MW00603763

The EBCC Atlas of
European Breeding Birds

EBCC acknowledges the support of:

landbouw, natuurbeheer
en visserij

and many other institutions and individuals

The EBCC Atlas of European Breeding Birds:
Their Distribution and Abundance

Edited by

Ward J M Hagemeijer[1]
and Michael J Blair[2]

Data editing team
Ward Hagemeijer[1]
Chris van Turnhout[1]
Johan Bekhuis[1]
assisted by
Mike Blair[2]
Simon Gillings[2]

Text editing team
Mike Blair[2]
Rob Bijlsma[1]
Ward Hagemeijer[1]
assisted by
Simon Gillings[2]
Chris van Turnhout[1]

[1]*SOVON Bird Census Work The Netherlands*
[2]*British Trust for Ornithology*

T & A D Poyser
LONDON

ISBN 0-85661-091-7

EBCC is keen to encourage use of the atlas data. If you wish to use the data-set, please contact either: **EBCC, p.a. SOVON, Rijkstraatweg 178, 6573 DG Beek-Ubbergen, The Netherlands;** or: **EBCC, c/o BTO, The Nunnery, Thetford, IP24 2PU, UK**

First published in 1997
by T & A D Poyser Ltd
24–28 Oval Road, London NW1 7DX

United States Edition published by
ACADEMIC PRESS
San Diego, CA 92101

A catalogue record for this book is available from the British Library

The **recommended citation** for this book is: E J M Hagemeijer and M J Blair (Editors). 1997. *The EBCC Atlas of European Breeding Birds: Their Distribution and Abundance.* T & A D Poyser, London.

Conversion of data to illustrate colour maps and charts by Hardlines, Charlbury
Text set in 10/12 pt ITC Garamond
Typeset by Selwood Systems, Midsomer Norton
Printed and bound in Great Britain by Jarrold Book Printing Ltd, Norfolk

This book is printed on acid-free paper

ISBN 0-85661-091-7

Contents

This book is dedicated to the memory of contributors and helpers who did not live to see its publication, those known to us being:

Hans Bub, Germany
Steve Carter, England
George Dunnet, Scotland
Olavi Hildén, Finland
Helmut Ölschlegel, Germany
Rumen Todorov, Bulgaria
Tony Whilde, Ireland

Foreword

The planning, the presentation and the completion of a distribution atlas for European breeding birds are each ambitious tasks. Scientific bodies and government officials throughout Europe undoubtedly will first question the value, let alone the meaning of such an effort. Those aware of the biological problems lying behind particular patterns of distribution, and who have noted the existence of clear, but usually varying boundaries which species rarely or reluctantly cross to breed, have been waiting for such a work in print for almost too long, and have had to satisfy themselves with more general works or with publications with a far more restricted scope. Others who know of the decline of the numbers and size of wild areas, which are subject to constant encroachment by man and his industrial and urban expansion and to the personal needs of the ever-increasing population, have also been far too long awaiting a reference base against which to measure and document the rate at which bird species are vanishing from regions where once they were plentiful.

The EBCC Atlas of European Breeding Birds is therefore not only of great scientific value, but it is also a tool in the hands and minds of conservationists who need evidence rather than assertions to persuade the uncommitted, convince the doubters, and weaken the hostility of the vested interests.

Planning an atlas project and implementing it are two widely different tasks. Perhaps only the European Ornithological Atlas Committee can understand and know fully the difficulties of integrating the efforts of ornithological field workers in nearly 40 countries which have different scientific standards and infrastructure, varying economic circumstances and distinct societies, despite them sharing the same ideals of science, bird protection and nature conservation.

Even when the excessive rationalism applied in agriculture and other land use can be demonstrated as the main cause of the disappearance of natural habitats and their characteristic birds, the problem remains of why so many bird species are declining in numbers across the continent, and so few are extending their ranges or showing substantial increases. Why has the White Stork disappeared from many parts of Europe within one or two generations, whereas it has thrived for hundreds of previous generations? What about Bittern, Capercaillie, Black Grouse, Partridge, Quail, Corncrake, Turtle Dove, and most of all the eagles and vultures and the millions of colonially nesting seabirds, now impressing us only in thousands? Where have the birds of the Mediterranean Sea gone? The geographical ranges and the breeding numbers of these and other birds should be documented now and monitored or counted regularly to agreed standards in future, in all European habitats, be they forests, marshes, wetlands, sea-coasts, mountains, or man-made.

Identifying species and counting individual birds, though apparently a trivial exercise, requires a thorough knowledge of more than just local birds. Government officials in their armchairs and desk-bound scientists are therefore invited to visualize and appreciate the tremendous commitment and effort which has gone into the preparatory work for this atlas, from the thousands of fieldworkers and voluntary birdwatchers, perhaps more than one hundred thousand overall, often in severe or inclement conditions, all over Europe. Their expert knowledge, enthusiasm and determination are at the heart of this book, and without them this *Atlas* would have never seen the light of day. It is also worth acknowledging that the often tedious work of collating and correcting the raw data by national organizers, the computerization and validation of these results, and the endless correspondence have been essential to the completion of the task.

The EBCC Atlas of European Breeding Birds is a monument to national and international cooperation, and to personal patience and dedication. It serves the scientific community and the organizations and public offices alike. The publication of this book is therefore a memorable event for Europe, and equally is of importance to all nations of the world interested in understanding and conserving their natural heritages. The field workers, national organizers and final editors and their staff, whether professionals or volunteers, are to be congratulated for this splendid result.

K H Voous, Huizen, The Netherlands

Preface

The EBCC Atlas of European Breeding Birds is the result of a huge international collaboration. Data have been gathered right across Europe, mainly collated by national co-ordinators in each country. The texts and vignettes that support the atlas maps have been written and drawn by authors and artists from 35 and 11 different countries respectively. To make the material as widely accessible as possible, the Introduction to the book is printed here in 14 languages as are the names of all the birds. In addition, summaries of the other sections of the book, including the accounts of each species, have been prepared and made available to the national organizations in each country, so that they can translate and publish it in their own languages. It has not been an easy task. It has, however, been enjoyable and exciting; furthermore, we believe that the result is an important contribution to ornithology and to conservation.

By the mid-1960s, it had become clear to ornithologists in several European countries that their avifaunistic work had reached a stage where it could be much enhanced by greater international collaboration. The first conference of the International Bird Census Committee (IBCC), at Hillerød (Denmark) in 1968, like all of the early meetings, involved relatively few people but it still had a broad international perspective, with North American as well as European delegates. Early conferences concentrated on census methods and the comparison of results; the ideas of monitoring populations and habitats, especially with a clear focus on monitoring for nature conservation purposes, later became prominent. While international exchange of ideas was important in the census and monitoring work (even with some attempt to lay down standard methods), there was little development of collaborative projects. The European Ornithological Atlas Committee (EOAC), independent of IBCC but holding joint conferences with it from 1972 onwards, however, had from the beginning the idea of an Atlas of European Breeding Birds. In order to achieve this objective, EOAC had to set up a network of contacts in every European country and to agree a common protocol for data collection. Where there was no strong ornithological organization in a country, EOAC had to find some way of establishing a national data-gathering mechanism. In this way, the European atlas project has not only helped establish pan-European collaboration in bird studies but has also strengthened the idea of national data-gathering in several countries.

At their joint conference in the Netherlands, *Bird Numbers 1992*, IBCC and EOAC decided to merge, forming a European Bird Census Council (EBCC). This was partly a recognition of the facts that most of the national organizations involved in census and atlas work were the same and that it was wasteful to have two separate committees trying to promote co-operation between European ornithologists. But, more importantly, it was a recognition that census and atlas work are closely connected, different and complementary ways of describing the status of bird populations, of monitoring changes, and of contributing a sound factual base for nature conservation.

Although it later proved possible to obtain semi-quantitative data on bird populations from many countries, the original method of simple qualitative recording (presence/absence) proved an excellent means of obtaining the co-operation of all the nations. Their heterogeneity in terms of the level of ornithological organization, number of skilled ornithologists, degree of financial support etc., was such that an attempt to use a more refined methodology might have failed. Because the methods were simple, the 50 × 50km grid relatively coarse, and the time-span was several years, even countries with a low density of ornithologists and birdwatchers could provide useful data. The project has thus proved good for establishing the first sustained pan-European collaboration in ornithology.

The European atlas project has stimulated distributional studies in many countries. This work has often been at a greater level of detail than required for the European atlas, showing that it will be possible to produce a better European atlas in future. That will be one of the aims of the EBCC, which will also encourage the development of improved atlas work within individual countries.

Apart from the obvious problems created by armed conflict, the atlas project has generally been made easier by the political upheavals that have occurred in Europe since it began. The 'Iron Curtain', though quite irrelevant to birds, was an impediment to the flow of ornithological knowledge and its removal has been a great benefit. Furthermore, ornithologists in many countries have been inspired both by greater freedom and by national pride to make great efforts to contribute well to the atlas.

The major political changes have done little to diminish the differences between countries in the way in which ornithological work is organized. In some, there is a single body that organizes most of the atlas, census, nest-recording and ringing work; in others, these areas of work are organized by different bodies; whilst in yet others there is little or no organization at national level, the work being organized regionally. Sometimes the work is organized by paid professionals but in other countries it depends wholly on volunteers. Some countries can call on the assistance of tens of thousands of fieldworkers, others on just a few. The degree of state support also varies considerably. Although these differences impede international collaboration, it would be unrealistic for EBCC to aim to eliminate them. What we can do is to assist the development of avifaunistic work within individual countries. This will have the benefit of strengthening the scientific base of nature conservation within countries and make international collaboration easier.

EBCC, like IBCC and EOAC before it, has the important function of encouraging the exchange of ideas in bird census and atlas work. This is the role of the conferences that take place at intervals of two to three years, of other seminars and workshops, and of the EBCC newsletter *Bird Census News*. This communication allows every country to benefit from the experience of the others. Discussion across national boundaries also stimulates the effective development of totally new techniques, especially for data interpretation.

Communication depends on language. In Europe there are about 40 independent countries and about the same number of languages. Though most ornithologists speak more than one language, there is no single language spoken by all. English comes closest to being a common language and for that reason has been taken as the working medium for EBCC and as the main language for the *Atlas*. But, aware of the need to make the *Atlas* contents as widely accessible as possible, we have not only included a multi-language Introduction but have produced a summary of the text which is available for people in non-English-speaking countries to translate and publish in their own languages. We have also tried to ensure that the text is as simple and clear as possible, for those whose first language is not English. Because international communication is also facilitated by greater stability of English names, of scientific names and of taxonomic order, we have followed the concise edition of *Birds of the Western Palearctic* in these matters.

Atlas and census work provide information that is of interest in its own right and that is valuable for answering a variety of questions in scientific ornithology and ecology. It also provides an essential database for bird conservation. Bird populations and their habitats are threatened across Europe by the diverse impacts associated with the growth of human populations and economic development. The resources available to mitigate these pressures are limited, so priorities must be set. Which species are rarest? Which are most rapidly declining? Which are concentrated in just a few sites? Which, although common in one country, are concentrated there and are scarce elsewhere? Which, although rare in one country, are common and widespread elsewhere? Answers to such questions are essential if priorities are to be assessed. They all depend on sound census or atlas work. Surveillance (regular repetition of surveys) is essential if we are to detect newly arising problems – not just declines of individual species but also problems for whole suites of species characteristic of particular habitats or biotopes (such as the general decline of farmland birds now being detected in many European countries). A proper monitoring programme (Furness & Greenwood 1993) provides the means not only of detecting such problems but of understanding their probable causes; without such understanding, any attempts to remedy problems are likely to be ineffective. Monitoring is also essential in order to determine the success of measures taken to conserve endangered species and biotopes. Because of the great value of conservation-directed monitoring work, EBCC aims both to encourage the development of sound monitoring programmes for birds in all European countries and to promote a system of pan-European bird monitoring. Atlases have two important roles in wildlife monitoring. The first is a direct one, because repeat atlases can reveal changes in range, which can be substantial over periods as short as a couple of decades (see, eg Fuller *et al* 1995). Another role of atlases in monitoring may be to provide a basis for stratification in the design of census studies, so that survey effort may be concentrated, for example, where key species are most abundant.

Monitoring birds across the whole of Europe will be an important step forward. It may not be easy but it will be easier than monitoring most other forms of wildlife. This is because birds are comparatively easy to observe, because we already have a comparatively good knowledge of their ecology (which makes understanding the causes of conservation problems easier), and, above all, because there are so many birdwatchers who enjoy carrying out the fieldwork. For this reason, the monitoring of the distribution and abundance of birds has an importance far beyond ornithology, for we can use the birds as indicators for wildlife more generally. For example, birds characteristic of agricultural land are declining in many parts of Europe, suggesting that farmland is declining in quality both for birds and for other forms of wildlife. Whilst it is still important to monitor the other forms of wildlife directly, there is no doubt that a well-developed programme of avian Euromonitoring would be a valuable means of detecting the problems facing wildlife and its habitats across the continent at an early stage.

The aims of the EBCC will best be realised if we liaise fully with other international organizations, such as BirdLife International and Wetlands International. As part of the work on the *Atlas*, we have co-operated with the former to collect and collate information on bird population sizes and trends in all European countries, some of which has already appeared in *Birds in Europe* (Tucker & Heath 1994). The joint database that we have established is already being used by the Commission of the European Union to improve its ornithological databases, set up under the Birds Directive to provide information on Annex 1 species. European birdwatchers may look forward to their fieldwork contributing even more in future to the work of both voluntary conservation bodies and official agencies.

It is the policy of EBCC to make its data widely available for scientific and conservation purposes, while safeguarding the interests of the EBCC network and its members, who have provided the original information. A system is in place for the provision of data not only for conservation and science but also for more commercial uses. By charging appropriate fees to commercial users, it will be possible to generate some income to fund EBCC activities.

Lack of independent funding is a major problem for the development of EBCC's work. Because all business is currently conducted by individuals working in their spare time or in time provided by national organizations, without the aid of a paid secretariat, progress is slow. Furthermore, the participation in EBCC activities of people from some countries, especially in eastern Europe, is restricted for purely financial reasons. We hope that one of the outcomes of the *Atlas* will be a greater recognition of the value of international collaboration in such work, leading to a greater general willingness to provide funds to promote it.

The *Atlas* proves what can be done if the ornithologists of Europe collaborate across national boundaries. We have the potential to expand bird census and atlas work throughout the continent, leading to a better scientific understanding of our avifauna and to a monitoring programme that will be invaluable for the future conservation of Europe's birds. Having recognized that potential, we present ornithologists and conservationists with a challenge – the challenge to realize the potential by putting the monitoring programmes in place. We believe that it is a challenge that can be taken up, that must be taken up, and that will be taken up.

Goetz Rheinwald & Jeremy J D Greenwood

Introduction

PURPOSE OF *THE EBCC ATLAS OF EUROPEAN BREEDING BIRDS*

Many bird books feature confidently drawn species distribution maps. Some of these maps are based on surveys of breeding bird populations but, except for some specialist atlases, many of the maps are derived from a collection of sources of variable reliability and sometimes they are only a reworking of earlier maps of doubtful authenticity. Furthermore, the maps are usually not quantitative: they do not indicate where a species is common nor where it is scarce.

However, there is an increasing number of excellent regional and national breeding bird atlases available, many of which have their roots or inspiration in the project which has produced this *Atlas* and, like it, contain semi-quantitative data. It was in 1971 that the European Ornithological Atlas Committee (EOAC) was formed with the objective of mapping the breeding distributions of those European species for which data could be obtained through fieldwork. This book presents the results of that endeavour.

The *Atlas* represents bird distributions over a limited period of time, but the data collected (whatever their minor inconsistencies) comprise a baseline of knowledge, against which future work (and indeed future changes in the distributions of the birds) may be measured. The EOAC of 1971 clearly saw a vision of the first continent-wide breeding bird survey ever attempted. Their vision has been rewarded. *The EBCC Atlas of European Breeding Birds* maps the distribution of birds breeding in Europe: it answers the question 'what bird breeds where'?

LAYOUT OF THE *ATLAS*

This **Introduction** briefly describes the purpose of the *Atlas*, details the methods of distribution and population data collection, computerization and mapping and explains the structure of the *Atlas*. It is vital to understanding the book in all its aspects. It is printed in a selection of languages so that it can be read by most European ornithologists.

Initial sections

In the **Foreword,** Professor Karel Voous outlines why the *Atlas* is important within the context of the changes occurring to avifauna in Europe. The **Preface** summarizes how the collaborative *Atlas* project meets the requirements of European ornithologists, and outlines the policies and purpose of the EBCC for future European bird monitoring schemes. Then comes the **Introduction**, including items like methods and area of coverage. The **Explanatory Figures** section following this **Introduction** shows coverage, data quality and a copy of the standardized data-collection form. The **History** section describes the progress and setbacks encountered by the European Ornithological Atlas project. Then, under the title **Evolution and History of the European Bird Fauna**, comes an essay by Professor Jacques Blondel to illustrate how the present range of European bird species came into existence. Finally, there are lists of **Acknowledgements** and of **National and Major Regional Bird Atlases of Europe**.

Species section

An **Introduction to the Maps and Population Graphs** prefaces the body of the *Atlas*, which deals with the European breeding species. Part 1 consists of distribution maps, species accounts, common names in 14 languages for each breeding species, and illustrations. The species appear in approximate Voous (1977) order and Euring sequence. Part 2 comprises accounts of species that are believed to breed in Europe but for which no data were received.

Final sections

The **Derived Maps** section details the species richness of breeding birds in Europe and of Species of European Conservation Concern (SPEC), as defined by BirdLife International (Tucker & Heath 1994). The **Technical Appendix** contains an explanation of how the *Atlas* grid differs from the theoretical Universal Transverse Mercator (UTM) projection and how island and coastal 50km squares were rationalized. It also explains how the *Atlas* used the Euring number system.

National-language booklets

Summaries of the initial sections (**Preface, History**, and **Evolution and History of the European Bird Fauna**) and of the species accounts have been made available for ornithologists from any country to translate into their national language and to disseminate to their colleagues, in order to increase the use of the book by those who do not read English. The list of names and addresses of those supplying national-language booklets (as known at the time of going to press) is given at the end of the **Technical Appendix**.

METHODS

The *Atlas* data presentation

Original ideas for data collection and compilation and an

account of how methods were chosen are described in the **History** section, as is the story of how the surveys came to be mounted.

The *Atlas* maps show differences in density (the number of birds per unit area) on a logarithmic scale (explained in the section **Qualitative versus semi-quantitative information**, below). This scale is especially appropriate for species whose densities vary markedly through their range. However, smaller differences in density will remain hidden on this scale.

The *Atlas* not only presents the distribution of European breeding birds, but also gives estimates of breeding population size and trends of most species in every European country. Only from an appraisal of soundly based national population sizes and trends can changes in distribution patterns be understood.

Area of intended *Atlas* coverage

The area of intended coverage is shown in **Figure 1**. Although it would have been desirable to have matched fully the boundaries of the western Palearctic as defined in *Birds of the Western Palearctic* (Cramp *et al* 1977–1994), this was simply impractical because few data were available from Asia Minor, northern Arabia and northern Africa, and so these areas were omitted. The *Atlas* therefore uses the base map of *Atlas Florae Europaeae* (Jalas & Suominen 1972, 1988) except that it includes Novaya Zemlya, Franz

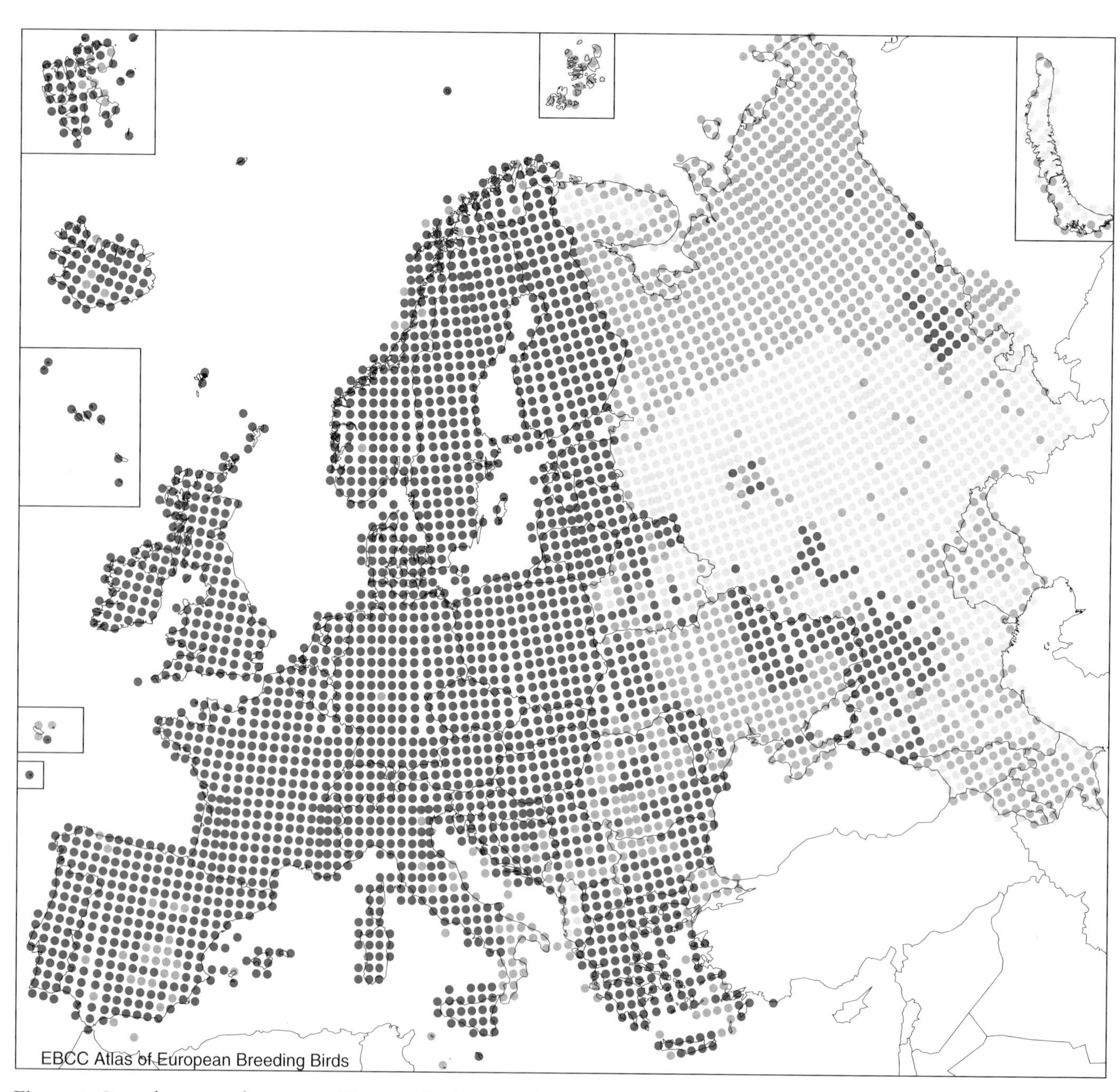

Figure 1 Completeness of coverage. The map limits show the area of intended coverage and the symbols show the area of achieved coverage.

- Data received for at least 75% of expected breeding species.
- Data received for less than 75% of expected breeding species.
- No data received.

Josef Land, all the Greek islands close to mainland Turkey, the Madeiran archipelago, the Azores, the Stavropol region of south-western Russia and the Caucasus republics. The remaining difference between the western Palearctic area and the *EBCC Atlas* coverage is that Cyprus, the Canary Islands and all North African-administered Mediterranean islands are omitted. The *Atlas* differs from the coverage of *Birds in Europe – their conservation status* (Tucker & Heath 1994) by omitting Turkey in Asia Minor and Greenland.

Not immediately apparent from **Figure 1** is that the boundaries of the western Palearctic, the *Atlas Florae Europaeae* and this *Atlas* omit a small area of Europe near Orenburg and include a part of Asian Kazakhstan between the Volga and the Ural rivers, and a part of Asian Russia east of Perm (Sverdlovsk region) unlike *Birds in Europe*.

Achieved coverage

In the **Explanatory Figures** section following the **Introduction, Figure 2** shows the censused squares and indicates the maximum data quality received per square, and **Figure 3** the minimum data quality received per square. The **Qualitative versus semi-quantitative information** subsection (see below) explains the meaning of these terms, but the categories of data quality shown in these maps were, in descending order of quality:

1. Semi-quantitative population estimate: breeding was either confirmed or assessed as probable.
2. Semi-quantitative population estimate: breeding was assessed as possible.
3. Qualitative presence: breeding was either confirmed or assessed as probable.
4. Qualitative presence: breeding was assessed as possible.

The data quality was usually the same for all species recorded in a square (but see below). Considerable areas of central Russia were not covered at all mainly because contacts could not be established. For much of the rest of Russia, parts of Belarus, Ukraine and the Caucasus republics, coverage was achieved for a restricted number of species. Coverage of most of former Yugoslavia was reasonably comprehensive (in some areas not for all species). There are gaps in Albania. Coverage was incomplete for the Russian arctic islands of Novaya Zemlya and Franz Josef Land.

Elsewhere, despite inevitable deficiencies, coverage essentially was complete.

The *Atlas* maps

The selected mapping projection had to meet three criteria: it must cover the *Atlas* area of intended coverage, it must be familiar to most European countries and it must be compatible with national projections. Only the Universal Transverse Mercator (UTM) projection met these basic criteria when the *Atlas* project began. Because the base map of the *Atlas Florae Europaeae* project uses the UTM grid, it was ideal as the basis of the map devised for the ornithological *Atlas*. The *Atlas Florae Europaeae* used 50km × 50km grid squares as recording units and the same squares were used for the ornithological *Atlas*. The work involved in collating and analysing data gathered at a finer scale would have been impractical.

The basic mapping unit of the UTM grid, the 100km × 100km square, is uniquely identified by a logically sequenced alphanumeric code of two numbers and three letters. For the flora and bird atlases each such square was subdivided into four 50km × 50km squares numbered thus:

1 3
2 4

and so each 50km square has a unique 6-character reference.

The layout of the UTM grid on the north–south axis is simple: the subdivided grid lines are at 50km intervals, parallel to lines of latitude and with a starting point at the Equator. The other axis is more difficult to manage because meridians of longitude converge towards the poles. Consequently, the number of 50km × 50km squares which can be accommodated diminishes towards the poles. The UTM cell arrangement compensates as follows. The cell layout pattern is based on 6° sectors of longitude (starting at 0°). The cells bordering each 6° meridian are diminished towards the poles until they become points, when they disappear and the new border squares then begin to diminish. The *Atlas Florae Europaeae* and this bird atlas have modified this system so that the variation in the size of the squares bordering the 6° meridians is less: border squares drop out when their width has declined to roughly 40km. (We refer to the cells as 'squares' in the *Atlas* for convenience, although they are not exactly square.) This pattern is shown clearly on the map of intended coverage (**Figure 1**) and full details are given in the **Technical Appendix**.

The EOAC provided 50km × 50km grid maps to national organizers to ensure that they used the correct grid for recording the data. Fieldwork was generally based on UTM grids finer than 50km × 50km or on non-UTM grids: in either case the national organizers had to convert data to a usable form for data input.

Dates of fieldwork and the validation process

It was planned that *Atlas* fieldwork should take place during 1985–1988. Nations organized their own fieldwork, however, and because of practical difficulties could not all meet that timescale. Where coverage was incomplete for the survey period, earlier or later data were evaluated to determine whether coverage or quality could be improved by including them. **Table 3** following this **Introduction** lists the participating countries, their data-collection periods, the national grids from which data were converted, and the type of recording.

Data gathering – species distribution data

Hundreds of thousands, perhaps more than a million, hours of fieldwork are the basis of the *Atlas*. Ideally, all participants would have used identical field methodology over the same period but this was impossible. The EOAC therefore issued broad guidelines rather than strict rules. In some countries, fieldwork for this *Atlas* and their national atlas was combined; in others, data from an independent national atlas project were used to provide data for this *Atlas*.

Methods used in the field ranged from single visits, through the accumulation of check-lists during many visits, to systematic surveys based on point- or line-transects or territory mapping on plots.

The standardized form produced by the Dutch Central

Bureau of Statistics is partially reproduced in **Figure 4** following this **Introduction**. A form was completed for each censused square. For squares lying across national borders, each nation compiled only its own component.

The general information requested for each square was:

1. Census period: the year, or sequence of years, from which the data originate.
2. The identity of the square (UTM50 code).
3. Survey completeness: indicates whether work in that square included more than 75% of the expected species (high) or less (low).
4. Altitude of square as a range to give minimum and maximum altitudes (metres).
5. Observers or coordinator(s): provided names and addresses in case of further queries.
6. Comments: allowed additional information to better explain the data on the form.
7. A short questionnaire on the habitats in the square.

The body of the form consists of a species list, (*c*440 species, following Voous (1977), numbered in Euring sequence) against which data were entered. The datafield format gave in Column 0 an abbreviated scientific name (eg Gav stell), in Column 1 the Euring code (eg 00020), and requested in Column 2 breeding evidence, and its code. There were 16 codes supplied, subdivided into three categories: Confirmed breeding, Probable breeding and Possible breeding. The codes are given in **Table 1**. Lastly, in Column 3 the datafield format requested an estimate of the number of breeding pairs in the square, expressed in a logarithmic scale (1 = 1–9, 2 = 10–99... 6 = > 100 000).

The form allowed separate recording of hybrids and unlisted species at the end of the list.

Overall, the sources of input breeding bird data were;

1. The EBCC national coordinators, who organized the data-collection and collated the results onto the data-collection forms.
2. Regional coordinators. Sometimes data-collection was organized by other than by national coordinators, especially when the country was large or when it was better delegated to an active member of an existing net of contacts. These regional coordinators worked in the same way as national coordinators.
3. Additional national sources, mainly literature, usually made available through a species expert. Where survey data were lacking, especially in remote areas, often the only source of data was in published or unpublished reports not available directly to the editors or national organizers.
4. Species text author. Very often, a species text author, having studied the species, would know of additional sources of information about distribution or numbers.

All data from these sources were treated within the data hierarchy: every addition to the database had to be approved at national coordinator level.

Qualitative versus semi-quantitative information

The *Atlas* uses semi-quantitative information (logarithmic population size estimates) calculated to the prescribed scale per square by regional and national coordinators and fieldworkers. The dots used represent numbers of breeding pairs, not densities, the increasing sizes of dot representing increasing order of magnitude (see key on page cxl). It is unfortunate that some countries wholly (Norway and Poland), mostly (Spain) or partly (Iceland, France and Italy) declined to provide semi-quantitative estimates. The project lost contact with Bosnia and Serbia, and could not upgrade their data. Some regions of France upgraded their data independently. The French national coordinator upgraded data nationwide for a limited number of species. Even log-scale estimates across a number of squares convey much more information than do mere indications of presence or absence.

Table 1 Breeding categories and codes

A: Possible breeding

1. Species observed in breeding season in possible nesting habitat
2. Singing male(s) present (or breeding calls heard) in breeding season

B: Probable breeding

3. Pair observed in suitable nesting habitat in breeding season
4. Permanent territory presumed through registration of territorial behaviour (song, etc.) on at least two different days a week or more apart at the same place
5. Courtship and display
6. Visiting probable nest site
7. Agitated behaviour or anxiety calls from adults
8. Brood patch on adult examined in the hand
9. Nest building or excavating nest-hole

C: Confirmed breeding

10. Distraction-display or injury-feigning
11. Used nest or eggshells found (occupied or laid within period of survey)
12. Recently fledged young (nidicolous species) or downy young (nidifugous species)
13. Adults entering or leaving nest-site in circumstances indicating occupied nest (including high nests or nest-holes, the contents of which can not be seen) or adult seen incubating
14. Adult carrying faecal sac or food for young
15. Nest containing eggs
16. Nest with young seen or heard

For border squares where each country submitted a population estimate for their component, the higher value was taken (logarithmic values should not be added), although in some cases this would result in an underestimate. Such approximations were more useful than downgrading these squares to qualitative status.

The dots on the maps refer to the following categories of information:

dark purple	= confirmed or probable breeding, qualitative
light purple	= possible breeding, qualitative
red	= confirmed or probable breeding, semi-quantitative
orange	= possible breeding, semi-quantitative
grey	= no survey work carried out for this species in this square
no dot	= square surveyed but species not recorded

Computerization – mapping data correction and input validation

The forms received from the national coordinators were examined for basic errors (omitted codes, illegal codes) before being computerized into an ASCII format file, each record having a national identity coding. Some countries provided data on floppy disk; these were also checked in the same way. The database constructed from the basic files has a single value per species per square.

Those national coordinators and other sources who promptly had supplied data quickly received interim maps and national listings per species as the first phase of the checking process. They were asked to check these and many corrections resulted. However, some countries submitted their original data late and others upgraded from qualitative to semi-quantitative data. Consequently, the data-correction and validation process began later and proceeded at different rates in different countries.

The production of interim maps was crucial in two respects:

1. It enabled national coordinators, and through them many data collectors, to validate that the data they had submitted had been input correctly: the maps showed whether the squares were in the correct locations for the correct species. Errors were more obvious from maps than from data listings alone.
2. It stimulated greater participation which often triggered new input data.

The second phase checked that the corrections from the first phase had been correctly input. This was achieved by sending national coordinators and other sources a second, corrected set of maps and data listings. Most coordinators completed these enormous tasks and submitted final corrections, but in countries like the former Yugoslavia updating and validation were often impossible. Those countries whose checking process had been subject to delay had to compress their efforts into a much shorter timescale, and the greater the delay, the greater were the difficulties encountered in finalizing the maps.

At a later stage updated figures came from some authors of species accounts and other species experts. Most of these have been examined by national coordinators and a decision made as to which figure to use. Where this has not been possible through lack of time, either the earlier figures have been retained or the text indicates that the author's opinion differs from some of the mapped material.

Where data based on atlas fieldwork were not available, which occurred particularly in northern Russia and Albania, data from other sources were appraised by local field ornithologists and a decision made as to the data's acceptability. Some semi-quantitative estimates were made for such squares by extrapolating from squares in the same region for which direct estimates were available, taking known areas of suitable habitat into account.

The final deadline for new data and corrections to be received was 1 July 1995, though to maximize coverage data received during the next few months from Albania, European Turkey, the Caucasus, parts of Ukraine and parts of Russia were used. Corrections arising from authors of species accounts were accepted up to 1 November 1995.

Data gathering – population size data

The national population graphs presented in the *Atlas* are derived from the European Bird Database. This contains population data collected collaboratively by EBCC and BirdLife International and was established to support this *Atlas* and the BirdLife Dispersed Species Project whose results are published in *Birds in Europe – their conservation status* (Tucker & Heath 1994). The collaboration also helped extend the depth of participation in some parts of Europe. Data were collected primarily by distributing questionnaires to national coordinators (listed in *Birds in Europe*) who in turn distributed them to appropriate experts, monitoring organizations and regional contributors. BirdLife International are the managers of the European Bird Database.

Each country supplied for breeding populations of all bird species:

1. Population size.
2. Population size trend (over the period 1970–1990).
3. Range trend (over the period 1970–1990).

Similar data were also collected for wintering populations, but are not presented here.

The reference sources used to evaluate population sizes and trends were recorded. Data verification codes, detailed in **Table 2** following this **Introduction**, were provided to indicate the accuracy and reliability of the population size and trend data.

Some authors of species accounts disagreed with the population estimates in the database but the information arrived too late to include in the database. In these cases, the authors have put their estimates in the text but the charts accompanying the species accounts always show the database figures.

Data limitations

The *Atlas* project has produced a high-quality dataset. Inevitably there are limitations to the data. Those wishing to use the data for further research must take into account these limitations, whose detail is beyond the scope of this book, and must be sought from the EBCC. However, some of the basic limitations affecting the general use of this book are:

1. There was no prescribed set of fieldwork methodologies for establishing presence or absence,

nor for determining population sizes. Many national projects which were the source of EBCC data had prepared their fieldwork methodologies for their own purposes, according to the resources available.
2. There was no universal set of methods of preparing the fieldwork results for collation onto the reporting forms, largely for reasons similar to those given above. Conversion methods were individual.
3. Differences in the quality of field ornithology and in the relative numbers of observers will result in varying data quality.
4. Some data are partly extrapolation data.
5. Some data come from literature (mainly arctic areas).

LAYOUT OF THE MAPS AND SPECIES ACCOUNTS IN THE *ATLAS*

In the *Atlas*, the species are in two groups: those for which we obtained satisfactory mapping data and those for which we did not. The former group all have full accounts in Part 1 of the species accounts; the second group have briefer accounts in Part 2. In both parts, species are in Voous order and in approximate EURING sequence, except for minor adjustments in Part 1 to ensure that any species whose map and text occupy a single page always faces another single-page species. Species whose maps and texts occupy two pages always have the map and text facing one another. In some cases, species with very restricted distributions do not require full treatment, allowing more than one species to be accommodated on a single page. Each species is illustrated, and common names (where available) are included in 14 languages. Most mapped species have a population graph which is explained in the pages preceding the species maps and accounts.

Derived maps (summary explanation)

Figure 5 illustrates the general species richness per square of breeding birds. **Figures 6–8** demonstrate the species richness of Species of European Conservation Concern (SPEC) Categories 1, 2 and 3, as defined by BirdLife International, and **Figure 9** combines the three Categories.

THE SPECIES ACCOUNTS

The species accounts cover (where applicable) a list of standard topics, usually in the following order (according to predetermined priorities); world distribution, breeding habitats in Europe, pattern of distribution and abundance in Europe, recent changes in distribution and population (and their possible causes), regional variation in abundance, possible factors limiting distribution, breeding density in prime habitat, migration and movement characteristics of the species in and beyond Europe, any special feature of the species, and concise reference to subspecies, covering distribution, range, overlap, and trends.

Unless a brief reference is absolutely essential to illustrate one of the standard topics, the following topics are omitted: breeding biology, behaviour, food, relations with other species, morphological features and physiology, detailed discussion of threats to the species (the province of *Birds in Europe*), abnormalities, oology, evolution and taxonomy (except where there are major recently accepted changes, or where subspecies are significantly different), mortality and other parameters of population dynamics, and voice and song.

Species-inclusion criteria

Species breeding in the area of intended coverage from 1985 onwards are included if they meet the criteria in **Table 1**. The principle of inclusion of introduced species breeding in the wild was that they had to have at least one population assessed as self-sustaining over five years. However, acceptance or interpretation of such rules varies widely across Europe and so selection or omission of some species with introduced populations may superficially appear arbitrary.

The *Atlas* includes 513 species plus *Passer* × *italiae*.

NOMENCLATURE AND TAXONOMY

Taxonomy

The EBCC has adopted a cautious and conservative position on taxonomic matters. This *Atlas* generally follows the taxonomy, order and English nomenclature adopted by *Birds of the Western Palearctic* (*BWP*), as amended for the Concise Edition.

Puffinus yelkouan, *Puffinus mauretanicus*, *Larus cachinnans*, *Anthus petrosus*, *Phylloscopus lorenzii* and *Pyrrhula murina* are treated as separate species and are mapped separately from *Puffinus puffinus*, *Larus argentatus*, *Anthus spinoletta*, *Phylloscopus collybita* and *Pyrrhula pyrrhula*. Separate mapping was possible either because they were recorded separately or are geographically separated. (The text for the three *Puffinus* species is integrated.)

Initially there was an attempt to record subspecies and forms of several species but the distinctions the EOAC had made are not observed uniformly across Europe, making mapping impossible. However, 'Italian Sparrow' was recorded separately and the *Atlas* follows *BWP* in treating it as a stabilized hybrid between *Passer domesticus* and *P. hispaniolensis*, describing it as *Passer* × *italiae*. Conversely, *Phylloscopus trochiloides* includes two geographically separate subspecies, *viridanus* and *nitidus*, previously regarded as separate species. The case for separating *Lanius meridionalis* from *L. excubitor* was generally accepted as the *Atlas* was being finalized; a diagram in the account indicates the boundary between the two forms. *Hippolais caligata* is sometimes considered to be distinct from *H. rama* but here the latter is treated as a subspecies. Relationships within some gull complexes are often unclear; *Larus armenicus* is treated separately here.

Euring numbers

The European Union for Bird Ringing (EURING), has an evolving list of five-figure reference numbers for species and subspecies, used primarily for ringing (banding). This list generally follows the Voous order, where applicable, and so was adopted as a useful method of collating data. The Euring numbers are given in the species accounts. The **Technical Appendix** gives details of how Euring numbers were used.

THE USE OF REFERENCE AND OTHER PUBLICATIONS

Authors were asked to avoid citing handbooks as references because space for citations was generally limited. Two current major European handbooks deserve special recognition. For basic understanding of any European breeding species, the texts and maps in this *Atlas* should be studied in conjunction with the appropriate entries in these pre-eminent reference publications: *Birds of the Western Palearctic* (Cramp *et al* 1977–1994) and *Handbuch der Vögel Mitteleuropas* (Glutz von Blotzheim *et al* 1966–1993). In the *Atlas* species accounts the abbreviations *BWP* and *HVM* are used for these books.

Birds in Europe – their conservation status (Tucker & Heath 1994) provides the first-ever review of European bird populations, the threats to them and their conservation status; it describes in detail those species with an unfavourable conservation status. The *Atlas* covers not only these species, also all the other species which are not at present threatened. The population graphs in the *Atlas* come from the same European Bird Database used for *Birds in Europe*, and so the species texts cite the latter frequently.

References cited in the *Atlas* appear at the end of the book, just before the indexes.

Michael Blair & Ward Hagemeijer

ABBREVIATIONS AND GLOSSARY OF TERMS

Compass directions

N = north
S = south
E = east
W = west, hence NW = northwest and WSW = west-southwest etc
C = central, hence S-C = south-central, etc.

General expressions

asl = above sea level (altitude)
c = approximately
et al = and others (in text citations)
pers comm = personal communication(s)
pers obs = personal observation(s)
unpubl = unpublished work

Dimensions and measurable quantities

bp = breeding pairs
ha = hectares
ind = individuals
m = metres
km = kilometres
km^2 = square kilometres
M = million

Acronyms

BTO = British Trust for Ornithology (GB)
BWP = Birds of the Western Palaearctic
HVM = Handbuch der Vögel Mitteleuropas
JNCC = Joint Nature Conservation Committee (GB)
RSPB = Royal Society for the Protection of Birds (GB)
SOVON = SOVON Bird Census Work The Netherlands
WWT = Wildfowl and Wetlands Trust (GB)

Glossary definitions

eutrophic — rich in mineral nutrients from animal or vegetable decomposition
lentic — pertaining to still or standing water, as in ponds and lakes
lotic — pertaining to running water
mesotrophic — neither rich nor poor in basic salts or nutrients
'mixotrophic' — a term coined for boreal zone lakes that are shallow and richly vegetated but whose shores are relatively poor in nutrients
oligotrophic — poor in basic salts and nutrients
phenology — the study of the times of recurring events
sclerophytic — pertaining to plants with thick, usually small leaves, which have low transpiration rates, suited to dry climates
xerophytic — pertaining to plants adapted to very dry conditions

Table 2 Population codes in the European Bird Database

POPMIN	= minimum population size (in pairs)
POPMAX	= maximum population size (in pairs)
MEAN	= geometric mean of population size (in pairs)
YRC	= year of population size estimate
PST	= population size trend
RST	= range size trend
PSV	= population size verification code
PTV	= population trend verification code
RTV	= range trend verification code

Population codes and range trend codes

The population and range trends apply to the period 1970–1990.

+2	= large increase of at least 50%
+1	= small increase of at least 20%, but less than 50%
0	= stable, with no overall change of more than 20%
−1	= small decrease of at least 20%, but less than 50%
−2	= large decrease of at least 50%
n	= new breeder within period
x	= gone extinct within period
f	= fluctuating, with changes of at least 20%, but no clear trend

Table 3 Participating countries, their data-collection periods and their methods

Country/ region	Code	Data-collection periods	Methods	Remarks
Albania		85 and 93	DR, LR and VR	
Armenia		85–93	LR	Validated, *Birds of Armenia* project
Austria	A	85–88 (some 89/90)	DR	
Azerbaijan	AZ	94 (few species only)	LR and VR	Vincent van der Berk, Roald Potapov
Azores		82–95	DR	
Belarus	BELA	72–92	DR	
Belgium	B	85–89	DR	
Bulgaria	BUL	80–89	DR	
Czech Republic	CZ	85–88 (some 89)	DR	
Croatia		85–88	DR	
Denmark	DK	85–88	DR	
Estonia	EST	85–88	DR	
Faeroes		81–89	DR	
Finland	FIN	86–90	DR	
France	F	80–92	DR and LR	DR and qualitative data, 85–89
Georgia		92	VR	Steffan Roth; biological expedition
Germany	D	79–90	DR	
Great Britain	GB	85–88 (some 89)	DR	
Greece	G	81–90	VR	
Hungary	H	79–91	DR	
Iceland	ICE	85–95	DR	
Ireland	IRE	85–88	DR	
Italy	I	79–92	DR and LR	
Latvia	LAT	85–88	DR	
Lithuania	LITH	85–88	DR	
Luxembourg	L	76–90	DR	
Madeira		85–95	DR	
Malta	MAL	85–88	DR	
Moldova		86–90	DR	
Netherlands	NL	84–90	DR	
Norway	N	50–89 (–94)	DR	Svalbard 50–94; DR, LR, VR
Poland	PL	86–93 (some 94/95)	DR	
Portugal	P	78–89	DR	
Romania	ROM	77–92	DR	
Russia	R	63–94	LR, DR and VR	
Slovak Republic	SLK	85–88	DR	
Slovenia	SLN	79–88	DR	
Spain	E	70–92	DR and LR	Includes Andorra
Sweden	S	86–91	DR	
Switzerland	CH	85–88 (some 89/90)	DR	Includes Liechtenstein
Turkey (Thrace)	TUR	88–95	DR	Gernant Magnin; European Turkey only
Ukraine	UKR	80–93	DR, LR and VR	
Ex-Yugoslavia		85–92	DR and LR	Bosnia, Serbia, Macedonia

The codes are the country codes used elsewhere in the *Atlas*.

The dates given do not imply that the whole country was surveyed, nor that every year the same area of a country was surveyed. Russia, for example, was unable to submit data for about 1000 50km squares. However, most countries' surveys covered a three-year period over the entire area, usually during 1985–88.

The listings under Methods mention the principal recording methods. Specialist species information was often made available from species studies.

Key: DR = Direct Recording for the *Atlas*; LR = Local Records, after validation, or provided in local survey format; VR = Visitors' Records.

ÚVOD

ÚČEL *ATLASU HNÍZDNÍHO ROZŠÍŘENÍ PTÁKŮ V EVROPĚ*

Mnohé knihy o ptácích obsahují důvěryhodně vypadající mapy rozšíření druhů. Některé z těchto map jsou založeny na mapování hnízdních populací ptáků, ale až na některé specializované atlasy je řada z nich odvozena z různě spolehlivých pramenů a někdy jsou to pouhá přepracování starších map pochybné věrohodnosti. Tyto mapy kromě toho obvykle neobsahují kvantitativní data: neudávají, ani kde je druh obecný, ani kde je vzácný.

Stále vzrůstá počet dostupných kvalitních regionálních a národních atlasů hnízdního rozšíření ptáků, z nichž mnohé byly inspirovány projektem, jehož výsledkem je i tento *Atlas* a stejně jako on obsahují semikvantitativní údaje. Projekt byl zahájen r. 1971, kdy byl vytvořen Evropský výbor pro ornitologický atlas (European Ornithological Atlas Committee, EOAC) s cílem zmapovat hnízdní rozšíření všech evropských ptačích druhů, u nichž bylo možno získat údaje terénní prací. Výsledky přináší tato kniha.

Atlas zachycuje nejen rozšíření ptáků v určitém omezeném časovém úseku, ale získaná data (i přes menší nesrovnalosti) představují základí, z kterého mohou vycházet další práce (především týkající se budoucích změn v rozšíření ptáků). EOAC měl v r. 1971 jasnou představu o prvním celoevropském mapování hnízdících ptáků, které do té doby nebylo provedeno. A jeho představa se skutečně naplnila. *EBCC* (European Bird Cencus Council) *Atlas hnízdního rozšíření ptáků v Evropě* mapuje rozšíření ptáků hnízdících na území Evropy: odpovídá na otázku "kde který pták hnízdí"?

USPOŘÁDÁNÍ *ATLASU*

Tento **Úvod** stručně popisuje účel *Atlasu*, podrobně líčí metody získávání údajů o rozšíření a populacích, jejich počítačovém zpracovávání a mapování a vysvětluje strukturu *Atlasu*. Je důležité porozumět knize ze všech hledisek. Je vytištěna v řadě jazyků, takže ji může číst většina evropských ornitologů.

Počáteční oddíly

V **Předmluvě** nastiňuje prof. Voous, proč je *Atlas* významný v kontextu se změnami, které nastávají v avifauně Evropy. **Předmluva** dále shrnuje, jak *Atlas*, vzniklý na základě rozsáhlé spolupráce, splňuje požadavky evropských ornitologů a podává nástin plánů EBCC pro budoucí monitorování evropských ptáků. Poté je zařazen **Úvod** včetně metod a zpracovaného území. Oddíl **Vysvětlující obrázky**, který následuje po úvodu, ukazuje pokrytí území, kvalitu údajů a ukázku standardizovaného dotazníku. Oddíl **Historie** popisuje úspěchy i překážky, s nimiž se projekt Evropský ornitologický atlas setkával. Prof. Jacques Blondel v kapitole nadepsané **Vývoj a historie ptačí fauny v Evropě** popisuje, jak došlo k současnému rozšíření evropských ptačích druhů. A konečně tu jsou kapitoly **Poděkování** a **Národní a hlavní regionální atlasy ptáků v Evropě.**

Oddíl druhů

Úvod ke kapitole **Mapy a populační grafy** předchází hlavní části *Atlasu*, která pojednává o druzích hnízdících v Evropě. Část 1 obsahuje mapy rozšíření, popisy druhů, název každého hnízdícího druhu ve 14 jazycích a jeho ilustrac. Druhy jsou uvedeny přibližně v pořadí podle Voouse (1977) a Euringu. Část 2 obsahuje popisy druhů, o kterých se předpokládá, že v Evropě hnízdí, ale k nimž nebyly získány žádné údaje.

Závěrečné oddíly

Oddíl **Odvozené mapy** podrobně uvádí pestrost druhů hnízdících v Evropě a druhů, jež jsou předmětem zájmu evropských ochranců přírody (Species of European Conservation Concern - SPEC) podle zásad BirdLife International (Tucker et Heath (1994). **Technická příloha** obsahuje vysvětlení, jak se mapovací síť *Atlasu* liší od teoretické Univerzální Transverzální Mercatorovy (UTM) projekce a jak byly upraveny pobřežní a ostrovní 50km čtverce. Vysvětluje též, jakým způsobem *Atlas* použil číselný systém Euringu.

Brožury v národních jazycích

Souhrny počátečních oddílů (**Předmluva, Historie** a **Vývoj a historie ptačí fauny v Evropě**) a popisů druhů se stanou dostupné ornitologům všech zemí tím, že budou přeloženy do příslušných jazyků a distribuovány v jednotlivých zemích, čímž se zvýší použitelnost knihy pro ty, kdo neovládají angličtinu. Seznam jmen a adres těch, kteří přispěli do brožur napsaných v jiných národních jazycích (jak byl znám v době před vytištěním) je zařazen na konec **Technické přílohy.**

METODY

Prezentace údajů v *Atlasu*

Původní představy o shromažďování a zpracování údajů a o výběru metod jsou popsány v oddílu **Historie**, stejně tak jako popis příprav mapování.

Mapy v *Atlasu* ukazují rozdíly v hustotě (počtu ptáků na jednotku plochy) v logaritmické stupnici,vysvětlené v části **Kvalitativní versus semikvantitativní informace**, viz níže. Tato stupnice je zvášte výhodná v případě druhů, jejichž hustoty se značně liší v různých částech jejich areálu. Menší rozdíly hustoty však tato stupnice nezachycuje.

Kromě rozšíření ptáků hnízdících v Evropě *Atlas* prezentuje odhady velikostí hnízdních populací a trendů většiny druhů v každé evropské zemi. Změny v rozšíření lze pochopit pouze z vyhodnocení národních populačních hustot založených na spolehlivých údajích.

Oblast zamýšleného pokrytí *Atlasem*

Oblast zamýšleného pokrytí ukazuje **obr. 1.** Přestože by bylo žádoucí, aby odpovídala západní palearktické oblasti, jak je uvedeno v díle Ptactvo západní Palearktidy (*The Birds of the Western Palearctic; Cramp et al 1977-1994*), nebylo to možné pro nedostatek dostupných údajů z Malé Asie, severní Arábie a severní Afriky. Proto byly tyto oblasti vynechány. Z tohoto důvodu *Atlas* vychází ze základní mapy Atlasu evropské flóry (*Atlas Florae Europaeae; Jalas et Suominen 1972, 1988*), navíc však zahrnuje Novou Zemi, Zemi Františka Josefa, všechny řecké ostrovy poblíž pevniny Turecka, souostroví Madeira, Azory, Stavropolskou oblast jihovýchodního Ruska a Kavkazské republiky. Do *Atlasu* nebyl zahrnut Kypr, Kanárské ostrovy a všechny středomořské ostrovy pod správou severoafrických států. Na rozdíl od území pokrytého dílem Ptáci Evropy - jejich ochranářský status (*Birds in Europe - their conservation status; Tucker et Heath 1994*) v *Atlase* chybí Turecko a Grónsko.

Z obr. 1 není na první pohled patrno, že hranice západní palearktické oblasti, *Atlas Florae Europaeae* a tento *Atlas* nezahrnují malou část Evropy poblíž Odenburgu a naopak zahrnují část asijského Kazachstanu mezi řekami Volhou a Uralem a asijskou část Ruska východně od Permu (oblast Sverdlovska), čímž se odlišují od *Birds in Europe.*

Dosažené pokrytí

Obr. 2 v oddíle **Vysvětlující obrázky**, který následuje po **Úvodu**, ukazuje sčítané čtverce a udává nejvyšší kvalitu údajů získaných na jeden čtverec. **Obr. 3** ukazuje nejnižší kvalitu údajů získaných na jeden čtverec. Oddíl **Kvalitativní versus semikvantitativní informace** (viz níže) vysvětluje význam těchto termínů. Byly použity následující kategorie kvality údajů:

1. Semikvantitativní odhad populace: hnízdění bylo buď potvrzeno nebo hodnoceno jako pravděpodobné.
2. Semikvantitativní odhad populace: hnízdění bylo hodnoceno jako možné.
3. Kvalitativní přítomnost: hnízdění bylo buď potvrzeno nebo hodnoceno jako pravděpodobné.
4. Kvalitativní přítomnost: hnízdění bylo hodnoceno jako možné.

Kvalita údajů ve čtverci byla obvykle stejná u všech zaznamenaných druhů. Výjimkou jsou značné části středního Ruska, kde čtverce nebyly pro nedostatečné kontakty pokryty vůbec. U většiny zbývající plochy Ruska, částí Běloruska, Ukrajiny a Kavkazských republik byly čtverce pokryty jen pro omezený počet druhů. Většiny území bývalé Jugoslávie byla pokryta poměrně dobře (v některých oblastech ne u všech druhů). Mezery jsou také v Albánii. Neúplné bylo pokrytí ruských arktických ostrovů Nová Země a Země Františka Josefa.

Jinde bylo pokrytí přes jisté nedostatky v podstatě úplné.

Mapy v Atlasu

Volba mapovací projekce musela splňovat tři hlediska: pokrývat oblast zpracovanou v *Atlase*, být známa ve většině evropských zemí a být kompatibilní s národními projekcemi. Když byl započat projekt *Atlas*, splňovala tato základní hlediska pouze Univerzální Transverzální Mercatorova projekce (UTM). Protože základní mapa v díle *Atlas Florae Europaeae* používá sítě UTM, byla tato síť ideální jako základ mapy vytvořené pro ornitologický *Atlas. Atlas Florae Europaeae* používal sítě čtverců 50 km x 50 km jako základních záznamových jednotek, týchž čtverců bylo použito i v ornitologickém *Atlasu*. Z hlediska srovnávání a analýzy údajů by použití jemnějšího měřítka bylo nevhodné.

Základní mapovací jednotka sítě UTM, čtverec 100 km x 100 km, je identifikována logicky sestaveným alfanumerickým kódem dvou čísel a tří písmen. Pro účely atlasů flóry a fauny ptáků byl každý čtverec dělen na čtyři čtverce 50 km x 50 km, očíslovaných takto:

1 3
2 4

a tedy každý 50 km čtverec má jedinečné šestimístné označení.

Rozložení sítě UTM podél severojižní osy je prosté: čáry omezující pododdíly čtverců leží ve vzdálenostech 50 km, jsou rovnoběžné s rovnoběžkami zeměpisné šířky a jejich výchozí bod leží na rovníku. Zvládnout druhou osu je obtížnější, neboť poledníky zeměpisné délky se směrem k pólům sbíhají. Následkem toho se počet čtverců 50 km x 50 km, které se mezi ně vejdou, směrem k pólům zmenšuje. Uspořádání buněk UTM to vyrovnává takto: způsob uspořádání buněk je založen na úsecích 6° zeměpisné délky (počínaje na 0°). Buňky, které hraničí s každým 6° poledníkem, se směrem k pólům zmenšují, až se z nich stanou body, které pak mizí a nové hraniční čtverce se pak začnou zase zmenšovat. *Atlas Florae Eropaeae* a tento *Atlas* ptáků systém modifikovaly tak, že proměnlivost velikosti čtverců hraničících s 6° poledníky je menší: hraniční čtverce vypadnou, jakmile se jejich šířka zmenší zhruba na 40 km. (V *Atlasu* tyto buňky označujeme jako "čtverce", přestože mnohé z nich nejsou přesně čtvercové.) Toto uspořádání je jasně patrné z mapy zamýšleného pokrytí (**obr. 1**) a podrobnosti jsou uvedeny v **Technické příloze**.

EOAC poskytl národním organizátorům mapy se sítí 50 km x 50 km, aby měl jistotu, že budou používat správnou síť při zaznamenávání údajů. Terénní práce byly obecně založeny na UTM sítích jemnějších než 50 km x 50 km nebo na sítích jiných než UTM; v obou případech museli národní organizátoři převádět data do formy použitelné v evropském měřítku.

Terénní data a ověřování správnosti

Bylo plánováno, že terénní práce pro *Atlas* by měly

proběhnout v letech 1985–1988. Avšak státy si organizovaly terénní práce po svém, a tak z praktických důvodů všechny nemohly toto období dodržet. Tam, kde pokrytí v období mapování nebylo úplné, byly k vyhodnocení použity dřívější či pozdější údaje. **Tabulka 3** , která následuje po tomto **Úvodu**, obsahuje seznam zúčastněných zemí, období sběru dat, národní sítě, z nichž byly údaje převáděny, a metody.

Shromažďování údajů - data o rozšíření druhů

Atlas je založen na statisících, možná více než miliónu hodin práce v terénu. V ideálním případě všichni účastníci měli použít stejné metodologie ve stejném období, ale to nebylo možné. Proto EOAC namísto striktních pravidel vydal široké směrnice. V některých zemích byly kombinovány terénní práce pro tento *Atlas* a pro jejich národní atlasy; v jiných zemích byly využity údaje získané v nezávislých národních mapovacích projektech. Metody užité v terénu vycházejí od jednotlivých návštěv přes vytvoření druhových seznamů v průběhu mnoha návštěv až k systematickým sčítáním založeným na bodových transektech, liniích nebo mapováních hnízdních okrsků.

Na **obr. 4** za tímto **Úvodem** je částečně otištěn standardizovaný formulář, který vytvořil nizozemský Ústřední statistický úřad (Dutch Central Bureau of Statistics). Formulář byl vyplněn pro každý sčítaný čtverec. U čtverců ležících na hranici dvou sousedních států, každý ze států uvedl pouze svoji část.

Obecné informace vyžadované pro každý čtverec byly následující:

1. Období sčítání: rok nebo řada let, z nichž údaje pocházejí.
2. Identita čtverce (kód UTM50).
3. Úplnost průzkumu: uvedeno, zda práce v příslušném čtverci zahrnovala více než 75 % očekávaných druhů (vysoká) nebo méně (nízká úplnost).
4. Nadmořská výška čtverce, udaná jako rozsah minimální a maximální výšky (v metrech).
5. Pozorovatelé nebo koordinátor (koordinátoři): uvedena jména a adresy pro případné další dotazy.
6. Poznámky: poskytovaly možnost lépe vysvětlit dalšími informacemi údaje ve formuláři.
7. Krátký dotazník o stanovištích ve čtverci.

Obsah formuláře tvoří seznam druhů (cca 440 druhů podle Voouse 1977, očíslovaných v pořadí Euringu), k nimž byla vyplňována data. Ve sloupci 0 bylo uváděno zkrácené vědecké jméno (např. Gav stell), ve sloupci 1 kód Euringu (např. 00020) a ve sloupci 2 důkaz o hnízdění a jeho kód. Kódů bylo 16 a byly dále rozděleny do tří kategorií: prokázané hnízdění, pravděpodobné hnízdění a možné hnízdění. Kódy jsou uvedeny v **Tabulce 1**. A konečně ve sloupci 3 byl zaznamenán odhad počtu hnízdících párů ve čtverci, vyjádřený v logaritmické stupnici (1 = 1–9, 2 = 10–99, ...6 = více než 100 000).

Formulář umožňoval oddělený záznam hybridů a neuvedených druhů na konci seznamu.

Vcelku byly zdroje údajů o hnízdících ptácích tyto:

1. Národní koordinátoři EBCC, kteří organizovali sběr dat a sestavili výsledky do formulářů.
2. Regionální koordinátoři. Sběr dat byl někdy organizován jinými osobami než národními koordinátory, zejména ve velkých státech, nebo v případě kdy bylo lepší předat existující síť kontaktů aktivnímu členu této sítě. Tito regionální koordinátoři pracovali stejným způsobem jako národní koordinátoři.
3. Další národní zdroje tvořila především literatura a údaje zpřístupněné odborníkem na určitý druh. Tam, kde chyběly údaje z mapování, zvláště v odlehlých oblastech, byly často jediným zdrojem dat publikované nebo nepublikované zprávy, které editorům nebo národním koordinátorům nebyly přímo přístupné.
4. Autor textu o druhu. Velmi často sám autor textu o konkrétním druhu získal další zdroje informací o jeho rozšíření či početnosti.

Všechny údaje z těchto zdrojů byly zpracovány podle hierarchie dat; každý dodatek k databázi musel být schválen na úrovni národních koordinátorů.

Tabulka 1. Hnízdní kategorie a kódy

A. Možné hnízdění
1. Druh pozorovaný v hnízdním období v možném hnízdním prostředí;
2. Pozorování zpívajícího samce (samců) nebo zaslechnutí hlasů souvisejících s hnízděním v hnízdním období;

B. Pravděpodobné hnízdění
3. Pár pozorovaný ve vhodném hnízdním prostředí v době hnízdění;
4. Stálý okrsek předpokládaný na základě pozorování teritoriálního chování (zpěv atd.) na témže stanovišti nejméně ve dvou různých dnech za týden či v ještě větším časovém odstupu;
5. Námluvy a tok;
6. Navštěvování pravděpodobného místa hnízdění;
7. Znepokojené chování nebo výstražný hlas dospělých ptáků;
8. Hnízdní nažina na dospělém ptákovi zkoumaném v ruce;
9. Stavba hnízda nebo hloubení hnízdní nory;

C. Prokázané hnízdění
10. Odpoutávání pozornosti nebo předstírání zranění;
11. Nález použitého hnízda (obsazeného) nebo vaječných skořápek (z vajec snesených v průběhu zkoumaného období);
12. Nedávno vyvedená mláďata (krmivých druhů) nebo mláďata v prachovém peří (nekrmivých druhů);
13. Dospělí ptáci zaletující do místa hnízda nebo je opouštějící za okolností nasvědčujících obsazenému hnízdu (včetně vysoko umístěných hnízd nebo hnízdních dutin, do nichž není vidět) nebo dospělí ptáci vysezující snůšky;
14. Dospělý pták odnášející trus nebo přinášející potravu mláďatům;
15. Hnízdo s vejci;
16. Hnízdo s mláďaty (viděnými nebo slyšenými).

Kvalitativní versus semikvantitativní informace

Atlas využívá semikvantitativních informací (logaritmických odhadů velikosti populací), vypočítaných pro předepsané měřítko na čtverec regionálními a národními koordinátory a terénními pracovníky. Použité body obecně značí počty hnízdících párů, nikoliv hustoty, a zvětšující se velikosti bodů značí vzrůstající řádové velikosti (viz klíč na str. cxl). Naneštěstí některé země jako celek (Norsko a Polsko), většinou (Španělsko) nebo zčásti (Island a Itálie) odmítly podat semikvantitativní odhady. Projekt ztratil kontakt s Bosnou a Srbskem a nemohl doplnit jejich údaje. Některé oblasti Francie zpřesnily své údaje nezávisle. Francouzský národní koordinátor zkvalitnil údaje z celé země u omezeného počtu druhů. I odhady v logaritmické stupnici, uvedené přes několik čtverců, podávají mnohem více informací než jen pouhý údaj o přítomnosti či nepřítomnosti druhu.

U hraničních čtverců, v nichž každá země poskytla odhad populace ze své části, byla vzata vyšší hodnota (logaritmické hodnoty nemají být sčítány), i když v některých případech to mohlo vést k podhodnocení. Takové přibližné hodnoty byly užitečnější než snížení hodnoty těchto čtverců na kvalitativní status.

Body na mapách znamenají následující kategorie informací:

tmavě nachová	=	prokázané nebo pravděpodobné hnízdění, kvalitativní hodnocení
světle nachová	=	možné hnízdění, kvalitativní hodnocení
červená	=	nebo pravděpodobné hnízdění, semikvantitativní hodnocení
oranžová	=	možné hnízdění, semikvantitativní hodnocení
zelená	=	žádné sčítání nebylo v tomto čtverci pro daný druh provedeno
žádný bod	=	čtverec byl sčítán, ale daný druh nebyl zaznamenán

Počítačové zpracování - oprava mapovacích dat a ověření jejich správnosti pro vkládání

Po kontrole základních chyb (vynechané kódy, nesprávné kódy) ve formulářích od národních koordinátorů bylya data převedena do formuláře ASCII, kde každý záznam měl kód národní identity. Některé země dodaly údaje na disketách; ty byly kontrolovány stejným způsobem. Databáze sestavená ze základních záznamů obsahuje jedinou hodnotu pro druh a čtverec.

Ti národní koordinátoři a jiné zdroje, které rychle poskytly údaje, obratem obdrželi předběžné mapy a národní seznamy pro jednotlivé druhy jako první fázi kontrolního procesu. Byli požádáni, aby je zkontrolovali; výsledkem byly četné opravy. Některé země však poskytly své originální údaje pozdě a jiné doplnily své kvalitativní údaje o semikvantitativní. V důsledku toho proces opravy dat postupoval v různých zemích různě rychle.

Předložení prozatímních map bylo velmi důležité ze dvou důvodů:

1. Dovolilo národním koordinátorům a jejich prostřednictvím i mnohým sběratelům dat ověřit, že údaje, které poskytli, byly vloženy správně: mapy ukázaly, zda čtverce jsou ve správných místech a pro správné druhy. Omyly byly z map patrnější než z pouhých seznamů dat.
2. Stimulovalo větší účast, která zase vedla k novým údajům.

Ve druhé fázi se kontrolovalo, zda opravy z první fáze byly správně vloženy. Toho bylo dosaženo tak, že národním koordinátorům a jiným zdrojům byla zaslána druhá, opravená série map a seznamů údajů. Většina koordinátorů vykonala tyto obrovské úkoly a poskytla konečné opravy, ale v takových zemích jako je bývalá Jugoslávie, bylo ověření a zpřesnění dat často nemožné. V zemích, kde se ověřovací proces opozdil, bylo nutno zvýšit úsilí při konečné úpravě dat. Čím větší bylo toto zpoždění, tím větší nastaly potíže.

V pozdějším stadiu zpracování byly od některých autorů druhových textů i jiných odborníků na určité druhy získány nejnovější údaje. Většina z nich byla zhodnocena, zda budou použity. Tam, kde to pro nedostatek času nebylo možné provést, byly buď ponechány dřívější údaje nebo se údaje v textu liší od některých údajů v mapě.

Tam, kde nebyly k dispozici údaje založené na terénní práci pro *Atlas*, což byl zvláště případ severního Ruska a Albánie, byly údaje získané z jiných zdrojů schváleny místními terénními ornitology a bylo učiněno rozhodnutí o jejich použitelnosti. Pro takové čtverce byly některé semikvantitativní odhady udělány extrapolací ze čtverců v téže oblasti, v nichž byly k dispozici přímé odhady, přičemž v úvahu byly brány známé plochy vhodných stanovišť.

Konečný termín pro dodání nových údajů a oprav byl 1. červenec 1995, ale aby se dosáhlo co největšího pokrytí, bylo použito i údajů dodaných v dalších několika měsících z Albánie, evropské části Turecka, Kavkazu, částí Ukrajiny a částí Ruska. Opravy učiněné autory popisů druhů byly přijímány do 1. listopadu 1995.

Shromažďování údajů - data o velikosti populace

Národní populační grafy v *Atlasu* jsou odvozeny z Evropské databáze ptáků (European Bird Database). Tato databáze obsahuje údaje o populacích, získané ve spolupráci mezi EBCC a BirdLife International a byla vytvořena jako podklad pro tento *Atlas* a pro projekt BirdLife nazvaný Rozptýlené druhy (Dispersed Species), jehož výsledky jsou publikovány v díle *Birds in Europe – their conservation status* (Tucker & Heath). Tato spolupráce také umožnila prohloubení účasti v některých částech Evropy. Údaje byly shromažďovány hlavně rozesíláním dotazníků národním koordinátorům (jejichž seznam je v Birds in Europe), kteří je dále rozesílali příslušným odborníkům, monitorujícím organizacím a regionálním přispěvatelům. BirdLife International jsou správci Evropské databáze ptáků.

Každá země dodala tyto informace o hnízdních populacích všech ptačích druhů:

1. Velikost populace.
2. Vývojový trend populace (za období 1979–1990).
3. Územní trend (za období 1970–1990).

Podobné údaje byly shromážděny také o zimujících populacích, ty zde však nejsou uvedeny.

Byly zaznamenány referenční zdroje použité při

vyhodnocování velikostí populací a jejich trendů. V **Tabulce 2** jsou podrobně uvedeny kódy ověřování dat, které udávají přesnost a spolehlivost údajů o velikosti populací a jejich trendech.

Někteří autoři popisů druhů nesouhlasili s populačními odhady v databázi, ale jejich informace došly příliš pozdě, aby do ní mohly být zařazeny. V takových případech autoři vložili své odhady do textu, ale grafy doprovázející popisy, vždy ukazují údaje z databáze.

Nedostatky dat

Projekt *Atlas* poskytl soubor údajů vysoké kvality. Jsou zde však nevyhnutelně i jisté nedostatky. Ti, kteří chtějí využít těchto dat pro další výzkum, musí vzít tyto nedostatky v úvahu; jejich podrobné vypsání je nad rámec této knihy a musí být vyžádáno od EBCC. V dalším textu uvádíme některá ze základních omezení, která mají vliv na obecné využití této knihy:

1. Nebyla předepsána žádná metodika terénních prací pro zjištění přítomnosti či nepřítomnosti nebo pro určení velikosti populací. Mnohé národní projekty, které byly zdrojem údajů pro EBCC, si vytvořily metodiky terénních prací pro vlastní účely podle dostupných zdrojů.
2. Nebyl tu žádný univerzální soubor metod, jak připravit výsledky terénních prací pro sestavení zprávy ve formulářích, většinou ze stejných důvodů jak je uvedeno výše. Metody přepočtů byly individuální.
3. Rozdíly v kvalitě terénní ornitologie a v relativních počtech pozorovatelů mají za následek údaje různé kvality.
4. Některé z údajů jsou zčásti extrapolace.
5. Některé z údajů pocházejí z literatury (hlavně pro arktické oblasti).

USPOŘÁDÁNÍ MAP A POPISŮ DRUHŮ V *ATLASU*

V *Atlasu* jsou druhy ve dvou skupinách: ty, pro něž jsme získali dostatečná mapovací data a ty, pro které jsme je nedostali. Všechny druhy v první skupině mají úplný popis v Části 1; druhy ve druhé skupině mají stručnější popisy v Části 2. V obou částech jsou druhy seřazeny podle Voouse a v přibližném pořadí Euringu, s výjimkou menších úprav v Části 1, které umožňují, aby druh, jehož mapa a popis tvoří jen jedinou stránku, byl vždy naproti jinému druhu obsahujícímu také jedinou stránku. Druhy, jejichž mapy a texty obsahují dvě stránky, mají vždy mapu a text proti sobě. V některých případech druhy s velmi omezeným rozšířením nevyžadují plné zpracování, takže bylo možno umístit na jedné straně více než jeden druh. Každý druh je vyobrazen a jsou uvedeny jeho názvy ve 14 jazycích (pokud byly dostupné). Většina mapovaných druhů má populační graf opatřený vysvětlivkami, které jsou před mapami a popisy druhů.

Odvozené mapy (souhrnné vysvětlení)

Obr. 5 ilustruje celkovou druhovou pestrost hnízdících ptáků v každém čtverci. **Obr. 6–8** ukazují druhovou pestrost druhů s významem pro Evropské životní prostředí (European Environmental Concern, SPEC) v kategoriích 1, 2 a 3, jak je definuje BirdLife International a **Obr. 9** slučuje tyto tři kategorie.

POPISY DRUHŮ

Popisy druhů obsahují (kde je to možné) řadu standardních údajů obvykle v tomto pořadí (podle předem stanovených priorit): světové rozšíření, hnízdní prostředí v Evropě, způsob rozšíření a početnost v Evropě, současné změny v rozšíření a populacích (a jejich možné příčiny), regionální kolísání početnosti, možné faktory omezující rozšíření, hnízdní hustota v hlavním prostředí, charakteristiky migrací a pohybů druhu v Evropě a mimo ni, jakékoliv zvláštní rysy druhu a stručný odkaz na subspecie, obsahující jejich rozšíření, území, překrývání a trendy.

Pokud nebyl k osvětlení standardních hledisek nutně zapotřebí alespoň krátký odkaz, byla vypuštěna následující hlediska: hnízdní biologie, chování, potrava, vztah k jiným druhům, morfologické znaky a fyziologie, podrobný popis ohrožení druhu (což je obsah díla *Birds in Europe*), abnormality, oologie, evoluce a taxonomie (vyjma případy, u nichž v nedávné době byly přijaty větší změny nebo kde se subspecie významně odlišují), mortalita a jiné parametry populační dynamiky a také hlas a zpěv.

Kritéria pro zařazení druhů

Druhy hnízdící v oblasti zamýšleného pokrytí od r. 1985 dále jsou do *Atlasu* zařazeny, pokud splňují kritéria

Tabulka 2. Populační kódy v Evropské databázi ptáků

Kód	Význam	Kód	Význam
POPMIN	= minimální velikost populace (v párech)		
POPMAX	= maximální velikost populace (v párech)		
MEAN	= geometrický průměr velikosti populace (v párech)	PSV	= ověřovací kód velikosti populace
YRC	= rok odhadu velikosti populace		
PST	= trend změn velikosti populace	PTV	= ověřovací kód populačního trendu
RST	= územní trend změn	RTV	= ověřovací kód územního trendu

Kódy populačních a územních trendů
Populační a územní trendy se vztahují k období 1970–1990.

+2	= velký vzrůst alespoň o 50 %
+1	= malý vzrůst alespoň o 20 %, ale méně než o 50 %
0	= stabilní, se změnami ne většími než 20 %
-1	= malý pokles alespoň o 20 %, ale méně než o 50 %
-2	= velký pokles alespoň o 50 %
n	= nový hnízdič ve sledovaném období
x	= druh vymizelý ve sledovaném období
f	= fluktuující, se změnami alespoň o 20%, ale s nejasným trendem

uvedená v **Tabulce 1**. Zásadou pro zařazení introdukovaných druhů hnízdících ve volné přírodě bylo, že musely mít alespoň jednu populaci, o níž bylo zjištěno, že je soběstačná po dobu pěti let. Dodržování nebo interpretace těchto pravidel se v různých zemích Evropy značně liší a výběr či vynechání některých druhů s introdukovanými populacemi se mohou při zběžném pohledu jevit jako libovolné.

Atlas obsahuje 513 druhů a *Passer x italiae.*

NOMENKLATURA A TAXONOMIE

Taxonomie

EBCC zaujímá v taxonomických otázkách opatrné a konzervativní stanovisko. Tento *Atlas* se obecně přidržuje taxonomie, pořadí a anglického názvosloví přijatých v díle *Birds of the Western Palearctic (BWP)*, jak byly upraveny pro jeho stručné vydání.

Puffinus yelkouan, Puffinus mauretanicus, Larus cachinnans, Anthus petrosus, Phylloscopus lorentzii a Pyrrhula murina jsou zpracovány jako samostatné druhy a jsou mapovány odděleně od *Puffinus puffinus, Larus argentatus, Anthus spinoletta, Phylloscopus collybita a Pyrrhula pyrrhula*. Oddělené mapování bylo možné jednak proto, že tyto druhy byly zaznamenávány odděleně nebo že jsou odděleny geograficky. Text pro tři druhy rodu *Puffinus* tvoří celek.

Zprvu byl činěn pokus zaznamenávat subspecie a formy několika druhů, avšak odlišnosti stanovené EOAC nejsou jednotně sledované ve všech evropských zemích, což znemožňuje mapování. Avšak "italský vrabec" byl zaznamenáván odděleně a *Atlas* ve shodě s *BWP* jej zpracovává jako stabilizovaného hybrida mezi *Passer domesticus* a *P. hispaniolensis* a popisuje jej jako *Passer x italiae*. Naproti tomu *Phylloscopus trochiloides* obsahuje dvě geograficky oddělené subspecie, *viridianus a nitidus*, které byly dříve považovány za dva samostatné druhy. Při konečném zpracovávání *Atlasu* byl obecně přijat důvod pro oddělení *Lanius meridionalis od L. excubitor*; diagram v popisu naznačuje hranici mezi těmito dvěma formami. *Hippolais caligata* se někdy považuje za odlišnou od *H. rama*, ale zde je *H. rama* zpracována jako subspecie. V některých komplexech racků jsou nejasné poměry; Larus armenicus je zde zpracován odděleně.

Čísla Euringu

Evropská unie pro kroužkování ptáků (Union for Bird Ringing – Euring) má stále doplňovaný seznam pětimístných referenčních čísel druhů a subspecií, kterého se používá především při kroužkování. Kde je to možné, je seznam většinou seřazen podle Voouse a byl přijat jako vhodná metoda pro srovnávání údajů. Čísla Euringu jsou uvedena v popisech druhů. V **Technické příloze** je podrobně uvedeno, jak bylo použito čísel Euringu.

POUŽITÍ ODKAZŮ A JINÝCH PUBLIKACÍ

Autoři byli požádáni, aby se vyhnuli citování příruček jako literatury, protože prostor určený pro citace byl obvykle omezený. Zvláštní uznání zasluhují dvě běžná hlavní evropská díla. Pro základní poznání kteréhokoliv druhu hnízdícího v Evropě by měly být texty a mapy v tomto *Atlasu* studovány ve spojení s patřičnými odstavci v těchto vynikajících základních publikacích: *Birds of the Western Palearctic (Cramp et al 1977–1994) a Handbuch der Vögel Mitteleuropas (Glutz von Blotzheim et al 1966–1994)*. V popisech druhů v tomto *Atlasu* jsou pro tato díla používány zkratky *BWP* a *HVM*.

Dílo *Birds in Europe - their conservation status (Tucker et Heath 1994)* podává vůbec první přehled evropských ptačích populací, jejich ohrožení a status ochrany; *Atlas* obsahuje nejen tyto druhy, ale také všechny ostatní, které v současnosti nejsou ohroženy. Populační grafy v *Atlasu* pocházejí z téže databáze o evropských ptácích, které bylo použito pro *Birds in Europe*, a tak tato publikace je často citována v textech jednotlivých druhů.

Odkazy citované v *Atlasu* jsou uvedeny na konci knihy před indexy.

Michael Blair, Ward Hagemeier
Karel Šťastný, Vladimír Bejček

ZKRATKY A REJSTŘÍK POJMŮ

Světové strany

N	= sever
S	= jih
E	= východ
W	= západ, z toho NW = severozápad a WSW = západojihozápad atd.
C	= střední, centrální, z toho S-C = jižně-centrální atd.

Obecné výrazy

asl	= nadmořská výška, nad mořem
c	= přibližně
et al	= a jiní (v citacích)
pers comm	= osobní sdělení
pers obs	= osobní pozorování
unpubl	= neuveřejněné dílo

Rozměry a měřitelná množství

bp	= hnízdící páry
ha	= hektary
ind	= jedinci
m	= metry
km	= kilometry
km^2	= čtvereční kilometry
M	= milión

Zkratky

BTO	= British Trust for Ornithology (GB)
BWP	= Birds of the Western Palearctic
HVM	= Handbuch der Vögel Mitteleuropas
JNCC	= Joint Nature Conservation Committee (GB)
RSPB	= Royal Society for the Protection of Birds (GB)
SOVON	= SOVON Bird Census Work The Netherlands (NL)
WWT	= Wildfowl and Wetlands Trust (GB)

Rejstříkové definice

eutrophic	bohatý na minerální živiny z rozkladu živočišných nebo rostlinných látek

lentic — týkající se stojatých vod, jako jsou rybníky a jezera
lotic — týkající se tekoucích vod
mesotrophic — ani bohatý, ani chudý na základní soli nebo živiny
„mixotrophic“ — termín vytvořený pro jezera v boreálním pásmu, která jsou mělká a bohatě zarostlá vegetací, ale jejichž břehy jsou poměrně chudé na živiny
oligotrophic — chudý na základní soli a živiny
phenology — studie období opakujících se dějů
sclerophytic — týkající se rostlin s tlustými, obvykle malými listy, které mají nízkou transpirační rychlost, vyžadující suché podnebí
xerophytic — týkající se rostlin přizpůsobených velmi suchým podmínkám

Einführung

DER EBCC ATLAS DER BRUTVÖGEL EUROPAS

Der vorliegende Atlas zeigt die Verbreitung der Brutvögel Europas Ende der 1980er Jahre. Im Unterschied zu den bisher verfügbaren Verbreitungskarten basiert er auf grossflächigen und aktuellen Kartierungen im Freiland, die nach allgemeinen Richtlinien mit 50x50-km-Quadraten als einheitliche Erfassungseinheiten durchgeführt wurden. In den meisten Ländern wurden zusätzlich für jedes Quadrat Bestandsschätzungen auf logarithmischer Basis durchgeführt. Die Karten dokumentieren also die gegenwärtige Brutverbreitung und Häufigkeitsverteilung der Vogelarten in ganz Europa.

Nachdem sehr viele europäische Länder einen nationalen Verbreitungsatlas vorgelegt haben (s. **List of national and regional Atlases in Europe**), hat das European Ornithological Atlas Committe EOAC jetzt auch sein 1971 formuliertes Ziel einer kontinentalen Brutvogelerfassung erreicht. Mit der heutigen Situationsbeschreibung stellt der Atlas die Basis für Vergleiche künftiger Arbeiten über grossflächige Veränderungen von Brutbeständen und deren Verbreitung dar.

Für Feldornithologen, die nicht englischer Muttersprache sind, wird das einleitende Kapitel in zahlreiche Sprachen übersetzt. Hier sollen Einzelheiten der Methode der Erfassung, Bestandsschätzung, Datenverarbeitung und Kartendarstellung, die für das Verständnis wichtig sind, geboten werden. Zudem werden Kurzfassungen einiger einleitender Kapitel und der Begleittexte zu den Arten in andere Sprachen übersetzt und als separate Beihefte zum englischen Atlas abgegeben. Die Namen und Adressen der Länder, die ein nationales Begleitheft erstellten, werden am Ende des **Technical Index** aufgelistet.

INHALT

Einführende Kapitel

Im **Geleitwort** stellt Karel Voous heraus, wo die Bedeutung dieses Atlanten in einer sich ändernden Vogelfauna Europas liegt. Das Vorwort (**Preface**) stellt dar, wie das gemeinsame Atlasprojekt die Anforderungen der europäischen Ornithologen erfüllt und skizziert die Politik des EBCC für künftige europäische Monitoring-Massnahmen. Dieser Einführung, die Aussagen über Methoden und Geltungsbereich des Atlas enthält, folgt ein Abschnitt mit den erklärenden Karten, die den Deckungsgrad und die Qualität der Angaben zeigen sowie eine Kopie des Erfassungsbogen für die Atlasdaten. Das Kapitel **History** beschreibt die Entwicklung des Projekts und die Rückschläge, die es erfahren hat. Jacques Blondel stellt in **Evolution and History of the European Bird Fauna** dar, wie die heutige Verbreitung der Vogelarten zustande kam. Danksagungen und eine Liste der nationalen und regionalen Vogelatlanten Europas beschliessen diesen Teil.

Die Artkapitel

Dem Hauptteil ist eine **Introduction to the Maps and Population Graphs** (Schlüssel mit den Symbolen, die in den Karten und den Bestandsgraphiken verwendet wurden) vorangestellt. Der Zentralteil des Atlanten behandelt die europäischen Brutvogelarten. Teil 1 enthält die sicheren Brutvogelarten Europas; jedes Artkapitel enthält den Namen der Art in 14 Sprachen, Zeichnung, Verbreitungskarte, Arttext und Grafik der Bestände und ihrer Änderungen. Teil 2 enthält solche Arten, von denen ein Brutvorkommen in Europa vermutet wird, wir aber keine Angaben erhielten.

Abschliessende Kapitel

Im ersten Kapitel werden auf **Auswertenden Karten** der Artenreichtum (Abb. 5) sowie die **Arten mit europäischer Verantwortung** (SPEC) (Abb. 6–9) dargestellt, so wie diese von BirdLife International durch Tucker & Heath (1994) definiert wurden.

Der **Technische Anhang** enthält Erläuterungen darüber, wie das Gitter im Atlas von der theoretischen UTM-Projektion abweicht und die Inseln und Küstenquadrate vereinfacht wurden. Es erklärt auch, wie der Atlas den Euring-Code verwendet.

METHODEN

Richtlinien

Im Idealfall hätten alle Länder Europas mit derselben Methode und in der gleichen Zeitspanne gearbeitet. Da dies nicht möglich war, formulierte das EOAC zwar allgemeine Regeln, gab aber keine strikten Richtlinien heraus. In nationalen Projekten wurden die Methoden den Zielsetzungen, Gegebenheiten und Möglichkeiten der Länder im Rahmen der vorgegebenen Richtlinien angepasst. In einigen Ländern wurde die Erfassung für diesen Atlas zusätzlich mit einem nationalen Projekt kombiniert; in anderen wurden die Ergebnisse aus einem früheren übernommen und ergänzt.

Daten zur Verbreitung

Für den vorliegenden Atlas wurden überall 'qualitative'

Angaben über die Verbreitung gesammelt (Anwesenheit der Arten zur Brutzeit in 50x50-km-Quadraten). Die Beobachtungen wurden entsprechend den Kriterien der Tab.1 eingeordnet und danach den drei Kategorien zugeteilt (A: mögliches, B: wahrscheinliches und C: gesichertes Brüten im Quadrat). In den Verbreitungskarten der Brutvogelarten werden allerdings 'wahrscheinliches' und 'gesichertes' Brüten zusammengefasst, so dass nur zwei Symbole für die Brutqualität verwendet werden.

Daten zur Häufigkeit

In der Mehrzahl der Länder wurden die Angaben über die Verbreitung der Brutvögel durch 'halb-quantitative' Schätzwerte der Grösse der Brutpopulation in 50x50-km-Quadraten ergänzt. Die dafür verantwortlichen nationalen und regionalen Koordinatoren und Fachleute konnten sich teils auf repräsentative, grossflächige Bestandsaufnahmen stützen, teils mussten sie auf lokale, kleinflächige Einzeluntersuchungen zurückgreifen, oder sie konnten nur eine grobe Schätzung wagen.

Die Bestandsschätzungen aus den verschiedenen Ländern basieren also auf sehr unterschiedlichen Grundlagen und werden auf einer logarithmischen Skala dargestellt (1 = 1 bis 9 Paare, 2 = 10–99, 3 = 100–999, 4 = 1000 bis 9 999, 5 = 10 000 bis 99 999, 6 = 100 000 Paare oder mehr pro 50x50-km-Quadrat). Angaben über Brutpopulationen sind immer mit (zum Teil systematischen) Fehlern behaftet, selbst wenn sie als Grössenklassen ausgewiesen werden. Wir halten das Vorgehen dennoch für gerechtfertigt. Selbst grobe quantitative Angaben sind aussagekräftiger als rein qualitative Informationen über die Anwesenheit einer Art.

Bei länderübergreifenden Quadraten, für die jedes betroffene Land einen Schätzwert für seinen Teil gegeben hatte, wurde der höchste Teilwert berücksichtigt, weil die verwendeten logarithmischen Klassen nicht zusammengezählt werden können. Dies kann zu einer Unterschätzung des Bestands entlang von Landesgrenzen führen.

Aus Norwegen und Polen konnten keine quantitativen Angaben für die Quadrate gewonnen werden, ebenso aus Bosnien und Serbien, wo die Kontakte wegen tragischer Ereignisse abrissen. Aus Frankreich, Spanien, Italien und Island liegen nur aus einzelnen Regionen und/oder zu einzelnen Arten quantitative Informationen vor.

Die Qualität der Daten in den bearbeiteten 50x50-km-Atlasquadraten Europas sind in Abb. 2 und Abb. 3 dargestellt; Abb. 2 zeigt die maximale Qualität, Abb. 3 die minimale – entsprechend der folgenden Differenzierung:

1. Halb-quantitative Bestandsangaben: Bruten sicher oder wahrscheinlich (in den Artkarten: roter Punkt).
2. Halb-quantitative Bestandsangaben: Bruten möglich (in den Artkarten: orangener Punkt).
3. Qualitative Brutangabe: Brutvorkommen sicher oder wahrscheinlich (in den Artkarten: dunkel-lila Punkt).
4. Qualitative Brutangabe: Brutvorkommen möglich (in den Artkarten: hell-lila Punkt).

In den Artkarten gibt es ferner graue Punkte, wenn für diese Art in diesem Quadrat keine Erfassung durchgeführt wurde; ein Quadrat ohne jeden Punkt heisst, dass das Quadrat untersucht, die Art aber nicht festgestellt wurde.

UTM-Raster

Die Kartenprojektion auf der Basis von Rasterquadraten hatte drei Kriterien zu erfüllen: Sie musste 1.) das ganze Untersuchungsgebiet umfassen, 2.) den meisten europäischen Ländern vertraut sein, und 3.) mit der geographischen Einteilung in den nationalen Karten direkt oder indirekt übereinstimmen. Einzig die 'Universal Transverse Merkator' (UTM)-Projektion genügt diesen Kriterien. Weil zudem die Grundkarte des *Atlas Florae Europaeae* das UTM-Rastergitter benutzt, ist diese Kartenprojektion auch für den ornithologischen Verbreitungsatlas verwendet worden. Wie im europäischen Pflanzenatlas dient auch im ornithologischen das 50x50-km-Gitter als Erfassungseinheit. Ein feineres Rasternetz wäre bei der Datensammlung und bei der Auswertung kaum zu bewältigen gewesen.

Die Grundeinheit des UTM-Gitters ist das 100x100-km-Quadrat. Dieses wird durch einen Code aus zwei Zahlen und drei Buchstaben eindeutig bezeichnet. Die vier 50x50-km-Quadrate innerhalb jedes 100x100-km-Quadrates werden nach folgendem Schema durch die Zusatzzahlen 1–4 charakterisiert: 1 = nordwestliches, 2 = südwestliches, 3 = nordöstliches, und 4 = südöstliches Viertel. Jedes 50x50-km-Quadrat hat somit einen Code aus drei Zahlen und Buchstaben.

In der Nord-Süd-Achse ist das UTM-Gitter durch Linien parallel zu den Breitengraden begrenzt. Sie liegen in Intervallen von 50 km und beginnen am Äquator. Die Längengrade konvergieren gegen die Pole, weshalb die Zahl der Quadrate polwärts abnimmt. Im UTM-Gitter ist dies kompensiert worden, so dass die "Quadrate" in Ost-West-Richtung nicht zu stark von 50 km abweichen. Das hat aber zur Folge, dass einzelne Felder nicht mehr exakt quadratisch sind. In Abb. 1 kommt die Korrektur im Muster der Quadrate deutlich zum Ausdruck und wird im **Technical Appendix** ausführlich dargestellt.

Jahre der Erfassung

Ursprünglich war vorgesehen, die Feldarbeit für den Atlas 1985–1988 durchzuführen. Da verschiedene Nationen ihre Erfassung nicht auf diesen Plan ausrichten konnten, mussten auch frühere und spätere Angaben verwendet werden, um den Erfassungsgrad zu verbessern. Tab. 3 (im Anschluss an **Introduction**) listet alle teilnehmenden Länder mit den Jahren ihrer Feldarbeit, dem nationalen Gitter und den angewandten Erfassungsmethoden auf.

Besonders in Nord-Russland und Albanien, wo keine Angaben aus der Atlaserfassung vorlagen, machten lokale Ornithologen Verbreitungsangaben und Bestandsschätzungen nach anderen Quellen. Wo die Zuverlässigkeit solcher Informationen gewährleistet war, wurden sie übernommen. In einzelnen Fällen wurde aufgrund von Bestandsangaben aus Quadraten derselben Region extrapoliert.

Organisation

Dieser Atlas ist ein Projekt des European Ornithological Atlas Committee EOAC. Die Durchführung übernahm im wesentlichen SOVON (Niederlande), das sich auf die nationalen Koordinatoren als Hauptvertreter der teilnehmenden Länder stützte.

Alle nationalen Koordinatoren erhielten vom EOAC die 50x50-km-Gitterkarten ihres Landes, um eine einheitliche Verwendung von Quadraten im ganzen Untersuchungsgebiet sicherzustellen. Wenn in einem Land feinere oder andere Rastereinheiten gewählt wurden, hatten die Koordinatoren die Aufgabe, die Angaben aus ihren Ländern in das UTM-Gitternetz zu überführen.

Alle Daten aus den einzelnen Ländern wurden von der SOVON in Zusammenarbeit mit dem Niederländischen Zentralamt für Statistik gesammelt, kontrolliert, in Absprache mit den Koordinatoren korrigiert und mit EDV ausgewertet.

Die nationalen Koordinatoren organisierten die Datenaufnahme in ihren Ländern, instruierten die Feldornithologen, sammelten die Daten und schätzten gegebenenfalls auch Bestände in den Quadraten. Sie füllten die Fragebogen aus, übermittelten die nationalen Angaben an die Zentrale in den Niederlanden und kontrollierten später die Computerausdrucke, um Übermittlungsfehler auszumerzen. Sie erhielten auch alle Daten von dritter Seite zur Stellungnahme.

In grossen Ländern und wo regionale Organisationen vorhanden sind, wurden die nationalen Koordinatoren durch regionale und lokale Feldornithologen und weitere Fachleute unterstützt. Angaben aus der Literatur und aus unveröffentlichten Berichten wurden durch die Autoren der Arttexte und andere Artspezialisten eingebracht. Für einzelne entlegene Gebiete waren sie die wichtigste Datenquelle.

Die Arbeit im Feld wurde von Tausenden von Ornithologen meist in ihrer Freizeit geleistet. Ihr Beitrag kann nicht hoch genug eingeschätzt werden. Hundertausende, vielleicht sogar über eine Million Beobachtungsstunden sind die Grundlage für den vorliegenden europäischen Atlas.

Datenaufnahme in den Ländern und Übermittlung an die Zentrale

Das Zentralamt für Statistik entwickelte ein Formular für die Datenaufnahme. Es ist in Abb. 4 (nach **Introduction**) teilweise wiedergegeben. Für jedes der 50x50-km-Quadrate war ein Formular auszufüllen. Randquadrate an den Landesgrenzen waren nur für den nationalen Teil zu bearbeiten. Es wurden folgende allgemeine Angaben zu jedem Quadrat verlangt:

1. Erfassungszeitraum: Jahre, aus denen die Angaben stammen.
2. UTM-50-Code des Quadrates.
3. Vollständigkeit der Erfassung: Gut, d.h. im Quadrat wurden mindestens 75% der zu erwarteten Brutvogelarten nachgewiesen; mangelhaft, d.h. < 75%.
4. Höhenlage: minimale und maximale Meereshöhe im Quadrat.
5. Adresse von Bearbeiter oder Koordinator.
6. Zusätzliche Informationen und Bemerkungen.
7. Kurze Beschreibung der Lebensräume im Quadrat.

Im Hauptteil des Fragebogens waren rund 440 Vogelarten mit dem wissenschaftlichen Namen in Kurzform und dem Euring-Code aufgelistet. Für nicht aufgeführte Arten, Bastarde etc. waren freie Zeilen vorhanden. Für jede im Quadrat nachgewiesene Art wurde der Brutnachweis in den drei Kategorien A–C, nach Atlas-Code 1–16 (s. Tab. 1) und die Zahl der Brutpaare im Quadrat als Schätzwert auf logarithmischer Basis eingetragen.

Die eingehenden Formulare bzw. Disketten wurden bei der Zentrale auf offensichtliche Fehler und Mängel geprüft (z.B. fehlende oder offensichtlich falsche Codes) und in einen ASCII-File der Datenbank eingegeben. Jeder Eintrag erhielt einen nationalen Identifizierungs-Code. Die Datenbank enthält einen einzigen Wert für jede der Grundinformationen je Art und Quadrat.

Kontrolle der Daten und Korrekturen

Länder mit fristgerecht abgelieferten Daten erhielten umgehend Arbeitskarten und Landeslisten je Art zur Kontrolle. Dieses Vorgehen erwies sich als sehr

Tab. 1 Kategorien des Brutnachweises und Codes

A: Mögliches Brüten	
1	Art während der Brutzeit im möglichen Bruthabitat beobachtet
2	Singende(s) Männchen zur Brutzeit anwesend oder Nestrufe gehört
B: Wahrscheinliches Brüten	
3	Ein Paar zur Brutzeit in geeignetem Bruthabitat beobachtet
4	Ständiges Revier durch Feststellen von Revierverhalten (Gesang etc.) an mindestens 2 verschiedenen Tagen im Abstand von mindestens einer Woche am gleichen Platz vermutet
5	Balzverhalten
6	Aufsuchen möglicher Neststandorte
7	Erregtes Verhalten oder Warnrufe von Altvögeln
8	Brutfleck bei Altvögeln, die in der Hand untersucht wurden
9	Nestbau oder Zimmern einer Höhle
C: Gesichertes Brüten	
10	Ablenkungsverhalten oder Verleiten (Flügellahmstellen)
11	Benutztes Nest oder Eischalen gefunden (von geschlüpften Jungen oder solchen, die in der aktuellen Brutperiode gelegt worden waren)
12	Eben flügge Junge (Nesthocker) oder Dunenjunge (Nestflüchter) festgestellt
13	Altvögel, die den Brutplatz anfliegen oder verlassen unter Umständen, die auf ein besetztes Nest hinweisen (einschliesslich hoch gelegene Nester oder unzugängliche Nisthöhlen)
14	Altvögel, die Kot oder Futter tragen
15	Nest mit Eiern
16	Junge im Nest gesehen oder gehört

zweckdienlich und effizient, weil Fehler auf Karten besser erkannt werden. Die anschaulichen Unterlagen stimulierten zudem andere Länder, ihre Daten abzuliefern.

In einem zweiten Kontakt von Zentrale und Koordinatoren wurde geprüft, ob die ersten Fehler in Verbreitungskarten und Listen korrigiert worden waren. Da die Angaben aus verschiedenen Ländern zu unterschiedlichen Perioden eintrafen, überlagerten sich diese Korrekturschritte. Die meisten nationalen Koordinatoren erledigten jedoch die enormen Kontroll- und Endkorrekturarbeiten fristgerecht, wenn auch zum Teil unter erheblichem Zeitdruck. In einzelnen Ländern wie dem früheren Jugoslawien war die Datenbearbeitung allerdings erschwert oder sogar unmöglich.

Zu einem späteren Zeitpunkt trafen weitere Zahlen und Korrekturvorschläge sowohl für die Verbreitung der Arten, als auch ihrer lokalen Dichte und ihrer nationalen Bestände von den Autoren der Arttexte und weiteren Spezialisten ein. Bei den meisten wurde durch die nationalen Koordinatoren überprüft und entschieden, welcher Zahl der Vorzug zu geben war. Wo dies aus Zeitmangel nicht mehr möglich war, wurde die ursprüngliche Zahl beibehalten und im Arttext vermerkt, dass sich die Ansicht des Autors in Teilen des Verbreitungsgebietes nicht mit den Kartenangaben deckt. Bei den nationalen Beständen konnten die Zahlen u.U. nicht mehr in die *European Bird Database* aufgenommen werden, aus denen die Bestandsgraphiken gefertigt wurden. Auch hier wird auf die abweichende Ansicht des Autors hingewiesen.

Der Schlusstermin für Angaben und Korrekturen war der 1. Juli 1995, doch wurden Daten aus Albanien, der europäischen Türkei, dem Kaukasus und Teilen der Ukraine und Russlands sowie Informationen der Artautoren bis zum 1. November 1995 berücksichtigt.

MATERIAL

Untersuchungsgebiet

Abb. 1 zeigt das beabsichtigte Bearbeitungsgebiet. Es wäre wünschenswert gewesen, die ganze Westpaläarktis zu bearbeiten, wie sie in *The Birds of the Western Palearctic* von Cramp et al (1977–1994) definiert ist. Da aber nur wenig Angaben aus Kleinasien, dem Norden der Arabischen Halbinsel und aus Nordafrika verfügbar sind, wurden diese Gebiete ausgeklammert. Das beabsichtigte Bearbeitungsgebiet entspricht daher im wesentlichen der Grundkarte des *Atlas Florae Europaeae* (Jalas & Suominen 1972, 1988). Es umfasst aber zusätzlich Novaya Zemlja, Franz-Josef-Land (wo die Angaben allerdings unvollständig sind), alle griechischen Inseln längs der türkischen Küste, Madeira, die Region um Stavropol in Südrussland und die Kaukasus-Republiken. Zypern, die Kanarischen Inseln und alle Mittelmeerinseln unter nordafrikanischer Verwaltung bleiben dagegen unberücksichtigt. Im Unterschied zum Erfassungsbereich von *Birds in Europe: Their Conservation Status* (Tucker & Heath 1994) schliesst der vorliegende Atlas den kleinasiatischen Teil der Türkei und Grönland aus.

Im Unterschied zu *Birds in Europe* schliessen Cramp et al (1977–1994), Jalas & Suominen (1972, 1988) und der vorliegende Atlas ein kleines Areal Europas bei Orenburg aus, berücksichtigen aber einen Teil des asiatischen Kasachstans zwischen Wolga und dem Uralfluss und einen Teil des asiatischen Russlands bei Sverdlovsk; dies ist in Abb. 1 nicht sofort ersichtlich.

Die tatsächlich bearbeitete Fläche zeigen die Karten der Abb. 2 und 3. Der Vergleich mit Abb. 1 zeigt, dass südliche Teile Russlands nicht und zusätzlich weite Teile von Russland, Weissrussland, der Ukraine und der Kaukasusländer nur für ausgewählte Arten bearbeitet sind.

Nationale Bestände

Die nationalen Gesamtbestände wurden vom EBCC und BirdLife International gemeinsam gesammelt. Die Zusammenarbeit förderte die Kontakte der beiden Organisationen zu den europäischen Ländern. Die nationalen Daten der Brutbestände sind die Grundlage für diesen Atlas und das Dispersed Species Projekt, dessen Ergebnisse in *Birds in Europe: Their Conservation Status* veröffentlicht wurden (Tucker & Heath 1994). Die Angaben wurden hauptsächlich durch Fragebogen an die nationalen Koordinatoren erhoben, welche in *Birds in Europe* aufgelistet sind (Tucker & Heath 1994). Diese leiteten die Formulare an geeignete Organisationen, Artspezialisten und regionale Fachleute weiter. Jedes Land schätzte die Grösse der nationalen Populationen seiner Brutvögel (minimale und maximale Zahl der Paare pro Land), deren Veränderungen in Prozent-Kategorien von 1970 bis 1990 sowie Veränderungen im Verbreitungsareal 1970–1990. Erfasst wurden auch die Zuverlässigkeit der Daten (vgl. Tab. 2) und die Quellen. Alle diese Grundlagen sind in der europäischen ornithologischen Datenbank (European Bird Database) gespeichert, die von BirdLife International verwaltet wird.

Bearbeitete Brutvogelarten

Berücksichtigt wurden Arten, welche seit 1985 im Untersuchungsgebiet gebrütet haben, falls sie die Kriterien in Tab. 1 erfüllten. Eingebürgerte Arten, welche über mindestens fünf Jahre in einer freilebenden und selbsterhaltenden Population vorkamen, werden ebenfalls dargestellt. Diese Regel wurde allerdings in verschiedenen Ländern unterschiedlich strikt angewandt.

Fehlerquellen und Grenzen, Aussagekraft

Im vorliegenden Atlas werden die Angaben grossflächig als halb-quantitative Verbreitungskarten dargestellt. Dazu sind die verfügbaren Daten im grossen und ganzen ausreichend zuverlässig. Wer sie jedoch für weitergehende Auswertungen benützen will, muss sich bewusst sein, dass die Genauigkeit und deshalb auch die Verlässlichkeit eingehenderer Aussagen begrenzt ist. Wir beschränken uns hier auf die wichtigsten Fehlerquellen, die bei der Interpretation der Verbreitungskarten zu beachten sind; Einzelheiten müssen beim EBCC erfragt werden.

1. Für die Feldarbeit wurden nur allgemeine Richtlinien ausgearbeitet, doch keine strikten Regeln festgelegt. Da die einzelnen Länder die Methoden ihren Möglichkeiten anpassten und bei den Bestandsschätzungen von unterschiedlichen Voraussetzungen ausgehen mussten, können systematische Fehler nicht ausgeschlossen werden.

Tab.2 Codes für Bestände in der *European Bird Database*

POPMIN	= Mindestbestand (in Paaren)		
POPMAX	= Höchstbestand (in Paaren)		
MEAN	= geometrisches Bestandsmittel	PSV	= Genauigkeit der Bestandsschätzung
YRC	= Jahr der Bestandsschätzung		
PST	= Bestandstrend	PTV	= Genauigkeit der Trendschätzung
RST	= Verbreitungstrend	RTV	= Genauigkeit der Trendschätzung

Masszahlen für Bestands- und Verbreitungstrends Bestand und Vorkommen beziehen sich auf 1970–1990

+2	= starke Zunahme von mindestens 50%
+1	= schwache Zunahme zwischen 20 und 50%
0	= stabil, Veränderung unter 20% in beiden Richtungen
-1	= schwache Abnahme zwischen 20 und 50%
-2	= starke Abnahme von mindestens 50%
n	= Neusiedler während des Zeitraumes
x	= ausgestorben während des Zeitraumes
f	= schwankend, mit Änderungen über 20% aber ohne klaren Trend

Übersetzung/Bearbeitung: Goetz Rheinwald
nach einer Vorlage von Michael Blair, Ward Hagemeijer

2. Auch für die Auswertung und Interpretation der Felddaten wurden keine detaillierten Vorgaben gemacht. Jedes Land musste eigenständig entscheiden, wie die Angaben der Feldornithologen umzusetzen und in geeigneter Form in die Formulare für den europäischen Atlas einzutragen waren. Dies betrifft insbesondere die Bestandsgrössen für die einzelnen Quadrate und für das ganze Land.
3. Die Zuverlässigkeit der Daten hängt von der individuellen Erfahrung und den Kenntnissen der Feldornithologen ab, von der Zahl der Beobachter eines Gebietes und ihren zeitlichen Möglichkeiten.
4. Gebietsweise mussten die Angaben aufgrund von Stichproben extrapoliert oder aus der Literatur übernommen werden.

PRÄSENTATION DER DATEN

Reihenfolge der Arten

Der Atlas behandelt 513 Arten (zuzgl. den Italiensperling). Sie werden im Hauptteil des Atlas artweise in der Regel in systematischer Reihenfolge angenähert nach Voous (1977) dargestellt. In der Artbearbeitung wird auch der fünfstellige Euring-Code mitgeteilt, der von der europäischen Beringungsorganisation Euring benutzt wird; er wurde beim Zusammentragen der Artinformationen in der Datenbank verwendet (Einzelheiten Technical Appendix). Abweichungen in der Reihenfolge der Arten ergaben sich wegen der unterschiedlichen Länge der Arttexte (s. unten).

Aufbau und Umfang der Arttexte

Jede Art ist mit einer Vignette abgebildet. Die Artnamen sind, soweit bekannt, in 14 Sprachen angegeben. Bei den meisten wird ein Säulendiagramm mit den nationalen Beständen gegeben (Zeichenerklärung vor den Artkapiteln). Arten mit aussagekräftigen und verlässlichen Angaben und einem weiten Verbreitungsgebiet werden auf einer Doppelseite dargestellt, solche mit einem eingeschränkten Verbreitungsgebiet auf einer Seite; dasselbe gilt für Arten, bei denen unzureichende Angaben eine Verbreitungskarte nicht rechtfertigen. In einigen Fällen erübrigten sich Bestandsgrafiken, so dass die Aussagen auf einer halben Seite Platz finden. Um zu gewährleisten, dass zweiseitige Arttexte auf einer Doppelseite stehen, wurde die Reihenfolge der Arten nötigenfalls leicht geändert.

Erläutert werden in der Regel in folgender Reihenfolge diese Themen: Weltverbreitung, Bruthabitate, Verbreitung und Häufigkeitsmuster in Europa, jüngste Veränderungen in Bestand und Verbreitung (und mögliche Ursachen), regionale Unterschiede in der Häufigkeit, Verbreitungsgrenzen und mögliche Einflussfaktoren, Siedlungsdichte im Primärhabitat, Zugverhalten innerhalb und ausserhalb Europas sowie besondere Merkmale und auffällige Unterarten, deren Verbreitung und Überlappung sowie Bestandstrends der Art.

Nicht behandelt werden Brutbiologie, Oologie, Verhalten, Nahrung, Beziehungen zu anderen Arten, Evolution und Taxonomie (ausser bei kürzlich vollzogenen Änderungen oder bei deutlich verschiedenen Unterarten), Sterblichkeit und weitere populationsdynamische Parameter. Verzichtet wird auch auf Angaben über die Gefährdung von Arten und deren Ursachen, welche in *Birds in Europe* (Tucker & Heath 1994) ausführlich besprochen werden, und das nach den Artkapiteln in knapper Form referiert wird.

Verbreitungskarten

Die in den Verbreitungskarten verwendeten Punktgrössen entsprechen den logarithmischen Grössenklassen der Brutpaare pro Quadrat und sind daher keine Siedlungsdichten. Mit besonderen Symbolen wird auch mögliches und wahrscheinliches/sicheres Brüten dargestellt (s. oben: Daten zur Häufigkeit im Abschnitt Methoden).

NOMENKLATUR UND TAXONOMIE

Das EBCC nimmt in den taxonomischen Fragen eine vorsichtig-konservative Haltung ein. Im allgemeinen folgt dieser Atlas in Taxonomie, systematischer Reihenfolge und englischer Nomenklatur den *Birds of the Western Palearctic* (BWP).

Puffinus yelkouan, Puffinus mauretanicus, Larus cachinnans, Anthus petrosus, Phylloscopus lorenzi und *Pyrrhula murina* werden als selbständige Arten behandelt und wurden in Verbreitungskarten *Puffinus puffinus, Puffinus mauretanicus, Larus argentatus, Anthus spinoletta, Phylloscopus collybita* und *Pyrrhula pyrrhula* gegenübergestellt. Dies war dann möglich, wenn sie entweder getrennt erfasst wurden oder wenn sie geographisch getrennt sind. (Die drei *Puffinus*-Arten werden zusammen dargestellt).

Es gab ursprünglich den Versuch, Unterarten und unterscheidbare Formen einiger Arten getrennt zu kartieren, doch die Unterscheidungen, die das EOAC getroffen hatte, wurden nicht einheitlich in ganz Europa beachtet. Dies machte eine Kartendarstellung unmöglich. Dennoch wurde der Italiensperling gesondert erfasst, und dieser Atlas folgt BWP, indem es ihn als stabilisierten Hybriden zwischen *Passer domesticus* und *P. hispaniolensis* auffasst und ihn als *Passer x italiae* bezeichnet. Im Gegensatz dazu enthält *Phylloscopus trochiloides* zwei geographisch getrennte Unterarten *viridanus* und *nitidus*, die früher als eigene Arten betrachtet wurden. *Lanius meridionalis* von *Lanius excubitor* zu trennen, wurde allgemein akzeptiert, als der Atlas beendet wurde; ein Diagramm im Arttext zeigt die Grenze zwischen den beiden Formen. *Hippolais caligata* wird manchmal als gesondert von *H. rama* betrachtet; im vorliegenden Atlas wird letzterer aber als Unterart behandelt. Die Beziehungen innerhalb einiger Möwengruppen sind oft unklar; *Larus armenicus* wird hier als selbständige Art betrachtet.

QUELLEN UND LITERATUR

In den Arttexten werden aus Platzgründen nur wenige, artspezifische Literaturzitate erwähnt (Anhang 1), nicht aber Handbücher. Für das Grundverständnis jeder europäischen Brutvogelart sollten Arttexte und Karten dieses Atlanten stets in Zusammenhang mit den Angaben in den beiden wichtigsten Handbüchern Europas gesehen werden: *Birds of the Western Palearctic* (Cramp et al 1977–1994) und *Handbuch der Vögel Mitteleuropas* (Glutz von Blotzheim et al 1966 bis vorläufig 1995). In den Arttexten werden diese beiden Standardwerke mit dem Kürzel BWP und HVM zitiert.

Birds in Europe: Their Conservation Status (Tucker & Heath 1994) gibt einen ersten Überblick über die europäischen Vogelpopulationen, ihre Gefährdung und ihren Schutzstatus. Das Buch beschreibt eingehend alle Arten, die einen ungünstigen Schutzstatus haben ('unfavourable conservation status'). Der vorliegende Atlas enthält dagegen **alle** Arten, auch die gegenwärtig nicht gefährdeten. Die Bestandsangaben entstammen der gleichen europäischen Datenbank, die auch für Birds in Europe verwendet wurde; deshab wird dieses Werk in den Arttexten häufig zitiert.

Die im Atlas zitierte Literatur findet der Leser im Literaturverzeichnis am Ende des Buches.

ABKÜRZUNGEN

asl	über Normal-Null (above sea level, Höhe ü.M.)
bp	Brutpaare
BTO	British Trust for Ornithology (Grossbritannien)
BWP	Birds of the Western Palearctic (Cramp et al 1977–1994)
c	circa, ungefähr
CBS	Central Bureau voor Statistics (Niederlande)
EBCC	European Bird Census Council (Europäische Organisation der Länder, welche sich mit der Überwachung von Vogelbeständen befassen; Herausgeberin des europäischen Brutvogelatlas)
EOAC	European Ornithological Atlas Committee (Arbeitsgruppe für den Europäischen Brutvogelatlas)
et al	und andere (in Zitaten)
ha	Hektare (10 000 m^2)
HVM	Handbuch der Vögel Mitteleuropas (Glutz von Blotzheim et al 1966 bis vorläufig 1995)
ind	Individuen
JNCC	Joint Nature Conservation Committee (Grossbritannien)
M	Million(en)
pers comm	persönliche Mitteilung(en)
pers obs	eigene Beobachtung(en)
RSPB	Royal Society for the Protection of Birds (Grossbritannien)
SOVON	SOVON Bird Census Work The Netherlands (Niederlande)
SPEC	Species of European conservation concern (Arten, für deren Schutz Europa die Verantwortung trägt; Tucker & Heath 1994)
unpubl	unveröffentlicht
UTM	'Universal Transverse Merkator' Projektion (Rastergitter als Erfassungseinheit im vorliegenden Atlas, Quadrate von 50x50 km)
WWT	Wildfowl and Wetlands Trust (Grossbritannien)

Introducción

ATLAS EBCC DE LAS AVES REPRODUCTORAS EN EUROPA

Muchos libros sobre aves incluyen mapas detallados de distribución de las especies. Algunos de estos mapas se basan en estudios de poblaciones de aves reproductoras pero, excepto en el caso de atlas especializados, muchos mapas se derivan de fuentes de distinta fiabilidad y algunas veces sólo se trata de reproducciones de mapas anteriores de dudosa exactitud. Además muchos mapas, al no incluir habitualmente información cuantitativa, no reflejan las diferencias en la abundancia de una especie entre zonas distintas.

Sin embargo, se dispone ya de un creciente número de excelentes atlas de aves reproductoras a nivel nacional o regional, muchos de los cuales surgieron a raíz del proyecto que originó este *Atlas* y, como él, contienen datos semicuantitativos. En 1971 se creó el Comité del Atlas Ornitológico Europeo (European Ornithological Atlas Committee, EOAC) con el objetivo de cartografiar la distribución en época de cría de aquellas especies en Europa para las que se pudiera obtener información mediante trabajo de campo. Este libro recoge los resultados de dicho empeño.

El *Atlas* representa la distribución de las aves en un periodo de tiempo limitado, pero los datos recogidos (a pesar de pequeñas imprecisiones) constituyen una referencia obligada frente a la que deberán contrastarse futuros trabajos (y desde luego futuros cambios en la distribución de las aves en Europa). El EOAC de 1971 tuvo una clara visión de lo que llegaría a ser el primer estudio de ámbito continental de aves reproductoras que se hubiera intentado jamás. Su sueño ha sido recompensado y la información finalmente contenida en el *Atlas EBCC de las Aves Reproductoras en Europa* permite conocer dónde cría cada especie al reflejar fielmente la distribución de las especies reproductoras en Europa.

ESTRUCTURA DEL ATLAS

Esta **Introducción** describe brevemente el propósito del *Atlas,* detalla los métodos utilizados para la obtención de los datos sobre distribución y población, así como para su informatización y cartografiado, y explica la estructura del *Atlas*. Además, está impresa en diversos idiomas de forma que pueda ser leída por la mayoría de los ornitólogos europeos.

Secciones iniciales

En el **Prefacio** el Profesor Karel Voous destaca la importancia del *Atlas* en el contexto de los cambios que están afectando a la avifauna en Europa. El **Prólogo** resume como este proyecto colectivo de *Atlas* cubre las expectativas de los ornitólogos europeos y destaca la política y proyectos del Consejo Europeo de Censos de Aves (European Bird Census Council, EBCC) para futuros programas de seguimiento de las aves europeas. Se incluye después la **Introducción**, con temas como metodología y ámbito geográfico, y a continuación una sección de **Figuras Explicativas**, que refleja la cobertura obtenida, la calidad de los datos y una copia de la ficha modelo para la compilación de los mismos. Una sección cronológica (**Historia**) describe después la evolución del proyecto de Atlas Ornitológico Europeo y los contratiempos a los que se ha enfrentado. A continuación, bajo el título **Evolución e Historia de la Avifauna Europea**, se incluye un ensayo del Profesor Jacques Blondel que ilustra cómo ha llegado a configurarse la actual distribución de las especies de aves europeas. Finalmente, se incluyen una sección de **Agradecimientos** y una relación de los **Atlas Ornitológicos Nacionales y Regionales de Europa**.

Sección de especies

Una Introducción a los Mapas y Gráficos de Población precede a la sección principal del *Atlas* que se ocupa de las especies reproductoras en Europa. La Parte 1 comprende los mapas de distribución, los comentarios por especie, los nombres comunes en 14 idiomas para cada especie reproductora, e ilustraciones. Las especies aparecen siguiendo aproximadamente el orden de Voous (1977) y la secuencia de la Unión Europea para el Anillamiento de Aves (European Union for Bird Ringing, EURING). La Parte 2 comprende los comentarios de aquellas especies que se cree se reproducen en Europa pero para las que no se recibieron datos precisos.

Secciones finales

En esta sección un nuevo grupo de mapas refleja la distribución de las aves reproductoras en Europa y la de especies que necesitan medidas de conservación en Europa (Species of European Conservation Concern, SPEC) según la definición establecida por BirdLife International (Tucker & Heath, 1994). El Apéndice Técnico explica cómo el retículo utilizado para el *Atlas* difiere de la proyección UTM teórica y como fueron consideradas las islas y las cuadrículas de 50 km que incluyen zonas costeras. También explica cómo utiliza el Atlas el sistema de numeración de EURING.

Suplementos en otros idiomas

A los delegados del EBCC en cada país se les ha proporcionado un resumen de las secciones iniciales del *Atlas* y de los comentarios por especie para que, en caso de que se consigan los fondos necesarios e independientemente del *Atlas,* sean traducidos a sus idiomas respectivos y publicados, en forma de suplemento, para que pueda así facilitarse el uso de este libro por parte de aquellos que no lean Inglés. Al final del Apéndice Técnico se incluye la lista de nombres y direcciones de quienes proporcionan estos suplementos (según confirmaciones en el momento de entrar en prensa este Atlas).

MÉTODOS

Presentación de los datos del Atlas

El planteamiento inicial para la recolección de datos y su compilación y la selección de los métodos de trabajo, se describen en la sección cronológica donde se detalla además cómo se organizaron los muestreos.

Los mapas del *Atlas* reflejan las diferencias en densidades (número de aves por unidad de superficie) en escala logarítmica (como se explica más abajo). Esta escala es especialmente apropiada para aquellas especies cuyas densidades varían notablemente entre zonas distintas de su área de distribución pero, por el contrario, las pequeñas diferencias en densidad no quedan claramente reflejadas a esta escala.

El *Atlas* no sólo ofrece la distribución de las aves reproductoras en Europa, sino que también incluye estimaciones del tamaño de las poblaciones reproductoras y las tendencias de la mayoría de las especies en cada país europeo. Los cambios en los patrones de distribución sólo pueden ser entendidos con una información detallada sobre tamaños de población y tendencias a nivel nacional.

Área de cobertura prevista del *Atlas*

El área de cobertura prevista se muestra en la Figura 1. Aunque hubiera sido deseable que coincidiera totalmente con los límites del Paleártico Occidental según han sido definidos en *The Birds of The Western Paleartic* (Cramp *et al.*, 1977–1994), esto resultó finalmente imposible porque se dispone de pocos datos para Asia Menor, norte de la Península de Arabia y norte de Africa, por lo que estas zonas fueron finalmente excluidas. Por este razón, el *Atlas* sigue el mapa base del *Atlas Florae Europaeae* (Jalas & Suominen 1972, 1988) con la diferencia de que éste incluye Novaya Zemlya, Franz Josef Land, todas las islas griegas próximas a Turquía, los archipiélagos de Madeira y Azores, la región de Stavropol al sureste de Rusia y las repúblicas del Cáucaso. Las diferencias existentes entre el área del Paleártico Occidental y la de cobertura del *Atlas EBCC* son que éste no las Islas Canarias, Chipre, ni otras pequeñas islas mediterráneas. La cobertura del *Atlas* difiere de la de *Birds in Europe: their conservation status* (Tucker & Heath, 1994) ya que no incluye Turquía y Groenlandia.

Aunque no resulta muy evidente en la Figura 1, los límites del Paleártico Occidental, los del *Atlas Florae Europaeae* y los de este *Atlas* no incluyen una pequeña área de Europa, cerca de Odenburg e incluyen una parte del Kazahkstán asiático entre los ríos Volga y Ural, y una parte de la Rusia asiática al este de Perm (región de Sverdlovsk), a diferencia de *Birds in Europe*.

Cobertura obtenida

En la sección de Figuras Explicativas que sigue a la Introducción, la Figura 2 muestra las cuadrículas censadas e indica la calidad máxima de los datos obtenidos para cada cuadrícula, y la Figura 3 refleja la calidad mínima de datos obtenidos para cada cuadrícula. Aunque en el apartado de Información cualitativa frente a semicuantitativa (ver más abajo) se explica el significado de estos términos, las categorías de calidad de los datos mostradas en esos mapas son, en orden descendiente:

1. Estima semicuantitativa de población, reproducción segura o probable.
2. Estima semicuantitativa de población, reproducción posible.
3. Presencia cualitativa, reproducción segura o probable.
4. Presencia cualitativa, reproducción posible.

La calidad de los datos fue en general homogénea para todas las especies registradas en una cuadrícula (pero ver más abajo). Extensas áreas de Rusia central no fueron cubiertas principalmente debido a que no pudieron establecerse los contactos apropiados. Para una gran parte del resto de Rusia, partes de Bielorusia, Ucrania, y las repúblicas del Cáucaso, sólo se logró una buena cobertura para un reducido número de especies. La cobertura de la mayor parte de la ex Yugoslavia fue razonablemente aceptable (aunque no para todas las especies en algunas áreas) y quedaron también zonas sin cubrir en Albania. La cobertura fue incompleta para las islas rusas del ártico de Novaya Zemlya y Franz Josef Land.

En el resto de las zonas, a pesar de inevitables deficiencias, la cobertura se considera esencialmente completa.

Los mapas del *Atlas*

La selección del sistema de proyección a emplear para los mapas se basó en tres criterios: que cubriera el área de cobertura prevista del *Atlas*; que fuera conocida por la mayoría de los países europeos, y que fuera compatible con los sistemas de proyección utilizados a nivel nacional. Sólo la proyección Universal Transverse Mercator (UTM) cumplía estos criterios básicos cuando se inició el proyecto de este *Atlas*. Dado que el mapa base del proyecto *Atlas Florae Europaeae* utiliza el retículo UTM, resultó ideal como base para el mapa que se diseñó para este *Atlas* ornitológico. El *Atlas Florae Europaeae* utilizaba cuadrículas de 50km x 50km como unidades de trabajo a la hora de reflejar la información y esas mismas cuadrículas fueron utilizadas para el *Atlas* ornitológico, ya que hubiera sido imposible recopilar y analizar los datos a una escala menor a nivel continental.

La unidad cartográfica básica del retículo UTM, los cuadrados de 100km x 100km, están identificados individualmente por un código alfanumérico secuencial de dos números y tres letras. Para los atlas de flora y aves, cada uno de tales cuadrados fue subdividido en cuatro cuadrículas de 50km x 50km numeradas en el orden:

1	3
2	4

y de esta forma, cada cuadrícula de 50km x 50 km tiene una referencia exclusiva de seis caracteres. La representación del retículo UTM en sentido norte-sur es sencilla ya que las líneas que subdividen el retículo reflejan intervalos de 50km, comenzando en el ecuador, y son paralelas a las líneas de latitud (paralelos). En el eje este-oeste resulta más complicado porque los meridianos convergen hacia los polos. Por ello, el número de cuadrículas de 50km x 50 km que pueden ser incluidas disminuye hacia los polos y la distribución de las celdas UTM se compensa de diversas maneras. Las celdas que bordean cada meridiano de 6° disminuyen hacia los polos hasta que se transforman en puntos. El *Atlas Florae Europaeae* y este atlas ornitológico han modificado este sistema de forma que la variación en el tamaño de las cuadrículas que bordean los meridianos de 6° es menor. El *Atlas* se refiere a estas celdas como "cuadrículas" por conveniencia, aunque muchas de ellas no son exactamente cuadradas. Esta distribución se muestra en el mapa de cobertura prevista (Figura 1) y se ofrecen detalles completos en el **Apéndice Técnico**.

El EOAC proporcionó mapas con la cuadrícula 50km x 50km a los coordinadores nacionales para asegurarse de que se usaba así la cuadrícula correcta para el registro de los datos. El trabajo de campo se basó generalmente en cuadrículas UTM menores que las de 50km x 50km o en cuadrículas no correspondientes a la proyección UTM (según como estuvieran organizados los distintos atlas nacionales), pero en ambos casos los coordinadores nacionales tuvieron que convertir los datos a cuadrículas de 50km x 50km de forma que fueran utilizables para el posterior tratamiento de los mismos.

Fechas de trabajo de campo

Se había previsto que el trabajo de campo para el *Atlas* se desarrollara entre 1985 y 1988. Cada nación organizó su propio trabajo de campo. Sin embargo, y debido a dificultades prácticas no todos los países pudieron cumplir este calendario. Allí donde la cobertura resultó incompleta para el periodo de estudio, se consideraron también datos anteriores o posteriores de forma que la cobertura o la calidad de la información pudieran ser mejoradas al incluirlos. La Tabla 3, a continuación de la Introducción, detalla los países participantes, sus fechas de obtención de datos, la cuadrícula nacional de la que estos datos fueron convertidos y los métodos utilizados.

Compilación de información - datos sobre distribución de especies

Cientos de miles, tal vez más de un millón de horas de trabajo de campo, constituyen la base de este *Atlas*. Hubiera sido ideal que todos los participantes utilizasen idéntica metodología de campo y en el mismo periodo de tiempo, pero esto resultó finalmente imposible. El EOAC estableció por tanto unos criterios generales más que normas estrictas. En algunos países se realizaron simultáneamente el trabajo de campo para este *Atlas* y su atlas nacional. En otros, se utilizaron los datos de un proyecto independiente de atlas nacional como fuente de información para este *Atlas*.

Los métodos de trabajo de campo variaron desde visitas aisladas o acumulación de observaciones durante muchas visitas, hasta muestreos sistemáticos basados en transectos, estaciones de escucha o parcelas.

En la Figura 4 se reproduce parcialmente la ficha estándar elaborada por la Oficina Central de Estadística de Holanda (Dutch Central Bureau of Statistics). Se utilizó una ficha para cada cuadrícula censada. Para las cuadrículas que incluyen límites nacionales, cada país recopiló únicamente la información correspondiente a su territorio. La información general solicitada para cada cuadrícula fue:

1. Periodo de censo: año o años durante los que se obtuvieron los datos
2. Identificación (código UTM50)
3. Efectividad de los muestreos: indica si el trabajo en esta cuadrícula refleja más del 75% de las especies esperadas (alta) o menos (baja)
4. Altitud (rango entre las altitudes mínima y máxima, en metros)
5. Observador(es) o coordinador(es): nombre(s) y dirección(es) para posibles solicitudes futuras de información
6. Comentarios que pudieran explicara mejor los datos de la ficha
7. Pequeño cuestionario sobre los hábitats presentes

La ficha contiene un listado de especies (unas 440, según el orden de Voous (1977) y numeradas con la secuencia de EURING) al que referir los datos. La columna 0 contiene la abreviatura del nombre científico (p.ej., Gav stell) y la columna 1 el código EURING (p.ej. 00020). La columna 2 se reserva para detallar la categoría de reproducción mediante alguno de los 16 códigos (Tabla 1) agrupados en tres categorías: reproducción segura, probable o posible. Finalmente, la columna 3 solicitaba una estimación del número de parejas reproductoras en la cuadrícula, en escala logarítmica (1 = 1–9, 2 = 10–99 ... 6 = > 100.000).

El diseño de la ficha permitía el registro al final de la lista de híbridos y otras especies no incluidas en ella.

En general, las fuentes de información sobre aves reproductoras fueron:

1. Coordinadores nacionales del EBCC, quienes organizaron la obtención de datos y trasladaron los resultados a las fichas proporcionadas.
2. Coordinadores regionales. Algunas veces la recopilación de datos fue organizada por personas distintas a los coordinadores nacionales, especialmente en los países de mayor superficie, o cuando se contactó con algún miembro activo de una red de colaboradores ya existente. Estos coordinadores regionales trabajaron de la misma forma que los coordinadores nacionales.
3. Otras fuentes adicionales, principalmente bibliografía disponible a través de expertos nacionales en distintas especies. Cuando no se pudo disponer de datos de campo, especialmente de áreas inaccesibles o remotas, muchas veces la única fuente de datos fueron informes publicados o inéditos, no asequibles fácilmente al editor u organizadores nacionales.
4. Autores de los textos de especies. El autor del texto de una especie, experto en la misma, muy frecuentemente proporcionó información adicional sobre distribución o cifras.

Tabla 1 Categorías de reproducción y códigos

A: Reproducción posible
1. Especie observada en época de cría en posible hábitat de nidificación
2. Macho(s) cantor(es) presente(s), o reclamos de cría oídos en época de cría

B: Reproducción probable
3. Pareja observada en hábitat de cría adecuado en la temporada de reproducción
4. Territorio permanente asumido del registro de comportamientos territoriales (cantos, etc.) en al menos dos días diferentes con intervalo de una semana o más en el mismo lugar.
5. Manifestaciones de cortejo y celo
6. Ave vista visitando probable emplazamiento de nido
7. Comportamiento agitado o llamadas de ansiedad de los adultos
8. Placa incubadora en adulto examinado en mano
9. Construcción de nido o excavación de agujero para nido

C: Reproducción segura
10. Comportamiento de distracción o simulación de heridas
11. Nido usado o cáscaras de huevos (ocupado o puestos durante el periodo de estudio)
12. Pollos volantones (especies nidícolas) o aœn con plumón (especies nidífugas)
13. Adultos entrando o saliendo del emplazamiento del nido en circunstancias que indican que está ocupado (incluyendo los nidos altos o en agujeros, cuyos contenidos no pueden ser vistos) o adultos vistos incubando
14. Adulto transportando saco fecal o cebo para los pollos
15. Nido con huevos
16. Nido con jóvenes vistos u oídos

Todos los datos procedentes de estas fuentes fueron cuidadosamente revisados, y su inclusión en la base de datos tenía que ser aprobada previamente por el coordinador nacional.

Información cualitativa frente a semicuantitativa

El *Atlas* ofrece información semicuantitativa (estimas logarítmicas del tamaño de población) para cada cuadrícula, proporcionada por los coordinadores nacionales y regionales y los colaboradores de campo. Los distintos tamaños de puntos utilizados representan números de parejas reproductoras, no densidades. Los tamaños de puntos representan órdenes crecientes de magnitud (ver clave en página cxl). Desafortunadamente, algunos países como Noruega y Polonia (para todas las especies), España (para la mayoría de las especies) y Francia, Islandia e Italia (para parte de las especies), no proporcionaron información semicuantitativa. Tampoco se pudo disponer, por razones obvias, de los datos de Bosnia y Serbia. Algunas regiones de Francia valoraron sus datos de forma independiente. El coordinador nacional para Francia valoró los datos a nivel nacional para un número limitado de especies. Incluso estimaciones a escala logarítmica para un determinado número de cuadrículas, ofrecen mucha más información que la simple indicación de presencia-ausencia.

Para cuadrículas fronterizas donde cada país envió estimas de población para su territorio, se consideró el valor más alto (los valores logarítmicos no pueden ser sumados), aunque en algunos casos esto resultó en infraestimas de la población. Tal aproximación fue más útil que reflejar en esas cuadrículas únicamente datos cualitativos.

Los puntos en los mapas equivalen a las siguientes categorías de información:

púrpura intenso	=	cría segura o probable, cualitativa
púrpura claro	=	cría posible, cualitativa
rojo	=	cría segura o probable, semicuantitativa
naranja	=	cría posible, semicuantitativa
gris	=	no ha habido prospección para esta especie en esta cuadrícula
sin punto	=	cuadrícula prospectada sin haberse registrado la especie

Informatización - corrección de los mapas y comprobación de datos

Las fichas recibidas de los coordinadores nacionales fueron revisadas a la búsqueda de errores básicos (ausencia de códigos o errores en los mismos) antes de ser informatizados en un fichero formato ASCII, cada registro con un código nacional de identificación. Algunos países proporcionaron su información en disquete, y fue también revisada de la misma manera. La base de datos construida a partir de los ficheros básicos contiene un valor simple para cada especie en cada cuadrícula.

Aquellos coordinadores nacionales y otros informadores que enviaron rápidamente los datos, recibieron mapas preliminares y listados nacionales de especies en una primera fase del proceso de revisión. Se les pidió comprobar estos datos y se detectaron así numerosos errores que pudieron ser corregidos. Sin embargo, algunos países enviaron sus datos originales y los transformados de cualitativos a semicuantitativos, con bastante retraso. Por ello, la corrección de datos y el proceso de revisión comenzó tarde y se desarrolló a ritmos diferentes en distintos países. La elaboración de mapas preliminares resultó muy importante por dos razones:

1. Permitió a los coordinadores nacionales, y a través de ellos a muchos colaboradores de campo, comprobar si los datos que enviaron habían sido correctamente informatizados. Los errores resultaron mucho más fácilmente detectables al revisar los mapas que las listas de registros.
2. Estimuló una mayor participación que frecuentemente se tradujo en nuevos aportes de datos.

En una segunda fase se comprobó que las correcciones

derivadas de la primera fueron introducidas en la base de datos. Esto se consiguió enviando a los coordinadores nacionales, y otros informadores, una segunda colección de mapas y datos ya corregidos. La mayoría de los coordinadores realizaron esta enorme labor y enviaron correcciones finales, pero en algunos países como la ex-Yugoslavia, la actualización y comprobación fueron prácticamente imposibles. Aquellos países en los que el proceso de revisión se retrasó tuvieron que concentrar sus esfuerzos en un plazo de tiempo mucho menor, y a mayor retraso mayores fueron las dificultades encontradas para completar definitivamente los mapas.

En una fase posterior, se recibieron mapas actualizados de algunos autores de textos de especies y otros expertos en diversas especies. La mayoría de estos mapas han sido revisados por los coordinadores nacionales, decidiéndose finalmente qué mapa utilizar. Cuando esto no fue posible, debido a la falta material de tiempo, o bien se incluye el mapa original o se señala en el texto que la opinión del autor del mismo en cuanto a la distribución de la especie difiere en alguna forma de la reflejada en el mapa.

En aquellos casos en que no se pudo disponer de datos basados en trabajos de campo, lo que ocurrió sobre todo en el norte de Rusia y Albania, ornitólogos locales proporcionaron datos de otras fuentes, debiendo decidirse entonces sobre la validez de estos datos. Para tales cuadrículas se realizaron algunas estimas semicuantitativas extrapolando datos de cuadrículas en la misma región para las que se disponía de estimas directas, teniendo en cuenta áreas conocidas de hábitat apropiado para la especie.

El plazo final para la recepción de nuevos datos y correcciones fue el 1 de julio de 1995, aunque para maximizar la cobertura fueron utilizados también algunos datos recibidos durante los siguientes meses correspondientes a Albania, Turquía europea, el Cáucaso, parte de Ucrania y parte de Rusia. Las correcciones por parte de los autores de los comentarios de especies fueron admitidas hasta el 1 de noviembre de 1995.

Compilación de datos – tamaños de población

Los gráficos nacionales de población que se ofrecen en el *Atlas* se derivan de la Base de Datos de Aves de Europa. Esta contiene datos de población recopilados conjuntamente por el EBCC y BirdLife International y se creó para apoyar el trabajo de este *Atlas* y el Proyecto Especies Dispersas de BirdLife, cuyos resultados fueron publicados en *Birds in Europe: their conservation status* (Tucker & Heath, 1994). Esta colaboración también ayudó a ampliar la participación en algunas partes de Europa. Los datos fueron inicialmente recopilados distribuyendo cuestionarios a los coordinadores nacionales (cuya relación aparece en *Birds in Europe*), quienes a su vez los distribuyeron a los expertos apropiados, organizaciones que realizan seguimiento de aves y colaboradores regionales. BirdLife International es el gestor de esta Base de Datos sobre Avifauna Europea.

Cada país proporcionó la siguientes información para las poblaciones reproductoras de todas las especies de aves en su territorio:

1. Tamaño de población
2. Tendencias del tamaño de población (en el periodo 1970–1990)
3. Cambios en el área de distribución (en el periodo 1970–1990).

Datos similares fueron también recopilados para poblaciones invernantes aunque no se incluyen aquí.

Se detallan también las fuentes de información utilizadas para evaluar los tamaños de población y las tendencias. Se establecieron códigos para verificar los datos, que se detallan en la Tabla 2 que sigue a esta Introducción, y que indican la exactitud y fiabilidad de los datos sobre tamaño de población y tendencias.

Algunos autores de los comentarios de especies discrepan de las estimaciones de población que figuran en la base de datos, pero la nueva información llegó demasiado tarde para ser incorporada a la misma. En estos casos, los autores han incluido sus propias estimaciones en el texto pero los mapas y gráficos acompañantes siempre muestran las cifras de la base de datos.

Limitaciones de los datos

Este proyecto *Atlas* ha generado un conjunto de datos de alta calidad. Inevitablemente, hay algunas limitaciones a estos datos. Aquellos que deseen utilizar los datos para posteriores investigaciones deben tener en cuenta estas limitaciones cuyo detalle escapa al alcance de este libro y deben requerirse, en su caso, del EBCC. Sin embargo algunas de las limitaciones básicas que afectan al uso de este libro son:

1. No había una metodología de campo preestablecida para determinar la presencia o ausencia ni para establecer tamaños de población. Muchos proyectos nacionales de atlas que fueron fuente de los datos del EBCC, habían preparado sus metodologías de trabajo de campo para sus propios propósitos de acuerdo con los recursos disponibles.
2. No existía una única propuesta para preparar los resultados del trabajo de campo para su registro en las fichas, principalmente por razones similares a las dadas arriba. Los métodos de conversión fueron individualmente seleccionados.
3. Las diferencias existentes en el desarrollo de la ornitología de campo y en los números relativos de observadores entre países se tradujeron también en una variable calidad de los datos.
4. Algunos datos son obtenidos mediante extrapolaciones.
5. Algunos datos son de origen bibliográfico (principalmente en las áreas árticas).

DISTRIBUCIÓN DE LOS MAPAS Y COMENTARIOS POR ESPECIES EN EL *ATLAS*

En el *Atlas* las especies se organizan en dos grupos, aquellas para las que se obtuvieron mapas de distribución completos y aquellas para las que no. Para todas las del primer grupo se incluye un amplio comentario en la Parte 1 de la sección de especies. Para el segundo grupo se incluyen comentarios más breves en la Parte 2. En ambos casos las especies siguen el orden de Voous y la secuencia aproximada de EURING excepto algunos cambios en la Parte 1, por motivos de maquetación del *Atlas*, para asegurar que cada especie cuyo mapa y texto ocupan una sola página, aparece siempre enfrentada a otra especie que ocupe una única página. Las especies cuyo mapa y texto ocupan dos páginas siempre presentan el mapa y el texto enfrentados. En algunos casos, las especies con distribuciones muy restringidas no requieren descripción completa, y esto permite incluir más de una de estas especies en una única página. Cada especie está ilustrada y se incluyen los nombres comunes (siempre que se han podido conseguir) en 14 idiomas. Para muchas de las especies cartografiadas se incluye además un gráfico de población que se explica en las páginas que preceden a los mapas de especies y comentarios.

La Figura 5 muestra la riqueza general en especies de aves reproductoras por cuadrícula. Las Figuras 6 a 8 ilustran la riqueza en especies que necesitan medidas de conservación en Europa (SPEC) de Categoría 1, 2 y 3, según han sido definidas por BirdLife International, y la Figura 9 combina la representación de estas tres categorías.

COMENTARIOS POR ESPECIES

Los comentarios incluyen, en general, una serie de aspectos habituales en los atlas ornitológicos y normalmente en el siguiente orden de acuerdo con prioridades predeterminadas: distribución mundial, hábitat de cría en Europa, patrones de distribución y abundancia en Europa, cambios recientes en distribución y población (y sus posibles causas), variaciones regionales en abundancia, posibles factores limitantes de la distribución, densidad de reproducción en los principales hábitats, migración y movimientos característicos de la especie en, y fuera de, Europa, así como cualquier aspecto destacable de la especie y referencias concretas a subespecies, distribución, solapamiento y tendencias.

A menos que se considere absolutamente necesaria una breve referencia para ilustrar alguno de los aspectos citados, en los comentarios no se incluye información sobre: biología de reproducción, comportamiento, alimentación, relaciones con otras especies, morfología y fisiología, discusión detallada de amenazas a la especie (incluidas en *Birds in Europe*), anormalidades, oología, evolución y taxonomía (excepto cuando existen cambios importantes recientemente adoptados o cuando las subespecies son apreciablemente diferentes), mortalidad y otros parámetros de la dinámica de poblaciones, así como voces y cantos.

Criterios de inclusión de especies

Se incluyen en el *Atlas* las especies reproductoras en el área de cobertura prevista, desde 1985 en adelante, si cumplen alguno de los criterios reflejados en la Tabla 1. En el caso de las especies introducidas que se reproducen en libertad, se incluyeron aquellas que han tenido al menos una población considerada como autosostenible a lo largo de cinco años. Sin embargo, la interpretación de tal norma varía ampliamente a través de Europa y por ello la selección u omisión de algunas especies con poblaciones introducidas puede parecer superficialmente arbitraria.

El *Atlas* considera un total de 513 especies, más Passer x italiae.

NOMENCLATURA Y TAXONOMÍA

Taxonomía

El EBCC ha adoptado una posición conservadora y cauta en relación con los aspectos taxonómicos. Este *Atlas* sigue generalmente la taxonomía, orden y nomenclatura inglesa adoptada por *The Birds of the Western Paleartic* (*BWP*), con las correcciones de su edición abreviada.

Puffinus yelkouan, Puffinus mauretanicus, Larus cachinnans, Anthus petrosus, Phylloscopus lorenzii y *Pyrrhula murina* se tratan como especies verdaderas y su distribución se cartografía separadamente de *Puffinus puffinus, Larus argentatus, Anthus spinoletta, Phylloscopus collybita* y *Pyrrhula pyrrhula*. El cartografiado independiente fue posible bien porque se registraron de forma separada los datos o porque están geográficamente separadas las especies (aunque se presenta un único texto integrado para las tres especies de *Puffinus*). Inicialmente se hizo un intento para registrar subespecies y formas de algunas especies pero las distinciones que el EOAC ha hecho no se tienen en cuenta uniformemente en Europa por lo que el mapeo es imposible. Sin embargo, el Gorrión Italiano fue registrado de forma independiente y el *Atlas* sigue al *BWP* tratándola como un híbrido estable entre *Passer domesticus* y *P. hispaniolensis* describiéndolo como *Passer* x *italiae*. A la inversa, *Phylloscopus trochiloides* incluye dos subespecies geográficamente separadas, *viridanus* y *nitidus*, que fueron previamente consideradas como especies separadas. La separación de *Lanius meridionalis* de *L. excubitor* fue generalmente aceptada cuando el *Atlas* estaba siendo terminado; un diagrama en el comentario indica los límites entre las dos formas. *Hippolais caligata* es considerado algunas veces como distinto de *H. rama* pero aquí este último es tratado como una subespecie. La relación entre algunos grupos de gaviotas es frecuentemente poco clara; *Larus armenicus* se trata aquí de forma independiente.

Códigos EURING

La Unión Europea para el Anillamiento de Aves (EURING) tiene una lista de referencia con un código de 5 dígitos para especies y subespecies que se utilizan fundamentalmente para anillamiento. Esta lista generalmente sigue el orden de Voous, siempre que es aplicable, y por ello se adoptó como un método útil para la recopilación de datos. Los códigos EURING se incluyen en los comentarios de las especies, y el Apéndice Técnico da detalles de como se utilizaron.

USO DE REFERENCIAS Y OTRAS PUBLICACIONES

Se pidió a los autores que evitaran las citas de manuales como referencias dado que el espacio para la bibliografía es bastante limitado. Para el conocimiento básico de cualquier especie reproductora de ave en Europa, los textos y mapas de este *Atlas* deben estudiarse conjuntamente con la información proporcionada por dos obras especialmente destacables: *The Birds of the Western Paleartic* (Cramp *et al.*, 1977–1994), y *Handbuch der Vögel Mitteleuropas* (Glutz von Blotzheim *et al.*, 1966-1993). En los comentarios de especies de este *Atlas* se utilizan las abreviaturas *BWP* y *HVM* para estos libros.

Birds in Europe: their conservation status (Tucker & Heath 1994) supone la primera revisión de las poblaciones de aves europeas, las amenazas que las afectan y su estado de conservación, describiendo en detalle aquellas especies con un estado de conservación desfavorable. El *Atlas* comprende no sólo estas especies sino también todas las otras que no están amenazadas actualmente. Los gráficos de población que figuran en el *Atlas* se han obtenido de la misma Base de Datos de la Avifauna Europea utilizada para *Birds in Europe* y por eso en los textos de especies se cita este último trabajo frecuentemente.

Las referencias citadas en el *Atlas* aparecen al final del libro, justo antes de los índices.

Michael Blair, Ward Hagemeijer

Traducción:
Ramón Martí
Sociedad Española de Ornitología
(SEO/BirdLife)

ABREVIATURAS Y GLOSARIO DE TÉRMINOS

Puntos cardinales

N = norte
S = sur
E = este
W = oeste (NW = noroeste y WSW = oeste-suroeste, etc.)
C = central

Expresiones generales

asl = sobre nivel del mar (altitud)
c = aproximadamente
et al = y otros (en referencias bibliográficas)
pers comm = comunicación personal
pers obs = observación personal
unpubl = trabajo inédito, sin publicar

Dimensiones y unidades de medida

bp = parejas reproductoras
ha = hectáreas
ind = individuos
m = metros
km = kilómetros
km^2 = kilómetro cuadrado
M = millón

Siglas

BTO = British Trust for Ornithology (GB)
BWP = Birds of the Western Palaeartic
HVM = Handbuch der Vögel Mitteleuropas
JNCC = Joint Nature Conservation Committee (GB)
RSPB = Royal Society for the Protection of Birds (GB)
SOVON = SOVON Bird Census Work The Netherlands (NL)
WWT = Wildfowl and Wetlands Trust (GB)

Introduction

OBJET DE L'ATLAS DES OISEAUX NICHEURS D'EUROPE DE L'E.B.C.C.

De nombreux ouvrages d'ornithologie représentent des cartes de répartition d'espèces qui ne reposent pas sur l'état des connaissances du moment. Certaines d'entre elles sont fondées sur des enquêtes concernant les populations d'oiseaux nicheurs mais, si l'on excepte quelques atlas spécialisés, un grand nombre de ces cartes sont obtenues à partir d'un ensemble de sources plus ou moins fiables et ne sont même parfois qu'une simple 'resucée' de cartes plus anciennes d'authenticité douteuse. De plus, ces cartes ne sont que très rarement quantitatives: elles ne nous montrent pas si une espèce est rare ou commune.

En revanche, un nombre sans cesse croissant d'atlas d'oiseaux nicheurs à une échelle régionale ou nationale, d'excellente facture, sont aujourd'hui disponibles. Nombre d'entre eux trouvent leur origine ou leur inspiration dans le projet qui a produit cet atlas. Comme lui, ils contiennent des données semi-quantitatives. Le Comité pour l'Atlas Ornithologique Européen (EOAC) fut formé en 1971. Son objectif était de mettre sur carte les aires de nidification des espèces européennes pour lesquelles les données pouvaient être obtenues sur le terrain. Ce livre présente le résultat de cette tentative.

L'Atlas représente les répartitions des oiseaux sur une période limitée de temps; les données collectées (indépendamment de défauts mineurs) constituent un fondement de notre connaissance à partir duquel de futurs travaux pourront s'effectuer, en particulier l'étude de tout changement de répartition. En 1971, l'optique de l'EOAC fut de réaliser une vaste enquête sur la répartition des espèces nicheuses, la première à l'échelle du continent. Le projet a pris corps. *L'Atlas des Oiseaux Nicheurs d'Europe* répond à la question: 'où niche cette espèce ?'.

COMMENT UTILISER CE LIVRE

L'**Introduction** décrit sommairement l'objet de l'*Atlas*, détaille les méthodes de collecte des données sur la distribution et l'effectif des populations, l'informatisation et la mise en carte, et présente la structure de l'ouvrage. Il est fondamental de comprendre le livre dans tous ces aspects. Pour ce faire, cette introduction a été traduite en plusieurs langues de sorte que la majorité des ornithologues européens puissent bien la comprendre.

Sections liminaires

Dans l'**Avant-propos**, le professeur Karel Voous souligne l'importance de l'Atlas dans le contexte de changements survenus au cours du temps dans l'avifaune européenne. La **Préface** résume la manière dont le projet *Atlas* peut répondre aux attentes des ornithologues européens et présente la politique et les intentions de l'EBCC en matière de 'monitoring' des oiseaux d'Europe. Vient ensuite l'**Introduction**. Une section comprenant les **Cartes explicatives** suit cette introduction. Celles-ci experiment la qualité des données de base et la couverture du territoire. La section '**Historique**' décrit les progrès et retards rencontrés pendant le déroulement du programme. Ensuite, sous le titre '**Histoire et évolution de l'avifaune en Europe**', le professeur Jacques Blondel illustre la mise en place des répartitions des espèces européennes. Le lecteur trouvera enfin les **Remerciements** ainsi qu'une **Liste des atlas nationaux et des principaux atlas régionaux en Europe**.

Section sur les espèces

En préambule à la section principale, on trouvera les **Symboles utilisés sur les cartes et graphiques de population**. Le corps de l'atlas traite des espèces nicheuses en Europe. La première partie contient les cartes et les commentaires sur chaque espèce ainsi que les illustrations et les noms vernaculaires en 14 langues. L'ordre des espèces suit à peu près celui proposé par Voous (1977) et l'ordre utilisé par EURING. La seconde partie traite des espèces à distribution restreinte et celles dont la cartographie est insuffisante. L'illustration des ces espèces et les noms vernaculaires sont présentés sur des pages séparées.

Sections terminales

Les **Cartes synthétiques** détaillent la richesse spécifique en 'SPEC', ou espèces à haute valeur patrimoniale en Europe, telles qu'elles furent définies par 'Birdlife International' (Tucker & Heath 1994). L'**Annexe 1** contient les références citées dans les textes spécifiques. L'index de l'atlas dans les 14 langues constitue l'**Annexe 2**. L'**Annexe** 3 est un appendice technique. Il rassemble les explications sur les différences entre le système de grille utilisé dans l'*Atlas* et la projection théorique universelle transverse de Mercator (UTM). Sont aussi expliqués le système de numérotation du type EURING et la manière dont les carrés côtiers et insulaires de 50 x 50 km ont été rationalisés.

Livrets en langues nationales

Dans l'idée d'accroître la diffusion du livre, les résumés des sections liminaires (**Préface, Historique** et **Histoire et évolution de l'avifaune eu Europe**) et des contributions sur les espèces ont été mises à disposition des ornithologues européens pour qu'ils puissent en effectuer une traduction destinées à leurs collègues ne lisant pas l'anglais. Les livrets en langues étrangères non couvertes par ce livre (**Introduction** et nom d'espèces) incluent également une traduction de cette introduction.

MÉTHODES

Présentation des données de l'Atlas

Dans la section **Historique**, outre l'histoire du projet proprement dite, sont présentées les idées nouvelles sur la collecte des données et leur compilation ainsi qu'un compte-rendu sur le choix des méthodes.

Les cartes de l'*Atlas* présentent les différences en densité (nombre d'oiseaux par unité de surface) sur une échelle logarithmique. Cette échelle convient tout spécialement pour les espèces dont les densités varient beaucoup sur l'étendue de leur aire de répartition. En revanche, à cette échelle, les plus petites différences sont masquées.

On trouvera dans l'*Atlas* non seulement la répartition des oiseaux nicheurs d'Europe, mais aussi une estimation de la taille de la population nicheuse et des tendances de chaque espèce dans tous les pays d'Europe. Les modifications des patrons de répartitions ne peuvent être appréhendés que lorsque une évaluation des tailles de population et des tendances nationales repose sur des bases méthodologiques solides.

Couverture géographique escomptée

Les objectifs, en terme de couverture géographique, sont présentés à la **Fig 1**. Bien qu'il eut été souhaitable d'atteindre les frontières du Paléarctique Occidental définies dans '*The Birds of the Western Palearctic*' (Cramp *et al.* 1977-1994), cela s'est révélé impossible à cause du peu d'informations disponibles pour l'Asie Mineure, le nord de l'Arabie et l'Afrique du Nord. Ces régions n'ont pas été incluses dans le projet. L'*Atlas* utilise par conséquent le fond de carte de '*Atlas Florae Europaeae*' (Jalas & Suominen 1972, 1988) augmenté de la Nouvelle Zemble, de l'archipel François-Joseph, de toutes les îles grecques proches de la Turquie, de Madère, de la région de Stavropol au sud-est de la Russie et des Républiques Caucasiennes, qui sont pris en compte dans le présent atlas. Les différences restant entre le Paléarctique Occidental et le territoire couvert par l'*Atlas* de l'EBCC, comprennent Chypre, les Iles Canaries et toutes les îles méditerranéennes administrées par un pays d'Afrique du Nord. La couverture de cet atlas diffère de celle de '*Birds in Europe - their conservation status*' (Tucker & Heath 1994) par l'omission de la Turquie d'Asie et du Groenland.

Sur la **Fig 1**, on ne perçoit pas immédiatement qu'à la fois les limites du Paléarctique Occidental, l'aire couverte par l'*Atlas Florae Europaeae* et par cet atlas excluent une petite zone d'Europe près d'Orenbourg et incluent une partie du Kazahkstan asiatique entre la Volga et le fleuve Oural, à l'opposé de '*Birds in Europe*'.

Couverture atteinte

Dans la section '**Cartes explicatives**' suivant l'**Introduction**, la **Fig 2** montre les carrés inventoriés et indique la qualité maximale des données reçues par carré. La **Fig 3** donne la qualité minimale. La sous-section **Information qualitative et information semi-quantitative** explique la signification de ces termes. Les 4 catégories de données sur ces cartes sont, par ordre décroissant de qualité:

1. Estimation de population semi-quantitative: nidification probable ou certaine.
2. Estimation de population semi-quantitative: nidification possible.
3. Présence (pas d'estimation): nidification probable ou certaine.
4. Présence (pas d'estimation): nidification possible.

Dans chaque carré, la qualité des données est généralement la même pour toutes les espèces signalées. D'importantes superficies du centre de la Russie n'ont pas du tout été couvertes, principalement parce qu'aucun contact n'a pu être établi. Pour une bonne partie du reste de la Russie, des portions de la Biélorussie, de l'Ukraine et des Républiques Caucasiennes, la couverture a été atteinte pour un nombre limité d'espèces. La couverture de presque toute l'ancienne Yougoslavie est raisonnablement bonne, mais pas pour toutes les espèces dans certaines régions. Il reste des lacunes en Albanie. La couverture est incomplète pour les îles de l'Arctique russe: la Nouvelle Zemble et l'Archipel François-Joseph.

Partout ailleurs, malgré d'inévitables déficiences, la couverture est quasiment complète.

Les cartes

Le choix de la projection cartographique avait à répondre à trois critères: elle devait englober la couverture territoriale escomptée, elle devait être familière dans tous les pays d'Europe et devait être compatible avec les projections nationales. Seul l'UTM répondait à ces critères au début du projet. C'était une base de travail idéale pour les ornithologues car le projet *Atlas Florae Europaeae* avait déjà opté pour la grille UTM. Dans ce dernier, les carrés UTM de 50 x 50 km sont utilisés lors de la collecte les données et les mêmes carrés l'ont aussi été pour l'*Atlas* ornithologique. Il eut été utopique de collecter et analyser les données sur une maille plus fine.

L'unité de base du maillage UTM est le carré de 100 x 100 km. Elle est identifiée, de manière non-équivoque, par un code alpha-numérique, fait de deux chiffres et trois lettres, suivant une séquence logique. Pour les atlas floristique et ornithologique, ces unités sont subdivisées en quatre carrés numérotés de la sorte:

1 3
2 4

de sorte que chaque carré de 50 x 50 km est référencé par 6 caractères.

Sur l'axe nord-sud, la disposition du maillage UTM est simple: des lignes (parallèles) partagent le territoire tous les 50 km. L'origine est l'équateur. L'autre axe est plus difficile à gérer car les méridiens se rejoignent aux pôles et ne sont donc pas parallèles. Par conséquent, le nombre de carrés que l'on peut aligner diminue vers les pôles. La projection UTM utilise des fuseaux de compensation. Ceux-ci sont disposés longitudinalement tous les six degrés, en commençant au méridien de Greenwich. Les cellules de ces fuseaux sont de plus en plus petites au fur et à mesure que l'on se rapproche du pôle, jusqu'à ne plus faire qu'un point et disparaître. Commence alors un autre fuseau ayant la même longitude. L'*Atlas Flora Europaeae* et l'*Atlas* de l'EBCC ont modifié le principe de base. La taille des cellules du fuseau de compensation ne diminue pas en deçà de 40 km de sorte que la cellule suivante, plus au nord, doit avoir 65 km de large. Malgré leur forme en trapèze, les cellules de ces fuseaux sont aussi, par la suite, appelées carrés, pour plus de clarté. On trouvera une illustration de ce qui précède à la **Fig 1** et plus de détails dans l'**Annexe 3**.

L'EOAC a procuré aux organisateurs nationaux des cartes avec les grilles utilisées de manière à assurer une utilisation correcte de la grille lors de la récolte des données. Le travail de terrain a souvent été basé sur un maillage inférieur aux carrés de 50 x 50 km, voire sur un autre système de projection. Dans ces cas, les organisateurs nationaux ont assuré la conversion.

Chronologie du travail de terrain et procédures de validation

Le travail de terrain avait été planifié pour la période 1985-1988. Les pays ont mis sur pied leurs propres enquêtes et, suite à des difficultés d'ordre pratiques, ne purent tous réaliser le travail dans les délais prévus. Lorsque, sur la période d'enquête, la couverture s'est révélée incomplète, se posait la question de savoir si l'ajout de données antérieures ou postérieures permettrait d'améliorer la qualité des informations ou le degré de couverture. Le **Tableau 3**, qui suit cette **Introduction**, donne la liste des pays participants, leur période de collecte des données, le maillage national qui a été converti et les méthodes.

Compilation des données sur la répartition des espèces

Des centaines de milliers, voire des millions d'heures de travail sur le terrain sont à la base de l'*Atlas*. Idéalement, tous les participants auraient dû utiliser les mêmes méthodes sur un même laps de temps. Cela s'est avéré impossible. Au lieu de directives précises, l'EOAC a préféré indiquer les orientations à prendre. Dans certains pays, les observateurs collectaient les données simultanément pour l'atlas national et pour l'atlas européen. Dans d'autres, les données de l'atlas national, collectées indépendamment, furent utilisées pour le présent travail.

Collecte des données

Le formulaire standard, mis au point par le Bureau Central de Statistiques des Pays-Bas, est en partie reproduit à la **Fig 4**, à la suite de cette introduction. Un formulaire était rempli pour chaque carré inventorié. Chaque pays s'est chargé de la portion des carrés frontaliers qui le concernait.

L'information demandée pour chaque carré était:

1. Période d'inventaire: l'année ou série d'années pendant lesquelles les données ont été collectées.
2. Identification du carré (code UTM50).
3. Etat d'achèvement de l'inventaire: indique si le carré contient plus (high) ou moins (low) de 75% des espèces suspectées y nicher.
4. Altitude: valeurs minimale et maximale.
5. Identité des participants: Nom et adresse du (des) coordinateur(s) ou de (des) l'observateur(s) en cas de besoin de renseignements complémentaires.
6. Commentaires: permet d'ajouter des informations pour mieux expliquer les données du formulaire.
7. Court questionnaire sur les habitats présents dans le carré.

Le corps du formulaire est une liste d'espèces (env. 440, selon l'ordre de Voous (1977), numérotées suivant le code EURING) en droit de laquelle les observations sont indiquées. Le format du champ de la colonne 0 est une abréviation du nom scientifique (ex Gav. stell.), en colonne 1, le code EURING (ex 00020) et en colonne 2, la preuve de nidification et son code. Seize codes ont été fournis, divisé en trois catégories: nidification certaine, possible, probable.

Tableau 1 Codification des indices de reproduction

A: Nidification possible
1. Espèce observée durant la saison de reproduction dans un habitat favorable à la nidification;
2. Mâle chanteur (ou cris de nidification) en période de reproduction;

B: Nidification probable
3. Couple observé dans un habitat favorable durant la saison de reproduction;
4. Territoire permanent présumé en fonction de l'observation de comportements territoriaux ou de l'observation à 8 jours d'intervalle au moins d'un individu au même endroit;
5. Parades nuptiales;
6. Fréquentation d'un site de nid potentiel;
7. Signes ou cris d'inquiétude d'un individu adulte;
8. Plaque incubatrice;
9. Construction d'un nid, creusement d'une cavité;

C: Nidification certaine
10. Adulte feignant une blessure ou cherchant à détourner l'attention;
11. Nid utilisé récemment ou coquille vide (oeuf pondu pendant l'enquête);
12. Jeunes fraîchement envolés (espèces nidicoles) ou poussins (espèces nidifuges);
13. Adultes entrant ou quittant un site de nid laissant supposé un nid occupé (incluant les nids situés trop haut ou les cavités et nichoirs, le contenu du nid n'ayant pu être examiné) ou adulte en train de couver;
14. Adulte transportant des sacs fécaux ou de la nourriture pour les jeunes;
15. Nid avec oeuf(s);
16. Nid avec jeune(s) (vu ou entendu).

Les codes sont donnés au **Tableau 1**. Enfin, en colonne 3, le champ 'données numériques', c.à.d. une estimation du nombre de couples nicheurs dans le carré sur une échelle logarithmique (1 = 1 à 9, 2 = 10 à 99, ... 6 → 100 000).

Le formulaire permet de noter aussi les hybrides et les espèces non prévues en bas de la liste.

Au total, les sources de données sur les oiseaux nicheurs sont:

1. Les coordinateurs nationaux de l'EBCC, qui ont organisé la collecte des données et ont complété les formulaires.
2. Les coordinateurs régionaux. Parfois, la collecte des données a été organisée par d'autres personnes que le coordinateur national, spécialement dans les grands pays, ou là où il a semblé préférable de déléguer le travail à un membre d'un réseau de contacts. Ces collaborateurs régionaux ont œuvré de manière similaire aux collaborateurs nationaux.
3. Sources de données additionnelles, surtout celles de la littérature ornithologique, généralement par l'entremise d'un bon connaisseur d'une espèce. Là où les données d'enquêtes faisaient défaut, en particulier dans les contrées reculées, la seule source d'information disponible était souvent des rapports, publiés ou non, qui n'étaient pas directement à la disposition des éditeurs ou des organisateurs nationaux.
4. Les auteurs des textes spécifiques. Très souvent un auteur, ayant étudié une espèce, connaissait des sources d'informations sur la répartition ou les effectifs ignorées des organisateurs.

Toute donnée provenant de ces sources était traitée dans la hiérarchie des données: chaque ajout à la base de donnée devait être approuvé au niveau du coordinateur national.

Information qualitative et semi-quantitative

L'*Atlas* exploite des données semi-quantitatives (estimations de taille de population semi-logarithmiques) calculées sur l'échelle prévue, par carré, par les coordinateurs régionaux ou nationaux ou par les observateurs. C'était là globalement la méthode la plus efficace et la plus précise. Les points représentent un nombre de couples nicheurs, et non une densité, une taille croissante signifiant une augmentation d'un ordre de grandeur (voir légende des cartes). Il est regrettable que certains pays aient refusé totalement (Norvège et Pologne), presque totalement (Espagne) ou partiellement (Islande et Italie), de fournir des estimations semi-quantitatives. On a perdu le contact avec la Bosnie et la Serbie, et leurs données n'ont pu être adaptées à l'échelle semi-quantitative. Certaines régions de France ont mis à jour leurs données semi-quantitatives indépendamment. Le coordinateur national français a utilisé l'échelle semi-quantitative pour quelques espèces seulement à l'échelon national. Même les estimations sur une échelle logarithmique, pour un grand nombre de carrés, sont plus riches en informations que la seule indication de présence-absence.

Pour les carrés frontaliers où chaque pays avait, de son côté, soumis des estimations des tailles de population, la valeur la plus élevée a été retenue (on ne peut sommer des valeurs logarithmiques). Ceci pourrait entraîner des sous-estimations mais il a semblé préférable de choisir cette approximation plutôt que de réduire toute l'information frontalière en présence-absence.

Informatisation, mise sur carte et corrections

Les formulaires reçus des coordinateurs nationaux furent examinés sommairement dans le but de repérer les erreurs grossières (codes erronés ou omis p. ex.) avant d'être informatisés sur des fichiers ASCII, en ajoutant un code national à chaque enregistrement. Certains pays ont fourni directement sur disquette leurs données correctement formatées. Elles ont aussi été testées de la même manière. La base de donnée définitive, construite à partir des fichiers de base, contient une seule information par espèce et par carré.

Ceux qui, parmi les coordinateurs nationaux ou autres collaborateurs, ont transmis leurs données rapidement ont reçu des cartes intermédiaires et des listes par espèce au niveau national. Pour cette première phase du processus de vérification, il leur a été demandé d'examiner soigneusement les cartes et nombre d'erreurs ont ainsi été repérées. Certains pays ont renvoyé leurs données de base assez tardivement tandis que d'autres transformaient le qualitatif en semi-quantitatif. Par conséquent, le processus de correction de données et de validation a commencé tard et a progressé à différentes vitesses selon les pays.

La production de cartes intermédiaires a été une étape cruciale à deux points de vue:

1. Cela a permis aux coordinateurs nationaux et, à travers eux, à de nombreux collecteurs de données, de vérifier que les données qu'ils avaient soumises avaient été correctement informatisées. Les cartes montraient si les carrés comprenaient bien les bonnes espèces. Les erreurs de ce type sont plus évidentes sur une carte que sur un simple listing.
2. Ces cartes ont en outre stimulé la participation.

La seconde phase a consisté en la vérification des modifications apportées lors de la première phase. Pour ce faire, un second jeu de cartes et listings comprenant les données modifiées a été envoyé aux coordinateurs nationaux et autres collaborateurs. La majorité des coordinateurs a effectué cette tâche gigantesque et remis ses corrections définitives. Toutefois, dans certains pays tel que l'ex-Yougoslavie, la mise à jour et la validation ont été impossible à assurer. Dans les pays où le processus de vérification a subi du retard, il a fallu fournir un effort important en un court laps de temps et, plus le retard a été important, plus les difficultés à finaliser les cartes ont été nombreuses.

Dans la dernière étape, des données chiffrées mises à jour furent fournies par certains auteurs de texte et autres spécialistes d'espèces. Elles ont, pour la plupart, été examinées par les coordinateurs nationaux et une décision sur la valeur à utiliser a été prise. Dans quelques cas, à cause d'un manque de temps, cela n'a pas été possible. Il a été alors soit retenu la valeur chiffrée précédente, soit signalé que l'opinion de l'auteur divergeait par rapport au matériel cartographié.

Dans le Nord de la Russie et en Albanie, et plus généralement là où les données provenant d'un travail de terrain n'étaient pas disponibles, les données de la littérature furent examinées par des ornithologues de terrain et une décision prise, comme pour l'acceptabilité des données. Les carrés concernés sont repérés sur la carte de couverture par un symbole spécifique (voir '**Map Key**'). Certaines estimations semi-quantitatives pour ce genre de carrés ont été obtenues en extrapolant à partir des carrés de la même région pour lesquelles une estimation chiffrée était disponible en prenant en compte les zones où le type d'habitat était connu.

L'échéance pour la remise des nouvelles données et des corrections était le 1er juillet 1995; cependant, les données reçues au cours des quelques mois qui suivirent en provenance de l'Albanie, de la Turquie d'Europe, du Caucase, de l'Ukraine ou de la Russie ont aussi été utilisées pour maximiser la couverture. La réception des corrections faites par les auteurs des textes a été close au 1er novembre 1995.

Compilation des données sur les tailles de population

Les graphiques des populations nationales présentés dans l'*Atlas* sont dérivés de la base de données sur les oiseaux d'Europe. Celle-ci contient des données récoltées en collaboration par l'EBCC et BirdLife International et a été mise sur pied comme soutien à cet *Atlas* et au projet BirdLife Dispersed Species, dont les résultats sont publiés dans *Birds in Europe - their conservation status*. Cette collaboration a aussi permis d'augmenter la participation de certaines parties de l'Europe. Les données ont été récoltées principalement sur des questionnaires distribués aux coordinateurs nationaux (liste dans *Birds in Europe*) qui, à leur tour, les ont distribués aux ornithologues concernés, aux organisations s'occupant de monitoring et aux responsables régionaux. BirdLife International est l'administrateur de la base de données en question.

Chaque pays a fourni pour les populations de toutes les espèces nicheuses:

1. La taille de la population.
2. La tendance numérique de la population pendant la période 1970-1990.
3. La tendance de la répartition géographique sur cette même période.

Des données similaires ont été également récoltées pour les populations hivernantes, mais elles ne sont pas présentées ici. Les références utilisées pour déterminer les tailles de population et les tendances ont été enregistrées. Les codes de vérification de données, détaillés au **Tableau 2** à la suite de cette **Introduction**, permettent de se rendre compte de la précision et de la qualité des estimations de tendance et d'abondance.

Limitations des données

Le projet *Atlas* a engendré un jeu de données de grande qualité. Mais il a inévitablement ses limites. Ceux qui, dans l'avenir, souhaiteraient utiliser ces données doivent être conscients de la chose. Les détails de ces limitations dépassent le cadre de ce livre mais peuvent être obtenus auprès de l'EBCC. Néanmoins, certains sont susceptibles d'affecter l'utilisation 'normale' de ce livre:

1. Absence de prescription méthodologique pour le travail de terrain, à la fois pour les présences-absences et pour les abondances. Beaucoup d'organismes nationaux qui ont fourni les données de cet *Atlas* avaient mis sur pied des programmes conçus par leurs soins, avec leur propre méthodologie, en accord avec les ressources disponibles.
2. Aucune technique pour préparer les résultats de terrain en vue de remplir les questionnaires, pour des raisons en grande partie similaire à celles développées au point précédent. En outre, les conversions cartographiques furent également réalisées indépendamment.
3. Des différences dans le niveau de l'ornithologie de terrain et dans le nombre d'observateurs de terrain peuvent amener des données de qualité variable.
4. Certaines données sont des extrapolations.
5. Certaines données viennent de la littérature (surtout régions arctiques).

DISPOSITION DES CARTES ET DES TEXTES DANS L'*ATLAS*

Dans l'*Atlas*, les espèces sont divisées en deux groupes, selon la quantité et la nature des données. Dans le premier groupe, les espèces sont traitées *in extenso* dans la première partie de la **Section principale**. Le second groupe comprend les espèces pour lesquelles les données étaient insuffisantes pour être présentées sur carte; elles sont présentées de manière plus succincte dans la Partie 2. Dans les deux groupes, l'ordre est celui de Voous et suit à peu près la séquence d'EURING, à l'exception de quelques réajustements mineurs de manière à ce que les espèces n'occupant qu'une seule page soient en vis-à-vis. Les espèces occupant deux pages ont toujours le texte face à la carte. Dans certains cas, les espèces à distribution très réduite, ne nécessitant pas de graphique populationnel, peuvent n'occuper qu'une demi-page. Chaque espèce est illustrée et les noms vernaculaires en 14 langues sont donnés également lorsqu'ils étaient disponibles. La plupart des espèces cartographiées ont un graphique de population qui est expliqué dans la légende précédant les cartes et textes.

Cartes synthétiques

Dans la **Section finale**, la **Fig 5** illustre la richesse spécifique par carré et les **Fig 6** à **8** montrent les richesses en espèces à haute valeur patrimoniale (SPEC, catégories 1, 2 et 3, définies par BirdLife International). La **Fig 9** combine ces trois catégories.

LES COMMENTAIRES SUR LES ESPÈCES

Les commentaires sur les espèces couvrent, dans le cas général, une liste de thèmes standards, habituellement dans l'ordre suivant (en fonction d'un ordre de priorité pré-établi): distribution mondiale, habitats de nidification en Europe, patrons de distribution et d'abondance en Europe, récents changements dans la répartition ou l'abondance et causes possibles, variations régionales d'abondance, facteurs supposés limiter la répartition, densités de nicheurs dans l'habitat de prédilection, migrations et mouvements en Europe et hors d'Europe, particularités diverses de l'espèce et brèves références aux sous-espèces, leurs répartition, couverture, sympatries, et tendances.

Certains sujets sont évités, à moins qu'une brève mention ne soit absolument nécessaire pour illustrer un point précis relevant des thèmes standards. Ce sont: biologie de reproduction, comportement, nourriture, relations interspécifiques, traits morphologiques ou physiologiques, discussion détaillée des menaces pesant sur l'espèce (le domaine de *Birds in Europe*), anomalies, oologie, évolution et taxonomie (excepté pour les changements récents importants et acceptés, ou lorsque les sous-espèces sont nettement distinctes), mortalité et autres paramètres de la dynamique des populations, voix et chant.

Critère d'inclusion d'une espèce

Les espèces qui ont niché, à partir de 1985, dans la zone de couverture escomptée, ont été incluses si elles répondent aux critères du **Tableau 1**. Le principe d'inclusion d'une espèce nicheuse introduite est le suivant: présence sur la zone d'au moins une population dont la viabilité intrinsèque a été attestée pendant 5 ans au moins. En fait, l'acception ou l'interprétation de ce critère varie assez largement à travers l'Europe et, de ce fait, l'ajout ou l'omission d'une espèce dont la population aurait été introduite peut apparaître au premier abord comme arbitraire.

L'*Atlas* traite de 506 espèces.

NOMENCLATURE ET TAXONOMIE

Taxonomie

L'EBCC a adopté une position prudente et conservatrice en matière de taxonomie. Cet *Atlas* suit en règle générale la taxonomie, l'ordre et la nomenclature anglaise adoptés dans '*Birds of the Western Palearctic*' (*BWP*), suivant les amendements de l'édition abrégée.

Puffinus yelkouan, Puffinus mauretanicus, Larus cachinnans, Anthus petrosus, Phylloscopus lorenzii et *Pyrrhula murina* sont traitées comme espèces séparées. Lorsque cela s'est avéré possible, *Puffinus puffinus, Larus argentatus, Anthus spinoletta, Phylloscopus collybita* et *Pyrrhula pyrrhula* ont été cartographiées séparément. Pour ces espèces, une cartographie propre a été rendue possible lorsque l'enregistrement des données s'est fait de manière séparée ou dans le cas ou les aires sont disjointes. Il avait été prévu initialement de tenter de noter séparément les sous-espèces et formes géographiques de certaines espèces mais la distinction suggérée par l'EOAC n'a pas été respectée dans toute l'Europe, rendant la cartographie impossible. Le Moineau cisalpin a été noté comme tel et l'*Atlas*, suivant l'exemple de *BWP*, l'a traité comme un hybride stable entre *Passer hispaniolensis* et *P. domesticus*, lui conférant le nom de *Passer × italiae*. Inversement, *Phylloscopus trochiloides* comprend deux sous-espèces séparées géographiquement, *viridanus* et *nitidus*, considérées auparavant comme des espèces. Le cas des Pies-grièches grises a été tranché lorsque l'*Atlas* a été finalisé et *Lanius meridionalis* a été acceptée. Un diagramme dans le texte indique la frontière entre les deux espèces. *Hippolais caligata* est parfois distinguée de *H. rama*, mais cette dernière a été considerée ici comme une sous-espèce. Les relations au sein du genre *Larus* sont souvent peu claires. *Larus armenicus* est ici traitée séparément.

Codes EURING

L'association européenne de baguage (EURING) possède une liste évolutive de codes de référence en 5 chiffres des espèces et sous-espèces, utilisée primitivement pour le baguage. En règle générale, cette liste suit l'ordre de Voous (1977) et cette méthode, lorsqu'elle pouvait s'appliquer, s'est révélée très utile dans la compilation des données. Les codes EURING apparaissent en tête des commentaires de chaque espèce. L'**Annexe 3** précise la manière dont ces codes ont été utilisés.

L'EMPLOI DES RÉFÉRENCES ET AUTRES PUBLICATIONS

Il a été demandé aux auteurs d'éviter de citer les traités comme des références ordinaires car l'espace était compté. Deux traités majeurs actuels méritent l'attention du lecteur. Pour une meilleure intelligibilité, les textes et cartes de l'*Atlas* de toutes les espèces nicheuses gagnent à être examinés conjointement avec les articles correspondant de ces deux traités. Il s'agit de '*Birds of the Western Palearctic*' (Cramp *et al.* 1977-1994) et de '*Handbuch der Vögel Mitteleuropas*' (Glutz von Blotzheim *et al.* 1966-1993). Tout au long du présent travail, ces deux ouvrages ont été abrégés par *BWP* et *HVM*, respectivement.

Birds in Europe - their conservation status (Tucker & Heath 1994) est le premier ouvrage sur les populations des oiseaux d'Europe, les menaces et leur statut de conservation. Il décrit les espèces à statut de conservation défavorable. L'*Atlas* traite non seulement de ces espèces mais également de toutes celles qui ne sont pas menacées à l'heure actuelle. Les graphiques de population de l'*Atlas* proviennent de la base de donnée utilisée pour '*Birds in Europe*' et cette référence est donc fréquemment citée dans les textes.

Les références citées dans l'Atlas se trouvent dans l'*Annexe 1*.

Michael Blair, Ward Hagemeijer
(Traduction: Christian Vansteenwegen)

ANNEXE À L'INTRODUCTION

ABRÉVIATIONS UTILISÉES ET GLOSSAIRE

Points cardinaux

N = nord
S = sud
E = est
W = ouest, donc NW = nord-ouest
C = central, donc S-C = central-sud, etc.

Expressions usuelles

asl = au-dessus du niveau de la mer
c = environ
et al = et autres (dans les références)
pers com = communication personnelle
pers obs = observation personnelle
unpubl = non publié

Mesures

bp = couples nicheurs

ha = hectares
ind = individus
m = mètres
km = kilomètres (donc km^2 = kilomètres carrés)
M = million

Abréviations

BTO = British Trust for Ornithology
JNCC = Joint Nature Conservation Committee (financé par le gouv. brit.)
RSPB = Royal Society for the Protection of Birds
SOVON = Samenwerkende Organisaties Vogelwerk Nederland
WWT = Wildfowl and Wetlands Trust

Glossaire

eutrophic (eutrophe) = riche en éléments minéraux issus de la décomposition des organismes;
lentic (lentique) = relatif aux eaux stagnantes;
lotic (lotique) = relatif aux eaux courantes;
mesotrophic (mésotrophe) = intermédiaire entre eutrophe et oligotrophe;
'mixotrophic' = désigne les lacs boréaux à eaux peu profondes et végétation riche dont les rives sont relativement pauvres en nutriments;
oligotrophic (oligotrophe) = pauvre en sels et en nutriments;
phenology (phénologie) = l'étude de la chronologie des phénomènes récurrents;
sclerophytic (sclérophytique) = relatif aux plantes à feuilles petites et épaisses, à faible transpiration, adaptées aux climats secs;
xerophytic (xérophytique) = relatif aux plantes adaptées aux climats très secs.

Johdanto

EUROOPAN PESIMÄLINTUATLAKSEN TARKOITUS

Monissa lintukirjoissa lajien levinneisyydet esitetään tarkoilta näyttävillä kartoilla. Jotkut niistä perustuvat pesimälinnuston tutkimukseen, mutta lukuun ottamatta joitakin erikoisatlaksia useimmat kartat on laadittu erilaisista lähteistä koottujen tietojen perusteella. Näiden luotettavuus kuitenkin vaihtelee. Joskus kartat on piirretty työstämällä aikaisempia karttoja, joiden alkuperä on epäluotettava. Tavallisesti kartat eivät ole kvantitatiivisia: ne eivät kerro, missä joku laji on yleinen ja missä harvinainen.

Eurooppaan perustettiin vuonna 1971 lintuatlastoimikunta (nykyään Euroopan lintulaskentatoimikunta, European Bird Census Committee, EBCC), joka otti tehtäväkseen kartoittaa eurooppalaisten lintulajien levinneisyydet, sikäli kuin ne olivat kenttätyön avulla selvitettävissä. Tavoitteena oli mantereenlaajuinen pesimälintukartasto, kaikkien aikojen ensimmäinen. Nyt tuo toive täyttyy. *The EBCC Atlas of European Breeding Birds* esittää levinneisyyskartat Euroopassa pesivistä linnuista. Se vastaa kysymykseen: "Mitä lintuja pesii missäkin?"

Nykyään on jo saatavilla yhä useampia erinomaisia alueellisia ja kansallisia pesimälinnustoatlaksia, joista monet on aloitettu nyt käsillä olevan Atlaksen innoittamina ja samojen ideoiden pohjalta. Niistäkin monet perustuvat tämän teoksen lailla osittain kvantitatiiviseen (puolikvantitatiiviseen) aineistoon, jossa lajien runsaudet on ilmaistu väljien luokkien avulla.

Atlas esittelee lintujen levinneisyydet tietyltä ajalta. Vaikka kerätty aineisto sisältäisikin vähäistä epäyhtenäisyyttä, on se kuitenkin perusta mahdolliselle uudelle levinneisyyksien kartoitukselle ja muutosten tutkimiselle.

ATLAKSEN RAKENNE

Tämä johdanto kuvaa lyhyesti Atlaksen tarkoituksen, levinneisyys- ja populaatioaineiston keruumenetelmien yksityiskohdat, tietokonekäsittelyn ja karttojen laadinnan sekä selittää sen rakennetta. Johdanto on välttämätön, jotta voi ymmärtää Atlaksen kaikki puolet. Se on painettu useilla eri kielillä, jotta useimmat eurooppalaiset lintuharrastajat voivat sen lukea.

Alkuluvut

Esipuheessa professori Karel Voous hahmottelee, miksi *Atlas* on tärkeä tutkittaessa Euroopan linnuston muutoksia. Alkusanoissa kuvataan, miten yhteinen atlashanke täyttää eurooppalaisten ornitologien tarpeita. Samalla kuvataan EBCC:n tavoitteita ja *Atlaksen* merkitystä tuleville linnustonseurantahankkeille. Näitä seuraa johdanto, jossa selostetaan menetelmät ja annetaan yleisiä tietoja *Atlaksesta*. Johdantoa seuraavassa jaksossa kuvataan *Atlaksen* kattavuus ja aineiston laatu sekä esitetään alkuperäinen vakiomuotoinen aineiston keruulomake. Historia-jaksossa kuvataan atlashankkeen edistymistä ja vaikeuksia. Omassa luvussaan professori Jacques Blondel kuvaa Euroopan linnuston historiaa ja millaisen kehityksen tulosta lintujen nykyiset levinneisyydet ovat. Lopuksi seuraavat kiitokset ja luettelo Euroopan kansallisista ja tärkeimmistä alueellisista lintuatlaksista.

Lajikuvaukset

Pääosa Atlaksesta käsittelee Euroopan pesimälintuja. Karttasymbolien ja populaatioita kuvaavien piirrosten selitykset edeltävät sitä. Osa 1 käsittää levinneisyyskartat, lajikuvaukset, jokaisen pesimälajin nimet 14 kielellä sekä lajikuvat. Lajit on esitetty suurin piirtein Voousin (1977) ja Euringin (Euroopan rengastusunioni, European Union for Bird Ringing) luettelon mukaisessa järjestyksessä. Osa 2 käsittää ne lajit, joiden uskotaan pesivän Euroopassa, mutta joista ei saatu aineistoa.

Loppuluvut

Lajikarttojen perusteella on laadittu karttoja, jotka esittävät pesimälajien lukumääriä sekä euroopanlaajuisesti suojelun tai erityishuomion tarpeessa olevien lajien määriä BirdLife International'in kriteerien mukaisesti (Species of European Conservation Concern eli SPEC; Tucker & Heath 1994). Lopussa olevassa teknisessä liitteessä selitetään, kuinka *Atlaksen* koordinaatisto eroaa teoreettisesta poikittaisesta Mercator-projektiosta (Universal Transverse Mercator Projection, UTM) sekä kuinka 50 x 50 km:n ruutuja on käsitelty saarilla ja rannikoilla. Lisäksi selitetään, kuinka Euring-koodia on *Atlaksessa* käytetty.

Erikieliset kirjaset

Alkulukujen (alkusanat, historia sekä Euroopan linnuston kehitys ja historia) sekä lajikuvausten englanninkieliset yhteenvedot ovat minkä tahansa maan ornitologien saatavissa kääntämistä varten. Näitä käännöksiä voi levittää edelleen, jotta teoksen käyttö olisi englantia taitamattomillekin mahdollista. Kansallisten kirjasten hankintaosoitteet on lueteltu teknisessä liitteessä, sikäli kuin ne ovat olleet *Atlaksen* julkaisuhetkellä tiedossa.

MENETELMÄT

Atlasaineiston esitystapa

Alkuperäiset ajatukset aineiston keruu- ja käsittelytavoista ja niiden valinnasta sekä selostus tutkimuksen toteutuksesta kuvataan historiaa koskevassa luvussa.

Atlaskartat osoittavat lintujen tiheysvaihtelut logaritmisella asteikolla, joka selitetään tuonnempana kohdassa Kvalitatiivinen ja puolikvantitatiivinen tieto. Se on erityisen sopiva lajeille, joiden tiheydet vaihtelevat merkittävästi levinneisyysalueen eri osissa. Haittapuolena on tietysti se, että vähäisemmät tiheyserot häviävät näkyvistä.

Atlas ei esitä Euroopassa pesiville linnuille vain levinneisyyksiä, vaan myös luotettavan arvion useimpien lajien maakohtaisesta populaatiokoosta ja sen muutoksesta. Levinneisyysmuutoksia ei voi ymmärtää ilman näitä tietoja.

Suunniteltu atlasalue

Alunperin suunniteltu atlasalue on esitetty Kuvassa 1. Suotavaa olisi ollut pyrkiä noudattamaan läntisen palearktisen alueen rajoja käsikirjan *The Birds of the Western Palearctic* (Cramp ym. 1977-1994) mukaisesti. Tämä ei kuitenkaan ollut mahdollista, koska Vähä-Aasiasta, Arabian niemimaalta ja Pohjois-Afrikasta on liian vähän tietoa saatavilla. Siksi teoksessa käytetään *Atlas Florae Europaeaen* (Jalas & Suominen 1972, 1988) pohjakarttoja, joihin on lisätty Novaja Zemlja, Frans Joosefin maa, kaikki Kreikan saaret Turkin rannikon läheisyydestä, Madeira, Azorit, Stavropolin alue Kaakkois-Venäjällä sekä Kaukasuksella sijaitsevat tasavallat. Vielä eroina läntisen palearktiksen alueeseen Atlas ei ulotu Kyprokselle, Kanarian saarille eikä Pohjois-Afrikan valtioihin kuuluville Välimeren saarille. Tuckerin ja Heathin (1994) teoksesta *Birds in Europe – their conservation status Atlas* eroaa siinä, että Turkki ja Grönlanti eivät ole mukana.

Kuvasta 1 ei välittömästi ilmene, että pieni alue Eurooppaa Orenburgin lähistöllä ei kuulu läntiseen palearktiseen alueeseen eikä ole mukana *Atlas Florae Europaeae*ssa tai tässä *Atlaksessa*. Sen sijaan mukana ovat toisin kuin teoksessa *Birds in Europe* Volgan ja Uraljoen väliin jäävä osa Aasiaan kuuluvaa Kasakstania sekä pala Aasiaan kuuluvaa Venäjää Permin itäpuolella (Sverdlovskin alue).

Toteutunut atlasalue

Johdantoa seuraavassa kuvallisesti selostavassa luvussa esitetään *Atlaksen* kattavuus. Kuva 2 osoittaa tutkitut ruudut ja näyttää aineiston ruutukohtaisen enimmäis- ja Kuva 3 vähimmäislaadun. Alaluku aineiston kvalitatiivisuudesta tai osittaisesta kvantitatiivisuudesta (tuonnempana) selostaa näiden käsitteiden merkityksen. Kartoissa käytetyt aineiston laatuluokat ovat parhaasta huonoimpaan seuraavat:

A. Populaatiokoosta on runsausluokitukseen perustuva arvio
1. Ruudut, joissa pesintä on varmistettu tai se oli todennäköinen.
2. Ruudut, joissa laji mahdollisesti pesi.

B. Kvalitatiivinen tieto (arvio populaatiokoosta puuttuu)
3. Ruudut, joissa pesintä on varmistettu tai se oli todennäköinen.
4. Ruudut, joissa laji mahdollisesti pesi.

Aineiston laatu oli tavallisesti sama kaikille tietyssä ruudussa havaituille lajeille. Keski-Venäjällä ei kuitenkaan tietoa saatu huomattavan laajoilta alueilta, koska yhteyshenkilöitä ei löydetty. Suuresta osasta muuta Venäjää, osista Valko-Venäjää, Ukrainaa ja Kaukasuksen tasavaltoja vain osasta lajeja saatiin kattava tieto. Entisen Jugoslavian alueelta saatiin jokseenkin kattava aineisto, joskaan joiltakin alueilta ei kaikista lajeista. Albaniassa on aukkoja. Kattavuus oli puutteellista myös Novaja Zemljalla ja Frans Joosefin maalla. Muualla peittävyys oli yleensä täydellinen. Lajikohtaisten laatuerojen takia kunkin ruudun aineiston enimmäis- ja vähimmäislaatu on esitetty erikseen Kuvissa 2 ja 3.

Atlaskartat

Karttaprojektion tulee täyttää seuraavat ehdot: kartan tulee kattaa koko tutkittava alue, sen tulee olla tuttu vähintäänkin useimmissa Euroopan maissa ja sen tulee olla yhteensopiva kansallisten projektioiden kanssa. Vain UTM-projektio täytti nämä ehdot silloin, kun atlashanke aloitettiin. Koska *Atlas Florae Europaeae*n pohjakartalla on UTM-koordinaatisto, oli se hieman muutettuna ihanteellinen ratkaisu lintuatlaksen tarpeisiin. *Atlas Florae Europaeae* käyttää 50 × 50 km:n ruutuja havaintoyksikköinään – lintuatlaksessa käytettiin samoja ruutuja. Tiheämmän koordinaatiston käyttö ei olisi ollut käytännöllistä kerätyn aineiston esittämiselle ja analysoinnille.

UTM-koordinaatistossa kartan 100 × 100 km:n perusruudut tunnistetaan yksiselitteisen kahden numeron ja kolmen kirjaimen yhdistelmän perusteella. Sekä kasvi- että lintuatlaksessa jokainen ruutu jaettiin neljään 50 × 50 km:n ruutuun ja numeroitiin yhdestä neljään järjestyksessä luoteinen, lounainen, koillinen ja kaakkoinen. Siten jokaiselle 50 × 50 km:n ruudulle tuli oma, ainutkertainen kuuden merkin tunnuksensa.

UTM-koordinaatiston ulkoasu on etelä–pohjois -suunnassa yksinkertainen: koordinaatit kulkevat 50 km:n välein leveyspiirien suuntaisesti päiväntasaajalta alkaen. Itä–länsi -suuntaiset koordinaatit ovat hankalampia, koska pituuspiirit lähenevät toisiaan napoja lähestyttäessä. Sen takia mahdollisten 50 × 50 km ruutujen lukumäärä vähenee napoja kohden. UTM:n ruutujärjestelmä ottaa ongelman huomioon seuraavasti. Ruudusto perustuu pituuspiirien mukaisiin 6°:n sektoreihin alkaen pituuspiiriltä 0°. Näiden sektorien rajoilla ruudut kapenevat napoja kohti kunnes ne katoavat ja uudet rajaruudut alkavat kaventua. *Atlas Florae Europaeae* ja tämä lintuatlas ovat muuntaneet systeemiä siten, että sektorien rajoilla ruutujen pinta-alavaihtelu pienenee: reunaruudut ovat mukana itsenäisinä vain, kunnes niiden leveys on vähentynyt suunnilleen 40 km:in. Seuraavalla 50 km:n vyöhykkeellä ne yhdistetään viereisiin ruutuihin. (Käytännöllisistä syistä kuvioita nimitetään *Atlaksessa* "ruuduiksi", olivatpa ne neliöitä tai puolisuunnikkaita.) Syntyvä kuvio näkyy selvästi suunnitellun atlasalueen kartalla (Kuva 1). Yksityiskohtaiset tiedot esitetään teknisessä liitteessä.

Euroopan lintuatlastoimikunta toimitti 50 × 50 km:n koordinaattiruutukartat jokaisen maan organisaattoreille varmistaakseen, että he käyttivät oikeaa koordinaatistoa aineiston keruuseen. Kenttätyö perustui tavallisesti pienempään UTM-ruutukokoon kuin 50 × 50 km tai peräti johonkin muuhun koordinaatistoon (Suomessa yhtenäiskoordinaatistoon). Kansallisten organisaattoreiden tuli silloin muuntaa aineisto UTM:n 50 × 50 km:n ruudukkoa vastaavaksi.

Kenttätyövuodet ja aineiston varmistus

Alunperin suunniteltiin, että *Atlaksen* kenttätyö tapahtuisi vuosina 1985-88. Kukin maa organisoi kuitenkin itse kenttätyönsä eikä käytännöllisten ongelmien takia aikataulusta kyetty pitämään kiinni. Alueilla, joilla kattavuus oli epätäydellistä tutkimusvuosien ajalta, arvioitiin, voidaanko sitä tai laatua parantaa ottamalla mukaan aiemmin tai myöhemmin kerättyä aineistoa. Taulukko 3, joka seuraa johdantoa, luettelee osallistuneet maat, niiden aineiston keruuvuodet, kansalliset koordinaatistot, joista aineisto siirrettiin UTM:ään, ja menetelmät.

Aineiston keruu – lajien levinneisyysaineisto

Atlas perustuu satoihin tuhansiin, ehkä yli miljoonaan kenttätyötuntiin. Ihannetilanteessa kaikki osallistujat olisivat soveltaneet samaa työskentelymenetelmää samojen vuosien aikana, mutta käytännössä tämä oli mahdotonta. Lintuatlastoimikunta laati tätä ennakoiden sangen yleisluonteiset ohjeet. Joissakin maissa kenttätyö tätä ja omaa kansallista atlasta varten yhdistettiin, toisissa taas alunperin erikseen tehdyn oman atlaksen aineisto luovutettiin myös tähän Euroopan *Atlakseen*. Kenttätyöskentelyssä menetelmä vaihteli yksittäisistä maastokäynneistä ja tietojen kartuttamisesta useiden käyntien aikana systemaattisiin tutkimuksiin, jotka perustuivat piste- tai linjalaskentoihin tai reviirikartoitukseen valituilla koealoilla.

Hollannin keskustilastokeskus tuotti ruutukohtaisen atlasaineiston keruuta varten vakiolomakkeen, joka on osittain esitetty Kuvassa 4. Valtioiden rajoilla sijainneista ruuduista kukin maa tuotti oman lomakkeen.

Jokaisesta ruudusta pyydettiin seuraavat yleiset asiat:

1. Tutkimusjakso: vuosi tai vuodet, jolloin aineisto kerättiin.
2. Ruudun UTM-koodi.
3. Tutkimuksen täydellisyys: löydettiinkö todennäköisesti yli vai alle 75 % ruudun lajeista.
4. Ruudun alimman ja ylimmän pisteen korkeus (metreinä) meren pinnan yläpuolella.
5. Havainnoitsijoiden ja koordinaattoreiden nimet ja osoitteet mahdollisia tarkistuskysymyksiä varten.
6. Mahdollinen lisätieto, jonka avulla aineistoa voidaan ymmärtää paremmin.
7. Ruudun elinympäristötyyppien kuvaus.

Pääosa lomakkeesta käsitti n. 440 lajin luettelon (Voousin (1977) mukaisessa järjestyksessä Euring-koodilla varustettuna), johon oli varattu tilaa havaintojen kirjaamiseen. Lomakkeen sarakkeet olivat: Sarake 0, tieteellisen nimen lyhenne (esim. Gav ste). Sarake 1, Euring-koodi (esim. 00020). Sarake 2, pesintävarmuusindeksi, joka kuvaa 16 vaihtoehdon mukaisesti havainnon laatua; ryhmiteltyinä vaihtoehdot ilmaisevat onko kyseinen laji pesinyt kyseisessä ruudussa varmasti, todennäköisesti vai mahdollisesti (Taulukko 1). Sarake 3, arvio pesivien parien määrästä ruudun alueella logaritmisella asteikolla, jossa 1 = 1–9, 2 = 10–99, ... ja 6 = >100000 paria. Lomakkeen loppuun oli mahdollista merkitä myös havainnot risteymistä ja muista kuin luetelluista lajeista.

Pesimälintuaineistoa saatiin loppujen lopuksi seuraavista lähteistä:

1. Kansallisilta koordinaattoreilta, jotka organisoivat aineiston keruun ja siirsivät sen lomakkeille.
2. Alueellisilta koordinaattoreilta, jotka tekivät työn joissakin suurissa maissa tai kun oli helpompaa lähestyä olemassa olevan havainnoitsijaverkon aktiivijäseniä.
3. Muista kansallisista, tietyn lajin asiantuntijan esille tuomista lähteistä, erityisesti kirjallisuudesta. Erityisesti hankalasti saavutettavilta ja joskus muiltakaan alueilta atlasaineistoa ei saatu. Tällöin voitiin käyttää ainoastaan asiantuntijoiden tuntemaa julkaistua tai julkaisematonta aineistoa.
4. Lajikuvauksen kirjoittajilta. Usein heillä oli käytettävänään lisätietoja levinneisyyksistä ja lukumääristä, erityisesti jos he olivat tutkineet lajia.

Kaikki tiedot tarkistutettiin kansallisilla koordinaattoreilla.

Kvalitatiivinen ja puolikvantitatiivinen tieto

Atlaksessa käytetään puolikvantitatiivista aineistoa (populaatiokoko- eli kanta-arviot logaritmisella asteikolla luokiteltuina), jonka koordinaattorit ja havainnoitsijat tuottivat. Karttapisteet siis ilmaisevat ruudun parimäärän, eivät pesimätiheyksiä (ks. karttamerkkien selostukset sivulla cxl). Kaikki maat eivät valitettavasti kyenneet tuottamaan puolikvantitatiivisia populaatiokoon arvioita lainkaan (Norja, Puola), pääosasta maata (Espanja) tai osasta maata (Islanti, Ranska, Italia). Atlashanke menetti kontaktinsa Bosniaan ja Serbiaan eikä kyennyt arvioimaan heidän aineistoaan. Jotkut Ranskan alueet tuottivat populaatioidensa kokoarviot itsenäisesti ja kansallinen koordinaattori tuotti maanlaajuiset arviot vain osalle lajeja. Logaritmisellakin asteikolla annetut populaatiokoon arviot ovat paljon informatiivisempia kuin kvalitatiivinen tieto eli pelkkä tieto esiintymisestä tai puuttumisesta.

Taulukko 1 Pesimisvarmuusluokat ja -indeksit

A: Mahdollinen pesintä
1. Yksittäishavainto lajista tyypillisessä pesimäympäristössä
2. Laulava koiras tai pesintään liittyviä ääniä havaittu pesimäkaudella

B: Todennäköinen pesintä
3. Pari havaittu kerran sopivassa pesimäympäristössä
4. Samalla paikalla reviirikäyttäytymistä osoittava koiras vähintään kahtena eri päivänä vähintään viikon välein (pysyvä reviiri)
5. Pariskunta kosiomenoissa tai soitimella
6. Lintu käy todennäköisellä pesäpaikalla
7. Lintu puolustaa todennäköistä pesää hyökkäilemällä tai varoittelemalla
8. Hautomalaikku pyydystetyllä linnulla
9. Lintu rakentamassa pesää tai keskeneräinen kolo

C: Varma pesintä
10. Lintu esittää siipirikkoreaktion
11. Löydetty samanvuotinen pesä tai munankuoria
12. Vastikään pesästä lähteneitä poikasia (pesäviipyiset lajit) tai untuvikkoja (pesäjättöiset lajit)
13. Emo meni pesään tai lähti pesästä (sisältää tapaukset, joissa pesää tai pesän sisältöä ei ole voitu nähdä) tai emo hautomassa
14. Emo kantaa ruokaa tai poikasten ulosteita
15. Munapesä
16. Poikaspesä nähty tai kuultu

Suomen lomakkeella luokittelu oli hieman toinen, mutta jako mahdollista, todennäköistä tai varmaa pesintää osoittaviin havaintoihin oli yhtenevä Euroopan lintuatlastoimikunnan ohjeiden kanssa.

Rajaruuduissa, joista kaksi maata tuotti oman populaatiokoon arvionsa, valittiin suurempi (logaritmisella asteikolla annettujen arvojen yhteenlasku ei ole tule kysymykseen), vaikka tämä joissakin tapauksissa saattoikin johtaa aliarvioon. Menettely antoi kuitenkin paremman tuloksen kuin, jos olisi tyydytty pelkkään kvalitatiiviseen tietoon.

Kartoilla pisteet on luokiteltu seuraavasti:

tumma purppuranpunainen	=	varmistettu tai todennäköinen pesintä, kvalitatiivinen tieto
vaalea purppuranpunainen	=	mahdollinen pesintä, kvalitatiivinen tieto
punainen	=	varmistettu tai todennäköinen pesintä, puolikvantitatiivinen tieto
oranssi	=	mahdollinen pesintä, puolikvantitatiivinen tieto
harmaa	=	lajia ei ole etsitty kyseisessä ruudussa
piste puuttuu	=	ruutu on tutkittu, mutta lajia ei ole löydetty

Esiintymisaineisto tietokannaksi – korjaukset ja tarkistukset

Kansallisilta koordinaattoreilta saadut lomakkeet tarkistettiin yksinkertaisten virheiden, kuten puuttuvien tai väärien koodien löytämiseksi ennen kuin ne vietiin ASCII-muotoiseen tietokantaan. Jokaiseen havaintoon lisättiin maatunnus. Joistakin maista aineisto saatiin levykkeillä; nämä tarkistettiin samalla tavalla. Aineistoja yhdistettäessä kullekin lajille tuli kuhunkin ruutuun vain yksi arvo, mahdolliset päällekkäisyydet siis poistettiin.

Ne kansalliset koordinaattorit ja muut aineiston toimittajat, joilta tieto saatiin aikataulun mukaisesti, saivat alustavat lajikartat ja -listaukset heti tässä vaiheessa tarkistuksia varten. Paljon korjauksia saatiinkin heiltä. Jotkut maat toimittivat kuitenkin alkuperäisen aineistonsa tai paransivat aineiston laatua kvalitatiivisesta puolikvantitatiiviseksi paljon myöhemmin. Sen takia myös aineiston tarkistus ja korjaus edistyivät eri tahdissa eri maissa.

Alustavien karttojen tuottaminen oli välttämätöntä kahdesta syystä:

1. Niiden avulla kansalliset koordinaattorit ja heidän kauttaan monet havainnoitsijat saattoivat tarkistaa, että heidän toimittamansa aineisto oli tallennettu oikein: kartat osoittivat oliko lajit merkitty oikeisiin ruutuihin. Virheet oli helpompi havaita kartoilta kuin listauksista.
2. Ne synnyttivät lisäinnostusta osallistumiseen ja sitä kautta saatiin vielä uuttakin aineistoa.

Jatkossa tarkistettiin vielä, että edellisen vaiheen korjaukset oli tehty oikein lähettämällä kansallisille koordinaattoreille ja muille tiedon toimittajille korjatut kartat ja listaukset. Useimmat koordinaattorit tekivät tämän valtavan työn ja toimittivat lopulliset korjaukset, mutta joissain maissa, kuten entisen Jugoslavian alueella, päivitykset ja tarkistukset olivat enimmäkseen mahdottomia. Alunperinkin myöhässä olleiden maiden tuli tehdä tämä kaikki lyhyessä ajassa, ja kuta enemmän oli viivästytty, sitä vaikeampaa oli lopullisten karttojen viimeistely.

Joiltakin kirjoittajilta ja muilta lajien erityistuntijoilta saatiin lisätietoja vieläkin myöhemmässä vaiheessa. Kansalliset koordinaattorit tutkivat useimmat näistä ja päättivät, mikä tulos hyväksyttiin aineistoon. Milloin ajan puutteen vuoksi tarkistusta ei voitu tehdä, joko alkuperäinen tieto säilytettiin tai tekstissä tuodaan esille, että kirjoittajan mielipide on toinen kuin aineiston perusteella saatu kuva.

Sellaisilla alueilla, mistä atlasaineistoa ei ollut saatavilla, erityisesti Pohjois-Venäjällä ja Albaniassa, paikalliset kenttäornitologit kokosivat aineiston muista lähteistä. Niissä lajien runsauksia arvioitiin yleistämällä tietoja lähialueen sellaisista ruuduista, joista tietoa oli saatavissa. Tällöin otettiin tietysti huomioon ruutujen elinympäristökoostumus.

Uuden aineiston ja korjausten viimeinen takaraja oli 1. heinäkuuta 1995, joskin vielä muutaman seuraavan kuukauden aikana Albaniasta, Turkin Euroopan puoleisesta osasta, Kaukasukselta sekä osista Ukrainaa ja Venäjää saatua aineistoa käytettiin kattavuuden maksimoimiseksi. Lajikuvausten kirjoittajilta saatuja korjauksia hyväksyttiin marraskuun 1. päivään asti.

Aineiston keruu – kanta-arviot

Maakohtaiset kanta-arviokuviot, jotka *Atlaksessa* esitetään, ovat peräisin eurooppalaisesta lintutietokannasta. Sen ovat yhdessä koonneet Euroopan lintulaskentatoimikunta ja BirdLife International *Atlasta* ja BirdLifen *Birds in Europe – their conservation status* – teoksen syntyyn (Tucker & Heath 1994) johtanutta hanketta varten. Tietokannan luominen auttoi myös parantamaan osallistumista joissakin Euroopan osissa. Aineisto kerättiin ensisijaisesti lähettämällä kyselyjä kansallisille koordinaattoreille (heidän nimensä on esitetty *Birds in Europe* -teoksessa), jotka edelleen levittivät kyselyä asiantuntijoille, linnustonseurantaorganisaatioille ja alueellisille koordinaattoreille ja tiedon toimittajille. BirdLife International huolehtii tietokannasta.

Jokainen maa toimitti kaikista pesivistä lajeista seuraavat tiedot:

1. Kannan koko.
2. Kannan koon kehityssuunta (vuosina 1970-90).
3. Levinneisyyden kehityssuunta (vuosina 1970-90).

Aineistoa kerättiin myös talvehtivan kannan koosta, mutta sitä ei käytetä Atlaksessa.

Jotkut lajikuvausten kirjoittajat eivät hyväksyneet lintutietokannassa olevaa kanta-arviota, mutta tieto saapui liian myöhään. Tällöin kirjoittajat esittävät omat arvionsa tekstissä. Lajikuvauksiin liittyvissä diagrammit perustuvat aina lintutietokantaan.

Aineiston rajoitukset

Atlashanke on tuottanut hyvälaatuisen aineiston. Kuitenkin sillä on myös rajoituksensa. Haluttaessa käyttää aineistoa jatkotutkimuksiin, on ne otettava huomioon, vaikkakaan niitä ei tässä yhteydessä ole tarpeen käsitellä (yksityiskohdat ovat saatavissa Euroopan lintulaskentatoimikunnalta). *Atlaksen* käyttöön vaikuttavat kuitenkin seuraavat yleiset perusrajoitukset:

1. Sille, miten lajin esiintyminen tai puuttuminen jostakin ruudusta todetaan, ei etukäteen esitetty yhteistä kenttätyömenetelmää. Sama koskee populaatiokoon arvioita. Monissa maakohtaisissa hankkeissa, joista aineisto on peräisin, kenttätyöt oli suunniteltu omia tarkoituksia varten käytettävissä olleiden mahdollisuuksien mukaisesti.
2. Yhteistä menetelmää ei liioin ollut kenttätulosten muokkaamiseksi atlaslomakkeille pääasiassa samoista syistä kuin edellä.
3. Kenttäornitologian yleisen tason ja havainnoitsijoiden

määrän vaihtelu aiheuttavat vaihtelua aineiston laatuun.

4. Joillakin alueilla tiedot perustuvat lähialueiden tietojen yleistämiseen.
5. Joillakin (pääasiassa arktisilla) alueilla tiedot ovat peräisin kirjallisuudesta.

ATLAKSEN KARTTOJEN JA LAJIKUVAUSTEN ESITYSTAPA

Lajit on *Atlaksessa* jaettu kahteen ryhmään. Toisessa ovat ne lajit, joista saatiin tyydyttävä kartoitusaineisto, ja toisessa ne, joista ei saatu. Kaikista edellisen ryhmän lajeista on täydet kuvaukset kirjan osassa 1 (Lajikuvaukset). Jälkimmäisen ryhmän lajeista on suppeammat kuvaukset osassa 2. Molemmissa osissa lajit on esitetty Voousin (1977) teoksen mukaisessa ja pääosin myös Euringin käyttämässä järjestyksessä. Ainoat poikkeukset ovat osassa 1 silloin, kun samalle aukealle oli mahdollista sijoittaa kaksi yhden sivun kuvauksen saanutta lajia. Kahden sivun lajeilla kartta ja kuvaus ovat aina samalla aukeamalla. Useimpien lajien populaatiokoot on esitetty piirroksina, joiden symbolit on selitetty ennen lajikuvauksia. Joistakin lajeista, joiden levinneisyydet ovat hyvin suppeat, ei populaatiokokoja esitetä kuvioina. Silloin samallekin sivulle on mahtunut kaksi lajia. Jokaisesta lajista on piirros. Lisäksi lajien nimet on esitetty 14 eri kielellä (jos nimet ovat olemassa).

Aineistosta työstetyt kartat

Kuva 5 esittää pesivien lintulajien lukumäärän kussakin ruudussa. Kuvat 6, 7 ja 8 puolestaan esittävät niiden lajien lukumäärän, jotka on luokiteltu eurooppalaisittain uhanalaisuutensa tai heikkenevän kannankehityksensä takia erityisen luonnonsuojelullisen huolen kohteiksi (BirdLife Internationalin Species of European Conservation Concern, luokat 1, 2 ja 3). Kuvassa 9 mainittuihin luokkiin kuuluvien lajien lukumäärät on yhdistetty.

LAJIKUVAUKSET

Lajikuvaukset on laadittu noudattaen seuraavaa kaavaa sen mukaan, miten aiheet kutakin lajia koskevat: levinneisyys maailmassa, elinympäristöt Euroopassa, levinneisyys ja runsaus Euroopassa, levinneisyyden ja populaatiokoon viimeaikaiset muutokset (ja niiden mahdolliset syyt), runsauden alueellinen vaihtelu, mahdolliset levinneisyyttä rajoittavat tekijät, pesimätiheys tärkeimmissä elinympäristöissä, muutto ja muut liikehdinnät Euroopan alueella ja sen ulkopuolella, lajin erityispiirteitä sekä alalajit levinneisyysalueineen ja mahdollisine alue- tai populaatiokoon muutoksineen.

Lajikuvauksissa ei käsitellä pesimäbiologiaa, käyttäytymistä, ravintoa, lajienvälisiä suhteita, morfologisia tai fysiologisia ominaisuuksia, uhanalaisuuden syitä (jotka on käsitelty teoksessa *Birds in Europe*), poikkeavuuksia, munia, evoluutiota ja taksonomiaa (paitsi jos lajin asemassa on äskettäin hyväksyttyjä muutoksia tai alalajit poikkeavat toisistaan merkittävästi), kuolleisuutta tai muita populaatiodynamiikkaan liittyviä tekijöitä ja ääniä ja laulua, ellei lyhyt maininta ollut erityisen tärkeä.

Lajisto – mukaan ottamisen kriteerit

Mukaan on otettu kaikki aiotulla tutkimusalueella vuodesta 1985 lähtien pesineet lajit, jos ne täyttävät Taulukossa 1 esitetyt ehdot. Ihmisen alueelle levittämät, luonnossa pesivät lajit otettiin mukaan, jos niillä on ollut vähintään yksi itseään ylläpitävä populaatio vähintään viiden vuoden ajan. Näiden ehtojen täyttymistä arvioidaan kuitenkin jossain määrin eri tavoin eri puolilla Eurooppaa, minkä vuoksi joidenkin ihmisen levittämien lajien mukaan ottaminen voi vaikuttaa keinotekoiselta.

Atlaksessa on mukana 513 lajia ja lisäksi *Passer* x *italiae*.

NIMISTÖ JA TAKSONOMIA

Taksonomia

Euroopan lintulaskentatoimikunta on omaksunut varovaisen ja konservatiivisen asenteen taksonomisiin kysymyksiin. *Atlas* noudattaa yleisesti sitä taksonomiaa, järjestystä ja englanninkielistä nimistöä, jota on käytetty käsikirjan *Birds of the Western Palearctic (BWP)* lyhennetyssä ja korjatussa laitoksessa.

Levantinliitäjä *Puffinus yelkouan*, baleaarienliitäjä *Puffinus mauretanicus*, valkopäälokki *Larus cachinnans*, vuorikirvinen *Anthus spinoletta*, lännenvuoritiltaltti *Phylloscopus lorenzii* ja azorienpunatulkku *Pyrrhula murina* käsitellään itsenäisinä lajeina. Niillä on myös omat kartat erillään pikkuliitäjästä *Puffinus puffinus*, harmaalokista *Larus argentatus*, luotokirvisestä *Anthus petrosus*, tiltaltista *Phylloscopus collybita* ja punatulkusta *Pyrrhula pyrrhula*. Erillisten karttojen tuottaminen oli mahdollista joko siksi, että ne oli kenttätyön yhteydessä kartoitettu erikseen tai niiden levinneisyysalueet ovat erillään. (Kolmen *Puffinus*-lajin kuvaukset on yhdistetty.)

Alunperin monien lajien alalajeja yritettiin kartoittaa erikseen, mutta lintuatlastoimikunnan laatimia ohjeita ei

Taulukko 2 Eurooppalaisessa lintutietokannassa käytetyt koodit

POPMIN	= vähimmäiskanta (pareja)		
POPMAX	= enimmäiskanta (pareja)		
MEAN	= kannan geometrinen keskiarvo (pareja)	PSV	= kannan koon vahvistuskoodi
YRC	= kanta-arvion vuosi		
PST	= kannan muutossuunta	PTV	= kannan muutossuunnan vahvistuskoodi
RST	= levinneisyysalueen muutossuunta	RTV	= levinneisyysalueen muutossuunnan vahvistuskoodi

Kantoja ja levinneisyysalueen muutosta kuvaavat koodit

+2	= voimakas kasvu (vähintään 50 %)
+1	= vähäinen kasvu (vähintään 20 %, alle 50 %)
0	= vakaa, ei yleistä vähintään 20 %:n muutosta
-1	= vähäinen pienentyminen (vähintään 20 %, alle 50 %)
-2	= voimakas pienentyminen (vähintään 50 %)
n	= uusi pesimälaji tutkimuskaudella
x	= tutkimuskaudella hävinnyt laji
f	= vaihteleva, muutos vähintään 20 %, mutta ei suuntausta

noudatettu yhteneväisesti kaikkialla Euroopassa eikä yritys onnistunut. Kuitenkin ìitalianvarpunenî esitetään erikseen ja *Atlas* kohtelee sitä *BWP*:n tavoin varpusen *Passer domesticus* ja pajuvarpusen *P. hispaniolensis* vakiintuneena risteymänä *Passer × italiae*. Sen sijaan idänuunilintu *Phylloscopus trochiloides* käsittää kaksi maantieteellisesti erillistä alalajia, *Ph. t. viridanuksen* ja *Ph. t. nitiduksen*. Jälkimmäistä, kaukaasianuunilintua, on pidetty myös itsenäisenä lajina *Ph. nitidus*. Etelänisolepinkäisen *Lanius meridionaliksen* erottaminen isolepinkäisestä *L. excubitorista* oli yleisesti hyväksytty, kun *Atlasta* viimeisteltiin; näiden kahden muodon välinen esiintymisraja on esitetty kaavakuvana. Pikkukultarinnan *Hippolais caligata* alalajille *rama* (aavikkokultarinta) annetaan joskus itsenäisen lajin asema, mutta *Atlaksessa* ei. Joidenkin lokkikompleksien suhteet ovat epäselviä. Armenianlokkia *Larus armenicus* pidetään *Atlaksessa* itsenäisenä lajina.

Euring-numerot

Euroopan rengastusunioni Euring on kehittänyt viisinumeroisen koodin lintujen lajeille ja alalajeille. Sitä käytetään ensisijaisesti rengastustietokantojen käsittelyssä. Euringin luettelo noudattaa yleisesti ottaen Voousin järjestystä. Siksi se otettiin käyttöön myös atlasaineiston käsittelyyn. Euring-numerot on ilmoitettu lajiartikkeleiden yhteydessä. Niiden käyttöperiaatteet selostetaan teknisessä liitteessä.

LÄHDELUETTELO

Kirjoittajia pyydettiin välttämään viittauksia käsikirjoihin, koska tilaa oli niukasti. Kaksi keskeistä eurooppalaista käsikirjaa on mainittava, nimittäin *Birds of the Western Palearctic* (Cramp ym. 1977-1994) ja *Handbuch der Vögel Mitteleuropas* (Glutz von Blotzheim ym. 1966-1993). Perustiedot mistä tahansa eurooppalaisesta pesimälintulajista löytyvät niistä. Atlaksessa niistä käytetään lyhenteitä *BWP* ja *HVM*.

Birds in Europe – their conservation status (Tucker & Heath 1994) tarjoaa kaikkien aikojen ensimmäisen katsauksen eurooppalaisten lintupopulaatioiden tilasta, uhkista ja suojelutilanteesta. Lajeista, joiden suojelutilanne on epäsuotuisa, on siinä yksityiskohtaiset käsittelyt. *Atlaksen* populaatioita kuvaavat diagrammit on laadittu saman eurooppalaisen lintutietokannan perusteella kuin mainittu kirjakin, johon sen vuoksi viitataan runsaasti.

Atlaksen lähdeluettelo on kirjan lopussa ennen hakemistoja.

Michael Blair, Ward Hagemeijer ja Juha Tiainen

KÄSITTEET JA NIIDEN LYHENTEET

Ilmansuunnat

N = pohjoinen
S = etelä
E = itä
W = länsi; siten NW = luode, WSW = länsilounas, jne.
C = Keski-, keski-; siten S-C = eteläinen Keski-, jne.

Yleisiä ilmaisuja

asl = meren yläpuolella (korkeus)
c = suunnilleen
et al = ynnä muut (lähdeviittauksissa)
pers comm = henkilökohtainen ilmoitus
pers obs = henkilökohtainen havainto
unpubl = julkaisematon tieto

Laadut

bp = pesiviä pareja
ha = hehtaari
ind = yksilöitä
m = metri
km = kilometri
km^2 = neliökilometri
M = miljoona

Akronyymit eli kirjainsanat

BTO = British Trust for Ornithology (Iso-Britannia)
BWP = Birds of the Western Palaearctic
HVM = Handbuch der Vögel Mitteleuropas
JNCC = Joint Nature Conservation Committee (Iso-Britannia)
RSPB = Royal Society for the Protection of Birds (Iso-Britannia)
SOVON = Samenwerkende Organisaties Vogelwerk Nederland (Hollanti)
WWT = Wildlife and Wetland Trust (Iso-Britannia)

ΕΙΣΑΓΩΓΗ

Ο ΑΤΛΑΝΤΑΣ ΤΩΝ ΑΝΑΠΑΡΑΓΟΜΕΝΩΝ ΠΟΥΛΙΩΝ ΤΗΣ ΕΥΡΩΠΗΣ

Σε πολλά ορνιθολογικά βιβλία μπορεί κανείς να βρεί φαινομενικά λεπτομερείς χάρτες εξάπλωσης των διαφόρων ειδών. Αρκετοί από τους χάρτες αυτούς βασίζονται σε καταγραφές των αναπαραγόμενων πληθυσμών μιας περιοχής ή χώρας αλλά, με εξαίρεση κάποιους εξειδικευμένους άτλαντες, συνήθως οι χάρτες αυτοί προέρχονται από διάφορες πηγές αμφιβόλου αξιοπιστίας ενώ συχνά πρόκειται για επανεκδόσεις παλαιότερου υλικού, το οποίο έχει πλέον χάσει την εγκυρότητα του. Επιπλέον, τέτοιοι χάρτες δεν περιέχουν ποσοτικά δεδομένα δηλαδή πολύ σπάνια δείχνουν κατά πόσο ένα είδος είναι κοινό ή σπάνιο στην περιοχή εξάπλωσής του.

Τα τελευταία όμως χρόνια έχουν δημοσιευθεί και εξακολουθούν να δημοσιεύονται με αυξανόμενο ρυθμό αρκετοί εξαιρετικής ποιότητας τοπικοί, περιφερειακοί ή εθνικοί άτλαντες αναπαραγόμενων πουλιών. Για πολλούς από αυτούς τα κίνητρα ή η έμπνευση προήλθαν από το πρόγραμμα του παρόντος *Ατλαντα* και, ακριβώς όπως αυτός, περιέχουν ημι-ποσοτικά δεδομένα. Ηδη από το 1971 συγκροτήθηκε η "Επιτροπή Ευρωπαϊκού Ορνιθολογικού Ατλαντα" (EOAC) με σκοπό τη χαρτογράφηση όλων των ειδών που αναπαράγονται στην Ευρώπη και για τα οποία θα ήταν δυνατό να συλλεχθούν αξιόπιστα δεδομένα με εργασία πεδίου. Η παρούσα έκδοση περιλαμβάνει τα αποτελέσματα αυτής ακριβώς της προσπάθειας.

Ο *Ατλαντας* δείχνει τη γεωγραφική εξάπλωση των διαφόρων ειδών πουλιών σε μια συγκεκριμένη και περιορισμένη χρονική περίοδο, αλλά τα στοιχεία που συγκεντρώθηκαν (παρά την κάποια ανομοιογένειά τους) συνθέτουν μια αξιόλογη βάση δεδομένων στην οποία μπορεί πλέον εύκολα να στηριχθεί κάθε αντίστοιχη εργασία στο μέλλον καθώς επίσης και να αξιολογηθούν όλες οι πιθανές αλλαγές στην κατανομή των ίδιων των ειδών. Η Επιτροπή του 1971 είχε ένα σαφές όραμα: να επιχειρήσει την πρώτη πανευρωπαϊκή απογραφή των πουλιών που αναπαρόγονται στον Ευρωπαϊκό χώρο. Ο *Ατλαντας των Αναπαραγόμενων Πουλιών της Ευρώπης* υλοποιεί αυτό το όραμα, δηλαδή χαρτογραφεί τη γεωγραφική εξάπλωση όλων αυτών των ειδών και απαντά στο ερώτημα "ποιό είδος πουλιού αναπαράγεται πού ...".

ΔΟΜΗ ΤΟΥ ΒΙΒΛΙΟΥ

Στην παρούσα **Εισαγωγή** περιγράφονται εν συντομία οι στόχοι του *Ατλαντα*, αναλύονται με λεπτομέρεια οι μέθοδοι συλλογής δεδομένων για την εξάπλωση και τους πληθυσμούς των ειδών, η χαρτογράφηση και ανάλυση μέσω ηλεκτρονικού υπολογιστή και δίνονται βασικές πληροφορίες για τη δομή του βιβλίου. Ο αναγνώστης πρέπει να διαβάσει αυτές τις οδηγίες για να μπορέσει να καταλάβει το βιβλίο σε όλες του τις λεπτομέρειες. Εξάλλου η εισαγωγή έχει τυπωθεί σε αρκετές γλώσσες για να μπορεί να γίνει κατανοητή από τους περισσότερους Ευρωπαίους ορνιθολόγους.

Εισαγωγικό μέρος

Στον **Πρόλογο**, ο καθηγητής Karel Voous εξηγεί συνοπτικά τη σπουδαιότητα του *Ατλαντα* όσον αφορά τις διάφορες μεταβολές που παρατηρούνται στην Ευρωπαϊκή ορνιθοπανίδα. Το **Προοίμιο** περιγράφει συνοπτικά το πώς η συλλογική αυτή προσπάθεια εξυπηρετεί τις ανάγκες των Ευρωπαίων ορνιθολόγων και ταυτόχρονα υπογραμμίζει την πολιτική και τους στόχους του Ευρωπαϊκού Συμβουλίου Ορνιθολογικής Απογραφής (EBCC) σε μελλοντικά επιμέρους προγράμματα αντίστοιχης μορφής. Ακολουθεί η **Εισαγωγή**, που περιγράφει μεταξύ άλλων τη μεθοδολογία και την περιοχή κάλυψης. Εν συνεχεία, ενα ειδικό κεφάλαιο με τίτλο **Επεξηγηματικά Σχήματα** δείχνει τη γεωγραφική κάλυψη, την ποιότητα των δεδομένων και το τυποποιημένο έντυπο συλλογής δεδομένων. Στο κεφάλαιο **Ιστορία** περιγράφονται τα προβλήματα και η εξέλιξη του προγράμματος του Ευρωπαϊκού Ορνιθολογικού Ατλαντα. Ακολουθεί το κεφάλαιο **Εξέλιξη και Ιστορία της Ευρωπαϊκής Ορνιθοπανίδας**, όπου ο Καθηγητής Jacques Blondel εξηγεί τους τρόπους με τους οποίους διαμορφώθηκε η σημερινή γεωγραφική εξάπλωση των διαφόρων ειδών της Ευρωπαϊκής ορνιθοπανίδας. Τέλος ακολουθούν οι **Ευχαριστίες** και κατάλογος με όλα τα βιβλία που έχουν εκδοθεί μέχρι σήμερα ως **Εθνικοί και Περιφερειακοί Ατλαντες στην Ευρώπη**.

Κείμενα ειδών

Η **Εισαγωγή στους χάρτες και τα γραφήματα των πληθυσμών** μας οδηγεί στα κείμενα των επιμέρους ειδών. Ο κύριος όγκος του βιβλίου περιλαμβάνει τα κείμενα για όλα τα είδη που αναπαράγονται στην Ευρώπη. Το πρώτο μέρος αποτελείται από τους χάρτες εξάπλωσης, κείμενα για κάθε είδος, την κοινή ονομασία του είδους σε 14 γλώσσες και σκίτσα του είδους. Η σειρά των ειδών ακολουθεί κατά προσέγγιση την ταξινόμηση του Voous (1977) και τη σειρά αρίθμησης του Euring. Το δεύτερο μέρος αποτελείται από κείμενα για τα είδη τα οποία πιστεύεται οτι αναπαράγονται στην Ευρώπη αλλά για τα οποία δεν συλλέχθηκαν νέες πληροφορίες.

Τελικό μέρος

Το τμήμα **Χάρτες Σύνθεσης** ασχολείται με την εξάπλωση των πουλιών που αναπαράγονται στην Ευρώπη και εκείνων των ειδών τα οποία θεωρούνται ως **Είδη Χρήζοντα Προστασίας** (SPEC) σύμφωνα με τον ορισμό του Birdlife International (Tucker & Heath 1994). Το **Τεχνικό Προσάρτημα** επεξηγεί τα σημεία στα οποία η κάναβος (τετραγωνισμός) του *Ατλαντα* διαφέρει από τη θεωρητική Παγκόσμια Εγκάρσια Μερκατορική (UTM) προβολή, καθώς και πώς αντιμετωπίστηκε η περίπτωση των νησιών και των παράκτιων περιοχών. Εξηγεί επίσης πως χρησιμοποίηθηκε το σύστημα αρίθμησης του Euring στον *Ατλαντα*.

Τεύχη άλλων γλωσσών

Περιλήψεις των αρχικών τμημάτων (**Προοίμιο, Ιστορία**, και **Εξέλιξη και Ιστορία της Ευρωπαϊκής Ορνιθοπανίδας**) καθώς και των κειμένων για τα είδη δόθηκαν σε ορνιθολόγους όλων των Ευρωπαϊκών χωρών, με στόχο να μεταφρασθούν στις γλώσσες τους και έτσι να γίνουν προσιτά σε όλους όσους δεν γνωρίζουν την Αγγλική. Στο τέλος του **Τεχνικού Παραρτήματος** υπάρχει κατάλογος (όπως είχε διαμορφωθεί πριν την εκτύπωση του παρόντος) με ονόματα και διευθύνσεις απ' όπου μπορεί κανείς να προμηθεύεται τα τεύχη άλλων γλωσσών.

ΜΕΘΟΔΟΛΟΓΙΑ

Παρουσίαση των δεδομένων

Η αρχική ιδέα για τη συλλογή και σύνθεση των δεδομένων καθώς και ο τρόπος με τον οποίο επελέγησαν οι αντίστοιχες μέθοδοι περιγράφονται στο κεφάλαιο **Ιστορία**.

Οι χάρτες του *Ατλαντα* δείχνουν την πληθυσμιακή πυκνότητα (αριθμός πουλιών ανά μονάδα επιφάνειας) σε λογαριθμική κλίμακα (λεπτομέρειες δίνονται κατωτέρω, στο **Ποιοτικά και ημι-ποσοτικά δεδομένα**). Η λογαριθμική κλίμακα κρίθηκε ως η καταλλλότερη μέθοδος επειδή στα περισσότερα είδη οι πυκνότητες ποικίλουν σημαντικά μέσα στην περιοχή εξάπλωσής τους. Δυστυχώς, στην κλίμακα αυτή αποκρύπτονται οι μικρές διαφορές πυκνότητας.

Ο *Ατλαντας* όχι μόνο παρουσιάζει την εξάπλωση των πουλιών που αναπαράγονται στην Ευρώπη αλλά περιέχει και εκτιμήσεις του συνολικού αναπαραγόμενου πληθυσμού και των αυξητικών ή μειωτικώντάσεων για τα περισσότερα είδη για κάθε μια Ευρωπαϊκή χώρα. Δεν είναι δυνατό να κατανοήσουμε σε βάθος τις διάφορες μεταβολές στην εξάπλωση των ειδών παρά μόνο μέσω εκτιμήσεων οι οποίες βασίζονται σε αδιαφιλονίκητα δεδομένα για κάθε μια χώρα.

Γεωγραφική κάλυψη του *Ατλαντα*

Η γεωγραφική κάλυψη στην οποία αποβλέπει ο *Ατλαντας* φαίνεται στο **Σχήμα 1**. Αν και θα επιθυμούσαμε πολύ να ταυτίσουμε τα όρια του παρόντος *Ατλαντα* με τα όρια της δυτικής Παλαιαρκτικής ζώνης, όπως αυτά καθορίζονται στο *The Birds of the Western Palearctic* (Cramp *et al* 1977–1994), κρίναμε τελικά ότι αυτό είναι ανέφικτο για το πρόγραμμά μας επειδή δεν διαθέταμε επαρκή δεδομένα από τη Μικρά Ασία, τη βόρεια Αραβία και τη βόρεια Αφρική, οι οποίες και εξαιρέθηκαν. Ο *Ατλαντας* συνεπώς στηρίζεται κυρίως στη χαρτογράφηση του *Atlas Florae Europaeae* (Jalas & Suominen 1972, 1988), αλλά περιλαμβάνει περιοχές όπως η Νεα Γη (Novaya Zemlya) και η Γη του Φραγκ. Ιωσήφ (Franz Josef Land), όλα τα Ελληνικά νησιά του Αιγαίου, το αρχιπέλαγος της Μαδέρας, τις Αζόρες, την περιοχή γύρω από τη Stavropol της ΝΑ Ρωσίας και τις Δημοκρατίες του Καυκάσου. Κάποιες άλλες διαφορές σε σχέση με τη δυτική Παλαιαρκτική είναι ότι στην παρούσα έκδοση έχουν εξαιρεθεί η Κύπρος, τα Κανάρια νησιά και όλα τα βορειοαφρικανικά νησιά. Ο *Ατλαντας* επίσης διαφέρει από το *Birds in Europe – their conservation status* (Tucker & Heath 1994) στο ότι δεν περιλαμβάνει το Ασιατικό τμήμα της Τουρκίας και τη Γροινλανδία.

Τέλος, αν και δύσκολα διακρίνεται στο **Σχήμα 1**, τόσο από τη δυτική Παλαιαρκτική όσο και από το *Atlas Florae Europaeae* και από την παρούσα έκδοση εξαιρείται μια μικρή περιοχή της Ευρώπης κοντά στο Odenburg ενώ αντίθετα περιλαμβάνεται ένα μέρος του ασιατικού Καζακστάν μεταξύ των ποταμών Βόλγα και Ουράλη και ένα τμήμα της Ασιατικής Ρωσίας ανατολικά του Perm (περιοχή Sverdlovsk).

Επιτευχθείσα κάλυψη

Στο τμήμα **Επεξηγηματικά Σχήματα** που ακολουθεί την **Εισαγωγή**, το **Σχήμα 2** δείχνει τα τετράγωνα (κελλιά) που απογράφηκαν καθώς και τη μέγιστη ποιότητα των δεδομένων ανά τετράγωνο, ενώ το **Σχήμα 3** δείχνει την ελάχιστη ποιότητα των δεδομένων ανά τετράγωνο. Οι όροι αυτοί επεξηγούνται καλύτερα υπο-κεφάλαιο **Ποιοτικά και ημι-ποσοτικά δεδομένα** (βλ. κατωτέρω) αλλά συνοπτικά οι κατηγορίες της ποιότητας των δεδομένων που δείχνουν οι χάρτες είναι οι εξής κατά φθίνουσα σειρά:

1. Ημι-ποσοτική πληθυσμιακή εκτίμηση: η αναπαραγωγή εκτιμήθηκε ως επιβεβαιωμένη ή πιθανή.
2. Ημι-ποσοτική πληθυσμιακή εκτίμηση: η αναπαραγωγή εκτιμήθηκε ως ενδεχομένη.
3. Ποιοτική παρουσία: η αναπαραγωγή εκτιμήθηκε ως επιβεβαιωμένη ή πιθανή.
4. Ποιοτική παρουσία: η αναπαραγωγή εκτιμήθηκε ως ενδεχομένη.

Η ποιότητα των δεδομένων ήταν συνήθως η ίδια για όλα τα είδη που καταγράφηκαν σε κάθε ένα τετράγωνο (βλ. όμως και κατωτέρω). Σημαντικές περιοχές της Κεντρικής Ρωσίας δεν καλύφθηκαν καθόλου, κυρίως λόγω έλλειψης συνεργατών. Για μεγάλο τμήμα της υπόλοιπης Ρωσίας, καθώς και για περιοχές της Λευκορωσίας, της Ουκρανίας και των Δημοκρατιών του Καυκάσου, η κάλυψη θεωρείται πλήρης για λίγα μόνο είδη. Για την πρώην Γιουγκοσλαβία η κάλυψη θεωρείται αρκετά καλή (αν και σε μερικές περιοχές όχι για όλα τα είδη). Υπάρχουν τέλος κενά στην Αλβανία και ανεπαρκής κάλυψη για τα Ρωσικά νησιά της Αρκτικής: την Νεα Γη (Novaya Zemlya) και τη Γη του Φραγκ. Ιωσήφ (Franz Josef Land).

Στις υπόλοιπες περιοχές, παρά τις αναπόφευκτες ελλείψεις, η κάλυψη θεωρείται επαρκής.

Οι χάρτες του *Ατλαντα*

Η επιλογή της κατάλληλης χαρτογραφικής προβολής έγινε με τρία κριτήρια: να καλύπτει όλη τη γεωγραφική περιοχή που μας ενδιαφέρει, να είναι οικεία στις περισσότερες Ευρωπαϊκές χώρες και να είναι συμβατή με προβολές εθνικής κλίμακας. Οταν ξεκινήσαμε το πρόγραμμα του *Ατλαντα*, η μόνη προβολή που εκπληρούσε και τα τρία αυτά κριτήρια ήταν η Παγκόσμια Εγκάρσια Μερκατορική (UTM). Επειδή και οι χάρτες του *Atlas Florae Europeae* χρησιμοποιούν τη UTM αποφασίσαμε ότι η προβολή αυτή ήταν η πλέον κατάλληλη για τους ορνιθολογικούς χάρτες. Επιπλέον, χρησιμοποίησαμε την ίδια κάναβο με βασική χαρτογραφική μονάδα τετράγωνα των 50km x 50km. Κάθε άλλη επιλογή (π.χ. τετράγωνα μικρότερου μεγέθους) θα έκανε τη συγκέντρωση και ανάλυση των δεδομένων ανέφικτη.

Η βασική χαρτογραφική μονάδα της κανάβου του UTM είναι το τετράγωνο των 100km x 100km. Κάθε τέτοιο τετράγωνο αναγνωρίζεται με ένα ειδικό κωδικό που αποτελείται από δύο γράμματα και τρεις αριθμούς. Για τους άτλαντες χλωρίδας και ορνιθοπανίδας κάθε τέτοιο τετράγωνο υποδιαιρείται σε τέσσερα μικρότερα τετράγωνα 50km x 50km, τα οποία αριθμούνται ως εξής:

1	3
2	4

Συνεπώς, κάθε τετράγωνο 50km x 50km αναγνωρίζεται με ένα κωδικό έξι χαρακτήρων.

Η δομή του τετραγώνου UTM στο νοητό άξονα Βορρά-Νότου είναι απλή: οι διαχωριστικές γραμμές είναι χαραγμένες σε αποστάσεις των 50km μεταξύ τους, είναι δε παράλληλες προς το γεωγραφικό πλάτος ξεκινώντας από τον Ισημερινό. Ο άλλος άξονας είναι πιο δύσκολος να χαραχθεί, επειδή οι μεσημβρινοί (του γεωγραφικού μήκους) συγκλίνουν προς τους δύο πόλους της Γης. Κατά συνέπεια, ο αριθμός των τετραγώνων 50km x 50km τείνει να μειώνεται καθώς κινούμεθα προς τους δύο πόλους. Στην κάναβο του UTM η δυσκολία αυτή αντιμετωπίζεται ως εξής. Ξεκινώντας από τις 0° γεωγραφικού μήκους, και για κάθε 6°, τα τετράγωνα που αγγίζουν τους μεσημβρινούς αυτούς (κάθε 6°) στενεύουν όπως προχωρούμε προς τους πόλους, μέχρι που να γίνουν λεπτές γραμμές μηδενικού εύρους, οπότε εξαφανίζονται. Στη συνέχεια, αρχίζει να λεπταίνει η επόμενη σειρά τετραγώνων που έρχεται σε επαφή με τους μεσημβρινούς αυτούς και ούτω καθεξής μέχρι τους πόλους. Τα τετράγωνα που βρίσκονται ανάμεσα στους αντίστοιχους μεσημβρινούς αλλά όχι σε επαφή με αυτούς διατηρούν σταθερό εύρος 50km. Στο *Atlas Florae Europeae* καθώς και στον παρόντα *Ατλαντα* η μέθοδος αυτή τροποποιήθηκε, με τρόπο ώστε η διακύμανση του εύρους των τετραγώνων που αγγίζουν τους μεσημβρινούς κάθε 6° να είναι μικρότερη: τα τετράγωνα αυτά ενώνονται μεταξύ τους ανά ζεύγη όταν το εύρος τους μειωθεί περίπου στα 40km. (Αναφερόμαστε στα κελλιά του χάρτη με τη λέξη "τετράγωνα" για ευκολία, αν και βέβαια πολλά από αυτά αποκλίνουν σημαντικά από το σχήμα τετραγώνου). Η διαρρύθμιση των τετραγώνων φαίνεται σαφώς στο χάρτη στο **Σχήμα 1** ενώ λεπτομερείς επεξηγήσεις δίνονται στο **Τεχνικό Παράρτημα**.

Η EOAC διένειμε έτοιμους χάρτες με τα τετράγωνα 50km x 50km στους υπεύθυνους του προγράμματος κάθε χώρας, έτσι ώστε η καταγραφή των δεδομένων να γίνει με ενιαίο τρόπο. Πολύ συχνά η εργασία πεδίου έγινε σε τετράγωνου μικρότερου μεγέθους ή σε χάρτες με άλλο τετραγωνισμό αλλά σε κάθε περίπτωση οι υπεύθυνοι σε κάθε χώρα μετέτρεψαν τα δεδομένα στη σωστή μορφή των 50km x 50km.

Περίοδος εργασίας πεδίου και η διαδικασία αξιολόγησης

Είχε εξαρχής αποφασισθεί ότι η εργασία πεδίου σε όλες τις χώρες έπρεπε να καλύπτει την περίοδο 1985-1988. Τελικά, αυτό στάθηκε αδύνατο για πολλούς λόγους αλλά κυρίως επειδή οι ορνιθολόγοι κάθε χώρας οργάνωσαν τη δική τους εργασία πεδίου όπως εκείνοι νόμιζαν καλύτερα. Στις περιπτώσεις όπου τα δεδομένα από την εργασία πεδίου κρίθηκαν ως ανεπαρκή, χρησιμοποιήθηκε προγενέστερο ή μεταγενέστερο υλικό, το οποίο όμως έπρεπε να αξιολογηθεί κατάλληλα. Ο **Πίνακας3** που ακολουθεί την **Εισαγωγή** δείχνει όλες τις χώρες που μετέχουν στον *Ατλαντα*, τη χρονική περίοδο κατά την οποία συγκέντρωσαν τα δεδομένα τους, την κάναβο που χρησιμοποίησαν και τη μεθοδολογία τους.

Συγκέντρωση του υλικού – εξάπλωση των ειδών

Χρειάστηκαν εκατοντάδες χιλιάδες, ίσως και πάνω από ένα εκατομμύριο συνολικά, ώρες εργασίας στο ύπαιθρο για να ετοιμασθεί ο παρών *Ατλαντας*. Το ιδανικό θα ήταν βέβαια όλοι όσοι εργάστηκαν στο πρόγραμμα να χρησιμοποιούσαν την ίδια ακριβώς μεθοδολογία στην ίδια χρονική περίοδο, κάτι που όμως στάθηκε αδύνατο. Ετσι στους ενδιαφερόμενους δόθηκαν απλώς γενικές κατευθύνσεις παρά αυστηροί κανόνες. Σε κάποιες χώρες, οι συμμετέχοντες ορνιθολόγοι συνδύασαν την εργασία πεδίου για τον *Ατλαντα* με παρόμοια προγράμματα εθνικής ή τοπικής κλίμακας ενώ σε άλλες χρειάστηκε να γίνει εξαρχής όλη η διαδικασία για τον παρόντα *Ατλαντα*. Για την εργασία πεδίου χρησιμοποιήθηκε ποικιλία μεθόδων, από μία μόνο επίσκεψη ή την κατάρτιση καταλόγου ειδών σε πολλές επισκέψεις έως συστηματικές καταγραφές βασισμένες σε δειγματοληψίες (διαδρομής ή σημειακές) και χαρτογράφηση επικρατειών.

Για κάθε τετράγωνο 50km x 50km χρησιμοποιήθηκε ειδικό τυποποιημένο δελτίο. Απόσπασμα του δελτίου αυτού, το οποίο σχεδιάσθηκε από το Ολλανδικό Κεντρικό Γραφείο Στατιστικής φαίνεται στο **Σχήμα 4**. Για όσα τετράγωνα τέμνονται από σύνορα δύο ή περισσότερων χωρών, η συμπλήρωση του εντύπου έγινε για κάθε χώρα χωριστά.

Για κάθε τετράγωνο έπρεπε να υπάρχουν οι εξής γενικές πληροφορίες:

1. Χρονική περίοδος της απογραφής: το έτος ή η σειρά ετών κατά τα οποία συγκεντρώθηκαν πληροφορίες.
2. Η ταυτότητα του τετραγώνου (κωδικός UTM50).
3. Η πληρότητα της καταγραφής: δείχνει κατά πόσο τα δεδομένα για το συγκεκριμένο τετράγωνο καλύπτουν το 75% των αναμενόμενων ειδών (υψηλή) ή χαμηλότερο ποσοστό (χαμηλή).
4. Υψόμετρο του τετραγώνου, με ελάχιστο και μέγιστο.
5. Παρατηρητές ή συντονιστής(ές): ονόματα και διευθύνσεις, για επίλυση πιθανών προβλημάτων ή για διευκρινίσεις.
6. Σχόλια: οποιαδήποτε άλλη πληροφορία, η οποία βοηθά στην καλύτερη ερμηνεία του δελτίου.
7. Σύντομο ερωτηματολόγιο για τους τύπους βιοτόπου που περιλαμβάνει κάθε τετράγωνο.

Το κύριο μέρος του δελτίου αποτελείται από ένα κατάλογο ειδών (περίπου 440 είδη, με την ταξινομική σειρά του Voous και με τον κωδικό του Euring) με τις αντίστοιχες στήλες. Στη στήλη 0 υπήρχε, σε σύντμηση, το επιστημονικό όνομα του είδους (π.χ. *Gav stell*), στη στήλη 1 ο κωδικός του Euring (π.χ. 00020), ενώ στη στήλη 2 οι κωδικοί των ενδείξεων αναπαραγωγής. Υπήρχαν 16 τέτοιοι κωδικοί ταξινομημένοι σε τρείς κύριες κατηγορίες: Εξακριβωμένη αναπαραγωγή, Πιθανή αναπαραγωγή και Ενδεχόμενη αναπαραγωγή (**Πιν. 1**). Τέλος, στη στήλη 3 έπρεπε να δοθεί εκτίμηση του μεγέθους του αναπαραγόμενου πληθυσμού (σε αριθμό ζευγών), σε λογαριθμική κλίμακα (1 = 1-9, 2 = 10-99, ..., 6 = >100.000).

Στο δελτίο υπήρχε πρόσθετος χώρος για είδη εκτός του καταλόγου ή για υβρίδια.

Συνολικά, οι πηγές πληροφοριών για τον παρόντα *Ατλαντα* ήταν:

1. Οι εθνικοί εκπρόσωποι του EBCC σε κάθε χώρα, οι οποίοι οργάνωσαν τη συλλογή των δεδομένων και συμπλήρωσαν τα δελτία.
2. Τοπικοί συντονιστές. Συχνά η συλλογή των δεδομένων έγινε από άλλους συντονιστές, ιδιαίτερα σε χώρες με μεγάλη έκταση ή όταν υπήρχε κάποιο άλλο δίκτυο συνεργατών με το οποίο ήταν ευκολότερο να υπάρξει συνεργασία. Οι τοπικοί συντονιστές εργάσθηκαν με τον ίδιο τρόπο όπως και οι εθνικοί εκπρόσωποι.
3. Πρόσθετα δεδομένα για κάθε χώρα, κυρίως βιβλιογραφικά, η συλλογή των οποίων ανατέθηκε σε ορνιθολόγους ειδικευμένους σε ένα ή περισσότερα είδη. Αυτό επιδιώχθηκε γιατί σε πολλές απομακρυσμένες περιοχές όπου δεν έγινε απογραφή υπήρχαν δημοσιευμένες ή

Πίνακας 1 Κατηγορίες αναπαραγωγής και κωδικοί

A: **Ενδεχόμενη αναπαραγωγή**

1. Το είδος παρατηρήθηκε κατά τη διάρκεια της αναπαραγωγικής περιόδου σε βιότοπο κατάλληλο για φώλιασμα.
2. Παρατηρήθηκαν ή ακούστηκαν αρσενικά πουλιά να κελαηδούν κατά τη διάρκεια της αναπαραγωγικής περιόδου.

B: **Πιθανή αναπαραγωγή**

3. Ζευγάρι παρατηρήθηκε σε κατάλληλο για φώλιασμα βιότοπο κατά την αναπαραγωγική περίοδο.
4. Υποτιθέμενη μόνιμη επικράτεια: καταγραφή επικρατειακής συμπεριφοράς (τραγούδι κλπ.) σε δύο τουλάχιστον διαφορετικές ημέρες, που να απέχουν μεταξύ τους τουλάχιστον μια εβδομάδα, στην ίδια τοποθεσία.
5. Ερωτικές επιδείξεις.
6. Επίσκεψη του πουλιού σε πιθανή θέση φωλιάς.
7. Εκνευρισμός ή φωνές ανησυχίας ενήλικων πουλιών που υποδεικνύουν ύπαρξη φωλιάς.
8. Σύλληψη ενήλικου πουλιού με γυμνό δέρμα στην κοιλιά (για κλώσσημα).
9. Κατασκευή φωλιάς ή σκάψιμο τρύπας για φωλιά.

C: **Εξακριβωμένη αναπαραγωγή**

10. Συμπεριφορά περισπασμού ή ψευδο-τραυματισμού.
11. Ανεύρεση χρησιμοποιημένης φωλιάς ή υπολειμμάτων από κελύφη αυγών, τα οποία προέρχονται από την περίοδο καταγραφής.
12. Νεοσσοί οι οποίοι ολοκλήρωσαν πρόσφατα την πτέρωσή τους ή νεοσσοί με πούπουλα.
13. Ενήλικα πουλιά τα οποία παρατηρήθηκαν να πηγαινο-έρχονται σε σημείο όπου υπάρχουν ενδείξεις οτι υπάρχει φωλιά εν χρήσει (ακόμα και φωλιές σε τρύπες ψηλών δέντρων ή βράχων) ή ενήλικα που παρατηρήθηκαν να κλωσσάνε αυγά.
14. Ενήλικο που μεταφέρει τροφή για τους νεοσσούς ή περιττώματα νεοσσών έξω από τη φωλιά.
15. Φωλιά με αυγά.
16. Οπτική ή ακουστική παρατήρηση φωλιάς με νεοσσούς.

αδημοσίευτες εργασίες, οι οποίες συχνά ήταν δύσκολο να βρεθούν από τους εθνικούς εκπροσώπους ή τους κεντρικούς οργανωτές του προγράμματος.

4. Συγγραφείς κειμένων για κάθε είδος. Πολύ συχνά κάποιος ορνιθολόγος ειδικευμένος σε κάποιο ή κάποια είδη είχε πρόσθετες πηγές πληροφοριών σχετικές με πληθυσμούς ή εξάπλωση.

Τα δεδομένα από όλες αυτές τις πηγές αξιολογήθηκαν ιεραρχικά: κάθε νέα προσθήκη στη βάση δεδομένων έπρεπε να εγκριθεί από τον εθνικό εκπρόσωπο.

Ποιοτικά και ημι-ποσοτικά δεδομένα

Ο *Ατλαντας* χρησιμοποιεί ημι-ποσοτικά δεδομένα (λογαριθμικές πληθυσμιακές εκτιμήσεις), υπολογισμένα για κάθε τετράγωνο 50km x 50km από τους εθνικούς εκπροσώπους και όσους εργάσθηκαν στο πεδίο. Οι κουκίδες στους χάρτες απεικονίζουν τον αριθμό των αναπαραγόμενων, ανά τετράγωνο, ζευγαριών κάθε είδους. Το μέγεθος των κουκίδων αντιπροσωπεύει την τάξη μεγέθους του πληθυσμού (βλ. κλείδα στη σελίδα cxl). Δυστυχώς κάποιες χώρες είτε συνολικά (Νορβηγία και Πολωνία) είτε σε μεγάλο ποσοστό (Ισπανία) είτε εν μέρει (Ισλανδία, Γαλλία και Ιταλία) αρνήθηκαν να δώσουν ημι-ποσοτικά δεδομένα. Κατά τη διάρκεια του προγράμματος χάσαμε κάθε επαφή με τη Βοσνία και τη Σερβία και έτσι δεν μπορέσαμε να αναθεωρήσουμε τα αρχικά τους δεδομένα. Μερικές περιφέρειες της Γαλλίας αναθεώρησαν ανεξάρτητα τα δεδομένα τους. Ο Γάλλος εθνικός εκπρόσωπος αναθεώρησε, σε επίπεδο χώρας, τα δεδομένα για λίγα μόνο είδη. Σε κάθε περίπτωση πάντως, τα ημι-ποσοτικά δεδομένα προσφέρουν πολύ καλύτερη πληροφόρηση από την απλή ένδειξη παρουσίας ή απουσίας ενός είδους.

Για τα διακρατικά τετράγωνα όπου οι ορνιθολόγοι κάθε χώρας έδωσαν τις δικές τους πληθυσμιακές εκτιμήσεις, χρησιμοποιήθηκε η μεγαλύτερη πληθυσμιακή μονάδα (οι λογαριθμικές τιμές δεν πρέπει να προστίθενται), αν και σε κάποιες περιπτώσεις αυτό ίσως είχε σαν αποτέλεσμα την υποεκτίμηση. Ακόμη και σ' αυτές τις περιπτώσεις αυτή η μέθοδος ήταν προτιμότερη από την ποιοτική παρουσίαση των δεδομένων.

Οι κουκίδες στους χάρτες αναπαριστούν τις εξής κατηγορίες:

σκούρο μωβ	=	αναπαραγωγή επιβεβαιωμένη ή πιθανή, ποιοτικό
ανοιχτό μωβ	=	αναπαραγωγή ενδεχόμενη, ποιοτικό
κόκκινο	=	αναπαραγωγή επιβεβαιωμένη ή πιθανή, ημι-ποσοτικό
πορτοκαλί	=	αναπαραγωγή ενδεχόμενη, ημι-ποσοτικό
γκρί	=	δεν έγινε προσπάθεια ανεύρεσης του είδους στο τετράγωνο
χωρίς κουκίδα	=	έγινε προσπάθεια ανεύρεσης του είδους στο τετράγωνο αλλά το είδος δεν βρέθηκε

Εισαγωγή σε υπολογιστή – διόρθωση των χαρτογραφικών δεδομένων και επιβεβαίωση του εισαχθέντος υλικού

Τα δελτία που στάλθηκαν από τους εθνικούς συντονιστές ελέγχθηκαν καταρχήν για την ύπαρξη τυχόν βασικών λαθών (π.χ. παράλειψη κωδικών) και κατόπιν εισήχθηκαν σε μορφή αρχείου ASCII, με ειδικό ανά χώρα κωδικό για κάθε εγγραφή. Μερικές χώρες παρέδωσαν τα δεδομένα τους έτοιμα σεδισκέττες, οι οποίες όμως ελέγχθηκαν ξανά. Η τελική βάση δεδομένων περιέχει μόνο μια εγγραφή για κάθε είδος και κάθε τετράγωνο.

Στους εθνικούς εκπροσώπους που παρέδωσαν το υλικό τους έγκαιρα στάλθηκαν προκαταρκτικοί χάρτες και κατάλογοι ανά είδος, έτσι ώστε να κάνουν οι ίδιοι τις πρώτες διορθώσεις, με αποτέλεσμα να προκύψουν πολλές βελτιώσεις του αρχικού υλικού. Κάποιες χώρες καθυστέρησαν αρκετά, ενώ σε άλλες οι υπεύθυνοι αναβάθμισαν τα ήδη υπάρχοντα δεδομένα τους από ποιοτικά σε ημι-ποσοτικά. Ετσι, η διόρθωση των δεδομένων προχώρησε με διαφορετικό ρυθμό από χώρα σε χώρα.

Η παραγωγή προκαταρκτικών χαρτών ήταν απαραίτητη για δύο λόγους:

1. Εδωσε τη δυνατότητα στους εθνικούς αντιπροσώπους και τους ορνιθολόγους κάθε χώρας να αξιολογήσουν έγκαιρα όλα τα δεδομένα τα οποία οι ίδιοι συγκέντρωσαν π.χ. να ελέγξουν τη σωστή γεωγραφική θέση των τετραγώνων,

την πληρότητα τους, τα είδη που απεγράφησαν σε κάθε τετράγωνο κ.λ.π. Η διαδικασία αυτή έδειξε ότι οι διορθώσεις ήταν πολύ ευκολότερο να γίνουν πάνω σε χάρτες παρά σε κείμενα ή καταλόγους.

2. Προκάλεσε νέο ενδιαφέρον και κίνητρα σε ακόμη περισσότερους ορνιθολόγους, πολλοί από τους οποίους πρόσφεραν στο πρόγραμμα νέα και συχνά αξιόλογα δεδομένα.

Η δεύτερη φάση ελέγχου έγινε για να διαπιστωθεί κατά πόσον οι πρώτες διορθώσεις μεταφέρθηκαν με σωστό τρόπο στον υπολογιστή. Αυτό έγινε πάλι με την αποστολή στους εθνικούς εκπροσώπους μιας νεότερης σειράς χαρτών και καταλόγων για κάθε είδος. Η πλειοψηφία των συντονιστών έλεγξε ξανά το ογκώδες αυτό υλικό, μια πράγματι επίπονη εργασία, και το επέστρεψαν ξανά διορθωμένο. Σε κάποιες όμως χώρες, όπως π.χ. στην πρώην Γιουγκοσλαβία, αυτό στάθηκε αδύνατο. Σε άλλες πάλι περιπτώσεις ζητήθηκε από τους υπεύθυνους να επισπεύσουν την όλη διαδικασία, αλλά βέβαια όσο καθυστερούσε μια χώρα τόσο καθυστερούσε και η συνολική αξιολόγηση του τελικού προϊόντος.

Σε μεταγενέστερες φάσεις του προγράμματος, ορνιθολόγοι εξειδικευμένοι σε ένα ή περισσότερα είδη βελτίωσαν ακόμη πιο πολύ το υλικό. Στις περιπτώσεις αυτές χρειάσθηκαν απευθείας συνεννοήσεις των ειδικών με τους εθνικούς εκπροσώπους, έτσι ώστε να αποφασισθεί τελικά ποιά δεδομένα θα χρησιμοποιηθούν. Οπου, κυρίως λόγω έλλειψης χρόνου, αυτό ήταν δύσκολο να γίνει είτε χρησιμοποιήθηκε το αρχικό υλικό ή με ειδική αναφορά στα κείμενο των ειδών διευκρινίζεται ότι οι απόψεις του συγκεκριμένου επιστήμονα διαφέρουν από τα δεδομένα που δείχνουν οι χάρτες.

Σε όποιες χώρες ή περιοχές δεν έγινε εργασία πεδίου, ιδίως στην Αλβανία και τη βόρεια Ρωσία, χρησιμοποιήθηκαν άλλες πηγές δεδομένων, οι οποίες αξιολογήθηκαν από τοπικούς ορνιθολόγους με σκοπό να εκτιμηθεί η αξιοπιστία τους. Κάποιο όμως ποσοστό ημι-ποσοτικών δεδομένων χρησιμοποιήθηκε ακόμα και σε πολλά από αυτά τα τετράγωνα, ιδιαίτερα όταν τα τετράγωνο αυτά ήταν δίπλα σε τετράγωνα με υψηλής ποιότητας πληροφορία και με όμοιους τύπους βιοτόπων.

Ως τελική προθεσμία παράδοσης όλων των δεδομένων ορίσθηκε η 1η Ιουλίου 1995, αν και κάποιο υλικό έγινε δεκτό για μερικούς μήνες ακόμη, έτσι ώστε να μπορέσει να περιληφθεί όσο το δυνατό περισσότερη πληροφορία από περιοχές όπως η Αλβανία, το Ευρωπαϊκό τμήμα της Τουρκίας, ο Καύκασος και ορισμένα τμήματα της Ουκρανίας και της Ρωσίας. Οι τελικές διορθώσεις στα κείμενα των ειδών έγιναν δεκτές μέχρι την 1η Νοεμβρίου 1995.

Συλλογή δεδομένων για το μέγεθος των πληθυσμών

Τα πληθυσμιακά δεδομένα για τα είδη κάθε χώρας τα οποία δίνονται σε γραφήματα του παρόντος *Ατλαντα*, προέρχονται από την Ευρωπαϊκή Βάση Ορνιθολογικών Δεδομένων. Αυτή η βάση δεδομένων περιλαμβάνει πληθυσμιακά δεδομένα τα οποία συγκεντρώθηκαν με κοινή προσπάθεια τόσο του EBCC όσο και του Birdlife International, συγκροτήθηκε δε με στόχο να βοηθήσει τόσο το παρόνπρόγραμμα όσο και το "Dispersed Species Project" του Birdlife. Το υλικό του τελευταίου προγράμματος έχει ήδη δημοσιευθεί στο βιβλίο *Birds in Europe - their conservation status* (Tucker & Heath 1994). Η συνεργασία αυτή βοήθησε εξάλλου σημαντικά στη διερεύνηση της συμμετοχής ορνιθολόγων σε πολλές Ευρωπαϊκές χώρες. Τα δεδομένα συγκεντρώθηκαν αρχικά μέσω ειδικών ερωτηματολογίων τα οποία στάλθηκαν στους εθνικούς συντονιστές (τα ονόματα τους δίνονται στο *Birds in Europe*) και αυτοί με τη σειρά τους τα προώθησαν σε ειδικούς ορνιθολόγους, επιστημονικούς φορείς και άλλους ενδιαφερόμενους. Το Birdlife International διαχειρίζεται την Ευρωπαϊκή Βάση Ορνιθολογικών Δεδομένων.

Κάθε χώρα έδωσε δεδομένα για τους αναπαραγόμενους πληθυσμούς όλων των ειδών ως εξής:

1. Πληθυσμιακό μέγεθος.
2. Τάσεις του μεγέθους του πληθυσμού (στην περίοδο 1970-1990).
3. Τάσεις της εξάπλωσης (στην περίοδο 1970-1990).

Παρόμοια δεδομένα συγκεντρώθηκαν και για τους διαχειμάζοντες πληθυσμούς, αλλά αυτά δεν παρουσιάζονται στον παρόντα *Ατλαντα*.

Καταγράφηκαν επίσης όλες οι βιβλιογραφικές πηγές που χρησιμοποιήθηκαν για την εκίμηση και αξιολόγηση των πληθυσμών και των τάσεων τους. Στον **Πίνακα 2** δίνονται εξάλλου και οι ειδικοί κωδικοί που χρησιμοποιήθηκαν για την επαλήθευση της ακρίβειας και πιστότητας των δεδομένων για τους πληθυσμούς και των τάσεων τους.

Πίνακας 2 Κωδικοί πληθυσμού στην Ευρωπαϊκή Βάση Ορνιθολογικών Δεδομένων

POPMIN	=	Ελάχιστο μέγεθος πληθυσμού (σε ζεύγη)
POPMAX	=	Μέγιστο μέγεθος πληθυσμού (σε ζεύγη)
MEAN	=	Γεωμετρικός μέσος όρος πληθυσμού (σε ζεύγη)
YRC	=	Ετος μέτρησης πληθυσμού
PSV	=	Κωδικός επαλήθευσης για την εκτίμηση του πληθυσμού
PST	=	Τάση πληθυσμού (αύξηση/μείωση)
PTV	=	Κωδικός επαλήθευσης για την τάση του πληθυσμού
RST	=	Τάση γεωγραφικής εξάπλωσης
RTV	=	Κωδικός επαλήθευσης για την τάση εξάπλωσης

Κωδικοί τάσης πληθυσμού και εξάπλωσης

Οι τάσεις πληθυσμού και εξάπλωσης αναφέρονται στην περίοδο 1970-1990.

+2	=	μεγάλη αύξηση πάνω από 50%
+1	=	μικρή αύξηση πάνω από 20% αλλά λιγότερο από 50%
0	=	σταθερό, χωρίς συνολική αλλαγή πέραν του 20%
-1	=	μικρή μείωση πάνω από 20% αλλά λιγότερο από 50%
-2	=	μεγάλη μείωση πάνω από 50%
n	=	νέο αναπαραγόμενο είδος κατά τη διάρκεια της περιόδου
x	=	εξαφανίστηκε κατά τη διάρκεια της περιόδου
f	=	κυμαίνεται, με μεταβολές πάνω από 20% αλλά χωρίς σαφή τάση

Μερικοί συγγραφείς κειμένων ειδών δεν συμφωνούσαν με τις εκτιμήσεις πληθυσμών στη βάση δεδομένων αλλά η πληροφορία έφτασε πολύ αργά για να περιληφθεί στη βάση δεδομένων. Σε αυτές τις περιπτώσεις, οι συγγραφείς έβαλαν τις δικές τους εκτιμήσεις στο κείμενο αλλά τα γραφήματα που συνοδεύουν το κείμενο δείχνουν πάντα την πληροφορία που υπάρχει στη βάση δεδομένων.

Ελλείψεις στα δεδομένα

Ο παρών *Ατλαντας* περιέχει δεδομένα υψηλής ποιότητας. Αναπόφευκτα όμως όλο αυτό το υλικό έχει και ελλείψεις και περιορισμούς. Αυτό θα πρέπει να λαμβάνεται υπόψη από όλους όσους θέλουν να χρησιμοποιήσουν τον *Ατλαντα* για περαιτέρω εξειδικευμένη εργασία. Για περισσότερες διευκρινίσεις οι ενδιαφερόμενοι πρέπει να απευθύνονται στο EBCC. Οι βασικότερες ελλείψεις που επηρεάζουν τη γενική χρήση αυτού του βιβλίου είναι οι εξής:

1. Δεν υπάρχουν προδιαγραφές για τη μεθοδολογία εργασίας υπαίθρου που ακολούθησαν οι εθνικοί εκπρόσωποι για να καταγράψουν την απουσία ή παρουσία των ειδών στα τετράγωνα ή για να προσδιορίσουν τα πληθυσμιακά μεγέθη. Σε πολλές χώρες, το EBCC χρησιμοποίησε δεδομένα τα οποία στηρίχθηκαν σε μεθοδολογίες και προδιαγραφές εθνικών προγραμμάτων ή εθνικών προτεραιοτήτων, ανάλογα με το διαθέσιμο ανθρώπινο δυναμικό ή τη χρηματοδότηση.
2. Για πολλούς από τους παραπάνω λόγους, δεν υπήρξε ομοιογενής και ενιαία μέθοδος μεταφοράς των δεδομένων στα απογραφικά δελτία, με αποτέλεσμα να υπάρχουν διαφοροποιήσεις από χώρα σε χώρα.
3. Υπήρξαν σημαντικές διαφορές στην ποιότητα της εργασίας πεδίου από χώρα σε χώρα, καθώς και στον αριθμό των ορνιθολόγων που συμμετείχαν στο πρόγραμμα.
4. Ενα ποσοστό δεδομένων προέρχεται εν μέρει από προβολή (extrapolation) υπαρχουσών εκτιμήσεων.
5. Ενα ποσοστό δεδομένων προέρχεται από τη βιβλιογραφία (κυρίως περιοχές της Αρκτικής).

Η ΠΑΡΟΥΣΙΑΣΗ ΤΩΝ ΧΑΡΤΩΝ ΚΑΙ ΤΩΝ ΚΕΙΜΕΝΩΝ ΓΙΑ ΤΑ ΕΙΔΗ

Τα είδη χωρίζονται σε δύο ομάδες: αυτά για τα οποία υπήρχε ικανοποιητικό υλικό και τα υπόλοιπα. Για την πρώτη ομάδα δίδονται πλήρεις περιγραφές στο 1ο Μέρος, ενώ για τη δεύτερη ομάδα οι περιγραφές είναι πιο συνοπτικές στο 2ο Μέρος. Και στα δύο Μέρη, η σειρά των ειδών ακολουθεί την ταξινόμηση του Voous και την αρίθμηση του Euring, εκτός από κάποιες μικροτροποποιήσεις τις οποίες απαιτούσε η σελιδοποίηση του βιβλίου έτσι ώστε όταν ο χάρτης και το κείμενο ενός είδους καταλάμβανε μία σελίδα, στην απέναντι σελίδα να χωράει επίσης χάρτης και κείμενο για κάποιο άλλο είδος. Σε άλλες πάλι περιπτώσεις π.χ. για είδη με σύντομα κείμενα, μία μόνο σελίδα επαρκούσε για να περιληφθούν δύο είδη. Ολα τα είδη εικονογραφούνται με σκίτσα ενώ οι κοινές ονομασίες για όλα τα είδη (όπου βεβαίως υφίστανται) δίδονται σε 14 γλώσσες. Η πλειοψηφία των ειδών για τα οποία υπάρχει χάρτης, συνοδεύεται και από το αντίστοιχο γράφημα πληθυσμιακού μεγέθους, το οποίο επεξηγείται στις σελίδες που βρίσκονται πριν από την αρχή του κεφαλαίου των ειδών.

Συνθετικοί χάρτες (περιληπτική επεξήγηση)

Το **Σχήμα 5** απεικονίζει τον αριθμό των αναπαραγόμενων ανά τετράγωνο ειδών. Τα **Σχήματα 6-8** δείχνουν τον αριθμό των ειδών τα οποία χρήζουν προστασίας (SPEC) των κατηγοριών 1, 2, και 3, όπως επεξηγείται στο βιβλίο *Birds in Europe* του Birdlife International, και το **Σχήμα 9** συνδυάζει τις τρείς αυτές κατηγορίες.

ΤΑ ΚΕΙΜΕΝΑ ΤΩΝ ΕΙΔΩΝ

Τα κείμενα των ειδών περιλαμβάνουν (όπου αυτό ήταν δυνατό) τα εξής επιμέρους θέματα, με την ίδια γενικά σειρά: παγκόσμια εξάπλωση, τύπος βιοτόπου του είδους στην Ευρώπη κατά την περίοδο αναπαραγωγής, εξάπλωση και αφθονία του είδους στην Ευρώπη, πρόσφατες μεταβολές στην εξάπλωση ή στον πληθυσμό του είδους (καθώς και οι πιθανές αιτίες), τοπικές διαφοροποιήσεις της πληθυσμιακής πυκνότητας, πιθανοί παράγοντες οι οποίοι περιορίζουν τη φυσιολογική εξάπλωση του είδους, αναπαραγωγική πυκνότητα στους καλύτερους διαθέσιμους βιότοπους, μετανάστευση και μετακινήσεις του είδους καθώς και συνοπτική αναφορά στα υποείδη όσον αφορά στην εξάπλωση, στην ανάμειξη και στις τάσεις τους.

Εκτός από εκεί όπου κρίθηκε απόλυτα αναγκαίο να γίνει μια σύντομη αναφορά, παραλείπονται εντελώς τα εξής επιμέρους θέματα: βιολογία αναπαραγωγής, συμπεριφορά, τροφικές συνήθειες, σχέσεις με άλλα είδη, μορφολογικά χαρακτηριστικά και φυσιολογία, λεπτομερή δεδομένα για τις απειλές κάποιων ειδών (τέτοιες πληροφορίες δίνονται στο *Birds in Europe*), μορφολογικές ανωμαλίες, ωολογία, εξέλιξη και ταξινόμηση (εκτός εάν πρόκειται για σημαντικές ταξινομικές αλλαγές οι οποίες έχουν γίνει αποδεκτές πρόσφατα, ή όταν πρόκειται για υποείδη που διαφέρουν σημαντικά μεταξύ τους), θνησιμότητα και άλλες παράμετροι πληθυσμιακών μεταβολών, και φωνή και τραγούδι.

Κριτήρια επιλογής ειδών

Στο βιβλίο αυτό περιλαμβάνονται όλα τα είδη πουλιών τα οποία αναπαράγονται στον Ευρωπαϊκό χώρο από το 1985 μέχρι σήμερα και τα οποία πληρούν τα κριτήρια του **Πίνακα 1**. Η προϋπόθεση για να περιληφθεί ένα εισαγμένο (μη-ιθαγενές) είδος στον *Ατλαντα* ήταν η ύπαρξη ενός τουλάχιστον αναπαραγόμενου πληθυσμού, ο οποίος διατηρήθηκε από μόνος του για τουλάχιστον μια πενταετία. Παρόλα αυτά, τέτοιου είδους κριτήρια ερμηνεύονται με διαφορετικούς τρόπους στις διάφορες χώρες και η επιλογή των ξενικών ειδών φαίνεται εκ πρώτης όψεως αυθαίρετη.

Ο *Ατλαντας* τελικά περιλαμβάνει 513 είδη, συν το *Passer* x *italiae*.

ΟΝΟΜΑΤΟΛΟΓΙΑ ΚΑΙ ΤΑΞΙΝΟΜΗΣΗ

Ταξινόμηση

Το EBCC υιοθέτησε επιφυλακτική και συντηρητική θέση σε ότι αφορά την ταξινόμηση των ειδών. Ο *Ατλαντας* γενικά ακολουθεί την ταξινόμηση, σειρά και ονοματολογία της έκδοσης *The Birds of the Western Palearctic (BWP)*, όπως αυτή τροποποιήθηκε για την υπό ετοιμασία επίτομη έκδοση του ίδιου έργου.

Θεωρούμε ως ξεχωριστά είδη τα: *Puffinus yelkouan*, *Puffinus mauretanicus*, *Larus cachinnans*, *Anthus petrosus*, *Phylloscopous lorenzii* και *Pyrrhula murina* και τα έχουν χωριστούς χάρτες από τα: *Puffinus puffinus*, *Larus argentantus*, *Anthus spinoletta*, *Phylloscopous collybita* και *Pyrrhula pyrrhula*. Η χωριστή χαρτογράφηση κατέστη δυνατή είτε επειδή έγινε ξεχωριστή καταγραφή είτε επειδή η γεωγραφική τους εξάπλωση ήταν σαφώς διακριτή. (Το κείμενο για τα τρία είδη *Puffinus* είναι ενιαίο). Αρχικά, έγινε προσπάθεια χωριστής χαρτογράφησης των φυλών ή υποειδών των διαφόρων ειδών, αλλά η ιδέα αυτή εγκαταλείφθηκε σύντομα, γιατί δεν υπάρχει ακόμα ομοφωνία ανά την Ευρώπη για την ύπαρξη ή όχι πολλών τέτοιων υποειδών. Αντίθετα, ο "Ιταλοσπουργίτης" χαρτογραφήθηκε ξεχωριστά επειδή όπως και στο *BWP* θεωρήσαμε οτι πρόκειται για σταθεροποιημένο υβρίδιο των *Passer domesticus* και *P. hispaniolensis* και αναφέρεται ως *Passer* x *italiae*. Αντίθετα, σε ένα άλλο είδος, το *Phylloscopus trochiloides* αποφασίσαμε να εντάξουμε και δύο διακριτά, από γεωγραφική άποψη, υποείδη, τα *viridianus* και *nitidus*, τα οποία πολλοί θεωρούν ως ξεχωριστά είδη. Στα τελικά στάδια του *Ατλαντα* διαχωρίσαμε επίσης το *Lanius meridionalis* από το *L. excubitor*, επεξηγώντας στο κείμενο το γεωγραφικό όριο εξάπλωσης των δύο αυτών υποειδών. Το *Hippolais calligata* συχνά διαχωρίζεται από το *H. rama*, αλλά στο παρόν βιβλίο το *rama* θεωρείται ως υποείδος του πρώτου. Ιδιαίτερα προβλήματα εμφανίζουν πολλά είδη γλάρων. Ο *Larus armenicus* θεωρείται ξεχωριστό είδος.

Η αρίθμηση του Euring

Η Ευρωπαϊκή Ενωση για τη Δακτυλίωση Πουλιών (Euring) έχει συντάξει ειδικό κατάλογο όπου όλα τα είδη και υποείδη αριθμούνται με ένα πενταψήφιο κωδικό, για χρήση των δακτυλιωτών. Ο κατάλογος αυτός ακολουθεί την ταξινομική σειρά του Voous και γι' αυτό κρίθηκε ως ο κατάλληλος για τη σύνταξη του *Ατλαντα*. Η αρίθμηση του Euring υπάρχει σε κάθε είδος που περιλαμβάνεται στο βιβλίο αυτό, ενώ στο **Τεχνικό Παράρτημα** επεξηγείται το πώς χρησιμοποιήθηκε αυτή η αρίθμηση.

ΒΙΒΛΙΟΓΡΑΦΙΚΕΣ ΠΑΡΑΠΟΜΠΕΣ ΚΑΙ ΑΛΛΕΣ ΔΗΜΟΣΙΕΥΣΕΙΣ

Λόγω περιορισμού στο χώρο που είναι διαθέσιμος στο απογραφικό δελτίο, ζητήθηκε από όλους να αποφεύγουν τις συνεχείς βιβλιογραφικές παραπομπές σε γνωστά ορνιθολογικά εγχειρίδια. Δύο όμως από αυτά τα εγχειρίδια χρήζουν ειδικής μνείας. Θεωρούμε οτι ο **Ατλαντας** πρέπει να χρησιμοποιείται σε συνδυασμό με δύο πασίγνωστα και σημαντικότατα εγχειρίδια: το *The Birds of the Western Palearctic* (Cramp *et al* 1977-1994) και το *Handbuch der Vφgel Mitteleuropas* (Glutz von Blotzheim *et al* 1966-1993). Στα κείμενα του *Ατλαντα* τα δύο αυτά εγχειρίδια αναφέρονται ως *BWP* και *HVM* αντίστοιχα.

Στο *Birds in Europe - their conservation status* (Tucker and Heath 1994) δημοσιεύεται για πρώτη φορά μια συνολική επισκόπηση των πληθυσμών των Ευρωπαϊκών πουλιών, οι απειλές και το καθεστώς προστασίας τους, ενώ περιγράφονται λεπτομερώς όλα εκείνα τα είδη για τα οποία χρειάζονταιμέτρα προστασίας. Ο *Ατλαντας* περιλαμβάνει όχι μόνον αυτά, αλλά και όλα τα υπόλοιπα είδη τα οποία θεωρούνται οτι τουλάχιστον σήμερα δεν κινδυνεύουν. Τα γραφήματα του *Ατλαντα* προέρχονται από υλικό το οποίο περιλαμβάνεται στην Ευρωπαϊκή Βάση Ορνιθολογικών Δεδομένων. Το *Birds in Europe* στηρίζεται στην ίδια βάση δεδομένων και έτσι το βιβλίο αυτό αναφέρεται συχνά ως βιβλιογραφική παραπομπή στην παρούσα έκδοση.

Η βιβλιογραφία που χρησιμοποιείται στον *Ατλαντα* παρουσιάζεται στο τέλος του βιβλίου, αμέσως πριν τα ευρετήρια.

Michael Blair, Ward Hagemeijer,
Γιώργος Χανδρινός, Φίλιος Ακριώτης

ΣΥΝΤΜΗΣΕΙΣ ΚΑΙ ΟΡΟΛΟΓΙΑ

Προσανατολισμοί

N	= Βορράς
S	= Νότος
E	= Ανατολή
W	= Δύση, επομένως NW = βόρειο-δυτικά, WSW = δυτικά-νοτιοδυτικά κ.λ.π.
C	= Κέντρο, επομένως S-C = νοτιο-κεντρικός κ.λ.π.

Γενικές εκφράσεις

asl	= πάνω από την επιφάνεια της θάλασσας (υψόμετρο)
c	= περίπου
et al	= και άλλοι (στη βιβλιογραφία)
pers comm	= προσωπική επικοινωνία
pers obs	= προσωπική παρατήρηση
unpubl	= αδημοσίευτα

Ποσότητες και διαστάσεις

bp	= αναπαραγόμενα ζευγάρια
ha	= εκτάρια
ind	= άτομα
m	= μέτρα
km	= χιλιόμετρα
km^2	=τετραγωνικά χιλιόμετρα
M	= εκατομμύριο

Ακρωνύμια

BTO	= British Trust for Ornithology (GB)
BWP	= Birds of the Western Palaearctic
HVM	= Handbuch der Vögel Mitteleuropas
JNCC	= Joint Nature Conservation Committee (GB)
RSPB	= Royal Society for the Protection of Birds (GB)
SOVON	= SOVON Απογραφή Πουλιών στην Ολλανδία (NL)
WWT	= Wildfowl and Wetlands Trust (GB)

Ορολογία

eutrophic	ευτροφικός: πλούσιος σε θρεπτικά άλατα ή συστατικά που προέρχονται από αποσύνθεση φυτικών ή ζωικών οργανισμών
lentic	ο σχετιζόμενος με στάσιμα νερά, π.χ. λίμνες, έλη
lotic	ο σχετιζόμενος με τρεχούμενα νερά
mesotrophic	μεσοτροφικός: μέτριος σε θρεπτικά άλατα ή άλλα συστατικά
"mixotrophic"	όρος που χρησιμοποιείται για λίμνες των βορείων ψυχρών δασών, οι οποίες είναι ρηχές και πλούσιες σε υδροχαρή βλάστηση αλλά φτωχές σε θρεπτικά άλατα ή άλλα συστατικά
oligotrophic	ολιγοτροφικός: φτωχός σε θρεπτικά άλατα ή άλλα συστατικά
phenology	φαινολογία: η μελέτη των περιοδικά επαναλαμβανόμενων φαινομένων
sclerophytic	σκληροφυτικός: ο σχετιζόμενος με τα φυτά που έχουν σκληρά και συνήθως μικρά φύλλα, με χαμηλούς ρυθμούς διαπνοής, χαρακτηριστικά των ξηρών κλιμάτων
xerophytic	ξηροφυτικός: ο σχετιζόμενος με φυτά προσαρμοσμένα σε πολύ ξηρές συνθήκες

Bevezetés

AZ EURÓPAI FÉSZKELŐ MADARAK EBCC *ATLASZ*ÁNAK CÉLJA

Számos madarakkal foglalkozó könyv ismertet magabiztosan madárelterjedési térképeket. A térképek között van, amelyik a költő fajok állományfelmérésén alapul, de egyes speciális atlaszokat kivéve legtöbbjük különböző megbízhatóságú és gyakran korábbi – kétes hitelességű – térképek újrafeldolgozását jelentik. Ugyanakkor ezek a térképek általában csak a fajok előfordulását jelzik, de a fajok állománynagyságáról nem adnak információkat.

Egyre több kiváló nemzeti és regionális atlaszt adnak ki, melyek szemikvantitatív adatokat tartalmaznak és amelyek ugyanannak a folyamatnak a hatására jöttek létre, mely végül létrehozta az *Atlasz*t. 1971-ben alakult meg az Európai Madáratlasz Tanács (European Ornithological Atlas Committee, EOAC) abból a célból, hogy azoknak az Európában költő madárfajoknak az állományfelmérését irányítsa, melyek állományát terepmunkával fel lehet mérni. Ennek a kihívásnak az eredménye e könyv.

Az *Atlasz* a madárállományok elterjedését mutatja be meghatározott időszakra. Az adatok (apróbb következetlenségeikkel együtt) jelenlegi ismereteinket tükrözik, melyekkel majd a jövőbeli felmérések eredményei (így az elterjedési változások is) összevethetőek. 1971-ben az EOAC előtt az a cél lebegett, hogy egy olyan, az egész kontinensre kiterjedő fészkelő madár állományfelmérést valósítson meg, amilyent még soha nem kíséreltek meg. A terv valóra vált. A *The EBCC Atlas of European Breeding Birds* az európai madárfajok elterjedését térképezi fel, választ adva arra a kérdésre, hogy "melyik faj hol költ".

AZ *ATLASZ* SZERKEZETE

Ezen **Introduction**, bevezetés, rész ismerteti az *Atlasz* célját, a fajok elterjedésének és állományfelmérésének módszereit, az adatfeldolgozást és térképezést, továbbá bemutatja az *Atlasz* felépítését. Elsődleges szempont volt, hogy a könyv minden tekintetben érthető legyen. Ezt a célt szolgálja a számos európai nyelvre lefordított **Introduction**, így az európai ornitológusok többsége anyanyelvén olvashatja a könyvet.

Bevezető részek

A **Foreword**, előszóban, Professzor Karel Voous körvonalazza az *Atlasz* fontosságát azoknak a változásoknak a fényében, melyek az európai avifaunában történnek napjainkban. A **Preface,** bevezetőben, összefoglalja, hogy az *Atlasz* program mennyiben felel meg az európai ornitológusok elvárásainak, és hangsúlyozza az Európai Madárszámlálási Tanács (EBCC, European Bird Census Council) irányelveit és szándékát a jövőbeni európai madár monitoring programokra vonatkozóan. Ezután az **Introduction**, bevezetés, következik, amely bemutatja a módszereket és a felmérést. Az **Introduction** követő **Explanatory Figures,** magyarázó ábrák, rész a vizsgált területeket és az adatok minőségét és az egységesen használt adatfelmérési nyomtatványt tárgyalja. A **History**, történet, rész tárja elénk a program fejlődését és a kudarcokat, amelyek a program során az *Atlasz* elkészítését hátráltatták. A **History and Evolution of the European Bird Fauna**, az európai madárfauna története és evolúciója, részben találjuk Jacques Blondel professzor írását arról, hogyan alakult ki az európai madárfajok jelenlegi elterjedési képe. Végül az **Acknowledgements**-ben a köszönetnyilvánítás, a **National and Regional Bird Atlases of Europe**-ban pedig a nemzeti és regionális madáratlaszok felsorolása található.

Fajok rész

Az *Atlasz* legnagyobb részét az európai fészkelő fajok leírása tölti ki, amelyet a **Qualitative versus semi-quantitative information**, kvalitatív kontra félig kvantitatív információk, rész mutat be az alábbiakban. A **Part 1**, első rész, az elterjedési térképekből, a fajleírásokból, a fajok 14 nyelvre lefordított nevéből és illusztrációkból áll. A fajok megközelítőleg Voous (1977) rendszere szerint, Euring sorrendben követik egymást. A **Part 2**, második rész, azon fajok leírását tartalmazza, amelyekről úgy tudják, hogy fészkel Európában, azonban fészkelésükről adatok nem érkeztek.

Befejező részek

A **Derived Maps,** származtatott térképek, fejezet részletezi az Európában fészkelő madarak fajgazdagságát és az európai természetvédelmi szempontból kiemelt fajok (SPEC) listáját a BirdLife International alapján (Tucker & Heath 1994). A **Technical Appendix,** technikai függelék, ismerteti, hogy az *Atlasz* négyzetrácsozása mennyiben különbözik az elméleti Univerzális Transzverz Mercator (UTM) vetülettől, illetve hogyan értelmezték az 50 km-es négyzeteket a szigetek és a parti területek esetében. Ez a rész ismerteti azt is, hogy az *Atlasz* hogyan alkalmazza az Euring számrendszert.

Nemzeti nyelvű füzetek

A bevezető részek (**Preface, History and Evolution of the**

European Bird Fauna) összefoglalóját és a fajleírásokat bármely nemzet lefordíthatta saját nyelvére, hogy szabadon terjeszthesse azt az ornitológusok között, hogy a könyv azoknak is hasznára váljon, akik nem tudnak angolul.

Azon nevek és címek listája, ahol a nemzeti nyelvre lefordított kiadványokat el lehet érni (ezen könyv nyomdába adásának időpontjáig terjedő információk alapján), a **Technical Appendix** rész végén található meg.

MÓDSZEREK

Adatközlés az *Atlasz*ban

Az adatgyűjtésre és a szerkesztésre vonatkozó eredeti elképzelések leírása, a módszerek kiválasztásának ismertetése illetve a program megszervezésének története a **History** fejezetben található.

Az *Atlasz* térképei az egyedsűrűség (egységnyi területre vonatkozó példányszám) különbségeit logaritmikus skálán ábrázolják, amelyet a **Qualitative versus semi-quantitative information** rész mutat be az alábbiakban. Ez a skála különösen azoknál a fajoknál alkalmazható, ahol az egyedsűrűség az elterjedési területen jelentősen változik. Azonban a skála az egyedsűrűség kisebb különbségeit elfedi.

Az *Atlasz* nemcsak a fajok elterjedését mutatja be, de becsléseket ad az európai populációk nagyságáról és a trendek alakulásáról a legtöbb faj esetében. Az elterjedési mintázatban bekövetkező változások csak a körültekintően tervezett és kivitelezett nemzeti felméréseken alapuló populáció méretek és trendek ismeretében érthetők meg.

Az *Atlasz* által felmérni kívánt területek

Az 1. ábra mutatja a felmérni kívánt területeket. Bár jó lett volna a felmért területeket pontosan fedésbe hozni a Nyugat-Palearktikum határaival (lásd a *The Birds of Western Palearctic*-ban, Cramp et al 1977-1994), de ez felesleges lett volna a Kis-Ázsiából, Észak-Arábiából és Észak-Afrikából származó kevés adat miatt, mely területek ezért kimaradtak. Emiatt az *Atlasz* az *Atlas Florae Europaeae* (Jalas & Souminen 1972, 1988) alaptérképeit használja fel, kivételt képez a Novaja Zemlja, a Ferenc József-föld, az összes Törökország közeli görög sziget, a Madeira szigetvilág, Azori szigetek, Délkelet-Oroszország sztavropoli régiója és a kaukázusi köztársaságok, melyek mind szerepelnek az *Atlasz*ban. A Nyugat-Palearktikum és az EBCC Atlasz által lefedett területek közti további különbség az, hogy Ciprus, a Kanári-szigetek és az összes észak-afrikai fennhatóságú mediterrán szigetek szintén kimaradtak az *Atlasz*ból. Az *Atlasz*ban vizsgált területek a *Birds in Europe – their conservation status* (Tucker & Heath 1994) című könyvétől abban térnek el, hogy az *Atlasz* Törökország kisázsiai területeire és Grönlandra vonatkozó adatot nem közöl.

Az 1. ábrából nem tűnik ki azonnal, hogy az *Atlas Florae Europaeae* és ez az *Atlasz* is – eltérően a *Birds in Europe*-tól – kihagyja Európa egy kis darabját Odenburg közelében, míg Kazahsztánnak a Volga és az Ural folyók közé eső egy részét, valamint Oroszország ázsiai részéről, Perm keleti részét (Szverdlovszky régió) magába foglalja.

A ténylegesen felmért terület

Az **Introduction** követő **Explanatory Maps** fejezetben a 2. ábra mutatja a felmért négyzeteket és jelzi minden négyzetben a maximális adatminőséget, míg a 3. ábra a minimális adatminőséget szintén négyzetenként. A **Qualitative versus semi-quantitative information** fejezet, lásd alább, ezeknek a kategóriáknak a jelentését magyarázza, de az adatminőség ezen térképeken jelzett kategóriái a minőség szerint csökkenő sorrendben a következőek:

1. Szemikvantitatív populációbecslés: a fészkelés bizonyított vagy valószínű
2. Szemikvantitatív populációbecslés: a fészkelés lehetséges
3. Kvalitatív jelenlét: a fészkelés bizonyított vagy valószínű
4. Kvalitatív jelenlét: a fészkelés lehetséges

Az adatok általában ugyanabba a minősítési kategóriába tartoztak négyzetenként (lásd alább) minden észlelt fajnál. Közép-Oroszország tekintélyes része egyáltalán nem lett felmérve a kapcsolatteremtés hiánya miatt. Oroszország fennmaradó részének többségén, Fehéroroszország, Ukrajna és a kaukázusi köztársaságok bizonyos részein a felmérések csak korlátozott számú fajra terjedtek ki. A volt Jugoszlávia területének legnagyobb részén széleskörű felmérés történt (néhány területen nem az összes fajra). Albánia számos területén nem történt felmérés. Az orosz sarkvidéki szigetvilág egyes részeinek felmérése (Novaja Zemlja, Ferenc József-föld) hiányosan történt.

Ezektől a kikerülhetetlen hiányosságoktól eltekintve a tervbe vett területeken a felmérések lényegében teljes körűek.

Az *Atlasz* térképei

A térképábrázolás módszerének kiválasztása a következő három szempont alapján történt: fedje le az *Atlasz*ban felmérni kívánt területeket, legyen a legtöbb európai országban ismert, valamint a nemzeti atlaszok térképeinek vetületi rendszereivel legyen kompatibilis. Az *Atlasz* projekt indulásakor mindezen alapvető követelményeknek egyedül az UTM vetületi rendszer felelt meg. Mivel az *Atlas Florae Europaeae* projekt is az UTM négyzethálót alkalmazza, így egy madártani atlasz számára is alkalmas választásnak tűnt. Az *Atlas Florae Europaeae* felmérési egységnek 50×50 kilométeres négyzeteket alkalmaz, ezért a madártani *Atlasz*hoz is ezt választottuk egységül. A gyűjtött adatok összeállítása és feldolgozása során nem lett volna értelme finomabb felosztás alkalmazásának.

A térkép alapvető egysége a 100×100 kilométeres négyzet, amely egy két számjegyből és három betűből álló, logikus sorrendben felépített kódrendszer segítségével egyedileg azonosítható. A florisztikai és madártani atlaszokban ezeket a négyzeteket további négy, 50×50 kilométeres négyzetekre osztották a következő sorrendben:

1 3
2 4

êgy minden 50 kilométeres négyzet egy 6 karakterből álló egyedi kóddal rendelkezik.

Az UTM négyzetháló kitűzése az észak-déli tengelyen egyszerű: a vonalakat az Egyenlítőtől kiindulva 50 kilométerenként, a földrajzi szélességi körökkel párhuzamosan vesszük fel. A másik tengely kezelése már bonyolultabb, mivel a hosszúsági körök (délkörök) a sarkok felé haladva összetartanak. Következésképpen a felrajzolható 50×50 kilométeres négyzetek száma a sarkok felé egyre csökken. Az UTM négyzetek elrendezését az alábbiak szerint oldották meg. A cellák (négyzetek) kialakításának a hosszúsági körök 6°-onként való felosztása az alapja (a 0°-tól indulva). Minden 6°-os délkört határoló cella mérete egyre csökken a sarkok felé, míg pontokká válva el nem tűnnek. Innen már az új határcellák mérete kezd el csökkenni. Az *Atlas Florae Europaeae* és ezen madártani atlasz úgy módosította a rendszert, hogy a 6°-os délköröket határoló négyzetek méretében kisebbek az eltérések: nevezetesen, ha egy határoló négyzet szélessége hozzávetőleg 40 km-re csökken, a négyzetet megszüntetjük. (Kényelmi szempontból az *Atlasz*ban a cellákat "négyzeteknek" hívjuk, bár tudjuk, hogy sokuk nem pontosan négyzet alakú.) Ez a mintázat a felmérni kívánt területeket ábrázoló térképről (1. ábra) világosan leolvasható, a részletes magyarázatot pedig a **Technical Appendix** tartalmazza.

Az EOAC 50×50 km-es felosztású térképekkel látta el az egyes országok szervezőit azért, hogy biztosítsa az adatok helyes négyzethez való rendelését. A terepmunkát általában 50×50 km-esnél finomabb felbontású térképeken végezték, de előfordult az is, hogy nem UTM négyzethálót alkalmaztak. Mindkét esetben a nemzeti koordinátorok feladata volt, hogy az adatokat a számítógépes rögzítéshez megfelelően konvertálják.

A terepmunka időpontjai, és az adatok érvényesítése

A tervek szerint a felméréseket az *Atlasz* számára 1985–1988 között kellett elvégezni. Az egyes országok maguk szervezték felméréseiket, azonban gyakorlati nehézségek miatt nem tudták mindenhol a fenti időszakban elvégezni a munkát. Ha ezen periódusra vonatkozó felmérések hiányosak voltak, akkor korábbi vagy későbbi adatok bevonásával becslés történt annak megállapítására, hogy vajon ezek az adatok javítják-e a felmérést akár a területek nagyságát, akár az adatok minőségét tekintve. Az **Introduction**-t követő 3. táblázat tartalmazza a felmérésben résztvevő országok felsorolását, az adatgyűjtés idejét, azt a nemzeti szinten használt rácsozatot amelyről az adatokat konvertálták, valamint a módszereket.

Adatgyűjtés – a fajok elterjedési adatai

Órák százezrei, talán több mint egy millió terepi munkaóra alapján készült az *Atlasz*. Ideális az lett volna, ha az összes résztvevő ugyanabban az időszakban ugyanolyan módszerrel végzi a terepmunkát, ezt azonban nem lehetett megoldani. Ezért az EOAC inkább széles körű irányelveket, mint szigorú szabályokat adott meg. Néhány országban a terepmunkát a nemzeti atlasz illetve ezen *Atlasz* elkészítéséhez együttesen végezték, míg más országok az adatokat az *Atlasz*tól függetlenül futó nemzeti atlasz projektek alapján szolgáltatták. A terepi felmérő módszerek az egyszeri területbejárástól a többszöri bejárás alapján készített fajlistákon át az olyan rendszeres felmérési módszerekig terjedtek, mint a pontszámlálás, sáv transzekt vagy territórium térképezés.

Az adatgyűjtéshez a Holland Központi Statisztikai Hivatal által készített standardizált formanyomtatványt vettük alapul, amely kérdőív az **Introduction**-t követő 4. ábrán látható. Ezt a kérdőívet töltötték ki minden egyes felmért négyzet esetében. Az országhatárok által kettészelt négyzeteknél az érintett országok csak a saját területükre eső részről szolgáltattak adatokat.

Az alábbi általános információkat kértük be a négyzetekről:

1. A számlálás időtartama: az adatgyűjtés éve vagy évei.
2. Az 50 km-es négyzetet jelölő UTM kód.
3. A felmérés teljessége: jelzi, hogy adott négyzetben a várható fajok több, vagy kevesebb, mint 75%-át mérték fel (magas illetve alacsony felmértség).
4. A négyzet tengerszint feletti magassága (a legalacsonyabb és a legmagasabb érték).
5. A megfigyelők vagy a koordinátor(ok): neve és címe, az esetleges további kérdések miatt.
6. Megjegyzések: további információk, magyarázatok a kérdőív adataihoz.
7. Egy rövid kérdőív az adott négyzetben található biotópokról.

A formanyomtatvány zömét a fajok felsorolása teszi ki (kb. 440 faj Voous (1977) rendszertani sorrendjében, Euring kódszám szerint). Az adatmező 0. oszlopában a tudományos név rövidítését (pl. Gav stell), az 1. oszlopában az Euring kódot (pl. 00020) adtuk meg, a 2. oszlopba a fészkelést, illetve ennek kódját kértük rögzíteni. 16 kód jelzi a fészkelés státuszát, amit három csoportra osztottunk: biztos fészkelő, valószínű fészkelő, lehetséges fészkelő. A kódok az 1. táblázatban láthatóak. Végül a 3. oszlop a fészkelő párok becsült számáról kért információt, logaritmikus skálán kifejezve (1 = 1–9, 2 = 10–99, ... , 6 = > 100 000).

A lista végén helyet hagytunk a hibrid és a felsorolásban nem szereplő fajoknak.

Végeredményben a fészkelő állományok adatforrásai a következők voltak:

1. Az EBCC nemzeti koordinátorai, akik az adatgyűjtést szervezték, és adatlapokon összegezték az eredményeket.
2. Területi koordinátorok. Egyes, főként nagy területű országok esetében az adatgyűjtést nem a nemzeti koordinátorok szervezték. Ha működött valahol egy megfigyelő hálózat, sokszor ennek egyik tagja látta el ezt a feladatot. Ezek a területi koordinátorok a nemzeti koordinátorokhoz hasonló módon tevékenykedtek.
3. Az országok egyéb adatforrásai, főként irodalmi adatok, melyeket egy adott faj szakértője gyűjtött össze. Ahol nem történt felmérés, főként a félreeső, eldugott helyeken, egyedüli adatforrásként a megjelent vagy a meg nem jelent írásos anyagok szolgáltak.
4. Fajleírások szerzői. Nagyon gyakran egy adott fajt tanulmányozó szerző szolgáltatott információt arról, hol lelhetők még fel az elterjedésre és az állománynagysága vonatkozó adatok.

Ezen adatforrásokból származó minden adatot a nemzeti

RÁBLÁZAT 1 *Fészkelési kódok és kategóriák*

A: Lehetséges fészkelés

1. A faj költési időben, lehetséges fészkelőhelyen történt megfigyelése.
2. Éneklő hím(ek) (vagy fészkelési hang) költési időben.

B: Valószínű fészkelés

3. Pár megfigyelése költési időszakban lehetséges fészkelőhelyen.
4. Állandó territórium tételezhető fel territoriális viselkedés (ének stb.) alapján egy hét legalább két különböző napján vagy még távolabbi időpontokban, ugyanazon a helyen.
5. Udvarlás és pózolás.
6. Valószínű fészek látogatása.
7. Izgatott viselkedés vagy adultok vészjelzése.
8. Kotlófoltos adult (kézben tartott madarat vizsgálva).
9. Fészeképítés vagy költőüreg kaparása.

C: Biztos fészkelés

10. Elterelő vagy sérülést tettető viselkedés.
11. Használt fészek vagy tojáshéj (a felmérési időszakból származó) találva.
12. Frissen kirepült fiatal (fészeklakó fajnál) vagy pelyhes fióka (fészekhagyónál).
13. Adult madár fészkelési helyet keres fel vagy repül le róla lakott fészekre utaló körülmények között (beleértve magasan levő fészket és odvakat, melyek belseje nem látható), vagy kotló adult látható.
14. Ürüléket vagy fiókáknak táplálékot szállító adult.
15. Tojásos fészekalj.
16. A fészekben fiókákat látni vagy hallani.

koordinátorok szintjén jóvá kellett hagyni ahhoz, hogy bekerülhessenek az adatbázisba.

Kvalitatív kontra szemikvantitatív információ

Az *Atlasz* szemikvantitatív információkat (a becsült populációméret logaritmusát) használja, amelyet az előírt skála alapján, négyzetenként, a regionális és országos koordinátor és a terepi felmérők állapítottak meg. A pontok a térképeken nem a költéssűrűséget, hanem a költő párok számát jelölik, a pont mérete pedig a mennyiségi kategóriát (lásd a térképjeleket a cxl oldalon). Sajnálatos, hogy egyes országok teljes mértékben (Norvégia és Lengyelország), mások jórészt (Spanyolország), megint mások részben (Izland, Olaszország és Franciaország) nem járultak hozzá a szemikvantitatív adatok közléséhez. Boszniával és Szerbiával a projekt kapcsolata megszakadt, így adataikat nem lehetett aktualizálni. Franciaország néhány régiója önállóan aktualizálta adatait. A francia nemzeti koordinátor csak korlátozott számú faj esetében frissítette meg az országos adatokat. Számos négyzet esetében még a becslések logaritmikus értékei is sokkal több információt hordoznak, mintha egy faj költéséről, illetve annak hiányáról lenne pusztán adatunk.

A határokon átnyúló négyzetek esetében, ahol minden ország, csak a saját területrészéről közölt adatot, a magasabb értéket vettük figyelembe (nem logaritmikus értéket számítva), annak ellenére, hogy néhány esetben ez alulbecslést eredményez. Ez a fajta közelítés hasznosabb volt, mintha ezen négyzetekről csupán kvalitatív adatokat közöltünk volna.

A térképen alkalmazott pontok az alábbi információs kategóriákat jelölik:

sötét lila	= biztos vagy valószínű fészkelő, kvalitatív
világos lila	= lehetséges fészkelő, kvalitatív
vörös	= biztos vagy valószínű fészkelő, szemikvantitatív
narancs	= lehetséges fészkelő, szemikvantitatív
szürke	= az adott négyzetben, az adott fajra nézve nem volt felmérés
nincs pont	= az adott fajra nézve volt felmérés, amely alapján nem fészkel a négyzetben

Számítógépes adattárolás – az adatok javítása és érvényesítése

A nemzeti koordinátoroktól beérkezett formanyomtatványok alapadatait az ASCII formátumú fájlként való tárolás előtt ellenőriztük (hiányzó vagy rossz kódok miatt) és minden rekordot egy nemzeti azonosító kóddal láttunk el. Néhány országból floppy lemezen érkeztek az adatok, amelyeket ugyanilyen módon ellenőriztük. Az alapfájlokból kialakított adatbázisban egy faj egy négyzetben egyetlen értékszámmal szerepel.

Azok a nemzeti koordinátorok és más adatszolgáltatók, akik időben küldték el az adatokat, előzetesen megkapták a megfelelő térképeket és a fajonkénti listákat ellenőrzés céljából. Ezen első ellenőrzés során is sok hibát sikerült kijavítani. Számos országból későn kaptuk meg az adatokat, míg mások esetében a kvalitatív adatokat szemikvantitatívra módosították. êgy ezeknél az adatellenőrzés későn kezdődött és a különböző országoknál eltérő szinten történt meg.

Az előzetes térképek előkészítése két szempontból is döntő fontosságú volt:

1. Lehetővé tette a nemzeti koordinátorok és rajtuk keresztül sok adatszolgáltató számára, hogy ellenőrizzék, pontosan történt-e az adatfelvitel: a térképekről leolvasható volt, hogy a négyzetek az egyes fajok esetén a megfelelő helyre kerültek-e. A tévedéseket a térképek szembetűnőbben jelezték, mint a puszta adatsorok.
2. Továbbá ösztönzőleg hatott új adatok közlésére is.

A második lépcsőben ellenőrizték, hogy az első fázisban

végrehajtott korrekciók számítógépes rögzítése hibátlanul történt-e. Ehhez másodszor is kiküldték a javított térképeket és adatsorokat a nemzeti koordinátoroknak. A legtöbb koordinátor elvégezte ezt a hatalmas munkát és visszaküldte a végső javításokat, de egyes országoknál, mint például a volt Jugoszlávia esetében az adatok ellenőrzése, javítása gyakran megoldhatatlan volt. Minél nagyobb volt egy adott ország csúszása a határidőt illetően, annál nagyobb nehézségekbe ütközött a térképek véglegesítése.

A későbbiekben is érkeztek javítások a fajleírások készítőitől és az egyes fajok szakértőitől. Ezeket az adatokat legtöbbször a nemzeti koordinátorokkal ellenőriztettük és ezek után dőlt el, hogy melyik szerepeljen az *Atlasz*ban. Ahol idő hiányában erre nem került sor, ott vagy meghagytuk a korábbi ábrákat, vagy a szövegben jeleztük, hogy a szerző véleménye eltér attól, ami a térképen szerepel.

Ahol terepi térképezéssel gyűjtött adatok nem álltak rendelkezésre, ez különösen Oroszország északi részére és Albániára volt jellemző, ott a helyi terepmadarászok más forrásból származó adatokat értékeltek. Az ilyen négyzetek esetében szemikvantitatív becsléseket végeztünk, a közölt adatokat extrapolációjával állapítottuk meg ugyanazon régió becsléssel felmért négyzetei alapján.

Az új adatok és javítások beérkezésének végső határideje 1995. július 1. volt, bár Albániából, Törökország európai részéről, a Kaukázusból, Ukrajna és Oroszország egyes részeiről a rákövetkező néhány hónap alatt érkezett adatokat is elfogadtuk, hogy az *Atlasz*t minél teljesebbé tegyük. Mennyiségi adatokra vonatkozó javításokat 1995. november 1-ig fogadtunk el a fajleírásokat készítő szerzőktől.

Adatgyűjtés – a populációméretre vonatkozó adatok

Az *Atlasz*ban szereplő nemzeti populációs adatok az Európai Madár Adatbázisból származnak. Ez olyan populációs adatokat tartalmaz, melyeket az EBCC-vel és a BirdLife International-el együttműködve az *Atlasz* illetve a BirdLife Dispersed Species Project-je számára gyűjtöttek, mely utóbbi eredményei a *Birds in Europe – their conservation status* című könyvben jelentek meg (Tucker & Heath 1994). Az együttműködés elősegítette a munkában való teljesebb részvételt is Európa egyes részeiben. Az adatokat elsősorban a nemzeti koordinátoroknak (*Birds in Europe*-ban felsoroltak) szétküldött kérdőívek alapján gyűjtöttük, akik továbbküldték ezeket a megfelelő szakembereknek és szervezeteknek. Az Európai Madár Adatbázist a BirdLife International kezeli.

Minden ország a következő populációs adatokat közölte az összes költő fajról:

1. Populációméret.
2. Populációméret változásai (1970 és 1990 között).
3. Elterjedési terület változásai (1970 és 1990 között).

A telelő populációkról hasonló adatokat gyűjtöttek, de ezeket az *Atlasz*ban nem közöljük.

A forrásanyagokat – amikből a populációk méreteit és változásait számítottuk – megőriztük. Az **Introduction**-t követő 2. táblázatban részletezett adat-ellenőrzési kódokat azért közöltük, hogy jelezzük a populációméretre és ezek változásaira vonatkozó adatok pontosságát és megbízhatóságát.

Néhány a fajleírást elkészítő szerző nem értett egyet az adatbázisban szereplő populáció becslésekkel, azonban ezen információk túlságosan későn lettek közölve ahhoz, hogy bekerüljenek az adatbázisba. Ezen esetekben a szerzők beírták becsléseiket a szövegbe, de a fajleírásoknál lévő grafikonok mindig az adatbázis adait mutatják.

Az adatok használhatósága

Az *Atlasz* projekt óriási értékű adatbázist állított fel. Az adatbázisnak szükségszerűen korlátai vannak. Azoknak, akik a további kutatásokban fel akarják használni a könyv adatait, figyelembe kell venniük ezeket a korlátokat, részletezésük azonban már túlmutatna ezen könyv célján, ezért javasoljuk, hogy az EBCC-től kérjenek további információkat. A könyv általános használata közben felmerülő alapvető korlátok a következők:

1. Sem egy faj előfordulásának vagy hiányának, sem a populációk méretének meghatározására nem írtunk elő egységes módszertant. Az EBCC forrásanyagát is képező számos nemzeti programban a helyi céloknak és lehetőségeknek megfelelően dolgozták ki az adatgyűjtési módszereket.
2. Nem volt általános módszere a terepmunka eredményeinek a formanyomtatványokon való megfelelő értékelésére a korábban említett okok miatt. Az adatokat országonként más-más módszerrel konvertálták.
3. Az adatok minősége változó a terepmunka színvonalában és a megfigyelők relatív számában meglévő eltérések miatt.
4. Egyes adatokat részlegesen extrapolálták.
5. Egyes adatok irodalmi adatok (főleg a sarki területre vonatkozók).

AZ ATLASZ TÉRKÉPEINEK SZERKEZETE ÉS A FAJOK LEÍRÁSA

Az Atlaszban a fajok két csoportban szerepelnek. Az

TÁBKÁZAT 2 *Az Európai Madár Adatbázis kódjai*

POPMIN	=	Minimális populációnagyság (pár)
POPMAX	=	Maximális populációnagyság (pár)
MEAN	=	Átlagos populációnagyság (pár)
YRC	=	Populációnagyság becslésének éve
PST	=	Populációnagyság változásának trendje
RST	=	Populáció elterjedési területe változásának trendje
PSV	=	a MEAN becslésének ellenőrző kódja
PTV	=	a YRC becslésének ellenőrző kódja
RTV	=	az RST becslésének ellenőrző kódja

egyikbe azok tartoznak, amelyekről megfelelő térképezési adatokkal rendelkezünk, a másikba pedig azok, amelyekről nem. Az első csoportra vonatkozó leírások teljesek és a fajleírások **Part 1** részben találhatók, a másik csoport rövidebb leírásait a **Part 2** rész tartalmazza. A fajok mindkét részben Voous rendszerében, és megközelítőleg az Euring kód szerinti sorrendben követik egymást, kivéve néhány kisebb módosítást az **Part 1** részben, mert arra törekedtünk, hogy ha egy faj térképe és a hozzá tartozó szöveg egyetlen oldalra került, akkor a szemben levő oldalt is egy faj töltse ki. Ha egy faj térképe és a szöveg egy-egy teljes oldalt kitöltött, akkor ezeket egymással szemben helyeztük el. Egyes, igen szűk elterjedésű fajok esetében nem volt szükség a teljes kidolgozásra, így lehetőség volt több, mint egy faj elhelyezésére egyetlen oldalon. Minden fajról közlünk ábrát, és közneveit (ahol lehetőség volt rá) 14 nyelven ismertetjük. A legtöbb fajról szerepel populációs grafikon, melyek magyarázata a térképeket és fajleírásokat megelőző oldalakon található.

Származtatott térképek (összefoglaló magyarázat)

Az 5. ábra mutatja be a költő madarakra vonatkozó általános fajgazdagságot négyzetenként. A 6-tól a 8-ig az ábrák a BirdLife International által meghatározott, az európai természetvédelmi szempontból kiemelt fajok (SPEC), 1., 2. és 3. kategóriái szerint mutatja be a fajgazdagságot. A 9. ábrán a három kategória összevontan szerepel.

A FAJOK LEÍRÁSAI

A fajok leírásai (ahol lehetséges volt) a következő általános témákat tartalmazzák: elterjedés a világon, európai fészkelési élőhelyek, elterjedési mintázat és abundancia viszonyok Európában, a populációméret és az elterjedés változásai napjainkban (és a lehetséges kiváltó okok), regionális változások az abundanciában, az elterjedést korlátozó lehetséges tényezők, költéssűrűség a legfontosabb élőhelyeken, a fajok vándorlásának és kóborlásának jellegzetességei Európában és azonkívül is, a fajok bármilyen különleges jellemvonása, végül tömör tájékoztatás az alfajokról, bemutatva azok elterjedését, az elterjedési terület átfedését más alfajokkal és a trendet.

A következő témák viszont nem szerepelnek (kivételt képeznek valamely általános témához kapcsolódó, elengedhetetlenül szükséges rövid ismertetők): költésbiológia, viselkedés, táplálék, más fajokkal való kapcsolatok, szervezettani és élettani sajátosságok, a veszélyeztető tényezők részletes ismertetése (ezzel a *Birds in Europe* foglalkozik), rendellenességek, tojástan, evolúció és rendszertan (kivéve, ha mostanában fogadtak el jelentős változásokat, vagy ha az alfajok jelentősen különböznek egymástól), halálozás vagy egyéb populációdinamikai változók illetve hang és ének.

Fajok – az *Atlaszba* való felvétel kritériumai

A felmérni kívánt területen 1985 óta fészkelő fajok közül azok szerepelnek, amelyek megfelelnek az 1. táblázat feltételeinek. Betelepített fajok csak akkor kerülhettek felvételre, ha legalább egy, öt éven át létező, önfenntartónak nyilvánított, vadon fészkelő populációja volt. Mindazonáltal a fenti szabályok elfogadása vagy értelmezése országonként igen eltérő volt, ezért néhány betelepített faj felvétele vagy kihagyása bizonyos mértékig önkényesnek tűnhet.

Az *Atlasz* 513 fajt tárgyal, plusz az olasz veréb, *Passer x italiae*.

NÓMENKLATÚRA ÉS TAXONÓMIA

Taxonómia

Az EBCC taxonómiai kérdésekben óvatos és konzervatív álláspontot követ. Az *Atlasz* általában a *Birds of the Western Palearctic* rövidített kiadásának (a továbbiakban BWP) helyesbítései szerinti taxonómiát, sorrendet és angol nómenklatúrát követi.

A *Puffinus yelkouan, Puffinus mauretanicus, Larus cachinnans, Anthus petrosus, Phylloscopus lorenzii* és *Pyrrhula murina* külön fajként, a *Puffinus puffinus, Larus argentatus, Athus spinoletta, Phylloscopus collybita* és *Pyrrhula pyrrhula* fajoktól elkülönített térképeken szerepelnek. A külön térképezés elkülönítetten történő felmérés, illetve földrajzi szeparáció esetén volt lehetséges. (A három *Puffinus* faj szöveges része együtt van megadva).

Kezdetben kísérlet történt számos faj alfajainak és változatainak külön térképezésére is, de az EOAC által megfogalmazott bélyegeket nem vették egyformán figyelembe az egyes országokban, emiatt a külön térképezés nem volt lehetséges. Mindazonáltal az olasz veréb külön lett felmérve, és az *Atlasz* a BWP-t követve a *Passer domesticus* és *P. hispaniolensis* állandósult hibridjeként tárgyalja, mint *Passer x italiae*. Ezzel szemben a *Phylloscopus trochlioides* két földrajzilag elkülönült alfajt is magába foglal (*viridanus* és *nitidus*), amelyeket azelőtt külön fajokként tárgyaltak. A *Lanius meridionalis* elkülönítése a *L. excubitor* fajtól csak az *Atlasz* elkészültére vált elfogadottá: a két alak elterjedése közötti határt diagram jelzi. A *Hippolais caligata*-t és a *H. rama*-t valamikor külön fajnak tekintették, de itt csak mint alfaj szerepel. A viszonyok néhány sirály fajkomplexben gyakran tisztázatlanok; a *Larus armenicus* itt elkülönítve szerepel.

Euring kódok

Az Európai Gyűrűzési Szövetség (Union for Bird Ringing, EURING) a fajok és alfajok azonosítására egy öt számjegyű kódrendszert alakított ki elsősorban a gyűrűzési adatokra. Ahol lehetséges az Euring-kódolás alapvetően a Voous-féle sorrendet követi, és az adatok egyeztetésének hasznos módszereként került alkalmazásra. Az egyes Euring-kódok a fajlistákban vannak megadva. A **Technical Appendix** részletezi az Euring kódok használatát.

A HIVATKOZÁSOK ÉS MÁS PUBLIKÁCIÓK HASZNÁLATA

A rendelkezésére álló szűk hely miatt, a szerzők kérésünkre elkerülték a kézikönyvekre történő hivatkozást. Két nagy, új európai kézikönyv azonban különös figyelmet érdemel. Az alapos értelmezéshez a fajhoz tartozó szövegeket és térképeket a következő kiemelkedőő publikációval együtt ajánlatos használni, ezek: *Birds of the Western Palearctic* (Cramp *et al.* 1977–1994) és *Handbuch der Vögel Mitteleuropas* (Glutz von Blotzheim *et al.* 1966–1993). Az

Atlasz szövegében ezek BWP és HVM rövidítéssel szerepelnek.

A *Birds in Europe – their conservation status* (Tucker & Heath 1994) című könyv volt az európai madárpopulációk, veszélyeztető tényezőik és védelmi helyzetük első áttekintése; de a könyv a kedvezőtlen státusú fajokat tárgyalja részletesen. Az *Atlasz* ezek mellett azokkal a fajokkal is foglalkozik, amelyek jelenleg nem veszélyeztetettek. A populációs adatok egy része a *Birds in Europe* által is használt Európai Madár Adatbázisból származik, ezért a szövegben gyakran történik utalás rá.

Az *Atlasz*ban levő hivatkozások a könyv végén a névmutató előtt találhatóak.

Michael Blair, Ward Hagemeijer, Tibor Szép

RÖVIDÍTÉSEK ÉS KIFEJEZÉSEK

Égtájak

N = észak
S = dél
E = kelet
W = nyugat, így NW=északnyugat és WSW=nyugat-délnyugat stb.

Általános kifejezések

asl = tengerszint feletti magasság (magasság)
c = körülbelül
et al = és mások (hivatkozásokban)
pers comm = személyes közlés(ek)
pers obs = személyes megfigyelés(ek)
unpubl = nem publikált munka

Dimenziók és mértékegységek

bp = fészkelő pár
ha = hektár
ind = példány
m = méter
km = kilométer
km^2 = négyzetkilométer
M = millió

Betűszavak

BTO = British Trust for Ornithology (Nagy Britannia)
BWP = *Birds of the Western Palaearctic*
HVM = *Handbuch der Vögel Mitteleuropas*
JNCC = Joint Nature Conservation Committee (Nagy Britannia)
RSPB = Royal Society for the Protection of Birds (Nagy Britannia)
SOVON = SOVON Bird Census Work The Netherlands (Hollandia)
WWT = Wildfowl and Wetlands Trust (Nagy Britannia)

Kifejezések

eutrophic állati vagy növényi bomlásból származó ásványi tápanyagokban gazdag
lentic állóvízi
lotic folyóvízi
mesotrophic nem gazdag, de nem is szegény alapvető sókban és tápanyagokban
'mixotrophic' boreális zónában levő, sekély és gazdag vegetációjú, de tápanyagokban szegény partszakaszú tavakra alkotott kifejezés
oligotrophic alapvető sókban és tápanyagokban szegény
phenology ismétlődő események vizsgálata
sclerophytic száraz klímához alkalmazkodott, alacsony párologtatású, általában vastag és kislevelű növények
xerophytic nagyon száraz körülményekhez alkalmazkodott növények

Introduzione

SCOPI DELL'*ATLANTE EBCC DEGLI UCCELLI NIDIFICANTI IN EUROPA*

Molti libri sugli uccelli presentano mappe di distribuzione delle specie. Alcune di queste mappe derivano da indagini sulle popolazioni nidificanti, ma, fatte salve alcune eccezioni, si tratta spesso di cartine distributive basate su sintesi di dati di ineguale attendibilità o non sono che rimaneggiamenti di precedenti mappe di dubbio valore. Nel più dei casi, inoltre, si tratta di carte non quantitative: esse non indicano, cioè, dove la specie è comune o dove è scarsa.

In effetti, è oggi disponibile un numero crescente di eccellenti atlanti regionali e nazionali sugli uccelli nidificanti; molti di questi atlanti hanno avuto origine o ispirazione dallo stesso progetto che ha prodotto il presente Atlante e, come questo, dispongono di dati semi-quantitativi.

L'EOAC, *European Ornithological Atlas Committee* (Comitato per l'Atlante Ornitologico Europeo) venne costituito nel 1971 con lo scopo di mappare, in periodo riproduttivo, la distribuzione di quelle specie per le quali era possibile ricavare dati tramite ricerche di campo. Con lungimirante intuito, l'EOAC prospettò allora la prima indagine sugli uccelli nidificanti, mai tentata sull'intero continente. L'intuizione è stata premiata e questo libro costituisce il risultato di quello sforzo.

L'Atlante delinea la distribuzione delle specie relativamente ad un periodo definito di tempo, ma i dati raccolti - qualunque sia il loro grado d'incompletezza - costituiscono una base di conoscenze con cui le future ricerche, come anche i futuri cambiamenti nella distribuzione delle specie, potranno essere confrontati. L' *Atlante EBCC degli Uccelli Nidificanti in Europa* mappa la distribuzione delle specie nidificanti nel nostro continente: esso risponde alla domanda 'quale specie nidifica dove ?'

IMPOSTAZIONE DELL'ATLANTE

In queste pagine sono brevemente illustrati gli scopi dell'Atlante, se ne descrivono i metodi di raccolta dati, di archiviazione informatica e di mappatura e se ne delinea la struttura. Per favorire la comprensione dell'opera in tutti i suoi aspetti, si è deciso di tradurre alcune parti in diverse lingue europee, così da rendere il testo accessibile alla maggior parte degli ornitologi del continente.

Sezioni iniziali

Nella Prefazione, il Professor Karel Voous spiega l'importanza dell'opera per la valutazione dei cambiamenti che si stanno verificando nell'avifauna europea.

Nelle Premesse, si evidenzia come il progetto complessivo dell'Atlante sia andato incontro alle richieste degli ornitologi europei e si illustrano le linee d'azione e gli obiettivi dell'EBCC per i futuri progetti di monitoraggio degli uccelli europei.

Segue quindi l'Introduzione, in cui sono anche trattati argomenti come i metodi di lavoro e l'area di copertura. La successiva sezione Figure Esplicative mostra la copertura territoriale, la qualità dei dati ed il modello di scheda standard per la raccolta dei dati.

Vi è poi un capitolo dedicato alla storia del progetto, dove sono descritti gli avanzamenti e le battute d'arresto incontrate nel corso del progetto.

Si prosegue con un capitolo su '**Evoluzione e storia dell'avifauna europea**', dove il Professor Jacques Blondel illustra come si siano originati gli areali attuali. Seguono, infine, un capitolo di ringraziamenti ed una lista degli atlanti ornitologici nazionali e di quelli regionali più importanti.

Sezioni monografiche

Una **Introduzione alle cartine distributive ed ai grafici di popolazione** fa da prefazione alla parte centrale dell'Atlante che tratta monograficamente le specie nidificanti. Nella parte 1 sono presentate, per ogni specie, la cartina distributiva, il testo di commento, un'illustrazione ed il nome volgare in 14 lingue. L'elenco segue all'incirca l'ordine sistematico di Voous (1977) e la sequenza di codice Euring. La parte 2 tratta le specie ritenute nidificanti in Europa, ma per le quali non si sono ricevuti dati di conferma al riguardo.

Sezioni finali

La sezione **Mappe derivate** tratta della ricchezza europea di specie nidificanti e di specie d'interesse conservazionistico (*SPEC*, *Species of European Conservation Concern*), come definite da *BirdLife International* (Tucker & Heath, 1994). L' **Appendice Tecnica** contiene spiegazioni riguardo le modifiche adottate, nella griglia cartografica di riferimento, rispetto alla proiezione Universale Trasversa di Mercatore (UTM) ed illustra gli adattamenti di reticolo effettuati per isole e limitate zone costiere. Questa Appendice spiega anche come si è utilizzato il sistema di codici numerici dell'Euring.

Fascicoli in lingue nazionali

I paragrafi iniziali (Premesse, Storia del progetto, Evoluzione e storia dell'avifauna europea) ed i testi monografici sulle specie sono stati riassunti in fascicoli in lingue nazionali per renderli accessibili agli ornitologi di ogni paese, così da consentire l'utilizzo del libro anche a coloro non famigliari con l'inglese. La lista dei nomi e degli indirizzi dei fornitori di questi fascicoletti in lingue nazionali (così come risulta al momento di andare in stampa) è riportata alla fine dell'**Appendice Tecnica**.

METODI

Presentazione dei dati dell'Atlante

La sezione storica descrive come il Progetto sia stato inizialmente organizzato nei suoi aspetti metodologici, ad esempio per la raccolta dati e per la compilazione delle schede.

Le differenze di densità (numero di individui per unità d'area) delineate nelle cartine distributive sono riferite ad una scala logaritmica (cfr. sotto-sezione successiva **Informazioni qualitative e semi-quantitative**). Questo tipo di scala è particolarmente appropriato per quelle specie la cui densità varia marcatamente nell'ambito dell'areale, ma non nel caso di differenze minime, che non vengono evidenziate.

L'Atlante non delinea unicamente la distribuzione delle specie nidificanti in Europa, ma fornisce anche, per la maggioranza delle specie e dei paesi europei, delle stime circa la consistenza numerica e la dinamica delle popolazioni. La comprensione delle variazioni degli areali in Europa può essere basata solo su stime affidabili della consistenza e dell'andamento delle popolazioni nazionali.

Ambito geografico considerato

La Fig. 1 mostra il quadro territoriale considerato nell'Atlante. Sebbene fosse auspicabile estendere l'ambito geografico del Progetto a tutto il Paleartico occidentale, così come questo è definito in *The Birds of the Western Paleartic* (Cramp *et al.*, 1977–1994), ciò non è stato possibile da realizzare per l'estrema scarsezza di dati disponibili per l'Asia Minore, l'Arabia settentrionale ed il Nord Africa, regioni che non sono quindi state considerate.

L'Atlante EBCC ha in effetti adottato la mappa base dell' *Atlas Florae Europaeae* (Jalas & Suominen, 1972; 1988), con l'aggiunta della Nuova Zemlya, della Terra di Francesco Giuseppe, di tutte le isole greche prossime alla Turchia, dell'arcipelago di Madera, delle Azzorre, della regione dello Stavropol nella Russia sud-orientale e delle repubbliche baltiche.

Le rimanenti differenze tra la regione Paleartica occidentale e l'ambito geografico qui considerato riguardano l'omissione dell'isola di Cipro, delle isole Canarie e di tutte le isole nord africane sotto amministrazione europea. Inoltre, rispetto all'opera di Tucker & Heath (1994): *Birds in Europe – their conservation status*, nel presente Atlante non sono incluse la Turchia asiatica e la Groenlandia.

Dalla Fig. 1 non emerge con immediata chiarezza che, diversamente da *Birds in Europe*, i limiti considerati in *The Birds of the Western Paleartic*, nell' *Atlas Florae Europaeae* e nel presente Atlante escludono una piccola parte d'Europa presso Orenburg (Russia sud-orientale) ed includono invece una porzione del Kazahkstan compresa tra il Volga ed i fiumi degli Urali, nonché una parte della Russia asiatica ad est di Perm (regione di Sverdlovsk).

Copertura raggiunta

La Fig. 2 della sezione Figure Esplicative mostra le unità cartografiche di rilevamento censite ed indica la 'massima qualità-dati' ottenuta per quadrato; la 'minima qualità-dati' è invece evidenziata in Fig. 3.

La sotto-sezione **Informazioni qualitative e semi-quantitative** (cfr. oltre) spiega il significato di questi termini; nelle cartine, comunque, le categorie di 'qualità-dati' illustrate sono (in ordine di valore decrescente):

1. Stime semi-quantitative di popolazione: nidificazione confermata o ritenuta probabile.
2. Stime semi-quantitative di popolazione: nidificazione ritenuta possibile.
3. Dati di presenza qualitativa: nidificazione confermata o ritenuta probabile.
4. Dati di presenza qualitativa: nidificazione ritenuta possibile.

La qualità-dati risulta generalmente la stessa per tutte le specie segnalate in un determinato quadrato (ma vedi oltre).

Aree piuttosto estese della Russia centrale non sono state coperte del tutto, principalmente a causa dell'impossibilità di stabilire contatti con corrispondenti locali. Per la gran parte del restante territorio russo, per parte della Bielorussia, per l'Ucraina e per le repubbliche caucasiche, la copertura è stata raggiunta solo per un ristretto numero di specie. Il grado di copertura della ex-Yugoslavia risulta nel complesso soddisfacente (in alcune aree non per tutte le specie). Esistono invece lacune importanti per l'Albania. Una copertura incompleta si registra anche per le isole russe artiche della Nuova Zemlya e della Terra di Francesco Giuseppe.

Nonostante inevitabili carenze, la copertura complessiva dell'Atlante può comunque considerarsi completa.

Reticolo cartografico

La scelta del tipo di proiezione cartografica doveva rispondere a tre criteri essenziali:

- riguardare tutta l'area geografica considerata nell' Atlante;
- essere conosciuta nella maggioranza dei paesi europei;
- essere compatibile con i sistemi cartografici nazionali.

Al momento d'inizio del Progetto, solo la proiezione Universale Trasversa di Mercatore (UTM) obbediva a questi tre criteri base.

La proiezione UTM risultava in effetti quella ideale anche per il fatto di essere stata già adottata come base per l'*Atlas Florae Europaeae*; inoltre, poiché quest'opera aveva adottato un reticolo di rilevamento composto da unità cartografiche di 50 km di lato, la stessa maglia a quadrati è stata scelta per l'atlante ornitologico. In effetti, il lavoro richiesto per raccogliere ed analizzare dati ad una scala cartografica più fine di rilevamento sarebbe stato inattuabile.

L'unità cartografica base del sistema UTM è la '*maglia fondamentale*', porzione reticolare di 100 × 100 km di lato; tale porzione è univocamente definita da un codice alfa-numerico sequenziale di due numeri (relativi ai fusi meridiani) e tre lettere (contrassegnanti le fasce parallele). Sia per l'atlante floristico che per quello ornitologico, ogni maglia di 100 × 100 km è stata suddivisa in quattro quadrati di 50 × 50 km, così numerati:

1 3
2 4

In tal modo, ogni quadrato di 50 km è identificabile da una sequenza univoca di 6 caratteri di riferimento.

La disposizione del reticolo UTM sull'asse dei paralleli è semplice: la superficie del globo è suddivisa in fasce disposte a intervalli di 50 km, conformemente ai paralleli e con punto di origine all'equatore.

La disposizione sull'asse dei meridiani è più complessa, poiché i meridiani convergono verso i poli. In questo caso, la definizione della celle del reticolo avviene per fusi di 6° di ampiezza in longitudine (con inizio a 0°); le celle in margine ai fusi si restringono gradualmente verso i poli fino a quando, divenute punti, non si annullano.

Tale sistema è stato leggermente modificato nell'*Atlas Florae Europaeae*, come anche nel presente atlante. Le variazioni dimensionali delle maglie marginali sono minori; i quadrati lungo i margini di fusi contigui non sono più considerati quando la loro larghezza si riduce a circa 40 km (nell'Atlante, le celle della griglia sono denominate 'quadrati' per convenienza, poiché nella realtà, come s'è visto, molte di esse tali non sono). Questa configurazione è chiaramente evidenziata nella carta del reticolo di riferimento (Fig. 1); ulteriori dettagli sull'argomento sono forniti nell'**Appendice Tecnica**.

L'EOAC ha fornito ai coordinatori nazionali del Progetto il reticolo predefinito di 50 × 50 km dell'Atlante allo scopo di garantire un corretto geo-referenziamento dei dati. La raccolta dei dati di campo si è spesso basata su griglie UTM in scala più fine o anche su reticoli diversi dall'UTM. In entrambi i casi, i coordinatori nazionali hanno poi provveduto a convertire i geo-referenziamenti nel reticolo cartografico ufficiale.

Periodo d'indagine

Il periodo d'indagine del Progetto era stato inizialmente fissato al quadriennio 1985–1988. La raccolta dati è stata autonomamente organizzata in ogni paese, ma, a causa di difficoltà pratiche, non tutte le nazioni sono poi riuscite a rispettare il quadro temporale previsto. Nei casi in cui il grado di copertura è risultato insufficiente per il periodo stabilito, si è considerata la possibilità di includere dati riferentisi ad anni precedenti o successivi, al fine di migliorare il quadro complessivo.

Nella Tab. 3, a seguito di questa *Introduzione*, sono elencati i paesi partecipanti, i relativi periodi di rilevamento-dati, il reticolo nazionale di riferimento e i metodi.

Raccolta dati e stime per classi numeriche delle specie

Centinaia di migliaia – forse più di un milione – di ore di lavoro di campo sono alla base dell'Atlante. Secondo l'impostazione ideale del Progetto, tutti i partecipanti all'inchiesta avrebbero dovuto utilizzare gli stessi metodi di raccolta dati, nello stesso periodo di tempo.

In realtà, ciò non si è verificato. L'EOAC ha in effetti preferito definire linee-guida generali piuttosto che regole rigorose. In alcuni paesi, le ricerche condotte per l'atlante europeo si sono abbinate con quelle realizzate nello stesso tempo per i progetti nazionali. In altri paesi, invece, i dati raccolti per la redazione di un autonomo progetto nazionale sono stati successivamente integrati al progetto europeo.

I metodi di raccolta dati utilizzati sul campo comprendono quindi sia semplici rilevamenti faunistici (singole o ripetute visite in un dato ambito territoriale) che censimenti qualitativi o quantitativi basati su metodi standardizzati (punti d'ascolto, transetti, mappaggio).

Il *Dutch Central Bureau of Statistics* ha realizzato la scheda standard riprodotta parzialmente in Fig. 4. Per ogni maglia ispezionata del reticolo si è compilata una scheda. Nel caso di maglie site a cavallo di confini nazionali, la compilazione della scheda è stata effettuata da entrambi i paesi per i territori di rispettiva pertinenza.

Le informazioni generali richieste per ogni maglia reticolare sono le seguenti:

1. Periodo d'indagine: anno, o sequenza di anni, a cui i dati vanno riferiti.
2. Codice UTM di identificazione della maglia.
3. Grado di completezza dei rilevamenti: viene richiesto di indicare se l'ispezione territoriale nel quadrato ha consentito di censire più del 75% (grado elevato) o meno del 75% (grado basso) delle specie attese.
4. Estremi altitudinali del territorio incluso nel quadrato.
5. Nomi e indirizzi del rilevatore o del coordinatore.
6. Commenti: spazio disponibile per informazioni suppletive sul tipo di dati forniti.
7. Descrizione dell'habitat: con riferimento ad un elenco predefinito di habitat, viene richiesto di indicare la percentuale approssimativa delle principali tipologie ambientali presenti sul territorio.

La maggior parte della scheda è poi occupata da una lista di 440 specie (nell'ordine tassonomico di Voous, 1977), numerate in sequenza Euring. I nomi delle specie sono riportati in forma abbreviata (ad es.: Gav stell) nella colonna 0. Al nome della specie si affianca, in col. 1, il codice Euring; la col. 2 è riservata ai codici delle categorie di nidificazione (in tutto 16, suddivise in tre categorie principali: nidificazione certa, probabile e possibile, cfr. Tab. 1). La col. 3, infine, concerne le stime numeriche (coppie nidificanti nel quadrato), espresse in scala logaritmica (1 = 1–9; 2 = 10–99; .... 6 = > 100.000). Al fondo della scheda sono previsti spazi aggiuntivi per segnalare specie non incluse nell'elenco.

Nel complesso, le fonti del Progetto sono state costituite da:

1. I coordinatori nazionali dell'EBCC, incaricati dell'organizzazione dei rilevamenti di campo nonché della raccolta dati sulle schede standard.
2. I coordinatori regionali, che in qualche caso (ad es. in paesi di grande estensione o dove un'efficiente rete di contatti ha funzionato autonomamente a livello locale, più che nazionale) hanno sostituito i coordinatori nazionali, svolgendone gli stessi compiti.
3. Le fonti complementari d'informazione nazionale, in particolar modo quelle bibliografiche, generalmente rese disponibili da un esperto. Nei casi in cui i dati di campo si sono rivelati insufficienti, le uniche fonti

TABELLA 1 *Categorie e codici di nidificazione*

A: Nidificazione possibile	
1.	Specie osservata in periodo riproduttivo in habitat potenzialmente idoneo alla nidificazione
2.	Maschio in canto (o altri richiami riproduttivi rilevati) in periodo riproduttivo
B: Nidificazione probabile	
3.	Coppia osservata in periodo riproduttivo in habitat favorevole alla nidificazione
4.	Territorio stabile, presunto in base al rilevamento, in due giorni diversi (distanziati di almeno una settimana) e nello stesso luogo, di comportamenti territoriali (canto, ecc.)
5.	Manifestazioni di corteggiamento e parate nuziali
6.	Visita ad un sito idoneo alla riproduzione
7.	Comportamenti irrequieti o richiami di allarme da parte di soggetti adulti
8.	Presenza di placca incubatrice in soggetti adulti esaminati in mano
9.	Attività di costruzione nido (trasporto materiale o scavo)
C: Nidificazione certa	
10.	Parate di distrazione o di simulazione di ferita
11.	Ritrovamento di nido usato o di guscio d'uovo (rispettivamente utilizzato o deposto durante il periodo dell'inchiesta)
12.	Giovani da poco involati (specie nidicole) o giovani in piumino (specie nidifughe)
13.	Adulti che entrano o che escono dal nido in circostanze che ne lasciano presumere l'occupazione (inclusi nidi alti o in cavità il cui interno non può essere controllato) o adulti visti incubare
14.	Adulti trasportanti sacche fecali o imbeccate
15.	Nido con uova
16.	Nido con giovani visti o sentiti

alternative d'informazione sono state costituite da lavori editi o inediti, spesso non facilmente reperibili dai coordinatori.

4. I testi monografici delle specie redatti da singoli autori. Molto spesso, gli specialisti incaricati della redazione dei testi monografici, hanno fornito informazioni suppletive sulla distribuzione e/o sulla consistenza delle specie loro affidate.

Tutti i dati provenienti dalle fonti sopra citate sono comunque stati sottoposti ad un processo gerarchico di validazione; qualsiasi informazione aggiuntiva all'archivio-dati è stata in effetti approvata a livello di coordinamento nazionale.

Informazioni qualitative e semi-quantitative

Nell'Atlante sono state richieste, per ogni maglia del reticolo, informazioni semi-quantitative sulla consistenza delle popolazioni, basate su stime per classi logaritmiche.

I tondi usati nelle cartine rappresentano numeri di coppie nidificanti (non densità riproduttive) e ad un incremento nella scala dimensionale dei tondi corrisponde quindi un ordine superiore di grandezza numerica (cfr. legenda a pag. cxl).

Sfortunatamente, alcune nazioni non hanno fornito stime sulla consistenza numerica delle popolazioni: Norvegia e Polonia (nessuna stima), Spagna (qualcuna) Islanda, Francia ed Italia (in parte). Nel corso del Progetto si sono inoltre persi i contatti con paesi come la Bosnia e la Serbia, i cui dati non sono quindi stati quantizzati. Il coordinatore francese ha fornito stime nazionali per un numero limitato di specie, ma informazioni semi-quantitative sono state indipendentemente fornite, per altre specie, a livello regionale. E' chiaro che anche un limitato numero di dati semi-quantitativi, relativi ad alcune maglie del reticolo, è più utile di semplici indicazioni di presenza-assenza.

Per le maglie del reticolo ricadenti su due o più paesi confinanti, e per le quali ogni paese ha fornito le proprie valutazioni semi-quantitative, si sono considerate le stime numeriche maggiori (i valori logaritmici non possono essere sommati). Questo sistema ha probabilmente comportato, in qualche caso, una sottostima degli effettivi, ma si tratta comunque di una approssimazione più informativa di una semplificazione a presenza qualitativa.

I tondi usati nelle cartine definiscono le seguenti categorie d'informazione:

- porpora scuro: nidificazione certa o probabile (dato qualitativo)
- porpora chiaro: nidificazione possibile (dato qualitativo)
- rosso: nidificazione certa o probabile (dato semi-quantitativo)
- arancio: nidificazione possibile (dato semi-quantitativo)
- grigio: quadrato non ispezionato
- nessun tondo: quadrato ispezionato, ma specie non rilevata

Informatizzazione – correzione dei dati cartografati e validazione degli archivi

Prima dell'informatizzazione in *file* in formato ASCII, i dati ricevuti dai coordinatori nazionali sono stati sottoposti a controlli per ricerca di errori sostanziali (codici omessi o errati); a ciascun *record* è stato associato un codice nazionale di identificazione. La stessa procedura è stata anche applicata ai dati trasmessi da alcuni paesi su supporto magnetico (*floppy disk*). Il *database* derivato dagli archivi di partenza contiene un singolo valore per specie per quadrato.

Una prima fase del processo di controllo è stata effettuata sottoponendo, ai coordinatori nazionali ed agli altri collaboratori che avessero trasmesso rapidamente i dati, delle carte distributive provvisorie e dei listati nazionali di specie. Alle richieste di verifica è corrisposto l'invio di un consistente numero di correzioni. In effetti, molti paesi hanno trasmesso tardivamente i propri dati ed altri hanno aggiunto le informazioni di tipo semi-quantitativo successivamente a quelle tipo qualitativo. Di conseguenza, la correzione dei dati e il processo di validazione sono iniziati più tardi e hanno avuto tempi diversi per aree diverse.

La produzione di carte provvisorie è stata determinante per due principali motivi:

1. ha permesso ai coordinatori nazionali, e – tramite essi - a molti rilevatori di campo, di verificare se i dati trasmessi erano stati archiviati correttamente e se i quadrati 'occupati' corrispondevano alle segnalazioni inviate per le specie;
2. ha stimolato una partecipazione più ampia, che ha spesso prodotto un invio di nuovi dati.

La seconda fase è coincisa con la verifica dei dati così aggiornati, tramite la spedizione ai coordinatori nazionali (ed alle altre fonti di dati) di una seconda versione, corretta, delle mappe provvisorie e dei listati. La maggior parte dei coordinatori ha potuto completare l'enorme lavoro di rilettura e di controllo e quindi sottoporre le ulteriori correzioni; tuttavia, l'aggiornamento e la validazione sono risultati impossibili in alcuni casi, come ad esempio per l'ex Jugoslavia. I paesi per i quali si è dovuta posticipare la procedura di controllo hanno avuto a disposizione un lasso di tempo ridotto per le verifiche; ovviamente, maggiore è stato il ritardo, più grandi sono state le difficoltà nel terminare le mappe.

Rappresentazioni aggiornate di carte sono state ricevute in una fase successiva da alcuni degli autori dei testi monografici o da altri esperti. Per decidere del loro impiego, molte delle modifiche proposte sono state sottoposte all'esame dei coordinatori nazionali. Nei casi in cui tale controllo non è stato effettuato per mancanza di tempo, si è utilizzata la mappa originale riportando nel testo le differenti indicazioni degli autori.

Per le aree non coperte da atlanti, in particolare per la Russia settentrionale e per l'Albania, si è fatto ricorso a dati di altra origine, raccolti e vagliati da ornitologi locali e successivamente sottoposti a valutazione in merito alla loro accettabilità. Per alcuni quadrati, parte delle stime semi-quantitative sono state estrapolate da quadrati limitrofi per i quali si disponeva di stime dirette, tenendo conto degli habitat rappresentati.

La scadenza ultima per l'invio dei nuovi dati e delle correzioni è stata fissata al primo luglio 1995; ciò nonostante, per massimizzare la copertura sono stati utilizzate anche informazioni ricevute nei mesi immediatamente successivi, relativamente all'Albania, alla Turchia europea, al Caucaso, a parte dell'Ucraina e della Russia. Correzioni segnalate da autori dei testi sono state accettate fino al 1° novembre 1995.

Assemblaggio dei dati - Consistenza numerica delle popolazioni

I grafici dell'Atlante relativi alla consistenza numerica delle popolazioni derivano dall' *European Bird Database*. Tale archivio contiene informazioni raccolte cooperativamente dall'EBCC e da *BirdLife International*, e destinate a integrare il presente Atlante e il *Dispersed Species Project* di *BirdLife*, i cui risultati sono pubblicati nel volume *Birds in Europe – their conservation status* (Tucker & Heath, 1994). Tale collaborazione ha contribuito anche a estendere la partecipazione all'Atlante in alcune parti d'Europa. I dati sono stati raccolti principalmente distribuendo questionari ai coordinatori nazionali (elencati in *Birds in Europe*), che a loro volta li hanno presentati ad esperti riconosciuti, ad organizzazioni di monitoraggio ed a coordinatori regionali. Il relativo archivio informatico (l' *European Bird Database*) è gestito da *BirdLife International*.

Per le popolazioni nidificanti di ciascuna specie, ogni paese ha fornito indicazioni su:

1. consistenza numerica della popolazione;
2. andamento della consistenza (periodo 1970–1990);
3. variazioni dell'areale occupato (periodo 1970–1990).

Le fonti di riferimento utilizzate per tali indicazioni sono state registrate; si è anche provveduto a fornire codici di verifica dell'accuratezza e dell'attendibilità delle stime (cfr. Tabella 2) (dati simili sono stati raccolti anche per le popolazioni svernanti, ma non vengono presentati in questa sede).

Alcuni Autori dei testi monografici di commento alle cartine non concordano con le stime di popolazione fornite dall'archivio. Le loro differenti valutazioni sono espresse nei testi, ma i grafici presentati si riferiscono sempre alle

TABELLA 2 *Codici di popolazione nell'* European Bird Database

POPMIN	=	consistenza minima di popolazione (in coppie nidificanti)			
POPMAX	=	consistenza massima di popolazione (in cp. nidificanti)			
MEAN	=	media geometrica della consistenza di popolazione (in cp. nidificanti)	PSV	=	codice di verifica della dimensione di popolazione
YRC	=	anno di stima della popolazione			
PST	=	andamento della consistenza di popolazione	PTV	=	codice di verifica dell'andamento di popolazione
RST	=	campo di variazione del PST	RTV	=	codice di verifica del campo di variazione

Codici di variazione dell'andamento di popolazione (riferiti al periodo 1970-1990)

+ 2	=	popolazione in netto incremento (50% almeno)
+ 1	=	popolazione in moderato incremento (minore del 50%, ma certamente superiore al 20%)
0	=	popolazione stabile o con fluttuazioni non superiori al 20% della consistenza complessiva
- 1	=	popolazione in moderato decremento (minore del 50%, ma certamente superiore al 20%)
- 2	=	popolazione in netto decremento (50% almeno)
n	=	nuovo nidificante nel periodo considerato
x	=	popolazione estinta come nidificante nel periodo considerato
f	=	popolazione con fluttuazioni di consistenza (dell'ordine di almeno il 20%), non chiaramente direzionate

stime d'archivio; in effetti, per ragioni di tempo, non è più stato possibile graficare le valutazioni alternative fornite dagli Autori.

Limiti dei dati

L'esecuzione del Progetto ha portato alla raccolta di un insieme di dati di elevata qualità. Inevitabilmente, però, alcune limitazioni sono insite nei dati. Coloro che intendessero utilizzarli in altre ricerche dovranno tenerne conto.

Entrare nel dettaglio di tali limitazioni va al di là degli scopi di questo libro; i ricercatori interessati possono richiedere informazioni direttamente all'EBCC. Sommariamente, i problemi di ordine più generale che possono influire sull'impiego delle informazioni contenute nel presente volume sono le seguenti:

1. Non è stato preparato alcun protocollo metodologico comune per il lavoro di campo, né per stabilire la presenza o l'assenza delle specie, né per stimare la dimensione delle loro popolazioni. Molti dei progetti nazionali i cui dati sono confluiti nell'Atlante EBCC hanno predisposto metodologie proprie finalizzate ai relativi scopi ed alle risorse disponibili.
2. Per le stesse ragioni di cui sopra, non è stato possibile suggerire una metodologia univoca per il confronto e per il trasferimento dei dati sulle schede di trasmissione. Ciascuno ha applicato metodi 'individuali'.
3. Le differenze di preparazione e del numero dei rilevatori sul campo hanno certamente determinando differenze nella qualità dei dati.
4. Alcuni dati derivano da una parziale estrapolazione.
5. Alcuni dati sono di origine bibliografica (principalmente per le aree artiche).

IMPOSTAZIONE DELLE MAPPE E DEI TESTI

Le specie presentate nell'Atlante sono suddivise in due gruppi: quelle per cui sono stati ottenuti dati distributivi soddisfacenti e quelle per le quali tale risultato non è stato raggiunto.

Le specie del primo gruppo sono trattate, con testo esteso, nella Parte 1 delle monografie distributive, mentre le altre sono presentate con testi più brevi nella Parte 2. In entrambe le parti le specie sono riportate secondo l'ordine sistematico di Voous, che corrisponde approssimativamente alla sequenza Euring. Vi sono tuttavia alcune eccezioni nella Parte 1, dovute alla necessità di affiancare quelle specie la cui trattazione si esauriva in una sola pagina; in questo modo, la mappa di distribuzione ed il testo di commento di tutte le specie a trattazione più estesa risultano appaiate e contemporaneamente consultabili. Nel caso poi di specie ad areale molto ristretto, si sono riuniti più testi in una sola pagina.

Ogni specie è illustrata ed i relativi nomi volgari (se esistenti) sono riportati in 14 lingue. Un grafico sulla consistenza numerica delle popolazioni si accompagna alla maggior parte delle specie la cui distribuzione è cartografata. La lettura dei grafici è illustrata nelle pagine che precedono le trattazioni monografiche.

Mappe derivate (spiegazione riassuntiva)

La Fig. 5 illustra la ricchezza generale di specie nidificanti per quadrato. Le Fig. 6, 7 e 8 evidenziano la ricchezza in *SPEC* (*Species of European Conservation Concern*), relativamente alle Categorie 1, 2 e 3 come definite da *BirdLife International*; la Fig. 9, infine, combina le tre Categorie.

LA TRATTAZIONE DELLE SINGOLE SPECIE

La trattazione delle singole specie comprende, quando possibile, una sequenza definita di argomenti, presentati di solito nel seguente ordine di priorità: distribuzione mondiale, habitat riproduttivi in Europa, quadro della distribuzione e abbondanza in Europa, variazioni recenti d'areale e di consistenza delle popolazioni (e loro possibili cause), variazioni regionali d'abbondanza, possibili fattori limitanti la distribuzione, densità di nidificanti negli habitat ottimali, migrazione e movimenti caratteristici all'interno e al di fuori d'Europa, eventuali caratteristiche particolari, brevi informazioni sulle sottospecie relativamente a distribuzione, areale, simpatria e andamenti.

Altri aspetti sono stati omessi, a meno che un loro breve richiamo non fosse indispensabile per la trattazione di uno degli argomenti di cui sopra. Si tratta di: biologia riproduttiva, comportamento, alimentazione, relazioni con altre specie, caratteristiche morfologiche e fisiologiche, dettagliate discussioni sulle minacce dirette (trattate in *Birds in Europe*), anormalità, caratteristiche delle uova, evoluzione e tassonomia (salvo che cambiamenti importanti, universalmente accettati, non siano sopravvenuti di recente o che siano riconosciute sottospecie marcatamente differenti), mortalità e altri parametri della dinamica di popolazione, vocalizzazioni.

Criteri di inclusione delle specie

Sono state incluse tutte le specie nidificanti, nell'ambito geografico precedentemente illustrato, a partire dal 1985, e rispondenti ai criteri di cui alla Tab. 1.

Le specie presenti in Europa a seguito di introduzioni sono state incluse soltanto se naturalizzate, ossia presenti con almeno una popolazione accertata per almeno cinque anni. L'accettazione e l'interpretazione di questa regola non è stata univoca in tutti i paesi, così che la selezione o l'omissione di qualche specie introdotta può superficialmente apparire arbitraria. L'Atlante include un totale di 513 specie, più *Passer x italiae*.

NOMENCLATURA E TASSONOMIA

Tassonomia

L'EBCC ha deciso di adottatare una posizione cauta e conservatrice riguardo ai problemi tassonomici. Il presente Atlante segue generalmente la nomenclatura e la tassonomia seguite nell'edizione ridotta di *The Birds of the Western Palearctic* (BWP).

I taxa *Puffinus yelkouan*, *Puffinus mauretanicus*, *Larus cachinnans*, *Anthus petrosus*, *Phylloscopus lorentzii* e *Pyrrhula murina* sono stati trattati come specie e mappati separatamente da *Puffinus puffinus*, *Larus argentatus*, *Anthus spinoletta*, *Phylloscopus collybita* e *Pyrrhula*

pyrrhula. Ciò è stata possibile perché tali taxa sono stati registrati separatamente, o perché hanno distribuzione geografica disgiunta (le tre specie di *Puffinus* sono trattate in un'unico testo).

Inizialmente si è anche tentato di tenere distinte le sottospecie e le forme geografiche di diverse altre specie, ma le indicazione dell'EOAC non sono state ovunque osservate, rendendo impossibile una restituzione cartografica distinta. Tuttavia, il Passero d'Italia è stato registrato come forma distinta e l'Atlante si adegua a BWP nel considerarlo un ibrido stabilizzato tra *Passer domesticus* e *P. hispaniolensis*, descrivendolo come *Passer x italiae*. Al contrario, *Phylloscopus trochiloides* include due sottospecie geograficamente separate, *viridanus* e *nitidus*, prima considerate come specie distinte. Al momento della conclusione dell'Atlante, l'idea di distinguere *Lanius meridionalis* da *L. excubitor* era ancora quella prevalente; il confine tra le due forme è indicato da un diagramma. *Hippolais rama*, talvolta trattata come forma distinta da *H. caligata*, viene qui considerata come una sua sottospecie. Le relazioni tassonomiche tra taxa di laridi sono spesso poco chiare; in questa sede *Larus armenicus* viene considerato una specie separata.

Codici Euring

L'Euring (*Union for Bird Ringing*, Unione Europea per l'Inanellamento degli Uccelli), ha definito una lista, regolarmente aggiornata, di codici numerici a cinque cifre per l'identificazione di specie e sottospecie; tali codici sono primariamente utilizzati per la trasmissione e l'archiviazione dei dati sull'inanellamento. La lista segue a grandi linee l'ordine sistematico di Voous, ed è pertanto stata adottata come utile metodo di raccolta e riordino dei dati. Ciascuna trattazione monografica è accompagnata dal relativo codice Euring. L'**Appendice Tecnica** spiega in dettaglio l'utilizzo dei codici.

Riferimenti bibliografici e pubblicazioni importanti

Agli autori è stati richiesto di non citare opere generali (gli *handbooks*) come fonti bibliografiche poiché lo spazio per le citazioni era generalmente molto ridotto. Due opere ornitologiche particolarmente importanti devono essere menzionate: si tratta di *The Birds of the Western Palearctic* (Cramp *et al.*, 1977–1994) e dell' *Handbuch der Vögel Mitteleuropas* (Glutz von Blotzheim *et al.*, 1966–1993). La piena comprensione dei testi e delle mappe delle specie europee contenute in questo Atlante non può prescindere dalla loro consultazione. All'interno dei testi, queste serie di volumi sono indicate rispettivamente con le sigle BWP e HVM.

Birds in Europe – their conservation status (Tucker & Heath, 1994) fornisce in assoluto il primo quadro generale sulle popolazioni europee di tutte le specie nidificanti, il loro stato di conservazione e le minacce relative, nonché descrive in dettaglio la situazione delle specie a status conservazionistico sfavorevole. Oltre a tali specie, l'Atlante comprende anche le specie che al momento non sono minacciate. I grafici relativi ai livelli di popolazione presentati nell'Atlante derivano dal medesimo archivio-dati (l' *European Bird Database)* utilizzato per *Birds in Europe*, e pertanto quest'opera è spesso citata nelle trattazioni delle singole specie.

I riferimenti bibliografici riportati nell'Atlante compaiono alla fine del libro, subito prima degli indici.

Michael Blair, Ward Hagemeijer
Lorenzo Fornasari & Toni Mingozzi

ABBREVIAZIONI E GLOSSARIO

Punti cardinali

N	= nord
S	= sud
E	= est
W	= ovest, per cui NW = nord-ovest, WSW = ovest-sud-ovest ecc.
C	= centrale, per cui S-C = centro-meridionale ecc.

Espressioni generali

asl	= altezza metri sul livello del mare (above sea level)
c	= circa
et al	= e altri (nelle citazioni)
pers comm	= comunicazione personale
pers obs	= osservazioni personali

Dimensioni e quantità misurabili

bp	= coppie nidificanti (breeding pairs)
ha	= ettari
ind	= individui
m	= metri
km	= chilometri
km^2	= chilometri quadrati
M	= milioni

Acronimi

BTO	= British Trust for Ornithology (GB)
BWP	= Birds of the Western Palearctic
HVM	= Handbuch der Vögel Mitteleuropas
JNCC	= Joint Nature Conservation Committee (GB)
RSPB	= Royal Society for the Protection of Birds (GB)
SOVON	= SOVON Bird Census Work The Netherlands (NL)
WWT	= Wildfowl and Wetland Trust (GB)

Glossario

eutrophic (eutrofico):	ricco di nutrienti minerali originatisi da decomposizione di animali o vegetali.
lentic (lentico):	di corpi d'acqua ferma, come laghi o stagni.
lotic (lotico):	di corpi d'acqua in movimento, come torrenti o fiumi.
mixotrophic (mixotrofico):	termine coniato per i laghi delle regioni boreali, poco profondi e ricchi di vegetazione ma le cui sponde

sono relativamente povere di nutrienti.

oligotrophic (oligotrofico): povero di sali e nutrienti minerali.

phenology (fenologia): lo studio cronologico degli eventi ricorrenti.

sclerophytic (sclerofitico): di piante, solitamente spinose e con foglie di piccole dimensioni, con basso tasso di traspirazione, adattate ai climi secchi.

xerophytic (xerofitico): di piante adattate a condizioni di estrema aridità.

Inleiding

DOEL VAN *THE EBCC ATLAS OF EUROPEAN BREEDING BIRDS*

In veel vogelboeken worden met de nodige stelligheid verspreidingskaarten van soorten afgedrukt. Een deel van die kaarten is gebaseerd op onderzoek aan broedvogelpopulaties, maar veel van die kaarten – uitgezonderd een aantal specialistische atlassen – zijn gebaseerd op niet altijd even betrouwbare bronnen. Soms zijn ze slechts een bewerking van vroegere kaarten van twijfelachtige authenticiteit. Daarnaast zijn de kaarten meestal niet kwantitatief: er wordt niet op aangegeven waar een soort algemeen is en waar schaars.

Er is echter een toenemend aantal zeer goede regionale en nationale broedvogelatlassen beschikbaar. Vele ervan komen direct of indirect voort uit hetzelfde project dat aan deze *Atlas* ten grondslag ligt, en bevatten net als deze *Atlas* semi-kwantitatieve gegevens. In 1971 werd het European Ornithological Atlas Committee (EOAC) gevormd, met als doel het verspreidingsgebied in kaart te brengen van die Europese soorten waarvoor door middel van veldwerk gegevens verzameld konden worden. In dit boek worden de resultaten van die inspanning gepresenteerd.

De *Atlas* is een momentopname van de verspreiding van de vogelsoorten, maar de verzamelde gegevens vormen (ondanks hun kleine inconsistenties) een vertrekpunt waartegen al het werk in de toekomst (en ook de toekomstige veranderingen in de verspreiding van de soorten) afgezet kan worden. Het EOAC van 1971 had duidelijk een broedvogelonderzoek voor ogen dat het hele Europese continent zou beslaan, het eerste dat ooit zou zijn ondernomen. Hun ideaal is uitgekomen. In *The EBCC Atlas of European Breeding Birds* (De EBCC-Atlas van de Europese broedvogels) wordt de verspreiding in kaart gebracht van de broedvogels van Europa; de *Atlas* geeft antwoord op de vraag: 'welke vogel broedt waar?'

INDELING VAN DE *ATLAS*

In deze **Inleiding** wordt in het kort het doel van de *Atlas* beschreven; wordt aangegeven hoe de verspreidings- en populatiegegevens zijn verzameld; hoe deze gegevens daarna werden verwerkt met de computer en in kaarten weergegeven; en hoe de *Atlas* is opgezet. Deze kennis is nodig om te begrijpen hoe het boek in elkaar zit. De inleiding wordt in meerdere talen weergegeven zodat het boek voor de meeste ornithologen van Europa toegankelijk is.

Initial sections (Inleidende hoofdstukken)

In het **Foreword** (Voorwoord) geeft Professor Karel Voous in grote lijnen aan waarom de *Atlas* belangrijk is in de context van de veranderingen waaraan de vogelwereld van Europa onderhevig is. In de **Preface** (Inleiding) wordt kort samengevat hoe een samenwerkingsproject als de *Atlas* tegemoet komt aan de eisen van de Europese ornithologen; en worden het beleid en de doelstelling van de EBCC uiteengezet wat betreft toekomstig broedvogelonderzoek op Europese schaal. Daarna volgt de **Introduction** (Introductie), waarin ook methode en onderzoeksgebied worden besproken. In het hoofdstuk met **Explanatory Figures** (Verklarende Figuren) worden de volledigheid van het onderzoek, de kwaliteit van de verzamelde gegevens en het data-verzamelingsformulier toegelicht. In het hoofdstuk **History** (Geschiedenis) worden de voortgang en de tegenslagen beschreven waar het Europese Ornithologische Atlasproject mee te maken heeft gehad. Daarna beschrijft Professor Jacques Blondel onder de titel **Evolution and History of the European Bird Fauna** (Evolutie en Geschiedenis van de Europese Vogelwereld) hoe de huidige verspreiding van de Europese vogelsoorten tot stand is gekomen. Tenslotte volgen er een lijst met **Acknowledgements** (medewerkers) en een lijst met **National and Major Regional Bird Atlases of Europe** (Nationale en belangrijke Regionale Broedvogelatlassen van Europa).

Species section (Soortbeschrijvingen)

Een **Introduction to the Maps and Population Graphs** (Inleiding op de kaarten en populatiegrafieken) gaat vooraf aan het hoofddeel van de *Atlas*, waarin de broedvogelsoorten van Europa behandeld worden. In Part 1 (Deel 1) worden de soorten behandeld waar redelijk wat gegevens over zijn; dit deel bestaat uit de verspreidingskaarten, soortbeschrijvingen en vogelnamen in 14 talen voor elke broedvogelsoort met hun afbeelding. Bij de rangschikking van de soorten wordt ongeveer de Voous-volgorde (1977) en die van de Euringcode aangehouden. Part 2 (Deel 2) bestaat uit die soorten waarvan wordt aangenomen dat ze in Europa broeden, maar waarvan geen gegevens werden ontvangen.

Final sections (Afsluitende hoofdstukken)

In het hoofdstuk **Derived Maps** (Samenvattende Kaarten) wordt de rijkdom aan broedvogels in Europa beschreven en van de Soorten met een Europese Beschermings Status (Species of European Conservation Concern), zoals gedefinieerd door BirdLife International (Tucker & Heath 1994). De **Technische Appendix** bevat uitleg over hoe het kaartraster van de *Atlas* verschilt van de theoretische

Universal Transverse Mercator (UTM) projectie en hoe gehandeld werd met de 50-kmblokken waarin eilanden of kustgedeelten liggen. In deze appendix wordt ook uitgelegd hoe het Euring-nummersysteem werd gebruikt in de *Atlas*.

Boekjes in de taal van het land

Van de inleidende hoofdstukken (**Preface**, **History**, en **Evolution and History of the European Bird Fauna**) en de soortbeschrijvingen zijn samenvattingen ter beschikking gesteld voor de ornithologen van elk land; zij kunnen deze vertalen in de eigen taal en verspreiden onder hun collega's zodat ook degenen die het Engels niet machtig zijn, gebruik kunnen maken van het boek. De lijst met namen en adressen van de organisaties die een boekje in hun nationale taal verzorgen (voor zover bekend bij het ter perse gaan van deze uitgave) wordt gegeven aan het einde van de **Technische Appendix**.

METHODEN

De wijze waarop de gegevens in de *Atlas* worden gepresenteerd

In het hoofdstuk **History** worden de idee'n beschreven die er oorspronkelijk waren omtrent het verzamelen van gegevens en het samenvoegen ervan; tevens wordt beschreven hoe de methoden werden gekozen; ook het verhaal over hoe de onderzoeken op poten werden gezet, heeft daar een plaats gekregen.

In de *Atlas*-kaarten worden de verschillen in dichtheid (het aantal vogels per oppervlakte-eenheid) volgens een logaritmische schaal weergegeven (verklaard in de sectie **Qualitative versus semi-quantitative information**, hieronder). Deze schaal is vooral nuttig bij soorten die in hun verspreidingsgebied in zeer verschillende dichtheden voorkomen. Kleinere verschillen blijven op deze schaal echter verborgen.

In de *Atlas* wordt niet alleen van elke Europese broedvogelsoort de verspreiding weergegeven, maar voor de meeste soorten ook schattingen van de populatiegrootte, en de trends in de meeste landen van Europa. Alleen vanuit een evaluatie van deugdelijk onderzochte populaties op landelijke niveau en de trends daarin, kunnen verspreidingspatronen verklaard worden.

Onderzoeksgebied voor de *Atlas*, zoals oorspronkelijk bedoeld

In **Fig. 1** staat het gebied aangegeven zoals dat oorspronkelijk zou worden onderzocht. Het zou wenselijk geweest zijn om de grenzen aan te houden van het West-Palearctisch gebied zoals gedefinieerd in *The Birds of the Western Palearctic* (Cramp *et al* 1977-1994). Dit had echter niet veel zin omdat er weinig gegevens waren over Klein-Azië, Noord-Arabië en Noord-Afrika; deze gebieden werden daarom niet opgenomen. Voor de *Atlas* is daarom de kaart overgenomen zoals gebruikt voor de *Atlas Florae Europaeae* (Jalas & Suominen 1972, 1988) met als aanvullingen Nova Zembla, Franz Jozefland, alle Griekse eilanden voor de kust van Turkije, de eilandengroep van Madeira, de Azoren, het gebied van Stavropol in het zuidoosten van Rusland en de Kaukasische republieken. Verder verschilt het gebied dat door de *EBCC Atlas* wordt behandeld van het West-Palearctisch gebied, doordat de eilanden in de Middellandse Zee die behoren tot Noord-Afrikaanse landen, Cyprus en de Canarische Eilanden niet zijn opgenomen. De *Atlas* onderscheidt zich van de *Birds in Europe – their conservation status* (Tucker & Heath 1994) door Aziatisch Turkije en Groenland niet op te nemen.

Wat niet direct uit Fig 1 naar voren komt, maar het werkgebied onderscheidt van dat van *Birds in Europe*, is dat de grenzen van de *western palearctic*, de *Atlas Florae Europaeae* en deze *Atlas* een klein stukje Europa nabij Orenburg buiten beschouwing laten en een deel van Aziatisch Kazachstan tussen de rivieren Wolga en Oeral, alsmede een deel van Aziatisch Rusland ten oosten van Perm (Sverdlovsk regio) wel meenemen.

Het uiteindelijke onderzoeksgebied

In het hoofdstuk **Explanatory Figures** volgend op de **Introduction** worden in **Fig. 2** de onderzochte blokken aangegeven, en de maximumkwaliteit van de daar verzamelde gegevens. In **Fig. 3** wordt de minimumkwaliteit van de gegevens per blok weergegeven. In het deel-hoofdstuk **Qualitative versus semi-quantative information** (Kwalitatieve versus semi-kwantitatieve informatie) (zie beneden) wordt de betekenis van deze begrippen uitgelegd. De kwaliteit van de gegevens, die op de kaarten worden weergegeven, wordt onderverdeeld in de volgende categorie'n, in aflopende volgorde van kwaliteit:

1. Semi-kwantitatieve populatieschatting: broeden bevestigd of waarschijnlijk.
2. Semi-kwantitatieve populatieschatting: broeden mogelijk.
3. Kwalitatieve presentie: broeden bevestigd of waarschijnlijk.
4. Kwalitatieve presentie: broeden mogelijk.

De kwaliteit van de gegevens was meestal gelijk voor alle genoteerde soorten in een blok. Grote delen van Rusland werden in het geheel niet onderzocht, vooral omdat er geen contacten konden worden gelegd. In het grootste deel van de rest van Rusland, delen van Wit-Rusland, de Oekraine en de Kaukasische republieken kon slechts voor een beperkt aantal soorten gebiedsdekkend worden gewerkt. In het voormalige Joegoslavië was het onderzoek redelijk gebiedsdekkend (in sommige gebieden niet voor alle soorten). In Albanië zijn er hiaten. Op de Russische arctische eilanden Nova Zembla en Franz Jozefland was de dekking onvolledig.

Elders was de dekking, ondanks onvermijdelijke tekortkomingen, grotendeels volledig.

De kaarten in de *Atlas*

De keuze van de kaartprojectie moest voldoen aan drie criteria: de projectie moest het oorspronkelijk bedoelde onderzoeksgebied beslaan, moest bekend zijn bij de meeste Europese landen en moest aansluiten op de nationale kaartprojectie. Bij het van start gaan van het *Atlas*-project voldeed alleen de Universal Transverse Mercator-projectie (UTM) aan deze drie criteria. Omdat voor de basiskaart van het *Atlas Florae Europaeae*-project gebruik wordt gemaakt van het UTM-raster, kon deze uitstekend gebruikt worden als kaart voor de ornithologische *Atlas*. In de *Atlas Florae*

Europaeae werden blokken van 50 x 50 km gehanteerd als verslageenheid; voor de ornithologische *Atlas* werden dezelfde blokken gebruikt. Het verzamelen en analyseren van gegevens op een fijnere schaal zou niet haalbaar zijn geweest.

De basiskaarteenheid van het UTM-raster, het 100 x 100 km-blok, wordt aangeduid met een logisch-oplopende alfanumerieke code van twee cijfers en drie letters. Voor de flora- en voor de vogelatlas werd elk blok onderverdeeld in vier blokken van 50 x 50 km, die als volgt werden genummerd:

1 3
2 4

Hierdoor kreeg elk 50-kmblok een unieke referentie van 6 cijfers/letters.

De lay-out van het UTM-raster langs de noord-zuidas is eenvoudig: de rasterlijnen liggen 50 km van elkaar, parallel aan de breedtegraden met als beginpunt de evenaar. De andere as is wat moeilijker te behandelen omdat de meridianen samenkomen bij de polen. Als gevolg daarvan kunnen er in de richting van de pool steeds minder van 50 × 50-kmblokken ingepast worden. De rangschikking van de cellen in het UTM-raster wordt daarom aangepast. Het cellenpatroon is gebaseerd op sectoren van 6°, beginnend bij 0°. Cellen grenzend aan elke 6°-meridiaan worden kleiner naarmate ze de polen dichter naderen totdat ze een punt vormen en verdwijnen, waarna de nieuwe grensblokken kleiner beginnen te worden. Voor de *Atlas Florae Europaeae* en deze vogelatlas is dit systeem zo gewijzigd dat de variatie in grootte van de blokken grenzend aan de 6°-meridianen geringer is: wanneer de grensblokken kleiner dan ongeveer 40 km worden, vallen ze weg. (In de *Atlas* worden de cellen voor het gemak 'blokken' genoemd, alhoewel ze niet precies vierkant zijn). Dit patroon wordt duidelijk op de kaart waarop het oorspronkelijke onderzoeksgebied staat weergegeven (**Fig. 1**); in de **Technische appendix** worden alle bijzonderheden vermeld.

Het EOAC leverde het kaartmateriaal met een 50 × 50-kmraster aan de organisatoren van het onderzoek in de verschillende landen om ervoor te zorgen dat zij het correcte raster gebruikten bij de verslaglegging van de gegevens. Het veldwerk was meestal gebaseerd op een UTM-raster dat fijner was dan 50 × 50 km, of er werd gebruik gemaakt van een ander raster dan het UTM-raster; in beide gevallen moesten de organisatoren in elk land zorgen voor de omzetting van de gegevens in een zodanige vorm dat deze verder verwerkt konden worden.

Veldwerkperiode en validering van de gegevens

Het was de bedoeling dat het veldwerk voor de *Atlas* zou plaats vinden in de jaren 1985–1988. De verschillende landen organiseerden echter hun eigen veldwerk; vanwege praktische problemen konden niet alle landen het werk klaar krijgen binnen die tijdgrenzen. Waar tijdens de onderzoeksperiode de dekking incompleet was, werden gegevens uit een eerdere of latere periode bekeken om te zien of de dekkingsgraad of de kwaliteit van de gegevens kon worden verbeterd wanneer die gegevens werden opgenomen. In **Tabel 3**, volgend op de **Inleiding**, worden de deelnemende landen opgesomd; de periode waarin de landen hun gegevens verzamelden; de nationale rasters vanwaaruit de gegevens werden omgezet; en de onderzoeksmethoden.

Het verzamelen van de gegevens – gegevens voor de soortverspreidingen

Honderdduizenden uren veldwerk, misschien wel meer dan een miljoen, vormen de basis van de *Atlas*. In het ideale geval zouden alle deelnemers dezelfde veldmethodiek over dezelfde periode gebruikt hebben, maar dat was onmogelijk. Het EOAC gaf daarom niet zozeer strakke regels alswel brede richtlijnen. In sommige landen werd het werk voor deze *Atlas* en dat voor de nationale atlas gecombineerd; in andere werden de gegevens van een onafhankelijk atlasproject gebruikt om de gegevens te leveren voor deze *Atlas*. Veldmethodes varieerden van het maken van lijsten van eenmalige bezoeken, via cumulatieve *checklists* van meerdere bezoeken, tot systematische onderzoeken gebaseerd op punt- of lijntransecten of territoriumkarteringen in plots.

In **Fig. 4**, volgend op de **Inleiding**, wordt een gedeelte van het gestandaardiseerde formulier weergegeven dat door het Nederlandse 'Centraal Bureau voor de Statistiek' werd gemaakt. Voor elk onderzocht blok werd een formulier ingevuld. Voor blokken die aan weerszijden van een landsgrens lagen, verzamelde elk land de gegevens voor het deel in het eigen land.

Voor elk blok werd de volgende algemene informatie opgevraagd:

1. Onderzoeksperiode: het jaar, of de opeenvolging van jaren, waarin de gegevens verzameld zijn.
2. De identiteit van het blok (UTM50-code).
3. Onderzoeksintensiteit: hoog (meer dan 75% van de voor dat blok te verwachten soorten zijn vastgesteld) of laag (minder dan 75%).
4. Hoogteligging van het blok, aangegeven in het hoogste en het laagste punt in dat blok.
5. Waarnemers of coördinator(en): hier werden namen en adressen opgegeven voor het geval er navraag moest worden gedaan.
6. Opmerkingen: hier kon aanvullende informatie worden gegeven om de gegevens op het formulier toe te lichten.
7. Een korte vragenlijst over de soorten habitat in het blok.

Het voornaamste deel van het formulier was een soortenlijst (ongeveer 400 soorten, volgens Voous (1977), genummerd volgens de Euringcode) waarin de gegevens moesten worden genoteerd.

In kolom 0 stond een verkorte wetenschappelijke naam (*bijv*. Gav stell), in Kolom 1 de Euring-code (*bijv* 00020); in Kolom 2 moest het eventuele broeden worden vermeld en de broedcode. Er waren 16 codes mogelijk, onderverdeeld in drie categorieën: zeker broedend, waarschijnlijk broedend en mogelijk broedend. Deze codes staan in **Tabel 1**. In kolom 3 tenslotte moest een schatting van het aantal broedparen in dat blok worden gegeven, volgens een logaritmische schaal (1 = 1-9, 2 = 10-99, ... 6 ≥ 100.000).

Aan het eind van de soortenlijst op het formulier konden apart hybriden en niet in de lijst opgenomen soorten worden genoteerd.

Tabel 1 Broedcategorie'n en hun codes

A: Mogelijk broedend
1. Soort waargenomen, in het broedseizoen, in het broedbiotoop.
2. Eenmalige waarneming van zingende of baltsende vogel in het broedseizoen.

B: Waarschijnlijk broedend
3. Waarneming van een paar in geschikt broedbiotoop in het broedseizoen.
4. Territoriumgedrag (zang, gevechten) op ten minste twee dagen, die meer dan een week uit elkaar liggen, op dezelfde plaats vastgesteld.
5. Baltsend paar (ook paring) in het territorium.
6. Bezoek van vogel aan een waarschijnlijke nestplaats
7. Angstkreten of ander gedrag (alarmeren), dat wijst op de aanwezigheid van een nest of jongen.
8. Vogel met broedvlekken.
9. Transport van nestmateriaal, nestbouw of uithakken van nestholte.

C: Zeker broedend
10. Afleidingsgedrag.
11. Pas gebruikt nest of verse eierschalen gevonden.
12. Pas uitgevlogen jongen van nestblijvers of donsjongen van nestvlieders.
13. Bezoek door ouders aan een nest, waarvan de inhoud niet vastgesteld kan worden, of waarneming van broedende vogel.
14. Transport van ontlastingspakketje of voedsel voor jongen.
15. Nest met eieren.
16. Nest met jongen gezien, of de jongen in het nest gehoord.

De broedvogelgegevens waren afkomstig uit de volgende bronnen:

1. De EBCC-coördinatoren op nationaal niveau; zij organiseerden het verzamelen van de gegevens en voegden de gegevens samen op een verzamelformulier.
2. Regionale coördinatoren. Soms werd het verzamelen van de gegevens georganiseerd door anderen dan de nationale coördinator, vooral wanneer het een groot land betrof, of wanneer het contact met een bestaand netwerk beter aan een van de actieve leden van dat netwerk kon worden gedelegeerd. De regionale coördinator ging op dezelfde manier te werk als de nationale coördinator.
3. Andere bronnen in het betreffende land. Meestal ging het om literatuur, die gewoonlijk via een soortexpert ter beschikking kwam. In de gevallen waar er geen onderzoeksgegevens beschikbaar waren – vooral voor afgelegen gebieden – vormden gepubliceerde en niet-gepubliceerde verslagen vaak de enige gegevensbron; deze verslagen waren vaak niet direct toegankelijk voor de redacteuren of de nationale coördinatoren.
4. De schrijver van de soorttekst. Heel vaak wist de schrijver van een soorttekst, door zijn/haar onderzoek naar de soort, andere bronnen van informatie aan te boren over de verspreiding en aantallen van een soort.

Al deze gegevens werden binnen de gegevenshiërarchie behandeld: elke toevoeging aan de database moest op het niveau van de nationale coördinator worden goedgekeurd.

Kwalitatieve versus semi-kwantitatieve informatie

In de *Atlas* wordt semi-kwantitatieve informatie gebruikt (schatting van populatiegroottes volgens een logaritmische schaal), die door de regionale en nationale coördinatoren en de veldwerkers per blok was berekend volgens de voorgeschreven schaal. De gebruikte stippen geven de aantallen broedparen weer, niet de broeddichtheid; hoe groter de stip hoe hoger de orde van grootte (zie de uitleg of pagina cxl). Het is jammer dat sommige landen weigerden om semi-kwantitatieve gegevens te leveren: Noorwegen en Polen geheel, Spanje voor het grootste deel, Frankrijk, IJsland en Italië gedeeltelijk. Het project verloor het contact met Bosnië en Servië en de gegevens uit die landen konden niet worden opgewaardeerd. Een aantal regio's in Frankrijk zorgden zelf voor de opwaardering van de gegevens. De nationale coördinator van Frankrijk zorgde voor opwaardering van de gegevens van een beperkt aantal soorten voor het hele land. Zelfs schattingen volgens een logaritmische schaal over een aantal blokken geven veel meer informatie dan alleen informatie over aan- of afwezigheid van een soort.

In het geval van grensblokken, waar elk land de populatieschatting opgaf voor het eigen deel, werd de hoogste waarde genomen (logaritmische waarden mogen niet bij elkaar worden opgeteld), alhoewel dat in sommige gevallen zou leiden tot een onderschatting. Een dergelijke benadering was bruikbaarder dan het degraderen van deze blokken tot kwalitatieve status.

De stippen in de kaarten verwijzen naar de volgende categorieën van informatie:

donker paars	= bevestigd- of waarschijnlijk broedend, kwalitatief
licht paars	= mogelijk broedend, kwalitatief
rood	= bevestigd- of waarschijnlijk broedend, semi-kwantitatief
oranje	= mogelijk broedend, semi-kwantitatief
grijs	= soort niet onderzocht in dit blok
geen stip	= blok onderzocht en soort niet broedend aangetroffen

Computerverwerking – correctie van op kaart gezette gegevens en validering van de input

De formulieren die door de nationale coördinatoren werden ingestuurd, werden nagekeken op primaire fouten (weggelaten codes, niet-bestaande codes), voordat ze met de computer werden verwerkt tot een ASCII-bestand; elk record kreeg een codering verwijzend naar het betreffende land. Sommige landen leverden hun gegevens aan op diskette; deze gegevens werden op dezelfde manier nagekeken. De uit deze basisbestanden gevormde database bevat één waarde per soort per blok.

De nationale coördinatoren en andere dataleveranciers die hun gegevens direct hadden ingeleverd, kregen snel daarop voorlopige kaarten en lijsten per soort toegestuurd als eerste fase in het correctieproces. Hen werd verzocht deze te controleren op fouten. Dit leverde veel correcties op. Een aantal landen stuurde hun gegevens echter laat in; andere moesten hun gegevens opwaarderen van kwalitatief naar semi-kwantitatief. Daardoor begon in de deelnemende landen het corrigeren van de gegevens en het valideren ervan op verschillende tijdstippen en verliep het in een verschillend tempo.

Het maken van voorlopige kaarten was om twee redenen van doorslaggevend belang:

1. De nationale coördinatoren, en via hen veel dataverzamelaars, konden zien of de gegevens die ze hadden ingestuurd, correct waren ingevoerd: op de kaarten was na te gaan of de soortgegevens in de juiste blokken waren terechtgekomen. Op de kaarten waren fouten gemakkelijker op te sporen dan in de lijsten met gegevens.
2. Ze stimuleerden tot een grotere deelname; hieruit kwam vaak weer extra informatie voort.

Tijdens de tweede fase werd gecontroleerd of de correcties die uit de eerste fase waren voortgekomen, juist waren ingevoerd. De nationale coördinatoren en andere dataleveranciers kregen daarvoor een set gecorrigeerde kaarten en lijsten met gegevens toegestuurd. De meeste coördinatoren voltooiden deze enorme klus en zonden de laatste correcties in, maar in landen zoals het vroegere Joegoslavië was opwaarderen en validering vaak onmogelijk. In de landen waar de gegevenscontrole was vertraagd, moest de rest van de correctie in een kortere tijd worden afgerond; hoe groter de achterstand, des te groter de problemen bij het uiteindelijk afleveren van de kaarten.

In een later stadium kwamen er opgewaardeerde gegevens van een aantal schrijvers van een soorttekst, en van andere soortexperts. De nationale coördinatoren hebben daarvan het grootste deel nagekeken, waarna ze beslisten welk cijfer uiteindelijk gebruikt zou worden. Wanneer dit vanwege tijdgebrek niet mogelijk was, werd ofwel het oorspronkelijke cijfer gehandhaafd ofwel in de tekst vermeld dat de mening van de schrijver deels afwijkt van de weergave in de kaart.

Wanneer er geen gegevens uit veldwerk beschikbaar waren, wat vooral het geval was in Noord-Rusland en Albanië, beoordeelden (lokale) veldornithologen of gegevens uit andere bronnen aanvaardbaar waren; Voor dergelijke blokken werden semi-kwantitatieve schattingen gemaakt door te extrapoleren vanuit blokken in hetzelfde gebied waarvoor wel directe schattingen waren. Hierbij werd rekening gehouden met geschikt habitat in het betreffende blok.

De uiterste inleverdatum voor nieuwe gegevens en correcties was 1 juli 1995, maar om de dekkingsgraad te verbeteren, werden ook nog gegevens gebruikt die in de maanden daarna vanuit Albanië, Europees Turkije, de Kaukasus, delen van de Oekraine en delen van Rusland beschikbaar kwamen. Correcties die afkomstig waren van de schrijvers van een soorttekst, werden geaccepteerd tot 1 november 1995.

Het verzamelen van de gegevens – gegevens over populatiegrootte

De populatiegrafieken die in de *Atlas* per land worden gegeven, zijn gemaakt op basis van gegevens uit de European Bird Database. Hierin zijn de gegevens opgeslagen die gezamenlijk door de EBCC en BirdLife International zijn verzameld. De database werd gevormd om deze *Atlas* en het 'Dispersed Species Project' van BirdLife International te ondersteunen. De resultaten van het laatstgenoemde project zijn gepubliceerd in *Birds in Europe – their conservation status* (Tucker & Heath 1994). Dit samenwerkingsproject heeft ook gezorgd voor een grotere deelname in bepaalde delen van Europa. De gegevens werden vooral verzameld door het rondsturen van vragenlijsten aan nationale coördinatoren, organisaties met monitoringprojecten en regionale medewerkers. BirdLife International heeft de European Bird Database onder beheer.

Elk land leverde de volgende gegevens over de broedpopulaties van alle vogelsoorten:

1. Populatiegrootte.
2. Trend in populatiegrootte (over de periode 1970-1990).
3. Trend in verspreiding (over de periode 1970-1990).

Dergelijke gegevens werden ook verzameld voor winterpopulaties, maar deze worden hier niet gepresenteerd.

De referentiebronnen die werden gebruikt om de populatiegroottes en de trends daarin vast te stellen, werden genoteerd. Er werd een lijst met codes opgesteld (Zie **Tabel 2** volgend op deze **Inleiding**), om de nauwkeurigheid en betrouwbaarheid aan te geven van de gegevens voor de populatiegrootte en de trend.

Sommige auteurs waren het niet eens met de populatieschattingen in de database maar deze informatie kwam te laat binnen om bij te dragen aan de database. In deze gevallen, hebben de auteurs hun schattingen in de tekst vermeld. De grafieken bij de soortteksten tonen echter altijd de database getallen.

Beperkingen aan de gegevens

Door het *Atlas*-project is een hoogwaardig gegevensbestand ontstaan, maar onvermijdelijk zitten er beperkingen aan. Diegenen die deze gegevens voor verder onderzoek willen gebruiken, moeten hiermee rekening houden. In het kader van dit boek kan daar echter niet in detail op worden ingegaan. Enkele van de belangrijkste beperkingen aan het gebruik van dit boek zijn:

1. Er werd geen veldwerkmethode voorgeschreven voor het vaststellen van aan- of afwezigheid, noch voor het vaststellen van de populatiegrootte. Veel nationale projecten – de dataleveranciers voor de EBCC – hadden hun eigen veldwerkmethoden ontwikkeld, voor hun eigen doeleinden en naar de aanwezige middelen.
2. Er was geen algemeen geldende methode voor het

Table 2 Populatiecodes in de European Bird Database

POPMIN	= minimumgrootte populatie (in bp)		
POPMAX	= maximumgrootte populatie (in bp)		
MEAN	= geometrisch gemiddelde van popmin en popmax (in bp)	**PSV**	=valideringscode populatiegrootte
YRC	= jaar voor welke de schatting van populatiegrootte geldt		
PST	= trend in populatiegrootte	**PTV**	=valideringscode trend in populatiegrootte
RST	= trend in grootte areaal	**RTV**	= valderingscode in trend grootte areaal

Codes gebruikt om Trends in Populatie en Areaal aan te geven

De trends in populatie- en areaalgrootte gelden voor de periode 1970-1990.

+2	= grote toename, ≥50%
+1	= kleine toename, ≥20%, maar <50%
0	= stabiel, geen verandering of verandering <20%
-1	= kleine afname, ≥20%, maar <50%
-2	= grote afname, ≥50%
n	= nieuwe broedvogel binnen periode
x	= uitgestorven binnen periode
f	= fluctuerend, veranderingen ≥20%, maar geen duidelijke trend

verzamelen van de veldwerkgegevens op de verzamelformulieren, grotendeels vanwege de boven al genoemde redenen. De convertering van de gegevens werd aan het land overgelaten.
3. Verschillen in kwaliteit van veldwerk en in het aantal medewerkers leiden tot gegevens van wisselende kwaliteit.
4. Bij sommige soorten is een deel van gegevens gebaseerd op extrapolatie.
5. Een deel van de gegevens is afkomstig uit literatuur (vooral in het geval van arctische gebieden).

LAY-OUT VAN DE KAARTEN EN DE SOORTTEKSTEN IN DE *ATLAS*

In de *Atlas* zijn de soorten in twee groepen ingedeeld: de soorten waarover we voldoende gegevens verkregen hebben en de soorten waarvoor dat niet het geval was. De soorten van de eerste groep hebben alle een volledige tekst in Deel 1 van de soortteksten; de soorten van de tweede groep hebben een kortere tekst in Deel 2. Beide delen zijn gerangschikt volgens Voous en ongeveer in de Euring-volgorde; in Deel 1 zijn echter enkele kleine veranderingen aangebracht om ervoor te zorgen dat elke soort waarvan tekst en kaart samen één pagina beslaan, altijd tegenover een soort staat met eenzelfde indeling. Soorten waarvan de kaarten en de tekst twee pagina's beslaan, staan altijd op twee tegenover elkaar liggende pagina's. Sommige soorten met een zeer beperkte verspreiding hebben geen volledige layout nodig, waardoor er meer dan één soort per pagina geplaatst kan worden. Elke soort is afgebeeld, en voorzien van de naam in de landstaal (indien voorhanden) in 14 talen. Bij de meeste soorten met een kaart staat een populatiegrafiek; deze wordt verklaard op de pagina's, die voorafgaan aan de soortkaarten en -teksten.

Verzamelkaarten

Fig. 5 geeft de soortenrijkdom per blok weer; in **Fig. 6** tot **8** wordt getoond wat de soortenrijkdom is per blok wat betreft de SPEC-categorieën 1, 2 en 3 (Species of European Conservation Concern (SPEC) (Tucker & Heath 1994)), zoals gedefinieerd door BirdLife International. In **Fig. 9** worden de gegevens van die drie categorieën gecombineerd.

DE SOORTTEKSTEN

Vooraf werd bepaald welke vaste onderwerpen (waar toepasselijk) in de soortteksten moesten worden behandeld, meestal in deze volgorde: wereldverspreiding; soorten broedhabitat in Europa; verspreidingspatroon en talrijkheid in Europa; recente veranderingen in verspreiding en populatie (en de mogelijke oorzaken daarvan); regionale verschillen in talrijkheid; mogelijke factoren die de verspreiding beperken; broeddichtheid in optimaal habitat; migratie- en verplaatsingskenmerken van de soort binnen en buiten Europa; speciale kenmerken van de soort; en beknopte informatie over ondersoorten wat betreft verspreiding, verspreidingsgebied, overlap en trends.

Behalve wanneer een korte verwijzing absoluut noodzakelijk is om een van de vaste onderwerpen toe te lichten, worden de volgende onderwerpen weggelaten: broedbiologie; gedrag; voedsel; relaties met andere soorten; fysiologie en morfologische kenmerken; gedetailleerde bespreking van de bedreigingen voor een soort (dat is het terrein van de *Birds in Europe*); afwijkingen; oölogie; evolutie en taxonomie (behalve wanneer er zich recentelijk belangrijke veranderingen hebben voorgedaan, of wanneer de ondersoorten aanmerkelijk verschillen); mortaliteit en andere parameters van populatiedynamiek; en geluid en zang.

Soorten – criteria voor opname

Opgenomen zijn die soorten die in de periode vanaf 1985 broedden in het oorspronkelijke onderzoeksgebied, volgens de criteria vermeld in **Tabel 1**. In het wild geïntroduceerde soorten werden opgenomen wanneer minimaal één populatie minimaal vijf jaar zonder menselijke tussenkomst heeft kunnen overleven. De aanvaarding of de interpretatie van die regels varieerde echter enorm in Europa; selectie of weglating van een aantal soorten met in het wild geïntroduceerde populaties lijkt op het oog wat arbitrair.

In de *Atlas* worden 513 soorten behandeld, plus *Passer* x *italiae*.

NOMENCLATUUR EN TAXONOMIE

Taxonomie

De EBCC heeft in taxonomische kwesties een voorzichtig

en conservatief standpunt ingenomen. Deze *Atlas* volgt over het algemeen de taxonomie, de volgorde en de Engelse nomenclatuur die in *Birds of the Western Palearctic* (*BWP*) worden gebruikt, zoals aangepast voor de Concise Edition.

Puffinus yelkouan, P. mauretanicus, Larus cachinnans, Anthus petrosus, Phylloscopus lorentzii en *Pyrrhula murina* worden behandeld als aparte soorten en worden in kaart gebracht apart van *Puffinus puffinus, Larus argentatus, Anthus spinoletta, Phylloscopus collybita* en *Pyrrhula pyrrhula*. Apart in kaart brengen was mogelijk ofwel omdat deze soorten apart waren genoteerd ofwel omdat ze geografisch gescheiden zijn. De tekst voor de drie *Puffinus* soorten is geïntegreerd. Aanvankelijk werd geprobeerd ondersoorten en vormen van verschillende soorten apart te vermelden, maar het onderscheid dat door EOAC was gemaakt, werd niet in heel Europa uniform gevolgd; het maken van kaarten was daardoor onmogelijk. De 'Italiaanse Mus' werd apart vermeld en de *Atlas* volgt de *BWP* door de soort te beschouwen als een stabiele hybride tussen *Passer domesticus* en *P. hispaniolensis*: *Passer* × *italiae*. Aan de andere kant omvat *Phylloscopus trochiloides* twee geografisch gescheiden ondersoorten, *viridanus* en *nitidus*, die eerder als aparte soorten werden beschouwd. Toen het werk aan de *Atlas* op zijn eind liep, was bijna besloten tot de afsplitsing van *Lanius meridionalis* van *L. excubitor*; in een diagram in de soorttekst wordt de grens tussen de vormen aangegeven. *Hippolais caligata* en *H. rama* worden soms als aparte soorten beschouwd, maar hier wordt de laatste gezien als een ondersoort. De relaties binnen de meeuwcomplexen zijn vaak onduidelijk; *Larus armenicus* wordt hier als een aparte soort beschouwd.

Euring-code

De European Union for Bird Ringing (EURING) heeft een groeiende lijst van referentienummers van vijf cijfers voor soorten en ondersoorten, vooral gebruikt bij het ringen. In deze lijst wordt grotendeels de Voous-volgorde gebruikt, waar toepasbaar; deze lijst werd daarom overgenomen als een bruikbare methode om gegevens te verzamelen. De Euring-code wordt in de soorttekst vermeld. In de **Technische Appendix** worden details gegeven over hoe de Euring-code werd gebruikt.

HET GEBRUIK VAN VERWIJZINGEN EN ANDERE PUBLICATIES

Aan de schrijvers werd gevraagd verwijzingen naar handboeken te vermijden, omdat de ruimte voor citaten over het algemeen beperkt was. Twee belangrijke Europese handboeken van dit moment verdienen bijzondere vermelding. Voor een goed begrip van alle Europese broedvogelsoorten moeten de tekst en kaarten in deze *Atlas* bestudeerd worden in samenhang met de overeenkomstige teksten in de volgende, uitstekende referentiehandboeken: *Birds of the Western Palearctic* (Cramp *et al* 1977-1994), en *Handbuch der Vögel Mitteleuropas* (Glutz von Blotzheim *et al* 1966-1993). In de soortteksten in de *Atlas* worden de afkortingen *BWP* en *HVM* gebruikt voor deze boeken.

In *Birds in Europe – their conservation status* (Tucker & Heath 1994) wordt voor het eerst een overzicht gegeven van de broedpopulaties van de Europese vogels, de bedreigingen waar ze aan bloot staan en hun beschermde status; in het boek worden in detail de soorten beschreven die een ongunstige beschermde status hebben. In de *Atlas* worden niet alleen die soorten behandeld, maar ook de soorten die op dit moment nog niet bedreigd zijn. De populatiegrafieken in de *Atlas* zijn gemaakt op basis van de European Bird Database die ook voor de *Birds in Europe* is gebruikt; in de soortteksten wordt dit boek dus regelmatig geciteerd.

De verwijzingen in de *Atlas* staan aan het eind van het boek, net voor de indexen.

Michael Blair, Ward Hagemeijer
Peter Brouwer (vertaling)

GEBRUIKTE AFKORTINGEN EN EEN VERKLARENDE WOORDENLIJST

Windrichtingen

N = noord
S = zuid
E = oost
W = west; vandaar NW = noordwest en WSW = west-zuidwest, etc.
C = centraal, midden; vandaar S-C = zuid-centraal, zuid-midden etc.

Algemene uitdrukkingen

asl = boven zeeniveau (hoogte)
c = ongeveer, ±
et al = en anderen (in citaten)
pers comm = persoonlijke mededeling(en)
pers obs = eigen waarneming(en)
unpubl = niet-gepubliceerd werk

Afmetingen en meetbare eenheden

bp = broedparen
ha = hectare
ind = individuen
m = meter
km = kilometer
km^2 = vierkante kilometer
M = miljoen

Afkortingen

BTO = British Trust for Ornithology (GB)
BWP = Birds of the Western Palearctic ('de Cramp')
HVM = Handbuch der Vögel Mitteleuropas ('de Glutz')
JNCC = Joint Nature Conservation Committee (GB)
RSPB = Royal Society for the Protection of Birds (GB)
SOVON = SOVON Vogelonderzoek Nederland (NL)
WWT = Wildfowl and Wetlands Trust (GB)

Verklaring van termen

eutrophic — rijk aan minerale voedingsstoffen van dierlijke of plantaardige oorsprong
lentic — stilstaand water betreffende, zoals in vijvers en meren
lotic — stromend water betreffende
mesotrophic — rijk noch arm in basiszouten of -voedingsstoffen

'mixotrophic' — een term ontwikkeld voor meren in de boreale zone die ondiep en dichtbegroeid zijn, maar waarvan de oevers relatief voedselarm zijn

oligotrophic — arm aan basiszouten en -voedingsstoffen

phenology — het onderzoek naar de momenten waarop steeds terugkerende gebeurtenissen plaatsvinden

sclerophytic — planten met dikke, meestal kleine bladeren betreffende; deze verdampen weinig vocht en zijn aangepast aan een droog klimaat

xerophytic — planten betreffende die aangepast zijn aan een zeer droog klimaat

Introdução

OBJECTIVO DO *ATLAS DO EBCC DA AVES NIDIFICANTES NA EUROPA*

Muitos livros de aves mostram mapas de distribuição de espécies bem delimitados. Alguns destes mapas baseiam-se em levantamentso das populações de aves nidificantes mas, com excepção de alguns atlas especializados, muitos daqueles mapas resultam de um conjunto de fontes de fiabilidade variável e, por vezes, eles são apenas actualizações de mapas anteriores, de autenticidade duvidosa. Para além disso, aqueles mapas não são normalmente quantitativos; não mostram onde a espécie é comum ou onde ela é pouco abundante.

No entanto, há hoje um número crescente de excelentes atlas regionais e nacionais, de aves nidificantes, muitos dos quais têm a sua génese ou buscaram inspiração no projecto que deu origem a este *Atlas* e, tal como este, fornecem informação de natureza semi-quantitativa. Em 1971 foi criado o Comité Europeu para o Atlas Ornitológico (EOAC) com o objectivo de mapear a distribuição das espécies nidificantes na Europa, para as quais fosse possível obter informação através de trabalho no terreno. Este livro apresenta os resultados obtidos na persecução daquele objectivo.

O *Atlas* apresenta as distribuições das aves relativas a um período limitado de tempo, mas a informação recolhida (apesar de algumas inconsistências menores) constitui-se como um conhecimento de base em referência ao qual o trabalho futuro (e certamente também as futuras alterações de distribuição das aves) será medido. Em 1971 o EOAC teve a visão clara do primeiro Atlas Continental de Aves Nidificantes alguma vez tentado. O *Atlas do EBCC das Aves Nidificantes na Europa* mapeia a distribuição das aves que nidificam na Europa, respondendo à questão: que ave nidifica e onde?

ESTRUTURA DO *ATLAS*

Esta **Introdução** descreve com brevidade o objectivo do *Atlas*, detalhando os métodos de recolha de dados relativos à distribuição e população, bem como o seu tratamento informático e gráfico, explicando ainda a estrutura do *Atlas*, sendo vital para a compreensão do livro em todos os seus aspectos. Esta introdução foi impressa numa variedade de línguas por forma a poder ser lida pela maioria dos ornitólogos europeus.

Secções iniciais

Na **Nota de Abertura** o Professor Karel Voous realça a importância do *Atlas* no contexto das alterações que ocorrem na avifauna europeia. O **Prefácio** sumariza a forma como o projecto atlas cooperativo serve os requisitos dos ornitólogos europeus e realça as políticas e objectivos do EBCC (European Bird Census Council) para futuros sistemas de monitorização de aves. Segue depois a **Introdução** que inclui dados sobre os métodos e a área de cobertura. A secção **Figuras Explicativas**, que surge a seguir a esta **Introdução**, mostra a cobertura, a qualidade dos dados e uma cópia da ficha normalizada de recolha de dados. A secção **História** descreve os avanços e atrasos enfrentados pelo projecto Atlas Ornitológico Europeu. Em seguida, sob o título **Evolução e História da Avifauna Europeia**, temos um ensaio pelo Professor Jacques Blondel para ilustrar como a distribuição das espécies de aves europeias se tornou no que é hoje. Finalmente há ainda uma lista de **Agradecimentos** e de **Atlas Nacionais ou Regionais de relevo, publicados na Europa**.

Secção de Espécies

Uma **Introdução aos mapas e gráficos de população** antecede o corpo do *Atlas* o qual trata das espécies nidificantes na Europa. A parte 1 do *Atlas* consiste nos mapas de distribuição, texto específico, nomes comuns para cada espécie, em 14 línguas, e ilustrações. As espécies seguem aproximadamente a sequência proposta por Voous (1977) e pela Euring. A parte 2 compreende as espécies que se acredita nidificarem na Europa, mas para as quais não foi recebida informação.

Secções Finais

A secção de **Mapas Derivados** apresenta em detalhe a riqueza específica para as aves que nidficam na Europa e das Espécies Europeias para as quais há Preocupações de Conservação (SPEC), de acordo com a definição do BirdLife International (Tucker & Heath 1994). O **Apêndice Técnico** contém as explicações sobre as diferenças entre a grelha usada no *Atlas* e a grelha teórica do Sitema Universal Transverso de Mercator (UTM), explicando também a forma como os quadrados de 50 × 50Km foram adaptados nos casos das ilhas e das zonas costeiras. Este apêndice explica ainda o modo com o *Atlas* utilizou o código numérico da Euring.

Fascículos em línguas nacionais

Foram disponibilizados sumários, das secções iniciais (**Prefácio, História** e **Evolução e História da Avifauna Europeia**) e dos textos específicos, por forma a que os ornitólogos de qualquer país os possam traduzir para a sua língua e assim dessiminá-los pelos seus colegas, alargando o seu uso àqueles que não lêem Inglês. A lista com os nomes e endereços daqueles que disponibilizarão fascículos em línguas nacionais, conhecidos à altura da impressão, é apresentada no fim do **Apêndice Técnico**.

MÉTODOS

A apresentação dos dados do *Atlas*

Na Secção de **História** descrevem-se as ideias originais relativas à forma como os métodos de recolha e compilação de dados foram escolhidos bem como a forma como os levantamentos foram efectivamente levados a cabo.

Os mapas do *Atlas* mostram diferenças na densidade (nº de aves por unidade de área) numa escala logarítmica (como explicado mais à frente na sub-secção **Informação qualitativa versus informação semi-quantitativa**,). Esta escala é especialmente apropriada para as espécies cujas densidades variam significativamente ao longo da sua área de distribuição. Contudo, as pequenas variações permanecem escondidas com a sua utilização.

O *Atlas* não apresenta apenas a distribuição das espécies mas fornece também estimativas da população nidificante e tendências nacionais para a maioria das espécies em cada país. Apenas com uma avaliação da dimensão das populações e das tendências nacionais, estimadas com base em informação fidedigna, se podem compreender as variações nos padrões de distribuição.

Área de cobertura pretendida pelo Atlas

Na Figura 1 mostra-se a área de cobertura pretendida. Embora fosse desejável fazê-la coincidir com os limites do Paleártico Ocidental, conforme definidos no *Birds of Western Palearctic* (Cramp *et al.* 1977–1994), tal objectivo revelou-se impraticável dada a ausência de informação para a Ásia Menor, o norte da Península Arábica e o Norte de África, tendo estas áreas sido, por isso, omitidas. O *Atlas* usa assim o mapa base do *Atlas Florae Europaeae* (Jalas & Suominen 1972, 1988) exceptuando o facto de incluir a Nova Zêmblia, a Terra de Francisco José, todas as ilhas Gregas situadas junto à Turquia, os arquipélagos da Madeira e dos Açores e a região de Stravopol, situada no sueste da Russia e das Repúblicas do Cáucaso. As restantes diferenças entre o Paleártico Ocidental e o *Atlas do EBCC* resultam do facto de este não incluir Chipre, as Ilhas Canárias e todas as ilhas do Mediterrâneo administradas por países norte Africanos. Em termos de cobertura, o *Atlas* difere do *Birds in Europe: their conservation status* (Tucker & Heath 1994) por omitir a Turquia, a Ásia Menor e a Gronelândia.

Embora não seja imediatamente aparente na Figura 1, o Paleártico Ocidental, o *Atlas Florae Europaeae* e o presente *Atlas* omitem uma pequena parte da Europa, junto a Orenburg, e incluem uma parte do Kazaquistão asiático, entre os rios Volga e Ural e uma parte da Rússia asiática, a leste de Perm (Região de Sverdlovsk), contrariamente ao *Birds in Europe*.

Cobertura conseguida

A seguir à **Introdução**, na secção das **Figuras Explicativas**, a Figura 2 mostra os mapas recenseados e a qualidade máxima obtida por quadrado enquanto a Figura 3 mostra a qualidade mínima recebida por cada quadrado. A sub-secção **Informação qualitativa versus informação semi-quantitativa** (mais à frente) explica o significado destes termos, mas as categorias de qualidade de informação que foram utilizadas naqueles mapas são, por ordem decrescente:

1. Estimativa semi-quantitativa da população: a nidificação foi confirmada ou dada como provável.
2. Estimativa semi-quantitativa da população: a nidificação dada como possível.
3. Informação qualitativa: a nidificação foi confirmada ou dada como provável.
4. Informação qualitativa: a nidificação dada como possível.

A qualidade da informação é normalmente a mesma para todas as espécies num quadrado (veja explicações mais à frente). Áreas consideráveis da Russia não foram cobertas de todo pela impossibilidade de estabelecer contactos. Para uma parte apreciável do remanescente da Rússia, partes da Bielorrússia, Ucrânia e das Repúblicas Caucasianas, a cobertura conseguida refere-se a um número restrito de espécies. Para a maior parte da antiga Jugoslávia a cobertura é razoavelmente completa (em algumas áreas não para todas as espécies). Na Albânia há algumas zonas não cobertas. A cobertura das Ilhas do Ártico Russo, Nova Zêmblia e Terra de Francisco José, foi também incompleta.

No resto da área, apesar das inevitáveis deficiências, a cobertura conseguida foi essencialmente completa.

Os mapas do *Atlas*

A projecção cartográfica a seleccionar tinha que preencher os seguintes requisitos: deveria ser conhecida de todos os países Europeus e deveria ser compatível com as projecções cartográficas nacionais, apenas o Sistema Universal Transverso de Mercator (UTM) preenchia estes critérios básicos quando o *Atlas* teve início. Tendo que o projecto *Atlas Florae Europaeae* usou uma grelha UTM como base, este tornou-se a base ideal para o mapa delimitado para o *Atlas Ornitológico*. O *Atlas Florae Europaeae* usou a grelha de quadrados de 50 × 50Km como unidade de registo sendo esta também utilizada no *Atlas Ornitológico*. O trabalho que resultaria da compilação e análise de dados recolhidos usando uma escala mais fina teria sido impraticável.

A unidade base da grelha UTM, o quadrado de 100 x 100Km, é identificado por um código alfanumérico lógico-sequencial de dois números e três letras. Para os Atlas da Flora e das Aves cada quadrado foi subdividido em quatro quadrados 50 × 50Km numerados da seguinte forma:

1 3
2 4

Tendo assim, cada quadrado, uma referência única de seis caracteres.

A organização da grelha UTM no sentido Norte-Sul é simples: a subdivisão faz-se a 50Km de intervalo, em linhas paralelas à latitude, com a origem no Equador. O outro eixo é de mais difícil organização uma vez que os meridianos convergem na direcção dos pólos. A grelha UTM está concebida para compensar este efeito da seguinte forma; o padrão de organização das quadrículas está baseado em sectores de 6° de longitude, com início no 0°. As células da orla de cada meridiano de 6° vão diminuindo na direcção dos pólos até se tornarem pontos, então as novas células da orla começam também a diminuir. O *Atlas Florae Europaeae* e este *Atlas* das aves modificaram este sistema por forma a reduzir a variação de tamanho dos quadrados de orla dos meridianos do intervalo de 6°; os quadrados da orla são retirados quando a sua largura se reduziu até aproximadamente 40Km, (chamamos aqui quadrados às células do *Atlas*, embora muitas delas não sejam exactamente quadrados). O padrão obtido é visível no mapa de cobertura pretendida (Figura1) e detalhes mais completos são fornecidos no **Apêndice Técnico**.

O EOAC forneceu mapas com a grelha de 50 × 50Km aos organizadores nacionais, para assegurar que a grelha correcta era utilizada para o registo da informação. O trabalho de campo foi normalmente baseado em grelhas UTM mais finas que a 50 × 50Km, em qualquer dos casos os organizadores tiveram que converter as informações para a tornar utilizável.

Períodos de trabalho e Processo de validação

O plano inicial previa que o trabalho de campo deveria decorrer entre 1985 e 1988. No entanto, os diferentes países organizaram o seu próprio trabalho de campo e, por razões várias, nem todos conseguiram cumprir aquele calendário. Quando a cobertura conseguida para aquele período era incompleta, dados anteriores ou posteriores foram avaliados para saber se a sua inclusão viria a melhorar a cobertura.

Na tabela 3, a seguir a esta *Introdução*, listam-se os países participantes, o seu período de recolha de informação, as grelhas nacionais a partir das quais a informação foi convertida e os métodos utilizados.

Recolha de dados – Dados sobre a distribuição das espécies

Centenas de milhares de horas, talvez mais de um milhão, foram a base deste *Atlas*. Idealmente todos os participantes deveriam utilizar metodologias de campo idênticas mas isto foi impossível. Por isso mesmo, o EOAC editou regras gerais em vez de normas estritas. Em alguns países, o trabalho de campo para este *Atlas* e para o Atlas Nacional decorreu em simultâneo, noutros os dados os dados do Atlas Nacional foram utilizados para este *Atlas*.

Os métodos utilizados no terreno variaram entre visitas únicas, acumulução de informação ao longo de várias visitas e levantamentos sistemáticos, baseados em recenseamentos por pontos de escuta, transectos lineares ou método dos mapas.

Na Figura 4, a seguir a esta **Introdução**, reproduz-se parcialmente a ficha padronizada criada pelo Departamento Central de Estatítica da Holanda. Para cada quadrado recenseado preencheu-se uma ficha. Nos quadrados partilhados por vários países, cada um preencheu uma ficha correspondente à sua parte.

A informação geral requerida para cada quadrado era:

1. Período de recenseamento: ano, ou sequência de anos, durante os quais se recolheram dados.
2. Identificação do quadrado (código UTM 50).
3. Grau de cobertura: indicando se o resultado nesse quadrado inclui mais de 75% das espécies esperadas (elevado) ou menos (baixo).
4. Altitude do quadrado sob a forma de intervalo de variação, fornecendo-se a altitude máxima e mínima em metros.
5. Observadores ou coordenador(es): nome e endereço a utilizar em caso de necessidade de contactos posteriores.
6. Comentários: possibilitando o fornecimento de informação que explique melhor os dados contidos na ficha.
7. Um curto questionário sobre os habitats existentes no quadrado.

O corpo central da ficha consistia numa lista de espécies (cerca de 440, de acordo com Voous (1977) numeradas na sequência da Euring), com espaço para introdução de dados.

O campo para introdução de dados incluia na coluna 0 uma abreviatura do nome científico (por ex. Gav stell), na coluna 1 o código da Euring (por ex. 00020) e pedia na coluna 2 a evidência de nidificação e o seu código. Havia 16 códigos possíveis, agrupados em três categorias; nidificação confirmada, nidificação provável e nidificação possível. Os códigos apresentam-se na tabela 1. Finalmente na coluna 3 solicitava-se uma estimativa do número de casais no quadrado, expresso numa escala logarítmica (1 = 1–9, 2 = 10–99, ..., 6 >100.000). A ficha permitia ainda a inclusão de híbridos e de espécies não listadas.

No conjunto, as fontes de dados sobre a nidificação foram:

1. Os coordenadores do EBCC, que organizaram a recolha de dados e compilaram os resultados nas fichas.
2. Os coordenadores regionais; por vezes a recolha de dados foi organizada por outras pessoas além dos coordenadores nacionais, especialmente em países de grandes dimensões, ou quando uma rede de contactos delegava num membro activo dessa rede. Estes coordenadores regionais trabalhavam de forma idêntica à dos coordenadores nacionais.
3. Fontes de informação adicionais, ao nível nacional, normalmente bibliográficas e disponibilizadas por especialistas. Em áreas remotas, para as quais não existia informação, muitas vezes a única informação disponível era aquela que constava de relatórios, publicados ou não, que não estavam directamente acessíveis aos editores ou organizadores nacionais.
4. Autores de textos de espécies. Muitas vezes, os autores dos textos, sendo conhecedores desta espécie, tinha conhecimento de fontes de informação adicionais sobre distribuição e números.

Toda a informação recolhida através destas fontes foi sujeita ao tratamento hierárquico; qualquer adição à base tinha que ser aprovada pelo coordenador nacional.

Informação qualitativa versus Informação semi-quantitativa

O *Atlas* usa informação semi-quantitativa (estimativas da

Tabela 1 *Categorias de Nidificação e Códigos*

A : Nidificação Possível

1.	espécie observada durante a época de reprodução em habitat favorável à nidificação
2.	Macho(s) a cantar presente (ou chamamentos ouvidos)na época de reprodução

B : Nidificação Provável

3.	Par observado em habitat favorável durante a época de reprodução
4.	Presumível comportamento território (canto, etc.)em pelo menos dois dias diferentes da mesma semana ou não e no mesmo local
5.	Parada nupcial
6.	Visitando provável local de ninho
7.	Comportamento agitado ou chamamentos ansiosos de aves adultas
8.	Pelada de incubação observada em ave adulta manuseada
9.	Construindo ninho

C : Nidificação Confirmada

10.	Comportamento de distração ou dissimulação
11.	Ninho usado ou cascas de ovos (ocupado ou encontrados durante o período de inventário)
12.	Juvenil que abondonou recentemente o ninho (com plumagem incompleta ou com penugem)
13.	Adultos entrando e saindo de local de ninho em circunstâncias indicando ninho ocupado (incluindo em ninhos ocupados em locais elevados, ninhos em buracos, e cujo conteœdo não pode ser visto) ou adulto visto a incubar
14.	Adultos transportando saco fecal ou comida para os juvenis
15.	Ninho com ovos
16.	Ninho com juvenis, visto ou ouvido

população numa escala logarítmica) calculada para cada quadrado pelos coordenadores, nacionais ou regionais, ou por aqueles que fizeram o trabalho de campo. Os símbolos utilizados representam o número de casais nidificantes, não as densidades, o aumento na dimensão destes símbolos representa um aumento no número de casais (legenda na página cxl). Infelizmente alguns países não forneceram dados semi-quantitativos, ou na totalidade, como a Noruega e a Polónia, ou para a maior parte do território como a Espanha, ou parcialmente como a Islândia, a França e a Itália. O projecto perdeu o contacto com a Bósnia e a Sérvia, e não pode por isso melhorar a qualidade da informação recebida. Algumas regiões de França melhoraram a informação fornecida independentemente, enquanto o coordenador nacional de França melhorou a informação relativa a algumas espécies à escala nacional. As estimativas em escala logarítmica para cada quadrado contém mais informação do que a mera informação de presença / ausência. Para quadrados de fronteira cada país forneceu uma estimativa para a parte que lhe corresponde. O valor mais alto foi o escolhido, uma vez que as escalas logarítmicas não são adicionáveis, mesmo que isso resultasse numa sub-estimação. Estas aproximações eram melhores do que considerar apenas a informação qualitativa.

Os símbolos nos mapas representam as seguintes categorias de informação:

Rôxo	= nidificação confirmada ou provável, informação qualitativa.
Lilás	= nidificação possível, informação qualitativa.
Vermelho	= nidificação confirmada ou provável, informação semi-quantitativa.
Laranja	= nidificação possível, informação semi-quantitativa.
Cinza	= Não foram efectuados levantamentos para esta espécie neste quadrado.
ausência de símbolo	= foram efectuados levantamentos mas a espécie não foi detectada.

Informatização – correcção da informação relativa aos mapas e validação das entradas

As fichas recebidas dos coordenadores nacionais foram examinadas em busca de erros básicos (omissão de códigos, códigos incorrectos, etc.) antes de serem transformadas em ficheiros no formato ASCII, tendo cada registo um código de identidade nacional. Alguns países forneceram a informação em 'diskette' tendo esta informação também sido verificada da mesma forma. A base de dados construida a partir das fichas padronizadas tem um único valor para cada espécie e quadrado.

Os coordenadores nacionais e outras fontes que forneceram informação atempadamente receberam mapas provisórios e listas nacionais, por espécie, para uma verificação inicial. Foi-lhes pedido que os verificassem e muitas correcções foram efectuadas nesta fase. No entanto, alguns países submeteram a sua informação já tarde ou melhoraram a qualidade da informação inicialmente enviada, de qualitativa para semi-quantitativa, em consequência, as correcções e o processo de validação começaram aí mais tarde e a um ritmo diferente entre os vários países.

A produção de mapas provisórios foi crucial a dois níveis:

1. Permitiu aos coordenadores nacionais, e através deles a muitos outros colaboradores, confirmar se a informação que tinham fornecido tinha sido introduzida correctamente: os mapas mostravam se as espécies estavam correctamente alocadas aos quadrados. Os erros eram mais óbvios nos mapas do que nas listagens.
2. Estimulou a participação levando à introdução de novos dados.

Numa segunda fase verificou-se se as correcções da primeira fase tinham sido correctamente introduzidas. Para alcançar este objectivo enviaram-se para correcção, aos coordenadores nacionais, mapas e listas corrigidas. A maioria dos coordenadores nacionais cumpriu esta enorme tarefa e submeteu as correcções finais, mas em países como a Jugoslávia a correcção e validação foram impossíveis. Nos países relativamente aos quais o processo de revisão e validação foi atrasado o tempo disponível para estas tarefas foi muito reduzido, sendo que quanto maior o atraso menor o tempo disponível, as dificuldades para finalizar os mapas foram crescentes.

Numa fase posterior receberam-se estimativas mais recentes de alguns autores e outros especialistas. Na sua maioria estas informações foram examinadas pelos coordenadores nacionais tendo-se tomado posteriormente uma decisão relativamente a estas propostas de alteração. Quando isto não foi possível, por falta de tempo, ou se mativeram as estimativas iniciais ou o autor indica no texto que a sua opinião difere da informação mapeada.

Quando não existia informação proveniente de trabalho de atlas, o que ocorreu particularmente no norte da Rússia e na Albânia, a informação disponível de outras fontes foi avaliada por ornitólogos locais para se chegar a uma decisão sobre a aceitação desta informação. Algumas estimativas semi-quantitativas forma efectuadas para estes quadrados, extrapolando de quadrados situados na mesma região, para os quais havia estimativas directas, e considerando as disponibilidades de habitat adequado.

A data limite para a recepção de novas informações e correcções foi 1 de Julho de 1995, embora para maximizar a cobertura se tenha aceite informação recebida nos meses seguintes relativa à Albânia, território europeu da Turquia, Cáucaso, parte da Ucrânia e parte da Rússia. As correcções vindas dos autores dos textos específicos foram aceites até 1 de Novembro de 1995.

Recolha de dados – informação sobre o tamanho das populações

Os gráficos de populações nacionais são derivados da Base de Dados de Aves. Esta contém dados sobre as populações recolhidos em conjunto pelo EBCC e pelo BirdLife International e criada para apoiar este *Atlas* e o 'Projecto Espécies Dispersas do BirdLife' cujos resultados foram já publicados no *Birds in Europe : their conservation status* (Tucker & Heath 1994). Esta colaboração ajudou ainda ao aprofundamento da participação em certas zonas da Europa. A informação foi recolhida inicialmente através da distribuição pelos coordenadores nacionais (conforme lista no *Birds in Europe*) que por sua vez os distribuiram pelos especialistas adequados, organizações dedicadas à monitorização e participantes regionais. O BirdLife International é o gestor da Base de Dados de Aves.

Cada país forneceu a seguinte informação sobre as populações de aves:

1. Tamanho da população
2. Tendência populacional em termos numéricos (para o período de 1970–1990).
3. Tendência populacional em termos de área de distribuição (para o período de 1970–1990).

Informação semelhante foi recolhida para as populações invernantes mas não é aqui apresentada.

As fontes bibliográficas utilizadas para a avaliação das tendências populacionais foram registadas. Na **Tabela 2**, apresentada a seguir a esta **Introdução**, detalham-se os códigos de verificação utilizados para indicar o grau de certeza e a fiabilidade das informações relativas às tendências, numéricas e de área.

Alguns autores de textos de espécies não concordaram com as estimativas de populações contidas na base de dados, mas esta informação chegou demasiado tarde para nela poder ser incluida. Nestes casos, os autores usaram as suas próprias estimativas no texto, mas os gráficos que acompanham estes textos usam sempre a informação disponível na base de dados.

Limitações dos dados

O projecto *Atlas* produziu um conjunto de dados de grande qualidade, mas inevitavelmente há limitações nestes dados. Aqueles que quiserem utilizá-los em investigações futuras deverão ter em atenção estas limitações, cujo detalhe está para além do objectivo deste livro, e que deverá por isso ser esclarecido pelo EBCC. No entanto, algumas limitações básicas que afectam uma utilização geral deste livro são:

TABELA 2 Códigos de população na Base de Dados Europeia de Aves

POPMIN	=	tamanho mínimo da população (em casais)			
POPMAX	=	tamanho máximo da população (em casais)			
MEAN	=	média geométrica do tamanho da população (em casais)	PSV	=	código de verifiçã do tamanho da população
YRC	=	ano a que se refere a estimativa da população			
PST	=	tendência da dimensão da população	PTV	=	código de verificação da tendência populacional
RST	=	tendência da distribuição da população	RTV	=	códice de verificação da tendência da distribuição

Códigos de População e Códigos de Tendência da distribuição
Estes códigos aplicam-se ao período de 1970–1990

+ 2	=	grande aumento de pelo menos 50%
+ 1	=	pequeno aumento de pelos menos 20%, mas inferior a 50%
0	=	estávelm, sem alterações superiores a 20%
- 1	=	pequena redução de pelos menos 20%, mas inferior a 50%
- 2	=	grande redução de pelo menos 50%
n	=	nidificação registada pela primeira vez neste período
x	=	extingiu-se durante este período
f	=	fluctuando, com variações de pelo menos 20% mas sem tendência definida

1. Não foi definido um conjunto de metodologias padronizadas, quer para a determinação da presença / ausência quer para a estimativa das populações. Muitos projectos nacionais, que foram a fonte de informação do EBCC definiram as metodologias de campo em função dos seus objectivos, de acordo com os recursos disponíveis.
2. Não houve uma metodologia universal na preparação e compilação dos dados, fundamentalmente pelas mesmas razões apresentadas acima. Os métodos de conversão foram escolhidos individualmente.
3. Diferenças na qualidade da ornitologia de campo e na abundância relativa de observadores resultam numa informação de qualidade variável .
4. Alguns dos dados são parcialmente extrapolados.
5. Alguns dos dados provêm da literatura (sobretudo nas zonas árticas).

APRESENTAÇÃO DOS MAPAS E TEXTOS ESPECÍFICOS DO *ATLAS*

No *Atlas* as espécies estão separadas em dois grupos, o daquelas que para os quais obtivemos informação satisfatória que permite mapear a sua distribuição e o daquelas para as quais não obtivemos. Para o primeiro grupo haverá textos específicos completos na Parte 1 dos **Textos específicos** e para o segundo grupo, textos específicos reduzidos na Parte 2. Nas duas Partes as espécies são apresentadas na ordem proposta por Voous e seguindo aproximadamente a sequência da Euring, com excepção de alguns ajustamentos efectuados na Parte 1, por forma a que qualquer espécie cujo mapa e texto ocupa apenas uma página esteja em face de uma espécie que ocupe idêntico espaço. Para as espécies que ocupam duas páginas o mapa e o texto estão sempre em face um do outro. Em alguns casos, espécies com distribuições tão restritas que não permitiam um tratamento completo, inseriram-se dois textos na mesma página. Para cada espécie há uma ilustração e os nomes vulgares (quando disponíveis) foram incluidos em 14 línguas. A maioria das espécies tem um gráfico de população que é explicado nas páginas que antecedem os mapas e os textos.

Mapas derivados (explicação abreviada)

A Figura 5 ilustra a riqueza específica de aves nidificantes por quadrado. As Figuras 6 e 8 mostram a riqueza específica em termos de Espécies Europeias com Preocupação de Conservação (SPEC), categorias 1,2 e 3, conforme definidas pelo BirdLife International e a Figura 9 combina estas três categorias.

TEXTOS ESPECÍFICOS

Os textos específicos, sempre que adequado, cobrem um conjunto de tópicos padronizado, normalmente na seguinte ordem, de acordo com as prioridades pré-determinadas; distribuição mundial, habitats de nidificação na Europa, padrão de distribuição e abundância na Europa, alterações recentes na distribuição e nos efectivos populacionais (e as suas causas possíveis), variações regionais na abundância, possíveis factores limitantes da distribuição, densidades na nidificação nos habitats mais favoráveis, migração e movimentos característicos da espécie, na Europa e fora dela, qualquer característica particular da espécie, e referências detalhadas a sub-espécies cobrindo, distribuição, área, sobreposições e tendências.

Os seguintes tópicos foram omitidos excepto nos casos em que eram absolutamente necessário para ilustrar algum dos tópicos padronizados; bilogia reprodutiva, comportamento, alimentação, interacções com outras espécies, características morfológicas e fisiológicas, discussão detalhada sobre as ameaças a que estejam sujeitas (o domínio do Birds in Europe), anormalidades, oologia, evolução e taxonomia (excepto nos casos em que houve alterações de monta aceites recentemente ou quando as sub-espécies são significativamente diferentes), mortalidade e outros parâmetros da dinâmica de populações, voz e canto.

Espécies – critérios de inclusão

As espécies que nidificam na área de cobertura pretendida desde 1985 foram incluidas desde que preenchessem os critérios definidos na **Tabela 1**. O princípio de inclusão de espécies introduzidas que nidificam no estado selvagem era o de que elas tivessem pelo menos uma população avaliada com sendo àuto-sustentada durante cinco anos. No entanto, a aceitação ou interpretação desta regra varia largamente através da Europa e assim a selecção ou omissão de algumas espécies com populaçõpes introduzidas poderá, superficialmente, parecer arbitrária.

O *Atlas* inclui 513 espécies mais *Passer x italiae*.

NOMENCLATURA E TAXONOMIA

Taxonomia

O EBCC adoptou uma posição cautelosa e conservadora em matéria de taxonomia. Este *Atlas* segue na generalidade a taxonomia, ordem e nomenclatura inglesa adoptadas pelo *Birds of Western Palearctic* (BWP), conforme emendado na Edição Concisa.

Puffinus yelkouan, *Puffinus mauretanicus*, *Larus cachinans*, *Anthus petrosus*, *Phylloscopus lorentzii* and *Pyrrhula murina* foram tratados como espécies e foram mapeados em separado de *Puffinus puffinus*, *Larus argentatus*, *Anthus spinoletta*, *Phylloscopus collybita* e *Pyrrhula pyrrhula*. O mapeamento separado foi possível quer porque elas foram registadas em separado, quer porque as suas distribuições estão geográficamente separadas (o texto para os três *Puffinus* foi integrado). Inicialmente tentaram-se registar graficamente as sub-espécies e formas de diversas espécies mas as distinções que o EOAC propôs não se observam de uma maneira uniforme através da Europa, tornando o mapeamento impossível. No entanto, o 'Pardal Italiano' foi incluido separadamente e tratado com um híbrido estabilizado entre *Passer domesticus* e *P. hispaniolensis*, descrevendo-o como *Passer* x *italiae*. Inversamente, o *Phylloscopus trochiloides* inclui duas subespécies separadas geográficamente, *viridianus* e *nitidus*, anteriormente tratadas como espécies separadas. A separação entre *Lanius meridionalis* e *L. excubitor* foi geralmente aceita na altura em que este *Atlas* estava em fase final pelo que o mapa de distribuição apresenta linha divisória entre as duas formas. O *Hippolais caligata* é por vezes considerado como distinto do *H. rama* mas neste trabalho este último é tratado como uma subespécie. As relações dentro de alguns complexos de Gaivotas são muitas vezes complexas; *Larus armenicus* é aqui tratado em separado.

Numeração da EURING

A União Europeia para a Anilhagem de Aves (EURING) tem uma lista numérica aberta, de cinco algarismos, para espécies e subespécies, que é utilizada principalmente na anilhagem. Esta lista segue na generalidade a ordem de Voous, quando aplicável, e por isso foi adoptada como um bom método para a compilação de dados. Os números de código da Euring são fornecidos na secção de textos específicos. No **Apêndice Técnico** detalha-se a forma como estes números foram utilizados.

O USO DE LIVROS DE REFERÊNCIA E OUTRAS PUBLICAÇÕES

Foi pedido aos autores que evitassem citar manuais porque o espaço para citações era geralmente limitado. Dois importantes manuais europeus merecem reconhecimento especial. Para a compreensão básica de qualquer espécie nidificante na Europa, os textos e mapas deste *Atlas* devem ser estudado em conjunto com estas proeminentes publicações de referência; *Birds of Western Palearctic* (Cramp *et al* 1977–1994) e *Handbuch der Vogel Mitteleuropas* (Glutz von Blotzheim *et al* 1966-1993). Nos textos específicos deste *Atlas* usaram-se as abreviaturas *BWP* e *HVM* para estes livros.

O livro *Birds in Europe: their conservation status* (Tucker & Heath 1994) fornece pela primeira vez uma perspectiva das populações de aves na Europa, as ameaças a que estão sujeitas e o seu estatuto de conservação, descrevendo em detalhe aquelas espécies cujo estatuto de conservação é desfavorável. O *Atlas* cobre não apenas estas espécies mas todas as outras que não estão presentemente sujeitas a ameaças. Os gráficos de populações do *Atlas* vêm da mesma Base de Dados de Aves usada no *Birds in Europe* e por isso os textos específicos citam frequentemente este trabalho.

As referências citadas aparecem no fim do livro, antes dos índices.

Michael Blair, Ward Hagemeijer
(Tradução de Rui Rufino & Renato Neves)

ABREVIATURAS E GLOSSÁRIO

Direcções

N = Norte
S = Sul
E = Leste
W = Oeste, e assim NW = noroeste e WSW = oeste-sudoeste, etc.
C = Centro, e assim S-C = Centro-Sul, etc.

Expressões gerais

asl = acima do nível do mar (altitude)
c = aproximadamente
et al = e outros (em citações)
pers comm = comunicação(ões) pessoal(ais)
pers obs = observação(ões) pessoal(ais)
unpubl = trabalho não publicado

Dimensões e medidas

bp = casais nidificantes
ha = hectares
ind = indivíduos
m = metros
km = quilómetros
km^2 = quilómetros quadrados
M = milhão

Acrónimos

BTO = British Trust for Ornithology (GB)
BWP = Birds of the Western Palearctic
HVM = Handbuch der Vögel Mitteleuropas
JNCC = Joint Nature Conservation Committe (GB)
RSPB = Royal Society for the Protection of Birds (GB)
SOVON = SOVON Bird Census Work The Netherlands (NL)
WWT = Wildfowl and Wetlands Trust (GB)

Glossário

eutrophic = eutrófico = rico em nutrientes minerais de origem animal ou vegetal em decomposição.
lentic = lêntico = pertencente a água de curso lento ou parada, como em charcos ou lagos
lotic = lótico = pertencente a água corrente
mesotrophic = mesotrófico = nem rico nem pobre em sais e nutrientes básicos
'mixotrophic' = 'mixotrófico' = um termo arranjado para lagos em zonas boreais que têm baixa profundidade e vegetação abundante mas cujas margens são relativamente pobres em nutrientes
oligotrophic = oligotrófico = pobre em sais e nutrientes básicos
phenology = fenologia = o estudo dos tempos em acontecimentos recorrentes
sclerophytic = esclerófilo = pertencente a a plantas com folhas espessas, normalmente pequenas, que têm taxas de transpiração reduzidas estando adaptadas a climas secos
xerophytic = xerofítico = pertencente a plantas adaptadas a condições de secura

WSTĘP

CEL OPRACOWANIA *THE EBCC ATLAS OF EUROPEAN BREEDING BIRDS*

Wiele książek o ptakach zawiera mapy rozmieszczenia gatunków. Niektóre z tych map powstały w oparciu o specjalne badania populacji lęgowych ptaków, lecz pomijając niektóre specjalistyczne atlasy, mapy takie są najczęściej kompilacjami z wielu źródeł o rozmaitej wiarygodności; niekiedy są to jedynie przeróbki wcześniejszych map o wątpliwej autentyczności. Co więcej, mapy te zazwyczaj nie prezentują aspektu ilościowego, tzn. nie pokazują, gdzie dany gatunek jest pospolity, a gdzie rzadki.

Z drugiej jednak strony, pojawia się coraz więcej doskonałych regionalnych i narodowych atlasów rozmieszczenia ptaków lęgowych. W większości, ich inspiracją był ten sam program, którego zwieńczeniem jest niniejszy *Atlas* i podobnie jak on, opracowania te zawierają dane półilościowe. Jeszcze w roku 1971 powołany został Komitet Europejskiego Atlasu Ornitologicznego (European Ornithological Atlas Committee, dalej EOAC); celem istnienia tej organizacji było zmapowanie rozmieszczenia lęgowego wszystkich europejskich gatunków, dla których, poprzez prace terenowe, możliwe było uzyskanie odpowiednich danych. Niniejsza książka prezentuje wyniki tych starań.

Atlas przedstawia rozmieszczenie ptaków odnoszące się do określonego okresu czasu; niemniej jednak, zgromadzone tu dane (bez względu na drobne odstępstwa) wyznaczają swego rodzaju fundamenty wiedzy, będące punktem odniesienia dla przyszłych prac, w szczególności dla przyszłych badań zmian zasięgów samych ptaków. W roku 1971, Komitetowi przyświecała jasna wizja realizacji pierwszego na skalę kontynentalną programu zbadania rozmieszczenia wszystkich ptaków lęgowych. Wizja ta urzeczywistniła się; *The EBCC Atlas of European Breeding Birds* przedstawia mapy rozmieszczenia ptaków lęgowych w Europie, odpowiadając na pytanie 'gdzie jaki ptak się gnieździ'.

UKŁAD *ATLASU*

Niniejszy **Wstęp** pokrótce opisuje przeznaczenie *Atlasu*, omawia metody zbierania danych o rozmieszczeniu i liczebności ptaków, zastosowane techniki komputeryzacji i mapowania, a także objaśnia strukturę *Atlasu*. Przeczytanie **Wstępu** jest konieczne do pełnego zrozumienia tej książki. Wydrukowany on został w wielu wersjach językowych, tak by mogła go przeczytać większość europejskich ornitologów.

Rozdziały wstępne

W **Przedsłowiu**, profesor Karel Voous opisuje pokrótce dlaczego *Atlas* jest tak istotny w kontekście zmian zachodzących w awifaunie Europy. **Przedmowa** podsumowuje, na ile oparty na szerokiej współpracy program *Atlasu* zaspokaja potrzeby europejskich ornitologów; zarysowana jest tam również polityka i zadania EBCC w przyszłych programach monitoringu ptaków w Europie. Po tych rozdziałach następuje **Wstęp**, opisujący takie zagadnienia jak metody i obszar objęty opracowaniem. Kolejny rozdział, **Rysunki objaśniające**, pokazuje stopień zbadania i jakość uzyskanych danych oraz kopię standardowego formularza używanego do zbierania danych. Rozdział **Historia** opisuje wzloty i upadki jakich doświadczył program Europejskiego Atlasu Ornitologicznego. Następnie, w eseju zatytułowanym **Ewolucja i historia europejskiej awifauny**, profesor Jacques Blondel omawia, jak powstały współczesne zasięgi europejskich gatunków ptaków. Tę część książki zamykają **Podziękowania** oraz lista **Krajowych i większych regionalnych atlasów rozmieszczenia ptaków w Europie**.

Rozdziały gatunkowe

Zasadnicza część *Atlasu* dotyczy gatunków gnieżdżących się w Europie. Otwiera ją **Legenda do symboli występujących na mapach i diagramów populacyjnych**. Na Część 1. składają się mapy rozmieszczenia, opisy gatunkowe, nazwy każdego gatunku w 14 językach oraz ilustracje. Gatunki omawiane są w kolejności odpowiadającej z grubsza porządkowi zastosowanemu przez Voousa (1977) oraz numeracji EURINGu. Część 2. zawiera opisy gatunków, które najprawdopodobniej gnieżdżą się w Europie, ale dla których nie udało się w toku prac nad *Atlasem* uzyskać danych to potwierdzających.

Rozdziały końcowe

Rozdział **Mapy pochodne** szczegółowo przedstawia zróżnicowanie bogactwa gatunkowego wszystkich europejskich gatunków ptaków lęgowych oraz gatunków szczególnie zagrożonych w Europie (Species of European Conservation Concern, SPEC) zdefiniowanych jako takie przez BirdLife International (Tucker & Heath 1994). **Dodatek techniczny** zawiera objaśnienia odnośnie różnic pomiędzy siatką zastosowaną w *Atlasie* a teoretycznym odwzorowaniem UTM, oraz odnośnie sposobu potraktowania 50-kilometrowych kwadratów zawierających wyspy i odcinki wybrzeża. Dodatek ten objaśnia też, w jaki sposób *Atlas* wykorzystuje system numeracji EURINGu.

Broszury w językach obcych

Streszczenia rozdziałów wstępnych (**Przedmowa, Historia** oraz **Ewolucja i historia europejskiej awifauny**) oraz tekstów gatunkowych zostały udostępnione ornitologom ze wszystkich krajów, by po ich przetłumaczeniu na języki ojczyste i rozpowszechnieniu wśród kolegów, książka była użyteczna także dla osób nie znających języka angielskiego. Nazwiska i adresy osób rozprowadzających broszury w językach obcych (aktualne w chwili oddawania książki do druku) zestawione są na końcu **Dodatku technicznego**.

METODY

Prezentacja danych w *Atlasie*

Pierwotne koncepcje zbierania i kompilacji danych oraz tekst o wyborze metod opisane są w rozdziale **Historia**; tam również opisana jest historia organizacji zbierania danych.

Atlas przedstawia zagęszczenia (ilość ptaków na jednostkę powierzchni) w oparciu o skalę logarytmiczną (patrz rozdział **Informacja jakościowa a półilościowa**, niżej). Ta skala jest szczególnie użyteczna dla gatunków wykazujących znaczne zróżnicowanie zagęszczenia w obrębie ich zasięgu. Jednakże przy jej użyciu, mniejsze różnice w zagęszczeniach pozostają niewidoczne.

Atlas nie tylko przedstawia rozmieszczenie europejskich ptaków lęgowych, lecz również zawiera oceny liczebności populacji lęgowych i ich trendów w większości krajów Europy. Zmiany w schematach rozmieszczenia można bowiem zrozumieć jedynie w powiązaniu z rzetelnymi ocenami wielkości populacji krajowych i ich trendów.

Planowany zasięg *Atlasu*

Planowany zasięg pokrycia *Atlasu* przedstawiony jest na ryc. 1. Pomimo, iż pożądana byłaby tu zgodność z granicami zachodniej Palearktyki zdefiniowanymi w podręczniku *The Birds of the Western Palearctic* (Cramp *et al* 1977–1994), podejście to okazało się niepraktyczne ze względu na ubóstwo danych z Azji Mniejszej, północnej Arabii i północnej Afryki. W rezultacie, tereny te nie zostały uwzględnione. *Atlas* wykorzystuje zatem podstawową mapę z opracowania *Atlas Florae Europaeae* (Jalas & Suominen 1972, 1988), poszerzoną o Nową Ziemię, Ziemię Franciszka Józefa, wszystkie wyspy greckie leżące w pobliżu wybrzeża Turcji, Maderę, Azory, rejon Stawropola w południowo-wschodniej Rosji oraz republiki Kaukazu. Pozostałe różnice pomiędzy terenem zachodniej Palearktyki a zasięgiem *EBCC Atlas* polegają na pominięciu Cypru, Wysp Kanaryjskich oraz wszystkich wysp śródziemnomorskich administrowanych przez kraje północnej Afryki. *Atlas* różni się od zasięgu opracowania *Birds in Europe – their conservation status* (Tucker & Heath 1994) przez nie uwzględnienie Turcji i Grenlandii.

Ryc. 1 dokumentuje również – co łatwo przeoczyć – że w odróżnieniu od *Birds in Europe*, granice obszaru zachodniej Palearktyki, opracowania *Atlas Florae Europaeae* oraz niniejszego *Atlasu* nie obejmują małego fragmentu Europy w okolicach Orenburga, zawierając natomiast fragment azjatyckiego Kazachstanu pomiędzy rzekami Wołgą i Uralem oraz fragment azjatyckiej Rosji położony na wschód od Permu (rejon Swierdłowska).

Zrealizowany zasięg *Atlasu*

W rozdziale **Rysunki objaśniające** (następującym po niniejszym **Wstępie**), na ryc. 2 przedstawione są kwadraty zbadane, z zaznaczeniem maksymalnego poziomu jakości uzyskanych danych w poszczególnych kwadratach; natomiast ryc. 3 przedstawia minimalny poziom jakości danych uzyskanych z poszczególnych kwadratów. Szczegółowo znaczenie tych terminów objaśnione jest w rozdziale **Informacja jakościowa a półilościowa** (patrz niżej). Generalnie, kategorie jakości danych przedstawione na tych mapach są następujące (uporządkowane wg malejącej jakości):

1. Półilościowe oceny liczebności populacji: gdy gniazdowanie było pewne lub ocenione jako prawdopodobne;
2. Półilościowe oceny liczebności populacji: gdy gniazdowanie oceniono jako możliwe;
3. Obecność gatunku: gdy gniazdowanie było pewne lub ocenione jako prawdopodobne;
4. Obecność gatunku: gdy gniazdowanie oceniono jako możliwe.

W poszczególnych kwadratach jakość danych była zwykle taka sama dla wszystkich stwierdzonych gatunków (patrz jednak niżej). Rozległe obszary środkowej Rosji nie zostały w ogóle przebadane, głównie z powodu niemożności nawiązania kontaktów z lokalnymi ornitologami. Dla większości pozostałych terenów Rosji oraz dla części Białorusi, Ukrainy i republik Kaukazu, uzyskano obraz rozmieszczenia ograniczonej liczby gatunków. Stopień zbadania większości terytorium byłej Jugosławii był stosunkowo dobry (w niektórych regionach nie dla wszystkich gatunków). Luki istnieją też dla Albanii. Niekompletny stopień zbadania osiągnięto też dla rosyjskich wysp arktycznych: Nowej Ziemi i Ziemi Franciszka Józefa.

Na pozostałych obszarach, pomimo nieuniknionych braków, zbadanie było zasadniczo kompletne.

Mapy w *Atlasie*

Wybór odwzorowania w którym sporządzone są mapy musiał uwzględniać trzy kryteria; musiało ono obejmować całość obszaru objętego opracowaniem, być dobrze znane w większości krajów europejskich oraz kompatybilne z odwzorowaniami przyjętymi w poszczególnych państwach. Gdy rozpoczynano program *Atlasu*, jedynym odwzorowaniem spełniającym te podstawowe kryteria było uniwersalne poprzeczne odwzorowanie Merkatora (UTM). Ponieważ podstawowa mapa z programu *Atlas Florae Europaeae* wykorzystuje właśnie siatkę UTM, była ona idealna również jako podstawa dla mapy zaprojektowanej dla *Atlasu* ornitologicznego. *Atlas Florae Europaeae* używał siatki kwadratów 50 km × 50 km jako jednostek podstawowych, i te same kwadraty zostały wykorzystane w atlasie ornitologicznym. Praca związana z zestawianiem i analizą danych zbieranych w dokładniejszej skali byłaby niepraktyczna.

Każda podstawowa jednostka mapowania w siatce UTM, kwadrat 100 km × 100 km, jest oznaczona unikatowym, uporządkowanym w oparciu o logiczną sekwencję, kodem alfanumerycznym, składającym się z 2 cyfr i trzech liter. Dla potrzeb atlasów florystycznych i ornitologicznych każdy taki kwadrat został podzielony na 4 kwadraty 50 km × 50 km, ponumerowane jak niżej:

1 3
2 4

W efekcie, każdy kwadrat o boku 50 km posiadał unikatowy identyfikator składający się z 6 znaków.

Układ siatki UTM wzdłuż osi północ-południe jest prosty; linie podziałowe siatki biegną w odstępach 50 km, równolegle do przebiegu równoleżników, z równikiem jako punktem początkowym układu. Układ siatki wzdłuż drugiej osi jest bardziej skomplikowany, gdyż południki zbliżają się do siebie w miarę przybliżania się do bieguna. W rezultacie, ilość mogących się między nimi pomieścić kwadratów 50 km × 50 km – zmniejsza się ku biegunom. Jest to skompensowane w UTM w sposób następujący. Układ oczek siatki UTM opiera się o odcinki odpowiadające 6° długości geograficznej, poczynając od południka 0°. Pola przylegające do każdego południka będącego wielokrotnością 6° zmniejszają się ku biegunom, dopóki nie staną się punktami, kiedy to znikają, a zmniejszać się zaczynają następne kwadraty graniczne. *Atlas Florae Europaeae* i niniejszy atlas rozmieszczenia ptaków zmodyfikowały ten system, tak by zmienność wielkości kwadratów przyległych do południków 6° nie była tak duża: kwadraty graniczne znikają gdy ich szerokość zmniejszy się do około 40 km. (W *Atlasie*, dla wygody, określamy wszystkie pola jako 'kwadraty', pomimo że wiele z nich nie jest dokładnie kwadratowe). Ten schemat jest zilustrowany dokładnie na mapie planowanego stopnia zbadania (ryc. 1) a szczegóły podane są w **Dodatku technicznym**.

EOAC dostarczył mapy z siatką 50 km × 50 km krajowym koordynatorom, tak by mieć pewność, że używają oni właściwej siatki do zbierania danych. Prace terenowe z reguły bazowały na siatkach UTM dokładniejszych niż 50 km × 50 km lub na siatkach innych niż UTM. W każdym przypadku, krajowi koordynatorzy musieli przetransponować dane do formy umożliwiającej wprowadzanie danych.

Terminy prac terenowych oraz proces sprawdzania danych

Pierwotnie planowano, że prace terenowe związane z *Atlasem*, powinny mieć miejsce w latach 1985-1988. Jednak w poszczególnych państwach zbieranie danych w terenie było organizowane osobno i z racji różnych trudności praktycznych, nie zawsze możliwe było dostosowanie się do tej skali czasowej. Tam gdzie stopień zbadania w planowanym terminie był niekompletny, sięgnięto po dane z okresu wcześniejszego lub późniejszego, oceniając czy ich uwzględnienie przyczyniłoby się do poprawy jakości obrazu lub stopnia zbadania. Tab. 3. za tym **Wstępem** zawiera listę państw uczestniczących w programie, okresy zbierania danych, krajowe siatki z których przetransponowano dane oraz stosowane metody.

Zbieranie danych – rozmieszczenie gatunków

Atlas powstał w oparciu o setki tysięcy, być może ponad milion godzin prac terenowych. W idealnej sytuacji, wszystcy uczestnicy powinni używać identycznych metod terenowych, pracując w tym samym okresie czasu; było to jednak niemożliwe. Z tego powodu EOAC wydał raczej szeroko rozumiane zalecenia, aniżeli ścisłe reguły. W niektórych krajach, prace terenowe nad tym atlasem połączone były z pracami nad atlasami krajowymi. W innych, dla potrzeb tego *Atlasu* użyto danych z niezależnie przeprowadzonego już programu atlasu krajowego. Metody pracy w terenie były zróżnicowane: od pojedynczych wizyt, poprzez wielokrotne kontrole połączone z kumulowaniem informacji, aż po systematyczne oceny liczebności oparte na liczeniach punktowych, transektach lub mapowaniu terytoriów na powierzchnuiach próbnych.

Standardowy formularz przygotowany przez Holenderski Centralny Urząd Statystyczny jest częściowo przedstawiony na ryc. 4 (za tym **Wstępem**). Formularz wypełniano dla każdego kontrolowanego kwadratu. W przypadku kwadratów położonych w poprzek granic państwowych, każdy kraj zestawiał dane jedynie dla swej własnej części.

Ogólna informacja wymagana dla każdego kwadratu zawierała:

1. Okres obserwacji: rok lub lata z których pochodzą dane.
2. Identyfikator kwadratu (kod UTM50).
3. Kompletność danych: wskaźnik ten określa czy w danym kwadracie stwierdzono ponad 75% oczekiwanych tu gatunków (wysoka) czy też mniej (niska).
4. Zakres wysokości (maximum, minimum) nad poziomem morza na terenie kwadratu (m npm).
5. Obserwatorzy lub koordynator (-rzy): załączone nazwiska i adresy w razie niejasności.
6. Uwagi: dopuszczalna dodatkowa informacja celem lepszego objaśnienia danych na formularzu.
7. Krótki kwestionariusz odnośnie siedlisk występujących w kwadracie.

Podstawową informacją podaną na formularzu jest lista gatunków (ok. 440 gatunków, za Voous'em (1977), w kolejności EURINGu), dla których wprowadzano dane zasadnicze. W kolumnie 0 formularza wpisany był skrót nazwy łacińskiej (np. Gav stell), w kolumnie 1 – kod EURINGu (np. 00020), zaś w kolumnie 3 wymagany był wpis odnośnie statusu lęgowego i jego kod. Istniało 16 takich kodów, zgrupowanaych w 3 kategoriach: gniazdowanie pewne, gniazdowanie prawdopodobne i gniazdowanie możliwe. Odpowiednie kody zestawione są w tab. 1. Na koniec, w kolumnie 3 formularza wpisywana była ocena liczebności par lęgowych w obrębie kwadratu, wyrażona w skali logarytmicznej (1 = 1–9, 2 = 10–99... 6= >100 000).

Formularz umożliwiał osobne zapisanie na końcu listy hybrydów i gatunków pierwotnie nie wymienionych.

Generalnie, wykorzystane były następujące źródła danych wejściowych o ptakach lęgowych:

1. Krajowi koordynatorzy EBCC, którzy organizowali zbieranie danych i zestawiali wyniki na formularzach.
2. Regionalni koordynatorzy. Czasami zbieranie danych

Tabela 1 *Kategorie gniazdowania i ich kody*

A: Gniazdowanie możliwe

1. Gatunek obserwowany w sezonie lęgowym w siedlisku lęgowym;
2. Śpiewający samiec widziany lub słyszany w sezonie lęgowym;

B: Gniazdowanie prawdopodobne

3. Para obserwowana w sezonie lęgowym w siedlisku lęgowym;
4. Zajęte terytorium, potwierdzone przez rejestrację zachowań terytorialnych (śpiew itp.) co najmniej dwukrotnie w odstępach przynajmniej tygodniowych, w tym samym miejscu;
5. Toki i pokazy godowe;
6. Odwiedzanie miejsca możliwego gniazdowania;
7. Ptaki dorosłe zaniepokojone lub wydające głosy zaniepokojenia;
8. Plama lęgowa u ptaka dorosłego trzymanego w ręku;
9. Budowa gniazda lub drążenie dziupli/nory.

C: Gniazdowanie pewne

10. Odwodzenie lub symulowanie zranienia;
11. Znalezione gniazdo (zajęte w okresie badań) lub skorupy jaj;
12. Świeżo lotne młode (podloty; gniazdowniki) lub pisklęta puchowe (zagniazdowniki);
13. Ptaki dorosłe widziane wysiadujące lub odwiedzające miejsce gniazdowania w okolicznościach sugerujących zajęte gniazdo (odnosi się do wysoko umieszczonych gniazd lub dziupli, których zawartości nie da się skontrolować);
14. Ptak dorosły z odchodami lub pokarmem dla młodych w dziobie;
15. Gniazdo z jajami;
16. Gniazdo z pisklętami (widzianymi lub słyszanymi);

było organizowane przez kogoś innego, aniżeli koordynator krajowy, szczególnie gdy kraj był rozległy lub gdy istniejąca sieć kontaktów lepiej funkcjonowała w oparciu o aktywnego członka takiej sieci.

3. Dodatkowe źródła danych krajowych, głównie literatura, zazwyczaj udostępniona przez ekspertów gatunkowych. Tam gdzie brakowało danych ilościowych, przede wszystkim na terenach odległych, jedynym źródłem danych były publikowane lub niepublikowane sprawozdania niedostępne bezpośrednio dla redaktorów lub krajowych organizatorów.
4. Autor tekstu gatunkowego. Bardzo często, autor tekstu gatunkowego dysponujący wiedzą na jego temat, znał dodatkowe źródła informacji odnośnie rozmieszczenia lub liczebności.

Wszystkie informacje z tych źródeł były traktowane zgodnie z hierarchią danych: każde uzupełnienie w bazie danych musiało uzyskać aprobatę na poziomie kordynatora krajowego.

Informacja jakościowa a półilościowa

Atlas wykorzystuje informację półilościową (logarytmiczna ocena wielkości populacji) oszacowaną w skali kwadratu przez regionalnych i krajowych koordynatorów oraz obserwatorów terenowych. Kropki na mapach reprezentują liczbę par lęgowych, nie zaś zagęszczenie, a wielkość kropek odpowiada kategorii liczebności (patrz objaśnienia na stronie cxl). Niestety, niektóre państwa nie były w stanie dostarczyć ocen półilościowych dla całości (Norwegia i Polska), większości (Hiszpania) lub części (Islandia, Francja i Włochy) swego terytorium. W trakcie trwania programu stracono kontakt z Bośnią i Serbią, co uniemożliwiło uaktualnienie ich danych. Niektóre regiony Francji podniosły jakość swych danych samodzielnie. Francuski koordynator krajowy podniósł jakość danych w skali kraju dla ograniczonej liczby gatunków. Nawet oceny w skali logarytmicznej, podane dla pewnej liczby kwadratów, zawierają daleko więcej informacji, niż proste wskazanie obecności lub nieobecności gatunku.

Dla kwadratów granicznych, gdzie każdy kraj dostarczył ocenę liczebności populacji dla swej części, używano wyższej z dwóch liczb (wartości w skali logarytmicznej nie należy dodawać), choć w niektórych przypadkach mogło to prowadzić do zaniżenia oceny. Takie szacunki były bardziej użyteczne niż degradacja tych kwadratów do statusu jakościowego.

Kropki na mapach oznaczają następujące kategorie informacji:

ciemnopurpurowe	= gniazdowanie pewne lub prawdopodobne, dane jakościowe
jasnopurpurowe	= gniazdowanie możliwe, dane jakościowe
czerwone	= gniazdowanie pewne lub prawdopodobne, dane półilościowe
pomarańczowe	= gniazdowanie możliwe, dane półilościowe
szare	= nie zbierano danych odnośnie danego gatunku w danym kwadracie
brak kropki	= kwadrat kontrolowany, lecz gatunku nie wykryto.

Komputeryzacja – mapowanie poprawek i sprawdzanie poprawności wprowadzenia danych

Formularze uzyskane od krajowych koordynatorów były sprawdzane celem wykrycia podstawowych błędów (brak kodów, kody niedozwolone) przed wprowadzeniem do komputera w postaci pliku ASCII, gdzie każdy rekord zaopatrywany był dodatkowo w kod państwa. Niektóre kraje dostarczyły dane na dyskietkach w formacie bazy danych; dane te były weryfikowane w ten sam sposób. Baza danych, która powstała z plików podstawowych zawiera dla poszczególnych gatunków jedną wartość na kwadrat.

Ci koordynatorzy krajowi, którzy szybko dostarczyli dane, szybko otrzymali robocze mapy i krajowe wydruki danych dla gatunków w ramach pierwszej fazy procesu weryfikacji. Byli oni proszeni o sprawdzenie tychże, co przyniosło w efekcie wiele poprawek. Jednakże niektóre kraje dostarczyły swe oryginalne dane późno, inne zaś uaktualniły swe dane z jakościowych na półilościowe. W rezultacie, proces weryfikacji i poprawiania danych rozpoczął się tam później, i generalnie prtzebiegał w różnym tempie w różnych krajach.

Produkcja roboczych map miała kluczowe znaczenie z dwóch powodów:

1. Umożliwiła koordynatorom krajowym, a poprzez nich wielu obserwatorom terenowym, sprawdzenie, czy dane które dostarczyli zostały bezbłędnie wprowadzone: mapy pokazywały czy dane symbole były we właściwym miejscu dla właściwych gatunków. Błędy były bardziej widoczne na mapach aniżeli wyłącznie na wydrukach danych.
2. Stymulowała szerszy współudział w programie, co często owocowało napływem nowych danych.

W drugiej fazie sprawdzano czy poprawki z pierwszej fazy zostały prawidłowo wprowadzone. Uzyskano to wysyłając koordynatorom krajowym drugi zestaw map roboczych wraz z wydrukami. Większość koordynatorów podołała temu ogromnemu obciążeniu i dostarczyła ostateczne poprawki, lecz w krajach takich jak była Jugosławia uzupełnienia i poprawki były często niemożliwe. Te kraje, dla których proces weryfikacji był opóźniony musiały skoncentrować swój wysiłek w daleko krótszym czasie; im większe było to opóźnienie, tym większe były trudności w finalizacji map.

W kolejnym etapie, uaktualnione dane otrzymano od autorów opracowań gatunkowych oraz innych ekspertów. Większość z nich została oceniona przez koordynatorów krajowych, celem podjęcia decyzji, których danych użyć. Tam, gdzie z braku czasu było to niemożliwe, utrzymane zostały dane wcześniejsze, względnie autor opracowania gatunkowego zaznaczał w tekście, że w jego opinii przedstawiony na mapie materiał posiada określone braki.

Tam, gdzie nie istniały dane zebrane w ramach atlasowych prac terenowych, a w szczególności w północnej Rosji i Albanii, miejscowi ornitolodzy terenowi oceniali dane pochodzące z innych źródeł i podejmowali decyzję odnośnie ich użyteczności dla *Atlasu*. Niektóre oceny półilościowe dla takich kwadratów uzyskano poprzez ekstrapolację z tych kwadratów w danym regionie, dla których bezpośrednie oceny były dostępne, biorąc pod uwagę powierzchnię odpowiednich siedlisk.

Ostatecznym terminem przyjmowanie nowych danych i poprawek był 1 lipca 1995; jednak dla maksymalizacji stopnia zbadania użyto także danych uzyskanych w ciągu kilku następnych miesięcy z Albani, europejskiej części Turcji, Kaukazu, części Ukrainy i części Rosji. Poprawki zgłaszane przez autorów opracowań gatunkowych były przyjmowane do 1 listopada 1995.

Zbieranie danych – liczebności populacji

Przedstawione w *Atlasie* diagramy wielkości krajowych populacji pochodzą z Europejskiej Bazy Danych o Ptakach (European Bird Database, dalej EBD). Zawiera ona dane o populacjach ptaków uzyskane we współpracy EBCC i BirdLife International, i założona została dla potrzeb niniejszego *Atlas*u oraz Programu Gatunków Rozproszonych prowadzonego przez BirdLife, którego wyniki zostały opublikowane w książce *Birds in Europe – their conservation status* (Tucker & Heath 1994). Ta współpraca ułatwiła również dotarcie z programem *Atlasu* do niektórych części Europy. Dane były zbierane w pierwszym rzędzie poprzez kwestionariusze rozesłane do narodowych koordynatorów (wymienionych w *Birds in Europe*), którzy z kolei rozprowadzili je wśród odpowiednich specjalistów, organizacji monitoringowych i współpracowników regionalnych. Zarządcą EBD jest BirdLife International.

Każdy kraj dostarczył następujących danych dla populacji lęgowych wszystkich swoich gatunków ptaków:

1. Liczebność populacji.
2. Trend liczebności populacji (w okresie 1970-1990).
3. Trend zmian zasięgu (w okresie 1970-1990).

Podobne dane zebrano również dla populacji zimujących; nie są one tu jednak przedstawione.

Źródła danych użytych do oszacowania wielkości populacji i ich trendów były rejestrowane. Kody dokładności oceny, wymienione w tab. 2 za tym **Wstępem**, określają dokładność i wiarygodność ocen wielkości populacji i jej trendu.

Niektórzy autorzy opracowań gatunkowych zakwestionowali oceny liczebności populacji zawarte w bazie danych (EBD), lecz było za późno, by te poprawki wprowadzić do bazy. W takich wypadkach, autorzy uwzględnili swoje oceny liczebności w tekstach opracowań gatunkowych, lecz towarzyszące diagramy zawsze pokazują liczby z bazy danych.

Ograniczenia danych

Program *Atlasu* zaowocował zestawem danych o wysokiej jakości. Nie dało się jedak uniknąć pewnych ograniczeń związanych z jakością zebranych danych. Ci, którzy chcą używać ich dla dalszych analiz, muszą ograniczenia te wziąć pod uwagę. Szczegółowe ich omówienie wykracza poza zakres tej książki i należy je uzyskać z EBCC. Niemniej jednak, niektóre ważniejsze ograniczenia, mające wpływ na ogólne wykorzystanie książki są następujące:

1. Nie istniał zawczasu ustalony zestaw metod terenowych dla określania obecności i nieobecności gatunków jak również dla określania wielkości populacji. Wiele programów krajowych, będących źródłami danych dla EBCC przygotowało własne metodyki pracy terenowej dla własnych potrzeb, w relacji do dostępnych zasobów.
2. Nie istniał uniwersalny zestaw metod konwersji danych terenowych na informacje zestawiane na formularzach zbiorczych, głównie z przyczyn zbliżonych do wymienionych wyżej. Metody tej konwersji danych były indywidualne.
3. Zróżnicowanie w poziomie ornitologii terenowej i

względnej liczbie obserwatorów wpłynęło na zróżnicowanie jakości danych.
4. Niektóre dane pochodzą częściowo z ekstrapolacji.
5. Niektóre dane pochodzą z literatury (głównie obszary arktyczne).

UKŁAD MAP I OPRACOWAŃ GATUNKOWYCH W *ATLASIE*

W niniejszym *Atlasie*, gatunki przedstawione są w dwóch grupach: te dla których uzyskano satysfakcjonujące dane dla potrzeb mapowania, oraz te, dla których nie udało się takich danych zebrać. Opracowania gatunkowe dla ptaków z pierwszej grupy znajdują się w części 1.; druga grupa posiada krótsze teksty w części 2. W obu częściach, gatunki uszeregowane są wg podziału Voous'a i z grubsza w kolejności numeracji EURINGu; wyjątkiem są drobne odstępstwa w części 1., służące temu, by każdy gatunek, dla którego mapa i tekst zajmują pojedynczą stronę, był zawsze ulokowany naprzeciw inego gatunku 'jednostronicowego'. Gatunki, których mapa i tekst zajmują dwie strony, zawsze mają mapę i tekst na stronach naprzeciwległych. W niektórych przypadkach, gatunki z bardzo ograniczonym zasięgiem nie wymagały obszernego omówienia, umożliwiając zestawienie na jednej stronie opracowań więcej niż tylko jednego gatunku. Każdemu gatunkowi towarzyszy jego ilustracja; zestawione są również jego nazwy w 14 językach. Większość zmapowanych gatunków posiada diagram populacyjny, który jest objaśniony na stronach, poprzedzających mapy i teksty gatunkowe.

Mapy pochodne

Ryc. 5 ilustruje ogólne bogactwo gatunkowe ptaków lęgowych w poszczególnych kwadratach. Ryc. 6 – 8 przedstawiają bogactwo gatunków wymagających szczególnych przedsięwzięć ochronnych (SPEC) w ich kategoriach 1, 2 i 3, zdefiniowanych przez BirdLife International. Ryc. 9 podsumowuje informację dla tych trzech kategorii.

OPRACOWANIA GATUNKOWE

Opracowania gatunkowe poruszają (tam, gdzie to możliwe) zestaw standardowych tematów, z reguły w następującym porządku (zgodnie z zawczasu ustalonymi priorytetami): rozmieszczenie na świecie, siedliska lęgowe w Europie, schemat rozmieszczenia i zagęszczenia w Europie, ostatnie zmiany w rozmieszczeniu i liczebności (i ich prawdopodobne przyczyny), regionalna zmienność w zagęszczeniach, prawdopodobne czynniki limitujące rozmieszczenie, zagęszczenia gniazdowe w podstawowym siedlisku, charakterystyka migracji i przemieszczeń gatunku w i poza Europą, cechy szczególne gatunku, oraz krótkie odniesienie się do podgatunków wraz z ich rozmieszczeniem i trendami.

Następujące tematy zostały pominięte (o ile krótka wzmianka nie okazywała się rzeczywiście konieczna, by zilustrować jedno ze standardowych zagadnień): biologia lęgowa, zachowanie, pokarm, stosunek do innych gatunków, cechy morfologiczne i fizjologia, szczegółowa dyskusja zagrożeń gatunku (przedmiot analizy w *Birds in Europe*), oologia, ewolucja i taksonomia (z wyjątkiem przypadków ogólnie zaakceptowanych, większych zmian, które nastąpiły ostatnio, względnie gdy podgatunki są istotnie różne), śmiertelność i inne parametry dynamiki populacji oraz głosy i śpiew.

Kryteria uwzględniania gatunków

W *Atlasie* uwzględnione są gatunki gniazdujące na obszarze planowanego zbadania od roku 1985 poczynając, jeżeli spełniają one jednocześnie kryteria wymienione w tab. 1. W przypadku gatunków introdukowanych, lecz gniazdujących w stanie dzikim, kryterium uwzględniania w opracowaniu stanowiło istnienie przynajmniej jednej populacji ocenianej jako samoodnawiająca się na przestrzeni pięciu lat. Akceptacja i interpretacja tego typu reguł jest silnie zróżnicowana w poszczególnych krajach Europy, tak więc uwzględnienie bądź pominięcie niektórych gatunków o introdukowanych populacjach może wydawać się na pierwszy rzut oka dosyć arbitralne.

W sumie, *Atlas* obejmuje 513 gatunków oraz *Passer* x *italiae*.

NOMENKLATURA I TAKSONOMIA

Taksonomia

EBCC przyjęło w kwestiach taksonomicznych ostrożne i konserwatywne stanowisko. Ten *Atlas* generalnie stosuje taksonomię, systematykę i angielską nomenklaturę przyjętą w opracowaniu *Birds of the Western Palearctic*, z uzupełnieniami dokonanymi w skróconym wydaniu tego podręcznika.

Puffinus yelkounan, Puffinus mauretanicus, Larus cachinnans, Anthus petrosus, Phylloscopus lorentzii oraz *Pyrrhula murina* są traktowane jako samodzielne gatunki, i mapowane oddzielnie od *Puffinus puffinus, Larus argentatus, Anthus spinoletta, Phylloscopus collybita* i *Pyrrhula pyrrhula*. Oddzielne mapowanie było możliwe gdyż były one osobno rejestrowane, albo są rozdzielone geograficznie (tekst dla trzech gatunków z rodzaju *Puffinus* jest jednak wspólny). Początkowo, próbowano również osobnego rejestrowania podgatunków i form w obrębie kilku gatunków, lecz podziały zastosowane przez EOAC nie były postrzegane tak samo w całej Europie, uniemożliwiając oddzielne mapowanie. 'Wróbel włoski' był jednak rejestrowany oddzielnie i *Atlas* – za BWP – traktuje go jako ustabilizowanego hybryda pomiędzy *Passer domesticus* a *P.hispaniolensis* i opisuje go jako *Passer x italiae*. Z drugiej strony, *Phylloscopus trochiloides* obejmuje dwa oddzielone geograficznie podgatunki, *viridanus* i *nitidus*, poprzednio uważane za odrębne gatunki. Argumenty za oddzieleniem *Lanius meridionalis* od *L.excubitor* były generalnie akceptowane w okresie, gdy *Atlas* był przygotowywany do druku; diagram w opisie gatunkowym wskazuje granicę pomiędzy tymi formami. *Hippolais rama* bywa czasem uważany za odrębny gatunek aniżeli *H.caligata*, lecz tutaj traktowany jest on jako jego podgatunek. Niejasne są też często relacje w obrębie niektórych kompleksów mew; tutaj *Larus armenicus* jest traktowany oddzielnie.

Numeracja EURINGu

Europejska Unia Obrączkowania Ptaków (EURING) posiada, modyfikowaną od czasu do czasu, listę pięciocyfrowych kodów identyfikacyjnych dla gatunków i podgatunków, używaną przede wszystkim dla celów obrączkowania ptaków. Generalnie, lista ta gdzie to możliwe przyjmuje porządek Voous'a, stąd też została tu wykorzystana jako użyteczna pomoc przy zestawianiu danych. Kody EURINGu podane są w opracowaniach gatunkowych. Szczegółowe objaśnienia odnośnie używania numeracji EURINGu zawiera **Dodatek techniczny**.

CYTOWANIE LITERATURY

Z uwagi na ograniczenia objętości, autorzy byli proszeni by unikać cytowania podręczników jako źródła danych. Jednakże na szczególną uwagę zasługują dwa współczesne podręczniki europejskie: *Birds of the Western Palearctic* (Cramp *et al* 1977–1994), oraz *Handbuch der Vogel Mitteleuropas* (Glutz von Blotzheim *et al* 1966–1993). W *Atlasie* książki te oznaczane są skrótami BWP oraz HVM. Znajdujące się w *Atlasie* teksty i mapy gatunkowe powinny być uzupełnione lekturą odpowiednich rozdziałów w tych fundamentalnych opracowaniach źródłowych.

Birds in Europe – their conservation status (Tucker & Heath 1994) jest pierwszym przeglądowym opracowaniem statusu i zagrożeń europejskich populacji ptaków; szczegółowo są tam opisane te gatunki, kórych status ochronny jest niekorzystny. *Atlas* omawia nie tylko takie gatunki, lecz również wszystkie pozostałe gatunki ptaków, które obecnie nie są zagrożone. Diagramy populacyjne w *Atlasie* pochodzą z tej samej Europejskiej Bazy Danych o Ptakach (EBD), wykorzystywanej w *Birds in Europe*, a teksty gatunkowe często odwołują się do tego źródła danych.

Bibliografia cytowana w *Atlasie* zestawiona jest na końcu książki, tuż przed indeksami.

Michael Blair, Ward Hagemeijer
(tłumaczenie: Przemysław Chylarecki)

SKRÓTY I SŁOWNIK UŻYTYCH TERMINÓW

Kierunki świata

N	= północny
S	= południowy
E	= wschodni
W	= zachodni; stąd NW = północno-zachodni, WSW = zachodni-południowo-zachodni itp.
C	= środkowy (centralny); stąd S-C = południowo-środkowa itp.

Wyrażenia ogólne

asl	= nad poziom morza (npm) (wysokość)
c	= około
et al	= i inni (przy cytowaniu literatury)
pers comm	= informacja ustna (lub listowna)
pers obs	= obserwacje własne
unpubl	= materiały niepublikowane

Wymiary i miary ilości

bp	= pary lęgowe
ha	= hektary
ind	= osobniki
m	= metry
km	= kilometry (km^2 = kilometry kwadratowe)
M	= miliony

Skróty nazw własnych

BTO	= British Trust for Ornithology (GB)
BWP	= Birds of Western Palearctic
HVM	= Handbuch der Vögel Mitteleuropas
EBCC	= European Bird Census Council
JNCC	= Joint Nature Conservation Committee (GB)
RSPB	= Royal Society for the Protection of Birds (GB)
SOVON	= SOVON Bird Census Work The Netherlands (NL)
WWT	= Wildfowl and Wetlands Trust (GB)

Definicje terminów

eutrophic	bogaty w składniki mineralne pochodzące z rozkładu materii roślinnej i zwierzęcej
lentic	odnosi się do wód stojących lub wolno płynących (np. w stawach i jeziorach)
lotic	odnosi się do wód płynących
mesotrophic	pośredni (ani bogaty ani ubogi) pod względem zawartości postawowych soli mineralnych i składników pokarmowych
'mixotrophic'	termin związany z jeziorami strefy borealnej, które są płytkie i z bogatą roślinnością, lecz ich plaże są relatywnie ubogie w składniki pokarmowe
oligotrophic	ubogi w podstawowe sole i składniki pokarmowe
phenology	badania rozkładu czasowego powtarzających się cyklicznie zjawisk
sclerophytic	odnosi się do roślin z grubymi, zazwyczaj małymi liśćmi, o małym tempie transpiracji, przystosowanych do suchych klimatów
xerophytic	odnosi się do roślin przystosowanych do bardzo suchych warunków

ВВЕДЕНИЕ

О ЗАМЫСЛЕ АТЛАСА ГНЕЗДЯЩИХСЯ ПТИЦ ЕВРОПЫ, СОЗДАННОГО ЕВРОПЕЙСКИМ СОВЕТОМ ПО УЧЕТАМ ПТИЦ

Многие книги содержат малодостоверные карты распространения птиц. Лишь некоторые из них базируются на наблюдениях за гнездящимися птицами. За исключением нескольких атласов, составленных специалистами, карты эти имеют первоисточники разной степени надежности, а иногда являются просто воспроизведением более ранних карт сомнительной достоверности. К тому же обычно на картах нет количественных характеристик: в лучшем случае они показывают, где виды обычны, а где редки.

В настоящее время появляется все больше новых, превосходных по качеству региональных и национальных атласов гнездящихся птиц. Многие из них имеют общие корни с проектом, который привел к созданию данного Атласа и, подобно ему, содержат полуколичественную информацию. В 1971 г. был организован Комитет по созданию Европейского Орнитологического Атласа (ЕОАС) с тем, чтобы картографировать гнездовое распространение тех европейских птиц, данные по которым могут быть получены с помощью полевых исследований. В Атласе представлены результаты этих работ.

В Атласе приведены данные по распространению птиц за ограниченный промежуток времени. Эти данные, несмотря на некоторые недостатки, являются той основой, с которой можно сопоставлять орнитологические исследования в будущем, особенно в отношении изменений в распространении птиц. Уже в 1971 г. ЕОАС представлял себе прообраз этого первого в истории всеевропейского обзора гнездящихся птиц. Эта мечта успешно осуществилась. В Атласе гнездящихся птиц Европы, созданном Европейским советом по учетам птиц, даны карты ареалов гнездящихся птиц Европы. В нем можно найти ответ на вопрос: "Какая птица где гнездится?"

СТРУКТУРА АТЛАСА

Введение кратко описывает назначение Атласа, детально знакомит с методами сбора данных по распространению и численности птиц, по их компьютерной обработке, а также объясняет структуру Атласа. Это необходимо для того, чтобы данное издание можно было использовать во многих аспектах. Введение напечатано на основных европейских языках, понятных большинству орнитологов этого континента.

ВСТУПИТЕЛЬНЫЕ РАЗДЕЛЫ

Во Вступлении профессор Карел Ваус (Нидерланды) показывает особое значение Атласа в связи с изменениями, происходящими в авифауне Европы. Предисловие объясняет, как совместный проект по созданию Атласа может удовлетворить потребности европейских орнитологов, а также разъясняет политику и намерения Европейского комитета по учетам птиц (EBCC) в проведении мониторинга птиц Европы в будущем. Затем идет Введение, включающее такие темы как методы и территорию, охваченную картамы Атласа. Раздел Справочные рисунки, следующий за Введением, показывает охваченную картографированием территорию, качество полученных данных, и экземпляр стандартизированной формы для представления собранных материалов. Исторический раздел рассказывает об успехах и трудностях, с которыми пришлось столкнуться при создании Атласа. Далее под заголовком 'Эволюция и история орнитофауны в Европе' помещен очерк профессора Жака Блонделя, объясняющий возникновение современных ареалов птиц в Европе. Затем приведены список благодарностей, а также список национальных и основных региональных атласов европейских птиц.

ВИДОВЫЕ ОЧЕРКИ

Введение в карты и графики изменения численности птиц предшествует основной части Атласа, которая посвящена видам, гнездящимся в Европе. Часть 1 состоит из карт распространения, видовых очерков, общепринятых названий каждого из гнездящихся видов на 14 основных европейских языках и иллюстраций. Группы птиц расположены в таксономическом порядке, предложенном К. Ваусом (1977), а виды - в последовательности, используемой Европейским Союзом кольцевания птиц. Часть 2 посвящена тем видам, чье гнездование в Европе предположительно, а по которым не получено никаких данных.

ЗАКЛЮЧИТЕЛЬНЫЕ РАЗДЕЛЫ

Раздел Дополнительные карты дает более подробные данные об обилии видов гнездящихся птиц Европы и "Видов Особого Европейского Внимания" (SPEC) в определении BirdLife International (Tucker & Heath 1994). В Техническом приложении разъяснены отличия проекции, принятой в Атласе, от проекции Меркатора; в нем говорится также о том, как изменено изображение островов и морских побережий с помощью 50-километровых квадратов. В этом же приложении дается объяснение использованной в Атласе системы международных кодов, используемых Европейским Союзом кольцевания птиц (Euring).

БУКЛЕТЫ НА ЯЗЫКАХ ЕВРОПЕЙСКИХ СТРАН

Для того, чтобы Атлас был использован более широкими кругами специалистов и любителей-орнитологов, включая и тех, кто не читает по-английски, резюме вводных разделов (Вступление, Исторический очерк, и Эволюция и история орнитофауны в Европе) и видовых очерков подготовлено в виде отдельных буклетов. Этот краткий текст был передан орнитологам неанглоязычных стран для перевода на свой родной язык и распространения среди своих коллег. Список имен и адресов лиц, выдающих буклеты на языках европейских стран (по информации, полученной ко времени сдачи Атласа в набор) помещен в конце Технического приложения.

МЕТОДЫ

ИСПОЛЬЗОВАННЫЕ МАТЕРИАЛЫ

В Историческом разделе представлены основополагающие идеи по сбору и обработке данных и объяснен выбор методов, использованных при подготовке Атласа.

Карты Атласа показывают различия в плотности (число птиц на единицу площади) в логарифмическом масштабе (объяснение в разделе Сравнение качественной и полуколичественной информации: см. ниже). Это весьма удобно для тех видов, плотность которых значительно варьирует на протяжении их ареала. Впрочем, незначительную разницу в плотности в этом случае выявить нельзя.

В Атласе представлено распространение птиц, гнездящихся в Европе, даны количественная оценка размножающихся популяций и характер изменений для большинства видов во всех европейских странах. Изменения в характере распространения птиц можно понять, лишь имея серьезно обоснованную оценку размеров популяций всех стран и тенденций динамики их численности.

ТЕРРИТОРИЯ, ПРЕДПОЛАГАВШАЯСЯ ДЛЯ ВКЛЮЧЕНИЯ В АТЛАС

Территория Европы, предполагавшаяся для включения в Атлас, показана на рис. 1. Было бы желательно, чтобы территория, покрытая картами Атласа, полностью соответствовала границам Западной Палеарктики, определенным в книге "Птицы Западной Палеарктики" (Cramp *et al* 1977-1994), но, к сожалению, это было невыполнимо. Данных из Малой Азии, Северной Аравии и Северной Африки оказалось столь мало, что пришлось исключить эти территории из Атласа. В результате за основу для Атласа были взяты карты Атласа Европейской флоры (Jalas & Suominen 1972, 1988). Кроме того, в Атлас включены Новая Земля, Земля Франца Иосифа, все греческие острова у берегов Турции, архипелаг Мадейра, Азорские острова, Ставропольский край юго-востока Европейской России и Кавказские республики. Таким образом, разница между границами Западной Палеарктики и территорией, охваченной Атласом, заключается в том, что в Атлас не включены Кипр, Канарские острова и все средиземноморские острова вдоль берегов Африки, принадлежащие североафриканским странам.

Территория, охваченная картами Атласа, отличается и от территории, рассматриваемой в книге "Птицы в Европе - их охранный статус" (Tucker & Heath 1994) - тем, что в него не включены малоазийская часть Турции и Гренландия.

При детальном рассмотрении рисунка 1 можно заметить, что в территорию Западной Палеарктики - как в Атласе Европейской флоры, так и в данном Атласе, в отличие от книги "Птицы в Европе"- не включена небольшая часть Европейской территории России рядом с Оренбургом и добавлены часть Казахстана между реками Волга и Урал и часть азийской России к востоку от г. Пермь (Свердловской обл.).

ФАКТИЧЕСКИЙ ОХВАТ ТЕРРИТОРИИ ЕВРОПЫ АТЛАСОМ

В разделе Справочные рисунки, который следует за Введением, на рис. 2 приведены учетные квадраты и указана максимальная качественная нагрузка, полученная для каждого квадрата; на рис. 3 показана их минимальная качественная нагрузка. Раздел Сравнение качественной и полуколичественной информации (см. ниже) объясняет значение этих терминов; уровень качественности данных, показанных на этих картах,отображен в нисходящем порядке:

1. Полуколичественная оценка популяции: размножение подтверждено или вероятно.
2. Полуколичественная оценка популяции: размножение возможно.
3. Качественное присутствие вида: размножение подтверждено или вероятно.
4. Качественное присутствие вида: размножение возможно.

Качество данных было обычно одинаковым для всех отмеченных видов в данном квадрате (но см. ниже). Значительные площади Центральной России не были охвачены вообще - в основном потому, что не удалось установить контакты со специалистами на этих территориях. Для большей части остальной территории России, для некоторых районов Белоруссии, Украины и Кавказских республик были получены данные только для ограниченного числа видов. Большая часть территории бывшей Югославии была обследована удовлетворительно (хотя в некоторых районах не по всем видам). Имеются пробелы в учетах в Албании. Охват территории не был полным и для арктических островов России: Новой Земли и Земли Франца-Иосифа.

Во всех других частях Европы, несмотря на неизбежные пробелы в информации, охват территории был, по существу, полным.

КАРТЫ АТЛАСА

Картографическая проекция выбиралась по трем критериям: она должна была отображать всю площадь, охваченную Атласом, быть хорошо известной в большинстве европейских стран и быть совместимой с национальными картографическими проекциями. Когда начиналась работа над Атласом, только равноугольная цилиндрическая проекция Меркатора удовлетворяла этим основным требованиям. Поскольку в картах Атласа Европейской флоры использована та же проекция, она идеально подошла и для Атласа птиц. Наш Атлас использовал в качестве основы квадраты 50 х 50 км - те же, что и в Атласе Европейской флоры. Использование квадратов более крупного масштаба для сбора и сопоставления данных было бы непрактичным.

Основной картографической единицей в сетке проекции Меркатора принято считать квадраты 100 х 100 км, обозначаемые с помощью логически последовательного цифро-буквенного кода, состоящего из двух чисел и трех букв. В Атласе флоры и Атласе птиц каждый такой квадрат разделен на четыре квадрата 50 х 50 км следующим образом:

1 3
2 4.

В итоге каждый 50-километровый квадрат имеет свое шестизначное название.

Деление сетки проекции Меркатора по оси "север-юг" осуществлено простым делением меридиана, начиная с экватора, на 50-километровые интервалы параллельно линиям широт. Деление другой оси сложнее ввиду того, что меридианы сходятся у полюсов и, стало быть, число 50- километровых квадратов также должно уменьшаться к полюсам. Проекция Меркатора компенсирует это следующим образом: в основе каждой ячейки ("квадрата") по долготе (начиная с нулевого градуса) лежит сектор в 6 градусов. Каждая ячейка, имеющая в основании сектор в 6 градусов, сужается к полюсу, где она исчезает, превратившись в точку; основание соседней ячейки тоже начинается с 6 градусов, уменьшаясь далее аналогичным образом. Атлас Европейской флоры и наш Атлас птиц несколько модифицировали эту схему, уменьшив различия в длине между основанием и вершиной данной ячейки ("квадрата") (мы говорим о ячейках градусной сетки в Атласе как о "квадратах" для удобства, хотя многие из них не являются квадратами.): ячейки исчезают, когда ширина их основания уменьшается приблизительно до 40 км. Эта модель продемонстрирована на карте предполагавшегося охвата территории (рис. 1), а полная ее детализация дана в Техническом приложении.

Комитет по созданию Европейского Орнитологического Атласа снабдил национальных координаторов картами с вышеописанной 50-километровой сеткой, чтобы они использовали одинаковую шкалу для регистрации своих данных. Поскольку полевые работы велись обычно с использованием карт, охватывавших меньшую площадь, чем 50 х 50 км, или с использованием другой картографической проекции, национальные координаторы, получив собранные в их стране данные, должны были придать им форму, удобную для дальнейшего унифицированного использования.

СРОКИ ПОЛЕВЫХ РАБОТ И ПРОЦЕСС ПРИНЯТИЯ ДАННЫХ

По плану полевые работы по сбору материалов для Орнитологического Атласа должны были проводиться в 1985-88 гг. Однако в каждой стране орнитологи организовали свои полевые работы по-разному, и из-за практических трудностей не все проводили учеты птиц именно в этот период. Там, где территория не была полностью обследована в эти годы, были использованы также данные наблюдений, проведенных раньше или позже 1985-88 гг. Это разрешалось в тех случаях, когда дополнительная информация увеличивала размер территории, покрытой учетами, или имела более высокое качество учетных данных. В таблице 3, следующей за Введением, имеется перечень стран-участниц, периоды сбора ими полевых данных, картографические сетки, используемые в этих странах и использовавшиеся методы работы.

СБОР ДАННЫХ ПО РАСПРОСТРАНЕНИЮ ВИДОВ

Сотни тысяч, а возможно, и более миллиона часов полевых наблюдений было затрачено при подготовке Атласа. В идеале все участники должны были использовать идентичные методы наблюдений в один и тот же период времени, что, конечно, было неосуществимо. В связи с этим Европейский Комитет по созданию Атласа предложил не строгие правила, а скорее лишь общие директивы по сбору информации. В некоторых странах орнитологи во время полевых работ собирали одновременно материалы для Атласа птиц Европы и для своих национальных атласов. Полевые работы проводились разными методами - от однократных посещений квадратов и составления списков обнаруженных видов во время многократных посещений, до систематических обследований методом учетных маршрутов (точечных или линейных трансектов) или картографирования гнездовых территорий на пробных площадях.

Стандартизированная форма для представления собранных материалов была составлена Нидерландским центральным статистическим бюро (см. рис. 4 после Введения). Такая форма заполнялась для каждого учетного квадрата. Для квадратов, территория которых принадлежала двум государствам, каждая страна представляла данные только по своей части территории. Для каждого квадрата требовалась следующая общая информация:

1. Период (год или ряд лет), когда собирались данные.
2. Соответствие площадок коду УТМ50 (проекция Меркатора, квадраты 50 х 50 км).
3. Полнота обзора (отмечено ли в данном квадрате более 75 от ожидавшегося числа видов - "высокая полнота"- или менее 75 % - "низкая полнота").
4. Гипсометрическое положение данного квадрата в виде интервала, дающего минимальную и максимальную высоты над уровнем моря в метрах.
5. Имена и адреса наблюдателей и координаторов - на случай возникновения вопросов к ним.
6. Комментарии: дополнительная информация, поясняющая данные, занесенные в форму.
7. Краткая анкета, описывающая местообитания данного квадрата.

Основная часть предложенной стандартной формы состоит из списка видов (около 440 видов - по К. Ваусу, 1977), перечисленных в последовательности, принятой Европейским Союзом кольцевания птиц (Euring). Около каждого вида помещаются полученные данные. В нулевом столбце дано сокращенное латинское название вида (например, Gav stell); в столбце 1 - порядковый номер кода Европейского Союза кольцевания птиц (например, 00020); в столбце 2 - подтверждение гнездования вида с условным кодом. Всего использовано 16 условных кодов, разделенных на три категории: подтвержденное, вероятное и возможное гнездование. Расшифровка этих кодов приведена в таблице 1. Наконец, в столбце 3 дана оценка числа гнездящихся пар на квадрат по логарифмической шкале (1 = 1-9 пар, 2 = 10-99 пар ... 6 = более 100 000 пар).

В конце списка допускался перечень гибридов и видов, не вошедших в основной список. Источники данных по гнездованию птиц:

1. Национальные координаторы всех стран Европы, которые организовали сбор данных и представили полученную информацию в виде стандартных форм учета.
2. Региональные координаторы. Иногда сбор данных был организован с помощью региональных, а не общенациональных координаторов: в крупных по площади странах или в странах, где существует хорошо налаженная сеть наблюдателей, один из них брал на себя координирующую роль. Такие региональные координаторы работали аналогично национальным координаторам.
3. Дополнительные национальные источники информации, в основном из орнитологической литературы, обычно использовались экспертами по отдельным видам. Там, где не хватало полевых данных, особенно в отдаленных районах, единственным источником материалов часто бывали

Таблица 1. КАТЕГОРИИ ГНЕЗДОВАНИЯ И ИХ КОДЫ

А: Возможное гнездование
1. Вид наблюдался в гнездовой период в местообитаниях, подходящих для его гнездования.
2. Слышали в гнездовой период пение самца (самцов) или брачные крики.

Б: Вероятное гнездование
3. Пара наблюдалась в гнездовое время в подходящем для гнездования биотопе.
4. Наблюдалось территориальное поведение (песни и т.п.) на постоянном участке на протяжении не менее чем двух разных дней в течение недели или большего промежутка времени.
5. Брачное поведение и демонстрации.
6. Посещение птицами вероятного места гнездования.
7. Беспокойное поведение и тревожные крики взрослых птиц.
8. Наседное пятно у взрослой птицы.
9. Строительство гнезда или выдалбливание дупла.

В. Подтвержденное гнездование
10. Птицы пытаются отвлечь наблюдателя или притворяются раненными.
11. Обнаружены занятое птицами гнездо или скорлупа яиц.
12. Встречены слетки (для птенцовых видов птиц) или пуховики (для выводковых видов).
13. Встречены взрослые птицы, прилетающие на свой гнездовой участок и покидающие его при обстоятельствах, указывающих на жилое гнездо (например, когда гнездо не видно, т.к. находится высоко на дереве или в дупле), или же видна насиживающая птица.
14. Встречены взрослые птицы с птенцовыми фекалиями или кормом для птенцов.
15. Найдено гнездо с кладкой.
16. Обнаружено гнездо с птенцами, которых видно или слышно.

опубликованные или неопубликованные отчеты, недоступные национальным координаторам.

4. Авторы видовых очерков. Очень часто авторы видовых очерков, хорошо знающие конкретные виды, имели свои дополнительные источники информации о распространении или численности этих видов.

Все данные, полученные из вышеперечисленных источников, рассматривались согласно принятой иерархии: каждое дополнение, вносимое в базу данных, требовало одобрения на уровне национального координатора.

СРАВНЕНИЕ КАЧЕСТВЕННОЙ И ПОЛУКОЛИЧЕСТВЕННОЙ ИНФОРМАЦИИ

В Атласе использованы полуколичественные показатели (логарифмическая оценка численности популяции), подсчитанные в необходимом масштабе на единицу площади национальными или региональными координаторами и полевыми наблюдателями. В совокупности точки на картах представляют не плотность, а число гнездящихся пар; возрастающие размеры точек отображают рост размера популяции (см. пояснения на стр. cxl). К сожалению, некоторые страны полностью (Польша, Норвегия), в основном (Испания) или частично (Исландия, Франция и Италия) отказались от использования полуколичественных оценок. Комитет по созданию Атласа утратил также связи с орнитологами Боснии и Сербии и поэтому не смог улучшить качество их данных. В некоторых районах Франции данные наносились на квадраты независимо от французского национального координатора, который сумел собрать в масштабах всей страны данные лишь для небольшого числа видов. Даже логарифмические оценки, относящиеся к нескольким квадратам передают гораздо больше информации чем простое указание на присутствие или отсутствие видов.

Для квадратов, разделяемых государственными границами, каждая страна давала свою оценку численности птиц для своей части квадрата. В этом случае для карты выбирали более высокие количественные показатели. Даже такие приближенные количественные оценки более полезны, чем сведение всех данных только к качественной информации.

Точки на картах относятся к следующим категориям информации:

темнопурпурная	= размножение подтверждено или вероятно, качественное присутствие вида
светлопурпурная	= размножение возможно, качественное присутствие вида
красная	= размножение подтверждено или вероятно, полуколичественная оценка популяции
оранжевая	= размножение возможно, полуколичественная оценка популяции
серая	= в данном квадрате полевые работы по этому виду не проводились
без точки	= квадрат был обследован, но данный вид не обнаружен

КОМПЬЮТЕРНАЯ ОБРАБОТКА КОРРЕКЦИЯ ДАННЫХ КАРТОГРАФИРОВАНИЯ И ИХ ВВОД

Формы, полученные от национальных координаторов, были проверены на основные ошибки (пропущенные и неправильные индексы) до введения в компьютер в формате десятичных кодов (формат ASCII); при этом каждая запись имела код своей страны. Некоторые страны представили свои данные на дискетах; этот материал прошел аналогичную проверку. Полученная из таких файлов база данных имеет единственное значение для каждого вида на каждый квадрат.

Национальные координаторы, оперативно представившие данные, вскоре получили предварительные карты и списки видов птиц своей страны в качестве первого этапа проверки полученных данных. Однако часть стран представила свои материалы поздно, другие преобразовали свои качественные данные в полуколичественные. В результате корректировка этих данных и процесс их утверждения начался позже и проходил в разных странах с различной скоростью.

Подготовка предварительных карт была особенно важна по двум причинам:

1. Это дало возможность национальным координаторам, а через них и многим орнитологам, представившим материал, проверить, насколько правильно введены их данные: ошибки легче выявляются на карте, чем при анализе списка видов.
2. Предварительные карты стимулировали включение в работу орнитологов, еще не задействованных в данном проекте. В итоге была получена дополнительная информация.

На второй стадии обработки проверяли, правильно ли введены исправления, выявленные при анализе предварительных карт. В результате национальные координаторы и другие участники представили второй, скорректированный набор карт и списков видов. Большая часть координаторов справилась с этой титанической задачей и представила окончательные поправки во-время. Только в таких странах, как бывшая Югославия, получение новых данных и проверка имеющихся зачастую оказалась невозможной.

Страны, не успевшие во-время проверить данные, должны были провести эту работу в более сжатые сроки. Задержки с выверкой собранных материалов создавали большие трудности на заключительных этапах создания карт Атласа.

На завершающей стадии подготовки Атласа от некоторых авторов видовых очерков и других экспертов пришли новейшие материалы. Большая их часть была проверена национальными координаторами, определявшими, что с ними делать. Если времени на это не было, то либо были сохранены первоначальные данные, либо в тексте было отмечено, что мнение авторов очерков не совпадает с закартированными материалами.

Там, где нельзя было провести специальные полевые работы по сбору материалов для Атласа (например, на Севере России или в Албании), местные орнитологи анализировали всю прочую имевшуюся информацию и приходили к заключению о ее пригодности. Часть полуколичественных показателей для этих квадратов была получена путем экстраполяции данных из соседних квадратов, в которых проводились полевые наблюдения в сходных местообитаниях.

1 июля 1995 г. было крайним сроком приема новых данных и поправок, однако, чтобы увеличить площадь, охваченную картами Атласа, в нем были использованы данные, полученные в последующие несколько месяцев из Албании, Европейской части Турции, с Кавказа, из отдельных областей Украины и России. Поправки, внесенные в предварительные данные авторами видовых очерков, принимались до 1 ноября 1995 г.

СБОР ДАННЫХ ПО ЧИСЛЕННОСТИ

Помещенные в Атласе графики изменений численности птиц на территориях отдельных стран взяты из Европейской Орнитологической базы данных. Она содержит данные по численности птиц, собранные совместно Европейским комитетом по учетам птиц и BirdLife International, и предназначается для использования в этом Атласе, а также в Проекте BirdLife International по дисперсно распространенным видам. Результатом последнего проекта стала публикация книги "Птицы в Европе - их охранный статус" (Tucker & Heath 1994). Это сотрудничество также помогло расширить круг участников из некоторых стран Европы.Данные собирались прежде всего с помощью анкет, разосланных национальным координаторам (перечисленным в "Птицах в Европе"), которые, в свою очередь,распространяли эти анкеты среди соответствующих специалистов, организаций, осуществляющих мониторинг, и среди региональных координаторов. BirdLife International является организацией, управляющей Европейской Орнитологической базой данных. Каждая страна представила следующие данные по численности всех гнездящихся видов птиц:

1. Общая численность.
2. Тренд изменений численности за период 1970-1990 гг.
3. Тренд изменений ареала вида за период 1970-1990 гг.

Аналогичная информация была собрана для зимующих птиц, но в данный Атлас она не включена.

Были зарегистрированы все источники информации о численности птиц и трендах ее изменений. Данные о точности и достоверности использованных материалов по общей численности и трендам приведены в таблице 2 после Введения.

Некоторые из авторов видовых очерков не согласились с оценками численности в базе данных, но такая информация была получена поздно, так что нельзя было включить ее в базу данных. В таких случаях, авторы привели свои оценки в тексте, а надо отметить, что в графике при видовом очерке всегда показаны оценки в базе данных.

НЕДОСТАТКИ СОБРАННЫХ ДАННЫХ

При создании Атласа был собран значительный объем высококачественных данных. Естественно, что не все данные идеально сравнимы. Те орнитологи, которые хотят использовать эти данные для дальнейших исследований, должны иметь это в виду. Детальное описание недостатков этих данных выходит за рамки этого Атласа. В случае необходимости нужно обращаться в Европейский Комитет по учетам птиц. Ниже приведены несколько основных недостатков, влияющих на возможности использования Атласа:

1. Специально рекомендованной методологии полевых работ для установления наличия или отсутствия видов птиц или их численности не существовало. Многие проекты из разных стран, служившие источником сведений для Европейского Комитета по учетам птиц, использовали свою методологию полевых исследований, в соответствии со своими целями и возможностями.
2. Не существовало универсальных методов модификации результатов полевых исследований для их соответствия учетным анкетам. Методы преобразования были индивидуальными.
3. Различия в качестве полевых исследований и в относительном числе наблюдателей, несомненно, тоже сказались на качестве собранных данных.
4. Некоторые данные отчасти являются результатом экстраполяции.
5. Некоторые данные (в основном по арктическим регионам) основаны на использовании орнитологических публикаций.

СХЕМА ИЗЛОЖЕНИЯ КАРТ И ВИДОВЫХ ОЧЕРКОВ

Все виды птиц Атласа разделены на две группы. К первой относятся виды, по которым был получен удовлетворительный объем данных для составления подробных карт. Полные очерки по этим видам помещены в Части 1 видовых очерков. Ко второй группе относятся виды, по которым не было получено такого объема данных. Более краткие очерки по этим видам приведены в Части 2. В обеих частях таксономические группы расположены в порядке, предложенном профессором К.Ваусом, а виды - приблизительно в последовательности, используемой Европейским Союзом кольцевания (Euring) за исключением следующих технических корректировок в Части 1: Вид, у которого карта и текст занимают одну страницу, всегда имеет на второй странице разворота тоже "одностраничный" вид. Если карта и текст вида занимают две страницы, то они всегда расположены на одном развороте. В некоторых случаях виды с очень ограниченным ареалом не нуждаются в полной трактовке и поэтому могут размещаться по два-три на одной странице. Каждый вид иллюстрирован; его общепринятое название (где это возможно) приведено на 14 языках. Большинство видов, имеющих карту ареала, имеет также график изменений численности, который объясняется на страницах перед видовыми картами и очерками.

ДОПОЛНИТЕЛЬНЫЕ (ПРОИЗВОДНЫЕ) КАРТЫ (СУММАРНОЕ ОБЪЯСНЕНИЕ)

Рис. 5 иллюстрирует общее обилие видов гнездящихся птиц на каждый квадрат. Рисунки 6-8 показывают обилие видов, включенных в 1, 2 и 3 категории SPEC (виды особого европейского внимания) - в том виде, в каком они определены BirdLife International, и Рис. 9 представляет собой комбинацию этих трех категорий.

ВИДОВЫЕ ОЧЕРКИ

Видовые очерки состоят (там, где это возможно) из перечня стандартных характеристик, обычно в нижеследующем порядке (в соответствии с заранее определенными приоритетами):

- распространение в пределах мирового ареала;
- гнездовые местообитания в Европе;
- характер распространения и численность в Европе;
- современные изменения в распространении и численности и их возможные причины;
- региональные изменения численности;
- возможные факторы, ограничивающие распространение и плотность гнездования в изначальных местообитаниях;
- миграции и описание передвижения вида внутри и за пределами Европы;
- другие особенности вида;
- краткий список подвидов с указанием их распределения, границ ареалов, перекрывания территориями других подвидов, трендов изменений.

Следующие характеристики видов не включены в очерк, если только краткое упоминание о них не является абсолютно необходимым для разъяснения одного из основных показателей: гнездовая биология, поведение, питание, взаимоотношения с другими видами, морфология и физиология, детальное обсуждение неблагоприятных для вида факторов (этому посвящен один из разделов книги "Птицы в Европе - их охранный статус"), отклонения от нормы, оология, эволюция и таксономия (за исключением тех случаев, когда существуют значительные изменения за последнее время или в случае существенных подвидовых различий), смертность и другие параметры популяционной динамики, описание голоса и песен.

КРИТЕРИИ ВКЛЮЧЕНИЯ ВИДОВ В АТЛАС

В Атлас включены виды, найденные на гнездовании на территории Европы в период с 1985 г., если они соответствуют критериям, приведенным в табл.1. Интродуцированные виды, гнездящиеся в дикой природе, включены в Атлас в том случае, если вид имел по крайней мере одну популяцию, которая считается самовоспроизводящейся на протяжении более чем 5 лет. Этот критерий интерпретируется в различных странах Европы по-разному, поэтому включение или не включение в Атлас некоторых видов иногда выглядит произвольным.

Атлас включает 513 видов птиц, плюс *Passer* x *italiae*.

НОМЕНКЛАТУРА И ТАКСОНОМИЯ

ТАКСОНОМИЯ

Европейский Комитет по учетам птиц занял в отношении таксономии осторожную и консервативную позицию. Атлас в целом следует таксономии, последовательности видов и английской номенклатуре, принятым для краткого издания "Птиц Западной Палеарктики", которое в настоящее время готовится к печати.

Puffinus yelkouan, *Puffinus mauretanicus*, *Larus cachinnans*, *Anthus petrosus*, *Phylloscopus lorenzii* и *Pyrrhula murina* рассматриваются как самостоятельные виды и закартированы отдельно от *Puffinus puffinus*, *Larus argentatus*, *Anthus spinoletta*, *Phylloscopus collybita* и *Pyrrhula pyrrhula*. Раздельное картографирование было возможно или когда эти виды наблюдались отдельно, или когда они были разделены географически. (Текст для трех видов рода *Puffinus* объединен.)

Первоначально мы пытались отмечать отдельно подвиды и формы некоторых видов. Однако различия между ними, предложенные Комитетом по созданию Европейского Орнитологического Атласа, не отмечались равномерно по всей Европе, что сделало их картографирование невозможным. Вместе с тем, например, "итальянский воробей" отмечался отдельно, и Европейский Орнитологический Атлас, вслед за книгой "Птицы Западной Палеарктики", рассматривает его как стабилизировавшийся гибрид *Passer domesticus* и *P. hispaniolensis* и обозначает эту форму как *Passer* x *italiae*. Наоборот, *Phylloscopus trochiloides* включает два географически разделенных подвида: *viridanus* и *nitidus*, раньше считавшихся самостоятельными видами. Выделение в отдельный вид *Lanius meridionalis* из вида *L. excubitor* было принято, когда работа над Атласом уже завершалась; поэтому в иллюстрации к видовому очерку показана граница между этими формами. Иногда предлагают отделять *Hippolais caligata* от *H. rama*, но в этом Атласе *H. rama* рассматривается в качестве подвида. Взаимоотношения внутри некоторых комплексов видов чаек также часто неясны; *Larus armenicus* рассматривается в Атласе как отдельный вид.

КОДЫ ЕВРОПЕЙСКОГО СОЮЗА КОЛЬЦЕВАНИЯ

В Европейском Союзе кольцевания птиц (EURING) имеется постоянно дополняемый список пятизначных кодов для видов и подвидов, который применяется в первую очередь при кольцевании (мечении) птиц. Этот список обычно соответствует таксономическому порядку профессора К.Вауса; поэтому он использовался как удобный метод для сопоставления данных. Коды Европейского Союза кольцевания приведены в видовых очерках. В Техническом приложении подробно объяснено, как эти коды использовались.

ПОРЯДОК ЦИТИРОВАНИЯ ПУБЛИКАЦИЙ

Авторов просили избегать цитирования справочной литературы из-за ограниченного объема Атласа. В связи с этим следует упомянуть два наиболее распространенных европейских справочника. Для лучшего понимания материалов по гнездящимся птицам Европы, тексты и карты данного Атласа необходимо использовать совместно с соответствующими разделами этих превосходных справочников: "Птицы Западной Палеарктики" (Cramp *et al, Birds of the Western Palearctic* 1977-1994) и "Справочник птиц Центральной Европы" (Glutz von Blotzheim *et al, Handbuch der Vögel Mitteleuropas* 1966-1993). В видовых очерках Атласа для этих книг даны специальные аббревиатуры: соответственно BWP и HVM.

Книга "Птицы в Европе - их охранный статус" (Tucker & Heath 1994) впервые приводит численность всех европейских видов птиц, статус их охраны и воздействующие на них неблагоприятные факторы. Подробно описаны виды с неблагоприятным охранным статусом. Атлас рассматривает не только птиц, требующих охраны, но и все другие виды птиц, в том числе и широко распространенные. Графические иллюстрации изменений численности птиц в Атласе взяты из Европейской Орнитологической базы данных , которая использовалась при создании "Птиц в Европе", поэтому эта книга также часто цитируется в Атласе.

Список литературы, цитированной в Атласе, помещен в окончательной части книги, непосредственно перед указателями.

Майкл Блэйр, Вард Хагемейер
Перевод Э. В. Рогачевой

СПИСОК СОКРАЩЕНИЙ И ТЕРМИНОВ

Стороны света

N = север, северный
S = юг, южный
E = восток, восточный
W = запад, западный; соответственно NW = северо-западный, а WSW = западный-юго-западный и т.п.
C = центральный; соответственно S-C = южно-центральный и т.п.

Общие выражения

asl = выше уровня моря (высоты)
c = приблизительно
et al = и другие (цитаты в тексте)
pers comm = личное сообщение
pers obs = личные наблюдения
unpubl = неопубликованные материалы

Количественные показатели

bp = гнездящиеся пары
ha = гектары
ind = особи
m = метры
km = километры (соответственно km2 = квадратный километр)
M = миллион

Аббревиатуры названий организаций и справочников

BTO = Британский Орнитологический Трест (Великобритания)
BWP = "Птицы Западной Палеарктики"
HVM = "Справочник Птиц Центральной Европы"
JNCC = Объединенный Комитет по Охране Природы (Великобритания)
RSPB = Королевское Общество Охраны Птиц (Великобритания)
SOVON = Организация СОВОН по учетам птиц в Нидерландах (Нидерланды)
WWT = Трест по водоплавающим птицам и водно-болотным угодьям (Великобритания)

Определения терминов

ксерофитный (xerophytic) - относящийся к растениям, приспособленным к крайне засушливым условиям.
лентический (lentic) - имеющий отношение к спокойным или стоячим водоемам (пруды, озера);
лотический (lotic) - имеющий отношение к проточной воде;
мезотрофный (mesotrophic) - имеющий умеренное содержание минеральных и органических питательных веществ;
"миксотрофный" ("mixotrophic") - имеющий смешанное питание неорганическими и органическими веществами (термин применен для мелководных озер бореальной зоны);
олиготрофный (oligotrophic) - бедный по содержанию основных солей и питательных веществ;
склерофитный (sclerophytic) - относящийся к растениям с жесткими побегами и мелкими листьями,слабо испаряющими влагу (признак сухого климата);
фенология (phenology) - система знаний о сезонных явлениях природы, их сроках и причинах;
эвтрофный (eutrophic) - обогащенный органическими и минеральными веществами;

Inledning

SYFTET MED *THE EBCC ATLAS OF EUROPEAN BREEDING BIRDS*

Många fågelböcker innehåller skenbart trovärdiga utbredningskartor. En del av dessa kartor grundar sig på inventeringar av häckande populationer, men med undantag för vissa specialatlaser härrör många kartor från källor av varierande tillförlitlighet, och ofta är de bara omarbetningar av tidigare kartor av tveksamt ursprung. Kartorna är vidare oftast inte kvantitativa: de visar inte var en art är allmän eller sällsynt.

Numera finns det dock ett ökande antal utmärkta regionala eller nationella fågelatlaser. Många av dessa har sitt ursprung i eller har inspirerats av det projekt som skapat denna *Atlas*, och innehåller, liksom denna, halvkvantitativa uppgifter. Den europeiska atlaskommittén (EOAC, European Ornithological Atlas Committee) bildades 1971 med syfte att med fältarbete kartlägga häckningsutbredningen för Europas fåglar. Denna bok presenterar resultatet av detta arbete.

Atlasen presenterar utbredningen för en begränsad tidsperiod, men den insamlade informationen (oberoende av mindre brister) ger en kunskapsbas mot vilken framtida inventeringsresultat (och särskilt förändringar i fåglarnas utbredning) kan jämföras. EOAC hade 1971 en klar vision av den första heleuropeiska kartläggningen av fåglarnas häckningsutbredning som någonsin utförts. Denna vision har nu belönats. *The EBCC Atlas of European Breeding Birds* visar i kartform utbredningen av alla häckande fåglar i Europa: den svarar på frågan Vilken fågel häckar var?

ATLASENS UPPLÄGGNING

Denna **Inledning** beskriver kortfattat syftet med *Atlasen*, ger detaljer om hur informationen insamlats, datalagts och bearbetats till kartor samt förklarar uppläggningen av boken. Den är vital för att förstå boken i alla dess aspekter. Inledningen trycks på flera språk så att den kan läsas av de flesta europeiska ornitologer.

Inledande sektioner

I **Forword** förklarar professor Karel Voous varför *Atlasen* är viktig i samband med de förändringar som sker i Europas fågelfauna. I **Preface** sammanfattas hur atlasprojektet uppfyller de europeiska ornitologernas behov och skisseras de planer och mål som EBCC har för framtida europeisk fågelövervakning. Därefter följer **Introduction,** inklusive uppgifter som metoder och täckningsområde. Den efterföljande sektionen **Explanatory Figures** visar täckningen, datakvaliten och en kopia av det standardiserade formuläret för datainsamlingen. Sektionen **History** beskriver framgångar och motgångar under projektets gång. Därefter, under titeln **Evolution and History of the European Bird Fauna,** följer en uppsats av professor Jacques Blondel om hur fåglarnas nuvarande utbredningsgränser i Europa uppstått. Slutligen finns det **Acknowledgements** och en lista över nationella och regionala fågelatlaser under **National and Major Regional Bird Atlases of Europe.**

Artsektion

En **Introduction to the Maps and Population Graphs** föregår huvuddelen av *Atlasen* som behandlar de häckande fåglarna i Europa. Del 1 består av utbredningskartor, arttexter, artnamnen på 14 språk och bilder. Arterna kommer ungefärligen i den ordning som ges av Voous (1977) och Euring. Del 2 omfattar arter som antas häcka i Europa men för vilka inga uppgifter erhölls.

Avslutande sektioner

Sektionen **Derived Maps** ger detaljer om artrikedomen för Europas häckande arter och om 'Species of European Conservation Concern' (SPEC) enligt BirdLife Internationals definition (Tucker & Heath 1994). **Technical Appendix** förklarar hur rutnätet för atlasen skiljer sig från den teoretiska Universal Transverse Mercatorprojektionen (UTM) och hur öar och rutor vid kusterna i vissa fall behandlats. Det förklarar också hur Eurings numreringssystem använts.

Häften på olika språk

Sammanfattningar av de inledande sektionerna (**Preface, History,** och **Evolution and History of the European Bird Fauna**) samt av arttexterna har gjorts tillgängliga för ornitologer från alla länder för översättning och för spridning, allt i syfte att göra boken tillgänglig för dem som inte kan engelska. Listan med namn och adresser till dem som tillhandahåller nationella språkversioner (så långt känt vid pressläggningen) ges i slutet av **Technical Appendix.**

METODER

Presentationen av data i *Atlasen*

Ursprungliga ideer om insamling och sammanställning av data samt metodval återfinns i sektionen **History**. Där finns också historien om hur projektet byggdes upp.

Atlaskartorna visar skillnader i täthet (antal fåglar per ruta) i logaritmisk skala (förklaring i sektionen **Qualitative versus semi-quantitative information**, nedan). Denna skala är särskilt lämplig för arter vars täthet varierar starkt inom utbredningsområdet. Små täthetsskillnader förblir däremot dolda med denna skala.

Atlasen ger inte bara utbredning utan också uppskattningar av den häckande populationens storlek och trender för de flesta arter i varje europeiskt land. Endast med utgångspunkt från välgrundade uppskattningar av bestånd och trender kan man förstå förändringar i utbredningen.

Område som *Atlasen* avsåg att täcka

Området med planerad täckning visas i **Fig. 1.** Även om det hade varit önskvärt att täcka hela Västpalearktis enligt definitionen i *The Birds of the Western Palearctic* (Cramp *et al.* 1977–1994) så var detta inte praktiskt möjligt eftersom så få uppgifter finns tillgängliga från Mindre Asien, norra Arabien och norra Afrika. Därför uteslöts dessa områden. *Atlasen* använder därför baskartan för *Atlas Florae Europaeae* (Jalas & Suominen 1972, 1988) förutom att den även innefattar Novaja Zemlja, Frans Josefs land, alla grekiska öar nära turkiska fastlandet, Madeira-arkipelagen, Azorerna, Stavropol-regionen i sydöstra Ryssland och de Kaukasiska republikerna. Den återstående skillnaden mellan västra Palearktis och *Atlasens* täckning är att Cypern, Kanarieöarna och de Medelhavsöar som administreras från Nordafrika uteslutits. *Atlasen* skiljer sig från täckningen i *Birds in Europe – their conservation status* (Tucker & Heath 1994) genom att Turkiet och Grönland inte är med.

Det är inte omedelbart klart av kartan i **Fig. 1** att Västpalearktis, *Atlas Florae Europaeae* samt denna *Atlas* utesluter ett litet område av Europa nära Orenburg samt inkluderar en del av asiatiska Kazachstan mellan Volga och Uralfloden samt en del av asiatiska Ryssland öster om Peru (Sverdlovskregionen), till skillnad från *Birds in Europe*.

Uppnådd täckning

I sektionen **Explanatory Figures** efter **Introduction** visar **Fig. 2** de rutor som inventerats samt den högsta datakvalitet som uppnåtts för varje ruta. **Fig. 3** visar den lägsta datakvalitet som erhållits per ruta. Undersektionen **Qualitative versus semiquantitative information** (se nedan) förklarar betydelsen av dessa termer, och de kategorier av datakvalitet som dessa kartor visar är i sjunkande ordning:

1. Halvkvantitativ populationsuppskattning: häckning bedömdes vara säker eller trolig.
2. Halvkvantitativ populationsuppskattning: häckning bedömes vara trolig.
3. Kvalitativ bedömning: häckning säker eller trolig.
4. Kvalitativ bedömning: häckning trolig.

Datakvaliten var vanligen densamma för alla registrerade arter i en ruta. Stora områden i centrala Rysland täcktes inte alls, huvudsakligen på grund av att kontakter inte kunde etableras. För mycket av resten av Ryssland, delar av Vitryssland, Ukraina och Kaukasusrepublikerna erhölls data för ett begränsat antal arter. Täckningen av tidigare Jugoslavien blev tämligen fullständig (i vissa områden inte för alla arter). Det finns luckor i Albanien. Täckningen blev komplett för Novaja Zemlja och Frans Josefs land. I övrigt blev täckningen fullständig med undantag för enstaka luckor.

Atlaskartorna

Valet av koordinatnät för *Atlasen* skulle uppfylla tre kriterier: det måste täcka den avsedda atlasregionen, det måste vara känt i de flesta europeiska länder och det måste stämma med nationella koordinatnät. Det var endast UTM-nätet som uppfyllde dessa kriterier. Eftersom baskartan för *Atlas Florae Europaeae* använder detta nät, passade denna karta utmärkt för denna fågelatlas. *Atlas Florae Europaeae* använder rutor om 50 × 50 km för sin registrering och samma rutor har använts för denna *Atlas*. Att insamla och bearbeta data i finare skala hade varit omöjligt.

Basrutorna om 100 × 100 km i UTM-nätet identifieras unikt av koder med två siffror och tre bokstäver. För både flora- och fågelatlasen har dessa rutor sedan delats i fyra 50 × 50 km-rutor som numrerats sålunda (varför varje ruta har en unik kod med sex tecken):

1 3
2 4

Utläggningen av UTM-nätet i nord-sydling riktning är enkel: rutornas gränslinjer stämmer med latituderna på 50 km avstånd från varandra och med start vid ekvatorn. Den andra axeln är svårare att hantera eftersom longituderna konvergerar mot nordpolen. Därför minskar antalet 50 × 50 km-rutor när man rör sig norrut. Man kompenserar för detta på följande sätt. Utläggningen av rutorna baserar sig på sektorer om 6 grader longitud (start vid 0 grader). De rutor som gränsar till varje sådan 6 gradersmeridian blir allt smalare norrut tills de helt försvinner och nästa nord-sydliga rad av rutor börjar minska. Både *Atlas Florae Europaeae* och denna fågelatlas har modifierat detta system så att storleksvariationen hos rutorna som gränsar till 6-gradersmeridianerna blir mindre. Gränsrutorna utesluts när de minskat till ungefär 40 km. (I *Atlasen* talar vi genomgående om rutor fastän inte alla är kvadrater.) Rutindelningen visas tydligt på kartan över *Atlasens* täckning (**Fig. 1**) och fullständiga detaljer ges i **Technical Appendix**.

EOAC sände kartor med 50 × 50 km-rutnätet till de nationella organisatörerna för att säkerställa att de använde rätt nät för dataregistreringen. Fältarbetet baserades vanligen på mindre rutor än 50 × 50 km eller på nationella nät som inte stämde med UTM-nätet. I dessa fall överförde de nationella organisatörerna den insamlade informationen till rätt koordinatsystem.

Tid för fältarbetet och kontroll av data

Det planerades att fältarbetet skulle ske åren 1985–1988. De olika länderna organiserade dock sina egna arbeten och av praktiska skäl kunde denna tidsperiod inte alltid hållas. I de fall som data saknades från dessa år användes tidigare eller senare data efter kontoll av att de var användbara. **Tabell 3** efter **Introduction** ger en lista över deltagande länder, deras datainsamlingsperioder, det nationella nätet från vilket data konverterades och metodiken.

Datainsamling – utbredningsdata

Hundratusentals, kanske mer än en miljon timmar fältarbete utgör grunden för *Atlasen*. Idealet hade varit att alla hade använt samma fältmetod under samma tidsperiod, men detta var omöjligt. EOAC gav därför allmänna riktlinjer i stället för strikta regler. I vissa länder kombinerades fältarbete för denna *Atlas* och arbete för en nationell atlas, i andra användes data från en oberoende nationell atlas för denna *Atlas*. Fältmetoderna varierade från enstaka besök, via sammanställning av artlistor från flera besök, till inventeringar baserade på punkt- eller linjetaxeringar eller revirkartering av provytor.

Det standardiserade formulär som producerades av statistiska centralbyrån i Holland visas delvis i **Fig. 4** efter denna **Introduction**. Ett formulär fylldes i för varje inventerad ruta. För rutor som sträckte sig över en nationsgräns gjorde varje land bara sin egen del.

Den allmänna information som efterfrågades för varje ruta var:

1. Inventeringsperiod: år eller följd av år för inventeringen.
2. Rutans identitet (UTM-kod).
3. Inventeringseffektivitet: mer än 75 % av förväntade arter (hög) eller mindre (låg).
4. Rutans högst och lägsta höjd över havet i meter.
5. Observatörer eller koordinator: namn och adress för ev. förfrågan.
6. Kommentarer: ev. ytterligare information för att förklara uppgifterna på formuläret.
7. Kort biotopbeskrivning.

Huvuddelen av formuläret består av en artlista (c. 440 arter i ordning enligt Voous (1977), numrerade enligt Euring) med utrymme för att skriva in data. Datafältet hade i kolumn 0 ett förkortat latinsk namn (t.ex. Gav stell), i kolumn 1 Euringkoden (t.ex. 00020). I kolumn 2 fyllde man sedan i häckningsindicium. Det fanns koder för 16 sådana indicier, vilka grupperades i tre kategorier: säker häckning, trolig häckning och möjlig häckning. Koderna ges i **Tabell 1**. I kolumn 3, slutligen, efterfrågades en uppskattning av antalet häckande par i rutan, uttryckt i en logaritmisk skala (1 = 1–9, 2 = 10–99, 3 = 100-999, 4 = 1000–9999, 5 = 10.000–99.999, 6 = > 100.000).

Formuläret tillät separat registrering av hybrider och olistade arter i slutet.

Totalt sett kom data från följande källor:

1. Nationella koordinatörer som organiserade datainsamlingen och förde in resultaten på formulären.
2. Regionala koordinatörer. Ibland organiserades datainsamlingen på annat sätt än genom en nationell koordinatör, särskilt om landet var stort eller när det var bättre att delegera uppgiften till en aktiv koordinatör i ett existerande regionalt nät. Dessa regionala koordinatörer arbetade på samma sätt som en nationell koordinatör.
3. Ytterligare nationella källor, främst litteratur, vanligen via en artexpert. Där fältdata saknades, särskilt i avlägsna områden, var ofta publicerade eller opublicerade rapporter den enda källan, ofta inte direkt tillgängliga för redaktörerna eller den nationelle koordinatorn.
4. Författaren till arttexten kompletterade ofta med ytterligare information om arten, ibland från egna studier.

Alla data från dessa källor kontrollerades först av den nationelle organisatören innan de fördes in i databasen.

Kvalitativ i förhållande till halvkvantitativ information

Atlasen använder halvkvantitativ information (logaritmiska populationsuppskattning) för varje ruta, beräknad av den nationelle koordinatorn eller fältarbetarna. Prickarna på kartorna representerar antal häckande par, inte tätheter. Ökande storlek på prickarna representerar successivt högre antal par enligt skalan (förklaring på sid. cxl). Beklagligtvis

Tabell 1 *Häckningsindicier*

A: Möjlig häckning

1. Art observerad under häckningssäsong i möjlig häckningsbiotop
2. Sjungande hane (eller annat häckningsläte) under häckningssäsong

B: Trolig häckning

3. Par i lämplig häckningsbiotop under häckningssäsong
4. Permanent revir: revirbeteende (sång, etc.) vid två tillfällen minst en vecka isär på samma plats
5. Parningsspel och lekar
6. Besök vid trolig boplats
7. Varningsbeteende från adulta
8. Ruvfläck noterad på adult i handen
9. Bobygge eller utgrävning av bohål

C: Säker häckning

10. Avledningsbeteende eller spelar skadad
11. Använt bo eller äggskal (från atlasperioden)
12. Nyligen flygga ungar (bostannare) eller dunungar (borymmare)
13. Adult till/från eller ut ur/in i boplats under omständigheter som indikerar häckning (högt belägna bon eller bohål som inte kan inspekteras) eller adulta som setts ruva
14. Adulta som bär mat till ungar eller spillning
15. Bo med ägg
16. Bo med ungar sedda eller hörda

kunde inte alla länder (Norge, Polen och det mesta av Spanien) samt delar av Island, Frankrike och Italien inte ge halvkvantitativa data. Projektet förlorade kontakten med Bosnien och Serbien och kunde inte uppdatera deras data. Några regioner i Frankrike uppdaterade sina data oberoende. Den franske koordinatorn uppdaterade sina data för hela landet avseende ett begränsat antal arter. Även logaritmiska uppskattningar för ett antal rutor ger mycket mer information än bara information om frånvaro eller närvaro.

För gränsrutor där varje land sände in sina respektive uppskattningar användes det högre värdet (logaritmiska värden bör inte adderas), trots att detta i vissa fall ger en underskattning. Dessa approximationer var bättre än att nergradera en ruta till bara kvalitativ status.

Prickarna på kartorna hänvisar till följande kategorier

mörklila	= säker eller trolig häckning, kvalitativt
ljuslila	= möjlig häckning, kvalitativt
röd	= säker eller trolig häckning, halvkvantitativ
orange	= möjlig häckning, halvkvantitativ
grå	= ingen inventering gjord för arten i rutan
ingen prick	= rutan inventerad men arten ej påträffad

Databearbetning – kontroll och rättning av kartdata

Formulären som sändes in av den nationelle koordinatorn granskades med avseende på elementära fel (saknade koder, felaktiga koder) innan de överfördes till en ASCII-fil. Varje post gavs en landskod. Vissa länder sände in datalagt material på diskett. Dessa filer kontrollerades på samma sätt. Databasen som byggdes upp på detta sätt har ett värde per art och ruta.

De nationella koordinatörer och andra uppgiftslämnare som hade sänt in data snabbt erhöll kartutskrifter och artlistor för kontroll på ett tidigt stadium. Många rättelser erhölls efter denna kontroll. Några länder sände in sina data eller uppdaterade sina data från kvalitativa till halvkvantitativa sent. Kontrollen och rättningen gick således i olika takt för olika länder.

Proceduren med provisoriska kartor var viktig i två avseenden:

1. Det möjliggjorde för den nationelle koordinatorn eller övriga inblandade att säkerställa att de data man sänt in också hade förts in på ett korrekt sätt: kartorna visade om prickarna satt på rätt plats för rätt art. Felen framgick tydligare på kartorna än i datalistorna.
2. Det stimulerade till ökat insamlingsarbete som ofta gav nya data.

I en andra fas kontrollerades att rättningarna hade förts in på ett korrekt sätt. Detta skedde genom att den nationelle koordinatorn erhöll en ny uppsättning korrigerade kartor plus en datalista. De flesta koordinatörer genomförde detta stora arbete och sände in de slutliga rättningarna, men i länder som tidigare Jugoslavien var uppdatering ofta omöjlig. De länder som hade drabbats av förseningar fick kortare tid på sig att kontrollera och rätta sina kartor.

I ett senare skede kom ytterligare en del kompletteringar från författarna till arttexterna eller andra experter. De flesta av dessa har kontrollerats av de nationella koordinatörerna. I de fall som detta inte hunnits med har antingen de ursprungliga uppgifterna behållits eller har det angivits att författarens uppfattning avviker.

Då det saknades uppgifter grundade på fältarbete, vilket särskilt var fallet i norra Ryssland och Albanien, granskades uppgifter från olika källor av lokala ornitologer, som avgjorde om data kunde accepteras. Vissa halvkvantitativa uppskattningar gjordes för sådana rutor genom interpolering från rutor med goda data i samma region, varvid kännedom om biotoperna vägdes in.

Slutpunkten för intagning av nya data och rättningar var 1 juli 1995, men för att maximera täckningen medtogs nya data under ytterligare några månader från Albanien, europeiska Turkiet, Kaukasus, delar av Ukraina och delar av Ryssland. Rättningar som kom från författarna till arttexterna accepterades fram till 1 november 1995.

Datainsamling – populationsstorlekar

De nationella populationsdiagrammen som presenteras i *Atlasen* kommer från European Bird Database. Denna innehållar populationsuppskattningar som insamlats gemensamt av EBCC och BirdLife International. Den etablerades för att stödja detta atlasprojekt och BirdLife Dispersed Species Project, vars resultat har publicerats i *Birds in Europe – their conservation status* (Tucker & Heath 1994). Samarbetet bidrog också till att fördjupa inventeringsarbetet i delar av Europa. Uppgifterna insamlades främst via formulär till de nationella koordinatörerna (listade i *Birds of Europe*), vilka i sin tur distribuerade dem till lämpliga experter, övervakningsorganisationer eller regionala bidragsgivare. BirdLife International har hand om European Bird Database.

Varje land gav följande uppgifter om alla häckande arter:

1. Populationsstorlek.
2. Populationstrend (under perioden 1970–1990).
3. Förändring av utbredningsområdet (1970–1990).

Liknande uppgifter insamlades också för övervintrande bestånd, men presenteras inte här.

Källorna som användes för att utvärdera populationsstorlekar och trender registrerades. Verifikationskoder, givna i **Tabell 2** efter denna **Introduction**, ges för att indikera tillförlitligheten i uppskattningarna av beståndsstorlek och trender.

Vissa författare till arttexterna accepterade inte uppskattningarna i databasen, men informationen kom in för sent för att kunna inkluderas. I dessa fall har författarna fört in sina uppskattningar i texten medan diagrammen som åtföljer arttexterna alltid visar databasens värden.

Begränsningar i datamaterialet

Atlasprojectet har producerat en databas av hög kvalitet. Men ändå finns det begränsningar i materialets användbarhet. Personer som vill använda materialet för fortsatt forskning måste ta hänsyn till dessa begränsningar, vilka dock inte kan listas här. Hänvändelse måste ske till EBCC. De viktigaste begränsningarna för att användna boken är dock dessa:

1. Det fanns ingen föreskriven fältmetod för att fastställa

Tabell 2 *Populationskoder i European Bird Database*

POPMIN	=	minsta populationsstorlek (i par)		
POPMAX	=	största populationsstorlek (i par)		
MEAN	=	geometriskt medeltal av populationsstorlek (i par)	PSV	= verifikationskod för populationsstorlek
YRC	=	år för uppskattning av populationsstorleken		
PST	=	trend för populationsstorleken	PTV	= verifikationskod för populationstrend
RST	=	trend för utbredningsområde	RTV	= verifikationskod för utbredningsområde

Koder för trender i populationsstorlek och utbredningsområde
(gäller för perioden 1970-1990)

+2	=	ökning med minst 50%
+1	=	ökning med minst 20%, men mindre än 50%
0	=	förändring mindre än 20%
-1	=	minskning med minst 20%, men mindre än 50%
-2	=	minskning med minst 50%
n	=	ny häckfågel inom perioden
x	=	utdöd inom perioden
f	=	fluktuerande, med ändringar på minst 20%, men utan tydlig trend

om en art fanns eller ej i en ruta, inte heller för att fastställa beståndsstorleken. Många nationella projekt som utgjorde källor för EBCC hade sina egna fältmetoder, bestämda av egna mål och resurser.
2. Det fanns inga allmänna metoder för att behandla fältdata inför rapporteringen på formulären, i huvudsak av samma skäl som angivits ovan. Överföringsmetoderna var individuella.
3. Skillnader i ornitologernas kvalitet och antalet observatörer i olika länder har resulterat i varierande datakvalitet.
4. Vissa uppgifter är resultat av extrapoleringar.
5. Vissa uppgifter kommer från litteraturen (främst arktiska områden).

UTFORMNING AV KARTORNA OCH ARTTEXTERNA I *ATLASEN*

Arterna har indelats i två grupper i *Atlasen*, dels de för vilka vi fick tillfredsställande kartläggning och dels de för vilka vi inte fick det. De förra arterna har alla fullständiga texter i Del 1 sektionen med arttexterna. Den andra gruppen behandlas kortfattat i Del 2. I båda delarna står arterna i ordning enligt Voous och i ungefär Eurings sekvens. Undantag är några få arter i Del 1 för att tillse att arter som behandlas på en sida står emot en annan art som också behandlas på bara en sida. Arter som behandlas på två sidor finns alltid på ett uppslag. Några arter med mycket begränsad utbredning kräver inte fullständig behandling och tillåter mer än en art på samma sida. Varje art är illustrerad och namnet ges (om det finns) på 14 språk. De flesta arter har ett populationsdiagram som förklaras på sidorna som föregår artkartorna.

Deriverade kartor (sammanfattad förklaring)

Fig. 5 visar artrikedomen per ruta för alla häckfåglar. I **Fig. 6–8** visas på samma sätt artrikedomen för 'Arter av europeiskt bevarandeintresse', Species of European Environmental Concern (SPEC), kategorierna 1, 2 och 3, enligt BirdLife Internationals definition. **Fig. 9** kombinerar de tre kategorierna.

ARTTEXTERNA

Artexterna täcker (där det är tillämpligt) ett antal standardrubriker, vanligen i följande ordning: världsutbredning, häckningsbiotoper i Europa, utbrednings- och täthetsmönster, sentida förändringar i utbredning och antal (och möjliga orsaker), regional variation i antal, möjliga faktorer som begränsar utbredningen, täthet i huvudbiotop, flyttning och rörelser typiska för arten inom och utom Europa, speciella egenskaper hos arten samt kortfattat om underarter, deras utbredning, överlappning och trender.

Om det inte är absolut nödvändigt för någon av huvudrubrikerna har följande ämnen ej behandlats: häckningsbiologi, beteende, föda, relationer till andra arter, morfologi och fysiologi, detaljer rörande hot (behandlas i *Birds of Europe*), abnormaliteter, oologi, evolution och taxonomi (utom då det finns viktiga nyligen accepterade ändringar eller när underarter är klart olika), dödlighet och andra populationsdynamiska egenskaper samt läten och sång.

Arterna – kriterier för att tas med

Arter som häckar i området för *Atlasen* från 1985 och därefter har tagits med om de uppfyller kriterierna i **Tabell 1**. Introducerade arter måste ha häckat med minst en självföryngrande population under fem år för att tas med. Bedömningarna härvidlag har dock varierat i olika delar av Europa och urvalet av arter kan därför delvis förefalla godtyckligt.

Atlasen omfattar 513 arter plus *Passer x italiae*.

NOMENKLATUR OCH TAXONOMI

Taxonomi

EBCC har valt att inta en försiktig och konservativ hållning i taxonomiska frågor. Denna *Atlas* följer därför huvudsakligen den taxonomi, ordning och engelska nomenklatur som finns i *Birds of the Western Palearctic* (*BWP*), så som den ändrats för 'Concise Edition'.

Puffinus yelkouan, Puffinus mauretanicus, Larus

cachinnans, Anthus petrosus, Phylloscopus lorentzii och *Pyrrhula murina* behandlas som egna arter. De har separata kartor från *Puffinus puffinus, Larus argentatus, Anthus spinoletta, Phylloscopus collybita* och *Pyrrhula pyrrhula*. Separata kartor kunde göras antingen om de hade registrerats separat eller har olika utbredningsområden. (De tre Puffinus-arterna har gemensam text.)

I början fanns en avsikt att registrera flera underarter och former, men den uppdelning som EOAC hade gjort accepterades inte i hela Europa, varför kartläggningen inte blev möjlig. 'Italiensk sparv' registrerades dock separat och *Atlasen* följer *BWP* och behandlar den som en stabil hybrid mellan *Passer domesticus* och *P. hispaniolensis*, kallad *P.* x *italiae*. I motsats till detta omfattar *Phylloscopus trochiloides* två geografiskt skilda underarter, *viridanus* och *nitidus*, tidigare betraktade som olika arter. Argumenten för att separera *Lanius meridionalis* från *L. excubitor* accepterades i atlasarbetets slutskede; ett diagram i arttexten visar gränsen mellan formerna. *Hippolais caligata* anses ibland vara artskild från *H. rama*, men här behandlas den senare som en underart. Relationerna inom vissa måskomplex är ofta oklara; *Larus armenicus* behandlas som egen art här.

Eurings numrering

The European Union for Bird Ringing (EURING) har utvecklat en lista med femsiffriga nummer för arter och underarter främst för ringmärkning. Denna lista följer i huvudsak Voous' ordning och användes därför vid datainsamlingen. Eurings artnummer ges i arttexterna. The **Technical Appendix** ger detaljer om hur Euringnumren användes.

ANVÄNDNINGEN AV REFERENSER OCH ANDRA PUBLIKATIONER

Författarna ombads att undvika att referera till handböcker med tanke på att utrymmet för referenser var begränsat. Två sentida stora europeiska handböcker bör omnämnas särskilt. För grundläggande förståelse av varje europeisk arts utbredning bör kartor och texter i denna *Atlas* studeras tillsammans med motsvarande avsnitt i dessa eminenta referensverk: *Birds of the Western Palearctic* (Cramp *et al.* 1977–1994) och *Handbuch der Vögel Mitteleuropas* (Glutz von Blotzheim *et al.* 1966–1993). I *Atlasen* används förkortningarna *BWP* och *HVM* för dessa böcker.

Birds in Europe – their conservation status (Tucker & Heath 1994) ger för första gången en översikt av Europas fågelpopulationer, hoten mot dem och deras bevarandestatus. Den beskriver i detalj de arter som befinner sig i fara. Atlasen behandlar inte bara dessa arter utan också alla andra arter som för närvarande inte är hotade. Populationsdiagrammen i *Atlasen* kommer från samma 'European Bird Database' som använts för *Birds in Europe*, varför det ofta förekommer hänvisningar till denna bok.

Citerade referenser i Atlasen finns förtecknade i slutet av boken.

Michael Blair, Ward Hagemeijer, Sören Svensson

FÖRKORTNINGAR OCH ORDFÖRKLARINGAR

Kompassriktningar

N = norr, S = söder, E = öster, W = väster, NW = nordväst, WSW = västsydväst, etc.
C = centrala, S-C = södra till centrala, etc.

Allmänna uttryck

asl	=	höjd över havsytan
c	=	cirka, ungefär
et al	=	med flera (i referenser)
pers comm	=	personligt meddelande
pers obs	=	personlig observation
unpubl	=	opublicerat arbete

Antals- och måttangivelser

bp	=	häckande par
ha	=	hektar
ind	=	individer
m	=	meter
km	=	kilometer
km^2	=	kvadratkilometer
M	=	miljon

Acronymer

BTO	=	British Trust for Ornithology (GB)
BWP	=	Birds of the Western Palaearctic
HVM	=	Handbuch der Vögel Mitteleuropas
JNCC	=	Joint Nature Conservation Committee (GB)
RSPB	=	Royal Society for the Protection of Birds (GB)
SOVON	=	SOVON Bird Census Work The Netherlands (NL)
WWT	=	Wildfowl and Wetlands Trust (GB)

Ordförklaringar

eutrophic	=	näringsrik
lentic	=	avser stillastående vatten, som i dammar och sjöar
lotic	=	avser rinnande vatten
mesotrophic	=	varken fattig eller rik på näring
'mixotrophic'	=	grund vegetationsrik sjö i boreala zonen med relativt näringsfattiga stränder
oligotrophic	=	näringsfattig
phenology	=	studiet av årstidsbundna händelser
sclerophytic	=	växter med tjocka, vanligen små blad, med liten transpiration, anpassade till torrt klimat
xerophytic	=	växter anpassade till mycket torrt klimat

Explanatory Figures

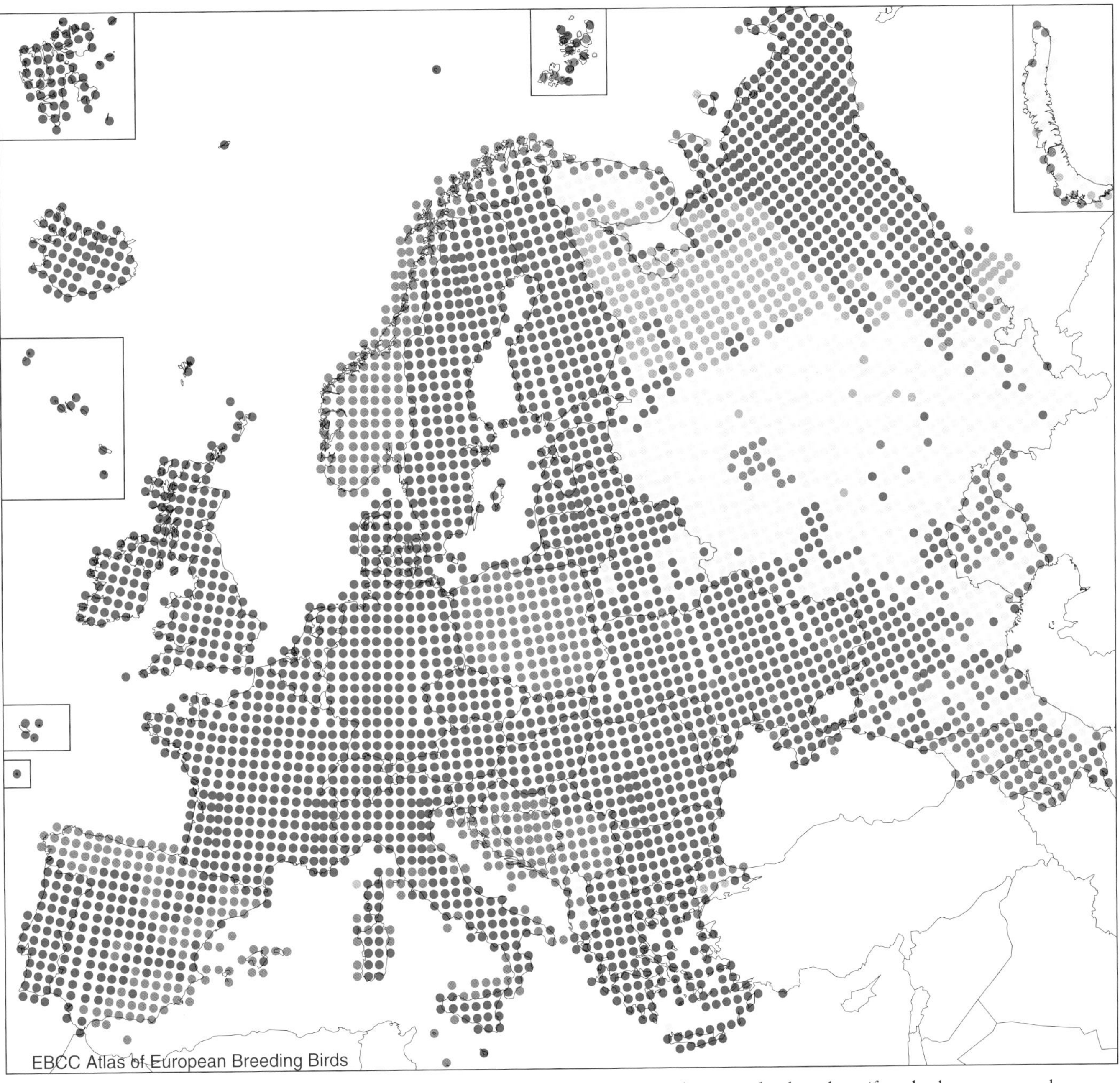

Figure 2 Map showing the maximum data quality per square. The map indicates whether data (for the best-covered species) for a square are semi-quantitative (*ie* include an estimate of numbers) or qualitative (presence/absence information), or whether they represent 'Confirmed and probable breeding' or 'Possible breeding'.

- ● Semi-quantitative data, confirmed and probable breeding.
- ● Semi-quantitative data, possible breeding.
- ● Qualitative data, confirmed and probable breeding.
- ● Qualitative data, possible breeding.
- No data.

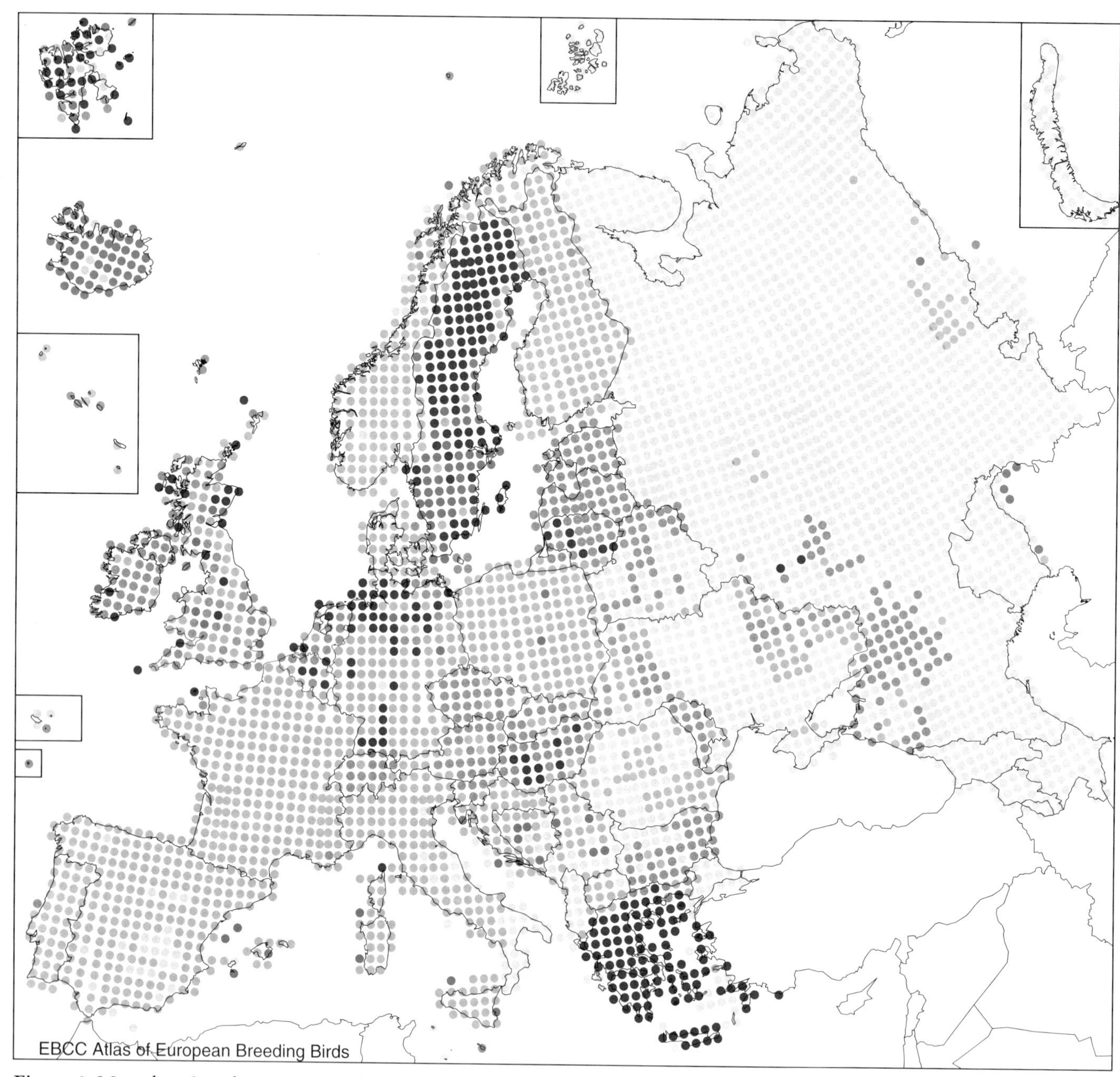

Figure 3 Map showing the minimum data quality per square. The map indicates whether data (for the least-covered species) for a square are semi-quantitative (*ie* include an estimate of numbers) or qualitative (presence/absence information) whether they or represent 'Confirmed and probable breeding' or 'Possible breeding'. It therefore follows that the minimum data quality for squares with an incomplete dataset (*ie* data were received for less than 75% of the species, see **Figure 1**) is equivalent to 'no data'.

- Semi-quantitative data, confirmed and probable breeding.
- Semi-quantitative data, possible breeding.
- Qualitative data, confirmed and probable breeding.
- Qualitative data, possible breeding.
- No data.

E.O.A.C.
European Atlas of Breeding Birds

01 1 9 _ _ – 1 9 _ _

02 50 km UTM square

03 Completeness of survey

☐ high

☐ low

04 Altitude

min.

max.

Comments

Name

Address

05 Habitat Description

10 Islets
11 Sea inlets
12 Tidal rivers and estuaries
13 Mud flats and sand flats
14 Salt marsh, salt pastures
15 Sand dunes and sand beaches
16 Shingle (stoney beach and river gravels)
17 Sea cliffs and rocky coast
18 Open sea
19 Machair
20 Wetlands (unspecified)
21 Lagoons
22 Standing water (fresh)
23 Standing water (brackish)
24 Running water
30 Scrub/grass (unspecified)
31 Heath or scrub
32 Sclerophyllous scrub (maquis, garrigue, phrygana)
33 Neutral grassland
34 Calcareous grassland
35 Acid grassland
36 Calcareous alpine and boreal grassland
37 Acid alpine and boreal grassland
40 Woodland (unspecified)
41 Broad-leaved deciduous woods
42 Coniferous woods
43 Mixed woodland
44 Alluvial forest
45 Broad-leaved evergreen woods
50 Peatlands (unspecified)
51 Raised bog
52 Blanket bog
53 Marsh, fen, water fringe vegetation
54 Other bogs and mires including rich fen
60 Rocky habitats (unspecified)
61 Scree
62 Exposed bedrock, inland cliffs
63 Permanent snow or ice
64 Inland sand dunes
80 Agricultural land and highly artificial landscapes
81 Crops, including heavily fertilised grassland
82 Orchards, poplar plantations
83 Shelterbelts, small woods, hedges, bocage
84 Urban parks and large gardens
85 Urbanised and industrial

06 Species list

Estimate (column 3)
Breeding evidence (column 2)
Euring code (column 1)

0	1	2	3
Gav. stell	00020		
Gav. arcti	00030		
Gav. immer	00040		
Tac. rufic	00070		
Pod. crist	00090		
Pod. grise	00100		
Pod. aurit	00110		
Pod. nigri	00120		
Ful. glaci	00220		
Cal. diome	00360		
Puf. puffi	00460		
Hyd. pelag	00510		
Oce. leuco	00550		
Sul. bassa	00710		
Pha. carbo	00720		
Pha. arist	00800		
Pha. pygme	00820		
Pel. onocr	00880		
Pel. crisp	00890		
Bot. stell	00950		
Ixo. minut	00980		
Nyc. nycti	01040		
Ard. rallo	01080		
Bub. ibis	01110		
Egr. garze	01190		
Egr. alba	01210		
Ard. ciner	01220		
Ard. purpu	01240		
Cic. nigra	01310		
Cic. cicon	01340		
Ple. falci	01360		
Pla. leuco	01440		
Pho. ruber	01470		
Cyg. olor	01520		
Cyg. colum	01530		
Cyg. cygnu	01540		
Ans. fabal	01570		
Ans. brach	01580		
Ans. eryth	01600		
Ans. anser	01610		
Ans. indic	01620		
Bra. canad	01616		

Figure 4 Standardized data-collection form (front page only) and instructions for its completion.

E.O.A.C.
European Atlas of Breeding Birds

INSTRUCTIONS

01 Fill in the year from which the data originate. If data are summarised from several years, fill in the first and last year of the period.

02 100 x 100 km UTM-squares are defined by a two letter code on UTM maps. The 50 x 50 km UTM-squares which are used for this atlas project, are derived from the 100 km squares and are numbered as follows

1	3
2	4

03 Completeness of the survey. Please indicate whether in your opinion the survey in this square included over ± 75% of the expected breeding species (high) or not (low).

04 Altitude. Please enter minimum and maximum altitudes in the square (in metres).

Name and address of person to be contacted if there are questions regarding this square.

Comments. If you think additional information on the survey, habitat types or recorded species is required for better understanding, please mention briefly here. Some possible examples: 'Surveyed by visitors who did not know the area well.' 'Square contains a frontier area near which observations cannot be made.' 'Half the square lies in another country; our species list applies to our part alone but we have estimated the breeding populations for the whole square.' 'Pollution damage has greatly affected the woodlands during the last x years.'

05 Habitat description. Give approximate percentages of the major habitat types. Also include entries for any habitat types which, though small in area, make a significant contribution to the list of breeding species. Some examples: an area of sand dunes with the only breeding colony of Sterna species in the square; a small rocky island with the only breeding colony of sea-birds in the square; a lake or reservoir specially important for breeding water birds.

06 Species list (according to Voous 1977). Only subspecies which can easily be identified in the field, have been included. Only record feral species (e.g. Columbia livia forma domestica, Alopochen aegyptiacus, etc.) if they breed in the wild in this square. Enter hybrids (e.g. Larus ridibundus x Larus melanocephalus, Corvus corone corone x Corvus corone cornix, etc.) separately at the end of the species list. Column 0 gives an abbreviation of scientific names and column 1 gives the new Euring code numbers. Column 2: Breeding evidence.
Where the code numbers 1 to 16 are available, please enter them in column 2, giving for each species the highest category recorded. In some cases the actual category of evidence is not easily available to the national organiser, but only the summarised information 'possible' (codes 1 or 2), 'probable' (codes 3 to 9) or 'confirmed' breeding (codes 10 to 16). If this is the case, please enter 'A' for possible breeding, 'B' for probable breeding, or 'C' for confirmed breeding, in column 2.

In column 3 please give an estimate of the number of breeding pairs in the square. Fill in the code number of the appropriate logarithmic scale:

1 = 1 - 9
2 = 10 - 99
3 = 100 - 999
4 = 1000 - 9999
5 = 10000 - 99999
6 = 100000 - 999999
etc.

Breeding evidence

A : possible breeding
1 Species observed in breeding season in possible nesting habitat
2 Singing male(s) present (or breeding calls heard) in breeding season

B : probable breeding
3 Pair observed in suitable nesting habitat in breeding season
4 Permanent territory presumed through registration of territorial behaviour (song, etc.) on at least two different days a week or more apart at same place
5 Courtship and display
6 Visiting probable nest-site
7 Agitated behaviour or anxiety calls from adults
8 Brood patch on adult examined in the hand
9 Nest-building or excavating of nest-hole

C : confirmed breeding
10 Distraction-display or injury-feigning
11 Used nest or eggshells found (occupied or laid within period of survey)
12 Recently fledged young (nidicolous species) or downy young (nidifugous species)
13 Adults entering or leaving nest-site in circumstances indicating occupied nest (including high nests or nest-holes, the contents of which cannot be seen) or adult seen incubating
14 Adult carrying faecal sac or food for young
15 Nest containing eggs
16 Nest with young seen or heard

V-37046

History of the European Ornithological Atlas Project

BACKGROUND

The European Ornithological Atlas Committee (EOAC) was formed in 1971. At the Conference on the Co-ordination and Encouragement of Amateur Ornithology in Europe, held at Tring, England, in December 1971, the objectives of the EOAC were reviewed. The EOAC Chairman was Dr Einhard Bezzel, and the joint convenors were Tommy Dybbro and Dr J.T.R. (Tim) Sharrock. Some of the earliest EOAC national delegates went on to make substantial contributions to the *Atlas*; Dr Stephan Dontchev (Bulgaria), Dr Ludwik Tomiałojć (Poland) and Dr Sören Svensson (Sweden). The EOAC decided to adopt the 50km x 50km grid for the EOA, and to plan for the fieldwork period to be 1985–88. This would allow prior pilot mapping studies of sample species to be carried out, and some national projects at finer resolution to be completed, so that the EOA project could be based on proven methods. The EOAC had already defined the breeding evidence categories (see **Table 1** on p.xx), and resolved to encourage and promote collaborative and coordinated work.

The aims of the EOAC were to:

1. Encourage national atlas projects in as many European countries as possible, coordinating national schemes through a standard set of methods.
2. Promote a European Ornithological Atlas (EOA) project, using data from national schemes and encouraging work within countries where no national scheme existed.
3. Build and maintain a European network of national delegates.

By the second EOAC meeting in September 1972 in Dziekanów near Warsaw, the drive for delegates from every European country had been launched. The meeting agreed the use of Euring numbers as a standard administrative method of listing species; an initial list of breeding species was circulated. The EOAC initially had intended to include all introduced species breeding in a feral state.

The International Bird Census Committee (IBCC) then invited the EOAC to hold meetings at the biennial IBCC conferences. By 1975 the pilot mapping studies were using the base map of *Atlas Florae Europaeae*. Between 1977 and 1981, *British Birds* and several other European journals published selected maps (transposed on to the European Invertebrate Survey base map) from the pilot studies' fieldwork; the maps depicted only breeding evidence, not population estimates. The partial coverage achieved showed that even the lengthy preparatory period allowed for prior to the main *Atlas* fieldwork in 1985 was likely to be insufficient in some countries, although the achieved mapping had reached an admirable standard.

Originally, the EOAC had made quantification of the breeding evidence (confirmed, probable or possible breeding numbers per 50km square) optional for national projects, although strongly recommending its adoption; quantification did not become agreed EOAC policy until 1989. In 1983 one pilot study had sought from EOAC national delegates semi-quantitative estimates of breeding numbers for the purposes of extrapolation over the area of each species' habitats in Europe, to obtain average densities. However, the quality of habitat data was insufficient to justify this approach; furthermore, pilot study results were non-uniform and therefore were not representative across Europe.

PROJECT ORGANIZATION

Project management

Since 1986 it had been apparent that the EOAC Executive Committee comprising chairman, treasurer and secretary was insufficient to deal with the increasing tasks of maintaining contact with participating countries and managing the data-processing. In 1987, the first Editor, Johan Bekhuis, was employed at the Dutch bird survey organization SOVON Bird Census Work The Netherlands, to deal with the mapping. More active steps began to be taken to raise funds to support such central data-processing and editing work. In 1992, Ward Hagemeijer (SOVON) took over the role of editor from Johan Bekhuis and work on the *Atlas* intensified. The Executive Committee took an increasingly active role, supported particularly by Dachverband Deutscher Avifaunisten (Germany), Schweizerische Vogelwarte Sempach (Switzerland), SOVON and the British Trust for Ornithology (BTO). The second Editor, Michael Blair, was employed in early 1993 at the BTO to recruit species account authors and artists.

By mid-1987, despite confirmation from the Helsinki IBCC/EOAC Conference that fieldwork generally had progressed well, relatively little data had reached SOVON. From then onwards, SOVON exercised centralized management under Johan Bekhuis, who ran the EOAC secretariat. The editor of *Bird Census News* from 1987 to 1992 was Rob Bijlsma. His remit was to keep IBCC and EOAC members in touch between triennial conferences, to provide an informal platform for debate and to present preliminary atlas (and monitoring) results; this would ensure that IBCC and EOAC remained active organizations between conferences. By 1993, *Bird Census News*, as a Europe-wide focus for bird-survey work, had become a recognized part of ornithological literature.

Overall project management simplified in 1992 when the IBCC and the EOAC merged into the European Bird Census Council (EBCC), which established the European Ornithological Atlas Working Group (EOA WG), initially of ten experienced specialists from six countries, to manage the project on its behalf. Dr Goetz Rheinwald became chairman. The EOA WG reported directly to the EBCC, and both bodies met regularly. Representatives from BirdLife International have attended the EOA WG meetings since 1992, as has the publisher since 1993. Text editing work had to be suspended for eight months from early 1994 after projected sponsorship fell through. (Data editing by SOVON continued.) After the restart, text editing continued at a low level until the funds promised from a fundraising campaign had materialized. Full resumption came in early 1995. The backlog of data processing and each nation's tranche of verification checks took many months to clear.

Data collection period

The original EOAC concept of compiling the EOA from data presented in national atlases proved impossibly labour-intensive, and so in 1979 the EOAC adopted the simpler, but more useful alternative of collating the raw data originally collected for each national atlas. Because some countries started national atlas fieldwork before 1985 and others, through lack of resources, could not begin until much later, the collection and delivery of EOA data took longer than intended. Furthermore, some countries had data covering far longer periods, or had earlier data, particularly for remote areas. The EOAC agreed that each country would organize its own fieldwork and would submit interim results annually. The first EOA data were available by 1986, but not until SOVON had organized practical means and methods of handling the data in 1987 could processing begin.

Data collection

Standardized recording form

There was initially no standard method of survey data collation and submission. In 1988 the Dutch Central Bureau for Statistics (CBS) designed and produced a special European Atlas recording form, usable by all countries. On receipt of these forms in February 1989, the EOAC representatives quickly formed a national coordinator network to complete them from national data.

Collaboration

By early 1990, the data-collection process was working well in many countries. The existence of the EOAC allowed collaboration to succeed in convincing doubters; countries with strong ornithological reputations and those whose scientific ornithology was in its infancy agreed to participate; the preliminary maps (see below) produced from initial data were the best evidence.

Submission deadline

The EOAC had intended that the final data would be submitted to SOVON by the end of 1989, but the size of the national coordinators' tasks of checking their data and compiling the EOAC forms was much greater than had been anticipated. Furthermore, they had not then validated SOVON's output maps and data lists. All coordinators were urged to plan to complete all their tasks by 1991, there being little chance of accommodating further delays without prejudicing the projected 1993 publication date.

BIRD NUMBERS '92

The EBCC Conference **Bird Numbers '92** in The Netherlands saw the EOAC working report *Breeding Bird Atlas of Europe* published; it contained the preliminary distribution maps and population data. The aims of the report were to:

1. Give feedback to everyone who had supported the EOAC project.
2. Allow countries which had submitted data to visualize and check their contribution.
3. Encourage non-contributing countries to submit data quickly.
4. Encourage countries contributing only qualitative information to upgrade it to semi-quantitative data.
5. Permit authors to use the maps when writing species accounts.
6. Use this 'dummy' atlas to help raise funds and assure publishers.

Every **Bird Numbers** delegate and national coordinator was asked to criticize the maps and to report errors and omissions; their helpful response was repeated throughout the correction process. At this Conference Johan Bekhuis retired as EOA WG secretary and as overall project coordinator; Ward Hagemeijer succeeded him.

ADDITIONAL PARTICIPATION IN THE PROJECT

Eastern Europe

Not until 1991 did the EOAC succeed in obtaining breeding bird data from Estonia, Latvia, Lithuania and Western Ukraine. Thanks to an invitation from Prof. E. Syroechkovski of the Academy of Sciences in Moscow, Johan Bekhuis attended the All-Union Ornithological Conference in 1991 and managed to establish new contacts and coordinators in all former Soviet republics or regions. Time did not permit the new coordinators to organize special mapping projects to produce data for the EOA. Instead, they contacted ornithologists working in their region to extract available breeding bird distribution data, whether from censuses or other records. Success was variable. In addition, Michael Blair, in his endeavours to recruit authors, had corresponded with individuals who would provide information on bird breeding distribution, and sometimes on populations; such arrangements produced most of the data from NE and SE European Russia and from Transcaucasia. These sources are recognized in the **Acknowledgements** section. Ward Hagemeijer, the mapping editor, developed contacts in Ukraine and S-C Russia to similar effect, and helped collect data from Albania.

Remaining areas in Europe

By the early 1980s it was obvious that Greece lacked an organization with sufficient status and resources to organize mapping or contribute data to the EOA. Tim Sharrock, at that time EOAC Chairman, recruited the German ornithologist Hartmut Heckenroth who knew Greek avifauna well and had many contacts with visiting ornithologists and bird tourists. Heckenroth was able to supply not only breeding evidence information, but even semi-quantitative population estimates for Greece. In 1993–94, when the *Atlas* coverage area was being finalized, Michael Blair made arrangements to obtain data for European Turkey and from the Azores and Madeiran archipelagos.

PRELIMINARY MAPS

Maps are vital to any atlas project. In 1987 the EOAC proposed that the *Atlas* maps should include both breeding evidence and estimates of breeding numbers for each species per 50km square. Such maps generally were similar to the early versions published in *British Birds*, except for a range of dot-sizes corresponding to semi-quantitative estimates. In preliminary form, these new maps stimulated completion of delayed tasks and encouraged not only further participation but also other atlas projects. The **List of Atlases** section demonstrates the success of these maps.

HABITAT DATA

The project originally collected proportionate habitat data per 50km square to compile a reserve data-set to help estimate breeding bird densities, but this idea was superseded when nations produced their own estimates of breeding numbers. Processing habitat data ceased after 1990. However, these data remain on many collection forms and may be useful in future.

POPULATION DATA QUESTIONNAIRE

The EOAC had long decided that each map should have a species account to explain the species' distribution pattern. The 1987 Conference decision to include habitat preferences, breeding densities, distribution changes, estimates of population sizes and trends and the conservation status in the species accounts required national breeding bird population estimates, so a population data questionnaire was sent to national coordinators.

The European Continental section of the International Council for Bird Preservation (ICBP, now BirdLife International) began work in 1990 on the Dispersed Birds Project, which was concerned with breeding, non-breeding and wintering populations. EOAC and ICBP therefore agreed to cooperate over the population data collection. ICBP distributed questionnaires to its national representatives in each European country, the section dealing with breeding bird populations having been devised jointly by ICBP and EOAC.

ICBP then collated and computerized the questionnaire data, thus establishing what eventually became the joint EBCC/BirdLife European Bird Database, and supplied EOAC with the output, which was also the basis of the population tables in *Birds in Europe: their conservation status*, published by BirdLife International in 1994.

FUNDING

Despite the early EOAC decision to fund the employment of a full-time coordinator to manage and process the fieldwork data and to cover working expenses, fundraising initially was unsuccessful. Data collection started on a volunteer basis in 1985, but the centralized plan for data handling and processing could not proceed without funding. Fundraising in The Netherlands, Germany and Britain had enabled SOVON to initiate much of the basic coordination of the data collection in the expectation that further funding would be obtained, and without this initiative, the EOA project would have foundered.

However, in 1991 a joint fundraising campaign by the BTO, SOVON and the CBS succeeded in obtaining a one-year grant from Eurostat (Statistical Office of the European Community) in 1991. This financial support proved to be crucial in funding the continuation of data collection and the development of the data processing.

Financial support and help with the data processing and the map production, especially from 1992 to 1994, came from the National Reference Centre for Nature, Forests and Landscape, an institute of the Dutch Ministry of Agriculture, Nature Management and Fisheries. An announcement to this intent was made during the opening ceremony of **Bird Numbers '92** by the Dutch States Secretary of Agriculture, Nature Management and Fisheries, Drs Gabor. A substantial British Government contribution was announced during the same session. In 1993 the EBCC entered lengthy negotiations with a European commercial firm for sole sponsorship of the *Atlas* but these proved fruitless. A new fundraising initiative was devised, but text editing work had to be suspended temporarily.

The 1993–1994 fundraising campaign brought donations from trusts, individuals, and further funds from the Department of the Environment in Britain. The German government also provided funds to employ the species account Editor for several months and to finance the translation of the summary of this *Atlas* into Russian, and to produce it as a booklet. Perhaps the most imaginative idea was the 'sponsor-a-species' campaign, which sprang from a concept of Ms E. Witt of Berlin. Over 100 species have been sponsored by individuals, organizations and firms. Without the support of so many, the editorial work could not have been completed.

THE EDITING PROCESS

In 1993 data-gathering and database correction approached completion. EBCC delegates were asked to nominate species specialists from their countries. With this list and others as a basis, Michael Blair recruited almost 500 species account authors from 37 countries (34 in Europe) for 512 species accounts, endeavouring to team up experts from opposite ends of Europe where possible, to emphasize the cooperative nature of the project and the vast ranges of many species. It was important to encourage authors from countries where ornithology and conservation were developing. The response was extraordinarily generous and enthusiastic. Rob Bijlsma rejoined the project in 1995, as reference editor, to ensure accounts had a proper European perspective, and especially for the older texts, to update and validate the references cited.

Michael Blair also had the responsibility of recruiting artists from as many countries as possible to provide vignettes. Twenty-seven artists from 11 countries, recruited as the authors had been, produced vignettes for this book.

ATLAS PUBLICATION

In early 1996 the EOA WG provided T & AD Poyser with the materials required to produce the *Atlas*. Since then, the struggles to overcome the complex technical problems of publishing the *Atlas* have sometimes seemed endless, but the publishers and editors have finally triumphed.

UPON REFLECTION

Europe is just beginning to coalesce. When the EOAC set out on this project, there was no example to follow for such a huge collaborative task. Many of the objectives were achieved in roundabout ways, and certainly many mistakes were made. We succeeded with most people; to those whom we failed, we apologize. Few would have anticipated the difficulties which had to be overcome. We learned much about differences and peculiarities on an individual, local or regional scale, but much more important we learnt we had so much in common, and we could tap the huge desire to cooperate. Perhaps our example may serve to encourage others working to the benefit of Europe, no matter what their subject.

Frank Saris & Goetz Rheinwald

Evolution and History of the European Bird Fauna

Since current biogeographic patterns result from a combination of historical factors and present ecological conditions, knowledge of the history of a fauna is crucial for understanding its origin, distribution and diversification. Europe is but a small peninsula of Eurasia and its fauna a sample of that of the entire Palearctic, but it is not a random sample, even if few bird species evolved within the limits of Europe such as they have been defined in this *Atlas*. Although most Palearctic biotas experienced a similar Plio-Pleistocene history, there are many differences in origin and composition of biota between the eastern and the western parts of Eurasia (Hino 1990). Stegmann (1938) coined the concept of 'faunal types' to classify bird assemblages of the Eurasian continent, each faunal type encompassing a group of species that share a common history and common ecological adaptations related to particular vegetation formations. More recently, another attempt was made by Voous (1960, 1963) who assigned the European bird species to 24 main 'faunal types' on the basis of a number of geographical–historical variables. However, a methodological problem with faunal types is that this concept combines extant distributions and faunal history so that assigning species to faunal types presupposes knowledge of the history of each of the taxa, which is far from being the case. An insight in the influence of history in shaping patterns of bird diversities and distributions may be obtained from several sources including fossil records, biosystematic studies of extant taxa, historical data on geography, climates and especially vegetation. This chapter does not give any details of the history of individual species or groups of species. Rather, it gives a brief overview of the main historical events that shaped the modern European bird fauna as a whole.

The story of birds began in the last two periods of the Mesozoic (Jurassic and Cretaceous), but not until the early Tertiary, and especially in the Miocene (*c* 30–40 million years ago) did the main characters of avifaunas become recognizable. Because the pneumatized bones of birds, especially those of small-sized land-birds, are a weak material for fossilization, the fossil record is still too scanty to give more than fragmentary indications about changes at the level of regional faunas. However, the fossil records do provide some insight into faunal turnover on the scale of higher taxonomic units (orders and families). Only representatives of some aquatic groups (eg divers, grebes, cormorants, flamingoes, ibises, rails, sandpipers) have so far been found from the late Cretaceous, and only few Paleocene birds are known at present (Brodkorb 1971, Olson 1985, Bochenski 1985).

During the early history of birds in the late Cretaceous–early Tertiary period, tropical and subtropical forests dominated by oaks, laurels and palms covered the low-middle latitudes of Eurasia and North America (Axelrod 1975). The climate of the earth was subtropical and semitropical conditions prevailed as far as 50°N. Continents were flat, without ice caps and large cordilleras, and Eurasia and North America were connected through Beringia, allowing exchanges between the two landmasses. The faunal interchange across this land-bridge resulted in considerable similarities in the modern avifaunas between the Palearctic and Nearctic regions, especially in the northern part of the continents. For example, half of the 44 arctic waterfowl and wader species have a circumpolar distribution whereas only 10% of bird species of the coniferous taiga occur in both Europe and North America (Haila & Järvinen 1990). At the very beginning of the Tertiary, the world avifauna was poorly diversified, and most groups of birds were presumably very widespread, so that many extinct families of the Tertiary are known from both Eurasia and the New World (Bochenski 1985). Many families now restricted to the tropics such as Trogonidae, Bucconidae, Bucerotidae, Coliidae, Capitonidae and Cracidae were then widespread in what is today the temperate zone (Brodkorb 1971, Mourer-Chauviré 1982, Olson 1985).

As the climate became drier in Eurasia from the late Eocene, xerophyllous plants started to evolve, especially mediterranean-type taxa, from the Iberian plate to central Asia (Axelrod 1975). The North Pacific land bridge ceased to exist so that the formerly homogeneous Holarctic avifaunas split in two blocks that evolved under conditions of increasing continental isolation, increasing dryness and falling temperatures. By the late Eocene–early Oligocene, which was a time of great radiation in both land and water birds, most extant orders (26 of 32) of birds had become established (Brodkorb 1971). As a consequence of these climatic changes, many tropical birds (eg Cracidae, Psittacidae, Musophagidae, Coliidae, Trogonidae and Bucerotidae) were wiped out in Europe and never returned. At the same time, reduction of forests and expansion of grasslands provided opportunities for differentiation into new niches (Brodkorb 1971). In contrast with the North American extant bird fauna, which includes many families of Neotropical origin, the Eurasian avifauna, and especially that of Europe, includes a very low proportion of tropical elements (Moreau 1966). This is because the south–north orientation of the major barriers (Andes, Rocky Mountains) favoured intercontinental dispersal of birds in the New World whereas the west–east orientation of massive barriers in the Old World (the eremian desert belt from the Sahara to

Mongolia and the mountain wall of Himalaya and associated ranges) effectively prevented intercontinental south–north dispersal (Snow 1978). Thus, such important North American families as Parulidae, Vireonidae, Tyrannidae, and Icteridae are of Neotropical, rather than Nearctic, origin whereas their ecological counterparts in Europe (Sylviidae, Muscicapidae, Turdidae) originated in the Palearctic. Diversification and continental specialization of the world avifauna increased when the zonal differentiation of the main vegetation belts began to develop by the late Oligocene/Miocene (Axelrod 1976, Keast 1990a, b). By the end of the Miocene, all the non-passerine and most of the passerine families were established.

The continuing climatic stresses of the late Tertiary peaked in the Plio-Pleistocene. The extant European bird fauna is a legacy of this epoch of exceptional climatic instability, which was characterized by strong short-term wet/dry and cool/warm fluctuations. Van Donk (1976) estimated 21 glacials or near-glacials as having occurred during the last 2.3 million years. They had considerable effects on vegetation and associated faunas everywhere on the earth. The repeated shifts back and forth and fragmentation of forest blocks had a decisive influence on the evolution of modern avian species and the establishment of current distributional patterns. However, a large proportion of the living bird species probably originated before the Pleistocene, which makes their origin more ancient than formerly thought (eg Brodkorb 1971). The main consequences of the Pleistocene climatic crises may be summarized in three points (see Blondel 1988):

1. At the height of the full glacial periods, virtually no arboreal vegetation persisted north of the Pyrenees, the Alps and the Carpathians (Pons 1981, Huntley & Birks 1983). Accordingly, all forest biomes including the birds must have withdrawn to somewhere south of 45°N.
2. Contrary to what has been believed for a long time (eg Moreau 1954), the Mediterranean biomes did not shift as a whole to the south in what is now the Sahara during the glacial episodes, but remained in local refugia mostly within the limits of the Mediterranean region, which was larger than today because the sea level had regressed by 100–150m (Zeuner 1952, Hopkins 1967). Paleobotanical and paleontological records have shown that the diversity of both geography and conditions of temperature and moisture within the Mediterranean during either glacial or interglacial periods has allowed the coexistence on a regional scale of all the European vegetation belts and their associated faunas (Blondel 1988). One example is that fossil remains of *Falco naumanni* (thermophilous Mediterranean species), *Lagopus mutus*, *Nyctea scandiaca* (birds of the tundra and the alpine belt), and *Monticola saxatilis* (turdid of the Mediterranean mountains) together with several forest species have been found in the same deposits of Würm II (70 000 BP {Before Present}) in southern France (Mourer-Chauviré 1975). Assuming that the species-specific habitat preferences we observe today have been approximately constant in time, such puzzling and apparently aberrant assemblages suggest that local landscapes in the Mediterranean during full glaciations might have been a kaleidoscope of such habitats as tundras, steppes, and both coniferous and broad-leaved forests. Hence, there has been a striking compression of the European faunas within the Mediterranean Basin.
3. Different types of more or less isolated patches of matorral already existed in the Mediterranean region in the late Miocene (Suc 1978) and persisted during the whole Quaternary in local areas where climatic, edaphic and topographical conditions allowed the existence of only a shrubby vegetation (Pons 1981). The present extension of matorrals is a modern and secondary feature caused by human deforestation that has continued since the early Neolithic until the last 50 years or so in the Mediterranean countries of Europe. Most Mediterranean endemics (eg *Sylvia* spp, *Alectoris* spp) evolved in the patches of matorral that have persisted in the region since the Pliocene.

To sum up, the Quaternary history of European forests is characterized by huge shifts back and forth of forest belts without any obvious geographic delimitation between them. Forest habitats were extensive, but there is no evidence that they became fragmented enough to allow for allopatric speciation in birds. This explains both the very low level of local and regional endemism of forest species and the homogeneity of forest bird faunas everywhere in Europe with a large number of 'core species', ie species that are widespread and that tend to be abundant wherever they occur. At the height of full glaciations, the Mediterranean region as a whole, and especially the three main peninsulas (Iberian, Ligurian, Balkan), acted as refuges from which species spread again to the north during each climatic amelioration. Populations of most species were dramatically reduced in numbers, especially those of deciduous broad-leaved forests which were concentrated in small areas, within the narrow limits of the Mediterranean region. But probably very few extinctions occurred: all the genera and species found as fossils in the Pliocene still exist today somewhere in Europe (Moreau 1954, Brodkorb 1971). This means that there have been no lasting revolutionary changes in the avifauna since the end of the Pliocene, which demonstrates a remarkable ecological persistence and resilience of taxa through a whole series of vicissitudes. Since the effects of previous glaciations have been somewhat obliterated by subsequent ones, the last glaciation, especially its second phase (Würm-Weichsel, 70 000 BP), seems to explain most of the present patterns of distribution and diversification of European birds. Post-glacial evolution has been mostly restricted to the subspecific level, including many cases of secondary hybridization between formerly isolated populations or semi-species as they have come into contact (Haffer 1977). One may imagine that species ranges that were more or less continuous during interglacials became fragmented in several refugia during full glaciations where populations evolved in isolation. Many taxa exhibit clear east–west replacement patterns of two sister taxa (eg semi-species) that probably evolved in isolation during glacial times (Haffer 1977, Harrison 1982). Conversely, the marine fauna of Europe, as in other regions of the world, shows little diversification. The climatic vicissitudes of the Plio-Pleistocene resulted in the present zonation of the main climatic–vegetational belts to which faunas are closely linked. Some features that reflect the past history of the most important of them are worth mentioning.

- The Arctic covers an enormous land area of some 25 million km² with tundra as the only vegetational type. Although a young formation going back at most to the Pliocene, this very distinctive region hosts as many as 141 breeding species (Salomonsen 1972). Only a small proportion of them (44) belong to the Arctic faunal type (*sensu* Voous 1960), and many have a circumpolar distribution.

- The northern belt of conifers (taiga) is one of the most extensive biogeographic formations on earth between 50° and 70°N. As a vegetation formation, it originated in the mountains of eastern Siberia during the gradual cooling of the climate that preceded the onset of Pleistocene glaciations, some 2.4 million years ago. Like the tundra, the taiga is recent as a vegetation formation, differing greatly from all vegetation types present on earth before the Pleistocene (Haila & Järvinen 1990). As a result, its fauna is of recent origin. During Pleistocene glaciations large parts of this belt were covered by ice, and therefore the taiga was restricted to very small areas. For these reasons, the taiga bird fauna includes only a relatively small number of species, most of them being exceptionally widespread. According to Brunov (in Haila & Järvinen 1990), the fauna of the central and northern taiga includes 32 species that are strict conifer dwellers, most of which are resident and specifically adapted to conifers (Haila *et al* 1987).

- The Palearctic steppes of SE Europe are poor in indigenous birds (Stegmann 1958) since only 40 species are characteristic of this vegetational type. As pointed out by Mayr (1972), the small number of steppe species may be related, as for the Arctic and taiga zones, to the very recent origin of this formation which originated in the late Tertiary.

- One of the most important and richest vegetation formations of Europe is broad-leaved deciduous forest. At the scale of Eurasia, this belt is split into two large blocks separated by large areas of steppe, deserts and massive mountains of central Asia that acted as barriers isolating Eurasian forests from the tropical rainforests of the monsoon zone. Hence, contrary to the previous zones, the deciduous forest blocks of the eastern and western sides of the continent experienced rather different Pleistocene histories. Because of the geographical configuration of landmasses, there were more opportunities for forests and their associated bird faunas to find refuge in the southeastern part of Eurasia during the most severe episodes of the glacial times than in the southwestern part. Hence the forests of eastern Eurasia moved to a lesser extent to the south and found larger and less fragmented refuge areas than those of western Eurasia (Hino 1990). This explains why present floras and faunas are on average more diversified in the east with more endemic and tropical elements (eg Zosteropidae, Pycnonotidae, Timalidae and Campephagidae).

- The bird diversity of the Mediterranean region is extremely high: 343 species breed at present in an area of 3 million km², a number to be compared with the 419 species which breed in the 10 million km² of the whole of Europe (Voous 1960). This region is a melting pot into which species from many faunal types dispersed from different biogeographic regions. Two of these played the most important roles: Eurasia (153 species) and the semi-arid belts of the south and south-east margins of the region (85 species). A striking feature of the Mediterranean fauna is the very low level of endemism, although Stegmann (1938) recognized the Mediterranean region as a well-defined subunit of the Palearctic: no more than 47 species (14% of the fauna) are regional endemics. In particular, although we should expect shrubland species to be numerous and dominant in the many types of matorrals that extend over more than half the region, this category is poorly represented (12%) whereas forest birds are widespread and dominant everywhere, including North Africa. The small proportion of endemics in the Mediterranean, in spite of high habitat diversity and many geographic barriers, may be explained by the common history shared by mid-European and Mediterranean forests and by the secondary extension of most matorrals (Blondel 1988, 1990). Thus this fauna, especially that of forests, is not fundamentally different from those of cold and temperate Europe, which mainly belong to Holarctic faunal types; the compositions of forest bird assemblages differ much more between the northern belt of conifers and the deciduous belt than between the latter and the Mediterranean forests.

Because more than two thirds of Europe are (or should be) forested, woodland birds represent an important and well-defined set of the terrestrial avifauna. At the scale of Eurasia where most forest species evolved, as many as 39 families and 126 genera are specialized to forest habitats. From an evolutionary viewpoint, the present forest avifaunas are a legacy of the long common history of birds and plants, with close interactions since the Eocene. Evidence of these interactions is given by many coevolutionary traits; birds are often the major seed dispersers and sometimes the pollinators of trees and shrubs which, in turn, provide them with food (Estrada & Fleming 1986, Snow & Snow 1988). Coadaptation between birds and plants may be traced over a long evolutionary time through current patterns of coadaptation of the present bird-plant assemblages (Ferry 1984), so that long-term plant–bird interactions resulted in highly integrated constructs. Regal (1977) suggested that in many important ecosystem processes such as the limitation of insect populations, seed dispersal and pollination, birds played a fundamental role in the radiation of angiosperms in the Cretaceous and early Tertiary. They certainly played an important role for the northward expansion of vegetation belts in relation to climatic changes. For instance, Beech *Fagus sylvatica* spread from southern Europe to southern Scandinavia within less than 3000 years, a rate of about 1 km/year (Moreau 1954). Birds and mammals must have been very important in the repeated processes of forest spreading after each glacial episode.

The overall picture of the European bird fauna such as it

has developed since the end of the glaciation is a dynamic one. Many changes in the distribution and abundance of species are natural processes, some of them perhaps as a consequence of climatic changes (eg Kalela 1949), but natural changes are slow and inconspicuous when compared with the tremendous changes due to human impact. Man-induced changes through agriculture have had effects on the abundance and distribution of species for as long as 5000 years in most of Europe and probably up to 10 000 years in the eastern Mediterranean. Clearly, traditional agriculture and forestry had positive effects on some components of diversity at the scale of landscapes. One example is that of the traditional land-use patterns (the *sylva–saltus–ager* triad) in Mediterranean landscapes (Blondel & Aronson 1994). A well-documented example of changes in the distribution of species is that of Fennoscandia (von Haartman 1973, Järvinen & Ulfstrand 1980, Haila & Järvinen 1990) where 98 species colonized the region during the period 1850–1970, that is a colonization rate of 2.8 species per decade, whereas 22 species vanished, a loss rate of 0.6 species per decade, resulting in a net gain of 2.2 species per decade. Most of these colonization events in North Europe since 1850 have been attributed to the role of man (Järvinen & Ulfstrand 1980). The evidence suggests that there is an optimum level at which man's activities result in a maximum gain of species, just as natural disturbance events that are a starting point for ecological successions regulate species diversities in forest ecosystems. But nowadays, human impact on landscapes are far beyond this optimal level. Dramatic changes in distribution and local abundance of birds are attributable to modern land-use practices including habitat destruction and fragmentation, deforestation, wetland drainage, eutrophication, pollution and modern industrial agriculture and forestry. The gamma component of bird species diversity, that is the total number of species at the scale of a landscape, probably has not changed much, but its alpha (local richness) and beta (among-habitat turnover of species) components are very sensitive to habitat alteration. One must hope that the current concern about the modern biodiversity crisis will help us to stop the decline of birds (and other wildlife) and restore as much as possible of our historical heritage.

I am most grateful to Staffan Ulfstrand for his useful comments on an earlier draft of this chapter which was written in the Department of Zoology of the University of Uppsala.

Jacques Blondel

Acknowledgements

The fieldworkers

This *Atlas*, like so much ornithological work in Europe, depends on the input of tens of thousands of skilled fieldworkers, almost all of them amateurs working in a voluntary capacity. We thank them for their hard work and dedication and hope that the published *Atlas* meets their hopes and expectations.

The European Bird Census Council (EBCC) Board

The editors are grateful for the support of EBCC Board members throughout the period of their employment. We pay special tribute to all previous Board members of the EBCC, and of its forerunner organization, the IBCC, without whom the project would not have begun. At the time of writing, the EBCC Board comprises: Dr Jeremy J.D. Greenwood, Chairman (GB); Ward Hagemeijer, Secretary (NL); Dr Anny Anselin, Treasurer and *Bird Census News* Editor (B); Dr Martin Flade (D); Dr Michael Pienkowski (GB); Prof Helena Rogacheva (R); Rui Rufino (P); Dr Luc Schifferli (CH); Dr Tibor Szép (H); and Dr Juha Tiainen (FIN). Dr Goetz Rheinwald (D) was a stalwart member until he stood down in late 1995, as did Andres Kuresoo (EST).

The European Ornithological Atlas Working Group (EOA WG)

The editors express their enthusiastic appreciation of all other members of the EOA WG who assisted in so many ways. When it was dissolved, the EOA WG comprised: Dr Goetz Rheinwald, Chairman (D); Michael Blair, text editor (GB); Dr Jeremy Greenwood (GB); Ward Hagemeijer, secretary, mapping editor (NL); Frank Saris (NL); Dr Luc Schifferli (CH) and RNDr Karel Šťastný (CZ). Invited members were Dr David Cole (Joint Nature Conservation Committee, GB), Melanie Heath and Dr Graham Tucker (BirdLife International) and Dr Andrew Richford (T & AD Poyser).

Atlas Coordinators

The collection, collation and correction of data were organized by national coordinators who formed a vital link in the project. Without them the surveys would not have taken place, nor would gaps in coverage been filled. Their workload, described in the *Introduction*, was heavy and demanding. The editors thank the EBCC coordinators for their magnificent effort. The list of EBCC coordinators follows these Acknowledgements.

European Bird Database Contributors

We also acknowledge the sterling efforts of the national contributors to the EBCC/BirdLife European Bird Database (see **Introduction**), who are also listed after these Acknowledgements. Melanie Heath and Graham Tucker (BirdLife International) managed the database on behalf of both BirdLife and EBCC, as well as producing its first fruit *Birds in Europe: their conservation status.*

EBCC Delegates

EBCC delegates form the routine national points of contact with the EBCC board, often via *Bird Census News* which is issued several times per year, on matters involving bird census work. Their invaluable assistance to the *Atlas* took the form of recruiting authors of the species accounts and artists to draw the vignettes. Naturally, when unexpected difficulties arose, the editors had to rely heavily on the EBCC delegates to help solve the problems. Their response was enthusiastic, and invariably encouraging. The list of EBCC delegates follows these Acknowledgements.

Species account authors

Most species accounts have two authors. Species account authors were recruited from 38 countries. Their names follow the texts in the *Atlas* (in alphabetical order except where all parties agreed a different sequence) and are listed below, after the EBCC delegates. Our admiration for the text authors is unbounded, and we feel we have made many personal friends through their support and goodwill. Of necessity, editing had to shorten and shape texts; those species accounts produced early in the project occasionally required updating to reflect recent work. Because not all authors had full access to references across Europe, especially for recent work, Rob Bijlsma, whose knowledge of the European avifauna is both wide and deep, was employed as Reference Editor to ensure a wide European perspective. His contribution has been invaluable.

The *Atlas* is dedicated to those who did not live to complete their contribution, or see the final result, but we should not forget those authors who were forced by circumstances to withdraw.

Artists

The provision of over 500 vignette illustrations is no small task. We endeavoured to recruit artists from as many countries as possible. Pressure of work forced many artists to decline participation, or to withdraw after accepting. One consequence is that many of the featured artists illustrated more species than they were originally allocated, often at short notice. All participating artists deserve our heartfelt thanks for marvellous illustrations in a variety of styles, particularly those who rallied to the cause in an emergency! Each artist was asked to place their initials within the illustration area to ease identification. They are listed below, after the authors. We express our gratitude to Eng. Tito Costa for kindly waiving priority on ten illustrations (by José Projecto), originally intended for the *Atlas of the Birds of the Peneda National Park* (Portugal) where he is the Director.

Data organizers

Johan Bekhuis, who was involved in the project from its beginnings, played a pivotal role in making it function properly. The sound precepts he applied for recording and handling the data stood the test of time, and his enthusiasm and knowledge of European ornithology brought the necessary momentum. From the beginning, the National Reference Centre for Nature Management (IKC Natuurbeheer) of the Dutch Ministry of Agriculture, Nature Management and Fisheries have processed the standard recording forms. IKC's Johan Thissen, Peter Frigge and Kees van Kessel invested much effort and time into the database design and into preparing the transfer of the data to SOVON. They prepared the maps for the working reports, Peter Frigge developing a mapping program for this purpose. Latterly, Peter Frigge fine-tuned the program to a standard which was electronically compatible with the requirements of the publisher's typesetters. To the national coordinators fell the responsibility of collating the data onto the standard recording forms or floppy discs. Data received in non-standard formats (maps, lists and corrections) were transcribed carefully and matched to *Atlas*-standard formats. Here Willibrord Schuurman, André van Kleunen (both volunteers at SOVON) and Johan Thissen were of enormous assistance.

The final stages of data-processing, error-correction and text-editing created a huge workload. At SOVON, Chris van Turnhout gave indispensable support and acted as a sounding-board in the process of producing the final maps and graph data. At the BTO, Simon Gillings rendered invaluable assistance in researching apparent anomalies between text contents and supporting database information.

Donors

The editors would like to express their personal gratitude to SOVON Bird Census Work The Netherlands and to the British Trust for Ornithology for hosting them, for facilitating the EOA project and for the realization of the *Atlas*. These organizations allowed the editors to develop the project and gave strong support when it faced major difficulties, thus ensuring its continuity. Their faith in the project gave time for adequate funding to be secured.

The project could not have succeeded without the financial and material support of individuals, trusts, and organizations. Funding for the project was received from (in approximate chronological sequence) DG11 of the European Commission, Eurostat of the EU, the Directorate of Nature, Forests, Landscape and Fauna of the Ministry of Agriculture, Nature Management and Fisheries (NL), the Joint Nature Conservation Committee (GB), Bundesminesterium für Umwelt, Naturschutz und Reaktorsicherheit (D), Luc Hoffmann (CH), Lady Y.P. McNeice of the Loke Wan Tho Foundation (Singapore), Schweizerische Vogelwarte Sempach (CH), the Peacock Trust (GB) and the Department of the Environment (GB). We also acknowledge the considerable input of time to the project by individuals representing SOVON Bird Census Work The Netherlands (NL), the British Trust for Ornithology (GB), the National Reference Centre for Nature Management of the Ministry of Agriculture, Nature Management and Fisheries (NL), Statistics Netherlands (NL), Zoologisches Forschungsinstitut und Museum Alexander Koenig (D), Dachverband Deutscher Avifaunisten (D), Schweizerische Vogelwarte Sempach (CH) and the Czech Ornithological Society (CZ).

We are particularly grateful to Dr Gerard C. Boere who, at a very difficult time for the project, showed his trust in the *Atlas* by helping to secure funding to finalize the project.

The 'Sponsor-a-species' campaign brought both individual and corporate support, acknowledged on the species' entries in the *Atlas*.

Special acknowledgements

It would be possible to write a book about all those from 1971 onwards who gave such excellent support, especially towards the creation of a unified, European approach. Rather than attempt imperfectly to list all deserving names, we ask that the book should be regarded as a tribute to their belief and commitment. Special thanks are due to all those people and organizations who helped solve what seemed at the time insuperable problems concerning contacts, data, mapping shortfalls and accounts for difficult species. We cite as a particular example Jacques van Impe, whose past work with Yuri N. Mineyev of the Komi Science Centre at Syktyvkar helped establish and maintain a link to Komi through Alexey A. Estafiev, Head of the Animal Ecology Laboratory, and Sergey K. Kotchanov and Vladimir M. Anufriev. This link provided virtually all the data for north-east European Russia and many of the associated species accounts. Victor P. Belik, Vladimir V. Morozov, Eugene Potapov, Peter Til'ba and Pavel S. Tomkovich, were generous with their guidance and assistance on many aspects of Russian bird distribution.

At the time of writing, *The Birds of Armenia* project was at the data-collating stage, but generously provided us with validated data pre-dating their 1995 fieldwork. We are grateful indeed to Mr Sarkis Acopian, that project's inspiration and to Peter B. Saenger, the project manager.

Hartmut Heckenroth played a vital role in securing data from Greece.

Rod Martins provided much thoughtful comment on biogeographical boundaries in relation to the *Atlas*' area of coverage. We look forward to his and Erik Hirschfeld's suggested revision of the western Palearctic southeastern boundaries.

We are grateful to the Finnish Museum of Natural History, acknowledging that the basis of our 50km grid lies in their *Atlas Florae Europaeae* amended for our purposes as described in the *Introduction*. The Scott Polar Institute kindly made available to us copies of maps of Franz Josef Land and Novaya Zemlya to act as vital references. We thank Rui Rufino for his help in establishing links with the Azores and Madeira. Vidar Bakken at the Norsk Polarinstitut was generous with his time in analysing records for Svalbard, Jan Mayen, and Bear Island. Some authors preferred to write in their own language rather than in English. In such cases the translators were Michael G. Wilson, from *Birds of the Western Palearctic* (Russian), Susan Fleming (German), Anny Anselin (French) and Sandy Hill (Spanish).

We are especially grateful to Professor C.M. Perrins for permission to superimpose the mapped breeding distributions of species contained in *Birds of the Western Palearctic* (Concise edition) in areas of Europe for which we lacked coverage.

ATLAS COORDINATORS

Note: national coordinators' names are without a suffix. Regional coordinators are indicated thus: [R]. Coordinators of additional data are indicated thus: [A]

Albania
Giuseppe Bogliani[A]
Ward Hagemeijer[A]

Armenia
Peter Saenger
Yuri Zharikov

Austria
Andreas Ranner

Azerbaijan
Vincent van den Berk[A]
Roald Potapov[A]

Belarus
Alexei Tishechkin

Belgium
Pierre Devillers
Jean-Paul Jacob
Anny Anselin[A]
Patrick Meire[A]

Bulgaria
Petar Iankov
Tanju Michev

Croatia
Goran Sušic
Tibor Mikuska

Czech Republic
Karel Šťastný

Denmark
Rene Christensen
Uffe Gjøl-Sörensen
Søren Sørensen[R] (Faeroes)

Estonia
Eerik Leibak
Olav Renno

Finland
Risto Väisänen

France
Dosithée Berthelot
Patrice Cramm[R]
Daniel Gilardot[R]
Daniel Ingremeau[R]
Pierre Piotte[R]
Jean-Charles Tombal[R]

Georgia
Steffan Roth[A]

Germany
Goetz Rheinwald

Greece
Hartmut Heckenroth

Great Britain
David Wingfield Gibbons
Michael Taylor

Hungary
Tibor Szép
Zoltán Waliczky

Iceland
Aevar Petersen
Kristinn Skarphédinsson

Ireland
Chris Wilson

Italy
Pierandrea Brichetti
Lorenze Fornasari[R]
Maurizio Fraissinet[R]
Enrico Meschini

Latvia
Jānis Priednieks
Māris Strazds

Lithuania
Pranas Mierauskas

Luxembourg
Jean Weiss

Macedonia
Branko Micevski

Malta
Joe Sultana

Moldova
I. Ganea

The Netherlands
Johan Bekhuis

Norway
Jan-Ove Gjershaug
Vidar Bakken[A] (Svalbard)

Poland
Przemek Chylarecki
Maciej Gromadski

Portugal
Rui Rufino
Luisa Braz[R] (Azores)
Henrique Costa Neves[R] (Madeira)
Paulo Oliveira[R] (Madeira)

Romania
Dan Munteanu

Russia
Victor V. Belik[R]
Alexey A. Estafiev[R]
Gennady Grishanov[R]
Yuri Mineyev[R]
Alexander Numerov[R]
Martin Poot[R]
Roald Potapov[R]
Alexander Skepel[R]
Peter Til'ba[R]
E.E. Syroechkovski[R]
Victor Zubakin[R]

Slovakia
Aladar Randik

Slovenia
Iztok Geister

Spain
Ramón Martí
Francisco Purroy

Sweden
Sören Svensson

Switzerland
Luc Schifferli

Turkey (Thrace)
Gernant Magnin

Ukraine
Joseph Chernichko
Irena Galinskaya
Igor Gorban
Yuri Vergeles
Valentin Serebryakov[R]
Jan van der Winden[A]

former **Yugoslavia**
Dragan Radovic
Jelena Kralj
Jozsef Gergely

EUROPEAN BIRD DATABASE CONTRIBUTORS

Albania
B. Hallmann and F. Lamani

Andorra
Associació per a la Defensa de la Natura, J. Argelich, A. Clamens, J. Crozier, M.-J. Dubourg, A. Matschke and M. Pilkington

Austria
A. Ranner, with contributions from K. Bauer, H.-M. Berg, M. Dvorak, A. Gamauf, A. Grüll, R. Kilzer, A. Landmann, H. Lauermann, C. Medicus, P. Sackl, O. Samwald, N. Winding and T. Zuna-Kratky

Belarus
V. V. Ivanovsky, A. V. Kozulin, M. E. Nikiforov, I. E. Samusenko, A. K. Tishechkin and B. V. Yaminsky

Belgium
A. Anselin, with contributions from K. Devos, J.-P. Jacob, P. Meire and J. van Vessem

Bulgaria
P. Iankov, with contributions from T. Michev, L. Profirov, B. Ivanov, V. Pomakov, B. Milchev (Bulgarian Society for the Protection of Birds)

Croatia
G. Susic and D. Radovic, with contributions from T. Mikuska and J. Mikuska

Cyprus
M. Charalambides (Cyprus Ornithological Society)

Czech Republic
K. Šťastný and V. Bejcek, with contributions from K. Hudec and J. Hora

Denmark
M. F. Munk, with contributions from K. Biledgaard, F. P. Jensen, H. E. Jørgensen, J. Madsen, U. G. Sørensen and R. Christensen
Faeroe Islands
S. Sørensen
Greenland
D. Boertmann, with contributions from K. Kampp and K. Falk

Estonia
V. Lilleleht, with contributions from T. Kastepõld, A. Kuresoo, E. Leibak, A. Leito, A. Leivits, L. Luigujoe, E. Mägi, T. Randla, O. Renno, E.Tammur, E. Viht and H. Vilbaste

Finland
P. Koskimies, with contributions from E. Lammi, M. Mikkola, J. Södersved and R. A. Väisänen

France
G. Rocamora (Ligue pour la Protection des Oiseaux), with contributions from D. Yeatman-Berthelot and the Société Ornithologique de France

Germany
G. Rheinwald, with contributions from M. Flade, J. Melter, J. Mooij and Dachverband Deutscher Avifaunisten

Greece
G. Catsadorakis and B. Hallmann, with contributions from S. Bourdakis, S. Csirouhakis, K. Economidis, V. Hatzirvassanis, M. Malakou, P. Mollat and K. Poirazidis

Hungary
Z. Waliczky, with contributions from J. Bagyura, A. Bankovics, L. Haraszthy, L. Holnár, Z. Kalotás, F. Markus, L. Molnár, E. Schmidt and T. Szép

Iceland
Æ. Petersen and O. K. Nielsen, with contributions from J. Ó. Hilmarsson

Republic of Ireland
E. Callaghan, J. Coveney, D. W. Gibbons and O. Merne

Italy
G. Tallone, M. Gustin, M. Lambertini, E. Meschini and P. Brichetti, with contributions from M. Fraissinet

Latvia
M. Strazds and J. Priednieks (breeding data), and G. Vaverinš, J. Priednieks and M. Strazds (winter data), with contributions from J. Bauga, J. Baumanis, M. Bergmanis, U. Bergmanis, P. Blums, M. Janaus, J. Kazubiernis, M. Kreilis, J. Lipsbergs, A. Mednis, A. Petrinš, A. Stipniece and J. Viksne

Liechtenstein
G. Willi

Lithuania
P. Mierauskas, with contributions from R. R. Budrys, E. Drobelis, G. Grazulevicius, E. Greimas, V. Jusys, P. Kurlavicius, G. Margis, G. Matiukas, S. Paltanavicius, V. Pareigis, A. Pranaitis, L. Raudonikis and S. Sinkevicius

Luxembourg
D. Crowther and J. Weiss, with contributions from E. Melchior

Malta
J. Sultana, with contributions from the Research Committee of the Malta Ornithological Society

Moldova
I. Ganea and N. Zubcov

The Netherlands
F. Hustings and J. F. Bekhuis (SOVON)

Norway
J. O. Gjershaug, P. G. Thingstad and S. Eldøy, with contributions from T. Axelsen, I. Byrkjedal, A. O. Folkestad, A. Heggland, J. A. Kålås, V. Ree, J. Sandvik and G. Bangjord
Svalbard
V. Bakken

Poland
M. Gromadzki, P. Chylarecki and A. Sikora, with contributions from J. Bednorz, R. Czeraszkiewicz, A. Dombrowski, W. Górski, A. Jermaczek, J. Slupek, A. Staszewski, T. Stawarczyk, L. Tomiałojć, Z. Wojciechowski and J. Wójciak

Portugal
R. Rufino and R. Neves, with contributions from P. Catry,

J. C. Farinha, L. Palma, M. Pimenta, M. Pinto, A. M. Teixeira, M. de Lourdes Santarém and L. Reino
Azores
F. M. Medeiros and L. Monteiro
Madeira
F. Zino

Romania
D. Munteanu

Russia
V. G. Krivenko, V. O. Avdanin, V. E. Flint, V. M. Galushin, A. N. Golovkin, A. S. Koriakin, Y. N. Mineyev, E. S. Ravkin and V. G. Vinogradov, with contributions from V. P. Belik, V. T. Butiev, A. V. Filchagov, A. L. Mischenko, V. Y. Semashko and P. S. Tomkovich

Slovakia
B. Murin, A. Darolová and Š. Danko, with contributions from M. Balla, M. Bohuš, J. Chavko, M. Fulín, S. Harvanclk, P. Kanuch, D. Karaska, P. Karc, D. Kerestúr, L. Kocian, M. Kornan, J. Kornan, A. Krištín, R. Kropil, L. Mošanský, S. Pacenovský, Š. Pcola, P. Pjencák, R. Potocny, P. Rác, J. Salaj, J. Sládek, J. Somogyi, A. Štollmann, K. Takác, A. Tirinda, A. Trnka, I. Turcek and P. Zach

Slovenia
I. Geister and A. Sovinc, with contributions from A. Bibic, F. Bracko, J. Gregori, T. Jancar, F. Janzekovic, M. Perušek, B. Štumberger, P. Trontelj and M. Vogrin

Spain
F. J. Purroy, A. Onrubia and J. L. Robles
Canary Islands
J. J. Naranjo Pérez (breeding data), K. W. Emmerson and J. A. Lorenzo (winter data)

Sweden
L. Risberg

Switzerland
O. Biber, with contributions from L. Schifferli and H. Schmid

Turkey
S. Baris, J. C. Eames, I. Green, M. Kasparek, G. Magnin, R. P. Martins, R. F. Porter, G. Sarigül, G. M. Tucker and M. Yarar, with contributions from V. van den Berk and G. Kirwan

Ukraine
I. M. Gorban, with contributions from T. B. Ardamatskaya, V. T. Afanasyev, I. Y. Vergeles, V. V. Vetrov, M. A. Voinstvensky, V. I. Gulay, V. N. Grishchenko, N. L. Klestov, M. P. Knysh, A. I. Koshelev, V. I. Lysenko, G. N. Molodan, V. D. Siohin, I. V. Skilsky and I. I. Chernichko

United Kingdom
R. W. Hudson and D. W. Gibbons, with contributions from J. H. Marchant, R. E. Green, G. Williams and A. J. del Nevo
Gibraltar
C. Perez and J. Cortes, with contributions from P. Acolina, R. Attrill, K. Bensusan, M. Caruana, G. Durante, J. C. Finlayson, A. Fortuna, E. F. J. Garcia, H. van Gils, S. T. Holliday, T. Jesty, E. Lamb, J. Licudi, J. Mead, M. Mosquera, E. Olivares, D. Price, D. Ramos, N. Ramos, Sir Derek Reffel, P. Rocca, R. Rutherford, J. Saez, A. Sheldon and T. Walsh
Guernsey
B. Wells, with contributions from J. Medland
Isle of Man
J. P. Cullen
Jersey
G. Young, with contributions from J. M. Allan, I. Buxton, D. Buxton, M. Dryden, D. and F. Le Sueur, R. Long, M. L. Long, N. Milton, A. R. Paintin and S. J. Tonge

EBCC DELEGATES

Albania
Taulant Bino

Austria
Michael Dvorak
Andreas Ranner

Belarus
Mikhael Nikiforov
Alexei Tishechkin

Belgium
Koen Devos
Jean-Paul Jacob

Bulgaria
Petar Iankov
Tanju Michev

Croatia
Tibor Mikuska
Goran Sušic

Czech Republic
Karel Šťastný
Jiri Flousek

Denmark
Erik Mendrup Jacobsen
Michael Grell

Estonia
Eerik Leibak
Agu Leivits

Finland
Juha Tiainen
Risto Väisänen

France
Dosithée Yeatman-Berthelot
Christian Vansteenwegen

Georgia
Aleksander Abuladze

Germany
Martin Flade
Goetz Rheinwald
Klaus Witt

Greece
Filios Akriotis
Ben Hallmann
George Handrinos
Kostas Papakonstinou

Great Britain
Richard Gregory
Jeff Kirby

Hungary
Tibor Szép
György Szimuly

Iceland
Aevar Petersen
Kristinn Skarphedinsson

Ireland
John Coveney
Oscar Merne

Italy
Lorenzo Fornasari
Maurizio Fraissenet
Toni Mingozzi

Latvia
Elmars Peterhofs
Jānis Priedniks

Lithuania
Petras Kurlavičius
Gintaurus Matiukas
Pranas Mierauskas

Luxembourg
Jean Weiss

Malta
Paul Portelli
Joe Sultana

Moldova
I. Ganea

The Netherlands
Marc van Roomen
Frank Saris

Norway
Jan-Ove Gjershaug
Per Gustav Thingstad

Poland
Przemek Chylarecki
Maciej Gromadski
Ludwik Tomiałojć

Portugal
Julia Almeida
Luis Matos

Romania
Dan Munteanu
Peter Weber

Russia
Gennady Grishanov
Eugene Potapov
Yuri Ravkin
Helena Rogacheva
Eugenius Syroechkovski

Slovakia
Alzbeta Darolava
Rudolf Kropil

Slovenia
Iztok Geister
Janez Gregory

Spain
Ramón Martí
Francisco Purroy

Sweden
Sören Svensson

Switzerland
Roberto Lardelli
Luc Schifferli
Hans Schmid

Turkey
Murat Yarar

Ukraine
Igor Gorban
Valentin Serebryakov

SPECIES ACCOUNT AUTHORS, BY COUNTRY

A (Austria)
Michael Dvorak
Alfred Grüll
Erich Hable
Andreas Ranner
Peter Sackl
Otto Samwald

AZ (Azerbaijan)
Iljas P. Babayev

B (Belgium)
Gert Baeyens
Jean-Paul Fouarge
Paul Gailly
Jacques van Impe
Roland Libois
Dries van Nieuwenhuyse
Luc Schmitz
Jacques Tahon
Paula Ulenaers
Christian Vansteenwegen
Janine van Vessem

BELA (Belarus)
Vladimir Ivanowsky

BUL (Bulgaria)
Zlatozar Boev
Andon Darakchiev
Ventzeslav Delov
Stephan Dontchev
Petar Iankov
Bojidar Ivanov
Tañu Michev
Bojan Milchev
Tzeno Petrov
Jeko Spiridinov
the late Rumen Todorov
Ilia Vatev

CH (Switzerland)
Jean-Pierre Biber
Olivier Biber
Andreas Bossert
Heinz Hafner
Heinrich Haller
Rolf Hauri
Michel Juillard
Verena Keller
Roberto Lardelli
Hans Märki
Christian Marti
Paul Mosimann
Alfred Schifferli
Luc Schifferli
Hans Schmid
Werner Suter
Christine Breitenmoser-Würsten

CZ (Czech Republic)
Vladimír Bejćek
Jiri Flousek
Karl Hudec
Lubomír Peške
Miroslav Šálek
Karel Šťastný

D (Germany)
Franz Bairlein
Anita Bastian
Hans-Valentin Bastian
Wolfgang Baumgart
Rolf K Berndt
Peter Berthold
the late Hans Bub
Siegfried Eck
Martin Flade
Karl Schulze-Hagen
Hermann Hötker
Hans Hudde
Thomas Keller
Wilfried Knief
Klaus Liedel
Karl-Heinz Loske
Hermann Mattes
Johannes Melter
Bernd-Ulrich Meyburg
Reinhard Möckel
Ronald Mulsow
Frank Neuschulz
Bernd Nicolai
Markus Nipkow
Hans Oelke
Hartwig Prange
Gerhard Rothaupt
Klaus Ruge
Norbert Schäffer
Burkhard Stephan
Peter Südbeck
Ralf Wassmann

DK (Denmark)
Jens Gregersen
Jon Fjeldså
Hans Jerrentrup
Jesper Madsen
Anders Pape Møller
Michael Brinch Pedersen
Henrik Sell
Henrik Skov

E (Spain)
Juan C. Alonso
Fernando Barrios
Cristina Barros
Maria Nièves de Borbon
Francisco J. Cantos
Joan Castany
José A. Donázar
José A. Gil-Delgado
Mario Díaz Esteban
Secundino Gallego
Vicente Garza
Luis Mariano González
Borja Heredia
Rafael Heredia
Angel Hernández
Eduardo de Juana
Florentino de Lope
German López
Antonio Lucio
Manuel Mañez
Juan Manrique
Ramón Martí
Carmen Martinez
Jorge Muntaner
Alejandro Onrubia
Salvador J Peris
Manuel Puigcerver
Francisco Purroy
Cristina Ramos
Juan Real
José D. Rodriguez-Teijeiro
Manuel Soler
Carlos Urdiales
Miguel Yanes

EST (Estonia)
Taivo Kastepöld

F (France)
Christian Bavoux
Guy Burneleau
Alain Crivelli
Etienne Danchin
Bruno Faivre
Camille Ferry
Jean-Paul Fouarge
Jean-Claude Génot
Olivier Girard
Gérard Gory
Pierre Nicolau-Guillaumet

Paul Isenmann
Guy Jarry
Ariane Bernard-Laurent
Jean-Dominique Lebreton
Norbert Lefranc
Loïc Marion
Daniel Muselet
Christian Pietri
Jean-Marc Pons
Gérard Rocamora
Bertrand Trolliet
Jacques Trouvilliez
Pierre Yésou

FIN (Finland)
Michael Haldin
Martti Hario
Pekka Helle
the late Olavi Hildén
Lasse Iso-Iivari
Antero Järvinen
Pertti Kalinainen
Jukka Kauppinen
Mikael Kilpi
Erkki Korpimäki
Pertti Koskimies
Esa Lammi
Risto Lemmetyinen
Harto Lindén
Heimo Mikkola
Mikko Ojanen
Raimo Pakarinen
Timo Pakkala
Hannu Pietiäinen
Hannu Pöysä
Erkki Pulliainen
Pentti Rauhala
Lennart Saari
Pertti Saurola
Tapio Solenen
Jorma Sorjonen
Torsten Stjernberg
Seppo Sulkava
Juha Tiainen
Jari Tuomenpuro
Markku Ukkonen
Johan Ulfvens
Risto A. Väisänen
Raimo Virkkala
Seppo Vuolanto

GB (Great Britain)
Nicholas Aebischer
Rob T. Barrett
Michael Blair
W. R. P. Bourne
Anne Brenchley
John Callion
Nigel Clark
Peter Clement
Martin Cook
John Coulson
Humphrey Q. P. Crick
Roy Dennis
Paul Donald
Euan Dunn
the late George Dunnet
Brian Etheridge
Peter J. Ewins
Tony D. Fox
Robert W. Furness
David W. Gibbons
Simon Gillings
David Glue
Andrew G. Gosler
Murray Grant
Andy Green
Jeremy J. D. Greenwood
Adam Gretton
Michael P. Harris
Ian Henderson
David Hill
Ron Hoblyn
Philip Holland
Andrew Hoodless
David Houston
Baz Hughes
Rob Hume
Philip Jackson
Alan Johnson
Jeff Kirby
Alan Knox
Sir Christopher Lever
Philip J. K. McGowan
John Marchant
Chris Mead
Patricia Monaghan
John Morgan
Tony Morris
Greg Mudge
Ian Newton
Myrfyn Owen
Mariko Parslow-Otsu
Ian J. Patterson
Will Peach
Steve J. Petty
Nicholas Picozzi
Ian R. Poxton
Derek A. Ratcliffe
Eileen C. Rees
Mark Rehfisch
Colin Shawyer
Michael Shepherd
Denis Summers-Smith
Mark L. Tasker
Des B. A. Thompson
Patrick S. Thompson
Glen Tyler
Andrew Village
Sarah Wanless
Jeremy Wilson
Ian Wyllie

G (Greece)
Haralambos Alivizatos

H (Hungary)
Attila Bankovics
Emil Boross
Sandór Farago
László Haraszthy
Robert Horváth
Gabór Magyar
Sándor Mogyorósi
Zoltán Molnár
Támas Székely
Tibor Szép
Janos Török

I (Italy)
Nicola Baccetti
Giovanni Boano
Massimo Bocca
Pierandrea Brichetti
Andrea Ciaccio
Mauro Fasola
Lorenzo Fornasari
Ugo Foschi
Giancarlo Fracasso
Maurizio Fraissinet
Armando Gariboldi
Fulvio Genero
Marco Lambertini
Bruno Massa
Renato Massa
Danila Mastronardi
Mario Milone
Toni Mingozzi
Roberto Parodi
Giorgio Truffi
Mario Lo Valvo

ICE (Iceland)
Arni Einarsson
Arnthor Gardarsson
Gudmundur A. Gudmundsson

IRE (Ireland)
Brendan Kavanagh
Oscar J. Merne
the late Tony Whilde

ISR (Israel)
Hadoram Shirihai

LAT (Latvia)
Janis Baumanis
Ugis Bergmanis
Juris Lipsbergs
Aivars Mednis
Janis Priednieks
Māris Strazds
Janis Viksne

LITH (Lithuania)
Eugenijus Drobelis
Petras Kurlavičius
Bronius Sablevicius
Vitas Stanevičius

L (Luxembourg)
Jules Diederich

MAL (Malta)
Joe Sultana

N (Norway)
Torgrim Breiehagen
Svein Haftorn
Olav Hogstad
John Atle Kålås
Hans Chr. Pedersen
Nils Røv

NL (The Netherlands)
Albert Beintema
Johan Bekhuis
Leo van den Bergh
Vincent van den Berk
Rob G. Bijlsma
Kees Camphuysen
Barwolt S. Ebbinge
Ruud Foppen
Ward Hagemeijer
Ben Hallmann
Rob Hengeveld
Jan B. Hulscher
Fred Hustings
Marcel Klaasen
Peter de Knijff
Mardik F. Leopold
Roel Meijer
Peter L. Meininger
Eduard Osieck
Maarten Platteeuw
Frank Saris
Frans J. Schepers
Cor Smit
Peter Venema
J. J. Vlug
Rob Vogel
Berend Voslamber
Jan van der Winden
Ronald Zollinger
Pieter Zomerdijk

P (Portugal)
António Araújo
Manuel J. Biscoito
João Carlos Farinha
José P. Granadeiro
Paulo Moniz
Luiz Monteiro
Renato Neves
Paulo Oliveira
Nuno Onofre
Luis Palma
Marcia Pinto
Jaime A. Ramos
Rui Rufino

Antonio P. Teixeira
Francis Zino

PL (Poland)
Jan Bednorz
Zdzisław Bogucki
Marta Borowiec
Przemek Chylarecki
Andrzej Dyrcz
Jadwiga Gromadzka
Piotr Indykiewicz
Leszek Jerzak
Marek Keller
Jarosław Krogulec
Tadeusz Mizera
Tadeusz Stawarczyk
Ludwik Tomiałojć
Tomasz Wesołowski
Maria Wieloch

ROM (Romania)
Dan Munteanu
Peter Weber

R (Russia)
Vladimir N. Anufriev
Victor Belik
Alexey A. Estafiev
V. N. Kalyakin
Sergey K. Kotchanov
Elena G. Lappo
Yuri N. Mineyev
Vladimir V. Morozov
Evgeny N. Panov
Peter Til'ba
Roald L. Potapov
Pavel S. Tomkovich
Victor Zubakin

S (Sweden)
Sven Blomqvist
Bodil Enoksson
Lambart von Essen
Ulla Falkdalen
Björn Helander
Hans Källander
Bo-Göran Lillandt
Arne Lundberg
Sven Mathiasson
Ingvar N. Nilsson
Jan Åke Nilsson
Leif Nilsson
Sven G. Nilsson
Bodil Nyström
Hans Nyström
Lennart Risberg
Kjell Sjöberg
Roland Staav
Bengt-Olov Stolt
Bo W. Svensson
Sören Svensson
Christer G. Wiklund

SLK (Slovakia)
Štefan Danko
Marián Janiga
Dušan Karaska
Anton Krištín
Miroslav Saniga

SLN (Slovenia)
Iztok Geister
Peter Groselj
Dare Šere
Iztok Skornik
Borut Štumberger

TUR (Turkey)
Gernant Magnin

UKR (Ukraine)
Igor Gorban
Antonia G. Rudenko
Valentin V. Serebryakov

ARTISTS

The 27 artists from 11 countries have (mostly) initialled their vignettes.

CB	Christof Bobzin (D)
CCT	Carl Christian Tofte (DK)
DP	Dan Powell (GB)
EL	Ernest Leahy (GB)
GB	George Brown (GB)
JC	Jens Overgaard Christensen (DK)
JF	Jon Fjeldså (DK)
JLR	Joaquín López-Rojas (E)
JP	José Projecto (P)
JPPW	Jan Wilczur (GB)
JV	Juan Varela (E)
JZ	Jos Zwarts (NL)
KD	Koen Devos (B)
MH	Mark Hulme (GB)
MS	Māris Strazds (LAT)
PC	Przemek Chylarecki (PL)
PH	Paul Hirst (GB)
PP	Pavel Procházka (CZ)
PR	Petr Rob (CZ)
RA	Richard Allen (GB)
RH	Ren Hathway (GB)
SiG	Simon Gillings (GB)
SG	Silvia Gandini (I)
Ski	Michał Skakuj (PL)
SuG	Susan Gough (GB)
TC	Tomasz Cofta (PL)
TKS	Thelma K Sykes (GB)

TRANSLATORS, ETC

The value of the *Atlas* has been greatly increased by the translations of the Introduction that are printed in it. We thank the translators, whose names are given at the end of their translations. Many thanks are due to those who have produced translations of the summaries of the species accounts (see the last section of the Technical Appendix). We also thank those who provided information on names in languages other than English: Karel Šťastný (CZ), Goetz Rheinwald (D), Ramon Martí (E), Dosithée Berthelot (F), Juha Tiainen (FIN), Filios Akriotis (G), Tibor Szép (H), Alessandra Grattarola (I), Rui Rufino (P), Maciej Gromadski (PL), Eugene Potapov (R), and Sören Svensson (S).

PROOFREADERS

We thank Jeremy Greenwood, John Marchant and Chris van Turnhout for much work on the proofs, assisted by Dawn Balmer, Richard Bashford, Jez Blackburn, Caroline Dudley, Soph Foulger, Simon Gillings, Su Gough, Ian Henderson, Philip Jackson, Andy Musgrove, Mark Rehfisch, Jonathan Simons, Mike Toms, Derek Toomer, Ray Waters, Chris Wernham, and Andy Wilson.

National and Major Regional Bird Atlases of Europe

This list shows the extent of regional and national ornithological mapping across Europe. The European Ornithological Atlas project has inspired or influenced most of these projects, directly or indirectly. Yet the list is far from comprehensive, for a number of reasons:

1. The request from the European Ornithological Atlas Working Group (EOA WG) asking all EBCC national delegates to obtain details of all published and extant ornithological atlases had an incomplete response. A slightly later survey by the British Trust for Ornithology filled most of the gaps, but was not intended to obtain precisely the same details. Some atlases therefore are included through fortuitous discovery; others have been excluded because information was lacking.

2. A general principle adopted was to exclude local and urban ornithological atlases for reasons of space; their inclusion would have tripled the length of the list. Consequently an initial exclusion criterion was set of a minimum coverage area of 10 000km². These ideals inevitably required sensible interpretation in a number of cases, particularly to achieve completeness. For example, if one of a country's seven regions was less than 10 000km² in area, it was nonsensical to exclude it. However, in some countries, the administrative unit is always less than 10 000km², and ornithological mapping is often carried out at very fine resolution, sometimes down to a 1 km square; such countries, like Britain, have very many detailed ornithological atlases based on counties, and these have had to be omitted. One exception has been made for urban atlases: ornithological atlases of capital cities have been included.

3. Much distribution data have been published as inclusions in avifaunal accounts and in handbooks and fieldguides rather than as true atlases. Only publications which recognizably are atlases have been included.

Goetz Rheinwald

Austria, national

Atlas der Brutvögel Österreichs (*Atlas of breeding birds of Austria*) – Ergebnisse der Brutvogelkartierung 1981–1985 der Österreichischen Gesellschaft für Vogelkunde. 1993. DVORAK, M., A. RANNER and H.M. BERG. Österreichische Gesellschaft für Vogelkunde, Umweltbundesamt Vienna. pp527. ISBN 3-85457-121-6.

Austria, regional

Atlas der Brutvögel Oberösterreichs (*Atlas of breeding birds of Upper Austria*). 1987. MAYER, G. Vogelschutzstation Steyregg, Linz. pp189.

Atlas der Brutvögel Vorarlbergs (*Atlas of breeding birds of Vorarlberg*). 1991. KILZER, R., and V. BLUM. Österreichische Gesellschaft für Vogelkunde, Landesgruppe Vorarlberg, Vorarlberger Landespflegefonds, Bregenz. pp278. ISBN 3-900851-14 X.

Belarus, regional

[*Breeding bird atlas of western Belarus*]. In Prep. VINTCHEVSKY, A.E. and A. TISHECHKIN. ZBTAP [West Belarusian Society for Protection of Birds].

Belgium, national

Atlas des oiseaux nicheurs de Belgique (*Atlas of breeding birds of Belgium*). 1988. DEVILLERS, P., W. ROGGEMAN, J. TRICOT, P. del MALMOL, C. KERWIJN, J.-P. JACOB and A. ANSELIN. Institut Royal des Sciences Naturelles de Belgique, Brussels. pp395.

Belgium, regional

Oiseaux de Bruxelles. Atlas des oiseaux nicheurs (Atlas of breeding birds). 1995. RABOSÉE, D., H. de WAVRIN, J. TRICOT and D. van der ELST. (Eds). Aves, Liège. pp304.

Bulgaria, regional

Atlas of breeding birds of Sofia. 1992. IANKOV, P. SOVON, Beek-Ubbergen, The Netherlands. pp40.

Croatia, national

[*Croatian breeding bird Atlas 1985–1988*]. In Prep. SUŠIC, G. and J. KRALJ. Institute of Ornithology, Croatian Academy for Science and Arts, Zagreb.

Czechoslovakia (later the Czech and Slovak Republics), national

Atlas Hnizdního Rozšíření Ptákü v CSSR 1973–1977 (*Atlas of breeding birds of Czechoslovakia*). 1987. ŠŤASTNÝ, K., A. RANDÍK and K. HUDEC. Academia, Praha. pp483.

Atlas Zimního Rozšíření Ptákü v Ceśké Republice 1982–1985 (*Atlas of wintering birds of the Czech Republic 1982–1985*). 1995. BEJČEK, V., K. ŠŤASTNÝ and K. HUDEC. H and H, Praha. pp270. ISBN 80-85787-94-6.

Atlas Hnizdního Rozšíření Ptáků v Ceske republice 1985–1989 (*Atlas of breeding birds of the Czech Republic 1985–1989*). 1995. ŠŤASTNÝ, K., V. BEJČEK and K. HUDEC. H and H, Praha. ISBN 80-8536875-7.

Czechoslovakia (later the Czech and Slovak Republics), regional

Atlas Hnizdního Rozšíření Ptáků v jiznich Cechach 1985–1989 (*Atlas of breeding birds of Southern Bohemia*). 1990. PYKAL, J., J. JANDA and P. BÜRGER. Inf. zprav. Spravy CHKO Trebonsko. pp52.

Hnizdni Rozšíření Ptáků v Zapadoceskem kraji v letech 1985 az 1988 (*Distribution of breeding birds in West Bohemia in 1985–1988*). 1991. MATTAS, M. Sbor. Zapadoces. Muz., Plzen, Prir. 79. pp111.

Hnizdni Rozšíření Ptáků. Jihomoravsky region. Cast 1: Nepevci (*Distribution of breeding birds. Southern Moravia. Part 1: Non-passerines*). 1994. MARTISKO, J., K. ŠŤASTNÝ, V. BEJČEK, K. HUDEC, J. PELLANTOVA and M. VLASIN. Mor. zems. mus. Brno, CSOP Brno. pp247.

Hnizdini Rozšíření Ptáků. Jihomoravsky region. Cast 2 Pevci (*Distribution of breeding birds. Southern Moravia. Part 2: Passerines*). 1995. MARTISKI, J., K. ŠŤASTNÝ, V. BEJČEK, K. HUDEC, J. PELLANTOVA and M. VLASIN. Mor. zems. muz. Brno, CSOP Brno.

Denmark, national

De danske ynglefugles udbredelse (*The Danish breeding bird distribution*). 1976. DYBBRO, T. Dansk Ornitologisk Forening, Copenhagen. pp293. ISBN 87-87604-00-0.

Fuglenes Danmark – en Kortlægning af Danmarks Fugle og Fuglel-Kaliteter 1993–1996. (*Birds of Denmark – mapping the Danish birds and bird sites 1993–1996*). In Prep. GRELL, M. Dansk Ornitologisk Forening. Copenhagen.

Estonia

Eesti Linnuatlas (*Estonian Bird Atlas*). 1993. RENNO, O. Eesti Teaduste Akadeemia. pp256. ISBN 5-440-01074-2.

Finland, national

Suomen Lintuatlas (*Finnish Bird Atlas*). 1983. HYYTIÄ, K., E. KELLOMÄKI and J. KOISTINEN. SLY.n Lintutieto Oy, Helsinki. pp520. ISBN 951-95560-3-6. Appendix to Suomen Lintuatlas: Distribution and numbers of Finnish breeding birds. 1989. KOSKIMIES, P. SLY:n Lintutieto Oy, Helsinki. pp75.

Muuttuva pesimälinnusto (*Abundance and distribution of Finnish breeding birds*). In print. 1996. VÄISÄNEN, R.A., E. LAMMI and P. KOSKIMIES. Otava and Lintutieto Oy, Helsinki. cpp540.

France, national

Atlas des oiseaux nicheurs de France (*Atlas of breeding birds of France*). 1976. YEATMAN, L. Société Ornithologique de France, Paris. pp450.

Atlas des oiseaux de France en hiver (*Atlas of Birds of France in winter*). 1991. YEATMAN-BERTHELOT, D. Société Ornithologique de France, Paris. pp575.

Nouvel Atlas des oiseaux nicheurs de France 1985–1989 (*New Atlas of breeding birds of France*). 1994. YEATMAN-BERTHELOT, D. and G. JARRY. Société Ornithologique de France, Paris. pp776.

France, regional

Atlas ornithologiques Rhône-Alpes (*Atlas of breeding birds of Rhône Alps*). 1977. LEBRETON, P. Centre ornithologique Rhône-Alpes, Villeurbanne. pp453.

Histoire et géographie des oiseaux nicheurs de Bretagne (*History and Geography of breeding birds of Brittany*). 1980. GUERMEUR, Y., and J-Y. MONNAT. Société pour l'étude et la protection de la nature en Bretagne/Centrale Ornithologique Ar Vran, Brest. pp240.

Atlas ornithologique Rhône-Alpes – Compléments 1976–1979 (*Supplement 1976–1979*). 1980. LEBRETON, P. Le Bièvre 2, numéro spéciale. pp80.

Atlas ornithologique Rhône-Alpes – Compléments 1980–1982 (*Supplement 1980–1982*). 1983. BROYER, J., and P. LEBRETON. Le Bièvre 5, supplément. pp118.

Atlas des oiseaux nicheurs de Franche-Comté (*Atlas of breeding birds of Franche-Comté*). 1984. Groupe naturaliste de Franche-Comté, Besançon. pp161.

Atlas des oiseaux nicheurs d'Aquitaine (*1974–1984*) (*Atlas of breeding birds of Aquitaine, 1974–1984*). 1987. BOUTET, J-Y. and P. PETIT. Centre Régional Ornithologique Aquitaine-Pyrénées, Bordeaux. pp241.

Atlas ornithologique Rhône-Alpes – Compléments 1983–1985 (*Supplement 1983–1985*). 1987. BERNARD, A. Le BIÈVRE 9: 139-170.

Atlas des oiseaux hivernants, Allier, Aveyron, Cantal, Haute-Loire, Lozére, Puy-de-Dôme, 1976–1984 (*Atlas of wintering birds of Allier, Aveyron, Cantal, Haute-Loire, Lozére, Puy-de-Dôme, 1976–1984*). 1987. DUBOC, P., and J.-J. LALLEMENT. Centre Ornithologique Auvergne, Clermont-Ferrand. pp181.

Atlas des oiseaux nicheurs du departement du Puy-de-Dôme (Atlas of breeding birds of the department of Puy-de-Dôme). 1989. Centre Ornithologique Auvergne. L.P.O. Clermont-Ferrand.

Les oiseaux de Champagne-Ardenne (*The birds of Champagne-Ardenne*). 1991. Centre Ornithologique de Champagne-Ardenne, St-Rémy-en-Bouzemont. pp290.

Oiseaux nicheurs du Gard (*Breeding birds of Gard*). 1993. Centre Ornitholgique du Gard. C.O. Gard, Nimes.

Atlas des oiseaux nicheurs de Normandie et des îles Anglo-Normandes (*Atlas of breeding birds of Normandy and the Channel Islands*). 1993. GON, Group Ornithologique Normand, Caen (2nd corrected edition). pp247.

Atlas des oiseaux nicheurs du Limousin (*Atlas of breeding birds in Limoges*). 1993. S.E.P.O.L. Edition Souny, Limoges. pp222.

Atlas des oiseaux nicheurs de Picardie (*Atlas of breeding birds of Picardie*). 1995. COMMECY, X. (Coord). Picardie Nature, C.O.P., Amiens. pp234.

Atlas des oiseaux nicheurs de Midi-Pyrénées (*Atlas of breeding birds of Southern France and the Pyrenees*). 1996. Association Régionale Ornithologique du Midi et des Pyrénées, Toulouse.

Atlas ornithologique de Bretagne (*Ornithological atlas of Brittany*). 1996. Groupe Ornithologique Breton.

Atlas des oiseaux nicheurs de Franche-Comté (*Atlas of breeding birds of Franche-Comté*). 1996. Groupe

naturaliste de Franche-Comté, Besançon.
Les Oiseaux d'Ile-de-France (*The birds of Ile-de-France*). In print, 1996. Le MARÉCHAL, P., G. LESAFFRE and C.O.R.I.F. *Avifauna de Lorraine (avec cartographie des oiseaux nicheurs 1985-1992)* (*Avifauna of Lorraine*). In print, 1996. Ligue pour la Protection des Oiseaux, délégation Lorraine.
Atlas des oiseaux nicheurs de la région Nord-Pas-de-Calais (2ème ètat 1984-1993) (*Atlas of breeding birds in the Nord-Pas-de-Calais region*). In print, 1996. TOMBAL, J.-C. Groupe Ornithologique Nord, Lille.

Germany, national

Atlas der Verbreitung und Häufigkeit der Brutvögel Deutschlands-Kartierung um 1985. (*Atlas of distribution and abundance of breeding birds in Germany – mapping around 1985*). 1993. RHEINWALD, G. Dachverband Deutscher Avifaunisten. pp264.

Germany, regional

Atlas der Brutvögel Niedersachsens 1980 (*Atlas of breeding birds in Lower Saxony 1980*). HECKENROTH, H. Naturschutz und Landschaftspflege in Niedersachsen 14. pp428.
Die Vögel des Bodenseegebietes (*Birds in the Lake Constance region*). 1983. SCHUSTER, S., *et al.* Orn. Arb. gem. Bodensee, Konstanz, pp379.
Brutvogelatlas Berlin (West) (*Breeding bird atlas of West Berlin*). 1984. WITT, K. Ornithologischer Bericht für Berlin (West) 9 (1984). pp384. ISSN 0344-4171.
Atlas der Brutvögel Bayerns 1979–1983 (*Atlas of breeding birds in Bavaria 1979–1983*). 1987. NITSCHE, G. and H. PLACHTER. Ornithologische Gesellschaft in Bayern/Bayerisches Landesamt für Umweltschutz. pp269.
Die Vögel des Rheinlands 3: Atlas zur Brutvogelverbreitung (*Birds in the Rhineland 3: Atlas of breeding birds*). 1987. WINK, M. pp236.
Atlas der Brutvögel Ostdeutschlands (*Atlas of breeding birds in Eastern Germany*). 1993. NICOLAI, B. Gustav Fischer Verlag. pp314. ISBN 3-334-6-440-3.

Great Britain and Ireland, national

The Atlas of Breeding Birds in Britain and Ireland. 1976. SHARROCK, J.T.R. (Compiler). T & AD Poyser. Calton. pp479. ISBN 0-85661-018-6
The Atlas of Wintering Birds in Britain and Ireland. 1986. LACK, P. T & AD Poyser, Calton. pp447.
The New Atlas of Breeding Birds in Britain and Ireland: 1988–1991. 1993. GIBBONS, D. W., J.B. REID and R.A. CHAPMAN. T & AD Poyser, London. pp520. ISBN 0-85661-075-5.

Great Britain, regional

Atlas of breeding birds of the West Midlands. 1970. LORD, J., and D. J. MUNNS. Collins, London. pp276.
Atlas of the breeding birds of the London area. 1977. MONTIER, D. (Ed.) London Natural History Society. pp288.
The birds of North-east Scotland. 1990. BUCKLAND, S.T., M.V. BELL and N. PICOZZI (Eds). North-east Scotland Bird Club, Aberdeen. pp473. ISBN 0-7136-4235-1.

Hungary, national

Magyarszág Fészkelõ mdarai (*Breeding birds of Hungary*). 1984. HARASZTHY, L. HOS (Hungarian Ornithological and Nature Conservation Society) Natura, Budapest.

Iceland, national

Atlas of breeding birds in Iceland. In Prep. SKARPHÉDINSSON, K.H. Icelandic Institute of Natural History.

Iceland, regional

Atlas of breeding birds in southwestern Iceland. SKARPHÉDINSSON, K.H. 1994. Icelandic Institute of Natural History. pp126.

Italy, national

Atlante degli uccelli nidificanti in Italia (*Atlas of breeding birds in Italy*). 1993. MESCHINI, E., and S. FRUGIS. Centro Italiano Studi Ornitologici, I.N.S.S., Suppl. Ric. Biol. Selvaggina 20. pp344.

Italy, regional

Atlante degli uccelli nidificanti sulle Alpi italiane I–IV (*Atlas of breeding birds in the Italian alps, parts 1–4*). 1982-1988. BRICHETTI, P. Gruppo Ricerca Avifauna Nidificante, Riv. ital. Ornithol. 52: 3-50; 53: 101-144; 56: 3-39; 58: 3-39.
Atlanta degli uccelli nidificanti in Provincia di Brescia (Lombardia) 1980–1984 (*Atlas of breeding birds in the Brescia District, Lombardy 1980–1984*). 1985. BRICHETTI, P. and D. CAMBI. G.R.A.N., Monografia di Natura Bresciana 8, Museo Civico di Scienze Naturali di Brescia. pp142.
Atlante degli uccelli nidificanti in Sicilia, 1979–1983 (*Atlas of breeding birds in Sicily, 1979–1983*). 1985. MASSA, B. L.I.P.U. Natur. Siciliano 11, num.spec., Palermo. pp242.
Atlante degli uccelli nidificanti in Provincia di Forli, Emilia-Romagna, 1982–1986 (*Atlas of breeding birds in the Forli District, Emilia-Romagna, 1982–1986*). 1987. FOSCHI, U.F., and S. GELLINI. Museo Ornitologico di Forli, Maggioli Editore, Forli. pp176.
Atlante degli uccelli nidificanti in provincia di Pordenone (Friuli-Venezia Giulia) 1981–1986 (*Atlas of breeding birds in the Pordenone District, Friuli-Venezia Giulia, 1981–1986*). 1987. PARODI, R. Museo Civico di Storia Naturale di Pordenone, Quaderno 1. pp118.
Atlante degli uccelli nidificanti in Provincia di Varese, Lombardia, 1983–1987 (*Atlas of breeding birds in the Varese District, Lombardy, 1983–1987*). 1988. GUENZANI, W. and F. SAPORETTI. L.I.P.U. Edizioni Lativa, Varese. pp176.
Atlante degli uccelli nidificante in Piemonte e Val d'Aosta 1980–1984 (*Atlas of breeding birds in Piedmont and the Aosta Valley 1980–1984*). 1988. MINGOZZI, T., G. BOANO, C. PULCHER and coll. G.P.S.O., Monografia 7, Museo Regionale di Scienze Naturali di Torino. pp514.
Atlante degli uccelli nidificanti in Campania, 1983–1987 (*Atlas of breeding birds in Campania, 1983–1987*). 1989. FRAISSINET, M. and M. KALBY, A.S.O.I.M., Monogr. 1, Napoli. pp230.

Atlante degli uccelli nidificanti nelle province di Treviso e Belluno, Veneto, 1983–1988 (*Atlas of breeding birds in the Treviso and Belluno District, Venetia, 1983–1988*). 1989. MEZZAVILLA, F. Museo Civico di Storia e Scienze Naturali di Montebelluna (TV). pp116.

Atlante degli uccelli nidificanti in Liguria 1981–1986 (*Atlas of breeding birds in Liguria 1981–1986*). 1989. SPANO, S., G.TRUFFI and coll. L.I.P.U. Cataloghi dei beni naturali 1, Regione Liguria, Genova. pp210.

Atlanta degli uccelli svernanti in Provincia di Brescia (*Lombardia*). *Inverni dal 1984–88* (*Atlas of wintering birds in the Brescia District, Lombardy, winters of 1984/85–1987/88*). 1990. BRICHETTI, P. and D. CAMBI. G.R.A., Monografia di Natura Bresciana 14, Museo Civico di Scienze Naturali di Brescia. pp112.

Atlante degli uccelli nidificanti in Lombardia 1983–1987 (*Atlas of breeding birds in Lombardy 1983–1987*). 1990. BRICHETTI, P. and M. FASOLA. Dipart. Biologia Animale Univ. Pavia e Gruppo Ricerche Avifauna Nidificante – Editoriale Ramperto, Brescia. pp241.

Atlante degli uccelli nidificanti in Provincia di Verona (*Veneto*) *1983–1987* (*Atlas of breeding birds in the Verona District, Venetia 1983–1987*). 1991. De FRANCESCHI, P. G.Vr.S.O. Memorie del Museo Civico di Storia Naturale di Verona (A: Biologica) 9, Verona. pp154.

Atlante degli uccelli svernanti in Lombardia (*Atlas of wintering birds in Lombardy*). 1992. FORNASARI, L., L. BOTTONI, R. MASSA, M. FASOLA, P. BRICHETTI and V. VIGORITA (Eds). Regione Lombardia Università degli Studi di Milano. pp378.

Atlante degli uccelli nidificanti in provincia di Modena, 1982–1990 (*Atlas of breeding birds in the Modena District, Emilia-Romagna 1982–1990*). 1992. GIANELLA, C., and R. RABACCHI. Provincia di Modena e S.O.M., Relazione sullo stato dell'ambiente in Provincia di Modena 3, Modena. pp196.

Atlante degli uccelli nidificanti nella Provincia di Vicenza, Veneto (*Atlas of breeding birds in the Vicenza District, Venetia*). 1994. Gruppo Vicentino Studi Ornitologici 'NISORIA'. Gilberto Padovan Editore, Vicenza. pp206.

Uccelli e paesaggio in Sicilia alle soglie del Terzo Millennio (*Birds and landscape in Sicily at the threshold of the third millennium*). 1994. lo VALVO, M., B. MASSA and M. SARA. Suppl. Natur. Siciliano 17, Palermo. pp271.

Atlante degli uccelli svernanti della Basilicata 1989–1995. (*Atlas of wintering birds in Basilicata 1989–1995*). 1996. KALBY, M. and M. MILONE. Università degli Studi 'Federico II', Napoli.

Atlante degli uccelli nidificanti in provincia di Livorno, 1981–1986 (*Breeding bird atlas of the province of Livorno, Tuscany 1981–1986*). In press. ARCAMONE, E., and E. MESCHINI. Quad. Mus. St. Nat. Livorno 13.

Atlante degli uccelli nidificanti e svernanti in Toscana 1982–1986 (*Breeding and wintering bird distribution atlas of Tuscany, 1982–1986*). In press. TELLINI, G., E.ARCAMONE, N. BACCETTI, E. MESCHINI and P. SPOSIMO. Monogr. Museo St. Nat. Livorno 1.

Latvia, national

Latvijas Ligzdojošo Putnu Atlants (*Latvian Breeding Bird Atlas*). 1989. VIKSNE, J., J. PRIEDNIEKS, M. STRĀZDS, A. STRĀZDS and A. PETRINS. Zinatne, Rīga Zinātne. pp352. ISBN 5-7966-0375-2.

Luxembourg, national

Atlas of Breeding Birds in Luxembourg. 1987. MELCHIOR, E., E. MENTGEN, R. PELTZER, R. SCHMIDT and J. WEISS. Lëtzebuerger Natur- a Vulleschutzliga. pp336.

The Netherlands, national

Atlas van de Nederlandse Broedvogels (*Atlas of breeding birds in the Netherlands*). 1979. TEIXERA, R.M. Natuurmonumenten, s' Graveland.

Atlas van de Nederlandse Vogels (*Atlas of Netherlands' birds*). 1987. BEKHUIS, J, R.G. BIJLSMA, A van DIJK, F. HUSTINGS, R. LENSINK and F. SARIS (Eds). SOVON, Beek-Ubbergen. pp595. ISBN 90-72121-01-5.

Ecologische Atlas van de Nederlandse Roofvogels (*Ecological Atlas of Dutch raptors*). 1993. BIJLSMA, R.G. Schuyt & Co, Haarlem. pp350. ISBN 90-6097-348-8.

The Netherlands, regional

Vogels in Friesland 1–3 (*Birds in Friesland*). 1976. van der PLOEG, D.T.E., W. de JONG, M.J. SWART, B. van der VEEN, J.A. VRIES, J.H.P. WESTHOF and A.G. WITTEVEEN. De Tille, Leeuwarden. pp495. ISBN 90-70001-042-9.

Vogels van Drenthe (*Birds of Drenthe*). 1982. van DIJK, A.J. and B.L.J. OS. Van Gorcum, Assen. pp348. ISBN 90-23219-35-3.

Broedvogels van Noord-Holland (*Breeding birds of North Holland*). 1990. RUITENBEEK, W., C. SCHARRINGA and P.J. ZOMERDIJK. Stichting Samenw. Vogelwerkgr. Noord-Holland, Assendelft. pp440. ISBN 90-90036-31-8.

Vogelatlas van Groningen (*Bird atlas of Groningen*). 1992. BRINK, H. van den, J. Furda, J. van KLINKEN and K. van SCHARENBURG. Avifauna Groningen, Groningen. pp237.

Broedvogels van Zeeland (*Breeding birds of Zeeland*). 1994. VERGEER, J.W. and G. van ZUYLEN. Uitgeverij KNNV/Stichting Uitgeverij SOVON, Utrecht. pp426. ISBN 90-5011-067-3.

Norway, national

Norsk Fugleatlas (*Norwegian Bird Atlas*). 1994. GJERSHAUG, J.O., P.G. THINGSTAD, S. ELDØY and S. BYRKJELAND (Eds). Norsk Ornitologisk Forening, Klæbu. pp552. ISBN 82-990868-2-5.

Poland, national

[*Polish Ornithological Atlas*]. In Prep. GROMADZKI, M. and A. SIKORA. Polish Institute of Ecology, Gdańsk.

Poland, regional

Atlas Ptaków Lęgowych Małopolski 1985–1991 (*The atlas of breeding birds in Malopolska 1985–1991*). 1992. WALASZ, K. and P. MIELCZAREK. Biologica Silesiae, Wrocław. pp522. ISBN 83-900021-2-4.

Portugal, national

Atlas das Aves que nidificam em Portugal Continental (*The atlas of breeding birds in continental Portugal*). 1989. R. RUFINO (coord.). CEMPA/SNPRCN Lisboa. pp215.

Portugal, regional

Atlas das aves invernantes do Baixo Alentejo (*Atlas of the wintering birds of the Baixo Alentejo*). In Prep. ELIAS, G.I. and L.M. REINO. SPEA. Lisboa.

Romania, national

Pasarile clocitoare din România (*Breeding birds in Romania*). 1992. COCHIA, V. Editura Stiinfifica, Bucharest. pp386. ISBN 973-44-0060-6.

Atlasul provizoriu al Pasarilor clocitoare din România (*Provisional atlas of breeding birds in Romania*). 1994. WEBER, P., D. MUNTEANU and A. PAPADOPOL. Publicatiile Societatii ornitologice Romane. pp148.

Slovenia, national

Zmiski Ornitološki Atlas Slovenije (*The atlas of wintering birds in Slovenia*). 1994. SOVINC, A. Tehniska zalozba Slovenije Ljubljana. pp452. ISBN 86-365-0160-1.

Ornitološki Atlas Slovenije (*Ornithological atlas of Slovenia*). 1995. GEISTER, I. Ljubljana: DZS. pp287. ISBN 86-341-1252-7.

Spain, national

Invernada de Aves en la peninsula Iberica (*Atlas of wintering birds of the Iberian peninsula*). 1988. TELLERÍA, J.L. (Ed). Sociedad Española de Ornitologia. Monografia No 1. pp208. ISBN 84-404-1923-6.

Atlas de las aves nidificantes de España (*Atlas of breeding birds in Spain*). In Prep. PURROY, F.J. and R. MARTÍ. Sociedad Española de Ornitologia.

Spain, regional

Avance del Atlas de Aves nidificantes de Mallorca (Preliminary breeding bird atlas of Mallorca). 1983. AVELLA, X. and J.M. GONZALES. GOB.

Atlas dels ocells nidificants de Catalunya i Andorra (*Atlas of the breeding birds of Catalonia and Andorra*). 1983. MUNTANER, J, X. FERRER and A. MARTINEZ. Hetres Editora, Barcelona.

Atlas de Aves Nidificantes de Navarra (*Atlas of breeding birds of Navarre*). 1985. ELOSEGUI, J. Casa de Ahorros de Navarra.

Atlas Ornitologico de la Rioja (*Ornithological atlas of Rioja*). 1985. de JUANA, E. Biblioteca de Temas Riojanos, pp661. ISBN 84-7359-091-0.

Atlas ornitologico de la provincia de Salamanca (*Ornithological Atlas of Salamanca province*). 1988. PERIS, S.J. and I. CARNERO. Diputación de Salamanca. pp244.

Atlas de las Aves nidificantes de la Comunidad Valenciana (*Atlas of breeding birds of Valencia district*). 1991. URIOS, V, J.V. ESCOBAR, R.PARDO and J.A. GOMEZ. Direccion General de Politica Forestal y Pesquera, generalitat Valenciana.

Atlas de las aves nidificantes de la Cominidad de Madrid (Atlas of breeding birds of the Madrid district). 1994. Agencia de Redio Ambiente, Madrid.

Atlas de Vertebrados de Galicia. Tomo II: Aves. (*Atlas of the Vertebrates of Galicia, Vol.II: Birds*). 1995. Soc. Galega de Historia Natural. Colección do Patrimonio Ecoloxico, Consello de Cultura Galega. Santiago de Compostela. pp305. ISBN 84-87172-89-X.

Sweden, national

Svensk Fågelatlas (*Swedish bird atlas*). 1996. SVENSSON, S. Swedish Ornithological Society and Dept. of Ecology, Lund University.

Switzerland, national

Verbreitungsatlas der Brutvögel der Schweiz (*Distribution atlas of breeding birds of Switzerland*). 1980. A. SCHIFFERLI, P. GÉROUDET and R. WINKLER. Schweizerische Vogelwarte Sempach, Sempach. pp462. ISBN 3-85949-001-X.

Neuer Verbreitungsatlas der Brutvögel der Schweiz (*New distribution atlas of breeding birds of Switzerland*). In Prep. SCHIFFERLI, L. *et al.* Schweizerische Vogelwarte Sempach.

Switzerland, regional

Les oiseaux nicheurs du canton de Genève (*The breeding birds in Geneva canton*). 1983. GÉROUDET, P., C. GUEX and M. MAIRE. Mus. d'Hist. Nat., Genève. pp351. ISBN 2-88139-000-5.

Oiseaux nicheurs de la haute vallée de l'Orbe (*Breeding birds in the high valley of Orbe*). 1984. GLAYRE, D. and D. MAGNENAT. Nos Oiseaux 37, fasc. spéc. no. 398. pp143.

Atlante degli uccelli nidificanti nel Mendrisiotto (*Atlas of breeding birds in Mendrisiotto*). 1988. LARDELLI, R. Soc. Ticinese Sci. Nat. Vol. II. Lugano. pp222. ISBN 88-85118-00-3.

Brutvögel des Kanton Zürich (*Breeding birds in Zurich canton*). 1991. WEGGLER, M. Züricher Vogelschutz, Zürich. pp304. ISBN 3-9070-1211-9.

Atlante degli uccelli del Ticino in inverno (*Atlas of birds in Ticino in winter*). 1992. LARDELLI, R. Ficedula, Gravesano. pp301. ISBN 88-85118-21-6.

Verbreitungsatlas der Brutvögel des Kantons Freiburg/Atlas des oiseaux nicheurs du canton de Fribourg (*Atlas of breeding birds in Freiburg canton*). 1993. Cercle ornithologique de Fribourg. pp389.

Les oiseaux du Pays d'Enhaut, canton de Vaud. Atlas des oiseaux nicheurs. (*Birds of Pays d'Enhaut, Vaud canton. Atlas of breeding birds*). 1995. BEAUD, P., F. MANUAEL and E. BEAUD. Nos Oiseaux, La-Chaud-de-Fonds. pp304. ISBN 2-790085-4-8.

Ukraine, regional

[*The Atlas of wintering birds in the Lviv region, Western Ukraine*]. 1989. GORBAN, I., A. BOKOTEJ and V. POGRANCZNY. Parts 1 and 2. pp61 and pp59.

The Species Accounts

INTRODUCTION TO THE MAPS AND POPULATION GRAPHS

Layout of the *Atlas*

In the *Atlas,* the species are in two groups; Part 1 contains 496 full species accounts, accompanying distribution maps and population graphs where appropriate. Part 2 has 17 species for which satisfactory mapping data are lacking. Species are arranged in approximate Voous order, generally being in Euring sequence. In Part 1 the majority of species take up two facing pages for the map and account. The remainder are accommodated mostly as single-page species (with maps trimmed to fit the page), but occasionally three or four share a double-page spread. Inevitably this means that some species occur out of sequence so that single-page species always face one another, but in each case the out-of-sequence species remains associated with the Family or Genus.

Maps presentation — symbols and keys

The *Atlas* maps show the distribution of every European breeding species for which data were obtained and give an indication of the abundance (where available), by dot size, as described below.

The maps contain insets which appear in all full maps. Along the top of the map, the insets from left to right are Svalbard, Franz Josef Land and Novaya Zemlya. Below the Svalbard inset along the left-hand edge the insets, from top to bottom, are the Azores archipelago, the Madeiran archipelago and the Selvagens (Salvage Islands).

The dots on the maps refer to the following categories of information:

dark purple = confirmed or probable breeding, qualitative
light purple = possible breeding, qualitative
red = confirmed or probable breeding, semi-quantitive
orange = possible breeding, semi-quantitative
grey = no survey work carried out for this species in this square
no dot = square surveyed but species not recorded

The size of each red or orange dot indicates the estimated population size per square, thus:

- . = 1–9 breeding pairs (bp)
- • = 10–99bp
- • = 100–999bp
- ● = 1000–9999bp
- ● = 10 000–99 999bp
- ● = more than 100 000bp

Besides coloured dots, the maps present a buff shading in Russia for species that occur in areas of Russia where there was no coverage for the *Atlas.* This shading corresponds with the species' range as presented in *Birds of the Western Palearctic.* This was done to make the large areas with missing data in Russia better interpretable. Shading in an area with grey dots means that BWP indicates the species occurs there, but no information was received for this *Atlas.* Shading in an area without dots shows that BWP indicates the species occurs, but data for this *Atlas* indicate the species no longer occurs.

Key to population graphs

Nearly every Part 1 species account in the *Atlas* is accompanied by a graph and pie-chart presenting information on population sizes and trends by country.

The population graphs summarize information about breeding population sizes and trends for almost every species, as derived from the joint BirdLife/EBCC European Bird Database (EBD). The EBD contains minimum (popmin) and maximum (popmax) estimates. The geometric mean (geomean) of the popmin and popmax values is taken as the most generally reliable single population figure for a country. Each graph lists the ten most numerous national populations, and includes a summation of all other national populations. The exceptions are Turkey and Russia (values for these countries are given beside the graph). Turkey is omitted from the graph because the *Atlas* covers only European Turkey whereas the EBD covers the whole of Turkey. Russia is omitted from the graph because it often contains population sizes (and size-ranges) which are so large that other national totals could not be presented in a useful way on the graph.

It should be noted that the European Bird Database contains some geographical units that are not commonly understood to be countries. These are Azores, Faeroe Islands, Gibraltar, Guernsey, Isle of Man, Jersey and Madeira. Some true countries do not feature in the database (either their status was not yet clear during the preparation of the database or data were lacking). These are Armenia, Azerbaijan, Bosnia, Georgia, Macedonia and Serbia. This affects the count of countries given with the bar-chart. In addition, Poland did not supply estimates for some species and therefore does not appear in the list for these species.

The geomean (calculated as antilog (log(popmin) + log (popmax))/2) for each of the 'top ten' countries is displayed as a horizontal bar, increasing in value from left to right.

The difference between the popmin and popmax values is shown as a line through the right-hand end of the bar.

The colour of the bar indicates the trend of the species in the particular country and corresponds to the appropriate slice in the pie-chart, which indicates the proportion of the countries in Europe displaying particular population trends. (The trend codes are shown in Table 2 in the Introduction.)

To save space, the pie-chart has sometimes been omitted for species that breed in only one European country.

Below the pie-chart are:

- The total number of European countries (excluding Russia and Turkey) in which the species breeds. (Note that, as explained above, some countries may be omitted from this total.)
- The estimate of the size of the species' European population (excluding Russia and Turkey). Just as the geomean is the best estimate of national population sizes, so the European geomean (Eugeomean) is the best estimate for the European total. The Eugeomean is the sum of all national geomean values (except Russia and Turkey). Simply summing national popmin and popmax values to achieve European popmin (Eupopmin) and popmax (Eupopmax) estimates would overestimate the range between Eupopmin and Eupopmax. Better values of Eupopmin and Eupopmax estimates (and a more realistic difference between them) are obtained from:

$$\text{Eupopmin} = \text{Eugeomean} - \sqrt{(\Sigma(\text{geomean} - \text{popmin})^2)}$$

$$\text{Eupopmax} = \text{Eugeomean} + \sqrt{(\Sigma(\text{geomean} - \text{popmax})^2)}$$

  The estimates presented below the graphs are Eupopmin, Eupopmax (calculated as above) and (Eugeomean).
- The percentage of the total European population breeding in the top ten countries.
- The estimate of the size of the Russian population; popmin, popmax and (geomean).
- The estimate of the size of the population in the whole of Turkey; popmin, popmax and (geomean).

For some species, the authors' views on population sizes of individual countries or of the whole of Europe differ from the estimates in the EBD. This is then made clear in the text, with the EBD figure being given in the usual place near the pie chart.

Conservation status

Most species accounts are preceded by a statement of the species conservation status, in terms of SPEC category (see Table 4, page 773) and of its Threat Status (INS-Insufficiently known; S-Secure; L-Localised; D-Declining; R-Rare; V-Vulnerable; E-Endangered; *W-in Winter; see Tables 5 and 6, page 774). The relevant criteria have not been applied to introduced species and those which have bred only occasionally or very marginally in the *Atlas'* area.

Gavia stellata

Red-throated Diver

CZ	Potáplice malá	I	Strolaga minore
D	Sterntaucher	NL	Roodkeelduiker
E	Colimbo Chico	P	Mobêlha-pequena
F	Plongeon catmarin	PL	Nur rdzawoszyi
FIN	Kaakkuri	R	Краснозобая гагара
G	Κηλιδοβούτι	S	Smålom
H	Északi búvár		

SPEC Cat 3, Threat status V

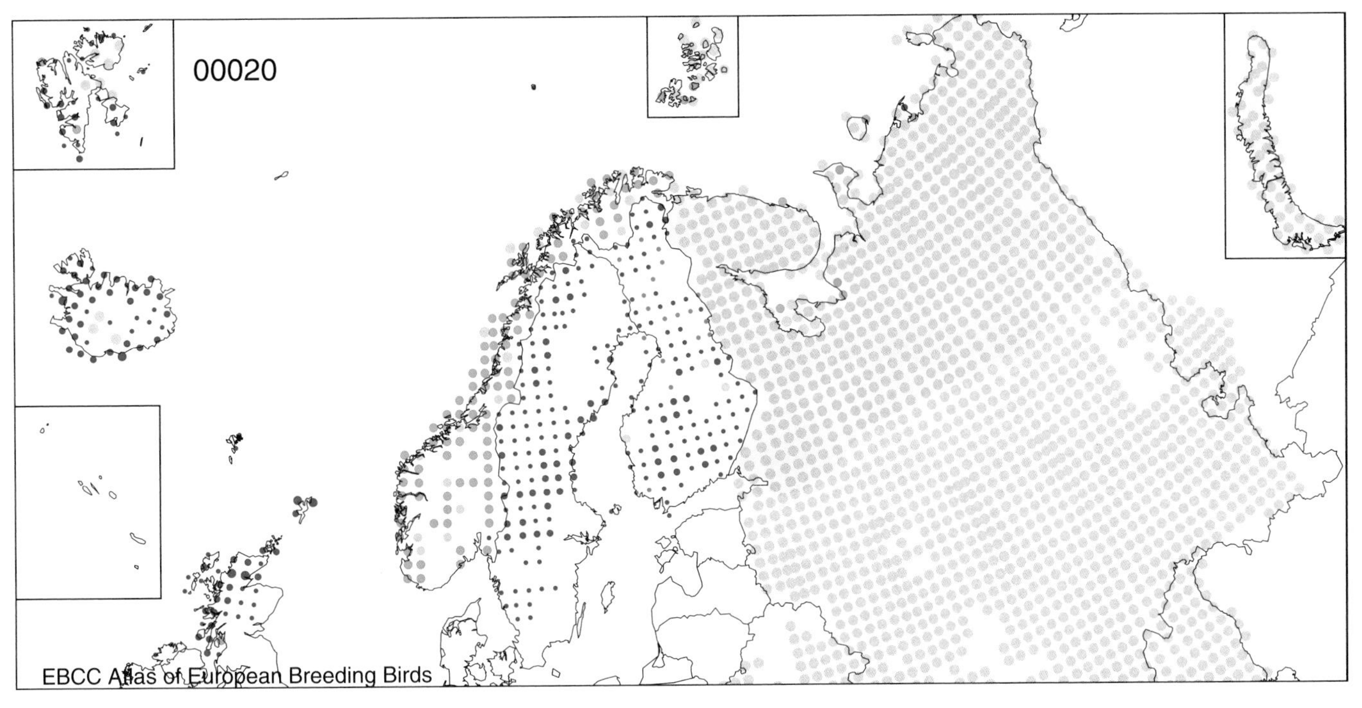

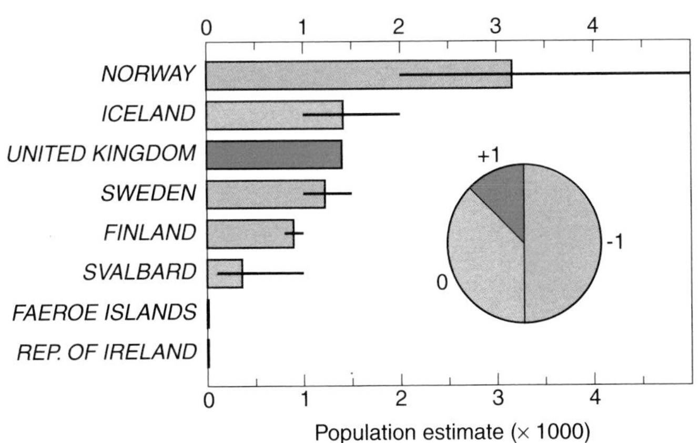

% in top 10 countries: 100.0
Total number of populated European countries: 8
Total European population 7158–10,502 (8434)
Russian population 50,000–100,000 (70,711)

The Red-throated Diver's distribution is circumpolar and Holarctic. Reaching 83°N in Greenland, it is amongst the most northerly of aquatic birds. Its southern boundary lies at 55°N in Scandinavia, Britain, Ireland, and at *c*60°N E of the Baltic. Its prime habitat is treeless tundra or heath terrain near oceanic coasts. It also breeds over much of the boreal coniferous forest zone. In treeless terrain it may occupy a pond smaller than 100m², but it needs at least 1–2ha to take off from a pond with forested shores. It seldom breeds on lakes larger than 20–30ha. The breeding ponds normally lack fish, so the birds must make fishing flights (up to 7–8km) to larger lakes, rivers, or the sea.

Highest breeding densities occur on oceanic islands, whereas in the forest zone, as in Sweden and Finland, densities are lower, normally 1bp per pond. The species is strictly territorial, but it tends to aggregate; a large bog with pools or a group of ponds in forest may accommodate 7–9 bp/10km². This gregariousness seems to be partly independent of fishing areas.

No major changes in range have been recorded. However, in Fennoscandia, the species clearly was more abundant around 1900. That the population has not generally increased after receiving legal protection indicates that there are reasons for the decline other than persecution (Pakarinen & Järvinen 1984). In Finland, the population decline seems to have stabilized, and in Scotland the trend is positive.

Acidification of fishing lakes, resulting in declining fish stocks, and increasing mercury levels may gravely endanger inland breeding birds (Eriksson & Sundberg 1991). Oil spillages pose a severe threat at sea.

Raimo Pakarinen (FIN)

Gavia arctica

Black-throated Diver

CZ	Potáplice severní	**I**	Strolaga mezzana
D	Prachttaucher	**NL**	Parelduiker
E	Colimbo Artico	**P**	Mobêlha-árctica
F	Plongeon arctique	**PL**	Nur czarnoszyi
FIN	Kuikka	**R**	Чернозобая гагара
G	Λαμπροβούτι	**S**	Storlom
H	Sarki búvár		

SPEC Cat 3, Threat status V

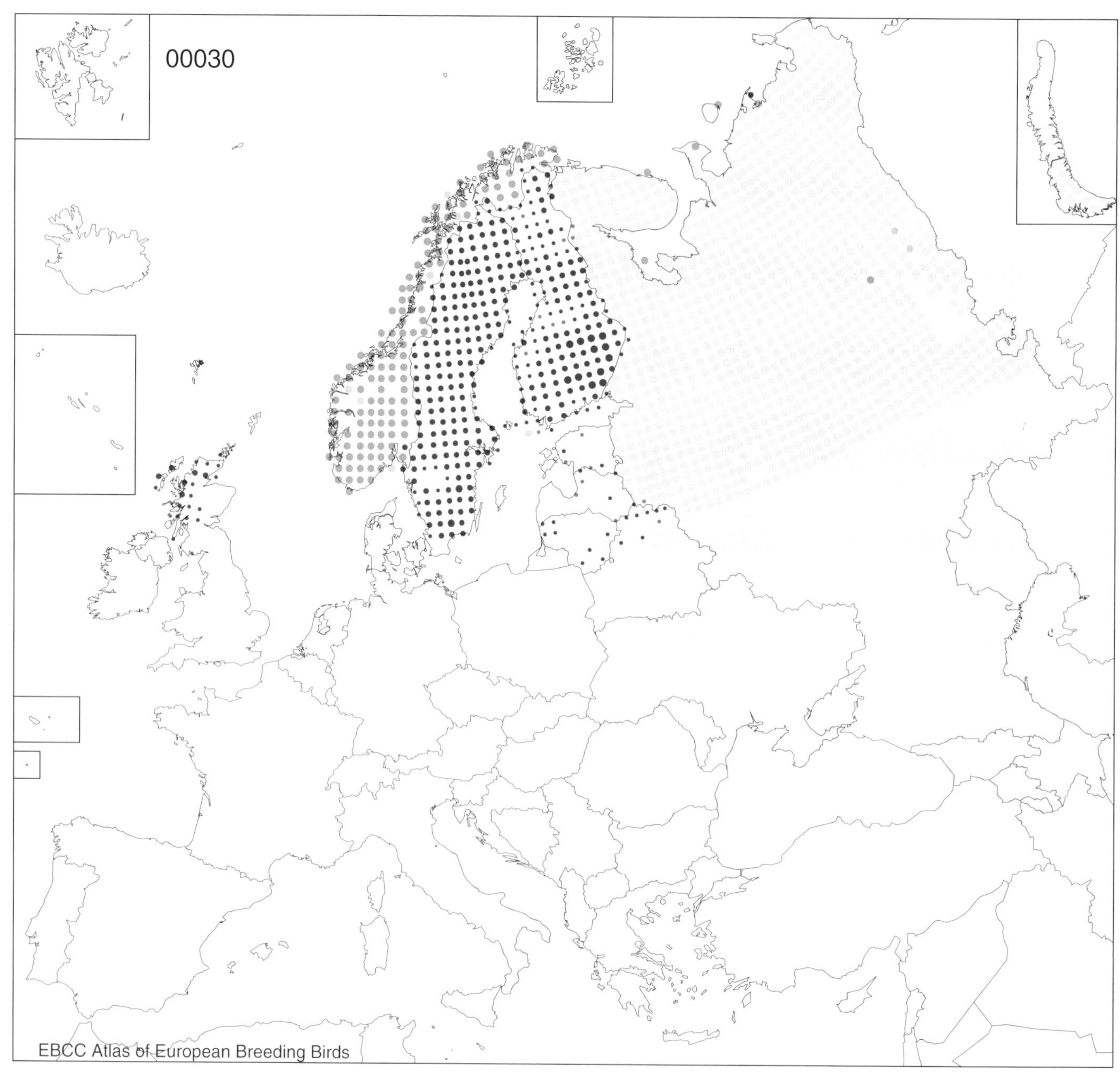

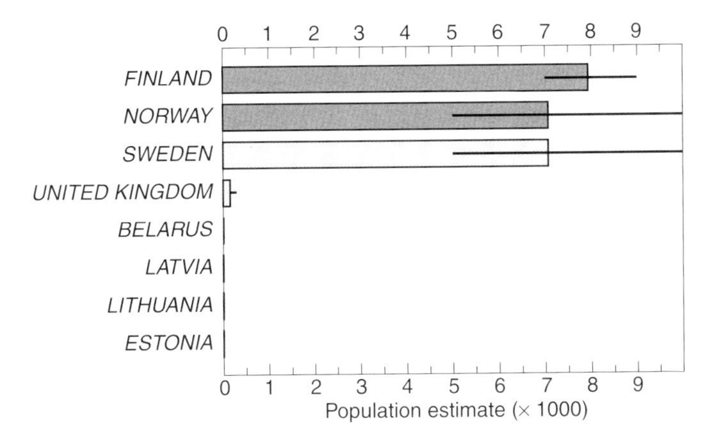

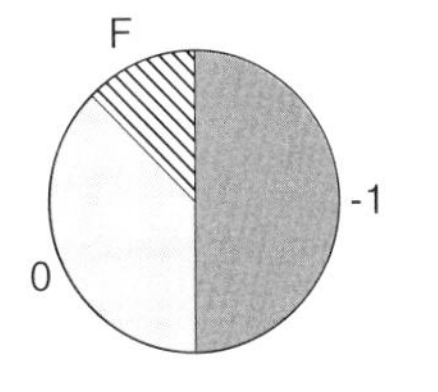

% in top 10 countries: 100.0
Total number of populated European countries: 8
Total European population 19,196–26,548 (22,272)
Russian population 100,000–200,000 (141,421)

The Black-throated Diver has a northern Holarctic breeding distribution. It occurs mainly in the arctic and boreal zones in Europe, Asia and North America. In its northernmost areas, it occurs in tundra and on arctic islands (to *c*73°N in S Novaya Zemlya) and in its southernmost areas it occurs in the Asian steppe zone (to perhaps 45°N) where its distribution is patchy. Its European distribution has a southern limit of 55°N. In Iceland, it is replaced by the Great Northern Diver *Gavia immer*. It winters mainly in coastal waters, such as the North, Baltic, Black and Caspian Seas, and in the Mediterranean. It also winters on large lakes in Europe and Asia.

The Black-throated Diver is strictly territorial with a fairly extensive territory. Breeding habitat varies in the western Palearctic from woodless tundra pools to boreal deep oligotrophic lakes with forested shores, but in the S of its range it also nests on shallow, more eutrophic lakes surrounded by arable land and on sea islands such as Åland. In boreal lakes ('*Gavia* lakes'; Kauppinen & Väisänen 1993) it is an indicator of oligotrophy. Typically, deep oligotrophic lakes have forested, sparsely vegetated shores and are no smaller than 15–20ha (Kauppinen 1993). Russia holds the great majority of the European breeding population, perhaps more than 100 000bp. The evenly distributed Finnish (*c*7000–9000bp) and combined Swedish and Norwegian (*c*10 000–20 000bp) populations are significant. Britain has *c*150bp in NW Scotland and the Hebrides, but not in Shetland. Altogether more sporadically distributed are the *c*20bp in N Belarus and the total of perhaps 30bp of Estonia, Latvia and Lithuania. Breeding censuses are liable to bias through counting unpaired individuals.

In Finland, the species is most abundant in the E and C lake districts. Breeding densities in Finland and Sweden range from 0.4 bp/km^2 (oligotrophic lakes larger than 1km^2), to 0.6 bp/km^2 (oligotrophic lakes smaller than 1km^2) (Kauppinen 1993). In moderately eutrophic lakes breeding density is much lower at *c*0.1 bp/km^2. Densities and breeding success are reduced where lakeshores are built-up or subject to disturbance. In S Finland, where this discrepancy between a stable population and its low breeding success is most marked, breeding population stability may depend partly on recruitment from the large Russian population (Pakarinen 1989).

However, on Finnish oligotrophic lakes, yearly population changes seem to be minor. On small lakes (*c*250ha) the water area regulates the occurrence of breeding pairs, the probability of occurrence increasing with lake size, from scarce on such small lakes, to regular on larger forested lakes (over 400ha). The species requires a long take-off distance which probably limits its choice of breeding sites. On larger lakes, each pair normally requires a territory of 50–100ha.

High breeding densities occur where there are broken shorelines, large numbers of islets and freedom from disturbance. Almost always, Black-throated Divers nest on islets (Lehtonen 1970). Breeding habitats in boreal lakes are deteriorating because these suffer not only eutrophication, acidification and often water level regulation, but also increasing construction work or other disturbance. Earlier in the 20th century, its southernmost range in Russia contracted. There have been no significant recent changes in range and population size. However, the recent population trend is apparently one of slight decline in many countries such as Russia, Finland, Norway, Latvia and Lithuania.

Jukka Kauppinen (FIN) Raimo Pakarinen (FIN)

Gavia immer

Great Northern Diver

CZ	Potáplice lední	**I**	Strolaga maggiore
D	Eistaucher	**NL**	IJsduiker
E	Colimbo Grande	**P**	Mobêlha-grande
F	Plongeon imbrin	**PL**	Nur lodowiec
FIN	Amerikanjääkuikka	**R**	Полярная гагара
G	Παγοβούτι	**S**	Svartnäbbad islom
H	Jeges búvár		

Non-SPEC, Threat status S (P)

The Great Northern Diver, a large member of its family, has an extensive, predominantly Nearctic breeding distribution extending through the Aleutians, Alaska, Canada and the northern United States, where it is known as the Common Loon. It also occurs in Greenland, where between 200 and 2000bp are found. Like the Black-throated Diver *G. arctica*, its breeding territories are found on relatively large freshwater lakes lacking tall vegetation along the shore.

Within Europe, regular breeding is currently confined to Iceland where there are about 300bp. Elsewhere in Europe, isolated pairs have bred occasionally. Its population size and distribution is not known to have changed substantially since the 1950s, although the species has not been monitored well on its European breeding grounds. The Great Northern Diver may have bred in the Faeroes in the 18th century, and possibly also on Bear Island and Jan Mayen Island. A lone pair bred in Scotland in 1970 (Hunter 1970). In recent years, also in Scotland, a mixed pair of Great Northern Diver and Black-throated Diver bred (G. Mudge, pers obs).

In Europe, the Great Northern Diver overwinters in coastal waters of Iceland, Norway, Britain, Ireland, Denmark, The Netherlands, France and Spain, probably staying further offshore than the smaller divers (Camphuysen & Leopold 1994), but individuals have wandered to the Baltic and the Azores. It is unclear whether Greenland birds regularly form part of the European wintering population. Nearctic birds winter off the North American Atlantic and Pacific coasts, sometimes forming large aggregations.

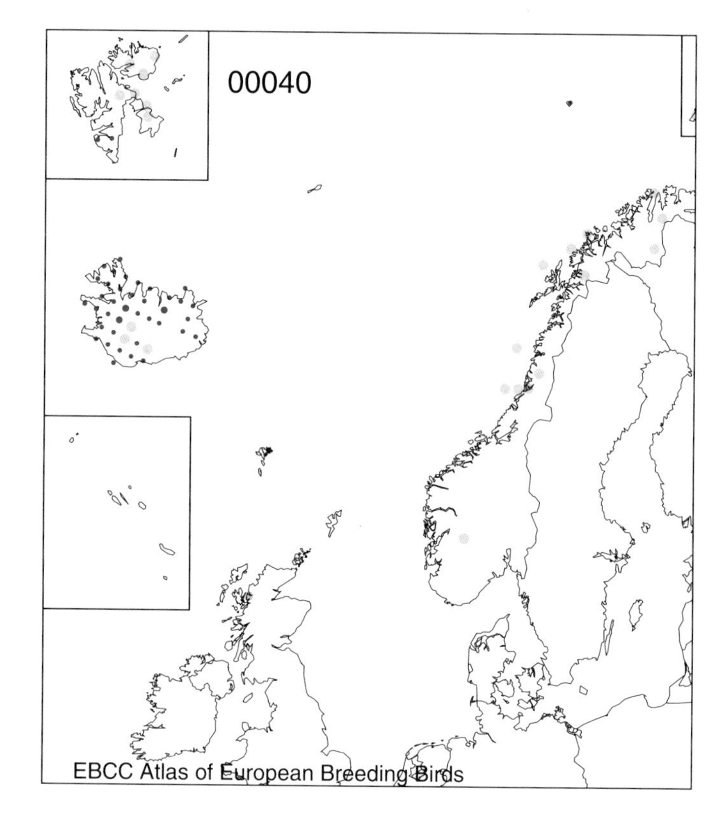

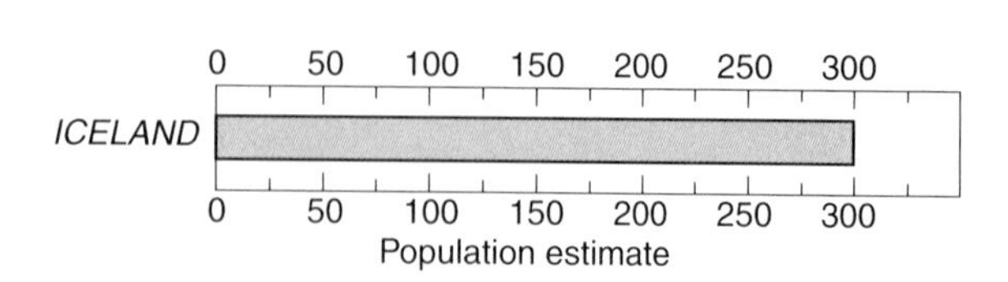

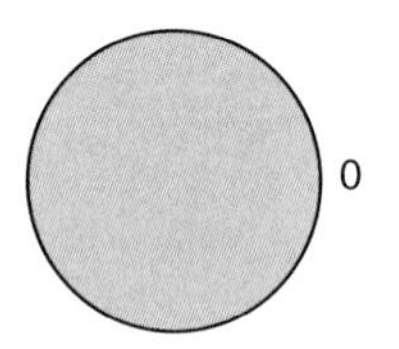

% in top 10 countries: 100.0
Total number of populated European countries: 1
Total European population 300–300 (300)

Greg Mudge (GB)

Gavia adamsii

White-billed Diver

CZ	Potáplice žlutozobá	I	Strolaga beccogiallo
D	Gelbschnabel-Eistaucher	NL	Geelsnavelduiker
E	Colimbo de Adams	P	Mobêlha-de-bico-branco
F	Plongeon à bec blanc	PL	Nur białodzioby
FIN	Jääkuikka	R	Белоклювая гагара
G	Κιτρινομύτικο Παγοβούτι	S	Vitnäbbad islom
H	Fehércsőrű búvár		

Non-SPEC, Threat status S (P)

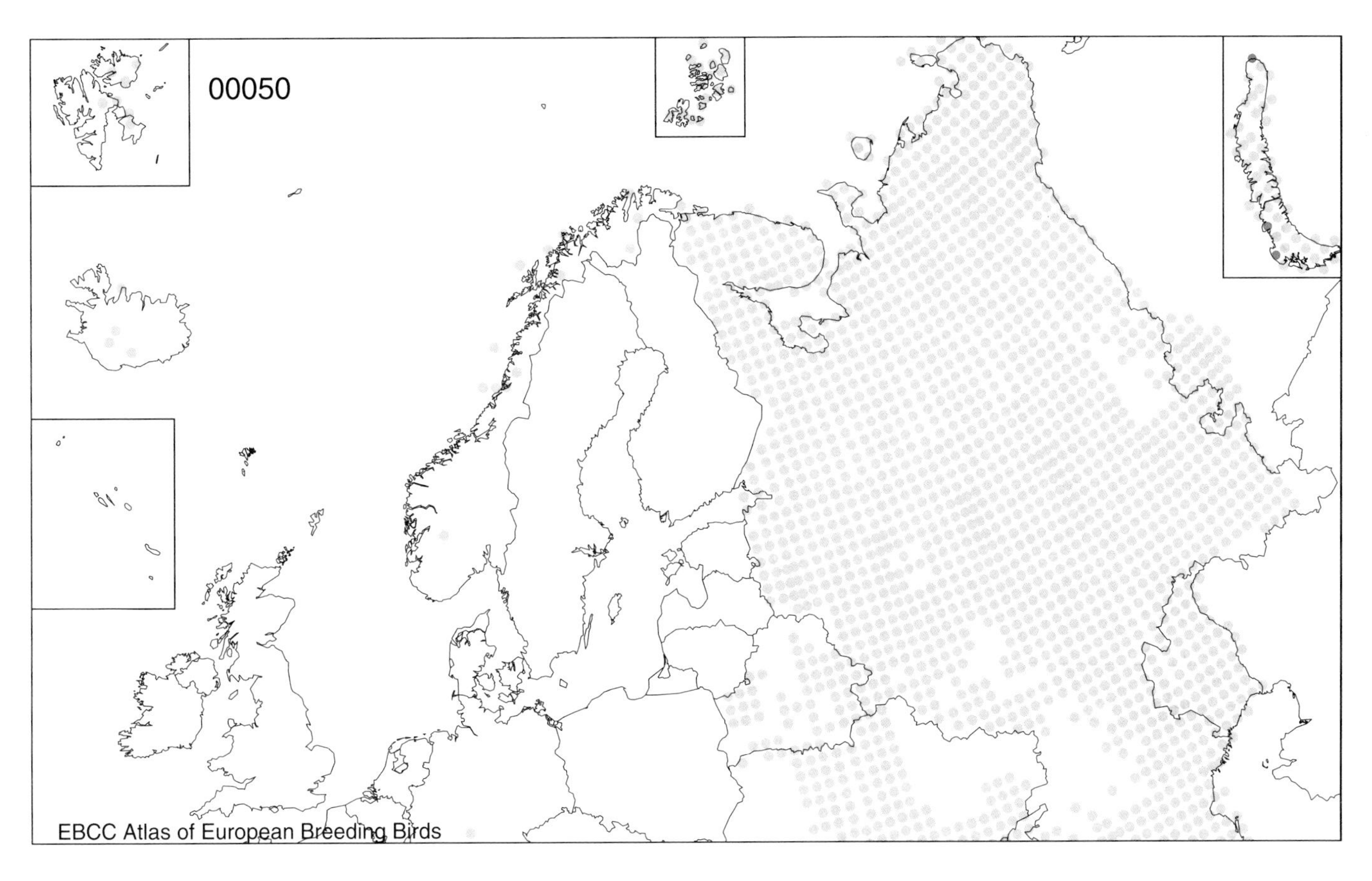

The White-billed Diver is a high-arctic species and breeds in the Arctic Ocean between the 0°C and 10°C July isotherms (C. Harrison 1982). In NW Canada its range extends from Cape Prince in Alaska to the Mackenzie River delta, and in Eurasia from Murmansk and Novaya Zemlya to Siberia (P. Harrison 1983). It is an extremely rare breeder within the western Palearctic and, because of the remoteness of its breeding grounds, its precise distribution remains unclear. In Siberian Russia breeding is often sporadic. Breeding density is highest in Kolyuchinskaya Guba in NE Siberia (Flint 1985). Within the *Atlas'* coverage area breeding was confirmed at three sites on Novaya Zemlya, and presence or breeding was suspected at two sites on the Kola Peninsula, on Kolguev Island and on Vaygach Island (M. Wilson, V.N. Kalyakin, pers comm).

The White-billed Diver is a lowland breeder but nests have been found on Alaskan lakes at 225m and 425m asl (Sage 1971). The species also nests by rivers, estuaries, deltas and sea coasts (C. Harrison 1982). Breeding in such habitats occurs irrespective of wetland size, island availability or fish abundance. Suitable habitat therefore does not appear to be in short supply, and may comprise up to 80% of the tundra surface (Sage 1971). However, it is often absent from sites which have optimal conditions (Flint 1985).

Like distributional data, population number and trend data are limited. The European Russian population is thought to be stable at 50–100bp but such data should be interpreted with caution. The North Sea wintering population is thought to comprise *c*100–200 birds, presumably most of which are European breeders (M. Wilson, V.N. Kalyakin, pers comm).

The White-billed Diver is migratory and when northern waterbodies become frozen it moves S, but generally it remains in arctic waters. In Europe, it winters chiefly off Norway where birds may be present from October until the following spring. Upon return to the breeding grounds, birds remain on the sea until the ice breaks up, when first they move to the rivers, and then to the tundra pools (Sage 1971, Flint 1985).

Simon Gillings (GB)

Tachybaptus ruficollis

Little Grebe

CZ	Potápka malá	I	Tuffetto
D	Zwergtaucher	NL	Dodaars
E	Zampullín Común	P	Mergulhão-pequeno
F	Grèbe castagneux	PL	Perkozek
FIN	Pikku-uikku	R	Малая поганка
G	Νανοβουτηχτάρι	S	Smådopping
H	Kis vöcsök		

Non-SPEC, Threat status S

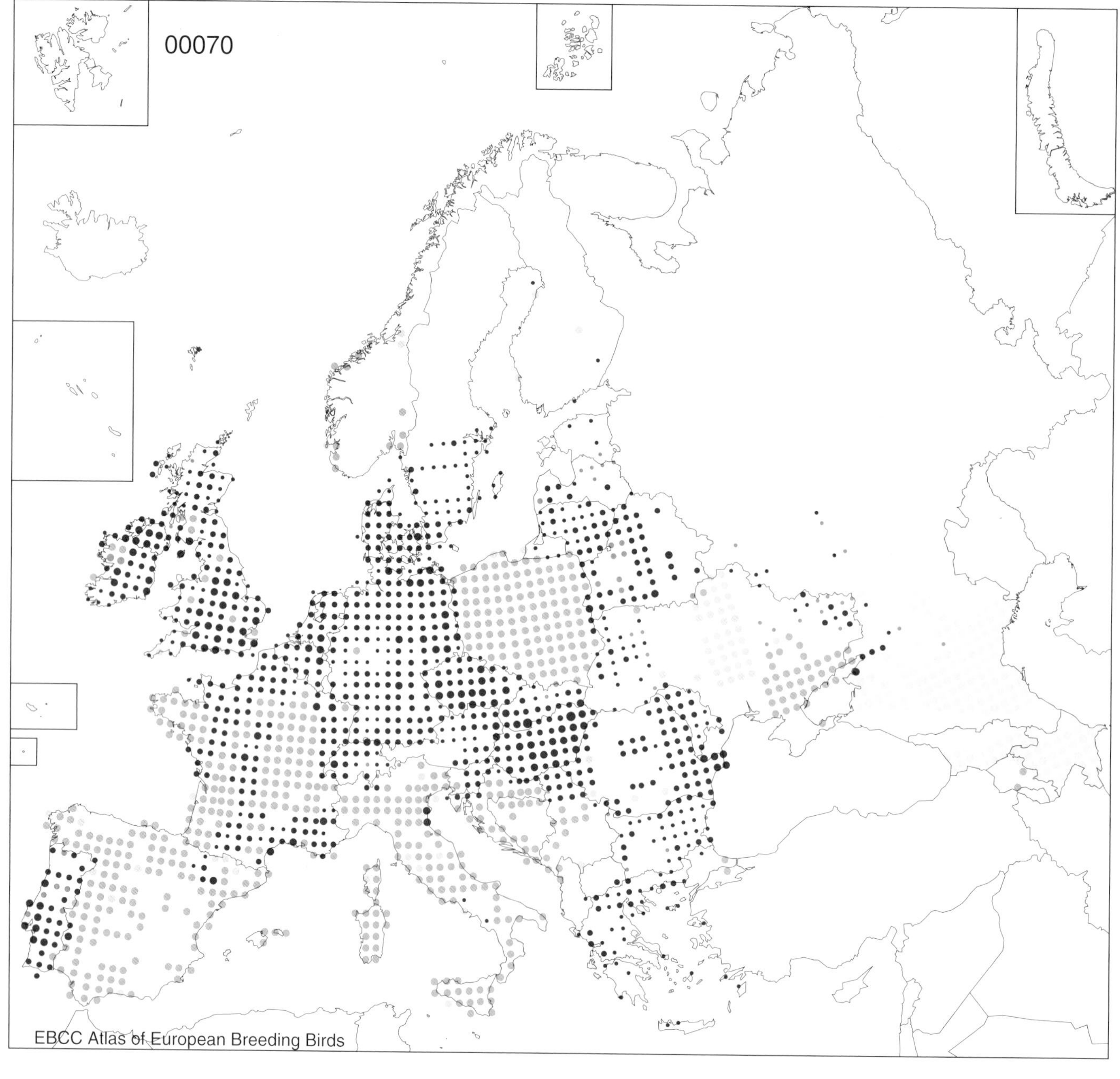

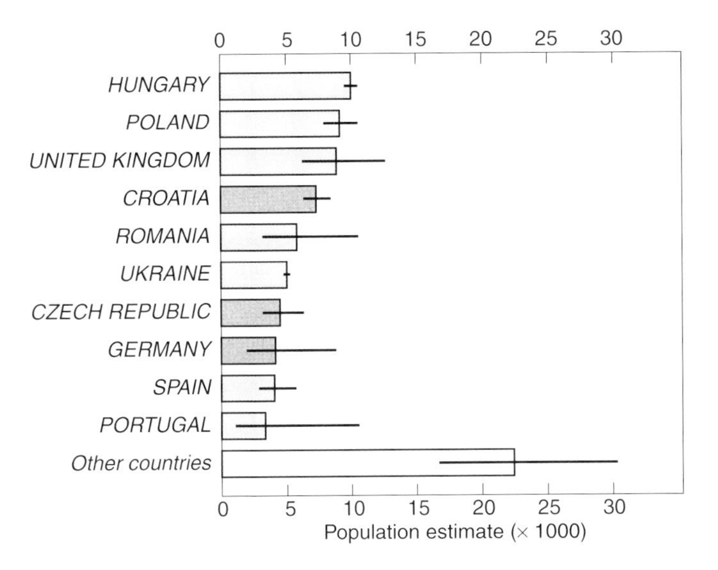

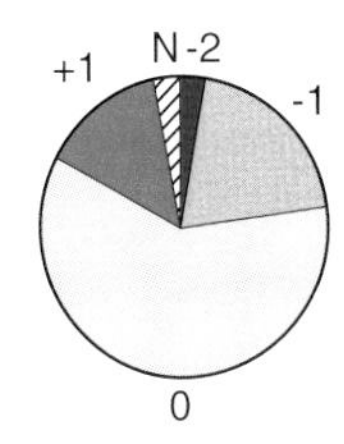

% in top 10 countries: 72.5
Total number of populated European countries: 35
Total European population 75,712–91,857 (81,136)
Russian population 500–5000 (1581)
Turkish population 5000–50,000 (15,811)

The Little Grebe is distributed in Europe from Portugal to the southern shores of Sweden and Norway at 60°N. It is evenly distributed in Britain, Ireland and C Europe, but it occurs increasingly sporadically southwards through S Europe. In Scandinavia, it nests regularly only in southern Sweden. Its distribution in E Europe cuts through the Baltic States, Belarus, W and SW Russia and E Ukraine, but then swings E reaching the Volga Delta and the W Caspian shore. Probably due to its largely sedentary nature, the Little Grebe has more subspecies (9) than any other grebe. In Europe the nominate subspecies extends over most of the mapped area, with *capensis* occurring in the SE corner. Extralimitally, it occurs in Japan, much of S Asia, the Indo-Malaysian archipelago and Africa S of the Sahara, including Madagascar. In small 20th-century range extensions it reached S Sweden (1905), Norway (1973) and spread to the Volga Delta (1967).

The Little Grebe's typical breeding habitats are small ponds, lakes and reservoirs, or any small stretch (<1ha) of slow-flowing water partly overgrown by swamp vegetation, the open-water proportion being as little as 0.1ha. Such prime habitat is disappearing from much of Europe, but the Little Grebe has adapted to some extent by using similar habitats with much less dense vegetation.

In Europe, the strongholds are in Hungary, Poland, Britain, Ireland, Portugal and Romania, with up to 12 000bp in a single country. Estonia, Finland, Luxembourg and Norway each hold fewer than 50bp, mostly because they are at the breeding range limit.

The Little Grebe nests as high as 600–610m asl in the Czech Republic (Šťastný *et al* 1987). Extralimitally, it has bred at 3016m asl in S Kazakhstan. In Poland, the Czech Republic, Slovenia and Hungary, up to 30% of the population breed on fishing ponds, but very few nest near larger open lakes. The Little Grebe, being highly territorial, does not form concentrations of nesting pairs, but it does exhibit a wide range of breeding densities across Europe. For example, in prime habitat in the Czech Republic, 9bp were located in separate ponds (2.8ha), part of a concentration of population which varied from 33 to 80bp over the years in only 193ha. The highest density in very dense habitat near Trebonsko was 7.8bp in 1ha, but the average overall ranged from 0.07 to 1.06 bp/ha (Šťastný *et al* 1987). In Poland, average densities are mostly lower: 0.03–0.06 bp/ha (Dyrcz *et al* 1991) and 0.05–0.07 bp/ha (Walasz & Mielczarek 1992). Local densities vary all over Europe, sometimes being very low in apparently suitable habitat.

Most European countries report largely stable breeding numbers, which sometimes fluctuate considerably depending upon weather conditions during preceding winters. Long-term declines are known for the Netherlands (from 2000bp in 1966–67 to 1000–1300bp in 1979), some areas of Germany (down 85% from 1960–85 near Gera, Lieder 1987), Britain and Ireland (range contractions, mainly in Ireland). Apart from temporal losses following severe winters, habitat destruction has contributed to these declines. Wintering numbers also seem to be on the decline, as in the Netherlands (P.L. Meininger, pers comm) and in Bavaria (Bezzel & Hashmi 1989).

The Little Grebe is a partial migrant. The most migratory populations are those to the N and E of its range. It arrives in C Europe in March, and in E Europe in late March and early April. The first birds leave their breeding grounds in September, but some remain until the ice begins forming, sometimes as late as January (Strautman 1963, Smogorgevskiy 1979). In favourable years, C Europe retains an overwintering population, but most winter annually in France and Italy. Eastern populations winter around the Black Sea and the Transcaucasus.

Igor Gorban (UKR)

This species account is sponsored by Ornis Consult, DK.

Podiceps cristatus | Great Crested Grebe

CZ	Potápka roháč	**I**	Svasso maggiore
D	Haubentaucher	**NL**	Fuut
E	Somormujo Lavanco	**P**	Mergulhão-de-crista
F	Grèbe huppé	**PL**	Perkoz dwuczuby
FIN	Silkkiuikku	**R**	Чомга
G	Σκουφοβουτηχτάρι	**S**	Skäggdopping
H	Búbos vöcsök		

Non-SPEC, Threat status S

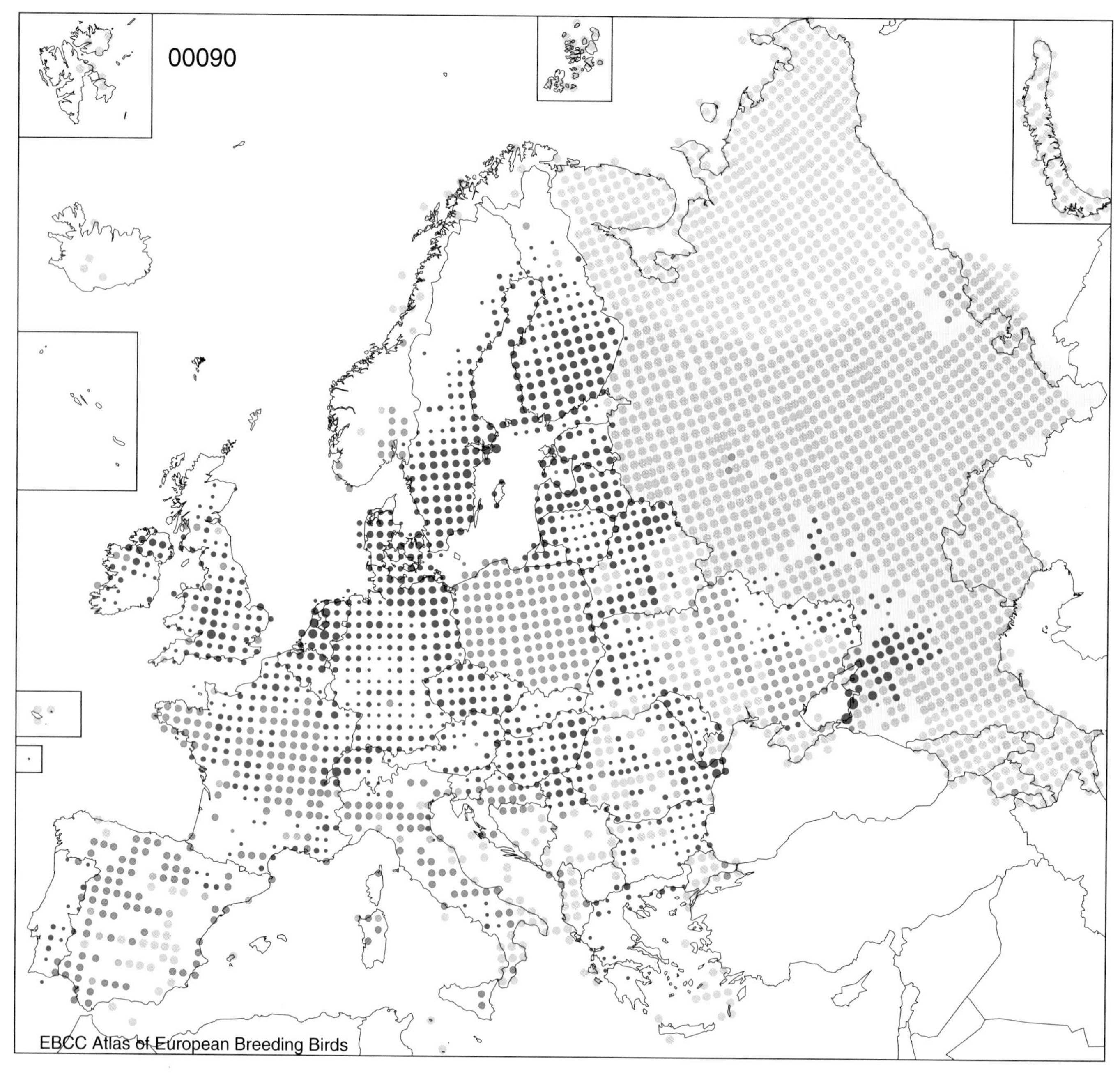

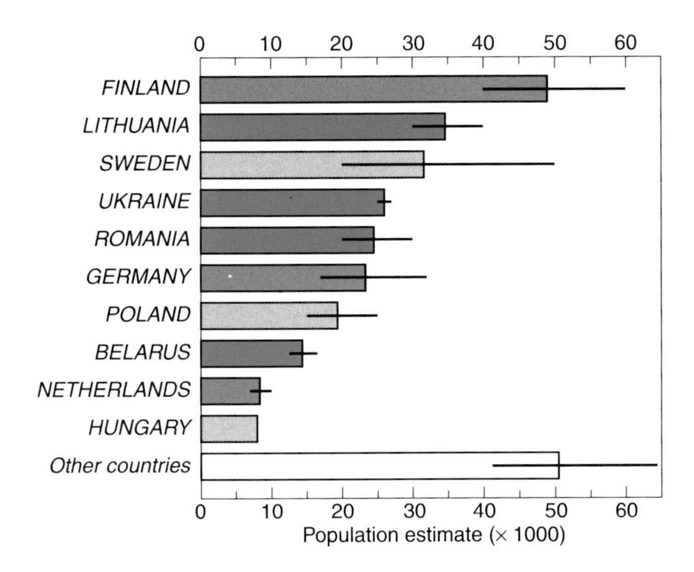

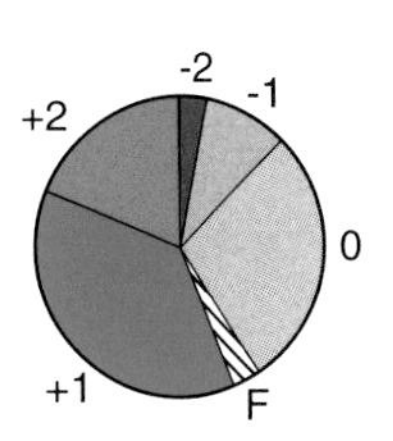

% in top 10 countries: 82.6
Total number of populated European countries: 32
Total European population 271,368–315,175 (289,581)
Russian population 100,000–1,000,000 (316,228)
Turkish population 1000–10,000 (3162)

The nominate form of the Great Crested Grebe *P.c. cristatus* occurs in Europe and W and C Asia. The subspecies *infuscatus* has a scattered distribution in Africa and the third subspecies *australis* is found in Australia and New Zealand.

During the breeding season the Great Crested Grebe is found on lakes, estuaries and in the Baltic Sea also in archipelagos. The majority of birds breed in lakes which combine a mosaic of reedbeds suitable for nest-building with extensive expanses of open areas in which to feed. The species seldom breeds on lakes smaller than 10ha. Although it breeds on oligotrophic waters, it achieves high breeding densities only on eutrophic lakes which normally have ample stocks of suitably sized fish, especially cyprinids (carp family), because its feeding activity is little hampered by water turbidity. In the Baltic Sea, the Great Crested Grebe has extended its breeding range to the most sterile and exposed offshore areas (Ulfvens 1988).

The species is widespread across almost the whole of Europe, being absent as a breeder from Iceland and elsewhere generally from above 67°N. In Norway it is restricted mostly to the SE and extreme SW. Its distribution is very scattered in the E and C Mediterranean countries (from Italy to Greece).

From the late 19th century onwards, the Great Crested Grebe has extended its range northwards, first breeding in Norway in 1904. Since 1900 it has expanded to the N in Finland by 200–300km, and occupied some gaps in its distribution in C Europe. However, it ceased to breed in Sicily, and outside the *Atlas*' area of coverage, in Cyprus and Israel, although these populations were never large. More recently the populations of France, Portugal and Italy have experienced both an increase and a range expansion.

The western European populations have undergone a marked increase since the late 19th century. In particular, the Fennoscandian population increased very rapidly during the 1960–70s. According to a recent estimate, the Finnish population of about 50 000bp may be ten times larger than that of the 1950s, at which time the population probably was underestimated. The most significant factor contributing to the population growth has been the increased eutrophication of standing waterbodies, a process which has increased not only the populations of small fish but also the areas of reedbeds. In many countries, reservoir construction also has played a role, but the effects of reduced hunting certainly were important initially, because the species had been hunted heavily for 'grebe fur' in the 19th century.

The breeding density of the Great Crested Grebe depends on the availability of suitable lakes and breeding sites. In many sites pairs form loose colonies, typically of 5–50bp, but sometimes up to 500bp (Goc 1986). In just a few lakes the breeding population exceeds 1000bp: the IJsselmeer in The Netherlands (1500bp), Lake Neuchâtel in Switzerland (2300) and Lake Vesijärvi in S Finland (1100–1600) (Fuchs 1978, Vlug 1983).

The Great Crested Grebe is often the most numerous waterbird in Fennoscandian lakes. In Finland the highest mean density, 14 bp/km^2, was achieved in large (mean size 300ha) eutrophic lakes (E. Lammi & R.A. Väisänen, in prep.). Densities ranging from 15 to 30 bp/km^2 have been recorded in many large lakes in N, W and C Europe.

The species is fully migratory in the N of its range, but further S it largely makes only cold-weather movements. The most important wintering areas (20 000–30 000 grebes at each) are the IJsselmeer, many of the Swiss lakes and in the Black Sea (Vlug 1983, Suter & Schifferli 1988). Marked changes in moulting and wintering distribution since 1975, suggesting a reduction in the extent of migration, and of migration distance, have been documented (Adriaensen *et al* 1993).

Jon Fjeldså (DK) Esa Lammi (FIN)

This species account is sponsored by Lions Club Aalsmeer, Aalsmeer, NL.

Podiceps grisegena

Red-necked Grebe

CZ	Potápka rudokrká	**I**	Svasso collorosso
D	Rothalstaucher	**NL**	Roodhalsfuut
E	Somormujo Cuellirrojo	**P**	Mergulhão-de-pescoço-ruivo
F	Grèbe jougris	**PL**	Perkoz rdzawoszyi
FIN	Härkälintu	**R**	Серощекая поганка
G	Κοκκινοβουτηχτάρι	**S**	Gråhakedopping
H	Vörösnyakú vöcsök		

Non-SPEC, Threat status S

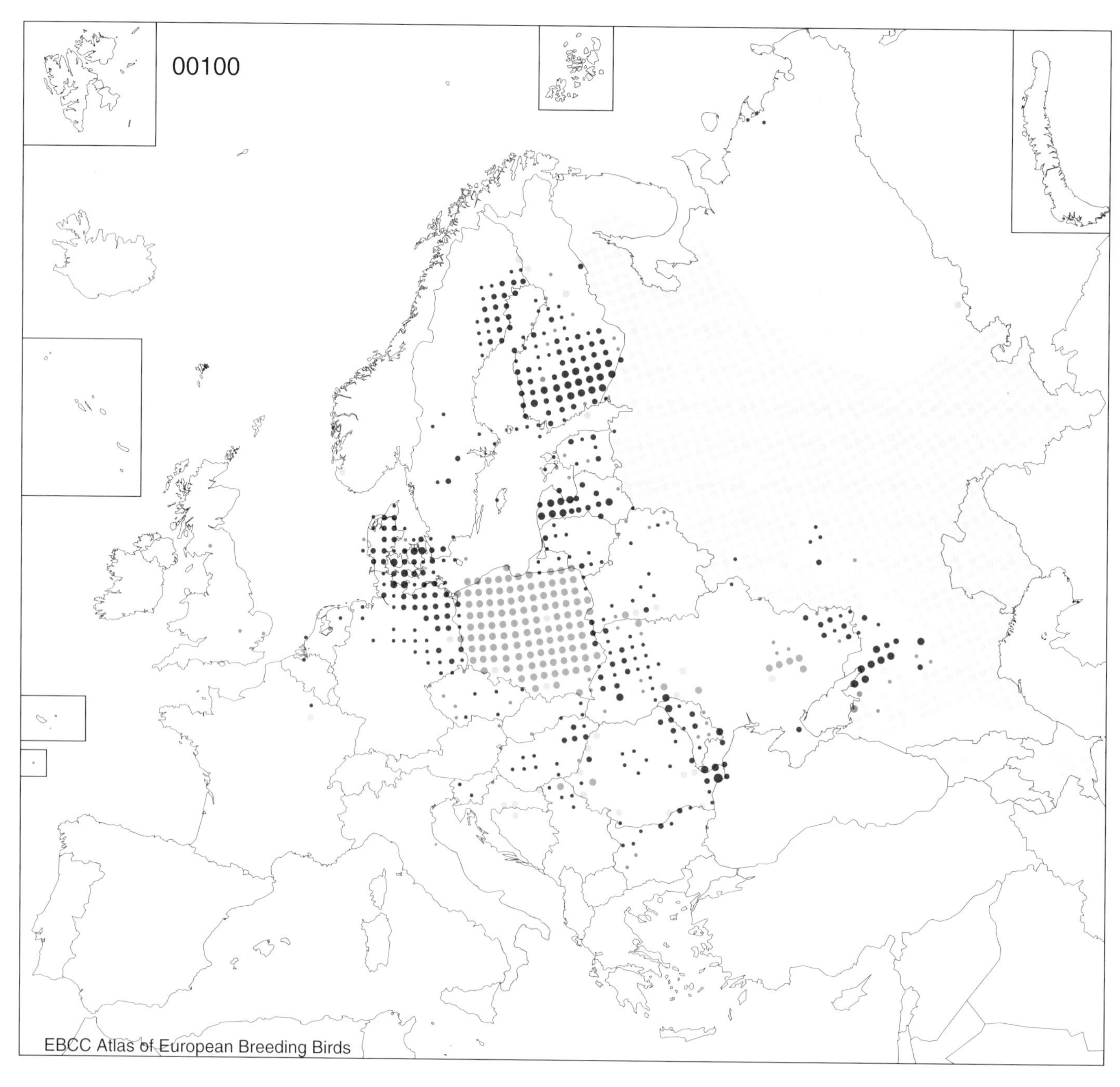

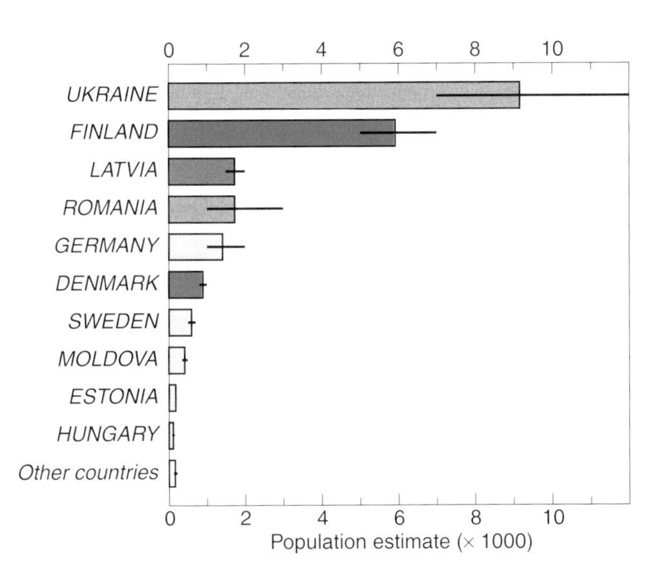

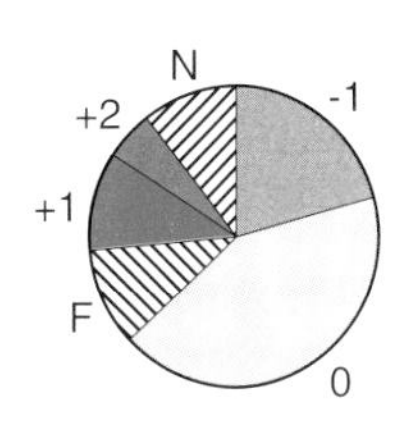

% in top 10 countries: 99.3
Total number of populated European countries: 19
Total European population 19,790–25,659 (22,302)
Russian population 10,000–100,000 (31,623)
Turkish population 100–1000 (316)

The Red-necked Grebe is a Holarctic breeding bird with distinct western and eastern subspecies. It nests mainly in the boreal but also in the temperate and steppe climatic zones. Its range extends far N, reaching 68°N in Scandinavia. In the W Palearctic this it predominantly in lowlands and on great plains, but exceptionally in mountains on lakes up to 1902m (Armenia) and 3016m asl (Kirghizstan). The nominate subspecies inhabits the Baltic area, C and E Europe, Turkey, Kazakhstan and W Siberia. The other subspecies, *holboellii*, is found E Asia and NW North America.

In Europe the major breeding locations are inland waterbodies, typically fairly small and shallow (often up to 1.5m deep), having at least some emergent plants and an abundant growth of submerged vegetation, in which invertebrates flourish. In C Europe the species is found primarily on fishponds of at least 0.1ha. In Fennoscandia and the Baltic States, it nests on smaller and shallower luxuriantly vegetated lakes, on peat-bog pools, ponds, small areas of open water in extensive reedswamps and in shallow bays of large lakes. In E Europe and Russia it shows similar preferences, frequenting ponds, marshy lakes, forest and steppe lakes, and oxbows. This kind of breeding habitat is fairly limited, and so the Red-necked Grebe has a patchy distribution.

The western border of its breeding range runs from Sweden (500–700bp) and Denmark (800–1000bp) through Germany (1500–2100bp), Hungary (80–150bp) and SE Europe to Turkey, which holds the southernmost breeding sites. In part because of climatic factors it seldom nests W of this limit (the Netherlands; 7 confirmed, 17 suspected breeding attempts since 1900 (van Dijk *et al* 1994a), Belgium, France and Austria two each). The Red-necked Grebe has also bred in Britain (firstly 1988), Slovenia (firstly 1990) and in SW Germany. At the range edge, it is relatively numerous in Denmark, the former East Germany (*c*1100bp) (Nicolai 1993b) and in Schleswig-Holstein (increased from *c*270bp in 1980 to *c*700 in 1990) (Vlug 1993). In the Czech Republic the Red-necked Grebe was a regular and locally numerous breeder before 1900, but now only single pairs (0–5) nest occasionally. In SE Europe the species is rare and is numerous only in a few places (such as the Danube Delta) (Romania 1000–3000bp, Moldova 350–500bp, Bulgaria 30–60bp). In Poland (*c*2000bp) it is widespread in the lowlands (Tomiałojç 1990). In Finland numbers increased considerably (20–40%) in the 1980s (1992, 5000–7000 bp; E. Lammi, pers comm). In the Baltic States and eastern Europe the species is, as everywhere, often sporadic, occurring irregularly, and only locally does it become fairly numerous (Latvia 1500–2000bp, Estonia 150–200, Lithuania 25–50, Belarus 50–75, Ukraine 7000–12 000). The population in European Russia is roughly estimated at 10 000–100 000bp. Some places hold many pairs (the Volga Delta), but in the NE (the Komi Republic), it does not breed.

In general only one bp occurs on a small pond, but sometimes many pairs nest on one pond (up to 8 bp/ha in the fishponds in Schleswig-Holstein and by the Baltic up to 8.67 bp/ha in waterbodies from which the adults make foraging flights to the sea) (Vlug 1993). Usually population density is much lower, perhaps up to 10–15 bp/km^2 on the most suitable lakes in Finland.

During winter the Red-necked Grebe becomes a truly marine species and lives in shallow, coastal waters of the W Baltic (up to 3600 in the NW Kattegat and *c*1200 in the Gulf of Pommern) (Durinck *et al* 1993), in the outer archipelago of the central W coast of Norway (up to 3000), in the North Sea and Dutch delta, and in the Caspian and Black Seas. Some individuals winter in inland waters.

J J Vlug (NL)

Podiceps auritus

Slavonian Grebe

CZ	Potápka žlutorohá	I	Svasso cornuto
D	Ohrentaucher	NL	Kuifduiker
E	Zampullín Cuellirrojo	P	Mergulhão-de-pescoço-castanho
F	Grèbe esclavon	PL	Perkoz rogaty
FIN	Mustakurkku-uikku	R	Красношейная поганка
G	Χειμωνοβουτηχτάρι	S	Svarthakedopping
H	Füles vöcsök		

Non-SPEC, Threat status S (P)

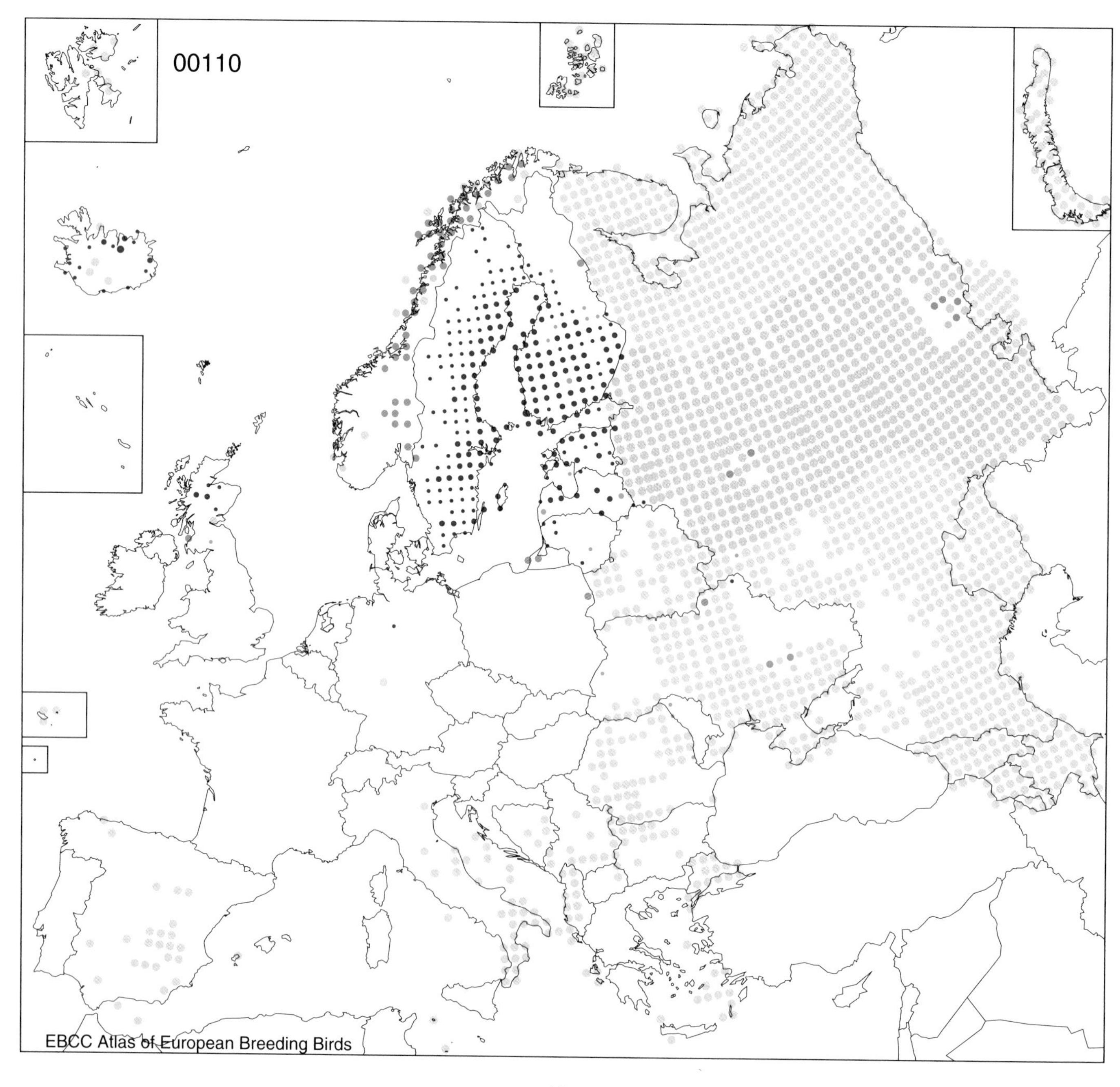

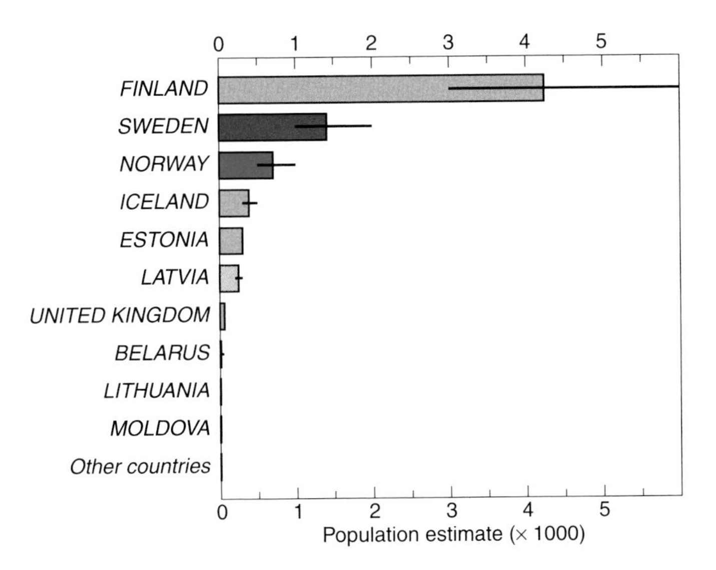

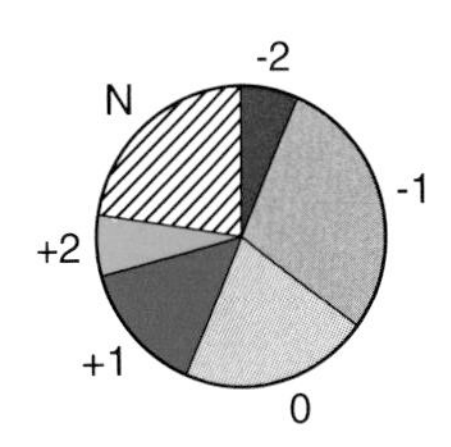

% in top 10 countries: 99.9
Total number of populated European countries: 14
Total European population 6058–9268 (7388)
Russian population 10,000–100,000 (31,623)

The range of this boreal, nearly circumpolar species (known in the Nearctic as the Horned Grebe) is characterized by three features. Firstly, the Slavonian Grebe is a more northerly species than its closest relatives. Secondly, in northern Asia and North America, the range is fairly continuous, reaching from coast to coast. Lastly, in western Europe, the Slavonian Grebe occurs more patchily, due to the Scandinavian mountain chain and an uneven distribution of breeding habitats.

The Slavonian Grebe prefers shallow, eutrophic lakes, usually of 1–10ha, with bays containing patchy stands of helophytes, but also uses oligotrophic lakes with barren shores (Iceland, Norway, Scotland), or even artificial habitats, such as gravel or sandpits. Along Baltic coasts it breeds frequently in brackish habitats.

The species is generally migratory, with birds from Norway and Iceland wintering on the Norwegian coast, in Britain or around the Faeroes and Ireland. Those from Russia, Finland and Sweden winter in the southern Baltic Sea, along North Sea coasts, in lakes in C Europe and in the Mediterranean.

The Slavonian Grebe has markedly extended its range in Europe since 1900, advancing through E and C Sweden and spreading through Norway. In Finland, its distribution has been stable at least since 1950. It became established in Scotland in 1908. During the *Atlas* period it bred for the first time in small numbers in Denmark, Germany, Greenland, Poland and Ukraine.

Outside Russia, the European population is estimated at 5000–10 000bp, being concentrated in Finland (3000–6000bp), Sweden (1000–2000bp), Norway (500–1000bp) and Iceland (300–500bp). Estonia has 300bp, Latvia 200–300bp and Lithuania 5–10bp. The Scottish population comprises *c*60bp. Small populations are found in Belarus and Moldova. Only isolated pairs occur in newly colonized countries. The Russian population is poorly known: estimates lie between 10 000 and 100 000bp, the authors estimating *c*30 000bp.

Despite its spread to new areas, the Slavonian Grebe has decreased in numbers certainly by 20–50% in Finland, Sweden, Iceland and Estonia. In Finland, the population was probably halved from 1950 to the late 1970s (Lammi 1983), but has apparently recovered somewhat since 1980. Population increases occurred in Norway, Scotland and Moldova.

Population trends are known in detail only from limited areas. The data show that large changes in numbers may occur over fairly short periods. In one decade the population in 29 lakes and coastal bays in Finland decreased by 67%. On the other hand, a well-studied population on the Finnish west coast decreased from 24 to 11bp in 1979–83, and then gradually increased to 43bp in 1991 (Ulfvens 1988, 1989, pers obs). The Scottish population rose from 52bp in 1971 to 80bp in 1978–80, and has now levelled out at *c*60bp. It is clear that hard winters deplete the Slavonian Grebe; variations in productivity between years may contribute (Fjeldså 1973, Ulfvens 1989).

The Slavonian Grebe populations have so far been able to recover rapidly and are therefore not endangered. However, permanently depleted breeding capacity may arise through acidification of breeding lakes. Locally, populations may clearly be under threat from human disturbance in the breeding season, or through habitat changes caused by afforestation, shore development, or fish stocking. Protection of local populations and their breeding habitats is clearly needed in many parts of Europe.

Roy Dennis (GB) Johan Ulfvens (FIN)

This species account is sponsored by Ulrich Radomski, Kiel, D.

Podiceps nigricollis

Black-necked Grebe

CZ	Potápka černokrká	I	Svasso piccolo
D	Schwarzhalstaucher	NL	Geoorde Fuut
E	Zampullín Cuellinegro	P	Mergulhão-de-pescoço-preto
F	Grèbe à cou noir	PL	Zausznik
FIN	Mustakaulauikku	R	Черношейная поганка
G	Μαυροβουτηχτάρι	S	Svarthalsad dopping
H	Feketenyakú vöcsök		

Non-SPEC, Threat status S

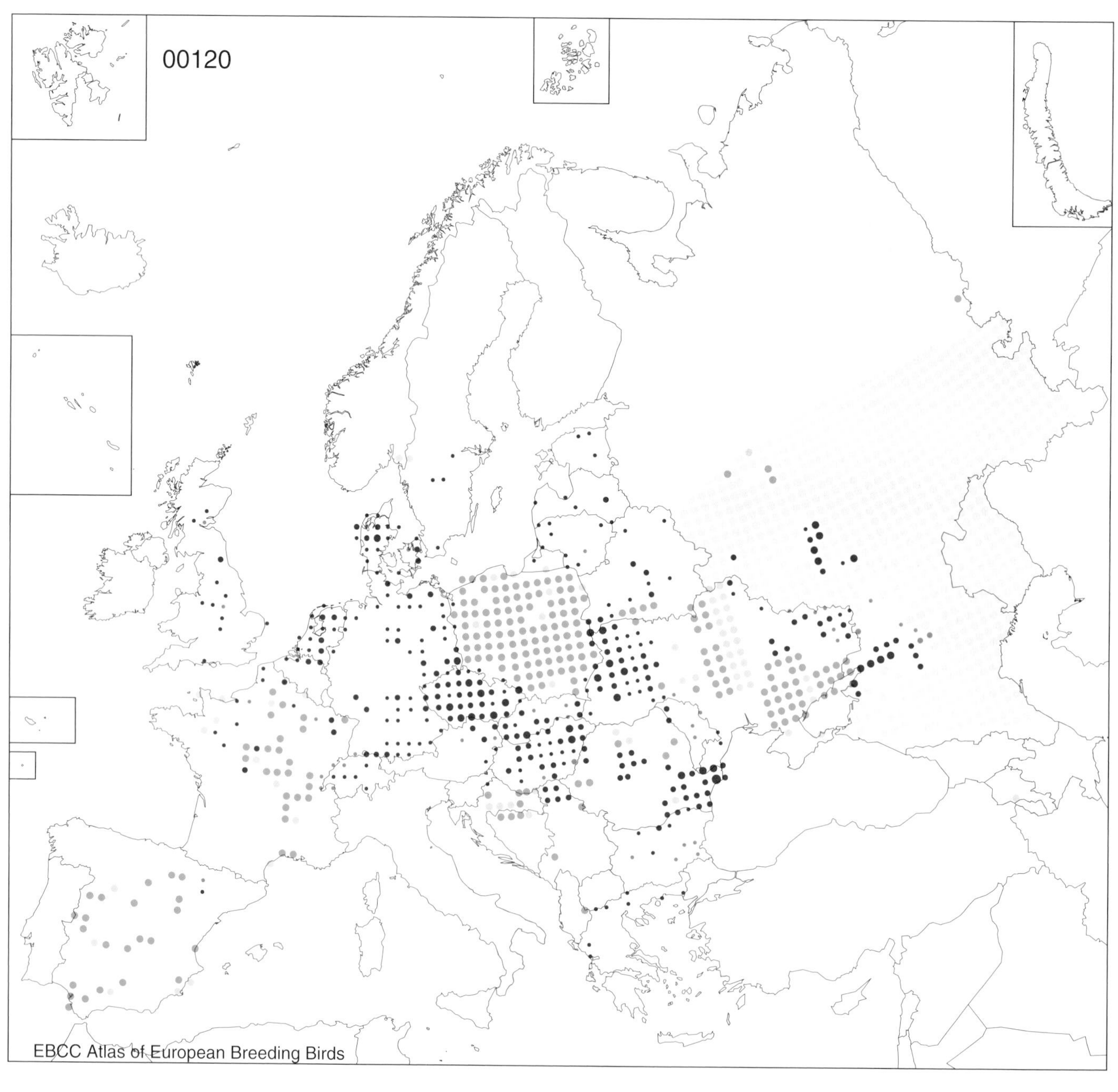

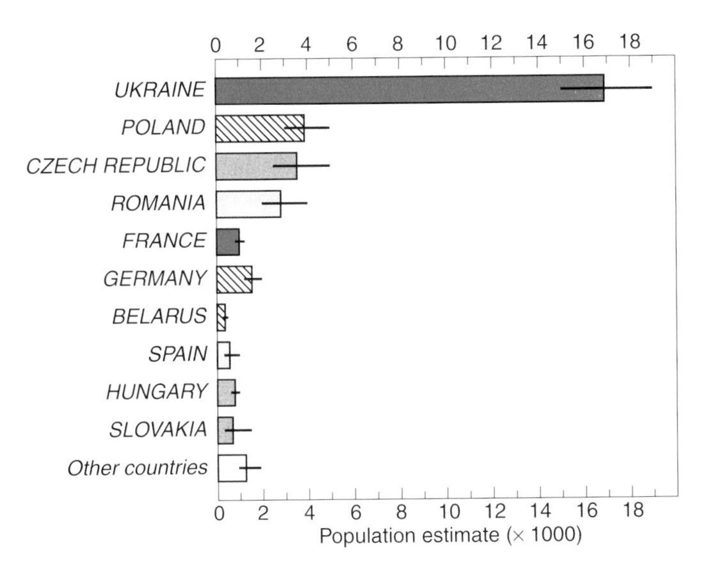

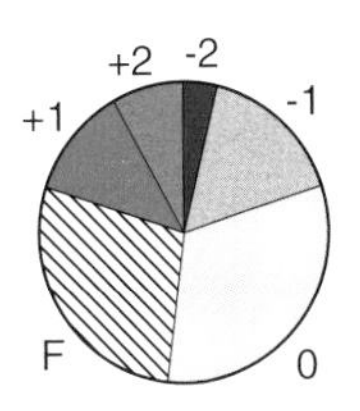

% in top 10 countries: 96.1
Total number of populated European countries: 25
Total European population 30,772–36,569 (33,319)
Russian population 10,000–100,000 (31,623)
Turkish population 2000–10,000 (4472)

The Black-necked Grebe, a colonial species, is distributed on three continents: the nominate *P.n. nigricollis* occurs from Spain to China, *gurneyi* inhabits southern Africa and occurs locally in East Africa, and *californicus* is found in C and W North America.

Its breeding habitats are shallow, highly productive, eutrophic waterbodies which may be either alkaline or saline. Reed *Phragmites* is important as protective cover but the Black-necked Grebe requires sufficient open water not only for its social displays but also to provide constant and easy access to the bottom, where it feeds. Its floating nest is anchored either to submerged aquatic plants such as pondweed *Potamogeton* or dock *Polygonum* spp, or to reeds. In W and C Europe the Black-necked Grebe's main habitat is fishponds; it also uses other artificial habitats such as sewage ponds, gravel-pits or reservoirs. The breeding site can be as small as 2–3ha in area. It has bred up to 1005m asl in Switzerland and 2000m asl in Transcaucasia. All three subspecies are known to breed in association with colonies of small gulls where they achieve higher than average breeding success.

In Eurasia, the Black-necked Grebe is latitude-dependent, breeding mainly between 45° and 55°N, except for a gap between 85° and 112°E, where it is absent. Although there is some degree of overlap, especially in C European Russia, it is replaced further N by its ecological counterpart, the Slavonian Grebe *P. auritus*. The Black-necked Grebe is rare in southern Europe and has probably disappeared from North Africa. Its core area runs from C France to S Russia. The total European population is between *c*37 000 and 142 000bp, of which *c*70% is held by Ukraine and southern Russia. Further W, populations are generally much smaller and more fragmented, not all the potential sites in any region being occupied (Fiala 1991). Although colonies of 2000bp exist in North America, the largest European colonies do not exceed 250bp. In Poland fewer than 10 colonies reach 50bp.

From the late 19th century to the 1930s, the species experienced a slight westward range extension of some 3% (Prinzinger 1979), but the reasons for it are unclear, although climatic changes in the Caspian area may have played a part. Since then, the species seems well-established, despite disappearing from Ireland. From 1970 to 1990 its breeding areas apparently were stable or increasing in all European countries except Germany, Austria and Latvia. However, numbers fluctuate markedly from year to year, particularly near the distribution limits. This is accentuated by its tendency to occupy irregularly flooded areas and by asynchronous trends at adjacent breeding sites (Hustings 1991). Population trends were stable or increasing except in C Europe. Fiala (1991) has estimated the annual decrease in the former Czechoslovakia to be 2.95% for the period 1971–87.

The Black-necked Grebe is particularly sensitive to disturbance during breeding. Habitat destruction either by removal or through degradation of quality (such as commercialization of fishponds) remains the main threat to the species. Increasing disturbance from recreational activities probably prevents nesting in many areas, but often acts indirectly, by driving away gull colonies amongst which the species has nested (Trouvilliez 1988).

Black-necked Grebe movements are not well-known. Birds begin dispersing after breeding, and reach their wintering grounds in November in western, but mainly Mediterranean (both sides) coastal regions (4000 at Formentera, Balearics), or on larger ice-free freshwater bodies. The Black, southern Caspian and northern Red Seas and Turkish lakes (186 000 known from Lake Burdur) hold large numbers, the Atlantic and North Sea coasts many fewer. In spring, after initially gathering in large waterborne flocks, birds reach their breeding grounds between mid-March and April.

Jacques Trouvilliez (F) Jon Fjeldså (DK)

Fulmarus glacialis **Fulmar**

CZ	Buřňák lední	**I**	Fulmaro
D	Eissturmvogel	**NL**	Noordse Stormvogel
E	Fulmar Boreal	**P**	Fulmar-glacial
F	Fulmar boréal	**PL**	Fulmar
FIN	Myrskylintu	**R**	Глупыш
G	Θνελλοπούλι	**S**	Stormfågel
H	Sirályhojsza		

Non-SPEC, Threat status S

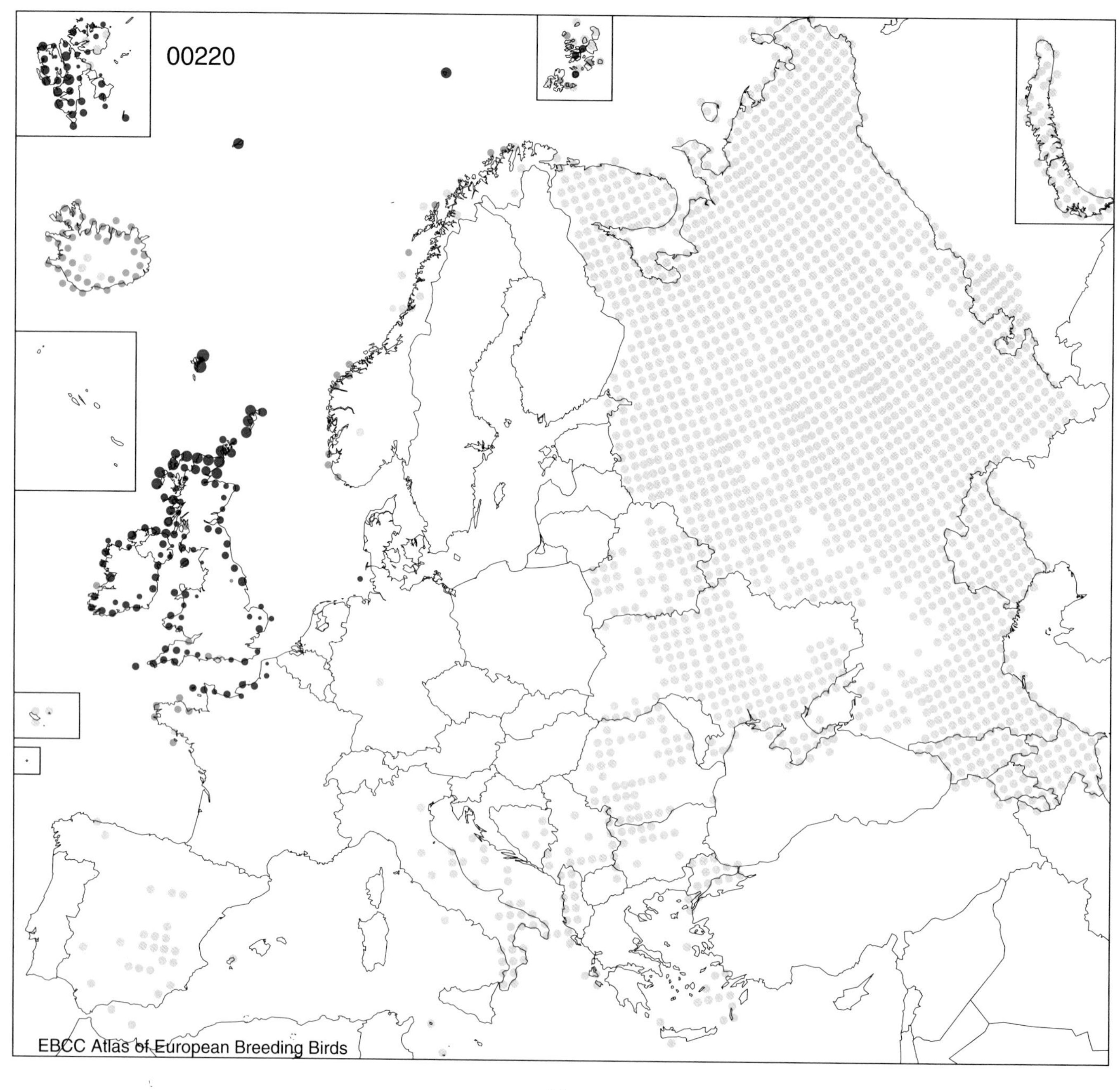

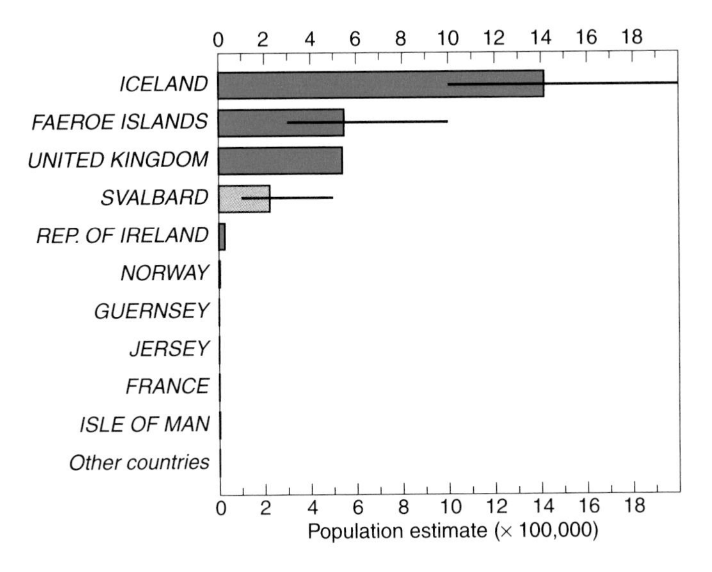

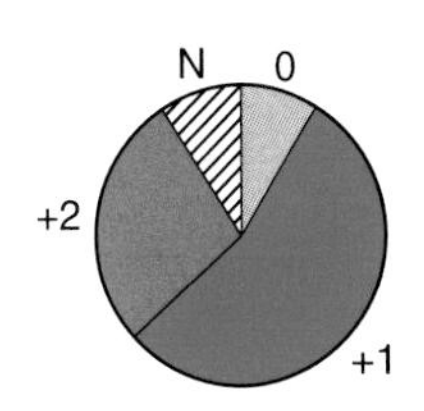

% in top 10 countries: 100.0
Total number of populated European countries: 11
Total European population 2,261,216–3,549,427 (2,759,431)
Russian population 26,000–26,000 (26,000)

Having increased its breeding range over the last 250 years or so from a boreal distribution in Iceland to the Faeroes and subsequently to the entire suitable coastline of Britain & Ireland, the Fulmar is now common and conspicuous at seacliffs, especially from spring to autumn, but also in winter. It is widely distributed throughout the Atlantic N of 45°N and the North Sea.

Now it breeds on almost all suitable marine coastal habitats in Iceland, the Faeroes, Britain & Ireland, and occurs in small isolated colonies in Brittany (first bred 1960) and Normandy (1972), on Heligoland (1972), and in SW (1920) and NW Norway. It is also widespread on Svalbard, Bear Island, Franz Josef Land, and on the northern island of Novaya Zemlya.

New colonies continue to be established in Britain & Ireland, filling gaps so that the total breeding range is not significantly extended. Breeding numbers in well-established colonies vary from year to year, but in general continue to grow. For example the Shetland breeding population has increased by 50% between 1977 and 1993 (Dunnet & Heubeck 1995). The more peripheral colonies on continental coasts increase and expand slowly. On the western side of the North Atlantic a southward extension of breeding range was detected in Labrador and Newfoundland in the early 1970s but has not developed as in the E.

Several explanations have been offered for the increase in range and numbers, including exploitation of a new food source of offal from whaling and trawling, and genetic or climatic change. All assumed that the expansion originated in Iceland. Bourne (1984) suggests that the population nesting on St Kilda (first recorded in 1697, but thought to have been there for at least 800 years; Fisher 1966), until the early 19th century the only breeding colony south of Iceland, may have been the source. That the Fulmar forms concentrations amongst fishing fleets has long been known, and still it continues (Hudson & Furness 1989), but similar behaviour in the North Pacific has not led to increases.

The traditional nesting habitat is the upper zones of high cliffs where grassy slopes and rock ledges provide suitable sites for the simple scrapes for the eggs. The Fulmar frequently consorts with other seabird species to form enormous multi-species colonies, and may itself number tens of thousands in large colonies. There are many small scattered colonies along coasts. Even during its period of rapid range expansion (admirably chronicled by Fisher 1952), it also nested on low-lying sand-dunes, in fields and on buildings and walls up to 15km from the nearest sea.

Recoveries of birds ringed in Britain show that for its first three or four years of life the Fulmar is dispersed widely throughout the North Sea and North Atlantic, as far as Newfoundland, Greenland, Iceland and the Barents Sea. Once it begins 'prospecting' at breeding colonies, when 5–10 years old, its pelagic distribution becomes much more restricted to a few hundred kilometres from colonies. This pattern is maintained by breeding adults.

The Fulmar occurs in light and dark phases with a continuum of intermediates between the extremes. The dark form occurs only occasionally in southerly populations, but predominates on Bear Island and parts of Svalbard. There is no clear cline in the distribution of the colour morphs.

In the North Pacific *F.g. rodgersii* breeds on the Kurile, Commander and Aleutian Islands, and on islands in the Bering Sea and Gulf of Alaska. It is unlikely that these could mix with North Atlantic birds, even in the high arctic. Neither of the northern populations can mix with the circumpolar breeding Southern Fulmar, *F. glacialoides*, which comes N in summer only to *c*35°S, except in the Humboldt Current where it reaches 10°S.

the late George Dunnet (GB)

This species account is sponsored by Technischer Überwachungsverein Rheinland, Rheinberg, D.

Pterodroma feae

Gon-gon/Fea's Petrel

CZ	Buřňák kapverdský	I	Petrello di Fea
D	Feasturmvogel	NL	Kaap Verdische Stormvogel
E	Petrel Gon-gon	P	Gon-gon
F	Pétrel gongon	PL	Petrel wyspowy
FIN	Kapverdenviistäjä	R	Тайфунник Гон-Гон
G	Πτεροδρόμα του Fea	S	Atlantpetrell
H	Gon-gon hojsza		

SPEC Cat 1, Threat status E

Fea's Petrel is a Macaronesian endemic. In Europe it is found only on the Madeira archipelago where probably *c*20% of the world population breeds on Bugio, the southernmost of the Deserta group (Zino & Biscoito 1994). There are two records from the Azores (Bibby & del Nevo 1991, Monteiro & Furness 1995), but it is doubtful whether breeding takes place there. The Cape Verde Islands hold *c*1000bp (Hazevoet 1994), the majority of the world population.

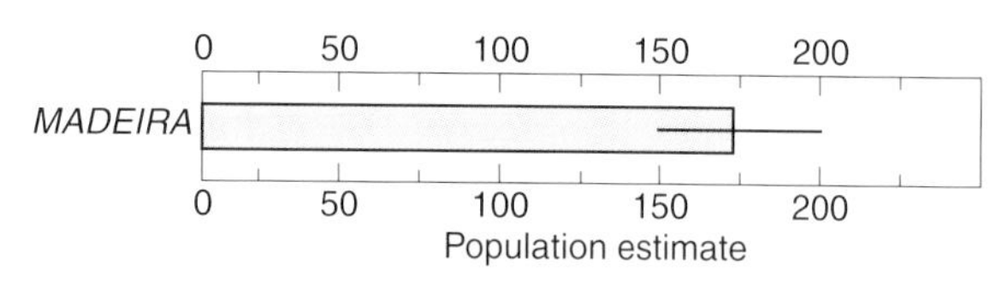

% in top 10 countries: 100.0
Total number of populated European countries: 1
Total European population 150–200 (173)

On Bugio the species is migratory. It arrives in May and June and departs in January and February. Its destination is unknown and rarely has it been seen other than in the waters round Madeira during the breeding season. Probably 90% of the Bugio population is on the southern end of the island, which may be related to the ground vegetation being sparser in the breeding area (Jouanin *et al* 1969, P.A. Zino & F. Zino 1986, Zino *et al* 1994a).

The site on Bugio is windswept and arid. Fea's Petrel builds long burrows in the rock-hard ground. The roots of what little vegetation there is are very important in binding the soil and stabilizing the nests (P.A. Zino & F. Zino 1986). Habitat deterioration is probably the only serious threat to the species.

Monitoring of the Bugio population started in 1967 (Jouanin *et al* 1969), intensifying since 1986 when the Freira Conservation Project started to build up the work. The population is probably stable; greater understanding from recent studies has allowed numbers to be estimated with greater confidence.

Manuel J Biscoito (P) Francis Zino (P)

Pterodroma madeira

Freira/Zino's Petrel

CZ	Buřňák madeirský	I	Petrello di Madeira
D	Madeirasturmvogel	NL	Madeira-stormvogel
E	Petrel Freira	P	Freira da Madeira
F	Pétrel de Madère	PL	Petrel maderski
FIN	Madeiranviistäjä	R	Мадейрский тайфунник
G	Πτεροδρόμα του Zino	S	Madeirapetrell
H	Madeira-hojsza		

SPEC Cat 1, Threat status E

Zino's Petrel is Europe's rarest seabird. Madeira holds the total world breeding population, now totalling a mere 20–30bp. It is questionable whether such a small population is large enough for the species to survive (P.A. Zino & F. Zino 1986; Zino & Biscoito 1994; Zino *et al* 1994b).

The species is migratory and comes to Madeira only to breed, arriving in late March or early April and leaving in late September or early October. Where it migrates to is unknown and there are no records of this bird other than in Madeiran waters.

On Madeira Zino's Petrel occurs only around its breeding area, on the high central mountain massif at about 1600m asl. It comes

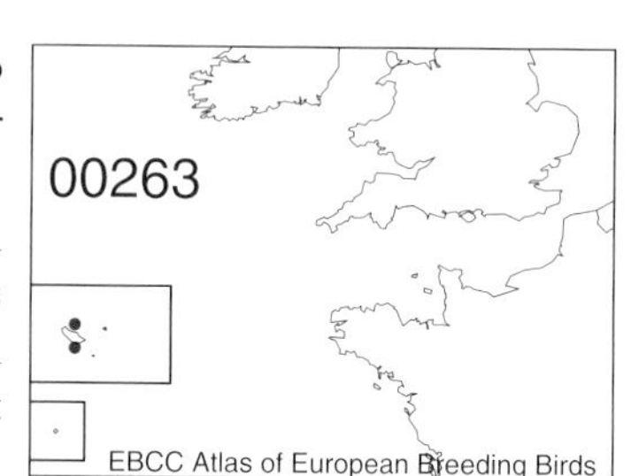

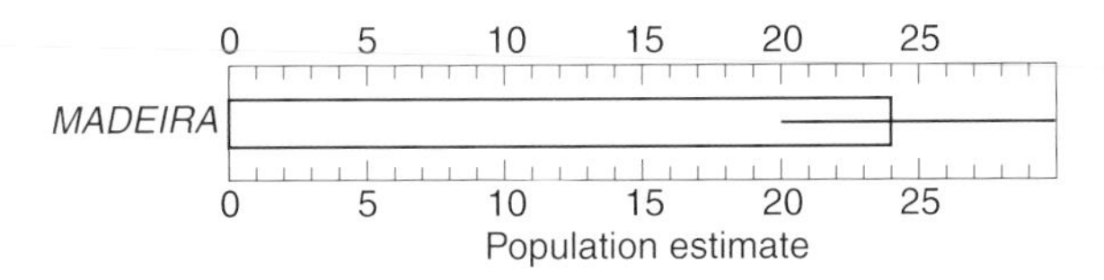

% in top 10 countries: 100.0
Total number of populated European countries: 1
Total European population 20–30 (24)

ashore only at night. It nests on ledges on inland cliffs which are well-vegetated and have sufficient soil for burrowing. These ledges are not browsed by herbivores which is probably highly significant.

The species was discovered in 1903, but scientific work only started in 1969 after its rediscovery because it had been considered extinct! In 1986 the Freira Conservation Project was started and since then the population has been monitored regularly, often with great difficulty. The principal limiting factors are human predation (collectors), rats *Rattus rattus* and feral cats. It is hoped that the human persecution is at an end. The rats have been brought under control after very considerable efforts from the project. However, cats continue to be a major problem (Zino 1992). Breeding success apparently has improved since the start of the project, but the total population still appears to be declining.

Manuel J Biscoito (P) Francis Zino (P)

Bulweria bulwerii

Bulwer's Petrel

CZ	Buřňák Bulwerův	I	Berta di Bulwer
D	Bulwersturmvogel	NL	Bulwers Stormvogel
E	Petrel de Bulwer	P	Pardela de Bulwer
F	Pétrel de Bulwer	PL	Tajfunnik cienkodzioby
FIN	Tyrskyliitäjä	R	Длиннохвостый тайфунник
G	Θαλασσοβάτης του βυλωερ	S	Spetsstjärtad petrell
H	Ékfarkú hojsza		

SPEC Cat 3, Threat status V

Bulwer's Petrel is found in both the Pacific and Atlantic Oceans. The Madeira archipelago and the Selvagens seem to be its principal European breeding grounds. The population is stable there (P. Harrison 1985). Once common on the Azores, its population there has been subjected to severe predation by both humans and ferrets *Mustela furo* in the past and as a result appears to be declining (Fructuoso 1981; le Grand *et al* 1984). The Canary Islands hold a small breeding population, also declining. The European population is *c*50% of the total Atlantic population, the remainder being found in the Cape Verde Islands.

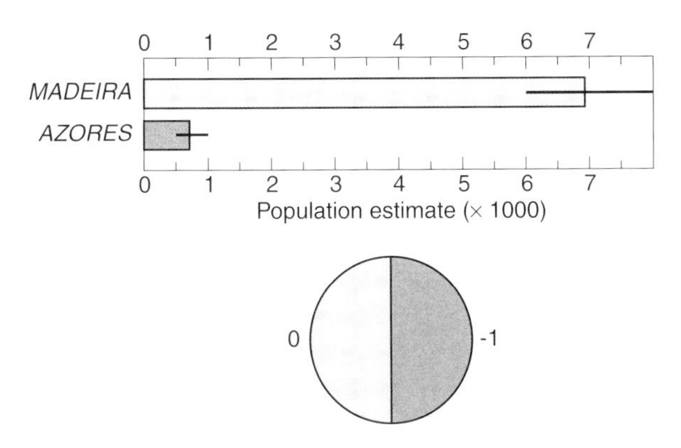

% in top 10 countries: 100.0
Total number of populated European countries: 2
Total European population 6684–8746 (7635)

The species is migratory, arriving in the breeding area towards the beginning of April and departing by the end of September. It migrates S into the tropical Atlantic.

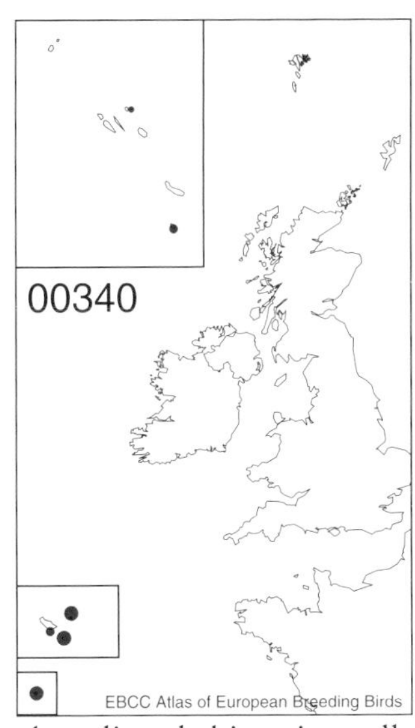

It breeds in very rough nests mostly in scree and rocks, which habitat is plentiful. On Selvagem Grande it competes for nest sites with the Little Shearwater *Puffinus assimilis*, and sometimes uses burrows dug by White-faced Storm-petrels *Pelagodroma marina* (Zino & Biscoito 1994).

Although the state of the breeding habitat is well-controlled there is heavy predation by the Yellow-legged Gull *Larus cachinnans*, especially within the Madeira archipelago (Zino & Biscoito 1994). On the Azores predation by ferrets and humans is believed to have ceased, but predation by the Buzzard *Buteo buteo rothschildi* has some effect. Cory's Shearwater *Calonectris diomedea* may kill some adults.

Luiz Monteiro (P) Francis Zino (P)

Calonectris diomedea

Cory's Shearwater

CZ	Buřňák šedý	I	Berta maggiore
D	Gelbschnabel-Sturmtaucher	NL	Kuhls Pijlstormvogel
E	Pardela Cenicienta	P	Pardela-de-bico-amarelo
F	Puffin cendré	PL	Burzyk żółtodzioby
FIN	Välimerenliitäjä	R	Желтоклювый буревестник
G	Αρτέμης	S	Gulnäbbad lira
H	Mediterrán vészmadár		

SPEC Cat 2, Threat status V (P)

A pelagic species, Cory's Shearwater breeds along rocky coasts and islands of the Mediterranean and Atlantic. On Berlenga alone the population is *c*50 000bp and we believe the entire Atlantic population to be 80 000–130 000bp. The Mediterranean population is 50 000–60 000bp (Massa & Lo Valvo 1986, Thibault 1993). The isolated and probably sedentary Cape Verde population is *c*10 000bp (Hazevoet 1994).

Most populations have been reasonably stable since *c*1975, except on the Selvagens where harvesting and vandalism have had significant effects (Mougin *et al* 1987). Permanent wardening has allowed some recovery (Mougin *et al* in press a & b).

Cory's Shearwater breeds mostly in burrows, crevices and caves. It is at risk mainly from rats *Rattus rattus* taking chicks, and from humans, through egg-collecting, building projects, tourism and poaching. The species displays high site tenacity, known cases of individuals changing colonies being very rare. Egg-laying is highly synchronized (between late May and the first week in June). Fledging occurs in September. Between October and February Atlantic birds migrate probably as far as waters off southern South America, and Mediterranean birds to waters off southern Africa (Mougin *et al* 1987), although some remain in the Mediterranean. North Atlantic observations are not uncommon.

Birds from different colonies differ in size, partly perhaps in relation to food availability and climate (Massa & Lo Valvo 1986, Randi *et al* 1989, Granadeiro 1993).

José P. Granadeiro (P) Bruno Massa (I) Mario Lo Valvo (I)

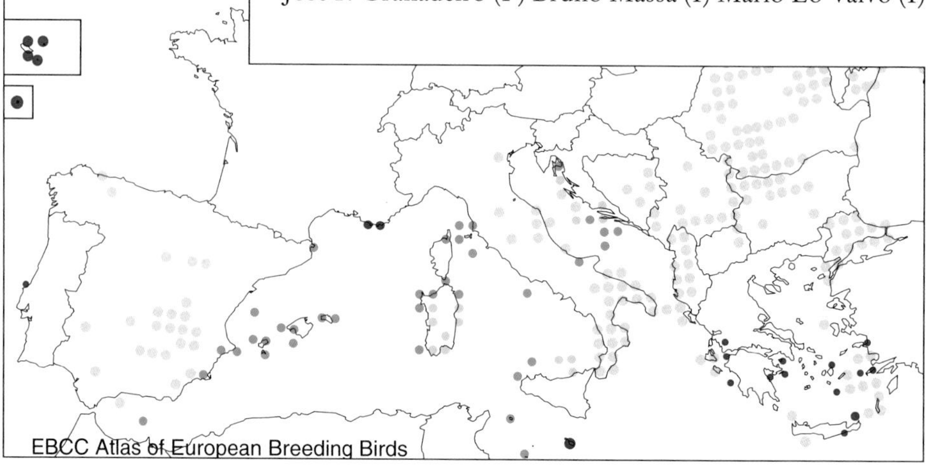

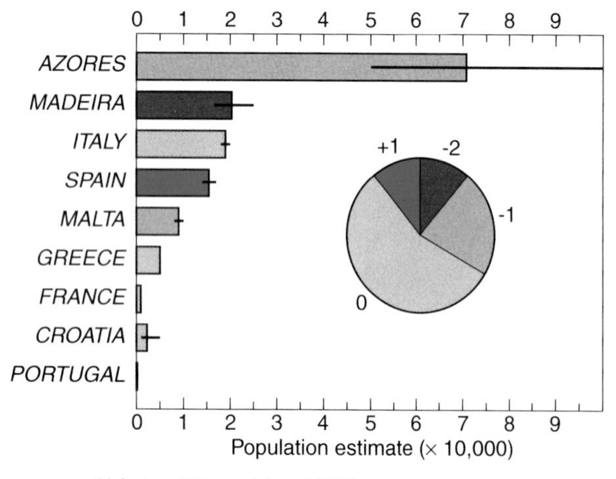

% in top 10 countries: 100.0
Total number of populated European countries: 9
Total European population 121,536–172,591 (142,722)

This species account is sponsored by

Instituto da Conservaçåo da Natureza, Lisboa, P.

Puffinus assimilis

Little Shearwater

CZ	Buřňák menší	I	Berta minore fosca
D	Kleiner Sturmtaucher	NL	Kleine Pijlstormvogel
E	Pardela Chica	P	Pardela-pequena
F	Puffin semblable	PL	Burzyk mały
FIN	Kääpiöliitäjä	R	Буревестник-крошка
G	Μικρός Μύχος	S	Dvärglira
H	Kis vészmadár		

SPEC Cat 3, Threat status V

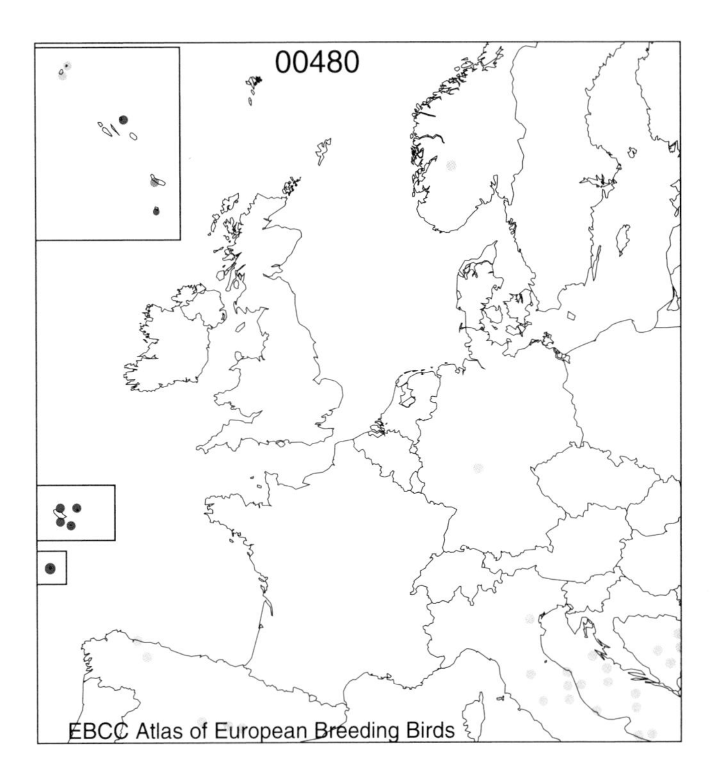

The Little Shearwater has a patchy distribution in the Atlantic, Pacific and Indian Oceans, the vast majority breeding in the Southern Hemisphere. Eight subspecies are known, the European population belonging to *P.a. baroli* which breeds in the Azores, Madeira (including the Selvagens), and Canary archipelagos.

In the Azores, breeding was first confirmed on São Miguel in 1953 (Bannerman & Bannerman 1964), then on Corvo (le Grand 1980) and recently on Santa Maria (Vila Islet) and Graciosa (Praia and Baixo Islets). The population of these three islets is estimated at 150bp (L. Monteiro *et al* unpubl). The most important breeding colony of *baroli* (estimated to be >2050bp; Oliveira & Moniz 1995) lies in the Selvagens. In other breeding areas in the Madeira archipelago numbers are relatively low, with the possible exception of the Desertas Islands where numbers may exceed 500bp.

The Little Shearwater is regarded as a comparatively sedentary species without long-distance migration (*BWP*). This view is supported by the recapture throughout the year during ringing at colonies (on the ground or in burrows) of many individual birds which have already bred successfully. In the Selvagens successful breeders were recorded at their nest site or its vicinity at least every 19 days during the non-breeding season (Oliveira & Moniz 1995). Despite being sedentary, these populations retain the Southern Hemisphere breeding cycle, nesting in the northern winter.

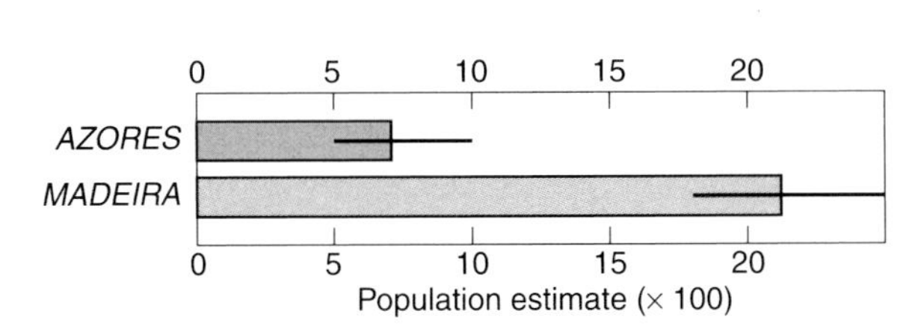

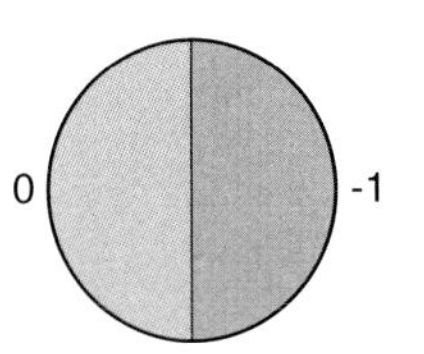

% in top 10 countries: 100.0
Total number of populated European countries: 2
Total European population 2446–3307 (2828)

The Little Shearwater nests either in burrows excavated in soil or underneath rocks. Inter-specific competition for these sites may be important in limiting population levels. In 1994 32% of breeding failures on Selvagem Grande were due to interference by the Cory's Shearwater *Calonectris diomedea*; on Vila Islet (Azores) other small procellariformes were recorded in 55% of the active nest sites in 1993 and 1994. Another factor limiting the Little Shearwater's breeding distribution (directly or indirectly) is the presence of rats *Rattus rattus*, goats *Capra* spp and rabbits *Oryctolagus cuniculus*.

Paulo Moniz (P) Luiz Monteiro (P)
Paulo Oliveira (P)

Puffinus puffinus (00461)

Manx Shearwater

CZ	Buřňák severní	I	Berta minore dell'Atlantico
D	Schwarzschnabel-Sturmtaucher	NL	Noordse Pijlstormvogel
E	Pardela Pichoneta	P	Pardela-sombria
F	Puffin des Anglais	PL	Burzyk północny
FIN	Pikkuliitäjä	R	Малый (обыкновенный) буревестник
G	Μύχος του Ατλαντικού	S	Mindre lira
H	Atlanti vészmadár		

SPEC Cat 2, Threat status L (P)

Puffinus yelkouan (00462)

Levantine Shearwater

CZ	Buřňák středomořský	NL	Yelkouanpijlstormvogel
D	Yelkouan-Sturmtaucher	P	Pardela do Mediterrâneo
E	Pardela Mediterránea	PL	Burzyk śródziemnomorski
F	Puffin de Méditerranée	R	Средиземноморский буревестник
FIN	Levantinliitäjä	S	Medelhavslira
G	Μύχος		
H	Bukdosó vészmadár		
I	Berta minore mediterranea		

SPEC Cat 4, Threat status S (includes P. mauretanicus)

Puffinus mauretanicus (00463)

Balearic Shearwater

CZ	Buřňák mauritánský	I	Berta minore delle Baleari
D	Balearen-Sturmtaucher	NL	Vale Pijlstormvogel
E	Pardela Balear	P	Pardela das Baleares
F	Puffin des Baléares	PL	Burzyk mauretański
FIN	Baleaarienliitäjä	R	Мавританский буревестник
G	Μύχος των Βαλεαρίδων	S	Medelhavslira
H	Baleári vészmadár		

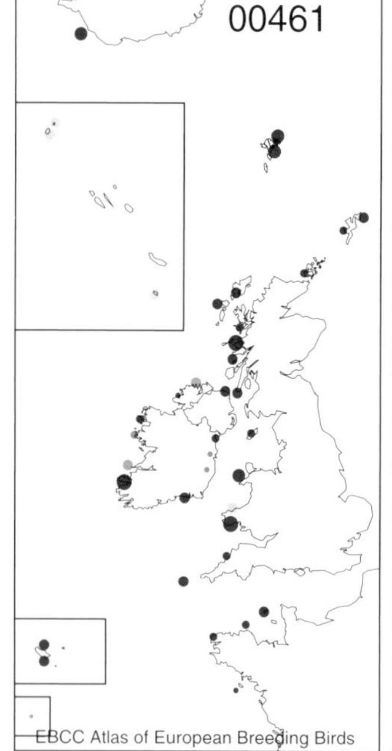

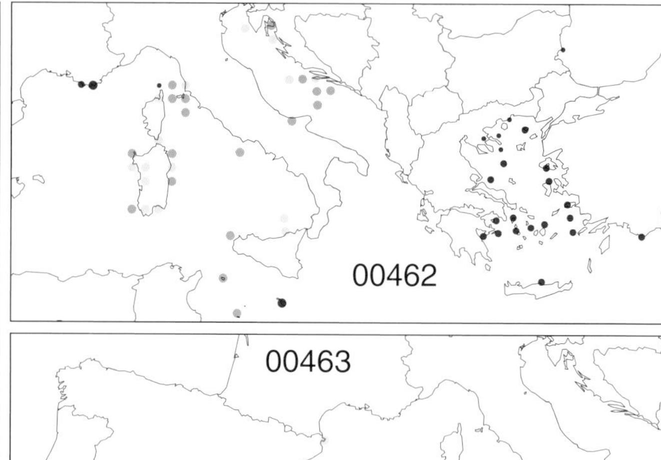

The taxonomy of the *Puffinus* shearwaters is complex and is constantly changing as it becomes better understood. At the time of the *Atlas* fieldwork the Manx Shearwater was considered to have three distinct subspecies: the nominate Manx Shearwater *P.p. puffinus* of the Atlantic coasts of Europe; the Balearic Shearwater *P.p. mauretanicus* breeding around the Balearic Islands in the western Mediterranean, *c*70% of the population being on Formentera; and the Levantine or Yelkouan Shearwater *P.p. yelkouan* of the eastern Mediterranean, from southern France and Sardinia to the Aegean Sea and the Black Sea coast of Bulgaria. The *Atlas* survey records therefore referred only to one species. When the species accounts were commissioned, the two Mediterranean forms had been separated as *P. yelkouan* (Bourne *et al* 1988). However, there is an increasing body of opinion that three full species should be recognised (*BWP, Concise Edition*, in press). The species account has been edited to reflect this. One of the authors of this species account (Pierre Yésou) disagrees with this conclusion, and believes that the balance of evidence strongly supports the retention of only two species, grouped as in Bourne *et al* (1988) but only on that point does the edited text not reflect his conclusions. Elsewhere in the world there are five closely related *Puffinus* shearwaters which some authors regard as subspecies of the Manx Shearwater and which others regard as distinct species.

These species are medium-sized shearwaters with generally black or dark brown plumage above and white below. Due to individual variation, many Balearic and Levantine Shearwaters are indistinguishable on plumage alone, having varying amounts of brown on the underparts and underwings. They are nocturnal at the nesting colonies, which are generally on small and often inaccessible islands. They breed in burrows or in caves, often in dense colonies, located between sea level and 700m asl. These factors make surveys and censuses of populations difficult. However, the *Atlas* survey coverage was fairly comprehensive. Only the breeding populations in S Iceland, Madeira and the W

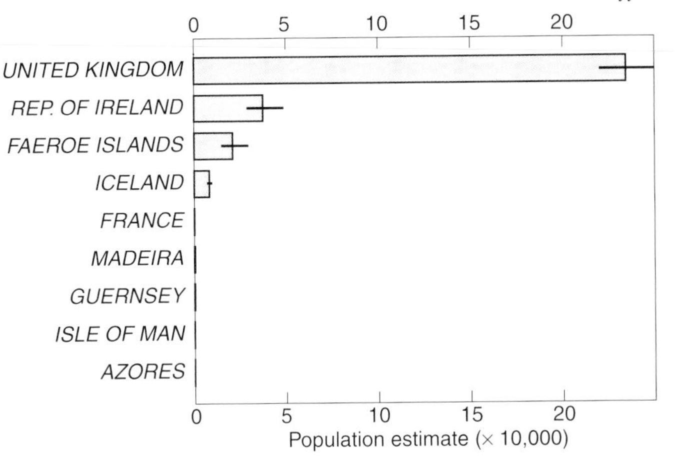

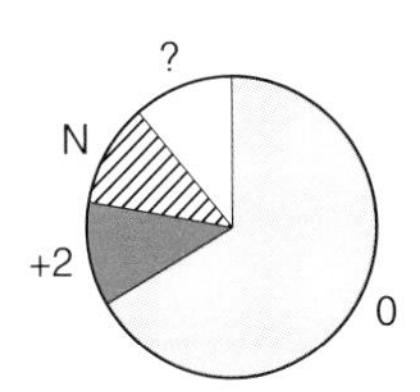

% in top 10 countries: 100.0
Total number of populated European countries: 9
Total European population 284,260–323,490 (302,342)

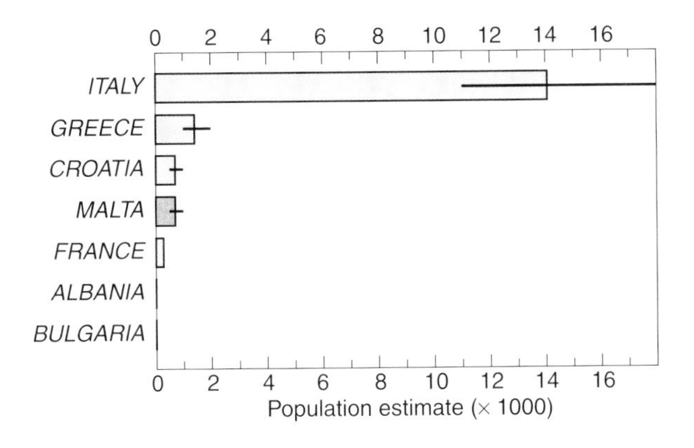

Puffinus yelkouan

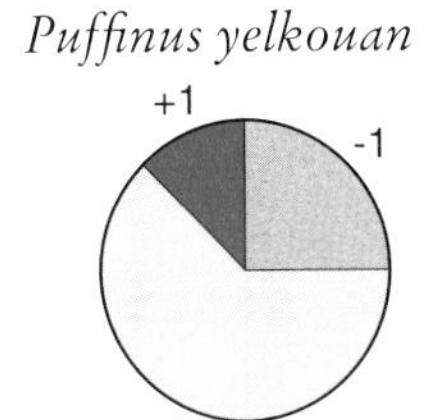

% in top 10 countries: 100.0
Total number of populated European countries: 7
Total European population 14,736–20,343 (17,179)
Turkish population 1000–30,000 (5477)

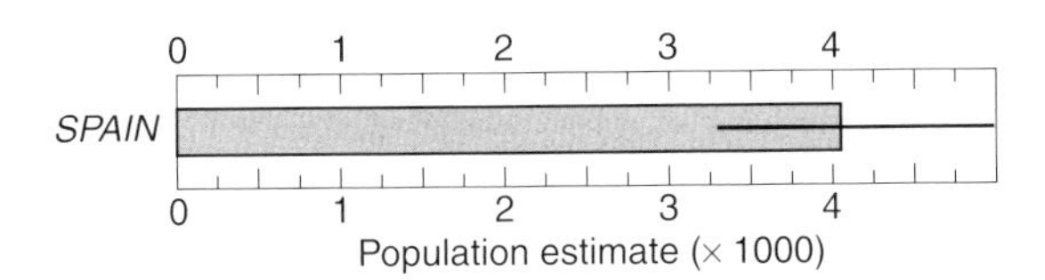

Puffinus mauretanicus

% in top 10 countries: 100.0
Total number of populated European countries: 1
Total European population 3300–5000 (4062)

Azores (currently, possible breeder; L. Monteiro, pers comm) were unrecorded.

During the breeding season all three species range widely over the surrounding seas, often up to several hundred kilometres from the colonies. After breeding, the Manx Shearwater moves SW across the Atlantic to spend the winter off NE and E South America. From June to October large numbers of the Balearic Shearwater population move W out of the Mediterranean to the Atlantic coast from Morocco to the North Sea, while the Levantine Shearwater population spreads throughout the Mediterranean and also into the Black Sea.

Because of censusing difficulties, it is impossible to determine population trends. However, it is thought there have been small decreases in the Balearics and Malta and a larger decrease in the Canary Islands. In Brittany, there have been declines in the small population up to 1985, but since then there has been a clear increase (Yésou 1994).

The distribution of these three species is restricted by the availability of islands with suitable nesting habitat, such as rock crevices (the commonest Mediterranean habitat) and burrows made by the rabbit *Oryctolagus cuniculus* or Puffin *Fratercula arctica* in earthen slopes or flat ground. Absence of ground predators such as brown rat *Rattus norvegicus* is important for breeding success, although some colonies are infested.

The European population of the Manx Shearwater may number 270 000–340 000bp, of which the majority breed in western Britain (200 000–250 000bp), especially on the islands of Rhum (Scotland), and Skokholm and Skomer (SW Wales) (Lloyd *et al* 1991). Ireland, the Faeroes and Iceland also have important colonies. The Levantine Shearwater's population may number 11 000–22 000bp for the W Mediterranean basin alone, where the Balearic Shearwater population is *c*3000–5000bp (Zotier *et al* 1992). The size of the Aegean colonies remains unknown. Outside the *Atlas*' area of coverage, there are small, recently established W Atlantic colonies of the Manx Shearwater in Newfoundland and in New England. There is also a small breeding population on the Canary Islands.

In the large Manx Shearwater colonies on Rhum, Skomer and Skokholm, densities of occupied burrows reach 460/ha (Brooke 1990). The largest known colonies in the Mediterranean are on Tavolara and Molara, Sardinia, totalling 6000–9000bp.

Oscar J. Merne (IRE) Pierre Yésou (F)

Hydrobates pelagicus

Storm Petrel

CZ Buřňáček malý
D Sturmschwalbe
E Paíño Europeo
F Océanite tempête
FIN Merikeiju
G Πετρίλος
H Viharfecske
I Uccello delle tempeste
NL Stormvogeltje
P Paínho-de-cauda-quadrada
PL Nawałnik burzowy
R Прямохвостая качурка
S Stormsvala

SPEC Cat 2, Threat status L (P)

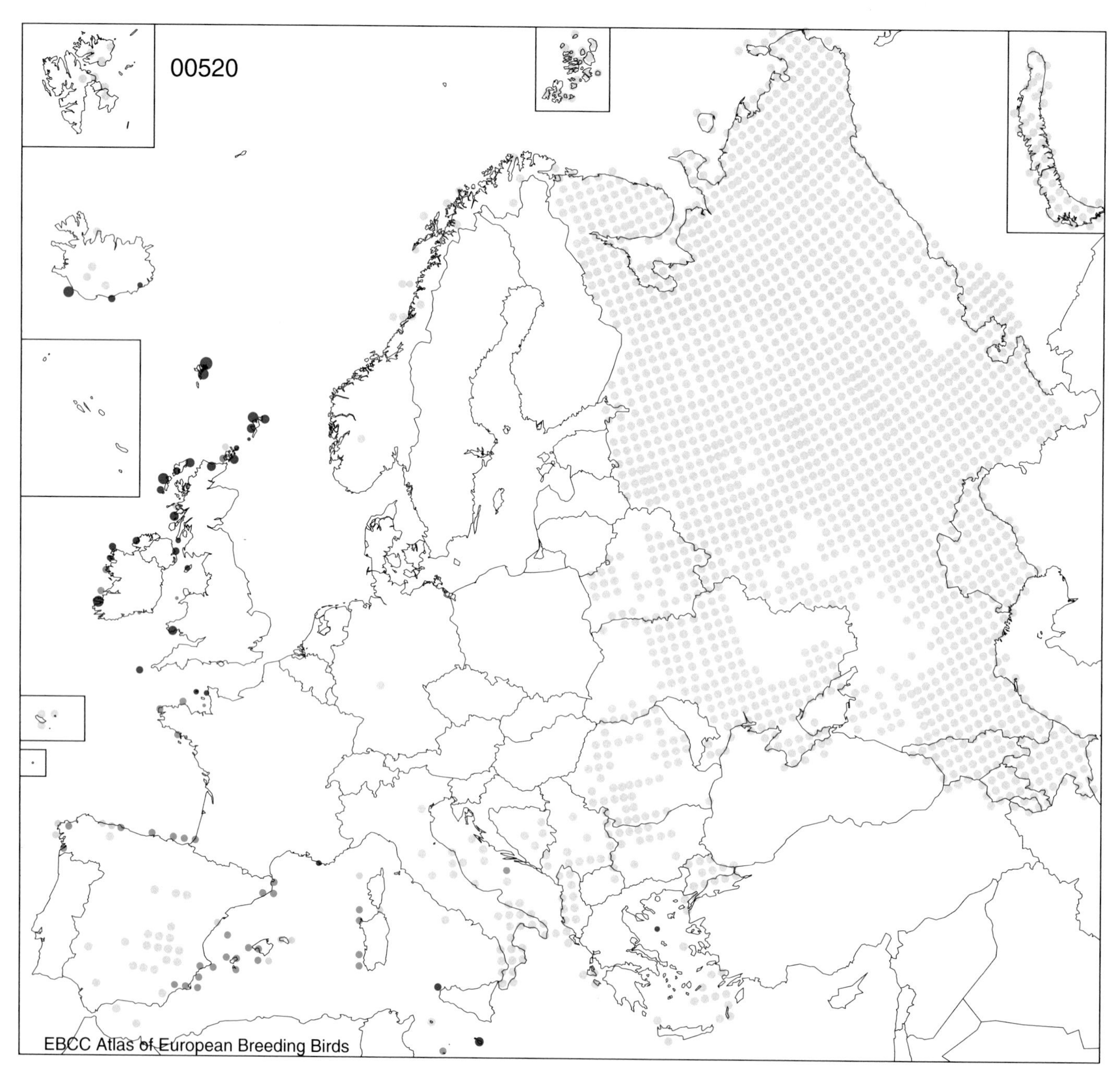

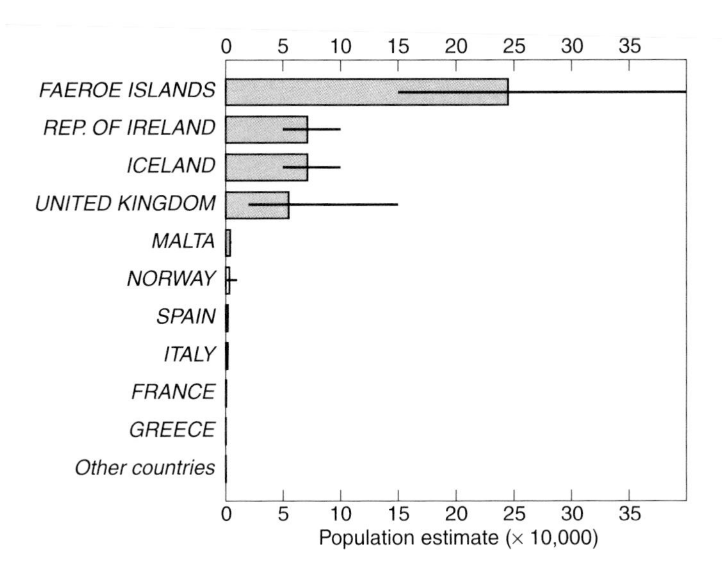

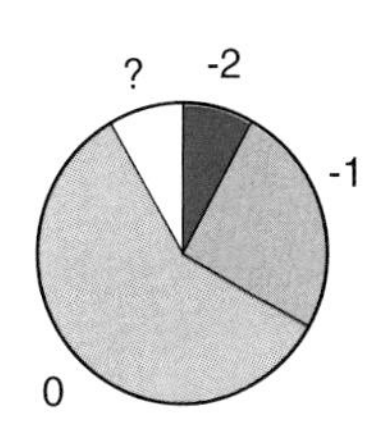

% in top 10 countries: 100.0
Total number of populated European countries: 12
Total European population 346,977–639,020 (452,278)

The Storm Petrel, whose name derives from its appearance to early mariners as an apparent harbinger of foul weather, is a pelagic species which has a scattered distribution along the rocky European coasts of the Atlantic Ocean and Mediterranean (mostly on inaccessible cliffs and islets).

It breeds in crevices, burrows of other species, walls, ruins, boulder and scree slopes, boulder beaches and inside moderately large caves. The entire world population breeds within the western Palearctic. Its distribution, falling almost entirely within the Atlas' area of coverage, includes a number of islets near Iceland, the Faeroes and Norway, numerous islets and seacliffs in Britain & Ireland, a few sites in NW France, parts of the Iberian Atlantic and Mediterranean coasts, the Canary Islands, Desertas, Madeira, the Salvagens and several W Mediterranean islands, especially Malta. There is also one breeding record from the Aegean Sea.

The Icelandic Westmann Islands population is estimated at 50 000–100 000bp and that of the Faeroes 150 000–400 000bp. The European population has been estimated as 280 000–800 000bp, of which only 15 000–20 000 are in the Mediterranean. Colonies in the Mediterranean vary from few bp to *c*5000–10 000 (Filfla, off Malta), but generally hold fewer than 100bp.

Because of the inaccessibility of many colonies and nest sites, the presence of large numbers of non-breeders and the species' nocturnal habits, any estimate of colony size will almost invariably be subject to a large degree of uncertainty, and therefore it is extremely difficult to ascertain trends in Storm Petrel populations. This constraint is applicable particularly to the large Atlantic colonies, but not so much so in the Mediterranean area, where the species has been decreasing since 1965, due mostly to human disturbance. Here, many previously inaccessible areas along coasts are now frequented by tourists and fishermen, or have been subjected to the boom in building construction. In crucial inshore areas, the mere presence of boats and dinghies during the breeding cycle is sufficient to discourage breeding. Rats *Rattus rattus*, often attracted by debris left by humans, are a major threat (Massa & Sultana 1991). Perhaps they may have already been the cause of decreasing numbers on several islands, or may even have forced the Storm Petrel to abandon island colonies. According to Lloyd *et al* (1991) all known Storm Petrel colonies in Britain & Ireland are on islands thought to be free of rats. One of the very few cases where there is reliable evidence of a decrease is that of the Isles of Scilly, but here an expanding gull colony is thought to have been responsible.

The Storm Petrel displays high site tenacity. Females are larger than males. Egg-laying is highly asynchronous, so that March sees the first arrivals at colonies, and October the latest fledging of young. Between October/November and January/February, Atlantic individuals migrate to winter as far S as waters off southern Africa, where they gradually replace all their flight feathers before returning to breed (Warham 1990). Equivalent data are lacking for Mediterranean birds, but apparently only a proportion migrates to the Atlantic Ocean, the others remaining quite sedentary, although some occur in the E Mediterranean and a few reach the Black Sea.

The Atlantic subspecies is *H.p. pelagicus*, whereas the larger *melitensis* is typical of the Mediterranean (Hémery & d'Elbée 1985, Catalisano *et al* 1988). However, minor biometrical differences have been recorded between individuals of different colonies (Furness & Baillie 1981). An unusual characteristic of the species is the incidence of seemingly deliberate aerial collisions during aerial chases at the nesting grounds, possibly a culmination of the aerial display (Warham 1990).

Bruno Massa (I) Oscar J Merne (IRE)

Pelagodroma marina

White-faced Storm-petrel

CZ	Buřňáček běločelý	H	Tengeri fecske
D	Weiβgesicht-Sturmschwalbe	I	Uccello delle tempeste fregata
E	Paíño Pechialbo	NL	Bont Stormvogeltje
F	Océanite frégate	P	Páinho-de-ventre-branco
FIN	Ulappakeiju	PL	Nawałnik białobrewy
G	Ασπρομέτωπος Κυματοβάτης	R	Морская качурка
		S	Fregattstormsvala

SPEC Cat 3, Threat status L

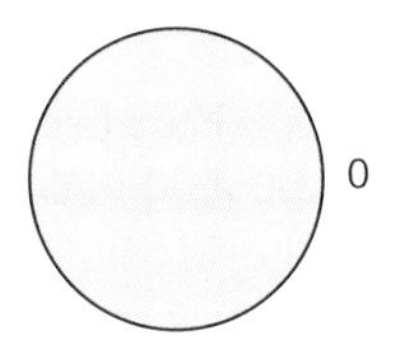

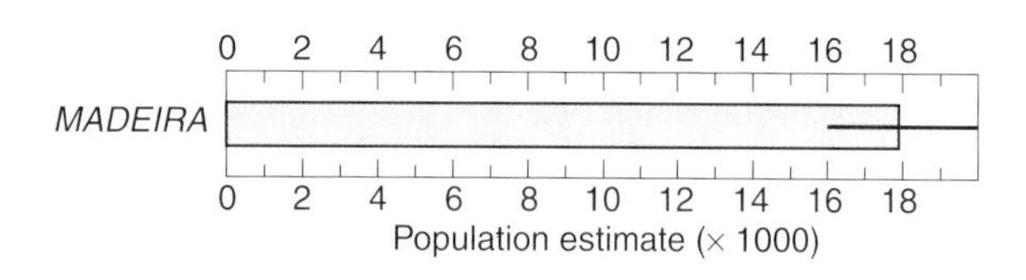

% in top 10 countries: 100.0
Total number of populated European countries: 1
Total European population 16,000–20,000 (17,889)

Within Europe the subspecies *P.m. hypoleuca* of the White-faced Storm-petrel breeds in large numbers only on the Selvagens (Zino & Biscoito 1994). Recently a small population of *c*10bp was discovered in the Canary Islands (Martín *et al* 1989), outside the Atlas coverage area. Within Macaronesia, but again outside the Atlas coverage area, there is another large population on the Cape Verde Islands, but this is comprised of the subspecies *eadesi*. The White-faced Storm-petrel is migratory and a winter breeder, returning to the Selvagens in December and remaining in the area until breeding is complete in July (Jouanin & Roux 1965, Jensen 1981, Mougin 1988). Its migration destination is not known.

A colonial breeder, it nests in sandy scrub terrain. Within the Selvagens there are two main breeding areas: on Selvagem Grande it nests mostly on Chão dos Caramujos and in the area round Pico dos Tornozelos and on Selvagem Pequena and Ilbeu de Fora it nests in all areas (Zino & Biscoito 1994). As a consequence of the permanent wardening of Selvagem Pequena in recent years it has been possible to reach more accurate estimates of breeding numbers. A recent study estimates at least 30 000bp on Selvagem Pequena. The present estimate for Selvagem Grande is in the region of 10 000bp but that may be an underestimate. The population is thought to be stable.

The breeding areas lie within a strict nature reserve and so the habitat is well protected. Predation by the Yellow-legged Gull *Larus cachinnans* is a problem because its population on the islands has increased dramatically. To a lesser extent the Short-eared Owl *Asio flammeus* is known to take petrels in some numbers, but probably not to a significant degree (Zino & Biscoito 1994).

Manuel J Biscoito (P) Francis Zino (P)

Oceanodroma leucorhoa

Leach's Storm-petrel

CZ	Buřňáček bělavý	I	Uccello delle tempeste codaforcuta
D	Wellenläufer	NL	Vaal Stormvogeltje
E	Paíño Boreal	P	Paínho-de-cauda-forcada
F	Océanite culblanc	PL	Nawałnik duży
FIN	Myrskykeiju	R	Северная качурка
G	Κυματοβάτης	S	Klykstjärtad stormsvala
H	Villás viharfecske		

SPEC Cat 3, Threat status L (P)

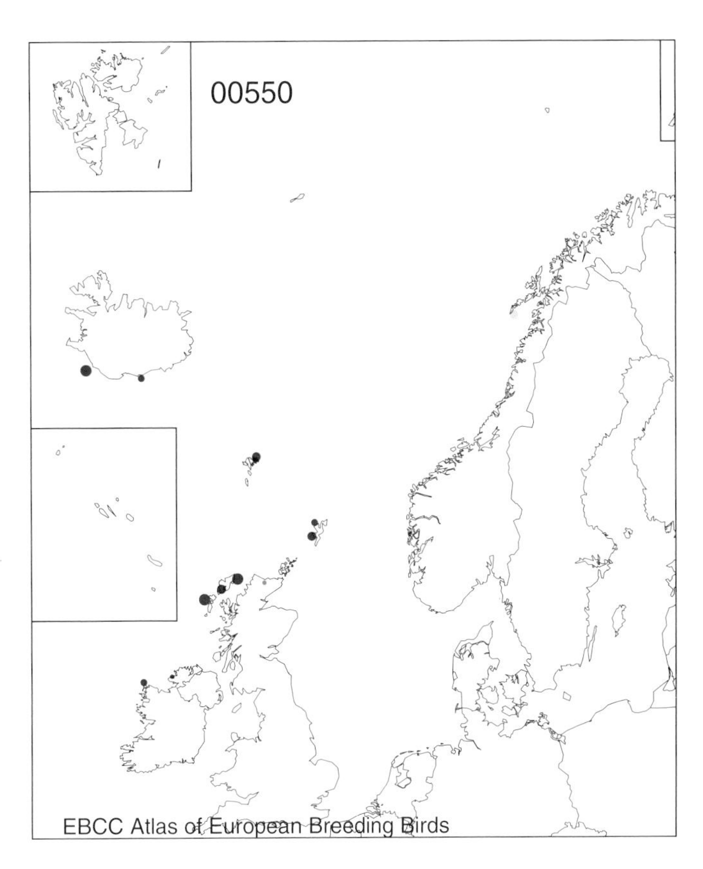

Leach's Storm-petrel breeds on oceanic islands both in the N Atlantic and N Pacific. In Europe, it has probably a more oceanic distribution than any other species, and breeds only on Atlantic islands comparatively near the continental shelf break. Colonies have been found from the extreme N of Norway to as far S as NW Ireland. The species' breeding distribution seems likely to be related to its feeding distribution; by day it is found mostly over or beyond the continental shelf edge (Webb *et al* 1990). It is difficult to census the species because it nests in burrows and crevices mostly on islands free of mammalian predators, and it appears on the surface only at night. The lack of mammalian predators appears to be crucial. No colonies are known from islands with rats *Rattus* spp, while on Foula (Shetland), where there are cats present, populations appear to be relict.

New colonies have been found in recent years, but it is impossible to tell if this is due to colonization, or to discovery of long-established sites (Fowler 1982). At the southern edge of its range in Ireland, special attempts have been made in the past to examine all likely islands (Ruttledge 1966), but no colonies were found. However, breeding has since been proved at the one island where it had been suspected. It seems likely that further colonies await discovery within or perhaps outside the current European range, perhaps especially in the Faeroes and Iceland.

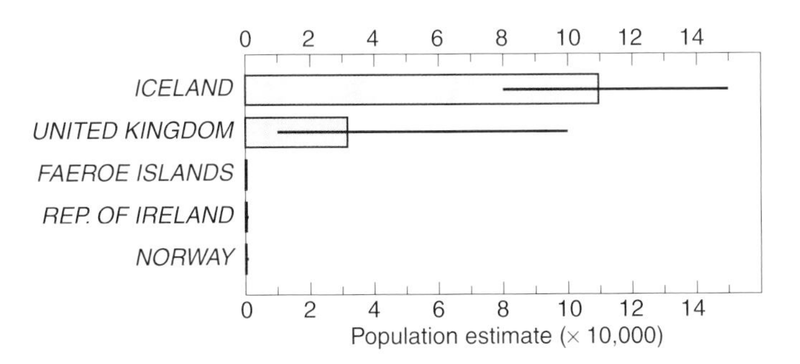

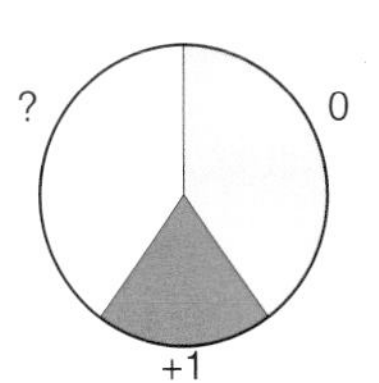

% in top 10 countries: 100.0
Total number of populated European countries: 5
Total European population 105,775–221,843 (142,389)

The difficulty of counting breeding pairs means that only orders of magnitude can be guessed at for most colonies. The largest numbers in Europe are found off Britain and off Iceland. Estimates of abundance have varied by a factor of 80 for Iceland (P.G.H. Evans (1984) with present estimates). Populations in Norway, Ireland and the Faeroes are very small. Several guesses of the size of the main breeding colony in Britain, on the St Kilda group, have been made. Most recently, Tasker *et al* (1988) found densities of between four and eight burrows in 100m² of short-cropped turf searched on Boreray. If this density be extrapolated to the remainder of the island, then between 3200 and 6400 burrows would be present.

Leach's Storm-petrel migrates southwards for the winter to the tropics and to waters off South Africa. The species is best known to most birdwatchers in Europe during autumnal migration, when during westerly gales this strongly oceanic bird is blown close to land, and occasionally inshore to occur on inland waters.

Mark L Tasker (GB)

Oceanodroma castro

Madeiran Storm-petrel

CZ	Buřňáček madeirský	I	Uccello delle tempeste di Madera
D	Madeirawellenläufer	NL	Madeirastormvogeltje
E	Paíño de Madeira	P	Paínho da Madeira
F	Océanite de Castro	PL	Nawałnik maderski
FIN	Madeirankeiju	R	Мадейрская качурка
G	Κυματοβάτης της Μαδέρας	S	Oceanlöpare
H	Madeirai viharfecske		

SPEC Cat 3, Threat status V

The small, pelagic Madeiran Storm-petrel breeds in the tropical and temperate sectors of the Atlantic and Pacific. Most of the Atlantic population is believed to be concentrated in the Macaronesian archipelagos, mainly in the Desertas and the Selvagens (Madeira), and in Graciosa and Santa Maria (Azores), representing >80% of the European population. Smaller colonies exist on an islet off Tenerife (Canary Islands) (Martín *et al* 1984) and on the Farilhões (off Portugal) (Teixeira & Moore 1983).

The species' clear preference for remote islets as nesting sites, its secretive, hole-nesting habits and exclusively nocturnal behaviour explain the generally imprecise understanding of its numbers and distribution. Few data on population trends are available. Probably most colonies are stable although a slight decline is suggested for the Azores (L. Monteiro, pers comm). On the Farilhões the population was tentatively estimated at 50bp in 1981 (Teixeira 1983) and although recent work suggests 200–400bp (J.P. Granadeiro unpubl), the difference probably reflects better-quality data rather than a real increase.

The Madeiran Storm-petrel nests in small rock crevices, holes in loose stone walls, caverns and burrows in the soil. Nests are sometimes shared with similar-sized species, such as Bulwer's Petrel *Bulweria bulwerii* and White-faced Storm-petrel *Pelagodroma marina*, suggesting the existence of interspecific competition at some breeding sites.

The species' distribution is limited by mammalian predators (such as rats *Rattus* spp and mustelids) and possibly by the rapidly increasing numbers of the Yellow-legged Gull *Larus cachinnans*. In the Azores, all main islands and some islets hold large rat populations, the Madeiran Storm-petrel occurring only in rat-free areas. On Berlenga Island, where the Black Rat *Rattus rattus* is abundant, birds probably prospecting from the nearby Farilhões (5km away) are often heard calling in flight, but nests have not been found, although recently remains have.

Analysis of Azores breeding data suggests the existence of two distinct populations on Graciosa (Azores) breeding annually, but out of phase by 4–5 months and overlapping in colony attendance in August–early September (L. Monteiro, pers comm), a circumstance also described for the Desertas and Selvagens (Zino & Biscoito 1994). Furthermore, the morphological differences between these two 'populations' may signify subspecific status.

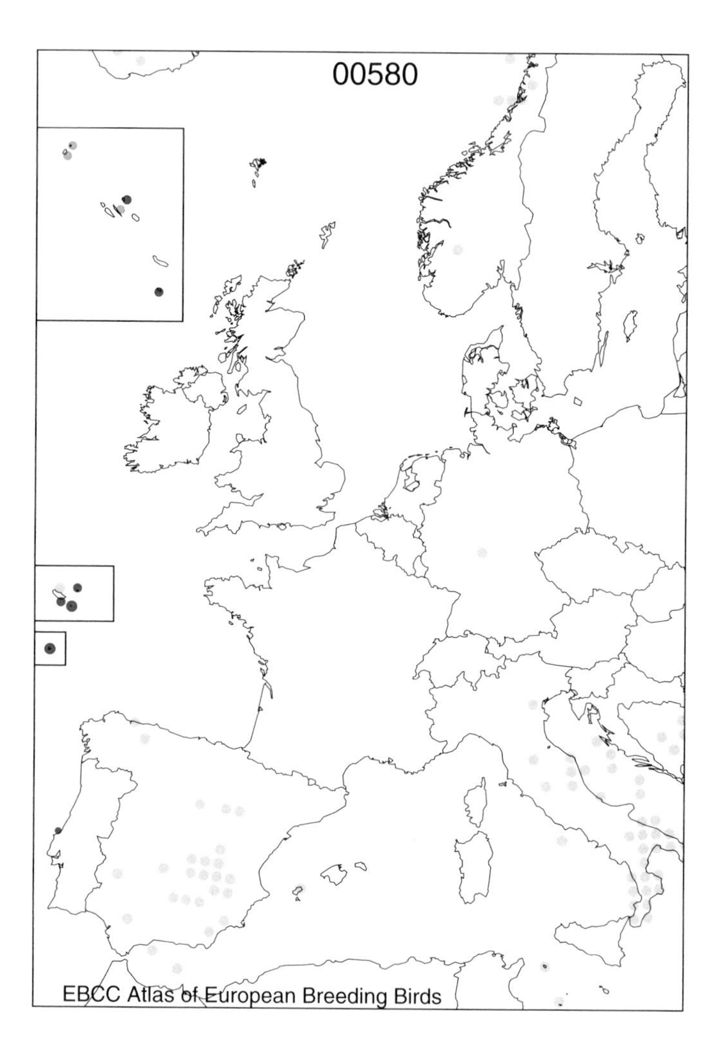

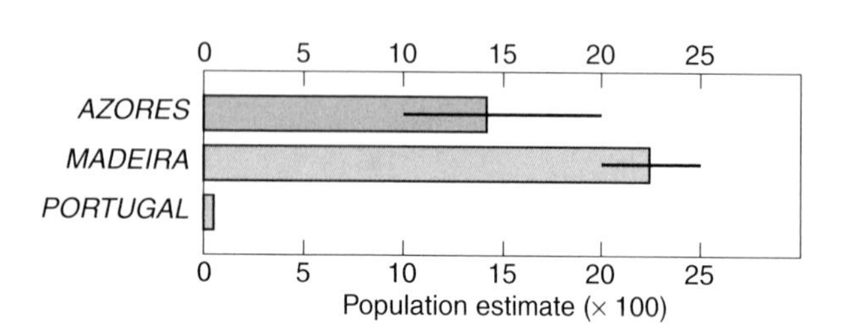

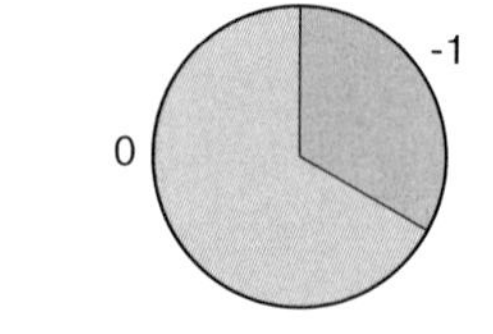

% in top 10 countries: 100.0
Total number of populated European countries: 3
Total European population 3224–4343 (3700)

José P Granadeiro (P) Antonio P Teixeira (P)

Phaethon aethereus

Red-billed Tropicbird

CZ Faeton červenozobý
D Rotschnabel-Tropikvogel
E Rabijunco Etéreo
F Phaéton à bec rouge
FIN Suomujouhipyrstö
G Ερυθρόρραμφος Φαέθων
H Piroscsõrû trópusi-madár
I Fetonte
NL Roodsnavelkeerkringvogel
P Rabo-de-palha
PL Faeton białosterny
R Красноклювый фаэтон
S Rödnäbbad tropikfågel

Criteria not applied

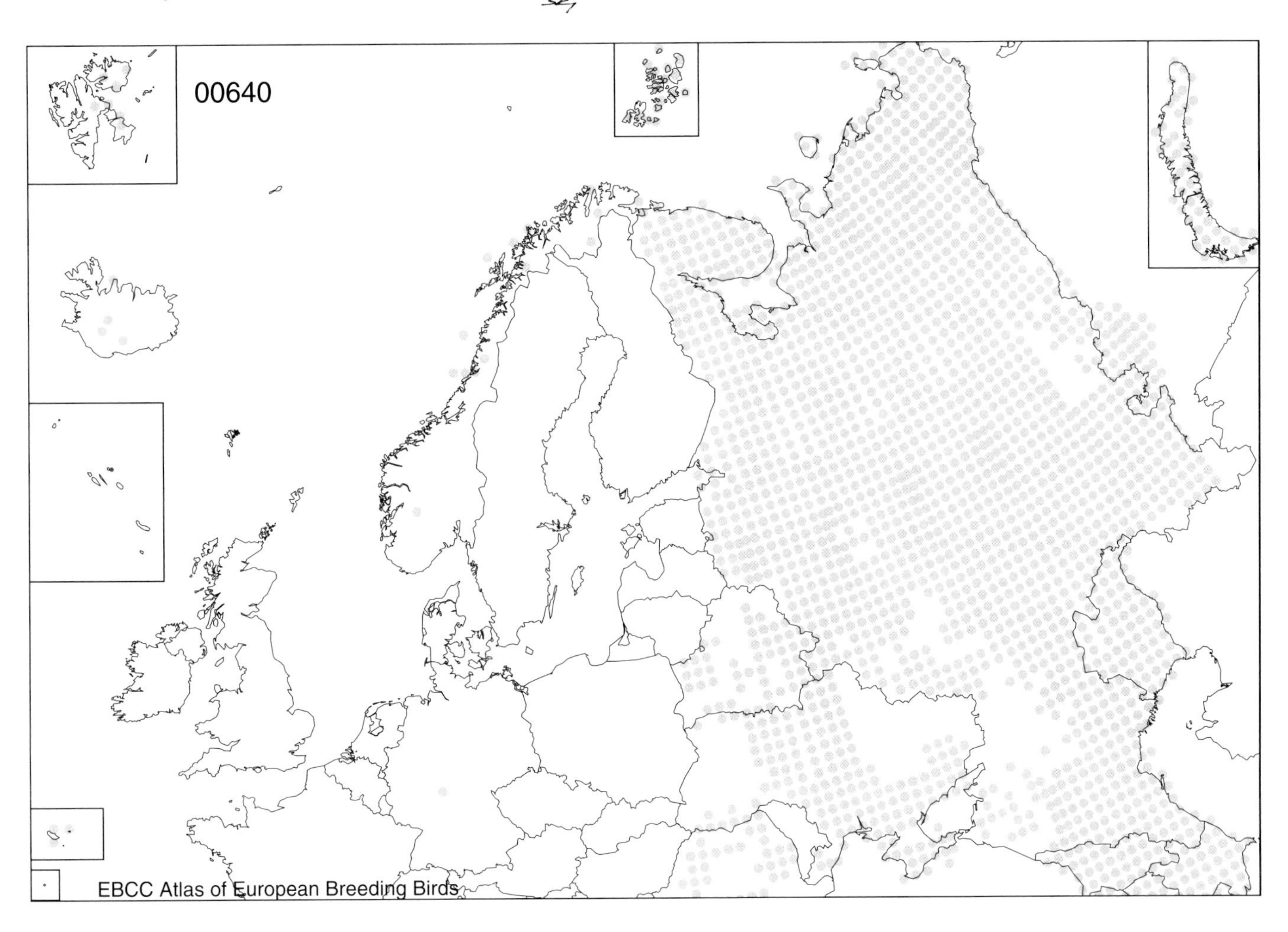

The Red-billed Tropicbird, a medium-sized tern-like seabird, lives for the most part a pelagic existence. It is widely distributed in tropical and subtropical waters of the eastern Pacific, northern Indian Ocean, Caribbean and Atlantic. In the western hemisphere, it frequents the vicinity of Ascension Island, St Helena, Fernando Noronha (the nominate subspecies *P.a. aethereus*), Cape Verde, Senegal and the West Indies. In the Indian Ocean (*indicus*) its core distribution is associated with breeding stations in the Red Sea, Arabian Gulf and Arabian Sea.

In 1993, a pair attempted to breed (egg laid but disappeared before hatching) on the rocky Ilheu de Baixo, off Graciosa in the C group of the Azores archipelago, the first European breeding record. The measurements of the egg and incubating bird fall within the range for the subspecies *mesonauta* (Furness & Monteiro 1995) which occurs from the eastern Pacific through the Caribbean to the Cape Verde Islands and Senegal.

European records of vagrants are scanty, consistent with the evidence that the species is not migratory, rarely straying outside its normal tropical range. However, since the 1980s apparently there has been an unusually large number of sightings N of its normal range around Cape Verde and Senegal. This increase simply may reflect better observer coverage. Nevertheless, the Azores birds could just as easily have been of West Indies provenance (Furness & Monteiro 1995).

Numbers on Cape Verde had apparently undergone an alarming decline (Bannerman & Bannerman 1968) to under 1000 birds by the late 1960s (de Naurois 1969). Hole-nesting in cliffs militates against accurate census work and on Cape Verde there has been no recent population estimate. However, the species still apparently breeds on São Tiago, probably no more than 25bp remain on Razo, and small populations may also exist on Boa Vista, Brava and Cima (Hazevoet & Haafkens 1989).

Euan Dunn (GB)

Morus bassanus

Gannet

CZ	Terej bílý	**I**	Sula
D	Baßtölpel	**NL**	Jan van Gent
E	Alcatraz Atlántico	**P**	Ganso-patola-comum
F	Fou de Bassan	**PL**	Głuptak
FIN	Suula	**R**	Олуша (Северная олуша)
G	Σούλα	**S**	Havssula
H	Szula		

SPEC Cat 2, Threat status L

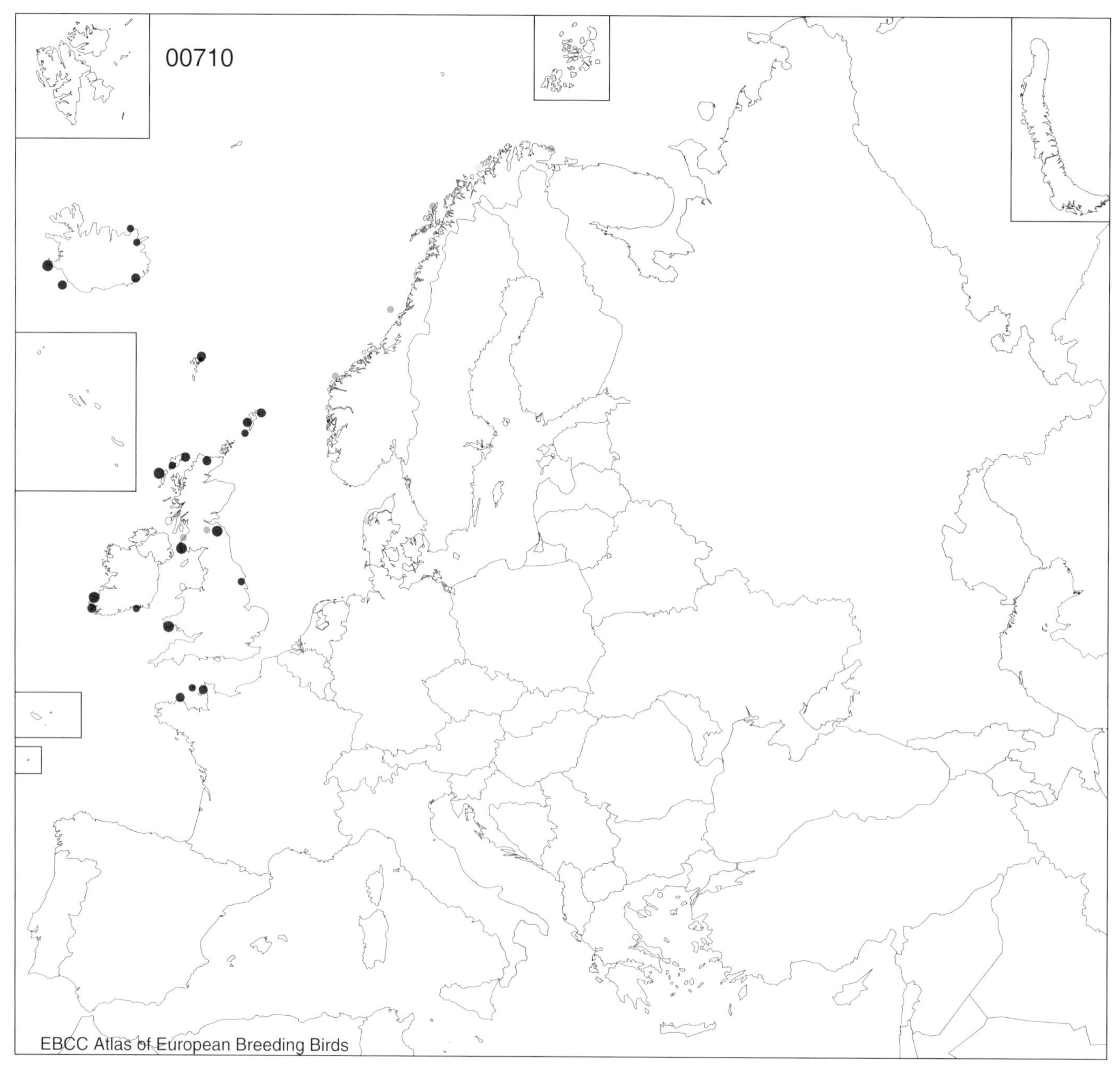

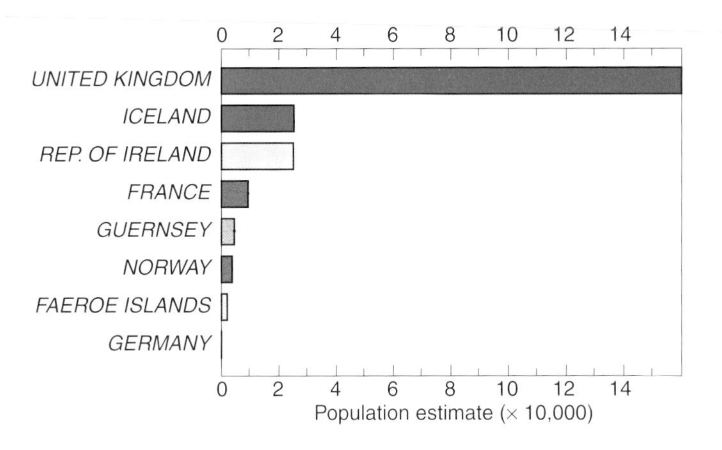

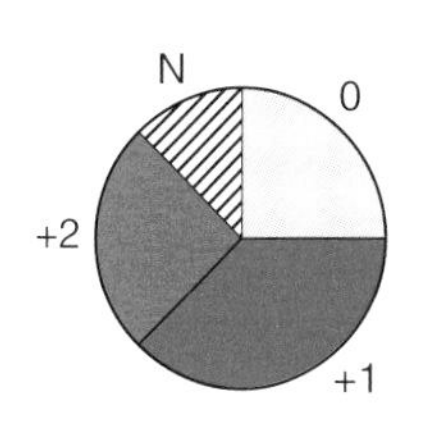

% in top 10 countries: 100.0
Total number of populated European countries: 8
Total European population 228,997–230,372 (229,656)

The Gannet, a large strikingly white seabird, spends most of its life at sea and comes ashore only during the breeding season. It is restricted mainly to the temperate waters of the North Atlantic and adjoining seas. On the eastern seaboard its breeding range extends from Norway and Iceland through Britain & Ireland and S to northern France. On the western side breeding is confined to the Gulf of St Lawrence and Newfoundland, Canada. The E and W Atlantic populations appear to be discrete.

The Gannet is highly colonial. Most of the long-established colonies are on isolated stacks or small, uninhabitated offshore islands, but some of the recently founded colonies are on inaccessible cliffs on the mainland, inhabited islands, or low rocky skerries. These rather specialized nesting requirements and the need to be close to favourable feeding areas contribute to the species' patchy breeding distribution along the coast of Europe and to the concentration of the population in NW Great Britain.

Around 1900 there were 13 European gannetries, mostly located in Britain & Ireland (Gurney 1913). Two of these, Grimsey in Iceland and Lundy in SW Britain no longer exist. The other 11 have increased in size. Many new colonies have been established. In 1988 there were 36 extant gannetries (Lloyd *et al* 1991).

In the late 1930s the Gannet's breeding range expanded south with new colonies in the Channel Islands (2) and France (1). Archaeological evidence suggests that Gannets may have bred in Norway in prehistoric times, but the first modern gannetry was not established there until 1946. Since then, several other colonies have been formed including Syltefjordstauran, the most northerly, near the Russian border (71°N). Colonies have also proliferated in Britain & Ireland during the 1970s and 1980s, including three sites mapped at the time of the surveys: Troup Head, NE Scotland; Clare Island, NW Ireland; and Ireland's Eye, Co. Dublin (Rockall is included in NW Hebrides). The most recent range expansion has been the establishment of a colony at Helgoland, Germany, in 1991.

Throughout this century the number of Gannets breeding in Europe has increased by about 3% per annum (Nelson 1978). This increase continues up to the present although during the 1970s and 1980s the rate slowed in some of the large or long-established colonies in Britain & Ireland and the Faeroes. In contrast, numbers at many of the newer gannetries, particularly those in Great Britain and Norway, increased rapidly (Wanless 1987). This sustained period of good fortune for the Gannet has been attributed to a marked reduction in the level of human persecution. Although most colonies are now protected, some young are still taken legally in the Faeroes, Iceland and at one British colony (Sula Sgeir).

At present *c*160 000 bp (70% of the European population) breed in Great Britain. This region has the world's largest (Atlantic) gannetry on St Kilda, Western Isles (an estimated 50 050 sites, 31% of the British total and 22% of the European total). Great Britain has three other gannetries holding over 20 000 sites. Ireland and Iceland both have *c*25 000bp (11% of the European total) while France, the Channel Islands, Norway and the Faeroes each contribute less than 4%.

The Gannet's distribution away from the colonies is relatively well known. Breeding birds are partial migrants, remaining near their colonies during winter or dispersing south to the Bay of Biscay and into the Mediterranean. Immatures range much further, reaching as far S as West Africa and N to SE Greenland and the seas around Jan Mayen and Bear Island.

Sarah Wanless (GB)

This species account is sponsored by Brian Hillcoat, Neuss, D.

Pelecanus onocrotalus

White Pelican

CZ	Pelikán bílý	**I**	Pellicano
D	Rosapelikan	**NL**	Witte Pelikaan
E	Pelícano Común	**P**	Pelicano-vulgar
F	Pélican blanc	**PL**	Pelikan różowy
FIN	Pelikaani	**R**	Розовый пеликан
G	Ροδοπελεκάνος	**S**	Vit pelikan
H	Rózsás gödény		

SPEC Cat 3, Threat status R

The White Pelican is distributed in widely scattered fashion in E Europe, Asia and Africa. Apart from small enclaves in India and Indochina, the Asian population is largely confined to C Asia. Crivelli & Schreiber (1984) distinguished two geographically separate populations, one in Europe and Asia and the other in Africa, but there are no subspecies. Half the Palearctic population breeds in Europe (Crivelli 1994). Breeding colonies can still be found in Greece (Lake Mikri Prespa), in Romania (Danube Delta) and in the Russian Federation (Lakes Manych and Manych-Gudilo). In the 19th century regular breeding occurred in Hungary, Bulgaria, Ukraine and former Yugoslavia, where drainage work and disturbance are probably the causes of their disappearance.

The E European and C Asian populations are migratory. The C Asian population winters in the Indus Delta, but the wintering grounds of the European population remain unknown (Crivelli *et al* 1991a).

The White Pelican's European breeding sites are nowadays confined to the remotest wetlands, colonies normally being located on rocky or bare-earth islands in lakes (Manych-Gudilo), or on the ground in reedbeds in deltas (Danube). More rarely, colonies occur at reservoirs. Only total isolation from the mainland offers protection from mammalian predators.

The largest European White Pelican colony (3500bp) is in the Danube Delta. Since 1989, the numbers at Lakes Manych and Manych-Gudilo have varied between 200 and 300bp (Linkov 1994). In Greece, the Mikri Prespa Lake breeding colony remains small, holding between 40 and 100bp since 1984 (A. Crivelli & G. Catsadorakis, pers obs). Because there are so few breeding colonies in Europe the species' survival will remain at risk.

Alain Crivelli (F)

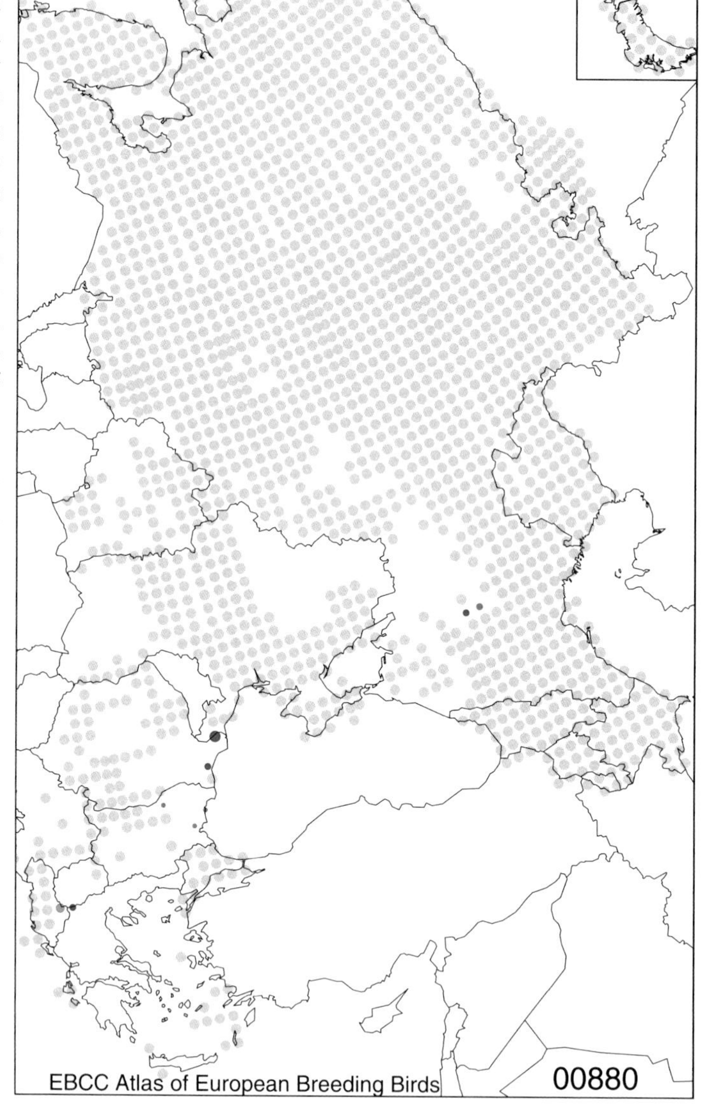

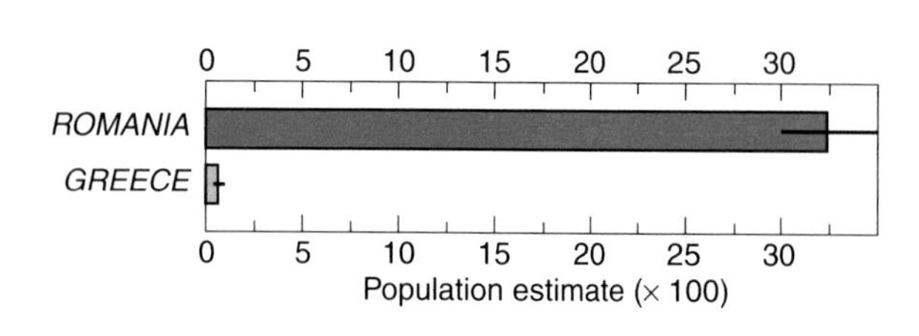

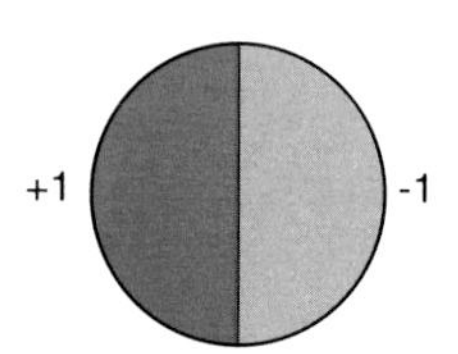

% in top 10 countries: 100.0
Total number of populated European countries: 2
Total European population 3062–3566 (3304)
Russian population 100–350 (187)
Turkish population 250–400 (316)

Pelecanus crispus

Dalmatian Pelican

CZ	Pelikán kadeřavý	I	Pellicano riccio
D	Krauskopfpelikan	NL	Kroeskoppelikaan
E	Pelícano Ceñudo	P	Pelicano-crespo
F	Pélican frisé	PL	Pelikan kędzierzawy
FIN	Kiharapelikaani	R	Кудрявый пеликан
G	Αργυροπελεκάνος	S	Krushuvad pelikan
H	Borzas gödény		

SPEC Cat 1, Threat status V

The Dalmatian Pelican is widely but patchily distributed in the Palearctic from Montenegro to Mongolia (Crivelli *et al* 1991b). A quarter of the world population (estimated at 3215–4280bp; Crivelli 1994), breeds in Europe from Montenegro to Greece to the Russian Federation. Since the 19th century, breeding colonies in Europe have vanished from Hungary (Tisza River), the former Yugoslavia (Vojvodina marshes), Greece (Evros Delta), Romania (Calafat floodplain), Ukraine (Dnestr Delta) and the Russian Federation (Azov Sea).

The Dalmatian Pelican breeds on inland and coastal wetlands from sea level up to 850m asl, but it is dependent on the availability of fish. It breeds on the ground, on floating islands in reedbeds or on halophytic vegetation-covered earthen islands totally isolated from mammalian predators on the mainland.

The European population is well-monitored and can be considered as stable. However, the breeding colonies may be expanding (Greece and Russian Federation) or shrinking (Albania) locally. In Romania, after a decline from the 1960s to the 1980s, an increase is now under way, more than 100bp being present in the Danube Delta (Botond Kiss, pers comm). In Montenegro and Bulgaria the population is stable (Lake Skadar 10–20bp, Lake Srebarna 70–90bp). In Albania however, only one breeding colony remains: 40–70bp at Karavasta lagoon (A. Crivelli, N. Peja, pers obs). Breeding colonies in Greece (Amvrakikos lagoons and Lake Mikri Prespa) are increasing. In Ukraine, the Dalmatian Pelican has started to breed again (Lysenko 1994). In the Russian Federation the numbers have also increased. However, the extent of remaining suitable habitats limits the recovery. It remains a species vulnerable to decline and extinction.

The Dalmatian Pelican is a dispersive species wintering mainly in Albania, Greece, Turkey, Iran, Iraq and along the western coast of the Caspian Sea as well as in India and in China. During mild winters flocks of up to 200 individuals also occur in Bulgaria.

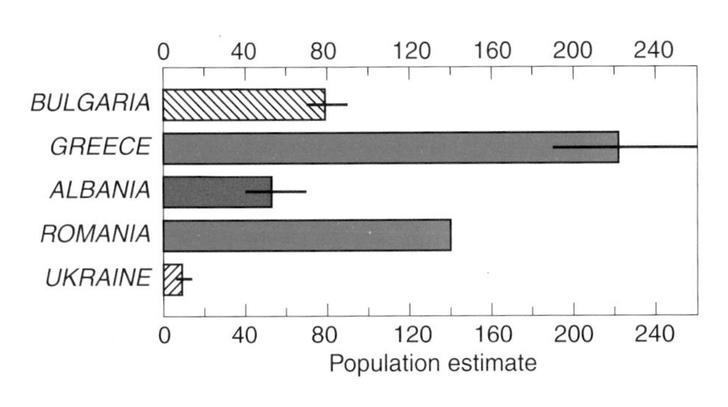

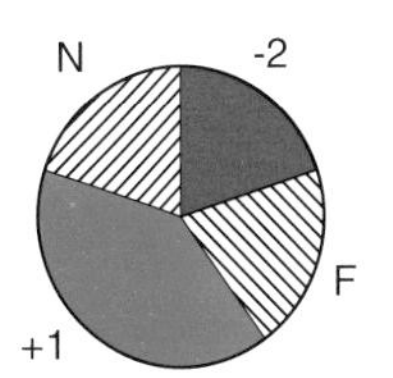

% in top 10 countries: 100.0
Total number of populated European countries: 5
Total European population 468–547 (504)
Russian population 400–450 (424)
Turkish population 100–150 (122)

Alain Crivelli (F) Tanu Michev (BUL)

Phalacrocorax carbo Cormorant

CZ	Kormorán velký	**I**	Marangone
D	Kormoran	**NL**	Aalscholver
E	Cormorán Grande	**P**	Corvo-marinho-de-faces-brancas
F	Grand Cormoran	**PL**	Kormoran
FIN	Merimetso	**R**	Большой баклан
G	Κορμοράνος	**S**	Storskarv
H	Kárókatona		

Non-SPEC, Threat status S

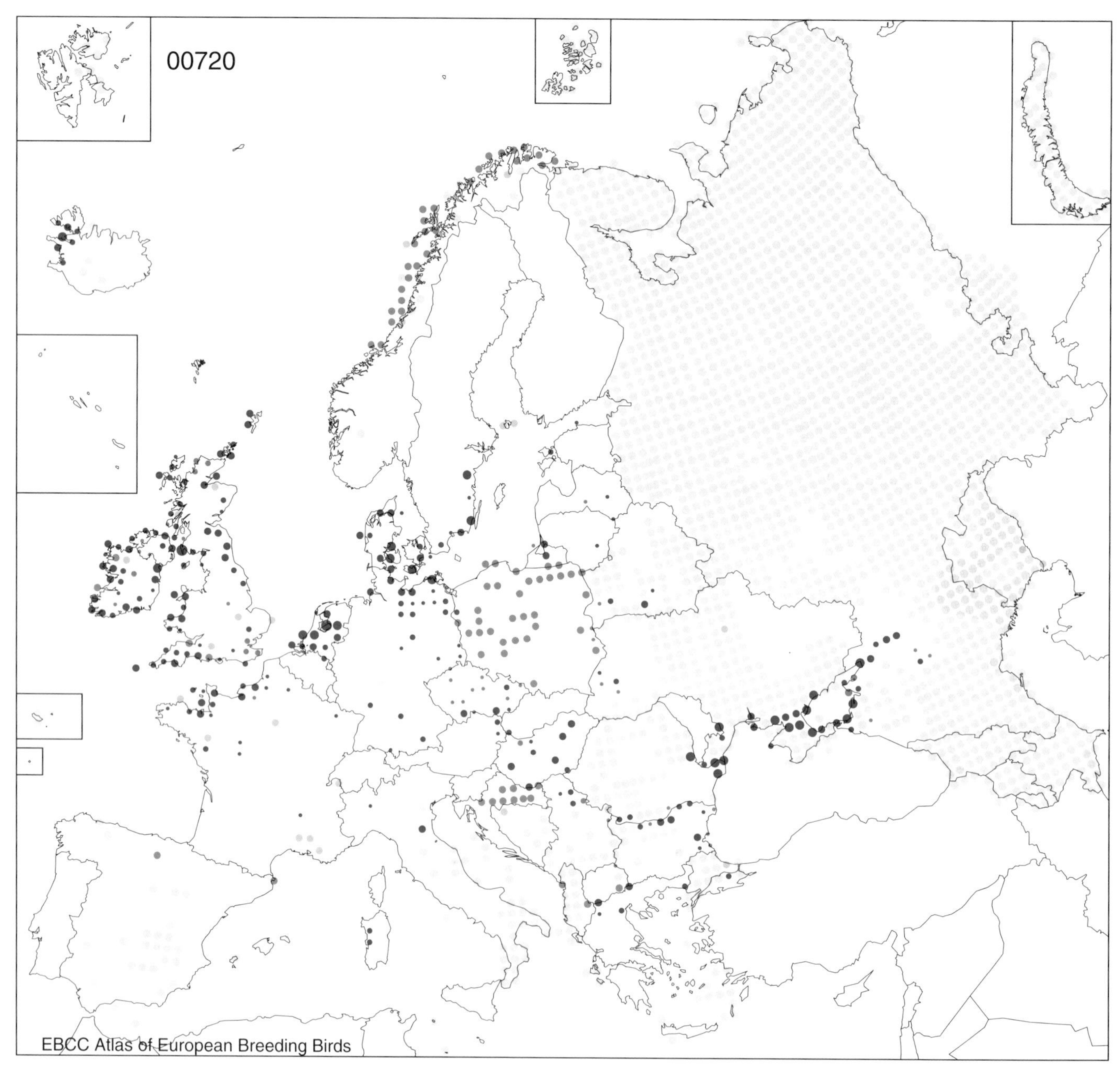

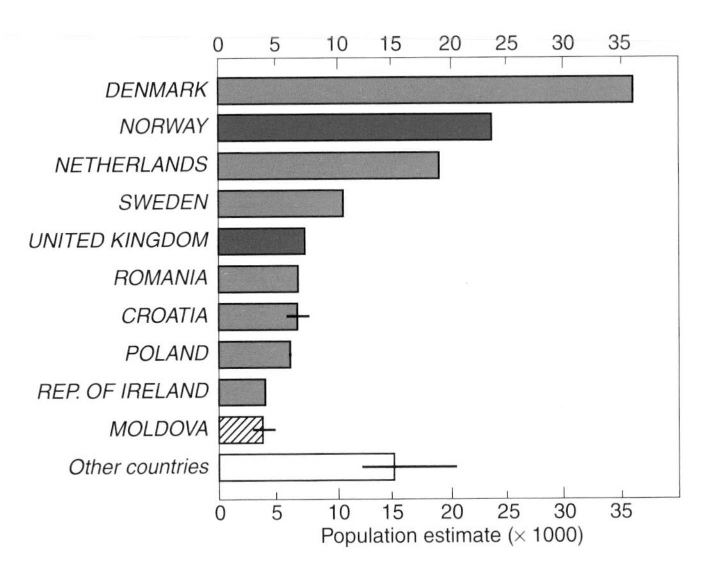

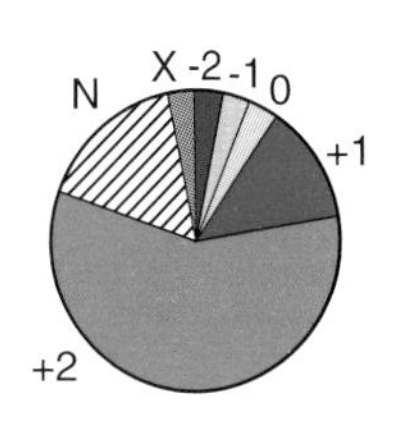

% in top 10 countries: 89.2
Total number of populated European countries: 31
Total European population 139,844–145,927 (141,954)
Russian population 20,000–35,000 (26,458)
Turkish population 1600–3000 (2191)

The Cormorant's wide distribution extends from Europe across Asia to Australia and New Zealand, and to East and South Africa, but reaches the Nearctic only marginally in W Greenland, SE Canada and the New England states. Habitat preferences differ between the two European subspecies *P.c. carbo* and *sinensis*, particularly during the breeding season, but also in winter (Marion 1994a). The nominate form breeds on seacliffs, with the exception of some inland colonies in Ireland. Its range encompasses the coasts of N France, Britain, Ireland, Iceland and Norway, with isolated extensions in W Greenland and on the Kola Peninsula, whereas *sinensis* occurs in the rest of Europe and in continental Asia S of the boreal zone. It prefers to nest on trees in wetlands but increasingly also on the ground on treeless islands and sand spits (the Baltic, Ukraine), and locally on cliffs (southern Europe) or shipwrecks. One distributional centre is the belt of coastal lowlands from the North Sea to the Baltic (the N-C European subpopulation), where colonies are associated with shallow fresh lakes and brackish inshore areas. The newly established tree-nesting colonies in SE England may be an offshoot of *sinensis* birds, as in inland western France (Marion 1994a). In E Europe, distribution mainly follows the larger rivers and inundation areas. Elsewhere, scattered colonies are often found in extensive fishpond areas.

Since the early 1970s, the European Cormorant population has been increasing rapidly. Much of the growth was contributed by the N-C European subpopulation which had numbered only 3000–5000bp throughout most of the 20th century. Between 1981/82 and 1992, it grew from 15 000bp in 28 colonies to 81 000bp in *c*170 colonies. The increase now seems to be slowing down from an exponential into a logarithmic pattern in some areas (the Netherlands; van Eerden & Gregersen 1995, Suter 1995). At the same time, new colonies are rapidly spreading northwards (Sweden) and eastwards into the Baltic states and Belarus. However, relatively few have been established in the W (England, France) and SW (S Germany, Italy). Reasons for this exceptional expansion are not known in detail but must be due to a combination of factors such as relaxed human persecution, availability of new colony sites (such as Dutch polders), and the greatly improved food supply deriving from water eutrophication. Eastern European numbers are less well known but have also grown, some at a similar rate (Ukraine; Koshelev *et al* 1992), others apparently more slowly or with some delay. The overall trend for *carbo* is positive too, but increase rates are lower than for *sinensis*, and vary regionally (Norway, Britain & Ireland). Persecution still seems to play a role locally (Scotland), but changes in the food supply must be the main driving force (Debout *et al* 1995). Most *carbo* colonies are relatively small (mostly <500bp, max 1600bp in Norway; N. Røv, pers comm). Continental birds, however, often form large colonies, several of these holding 3000–8000bp. The total European population reached at least 208 000bp in 1992, including 43 000bp of *carbo*. The authors believe that many of the national breeding populations are now larger than the graph indicates.

P.c. carbo winters primarily along the coasts of W Norway, the Kattegat and Skagerrak, Britain, Ireland, and Brittany, while *sinensis* winters from the southern Baltic to the southern Mediterranean. The two subspecies tend to be ecologically segregated, *carbo* being more associated with rocky coastlines, *sinensis* with estuaries, lagoons or inland lakes and rivers which do not normally freeze (Marion 1994a). Wintering Cormorants increased on inland waters throughout the range (Switzerland; Suter 1995), but France has recently become the main European wintering area (66 000, 1992), mostly on large rivers (Loire, Rhône, Rhine).

Loïc Marion (F) Werner Suter (CH)
with Jens Gregersen (DK) Jadwiga Gromadzka (PL)
Thomas Keller (D) Nils Røv (N)

This species account is sponsored by Dr Goetz Rheinwald, Bonn, D.

Phalacrocorax aristotelis Shag

CZ	Kormorán chocholatý	**I**	Marangone dal ciuffo
D	Krähenscharbe	**NL**	Kuifaalscholver
E	Cormorán Moñudo	**P**	Corvo-marinho-de-crista
F	Cormoran huppé	**PL**	Kormoran czubaty
FIN	Karimetso	**R**	Хохлатый баклан
G	Θαλασσοκόρακας	**S**	Toppskarv
H	Üstökös kárókatona		

SPEC Cat 4, Threat status S

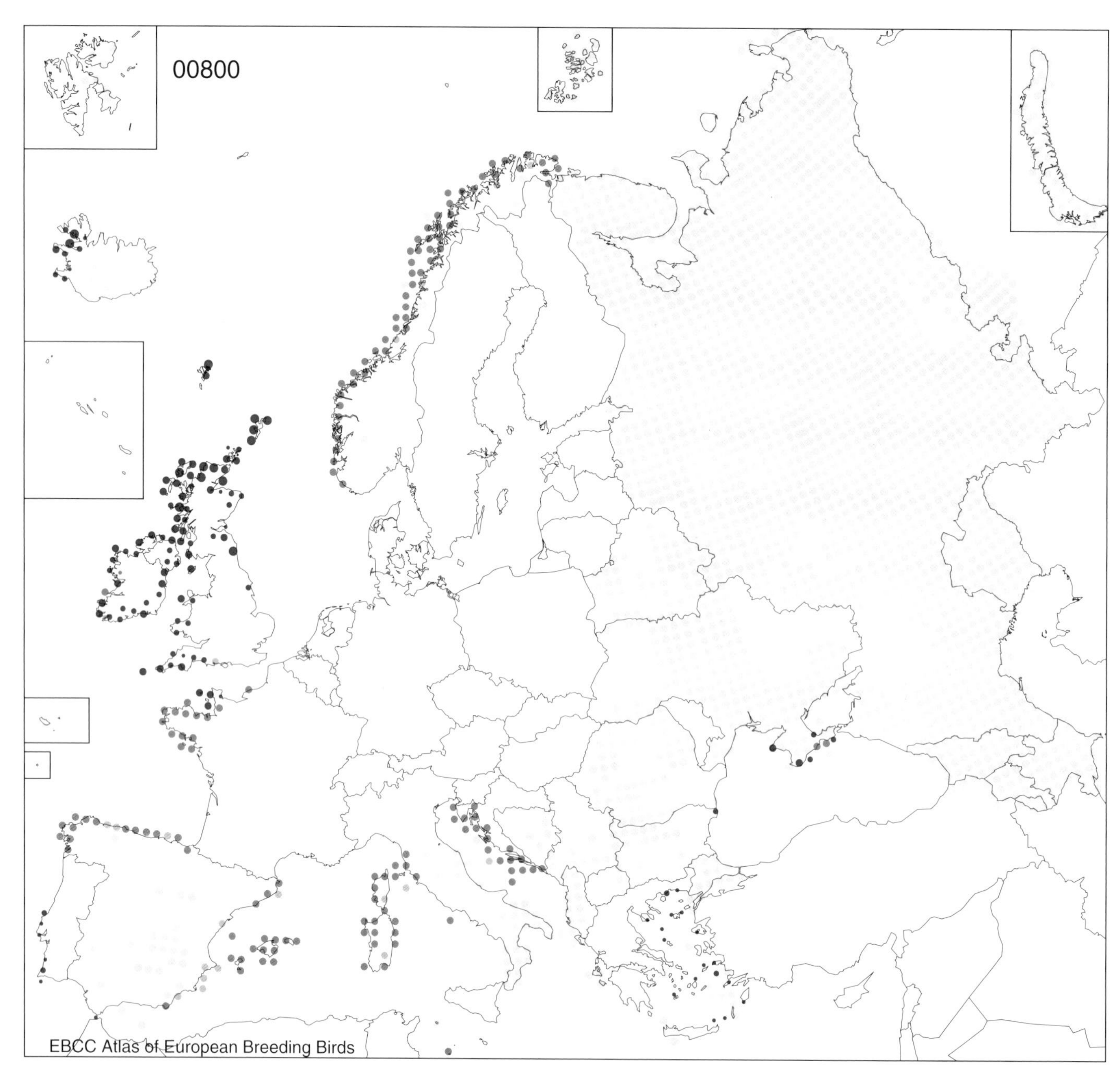

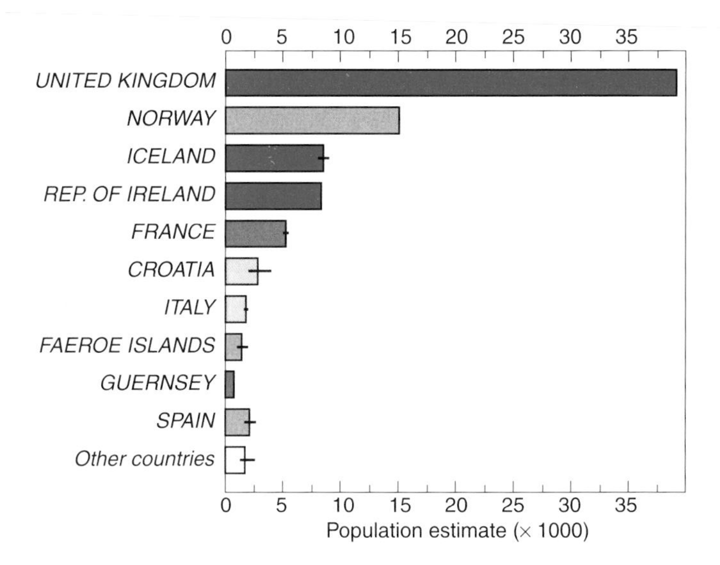

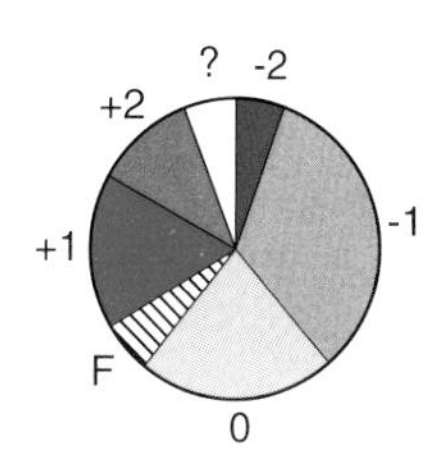

% in top 10 countries: 98.0
Total number of populated European countries: 18
Total European population 85,426–88,311 (86,632)
Russian population 1000–1500 (1225)
Turkish population 50–350 (132)

The Shag, a large seabird with dark glossy-green plumage is confined to the NE Atlantic and Mediterranean. It is found in both inshore and offshore marine habitats but is rarely encountered far from the coast or beyond the continental shelf. It is commonest along rocky coastlines and unlike the nominate form of its larger relative, the Cormorant *P. carbo*, is rarely found in estuaries or fresh water.

There are three subspecies: *P.a. aristotelis* breeds in Iceland, the Faeroes, Britain & Ireland. In mainland Europe it occurs from the Kola Peninsula south through Norway and locally along the Atlantic coasts of France, Portugal and Spain, whereas *P.a. desmarestii* occurs along the Mediterranean coast of France, Spain and Turkey, on many Mediterranean islands and on the shores and islands of the Black Sea, and *P.a. riggenbachi* is resident along the Atlantic coast of Morocco.

The Shag is a colonial breeder. Typically, it builds nests on cliff ledges but in some colonies, birds breed in crevices under large rocks. Sites need to be secure from terrestrial predators and sheltered from high seas and heavy rain. Within Europe the species has a widespread coastal distribution except where the habitat does not suit its breeding requirements. At present the species' stronghold is in northern and western Britain & Ireland. Substantial numbers also breed in NW Iceland and SW Norway. Population totals at the southern edge of the range are generally smaller than those in the N.

Apart from decreases in Ukraine, Albania and the Mediterranean coast of Spain, breeding distribution has changed little in recent years. In contrast, population trends have varied greatly, five countries showing an increase, eight a decrease, five no change and one fluctuating. Increases have occurred mainly at the range centre. Thus numbers in Great Britain increased by about 25% between 1969–70 and 1985–87. The largest increases occurred in NE England and only in the Orkney and Shetland Islands were numbers reduced (Lloyd *et al* 1991). Numbers also increased substantially in Ireland and on the Atlantic coast of France. The Norwegian population has almost halved since the 1930s. The present situation there is complex, sharp declines being recorded in several major colonies such as Runde, Røst and Lille Kamøy and numbers in Trøms showing a general decline (Røv 1990). However, elsewhere in Norway numbers have been stable, as at Froøyne, or have increased as at Rogaland and Sklinna. Little detailed information on population change appears to be available for the Faeroes or Iceland. At the southern edge of the range numbers are stable on the Atlantic coast of the Iberian Peninsula (Bárcena *et al* 1984), while in the Mediterranean, colonies on mainland Spain have almost totally disappeared and numbers on many of the islands are much reduced (de Juana 1984). It is likely that the species has also declined in colonies on the Takhaukut Peninsula in the Black Sea (Golovkin 1984). At subspecific level *aristotelis* is increasing but the much smaller *desmarestii* population is decreasing.

Increases have been attributed to a reduction in human persecution but the species appears to be particularly sensitive to changes in food supply and to 'red tide' incidents.

The Shag exhibits marked geographic, age-related and annual variations in movements outside the breeding season. Only in the N is it truly migratory; elsewhere it tends to be sedentary or make only small-scale movements away from the colonies. Younger birds generally make the longest movements and in Great Britain there are periodic large-scale eruptions of young birds.

Sarah Wanless (GB)

Phalacrocorax pygmeus

Pygmy Cormorant

CZ	Kormorán malý	**I**	Marangone minore
D	Zwergscharbe	**NL**	Dwergaalscholver
E	Cormorán Pigmeo	**P**	Corvo-marinho-pigmeu
F	Cormoran pygmé	**PL**	Kormoran mały
FIN	Kääpiömerimetso	**R**	Малый баклан
G	Λαγγόνα	**S**	Dvärgskarv
H	Kis kárókatona		

SPEC Cat 2, Threat status V

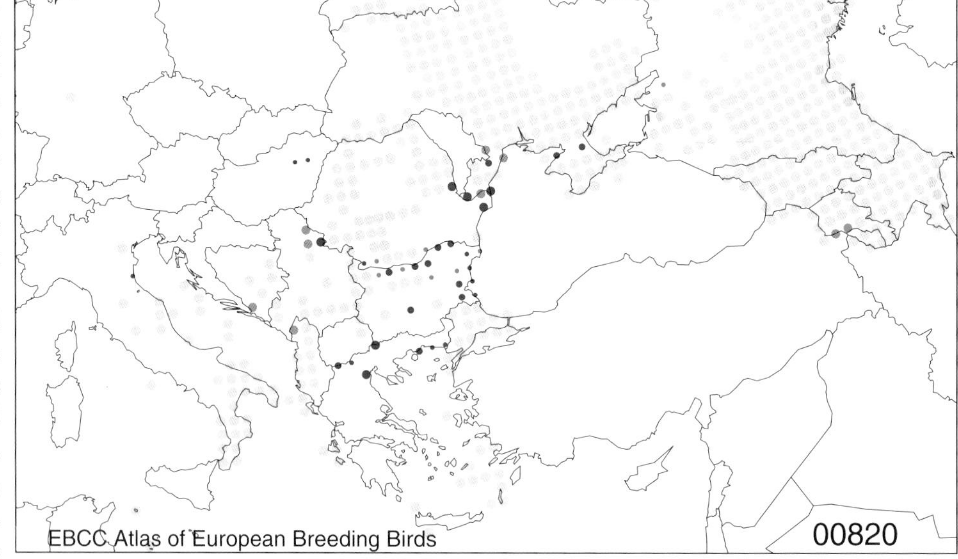

The Pygmy Cormorant breeds in the Balkans and on the Crimean Peninsula, in the coastal zones of the Azov, Caspian and Aral Seas, in Asia Minor and Iraq. The northern European populations winter mainly along the coast of the southern Balkan Peninsula; the remainder is mostly resident (Simeonov & Michev 1991).

In Europe it inhabits inland and coastal marshes, riverine forests and reedbeds from sea level up to 550m asl. It breeds in mixed colonies with herons and egrets, Glossy Ibis *Plegadis falcinellus*, Spoonbill *Platalea leucorodia*, Cormorant *Phalacrocorax carbo*, and Shag *P. aristotelis* (Simeonov *et al* 1990).

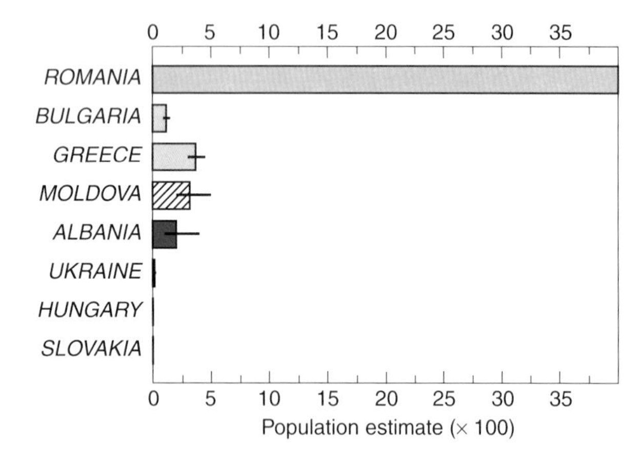

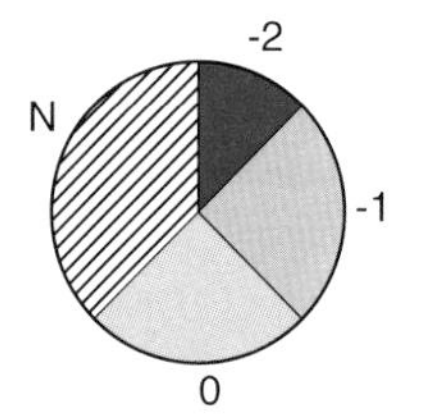

% in top 10 countries: 100.0
Total number of populated European countries: 8
Total European population 4852–5308 (5022)
Russian population 150–250 (194)
Turkish population 2000–5000 (3162)

Except for those in the Volga Delta, almost all European breeding colonies are concentrated in the Balkan Peninsula, especially the Danube Delta. The present sizes of the populations in Azerbaijan and other parts of the Caspian are not known. Small numbers breed in Hungary, Slovakia, Moldova, Ukraine and in Russia (excluding the Volga Delta), but there is no recent information from the former Yugoslavia, where it is known to breed.

After a sharp decline in the 1950s, the population of the Pygmy Cormorant is now increasing. It has reoccupied some former traditional breeding places such as in Hungary, Bulgaria and Russia (Nankinov 1989) and recently has created new colonies in Slovakia. Its status in the Caspian is unknown.

The species has suffered a serious decline in Albania, but quantitative data are lacking, as is the case for Russia and parts of Ukraine. The population trend is stable in Greece and Bulgaria. Small decreases are known from Ukraine and Romania. However, recent information suggests that the population in the Danube Delta is increasing, because water eutrophication has led to a large increase in smaller fish species (P. Weber, pers obs).

Tañu Michev (BUL) Peter Weber (ROM)

Ardeola ralloides

Squacco Heron

CZ	Volavka vlasatá	I	Sgarza ciuffetto
D	Rallenreiher	NL	Ralreiger
E	Garcilla Cangrejera	P	Papa-ratos
F	Crabier chevelu	PL	Czapla modronosa
FIN	Rääkkähaikara	R	Желтая цапля
G	Κρυπτοτσικνιάς	S	Rallhäger
H	Üstökösgém		

SPEC Cat 3, Threat status V

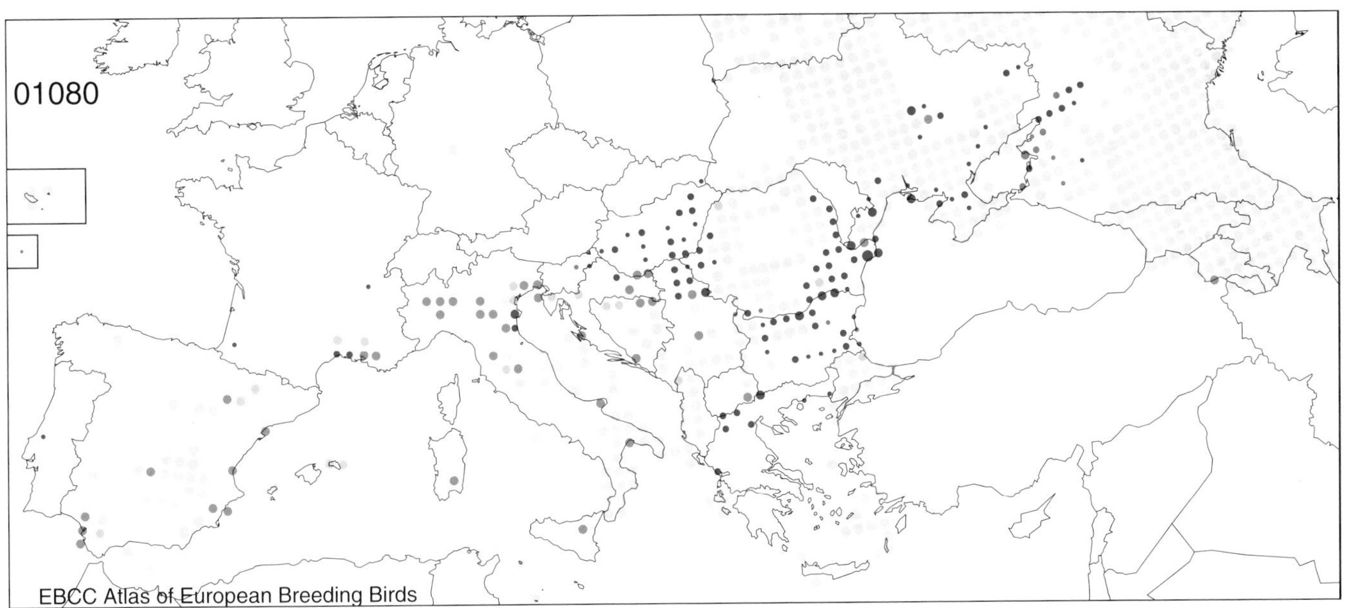

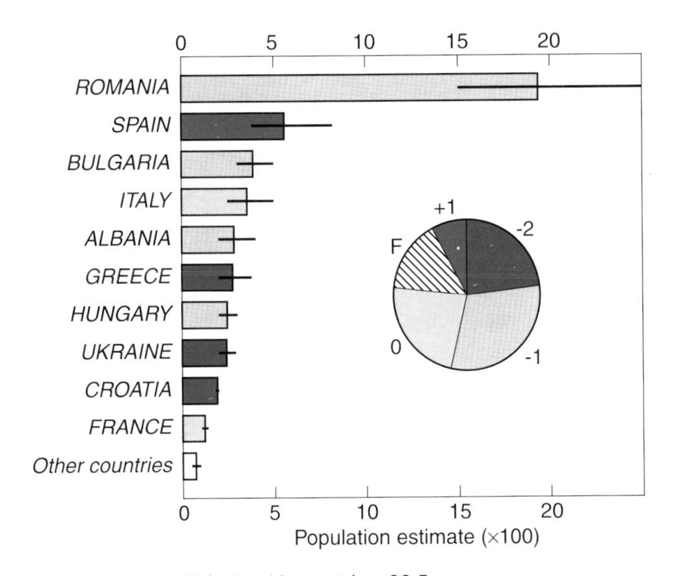

% in top 10 countries: 98.5
Total number of populated European countries: 13
Total European population 4154–5333 (4661)
Russian population 5500–6000 (5745)
Turkish population 3000–10,000 (5477)

This gregarious heron has a patchy distribution throughout southern Europe to E of the Aral Sea, N and tropical Africa, Madagascar and the Near and Middle East. In Europe it is a late breeder, nesting in mixed colonies with other *Ardeidae*. It is confined to extensive freshwater areas (natural or artificial) like the ricefield areas of Spain and N Italy. The rarity of the species in Portugal has been attributed to the scarcity of freshwater areas in this country (J.C. Farinha, pers comm).

The breeding populations in the western Mediterranean fluctuate but the species has recently increased in Italy, Spain and southern France. The largest populations in western Europe are in Italy (500–600 nests in 1995; M. Fasola, pers comm) and Spain (822 nests in 1990; Fernandez-Cruz *et al* 1992). In the Camargue, where the bulk of the French population breeds, numbers increased from 68bp in 1991 to a record of 142bp in 1992, but fell back to 96bp in 1993 (H. Hafner, pers obs). The largest populations, are in E Europe but are decreasing. In Greece, numbers declined from 1400bp before 1970 to only 201–377bp in 1985–86 (A. Crivelli, pers comm). In Croatia numbers declined in the most important breeding site of the country from 478bp in 1954 to less than 50bp during the mid-1980s (J. Mikuska, pers comm). Population changes may depend on conditions S of the Sahara, where European birds winter.

Heinz Hafner (CH)

This species account is sponsored by the Sociedad Española de Ornitologia/BirdLife, E.

Botaurus stellaris

Bittern

CZ	Bukač velký	**I**	Tarabuso
D	Rohrdommel	**NL**	Roerdomp
E	Avetoro Común	**P**	Abetouro-comum
F	Butor étoilé	**PL**	Bąk
FIN	Kaulushaikara	**R**	Выпь
G	Ηταυρος	**S**	Rördrom
H	Bölömbika		

SPEC Cat 3, Threat status V (P)

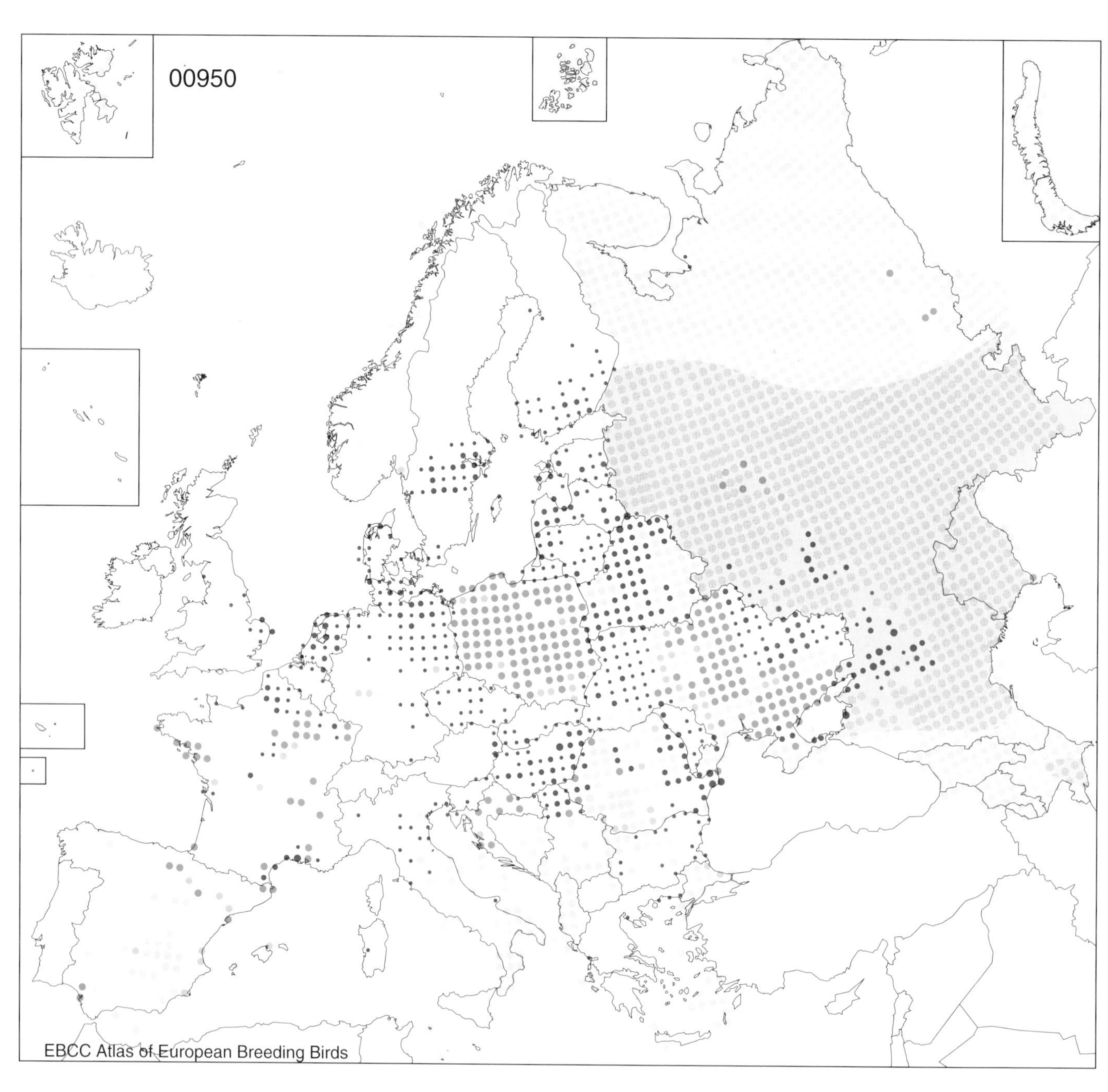

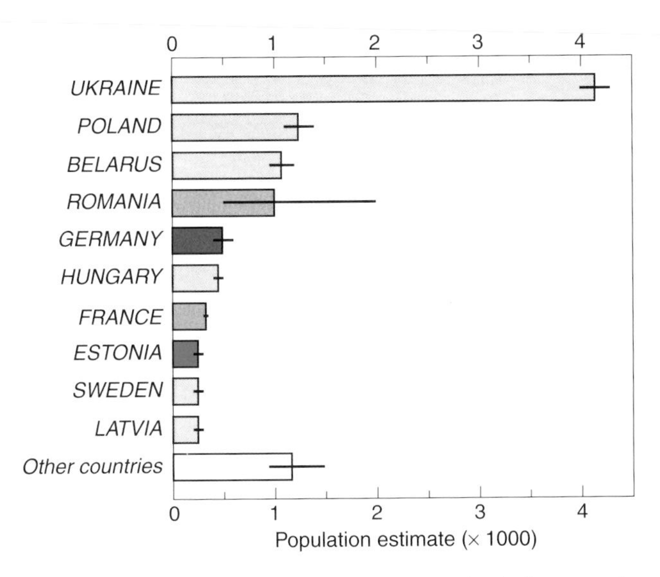

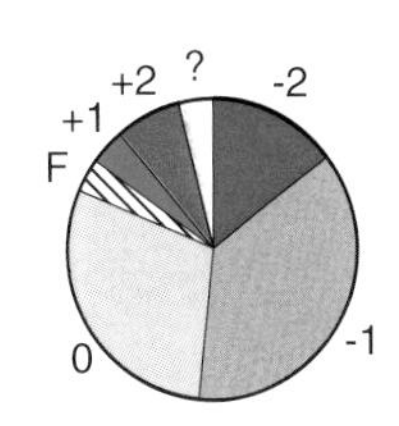

% in top 10 countries: 89.0
Total number of populated European countries: 27
Total European population 10,044–11,669 (10,618)
Russian population 10,000–30,000 (17,321)
Turkish population 30–500 (122)

The Bittern, a secretive and little-studied heron, is distributed in the warmer boreal and warm temperate zones from western Europe through C Russia to the Pacific. Discrete small populations exist in southern Africa.

Its European distribution is patchy, reflecting its virtual restriction to lowland swamps and densely vegetated wetlands featuring extensive stands of tall vegetation, usually reedbeds (*Phragmites*), which form thick cover beside sheltered pools, ponds and slow-moving rivers. It may also breed in dense reedmace *Typha* and bulrush *Scirpus latifolia* stands. It prefers stands in shallow fresh water, avoiding drier areas presumably because of mammalian predators.

The Bittern almost always hides in reedbeds throughout summer. It can only be mapped and monitored by recording singing (booming) males, whose sound carries for more than 5km. Males boom intensively day-long from March to May but mostly at night in June. Booming bouts peak just after dawn and dusk. Polygyny does occur, and so estimation of breeding female numbers is practically impossible.

Russia holds 10 000–30 000bp, *c*75% of the European population, and Ukraine 4000–4300. Poland (1100–1400bp), Belarus (950–1200bp) and Romania (500–2000) also have substantial populations. The graph shows the Bittern to be much scarcer in western Europe, only France (300–350bp) and The Netherlands (150–275) exceeding 100 booming males. Twelve countries' Bittern populations each comprise fewer than 100bp.

In larger reedbeds males show some tendency to exhibit a clumped distribution (P. Koskimies, unpubl). In C Europe, local densities may reach 1 male/8–10ha of reedbed (*HVM*). In an overgrown wetland in SE Finland density varied from 3.9 to 6.5 males/km^2 of reedbed (Koskimies 1989b), recently reaching 11 males/km^2 (P. Koskimies, unpubl). In Matsalu Bay in Estonia, the mean value is 0.7 bp/km^2 of reedbed (Leibak *et al* 1994), illustrative of the average density in N European extensive wetlands. The highest current density in Great Britain is 1 male/15.8 ha of reedbed, the smallest occupied reedbed being 2ha (G.A. Tyler, unpubl).

Common in W and C Europe in the 19th century, the Bittern has declined greatly since through human persecution and the drainage of hundreds of breeding areas. It became extinct in Great Britain and western Germany in the late 1800s, but soon after, in a northwards range expansion, it colonized southern Sweden and Finland and recolonized Great Britain. This expansion was probably due to a reduction of cattle grazing in reedbeds and to eutrophication leading to an increase in reedbed area. Persecution in most European countries is now much reduced.

The overall decline continues: half the countries with breeding populations suffered a decline from 1970 to 1990. In Germany, The Netherlands, Spain and Great Britain numbers declined by over 50% (Day 1981, Smith & Tyler 1993). Further breeding-site degradation comes from water pollution, abandonment of traditional wetland management and mechanization of reed harvesting. In E Europe populations have remained generally stable since the early 1970s, but increased by more than 20% in Estonia, by between 20 and 50% in Denmark (partly through site creation, K. Smith, pers comm) and by >100% in Finland (250–350 booming males, mid-1990s, P. Koskimies, pers obs).

In S and W Europe the Bittern is resident on waters that usually remain ice-free. Most northern and eastern birds disperse several hundred kilometres S or SW of their breeding quarters, to unfrozen waters. In Great Britain winter numbers correlate with the number of frosts (Bibby 1981, G.A. Tyler, unpubl). In severe winters many C European birds starve rather than emigrate. Therefore, especially in northern Europe, populations fluctuate considerably and may drop dramatically after harsh winters, as in Sweden (by 35–40% after the 1978/79 winter; Sveríges Ornitologiska Förening 1990). In Great Britain breeding numbers do not correlate with the previous winter's weather (Bibby 1981). From 1988 to 1990, after a period of mild winters, the number of booming males increased from 70 to 194 in Finland (Koskimies 1992b).

Pertti Koskimies (FIN) Glen Tyler (GB)

Ixobrychus minutus **Little Bittern**

CZ	Bukáček malý	I	Tarabusino
D	Zwergdommel	NL	Woudaapje
E	Avetorillo Común	P	Garça-pequena
F	Blongios nain	PL	Bączek
FIN	Pikkuhaikara	R	Волчок
G	Μικροτσικνιάς	S	Dvärgrördrom
H	Törpegém		

SPEC Cat 3, Threat status V (P)

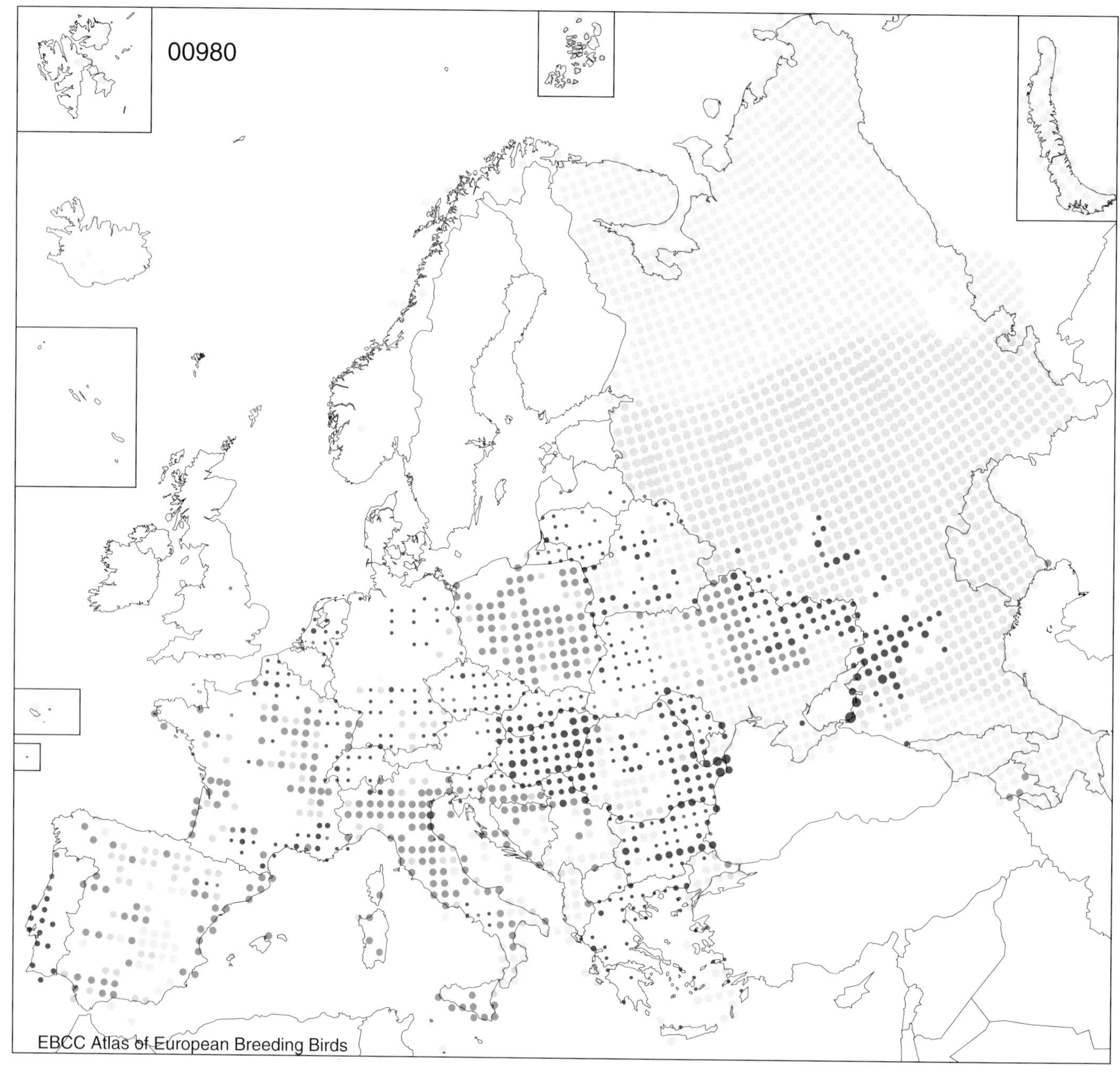

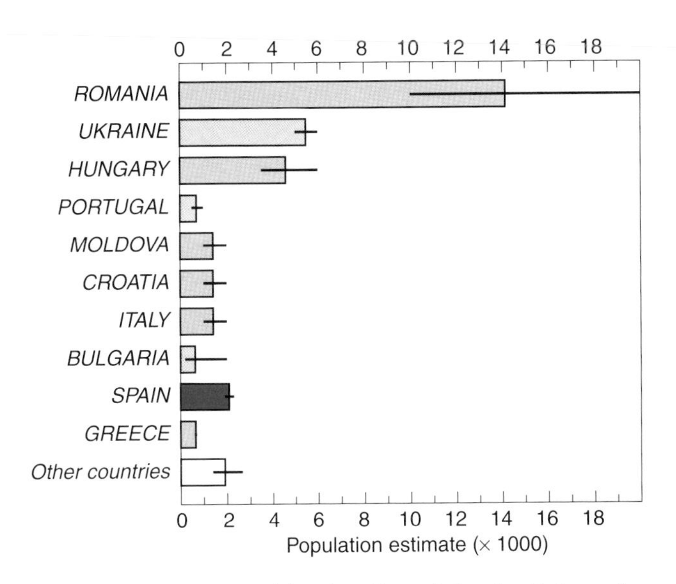

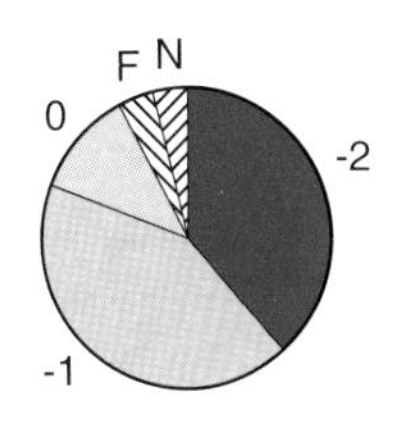

% in top 10 countries: 94.5
Total number of populated European countries: 26
Total European population 30,018–40,722 (34,420)
Russian population 10,000–50,000 (22,361)
Turkish population 1000–10,000 (3162)

The Little Bittern is widely distributed in the Palearctic, Afrotropical and Australasian regions. The nominate *minutus* occurs in Europe and W Asia, normally below 53°N in W Europe and below 60°N in Russia.

It is a rather secretive, small heron that arrives late in its breeding quarters (April–May), breeds solitarily or semi-colonially in inaccessible marshes and departs again in August and September. Censusing and monitoring the Little Bittern are therefore much more difficult than for most other heron species. It winters in Africa S of the Sahara, especially in wetlands in Sudan, Ethiopia and to a lesser extent in W Africa, crossing the Mediterranean in broad front migration, even during daylight.

Its breeding habitat comprises reedbeds or other dense vegetation along rivers, on lake margins or in marshes and even small fishponds, but preferentially where trees such as willow grow. Unbroken tracts of suitable habitat are not essential because it also frequents fragmented marshland. It uses only freshwater habitats, mostly in lowlands below 200m asl.

In Europe, the Little Bittern has a widespread but patchy distribution. It is absent from Great Britain (although it bred successfully in 1984 in S Yorkshire), Ireland, Denmark, Fennoscandia and Estonia. There is a general tendency for the species to become more widely distributed at higher densities towards C, E and SE Europe. Some 50% of the European population of *c*36 000–97 000bp is confined to Russia, Ukraine and Belarus, and between 30 and 45% to E and C Europe, the remainder being in W and SW Europe. Reliable quantitative data over large areas are scarce, however, and these figures should be used only as rough indications of where strongholds are located. At the local level, high densities may occur, such as 13–15bp on 7.6ha of fishponds in S Poland (Cempulik 1994).

Irregular short-term population fluctuations are typical of the Little Bittern, and are often asynchronous between neighbouring areas, such as found in different breeding localities in the Netherlands (Bekhuis 1990), S Germany (Hölzinger 1987) and S Poland (Cempulik 1994). However, long-term trends in Europe are decidedly negative, very few countries reporting a stable population and none an increasing trend. Except for Ukraine, Bulgaria and Portugal, the prevailing trends in most European populations from 1970 to 1990 were of range contractions and rapidly reducing numbers. Numerical declines of >50% in 1970–90 were found in Latvia, the Netherlands, Germany, France, Austria, Czech Republic, Slovakia, Slovenia and Spain, countries which mostly are on the breeding range limit and contain less than 5% of the European population. Elsewhere, declines ranged between 20 and 50%. The Dutch population, for example, declined from 170–225bp in 117 5km squares in the 1960s to 100–135 in 80 squares in 1973–77 and only 35–75 in 21 squares in 1985–89 (Bekhuis 1990); this trend still continues, only 9bp being left in 1992 (SOVON, pers comm). A similar decline has been quantified for Baden-Württemberg, Germany (including the Bodensee): 220–290bp in 1969, but only 40–50bp in 1980 (Hölzinger 1987).

The magnitude and extent of the Little Bittern's decline in Europe, even in protected wetlands, probably imply high mortality during migration or in the wintering grounds (Marion *et al* 1996). The parallel with Purple Heron *Ardea purpurea*, where the severity of drought in the wintering areas was correlated with survival of birds older than one year, is evident (Cavé 1983). Although many individuals overfly the Mediterranean and Sahara without stopping, the increasing desertification of the semi-arid zone S of the Sahara in the 1970s may have affected negatively survival rates during migration (Marion 1994b). However, favourable rainfall conditions in W Africa in the 1990s did not result in the European Little Bittern population recovering, probably because this area represents only a part of the wintering range. Habitat degradation in the breeding and wintering ranges since the 1960s may also be responsible for this failure.

Loïc Marion (F)

Nycticorax nycticorax — Night Heron

CZ	Kvakoš noční	**I**	Nitticora
D	Nachtreiher	**NL**	Kwak
E	Martinete Común	**P**	Goraz
F	Bihoreau gris	**PL**	Ślepowron
FIN	Yöhaikara	**R**	Кваква
G	Νυχτοκόρακας	**S**	Natthäger
H	Bakcsó		

SPEC Cat 3, Threat status D

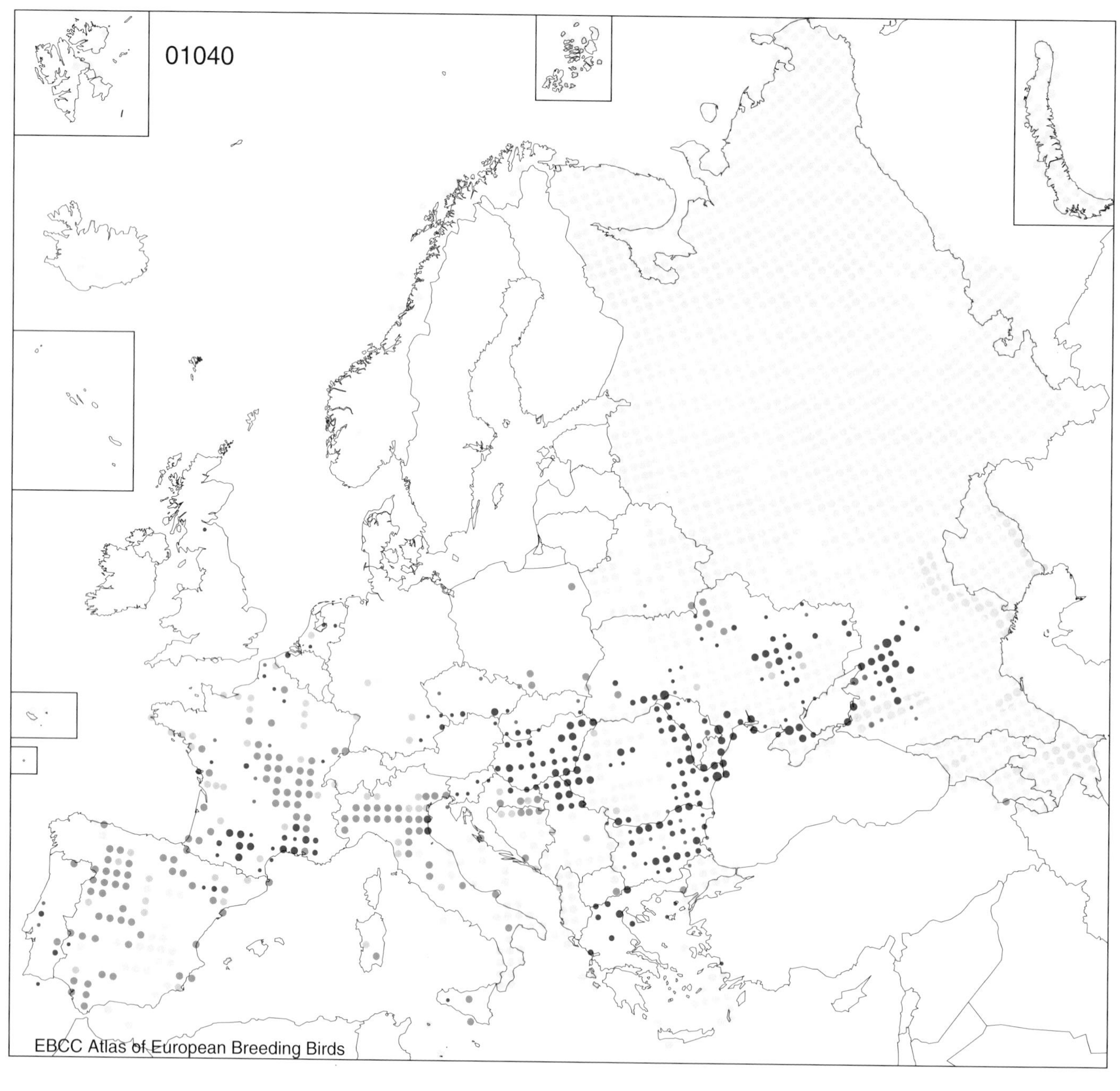

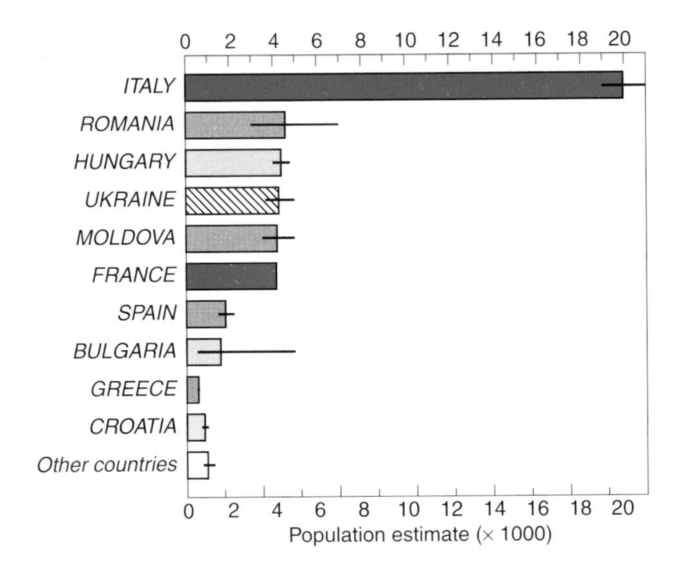

+2 N -2 +1 -1 F 0

% in top 10 countries: 98.0
Total number of populated European countries: 21
Total European population 44,859–51,753 (47,261)
Russian population 9000–11,000 (9950)
Turkish population 1000–3000 (1732)

This medium-sized heron breeds in small to very large colonies and on every continent except Australia and Antarctica. There are three subspecies in the New World, but the nominate *N.n. nycticorax* is found everywhere else. Within the Palearctic, it inhabits a variety of inland wetlands and coastal freshwater wetlands in the temperate and Mediterranean regions.

Colony sites in Europe are often shared with other herons and with egrets and typically are located in small clumps of low trees such as alder *Alnus* spp and willow *Salix* spp on wet soils in cultivated regions, in large riverine woodlands and, less frequently, in reedbeds in river deltas like the Ebro. Heronries of over 100 nests occur in sites where at least 500ha of permanent freshwater marshes are within a 5km foraging radius (Hafner & Fasola 1992). Ricefields are the main foraging habitat in NW Italy and to a lesser extent also in other regions with rice cultivation in Spain and Greece (Fasola & Ruiz 1996). The species commonly forages in canals, rivers and ponds, but less so in saltwater marshes.

The species is distributed at very low altitudes in Europe where there are extensive wetlands. However, the once (17th and 18th century) flourishing colonies in wetlands below sea level in The Netherlands became extinct due to habitat destruction. It is still widely distributed across the lower catchment areas of larger rivers such as the Rhône, Po, Danube and Volga. It is more patchily distributed in the inland wetlands, ponds and small lakes of C and S Europe. At the northern limit of its range in C Europe, colonies are mostly small and widely dispersed; nest numbers fluctuate and colony sites shift frequently. Its extraordinary abundance in N Italy is due to the availability of large areas of ricefields, which abound in food (Fasola *et al* 1996). For no apparent reason the Night Heron is scarce (Ebro Delta, Evros Delta) or rare (Camargue) in other regions with ricefields.

Although population and range size have increased in a few regions, as in N Italy, decreases, as in Spain, are much commoner in the long term, possibly due to the destruction of wetlands for land reclamation. Population fluctuations may be tied to variations in local hydrology (Ham 1975), but the size of the breeding population seems to depend heavily on the hydrological conditions encountered in the wintering areas in tropical Africa (den Held 1981).

The species' distribution is limited by the availability both of foraging and nesting habitats. Colony site availability places limits on breeding, especially in regions with unlimited food supplies, as in the NW Italian ricefields. In such regions, protection of the few remaining breeding sites possessing patchy natural vegetation is a priority for the conservation of the species (Fasola & Alieri 1992b).

The Night Heron reaches its highest breeding densities in NW Italy, where the largest known European colony (2950 nests) was recorded in 1990 and where various colonies, each with hundreds or even thousands of nests, occur at distances of 4–10km from one another. The same colony sites are occupied year after year, although the number of nests in any one colony may fluctuate considerably.

The Night Heron leaves Europe from July to September for its wintering ranges in Africa S of the Sahara and returns in March and April. Less than 1% of the birds overwinter in S Europe.

Mauro Fasola (I) Karl Hudec (CZ)

This species account is sponsored by the Institute for Inland Water Management and Waste Water Treatment, Lelystad, NL.

Egretta garzetta **Little Egret**

CZ	Volavka stříbřitá	**I**	Garzetta
D	Seidenreiher	**NL**	Kleine Zilverreiger
E	Garceta Común	**P**	Garça-branca-pequena
F	Aigrette garzette	**PL**	Czapla nadobna
FIN	Silkkihaikara	**R**	Малая белая цапля
G	Λευκοτσικνιάς	**S**	Silkeshäger
H	Kis kócsag		

Non-SPEC, Threat status S

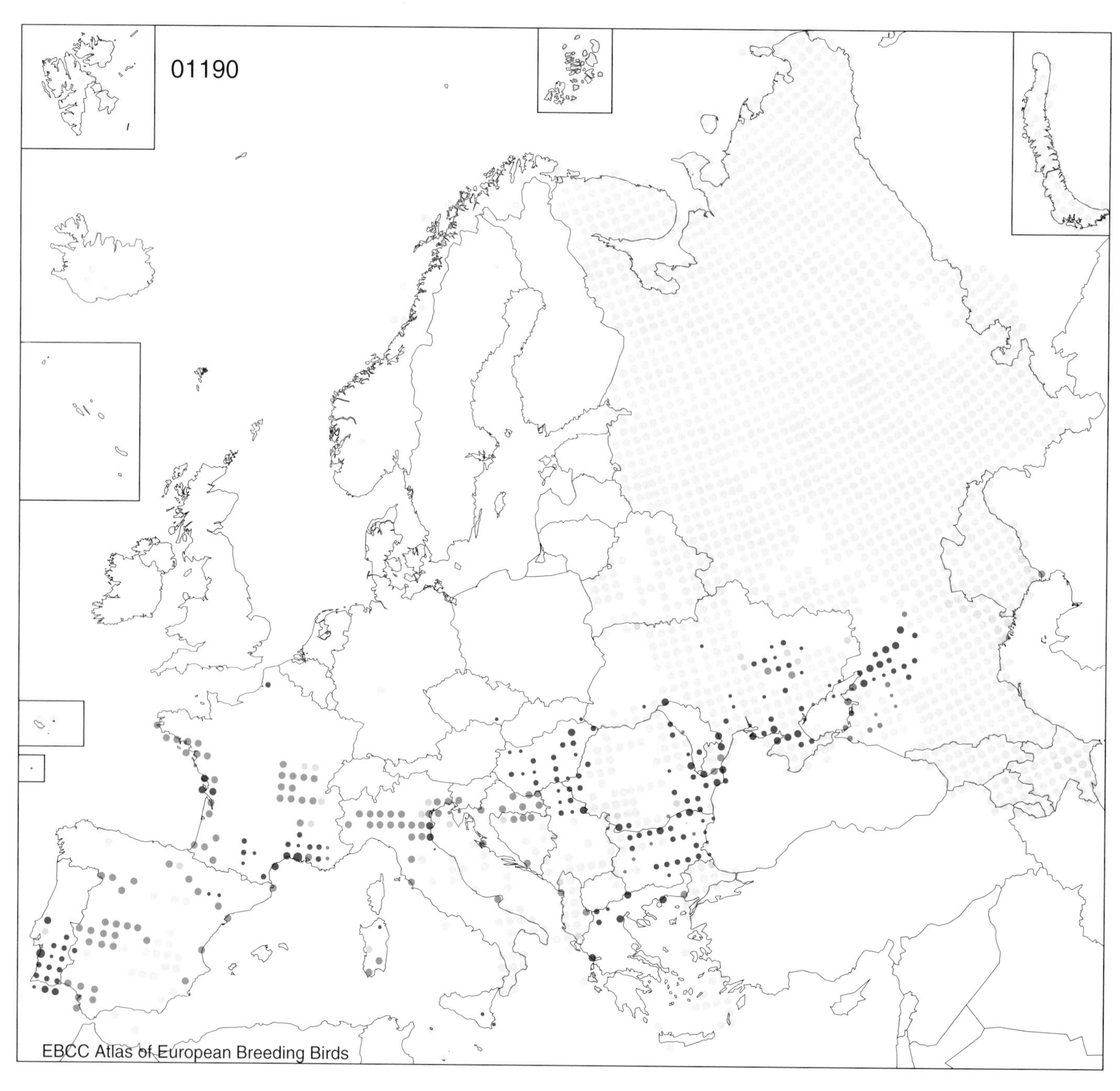

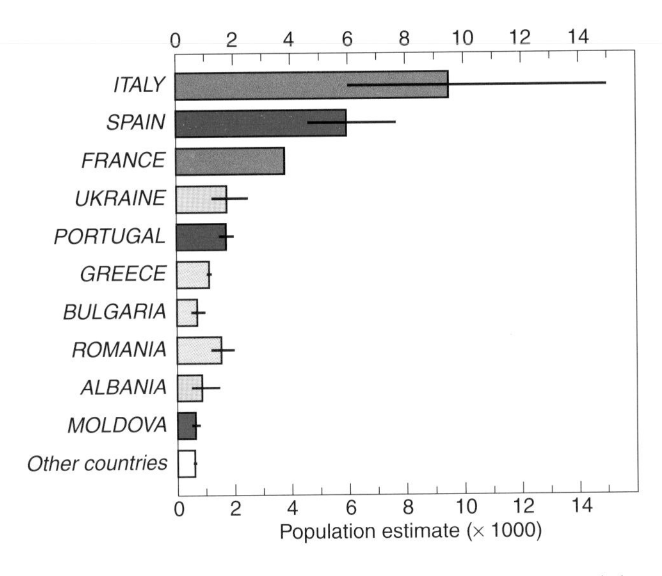

+2 -2 +1 -1 F 0

% in top 10 countries: 97.9
Total number of populated European countries: 14
Total European population 24,401–34,121 (28,224)
Russian population 4500–6000 (5196)
Turkish population 5000–10,000 (7071)

The slender, medium-sized Little Egret is widely distributed throughout the temperate and tropical latitudes in the Palearctic, African and Oriental regions, and also in Australia. The nominate form *E.g. garzetta* occurs in Europe, and there are two other subspecies elsewhere.

Colonies in Europe are usually located in low clumps of trees, often alder *Alnus* spp and willow *Salix* spp, and less frequently in taller trees (mainly along rivers) and in reedbeds (in deltas). The species normally forms mixed colonies with other heron species. The Little Egret selects nest sites at lower heights than the Night Heron *Nycticorax nycticorax* and the Grey Heron *Ardea cinerea*, because vertical nest distribution among herons is related to body size (Fasola & Alieri 1992a). It forages in a variety of freshwater, brackish and saltwater habitats. It is found more often in salt water than other *Ardeidae*, and its colonies amid salt water tend to be monospecific (Hafner & Fasola 1992).

Italian Little Egret heronries 1983–1989. Twenty-nine of the 62 heronries are clumped in the small rice cultivation region (hatching).

It is widely distributed in Europe in low-lying regions containing abundant foraging habitats, such as occur in the lower catchments of the largest rivers (Tagus, Ebro, Rhône, Po, Danube and Volga) and in those coastal areas of Italy, France and Spain which have large lagoons.

The breeding populations and the breeding ranges have recently increased in the Mediterranean (Spain, France and Italy), while they have mainly decreased in E Europe. Massive mortality was observed in S Europe during particularly severe winters. Population levels may depend on winter survival.

The highest abundance occurs in N Italy, where there are large areas of ricefields. Hundreds of nests are spaced in colonies separated by 4–10km. The largest known colony in this region had 1370 nests in 1992. The Little Egret is also abundant in regions with large lagoons (in Spain and France) and in countries with large inland wetlands (inner Russia), whereas they are widespread at low densities in other regions of inland wetlands (Hungary).

Its breeding distribution is determined by the availability both of foraging habitats and colony sites. Either can be a limiting factor, as exemplified by the circumstances in N Italy where food supply abounds in the ricefields but the number of potential breeding sites is restricted as a result of widespread intensive agricultural activities (Fasola & Alieri 1992b).

The majority of the Little Egret populations move to winter in North Africa, but since the 1950s an increasing number of birds (presently about 10% of the total population) overwinter on the European side of the Mediterranean.

Mauro Fasola (I) Heinz Hafner (CH)

Egretta alba

Great White Egret

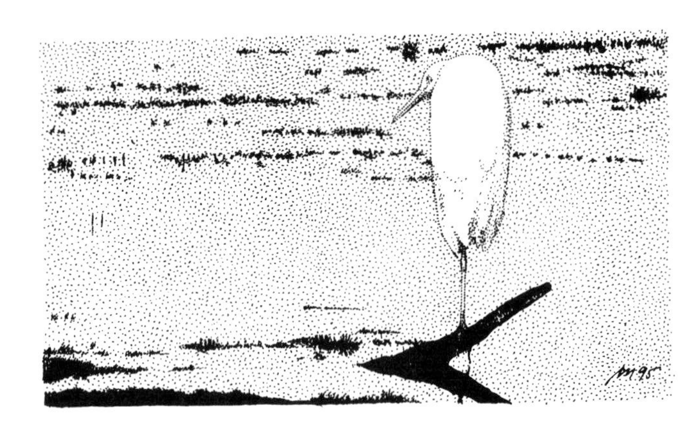

CZ	Volavka bílá	**I**	Airone bianco maggiore
D	Silberreiher	**NL**	Grote Zilverreiger
E	Garceta Grande	**P**	Garça-branca-grande
F	Grande Aigrette	**PL**	Czapla biała
FIN	Jalohaikara	**R**	Большая белая цапля
G	Αργυροτσικνιάς	**S**	Ägretthäger
H	Nagy kócsag		

Non-SPEC, Threat status S

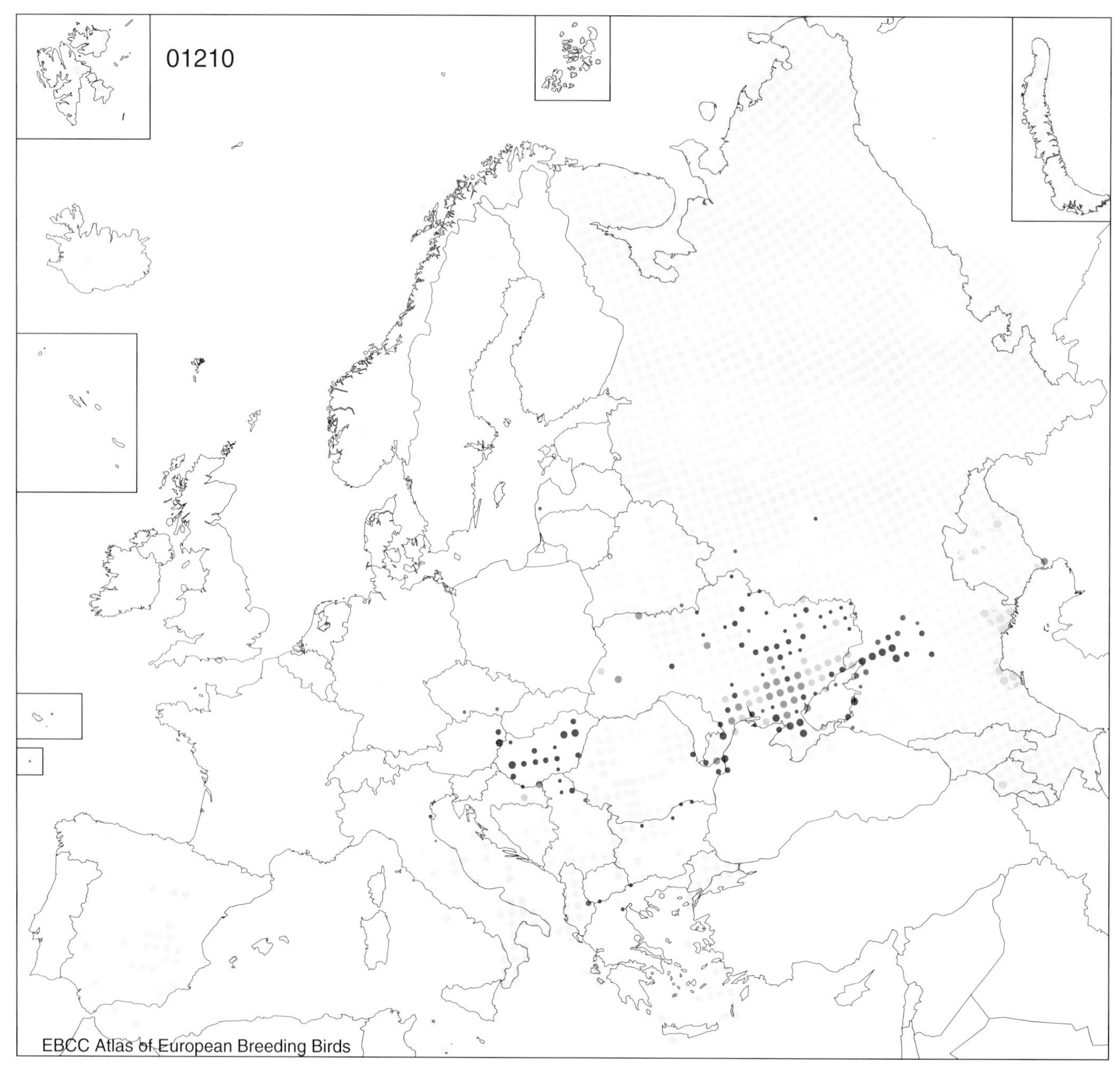

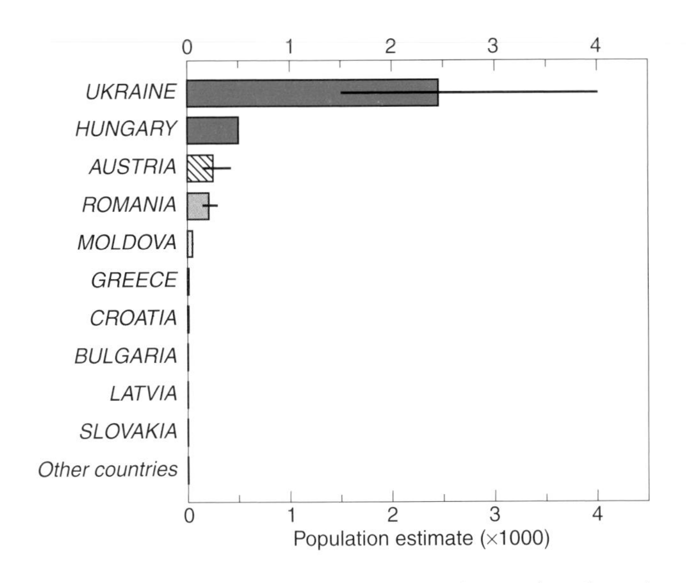

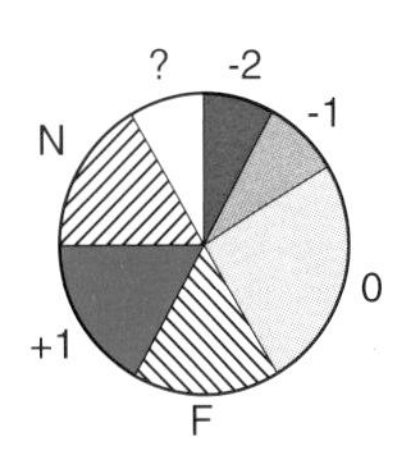

% in top 10 countries: 99.9
Total number of populated European countries: 12
Total European population 2542–5062 (3499)
Russian population 10,000–11,500 (10,724)
Turkish population 100–500 (224)

The Great White Egret is cosmopolitan, being distributed over temperate and tropical lowland areas of the world. In Europe it breeds mostly in extensive wetlands lying within the 20°C July isotherm. It is found in large reed-swamps, on lake shorelines, in riverine forest, estuaries and along coasts. For nesting it requires large undisturbed reedbeds, but sometimes uses bushes or low trees like willow *Salix* spp. It is a colonial breeder and often associates with Spoonbill *Platalea leucorodia*, Glossy Ibis *Plegadis falcinellus* or other breeding herons. In the Romanian Danube Delta it also forms loosely dispersed breeding groups, inter-nest distances being *c*10–50m (D. Munteanu, pers obs). It forages frequently on pastures, along ditches, in ricefields or amongst winter-rape.

The scarcity of large undisturbed wetlands and the species' climatic limitations explain its distribution pattern in Europe, for it occurs patchily in E and SE Europe westwards to the Hungarian Plain. In Russia, it breeds in the lower Volga and Ural river plains and along the Black Sea coast. It is widespread in E and C Ukraine, particularly along the Dnepr and Dnestr Rivers and Black and Azov Sea coasts. It recently bred in N and W Ukraine (I. Gorban, pers comm, Mikhalevich *et al* 1994). It also breeds in NE Moldova. Up to 150bp (155 in 1990) nest in the Romanian Danube Delta, further colonies being on the Ukrainian side. Further upstream, Bulgaria and the former Yugoslavia hold a few pairs. Small isolated colonies exist in N Greece and Albania. In the Hungarian Plain the species is widely distributed, the largest colonies being at Kisbálaton and E of the Tisza River. A few pairs breed annually in E Croatia, and since 1989, in E Slovakia. The present westernmost colonies on its traditional range are at Neusiedlersee in E Austria.

Following its recent increasing non-breeding occurrence W and N of its present European range, the species bred for the first time in the Netherlands in 1978; since 1991 breeding has become a regular event, with at least 5bp in 1995 (M. Zijlstra, pers comm). Similarly, it probably has bred irregularly in Latvia since 1977 (Celmins *et al* 1993), far beyond its traditional breeding range.

Great White Egret populations continually suffer strong fluctuations, but from the late 1800s to the 1950s it decreased over much of its European range. Since 1965 it seems to have recovered from this decline and has begun to colonize anew. From the 1970s onwards it increased in numbers in Hungary and started to breed at several new sites (Schmidt 1977). Since the late 1980s numbers have also grown in Austria (Dvorak *et al* 1993) and Ukraine, where it has spread to new areas (I. Gorban, pers comm). However, the tendency of its populations to undergo large fluctuations makes long-term trend analysis difficult. For example, the Austrian Neusiedlersee population has fluctuated from the late 1970s' *c*320bp to 152bp in 1985, 429 in 1989 and 174 in 1991. Since 1991, numbers rose steadily to reach 554bp in 1994 (Dvorak *et al* 1993, A. Grüll & A. Ranner, in prep).

Whereas past persecution by humans and recent protection measures probably are underlying reasons for the overall trends, the causes of year-to-year fluctuations are not fully understood, but changing water-levels at the breeding grounds may be implicated at Neusiedlersee, (A. Grüll & A. Ranner, in prep) and in the Oostvaardersplassen, the Netherlands (Zijlstra 1994).

The European population winters mostly in North Africa and the E Mediterranean, a few crossing the Sahara. However, increasingly more birds are overwintering in C Europe (rarely Romania, D. Munteanu, pers obs) and the Netherlands (Zijlstra 1994). In January 1993, 215 birds were in Croatia and at least 75 in E Austria (BirdLife Austria). Furthermore, individuals are increasingly dispersing to winter in W and C Europe.

Dan Munteanu (ROM) Andreas Ranner (A)

Ardea cinerea

Grey Heron

CZ	Volavka popelavá	**I**	Airone cenerino
D	Graureiher	**NL**	Blauwe Reiger
E	Garza Real	**P**	Garça-real
F	Héron cendré	**PL**	Czapla siwa
FIN	Harmaahaikara	**R**	Серая цапля
G	Σταχτοτσικνιάς	**S**	Gråhäger
H	Szürke gém		

Non-SPEC, Threat status S

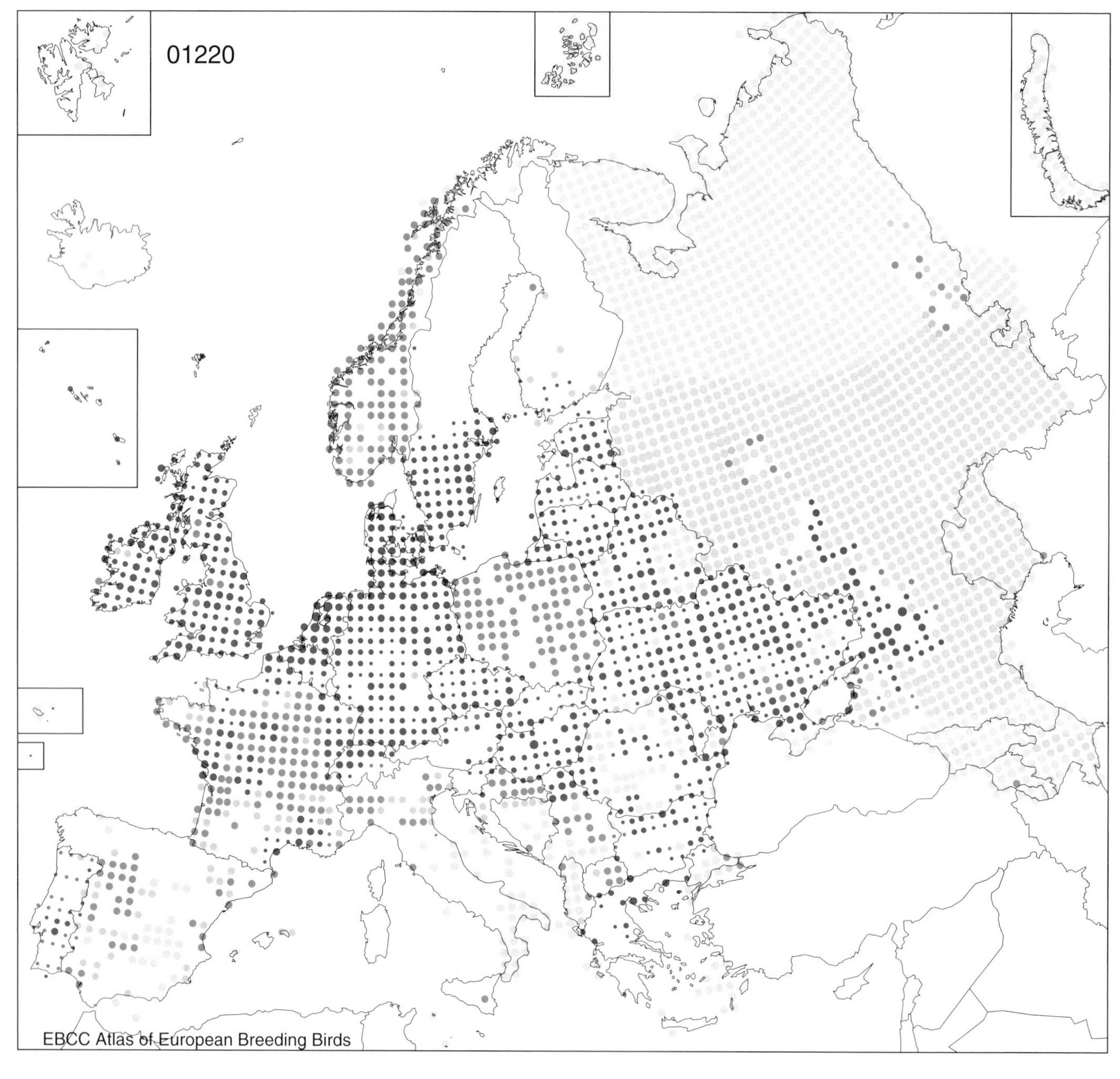

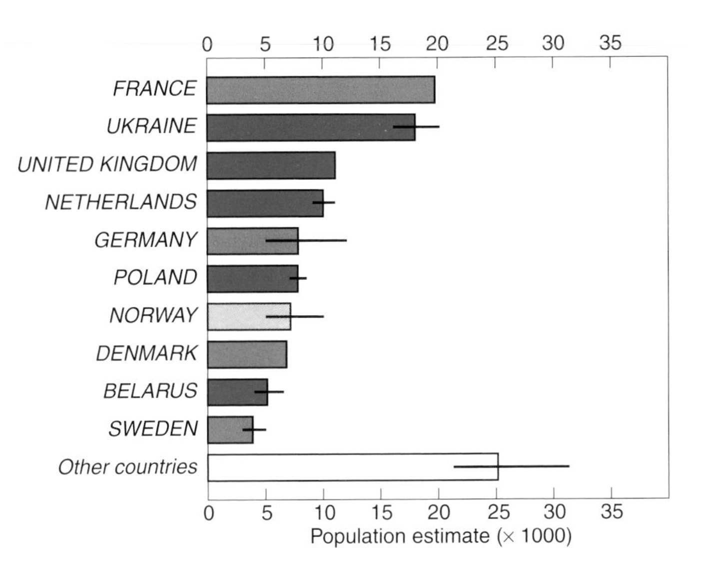

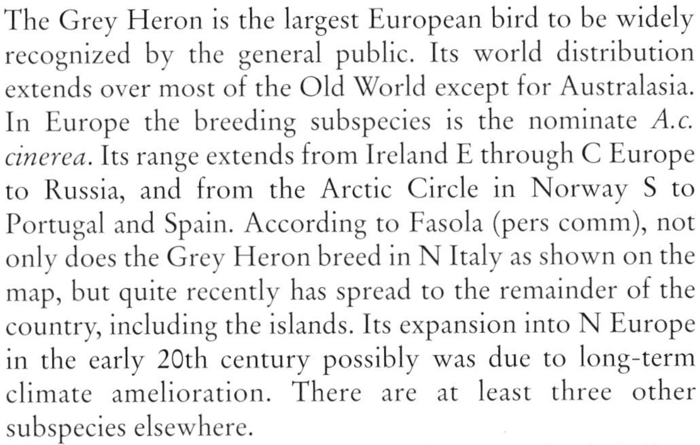

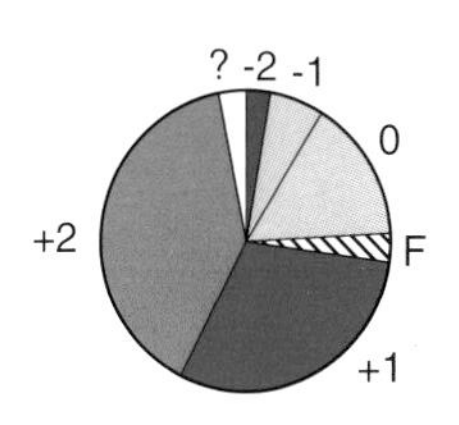

% in top 10 countries: 79.2
Total number of populated European countries: 33
Total European population 117,500–128,503 (122,046)
Russian population 20,000–25,000 (22,361)
Turkish population 2000–5000 (3162)

The Grey Heron is the largest European bird to be widely recognized by the general public. Its world distribution extends over most of the Old World except for Australasia. In Europe the breeding subspecies is the nominate *A.c. cinerea*. Its range extends from Ireland E through C Europe to Russia, and from the Arctic Circle in Norway S to Portugal and Spain. According to Fasola (pers comm), not only does the Grey Heron breed in N Italy as shown on the map, but quite recently has spread to the remainder of the country, including the islands. Its expansion into N Europe in the early 20th century possibly was due to long-term climate amelioration. There are at least three other subspecies elsewhere.

The Grey Heron prefers natural and artificial shallow waterbodies, whether fresh, brackish or salt, anywhere from the coast up to 500m asl, and occasionally above 1000m asl. If not persecuted, it can become habituated to human presence, and will even breed in the centre of large cities, such as Amsterdam. The nests, single or in colonies, are usually situated near its feeding grounds, although sometimes they can be 10–30km away. Typically, the Grey Heron nests in trees, but it will also nest on the ground in reedbeds, on rocky islands near the coast (in N Europe) or on cliffs, as in Scotland.

High densities of breeding pairs have been reported from The Netherlands (26.9 bp/100km^2), Denmark (15.6 bp/100km^2) and Germany (Schleswig-Holstein, 12.8 bp/100km^2) (Bezzel & Geiersberger 1993). In 1975, 92 bp/100km^2 were found in Noord-Holland in The Netherlands (Teixeira 1979). In 1973, 777 pairs bred in five colonies on the Eiderstedt Peninsula in Schleswig-Holstein, a density of 130 bp/100km^2 (Drenckhahn 1974). In the early 20th century, some heronries containing more than 1000bp existed in the Netherlands (Horstermeer, Hoog Soeren and Gooilust, the last-named having 1025 nests in 1925) (Teixeira, 1979) and in Schleswig-Holstein at Julianka (Drenckhahn 1974). Even as late as 1962, 1300bp may have bred in a single colony in Grandieu in the Loire Valley (Creutz 1981).

After fledging, juveniles disperse widely in all directions, but re-orientate to the SW in August and September for autumn migration. Outside the breeding season the species is widely scattered, but important wintering areas are the Upper Rhine Valley, the lowlands of the River Po, in France the pond area of Les Dombes, the deltas of the Loire, Gironde and Rhône and in Spain the Ebro Delta and the lagoons near Valencia (Creutz 1981). Northerly populations, except the British and Irish breeders, are migratory. Other populations from W Europe eastwards to Siberia are partially migratory, many moving S to the Mediterranean or beyond the Sahara, but others winter locally. The Mediterranean breeders are resident.

Because it feeds mainly on fish, the Grey Heron was heavily persecuted in the early 20th century. The severe winter of 1962/63 took a heavy toll and the breeding population reached a minimum. Water pollution, pesticides and habitat destruction may also have contributed towards this massive decline (Mead *et al* 1979). By the mid-1960s and early 1970s, the Grey Heron had become threatened in many parts of its range in C Europe, or even extinct (Bezzel & Geiersberger 1993). Creutz (1981) estimated the total European population (excluding the former USSR) as being only 30 000bp in that period. Since then, the Grey Heron population has increased in most European countries (Slovenia has experienced range and population increases of 20–50%; Geister 1995), due perhaps to a combination of better protection and a series of mild winters. By the late 1980s, its population had risen to *c*150 000bp. It remains an efficient and opportunistic predator of unprotected fish stocks and collections in ponds.

Wilfried Knief (D) Paula Ulenaers (B)
Janine van Vessem (B)

This species account is sponsored by Gunther Stöckmann-Klotz, Rheinberg, D.

Ardea purpurea — Purple Heron

CZ	Volavka červená	**I**	Airone rosso
D	Purpurreiher	**NL**	Purperreiger
E	Garza Imperial	**P**	Garça-vermelha
F	Héron pourpré	**PL**	Czapla purpurowa
FIN	Ruskohaikara	**R**	Рыжая цапля
G	Πορφυροτσικνιάς	**S**	Purpurhäger
H	Vörös gém		

SPEC Cat 3, Threat status V

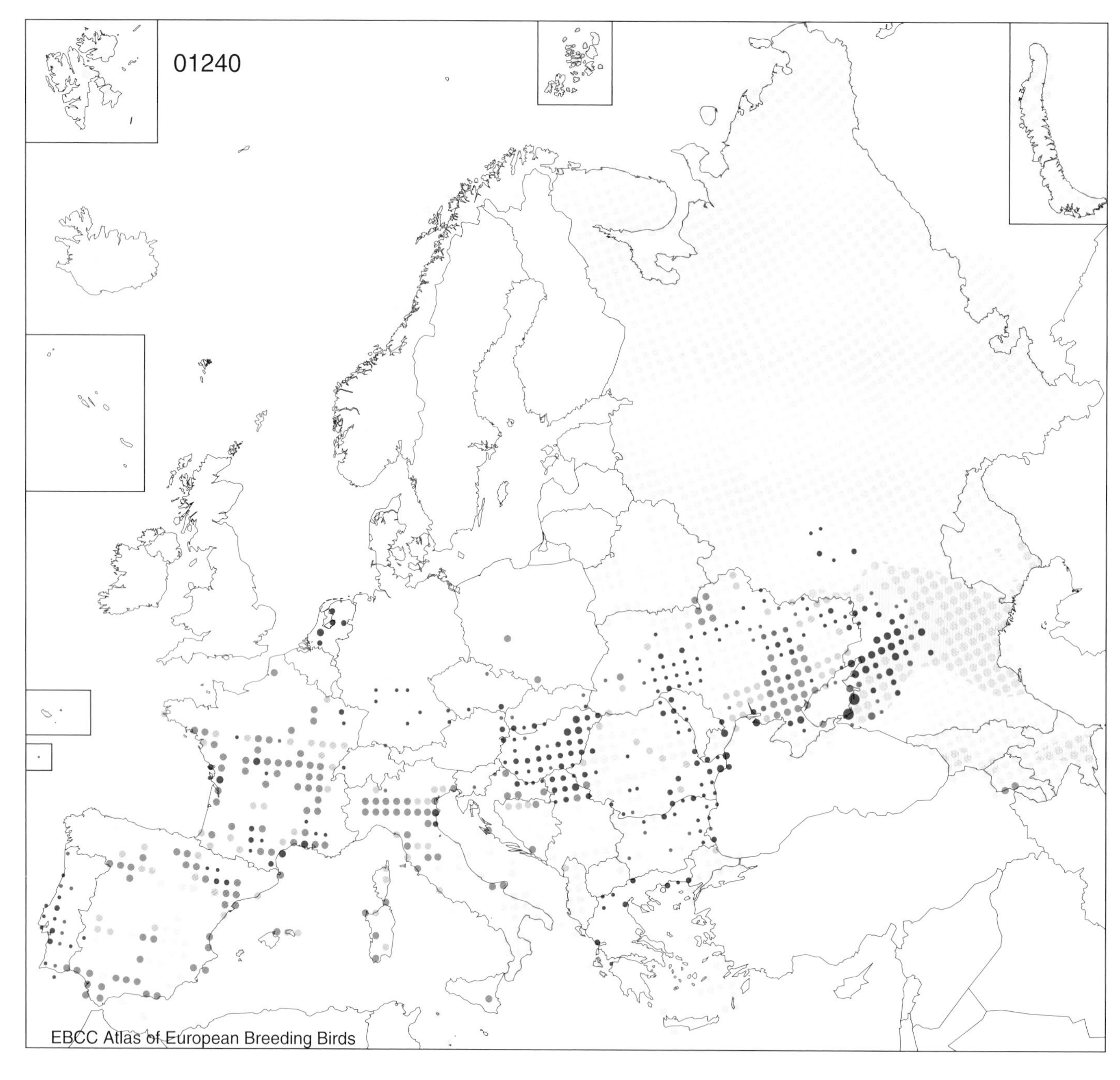

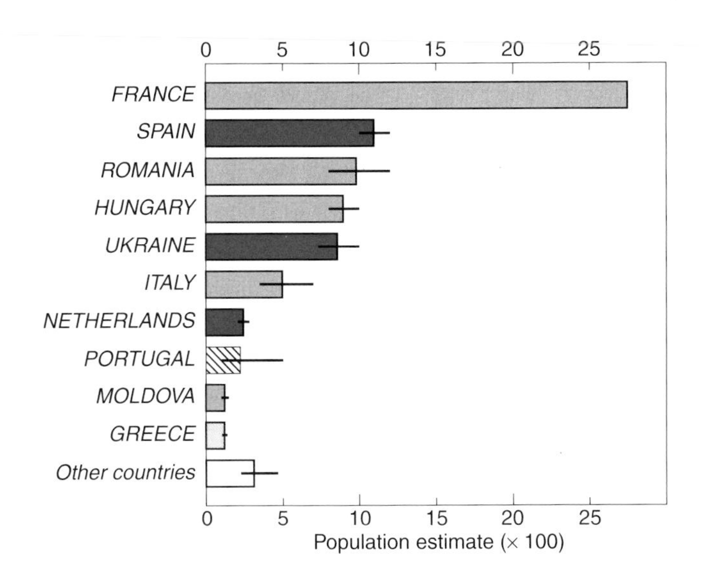

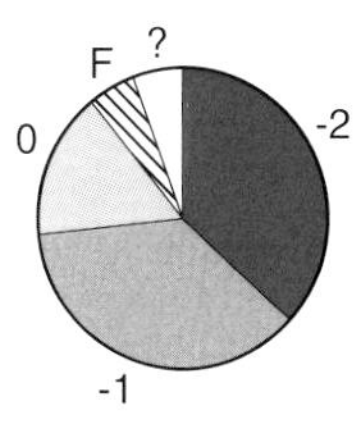

% in top 10 countries: 96.1
Total number of populated European countries: 19
Total European population 7766–8556 (8090)
Russian population 40,000–90,000 (60,000)
Turkish population 2000–5000 (3162)

The breeding distribution of the Purple Heron covers the Palearctic, Oriental and Ethiopian regions. In Eurasia it occurs mainly in southern Europe, E through C Asia and India to Ussuriland (140°E) and the Indo-Malaysian archipelago. In East Africa it is distributed continuously from the Equator S to Botswana, and locally in the Cape Verde Islands, Madagascar and the Cape of Good Hope region. European breeding birds (the nominate subspecies *A.p. purpurea*) winter in sub-Saharan Africa, from Senegal to East Africa. At least three other subspecies are recognized. There are several well-separated breeding populations: Europe and C Asia; Ussuriland to the Chang-Jiang (Yangtse) River; India and SE Asia; the Sundas and the Philippines, and Africa. Palearctic populations are migratory, the others resident.

The Purple Heron's breeding area is disjunct in much of W Europe, but becomes more continuous in C and E Europe, mostly below 53°N, especially along the Danube and in the Balkans (the exception being The Netherlands). Large numbers occur in broad swathes along the Dnestr, Dnepr, Don, Volga and Ural Rivers and also around the intervening steppe lakes in S Ukraine and S Russia.

The Purple Heron inhabits a variety of climatic zones, such as temperate, mediterranean, forest-steppe and steppe (and also savanna and rainforest outside Europe). It is well-adapted to dense marshy vegetation, its most important European habitats being freshwater marshes and reedbelt-fringed lakes, bordered by feeding areas like ricefields, farmland ditches and swampy river valleys. In the Carpathian basin it prefers large marshes like Kisbálaton and Lake Velence, but also uses fishpond reedbeds (Hortobágy, Szeged-Fehér-tó) and small natural alkaline lakes. Small colonies or scattered breeding pairs use oxbows and small riverside marshes (Danube and Tisza).

Most of the European population (*c*45 000–98 000bp) breed in Russia, whose numbers are poorly known. Significant numbers occur in France, Spain, Romania (mostly Danube Delta), Hungary, Ukraine (*c*1000–1500bp; Mikhalevich *et al* 1994), Italy (*c*40 sites, *c*550bp 1985–86; Barbieri & Brichetti 1992), The Netherlands and Portugal. The remaining populations each have fewer than 150bp. The largest western populations breed in just a few sites, such as Coto Doñana, the Tejo and Ebro Valleys in Spain, the French Gironde and Rhône Valleys and the Dutch Nieuwkoop marshland.

Several populations have been monitored closely since 1985 at least. The Netherlands population crashed from 900bp (early 1970s) to 215–300bp (1984–93), only 270bp (14 colonies) remaining in 1993 (van der Kooy 1994). Similar declines have occurred in southern France, where 1874bp (1982) declined slowly to 712bp (1992) (Kayser *et al* 1994) and in Austria where 320bp (1970s) decreased to 100bp (1990) (Dvorak *et al* 1993). The author believes that the core Russian population is also declining. Overall, only four national populations were stable from 1970 to 1990, whereas eight suffered at least a 20% decline, and seven a >50% decline. Falling water tables, desiccation, declining food supplies and habitat destruction were involved locally, but do not explain the Europe-wide trends of range contraction and losses; low winter survival rates would. Recoveries of nestlings ringed in The Netherlands showed a significant correlation between reduced survival rates of birds over one year old (but not first-year birds) and drought severity in West Africa, the main wintering area (Cavé 1983).

European populations winter in equatorial Africa, chiefly N of the Equator. French and Dutch ringing records confirm that western birds winter in the Niger and Senegal floodplains. C European ringing recoveries show that Carpathian basin birds also winter in West Africa, probably crossing the western Sahara. Hungarian birds migrate SW through Italy and Sicily to reach the Tunisian and Algerian coasts (Bankovics 1978). East Africa (upper Nile, Sudan, Ethiopia) may host Russian and Ukrainian populations.

Attila Bankovics (H)

This species account is sponsored by Netherlands Ornithological Union, Culemborg, NL.

Bubulcus ibis

Cattle Egret

CZ	Volavka rusohlavá	I	Airone guardabuoi
D	Kuhreiher	NL	Koereiger
E	Garcilla Bueyera	P	Garça-boieira
F	Héron garde-boeufs	PL	Czapla złotawa
FIN	Lehmähaikara	R	Египетская цапля
G	Γελαδάρης	S	Kohäger
H	Pásztorgém		

Non-spec, Threat status S

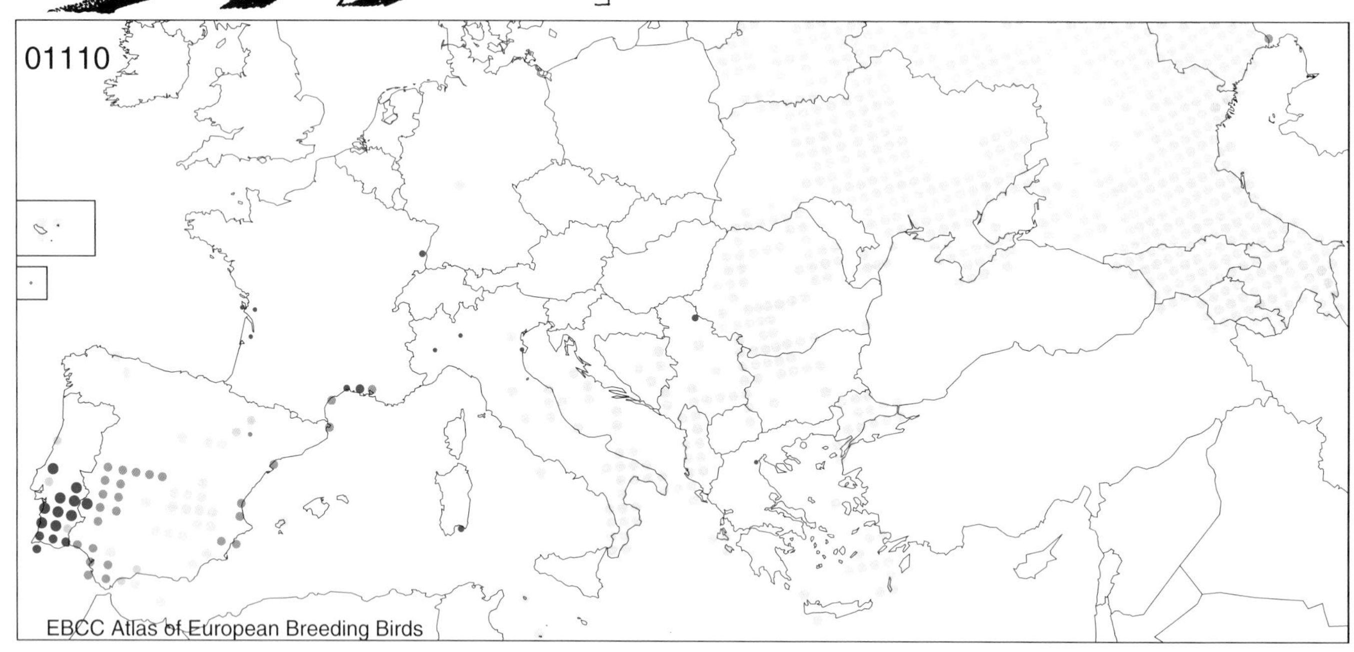

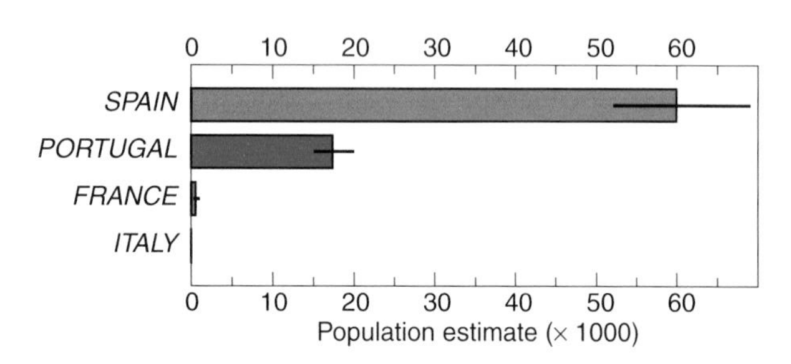

N +1 +2

% in top 10 countries: 100.0
Total number of populated European countries: 4
Total European population 69,527–87,306 (77,782)
Russian population 30–50 (39)
Turkish population 1–50 (7)

A vigorous colonizer, the Cattle Egret now has an almost worldwide distribution: Africa, SW Europe, S and E Asia and the Americas. In Europe it inhabits open grassy areas and freshwater habitats, avoiding saltwater biotopes, but it is less restricted to aquatic habitats than other herons. In 1990, a colony along the Guadiana River held more than 10 000bp.

The Cattle Egret's European range expansion has progressed slowly. In the 19th century it was resident and common only in Andalucía. Since 1930 it has bred in southern Portugal, and from 1961 it occurred increasingly frequently in Iberia, further colonies becoming established in the SW after 1970 and soon reaching 50 000bp. Censuses in Spain (1990) (Fernandez-Cruz *et al* 1992) and Portugal (1991) (J.C. Farinha, in prep) revealed 85 000bp at 63 breeding sites. In the Camargue, two pairs bred successfully for the first time in 1969 (following earlier failures); the population increased to 352bp in 1984, dropped to 74bp in 1985 (severe frosts in January 1985) and then increased to 1800bp in 1993 and 3540bp in 1996 (H. Hafner pers comm). In W France, at Lac de Grand Lieu, the species has bred irregularly since 1981 (*c*10bp in 1984), as it has in the E (Alsace) in the 1980s (through introductions). Several new colonies appeared in the early 1990s, as in the Aude district and in the Indre and near Brenne (Hafner 1994). It has bred in Sardinia since 1985, reaching *c*65bp in 1992 (Grussu 1994). Further colonization depends on man-made habitat changes, such as the creation of ricefields or pastures, and on warm enough summers to provide sufficient insects and amphibians.

The European population is partially migratory, wintering mainly in S Iberia and North Africa. In January 1993, *c*160 000 birds were reported in Iberia alone (Sarasa *et al* 1993).

João Carlos Farinha (P)

Plegadis falcinellus

Glossy Ibis

CZ	Ibis hnědý	I	Mignattaio
D	Braunsichler	NL	Zwarte Ibis
E	Morito Común	P	Maçarico-preto
F	Ibis falcinelle	PL	Ibis kasztanowaty
FIN	Pronssi-iibis	R	Каравайка
G	Χαλκόκοτα	S	Bronsibis
H	Batla		

SPEC Cat 3, Threat status D

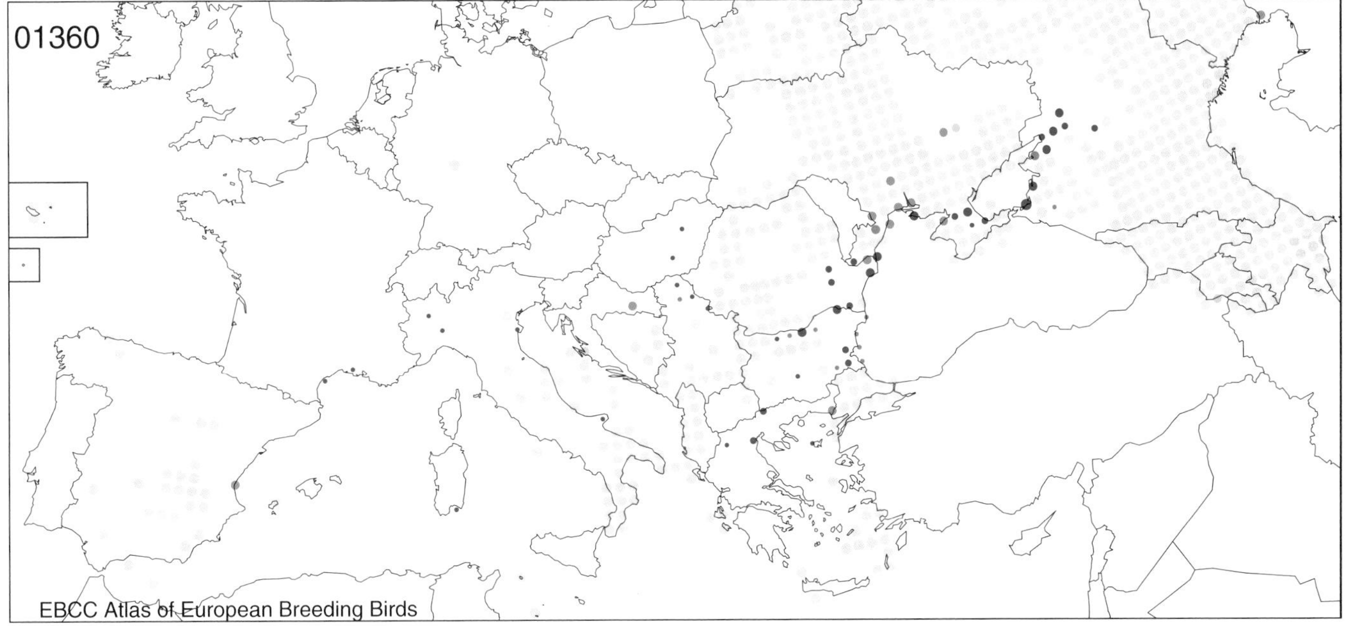

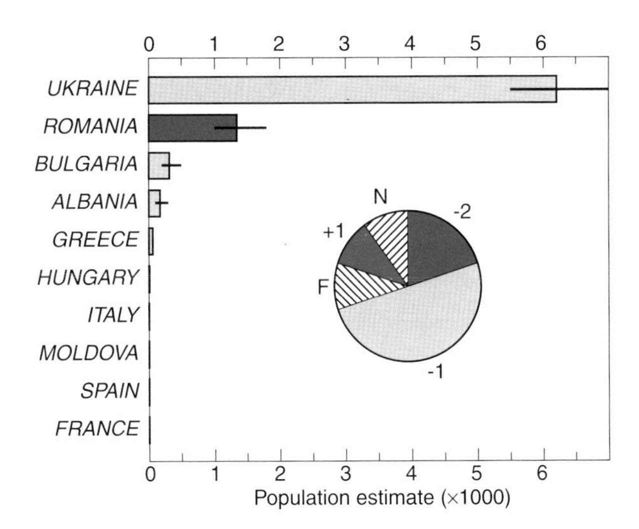

The Glossy Ibis' vast discontinuous range covers Australasia to India, C Asia to the Caspian and the Balkans, Africa, the eastern USA and the Caribbean but has diminished considerably since 1965. Some populations in W and C Europe were extirpated, mostly through the destruction of breeding and foraging habitats. Some 99% of European birds now breed W and N of the Black Sea (Koshelev *et al* 1991) and around the Caspian. Most European birds migrate to sub-Saharan Africa in September but Caspian birds winter in India and Ethiopia.

The species' requires extensive wetlands containing deep water and abundant vegetation. Occasionally it uses riverine forest. It forages in invertebrate-rich shallow waters, marshes and swamps, wet pastures, flooded meadows, sometimes far from the colony. It usually nests in willow *Salix*, or sometimes in reedbeds where willow is absent, and tends to form mixed colonies with the smaller herons and Pygmy Cormorant *Phalacrocorax pygmeus*. Colony-fidelity is low (Koshelev *et al* 1991).

Russia (6500–8000bp), Ukraine (5500–7000bp) and Romania (1000–2000bp) hold the largest European populations. Bulgaria has 100–700bp (Simeonov *et al* 1990), Albania 100–300bp, and Hungary, Serbia, Croatia and Greece altogether probably possess fewer than 100bp. Breeding occurs irregularly in Italy (1973–77, 1985–87 and 1989–90, 8–9bp in Sardinia in 1990; Brichetti 1992), Spain and France (one pair 1988 (Aude), 3bp 1991 (Camargue); Frémont 1994). Local breeding populations normally suffer significant yearly fluctuations (Simeonov *et al* 1990, Tchernitchko *et al* 1991). The general decline of E European populations is due mainly to habitat destruction, water pollution and human pressure. The Danube Delta population, 12 000bp in 1976–77, comprised a maximum of 2000bp in 1995 (D. Munteanu, unpubl).

Dan Munteanu (ROM)

Ciconia nigra Black Stork

CZ	Čáp černý	**I**	Cicogna nera
D	Schwarzstorch	**NL**	Zwarte Ooievaar
E	Cigüeña Negra	**P**	Cegonha-preta
F	Cigogne noire	**PL**	Bocian czarny
FIN	Mustahaikara	**R**	Черный аист
G	Μαυροπελαργός	**S**	Svart stork
H	Fekete gólya		

SPEC Cat 3, Threat status R

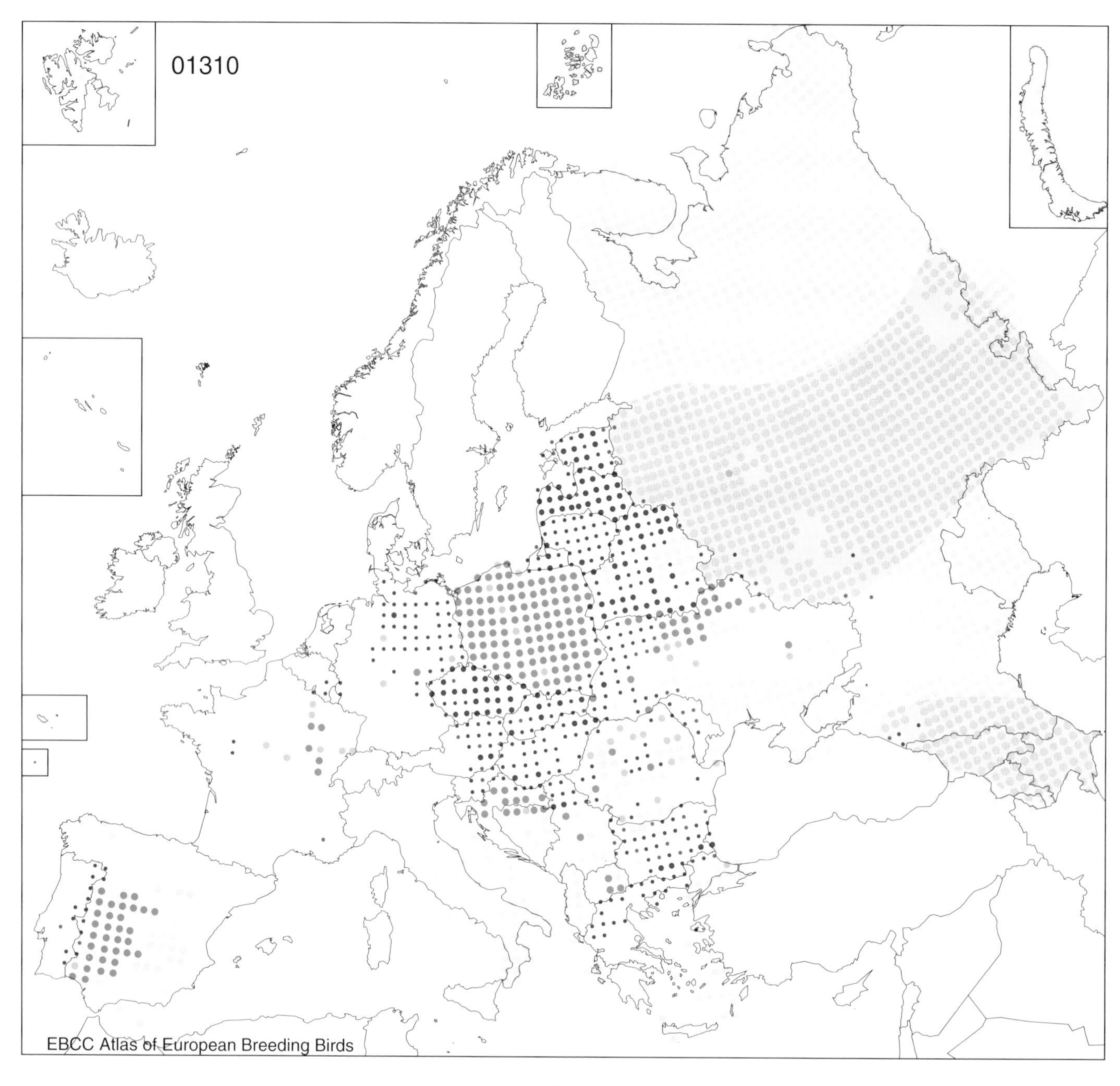

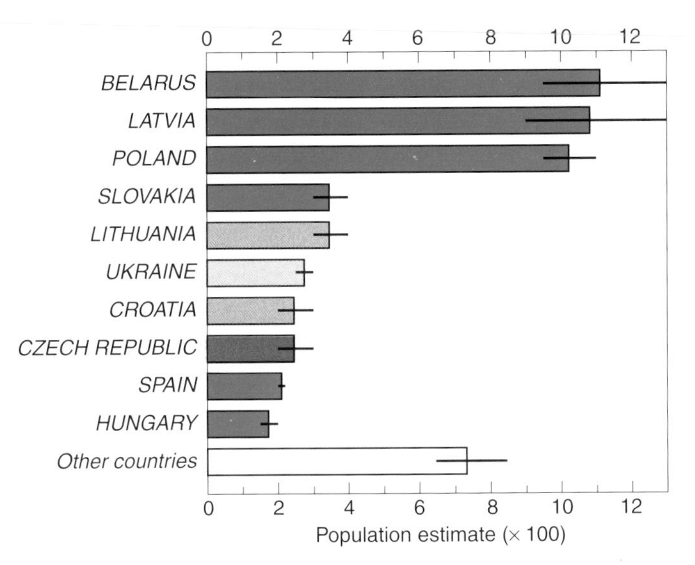

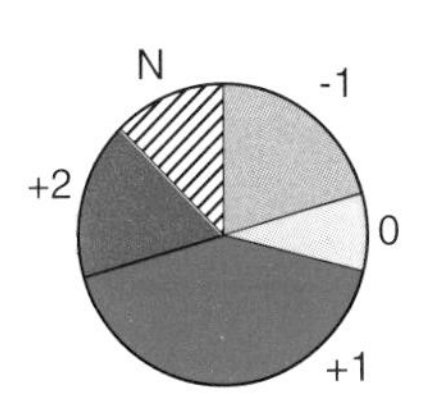

% in top 10 countries: 87.3
Total number of populated European countries: 24
Total European population 5513–6111 (5787)
Russian population 1000–10,000 (3162)
Turkish population 500–2000 (1000)

The Black Stork has the most extensive breeding area of the *Ciconiidae*. It is distributed throughout the forests of the warmer boreal zone to the warm temperate climatic zone between 30° and 61°N. Its range extends from C Europe eastward across the Siberian forests to NE China and Korea. To the S it inhabits the mountainous highlands of C Asia, the Middle East and Asia Minor, and also the Balkan and Iberian Peninsulas. Separated from the main Palearctic breeding area and thought to originate from migrants, is a small population on the South African low velds and dry highlands.

Apart from the few overwintering in Bulgaria and S Spain (Ferrero *et al* in press, Petrov *et al* in press), the Palearctic Black Stork is highly migratory. On migration it forms smaller flocks than the White Stork *C. ciconia*, entering Africa mainly through Sinai and Gibraltar. Some cross the C Mediterranean in a broader front generally via Sardinia, Sicily and Malta. Most E European birds apparently winter in NE and E Africa, scarcely crossing the Equator, the more westerly populations occupying the moist savannas and woodlands of sub-Saharan West Africa. Breeders from C and E Asia winter primarily in the Himalayan foothills in N India and in S China.

Prime breeding habitat in C and E Europe comprises deciduous and coniferous woodlands interspersed with rivers, creeks, lakes and other wetlands. In spring the Black Stork usually returns to the nest site from late March to early April. A solitary nester in the canopy of mature woodlands 60–170 years old, it favours regularly the oldest trees beside watercourses or by clearing edges. Throughout the Mediterranean it also prefers the more open dry forests of pine *Pinus* and cork oak *Quercus suber* (San Segundo Ontin in press). Cliff-nesting is more common in mountainous areas of Asia, the Mediterranean and C Europe, 61% and 28% respectively of all nests found in Spain and eastern Austria being on rocky outcrops and crags in steep-sided river valleys (González & Merino 1988).

Apart from Iberia, whose population comprises 250–300bp, the main breeding areas are concentrated on the European plain from N Germany, through Poland, Ukraine and Belarus to the Baltic States, whose total population in 1993 was estimated as 4300–5200bp (slightly higher than the graph indicates, and correctly so in our opinion), the majority being in Latvia, Belarus, Poland and Lithuania (Drobelis 1993).

Although the species had disappeared from most C European countries by the early 20th century, since the 1930s numbers have increased (in the Baltic States encouraged probably by a long-term improvement of feeding conditions) and the range has expanded gradually. The species now has not only recolonized much of its former breeding range in Slovenia, Austria, the Czech Republic, S Germany, Luxembourg, France (19–36bp in 1993; Duquet & Michel 1994), Belgium and Denmark, but also has extended its range in W Russia and C and S Ukraine (300–350bp in 1990–91, annual increase of 3%, perhaps now reaching the Khmelnitsky Region; Grishchenko 1994). These estimates, in our opinion, reflect the recent extent of the expansion. We believe that a comprehensive survey in Russia would produce higher estimates than given in the graph.

Breeding density in E European undisturbed woodlands lies between 1.3 and 1.8 bp/100km^2 (Belarus; Byshnev in press), but locally may reach up to 8.4 bp/100km^2 in E Poland (Keller & Profus 1992). In intensively cultivated forests of the Czech Republic and Austria densities between 0.2 and 1.7 bp/100km^2 occur (Pojer in press). In C Europe and the Balkan Peninsula most pairs breed in the lowland riverine forest and subalpine foothills of the Sumavan, Sudeten, Carpathian and Rhodopes mountains up to an altitude of 900–1300m asl. The Black Stork population of C Europe and the Balkans is reliably estimated at 1400–1900bp.

Peter Sackl (A) Māris Strazds (LAT)

This species account is sponsored by Dr Rüdiger Lück, Tosterglope, D.

Ciconia ciconia White Stork

CZ	Čáp bílý	**I**	Cicogna bianca
D	Weißstorch	**NL**	Ooievaar
E	Cigüeña Blanca	**P**	Cegonha-branca
F	Cigogne blanche	**PL**	Bocian biały
FIN	Kattohaikara	**R**	Белый аист
G	Πελαργός	**S**	Vit stork
H	Fehér gólya		

SPEC Cat 2, Threat status V

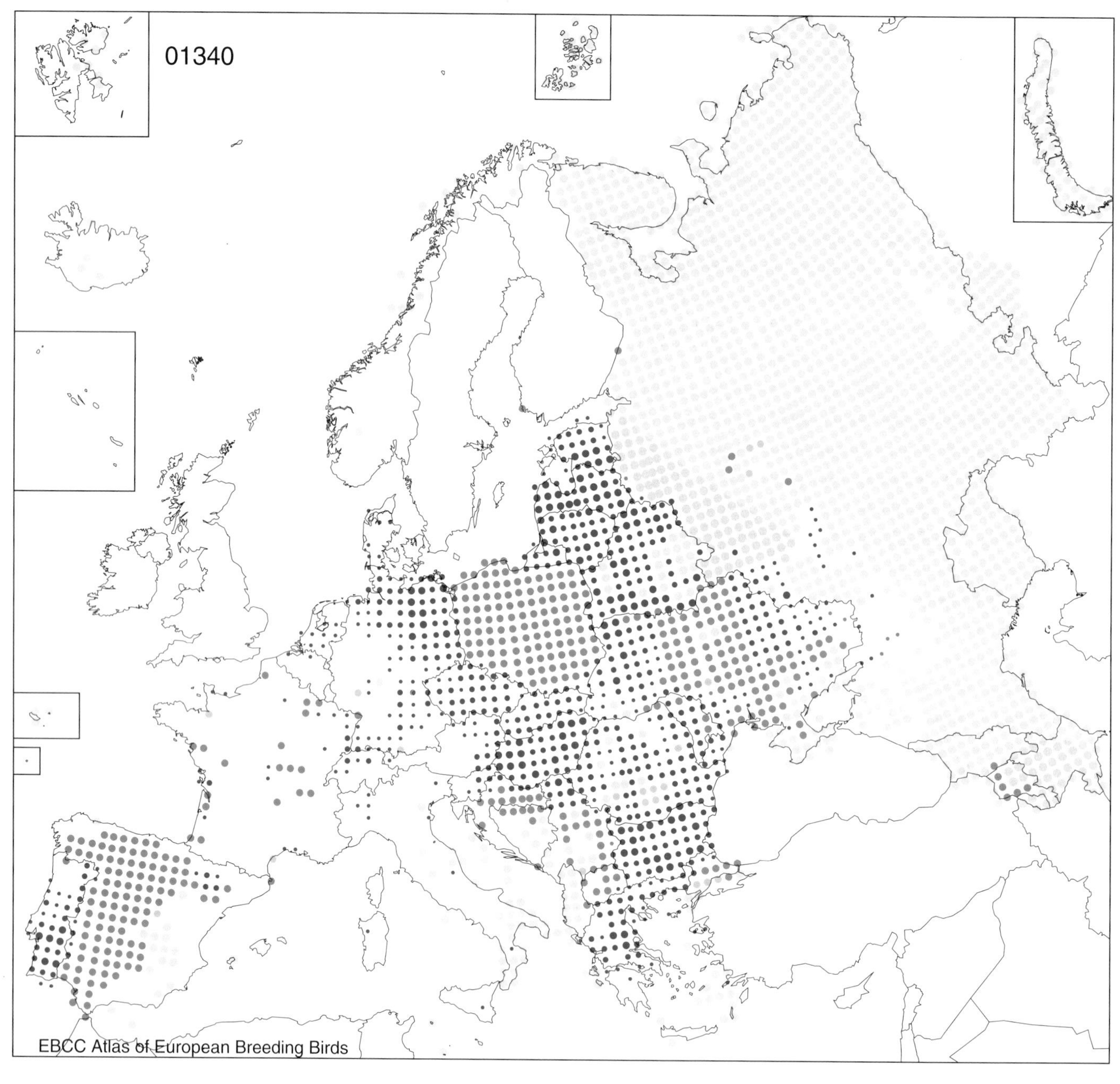

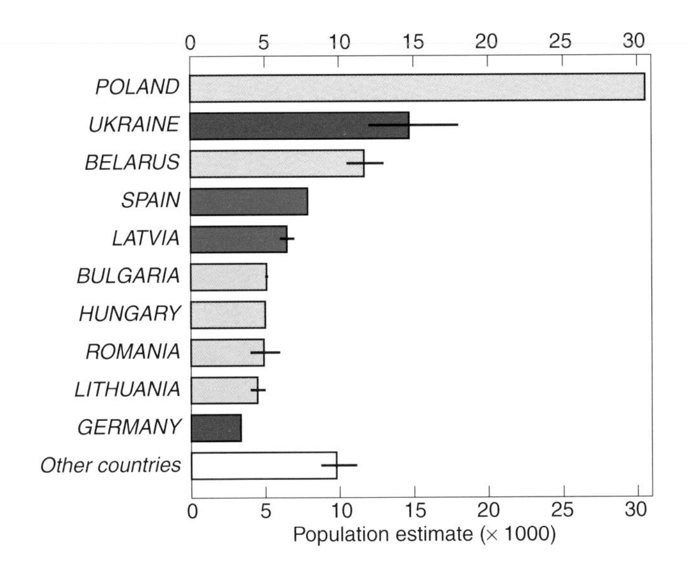

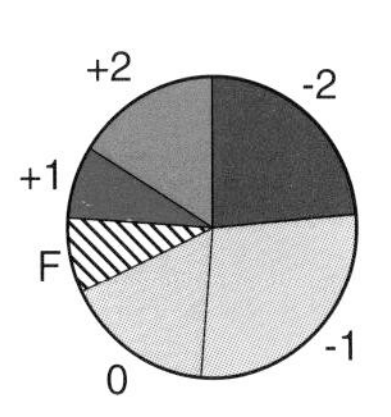

% in top 10 countries: 90.6
Total number of populated European countries: 26
Total European population 100,654–107,710 (103,850)
Russian population 3500–4000 (3742)
Turkish population 15,000–35,000 (22,913)

The distribution of the White Stork covers the temperate and warm Palearctic zones E to C Asia. It is widely distributed in E and C Europe (from eastern Germany to the Black Sea and from Estonia to Greece), in S and E Portugal and C, W and SW Spain. In NW Europe its distribution is patchier.

Only the nominate subspecies *C.c. ciconia* occurs in the Atlas' area of coverage, beyond which it is found E of the Sea of Azov, in Asia Minor, in NW Africa and even at the southern tip of Cape Province, South Africa. In Europe it breeds as far N as Denmark (formerly also S Sweden), Estonia and the St Petersburg region. Some 3000 have wintered in S Iberia since the 1980s (Tortosa *et al* 1995) but the majority migrate to the Sahelian belt and E and S Africa, and some to SW Asia. Now, only one other subspecies is recognized.

The White Stork occupies a variety of open habitats such as dry or wet grasslands, usually with fresh water nearby and scattered trees for nesting or roosting. Most of the western population breeds in farmland. In dry S Iberia, White Storks occur in places where widespread traditional agriculture is associated with open cork *Quercus suber* and holm oak *Q. ilex* woodland. In its winter range, it frequents savannas and open grasslands, sometimes gathering at waterbodies, but it also uses cultivated areas (southern Africa). The White Stork breeds in lowlands, mostly below 700m asl, avoiding persistently cold and wet areas. It nests in trees, sometimes on cliffs and on a wide variety of artificial objects. It readily accepts artificial nest-platforms.

The total European population numbers *c*105 000–120 000bp. Until recently the population trend was generally downward, especially in W and NW Europe. In the Netherlands numbers dropped from *c*500bp in 1910 to <10 in the 1980s (Bairlein 1991), in Alsace from 177bp in 1947 to some 20 in the 1980s (Bairlein 1991) and in Denmark from *c*4000bp in 1890 to 9 in 1991 (Sørensen 1995). A lesser decline occurred in the Balkans. Simultaneously, its numbers increased and its range expanded north- and eastwards in the Baltic states and European Russia, trends which continue. In Estonia (first nesting 1841), the *c*320bp of 1939 grew to 2000 by 1994 (Veromann 1994a). Similarly, in the Russian Pskov region numbers climbed from 400bp in 1958 to 1218 by 1974 (Veromann 1976). In Spain, numbers are again, albeit slowly, increasing since 1987, after a long-term decline had halved the population between 1948 and 1984 (Gómez-Manzaneque 1991). Switzerland, France (NE), Germany (SW), the Netherlands, Sweden and Italy, amongst others, have begun or completed reintroduction programmes.

The causes of the decline are complex (Bairlein 1991). Modern agricultural practices, often with considerable concomitant habitat losses, doubtless largely caused the decrease in many W European countries, such as the Netherlands, Denmark and Germany (N, and upper Rhine Valley). Furthermore, the long-term rainfall decrease in the western Sahel reduced food stocks and survival rates (Dallinga & Schoenmakers 1985, Kanyamibwa *et al* 1990). However, habitat conditions in the breeding area appear important, because different populations wintering in the same region in Africa show asynchronous trends, those from W and C Europe typically declining heavily, but those from E and S Europe being less affected, or even increasing.

As a long-range diurnal migrant dependent on thermal-soaring and gliding, the White Stork crosses deserts, but avoids large waterbodies and extensive forests. Most European birds therefore migrate either E or W of the Mediterranean, only a few risking the longer sea-crossing S of Sicily. The migration flyway divide runs from W Austria NNW through W Germany to the Netherlands.

António Araújo (P) Olivier Biber (CH)

This species account is sponsored by Naturschutzbund Deutschland, D.

Platalea leucorodia

Spoonbill

CZ	Kolpík bílý	**I**	Spatola
D	Löffler	**NL**	Lepelaar
E	Espátula Común	**P**	Colhereiro
F	Spatule blanche	**PL**	Warzęcha
FIN	Kapustahaikara	**R**	Колпица
G	Χουλιαρομύτα	**S**	Skedstork
H	Kanalasgém		

SPEC Cat 2, Threat status E

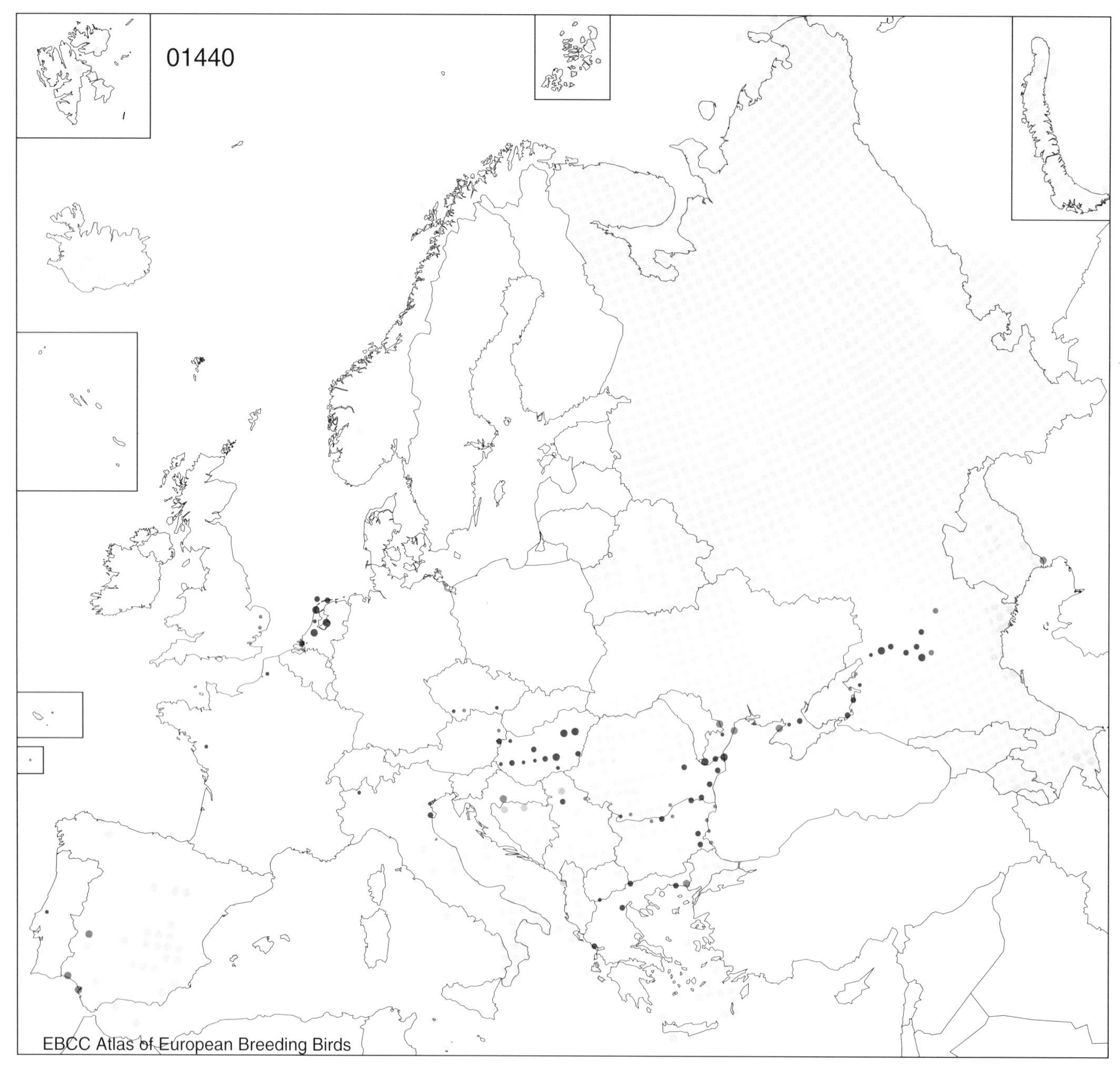

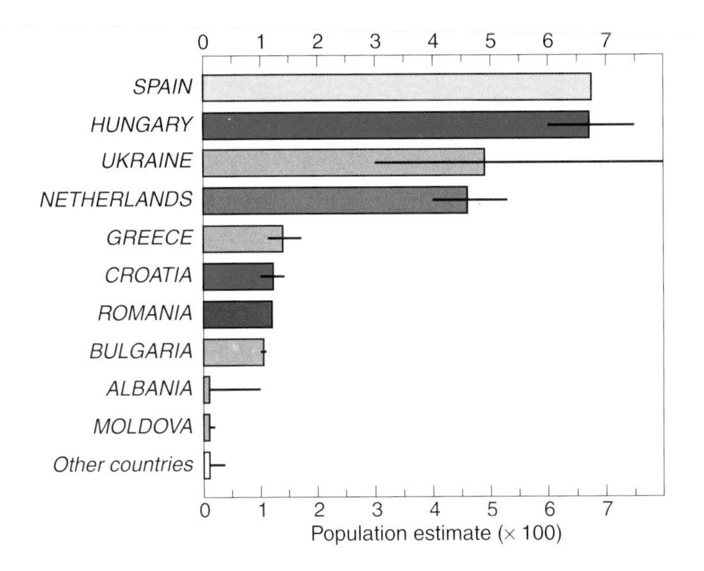

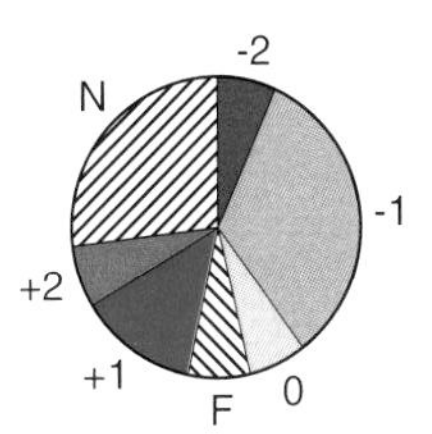

% in top 10 countries: 99.4
Total number of populated European countries: 15
Total European population 2631–3184 (2847)
Russian population 2300–2800 (2538)
Turkish population 500–3000 (1225)

The Spoonbill, a large specialized wading bird, is found in shallow wetlands from temperate and steppe zones in the N to the dry tropics in the S. Consequently, it has a patchy breeding distribution in Eurasia and Africa. The northernmost breeding colony lies in The Netherlands. Three subspecies are recognized, the nominate *P.l. leucorodia* breeding in Eurasia eastwards to the Sea of Japan and S as far as the Persian Gulf and Sri Lanka. The other two are confined to Africa.

Typical breeding habitat includes deltas, river floodplains and extensive marshes, where the species nests in reedbeds, on islands or in trees, safe from disturbance and ground predators. It flies up to 25km from the breeding colony to feeding areas. In winter and during migration, it is more dependent on marine habitats such as estuaries and coastal lagoons. For efficient feeding, it requires aquatic prey concentrations and shallow water free of vegetation.

In W and SW Europe breeding is largely restricted to the Netherlands and SW Spain (1075–1200bp) and a single colony in France at Lake Grand-Lieu (<10bp). In C and E Europe, it is more widely distributed, but it remains uncommon (Balkans 1000–1360bp; Ukraine and Russia 2600–3600bp). The major colonies, (>67% of the European population) are in Russia, Ukraine and Hungary. The Spoonbill recently extended its breeding range to the Czech Republic (1984), Slovakia, Italy (1989), France (1981) and Portugal. Dutch and Spanish birds winter in West Africa, especially Senegal (Poorter 1982). Those from the Balkans winter in the Mediterranean and East Africa. Part of the easterly European breeding population takes a south-easterly route to Iran and India.

In The Netherlands, the population declined from 300+ to about 150bp during the 1960s due to the effects of a build-up of pesticides. Since then there has been a steady increase to >600bp in 1993 (Voslamber 1994), in spite of the near-disappearance of two colonies on the mainland after fox *Vulpes vulpes* predation in the late 1980s. In Spain the population increased from <100 to >400bp during the 1960s and then to 675bp in the 1980s. Although Dutch birds transit through SW Spain during migration, there appears to be little exchange between the two breeding populations. In E and SE Europe, there have been declines in most countries, some slight, others significant. Early 20th-century strongholds in Serbia (500–1000) and Romania (400) have disappeared. The lower Volga population dropped from 2500bp in the early 1950s to 500bp around 1980 (Borodin 1984). The Spoonbill no longer breeds in Austria. In contrast, there has been a two- to threefold increase in Hungary. Overall, more than 67% of the European population showed a decline between 1970 and 1990, perhaps averaging 30%.

Its distribution is limited by the scarcity of suitable breeding habitat in the proximity of rich feeding areas. Its overall range has been reduced by human exploitation and by draining breeding areas. The recent decline in SE Europe is attributed to habitat loss, disturbance and water pollution. The loss of the Neusiedlersee colony is illustrative: an early decline caused by egg-collecting and reed-burning followed by another after 1970 coinciding with feeding-pool drainage (C.Y. Müller 1984). In the Netherlands, four new colonies have been established since 1988, perhaps triggered by fox predation (see above). Three are situated on fox-free Wadden Sea islands. Breeding success is highest in wet summers in the Netherlands and Spain (J.J. Chans, pers comm). The W Europe increase may be linked with increased protection along the migration route and in the wintering areas. Improvement of breeding conditions is a less likely reason. A breeding range extension into the German and Danish parts of the Wadden Sea might happen soon.

Eduard Osieck (NL) Berend Voslamber (NL)

This species account is sponsored by Vogelbescherming Nederland, Zeist, NL.

Phoenicopterus ruber

Greater Flamingo

CZ	Plameňák růžový	I	Fenicottero
D	Flamingo	NL	Flamingo
E	Flamenco Común	P	Flamingo-comum
F	Flamant rose	PL	Czerwonak
FIN	Flamingo	R	Большой фламинго
G	Φοινικόπτερο	S	Större flamingo
H	Rózsás flamingó		

SPEC Cat 3, Threat status L

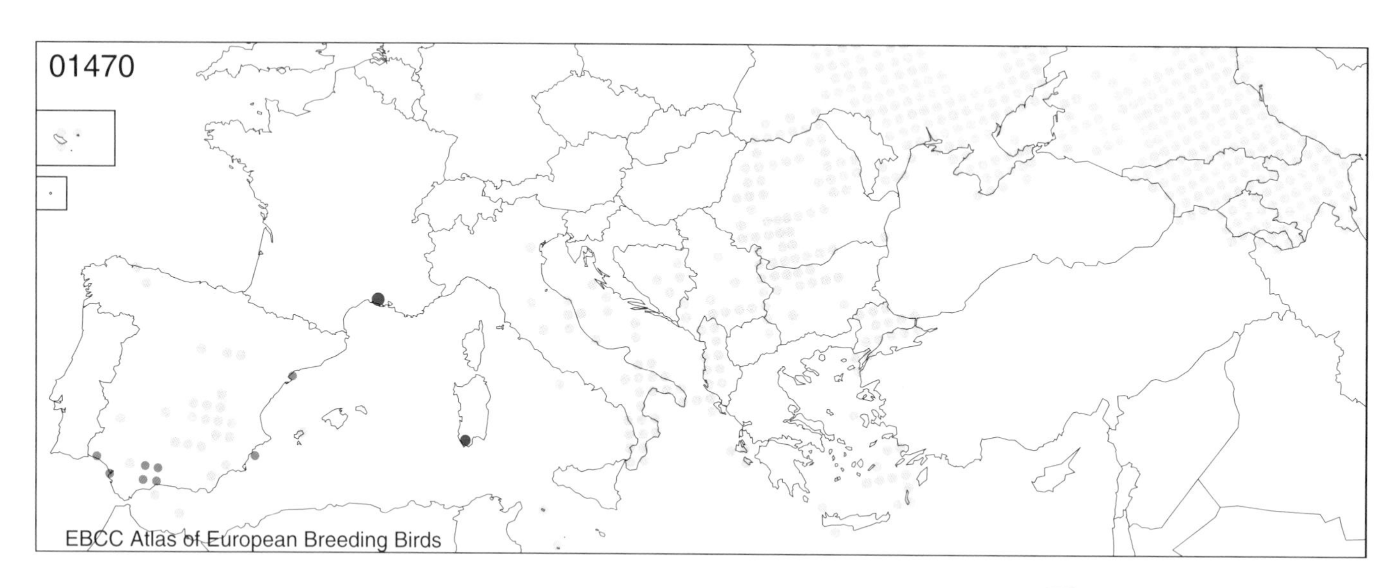

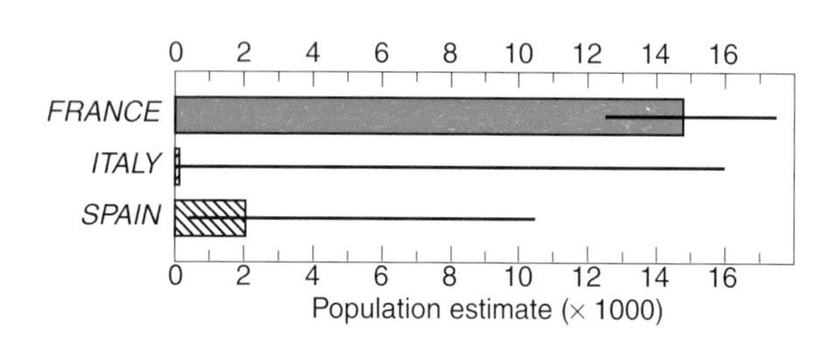

N F

+2

% in top 10 countries: 100.0
Total number of populated European countries: 3
Total European population 14,141–35,152 (16,966)
Turkish population 14,000–18,000 (15,875)

The Greater Flamingo prefers shallow, brackish and saline lagoons, salt pans and tidal flats. It breeds in dense colonies on low muddy or sandy islands and dykes, in widely separated areas throughout S Europe, C and SW Asia, Africa (*P.r. roseus*) and the Caribbean, even reaching the Galapagos (Caribbean Flamingo *P.r. ruber*). In many areas nesting is restricted to years of abundant rainfall prior to breeding. At Fuente de Piedra (Malaga) nesting is possible for the Greater Flamingo every other year on average, but in the Camargue it breeds annually on salinas (Johnson 1992). Only exceptionally does it nest elsewhere in Europe.

Specialized filter-feeders, flamingos are long-lived and do not breed before they are at least 4 years old. Colonies can number up to 20 000bp (Camargue). Birds forage for considerable distances; up to 70km from French sites and 160km from the Andalusian colony (Johnson 1992, Rendon *et al* 1991).

In Europe most sites are on or near the Mediterranean coast; in France the lagoons of Languedoc-Roussillon, the Rhone Delta and in Var, and in Spain the Ebro Delta, salinas in the SE, at Fuente de Piedra and wetlands from Cadiz up the Atlantic coast to Portugal on the Tejo Estuary. Since the *Atlas* surveys, it has bred successfully in Sardinia (Stagno di Molentargius) and the Ebro Delta. Numbers at all sites vary greatly. Since the early 1980s, it has colonized wetlands in Thrace and Tuscany, partly as a result of better protection and management at breeding sites. Flamingos are restricted in their distribution by availability of favourable habitat, and at present the Greater Flamingo occupies most areas which suit its needs.

There is great individual variation in the pattern of movements. Sightings of ringed birds show that while some individuals leave the Camargue for West Africa or the eastern Mediterranean, others have remained sedentary for 15 years (Johnson 1989). Furthermore, there is much exchange of birds between sites around the western Mediterranean where normally there are about 80 000 flamingos (Johnson *et al* 1991). The species is abundant on Sardinia and Cyprus in winter.

Alan Johnson (GB)

Cygnus columbianus

Bewick's Swan

CZ	Labuť malá	I	Cigno minore
D	Zwergschwan	NL	Kleine Zwaan
E	Cisne Chico	P	Cisne-pequeno
F	Cygne de Bewick	PL	Łabędź czarnodzioby
FIN	Pikkujoutsen	R	Малый или Тундровый лебедь
G	Νανόκυκνος	S	Mindre sångsvan
H	Kis hattyú		

*SPEC Cat 3*W, Threat status L*W*

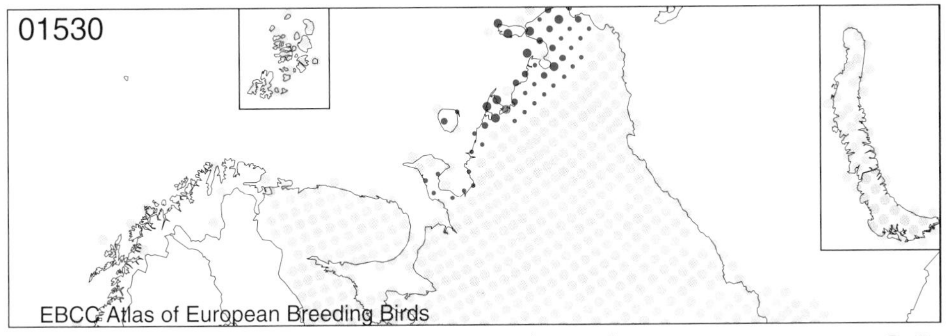

Bewick's Swan breeds on arctic tundra, across the northern Russian Palearctic, from the Kanin Peninsula to Kolyuchin Bay in the Chukchi Sea. Two main populations exist: one, estimated at 18 000 birds, breeding W of the Urals, migrates SW along the White Sea and Baltic coasts to winter in NW Europe; the other, some 30 000 birds, breeding E of the Lena Delta, winters mainly in Japan, China and Korea. The level of interchange between the two populations is not known, nor does their breeding range overlap. Small numbers also winter in the Caspian region of Iran, and occasionally in Turkey. Regular censuses of the birds wintering in NW Europe indicate that the western population has been stable since the early 1980s (Dirksen & Beekman 1991), although numbers fluctuate due to marked annual variation in breeding success. Earlier estimates of population size were lower (*c*10 000 during the late 1960s and 12 000 in 1980), but until recently there was no definite evidence for an increase in population after the mid-1960s, once the extent of incomplete coverage had been taken into account (Monval & Pirot 1989).

The main breeding habitat in European Russia is low-lying, sedge-grass, moss-lichen tundra, intersected by numerous lakes and river channels. Bewick's Swan rarely nests in shrub-tundra, and has been recorded in forest-tundra and taiga regions only during migration. Breeding densities recorded between 1973 and 1988 (Mineyev 1991) were: Malozemel'skaya tundra (including Russkiy Zavorot Peninsula, Kolokolkova Bay, Senyakha basin and between the Chesha and Shoina Rivers) 2.7–14.0 bp/10km^2; Bol'shezemel'skaya tundra (including Medynski Zavorot Peninsula, Bolvan Bay and southern Khaipudyr Bay in the Barents Sea) 0.2–1.8 bp/km^2; Yugor Peninsula (including the maritime Kara Sea lowlands) 0.8–6.6 bp/10km^2; Vaygach Island 1.0 bp/10km^2. The density variations reflect both tundra quality and the proportion of the population breeding each year. Few birds, either breeding or moulting, occur between the Kara River and the Yamal Peninsula. W of the main breeding area small numbers breed on the eastern Kanin Peninsula, which along with Chesha Bay is used mainly during migration. More recently, breeding densities of 35–40 bp/km^2 have been recorded on Russkiy Zavorot (J. Bowler, pers obs), but about 70% of the adult population probably remain in non-breeding flocks during the summer (Y.M. Shchadilov, Y.N. Mineyev, E.C. Rees & D.K. Scott, pers obs), indicating that recruitment to the European population may be based on the success of only 2000–3000bp.

Bewick's Swan uses only a few staging areas on migration, most notably Estonian wetlands, Novgorod near Lake Onega, and the White Sea region, which are of major importance for replenishing fat reserves (Beekman *et al* 1994). Winter distribution is also concentrated; up to 90% of the population occurs at fewer than 15 sites, mostly in the Netherlands, Britain and Ireland. A slight decline in the Netherlands population during the 1980s, and a corresponding increase in Britain, may be attributed to hard weather movements of swans from the continent (Monval & Pirot 1989). Numbers counted in Britain peaked during the 1991–92 winter, and have since declined (Waters & Cranswick 1993). Regional changes in winter distribution over the last 30 years also reflect a shift from traditional habitats, such as the shallow lakes, marshes and flooded pastures frequented until the mid-1960s (Poorter 1991), to increased use of arable land. Many of these changes were imposed by land reclamation and drainage, and the depletion of submerged macrophytes (a major food supply) due to water pollution, although the move to arable land may also be attributed to the swans preferring arable crops. Bewick's Swan continues to depend on areas of open water on which to roost.

Bewick's Swan is now generally regarded as conspecific with the Nearctic Whistling Swan *C.c. columbianus*; the collective name Tundra Swan has been proposed.

Eileen C Rees (GB)

This species account is sponsored by Northumbrian Water Ltd, Durham, GB.

NORTHUMBRIAN
WATER

Cygnus olor Mute Swan

CZ	Labuť velká	I	Cigno reale
D	Höckerschwan	NL	Knobbelzwaan
E	Cisne Vulgar	P	Cisne-vulgar
F	Cygne tuberculé	PL	Łabędź niemy
FIN	Kyhmyjoutsen	R	Лебедь-шипун
G	Κύκνος	S	Knölsvan
H	Bütykös hattyú		

Non-SPEC, Threat status S

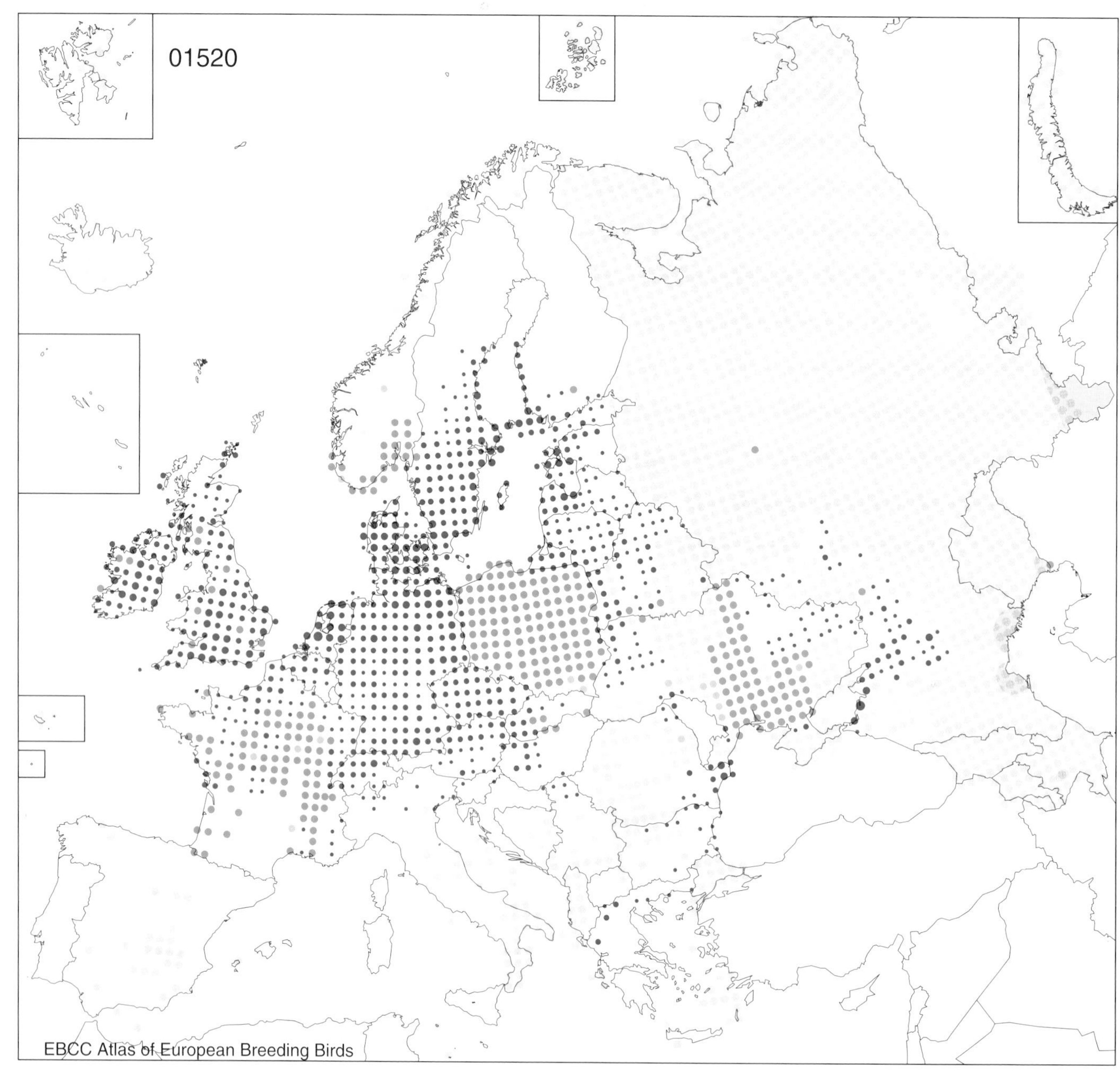

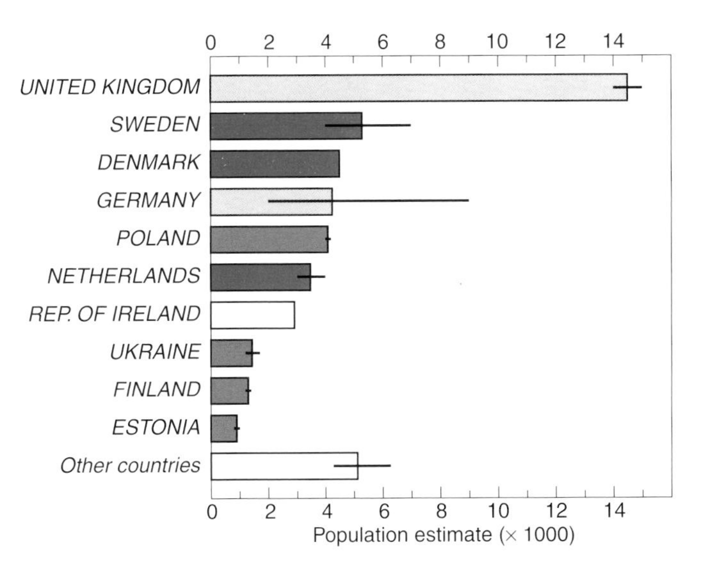

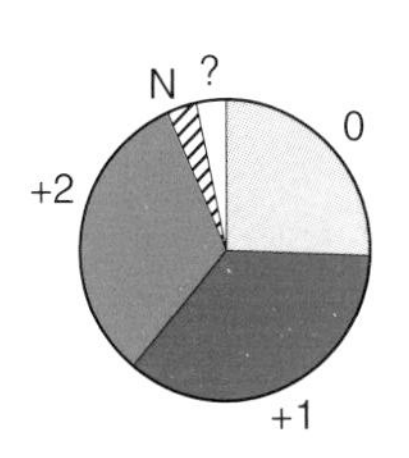

% in top 10 countries: 89.3
Total number of populated European countries: 31
Total European population 45,019–52,865 (47,726)
Russian population 7000–9500 (8155)
Turkish population 11–40 (21)

The Mute Swan has a patchy natural distribution across much of the Palearctic, but it is a popular ornamental species worldwide. In the Middle Ages it was a common captive breeder in Austria, Switzerland and S Germany, but wild birds and escaped 'park swans' formed a new mixed population which spread to W, C and S Europe (Köppen 1989). The Baltic held free-living populations from the early 1900s. The present continuous distribution stretches from *c*62°N in Sweden and *c*63°30'N in Finland (on coasts) S to 43°N in France and 40°N in Greece, and from Ireland to the N Caspian.

The Mute Swan breeds on a wide variety of fresh and saline waterbodies bordered by dense vegetation suitable for nesting. It also breeds on seaweed aggregations, saltwater islet beaches, barren cliffs, grasslands and increasingly since the 1960s in artificial reservoirs, ditches and gravel pits. Normally very territorial, the Mute Swan may breed in small concentrations or even colonies (where food is abundant), as in Denmark, England (Bacon & Andersen-Harild 1987) and Estonia (*c*68 bp/ha; Mägi *et al* 1992). It is less aggressive during incubation, but afterwards pairs defend water-borne territories (Bacon & Andersen-Harild 1987).

The highest overall breeding densities are: SW Finnish archipelago (1995), *c*50 bp/100km^2 on a *c*40km^2 island (L. Saari, pers obs), Denmark (>8bp), The Netherlands and NE Germany (4–8). N Polish densities are somewhat lower. In most of C Europe, <1bp/100km^2 is commonplace (Köppen 1989). Lowest values occur in highland regions (S. Mathiasson, pers obs) and in S Europe. Overall, population density (including non-breeders) varies, differing from breeding density patterns, which often are more localized (the Danube Delta, S Polish fishponds).

The European breeding population totals *c*35 000, but the wintering population comprises over 300 000 birds. Since the 1970s the species' numbers and range have increased rapidly in most areas. The Baltic population's expansion into western Ukraine now meets the Black Sea population's northwesterly extension (Wieloch 1991). The expansions have led to increasing numbers wintering in Hungary, Romania, the former Yugoslavia, Italy and Greece. In some areas (C Europe, SW Finnish archipelago) carrying capacity has been reached and natural regulation occurs (Köppen 1989, L. Saari, pers obs). Climate and weather set limits on the northeasterly range (S. Mathiasson, pers obs).

Mortality probably has lessened through reduced hunting pressure and generally milder winters since the 1970s. Mild winters in Finland correlate to subsequent increases in breeding and near-sedentary overwintering populations (L. Saari, unpubl). Severe winters cause high mortality (starvation, especially in the N) and low reproductive output the following breeding season (Esselink & Beekman 1991), but their effects may be reduced by widespread winter feeding and by the increase of eutrophic, ice-free waterbodies. Consequently the species has become more confiding and near-commensal, allowing it to extend its habitat use (Wieloch 1984). Conservation legislation has diminished hunting pressure, but culling and egg-removal remains common practice in The Netherlands, Germany and to a lesser extent elsewhere. In Britain, Ireland and Denmark lead poisoning (fishing weights, lead shot) has had a significant effect annually (P. Andersen-Harild, pers comm).

'Park swan' descendants generally are sedentary, whereas descendants of wild (feral) stock are mainly migratory (because of ice-cover; S. Mathiasson, pers obs). Some Baltic migration patterns have changed, mostly to shorter-distance movements. Finnish populations tend to overwinter, weather permitting, even when only shipping can break the ice to provide open water (L. Saari, pers obs). Since the 1970s Polish populations have migrated to the S and SW. Baltic birds now tend to winter close to their breeding and moulting area (1600 on the Vistula near Cracow; K. Walasz, pers comm). Many moulting grounds have changed.

Maria Wieloch (PL) Sven Mathiasson (S)
Lennart Saari (FIN)

This species account is sponsored by Northumbrian Water Ltd, Durham, GB.

Cygnus cygnus

Whooper Swan

CZ	Labuť zpěvná	I	Cigno selvatico
D	Singschwan	NL	Wilde Zwaan
E	Cisne Cantor	P	Cisne-bravo
F	Cygne chanteur	PL	Łabędź krzykliwy
FIN	Laulujoutsen	R	Лебедь-кликун
G	Αγριόκυκνος	S	Sångsvan
H	Énekes hattyú		

*SPEC Cat 4*W, Threat status S*

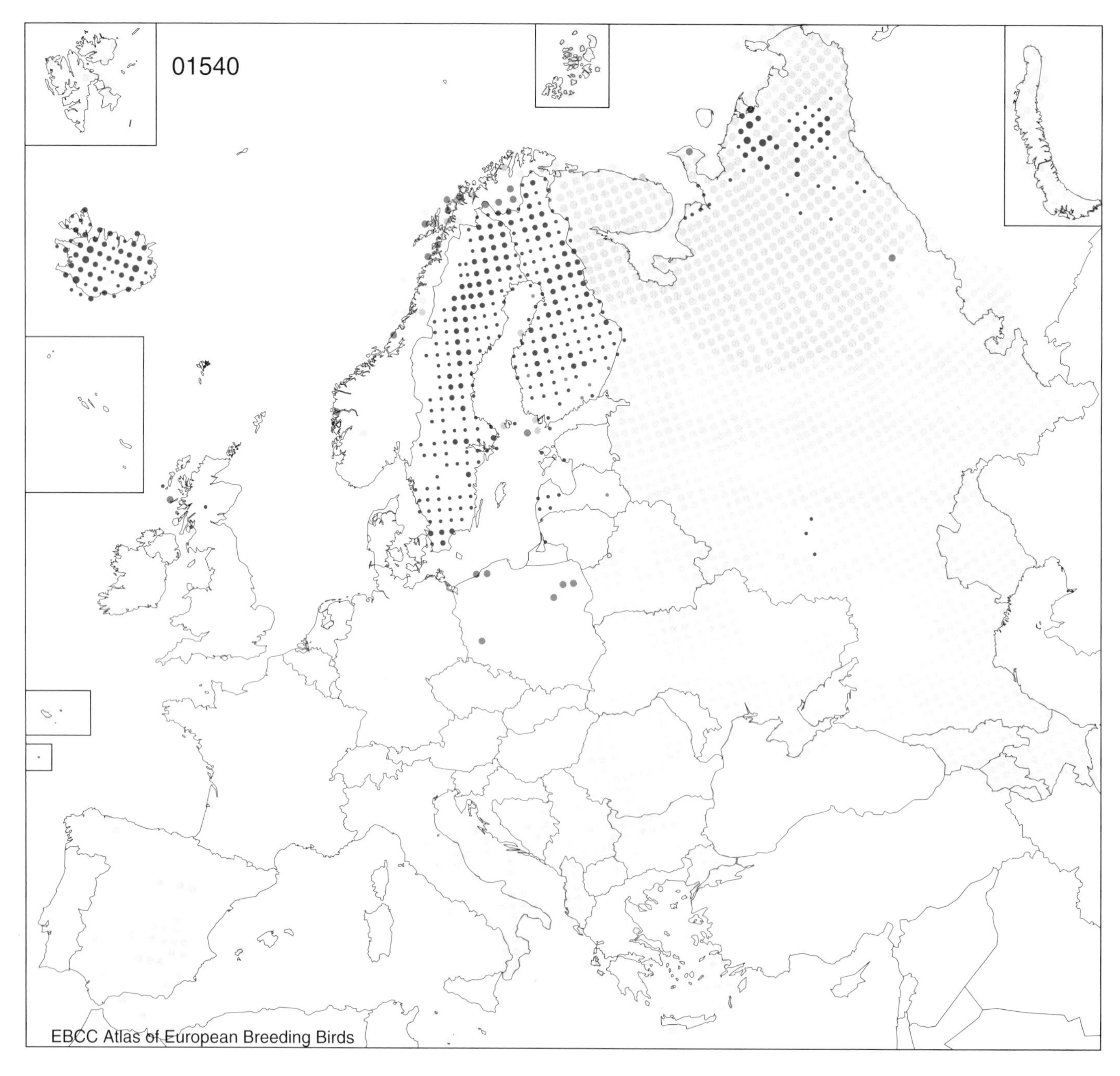

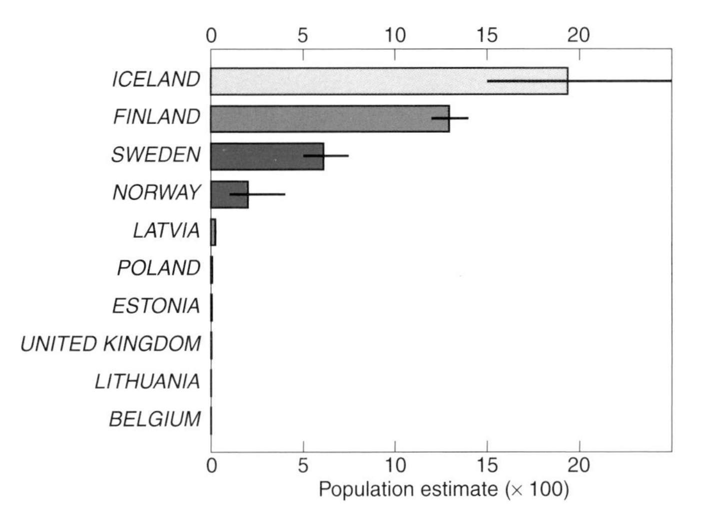

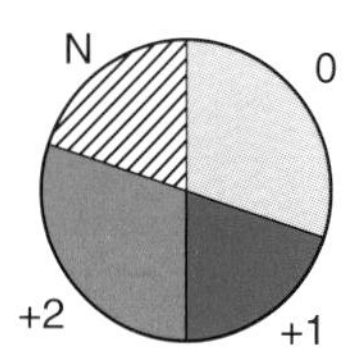

% in top 10 countries: 100.0
Total number of populated European countries: 10
Total European population 3616–4709 (4087)
Russian population 3000–3700 (3332)

The Whooper Swan is a trans-Palearctic boreal species distributed from Iceland to E Siberia. Some breed in tundra and steppe areas mainly occupied by other *Cygnus* species. In Finland breeding birds use two main habitat types: extensive wet peatlands and lakes with rich emergent vegetation (Haapenen *et al* 1973). In Iceland they are widely distributed in wetlands from 0 to 700m asl; most territories are on small lakes and ponds. Most nests are on islets, peninsulas or bars, also in sedge marshes, but rarely on seashore. Breeders occupy territories early in spring, as soon as the ice thaws. Pairs with small young spend time on mires and marshes. Broods usually stay on territories but sometimes move to richer feeding grounds.

In spring, arriving flocks occupy a variety of wetlands, including coastal lagoons, rivers and marshlands, and also cultivated fields. In early summer, non-breeders flock on wetlands and fields. Moulting concentrations (up to 3000 birds) form on shallow lakes, brackish lagoons and shallow sea-bays with dense bottom vegetation (*Potamogeton, Ruppia, Zostera,* green algae). Pre-migratory flocks in autumn form mainly on lakes, large rivers and brackish lagoons.

In Iceland the Whooper Swan winters mainly on spring-fed fresh waters in the volcanic zone, coastal waters attracting a minority, some of which have switched recently to urban habitat (Gardarsson & Skarphedinsson 1985). In Britain & Ireland it winters on natural wetlands and on agricultural land, but in Norway, Sweden and Denmark mostly on coastal waters. Birds wintering in S Sweden have recently moved away from the coast to inland areas where they feed on fields (L. Nilsson 1994).

A catastrophic decrease of eel-grass (*Zostera marina*) in the 1930s coincided with the disappearance of a large moulting concentration and a decline in numbers wintering coastally in W Iceland (Gardarsson & Skarphedinsson 1985). In Scotland and Ireland a shift to wintering on arable land occurred in the 1940s (Boyd & Eltringham 1962).

Breeding numbers have increased since 1950 in Norway, Sweden and Finland (by 11% per year, Haapenen 1991), a process associated with its spread from remote subarctic to boreal regions and usually regarded as recolonization of regions where the Whooper Swan had been eradicated previously by man. The Iceland population is stable or possibly increasing, but the long-term record is difficult to interpret, and counting efficiency may have improved. At Myvatn, N Iceland, numbers moulting show no trend from 1974 to 1994 and wintering numbers have also remained stable (A. Gardarsson pers obs).

The overall density in Iceland is only *c*2 bp/100km^2, or *c*5 bp/100km^2 when unsuitable ground is excluded. At Myvatn (200km^2, 280m asl) there are 3–4 bp/100km^2 (A. Gardarsson, pers obs). Much higher densities, 17–25 bp/100km^2, are reached in prime habitat, such as Skagafjördur (263km^2, 0–100m asl) and Jökuldalsheidi (188km^2, 500m asl) (Einarsson 1994). Densities are lower in Finland, about 0.9 birds/100km^2, or 0.14 bp/100km^2 (Haapenen 1991).

The Whooper Swan is migratory throughout its range. Even though 5–7% of the Icelandic population is resident, there is little overlap between breeding and wintering localities. In W Europe the main wintering areas are Ireland, N Britain, S Norway, SW Sweden, Denmark, N Germany and The Netherlands. Further E, the species winters along the Black and Caspian Seas, as well as in Kazakhstan, N China, Korea and Japan. Migration occurs on a broad front, W Icelandic birds going mainly to Ireland and W Scotland, and E Icelandic birds mainly to Scotland. Many make a further movement southwards in midwinter.

The Whooper Swan is polymorphic in eye colour and bill pattern. The proportion of yellow in the bill increases across the Palearctic from W to E (Brazil 1981). The Whooper Swan is replaced in Nearctic boreal wetlands by the similar Trumpeter Swan *Cygnus buccinator* (sometimes considered conspecific).

Arnthor Gardarsson (ICE)

This species account is sponsored by Northumbrian Water Ltd, Durham, GB.

Anser fabalis

Bean Goose

CZ Husa polní
D Saatgans
E Ansar Campestre
F Oie des moissons
FIN Metsähanhi
G Χωραφόχηνα
H Vetési lúd
I Oca granaiola
NL Rietgans
P Ganso-campestre
PL Gęś zbożowa
R Гуменник
S Sädgås

Non-SPEC, Threat status S

The Bean Goose is widely distributed across the northern Palearctic from N Norway to the E Siberian Khrebet Peninsula, a large range containing perhaps five subspecies, two of which occur in Europe: the Taiga Bean Goose *A.f. fabalis* and the Tundra Bean Goose *A.f. rossicus*. It is now generally accepted that populations should be separated into Taiga and Tundra types; some authorities have suggested full species status.

Taiga Bean Goose *A.f. fabalis*. The *fabalis* breeding range comprises the taiga of Scandinavia, Russian Karelia and the Kola Peninsula (Filchagov *et al* 1985). In Norway *fabalis* is virtually restricted to Finnmark, in Sweden it nests from Jämtland northwards, a small isolated population breeding in Dalarna, and in Finland it is scarce on the palsa (peat-mounds with permafrost cores) mire zones of Finnish Fjeld Lapland and absent from the southern raised bog complexes. Further E *fabalis* is reported to have bred in the forest tundra and the taiga of the Arkhangel'sk district, the Kani republic, and the Pechora-Ilych reserve (Lebedeva 1979, Yu.N. Mineyev pers comm).

The Taiga Bean Goose inhabits the forest zone, the home range always including a variety of mire types, mire forests, ponds, small lakes and streams. Among forest mire types

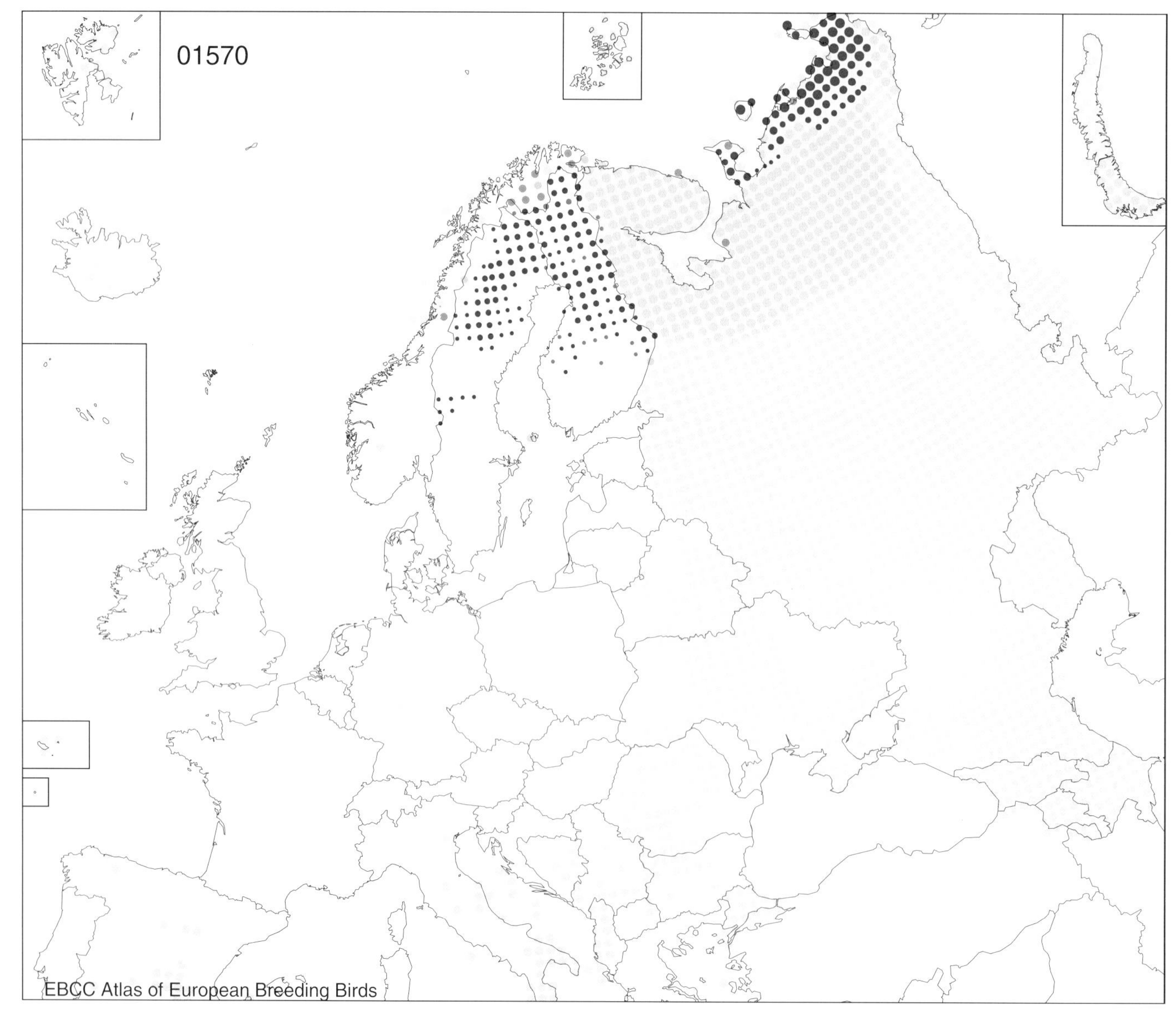

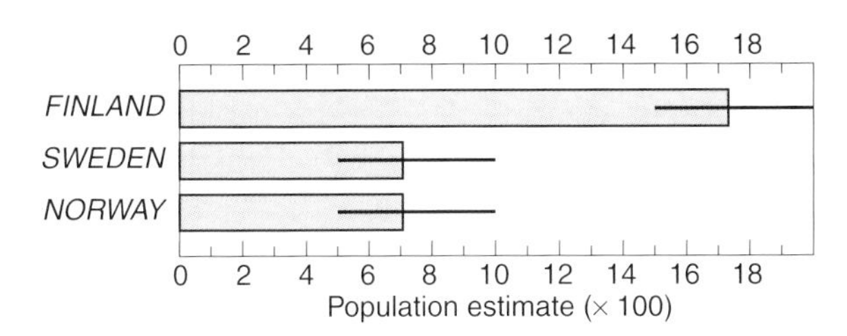

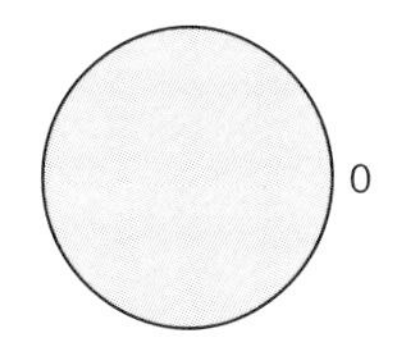

% in top 10 countries: 100.0
Total number of populated European countries: 3
Total European population 2773–3640 (3146)
Russian population 80,000–120,000 (97,980)

apparently it prefers spruce *Picea* mires, especially complex mire systems. The largest Bean Goose breeding concentrations in northern Finland occur on mesotrophic flark (pattern of wet areas in spring) fens in the aapa (wet, minerotrophic) mire zone comprising a mosaic of open fens and spruce mire. Sweden's sole area with dense Bean Goose populations lies in the northeastern aapa fen region. The dependence of *fabalis* on aapa mires may relate to suitable food plant production (Pirkola & Kalinainen 1984a, b). Probably the former dense populations further S in Sweden depended on suitable habitats being maintained by haymaking on the mires (Mellquist & von Bothmer 1984).

Censusing difficulties prevent the compilation of accurate breeding densities. S Swedish Lapland holds 1 bp/1165ha of wetland, but excluding unsuitable mires, holds *c*50–100 bp/16.245km^2 (P. Eriksson & Henricsson 1990). Roughly estimated, *fabalis* numbers are 500–1000bp each in Norway and Sweden, 1500–2000bp in Finland and 3000–6000bp in Russia.

The *fabalis* autumn migration in October sees 80 000 reach S Sweden, some 50 000 of which continue S of the Baltic. Smaller numbers pass W and S of the Baltic. By November, the remaining *c*30 000 either overwinter in Sweden, or move SW in sustained harsh weather (Nilsson & Persson 1984, Nilsson & Pirkola 1991).

Wintering *fabalis* numbers are estimated at 80 000–90 000 birds (Madsen 1991). An unknown proportion comprise *fabalis* populations breeding in the W Siberian lowlands, considered by Delacour (1951) as *johanseni*. However, the validity of *johanseni* is questionable, because Burgers *et al* (1991) showed that *fabalis* wintering in The Netherlands originate partly in the W Siberian taiga. Of the more eastern subspecies *middendorffii*, only 10 000–25 000 birds remain (Rose & Scott 1994); it is declining severely (Callaghan & Green 1993), a warning to protect *fabalis* in Europe.

Tundra Bean Goose *A.f. rossicus*. The *rossicus* breeding range lies in the tundra belt from the Kanin Peninsula E to the Khantanga River (Delacour 1951), along the Barents Sea coast, penetrating further S into the low-bush tundra than that of the White-fronted Goose *A. albifrons*; the summer habitat structure of *rossicus* is more diversified for it breeds in 12 of the 15 landscape types defined by Mineyev (1987). Typical *rossicus* breeding habitats comprise: poorly drained tussock-moss–crowberry *Empetrum* tundra (27% of nests found); poorly drained tussock-moss–willow *Salix* tundra patches (16%); slightly elevated tussock-moss tundra (16%); river and stream banks (15%), and much less frequently, grassland–tussock-moss tundra (5%) and willow–crowberry tundra on the edges of rolling uplands (5%) (Mineyev 1987).

Breeding density of *rossicus* in European Russia fluctuates between 2 and 10 bp/km^2, *c*50% of the population breeding at high densities, as in the Kanin Peninsula, the Vizhas-Oma watershed, the Malozemel'skaya and Bol'shezemel'skaya tundras and on Yugorskiy Peninsula (Mineyev 1990). On NE Vaygach Island, Syroechkovskiy *et al* (1991) reported 21, 20 and 61 nests/20km^2 respectively in 1986, 1987 and 1988.

In years of unfavourable ecological conditions the number of breeding geese finding optimum habitats reduces several-fold and in some years (1973, 1977, 1987) only odd solitary pairs may breed (Mineyev 1990). On Vaygach Island, breeding success is determined by weather conditions during egg-laying and incubation, by lemming cycles, and by Arctic Fox *Alopex lagopus* nest-predation (Syroechkovskiy *et al* 1991), the last-named seemingly being especially important. No successful nests were found on Yugorskiy Peninsula in 1984 because of high Arctic Fox density, but in 1985 many nests were successful when foxes were absent (Gritchik 1995, Yu.N. Mineyev, pers comm).

Allowing for seasonal changes, probably some 250 000–400 000 Bean Geese inhabit the NE European Russian tundra, *c*20–40% actually breeding (Mineyev 1990). Tentatively, the entire European breeding population, inclusive of Kolguyev Island and southern Novaya Zemlya, may total 85 000–150 000bp; perhaps 25 000–75 000 is more likely.

Populations of *fabalis* and *rossicus* perform 'leap-frog' migration, *rossicus* coming from further NE to winter further S on the Pannonian plain, in the Balkans, France, Italy and Spain, where few *fabalis* are recorded (Huyskens 1986, van Impe 1987). Some exchange occurs between the W European and the Danube basin wintering populations (van den Bergh 1984). W Palearctic *rossicus* wintering numbers probably total 300 000 birds (Madsen 1991); Spain's population has decreased sharply (Persson & Urdiales 1995).

NE Europe has experienced severe environmental degradation locally (Kotlyakov & Agranat 1994). New oilfields found on the Pechora bay coast will be exploited shortly (eg Sagers 1994). The Tundra Bean Goose may therefore face further long-term threats, especially given that its southern limit in C Siberia apparently is retreating northwards (Rogacheva 1992).

The eastern subspecies *serrirostris* has declined sharply in number since the mid-1970s in some Russian Far East tundras, probably partly through poorly regulated oil exploitation on the breeding grounds (Ler *et al* 1989). The Mace–Lande criteria suggest *serrirostris* is vulnerable (25 000–100 000 birds) (Callaghan & Green 1993).

Jacques Van Impe (B) Leif Nilsson (S) Lennart Saari (FIN) Mariko Parslow-Otsu (GB)

Anser brachyrhynchus

Pink-footed Goose

CZ	Husa krátkozobá	I	Oca zamperosee
D	Kurzschnabelgans	NL	Kleine Rietgans
E	Ansar Piquicorto	P	Ganso-de-bico-curto
F	Oie à bec court	PL	Gęś krótkodzioba
FIN	Lyhytnokkahanhi	R	Короткоклювый гуменник
G	Βραχυραμφόχηνα	S	Spetsbergsgås
H	Rövidcsőrű lúd		

SPEC Cat 4, Threat status S

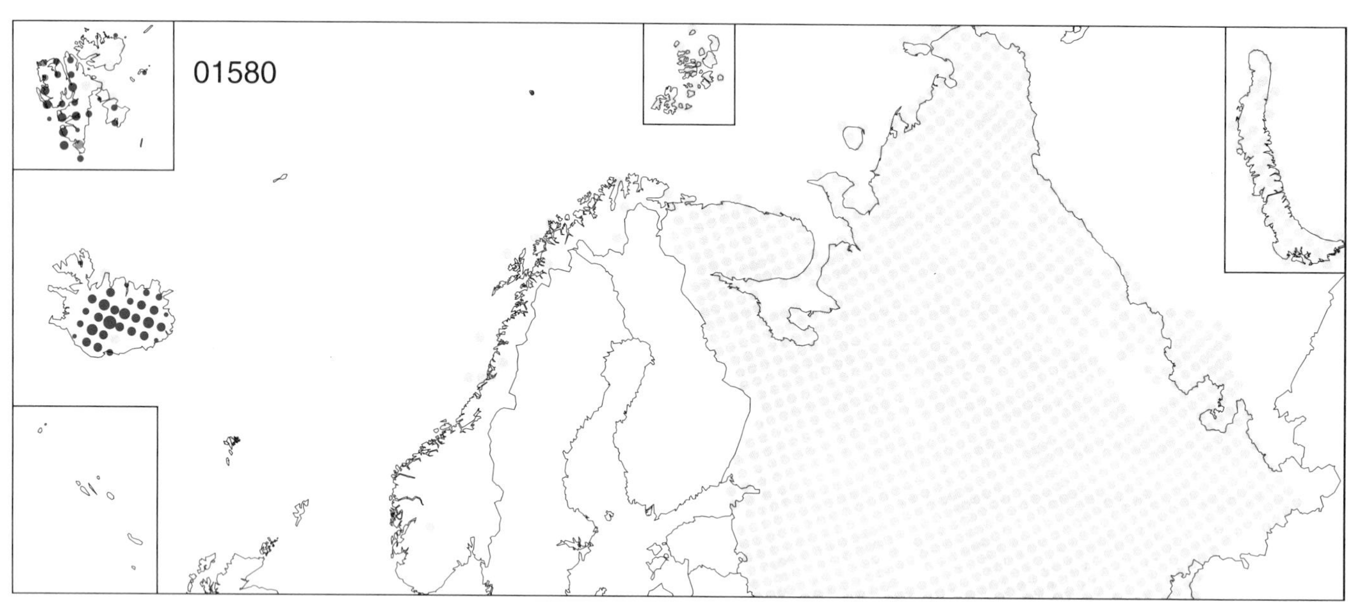

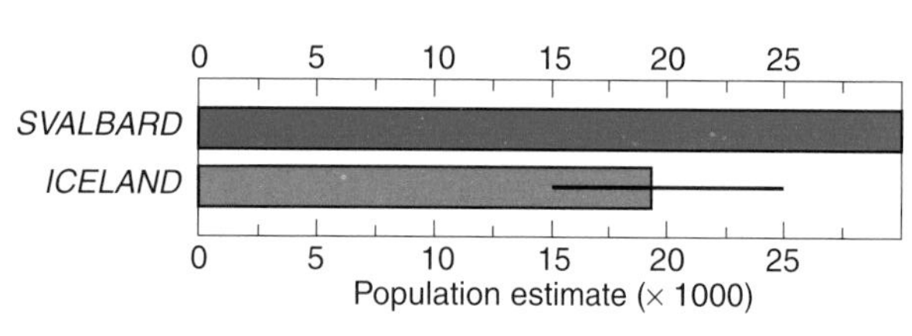

+2 +1

% in top 10 countries: 100.0
Total number of populated European countries: 2
Total European population 45,000–55,000 (49,365)

The world population of Pink-footed Goose breeds in Iceland, E Greenland and western Svalbard, while the Iceland/Greenland population migrates to wintering grounds in Britain & Ireland. The Svalbard population winters in Denmark, The Netherlands and Belgium, having autumn and spring stop-overs in Norway. There is only minor exchange of individuals between the two populations (Ebbinge *et al* 1984). In the Iceland/Greenland population, the majority nest in low-arctic conditions in Iceland, most geese breeding in large colonies in the central uplands close to the ice-caps. In the high arctic in E Greenland and Svalbard, the Pink-footed Goose nests on lowland tundras close to the sea as well as in inland valleys, often in small loose colonies. Since 1975 increasing numbers of geese have started to nest in lowland areas in Iceland as well, probably because human persecution has relaxed there. The highest nest densities are often found on hummocks or cliff sides near rivers or coasts.

In their wintering quarters the geese gather in large flocks which during daytime mostly feed on cultivated grasslands or arable land and roost on lakes or fjords at night.

In the early 1990s the Svalbard population numbered approximately 34 000 individuals, having increased slightly since 1975, while the Iceland/Greenland population has increased from fewer than 100 000 individuals in the early 1980s to more than 200 000 in the early 1990s (Madsen & Mitchell 1994). The increase of the total population coincides with the expansion into the lowland areas in Iceland, but the mechanisms behind the increase are not well understood. In our opinion, the graph of Svalbard breeding pairs is more representative of individual birds, and that of the Iceland proportion of the Iceland/Greenland population perhaps reflects earlier data.

In the central colonies in Iceland, densities of 36–544 nests/km^2 have been recorded (Ogilvie 1978), while densities are much lower in Svalbard at only 1–2 nests/km^2 in coastal lowland areas (Prokosch 1984). The difference between areas is mainly explained by foraging opportunities during nesting and brood-rearing. There are no subspecies.

Jesper Madsen (DK) Anthony David Fox (GB)

Anser albifrons

White-fronted Goose

CZ	Husa běločelá	I	Oca lombardella
D	Bläßgans	NL	Kolgans
E	Ansar Careto	P	Ganso-grande-de-testa-branca
F	Oie rieuse	PL	Gęś białoczelna
FIN	Tundrahanhi	R	Белолобый гусь
G	Ασπρομέτωπη	S	Bläsgås
H	Nagy lilik		

Non-SPEC, Threat status S

The White-fronted Goose breeds in the Eurasian tundra from the Kanin Peninsula in the W to the Kolyma tundra in the E. Its distribution is limited roughly between the July 4°C and 10°C isotherms.

Although the species' habitat preferences in the Bol'shezemel'skaya tundra are broadly comparable with those of the Tundra Bean Goose *Anser fabalis rossicus*, long-term research has shown they are confined to only 6 of the 15 tundra habitat types against the latter's 14 (Mineyev 1987). In particular, the White-fronted Goose is not found along the slopes bordering large lakes, whereas almost one sixth of all observations of Tundra Bean Geese occur in this habitat. Other principal breeding habitats of White-fronted Goose are seacoasts (23.3% of observations), tundras along rivers (22.2%), bogs (16.5%) and small temporary lakes (15.9%). Bird summer density per km^2 varies from 1.7 to 5.7 (1986–93) for the whole of the Malozemel'skaya tundra, and from 2.1 to 7.3 (1981–87) for the whole of the Yugorskiy Peninsula. From 1973 to 1993, the mean density averaged lowest (0.1–0.2 birds/km^2) in the Kanin Peninsula, the coastal area along the Chëshskaya Gulf, and the subarctic belt between the towns of Nar'yan Mar and Vorkuta. The island of Kolguyev yielded about 13 birds/km^2 and the southern part of Vaygach Island, 8 birds/km^2. The highest density of breeding birds was noted along Kolokolkova Bay (*c*90 birds/km^2).

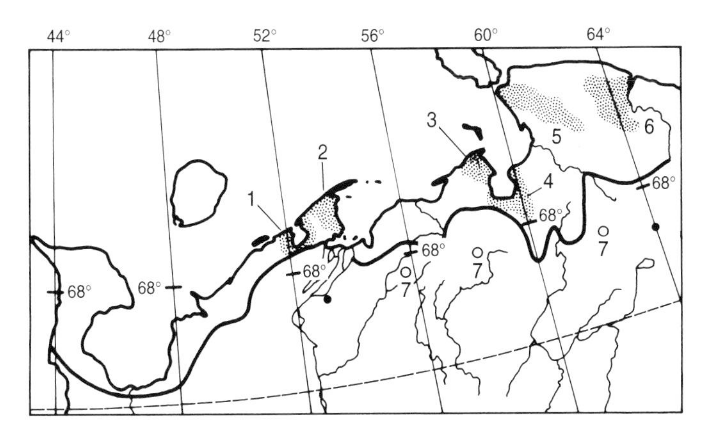

Map showing the distribution of the White-fronted Goose in Europe, in the far NE part of European Russia. Dotted areas indicate the breeding areas with highest densities. The drawn line indicates the distribution limit. The dots below the line (marked 7) indicate erratic breeding. The important areas are: (1) Kolokolkova Bay tundra; (2) Russki Zavorot Peninsula; (3) Medynski Zavorot Peninsula; (4) Khaypudir Bay coast; (5) Lymbadaykha-Bolshaya Oyu interfluvium; (6) Tabyu and Putyu interfluvium. (After Y. Mineyev, March 1994.)

The White-fronted Goose nests in several types of tundra; *Carex*-grassy areas in hilly tundras, seacoast meadows, along river coasts, in hummock grassy and hummock moss–shrubbery tundras, stone fields with sparse shrubby and grassy vegetation, and on *Carex–Eriophorum* bogs. Breeding densities vary from very low in the southernmost shrub tundra to very high in coastal areas, principally at lakes 0.1–0.5km^2 in area.

In the European tundras, Mineyev (1987) found large annual fluctuations. Nesting densities may reach 15–20 bp/km^2 in good ecological conditions. The species nests especially densely near breeding Rough-legged Buzzard *Buteo lagopus*, Merlin *Falco columbarius* and Peregrine *F. peregrinus*. The diagram indicates mass breeding areas.

Among the six subpopulations wintering in the W Palearctic, that in the Baltic/North Sea area comprises birds originating mainly from European breeding grounds (Perdeck & Speek 1964, Lebedeva 1979). Their number has grown from 55 000 to 80 000 in the 1960s to nearly 480 000 by January 1986. Subsequent winter counts estimate a slightly lower total (1988/89, 400 000–410 000; Kuyken & Meire 1990). These data suggest a marked increase of the breeding population in European Russia since 1965. However, ringing recoveries show that exchanges occur of wintering birds between the Baltic/North Sea population and the eastern Europe population (Lebedeva 1979). Because the latter group consists mainly of birds breeding in W and C Siberian tundras (Ptushenko 1952, Lebedeva 1979), the suggested increase of the European breeding population cannot yet be confirmed.

Comparative long-term studies of the Asian populations of the Taymyr Peninsula and the Anadyr River show that the latter's population is relict (Krechmar 1986). This accentuates the importance of protection of the westernmost breeding grounds, especially in the light of recent large-scale development of mineral extraction (Mineyev 1982a).

Yuri N Mineyev (R) Jacques van Impe (B)

Anser anser

Greylag Goose

CZ	Husa velká	I	Oca selvatica
D	Graugans	NL	Grauwe Gans
E	Ansar Común	P	Ganso-comum
F	Oie cendrée	PL	Gęgawa
FIN	Merihanhi	R	Серый гусь
G	Σταχτόχηνα	S	Grågås
H	Nyári lúd		

Non-SPEC, Threat status S

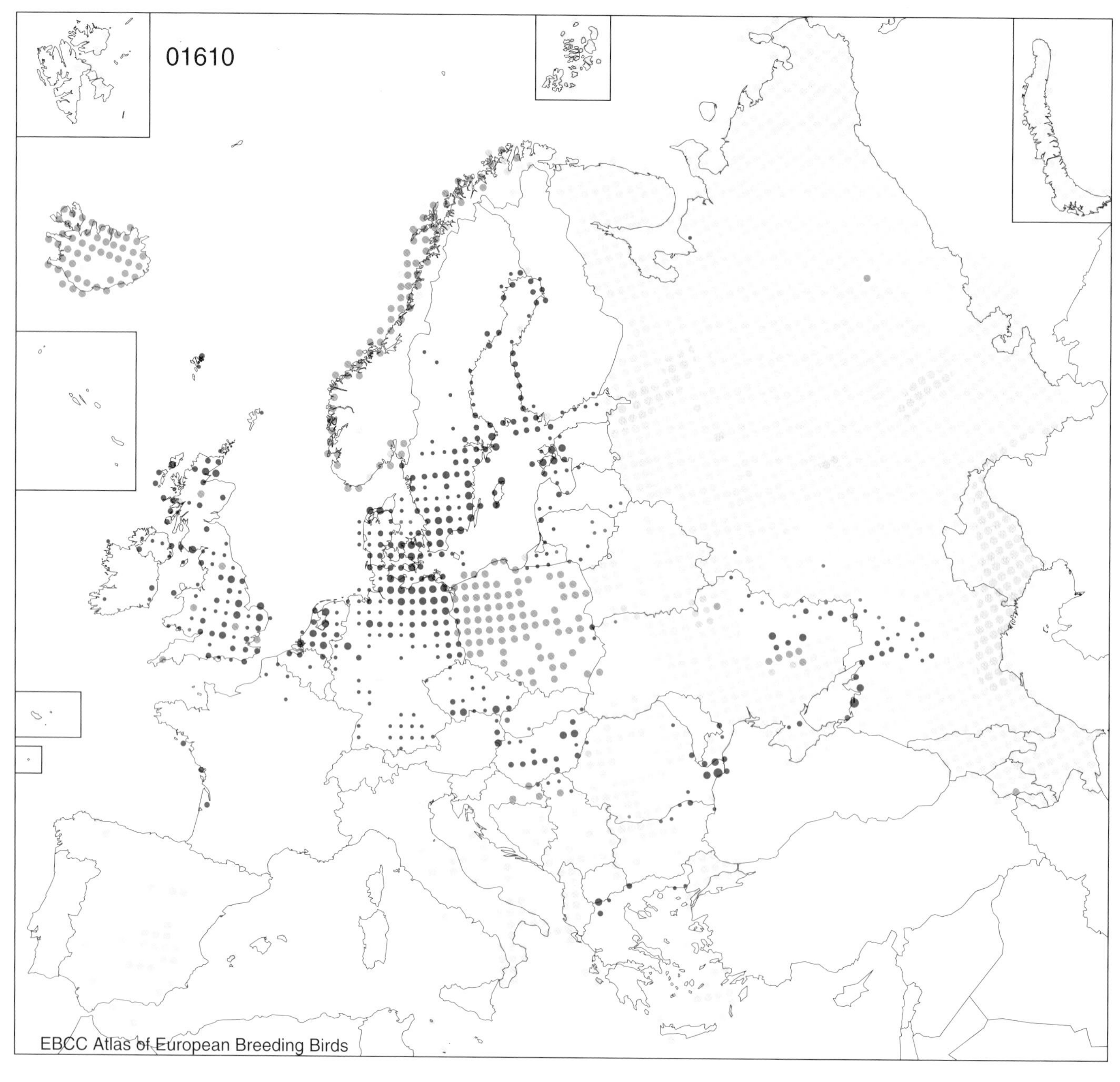

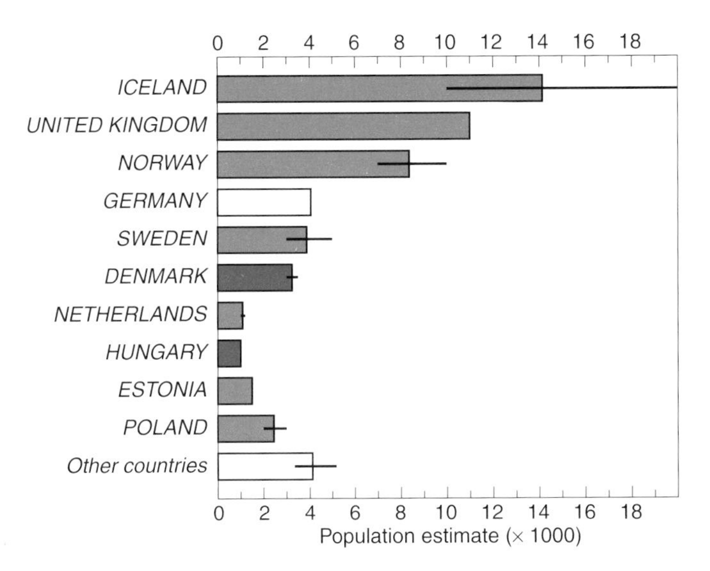

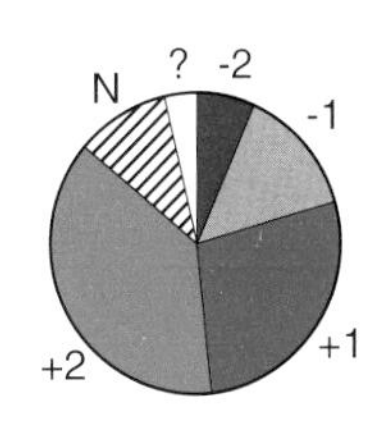

% in top 10 countries: 92.5
Total number of populated European countries: 29
Total European population 50,339–61,071 (54,834)
Russian population 8500–13,000 (10,512)
Turkish population 200–1000 (447)

The large Greylag Goose has the widest European distribution of any 'grey' goose. There are two subspecies, the nominate *A.a. anser* occurring mainly in Europe from the Arctic Circle south to 40°N, and *rubrirostris* which inhabits SE and E Europe, but predominantly occurs across much of Asia. Although the two subspecies are separable on their main ranges by bill coloration (*rubrirostris*' being pink), the occurrence of pink-billed individuals in *anser's* range is not unknown, and over a wide area from eastern Germany and the Czech Republic to the Urals many birds have varying amounts of pink in their bills (*BWP*).

The species' main breeding grounds are situated in Iceland (10 000–20 000bp), Great Britain, NW and C Europe and S Scandinavia. Several reintroduction programmes have resulted in thriving feral populations in Sweden, Great Britain, the Netherlands and Belgium. In Britain many feral Greylag have interbred with white domestic geese, resulting in variably marked offspring.

The Greylag Goose's breeding habitats comprise mainly various types of open freshwater marshes, usually near lakes, ponds, rivers or other waterbodies; in the Nordic countries, it also breeds along coasts and fjords. Occasionally, it breeds solitarily, but normally forms aggregations of varying sizes depending upon the size and quality of the habitat. Areas of extensive prime habitat can hold tens or even hundreds of breeding pairs.

The Greylag Goose assembles in large numbers at favoured locations to moult, most subpopulations remaining together during their flightless period. The Oostvaardersplassen in the Netherlands, with a carrying capacity of 35 000 geese (Loonen *et al* 1991), is one of the most important moulting areas, the birds coming from the breeding populations of the Netherlands, Germany, Denmark and Scandinavia. Other important moulting areas in continental Europe are Slonsk and Barycz in Poland and Neusiedlersee in Austria.

Because there are disjunct breeding populations in the western Palearctic, their distribution during migration and in their wintering areas is complicated. Breeders from Iceland winter mainly in Scotland and Ireland, while those from Britain are mostly resident. Geese from the Fennoscandian breeding population join up with those from Germany and the Netherlands. Until recently, these birds wintered mainly in Spain, but have switched to the SW Netherlands (up to 30 000) as a result of hunting pressure in the Coto de Doñana. The majority of breeding birds from NE and C Europe tend to winter in North Africa, especially in Tunisia and Algeria, but during mild winters a significant proportion of this population will either remain in C Europe or move no further than southern Europe.

The breeding population of the European continent has increased tremendously since 1950. For example, the Icelandic population increased from 25 000 birds in 1952 to 110 000 in 1987 (Madsen 1991) whereas the British population increased by 13% per annum during the 1980s, reaching some 19 500 birds in June–July 1991, scattered over 447 sites (Delany 1993). Overall, where trends were known, the species increased in 20 out of 25 European countries (by more than 50% in 11 from 1970 to 1990). Only Romania, Moldova, Slovakia, Bulgaria and Greece showed declines, which probably all involved *rubrirostris* alone. The present European breeding population is estimated at 56 300–80 000bp. The wintering population stands at some 270 000 birds, excluding those wintering in the Caspian area (Rose & Scott 1994).

The substantial overall increase demonstrates the success of some reintroduction projects, shows the adaptability of the geese to exploit new breeding places and makes evident the effect of improving hunting regulations in some countries. However, this success may bring problems, especially for resident populations. In Britain, the Greylag increase when considered with the increase in Canada Goose *Branta canadensis* numbers raises the issue of crop and amenity damage which can be significant, for example to the Hebridean machair, or to small reedbeds (Prater 1993).

Leo van den Bergh (NL)

Anser erythropus

Lesser White-fronted Goose

CZ	Husa malá	**I**	Oca lombardella minore
D	Zwerggans	**NL**	Dwerggans
E	Ansar Chico	**P**	Ganso-pequeno-de-testa-branca
F	Oie naine	**PL**	Gęś mała
FIN	Kiljuhanhi	**R**	Пискулька
G	Νανόχηνα	**S**	Fjällgås
H	Kis lilik		

SPEC Cat 1, Threat status V

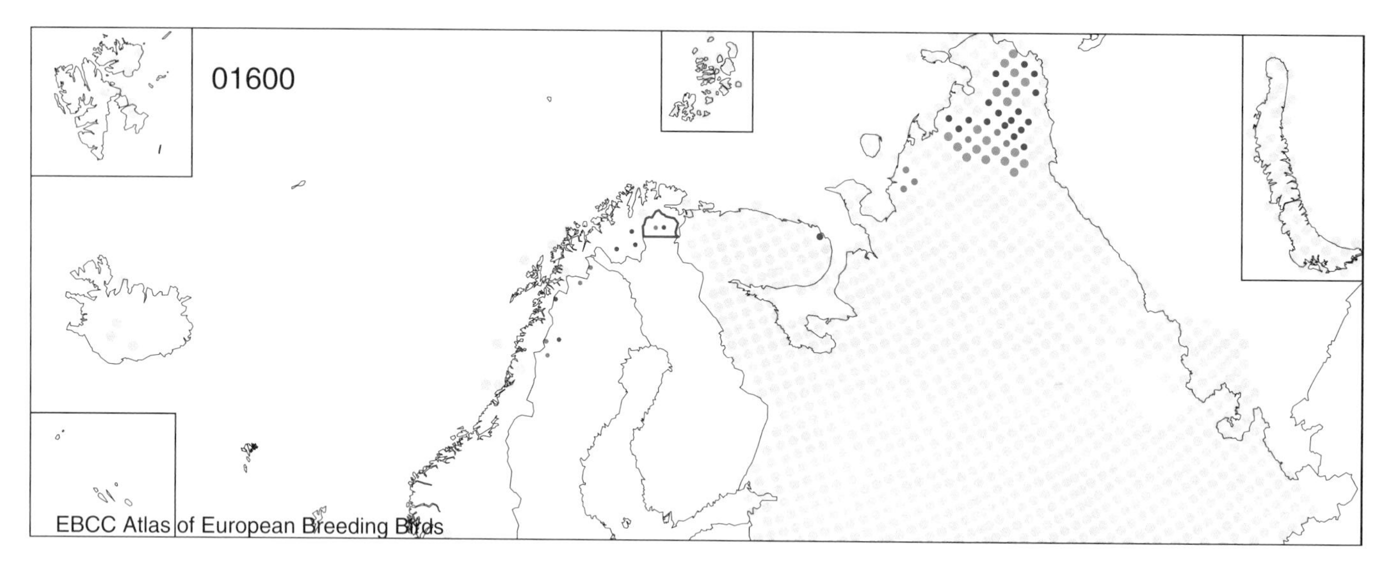

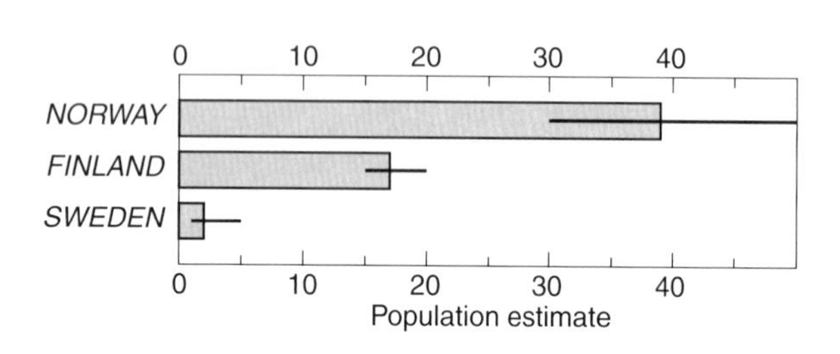

-1

% in top 10 countries: 100.0
Total number of populated European countries: 3
Total European population 49–70 (58)
Russian population 1000–2500 (1581)

The Lesser White-fronted Goose, the smallest 'grey' goose, breeds in the Palearctic region in the willow *Salix* and birch *Betula* forest belt between the arctic tundra and the taiga zone. It prefers hilly areas with small lakes and brooks, and also river valleys and deltas, where willow and dwarf birch are mixed with patches of low herbs.

In the early 1900s it was common from N Scandinavia and E through Siberia to the Bering Sea. Since the 1940s it has suffered a drastic decline, especially in Fennoscandia (Norderhaug & Norderhaug 1984) but also in E Siberia. W of the Urals (the Bol'shezemel'skaya tundra) the population now also seems to be declining (V.V. Morozov, pers obs) and may comprise only 1500 individuals (V.V. Morozov at *Anatidae 2000*). The decline's causes are unclear, but may lie in the wintering grounds, which for European birds lie round the S Caspian Sea, and S and W of the Black Sea. There, changes in habitat through drainage and altered land usage are likely contributory causes, as is greater hunting pressure (Vinogradov 1990). In the Fennoscandian breeding area heavier predation and increased human disturbance seem significant (von Essen *et al* 1994).

The migration routes are still not sufficiently well-known. The *c*100 000 (1920s) roosting on the Hortobágy puszta (E Hungary) have diminished to only a few hundred (Sterbetz 1982). During the spring migration, the Fennoscandian population uses roosting sites along the Bothnian Gulf and in Porsanger Fjord (Norway). The small groups wintering in the Netherlands comprise birds from the Swedish Lapland reintroduction project from 1981 to 1991 (von Essen 1991).

In the bushy and hilly breeding grounds numbers are difficult to assess, particularly because the birds may be scattered over a wide area. In its winter range the Lesser White-fronted Goose often associates with large flocks of the much commoner White-fronted Goose *A. albifrons*, and from a distance are difficult to distinguish during a survey.

Lambart von Essen (S) Vladimir V Morozov (R)

Branta canadensis

Canada Goose

CZ	Berneška velká	I	Oca del Canada
D	Kanadagans	NL	Canadese Gans
E	Barnacla Canadiense	P	Ganso do Canadá
F	Bernache du Canada	PL	Bernikla kanadyjska
FIN	Kanadanhanhi	R	Канадская казарка
G	Καναδόχηνα	S	Kanadagås
H	Kanadai lúd		

Criteria not applied

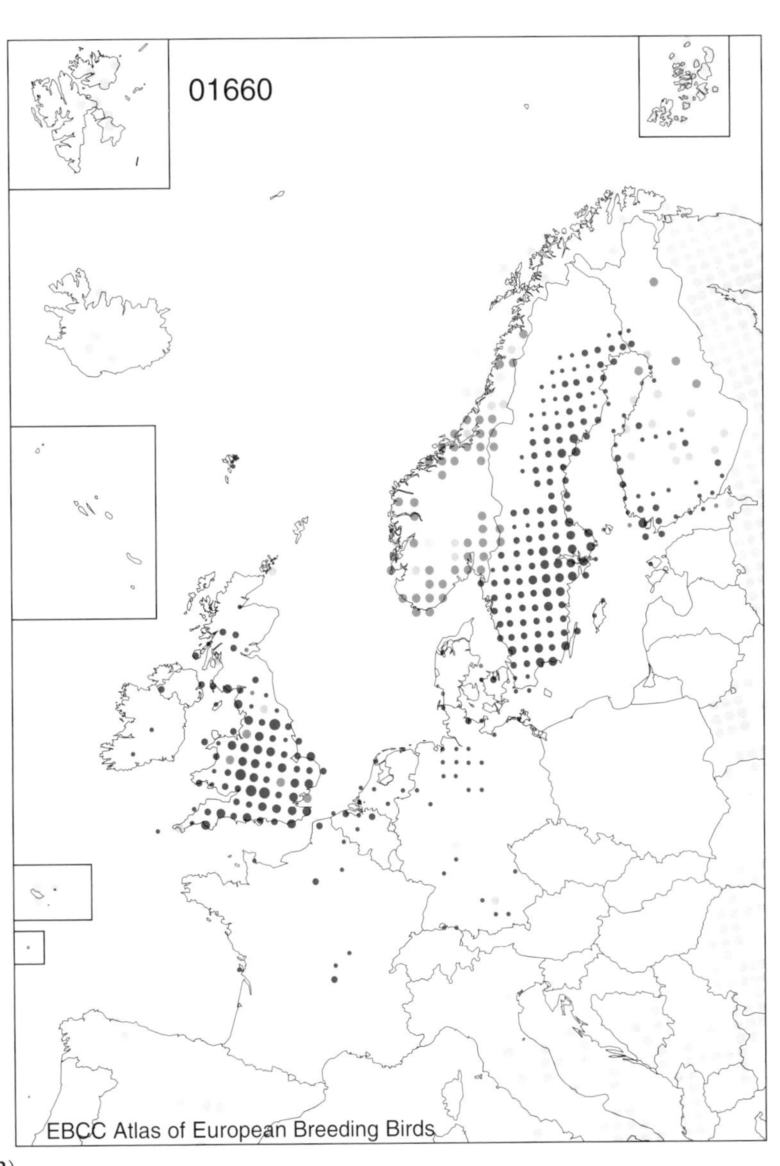

This N American species was introduced, especially in Britain, from *c*1650 onwards. In Scandinavia, released birds first bred in 1933 (Sweden), whence they have spread to Russia (Medvedev 1992). These introductions, the creation of much suitable habitat (reservoirs and gravel-extraction pits), and translocations to relieve local agricultural problems and provide hunting, have allowed rapid population growth. Some European populations suffer reduced genetic variability (Tegelström & Sjöberg 1995) but reduced viability has seldom been reported (Heggberget 1991). The Canada Goose is now abundant across much of Great Britain and Scandinavia, breeding in a variety of freshwater wetlands, favouring still waters containing well-vegetated nesting island, and in Fennoscandia bedrock islands along the Baltic coast and in larger lakes (Heggberget 1991, Tegelström & Sjöberg 1995).

The species is increasing rapidly across much of its European range. Britain (30 000bp) and Sweden (5000–10 000bp) currently support the majority and Norway, Finland and Germany up to 1000bp each. All other countries support 100bp or fewer but rapid increases have occurred in the 1990s in the Netherlands (R. Lensink, pers comm) and Belgium (Anselin & Geers 1994). The British population increased between 1953 and 1991 from 2200–4000 to 64 000 birds at an accelerating rate (Delany 1992). Population growth appears to be associated with the establishment of new colonies, either by natural processes or by forced introductions, rather than breeding numbers increasing at existing sites. Most sites support few birds even in autumn and winter; in Great Britain in 1991, 57% of the 1104 sites with Canada Geese held fewer than 25 birds (Delany 1992).

Apart from an annual summer moult migration, with N–S movements in excess of 500km, British birds are relatively sedentary, perhaps ranging only a few kilometres. Finnish and Swedish birds mostly winter around the Baltic and adjacent North Sea coast, Norwegian birds being largely sedentary (some move S within Norway) (Madsen & Andersson 1990). No moult migrations have been described for Fennoscandian birds.

The Canada Goose is now widely considered to be a pest and is sometimes the focus of heated debate, especially where there are allegations of serious agricultural or amenity damage. Other potential problems are interference with native waterfowl, threats to public health and excessive eutrophication of waterbodies, though the evidence is at best circumstantial (Allan *et al* 1995). It is ironic that introductions continue in Finland, Norway and in parts of eastern Europe, where the short-term gain for hunters is perceived as outweighing the risk of long-term deleterious effects.

Jeff Kirby (GB) Kjell Sjöberg (S)

This species account is sponsored by Dr Anny Anselin, Hasselt, B.

Branta leucopsis

Barnacle Goose

CZ	Berneška bělolící	I	Oca facciabianca
D	Nonnengans	NL	Brandgans
E	Barnacla Cariblanca	P	Ganso-de-faces-brancas
F	Bernache nonnette	PL	Bernikla białolica
FIN	Valkoposkihanhi	R	Белощекая казарка
G	Ασπρομαγουλόχηνα	S	Vitkindad gås
H	Apácalúd		

*SPEC Cat 4/2, Threat status L*W*

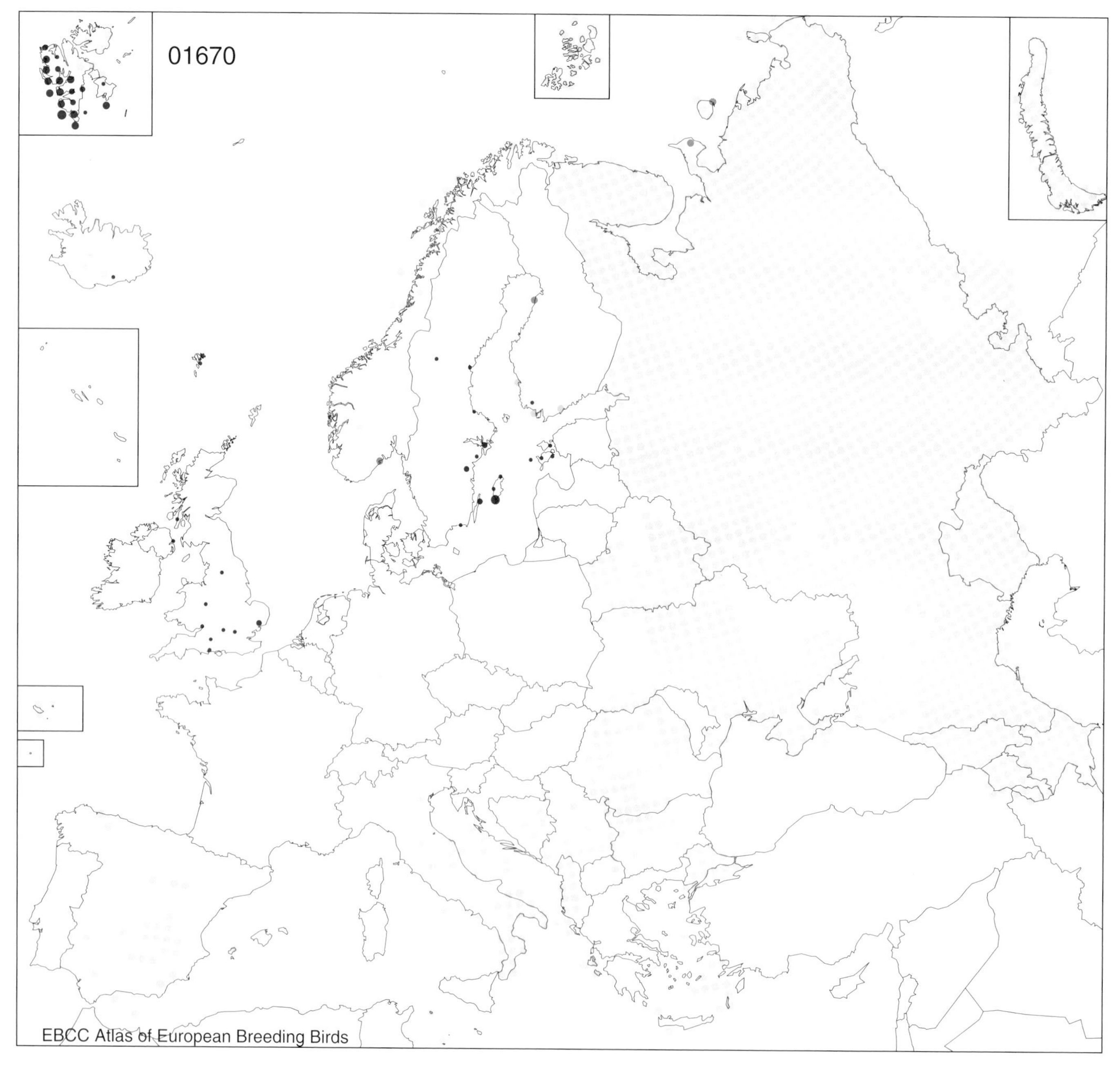

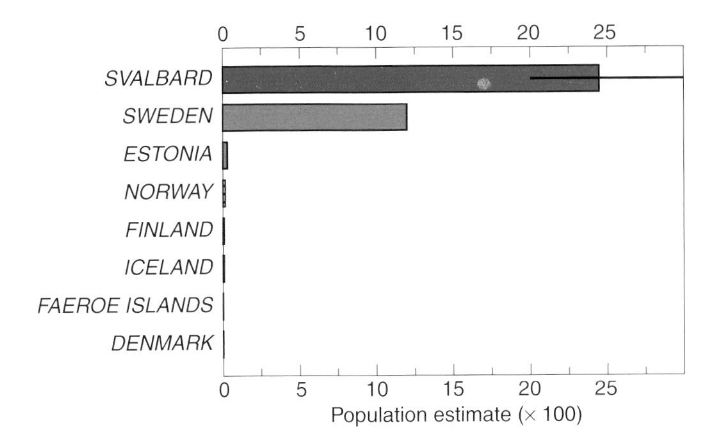

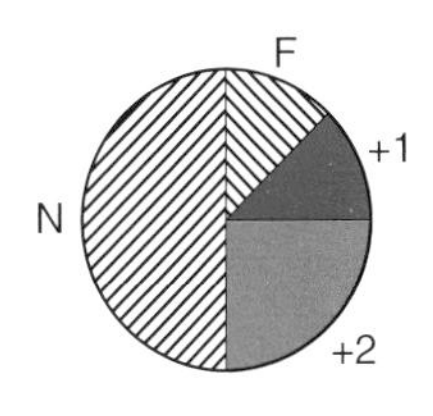

% in top 10 countries: 100.0
Total number of populated European countries: 8
Total European population 3261–4261 (3711)
Russian population 4000–5500 (4690)

The Barnacle Goose, a most gregarious species, breeds in four distinct areas: coastal plains and valleys of E Greenland, the Svalbard archipelago, coastal arctic Russia from 44° to 61°E and islands in the Baltic. Small numbers (5–10bp) breed in NW Iceland. A few feral birds breed in Great Britain.

The species is largely coastal throughout its life cycle. Being vulnerable to predators such as the Arctic fox *Alopex lagopus*, it nests in loose colonies in fox-free areas, such as steep cliffs above valleys or the sea or on offshore islands.

In winter, the three arctic populations remain discrete. The Greenland breeders congregate on the W coasts of Scotland and Ireland, staging through Iceland both in autumn and spring. The Svalbard population winters exclusively on the Solway Firth (W-C Britain), concentrated in three main coastal sites; the spring staging areas are in Helgeland, Norway. The Russian breeders stage through the Baltic and winter in The Netherlands where they are joined by the Baltic breeders. In cold winters the species concentrates in the southernmost wintering range and may overflow into Belgium and France.

All population sizes have increased since the mid-1970s. The Svalbard population has expanded its range slightly (Prestrud *et al* 1989) and the Russian population has extended its breeding westwards to the Kanin Peninsula (Filchagov & Leonovich 1992). The Baltic colonies were established as recently as 1975 (Larsson & Forslund 1994) and since have grown rapidly. They are well outside the species' normal latitudinal breeding limits, their success probably deriving from human alteration to the habitat. Winter distributions of all populations remain largely unchanged despite the increases in numbers.

The Greenland population has been censused by the WWT and the Irish National Parks and Wildlife Service every five years or so since 1959, when the population numbered 8300. Wintering populations were then about equally divided between Islay in the Inner Hebrides and the remainder of Scotland and Ireland. Wintering numbers have since increased, largely on Islay and on the Irish mainland. The most recent census in 1994 indicated a population of 38 400. The distribution proportions have changed, with 67% on Islay, 21% in Ireland and only 8% elsewhere in Scotland. Changes in grazing regimes in the remote Scottish island haunts and improved grazing and protection on Islay are probably responsible.

Svalbard breeding numbers increased from 300 in 1948 to 3500 in the 1960s and 7200 in 1976 (Owen & Norderhaug 1977), stabilizing in the late 1980s at *c*12 000–14 000 (WWT counts). Protection and improved feeding have allowed numbers to rise to the capacity of the breeding area, limiting further expansion (Owen & Black 1989). Breeding success is erratic, but in recent years only *c*1000bp on average nested successfully.

The Russian population, again following protection and the provision of winter feeding areas, has increased from 20 000 in 1960 to over 130 000 in the early 1990s (Larsson & Forslund 1994). The Baltic population grew to *c*2000bp in 1993, when the growth rate was declining rapidly (Larsson & Forslund 1994). This probably represents a post-breeding population in excess of 8000 individuals, *c*5% of the numbers wintering in The Netherlands, where small numbers have bred since 1988 (3bp), reaching 45–50bp in 1993 (Meininger & van Swelm 1994).

In all wintering areas and in spring in Norway and Iceland, the geese come into conflict with farming when feeding on agricultural pastures. On Islay a Goose Management Scheme is in operation, which offers payments to farmers for tolerating geese. A similar scheme is being piloted for the Solway, and authorities there and in Norway are collaborating on a Flyway Management Plan for the population. In The Netherlands, farmers receive compensation for goose damage, but this is not considered wholly satisfactory. The Dutch authorities are seeking a more strategic approach to managing the population and its relationship with agriculture.

Myrfyn Owen (GB)

Branta bernicla

Brent Goose

CZ	Berneška tmavá	I	Oca colombaccio
D	Ringelgans	NL	Rotgans
E	Barnacla Carinegra	P	Ganso-de-faces-negras
F	Bernache cravant	PL	Bernikla obrożna
FIN	Sepelhanhi	R	Черная казарка
G	Δαχτυλιδόχηνα	S	Prutgås
H	Örvös lúd		

SPEC Cat 3, Threat status V

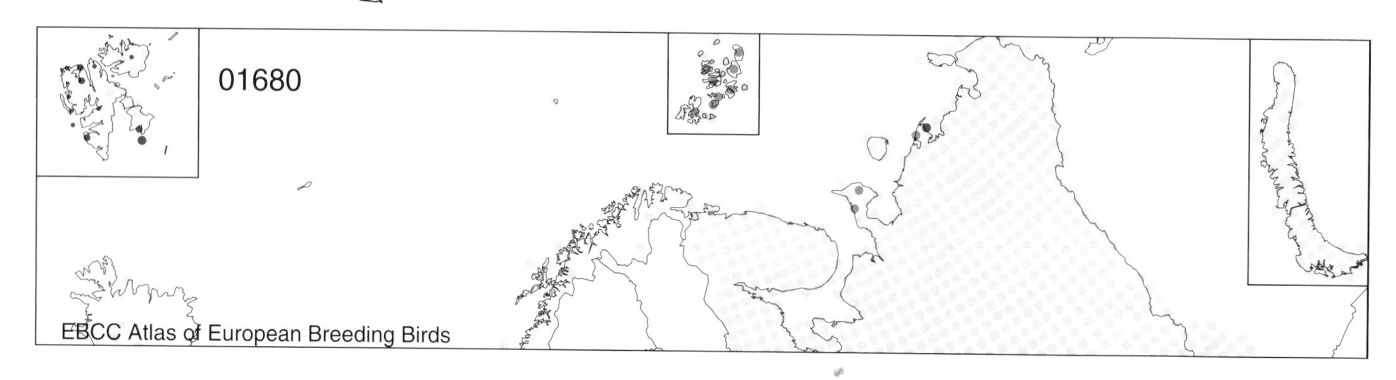

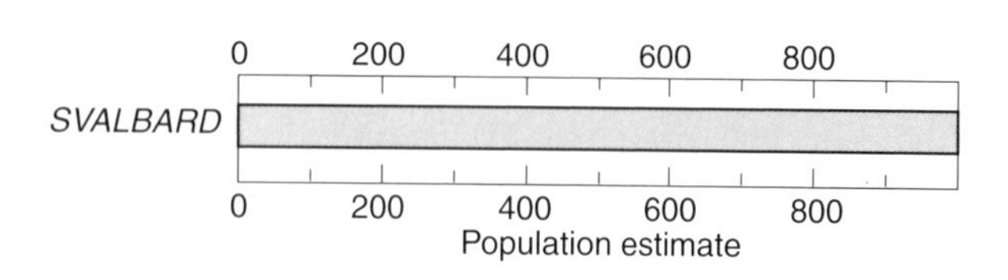

0

% in top 10 countries: 100.0
Total number of populated European countries: 1
Total European population 1000–1000 (1000)
Russian population 10–100 (32)

The Brent Goose has a circumpolar breeding distribution, nests on high-arctic coasts and winters in the Atlantic and Pacific temperate zones. In Europe two of the three subspecies breed and winter. *B.b. hrota* (light-bellied form) comprises the majority, whereas the nominate *B.b. bernicla* (dark-bellied) is an extremely rare breeder in the European Russian arctic. Two nests were found in 1990, and a pair possibly bred in 1994 on the Kanin Peninsula, all occurrences being within Barnacle Goose *B. leucopsis* colonies (A.V. Filchagov & E.E. Syroechkovski Jr, pers comm). Other broods were observed in 1994 along the Barents Sea Timan coast (E.E. Syroechkovski Jr, pers comm). Virtually the whole *bernicla* population breeds in Asian arctic Russia, predominantly on the Taymyr Peninsula. Most *hrota* breed in Svalbard, some using Franz Joseph Land, but all winter in Denmark and NE England. NE Canadian and N Greenland *hrota* winter in Ireland. Other Canadian *hrota* winter on W Atlantic coasts, and Asian, Alaskan and NW Canadian *nigricans* winter on N Pacific coasts.

The species usually nests in colonies, mostly on fox-free islets, but also scattered along mainland coasts. In Svalbard the tundra is arctic desert with extremely restricted feeding opportunities (Madsen *et al* 1989), whereas in Russia the breeding range extends to the lusher tundra vegetation, where, often on small islets, the species nests in association with the Taymyr Gull *Larus argentatus taimyrensis* (Spaans *et al* 1993). During lemming peak years it may also nest within Snowy Owl *Nyctea scandiaca* breeding territories (Summers *et al* 1994). In wintering and staging areas it feeds mostly in the intertidal zone and on saltmarshes (Ebbinge & Spaans 1995), but the continuing population increase has forced it to turn to pastures and winter cereals.

The *bernicla* world population increased from 40 000bp in the early 1970s to 300 000bp in the early 1990s (Ebbinge 1989, IWRB Goose Research Group 1994). However, poor breeding results from 1992 to 1994 have reduced numbers somewhat. The Svalbard *hrota* population has increased from *c*3000 to *c*5000bp during the same period, but numbers have remained relatively stable since (IWRB Goose Research Group 1994). In both populations, the initial increase was triggered by hunting bans on the wintering and staging grounds in western Europe. Heavy predation by polar bears *Ursus maritimus* and arctic foxes *Alopex lagopus* apparently limit the Svalbard population (Madsen *et al* 1989, 1992).

Jesper Madsen (DK) Barwolt S Ebbinge (NL)

This species account is sponsored by Solvey KG, Rheinberg, D.

Alopochen aegyptiacus

Egyptian Goose

CZ	Husice nilská	I	Oca egiziana
D	Nilgans	NL	Nijlgans
E	Ganso del Nilo	P	Ganso do Egipto
F	Ouette d'Egypte	PL	Gęś egipska
FIN	Afrikanhanhi	R	Нильский гусь
G	Αλωπόχηνα	S	Nilgås
H	Nilusi lúd		

Criteria not applied

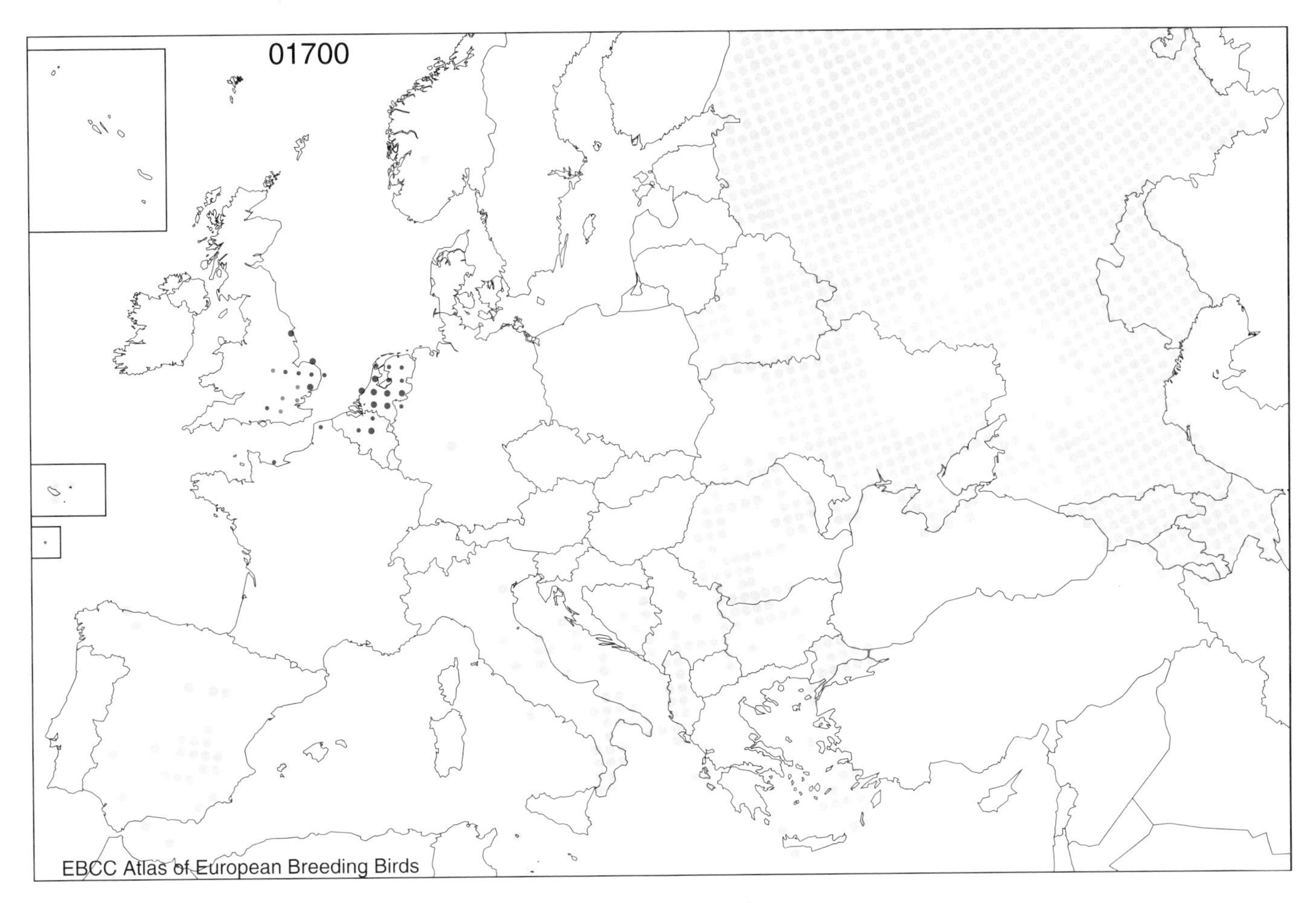

The first historical reference to the Egyptian Goose was a depiction at the grave of Mehu in Egypt around 2200 BC. Until the late 17th century, it had bred in SE Europe in Voyvodina, Hungary and Romania. Introductions failed in the USA, Australia and New Zealand. Its natural distribution covers most of Africa S of the Sahara.

In Europe, the Egyptian Goose prefers a richly structured habitat, consisting of ponds, gravel-pits, small lakes, meadows and woodland. Though some have adapted to city parks, most birds prefer rural areas. Its present distribution in Europe is restricted mainly to the lowlands of eastern Britain, Belgium and The Netherlands. It was first introduced to Great Britain, some certainly from Africa, in the 17th century, and in semi-domestication became quite widespread by the 19th century. The present feral population, mainly restricted to Norfolk, consists of 380–400bp (Sutherland & Allport 1991), but it is spreading slowly to the S and W, first breeding in Essex (1979), Somerset (1982) and Cambridgeshire (1988) (Prater 1993).

The thriving Dutch feral population originates from escapes since 1967, and after starting slowly is now booming, reaching 1300bp in 1994 (R. Lensink, in press). Meanwhile, its breeding range is expanding rapidly in the lowlands of NW Europe, having recently colonized NW France. There are 50–100bp in Belgium.

The Egyptian Goose is a successful colonizer, despite its maladaptive breeding strategy. It might spread further in W and S Europe if protected from hunting and egg-collecting. Northwards, its distribution is probably limited by submarginal ecological conditions (Lever 1987). At preferred breeding sites in The Netherlands, such as small lakes amid marshy woodland and meadows, densities of 19 bp/100ha have been recorded (P. Venema, pers obs).

Although the Egyptian Goose is usually sedentary throughout the year, it can form local concentrations during moulting.

Peter Venema (NL)

Tadorna tadorna Shelduck

CZ	Husice liščí	I	Volpoca
D	Brandgans	NL	Bergeend
E	Tarro Blanco	P	Pato-branco
F	Tadorne de Belon	PL	Ohar
FIN	Ristisorsa	R	Пеганка
G	Βαρβάρα	S	Gravand
H	Bütykös ásólúd		

Non-SPEC, Threat status S

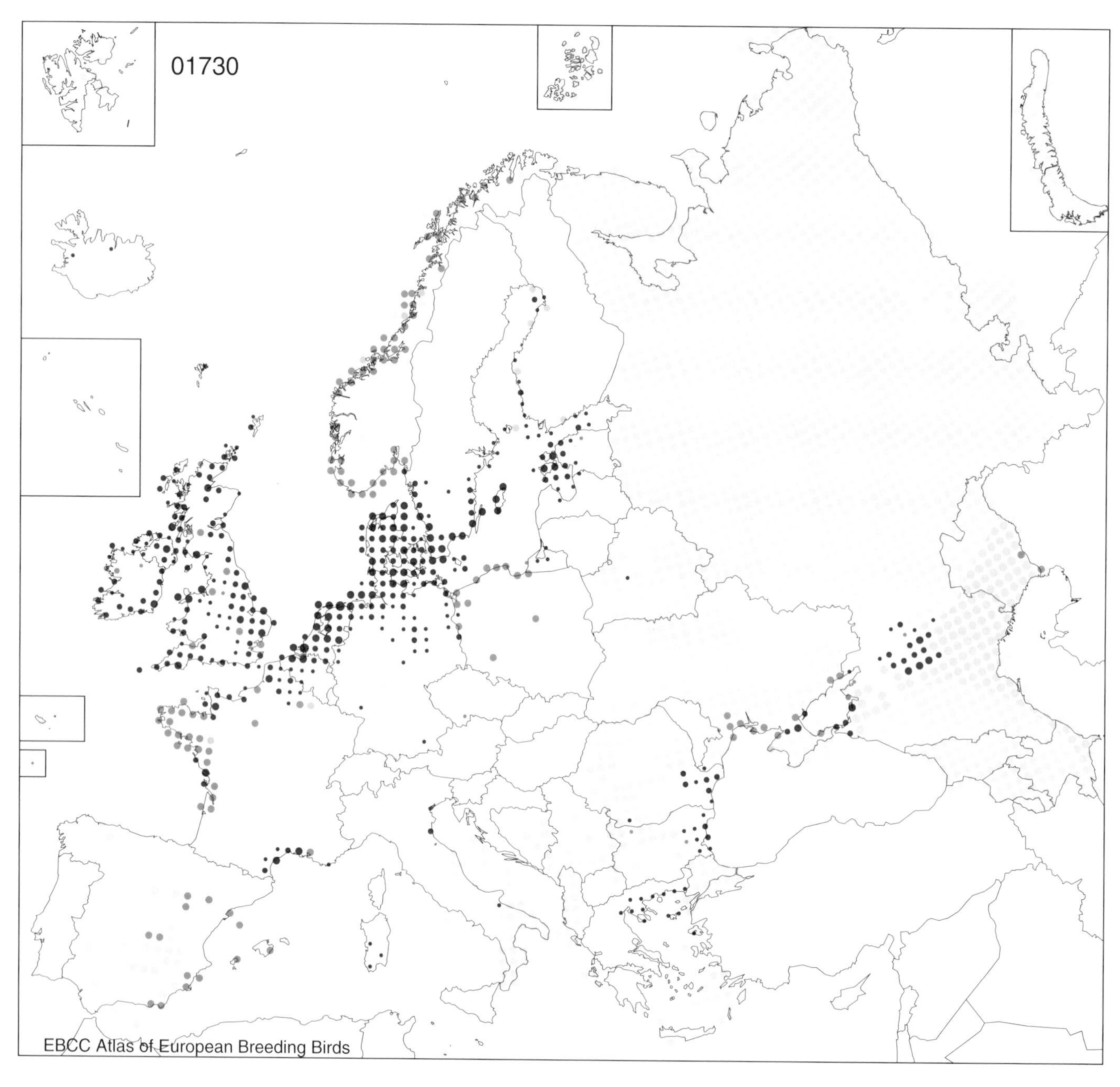

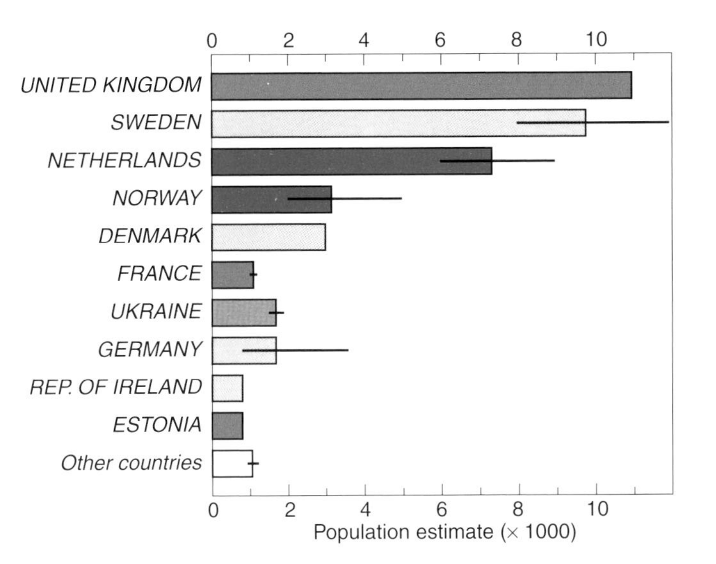

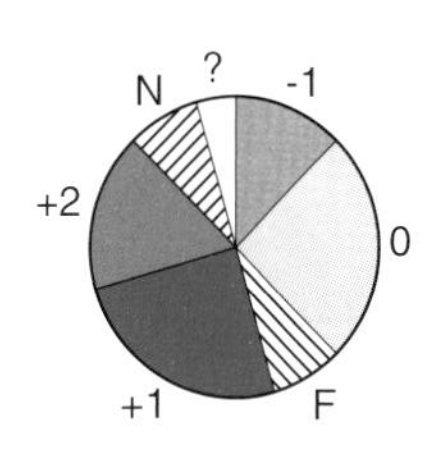

% in top 10 countries: 97.5
Total number of populated European countries: 24
Total European population 38,741–45,264 (41,434)
Russian population 2000–3500 (2646)
Turkish population 500–2000 (1000)

The Shelduck has a wide distribution, confined to the Palearctic but extending from W Ireland to W China in a fairly narrow latitudinal band (mainly 40°–60°N). There are two discrete European populations; one in the NW occupying muddy maritime shores, estuaries, brackish lagoons and inland freshwater bodies in countries bordering the Atlantic, North Sea and Baltic, and the other in the SE found mainly on inland seas and saline areas, extending from eastern Greece through Ukraine and Turkey to Asia. In both areas the Shelduck is patchily distributed, because it depends on the occurrence of suitable maritime or wetland feeding habitat adjacent to nesting locations containing burrows or other suitable cavities, which often are in sparsely vegetated sandy soil but sometimes also in dense prickly scrub.

Within Europe, the Shelduck is most abundant in its northwestern range, where some 34 200–47 400bp occur. Great Britain holds *c*11 000bp, Sweden 8000–12 000, The Netherlands 6000–9000, Norway 2000–5000, Denmark 3000, Germany *c*1500, Ireland *c*1100 (Patterson 1993) and France 1000–1200, other countries holding fewer, often much fewer, than 1000bp each. In the periphery of this area, such as in W France, Scotland and Norway, the species is largely coastal but in the centre, from NE France to Denmark, it occurs on freshwater bodies far inland.

In the SE of its European range, there are only 4100–7600bp (although Turkey holds perhaps as many as 2000bp). These form part of a much larger population extending to the E. The majority of the SE European population is found in S Russia (2000–3500) and Ukraine (1500–1900) and displays a strong tendency towards inland breeding beside saline waterbodies, especially in the former. Surprisingly, in view of the differences in habitat, there appear to be no differences in size or appearance between birds from the NW and SE parts of the range, and so it remains monotypic.

Shelduck numbers have been increasing in much of the NW population, possibly associated with an extension of breeding range away from the coast (Patterson 1982). The greatest increases have occurred in Great Britain (Linton & Fox 1991), France, Estonia and Finland with similar but smaller trends in (in order of population size) The Netherlands, Norway, Belgium, Poland, Spain and Lithuania. The increase in W Spain resulted in the colonization of six new coastal and inland sites on the Iberian Peninsula and one in the Balearic Islands during 1972–87, with a preference for hyper-saline wetlands (Robledano & Calvo 1989). No national population in N and W Europe has declined. In contrast, the largest population in the SE part of the range (S Russia) has merely remained stable while those in Ukraine, Romania and Greece have declined by 20–50%.

Perhaps the most striking feature of the Shelduck in Europe is the spectacular moult migration of almost all of the birds from the NW population to remote mudflats in the Heligoland Bight, off the coast of NW Germany where up to 180 000 birds gather in July each year (Nehls *et al* 1992). Because the birds are flightless for several weeks, this concentration in a small area close to the outflow of several major rivers makes the population very vulnerable to pollution. However, the existence of other smaller moulting areas in large estuaries (such as the Forth, Severn and Wash in Britain) ensures that the entire NW population is not exposed to risk at the same time. Increasing numbers of moulting Shelduck are appearing in the western Dutch Wadden Sea (30 000 birds in the early 1990s) and in the SW Netherlands delta (2000 birds in the late 1980s) (Swennen & Mulder 1995). Following the moult, the birds' range extends southwards during the winter, the complete breeding area being fully occupied only from late spring.

Ian J Patterson (GB)

This species account is sponsored by Prof. Dr Hans Oelke, Peine, D.

Tadorna ferruginea

Ruddy Shelduck

CZ	Husice rezavá	**I**	Casarca
D	Rostgans	**NL**	Casarca
E	Tarro Canelo	**P**	Pato-ferrugíneo
F	Tadorne casarca	**PL**	Kazarka
FIN	Ruostesorsa	**R**	Огарь
G	Καστανόχηνα	**S**	Rostand
H	Vörös ásólúd		

SPEC Cat 3, Threat status V

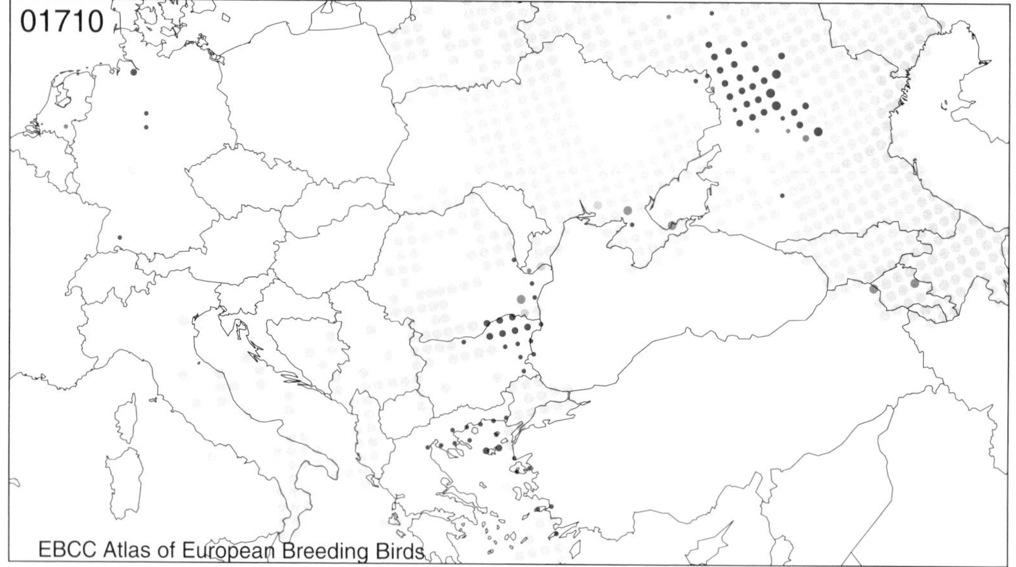

The world distribution of the Ruddy Shelduck lies principally in C Asia, but it stretches deep into SE Europe. A separate breeding population occurs in NW Africa. The European population is found mainly in the Black Sea region and in SE Russia and Transcaucasia. Turkey probably has the largest breeding population in the western Palearctic, at an estimated 4000–8000bp, followed by the Don region in S Russia (Tucker & Heath 1994). There are small populations in northern

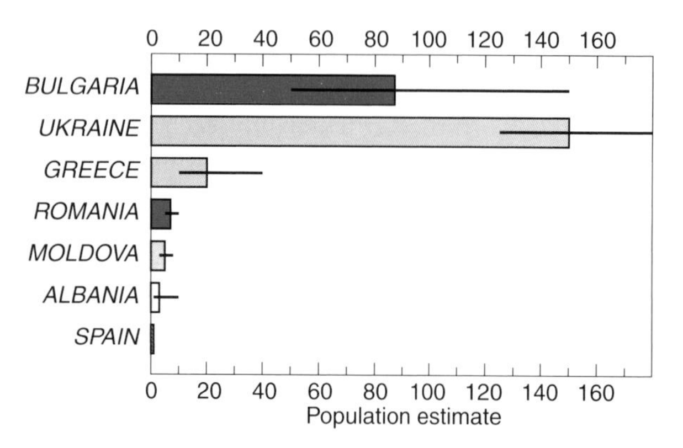

X -2 ? -1 +1 0

% in top 10 countries: 100.0
Total number of populated European countries: 7
Total European population 227–346 (273)
Russian population 1900–2900 (2347)
Turkish population 4000–8000 (5657)

Greece, Bulgaria, Romania, Moldova and Ukraine. What probably were introduced birds have bred in Ireland, The Netherlands (7bp 1992, with poor success) and Germany.

Most of the European and Turkish population is declining, but the Bulgarian and Russian populations apparently are increasing after former declines. The formerly thriving population along the coasts of Thrace and the Sea of Marmara has now largely disappeared, as have post-breeding and winter concentrations in the region's river deltas.

The Ruddy Shelduck is associated mostly with freshwater and brackish lakes and shores in open, arid and sparsely vegetated areas, although it has a variety of nesting habitats: holes in steep coastal and river cliffs and banks, in trees, dunes, dams and walls (*BWP*). It breeds from sea level up to 4800m asl (C Asia). Most populations are dispersive or nomadic, though a few are migratory.

The population of NE Greece and the Aegean islands (like Limnos) has almost disappeared, fewer than 5bp remaining. Pairs nest mainly on seacliffs, though usually close to freshwater or brackish marshes (Hölzinger 1991). In Turkish Thrace it is now only a possible breeder in Saros or the Kavak Delta (G. Magnin, pers comm to editors).

The main causes of the population decline probably lie in habitat changes due to agricultural development (particularly drainage of shallow marshland, and subterranean water extraction for irrigation), coastal housing development, shooting and nest-site disturbance. The future of the species seems greatly dependent on the implementation of conservation measures, particularly to prevent shooting at its wintering sites (Rose 1994).

Ben Hallmann (NL) Simon Gillings (GB)
Hans Jerrentrup (D)

Marmaronetta angustirostris

Marbled Teal

CZ	Čírka úzkozobá	I	Anatra marmorizzata
D	Marmelente	NL	Marmereend
E	Cerceta Pardilla	P	Pardilheira
F	Sarcelle marbrée	PL	Kaczka jarzębata
FIN	Marmorisorsa	R	Мраморный чирок
G	Στικτόπαπια	S	Marmorand
H	Márványos réce		

SPEC Cat 1, Threat status E

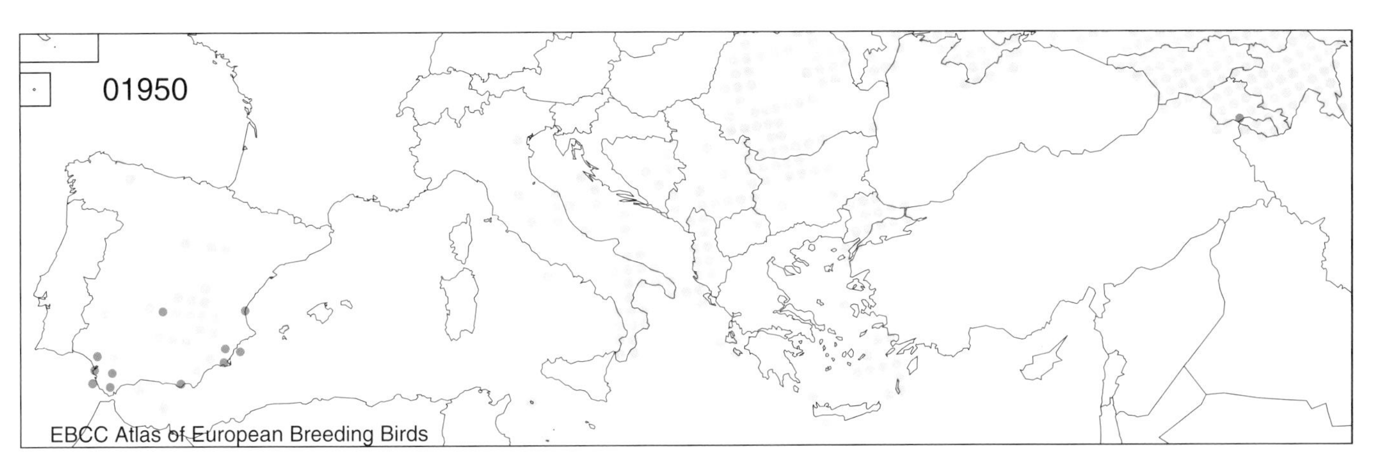

-2

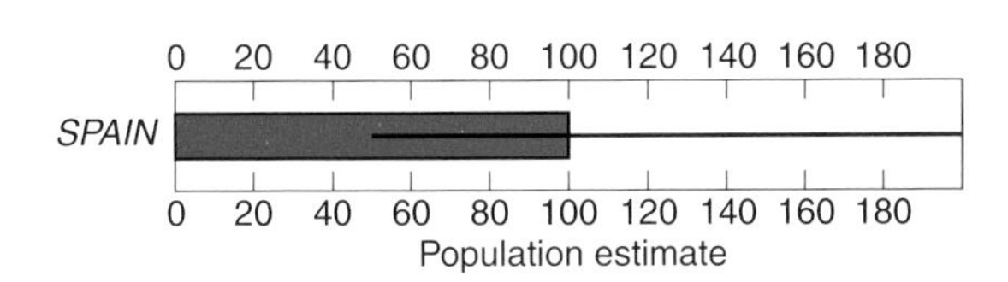

% in top 10 countries: 100.0
Total number of populated European countries: 1
Total European population 50–200 (100)
Turkish population 150–250 (194)

The world range of the Marbled Teal stretches from Spain and Morocco in the W through the S Mediterranean to Kazakhstan and Baluchistan in the E. Its distribution consists of small scattered populations. The two separate European populations, in Spain and in the Caucasus, are both severely threatened.

The Marbled Teal breeds annually in Andalusia and Valencia and it has a history of occasional breeding in France, Italy, Greece, Hungary and the former Yugoslavia (Green 1993). The Guadalquivir marshes comprise the main breeding area, where at several thousand bp in 1900, the species was extremely abundant (Valverde 1964). The crash in numbers since is associated with man-made habitat changes. Fewer than 50bp were left by the late 1970s. Numbers did recover partly in the late 1980s, peaking at 150–250bp (Mañez 1991), but since 1989 there has been a further consistent decline in population size to fewer than 50bp in 1993 (L. García, pers comm). Present fluctuations largely mirror rainfall patterns, almost all breeding habitat drying out in some years.

El Hondo and Salinas de Santa Pola in Alicante, Valencia support the only other sizeable Spanish population, *c*200bp being present in the 1960s. After a major decline it appears to have stabilized at 10–30bp over recent years (Dolz *et al* 1991, Navarro & Robledano 1992). One or two breeding pairs occupy other sites in Valencia, Murcia, Andalucía and Castilla La Mancha (Green 1993). A total of 3–11 pairs was dispersed between six such sites in 1993 (J. Navarro, pers comm).

Breeding is concentrated on shallow, brackish, relatively permanent wetlands, nests typically being made in dense beds of reedmace *Typha* or glasswort *Salicornia*. Outside the breeding season, it uses temporarily flooded areas, including ricefields and the extensive seasonal lakes of Doñana National Park. Ringing recoveries show that Spanish birds move regularly to Morocco and Algeria in winter, and probably at other times in a nomadic response to habitat availability. In times of abundance, huge differences in breeding densities occurred from year to year, suggesting that in some years most birds remained to breed in North Africa (Green 1993).

Little is known of the eastern population, but it breeds in Armenia (where the 1995 survey results may clarify its status); *c*200 pairs summer in the lake system of Azerbaijan, some breeding (M.V. Patrikeev, in prep).

Andy Green (GB)

Aix sponsa

Wood Duck

CZ	Kachnička karolinská	**I**	Anatra sposa
D	Brautente	**NL**	Carolina-eend
E	Pato Joyuyo	**P**	Pato-carolino
F	Canard carolin	**PL**	Karolinka
FIN	Morsiosorsa	**R**	Каролинская утка
G	Νυφόπαπια	**S**	Brudand
H	Karolinai réce		

Criteria not applied

The habits, habitat, diet and nesting requirements of the Wood Duck, a native of western and eastern but not C North America, are similar to those of its near relation, the Mandarin, *A. galericulata*, (*qv*). The former was first introduced to England in the 1870s, where by 1895 it was described in Devon as 'breeding freely and wandering at will over the country'. Why, then, has it failed to become as well and widely established in Great Britain and mainland Europe as its oriental congener?

The young of the Wood Duck have a 10-week fledging period compared to the Mandarin's 8 weeks, and so the former's ducklings are potentially vulnerable to predators for longer (Savage 1952). Furthermore, most Wood Duck breeding records in Europe have occurred in those S English counties where the more numerous Mandarin is well entrenched (Lever 1987). In North America the Wood Duck occurs between 31° and 51°N, whereas in the Far East the Mandarin is found from 36° to 55°N. This variation in latitude is likely to affect laying date, clutch size, duckling weight, incubation, fledging periods and the timing of moult and eclipse plumage, to the disadvantage of the Wood Duck's present population in Europe (Murton & Kear 1978).

Theoretically, the Wood Duck in Europe has three points in its favour: firstly, because it breeds earlier than most other hole-nesting species, it has an advantage in competition for nest-sites; secondly, since both the Wood Duck and the Mandarin cease laying around late May, the former has a breeding season a month longer than the latter; and thirdly, the Wood Duck lays a slightly larger clutch than the Mandarin (Kear 1990). None of these supposed advantages, however, have secured the species more than a toehold in Europe (Lever 1993a). The native North American population is now secure, which minimizes the conservation importance of the European birds.

Sir Christopher Lever (GB)

Aix galericulata

Mandarin

CZ	Kachnička mandarinská	I	Anatra mandarina
D	Mandarinente	NL	Mandarijneend
E	Pato Mandarín	P	Pato-mandarim
F	Canard mandarin	PL	Mandarynka
FIN	Mandariinisorsa	R	Мандаринка
G	Μανδαρινόπαπια	S	Mandarinand
H	Mandarinréce		

Criteria not applied

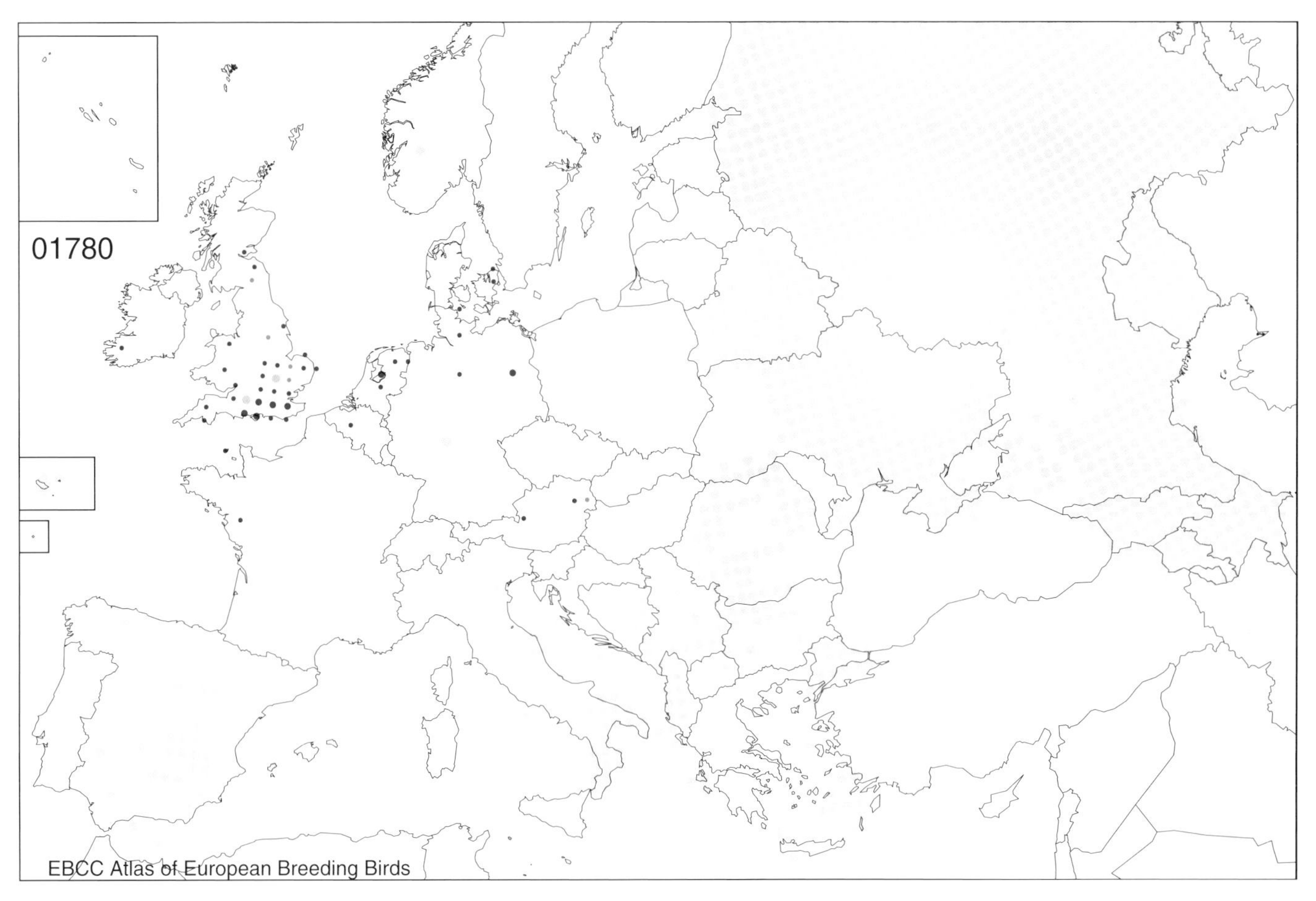

The Mandarin's native range is the Far East, principally Japan, China, Korea and the former USSR. It frequents lentic and lotic fresh waters with a dense marginal growth of woodland and shrubs (rhododendron is a favourite), especially where ample reeds, sedges or other emergent vegetation provide shelter. It normally nests in deciduous trees, occupying holes up to 3m deep and up to 18m above the ground. In Great Britain, it accepts nesting boxes readily even where natural sites occur (Davies & Baggott 1989).

Although the Mandarin was first introduced to Great Britain before 1745 (Lever 1977), its present patchy naturalized population there, and all those in continental Europe, are descended from escapes and deliberate releases in the 20th century (Lever 1987).

There are three principal reasons for the successful establishment of the Mandarin in Great Britain (and to a lesser extent in continental Europe): the existence of a vacant ecological niche for a hole-nesting duck which feeds largely on aquatic vertebrates in spring and summer, and on acorns, chestnuts and beechmast in autumn and winter; the availability of suitable habitats; and (in Britain at least) the particularly vigorous founding stock is descended directly from the wild (Lever 1993b).

The Mandarin's range and population in Great Britain (and perhaps in continental Europe) will probably continue slowly to expand and increase, being limited mainly by competition for nesting-sites (Bijlsma 1994a), the continued availability of suitable habitats, an adequate supply of nuts to enable it to survive hard winters (Davies 1988), and its relatively sedentary nature (in contrast to its behaviour in the Far East, where it migrates S in winter to S China and Taiwan). The British population is of major conservation importance, the total of *c*3500bp (a possible underestimate; Davies & Baggott 1989) equalling that of Japan, and surpassing that of the rest of Asia.

Sir Christopher Lever (GB)

Anas penelope Wigeon

CZ	Hvízdák eurasijský	**I**	Fischione
D	Pfeifente	**NL**	Smient
E	Silbón Europeo	**P**	Piadeira
F	Canard siffleur	**PL**	Świstun
FIN	Haapana	**R**	Свиязь
G	Σφυριχτάρι	**S**	Bläsand
H	Fütyülő réce		

Non-SPEC, Threat status S

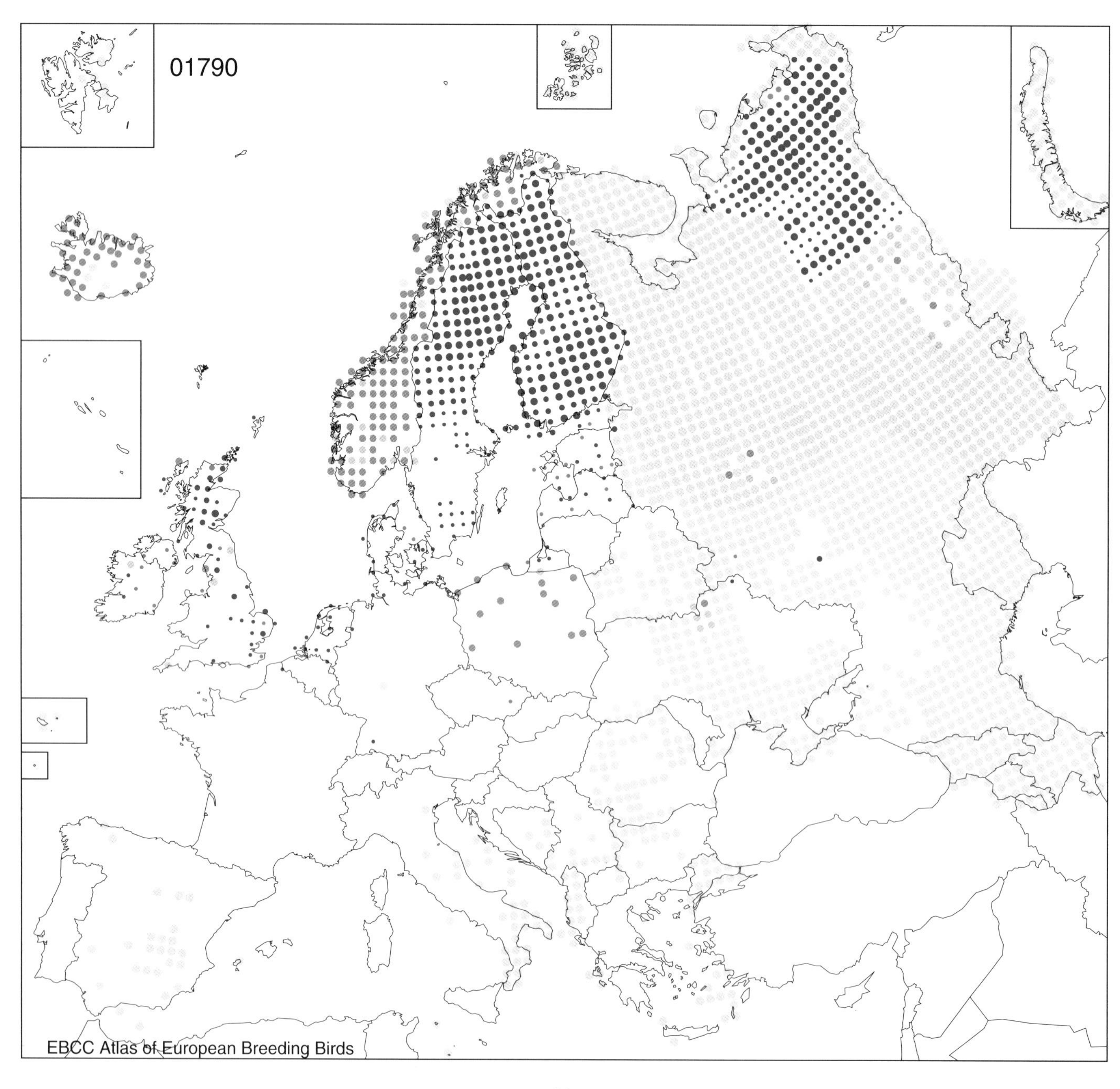

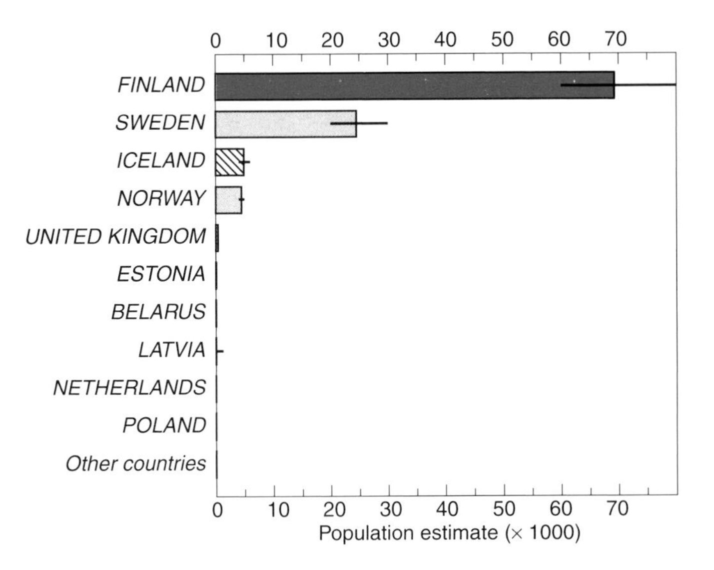

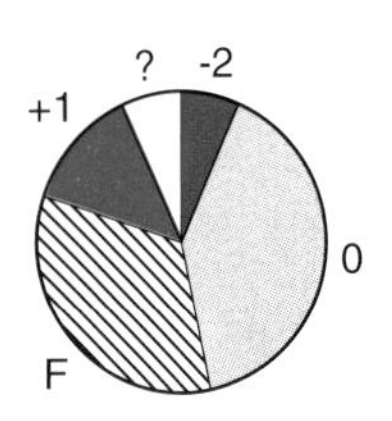

% in top 10 countries: 100.0
Total number of populated European countries: 15
Total European population 93,315–115,790 (103,678)
Russian population 170,000–230,000 (197,737)
Turkish population 1–10 (3)

The Wigeon has a northern Palearctic world breeding distribution. It occurs evenly in the subarctic and boreal zones, overlapping in the arctic tundra and temperate steppe zones, S to *c*50°N. To the E its range stretches to the Kamchatka Peninsula and N Sakhalin; to the W and NW it extends to Norway, Great Britain and Iceland.

The Wigeon is distributed to the N and NE in Europe, from *c*50° to 70°N. It is absent from the Arctic islands, although it inhabits much of Iceland, except the S and the interior. It is evenly spread at lower altitudes, but scattered in mountainous areas throughout Finland and most of Sweden and Norway (Haapanen & Nilsson 1979). It occurs sporadically in the Baltic states and is thinly spread across Great Britain. It is rare in Denmark, Germany and Ukraine and is an occasional breeder in The Netherlands, Ireland and Poland.

The wintering areas of European breeding populations are mainly in W and SW Europe, principally in the North Sea countries, but others exist in France, Iberia, Denmark and S Sweden. Western Europe has some local resident populations. Siberian breeding populations winter across a wide area, from NW Africa and the Mediterranean coast through the Caspian and Black Seas, to S and SW Asia.

The Wigeon breeds in a fairly wide range of freshwater habitats from open tundra and bogs to lakes surrounded by woodlands, mires and arable land in the boreal zone, to many types of wetlands in the temperate zone. Its preference is for shallow water and open habitats, avoiding closed forest landscapes, eutrophic lakes with tall, dense stands of emergent vegetation, mountains, and fast-flowing streams and rivers. The Wigeon occurs on all sizes of boreal lakes which have shallow wetlands and low vegetation with stands of sedge *Carex* and horsetail *Equisetum*. It avoids the smallest oligotrophic lakes, occurring regularly only where their area exceeds 1km^2 (Kauppinen 1993). In northern wetlands its habitats are humus and acid, but it tolerates alkaline and saline habitats in the S of its range.

Russia holds the great majority of the breeding population, *c*200 000bp, followed by Finland which has 60 000–80 000bp, Sweden 20 000–30 000bp, Iceland 4000–6000bp and Norway 4000–5000bp. Great Britain has only 300–500bp and the Baltic States a population varying between 10 and 100bp.

Prime S and C Fennoscandian habitat, where the Wigeon is a typical species, consists of boreal, shallow and richly vegetated lakes surrounded by bog and forest shores ('mixotrophic lakes'; Kauppinen & Väisänen 1993) where it reaches breeding densities of 3.0–5.0 bp/km^2, as it does on eutrophic lakes (Kauppinen 1993). However, on boreal oligotrophic and mesotrophic lakes in S and C Finland, it achieves 0.1–0.4 bp/km^2. Abundance is highest on northern wetland lakes where it is the commonest waterfowl species (Haapanen & Nilsson 1979). In terms of breeding density over the whole of northern Fennoscandia, it achieves 0.1–0.2 bp/km^2. The Wigeon has expanded southwards, colonizing Great Britain during the cooler climatic phase of the 1800s. The present population trend appears stable, and annual fluctuations are small in prime Finnish habitat.

Jukka Kauppinen (SF)

Anas strepera

Gadwall

CZ	Kopřivka obecná	**I**	Canapiglia
D	Schnatterente	**NL**	Krakeend
E	Anade Friso	**P**	Frisada
F	Canard chipeau	**PL**	Krakwa
FIN	Harmaasorsa	**R**	Серая утка
G	Καπακλής	**S**	Snatterand
H	Kendermagos réce		

SPEC Cat 3, Threat status V

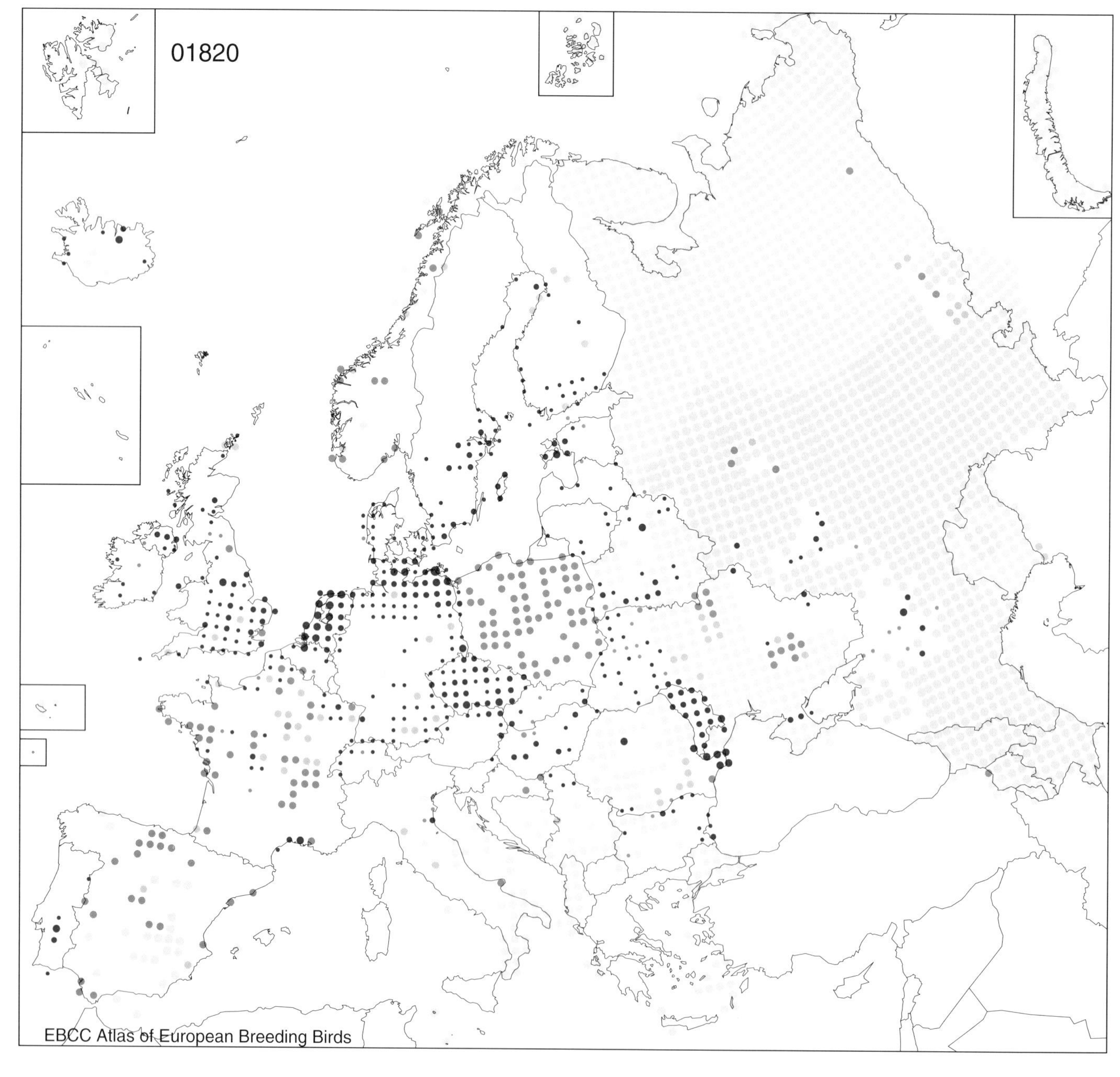

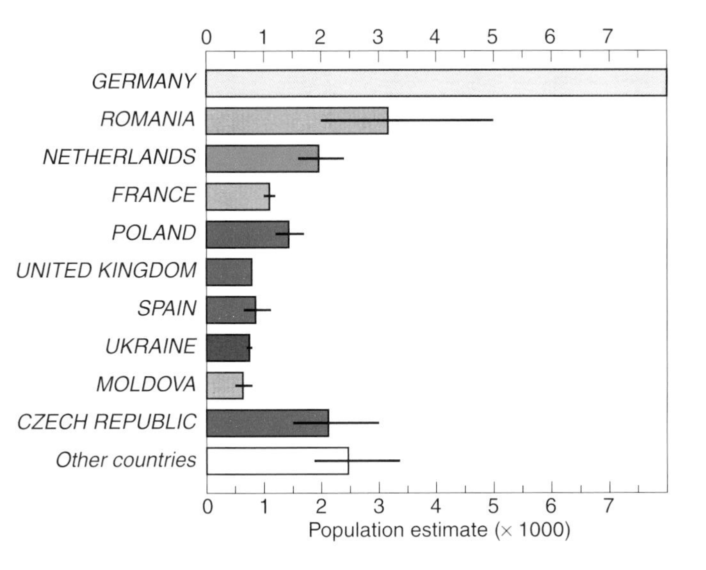

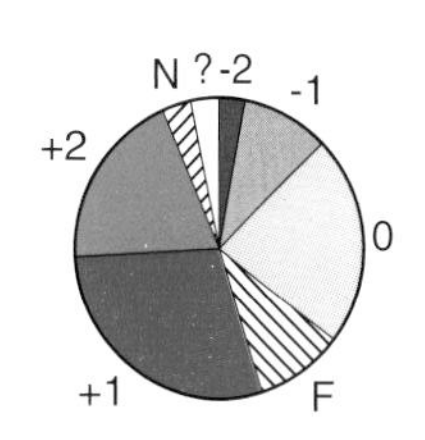

% in top 10 countries: 89.4
Total number of populated European countries: 31
Total European population 21,832–25,403 (23,255)
Russian population 55,000–85,000 (68,374)
Turkish population 500–5000 (1581)

The Gadwall breeds both in the Palearctic and in the Nearctic in relatively small areas in the mid-latitudes of the temperate and mediterranean zones, rather further S than the other dabbling ducks. It is concentrated in lowlands, in continental rather than coastal areas, and in open rather than in forested, hilly or especially mountainous terrain. Its Palearctic distribution extends from W Europe to the broad lowlands and steppes of Kazakhstan and W Siberia, as far as C Asian mountain ranges.

The Gadwall prefers large, shallow, open freshwater bodies possessing abundant shore and submerged vegetation. In N Germany it breeds mainly on eutrophic lakes and fishponds, in Great Britain on artificial waters such as reservoirs and gravel-pits, whereas on the steppes of continental Europe it frequents brackish waters. Recently, it has bred on brackish or even salt water in W Europe, as in the German Wadden Sea and W Baltic, where it breeds on lagoons, peninsulas and small marshy islands (Berndt & Busche 1991). Regionally, it tends to associate with gull and tern colonies.

In Europe its numbers fluctuate widely, but overall, the Gadwall has extended its range considerably, more so than other waterfowl, in C, W and SW Europe, and to a lesser degree in N and S Europe. This trend has been apparent for over 200 years. Early outposts in N Germany, S Sweden and Iceland were consolidated by the early or mid-19th century. Influxes to W Europe were evident in the 1940s and 1950s and led to new colonization, filling many gaps in distribution. The earliest influxes were interpreted as invasions as the consequence of steppe lakes in SE Europe and C Asia drying up temporarily (Kalela 1946). However, more recent expansions probably are influenced greatly by the development within the western European population since the 1960s of distinct breeding, moulting and wintering traditions.

Dynamic expansion and special habitat preferences have led to a patchy distribution in Europe. The Gadwall has widespread populations in Moldova, Poland, the Czech Republic, N Germany, the Netherlands and parts of England and France. Some of these countries show the most marked increases, such as the Netherlands where the population rose from 80bp in 1970 to 1600–2400bp in 1994, and France, where fewer than 100bp existed in 1976, but 1000–1200bp flourished in 1994. In 1990 in Schleswig-Holstein (15 700km^2) there were 650bp, one of the highest regional densities in Europe. In N and S Europe, except for S Sweden, Portugal and Spain, the Gadwall remains scarce. Where the Gadwall has colonized this century, the present population and distribution trends are generally considered to be positive, but in E Europe its numbers are stable or decreasing.

Fox (1988) suggested that the colonization of Great Britain derived largely from introduced stock, because 1000 or more birds were released in the 1960s. However, during the more recent expansions, wild birds are probably involved to a considerable degree, because many from the continent now winter there, as shown by ringing recoveries.

Little is known about the Gadwall's moulting areas. In winter the species favours a mild climate, but even then remains patchily distributed. Its major European wintering areas are in S Spain, S France, Romania, and the southern former USSR, including Transcaucasia. European birds also winter in North Africa, in the Nile Valley, Turkey and Mesopotamia. Further N a marked increase is apparent in wintering numbers in Great Britain, The Netherlands, Belgium, N France and S Germany, a change related to the recent series of mild winters. Asian populations winter from Pakistan to E China.

The Gadwall nowadays is monotypic, a Pacific Island subspecies *A.s. couesii* being extinct.

Rolf K Berndt (D)

Anas crecca **Teal**

CZ	Čírka obecná	**I**	Alzavola
D	Krickente	**NL**	Wintertaling
E	Cerceta Común	**P**	Marrequinho-comum
F	Sarcelle d'hiver	**PL**	Cyraneczka
FIN	Tavi	**R**	Чирок-свистунок
G	Κιρκίρι	**S**	Kricka
H	Csörgő réce		

Non-SPEC, Threat status S

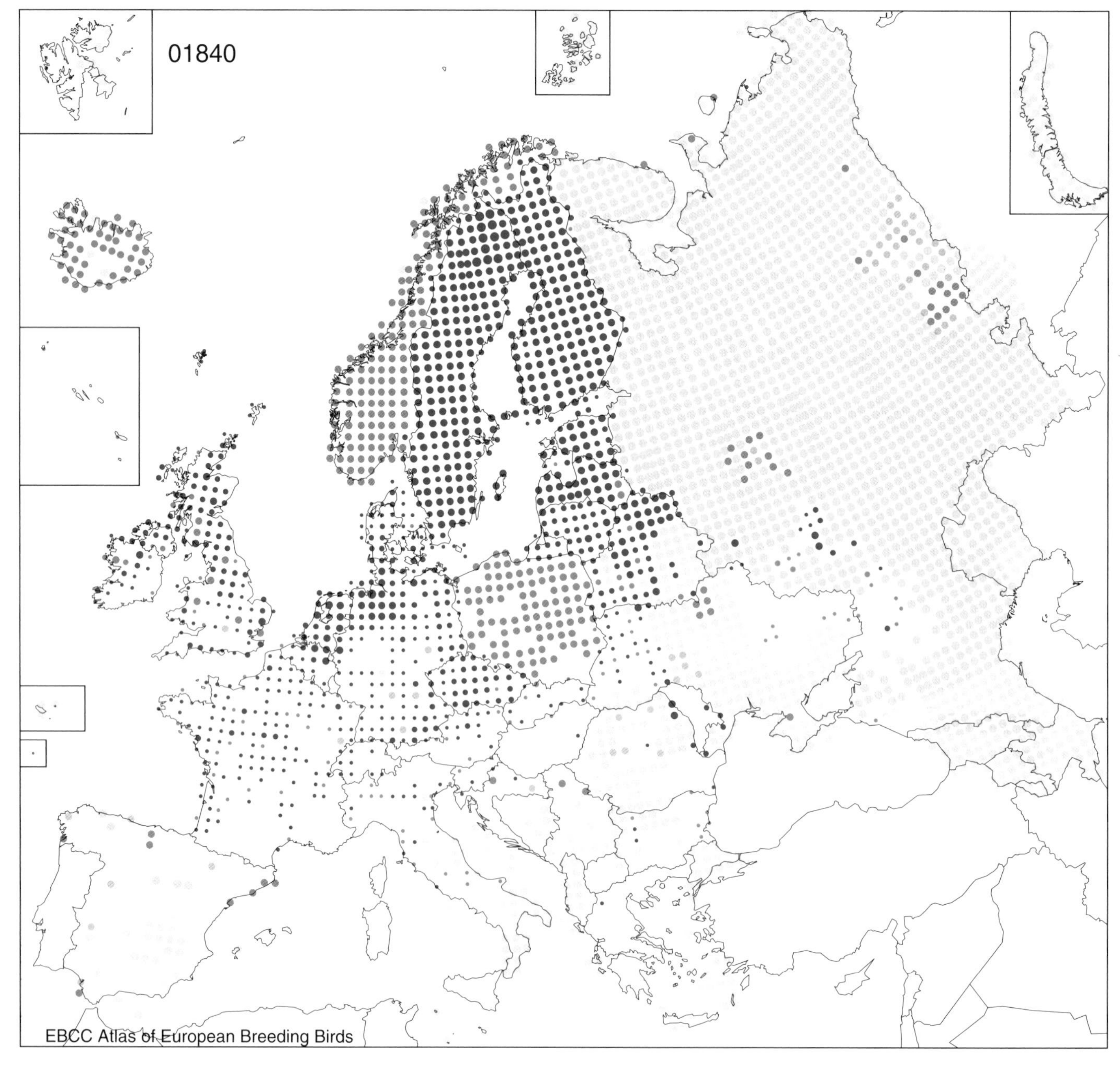

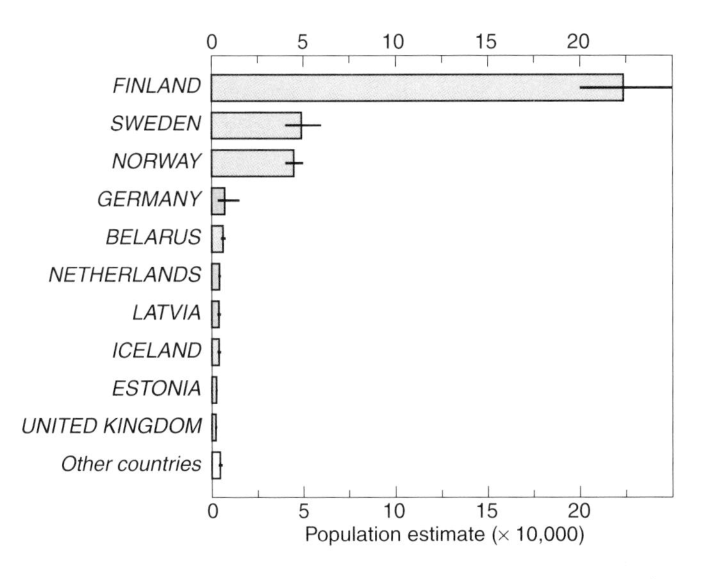

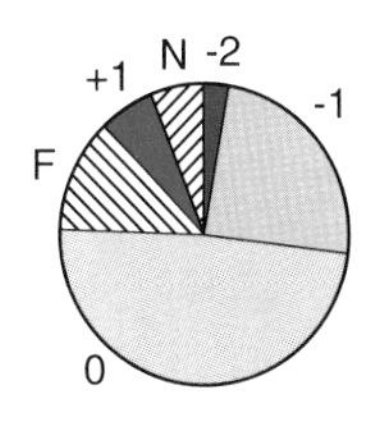

% in top 10 countries: 98.7
Total number of populated European countries: 33
Total European population 325,444–381,790 (351,495)
Russian population 775,000–1,170,000 (952,234)
Turkish population 100–1000 (316)

The Teal is an abundant holarctic species. In Europe the nominate subspecies *A.c. crecca* breeds throughout the middle latitudes of the W Palearctic in Europe and in N Asia. The other two subspecies inhabit the Nearctic, *nimia* in the Aleutian Islands and *carolinensis* on the North American mainland.

The Teal breeds on all kinds of shallow waters which have some dense border vegetation and emergent plants. It breeds inland as well as along some coasts and it frequently uses both natural and artificial small pools or ponds. Usually, rather open habitats are preferred, from tundra and bogs to farmland. Forest ponds, however, also provide important breeding habitat, especially in the northern parts of the range.

Teal originating from the northern half of Europe winter mainly in the countries bordering the North Sea or in SW Europe (some crossing the Mediterranean to reach the Canary Islands, North Africa and the Nile Valley), whereas those from S Russia and Ukraine winter in SE Europe, Turkey, the Middle East and the Caspian region. Ringing has shown use of different flyways in different years (*BWP*). Populations in the southern half of Europe are mainly sedentary. Asian breeders winter from Iran and Pakistan E to Japan.

In Europe hundreds of thousands of pairs breed in Russia and Fennoscandia. In the northern half of Europe the species is rather uniformly distributed. The map shows that almost every square is occupied in Fennoscandia and in the lowlands from N France through Germany and Poland well into Russia and the Baltic countries. Breeding densities tend to increase northwards. Overall trends in regional densities evidently correlate with the regional availability of suitable breeding habitats. Detailed studies of breeding densities in coniferous forest areas have yielded a density of 0.57 bp/km shoreline in southern Finland (P. Nummi & H. Pöysä, pers obs) and 0.24 bp/km shoreline in northern Sweden (Danell & Sjöberg 1979). In C Europe the species is less uniformly distributed, avoiding mountainous regions. Numbers per 50km square are generally low. In the southern half of Europe, S of a line from the Loire to the Danube, its distribution is irregular. In Great Britain it occurs most regularly in upland areas.

Long-term breeding population trends are poorly known for this species due to census problems (inconspicuous behaviour of breeding birds), a lack of census workers over much of its breeding area and marked short-term changes in breeding numbers in response to factors such as fluctuating water levels or winter mortality.

In most countries the trend is estimated to be stable or fluctuating. In Finland, for example, breeding numbers fluctuated considerably between 1986 and 1992 (Pöysä *et al* 1993). In the other countries a tendency towards decreasing numbers dominates, including some countries which hold (relatively) large populations (Russia, Germany, The Netherlands, Latvia). Changes in breeding range have usually not been recorded in these countries, with the exception of The Netherlands, where a probable decrease in the total area of bogs coincided with a modest colonization of grassland areas. The reasons for the downward trends are unclear, but destruction or deterioration of breeding habitats (through drainage developments in breeding areas) must be important factors.

Increasing trends are reported only from Denmark and some SE European countries holding small populations, such as Moldova, Romania and Hungary. Locally, the species may respond quickly to habitat management, such as restoration of high and stable water levels, resulting in better breeding opportunities and increased food supply (Fox 1986).

Despite breeding Teal populations in Europe apparently being stable or slightly decreasing, the numbers wintering in Europe (not all of European origin) increased markedly between 1967 and 1983, only to decline subsequently in 1983–86 (Monval & Pirot 1989).

Fred Hustings (NL) Hannu Pöysä (FIN)

This species account is sponsored by Dr Luc Schifferli, Sempach, CH.

Anas platyrhynchos **Mallard**

CZ	Kachna divoká	I	Germano reale
D	Stockente	NL	Wilde Eend
E	Anade Azulón	P	Pato-real
F	Canard colvert	PL	Krzyżówka
FIN	Sinisorsa	R	Кряква
G	Πρασινοκέφαλη	S	Gräsand
H	Tőkés réce		

Non-SPEC, Threat status S

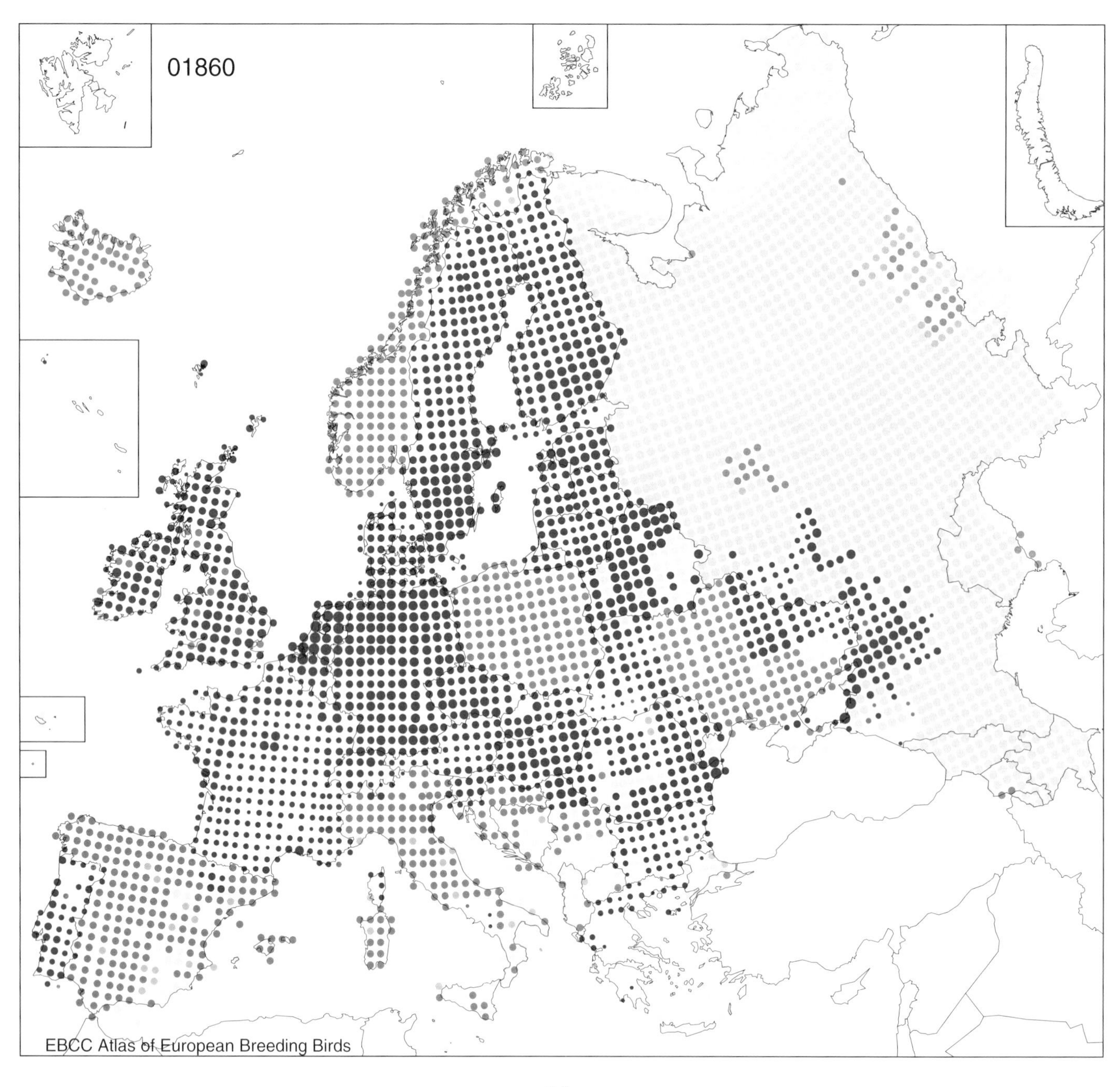

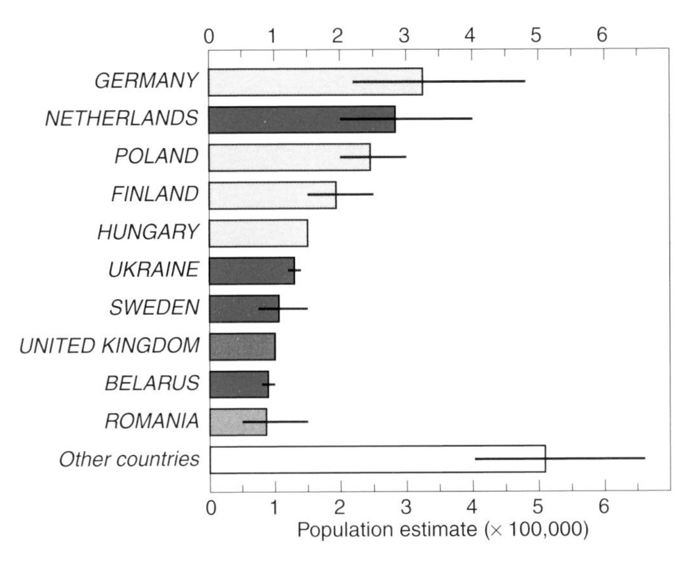

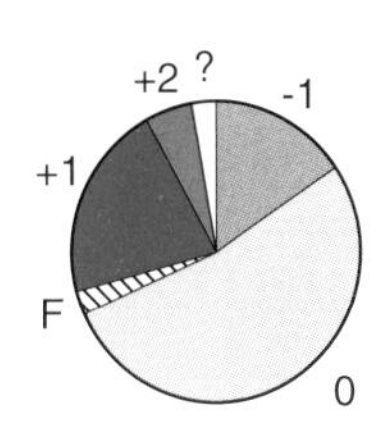

% in top 10 countries: 77.1
Total number of populated European countries: 38
Total European population 2,056,300–2,443,983 (2,215,429)
Russian population 650,000–800,000 (721,110)
Turkish population 5000–20,000 (10,000)

Holarctic in distribution, and the most abundant and widespread duck species in Europe, occurring in all countries, the Mallard is absent only from high altitude locations. Its ability to exploit habitats across a wide range of topographies is its outstanding feature. Its adaptability has brought it into closer contact with human beings than other duck species, resulting in a gradient of individuals from the truly wild to those living in parks. Some towns have populations containing every degree of hybrid with *A.p.* forma *domestica*.

The Mallard is essentially a bird of still or slow-flowing fresh water, brackish estuaries and lagoons, or coasts where saline water is shallow and sheltered. Consequently it reaches its highest densities in the lowlands. Its choice of habitat is governed by its need for water less than 1m deep in which to forage, and by its preference for emergent vegetation at wetland margins rather than open water in which to rest up. It requires wetlands subject to seasonal floods and containing significant amounts of submerged, floating, emergent and riparian vegetation, including dense stands of reeds and flooded swampy woodlands. It also frequents open waters incorporating mudflats, banks, spits and promontories, and uses reservoirs, ornamental waters, canals and sewage farms. It nests predominantly in vegetation up to 1m tall, favouring especially islands (D.A. Hill 1984a). Wetlands whose shorelines are convoluted rather than straight generally hold more breeding pairs because more of the males' established 'ranges' or 'activity centres' (where females are guarded from other males during the breeding period) may be condensed into a given area, making the regulation of local (site) breeding populations strongly density-dependent (D.A. Hill 1984b).

The species' distribution is ubiquitous, making patterns of variation difficult to identify from the 50 × 50km grid resolution. The population graph refers mostly to the 1980s and early 1990s but there is little significant change since then. The largest breeding population is in Russia, and with those of Germany, The Netherlands, Poland and Finland, comprises 60% of the European estimated breeding population. Population density, generally higher in the N, is highest on islands affording protection from mammalian predators. Here, the species may breed semi-colonially, with nests 5–10m apart (D.A. Hill 1984c).

Where altitude affects the Mallard's distribution, the restriction is comparatively slight. In major ranges such as the Pyrenees, the Italian Alps, Sicily and the Massif Central breeding may even occur above 2000m asl. The European population has remained relatively stable from 1970 to 1990. The large populations in The Netherlands, Ukraine, Sweden and Great Britain have increased, whereas those in Romania, Spain and the Czech Republic have decreased. Increases in Sweden and France contrast with other reports (in Marchant *et al* 1990) though Hustings (1988) confirmed the increases. In part the increases probably derive both from the profusion of permanent wetland areas left by mineral extraction and from the greater number of releases of hand-reared birds for hunting. Winter count totals for Europe also indicate a slow but general increase in Mallard populations (Monval & Pirot 1989).

Although the Mallard is mostly migratory, some populations as in S and W Europe are sedentary, apart from local movements in severe weather when they favour coasts. In N, E and C Europe, some individuals remain all year where waters remain unfrozen. Birds from NW Russia, Fennoscandia, the Baltic States, N Poland, N Germany and Denmark winter from Denmark to N France and Great Britain, some reaching northern Spain. Many Icelandic birds winter in Britain & Ireland. A proportion of Baltic breeding birds join those of C Europe, as do some from the Upper Volga basin. In western Europe most wintering birds concentrate in the countries bordering the southern Baltic Sea, and in The Netherlands, Belgium and N France.

Rolf K Berndt (D) David Hill (GB)

Anas acuta **Pintail**

CZ	Ostralka štíhlá	**I**	Codone
D	Spießente	**NL**	Pijlstaart
E	Anade Rabudo	**P**	Arrabio
F	Canard pilet	**PL**	Rożeniec
FIN	Jouhisorsa	**R**	Шилохвость
G	Ψαλίδα	**S**	Stjärtand
H	Nyílfarkú réce		

SPEC Cat 3, Threat status V

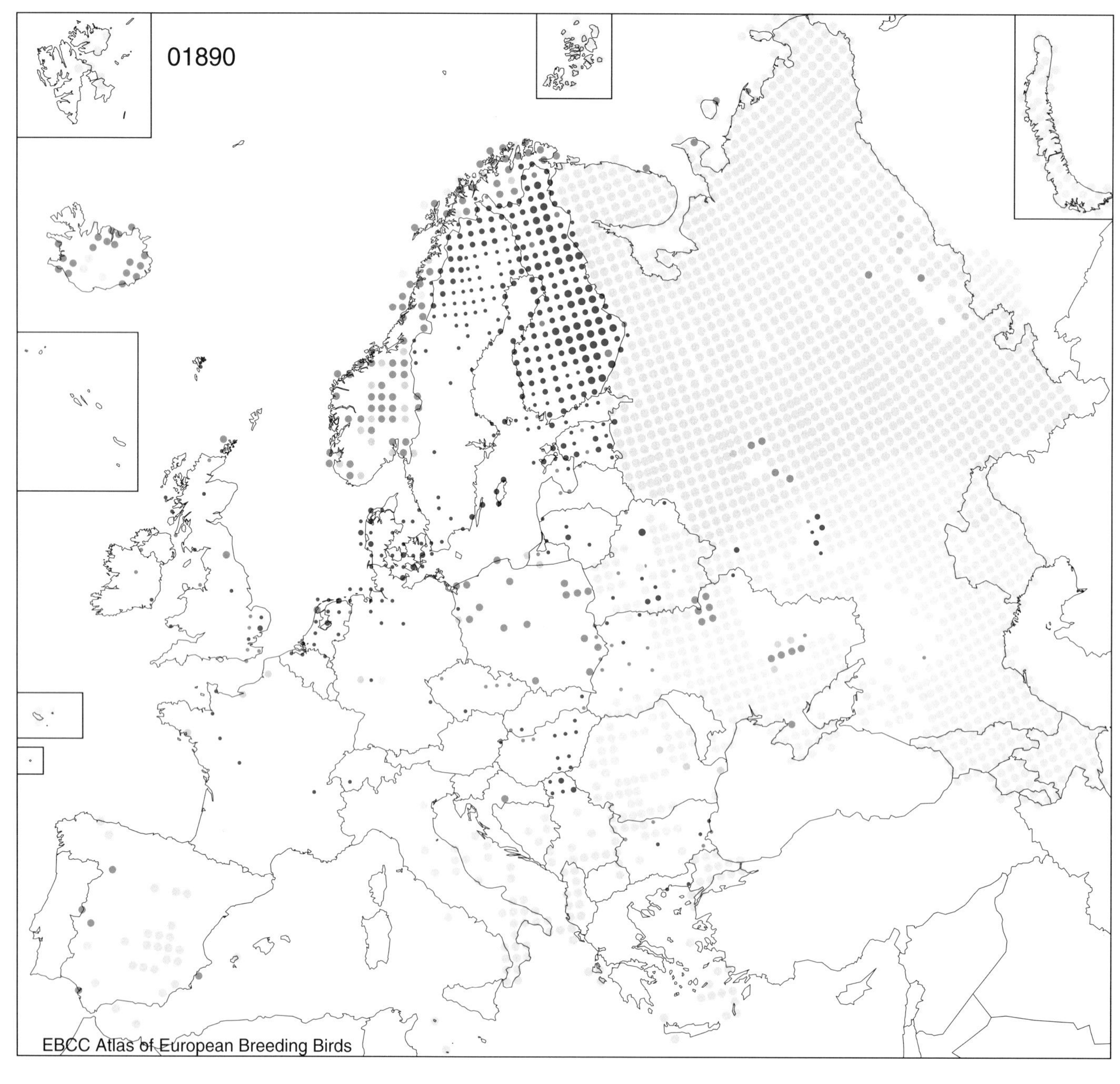

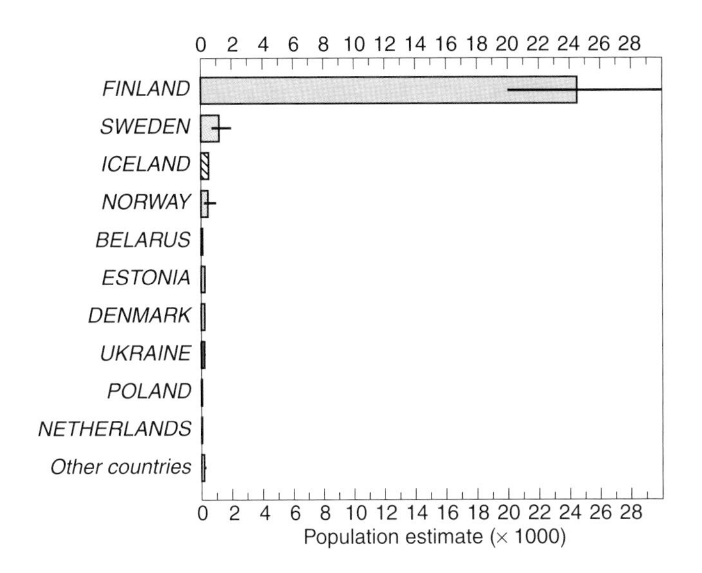

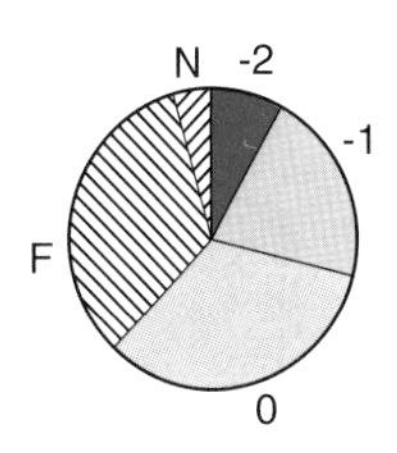

% in top 10 countries: 99.4
Total number of populated European countries: 24
Total European population 23,141–33,264 (27,670)
Russian population 150,000–300,000 (212,132)
Turkish population 500–1000 (707)

The holarctic distribution of the Pintail covers northern and temperate regions of Europe, Asia and North America. It is found throughout the Eurasian continent from E to W. Although it avoids arctic islands and the E Siberian coasts, it has a more northerly range than other dabbling duck species. Its southernmost limit lies usually at *c*40°N, except for small relict populations in Turkey and North Africa.

In Europe, the Pintail's largely continental distribution is reflected in the well-spread populations of Finland (20 000–30 000bp), Estonia (200–300bp) and especially of N and C Russia (150 000–300 000bp). At a much lower density, the same pattern is present inland in Sweden (700–2000bp) and Norway (100–500bp). In other European countries the Pintail has an extremely patchy distribution of isolated small groups, rarely exceeding a few dozen breeding pairs per country.

The Pintail's breeding habitat is characterized by open landscapes: shallow tundra wetlands with low vegetation and subarctic bogs, eutrophic lakes and seashore meadows in the boreal and temperate zones and grasslands and steppes in the S of its range. It also occurs on brackish or salty waters by the North Sea and in the Baltic archipelago. It avoids fast-running rivers and oligotrophic deep water bounded by continuous dense forests or tall emergent vegetation. Preferred habitats are either impermanent in character or vulnerable to drought or flooding, often requiring shifts to new breeding sites. Pintail populations in some wetlands therefore can be unstable. The populations in boreal eutrophic lakes, however, do appear to be relatively stable (Kauppinen 1993).

The Pintail is less abundant in northernmost Finnish Lapland than in the C boreal zone with its plethora of mires and dyseutrophic lakes (Haapanen & Nilsson 1979). On boreal lakes it prefers open habitats characterized by abundant vegetation including sedge *Carex* and horsetail *Equisetum* stands. On eutrophic reed *Phragmites* lakes, it tends to select open shores with low vegetation, often bordered by fields (Kauppinen 1993). On the C boreal zone dyseutrophic lakes, breeding density is *c*1–2 bp/km^2, but on eutrophic lakes in S Finland less than 0.5 bp/km^2 (Kauppinen 1993).

At present, there are no marked overall changes of range size in Europe, but some decline in numbers is recorded for Russia, Finland, Estonia, Denmark, Poland and Ukraine. The small breeding groups in the North Sea countries have increased since the 1900s, but their numbers remain insignificant.

Large moult gatherings occur in Russia and Kazakhstan. The northern breeding populations of the western Palearctic winter mainly in W Europe, the majority of Siberian birds migrating to the Mediterranean, the Balkans, the Black and Caspian Seas, some reaching Saudi Arabia and the Indian subcontinent. Other European populations winter in sub-Saharan Africa.

In winter the Pintail is one of the most concentrated duck species in the W Palearctic, because only very few wetlands, mainly in coastal areas, can hold such large flocks. Its winter distribution has a more southerly bias than most other dabbling duck species. Except in severe weather, the main wintering sites are usually in Great Britain, The Netherlands, Belgium and France. Cold weather movements take place predominantly to the W and S (Ridgill & Fox 1990), when the Marismas of the Guadalquivir Delta become a major wintering site. There have been no marked wintering population changes in W Europe since the 1960s, but little is known of changes over a longer period, although in the N Frisian Wadden Sea in the 19th century it was several times more abundant (Berndt & Busche 1991).

Rolf K. Berndt (D) Jukka Kauppinen (FIN)

Anas querquedula

Garganey

CZ	Čírka modrá	**I**	Marzaiola
D	Knäkente	**NL**	Zomertaling
E	Cerceta Carretona	**P**	Marreco
F	Sarcelle d'été	**PL**	Cyranka
FIN	Heinätavi	**R**	Чирок-трескунок
G	Σαρσέλα	**S**	Årta
H	Böjti réce		

SPEC Cat 3, Threat status V

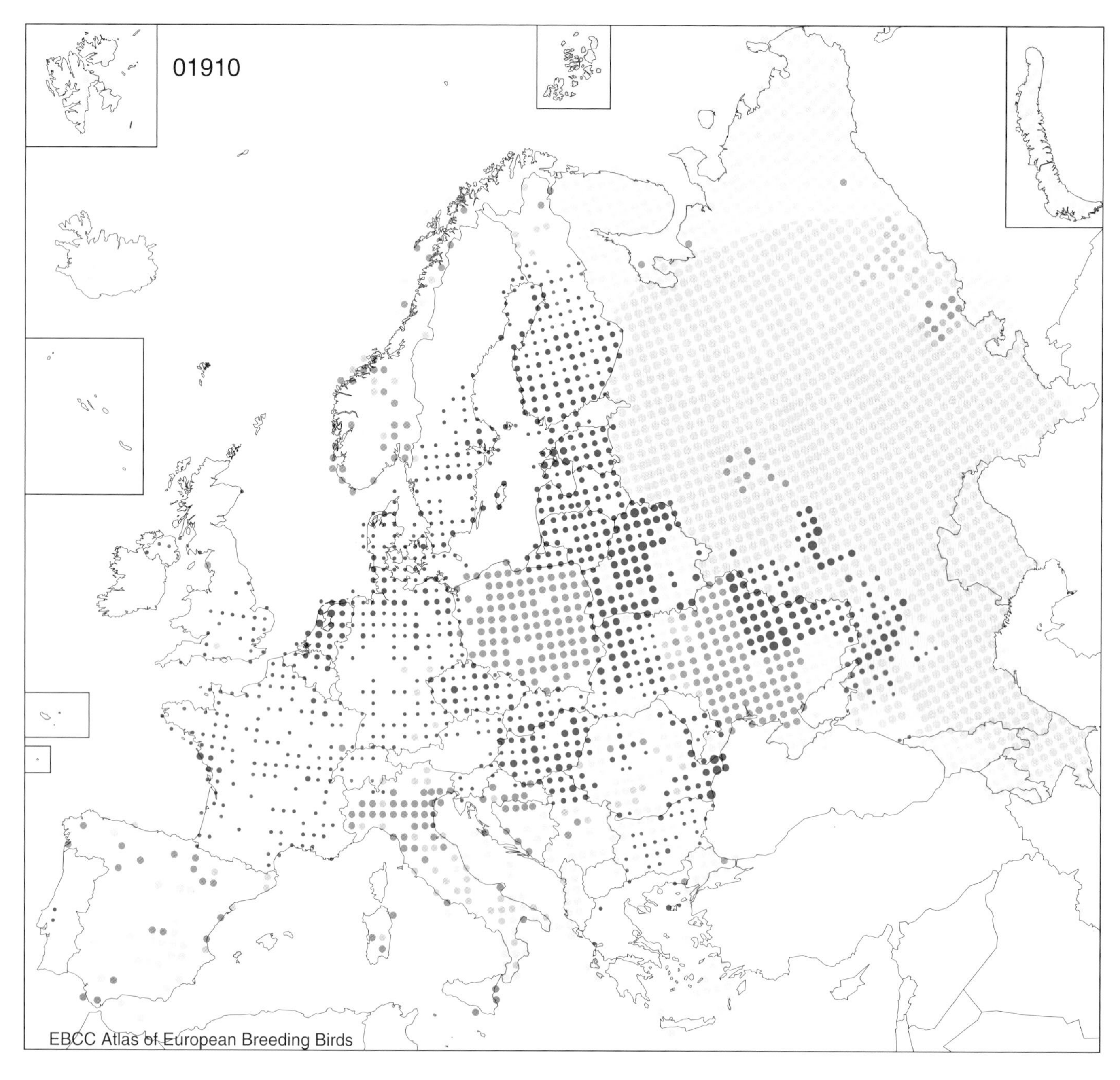

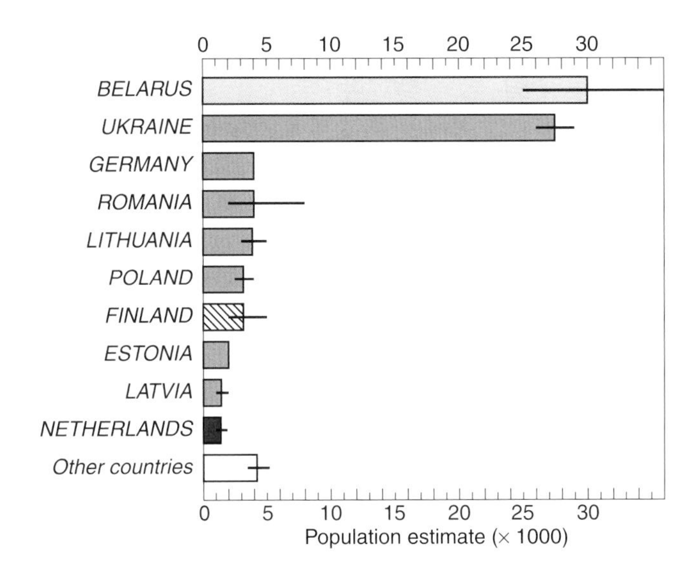

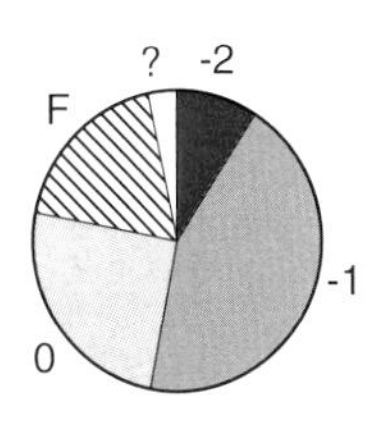

% in top 10 countries: 95.0
Total number of populated European countries: 32
Total European population 78,811–92,421 (84,647)
Russian population 570,000–960,000 (739,730)
Turkish population 500–1000 (707)

The monotypic Garganey is a trans-Palearctic breeding species distributed through the boreal, temperate, mediterranean, steppe and desert climatic zones E to Sakhalin and Kamchatka. Its range lies roughly between 45° and 65°N. It has tended to extend its breeding range northwards, possibly connected with increasing boreal zone summer temperatures.

Its precise habitat requirements have not been defined, but important elements are an open, rather treeless landscape, wet depressions, shallow water and shore vegetation. Hence the Garganey occupies marshes, moors, wet meadows near shallow freshwater pools, creeks, ditches, lakes and rivers. Often these habitats are bordered by a rich shore vegetation of reed and other marsh vegetation. Its general habitat requirements correspond to those of Teal *A. crecca*, but Garganey does not occur in mountains nor in dense woodland. It feeds mostly by making filtering movements with its bill on the water surface, and not by dabbling. Consequently, the proportion of invertebrate food is high and so the Garganey prefers eutrophic waters.

Except for small flocks wintering in the Mediterranean area, most European birds migrate to the wet river valleys and lakes in a 100km-broad belt in sub-Saharan Africa, probably flying non-stop across the Mediterranean and the Sahara. W European birds use two routes, via Iberia or Italy, but tend to return via Italy and the Balkans, the latter region perhaps also receiving E European breeders whose autumn migration route lies around the eastern Mediterranean (*BWP*). The species concentrates in extensive flooded depressions and wet meadows subject to dynamic hydrobiological conditions in the lower Senegal and upper Niger Rivers, and in the area adjacent to Lake Chad. Over 900 000 birds have been counted in aerial surveys (Roux & Jarry 1984), making it probable that almost the entire western Palearctic population winters there. Depending on the year's rainfall pattern, populations may shift laterally to the E or W. Most Asian populations winter from Pakistan and Indian through SE Asia to S China.

The largest breeding populations are in Russia, Belarus and Ukraine, which hold *c*750 000, 30 000 and 27 500bp respectively, but detailed distribution in these countries is poorly known, making the data incomplete. Elsewhere, numbers never exceed 4000bp, with Germany, Lithuania and Romania reaching that order, Poland and Finland each holding *c*3500bp and Estonia 2000bp. The lower numbers in The Netherlands (*c*1400bp) and France (*c*350bp) indicate well that distribution is concentrated mainly in the E and NE. Local density can be high, as in the Oka Valley SE of Moscow: 13bp/ha on extensive cultivated grassland (J. Philippona, pers comm).

In C and W Europe numbers decreased sharply in the 1970s. In The Netherlands an estimated 2500–10 000bp (1970, probably an underestimate) decreased to fewer than 1500bp by 1975, at which level numbers have stabilized (1987, 1250–1750bp). The steepest decline was noted in the early 1970s (Zomerdijk 1986). A similar decline, with fluctuations, occurred in N Europe, and has been paralleled by a decline in numbers migrating in or through W Europe.

Causes of this decline probably lie in both breeding and wintering areas. The main threat in breeding areas is a combination of intensification of cattle-rearing, lowering of the water table and early machine-mowing of grasslands; marshland reclamation is a contributing factor (Zomerdijk 1986, Kuschert & Ziesemer 1991). The gradual introduction of intensive farming methods in Russia, the Garganey's breeding stronghold, and into adjacent countries is likely to have a similar effect on these populations. In wintering areas flood-prevention measures, reservoir construction and the spread of rice and other crops into wetlands all have diminished the area of wetlands. Natural events, such as long periods of drought, may also adversely affect the Garganey population.

Sandór Farago (H) Pieter Zomerdijk (NL)

This species account is sponsored by Paul Simon, Gaurain-Ramecroix, B.

Anas clypeata Shoveler

CZ	Lžičák pestrý	**I**	Mestolone
D	Löffelente	**NL**	Slobeend
E	Cuchara Común	**P**	Pato-trombeteiro
F	Canard souchet	**PL**	Płaskonos
FIN	Lapasorsa	**R**	Широконоска
G	Χουλιαρόπαπια	**S**	Skedand
H	Kanalasréce		

Non-SPEC, Threat status S

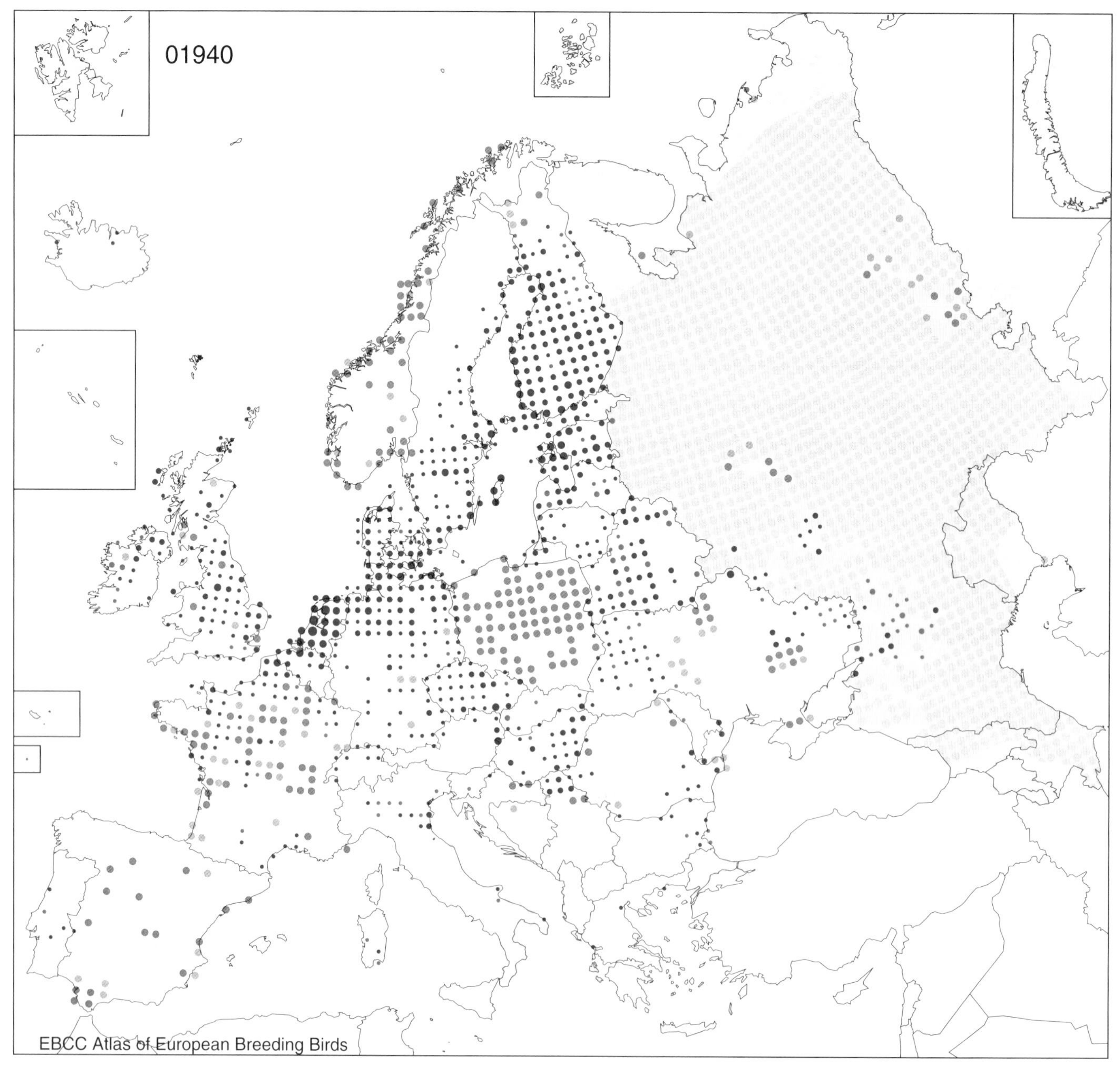

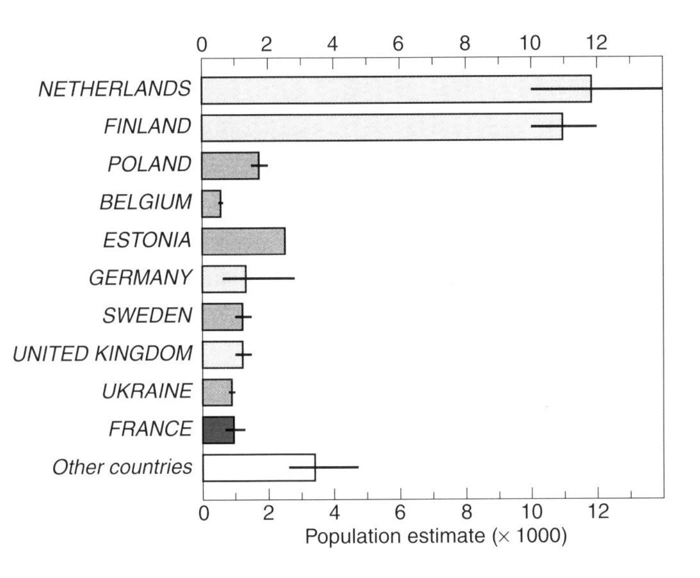

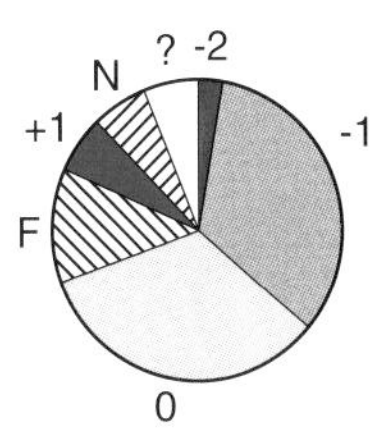

% in top 10 countries: 90.7
Total number of populated European countries: 33
Total European population 34,372–39,550 (36,623)
Russian population 65,000–95,000 (78,581)
Turkish population 100–1000 (316)

The monotypic Shoveler is an holarctic lowland species, breeding in the boreal, temperate, mediterranean, steppe and desert climatic zones, but mainly in the northern and temperate regions. Elsewhere, breeding is mostly marginal and scattered. Its range extends roughly between 45° and 70°N from Iceland to *c*162°E in the Palearctic and from Newfoundland to Alaska in the Nearctic.

The Shoveler breeds in spacious wet meadows, on moors, tundras, open parkland, short-grass steppes and inundated grasslands. In general it prefers poorly drained treeless meadows interspersed with eutrophic shallow stagnant freshwater pools and lakes, rivers with undisturbed creeks and muddy bottoms and banks, usually possessing lush emergent and floating vegetation. Its habitat choice is restricted as a result of its specialized, filtering feeding method (Dittberner & Dittberner 1987).

The main centre of the breeding population lies in Russia, which holds some 75% of the total population, but the data for large areas are incomplete, and so the mean estimate of 79 000bp must be treated with caution. The Netherlands (10 000–14 000bp) is a stronghold in western Europe, the highest densities (up to 15bp/ha) being attained in damp meadows in nature reserves and low-intensity farmland (Tanger & Zomerdijk 1985). In the S and SW of the range breeding birds are scattered and densities are usually very low. The species often breeds in areas subject to rapid dynamic change, such as flooding and fluctuating water tables, and so large year-to-year variations in numbers are typical.

The winter distribution of European birds is centred in North Africa and the Mediterranean, smaller numbers wintering in Sahelian Africa (Rüger *et al* 1986) or remaining in NW Europe. Those wintering in Transcaucasia, Mesopotamia and East Africa presumably originate from European Russia. Asian birds winter over an extensive range from Iran through the Indian subcontinent, SE Asia and China to Japan.

Following a sharp reduction in wintering numbers in Great Britain during the early 1960s, there was a sustained increase until 1971/72. The wintering population has subsequently decreased, albeit very slowly; numbers are still higher than in the 1960s (Kirby & Mitchell 1993). It is likely that the Shoveler's wintering conditions in Britain improved from the increasing availability of artificial wetlands, such as gravel-pits.

Up to the 1950s, but particularly during the first few decades of the 20th century, breeding numbers tended to increase in N and W Europe, probably due to climatic amelioration and eutrophication of inland waters improving food availability. This trend was accompanied by an expansion of the breeding range, such as in the Baltic states, Fennoscandia and Iceland. Since then, large annual fluctuations have occurred, making trend analysis and interpretation difficult.

In Finland, it is probably slowly increasing (Koskimies 1989a), but drainage and rapidly changing farming practices will inevitably cause declines over much of its range in W Europe. Thus, despite the provision of a network of protected areas leading to local increases in breeding pairs in Britain, the species showed a 12% reduction in the number of 10km squares in which the birds were recorded in 1968–72 and 1988–91 respectively, and a 39% reduction in number of squares from which breeding evidence was recorded (Mitchell 1994). Similarly, in the damp peat-meadows of Noord-Holland, The Netherlands, a decrease from 1250bp in 1973–74 to 800bp in 1981–89 was recorded, mainly as a result of earlier mowing dates, intensification of dairy farming and lowering of the water table. Highest densities (of >5 bp/100ha) are restricted to reserves that are specifically managed for meadow birds (Zomerdijk 1990a). The intensification of farming methods and the reclamation of wetlands in E Europe will, now that the political situation has drastically changed, have large-scale adverse effects on the Shoveler early in the 21st century.

Sándor Faragó (H) Pieter Zomerdijk (NL)

This species account is sponsored by Fa. Dünnwald, Rheinberg, D.

Netta rufina

Red-crested Pochard

CZ	Zrzohlávka rudozobá	**I**	Fistione turco
D	Kolbenente	**NL**	Krooneend
E	Pato Colorado	**P**	Pato-de-bico-vermelho
F	Nette rousse	**PL**	Hełmiatka
FIN	Punapäänarsku	**R**	Красноносый нырок
G	Φερεντίνι	**S**	Rödhuvad dykand
H	Üstökösréce		

SPEC Cat 3, Threat status D

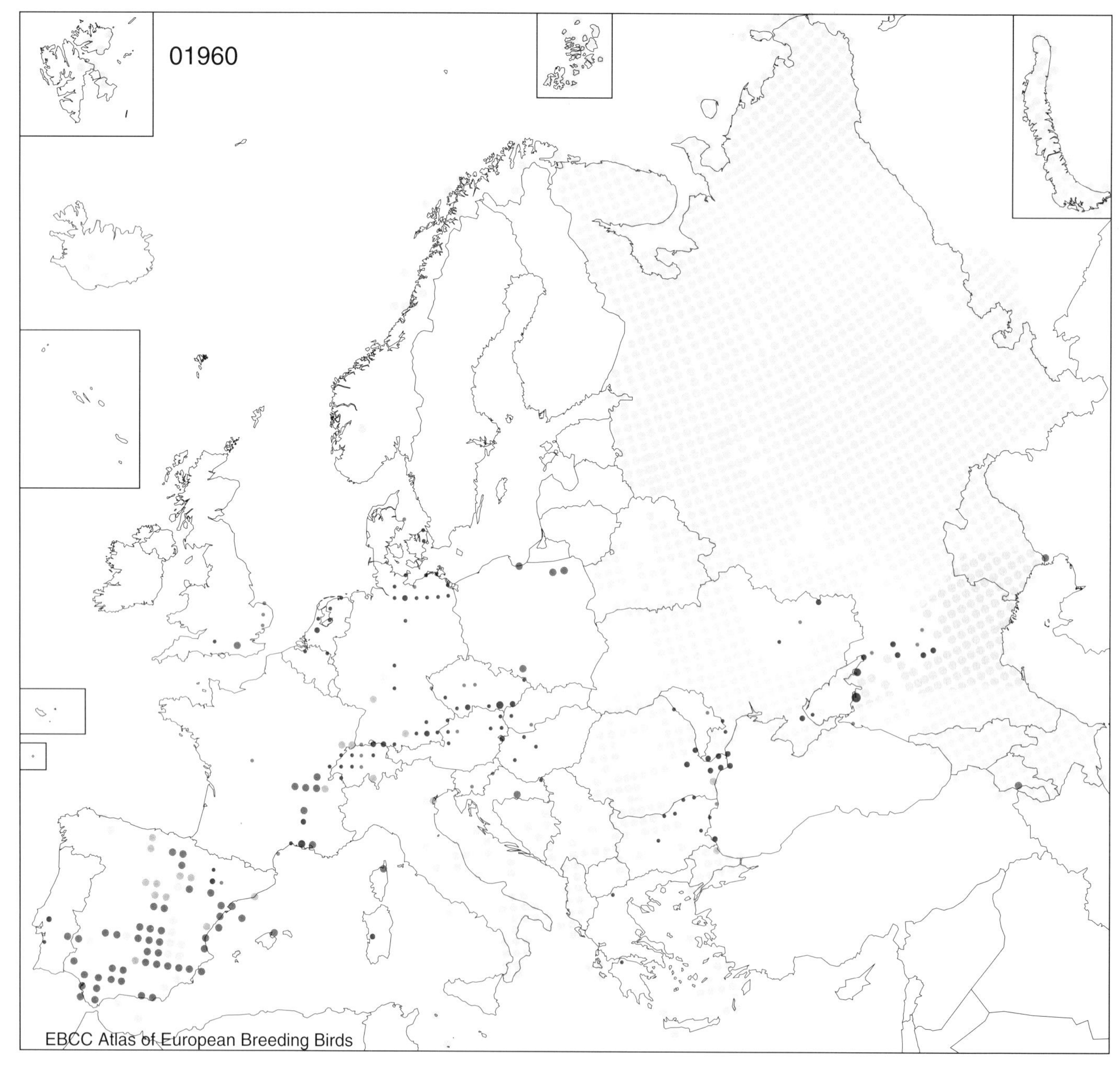

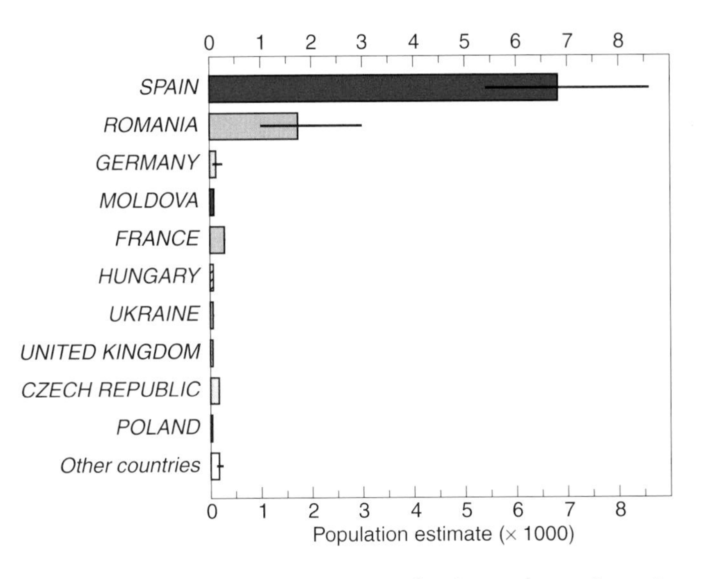

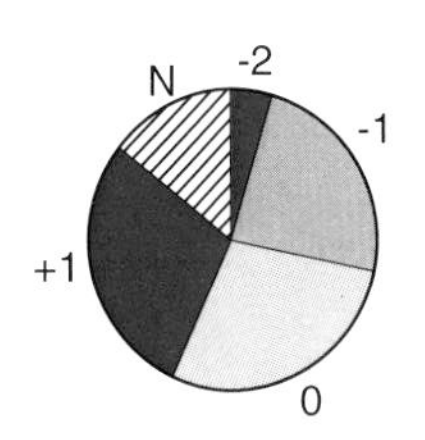

% in top 10 countries: 98.3
Total number of populated European countries: 21
Total European population 7991–11,780 (9586)
Russian population 5500–9000 (7036)
Turkish population 1000–5000 (2236)

The Red-crested Pochard is confined to the Palearctic temperate and mediterranean zones. Its distribution centre lies in the broad steppes and deserts E of the Caspian Sea as far as the mountain ranges of C Asia. In Europe its distribution is extremely patchy, consisting of several and sometimes very small breeding groups.

It prefers fairly large, shallow or moderately deep stretches of water with abundant shore and underwater vegetation. It also breeds in extensive marshes, deltas and on slow-running rivers. In Asia it often occupies brackish, salty or alkaline wetlands. The species prefers very different wetlands in Europe, especially lakes, lagoons and fishponds, although it will also choose small pools and impermanent freshwater bodies. In the western Baltic it breeds on brackish coastal waters. It displays an occasional affinity to gull and tern colonies.

The European distribution centres lie in the SE (Romania, Turkey, Russia) and in the SW (Spain). Near Valencia, the brackish Albufera (4000ha) is a major breeding site (200–400bp, Bernis 1972), as is Lake Constance; colonized in 1919, it held 50 pairs by 1970 and 300 by 1983, but only *c*33% bred successfully. In the N of its range (The Netherlands, N Germany, Poland) only small breeding groups occur. The Danish population formed in *c*1940, reaching 20bp in the 1950s, but by 1970 botulism had struck; the population has almost disappeared (possibly 1–2bp from 1986 to 1990; Sørensen 1995). British nesting records probably all concern a population originating from escapes, although continental birds are known to visit.

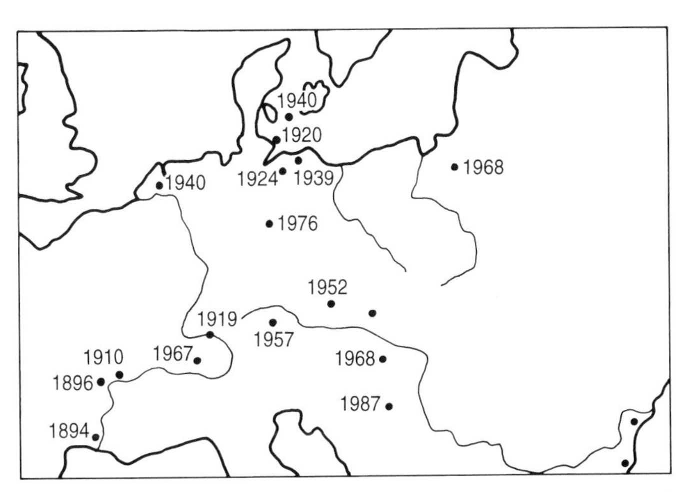

Map showing immigration into C Europe since 1894, indicating first proof of breeding (completed from Schneider-Jacoby & Vasić, 1989)

Colonization of C Europe dates from the late 1800s, and continues today (see diagram). These breeding groups show a temporal and spatial scattering throughout the continent, without significant discernible patterns of influxes or habitat preferences. In areas such as Spain, France, S Germany and the Czech Republic, populations have increased long-term. Elsewhere, reasons for breeding-site occupancy or abandonment are not known. European trends are therefore variable, but overall, numbers have increased slightly, and the range expansion continues. The Dutch increase from 6–15bp in the 1970s and 1980s to 20–30bp in 1991–93 is linked with improvement of water quality and transparency, allowing stonewort *Nitellopsis obtusa*, a favoured food of the Red-crested Pochard, to return. (Stonewort stores sulphate and calcium which aid feather-growth during the moult, and is an important addition to its diet; van der Winden *et al* 1994, Ruiters *et al* 1994).

Large moult gatherings occurred on Lake Constance (up to 9000) and Veluwemeer (The Netherlands; up to 1600) in the 1960s, but vanished following water pollution and the disappearance of stonewort. Today similar flocks occur mainly in Spain. Weather and feeding conditions permitting, the Red-crested Pochard tends to use traditional wintering grounds, but otherwise wintering locations differ from year to year (Szijj 1975). In SE Europe it winters mostly in the Danube Delta and on the Black Sea coasts, less commonly in Greece and the former Yugoslavia, but in SW Europe, except for the Camargue, it winters almost exclusively in Spain, the large lakes N of the Alps holding only moderate numbers. However isolated the numerous breeding groups in western Europe initially may appear, they share moulting and wintering places in merged flocks. Though yet unproven, it is probable that some from SE Europe reach the SW sector to winter in Spain.

Rolf K Berndt (D)

This species account is sponsored by Bureau Waardenburg bv, Culemborg, NL.

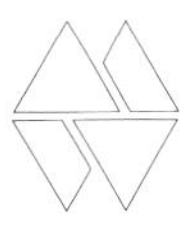

Aythya ferina

Pochard

CZ	Polák velký	I	Moriglione
D	Tafelente	NL	Tafeleend
E	Porrón Europeo	P	Zarro-comum
F	Fuligule milouin	PL	Głowienka
FIN	Punasotka	R	Красноголовый нырок
G	Γκισάρι	S	Brunand
H	Barátréce		

SPEC Cat 4, Threat status S

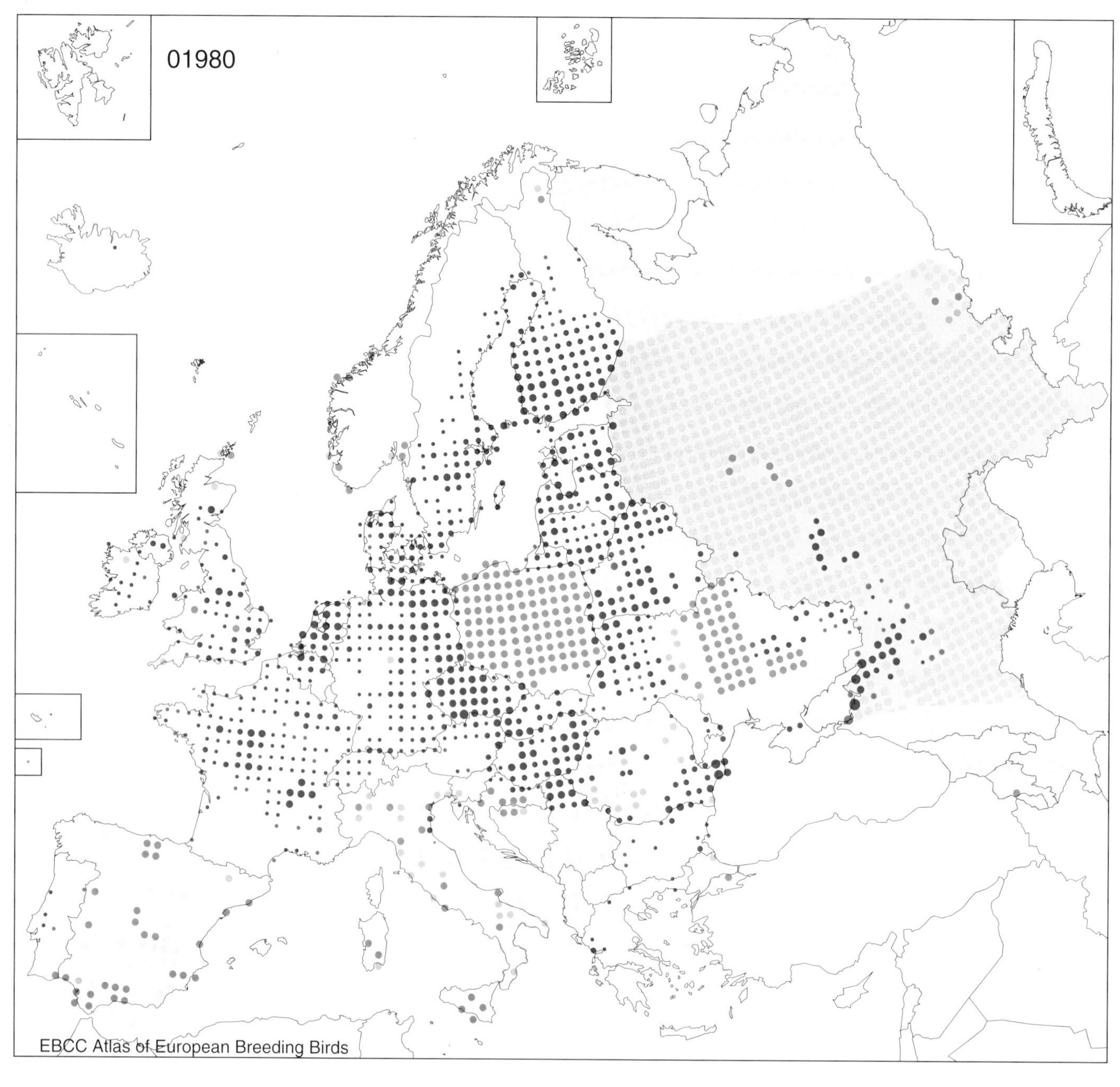

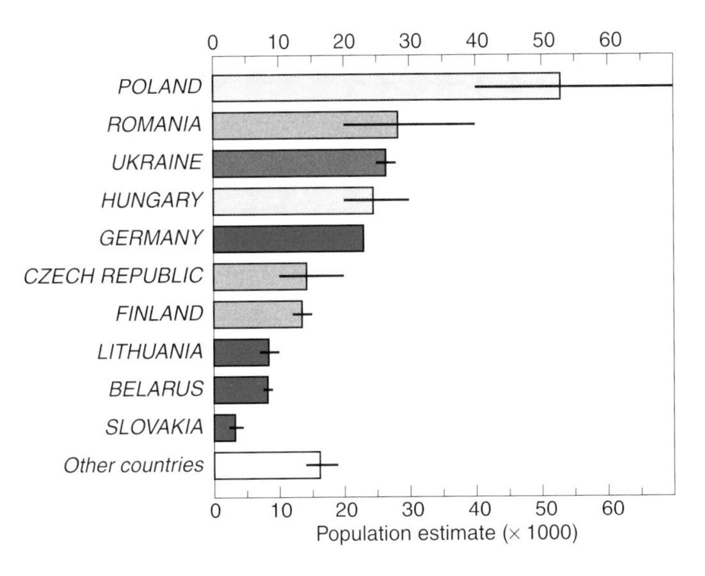

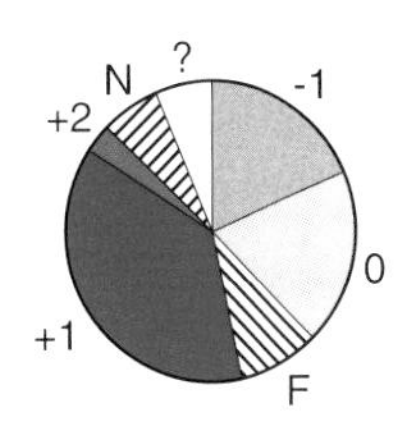

% in top 10 countries: 92.6
Total number of populated European countries: 32
Total European population 201,879–241,094 (218,633)
Russian population 90,000–100,000 (94,868)
Turkish population 500–1000 (707)

The Pochard is a Palearctic diving duck breeding from the Lake Baikal region (*c*118°E) in the E to Iceland, Ireland and Spain in the W, mostly between 45° and 60°N. Isolated populations occur in NW Africa and Turkey. Its counterparts in the Nearctic are the Canvasback *A. valisineria* and Redhead *A. americana*.

Originally a species of the base-rich, brackish and even saline lakes of the steppe region, the Pochard has expanded its range westwards to colonize more oceanic areas where it now occurs in a variety of different habitats, including oligotrophic lakes through to eutrophic and artificial waters. In the centre of its European range, in Poland, the Czech Republic, Hungary and E Germany, its favoured breeding habitats are fishponds. It may occupy suitable habitat up to 500–800m asl. In some areas, the Pochard shows a tendency to breed in association with gull colonies (*BWP*).

The main wintering areas for the European population, which is mostly migratory, are in NW and W Europe, the eastern Mediterranean, Black Sea and Caspian Sea, as well as North Africa (Rüger *et al* 1986). Others lie in Turkey, the Near East and Mesopotamia. Small numbers winter in sub-Saharan Africa, including Sudan and Ethiopia (*BWP*). Asian birds overwinter in Iran, Kazakhstan, and in a belt from Pakistan to SE China and Japan. Ringing recoveries suggest that a proportion of birds may wander widely over the wintering ranges (*BWP*). Some nesting populations are resident or partially migratory, such as the British and Irish breeders. Males commonly gather in western Europe in large numbers (from 2000 up to 50 000 are known) to moult. Eastern gatherings are much smaller (*BWP*).

Since the 1850s, the Pochard has expanded its range throughout much of Europe, when it colonized first Sweden and Finland, then Denmark and The Netherlands. In the early 20th century, it spread into C Europe, Britain and France and since 1950 has extended into the Mediterranean countries, such as Italy and Greece (see Bezzel 1969 for summary and map). At present, the Pochard is most numerous in C and E European countries, where the population is well-established and stable, although in our opinion some current estimates of numbers involved may be slightly exaggerated (eg Poland, T. Stawarczyk, pers obs). The large increase since the mid-1960s in Poland apparently is the result of the appearance of new suitable habitats there, particularly through increasing mineral extraction and reservoir construction and the establishment of intensive fish-farm ponds (Rutschke 1989). Small declines in population have been reported recently from the Czech Republic and Romania due to unfavourable changes in breeding habitats, while simultaneously, dramatic increases have occurred in neighbouring Ukraine. In Scandinavia, especially in Finland, the population increased until 1950 to *c*14 000–17 000, declining slightly more recently (Koskimies 1993a). In many W and S European countries at the edge of its range, the Pochard is patchily distributed and displays trends which are either stable, as in Great Britain (Fox 1991), or increasing.

The slight downturn in Pochard breeding numbers since a peak in 1978 in some countries correlates with the decreasing trend in the wintering population, a trend based on January counts throughout the Western Palearctic (Monval & Pirot 1989).

Breeding density in the species' distribution centre reaches *c*10 bp/10ha (Bezzel 1969) but in optimal breeding habitats such as at fishponds in Polish Silesia, the Pochard breeds at much higher densities, up to 29 bp/10ha of water surface. When associating with gull colonies on islets, the Pochard may assume semi-colonial behaviour, attaining a nest density of 130 nests/ha (T. Stawarczyk, pers obs). The total population is estimated at 250 000–350 000bp, the lower value probably being the more realistic.

There are no subspecies.

Tony Fox (GB) Tadeusz Stawarczyk (PL)

This species account is sponsored by the Institute for Inland Water Management and Waste Water Treatment, Lelystad, NL.

Aythya nyroca Ferruginous Duck

CZ	Polák malý	I	Moretta tabaccata
D	Moorente	NL	Witoogeend
E	Porrón Pardo	P	Zarro-castanho
F	Fuligule nyroca	PL	Podgorzałka
FIN	Ruskosotka	R	Белоглазый нырок
G	Βαλτόπαπια	S	Vitögd dykand
H	Cigányréce		

SPEC Cat 1, Threat status V

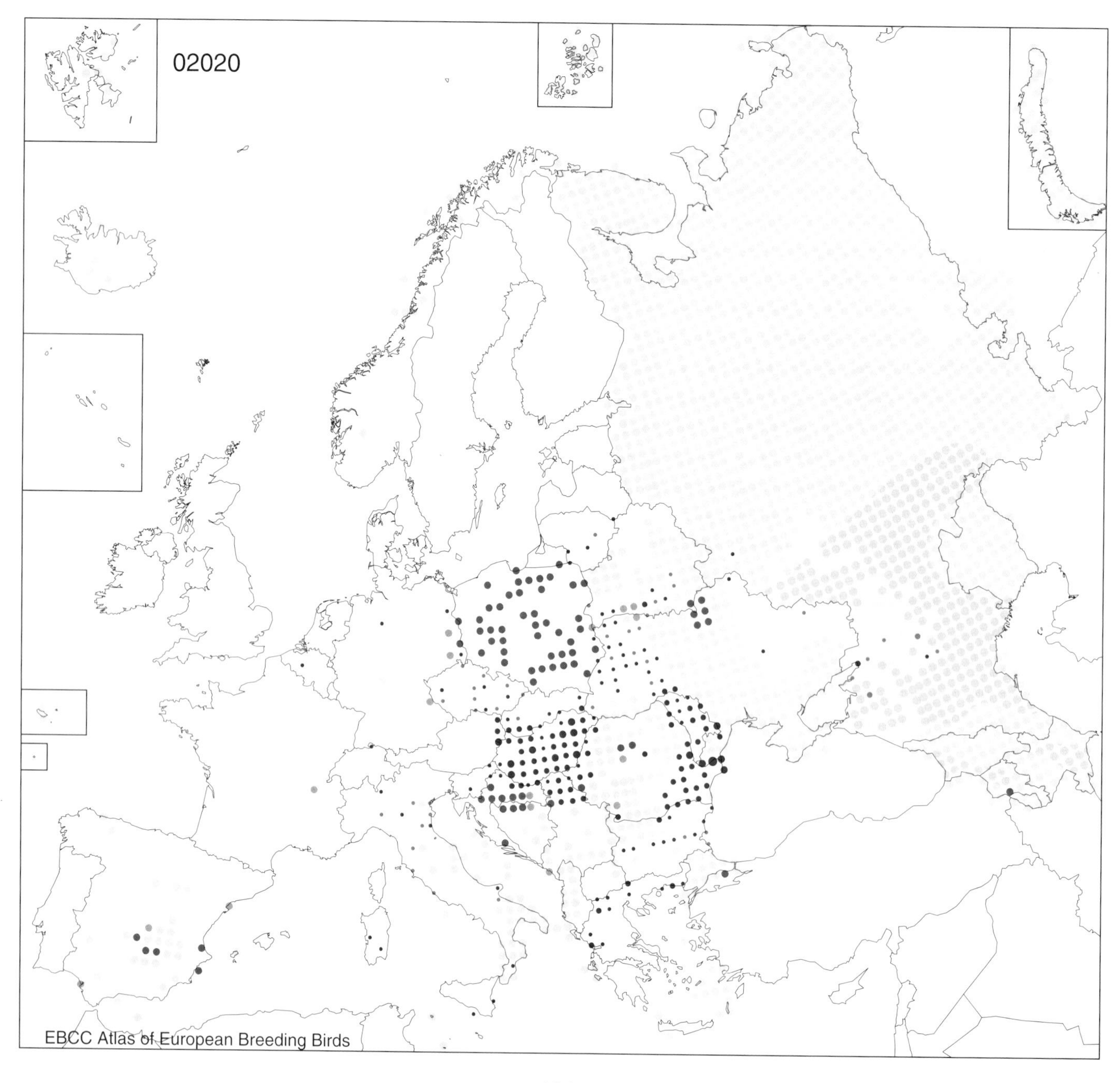

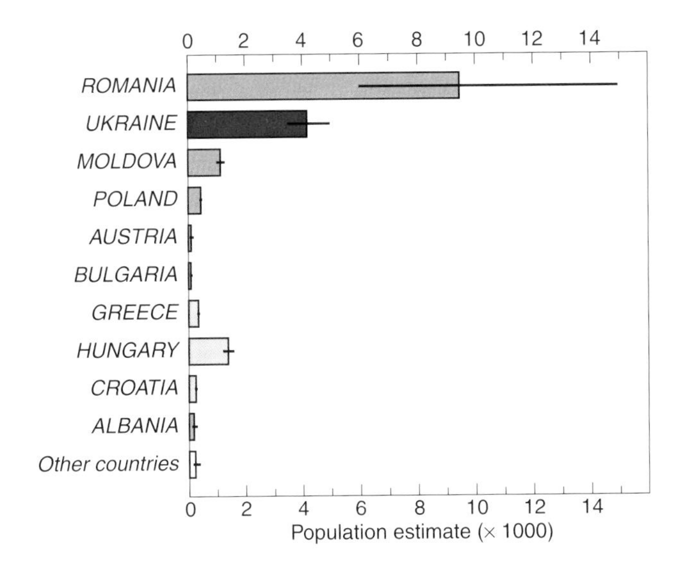

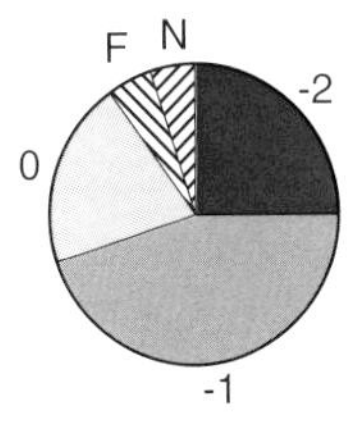

% in top 10 countries: 98.8
Total number of populated European countries: 20
Total European population 14,247–23,394 (17,810)
Russian population 500–1500 (866)
Turkish population 1000–3000 (1732)

Within its Palearctic distribution the Ferruginous Duck is strongly associated with wetlands in the forest steppe, steppe and semi-desert zones, ensuring a patchy occurrence. Relict numbers remain in a few isolated locations between Spain and C Europe. Its main range now stretches from C Europe eastward towards the Black and Caspian Seas. Further E there are two separate populations: one in C Asia centred around four main breeding sites (Amu-Darya region, Sir-Darya Valley, the saline marshes S of Betpak-Dala and the trans-Balhas area), and the other, comprising two groups, in W Mongolia near Jerentaj (Piechocki 1968) and the easternmost breeding site in E Tibet. The species is replaced in the Far East by the closely related Baer's Pochard *A. baeri*.

Although a freshwater diving-duck, it better tolerates luxuriant floating and submerged vegetation cover and shallow water (fresh or saline) than other European *Aythya* species (in Pannonia the shallow alkaline waters contain patchy dense sea club-rush *Bolboschoenus maritimus*). Its breeding habitats include dense marshy reedbeds containing small pools, sedge- or reedbelt-fringed fishponds, slow-flowing narrow channels, quiet winding rivers and oxbows. It avoids rapid streams and rivers, and deep oligotrophic lakes.

Since 1975 the species has bred occasionally in Spain, France, Belgium, The Netherlands, Germany, Switzerland and the Czech Republic. Other gradually shrinking disjunct breeding areas lie in Slovakia, Poland, Lithuania, Belarus, Italy and in the Balkan Peninsula. In the larger, insular breeding area of the Pannonian basin, numbers have also been declining.

Most of the European population, some 6000–15 000bp, breeds in Romania, largely concentrated in the Danube Delta (Weber *et al* 1994). Other sizeable populations occur below 500m asl in Hungary (1200–1600bp), Moldova (1000–1300bp) and Russia (500–1500bp). These have links with smaller populations of 100–500bp in Poland, Austria, Greece, Croatia, Albania and Ukraine, only the Carpathians forming a gap. All other national populations (under 100bp) are of little significance.

In the late 1890s in the Carpathian basin wetlands, it was one of the commoner and more widespread duck species (Chernel 1899). Because published data were lacking the Hungarian population has been underestimated (*HVM* 1969) until lately. Present knowledge of habitat distribution and the species' occurrence allows the 1960s population to be estimated at *c*2000bp. From the early 1980s it declined dramatically due to habitat changes arising from summer droughts and the generally drier weather conditions. Nevertheless, there were still *c*1200bp in Hungary in the late 1980s. Because of its vulnerable status, in 1993 Hungary legally designated it a strictly protected species. Numerous until the 1920s in Poland, it now is patchily distributed; two concentrations remain, Milicz fishponds (175bp in 1982) and >200bp near Tarnobrzeg and Janów Lub (Tomiałojć 1990), which I believe may represent a small recovery.

These trends are typical for much of its European range, where stable populations (1970–90) were recorded in only Hungary, Greece, Croatia and Lithuania, compared to declines of >20% in 10 countries and of >50% in 4 countries (mainly of marginal importance). Wetland drainage is probably the main reason for these declines. A notable exception is Russia, where range and numbers supposedly have increased, but possibly only as a local phenomenon (Krivenko *et al* 1994).

Most European birds winter in North Africa, mostly in Morocco, Algeria and Tunisia, arriving in October and November, but occasionally they migrate further S to sub-Saharan W Africa along the Niger and Senegal Rivers. Others winter along the Nile Valley chiefly in Sudan. The Ukrainian and S Russian populations probably winter around the Mediterranean basin, the Black Sea and the Lenkoran plain near the Caspian Sea. The Asian populations probably winter from Mesopotamia to S China.

Attila Bankovics (H)

Aythya fuligula Tufted Duck

CZ	Polák chocholačka	**I**	Moretta
D	Reiherente	**NL**	Kuifeend
E	Porrón Moñudo	**P**	Zarro-negrinha
F	Fuligule morillon	**PL**	Czernica
FIN	Tukkasotka	**R**	Хохлатая чернеть
G	Μαυροκέφαλη	**S**	Vigg
H	Kontyos réce		

Non-SPEC, Threat status S

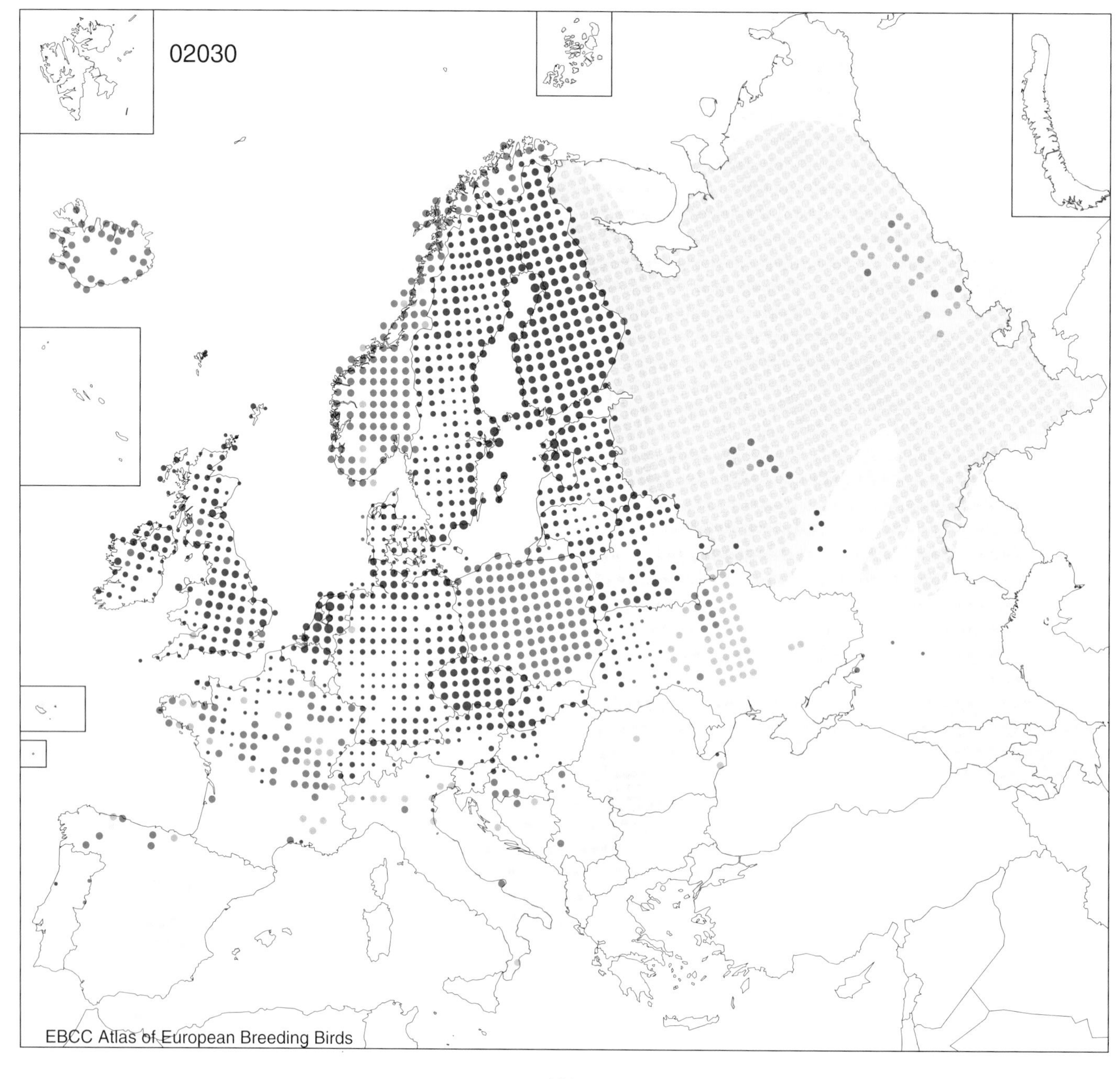

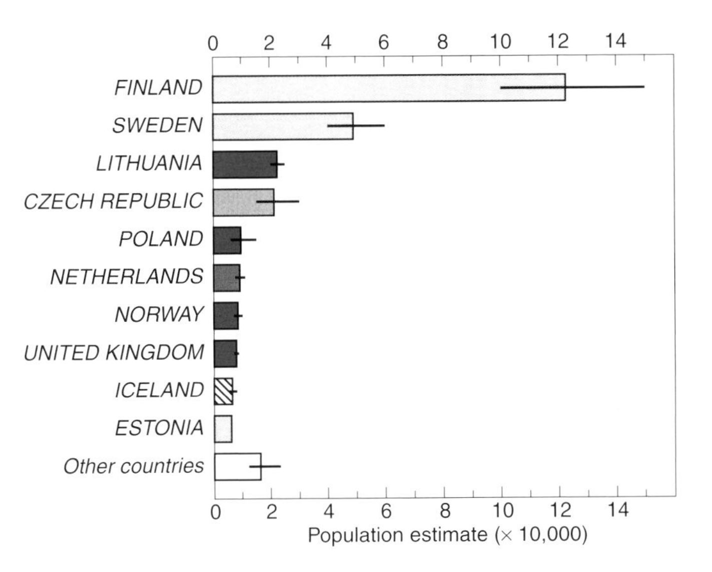

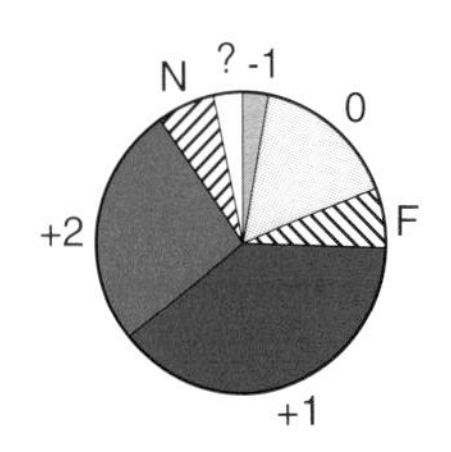

% in top 10 countries: 94.2
Total number of populated European countries: 31
Total European population 252,676–310,232 (278,250)
Russian population 395,000–490,000 (439,943)
Turkish population 50–500 (158)

The Tufted Duck is a trans-Palearctic breeding species, nesting in the boreal, temperate and steppe climatic zones. Its breeding range extends to 70°N in Norway and parts of Siberia and reaches 45°N in S Europe. Its main wintering grounds are located in NW Europe, where moult gatherings also occur on large lakes, such as Lake IJsselmeer in The Netherlands.

The Tufted Duck, almost universally a lowland species, breeds in freshwater lakes possessing abundant floating and emergent vegetation, ponds, quiet reaches of rivers, sheltered coastal areas, and sometimes on fell lakes. It shows a preference for nesting in Larid colonies, particularly in the N. The Tufted Duck is tolerant of human presence, inhabiting a variety of man-made waterbodies, ponds in city parks and even canals in intensive farmland where there is lush bankside vegetation.

A large proportion, probably more than 60%, of the western Palearctic population (600 000–830 000bp) breeds in Russia, numbers in neighbouring Fennoscandia (especially Finland) being estimated at 147 000–220 000bp. Maximum densities in Finland may reach 30 bp/km^2, but are normally *c*2–5 bp/km^2 (Koskimies 1989a). Where the Tufted Duck breeds in Black-headed *Larus ridibundus* and Common *L. canus* Gull colonies, it forms semi-colonial aggregations, reaching 5.2 bp/ha on islands in Lake Engure, Latvia (Priednieks *et al* 1989). Densities reduce gradually from Finland and Estonia towards the W and SW, except in The Netherlands (7500–11 000bp), where densities reach up to 100 bp/km^2 in prime habitat and 9 bp/km^2 overall in marshland in the province of Noord-Holland (Zomerdijk 1990b). In the Czech Republic and Poland it may reach similar densities on fishponds (Fiala 1988). In France and further S, distribution becomes very patchy and usually breeding density is low.

Since the 1950s the Tufted Duck has expanded greatly its European breeding range, coinciding with the spread of zebra mussel *Dreissena polymorpha* which has flourished in freshwater areas (Olney 1963). The Tufted Duck is particularly adept in exploiting this extensive feeding niche as its staple diet, either by taking larger mussels singly or by suction-feeding smaller mussels (de Leeuw & van Eerden 1992). High mussel densities, now commonplace, may affect favourably winter survival rates, unless extremely long cold spells occur late in winter (Suter & van Eerden 1992). Tufted Duck colonization rate was further boosted by increasing freshwater eutrophication and the construction of water reservoirs, which led to an increase in invertebrate biomass (particularly when ducklings require chironomid larvae), plant growth and potential nesting habitat.

From 1970 to 1990, some declines in breeding pair numbers occurred, notably in Russia, the Czech Republic and Ireland. The Fennoscandian and Baltic States' populations apparently are stable. However, in many countries the increase continues unabated (>50% in 1970–90), as in The Netherlands, Belgium, Austria, Switzerland, Slovakia, Hungary, Slovenia and Ukraine. Large-scale range expansion took place in Norway and France and in several C European countries. Where the Tufted Duck breeds in farmland, agricultural intensification may in future reduce breeding opportunities. Despite its tolerance of human presence, the species may be vulnerable locally to reduced breeding success through disturbance from increased leisure activity.

The Tufted Duck's European wintering population is centred around the Baltic, Danish inland waters, The Netherlands, Britain and Ireland, well-dispersed over inland freshwater and shallow coastal areas (Rüger *et al* 1986). Hard winters force movements towards the S and W. Smaller but increasing numbers winter on the northern shores of the Black Sea and Azov Sea and also in the upper basins of the Rhine, Danube and Rhône. Zebra mussel colonization may have influenced this gradual change. Sizeable numbers winter around the Mediterranean and Caspian, and others reach Mesopotamia and Ethiopia. Asian breeders winter in a belt stretching from Pakistan to Japan.

Aivars Mednis (LAT) Pieter Zomerdijk (NL)

This species account is sponsored by Manuel Galindo Widenmann, Valencia, E.

Aythya marila Scaup

CZ	Polák kaholka	**I**	Moretta grigia
D	Bergente	**NL**	Toppereend
E	Porrón Bastardo	**P**	Zarro-bastardo
F	Fuligule milouinan	**PL**	Ogorzałka
FIN	Lapasotka	**R**	Морская чернеть
G	Μαριλόπαπια	**S**	Bergand
H	Hegyi réce		

*SPEC Cat 3*W, Threat status L*W*

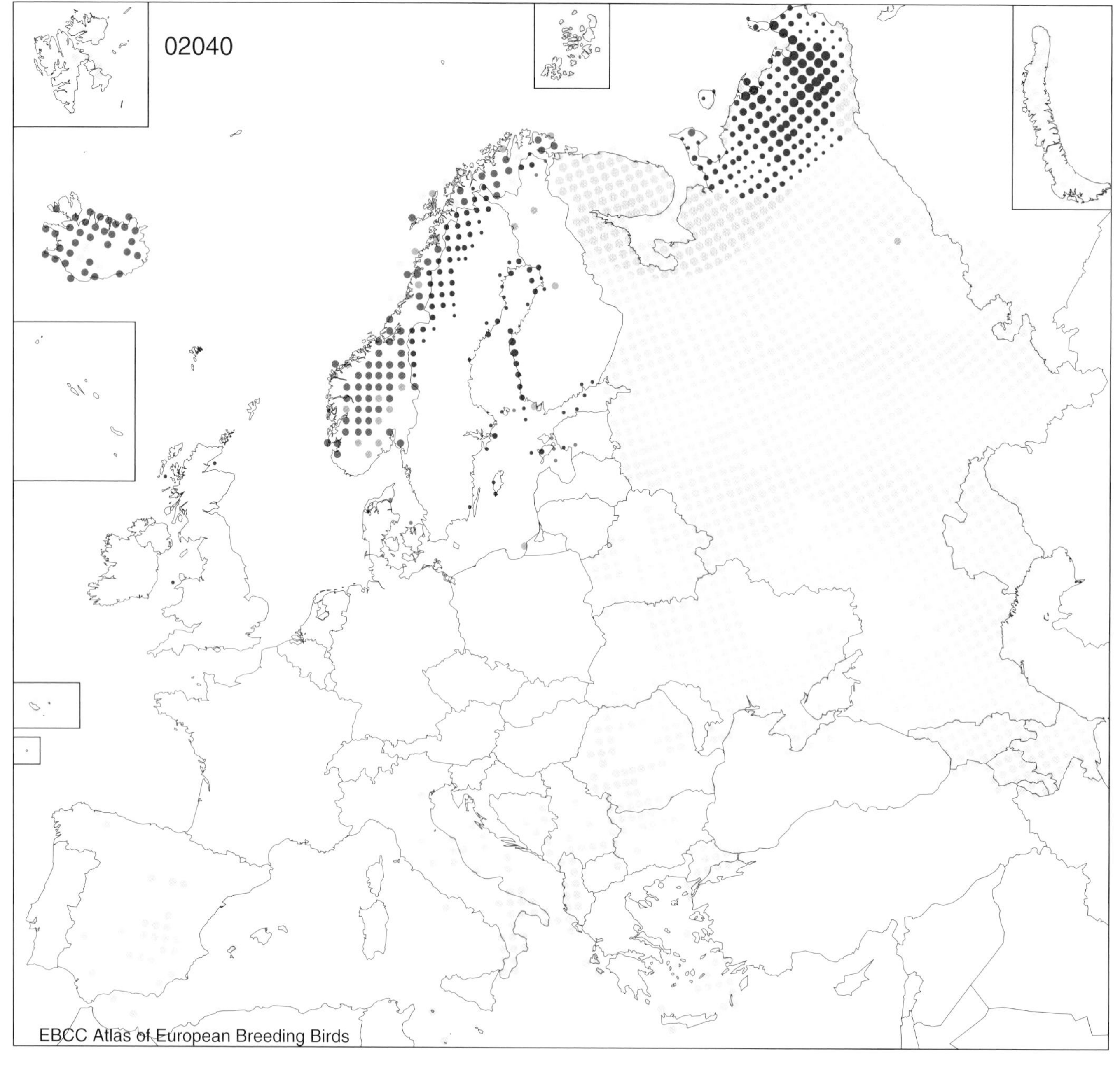

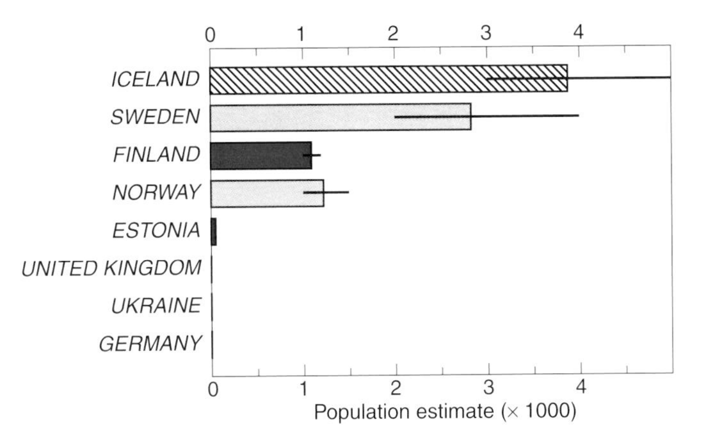

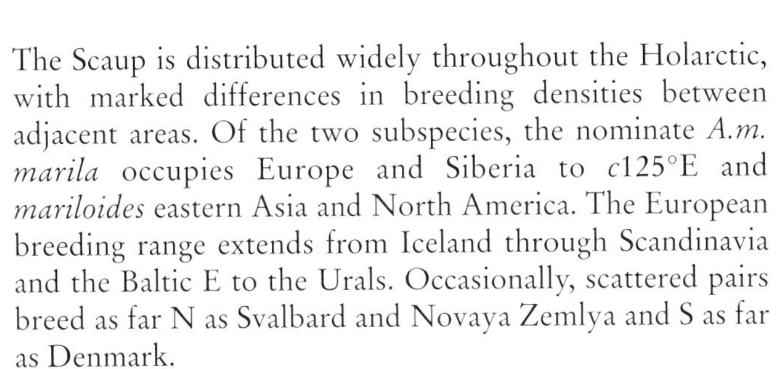

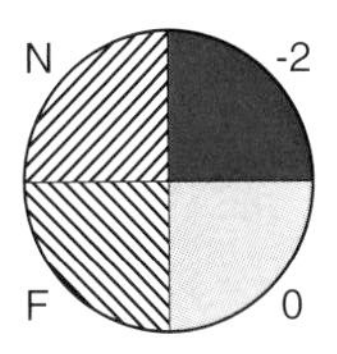

% in top 10 countries: 100.0
Total number of populated European countries: 8
Total European population 7847–10,727 (9075)
Russian population 40,000–80,000 (56,569)

The Scaup is distributed widely throughout the Holarctic, with marked differences in breeding densities between adjacent areas. Of the two subspecies, the nominate *A.m. marila* occupies Europe and Siberia to *c*125°E and *mariloides* eastern Asia and North America. The European breeding range extends from Iceland through Scandinavia and the Baltic E to the Urals. Occasionally, scattered pairs breed as far N as Svalbard and Novaya Zemlya and S as far as Denmark.

The Scaup's main breeding habitat is the tundra wetlands, mainly those small lakes and pools whose complement of aquatic insects and vegetation is adequate. Considerable numbers may nest close to larger waterbodies if sufficient shallows and open areas suitable for nesting exist, as at Lake Mývatn, Iceland (1700bp; Gardarsson 1979). In inland Fennoscandia the Scaup breeds close to small, sufficiently eutrophic lakes, mainly on the subalpine heath or in the upper subalpine birch *Betula* forest regions (600–800m asl), but patchily distributed in relatively small groups, partly reflecting the low abundance of suitable breeding habitats. The species' habitat requirements also explain its occurrence in the Baltic, where it breeds on small treeless, grassy islands in areas of productive, shallow waters, usually in association with the Tufted Duck *A. fuligula* and tern and gull colonies.

Data from spring and autumn migrations compared with the size of wintering populations show that the European population breeds mostly on the Russian tundra (40 000–80 000bp), although hard information is sparse. The abundance of Scaup in other European countries is comparatively low. Iceland holds 3000–5000bp, Norway *c*1000bp and Sweden 2000–4000bp, of which 200–300bp occurs in pockets along the Baltic coast from Gotland up to Haparanda. Estonia holds a small population of some 50bp. The Finnish population of 1000–1200bp breeds mainly along the Baltic coast. Approximately 900bp nest in a relatively small area (70km × 40km) immediately S of the Quark, one of the few regions with densities comparable to the Scaup's main breeding areas on the Russian tundra. The Finnish inland population is estimated at 100bp. Occasional nesting takes place in regions adjacent to the main breeding areas (including Denmark, Germany and Great Britain).

During winter the Scaup is present in most European countries, with some 90% of the population concentrated along the coasts of Denmark, Germany and The Netherlands. The total wintering population is estimated at 200 000 birds (Laursen 1989), although spatial and temporal fluctuations are substantial. The Adriatic, Black and Caspian Seas also hold wintering populations. Asian birds winter on N Pacific coasts.

The breeding populations in Western Europe have been characterized by large fluctuations since the mid-1960s. In some areas the population has declined quite drastically, while in others the mean population size has remained stable over a longer period, although considerable annual variations may exist. The reasons behind the fluctuations are not known, although one possible cause is the susceptibility to oil pollution during winter, because the Scaup forms large, dense flocks, sometimes of tens of thousands of birds. Another is hunting, with around 8000 birds shot annually (Bertelsen & Simonsen 1986). Although the number is small compared to the total wintering population, the effect on small breeding populations with differing wintering habits might be considerable.

Studies in Iceland (Gardarsson 1979) and in the Quark area in Finland (Hildén 1964, M. Haldin, pers obs) has shown considerable fluctuation in breeding success and production of ducklings between years. Given that close to 90% of the total European population breeds on the Russian tundra, where climatic variations can have an even more marked impact on the production of fledglings, it is possible that the variations in the smaller populations of western Europe in part reflect changes in the Russian population.

Michael Haldin (FIN)

Somateria mollissima

Eider

CZ	Kajka mořská	**I**	Edredone
D	Eiderente	**NL**	Eidereend
E	Eider Común	**P**	Eider-edredão
F	Eider à duvet	**PL**	Edredon
FIN	Haahka	**R**	Обыкновенная гага
G	Πουπουλόπαπια	**S**	Ejder
H	Pehelyréce		

Non-SPEC, Threat status S

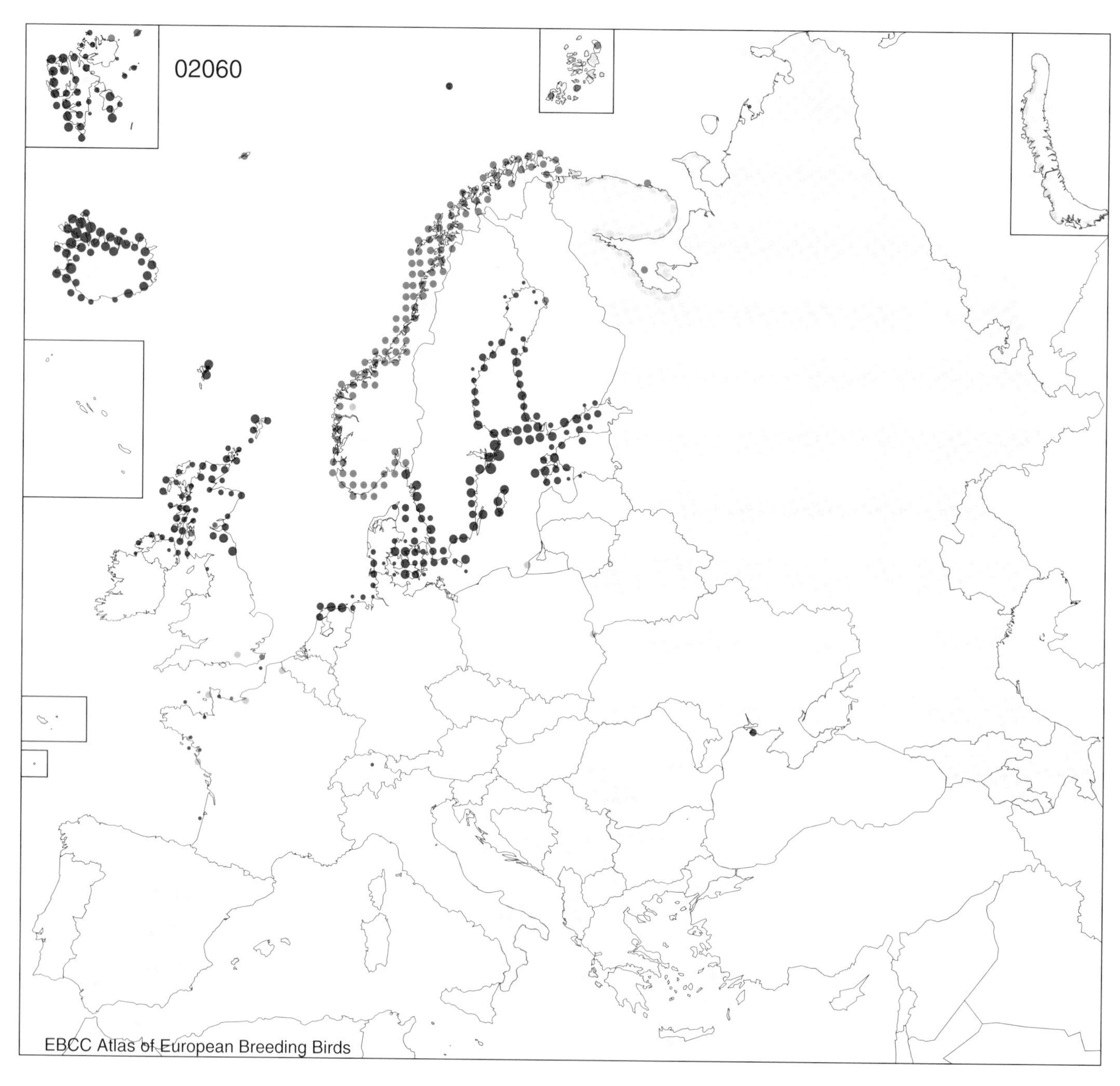

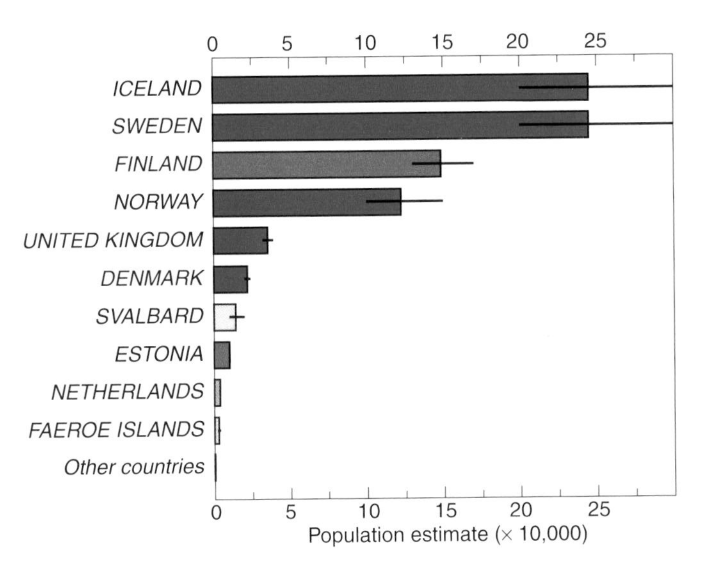

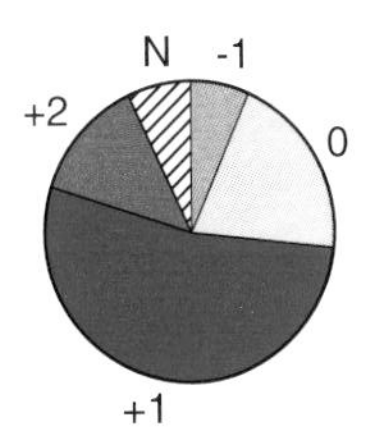

% in top 10 countries: 100.0
Total number of populated European countries: 15
Total European population 779,074–934,868 (849,264)
Russian population 20,000–30,000 (24,495)

A Holarctic species, the Eider is the most numerous and widespread European sea-duck. It has a circumpolar distribution, breeding up to 80°N. The nominate *S.m. mollissima* occupies most of the European distribution, *faroeensis* the Faeroes and *borealis* Franz Josef Land, Svalbard and Iceland, extending to Greenland and Baffin Island. The Nearctic contains three other subspecies.

During the breeding season it is found not only along rocky northern coasts but also south as far as the tidal zones of the Wadden Sea and in intervening estuaries, often forming large colonies where conditions are suitable. In Scotland, large breeding colonies are found mainly along the E coast in estuaries containing extensive mussel beds, whereas on rocky coasts there are scattered individual breeding pairs. In the northern Baltic Sea, large concentrations are found in the Finnish, Swedish and Estonian archipelagos. Females show a high degree of life-time philopatry to their natal colony, whereas males disperse widely (Swennen 1990).

Since the 1950s the Eider has extended its breeding range southwards. Populations in the Baltic increased tenfold during 1949–85. In the Gulf of Finland, Hario & Selin (1988) report a particularly steep increase for 1975–85, when the annual growth rate averaged 10%. Sweden had 200 000bp in the early 1970s and 270 000 in 1984. The Estonian population was estimated at 1400bp in 1960 and at 11 000–12 000 in 1985–86 (A. Kuresoo, pers comm). This well-established increase is thought to be due to improved feeding conditions resulting from the eutrophication of Baltic coastal waters. Other contributing factors include the setting up of vast waterfowl reserves, a ban on egg-collection and restrictions in spring hunting. Hunting pressure on juveniles in Denmark, the main wintering ground of Baltic populations, has also been very stable allowing a population growth in highly productive years (Hario & Selin 1988). In Great Britain too, numbers have increased since the mid-1970s at an average rate of 2–3% per annum. In the White Sea (Bianki & Koryakin 1990) and in the Gulf of Finland, however, populations currently are declining at 6–10% per year. In the Gulf of Finland, this trend has been linked with a lowered recruitment rate, resulting from heavy duckling mortality. Adult mortality has not been affected. A very low recruitment rate is typical also for the southern breeding areas (Swennen 1983), although large yearly variations may occur depending on food supply (Swennen 1989).

Breeding records outside the usual range are rare. In the Ukrainian Black Sea a colony was established in 1975, increasing steadily to 473 nests in 1989 (Ardamackaja 1990). In Switzerland, four successful broods have been recorded since 1988, following a long period of increasing numbers of oversummering birds.

Migration occurs mainly within the breeding range. The northern and eastern populations from Svalbard, Finland, Russia and the eastern Baltic make regular migratory movements, whereas those in The Netherlands, Britain & Ireland and Iceland are mainly resident or disperse only for short distances. The main concentrations of Eider in winter are found off the coasts of Denmark, Germany, The Netherlands, Norway, Iceland, Britain & Ireland and in the White Sea. In 1987, the total wintering population in the Western Palearctic was estimated at *c*3M birds (Laursen 1989).

A few birds of this otherwise purely marine species migrate inland and winter on the large lakes north of the Alps, where winter numbers have increased since the 1960s following the colonization of lakes by the zebra mussel *Dreissena polymorpha*. In Switzerland and its lakes bordering Germany and France, up to 600 birds now winter regularly, the largest numbers being on Lake Constance and Lake Geneva.

Extensive moult migrations, carried out mainly by birds from the Baltic, lead to large gatherings of moulting birds in the Wadden Sea, off Germany, The Netherlands and Denmark.

Verena Keller (CH) Martti Hario (FIN)

Somateria spectabilis

King Eider

CZ	Kajka královská	**I**	Re degli Edredoni
D	Prachteiderente	**NL**	Koningseidereend
E	Eider Real	**P**	Eider-real
F	Eider à tête grise	**PL**	Turkan
FIN	Kyhmyhaahka	**R**	Гага-гребенушка
G	Βασιλόπαπια	**S**	Praktejder
H	Cifra pehelyréce		

Non-SPEC, Threat status S

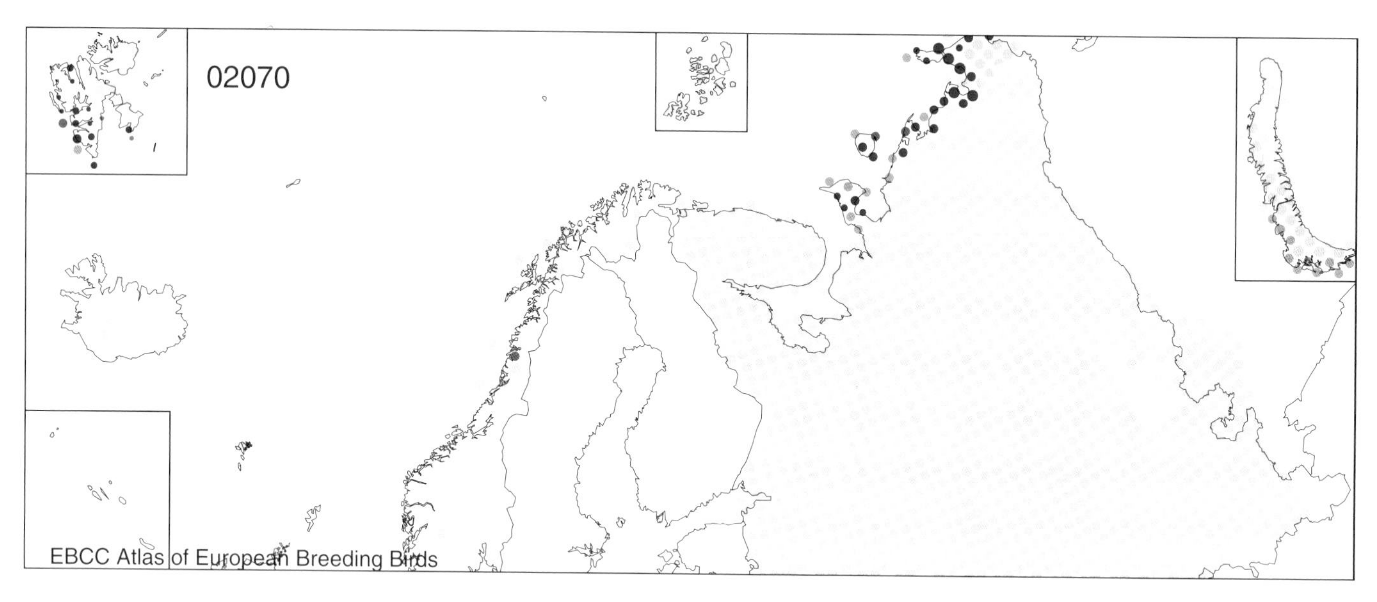

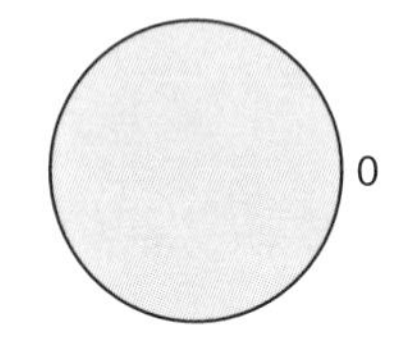

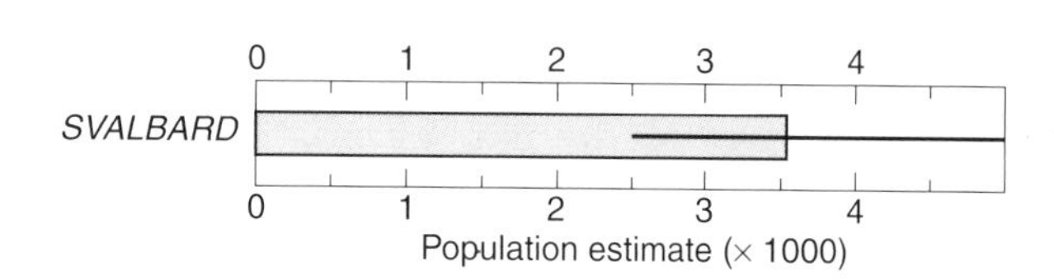

% in top 10 countries: 100.0
Total number of populated European countries: 1
Total European population 2500–5000 (3536)
Russian population 40,000–60,000 (48,990)

The monotypic King Eider, a large marine diving duck, slightly smaller than the Eider *S. mollissima*, has a circumpolar breeding range, except for the Kola Peninsula and Norwegian Sea coasts. In Europe, it occurs on mainland tundra from the Kanin Peninsula eastwards, and also on several islands, Kolguyev, Vaygach, Novaya Zemlya and W Svalbard. It breeds irregularly on the Solovetskiye Islands and in Kandalaksha Bay (White Sea) (Bianki *et al* 1993). In Europe the mainland tundra breeding area is a narrow 5–10km belt along the Arctic coast, but elsewhere in Asia (Yamal Peninsula, Gydan, Siberian river deltas) it can be 50km wide, and up to 220km in Taymyr.

The King Eider winters in the North Atlantic off the coasts of the Kola Peninsula, Norway, Iceland, Newfoundland and S Greenland, and in the Bering Sea off the coasts of the Kamchatka Peninsula, Alaska and Aleutian Islands.

The species usually breeds in isolated pairs, but in prime habitats (on islets in lakes and rivers) it forms loose colonies. In the E of its range, it may breed in association with Brent Goose *Branta bernicla* colonies or near breeding Snowy Owl *Nyctea scandiaca* (E Taymyr, Indigirka River; E.G. Lappo, unpubl).

Its habitat spectrum is quite wide, but generally it prefers (near coasts) flat lowlands possessing abundant small shallow lakes, large wet grassy bogs and marshes. In such sites, breeding density varies; 14–23 bp/km^2 at Khaypudyrskaya Bay (Mineyev 1987), 1.5–2.2 bp/km^2 at Karskaya Bay (Kara Sea) (Mineyev 1994) and up to 10 bp/km^2 at Baydaratskaya Bay (Kara Sea) (Kalyakin 1984). In wet polygonal sedge bogs, breeding density typically is 0.4–1.3 bp/km^2 and in dry hilly tundra with lakes 0.1–0.3 bp/km^2 (Mineyev 1994, V.V. Morozov, unpubl).

The European breeding population has declined slightly since the 1950s, but the Barents Sea moulting flocks remain as abundant as before (Uspenski 1965, Kalyakin 1984). Our opinion is that the European breeding population totals *c*2500–5000bp (V.N. Kalyakin, pers comm), most of the Russian population breeding further E.

Elena G Lappo (R) Vladimir V Morozov (R)

Polysticta stelleri

Steller's Eider

CZ Kajka bělohlavá
D Scheckente
E Eider Chico
F Eider de Steller
FIN Allihaahka
G Παρδαλόπαπια
H Steller-pehelyréce
I Edredone di Steller
NL Stellers Eidereend
P Eider de Steller
PL Birginiak
R Сибирская гага
S Alförrädare

*SPEC Cat 1, Threat status L*W*

The distribution of Steller's Eider, a high-arctic duck species, traditionally has been viewed as stretching from the Lena River delta in C Siberia E to the Chukotskiy Peninsula and to W and N Alaska. However, coverage since 1990 suggests the normal western limit is the Yamal Peninsula (*c*120km from Europe; Yésou & Lappo 1992), nests being found from W Yamal to Pronchishcheva Lake, E Taymyr (reviews in Yésou & Lappo 1992, Nygård *et al* 1995). Furthermore, the typically thin, consistent distribution, given low observer density, implies occupation of this western area for some time. The species may breed occasionally outside this range if persistent severe spring weather prevails.

Older, mostly unauthenticated records of occasional breeding in Europe on Novaya Zemlya, the Ainov Islands (near Norway) and in Norway (*BWP*) have been supplemented by others from the Murmansk coast (1987; Frantzen 1994a), the White Sea (Bianki 1992) and supplied directly to the *Atlas* in 1994. Since 1989, up to 1000 birds, some in full breeding plumage, have been observed in late spring in the White Sea (Nygård *et al* 1995).

Steller's Eider, perhaps the least coastal eider, shares range-wide the tendency of easternmost King Eider *Somateria spectabilis* populations to prefer inland nesting, although limited to the flat tundra zone coastal belt studded with irregular pools. It breeds on low peat mounds amid moss- and sedge-swamp vegetation, and on banks, overgrown by grass and sedge *Carex*, beside standing water (*BWP*). In extensive optimum habitat, estimated maximum breeding density is *c*1 bp/13km² (Yésou & Lappo 1992). Theoretical overall breeding density (if all European wintering birds bred in Taymyr) is 1 bp/10–20km² (Nygård *et al* 1995). Densest concentrations occur at river deltas (A.D. Fox, pers comm).

Europe holds important wintering numbers; 8000–15 000 off N Norway (mostly in Varangerfjord where 13 763 were counted in 1995; A.D. Fox & C. Mitchell, unpubl), up to 6500 off Estonia and Lithuania, perhaps another 500 elsewhere in the Baltic, and *c*25 000 from Kola E to Novaya Zemlya (Frantzen 1994a, Nygård *et al* 1995). Numbers off Estonia since 1990 have increased by more than 50%; in 1994, 28 500 were counted in Europe, supporting an estimated total of 40 000 (Nygård *et al* 1995). Such gatherings are vulnerable to oil-spills. Wintering Alaskan populations have declined from 200 000 to *c*30 000 (Kertell 1991, Dau 1992), making the species globally threatened (Collar *et al* 1994). It is unclear whether the Alaskan decrease (perhaps a continuation of declines noted since the 19th century in E Siberia and since the 1950s on the Commander Islands; *BWP*) is directly connected with the European increase.

Michael Blair (GB)

Histrionicus histrionicus

Harlequin Duck

CZ	Kačka strakatá	I	Moretta arlecchino
D	Kragenente	NL	Harlekijneend
E	Pato Arlequín	P	Pato-arlequim
F	Arlequin plongeur	PL	Kamieniuszka
FIN	Virta-alli	R	Каменушка
G	Αρλεκινόπαπια	S	Strömand
H	Tarka réce		

SPEC Cat 3, Threat status V

A small plump diving duck, the monotypic Harlequin Duck is a river specialist, remaining on fresh water in summer and migrating to the sea in winter. Its breeding range can be divided into Atlantic and Pacific segments. Iceland, Greenland and eastern Canada (mainly Labrador) form the Atlantic range. The Pacific segment reaches from the northern Lake Baikal region (*c*103°E) of E Siberia through Alaska (including the Kuriles and Aleutians) to W Canada, extending S of the US border to *c*37°N high in the Rocky Mountains (*BWP*).

Iceland comprises the sole European breeding area. There are no population estimates outside Iceland, and even the Icelandic population has not been properly censused (the main breeding area has been monitored for over 20 years), but it is unlikely that it exceeds 3000bp (Gardarsson 1975). There may be fewer than 2000. The Harlequin Duck is adapted to life in low-temperature, turbulent water, even rapids or waterfalls, and generally avoids contact with ice. Such waters, normally being poor in plant and animal life can support only low densities of the species (*BWP*). In Iceland the Harlequin Duck is widely distributed but reaches its highest breeding densities on rivers which drain lakes in the zone of postglacial volcanic activity (Gudmundsson 1971), because these rivers foster exceptionally dense populations of blackfly *Simulium vittatum* whose larvae and pupae form a significant part of the Harlequin Duck's breeding season diet (Bengtson & Ulfstrand 1971, Gardarsson & Einarsson 1994).

Breeding densities in Iceland from 1968 to 1971 ranged from 0.2 to *c*7.0 bp/km of river (Bengtson 1972). The River

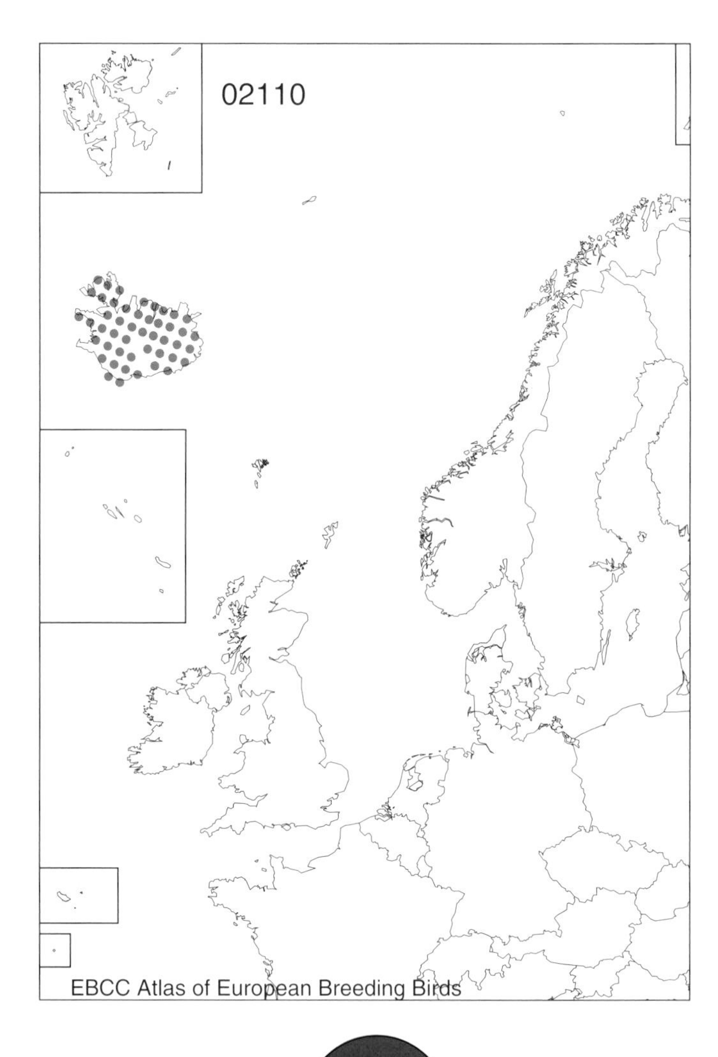

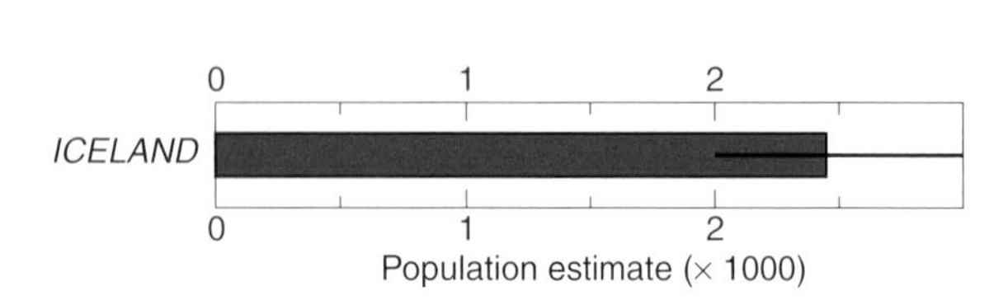

% in top 10 countries: 100.0
Total number of populated European countries: 1
Total European population 2000–3000 (2449)

Laxá (draining Lake Mývatn) and River Svartá (draining Lake Svartárvatn) hold notable densities of the Harlequin Duck during the breeding season (Gardarsson 1979). Pairs and unpaired adult males migrate up the rivers in spring. When the females are halfway through incubation the males leave to moult on the sea. Females and fledged young leave the rivers in the autumn. When on the sea the species remains on exposed rocky coasts. There are no records of Harlequin Duck migrating from Iceland to other countries (Gardarsson & Einarsson 1994). Vagrants to the Baltic may be of E Siberian origin. Some Siberian birds may migrate as far as the Yellow Sea (*BWP*).

Arni Einarsson (ICE)

Clangula hyemalis

Long-tailed Duck

CZ	Hoholka lední	I	Moretta codona
D	Eisente	NL	IJseend
E	Pato Havelda	P	Pato-de-cauda-afilada
F	Harelde Boréale	PL	Lodówka
FIN	Alli	R	Морянка
G	Χιονόπαπια	S	Alfågel
H	Jegesréce		

Non-SPEC, Threat status S

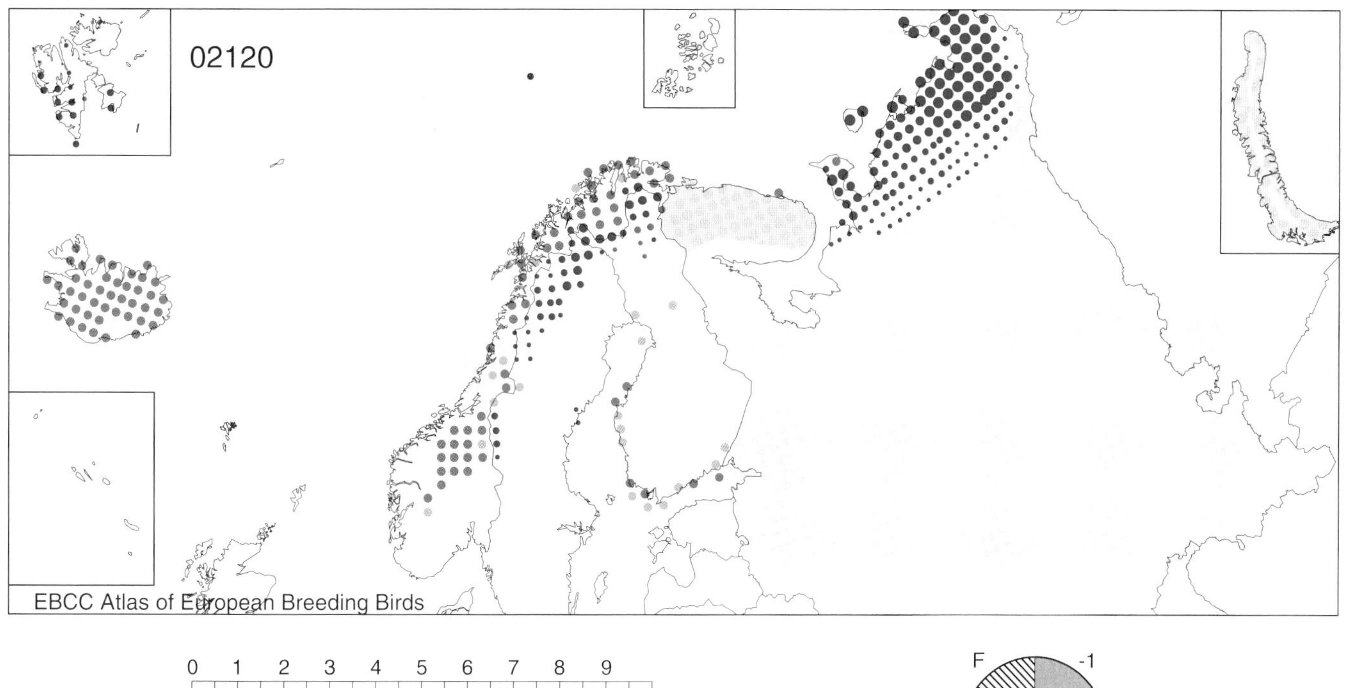

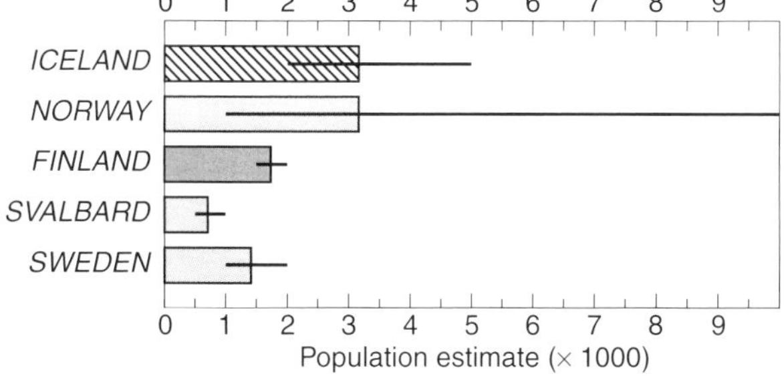

F -1
0

% in top 10 countries: 100.0
Total number of populated European countries: 5
Total European population 7669–17,294 (10,178)
Russian population 350,000–500,000 (418,330)

The Long-tailed Duck, a small sea-duck, has a circumpolar breeding range extending throughout the arctic zone. The vast bulk of the European population breeds on islands and coasts of high-arctic western Russia. The breeding population in western Russia has been estimated at roughly 5M birds (Uspenski 1970), while the number surveyed in wintering areas in NW Europe is assessed at 4.7M (Durinck *et al* 1994). Outside Russia the European population of Svalbard, Iceland, northern Finland and the mountainous regions of Norway and Sweden is comparatively very small. The Long-tailed Duck prefers low promontories, deltas adjacent to tundra with mosaics of low vegetation and lakes. Although birds occur in upland areas the species generally avoids wooded tundra. Due to its dispersed distribution, extensive breeding range and the absence of regular and systematic survey data of the winter population, any trends in the core breeding population in western Russia remain unknown.

During the non-breeding season the species appears in exposed offshore saltwater habitats. Recent surveys show the Baltic holding *c*90% of European wintering birds, which arrive from their moulting grounds in the White Sea in late October and remain until late May. In spring and during normal winters, three areas in the Baltic hold up to 1M birds: the Gulf of Pommern, Hoburgs Bank (S of Götland) and the Gulf of Riga. The majority feed in just a few extremely large extended aggregations, a habit which renders the species vulnerable to marine pollution. Oil pollution is believed to have increased in the Baltic following the expansion of the offshore oil industry and the growth in transportation of oil products, and this would be a major threat to the species. Oil pollution is probably the main cause of the decline of the Fennoscandian population (Risberg *et al* 1990, Thingstad 1994a).

Rolf K Berndt (D) Henrik Skov (DK)

Melanitta nigra

Common Scoter

CZ	Turpan černý	I	Orchetto marino
D	Trauerente	NL	Zwarte Zeeëend
E	Negrón Común	P	Pato-negro
F	Macreuse noire	PL	Markaczka
FIN	Mustalintu	R	Синьга
G	Μαυρόπαπια	S	Sjöorre
H	Fekete réce		

Non-SPEC, Threat status S

The Common Scoter, a sea-duck, breeds inland, dispersed across the boreal and low-arctic zones of Eurasia and North America. Within these zones it occupies a wide range of habitats from tundra and shrub vegetation to alpine terrain, and although it prefers sheltered nesting locations, it avoids enclosed areas. Banks of slow-flowing rivers are also favoured. In all locations pairs are normally widely separated (*BWP*).

The European subspecies, the nominate *M.n. nigra*, breeds from Iceland, NW Ireland, Scotland and Fennoscandia through Russia E to the River Lena in C Siberia. Some range extension occurred to the SW during the period of climatic amelioration between 1850 and 1950 (Burton 1995), first breeding records for Scotland and Ireland being 1855 and 1904 respectively. Very occasional breeding has occurred in Svalbard, the Faeroes and England. Only one other subspecies is recognized, *americana*, breeding from C Siberia to Alaska and in eastern Canada

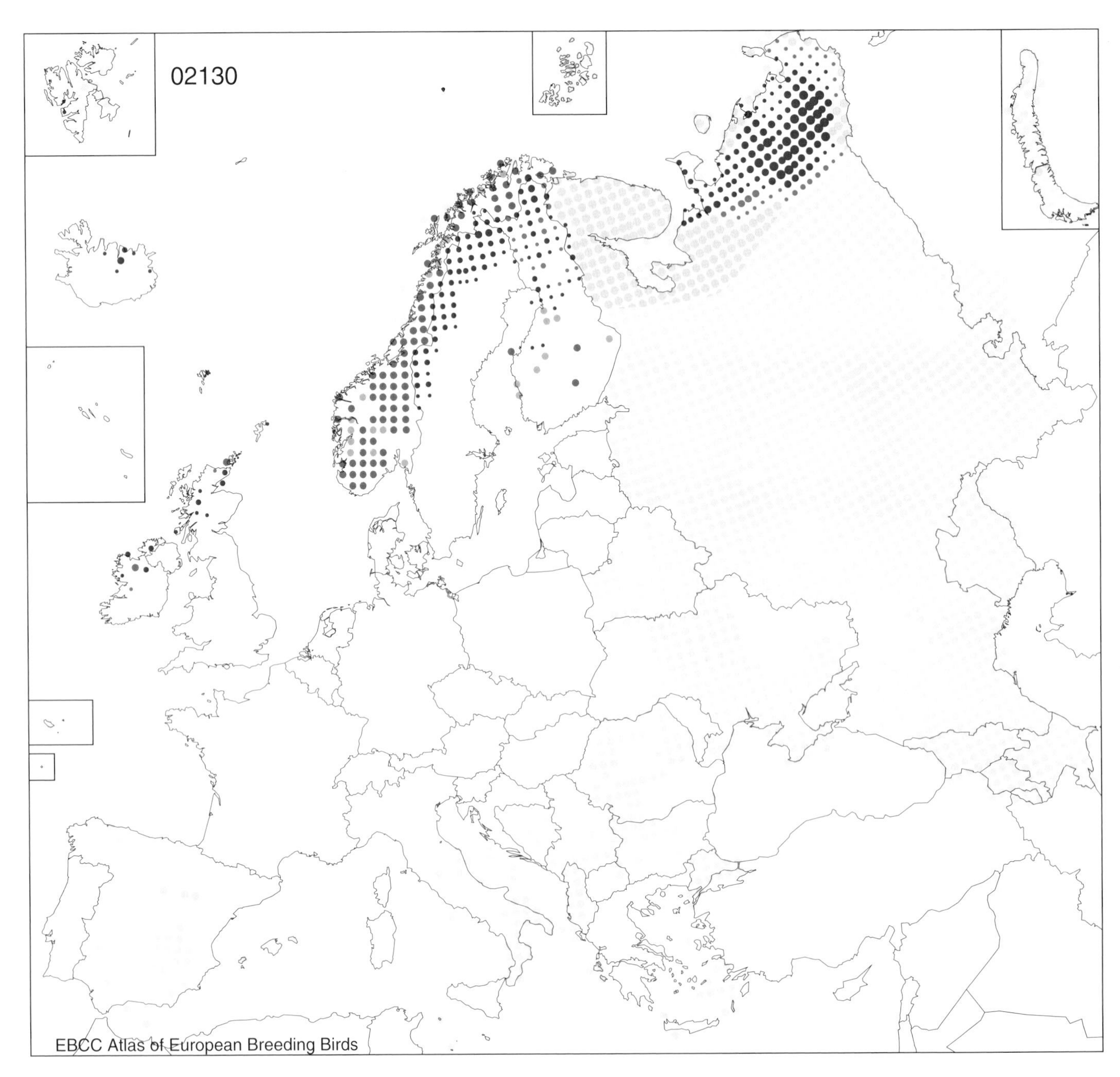

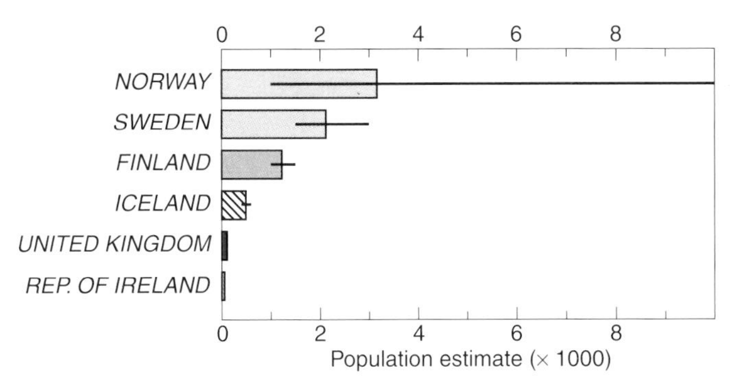

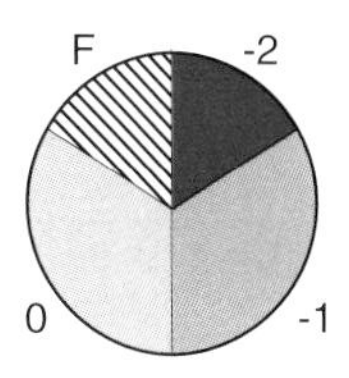

% in top 10 countries: 100.0
Total number of populated European countries: 6
Total European population 4903–14,066 (7166)
Russian population 100,000–120,000 (109,545)

and Newfoundland. Some Russian and American authors support *americana* as a separate species, Black Scoter.

Only a small proportion of the western Palearctic wintering population breeds in the region, between 100 000 and 120 000bp, but from winter counts some 1.3M birds are known to winter from Scandinavia to NW Africa (Durinck *et al* 1994) and from radar observations 1.5M have been estimated passing through the Baltic region on migration (Bergman & Donner 1964). If both these estimates are assumed correct, the total western Palearctic population size has been largely stable since the mid-1960s. *M.n. americana* winters mainly off N Pacific coasts, the small eastern and possibly the C Canadian populations moving to the NW Atlantic coast, down as far as *c*30°N.

The Common Scoter occurs mainly in marine habitats outside the breeding season, and it undergoes an extensive moult migration in Europe. To this end, large concentrations, often exceeding 10 000 birds, assemble in the western Baltic, the eastern North Sea, and offshore in Britain & Ireland and western France. Immatures moult first (from June onwards) and often remain in large numbers in Danish waters throughout the summer. This pattern is found elsewhere if conditions remain favourable, such as in The Netherlands (Leopold *et al* 1995). They are joined by the adult males in late June to August. Most females moult in August and September in the Baltic or further to the NE. Icelandic, Scottish and Irish breeders mainly moult locally.

After the summer moult, the Common Scoter remains highly gregarious. Large flocks concentrate in shallow waters (usually from 5 to 15m deep) which are reasonably sheltered and have a rich supply of bivalve prey. Flocks may remain at a chosen location throughout the winter, but there is usually much exchange between one location and the next, often over considerable distances. The most important wintering areas are the western Baltic and the Kattegat, where up to 940 000 birds have been counted. From here, birds cross over Jutland to another wintering area in the eastern North Sea (200 000), but many move on across the North Sea to winter in Britain & Ireland (30 000) or follow the eastern Atlantic seaboard and winter off France (40 000), Iberia (30 000) and NW Africa (5000–10 000). Because the various locations lie along the flyway and are subject to varying exchanges of birds, the numbers at any one location are subject to considerable inter-annual variation, depending on food availability (Durinck *et al* 1994, Skov *et al* 1995).

Moulting and wintering flocks of Common Scoter are vulnerable to oil pollution, because a single spill can have severe effects on the very large numbers which concentrate in a small area. Furthermore, wintering flocks are now under increasing pressure from the shellfish industry, which competes with the ducks for the same resources on the feeding grounds (Hunt in press).

Mardik F Leopold (NL) Henrik Skov (DK)

Melanitta fusca

Velvet Scoter

CZ	Turpan hnědý	I	Orco marino
D	Samtente	NL	Grote Zeeëend
E	Negrón Especulado	P	Pato-fusco
F	Macreuse brune	PL	Uhla
FIN	Pilkkasiipi	R	Турпан
G	Βελουδόπαπια	S	Svärta
H	Füstös réce		

*SPEC Cat 3*W, Threat status L*W*

The world distribution of the Velvet Scoter covers the whole of continental Eurasia and similar regions in W and C North America. Finland, Sweden and Estonia harbour the main breeding populations in NW Europe. The European subspecies is the nominate *M.f. fusca* whose eastern limit is the Yenisey, where *stejnegeri* replaces it eastwards in Asia. The third subspecies, *deglandi*, inhabits the Nearctic.

Originally a boreal tundra species, the Velvet Scoter is bound to freshwater and brackish water areas in its breeding range. Although breeding also occurs in northern Norway close to the ocean, small coastal lakes are selected and marine shores avoided. Its disjunct European breeding range includes the northern Scandinavian inland lakes and the vast archipelagos of the Baltic Sea. Both habitats bear close affinities to the forested inland lakes of the boreal coniferous zone where the species has its widest distribution in Siberian taiga and forest tundra. A seemingly

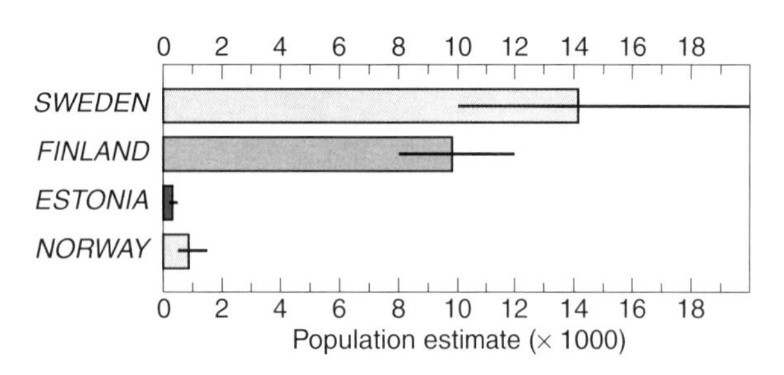

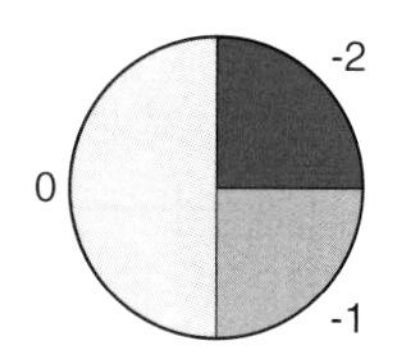

% in top 10 countries: 100.0
Total number of populated European countries: 4
Total European population 20,591–31,415 (25,122)
Russian population 50,000–70,000 (59,161)
Turkish population 15–50 (27)

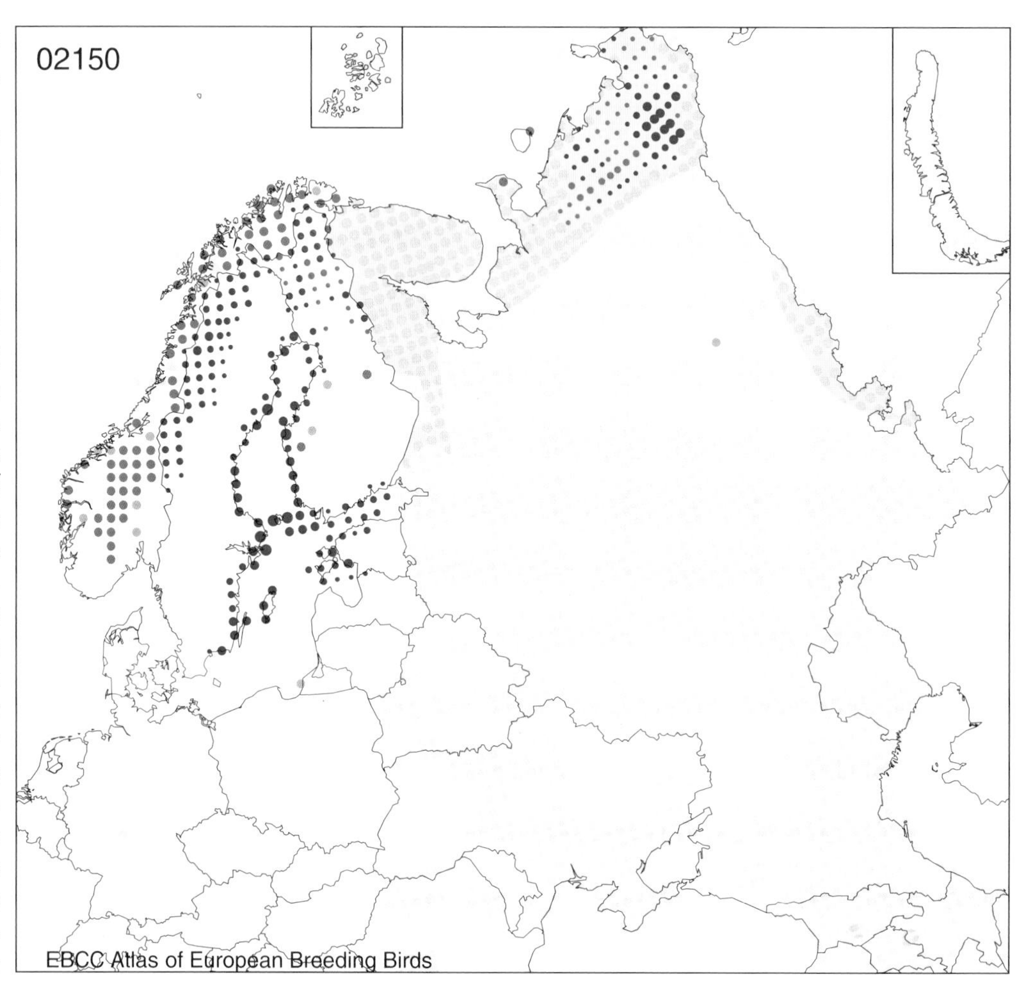

relict population occurs in Transcaucasia and NE Turkey, but its status is not known.

The bulk of the Scandinavian population breeds around the edge of the Baltic Sea. The northern inland populations are considered remnants of a larger and more widespread population. Hunting and illegal shooting in spring were the main reasons for the decline in N Scandinavia in the early 1900s. Spring hunting of males is still allowed in the Finnish Åland Islands, the annual bag averaging 25 000. Velvet Scoter is locally the most numerous sea-duck in the Baltic archipelagos (as in the Åland Islands); only Eider *Somateria mollissima* clearly outnumbers it over the whole Baltic area. Locally, populations are declining (as in the Gulf of Finland) due to the extremely poor fledging rates in most years. Broods are vulnerable to inclement weather conditions (Koskimies 1957). The species' late breeding coincides significantly with the peak of human disturbance, from activities such as boating and other summer leisure pursuits in the archipelago (Mikola *et al* 1994).

In Estonia, the species is entirely coastal, breeding on the sandy shores of low-lying marine islands. The Estonian population, which we believe to be *c*1000bp, is evenly distributed along the coast. Velvet Scoter is absent from Latvia westwards as a breeding species, but is locally numerous in winter.

The total wintering population in NW Europe exceeds 550 000 individuals (Durinck *et al* 1993). Of these, about 20% winter in Denmark, but other important wintering sites have recently been found in the Gulf of Pommern (286 000) and in the Gulf of Riga (137 000). At sea, the species tends to keep in shallow waters adjacent to the coast. However, it also visits inland waters more often and more regularly than the other sea-ducks. In cold winters, influxes of some hundreds of birds reach the interior of C Europe (Aubrecht *et al* 1990). Birds wintering from the Yellow Sea to Kamchatka presumably are *stejnegeri*, and those wintering from the Aleutians to Baja California *deglandi*.

On spring migration the species moves through the Gulf of Finland in a massive passage to the Siberian coniferous tundra. The main part of this spectacular movement follows the Estonian coast, where 200 000 birds have been recorded in a single day (Rusanen 1993). Just as this species seems largely to winter in large concentrations, so this shift to the breeding grounds is synchronous within such cohorts. The return autumn route and timing differ between sexes, males arriving in July nocturnally across the Baltic Sea, females and young in August and September, gradually along coasts. Males undergo complete post-breeding moult in Denmark in July and August and females in September and October. Danish waters then hold a significant proportion of the total NW European moulting population (Joensen 1976).

Rolf K Berndt (D) Martti Hario (FIN)

Bucephala islandica

Barrow's Goldeneye

CZ	Hohol islandský	I	Quattrocchi d'Islanda
D	Spatelente	NL	IJslandse Brilduiker
E	Porrón Islándico	P	Pato da Islândia
F	Garrot d'Islande	PL	Sierpiec
FIN	Amerikantelkkä	R	Исландский гоголь
G	Ισλανδική Κουδουνόπαπια	S	Islandsknipa
H	Izlandi kercerécе		

SPEC Cat 3, Threat status E

A hole-nesting diving duck, Barrow's Goldeneye is found on productive freshwater lakes and rivers in summer. Monotypic, it is highly territorial during the breeding season but gregarious at other times. Its world distribution is discontinuous. There is a Pacific population in NW North America, mainly in British Columbia and Alaska, where the birds are tree-nesters and winter mainly on the W coast of North America. Current population estimates are crude: *c*45 000 birds in Alaska; 70 000–186 000 in British Columbia, and in Washington, Oregon and California, fewer than 8000.

In the Atlantic, the origin of *c*2500 individuals (Reed & Bourget 1977) wintering mostly in the Bay of St Lawrence is unproven, and most often is assigned to a hypothetical breeding population in Labrador. Greenland's only breeding record dates from the 19th century. The well-studied Icelandic population numbers *c*2000 birds but has a skewed sex ratio of 1200 males to 800 females. It is resident but records of vagrants in Greenland and census data anomalies suggest some movements between Greenland or Labrador and Iceland; confirmation is lacking (Gardarsson 1978).

The Icelandic population mostly is confined to and resident in the north-eastern Lake Mývatn and River Laxá area which harbours 85–90% of the total (Gardarsson 1978, 1979, in prep). This area has not only an abundance of potential nest sites in the surrounding lava fields but also rich food supplies. The single most important breeding site lies at the Lake Mývatn outlet (Einarsson 1988, 1990). The population has been relatively stable at *c*2000 birds, although a significant declining trend seems evident, characterized by sudden reductions (in 1978 and 1989) coinciding with poor food supplies (Gardarsson & Einarsson 1994).

Barrow's Goldeneye winters mainly on ice-free fresh water in the breeding area but small numbers winter on other partially ice-free fresh waters, mostly within Iceland's volcanic zone (Gardarsson 1978). Coastal wintering grounds have not been found in Iceland.

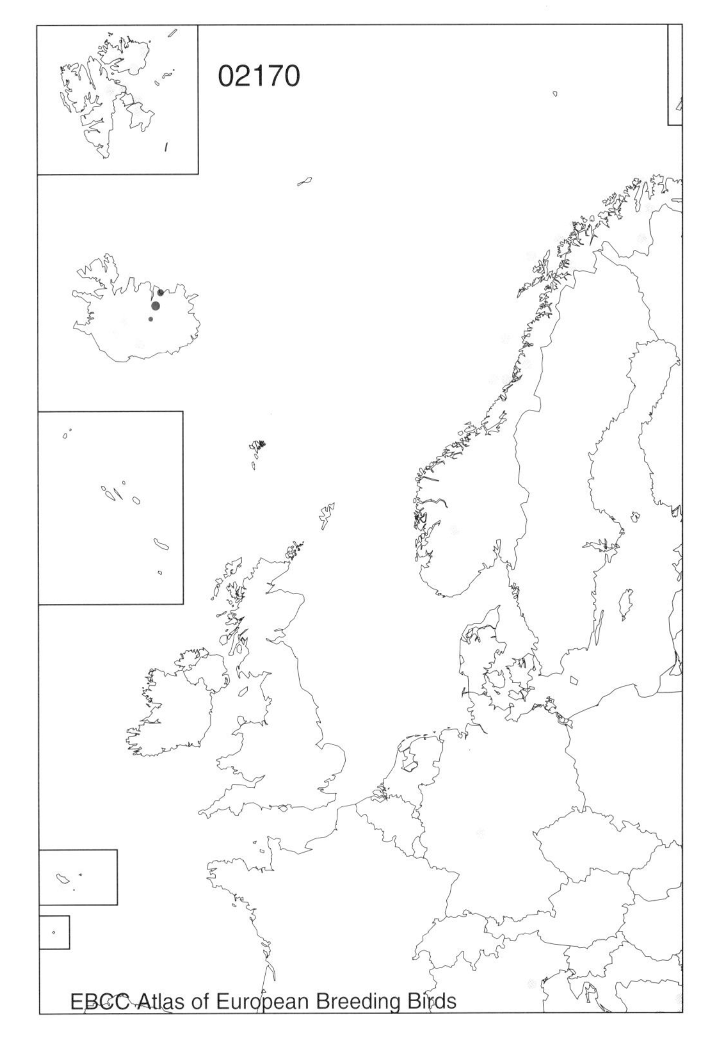

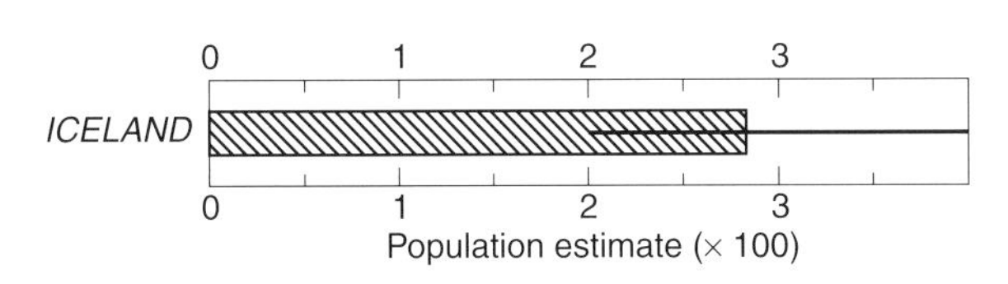

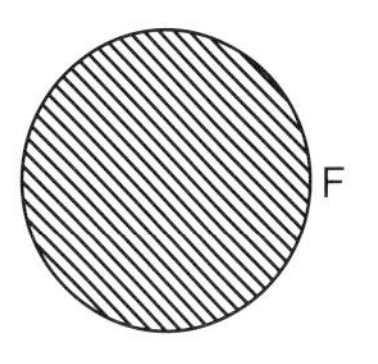

% in top 10 countries: 100.0
Total number of populated European countries: 1
Total European population 200–400 (283)

Arni Einarsson (ICE)

Bucephala clangula — Goldeneye

CZ	Hohol severní	**I**	Quattrocchi
D	Schellente	**NL**	Brilduiker
E	Porrón Osculado	**P**	Pato-olho-d'ouro
F	Garrot à oeil d'or	**PL**	Gągoł
FIN	Telkkä	**R**	Гоголь
G	Βουκεφάλα	**S**	Knipa
H	Kercerėce		

Non-SPEC, Threat status S

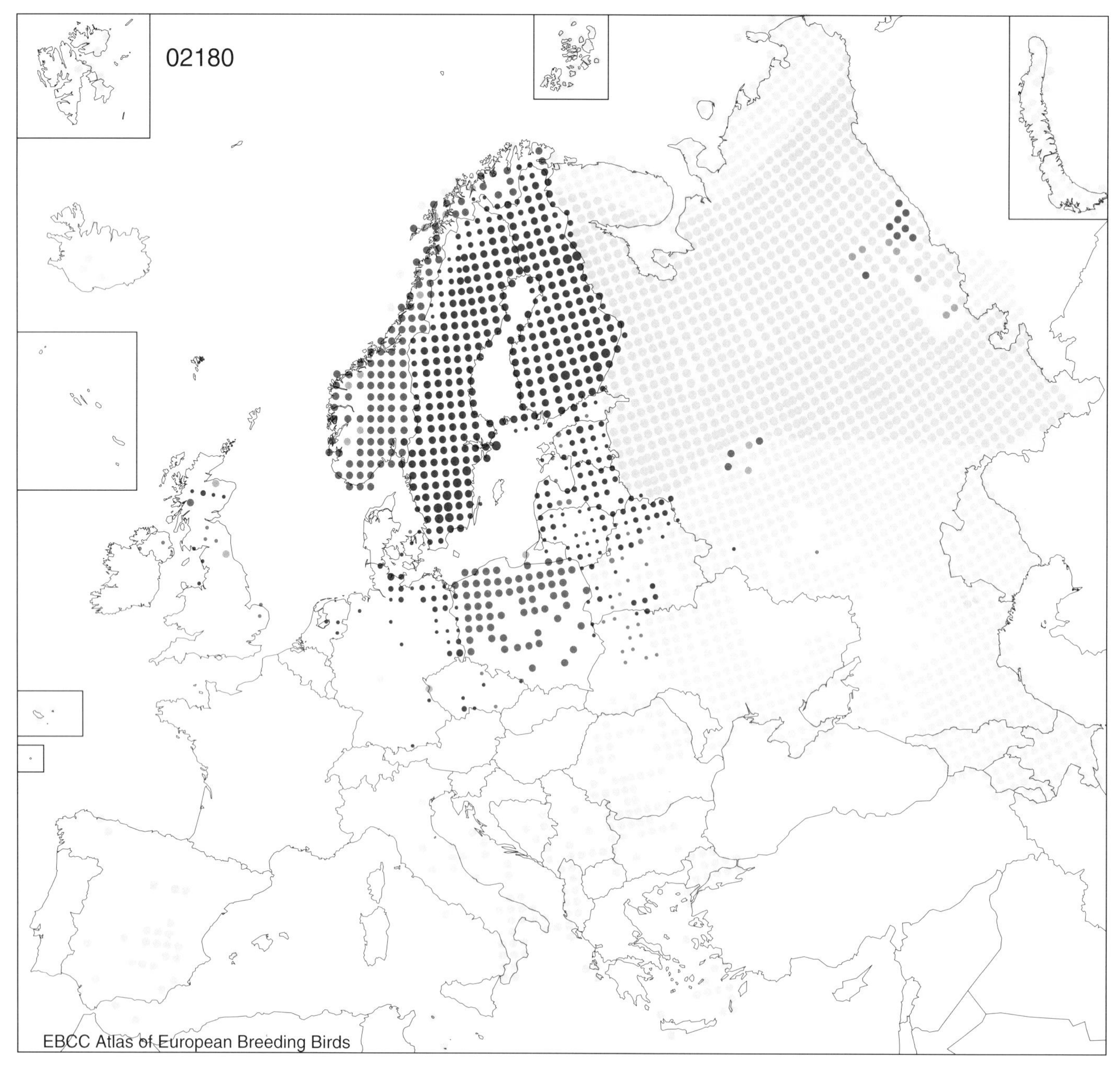

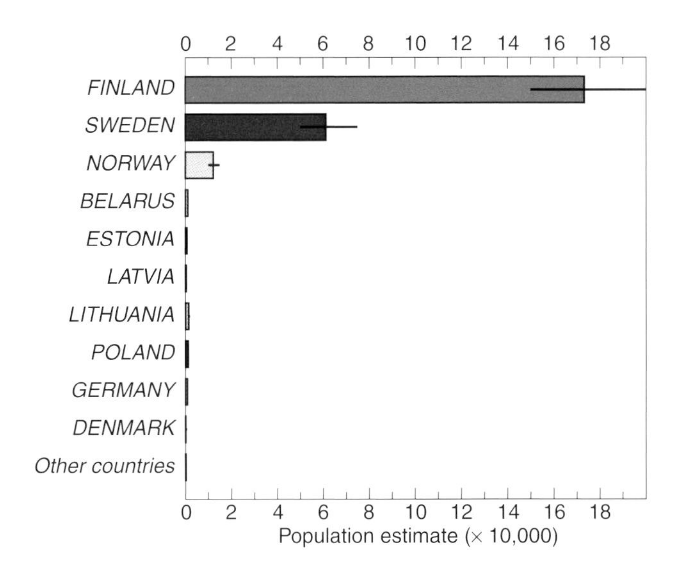

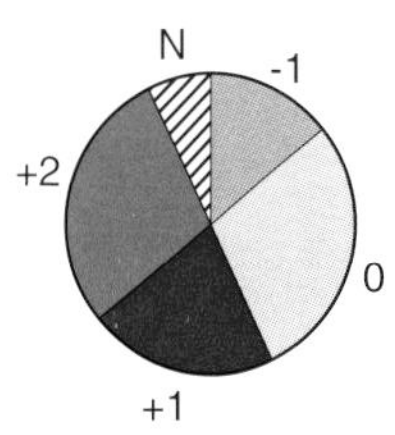

% in top 10 countries: 99.9
Total number of populated European countries: 14
Total European population 226,869–283,024 (252,758)
Russian population 28,000–48,000 (36,661)

The Goldeneye's breeding distribution covers most of the forest area, especially in the coniferous zone between 55° and 70°N, in Europe, N Asia (the nominate subspecies *B.c. clangula*) and North America (*americana*). A hole-nesting waterbird, it prefers older forests with mature and decaying trees which contain woodpecker nest sites and natural holes.

The Goldeneye has a northern European distribution, Finland holding at least 150 000bp and Sweden 50 000. Both countries' extensive nestbox schemes have significantly added to breeding numbers, even in areas rich in natural breeding habitats. There are also large populations in Russia and Norway, more than 30 000bp and 10 000bp respectively. The Goldeneye breeds on all kinds of open freshwater bodies, but it prefers relatively shallow lakes possessing moderate emergent vegetation (Nummi & Pöysä 1993).

The pattern of distribution largely follows the availability of suitable breeding opportunities. The Goldeneye may colonize new breeding areas after nestboxes have been provided, but success depends on such locations being in suitable breeding habitat and on their proximity to the population centre. In a study area in northern Finland, within the main range of the species, 29 nestboxes were set up for the 1959 breeding season. The first breeding was recorded in the same year and nine nestings were recorded two years later after which the number of breeding attempts stabilized (Rajala & Ormio 1970). In another study area in Scotland, at the extreme western limit of the range, 24 nestboxes were set up for the 1961 breeding season. Breeding was first recorded 14 years later in 1974, but four years after that the number of breeding attempts increased to 13 (Dennis & Dow 1984). The present population is estimated as more than 120bp. Interestingly, prior to the 1970s there were only two breeding records in Great Britain and these were probably injured birds.

Since the 1970s the numbers of breeding Goldeneye have definitely increased in Finland, Estonia, Denmark, Poland and Great Britain. The species has slightly extended its range, especially in Britain. There is a new breeding population in The Netherlands. However, the availability of suitable nest holes may limit distribution and population size of the species. In most countries modern forestry management techniques do not encourage widespread retention of old and decaying trees which contain likely nest holes.

The national waterfowl monitoring programme started in 1986 in Finland indicates that breeding numbers do fluctuate but there is no clear trend for the period 1986–93 (H. Pöysä, pers obs). The international waterfowl census (Monval & Pirot 1989) showed that the total wintering population in NW Europe had increased in the late 1970s, but since then the regional trends have been stable. In C Europe the wintering population has been stable since the late 1960s.

The results of an extensive aerial survey of breeding populations of waterfowl in the early 1970s in northern Fennoscandia revealed that Goldeneye breeding density varies between 0.04 and 0.34 bp/km of shoreline (Haapanen & Nilsson 1979). The highest densities were found in the Swedish woodland zone where boreal coniferous forests and mires are the dominant habitat types. Ground pair counts in coniferous forest areas have yielded a density of 0.35 bp/km of shoreline in northern Sweden (nestbox availability low or zero; Danell & Sjöberg 1979) and 0.53 bp/km of shoreline in southern Finland (nestbox availability high; P. Nummi, pers comm, H. Pöysä, pers obs).

Breeders from northern Europe migrate to the main wintering areas in Denmark, the western Baltic, The Netherlands, Great Britain, and to a lesser extent, S to mediterranean France. The larger lakes in Switzerland, Germany, Hungary and the former Yugoslavia also harbour wintering birds. Additional important wintering areas lie in Italy and in the Black Sea region. Asian birds winter on Pacific coasts from Taiwan to Kamchatka.

Roy Dennis (GB) Hannu Pöysä (FIN)

Mergus albellus Smew

CZ	Morčák bílý	**I**	Pesciaiola
D	Zwergsäger	**NL**	Nonnetje
E	Serreta Chica	**P**	Merganso-pequeno
F	Harle piette	**PL**	Bielaczek
FIN	Uivelo	**R**	Луток
G	Νανοπρίστης	**S**	Salskrake
H	Kis bukó		

SPEC Cat 3, Threat status V

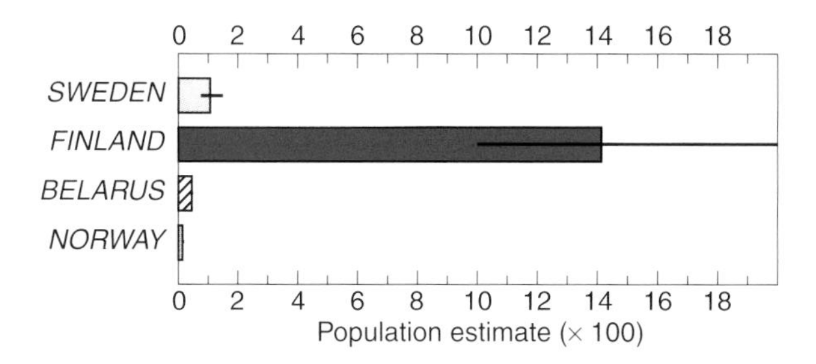

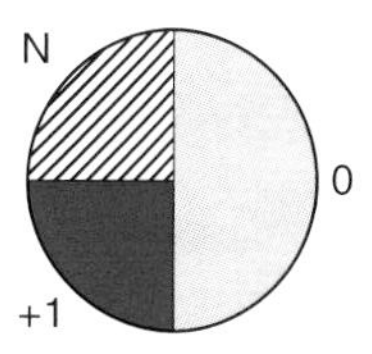

% in top 10 countries: 100.0
Total number of populated European countries: 4
Total European population 1164–2167 (1579)
Russian population 7000–15,000 (10,247)

The Smew, the smallest sawbill species, breeds in the Palearctic boreal taiga zone, occurring from N Sweden and Finland eastward through Siberia. Its precise eastern distribution limits are unclear. A tree-hole nester, often using old nest holes of Black Woodpecker *Dryocopus martius*, usually it selects sites close to small freshwater bodies possessing emergent aquatic or halophytic vegetation (small lakes, ponds or slow-flowing rivers; Koskimies 1989a) in the coniferous and mixed forest zones. Normally it prefers eutrophic rather than oligotrophic waters, but nest-hole availability is the dominant factor. It will also use nestboxes. Seemingly dominant over the Goldeneye *Bucephala clangula*, it will evict the latter from suitable nest sites, whether natural or artificial, sometimes laying eggs over the Goldeneye's. Where nesting sites are abundant, mixed 'colonies' may occur, sometimes with mixed clutches and exceptionally with mixed pairs.

Smew densities may reach 2–3 bp/100m of shoreline, or overall, 1–2 bp/km^2, but in N Finland usually they are lower, at 0.05–0.1 bp/km^2 in oligotrophic lakes (Koskimies 1989a) or 1–2 bp/km^2 in eutrophic waters (E. Lammi & R. Väisänen, pers comm). Breeding pairs tend to be secretive. The female behaves inconspicuously, the brood are adept at concealment and the male may leave the nest area during incubation. It is therefore difficult to establish distribution patterns and breeding densities.

The large European Russian population comprises 7000–15 000bp. In the 19th century the species was common in the forest-tundra, taiga and mixed-forest zones of the E European plain, occurring as far S as Romania, Ukraine, Belarus, S Russia and near the Kazakhstan border. These southern populations mostly have vanished. Population numbers have also dropped considerably through habitat loss, firstly through river valley deforestation between 1870 and 1890 and then by intensive industrial exploitation of the European taiga forests from 1920 to 1930 and from the 1950s to the early 1970s. Predation by American mink *Mustela vison* has been a contributory cause. Consequently the Smew was extirpated as a breeder along the Dnepr and in the Volga–Akhtuba floodplain. By the mid-1970s, Smew populations locally had stabilized or expanded slightly, as in the Leningrad region (Vinogradov 1994).

Smew distribution has been mapped reliably only in Fennoscandia, producing a rather even pattern between 65° and 70°N and E of 15°E, where estimated densities range from 1.0 to 100 bp/50km square. This region holds an estimated total of 1050–2100bp (Sweden 50–100bp, Finland 1000–2000bp). The Finnish population has developed favourably since the mid-1950s, recovering from near-extinction in the early 20th century. The 100–200bp of 1950 reached its present level by 1990 (M. Haldin, pers comm). Areas adjacent to the Finnish breeding nucleus are likely to contain similar densities in suitable breeding habitat. Higher breeding densities must occur further E, considering the numbers wintering regularly in the Szczecin lagoon in the Polish Baltic (Švažas *et al* 1994), on the Dutch IJsselmeer (Beekman & Platteeuw 1994, Durinck *et al* 1994) (*c*25 000 birds altogether) and in areas around the Black and Caspian Seas, mainly the Volga Delta and Sea of Azov, which together hold up to 65 000 birds (Isakov 1970). Here birds from Asian Russia may be present. Localized breeding has occurred in C Norway, S Finland and Belarus, the Belarussian 40–50bp comprising by far the southernmost breeding population.

In European Russia numbers probably fluctuate annually by at least 20% but without any clear trend, yet a range contraction of 20–50% in 1970–90 has been suggested for that region. Only regular surveys could disentangle the effects of variable severity of spring weather, inter-regional movements and true changes in range. During the same period, the Finnish population expanded its range and increased its numbers, both by 20-50%. In Sweden, distribution and numbers remained stable in recent years.

Maarten Platteeuw (NL)

This species account is sponsored by G. A. de Vries, Baarn, NL.

Mergus serrator

Red-breasted Merganser

CZ	Morčák prostřední	**I**	Smergo minore
D	Mittelsäger	**NL**	Middelste Zaagbek
E	Serreta Mediana	**P**	Merganso-de-poupa
F	Harle huppé	**PL**	Szlachar
FIN	Tukkakoskelo	**R**	Средний крохаль
G	Σκουφοπρίστης	**S**	Småskrake
H	Örvös bukó		

Non-SPEC, Threat status S

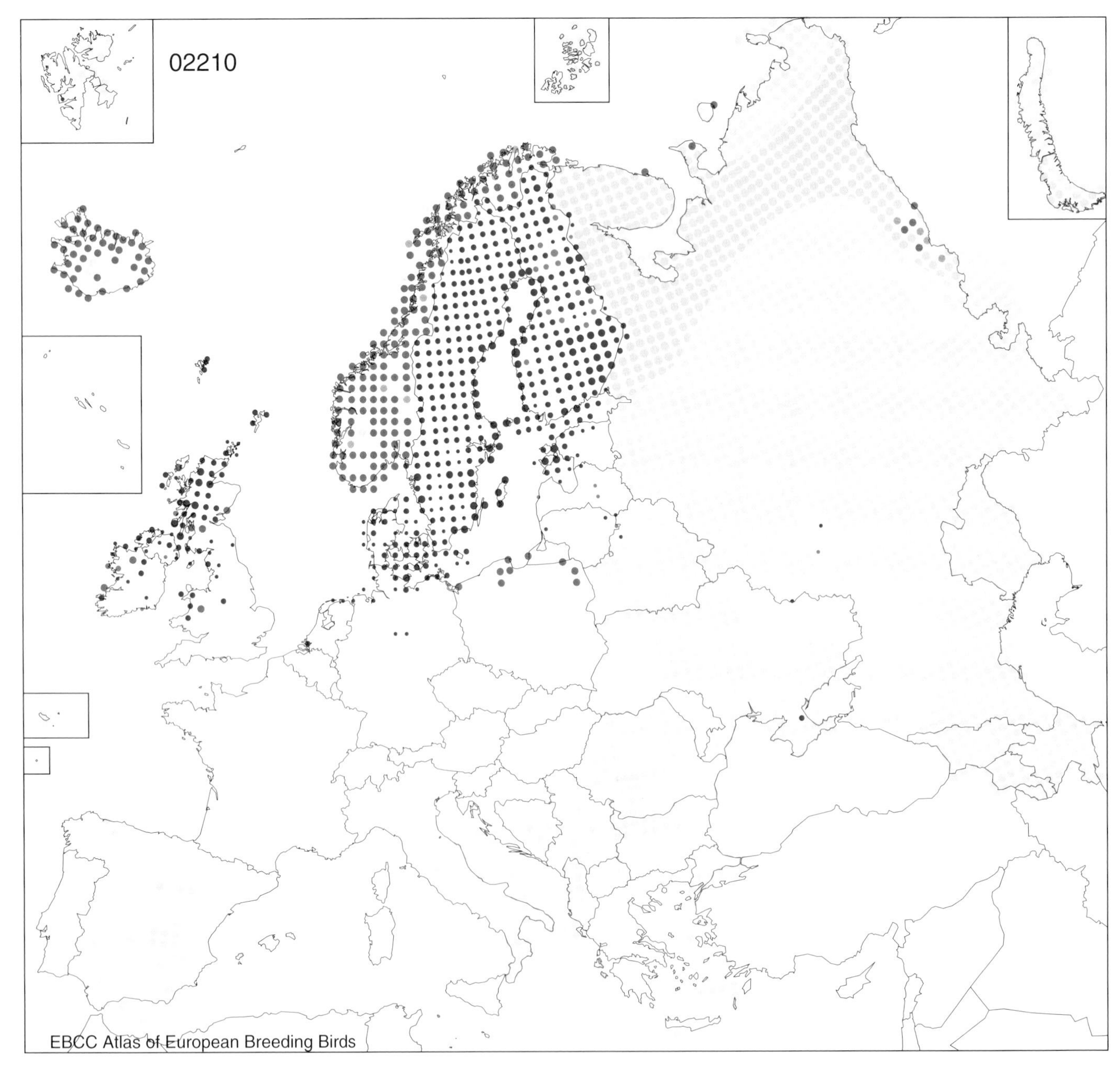

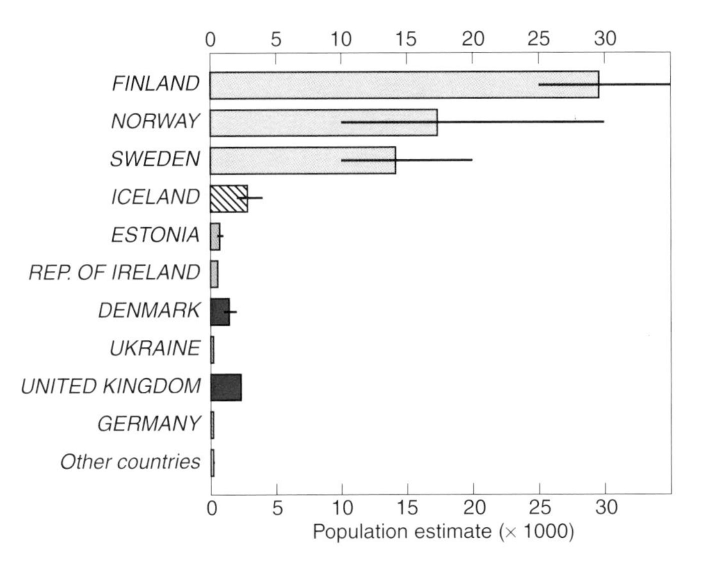

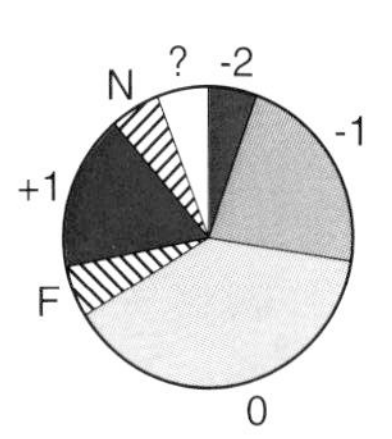

% in top 10 countries: 99.7
Total number of populated European countries: 18
Total European population 59,818–84,484 (69,442)
Russian population 5000–10,000 (7071)

The monotypic Red-breasted Merganser has a widespread Holarctic breeding distribution mostly above 50°N, covering Eurasia, North America and S Greenland. In Europe it is common in Iceland, Ireland, NW Britain, Fennoscandia, Estonia and northern Russia. Its southern distribution border reaches from Ireland to northern Poland and Belarus. However, pairs or small groups quite commonly breed much further S, as in The Netherlands, the Czech Republic and Ukraine.

It breeds mostly in forested regions, mainly on rather deep oligotrophic lakes and on small rivers with little emergent vegetation. Where breeding densities are high, the breeding lakes usually contain many wooded islets and possess shorelines which are indented and broken. Unlike the Goosander *M. merganser*, which otherwise shares almost identical habitats and is similarly distributed, it is also commonly found along tidal Atlantic coasts in Britain, Ireland and Norway (Carter 1993a, Frantzen 1994b). Numerous also along coasts and in the archipelagos of the Baltic Sea, the species in N Norway occurs up to 1000m asl in tundra-like habitat (Frantzen 1994b).

Its range has remained largely unchanged since the late 19th century, although it has moved southwards in Britain and Ireland as a result of marked population growth. According to recent population trends, the western European range still seems to be expanding slowly southward; elsewhere this is not the case. From 1975 onwards there has been a slight numerical increase in Denmark, SW Netherlands (2bp in 1977, 21bp in 1992; Meininger & de Kraker 1992, SOVON) and Britain. It first bred in France (2bp successfully) on the Chausey Islands, Normandy, in 1993 (Demongin 1994). The observed trends in Germany and Poland have been stable, but the Baltic countries show a clear decreasing trend. In the main breeding area of Fennoscandia and Russia, populations seem stable or are fluctuating without any long-term trend. The reasons for the varying population trends in different parts of the range are not known, but water reservoir construction and changes in hunting pressure may be involved.

Breeding densities depend greatly on the availability of suitable waterbodies. In Finland the Red-breasted Merganser prefers large lakes and in the archipelagos, sandy areas and moraines. In the Finnish lake region, it occurs on all lakes larger than $4km^2$, but infrequently on lakes smaller than $1km^2$, where the stock of fish sizes suitable for its broods may be inadequate. It seldom breeds in shallow eutrophic waters. In most breeding sites the species is widely scattered and breeding density in oligotrophic lakes varies from 0.4 to 0.7 bp/km^2 (Kauppinen 1993). In S Sweden the species is less abundant than in Finland and occurs only on lakes larger than $5km^2$ (Nilsson & Ås 1985).

In the Finnish and Swedish archipelagos the Red-breasted Merganser is one of the most numerous waterbirds. Towards the N it displays wider habitat requirements and generally achieves a higher breeding density, up to 9 bp/km^2. In breeding areas of extensive optimum habitat, where many breeding pairs are concentrated, the most dominant females often take broods from other females, sometimes forming large 'super-broods' up to 100 young strong (Hildén & Hario 1993)! In British rivers a density range of 1 bp/17–50km has been estimated (Carter 1993a), but in N Finland in large rivers 1 bp/5–10km is typical (E. Lammi & R. Väisänen, unpubl).

In its northernmost breeding areas the Red-breasted Merganser is migratory, but southern populations do not move far. Birds from Scandinavia, Finland and probably from much of western Russia winter mostly along Atlantic coasts and along the southern Baltic coasts. The Mediterranean basin and the Black Sea are also important wintering areas. According to international midwinter counts *c*150 000 individuals may winter in the western Palearctic, *c*100 000 of them in NW Europe.

Esa Lammi (FIN)

Mergus merganser Goosander

CZ	Morčák velký	**I**	Smergo maggiore
D	Gänsesäger	**NL**	Grote Zaagbek
E	Serreta Grande	**P**	Merganso-grande
F	Harle bièvre	**PL**	Nurogęś
FIN	Isokoskelo	**R**	Большой крохаль
G	Χηνοπρίστης	**S**	Storskrake
H	Nagy bukó		

Non-SPEC, Threat status S

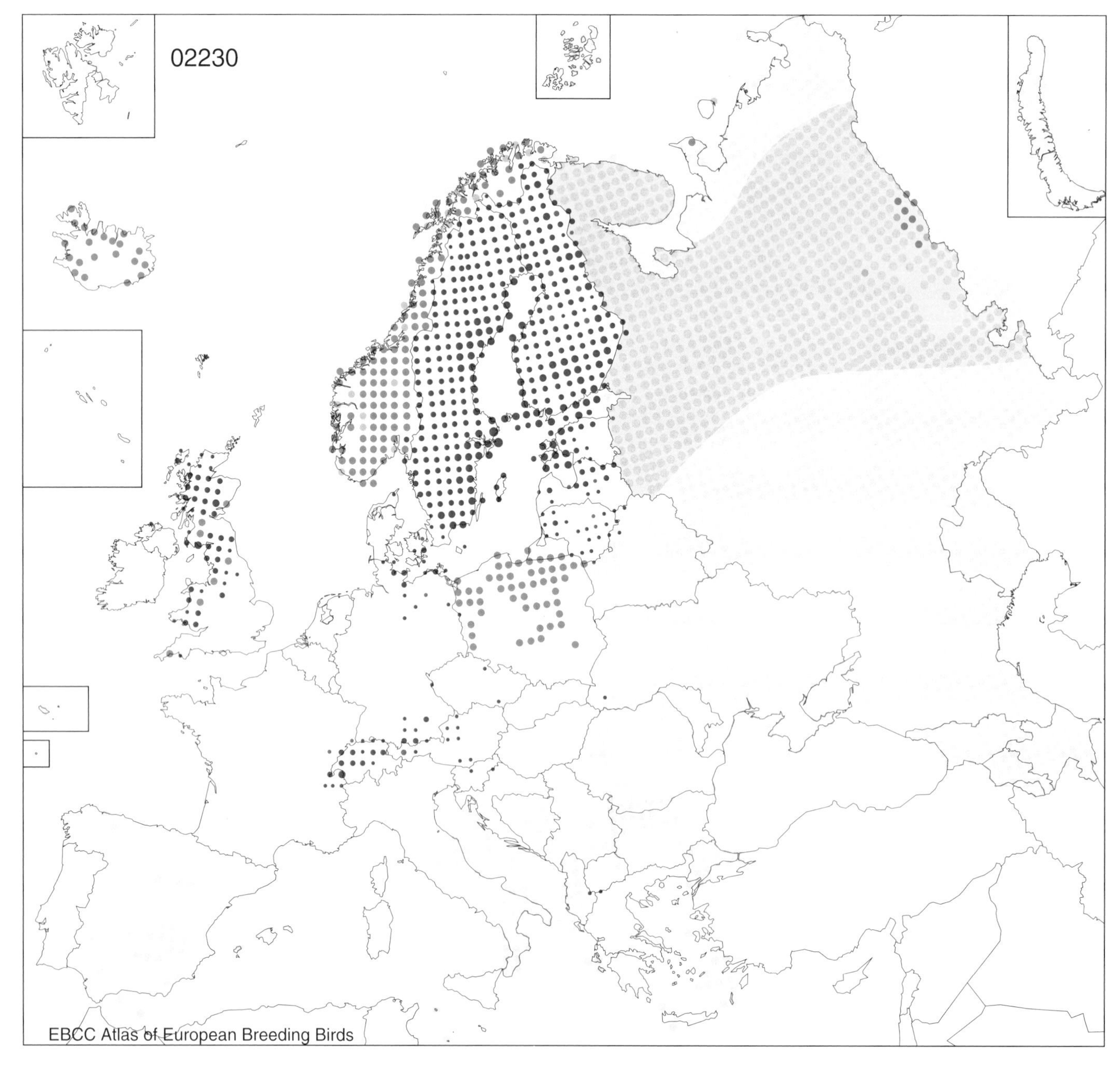

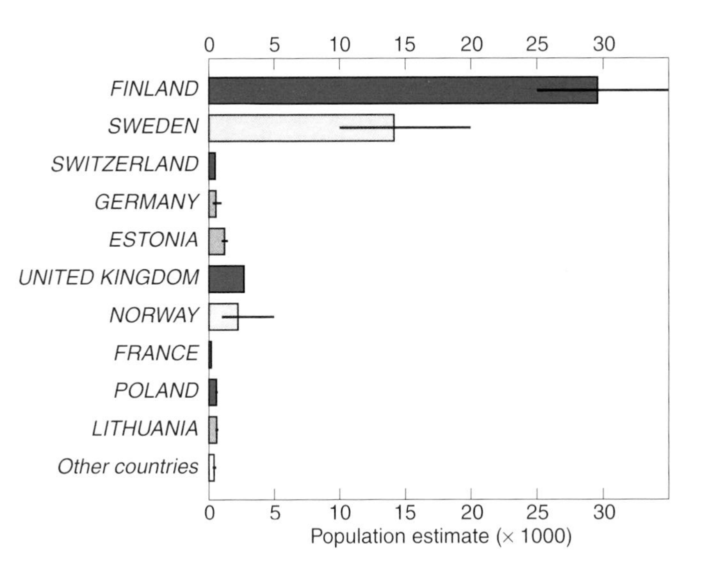

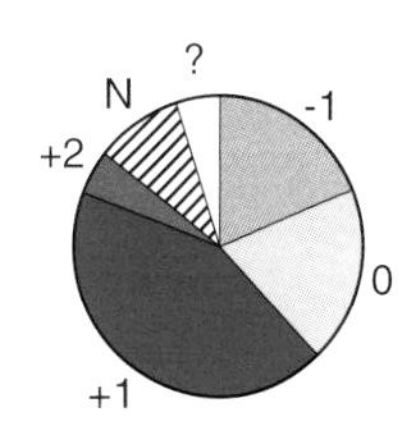

% in top 10 countries: 99.2
Total number of populated European countries: 21
Total European population 46,409–61,183 (52,718)
Russian population 10,000–20,000 (14,142)

The Goosander's breeding range overlaps with that of the Red-breasted Merganser *Mergus serrator*, but does not extend so far N in the tundra. The nominate Goosander subspecies *M.m. merganser* breeds in Europe and N Asia, *comatus* occurs in C Asia (highlands of Pamir and Tibet) and *americanus*, which resembles the nominate, is widely distributed in North America.

During the breeding season the Goosander occupies clear-water lakes and rivers, preferably in extensive forests or in mountainous regions. Birds from the alpine population are increasingly breeding in towns and parks by lakeshores where old trees offer suitable nesting places for this hole-nesting species (Géroudet 1985).

The Goosander is widespread in Iceland, N and W Great Britain, Fennoscandia, N Russia and Siberia. It is an extremely common breeding bird in the C and N Baltic, whereas in the E, S and W Baltic it is much less so, from Estonia to N Germany. The separate alpine population is distributed from France (Savoie), Switzerland and Bavaria to Austria. Additional tiny populations exist in SE Europe (Slovenia, Albania and Greece).

Since the 1850s the Goosander has extended its range southwards. In C Europe it was then a very rare breeding species, only a few broods being recorded from Lake Constance and Lake Neuchâtel. It first bred in Scotland in 1871, gradually extending its range S to England by 1941.

Population trends vary between regions. The largest population, in Fennoscandia, is increasing (36 000–60 000bp). In Finland the increase arose because water eutrophication improved the species' food supply, and the boom in construction of lakeside summer-houses inadvertently created many suitable nesting cavities. The British population has also increased to cover much of Scotland, then expanding into N England, Wales and SW England. Between 1968–72 and 1988–91, Scotland experienced a range contraction and further expansion seems to have slowed because of persecution (Carter 1993b). In contrast, numbers are decreasing in the Baltic States and in N Germany. However, the small alpine population (*c*550–700bp in 1994) continues to increase, probably because of the widespread hunting ban. Water eutrophication and nestbox schemes also may have contributed to this increase. Locally, however, canalization of rivers, the loss of nest sites or human disturbance have caused decreases. The alpine population remains vulnerable because of its size and scattered nature.

Although the map shows consistent characteristic densities across Fennoscandia and C Europe, it may be that numbers of Goosander breeding S of the Baltic have until recently been underestimated. Mizera *et al* (1994) showed the Oder River basin is a very important C European breeding (164–267 females with young, 1980–93) and wintering (up to 80 000 birds in cold winters) area.

Breeding densities depend greatly on the availability of suitable rivers and lakes. In Finnish coastal areas with offshore islands densities reached 3.4 bp/km^2, but elsewhere values mostly are lower (down to 0.15 bp/km^2); on lakes densities ranged from 0.1 to 2.0 bp/km^2, but in a river system in N Lapland averaged 0.2 bp/km^2 (overview in Niittylä 1980; E. Lammi & R.A. Väisänen, unpubl). Where locally many pairs concentrate, nest-site competition may lead several females to use one nest (up to 39 eggs; Géroudet 1985).

In the N of its breeding range the Goosander is migratory; further S only partially so. Scandinavian birds winter along the shores of the North Sea and in the Baltic region, occasionally moving further S (Hansen 1976). The alpine population is mostly sedentary (Hofer & Marti 1988). During moult migration in July and August, a significant proportion of European males congregate in N Norway at the Tana River mouth where in early September Frantzen (1984) counted 30 000 birds, almost the entire European population. This area might be the centre of the species' original range (Little & Furness 1985).

Christian Marti (CH) Esa Lammi (FIN)

Oxyura jamaicensis

Ruddy Duck

CZ	Kachnice kaštanová	I	Gobbo rugginoso della Giamaica
D	Schwarzkopf-Ruderente	NL	Rosse Stekelstaart
E	Malvasía Canela	P	Pato-rabo-alçado-americano
F	Erismature rousse	PL	Sterniczka jamajska
FIN	Kupariviuhkasorsa	R	Американская савка
G	Κοκκινόπαπια	S	Amerikansk kopparand
H	Feketefejű halcsontfarkú réce		

Criteria not applied

The Ruddy Duck is native to North America and was introduced into Europe from captive collections mainly in Great Britain. Birds first escaped in 1953, and since first breeding in 1960, the feral population has increased to *c*570bp by 1991 (Hughes & Grussu 1994). Captives have also escaped from other European countries, including Belgium and The Netherlands.

The Ruddy Duck was first recorded in Europe outside Britain in Sweden in 1965. Up to 1993 there were some 600 western Palearctic records from 19 countries (B. Hughes, in prep). The first breeding records from mainland Europe came from The Netherlands in 1977, France in 1988 and Belgium in 1991. Birds are now probably attempting to breed annually in these countries and also in Ireland, but the number of breeding pairs is still small. However, Iceland now has an established migratory breeding population (some 10–15 birds) which is thought to originate from Britain (Nielsen 1995). In Spain, the Ruddy Duck has bred intra-specifically and has crossbred with the White-headed Duck *O. leucocephala*. To preserve the latter's genetic purity, all Ruddy Ducks and hybrids occurring in Spain are now shot. Fourteen pure Ruddy Ducks and 33 hybrids had been controlled by December 1993 (Torres Esquivias 1995).

Northern European countries have mainly spring and summer Ruddy Duck records as birds disperse northwards to breed. Most records come from Sweden (21 records) and Norway (20) with fewer from Denmark (6) and Finland (3); although the majority refer to single birds (mostly males), pairs have occurred in Norway and Sweden, breeding being likely in the near future. Germany (40 records) has birds present all year round, but spring and summer records are exclusively from N Germany (Bauer 1994).

Most European countries are now assessing the feasibility of reducing Ruddy Duck numbers to help safeguard the White-headed Duck. However, concerted action across Europe will be necessary if the spread of the Ruddy Duck is to be halted. Unless countries act immediately, the Ruddy Duck undoubtedly will colonize the multitude of small, reed-fringed wetlands across Europe and the fate of the White-headed Duck in W Europe will be sealed.

Baz Hughes (GB)

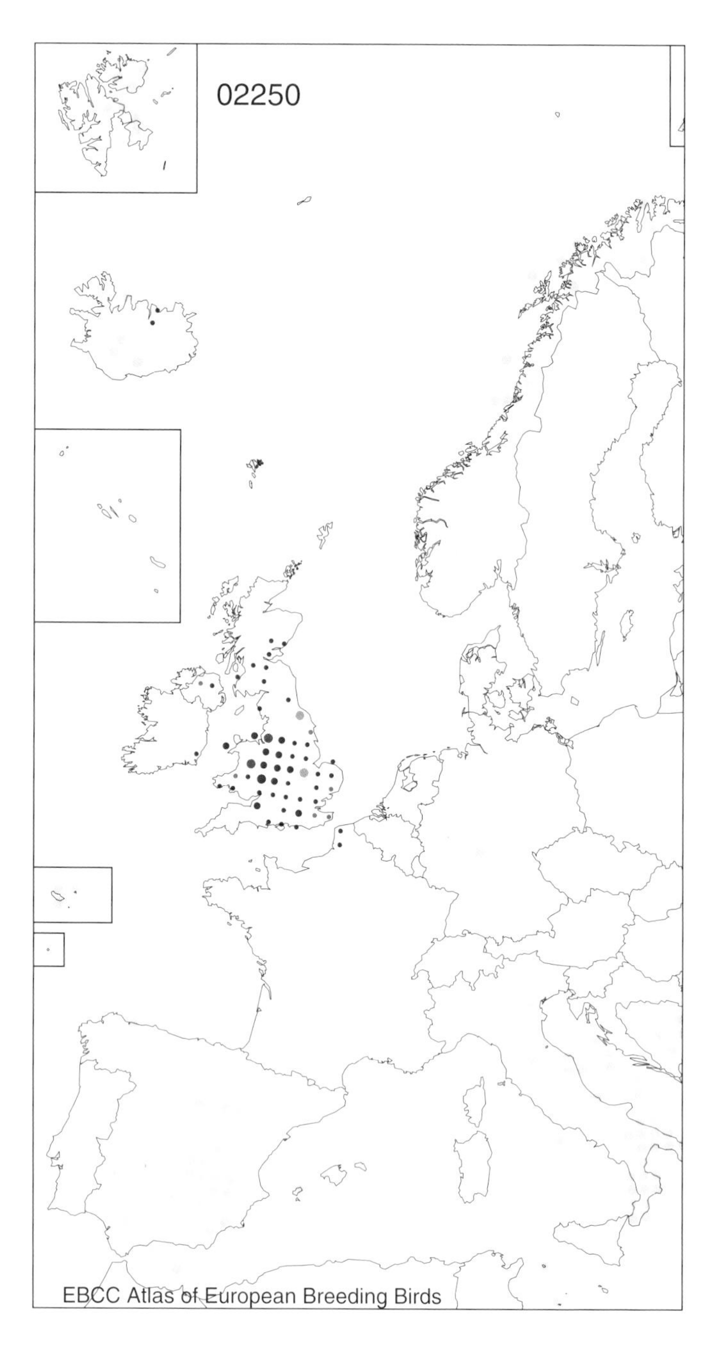

Oxyura leucocephala

White-headed Duck

CZ	Kachnice bělohlavá	I	Gobbo rugginoso
D	Weißkopf-Ruderente	NL	Witkopeend
E	Malvasía Cabeciblanca	P	Pato-rabo-alçado
F	Érismature à tête blanche	PL	Sterniczka
FIN	Viuhkasorsa	R	Савка
G	Κεφαλούδι	S	Kopparand
H	Kékcsőrű réce		

SPEC Cat 1, Threat status E

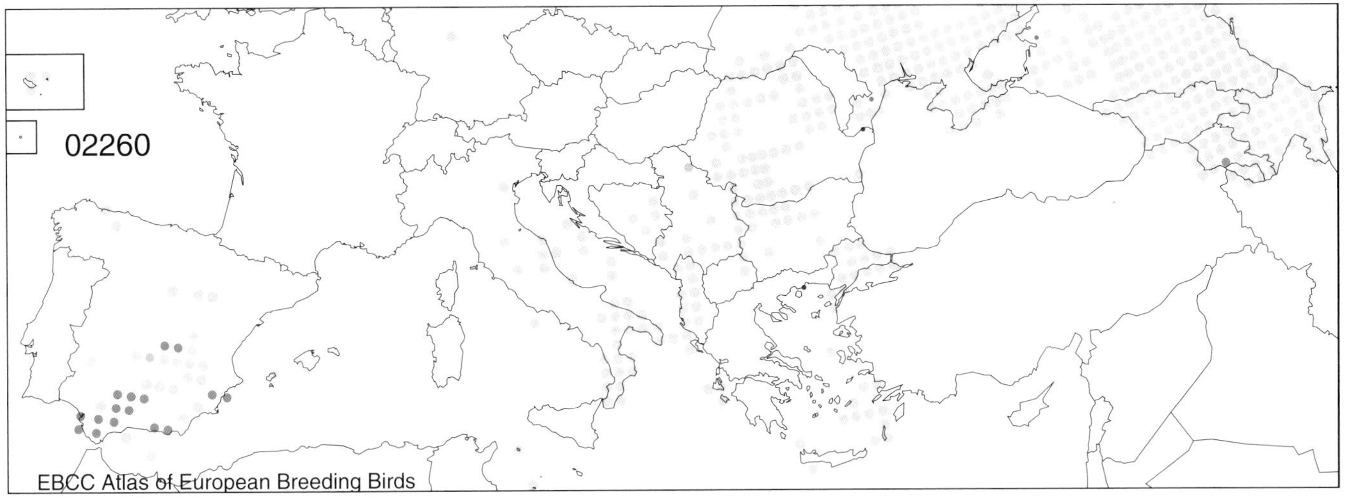

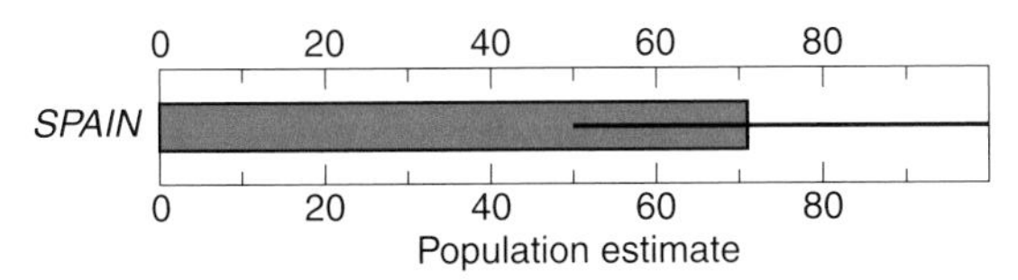

% in top 10 countries: 100.0
Total number of populated European countries: 1
Total European population 50–100 (71)
Russian population 10–40 (20)
Turkish population 150–250 (194)

The White-headed Duck has a distribution fragmented into a small resident population in the W Mediterranean and a larger, mainly migratory population in the E Mediterranean to C Asia. Breeding occurs on small, stagnant wetlands, usually brackish with no outflow and fringed with dense emergent vegetation. In Europe, breeding is now concentrated in southern Spain but it also occurs in Russia and Romania. NE Greece and the W Black Sea coast and probably Turkey are important wintering areas for birds breeding in European Russia or further E (Anstey 1989, Green & Anstey 1992). Azerbaijan holds important wintering populations of unknown origin (M.V. Patrikeev, in prep). Small numbers formerly bred in Italy until 1977 (Brichetti *et al* 1992) and Corsica, Hungary and former Yugoslavia (Vojvodina, now part of Serbia) until the 1960s. Historically, breeding also occurred in the Ukraine, Greece and Albania (Anstey 1989, Green & Anstey 1992).

In Spain, the species is concentrated in Andalucía where until recently it was almost confined to lagoons in Cordoba, Càdiz and Sevilla provinces. However it is currently expanding and bred for the first time in Jaén and Almeria provinces in 1988, in Malaga province in 1990 and has become established in Valencia and Castilla La Mancha since 1990 (Agencia de Medio Ambiente (AMA), Junta de Andalucía, pers comm). This expansion is due to a dramatic population increase since 1980, following the effective protection of the species from hunting (Torres Esquivias *et al* 1986, AMA Cordoba 1991). The peak annual census increased from 22 individuals in 1977 to 786 in 1992 and there are now an estimated 100–200 breeding females. The species was introduced to Mallorca in 1993 (J. Mayol, pers comm). In Russia, breeds in small numbers in one to three sites in the Volga Delta area (V. Moseikin, pers comm) while at least one pair bred in the Danube Delta, Dobrodja, Romania in 1986 (D. Ilhes, pers comm).

The White-headed Duck is extremely easy to shoot (A.J. Green *et al*, in prep) and hunting is undoubtedly a partial explanation for its extinction of the species in various European countries. The species reaches high densities in Spain, with up to six females breeding together in Laguna Rincón, Cordoba (4ha) and up to 559 birds wintering in Laguna Medina, Càdiz (120ha) (AMA Andalucía, pers comm). Nevertheless, the species' distribution is very patchy due to the small number of suitable wetlands remaining. Many breeding sites are temporary wetlands, and distribution varies considerably in response to annual variation in rainfall. The Spanish population is resident, but occasional exchange may occur with North Africa. The wintering location of Russian birds is unclear, but may be Turkey. There are no recognized subspecies, but the Spanish population contains a larger proportion of dark-bodied birds than those to the east, possibly due to a genetic bottleneck experienced in the 1970s.

Andy Green (GB)

Pernis apivorus

Honey Buzzard

CZ	Včelojed lesní	**I**	Falco pecchiaiolo
D	Wespenbussard	**NL**	Wespendief
E	Abejero Europeo	**P**	Falcão-abelheiro
F	Bondrée apivore	**PL**	Trzmielojad
FIN	Mehiläishaukka	**R**	Осоед
G	Σφηκιάρης	**S**	Bivråk
H	Darázsölyv		

SPEC Cat 4, Threat status S

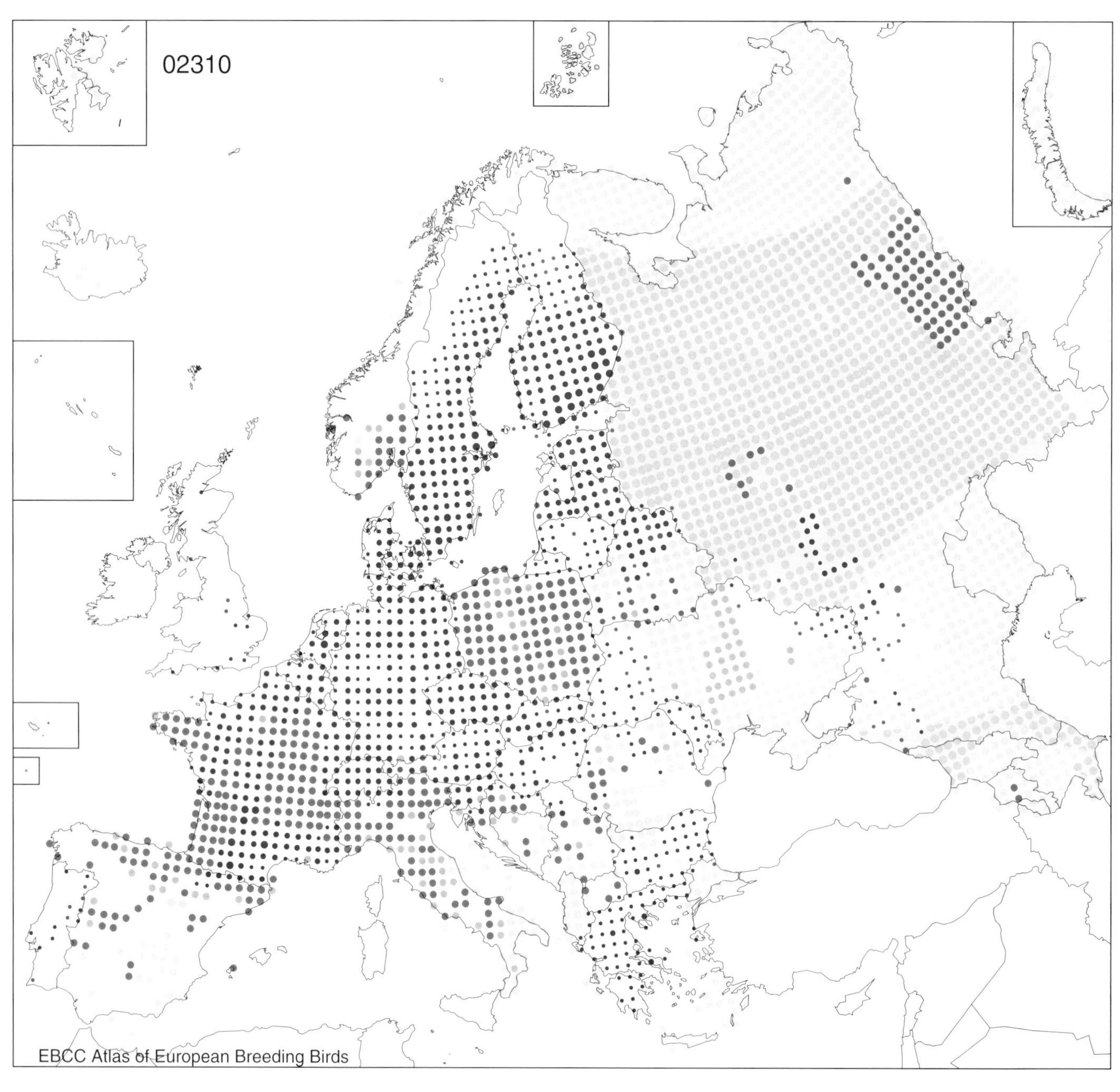

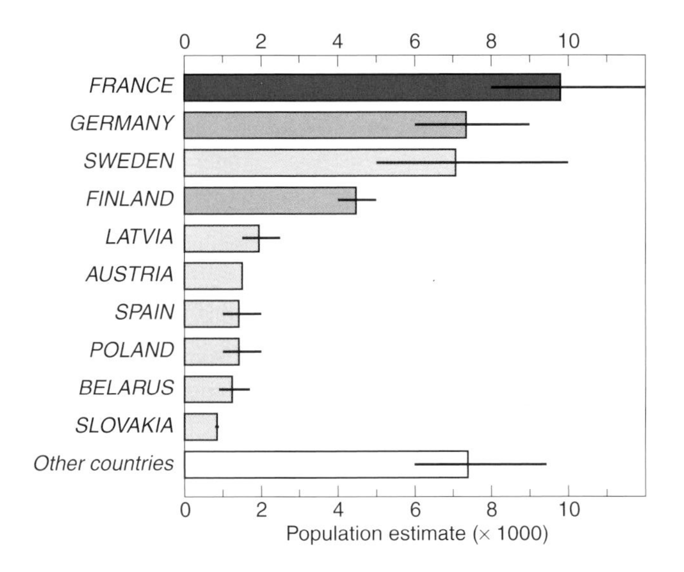

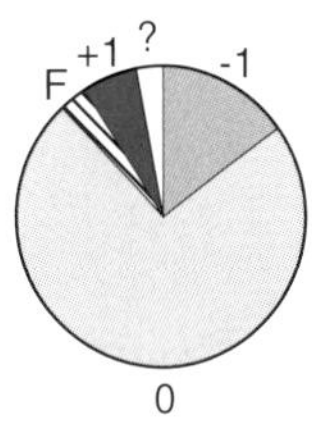

% in top 10 countries: 83.4
Total number of populated European countries: 33
Total European population 41,200–48,677 (44,424)
Russian population 70,000–100,000 (83,666)
Turkish population 50–500 (158)

The enigmatic Honey Buzzard, a specialized raptor, breeds in Europe and W Asia and winters in Africa S of the Sahara. Most of its year is spent in Africa or on migration. Monotypic, it forms a superspecies with the Crested Honey Buzzard *Pernis ptilorhyncus*, resident in E and SE Asia and the Indian subcontinent.

The Honey Buzzard's specialized feeding habit of excavating wasps' nests to extract larvae from the cells normally does not limit breeding performance, because if wasps' nests are scarce in any season, it compensates by feeding on amphibians and on pigeon and passerine nestlings, unless weather conditions are particularly adverse (Bijlsma 1993). Its short residency on its breeding grounds (May–August) and characteristic unobtrusive behaviour have made it one of the least-studied of the abundant raptors. Little is known of its life in the wintering areas.

The Honey Buzzard is rather catholic in its habitat choice, breeding in even-aged coniferous stands or high-quality mixed and deciduous forests, large or small, with or without water. Normally, it ignores the presence of human beings or other raptor species (Kostrzewa 1991, Bijlsma 1993, Amcoff *et al* 1994). Home range sizes are large (>1000ha) and foraging flights from the nest may be 7km in radius. In well-studied populations, such as in The Netherlands, the birds show high site and mate fidelity (R.G. Bijlsma, pers obs). The species is long-lived, has a small clutch size (almost invariably two eggs), low productivity, high site fidelity, delayed breeding commencement, but not deferred maturity (Bijlsma 1993, Tjernberg & Ryttman 1994); characteristics of a K-selected bird species but most unlike other similar-sized Palearctic raptors.

Between 49° and 67°N, the Honey Buzzard is widespread and relatively abundant throughout Europe. It occurs more patchily in Iberia, Italy, Greece, S England and Scotland (≈30bp in Britain). Its thin distribution in the Balkans, Ukraine and S Russia probably reflects the lack of observers. The Honey Buzzard has adapted well to maritime and mediterranean climate zone conditions and although generally it is a typical continental climate zone species, its breeding density and performance apparently are similar in each area. (Kostrzewa 1991, Bijlsma 1993).

The overall impression of population trends in Europe is one of stability. However, very few reliable long-term studies are available. Based on systematic counts of concentrated bird migration in S Sweden in 1973–92 (Tjernberg & Ryttman 1994), the Swedish population size appears to have declined significantly, as has the Finnish. Small increases may occur where afforestation enlarges the area of suitable breeding habitat, as in The Netherlands (Bijlsma 1993). Pesticide-related fluctuations, as experienced by bird- and vole-eating raptors in the mid-1900s, have not afflicted the Honey Buzzard, presumably because its food-chain was less contaminated.

The European population amounts to some 160 000bp, mainly concentrated in Russia, Finland, Sweden, Germany and France (some 85% of the total). Given an average reproductive rate of 0.3 young/bp (Tjernberg & Ryttman 1994), 800 000 birds should pass through migratory bottlenecks in S Spain and the Middle East. Highest figures for Gibraltar and Eilat have been 115 000 (in 1972) and 850 000 (in 1985) respectively (Shirihai & Christie 1992). The European population plus those breeding E of the Urals, probably numbers over 1M birds.

Shooting is a serious threat to the species. Juveniles, being confiding during migration, are particularly vulnerable. Consequently, first-year mortality is high (between 50 and 70%), although survival rates of adult birds are much better (Bijlsma 1993, Tjernberg & Ryttman 1994). The average reproductive rate of 0.3 young/pair in Sweden would only just suffice to maintain a stable population if hunting losses were zero (Tjernberg & Ryttman 1994). Hunting pressure in the Mediterranean region apparently is decreasing (McCulloch *et al* 1992), but it remains a major threat to the species.

Rob G Bijlsma (NL)

Milvus migrans

Black Kite

CZ	Luňák hnědý	**I**	Nibbio bruno
D	Schwarzmilan	**NL**	Zwarte Wouw
E	Milano Negro	**P**	Milhafre-preto
F	Milan noir	**PL**	Kania czarna
FIN	Haarahaukka	**R**	Черный коршун
G	Τσίφτης	**S**	Brun glada
H	Barna kánya		

SPEC Cat 3, Threat status V

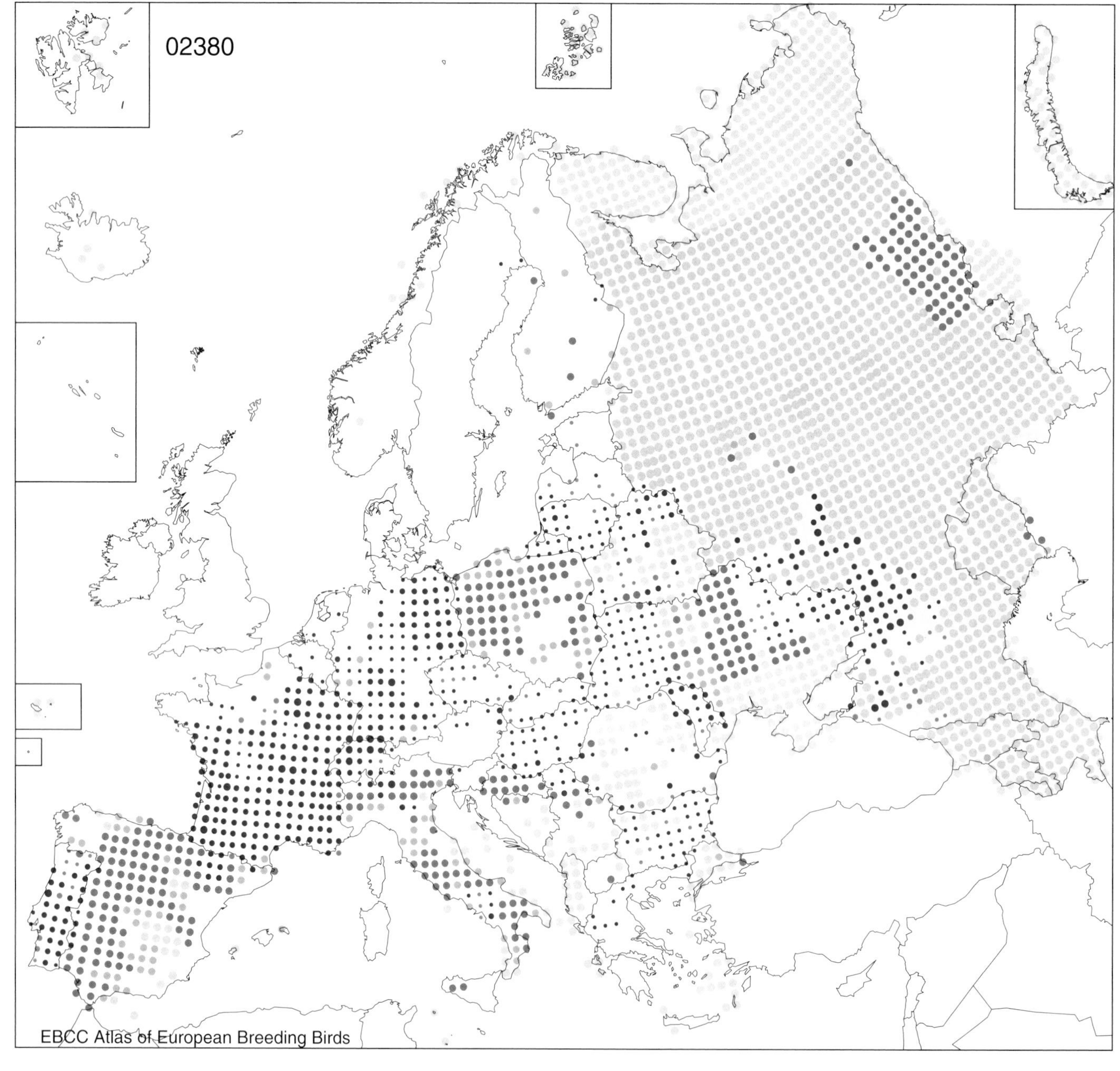

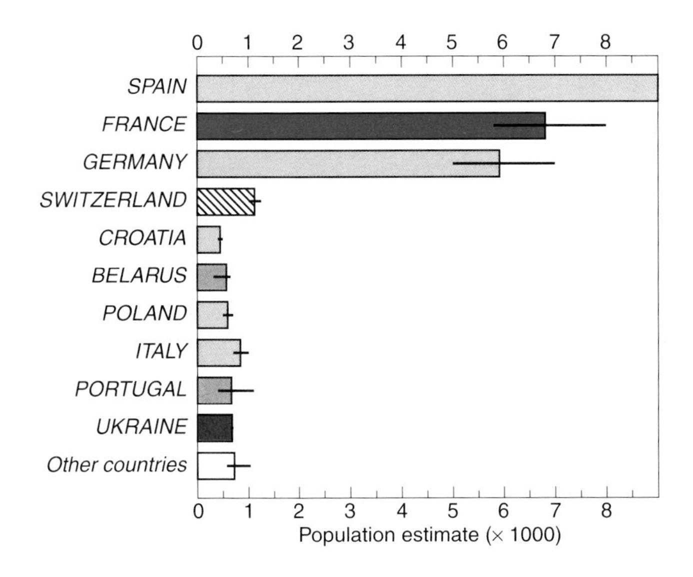

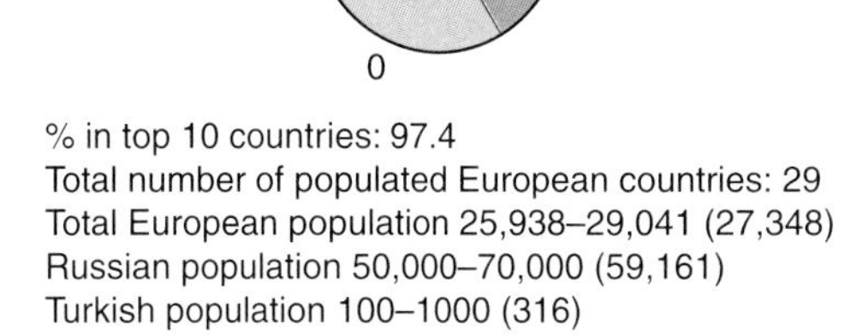

The Black Kite, a successful, medium-sized raptor, is distributed throughout Eurasia, Africa and Australia. The nominate *M.m. migrans* breeds in Europe and North Africa, intergrading with *lineatus* in C Asia, from where the range extends into the E Palearctic and China. European birds are markedly migratory and winter in sub-Saharan Africa.

The species is almost ubiquitous, inhabiting semi-deserts, cultivated areas and fragmented woodland, preferring lowlands (<1000m asl) with adjacent aquatic environments. Unlike the Asian and African subspecies, European birds generally avoid breeding in cities, although suburban areas around lakes may attract breeding clusters when food is plentiful. It is predominantly a bird of the mediterranean and low-latitude steppe zones, extending its range during the continental summer into the temperate and even the boreal zone (up to 65°N in Russia).

Worldwide, the Black Kite is gregarious and commensal with man, especially in Asia and Africa. In Europe it is rather more solitary. Semi-colonial nesting behaviour occurs at Lakes Léman and de Neuchâtel (Switzerland). Near the latter, 337 occupied nests were located in 484km^2; 71% were within 1km of the shore, the minimum nest-separation distance being 8m (Sermet 1980a). The species is almost omnivorous, eating much fish in aquatic habitats but taking a wide variety of small mammals, birds, insects and carrion elsewhere (Stubbe *et al* 1991).

Outside the mediterranean and temperate zones, the species breeds in small numbers in Sweden, Finland and Estonia and avoids maritime regions, hence its absence from Britain & Ireland and Denmark and its tiny numbers in the Low Countries and NW France. Russia's 50 000–70 000bp form by far the largest population. Elsewhere in Europe, only four core countries (Spain, France, Germany and Switzerland) account for >80% of the remaining 28 000bp, the highest densities occurring in Spain, E and S France and Switzerland. My view is that the graph's estimated 5000–7000bp for Germany is probably overoptimistic, 2500bp in 1993 being more likely (Kostrzewa & Speer 1995). Towards the SE and E, the numbers show a sharply declining trend. The Black Kite is distributed sparsely from C Europe to much of the Balkans (N Croatia and N Serbia hold reasonable numbers) and Greece. The large river basins and lake systems in Moldova, S Ukraine, S Russia and S Kazakhstan may hold substantial numbers.

Except in Russia, where apparently the Black Kite declined slightly and showed some range contraction during 1970–90, populations have been stable in its European core areas. France experienced a 100km northwards range extension in the 1970s and 1980s (Doumeret 1994), a trend supported by tiny increases in Luxembourg and Belgium and sporadic breeding attempts in The Netherlands in the 1980s. However, outside that core, declining trends predominated. In E Europe and the Balkans, declines in numbers and range contractions occurred, the most significant (>50%) in Ukraine.

The species' status in Europe is confused because of large annual variations in numbers and contradictory trends in adjacent regions. Consistent declines generally correlate with habitat deterioration, chemical pollution of waterbodies and poisoning. In several eastern German regions, the Black Kite recovered from the organochlorine poisoning era (1950–70s), sometimes by a factor of 5 (Stubbe *et al* 1991).

During migration, birds gather in flocks and avoid long sea-crossings, bypassing the Mediterranean via Gibraltar (up to 60 000 birds) and the Near East (up to 36 000 in spring in Israel). Given the relative dearth of autumn migrants in the Near East, presumably many take a Middle Eastern route through the Arabian Peninsula (Shirihai & Christie 1992). In Africa, kites often follow rain-belts to profit from swarming alate termites (L. Brown 1971). The chemicals used in locust-spraying may be particularly hazardous to Black Kites, which readily exploit locust swarms.

Rob G Bijlsma (NL)

This species account is sponsored by the Institute for Inland Water Management and Waste Water Treatment, Lelystad, NL.

Milvus milvus

Red Kite

CZ	Luňák červený	**I**	Nibbio reale
D	Rotmilan	**NL**	Rode Wouw
E	Milano Real	**P**	Milhano
F	Milan royal	**PL**	Kania ruda
FIN	Isohaarahaukka	**R**	Красный коршун
G	Ψαλιδιάρης	**S**	Röd glada
H	Vörös kánya		

SPEC Cat 4, Threat status S

The Red Kite inhabits only *c*1.8Mkm² of the SW Palearctic. It occurs mostly in the temperate and W mediterranean zones. Save for few on the Canary Islands, the Cape Verde Islands (*M.m. fasciicauda*), in NW Africa, and possibly still in W Transcaucasia, the map shows its entire range. It is very much a European bird.

The small Welsh population is sedentary. The continental populations winter in the S of the breeding distribution,

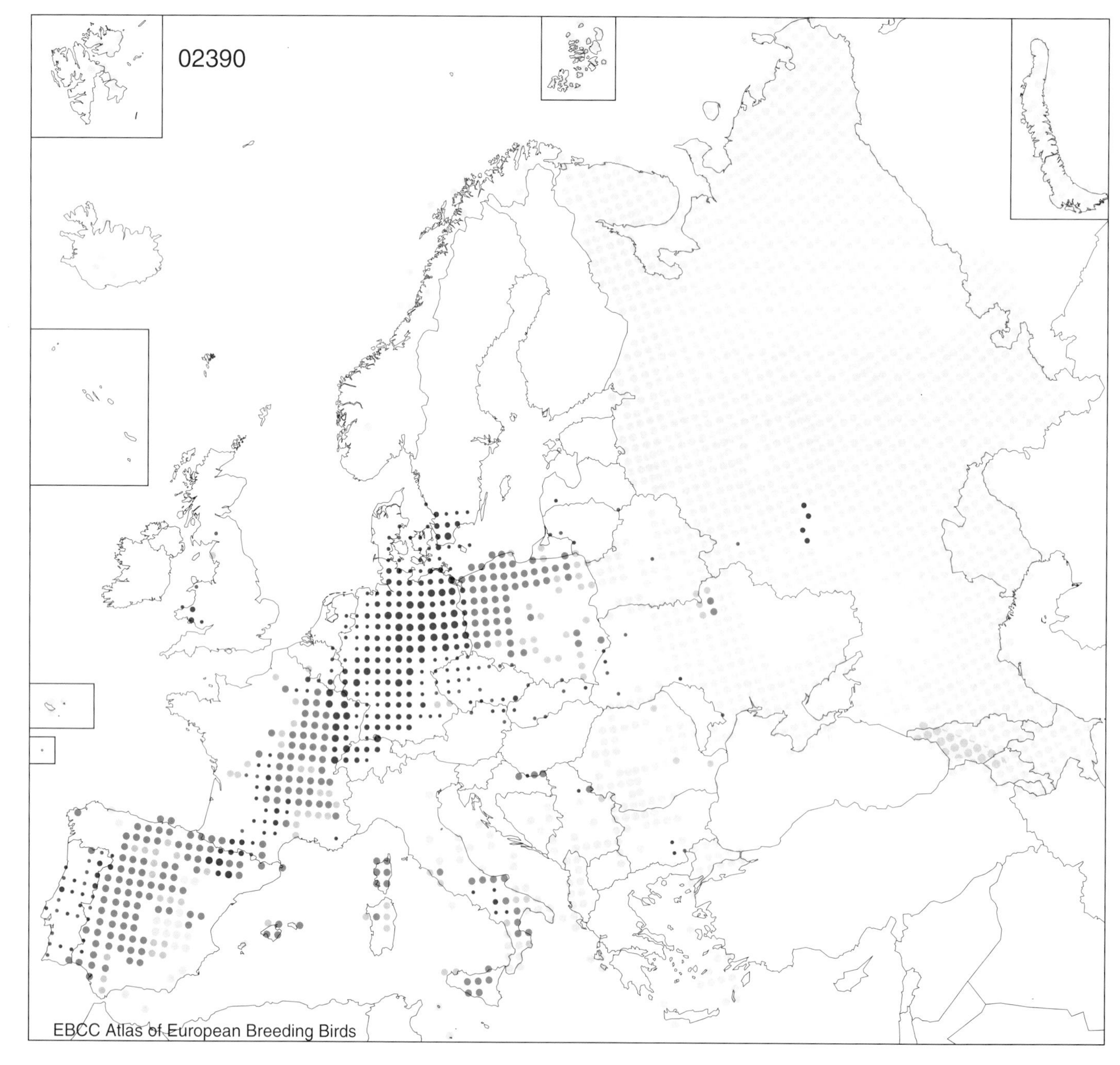

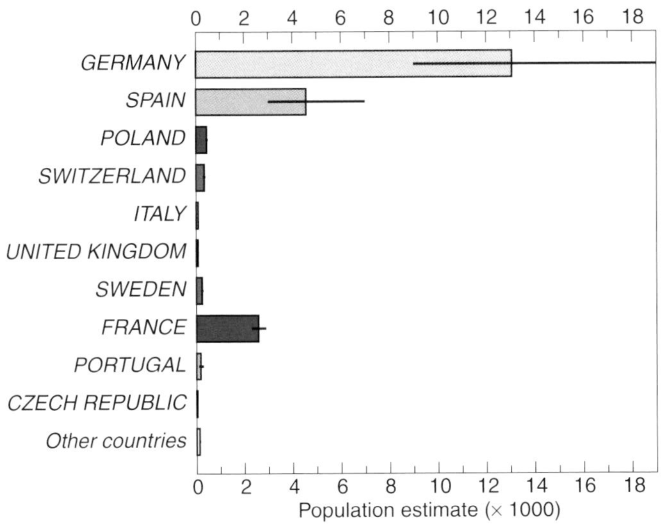

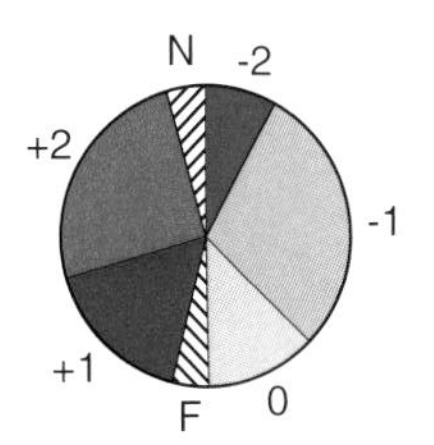

% in top 10 countries: 99.4
Total number of populated European countries: 24
Total European population 17,394–28,185 (21,777)
Russian population 1–50 (7)

biased towards Iberia, where recently 60 775 were counted (J. Bustamente, pers comm). There the local population also migrates from NE to SW. Since the late 1950s in Sweden and C Europe an overwintering tendency has developed, as in the NE Harz foothills where recently roosts of *c*100 birds have formed. However, in sustained severe wintry conditions most such birds will initiate a delayed migration, even as late as February (George 1994).

The Red Kite occupies open or fragmented habitats in lowlands or hilly countryside mostly below 600m asl, exceptionally up to 1000m. A tree-nester, it prefers woodland edges. In the S, in coastal areas and on islands, it often breeds on cliffs. Long foraging flights to meadows and agricultural steppe, up to 10km from the nest, are typical (Ortlieb 1989).

Breeding population density varies greatly. Of the world population of 19 000–32 000bp (Nicolai, in press), 22% is concentrated in Spain, and 67% in C Europe (E France to NE Germany), centred around the Harz Mountains. The productive Lower Saxony agricultural plains offer optimal hunting grounds. In the N Harz foothills densities of 37–47 bp/100 km^2 occur over a wide area (Nicolai 1993a). The Hakel forest (13km^2) held the highest concentration (136bp, 1979) (Stubbe 1982).

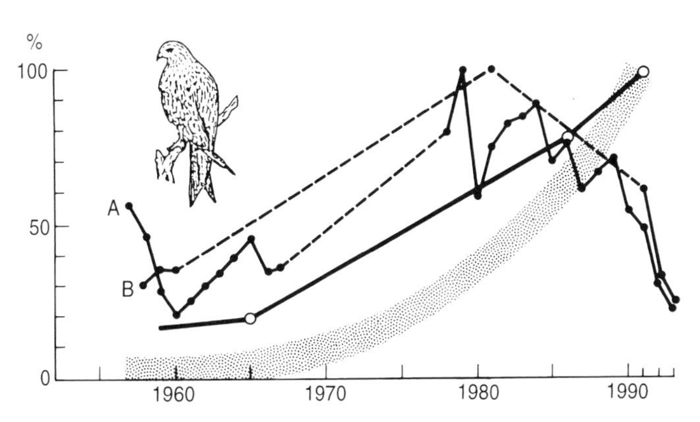

Title: Population trends of Red Kite in the north Harz foothills.

Key: Fine lines: trends in two large forests (A: Hakel, 13 km^2; B: Huy 20 km^2). Shaded strip: trend in open landscape. Broad line: trend over total study area (1500 km^2).
NB In 1991, total bp = 730 (= 100 %); further increase 1993.

Population trends show both historical and regional differences. When C Europe was covered in woodland, the species was scarce, but numbers increased with the advent of agriculture and the creation of cultivated steppe farmed at low intensity. Before the 20th century, the breeding range was clearly larger than at present. Populations suffered from intensive human persecution until the mid-1950s, but especially so between 1850 and 1900 (Ortlieb 1989). The species is particularly sensitive to poisoning which prevented further expansion in NW Europe and Britain (Evans & Pienkowski 1991).

Since the 1960s, habitat destruction in the S and E of its range has been paralleled by a reduction in numbers (Iberia, Italy, the Balkans and the Baltic). However, from the 1970s numbers increased in S Sweden (80bp 1982, 480bp 1993; Kjellén 1994), C Europe (locally in Germany by up to 400%; see diagram), France and Britain (including reintroductions in England and Scotland; Evans & Pienkowski 1991). This increase was triggered by better protection, adaptations to the changing landscape (breeding in isolated clumps of trees or avenues in open landscapes, along roads, in towns and on pylons) and recently possibly by higher survival rates.

Agricultural and forestry intensification will soon spread to E and C Europe and will affect adversely (severely so) the distribution and numbers of small mammals, especially the common hamster *Cricetus cricetus*, which not only inhabits steppes and arable land on loamy and loess soils, but is also important Red Kite prey; it is probably no coincidence that density gradients for both species peak in eastern Germany. The continuation of a form of low-intensity agriculture is therefore crucial to the future of the Red Kite world population.

Bernd Nicolai (D)

This species account is sponsored by Dachverband Deutscher Avifaunisten, D.

Haliaeetus albicilla — White-tailed Eagle

CZ	Orel mořský	**I**	Aquila di mare
D	Seeadler	**NL**	Zeearend
E	Pigargo Europeo	**P**	Águia-rabalva
F	Pygargue à queue blanche	**PL**	Bielik
FIN	Merikotka	**R**	Орлан-белохвост
G	Θαλασσαετός	**S**	Havsörn
H	Rétisas		

SPEC Cat 3, Threat status R

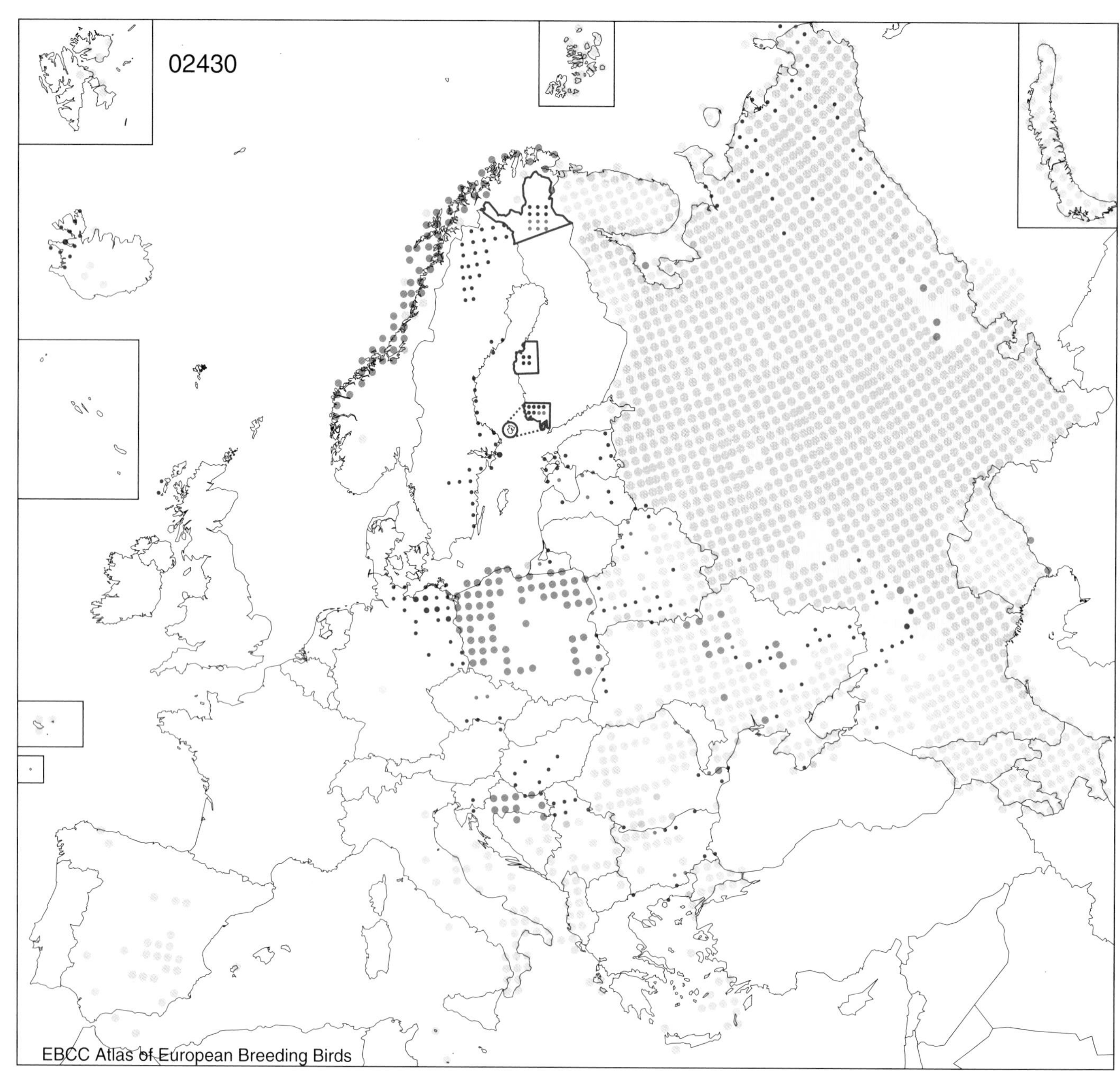

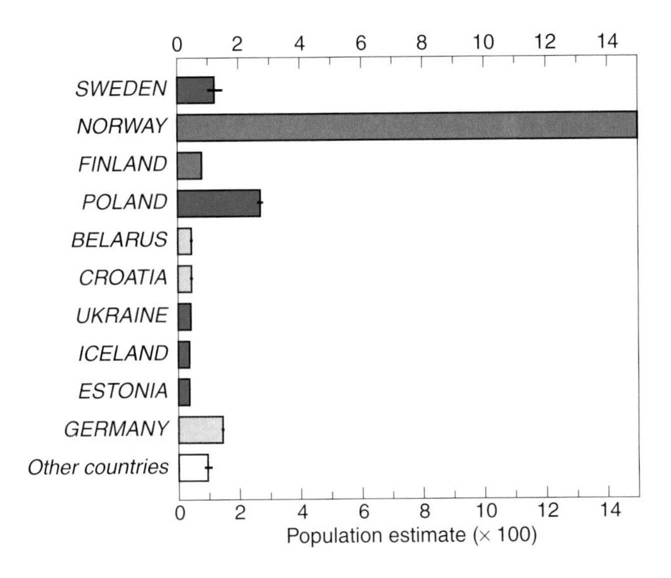

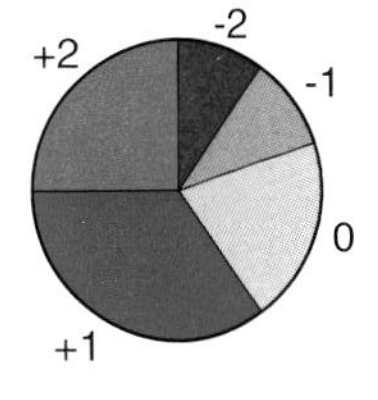

% in top 10 countries: 96.1
Total number of populated European countries: 20
Total European population 2392–2450 (2419)
Russian population 900–1100 (995)
Turkish population 10–30 (17)

The huge, magnificent White-tailed Eagle breeds over much of the northern Palearctic from Japan, Kamchatka and the Bering Strait in the E, to Germany, Scotland (reintroduced, Love 1983) and Iceland in the W, extending to Greenland in the Nearctic zone. In the N, its range extends from the Barents Sea coasts along *c*70°N through Siberia. In the S, it occurs from Croatia to the Caspian Sea and between 30° and 40°N eastwards to the Pacific. In Europe it bred formerly in Ireland, Denmark, Corsica, Portugal, Spain, Austria, Sardinia and Malta.

It associates closely with water habitats, fresh and saline, but especially those rich in fish or supporting large waterfowl populations. In Norway (Willgohs 1961), Iceland and Greenland it breeds mainly on sea-coast islands and in fjords, where it nests on cliff ledges, sometimes on the ground, or in trees when available. On the brackish Baltic coasts (Helander 1990) and in most freshwater habitats surrounded by woodland in central N and S Europe, it is exclusively a tree-nester.

Its distribution is uneven, matching the distribution and richness of water habitats. Persecution has affected its natural distribution, the species being exterminated from many parts of Europe since 1800. Reduced numbers survived in refuges in Norway, Sweden, Finland, NE Germany, NW Poland and the Danube Valley until protection permitted population growth. For example, Norway's total increased from 700–800bp in 1968 to 1500bp in 1993. However, the increase in many areas was reversed from the mid-1950s to the 1970s by the influence of chemical pollutants (DDT, PCBs), particularly in the Baltic. Fortunately, positive trends are now being observed in most populations in N and C Europe. This region, including Hungary, Romania and the former Yugoslavia, holds an estimated 3500bp. In southern Europe, however, the White-tailed Eagle remains very rare, fewer than 50bp remaining (Jerrentrup 1988) with no substantial signs of recovery.

Although the graph is representative, we suggest that recently published literature and current research support the following population estimates: Norway 1350–1650bp (1993), Poland 220–280bp (1992), Sweden 150bp (1993), Finland 100bp (1993), the former Yugoslavia 80bp (1991) and Lithuania 11bp (1992).

Population densities vary strongly with habitat quality. Average distance between breeding pairs in prime habitat is *c*4km, occasionally reduced to 1–2km in Norway, Sweden, Poland (Meyburg *et al* 1992) and Germany (Oder Delta). A 1300ha forest in NE Poland held 6–7 bp/km², the shortest distance between breeding pairs being 280m (T. Mizera, pers obs).

Historically, White-tailed Eagle distribution and numbers have been limited in part by persecution and egg- and specimen-collection. More recently, its survival is threatened more by the effects of human activities on the environment. Being a top predator in aquatic food webs, the species is very vulnerable to persistent pollutants, and many birds remain highly contaminated by organochlorines, especially in the Baltic (Falandysz *et al* 1994). Clearance of mature tree stands, currently a severe threat, reduces nesting opportunities, as happened in the Barycz Valley, Poland, where wasteful forest management reduced suitable nesting tree numbers twenty-fold (Mizera & Szymkiewicz 1990). The exploitation of shores for house-building, recreation and other leisure activities seriously reduces the availability of otherwise suitable habitat.

Mated pairs are mainly sedentary within their breeding home range, unless forced to migrate like arctic freshwater populations by seasonal climatic conditions (Helander 1990). Juveniles usually wander from their natal areas, occasionally very far (Finland–Bulgaria, Swedish Lapland–Hungary). The species winters mainly on the Norwegian coast (the resident population and a few arctic migrants), and the C and S Baltic coasts (the resident and many migrants from arctic areas and river deltas). The Oder Delta winter population comprised 120–150 birds in 1993.

Björn Helander (S) Tadeusz Mizera (PL)

This species account is sponsored by Ornithologische Arbeitsgemeinschaft Mecklenburg-Vorpommern, D.

Gypaetus barbatus

Lammergeier

CZ	Orlosup bradatý	**I**	Gipeto
D	Bartgeier	**NL**	Lammergier
E	Quebrantahuesos	**P**	Quebra-osso
F	Gypaète barbu	**PL**	Orłosęp
FIN	Partakorppikotka	**R**	Бородач
G	Γυπαετός	**S**	Lammgam
H	Saskeṣelyû		

SPEC Cat 3, Threat status E

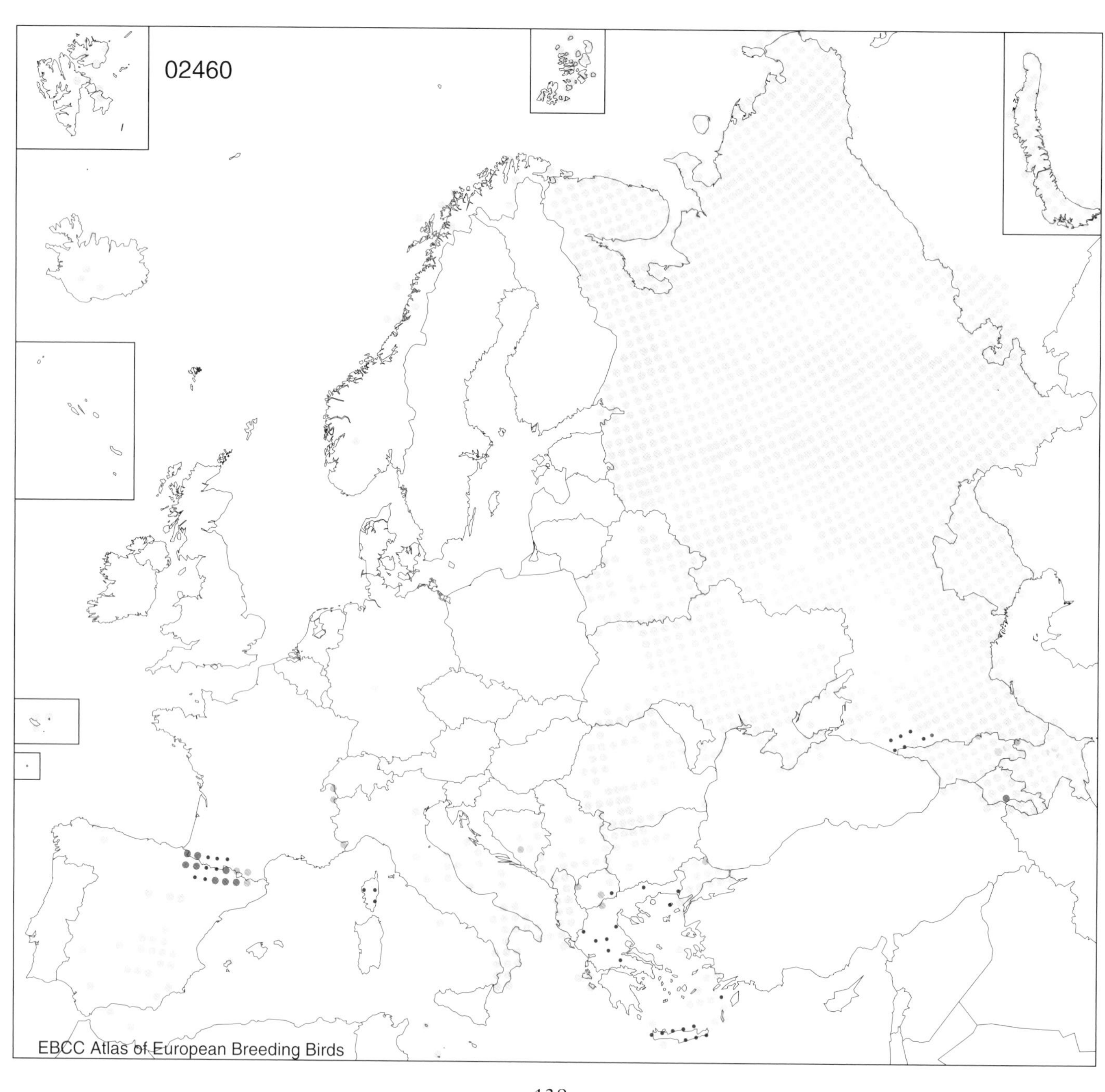

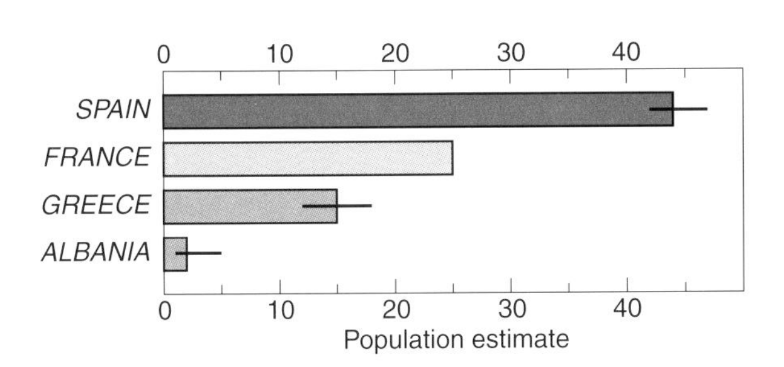

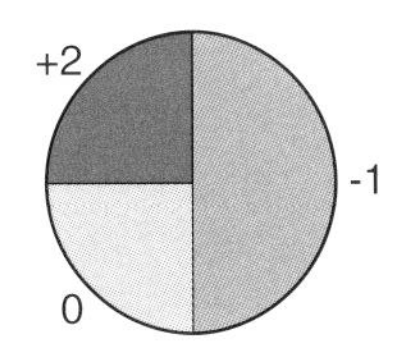

% in top 10 countries: 100.0
Total number of populated European countries: 4
Total European population 83–91 (86)
Russian population 20–40 (28)
Turkish population 100–500 (224)

The Lammergeier, or Bearded Vulture, as a carrion-eater has a predilection for bones, which if too large to swallow or too strong for the bird to break on the ground, are dropped from flight to shatter below on the rocks. The pieces can then be more easily digested. This peculiarity gives rise to its Spanish popular name of 'Quebrantahuesos', which translates as 'bone-breaker'.

Its world range stretches from Spain and NW Africa in the W through Asia Minor to the Himalayas and C Asia in the E, and S to East and South Africa, always in mountainous regions, and usually nesting above 1000m asl. The European population consists of a few isolated groups from the Caucasus to the Pyrenees. On all three continents the present population is but a fraction of what it was. The greatest decline has occurred in Europe.

With the exception of the Pyrenees, the species continues to decline in the rest of Europe to such an extent that urgent conservation action is required. In Albania there are only a few left, and there may be just one pair in S Albania (Grubac 1991). In the former Yugoslavia it is restricted to Macedonia, where 3bp were located in 1980–86 (Grubac 1991). The Greek breeding population was estimated at 35 pairs in the early 1980s (Handrinos 1985), of which 10 (30 individuals) were in Crete (Vagliano 1981). In the early 1990s the Greek population may have reduced to only 12–18bp; in 1995 only a few appeared to be nesting in Crete (S Coghlan, pers comm to the Editors). In mainland France there are 15 pairs (of which 12 bred) in the Pyrenees and 8 pairs in Corsica (J.F. Terrasse, pers comm), a slight improvement from 1989, when 14–16 territories were recorded over the whole of France (Fasce *et al* 1989, Terrasse 1991). Since 1986, there has been a reintroduction programme, using the 'hacking' method, in the Swiss and Italian Alps. These birds originate from the young of captive zoo stock. Of 35 releases in 1987–91, seven died, went missing or were taken back into captivity. The remaining birds spread over the Alps, covering distances of over 600km. First pair formation took place in 1989 and nest construction was witnessed in 1991 (Frey & Bijleveld 1994). The status of the Caucasus population is not known.

In the Iberian Peninsula the Lammergeier breeds as yet only in the Pyrenees, but each year there are increasingly frequent sightings of wandering juveniles and adults from the Pyrenean population visiting not only the great Cantabrican range, but also ranges in the centre of Spain. Nesting elsewhere in Spain has yet to be proved (Heredia & Heredia 1991). Seventy-six pairs, representing 65% of the presently known European population (excluding the Caucasus and the introductions in the Alps), are resident in the Pyrenees, making this the single most important European community. Of that total, in 1994 80% (61 pairs holding territory, 51 of which bred; R. Heredia, in prep) were on Spanish soil. Of the 61 S Pyrenean territories, 21% were occupied by trios made up of 2 males and 1 female. Monitoring of the Spanish Pyrenean population started in 1970, developing into systematic annual monitoring in 1982. Between 1986 and 1994 this population increased by 21bp, a remarkable 52% improvement. The highest breeding density, in the outer Pyrenees, is 1.9 bp/100 km^2, the average across suitable habitat in the entire mountain range being 0.53 bp/100 km^2.

The increase in the Pyrenean population is attributed to a reduction in the causes of mortality and to the availability of an adequate food supply. Here, the main causes of unnatural death are shooting and collisions with, and electrocution by overhead power lines. In the rest of Europe the main reasons for the species' drastic decline are poisoning, shooting, insufficient food supply and habitat disturbance or destruction.

Two subspecies are generally recognized, *G.b. barbatus* of Eurasia and North Africa, and *meridionalis* of East and South Africa. The latter is smaller on average, lacks black ear-feathering and has little plumage on the tarsi.

Rafael Heredia (E)

Neophron percnopterus

Egyptian Vulture

CZ	Sup mrchožravý	I	Capovaccaio
D	Schmutzgeier	NL	Aasgier
E	Alimoche Común	P	Abutre do Egipto
F	Vautour percnoptère	PL	Ścierwnik
FIN	Pikkukorppikotka	R	Стервятник
G	Ασπροπάρης	S	Smutsgam
H	Dögkeselyû		

SPEC Cat 3, Threat status E

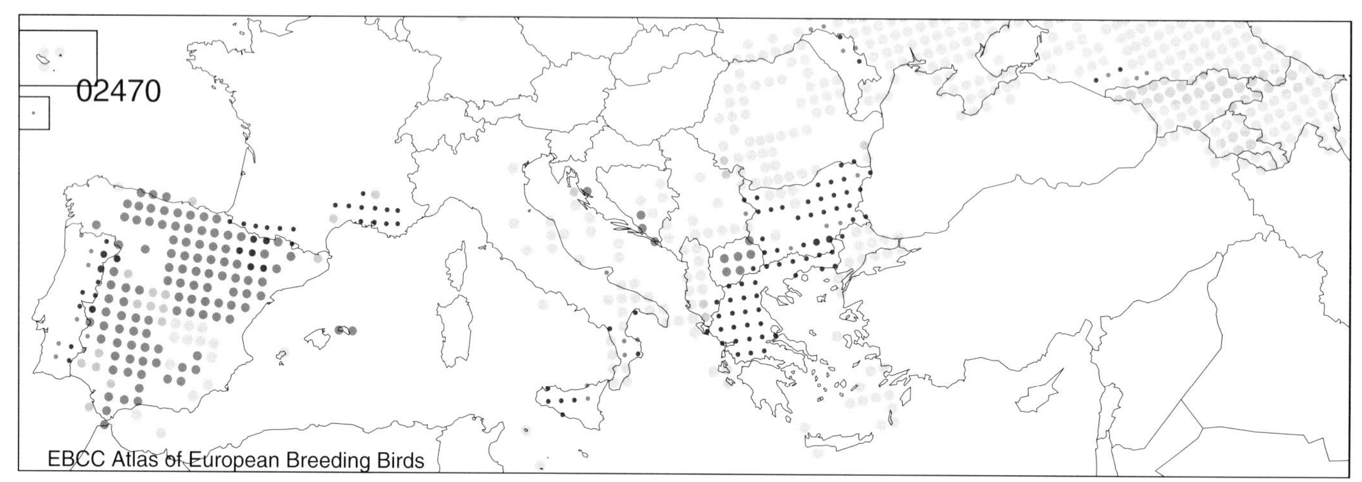

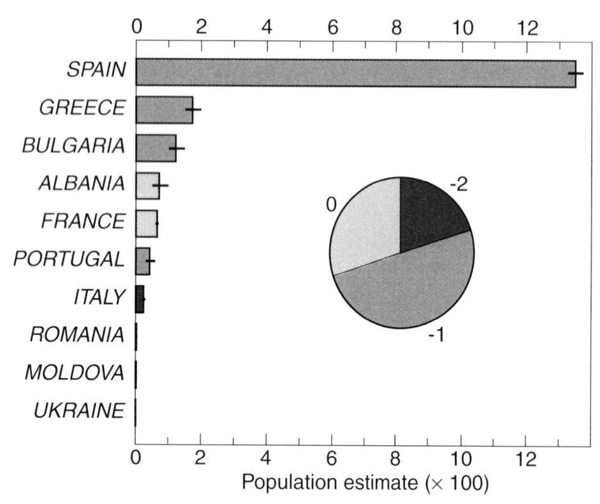

% in top 10 countries: 100.0
Total number of populated European countries: 10
Total European population 1805–1911 (1853)
Russian population 40–60 (49)
Turkish population 1000–5000 (2236)

The range of the Egyptian Vulture stretches from the Mediterranean countries and the Middle East through C Asia to India, and in the S reaches the Sahel and North and East Africa. Most European birds winters in sub-Saharan Africa in a belt between 14° and 17°N. A few winter in Spain (Coto Doñana and Menorca). Transcaucasian birds may winter in S Arabia, C Asian birds in India.

Spain holds the largest population, *c*1400bp. The number in Turkey is uncertain. There are no populations exceeding 200bp in any other European country, but 400–450bp remain in Transcaucasia (1990; 50bp Armenia, 200bp Azerbaijan, 150bp Georgia) and 1500–2000bp in C Asia (Kazakhstan, Turkmenistan, Kirghizstan, Tadzhikistan, Uzbekistan) (A. Abuladze, pers comm to the Editors).

The western European populations are concentrated below 1800m asl, largely in the Mediterranean mountains, but the Caucasus population breeds up to 3000m asl. The highest known breeding density (up to 1 bp/km^2) occurs on Menorca and in the Ebro basin (Donázar *et al* 1989). Under optimal conditions (as in N Spain) the species' distribution is limited only by breeding cliff availability, and not by such habitat's remoteness; the Egyptian Vulture tolerates human presence rather well, breeding close to villages (Donázar *et al* 1989).

Numbers have decreased throughout Europe. Only a few remain in S France, S Italy (including Sicily), Moldova, Romania and the former Yugoslavia (mostly Macedonia; 60bp 1980–86; Grubac 1989). Those in Portugal and the French Pyrenees are an integral part of the Iberian population (Elósegi 1989). Population trends recorded in some Spanish regions since 1985 have been irregular, but tend towards stability (Perea *et al* 1991). The main cause of decline remains human persecution, especially hunting and poisoning, the latter being responsible for the species' disappearance from many Spanish regions (Donázar 1993), Macedonia, Greece, Italy, and probably Turkey (Grubac 1989, Elósegi 1989, R. Hartasánchez, pers comm).

José A Donázar (E)

Gyps fulvus

Griffon Vulture

CZ	Sup bělohlavý	I	Grifone
D	Gänsegeier	NL	Vale Gier
E	Buitre Leonado	P	Grifo-comum
F	Vautour fauve	PL	Sęp płowy
FIN	Hanhikorppikotka	R	Белоголовый сип
G	Όρνιο	S	Gåsgam
H	Fakó keselyû		

SPEC Cat 3, Threat status R

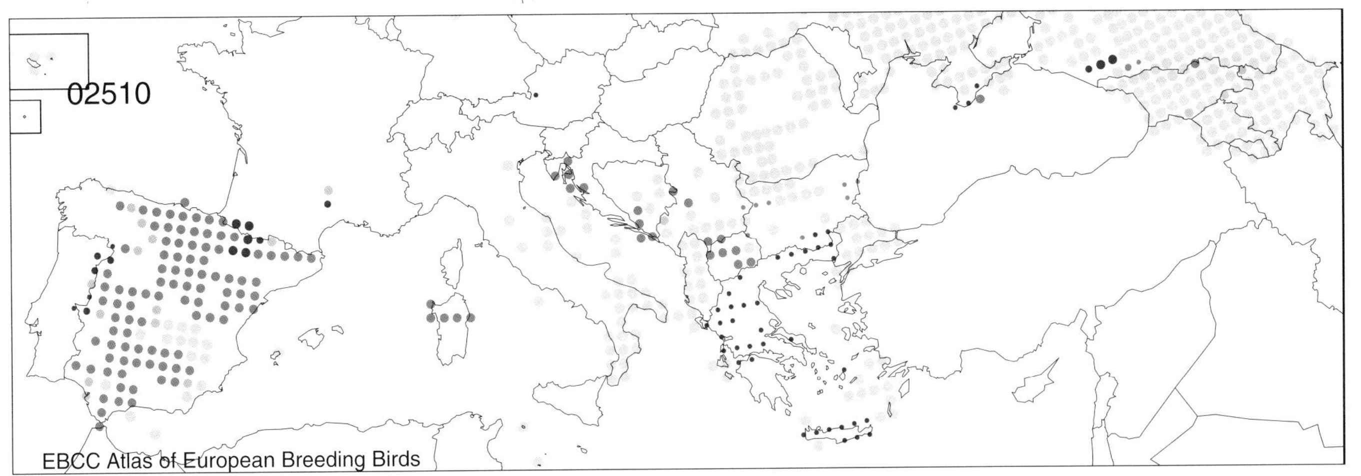

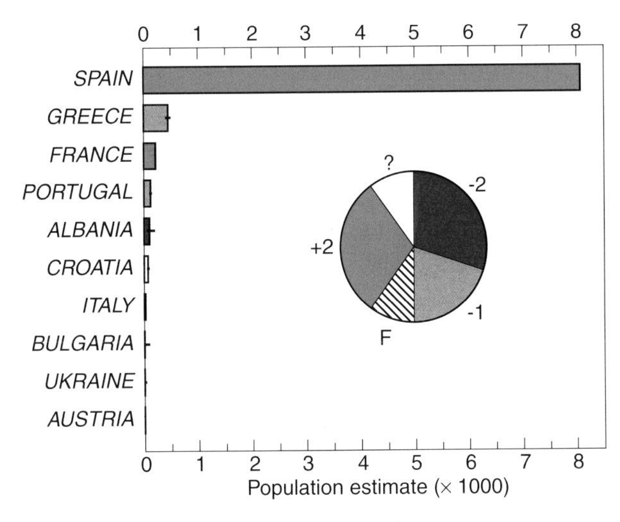

% in top 10 countries: 100.0
Total number of populated European countries: 10
Total European population 8988–9184 (9064)
Russian population 250–350 (296)
Turkish population 100–1000 (316)

The Griffon Vulture is distributed from S Europe to the Maghreb, the Middle East, Arabia and the mountains of C Asia and India. A mainly sedentary species, juveniles and non-breeders disperse to S Spain, Morocco, the Sahel and the Balkans (Bernis 1983, Susic 1994).

Spain holds more than 80% of the European population and Greece *c*450bp. Caucasus numbers are unknown. In the Pyrenees the species prefers mountains, remaining below 1950m asl to breed, but in the Caucasus it breeds up to 2750m asl. The limestone mountains of N and C Spain hold the largest colonies, some larger than 150bp. The Griffon Vulture is scarcer in Atlantic climate (Cantabrian Mountains) or very mountainous regions (the High Pyrenees). In Spain it is quite tolerant of human presence and may breed on a cliff close to habitation if food is availabile (Donázar *et al* 1989, Donázar 1993).

Since the 19th century the species has become extinct in the Carpathians, Dobrudja, Sicily, the southern Alps, over much of the Balkans and parts of Iberia (Elósegi 1989). In Spain two comprehensive counts in 1979 and 1989 revealed an increase from 2761 ± 478 pairs to 7808 ± 279 pairs (Arroyo *et al* 1990b). In parts of N Spain the increase has been apparent since the mid-1970s (Fernández 1994). An identical trend occurs in the French Pyrenees, but in the rest of Europe the trend is negative (Eloségi 1989) and severely so in Turkey (R. Hartasánchez, pers comm). The main causes of decline are hunting and poisoning (Donázar & Fernández 1990). Food availability may be important locally but does not explain population trends since 1965, at least in Spain (Arroyo *et al* 1990b). Recovery may come from widespread food availability and cessation of persecution. Successful reintroduction and restocking conservation projects are running in SE France and C and NE Italy.

José A Donázar (E) Fulvio Genero (I)

This species account is sponsored by Cellulose Beira Industrial, Leirosa, P.

Aegypius monachus　　**Black Vulture**

CZ	Sup hnědý	**I**	Avvoltoio monaco
D	Mönchsgeier	**NL**	Monniksgier
E	Buitre Negro	**P**	Abutre-preto
F	Vautour moine	**PL**	Sęp kasztanowaty
FIN	Munkkikorppikotka	**R**	Черный гриф
G	Μαυρόγυπας	**S**	Grågam
H	Barátkeselyû		

SPEC Cat 3, Threat status V

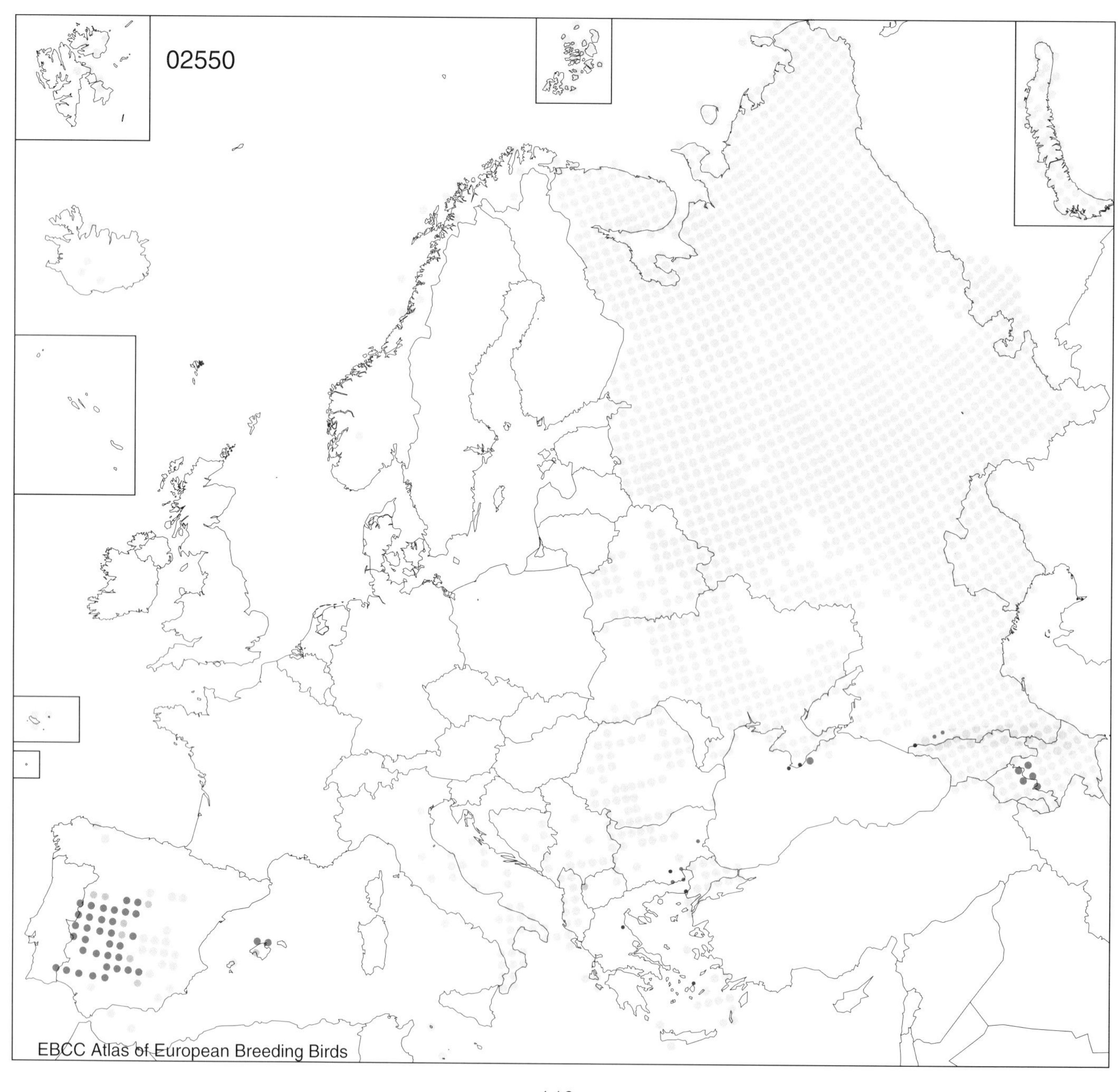

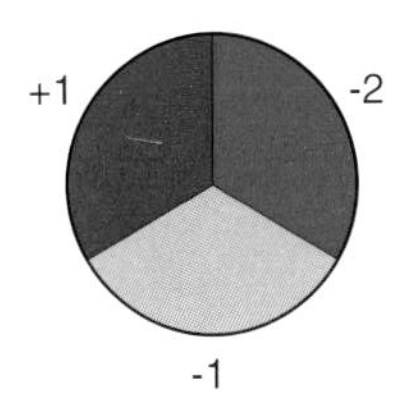

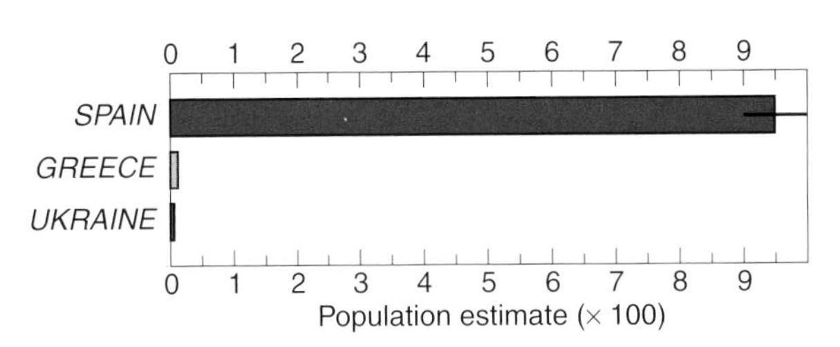

% in top 10 countries: 100.0
Total number of populated European countries: 3
Total European population 918–1018 (967)
Russian population 30–50 (39)
Turkish population 100–500 (224)

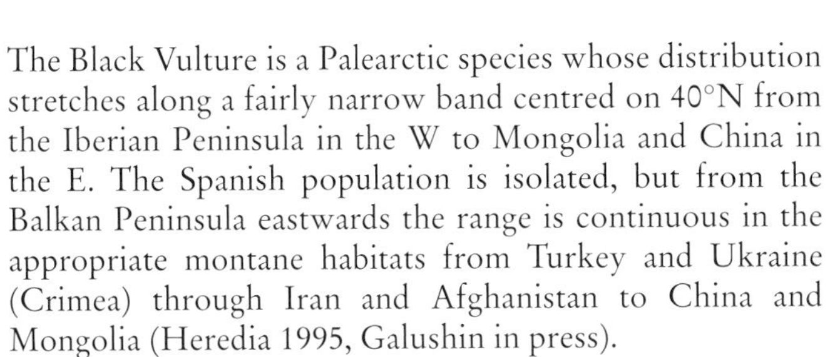

The Black Vulture is a Palearctic species whose distribution stretches along a fairly narrow band centred on 40°N from the Iberian Peninsula in the W to Mongolia and China in the E. The Spanish population is isolated, but from the Balkan Peninsula eastwards the range is continuous in the appropriate montane habitats from Turkey and Ukraine (Crimea) through Iran and Afghanistan to China and Mongolia (Heredia 1995, Galushin in press).

In Europe it breeds in C and SW Spain, Mallorca, eastern Greece (Thrace), Crimea, southern Bulgaria (Rhodopes, possibly also the Strandzha Mountains; Iankov *et al* 1995) and SE Georgia, Armenia and W Azerbaijan (Heredia 1995, Galushin in press). A reintroduction project is under way in France (Cevennes National Park) and another is planned for Sardinia.

Its breeding habitats are mountain forests, such as pine *Pinus* spp, Mediterranean oak *Quercus* spp or juniper *Juniperus* spp, in two different eco-geographical categories, lowland sierras covered by dense Mediterranean maquis (Spain and Greece) and subalpine pine forests (Spain). Occasionally it nests on rocks. It needs slopes to aid take-off, and old mature trees strong enough to carry the huge nest-structure, but it is essential that the habitat be undisturbed. In Europe it breeds from 300 to 1500m asl, such areas normally being bounded by plains where it forages, although it also seeks food in the forest.

The Black Vulture breeds in loose colonies or breeding nuclei, nest-separation distance being from 100m to several kilometres, its distribution following mountain ranges where nest-groups in core areas are concentrated in the more remote, undisturbed and mature valley forests. In expanding populations, if there be adequate adjacent habitat, core areas act as sources from which the species may radiate to occupy new territory; gaps between core areas tend to be filled by either isolated pairs or small groups. In shrinking populations only core areas remain.

Except in Spain the Black Vulture population has declined severely in Europe. It is now extinct in Portugal, France, Italy, Poland, Slovakia, Austria, the former Yugoslavia, Albania, Romania, Moldova and Cyprus (Tewes in press), the main causes being the alteration and destruction of breeding habitat. Persecution and secondary poisoning also played prominent roles. In Spain the reverse has occurred, the population recovering spectacularly from 200bp in 1970 to 1027 in 1994 (Sánchez in press). The key factors were the protection of core breeding areas, the ban on poisoning and an overall improvement in conservation standards and public awareness (González 1990). In Transcaucasia, there are probably 20bp in Georgia, 20bp in Armenia and 40bp and perhaps 50 non-breeders in Azerbaijan (A. Abuladze, pers comm to Editors).

Where suitable habitat exists, the species' distribution pattern is affected mainly by the existence of adequate food resources, and either an extensive livestock economy of sheep, goats, cows and horses or an abundance of wild ungulates (deer, wild boar) or other suitable mammals (rabbit, rodents) (Heredia 1995).

European populations largely are resident, the young dispersing widely. Adults remain all year in the general vicinity of the nest site. Immatures roost separately, some outside the breeding range. In SE Europe small-scale dispersive movements also occur, immatures taking up residency in non-breeding areas. The few birds crossing the Bosphorus in autumn probably are continuing their dispersal rather than migrating.

European Black Vulture conservation policy relies largely on protecting the remaining breeding colonies and banning predator control methods which use poison. The successful Mallorcan reintroduction scheme should be repeated elsewhere in Europe where appropriate ecological conditions still prevail. Although the species does breed in zoos, wild-bred Spanish birds are a proven source of successful reintroductions. Continued careful monitoring throughout the species' range remains essential, but determining the distribution and status of the Turkish, Ukrainian and Caucasus populations is the most immediate requirement.

Borja Heredia (E)

Circaetus gallicus — Short-toed Eagle

CZ	Orlík krátkoprstý	**I**	Biancone
D	Schlangenadler	**NL**	Slangearend
E	Culebrera Europea	**P**	Águia-cobreira
F	Circaète Jean-le-Blanc	**PL**	Gadożer
FIN	Käärmekotka	**R**	Змееяд
G	Φιδαετός	**S**	Ormörn
H	Kigyászölyv		

SPEC Cat 3, Threat status R

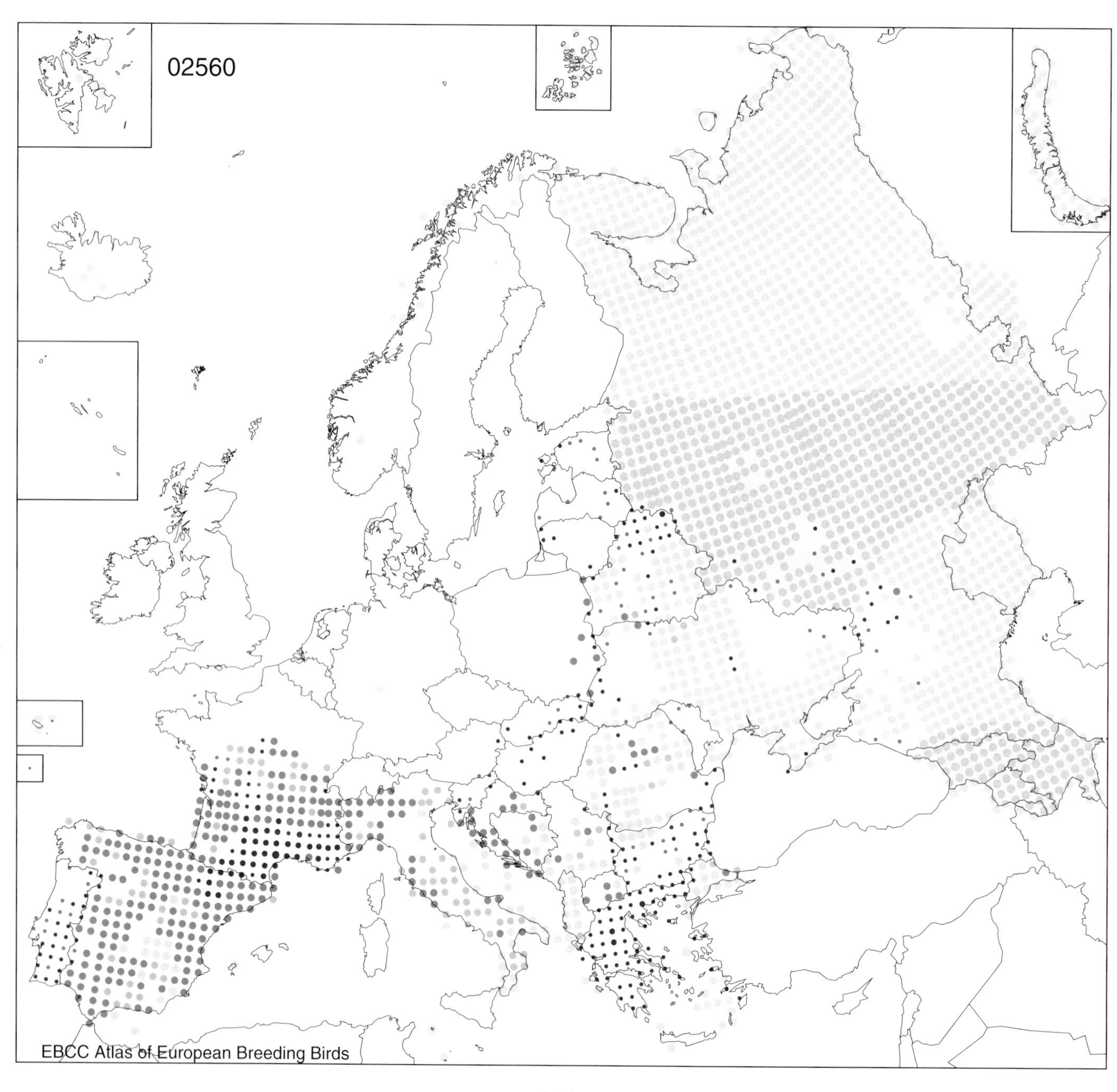

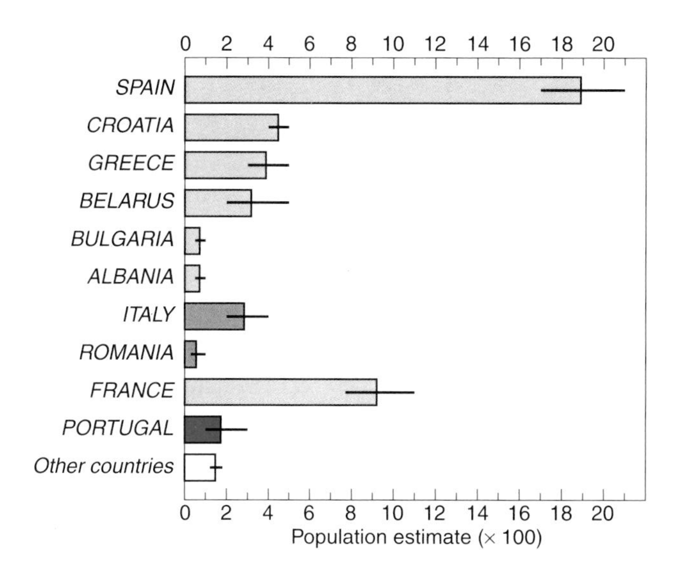

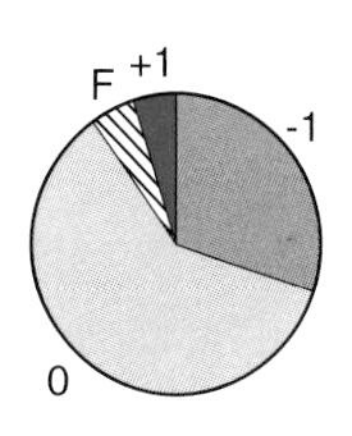

% in top 10 countries: 96.9
Total number of populated European countries: 20
Total European population 4450–5159 (4760)
Russian population 1000–3000 (1732)
Turkish population 1000–5000 (2236)

The breeding range of the Short-toed Eagle covers much of S and E Europe, NE Africa, the Caucasus, the Middle East, C Asia and SW Siberia. Its principal wintering grounds lie in the *Acacia* savannas S of the Sahara, only small numbers remaining in southern Europe and North Africa.

A warm climate and low rainfall (especially when there are nestlings) are typical of breeding habitats and favour an abundance of reptiles, which comprise the species' principal diet. Snakes are especially favoured. The Short-toed Eagle therefore prefers warm, open habitats where such prey abounds. For breeding it requires plains and hills (up to 2000m asl) interspersed with mature woodlands, and although it may nest in isolated trees, its preferred habitats in S Europe are broad-leaved and coniferous woodlands possessing ample open and semi-open foraging areas (Petretti 1988). Its hunting grounds comprise sclerophytic shrubland, rocky areas, stony and sandy pastures, fallow and uncultivated fields and arable land margins (Amores & Franco 1981). In eastern Europe it inhabits steppe areas, sometimes containing forests. In the N of its eastern range it prefers pine forests containing small open wetlands, but in the S chooses mainly patchy broad-leaved forests on ravine slopes. In Belarus the split was 79% of nests in pine bogs and 21% in dry pine forests interspersed with clearfells and wetlands (Ivanowsky 1992).

Densities in prime habitat varied between 2 bp/km^2 in the Tyrrhenian Hills in Italy (Petretti 1988) and 15.7 bp/km^2 in NE Greece (Vlachos & Papageorgiou 1994). The minimum distance between active nests in Belarus was 6km (Ivanowsky 1992).

Quantitative censuses are scarce and of varying quality. Recent conservative estimates suggest a population of 3000bp in Russia (V. Belik, E. Korshunova & Y. Pukinsky, pers comm), but comprehensive surveys of hitherto poorly studied areas are badly needed. Likewise, the flourishing population in Belarus may approach 500bp (Ivanowsky 1992). SE European countries surpassing 100bp are Croatia (400–500bp) and Greece (300–500bp). The above populations are considered stable, apart from some range contraction at the northern limit. The trend in Turkey (numbers roughly estimated at 1000–5000bp) is probably stable. Much smaller numbers exist in most other E European countries where declining population and range trends are common, as in Ukraine, Romania, Poland, Lithuania and Moldova.

The SW European population core lies in Spain (1700–2100bp) and France (770–1100bp), smaller numbers occurring in Portugal (100–300bp) and Italy (380–415bp, Petretti 1988). These populations are mostly stable, except for Portugal (locally increasing) and Italy (decreasing). The apparent occurrence mapped for the Balearics may represent long-staying spring migrants, because the species no longer breeds on any Mediterranean island.

The Short-toed Eagle suffered a marked decline and range contraction from the 19th century onwards. It no longer breeds in countries in N and C western Europe. Vicissitudes suffered by local populations largely depend on land use, declines being noted after introduction of intensive agriculture and forestry and increases where farmland is laid fallow (Barbraud & Barbraud 1994). The near-complete disappearance of traditional cattle-grazing has been particularly detrimental. The increasing human population, with habitat fragmentation and persecution as side-effects, also had a negative impact, as has all-too-frequent electrocution on power lines.

Being a broad-winged soaring raptor, the Short-toed Eagle travels on its migration S by the shortest possible sea-crossing, via Israel and Egypt in the E and Gibraltar and environs in the W. Maximum counts respectively have been 12 000+ and 4000–8800 birds (Bijlsma 1987b), figures which are reasonably consistent with the estimated European population size of 5000–7500bp, given an average fledgling production of 0.3–0.7/pair in France (Barbraud & Barbraud 1994), 0.75/pair in C Italy (Petretti 1988) and 0.9/pair in NE Greece (Vlachos & Papageorgiou 1994) and given the methodological difficulties of counting raptor migration.

Vladimir Ivanowsky (BELA) Nuno Onofre (P)
Gérard Rocamora (F)

Circus aeruginosus **Marsh Harrier**

CZ	Moták pochop	**I**	Falco di palude
D	Rohrweihe	**NL**	Bruine Kiekendief
E	Aguilucho Lagunero Occidental	**P**	Tartaranhão-ruivo-dos-paúis
F	Busard des roseaux	**PL**	Błotniak stawowy
FIN	Ruskosuohaukka	**R**	Болотный лунь
G	Καλαμόκιρκος	**S**	Brun kärrhök
H	Barna rétihéja		

Non-SPEC, Threat status S

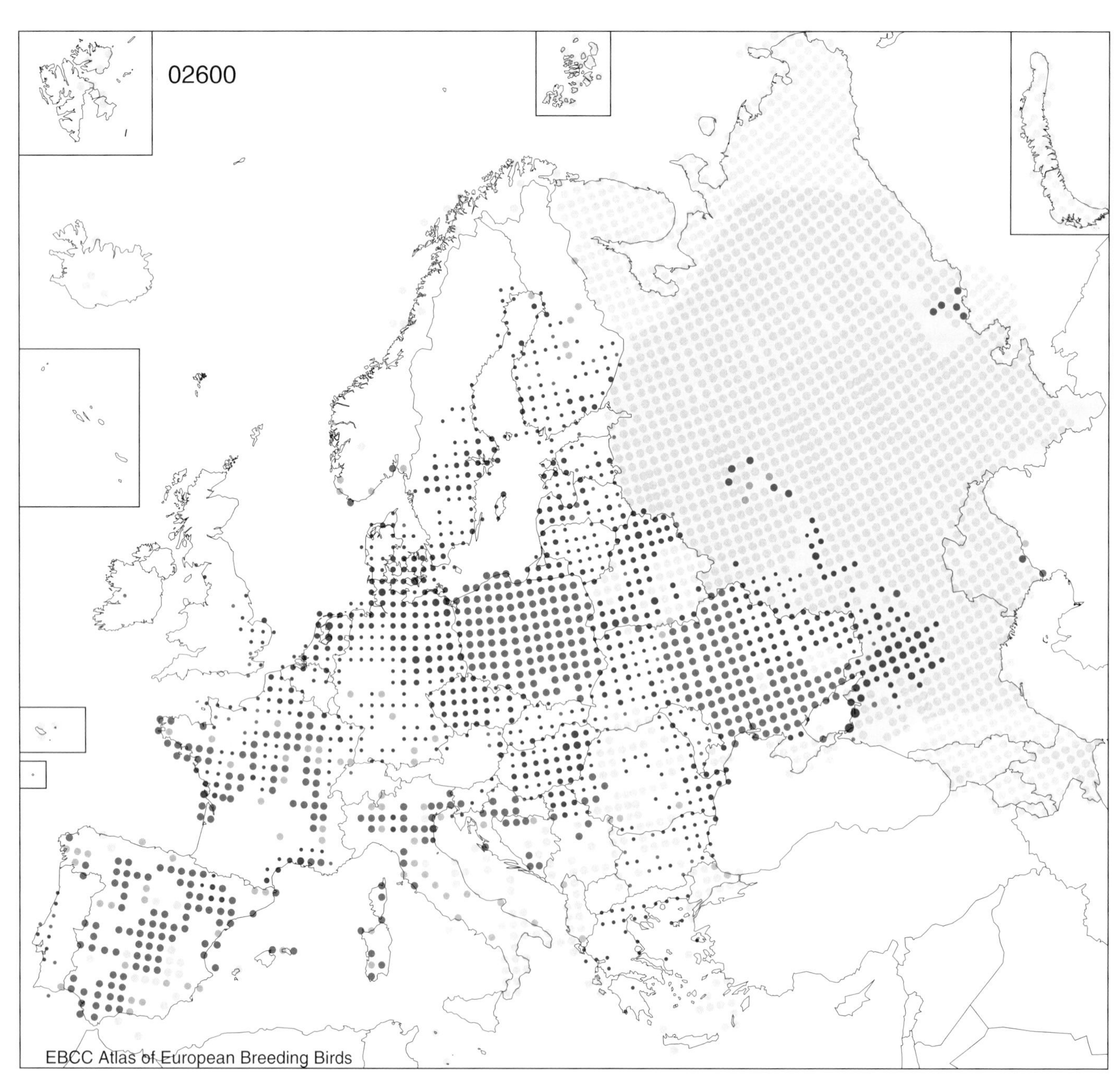

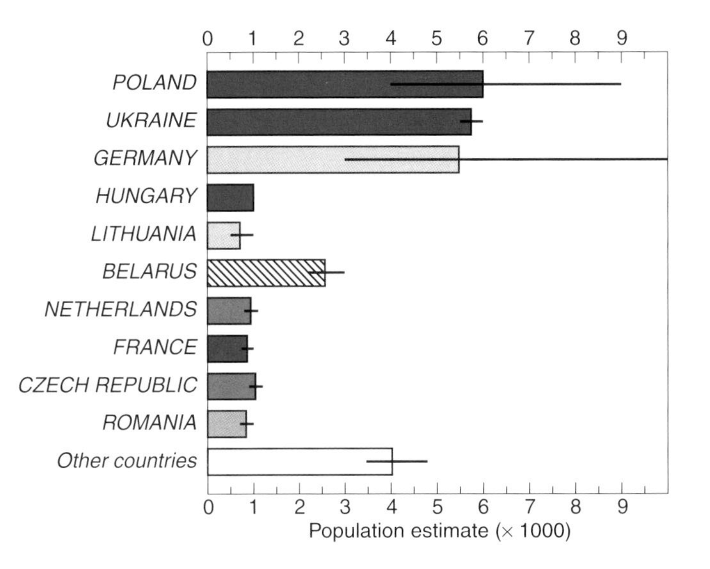

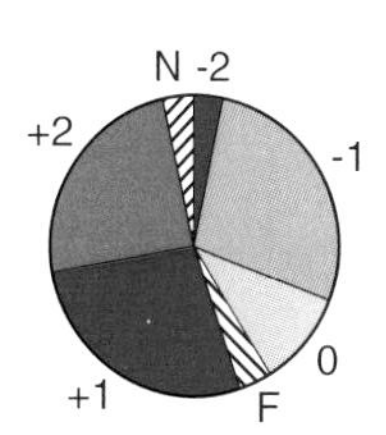

% in top 10 countries: 86.2
Total number of populated European countries: 29
Total European population 25,955–34,675 (29,197)
Russian population 25,000–40,000 (31,623)
Turkish population 500–5000 (1581)

The Marsh Harrier, the largest of the European harriers, has a wide distribution, the nominate subspecies *C.a. aeruginosus* occurring in the lowlands of Europe and Asia, others in northern Africa, in the Indian Ocean and in the Australasian and Pacific regions. Some authorities support full specific status for at least two of the latter subspecies.

In Europe, the Marsh Harrier breeds up to 55°N in the W of its range, whereas in the E, it reaches the Arctic Circle. It employs a wide variety of migratory strategies, from the wholly migratory of the northern and eastern populations which winter mostly in West and East Africa (some further S) to the sedentary of the southern populations, especially in western Europe and the Caucasus.

The Marsh Harrier prefers open wetlands with an abundant dense and high herbaceous vegetation, from sea level up to 400m asl, but reaches 2000m asl in C Asia. Avoiding hilly and forested terrain, it favours equally fresh and brackish waters, being found at marshes, ponds, lakes, lagoons and riverbanks of substantial watercourses. Locally, it has adapted to drier habitats and may breed in hedges and even in fields. It usually builds its nest on the ground or at water level, hidden in the vegetation. Occasionally it nests in shrubs and exceptionally in trees. In W-C France a study of 920 nests (C. Bavoux, pers obs) showed that 506 were in reed *Phragmites australis*, 112 in reedmace *Typha* spp and 101 in clubrush *Scirpus* spp.

The largest numbers are found E and C Europe, mostly in Russia, Poland and Ukraine which share a total of 34 500–55 000bp. The southern climatic zones are much less densely populated; Portugal, Italy and Greece now hold a total population of only a few hundred breeding pairs. After a long period of persecution, numbers have increased since the 1970s in 16 of the 31 countries with quantitative information, particularly in the Baltic States, Fennoscandia, Denmark, The Netherlands and Great Britain. In The Netherlands, the population of 1370–1410bp in 1991-92 (Bijlsma 1993) was more than double that of the early 1970s. In the same timespan, the Danish population increased from <100bp in 1970 to 610bp in 1987 (Jørgensen 1989) and in Britain the annual yearly increase averaged 19.6% between 1970 and 1991 (Underhill-Day 1993). In contrast, in the S of its European range, the species is generally decreasing, Spain having lost several hundred breeding pairs since 1974.

The population increases occurred mainly through several factors whose impact varied considerably in time and place. Most important was the stepwise banning of persistent pesticides, particularly DDT (Witkowski 1989), allowing populations in N, E and W Europe to recuperate, a process enhanced in The Netherlands by the reclamation of parts of the IJsselmeer; huge reedbeds developed in the newly created polders, providing optimal breeding and feeding conditions (Bijlsma 1993). At the same time, hunting pressure was significantly reduced in S Europe (McCulloch *et al* 1992). Present threats are habitat destruction (wetlands in E Europe), natural drying out of wetlands (which caused a catastrophic decline in Spain) and lead poisoning in France (and probably elsewhere in S Europe) through ingestion of gunshot imbedded in shot waterfowl and mammals (Pain *et al* 1993). The population dynamics of local populations are complicated. One study, of the sedentary population in W-C France (Île d'Oleron), began in 1982 and revealed a rapid population increase in the late 1980s (22% annually), possibly (because of a similar increase in wintering numbers) as a result of recruitment from other areas. A rapid decrease then occurred, followed by a period of stability. No local factors influencing this process have been identified so far (Bavoux *et al* 1989).

Christian Bavoux (F) Guy Burneleau (F)
Pierre Nicolau-Guillaumet (F)

This species account is sponsored by Büro für Landschaftsplanung, B. Böhling, Bedburg-Hau, D.

Circus cyaneus

Hen Harrier

CZ	Moták pilich	**I**	Albanella reale
D	Kornweihe	**NL**	Blauwe Kiekendief
E	Aguilucho Pálido	**P**	Tartaranhão-azulado
F	Busard Saint-Martin	**PL**	Błotniak zbożowy
FIN	Sinisuohaukka	**R**	Полевой лунь
G	Βαλτόκιρκος	**S**	Blå kärrhök
H	Kékes rétihéja		

SPEC Cat 3, Threat status V

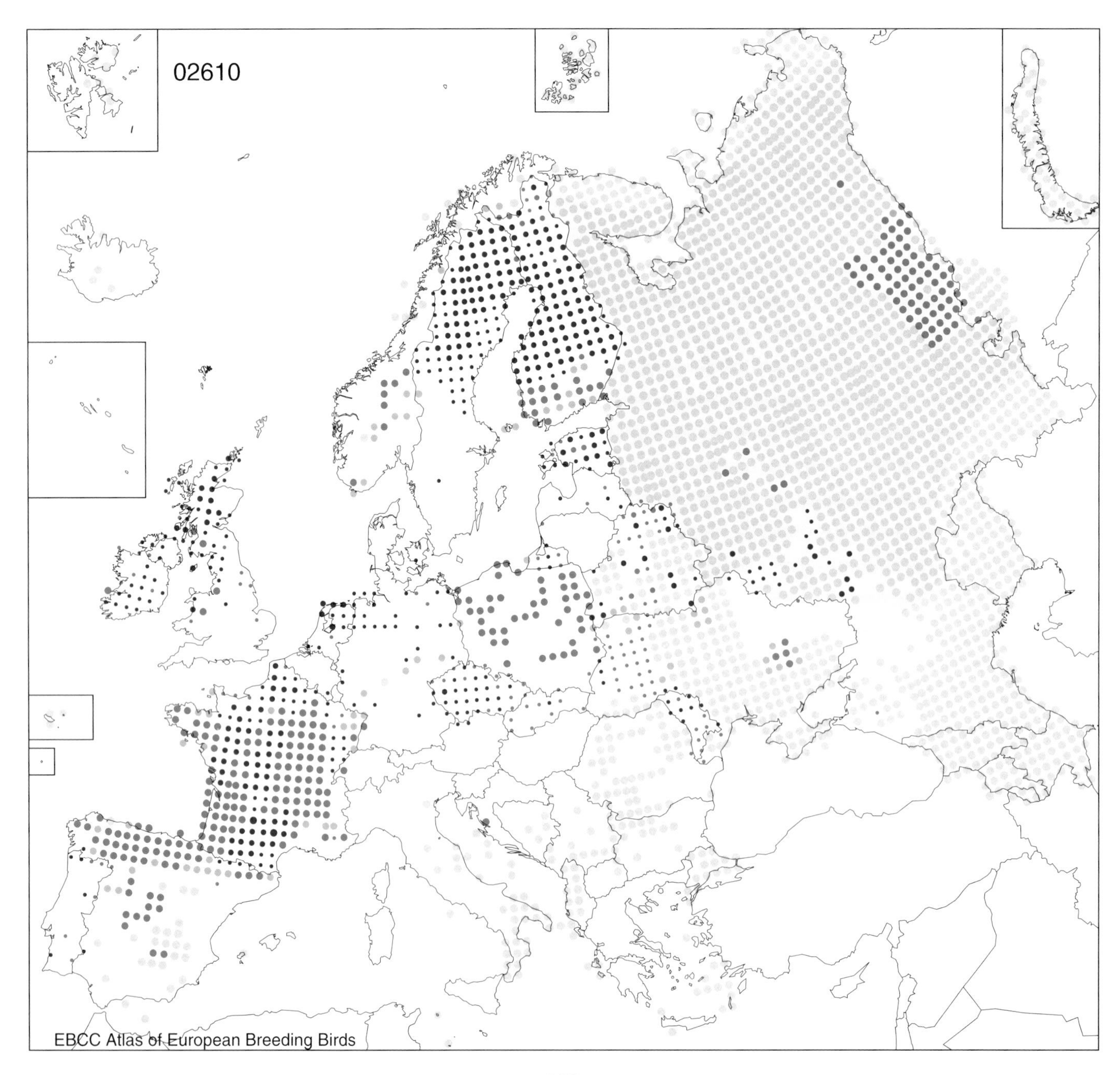

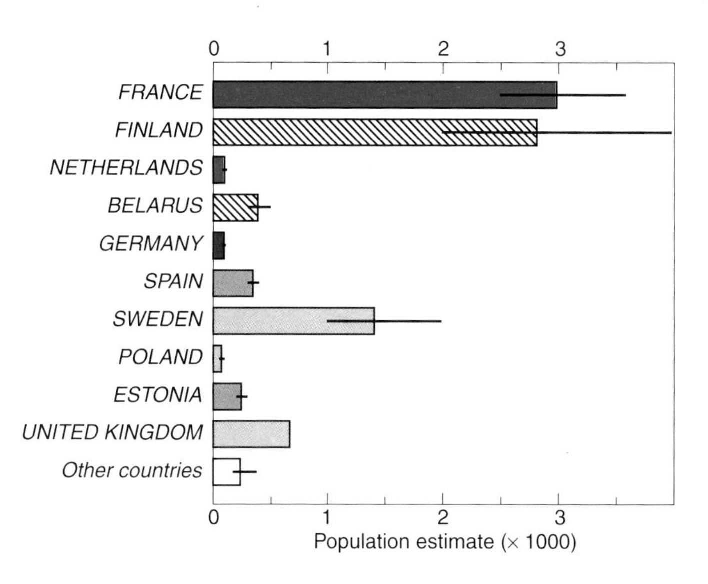

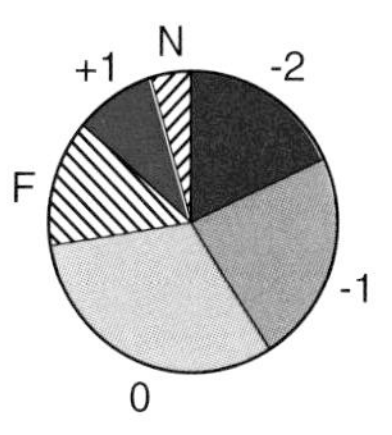

% in top 10 countries: 97.5
Total number of populated European countries: 22
Total European population 8332–10,840 (9391)
Russian population 15,000–20,000 (17,321)

The extensive breeding range of the nominate subspecies of the Hen Harrier *C.c. cyaneus* stretches from the Republic of Ireland in western Europe E to Kamchatka and Sakhalin in Siberia. In Europe it is absent as a breeding bird from the Balkans, Italy, Switzerland and Austria. The other subspecies *hudsonius* is confined to North America.

The Hen Harrier nests in a variety of open habitats containing low vegetation. Examples are fen, steppe, heath, sand-dune with scrub, overgrown marshes, forest clearings, plantations of young trees and arable farmland. Populations in N and NE Europe are migratory and they winter mainly in W and S Europe. Elsewhere in Europe the species is sedentary or partially migratory.

In Europe breeding populations in excess of 1000bp are known from Sweden, Finland, Russia and France. Of the other countries only Great Britain, Belarus, Spain and Estonia have populations of more than 200bp. In Belgium, Luxembourg and Denmark this raptor breeds only irregularly. Its distribution pattern is uniform over large parts of France, N Spain, Sweden and Finland, where the species is mapped in most squares. In C and eastern Europe, its distribution is much less regular.

Hen Harrier breeding densities generally are low, in western Finland and Scotland reaching 5–10 bp/100km^2 (Koskimies 1989a, Bibby & Etheridge 1993) but on the Dutch Wadden Islands, varying in size from 3300 to 18 400ha, up to 40 bp/100km^2 bred in the early 1990s (Bekhuis & Zijlstra 1991).

Recent population trends are downward in many European countries, including core areas like Russia, Spain and Estonia. Severe decreases of more than 50% are reported from Germany, Portugal, Latvia and Ukraine. In Portugal, Latvia and Ukraine numbers are currently small (fewer than 20bp) and there the species may become extinct. In Finland and Sweden, marked fluctuations in line with vole abundance (the vole is the main prey item in Fennoscandia) are characteristic.

The reasons for the downward trends reported from many countries are not completely clear. However, habitat destruction or deterioration (draining of marshes, maturation of afforested uplands, intensified farmland use) are main factors, as is increased persecution locally (Bibby & Etheridge 1993). In most countries, the decrease in numbers has been paralleled by important losses in breeding range. This contrasts with recent findings in France, where the species has extended its range in the N and NW of the country (Cormier 1994).

A long-term increase has been occurring in The Netherlands, from fewer than 20bp prior to 1950 to about 100bp in 1990. Formerly restricted to the mainland, nearly all breeding pairs are nowadays located on the Wadden Sea islands (first breeding in 1940). The increase was probably triggered by an improvement of the nesting habitat after grazing was reduced (Bekhuis & Zijlstra 1991).

In Great Britain a period of strong decline, caused by persecution, led to the extinction of the Hen Harrier on the mainland by 1900. Up to the 1930s it was confined to Orkney and the Outer Hebrides. Favoured by extensive afforestation in upland areas during the period 1940–70, the population increased rapidly, recolonizing much of the ground lost on the mainland. The expansion has continued in areas not subject to game preservation, but on many grouse moors numbers have declined. In this habitat, illegal persecution is an important limiting factor, as shown by differences in nesting success on grouse moors (23%) compared to other heather moorland (72%) and young conifer plantations (55%) (Etheridge & Summers in press). Long-term changes in Hen Harrier abundance have also occurred in Scandinavia. The small Norwegian population has increased throughout the 20th century, whilst in Finland an increase was recorded in 1940–70 (Saurola 1985). In the southern part of Sweden, however, the species has become scarcer.

Brian Etheridge (GB) Fred Hustings (NL)

This species account is sponsored by North West Water Properties Ltd, Warrington, GB.

Circus pygargus Montagu's Harrier

CZ	Moták lužní	I	Albanella minore
D	Wiesenweihe	NL	Grauwe Kiekendief
E	Aguilucho Cenizo	P	Tartaranhão-caçador
F	Busard cendré	PL	Błotniak łąkowy
FIN	Niittysuohaukka	R	Луговой лунь
G	Λιβαδόκιρκος	S	Ängshök
H	Hamvas rétihéja		

SPEC Cat 4, Threat status S

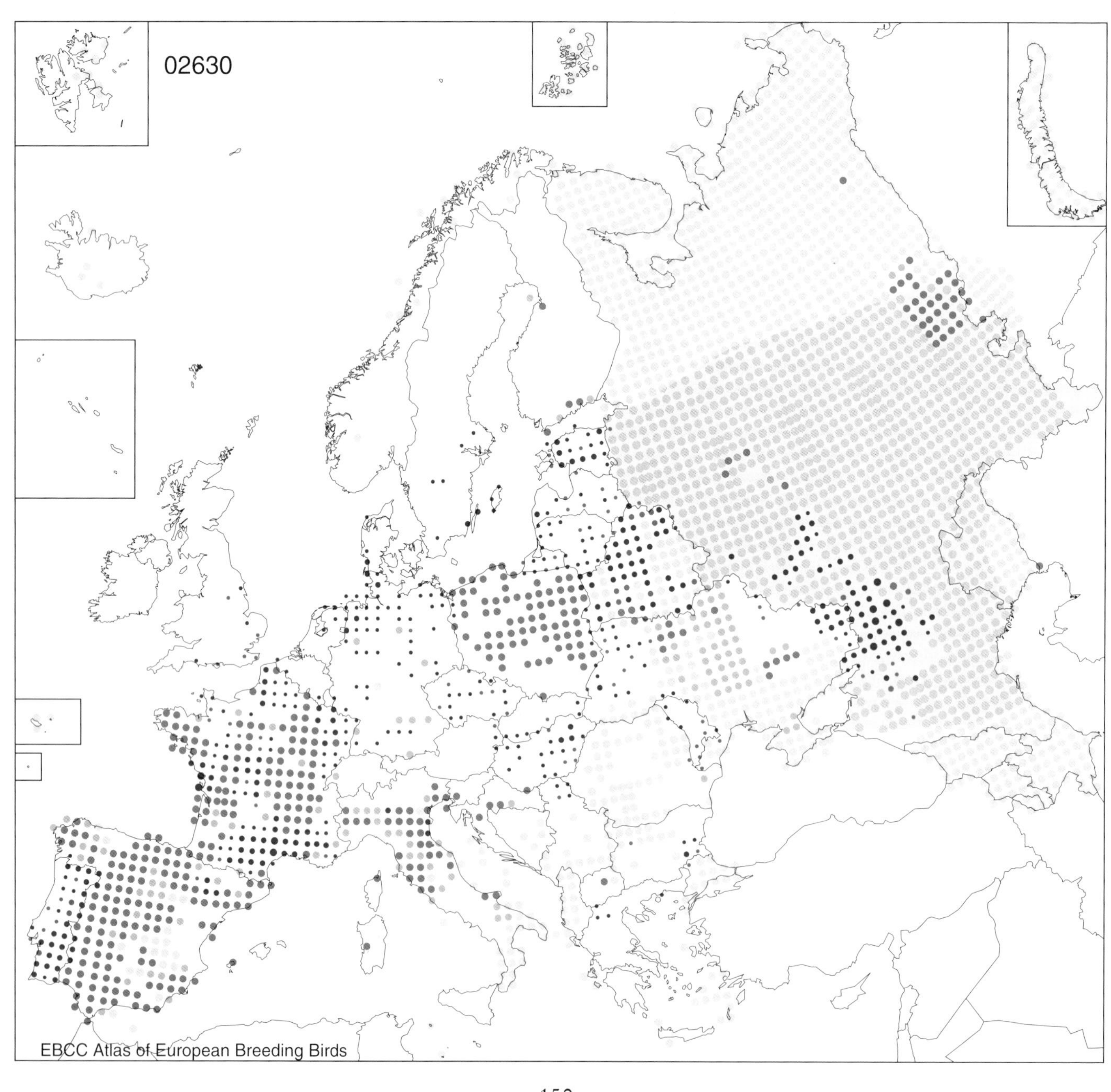

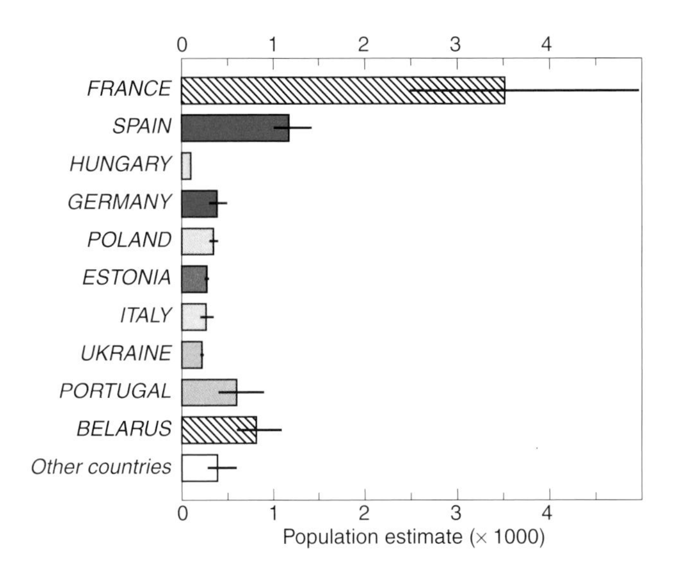

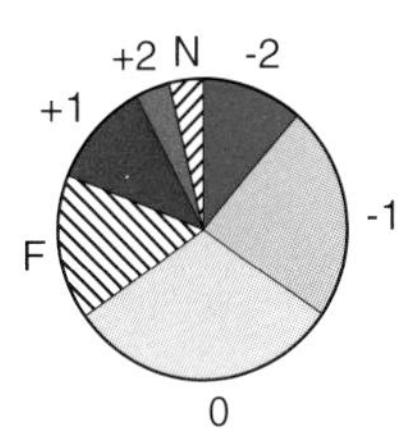

% in top 10 countries: 95.2
Total number of populated European countries: 26
Total European population 6976–9610 (8069)
Russian population 20,000–30,000 (24,495)
Turkish population 200–1000 (447)

The breeding distribution of Montagu's Harrier, a Palearctic species, covers the temperate, continental and steppe climate zones, from western Europe to C Siberia (*c*95°E). Its northern range limit touches the boreal zone at 61°N in S Fennoscandia and extends southwards into the mediterranean zone, including NW Africa. Western European populations winter in sub-Saharan Africa, mostly between 6° and 17°N, whereas those from N and E Europe winter mainly in Sudan, Ethiopia and East Africa.

Prime habitat for Montagu's Harrier once comprised steppes in the S and marshes in the N, but during the 20th century it has adapted to many habitat types such as fallow fields, saltmarshes, scrubby dunes, young conifer plantations and gorse-covered heaths. Since the mid-1970s in its Iberian stronghold, farmland (mostly cereals) has become the major breeding habitat, holding *c*95% of the Spanish (Ferrero 1993), and the majority of the Portuguese population (N. Onofre & R. Rufino, pers comm). In Great Britain, France, and through Germany to E Poland and Slovakia, Montagu's Harrier increasingly is breeding in cereal crops.

Where optimal habitat remains widespread, Montagu's Harrier tends to form breeding associations or semi-colonies. The densest known clusters were recorded in marshes in France (28bp on 22ha) and Poland (22bp on 210ha). In some years, the density on Marais de l'Ouest reached 2.7–4.3 bp/10km^2 and on the Polish Chelm Marshes 1.0–1.3 bp/10km^2 (Krogulec & Leroux 1994). Breeding density depends on the presence of optimal habitat but is even more strongly linked to prey availability on the hunting grounds.

The European population comprises 260 000–416 000bp, of which 75% occurs in Russia and 15% in Iberia and France. Overall, numbers and range have declined, in some cases even by >50% during 1970–90. In Spain the 6000bp of the early 1970s fell to 3300–3900bp in the early 1990s (Ferrero 1993), though probably not as low as the figure in the European Bird Database. In Germany, the population declined markedly to 230bp in 1992–93, especially in Brandenburg and Mecklenburg-Vorpommern, but stable or slightly increasing numbers have occurred in Schleswig-Holstein and Nordrhein-Westfalen since the mid-1970s (Kostrzewa & Speer 1995). The Dutch population suffered a catastrophic decline from 500–1000bp in 1900–30 to 250bp in 1950 and <10bp in the late 1980s (Zijlstra & Hustings 1992). Since then, a small recovery to 29–32bp took place in 1990–95 (B. Koks, pers comm to the Editors). The Danish population decreased from 350–400bp in 1940 to 35–54bp in 1976–87 (Jørgensen 1989). Portugal now holds only *c*400–900bp. Steadily decreasing populations featured in Britain (30bp in mid-1950s, extinct in 1974, 12bp in 1990), Lithuania (30bp), Latvia (50–150bp) and Ukraine (200–240bp).

Fluctuations, with declines in some regions and positive developments in others, have been noted since the mid-1970s both in countries with large populations, like France where a recent census revealed 2500–3500bp, and Belarus (600–1100bp), as well as those with small populations, like Slovakia (30–50bp). Increases in the late 20th century may imply a recovery from earlier losses (Poland, Hungary, Britain and The Netherlands), better coverage during recent surveys (France, and probably Russia) or a real increase, as in Estonia (20–30bp in 1900–30, 50–70bp in 1960s, 100–200bp in early 1990s; Leibak *et al* 1994), Finland and Sweden (colonized in the 20th century). Large-scale habitat destruction, and since the 1940s and 1950s widespread use of persistent pesticides over vast areas of Europe (including Russia) have caused the overall negative trend, as illustrated in The Netherlands, where the 600 000ha of prime habitat of the 1900s shrank to only 140 000ha of impoverished heaths by 1990, whilst food supply in nearby farmland had crashed (Zijlstra & Hustings 1992), a trend common to much of Europe. The change to farmland breeding probably is an adaptation to the loss of prime habitat, but without protective measures, reproductive output will remain low in such habitat (Nicklaus *et al* 1994).

Jarosław Krogulec (PL)

This species account is sponsored by Dansk Ornitologisk Forening, DK.

Circus macrourus

Pallid Harrier

CZ	Moták stepní	I	Albanella pallida
D	Steppenweihe	NL	Steppekiekendief
E	Aguilucho Papialbo	P	Tartaranhão-de-peito-branco
F	Busard pâle	PL	Błotniak stepowy
FIN	Arosuohaukka	R	Степной лунь
G	Στεπόκιρκος	S	Stäpphök
H	Fakó rétihéja		

SPEC Cat 3, Threat status E

The Pallid Harrier is distributed widely across steppes and semi-deserts from SE Europe to Lake Baykal. It is scarce in the steppe-forest zone, further W breeding sporadically. Its western range limit reaches Moldova, Ukraine and the Pripyat River (Belarus), the northern reaches the Moscow region, the southern runs along the Black Sea coastal belt to northern Transcaucasia and NW Iran, and the eastern extends to Sverdlovsk, Kazakhstan, the Altai and Mongolia.

The species usually inhabits drier and more open landscapes than Montagu's Harrier *C. pygargus*, preferring to breed in dry steppe uncultivated grasslands, mostly on the plains, but nests above 1000m asl in the Caucasus, the Altai and C Asia. It also occupies river valleys, agricultural areas, dry hills and plains scattered with blackthorn *Prunus spinosa* bushes (Zubarovsky 1977). In the C Siberian pre-Urals, it occupies primarily mesophyllic habitats, such as steppe brushwood, low-lying marshland and water-meadows, where densities average 2.2–6.2 bp/100km^2, but elsewhere values are much lower (Davygora & Belik 1994). In NE Ukraine it has nested in small steppe remnants and maize fields (V.T. Afanasjevś, pers comm) at *c*1–2 bp/300km^2 of suitable habitat, which intensive farming of virgin steppe has made scarce, incidentally also virtually eliminating the suslik *Citellus* spp, a main prey for many raptors.

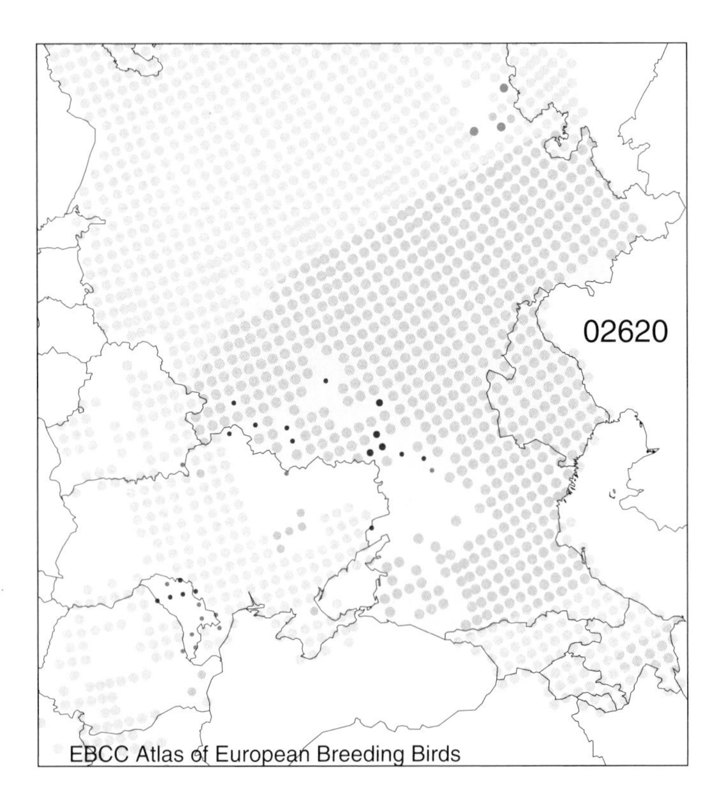

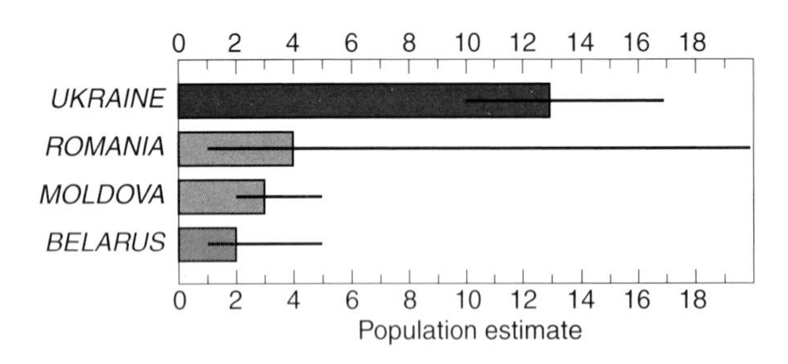

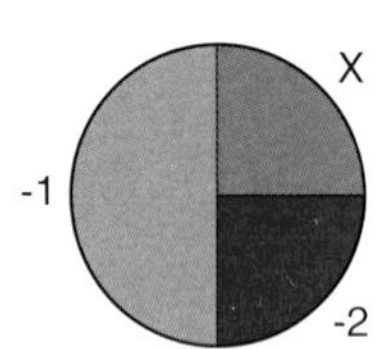

% in top 10 countries: 100.0
Total number of populated European countries: 4
Total European population 18–394 (23)
Russian population 1000–2000 (1414)

Very few breeding pairs remain in Ukraine, Moldova, Belarus and Romania; its status in Dobrudja needs clarification. At best the European Russian population may comprise 2000bp (*c*10% of the world population). Since the early 1900s the species has declined considerably, its European range now fragmented through changing land use and deteriorating food supplies. It has disappeared as a regular breeder from Sweden, Germany and the Baltic States (Hadasch 1994). Smaller, but significant negative trends have ensued in the range core in C Asia, following drainage schemes and overgrazing. However, the species is also spreading S to inhabit reedbeds by artesian wells in deserts N and E of the Caspian Sea (Davygora & Belik 1994).

The Pallid Harrier winters in SE Asia, Iran, India, and in Africa where it occupies most habitats S of the Sahara except tropical rainforest. A few may remain in the breeding grounds, in the Balkans, S Ukraine (Ivanov 1976), NW Caucasus (Averin 1938), the lower Volga region (Vorobyev 1931) and even the Aral-Caspian steppes (Bostanzhoglo 1911).

Contributions combined from Valentin V Serebryakov (UKR) Igor Gorban (UKR)

Elanus caeruleus

Black-winged Kite

CZ	Luněc šedý	I	Nibbio bianco
D	Gleitaar	NL	Grijze Wouw
E	Elanio Común	P	Peneireiro-cinzento
F	Élanion blanc	PL	Kaniuk
FIN	Liitohaukka	R	Дымчатый коршун
G	Ελανος	S	Svartvingad glada
H	Kuhi		

SPEC Cat 3, Threat status V

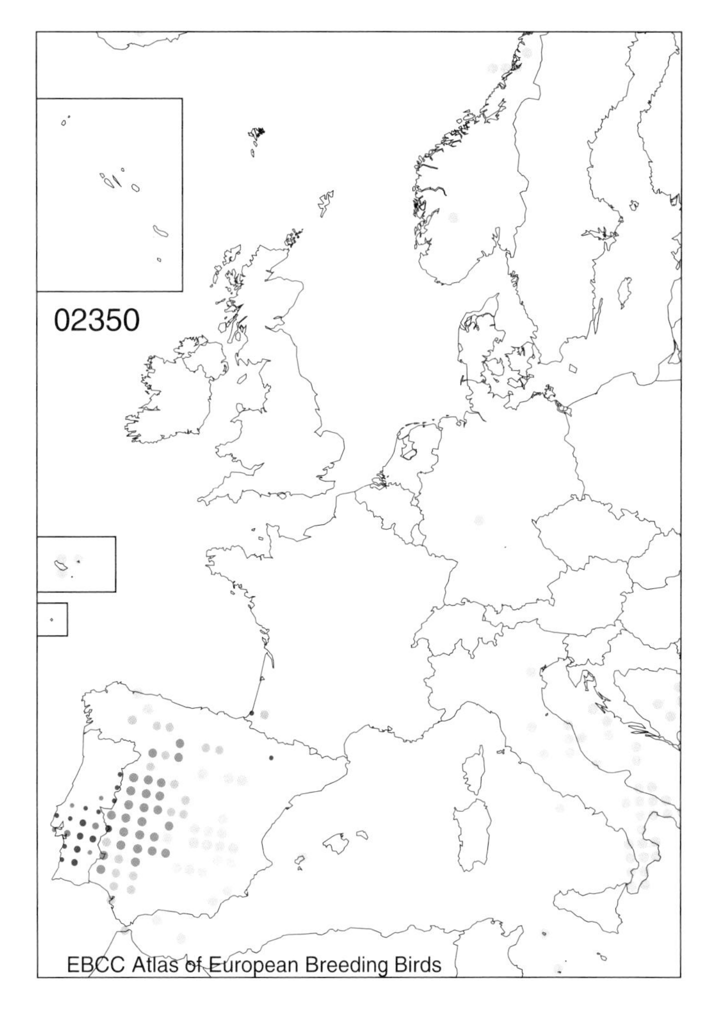

The Black-winged Kite has a discontinuous distribution throughout the Old World, and in Europe it occurs only in the extreme SW. It breeds locally in NW and NE Africa and is widespread elsewhere on that continent, especially in the E below the Equator. Other populations occur in the Indian subcontinent and SE Asia.

The European population breeds chiefly in open evergreen oak woodland, in association with low intensity cereal farming and pasture, the 'dehesas' or 'montados', where it can be locally common. In the areas recently colonized, in the northwestern and northern parts of its range, it occurs also in open deciduous oak woodland and in mosaic habitats of small pine woods, cereal fields and pasture. It is a tree-nesting species, occupying mostly lowland areas but it can be found at medium altitude plateaus, *c*800m asl. In any habitat, it clearly prefers flat landscapes.

The Black-winged Kite has expanded its range within Iberia and reached SW France recently (Guyot 1990). This range expansion has allowed the breeding population to increase overall, unaccompanied by any increase within its former range. These consequences result from the clearing of oak woodland in Spain during the 1950s and 1960s (Carbajo Molinero & Ferrero Cantisán 1985) and from the removal of understorey of the remnant evergreen oak woodland in Portugal and Spain (Palma 1985). As with other species which are expanding their range northwards, climatic factors may also be involved, but more information is required to prove any links.

In recent years it has lost breeding habitat due to the intensification of agriculture. A further decrease can be expected following the introduction of set-aside land.

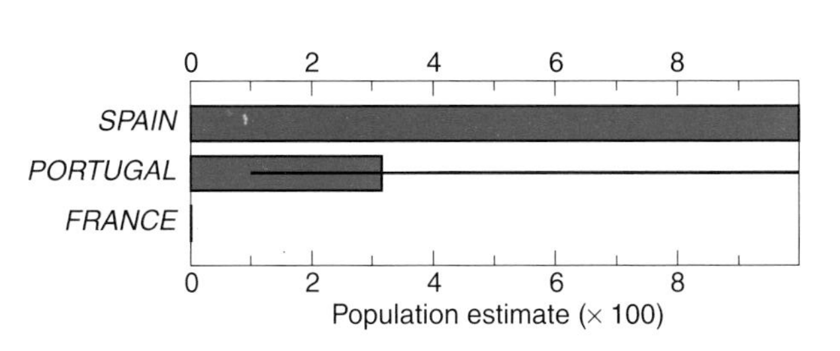

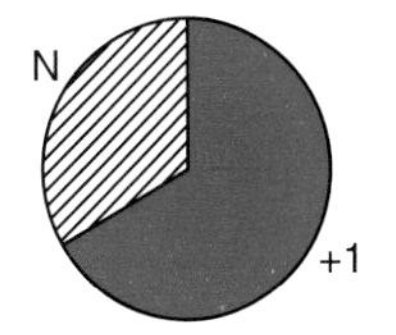

% in top 10 countries: 100.0
Total number of populated European countries: 3
Total European population 1101–2001 (1318)

The Black-winged Kite's European population is mostly resident but in winter disperses to more open farmland habitat, namely rice and corn stubble and fallows, where its prey, small mammals, reptiles and birds are more abundant.

Only one subspecies breeds in Europe, the nominate *E.c. caeruleus*. The Black-winged Kite is closely related to the White-tailed Kite, *E. leucurus*, of North and South America, and has been treated as conspecific.

Rui Rufino (P)

Accipiter gentilis

Goshawk

CZ	Jestřáb lesní	I	Astore
D	Habicht	NL	Havik
E	Azor Común	P	Açor
F	Autour des palombes	PL	Jastrząb
FIN	Kanahaukka	R	Тетеревятник
G	Διπλοσάϊνο	S	Duvhök
H	Héja		

Non-SPEC, Threat status S

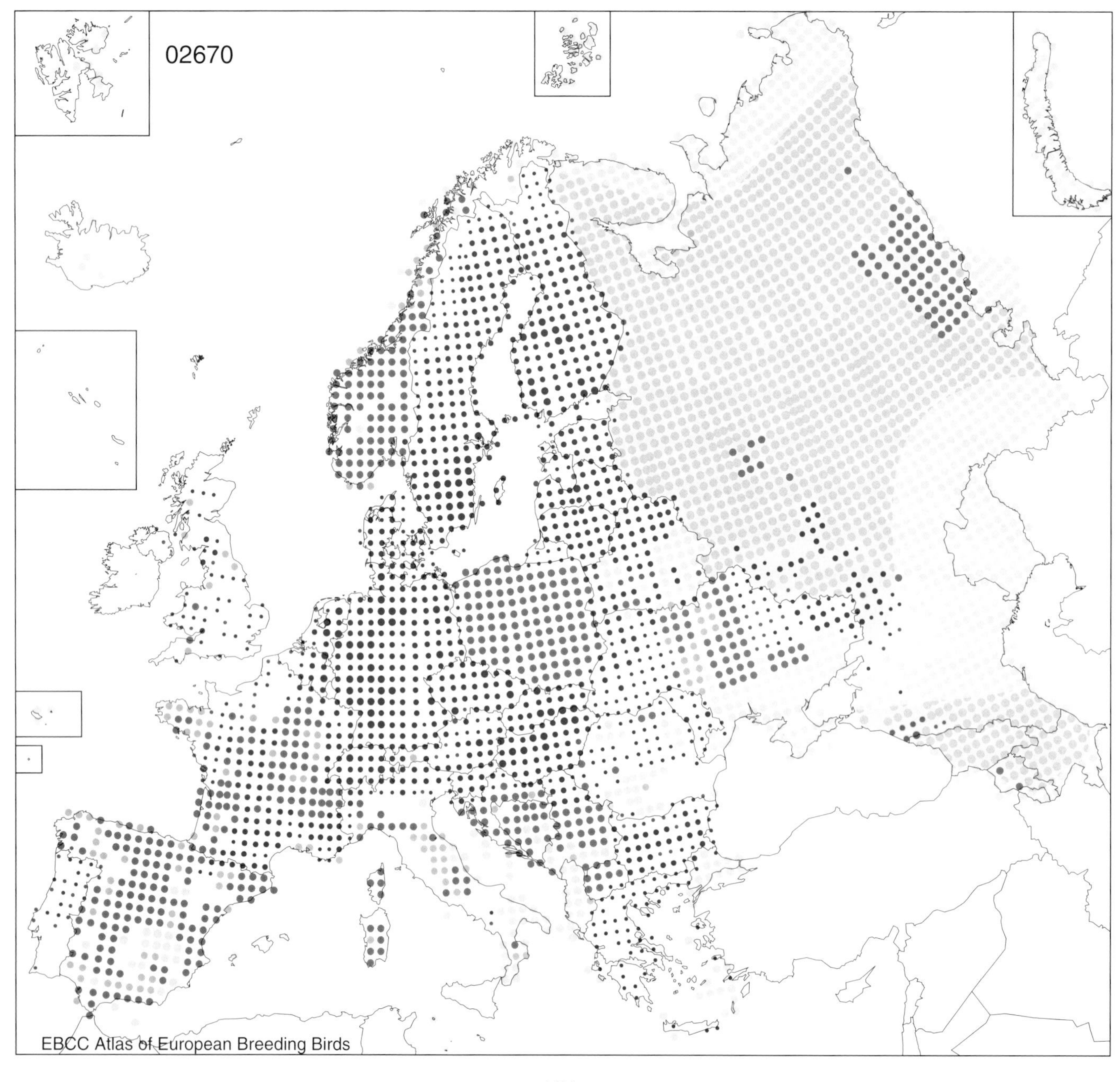

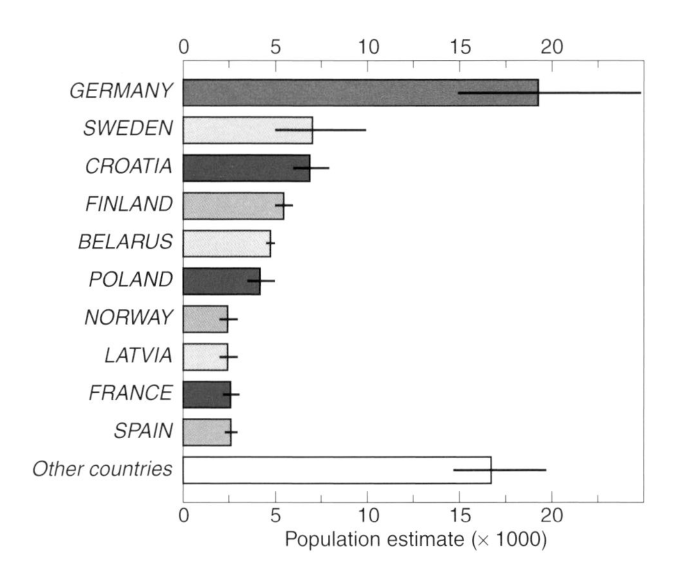

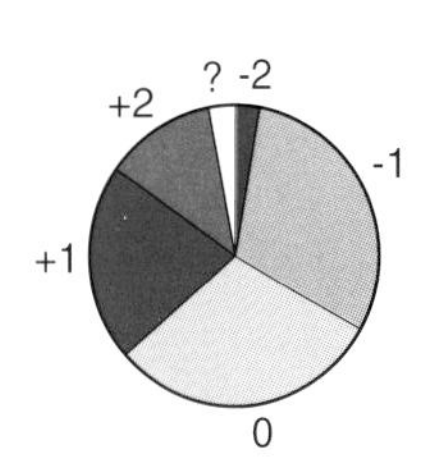

% in top 10 countries: 77.5
Total number of populated European countries: 33
Total European population 62,237–90,914 (75,221)
Russian population 70,000–100,000 (83,666)
Turkish population 100–1000 (316)

The Goshawk, a powerful hawk, has a widespread Holarctic distribution. In Europe it occurs from Spain to the Urals and from 70°N in Finland and 35°N in Crete. It is mostly resident throughout its range, but N Fennoscandian juveniles may be partial migrants, resulting from a genetic dimorphism or caused by food shortage (Marcström & Kenward 1981). Home range size and dispersive tendency fluctuate, depending on latitude, altitude, age (adults being often strictly sedentary), season and food supply. Most European birds are of the nominate subspecies *A.g. gentilis*; *buteoides* occurs from N Sweden eastwards and *arrigoni* on Corsica and Sardinia. There are several other subspecies elsewhere.

Once a typical woodland raptor, and remaining so in much of its range, the Goshawk has become much more adaptable, especially in western and C Europe. In northern Europe it breeds almost exclusively in the oldest parts of large forests; only in recent years has it begun to breed in smaller and younger woods. Elsewhere, especially in W Europe, it nests in all woodland types, coniferous, deciduous, large, small (<0.5ha of woodland suffices in open farmland), old or young (even scrub and young plantations), whether inhabited by people or not. Recently, it has even started colonizing parks in cities like Riga, Köln (Würfels 1994) and Amsterdam.

Its European distribution on the mapped scale has remained rather stable since the 1960s, except for an expansion in Great Britain. On a smaller scale, internal range expansions occurred within its western European distribution as it colonized other than woodland habitats. The population trend in northern Europe has remained rather stable since the 1950s. For example, in several extensive areas of coniferous and mixed forests in S and C Finland, the Goshawk maintained a breeding density of 3–6 bp/100km^2 from 1955 to 1975, in one case reaching 10 bp/100km^2 (Huhtala & Sulkava 1981). In western and C Europe a rapid decline during the 1950s and 1960s followed the use of highly toxic pesticides in agriculture. Stepwise banning of chlorinated hydrocarbons and mercury (used as seed dressing) in the early 1970s permitted spectacular improvements, such as twenty-fold increases in The Netherlands, Belgium, Denmark, Switzerland and locally in Germany. This trend generally stabilized in the 1980s, but some populations declined slightly in the late 1980s (Bijlsma 1991). The simultaneous increase in human persecution seldom led to long-term reduction of breeding densities nor has it prevented colonization of new areas (as in Britain), but it might disturb profoundly the age structure and reproductive output locally (Bijlsma 1993). Spreading human settlement and forest clearance may cause local decreases in N Europe. Declines in food resources in S Finland and Spain have had similar effects (Bijlsma 1991).

In Europe, nesting density in large (>200km^2) forested areas in the 1950s and 1960s was generally between 1 and 5 bp/100km^2. After the pesticide era, and especially during the 1980s, this increased to 6.6 bp/100km^2 in Belarus (V.V. Ivanovsky, pers comm), 6–7 bp/100km^2 in C Europe and 12–13 bp/100km^2 in western Europe. Much higher values (25–50 bp/100km^2) have been obtained in many E and W European study plots of <100 km^2, as in the fragmented Dutch landscape, rich in year-round prey (Bijlsma 1993). Dependent on local food supply, nest-separation distances (occupied nests) normally are fairly constant at 1.2km in Dutch forests (Bijlsma 1993), 1.5km in NE Spain (Mañosa 1994), 3–4km in Swiss mountain forests (Bühler & Oggier 1987), 3–5km in S and W Finland and 2–6km (mean 3.4) around Oulu in N Finland (R. Tornberg, in prep).

The European population is estimated at *c*160 000bp, *c*85 000 being in Russia. The Nordic countries have 13 000–20 000bp and C Europe (Poland to France) 29 000–44 000bp. S Europe, including the Balkans, contains 12 000–17 000bp.

Rob G Bijlsma (NL) Seppo Sulkava (FIN)

This species account is sponsored by Swarovski-Optik, Absam/Tirol, A.

Accipiter nisus — Sparrowhawk

CZ	Krahujec obecný	**I**	Sparviere
D	Sperber	**NL**	Sperwer
E	Gavilán Común	**P**	Gavião da Europa
F	Épervier d'Europe	**PL**	Krogulec
FIN	Varpushaukka	**R**	Перепелятник
G	Τσιχλογέρακο	**S**	Sparvhök
H	Karvaly		

Non-SPEC, Threat status S

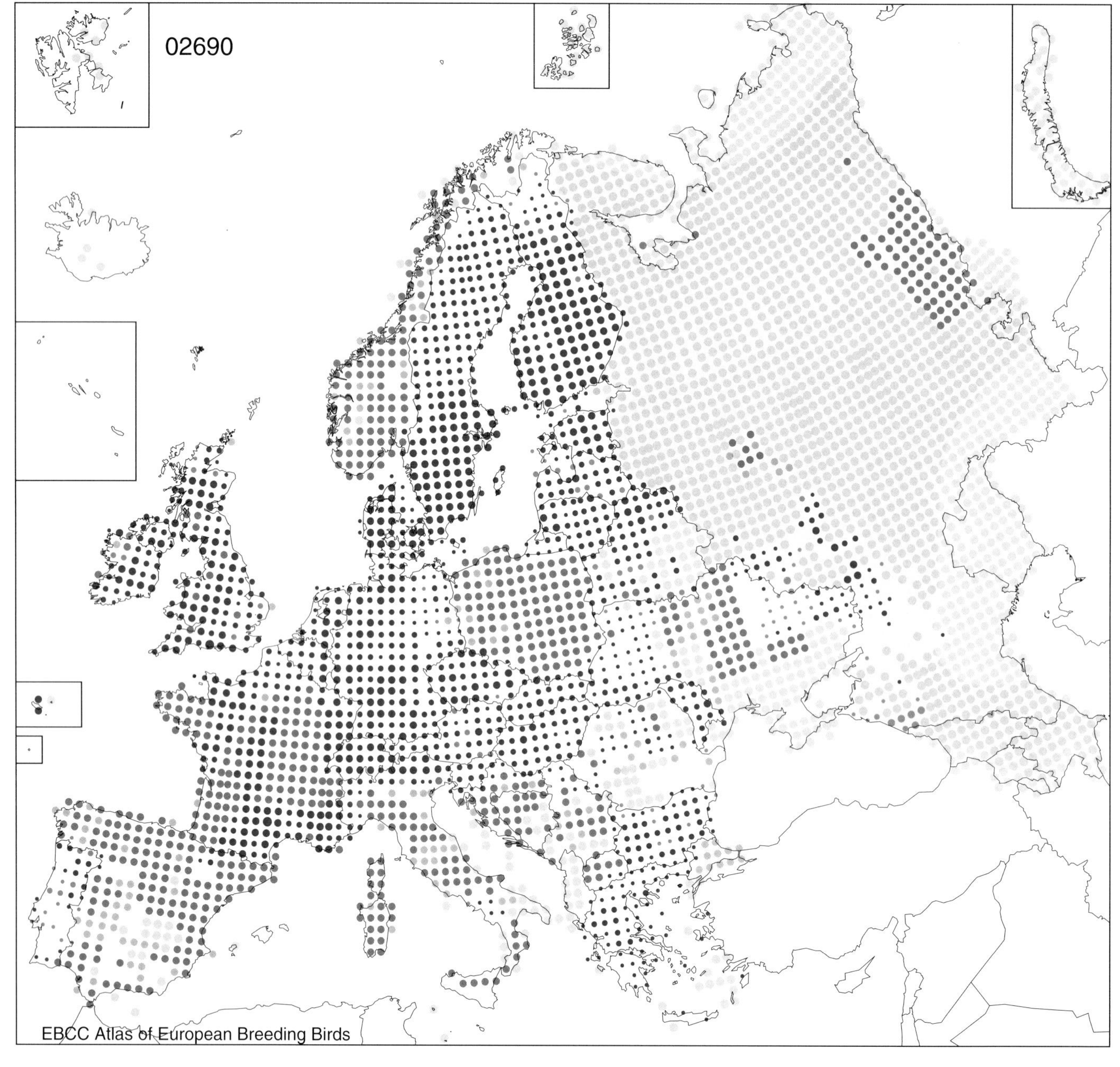

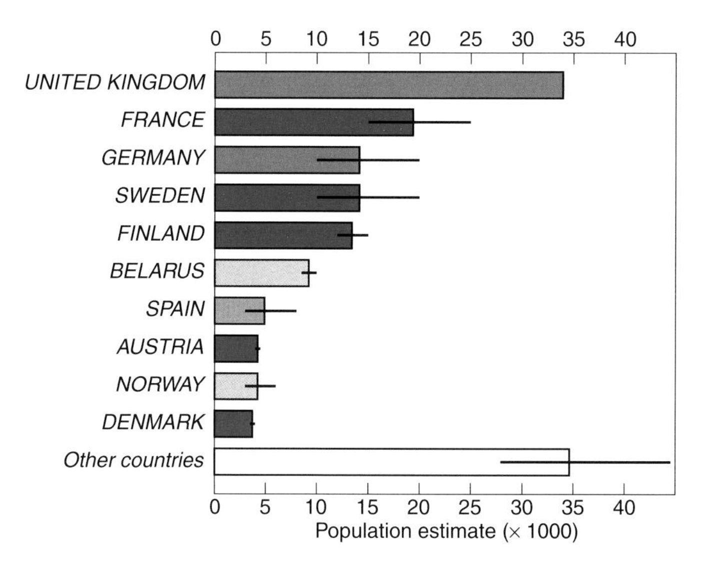

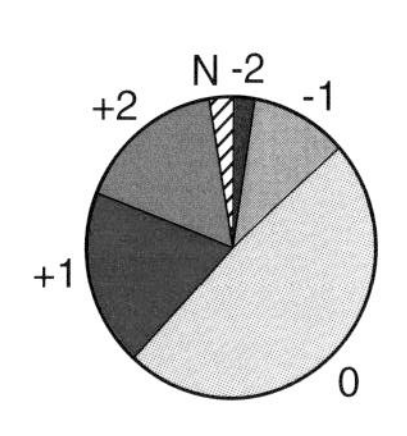

% in top 10 countries: 77.8
Total number of populated European countries: 37
Total European population 148,019–167,381 (156,078)
Russian population 140,000–180,000 (158,745)
Turkish population 3000–10,000 (5477)

The Sparrowhawk breeds in the Palearctic from Madeira and western Europe (excluding Iceland) to E Siberia, Sakhalin and Japan. It is polytypic, the nominate *nisus* intergrading with *nisosimilis* in W Siberia. There is an extralimital population in the Himalayas and the mountains of C Asia. Two island subspecies occur in Europe, *wolterstoffi* on Corsica and Sardinia and *granti* on Madeira (and the Canary Islands).

In Europe the Sparrowhawk inhabits all woodland types, preferring patchy 15–40-year-old coniferous forests interspersed with farmland and villages. However, since its recovery from pesticide-related declines (1950s–1970s), it has bred increasingly in purely deciduous woodland, tiny open-farmland woodlots (<1ha), marshes and urbanized areas. Being tolerant of human beings, it often breeds at high densities adjacent to or in built-up areas which abound in songbird prey. Peške (1990) recorded in inner Prague 82bp on 233km^2 in 1986–89.

In Europe, the Sparrowhawk is one of the most widespread raptors below the treeline. Breeding-pair spacing in woodland normally is regular. Density variations relate strongly to food supply, as in Britain, where increasing altitude and declining soil productivity correlates with increasing nest-separation distance (Newton 1986). Across the European continent, similarly varying densities occur in relation to breeding habitat availability and prey biomass. The average bp/50km-square per country figure roughly illustrates the point: the highest densities occur in W Europe; Britain 348, The Netherlands 273, Switzerland 210 and Denmark 217. These countries have in common large human populations, extensive prey populations and a predominance of farmland. Low densities of <50 bp/50km-square apply to most of southern Europe (Greece, Italy, Portugal, Spain) and to much of eastern Europe (Poland, Moldavia, Ukraine, Romania, Moldova), and intermediate values (150 bp/50km-square) occur in countries such as France, Germany, Austria, Croatia, Bulgaria, Sweden, Finland and Belarus. When related to woodland area, western European densities are much higher. Although only 10% of The Netherlands is forested, in five well-studied large plots values of 16–47 bp/100km^2 (Bijlsma 1993) are representative, as compared to 7–10 bp/100km^2 in Denmark (10 plots, Jørgensen 1989), 5–18 bp/100km^2 in France (5 plots, Joncourt 1986), 4–17 bp/100km^2 in Austria (7 plots, Gamauf 1991) and 3–23 bp/100km^2 in Switzerland (4 plots, Bühler 1991). Based on these data, the graph's Russian total of 140 000–180 000bp in *c*1500 50km squares is probably overoptimistic, especially when considering that much treeless steppe remains.

In NW Europe the population has increased considerably in range and size from 1970 to 1990 as a consequence of the ban on organochlorine pesticides. There has been a complete recovery of numbers. In most areas the species is more widely distributed at higher densities than prior to the first large-scale application of pesticides, and particularly so in large areas of intensive agriculture. In E-C England, recolonization took place within a decade (Newton & Wyllie 1992, Newton 1993a), whereas The Netherlands has witnessed a 15- to 20-fold increase since the 1960s (Bijlsma 1993). In Switzerland, the decline was worst in lowland farming areas, but barely detectable in the C Alps (Bühler 1991). The apparent stability of populations in much of C and E Europe is questionable because there pesticide use was also high. Other factors may apply across the Mediterranean range, where populations were either stable (Portugal, Croatia, Greece) or slightly decreasing (Spain, Italy).

In W, C and S Europe the species is mostly resident, but the extent of dispersive and migratory movements increases progressively to the N and NE, especially amongst juveniles. N European birds are migratory and move S and SW to winter from S Fennoscandia southwards, some reaching the Maghreb. The eastern *nisosimilis* migrates to wintering areas S as far as East Africa.

Ronald Zollinger (NL)

Accipiter brevipes

Levant Sparrowhawk

CZ	Krahujec krátkoprstý	I	Sparviere levantino
D	Kurzfangsperber	NL	Balkansperwer
E	Gavilán Griego	P	Gavião-grego
F	Épervier à pieds courts	PL	Krogulec krótkonogi
FIN	Sirovarpushaukka	R	Европейский тювик
G	Σαΐνι	S	Balkanhök
H	Kis héja		

SPEC Cat 2, Threat status R

This monotypic raptor is almost completely confined to Europe, where it breeds in low latitudes from the Balkan Peninsula to the middle reaches of the Urals, its range extending only to W Kazakhstan and Iran. It is fully migratory, but the extent of its wintering range in Africa is unknown. During migration, it typically forms single-species flocks that pass at high altitudes, sometimes even at night (Stark & Liechti 1993).

Its breeding habitat is mainly confined to fragmented deciduous forests along river basins (Esilevskaya & Bryukhanov 1991, Galushin 1994), but may include broad-leaved forests on foothills and mountain slopes (up to 2000m, but normally below 1000m asl). Its diet is diverse, consisting of birds (up to lark-size), small mammals (up to mole-size), lizards and insects. In terms of biomass, vertebrates are more important food items than insects or lizards (Simeonov 1984).

The main breeding grounds are found in Russia (1500–3000bp, in particular in the Don basin; Galushin 1994), and in Greece (1000–1200bp). Much lower numbers (<100bp) were recorded for the Balkan States and Hungary. However, the breeding numbers of this species are seriously underestimated, given the recent estimate (150bp) for Bulgaria being much higher than hitherto thought (G. Kouzmanov and G. Stayanov, pers comm), the number of migrants recorded in Israel (up to 49 000, spring 1987; Leshem 1994) and the difficulties of recording passage numbers accurately. The world population is probably in excess of 12 000bp, given an estimated fledgling production of 2 young/pair. Therefore, either the extent of the breeding range is underestimated, or breeding densities are much higher in the recorded breeding range, or both. Certainly, research on the middle Volga River in 1995 suggests an even distribution throughout deciduous woodlands, density averaging 17.3 bp/100km² (Galushin *et al* 1996).

Only Romania experienced a strong decrease in both range and numbers in 1970–90; elsewhere apparently demonstrated stability, consistent with the reasonably stable figures from autumn migration counts in Israel (Leshem 1994).

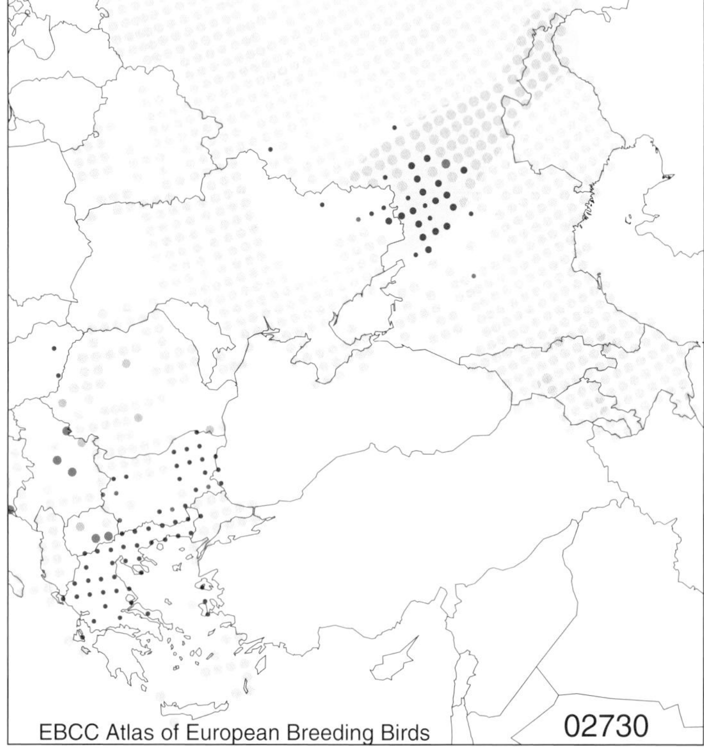

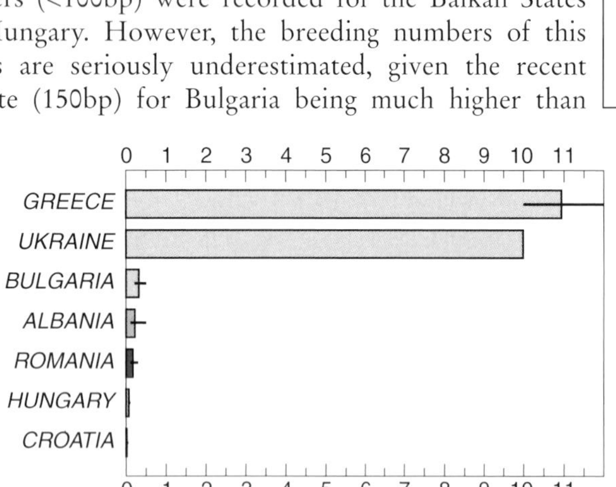

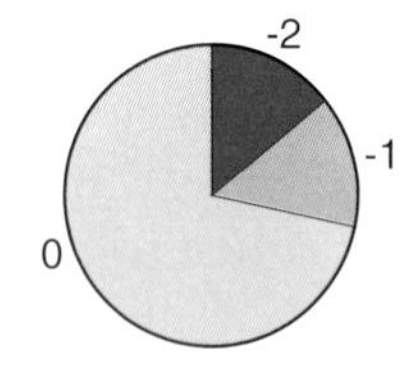

% in top 10 countries: 100.0
Total number of populated European countries: 7
Total European population 2079–2287 (2176)
Russian population 1500–3000 (2121)
Turkish population 10–500 (71)

Rob G Bijlsma (NL)

Buteo rufinus

Long-legged Buzzard

CZ	Káně bělochvostá	I	Poiana codabianca
D	Adlerbussard	NL	Arendbuizerd
E	Busardo Moro	P	Búteo-mouro
F	Buse féroce	PL	Kurhannik
FIN	Arohiirihaukka	R	Канюк-курганник
G	Αετογερακίνα	S	Örnvråk
H	Pusztai ölyv		

SPEC Cat 3, Threat status E (P)

The Long-legged Buzzard is distributed from SE Europe to Asia Minor, C Asia, and North Africa. It is a migrant or partial migrant, some wintering in the southern part of the breeding range, others moving to distinct, but imprecisely known areas in N India, Sudan and Nigeria. The nominate *B.r. rufinus* breeds in Europe and Asia. The other subspecies *cirtensis* occurs in North Africa.

In Europe, its range includes Greece (also several islands), Bulgaria, SW Russia, Ukraine, Albania, Romania, the Caucasus republics and possibly southern parts of former Yugoslavia. It probably breeds in European Turkey. Since the early 1990s, a few have bred in Hungary.

The Long-legged Buzzard prefers uncultivated and dry scrubby areas adjacent to suitable nest sites on crags and in gorges, and on mountains up to 1600m asl. It usually nests on cliffs, but sometimes uses trees in rural regions (Vatev 1987). Many nest sites are situated close to fresh water (Michev *et al* 1984), and occasionally along sea coasts.

The Long-legged Buzzard is most abundant in Russia (probably mostly in Asian Russia) and in Bulgaria, whose population density has gradually increased (Michev *et al* 1984, Nankinov *et al* 1991), accompanied by a significant northwards range extension. It is our opinion that the Bulgarian population now exceeds that given in the graph and comprises *c*300 bp (I. Vatev, pers obs) which occupy nearly all favourable habitats. The minimum recorded distance between two nests was *c*500m, in the W Balkan region. The northward range expansion is probably due to the species' adaptability to the available habitats, and also to an increasing tolerance of human activity. It is well-established in S Dobrujda (Romania; Kalabér 1984). In Ukraine and Greece, numbers appear stable, but the population in Russia seems to be in slight decline.

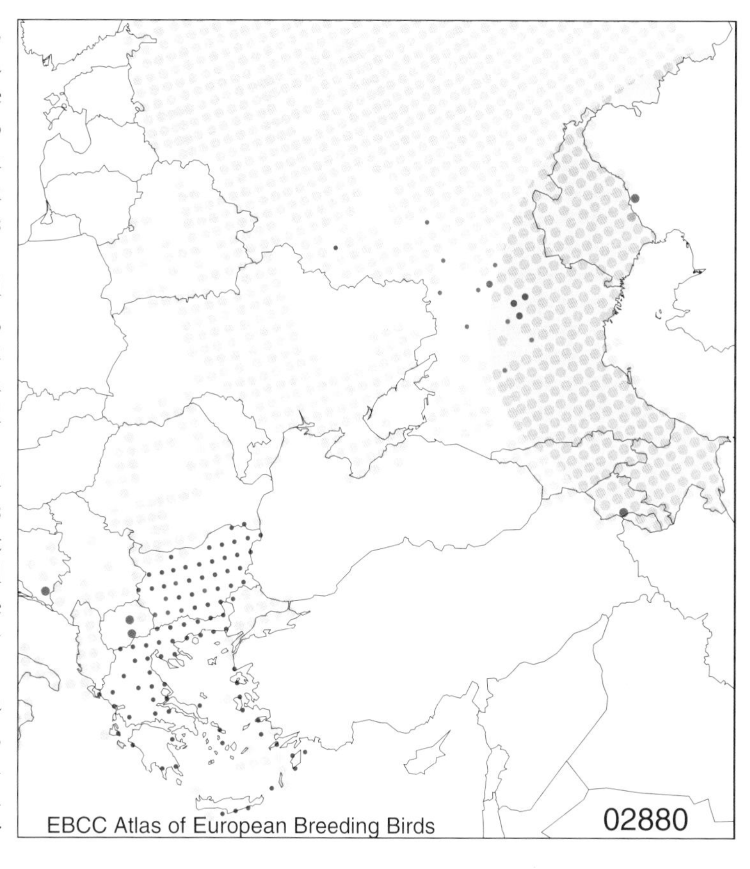

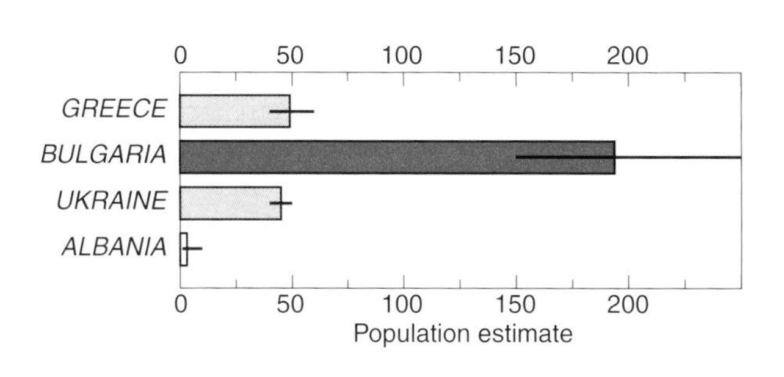

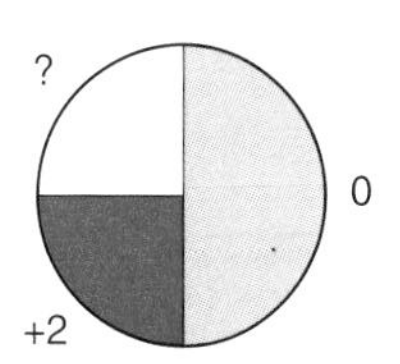

% in top 10 countries: 100.0
Total number of populated European countries: 4
Total European population 246–349 (291)
Russian population 800–1500 (1095)
Turkish population 1000–10,000 (3162)

Dan Munteanu (ROM) the late Rumen Todorov (BUL) Ilia Vatev (BUL)

Buteo buteo — Buzzard

CZ	Káně lesní	**I**	Poiana
D	Mäusebussard	**NL**	Buizerd
E	Busardo Ratonero	**P**	Águia-d'asa-redonda
F	Buse variable	**PL**	Myszołow
FIN	Hiirihaukka	**R**	Обыкновенный канюк
G	Γερακίνα	**S**	Ormvråk
H	Egerészölyv		

Non-SPEC, Threat status S

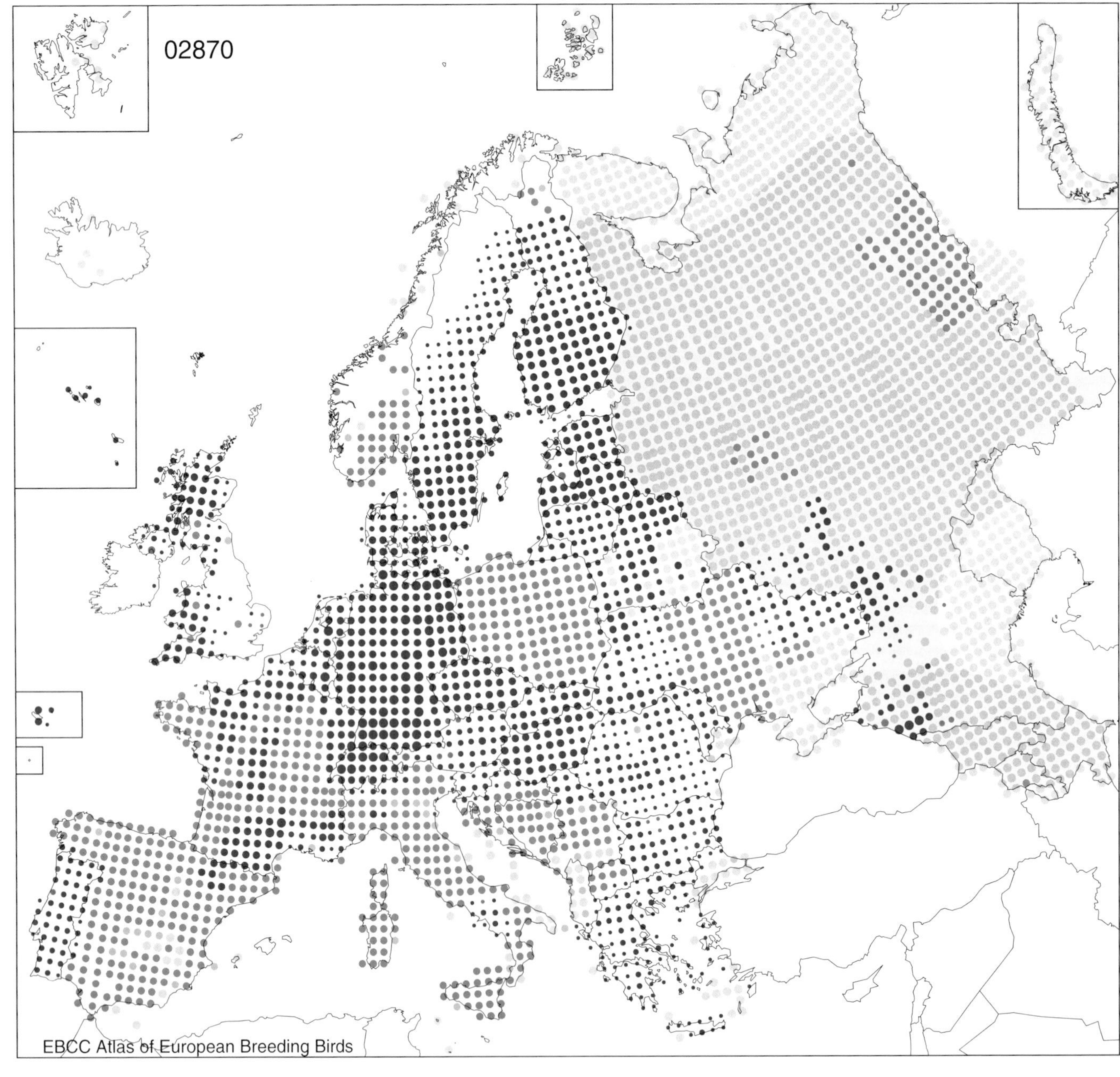

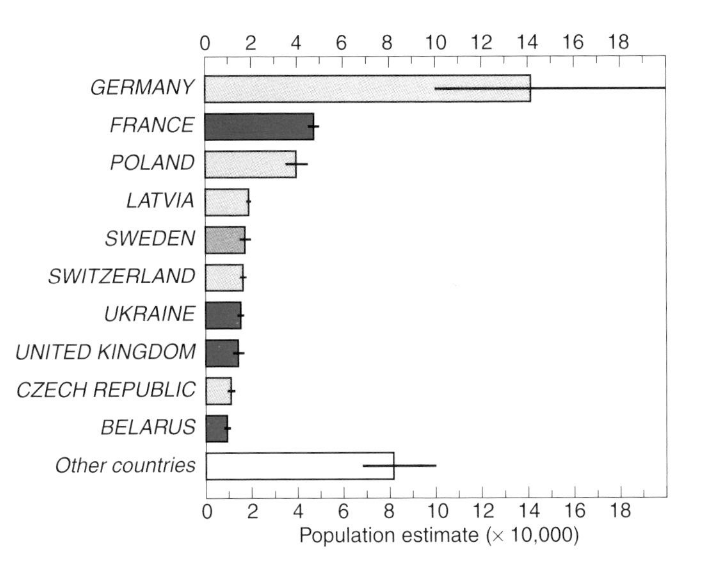

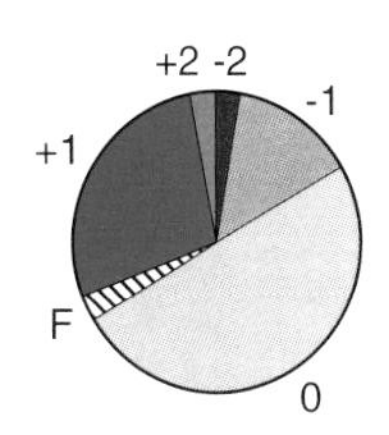

% in top 10 countries: 80.2
Total number of populated European countries: 36
Total European population 370,933–472,444 (413,101)
Russian population 400,000–600,000 (489,898)
Turkish population 1000–5000 (2236)

The Buzzard, a medium-sized raptor, is widespread throughout the Palearctic. The nominate subspecies *B.b. buteo* occurs in the W and in N Fennoscandia and eastern Europe intergrades with *vulpinus*, found E to *c*96°E. Island subspecies occur in the Mediterranean and Atlantic, and *menetriesi* occupies S Crimea, Transcaucasia and N Iran. The nominate is mostly resident or partly migratory (increasingly so, northwards), whereas *vulpinus* is a long-distance migrant: European *vulpinus* winter mostly in East and South Africa.

The Buzzard breeds almost anywhere with nesting trees more than 5m tall. It occupies uninterrupted forests, fragmented woodland, woodlots in cultivated landscapes, forested uplands and hillsides up to the tree-limit and overgrown marshland. It prefers forested habitats interspersed with or fragmented by short-vegetation fields or clearings; such a composition probably best suits its principal hunting method of wait-and-strike. It tolerates high precipitation but generally avoids warm, dry habitats. A typical denizen of the temperate and boreal zones, it is replaced at high latitudes by the Rough-legged Buzzard *B. lagopus* and in lowland, arid and semi-arid steppes in SE Europe by the Long-legged Buzzard *B. rufinus*.

Although one of the commonest European raptors, its breeding densities and performance fluctuate widely between years and regions, depending on food supply and local topography, and despite being a versatile predator, overall, its success mirrors vole-cycle peaks. Densities in Fennoscandia decrease gradually towards the spruce *Picea* forest northern limit. C and E England contain much suitable habitat, yet the species is absent, indicating unabated persecution by gamekeepers (K. Taylor *et al* 1988). Conversely, its colonization of Northern Ireland probably succeeded through reduced persecution. Low densities in upland Scotland and coastal areas of western Europe arise primarily through lack of suitable habitat or limited availability of nesting sites. Highest densities occur in temperate and boreal regions, averaging between 200 and 500 bp/50km square from the Low Countries through France, Germany, Denmark and C Europe to Poland and the Baltic States. In Fennoscandia, the average density per 50km square remains <100bp, as in S Europe (Portugal, Spain, Italy, Greece) and probably also in much of E Europe (Hungary, Romania, Moldova, Bulgaria, Ukraine).

Fragmented landscapes with a high proportion of cultivated land contain the highest breeding numbers. In The Netherlands, densities ranged from 46 to 185 bp/100km^2 in large plots containing suitable habitat; the low overall density of 16 bp/100km^2 demonstrates the scarcity of woodland (Bijlsma 1993). Breeding densities in Germany and Austria, probably typical of much of C Europe, averaged 11–28 bp/100km^2 (Gamauf 1991, Kostrzewa & Speer 1995), comparing favourably with Finland's 3–6 bp/100km^2 (Koskimies 1989a) where 20 bp/100km^2 is achieved only in the best habitats.

The species suffered from the massive application of persistent pesticides in the 1950s and 1960s, especially in agricultural areas in W and C Europe. Persecution was, and locally still is, another factor limiting distribution, depleting numbers, disrupting population turnover and reducing breeding success. The Buzzard takes carrion readily and so is particularly vulnerable to the illegal use of poisons (Bijlsma 1993). From 1970 to 1990, many European countries registered a slight increase (20–50%) in numbers, probably a recovery from pesticide-induced depletion (western Europe), combined with reduced persecution (Great Britain, Northern Ireland). Stable populations prevailed over much of C, E and N Europe in the 1980s, as in Denmark, where the 2000bp of 1965 increased to, and stabilized at, 5000bp in the 1980s; winter mortality and area of woodland apparently are limiting numbers (Noer & Secher 1990). The Swedish population may be decreasing by 1.7% per year, but the proposed cause (low reproductive rate; Ryttman 1994) needs substantiation. The Russian population, estimated at 500 000bp, has increased slightly. The remainder of Europe holds a possibly stable population of *c*420 000bp.

Rob G Bijlsma (NL)

This species account is sponsored by Heinrich Dierking, Reinbek, D.

Buteo lagopus

Rough-legged Buzzard

CZ	Káně rousná	I	Poiana calzata
D	Rauhfußbussard	NL	Ruigpootbuizerd
E	Busardo Calzado	P	Búteo-calçado
F	Buse pattue	PL	Myszołów włochaty
FIN	Piekana	R	Зимняк
G	Χιονογερακίνα	S	Fjällvråk
H	Gatyás ölyv		

Non-SPEC, Threat status S

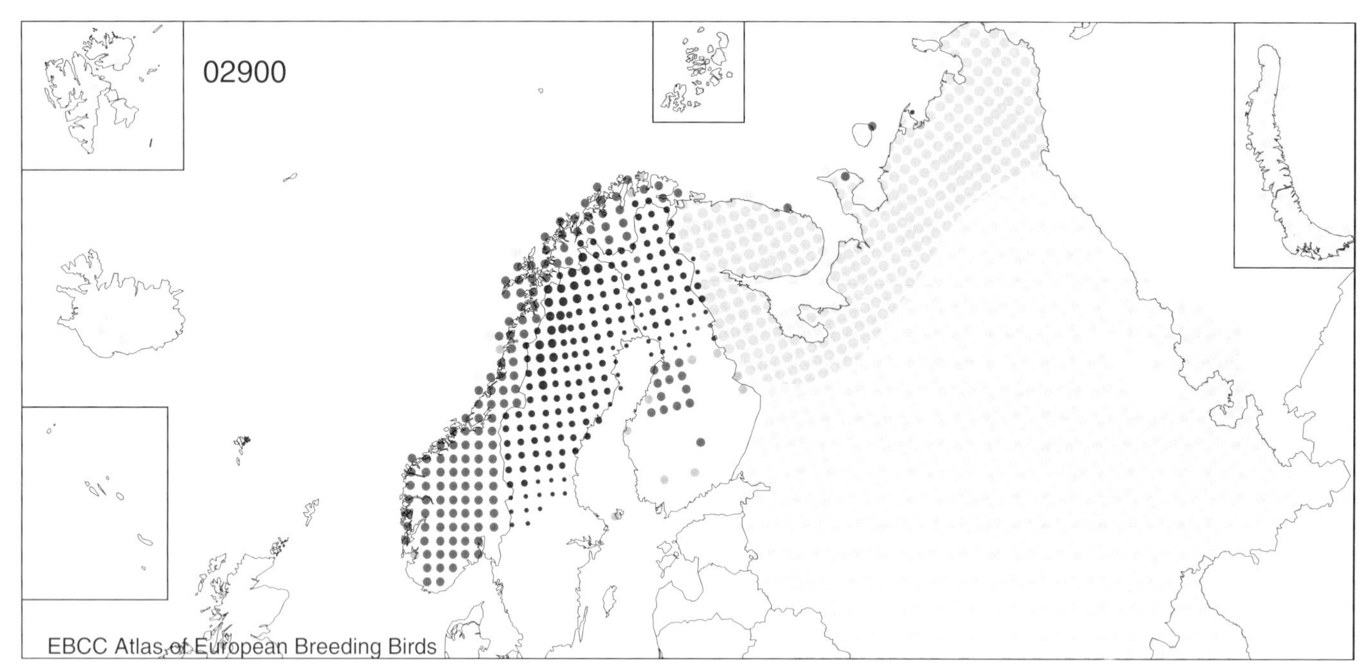

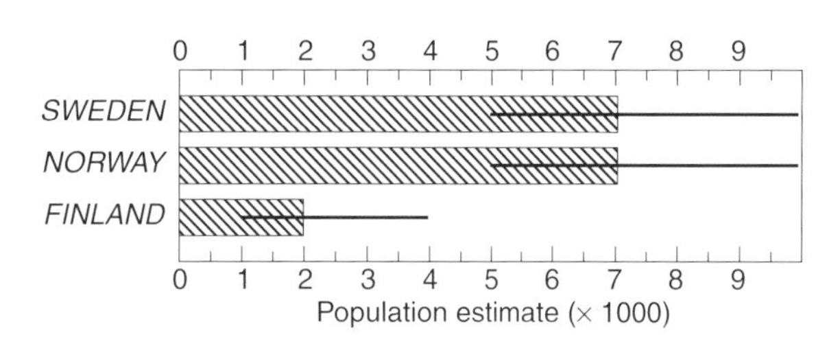

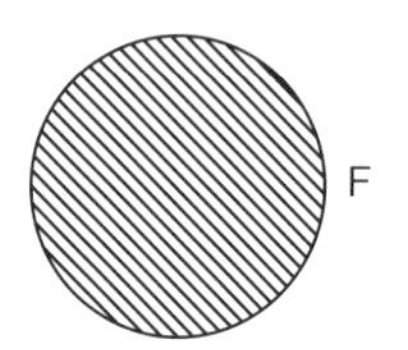

% in top 10 countries: 100.0
Total number of populated European countries: 3
Total European population 13,047–20,742 (16,142)
Russian population 80,000–120,000 (97,980)

The Rough-legged Buzzard has a Holarctic distribution in the arctic and subarctic zones, but it also nests in the S Scandinavian fells. In peak rodent years it may breed far into the boreal zone. In Finland it nests regularly N of 66°N (Lagerström 1993), exceptionally S to 63°N. In Sweden it breeds S to 60°N, and in Norway right to the S coast. Non-breeding birds wander much further S in summer, perhaps explaining some of the map's possible breeding records. The nominate *B.l. lagopus* breeds in Europe. There are three other subspecies.

In Fjell-Lapland it nests along river valleys near the treeless fells and in the subalpine birch forests, usually choosing the most inaccessible sites on slopes or in ravines. In Forest-Lapland it is a tree-nester in coniferous forest interspersed with rivers, lakes, clearfells or bogs, often near the forest edge.

It is the commonest raptor in Norway (Gjershaug 1994). In Finnish Fjell-Lapland breeding densities in peak rodent years may reach 18–19 bp/100km², locally 5bp on 3km² (Lagerström 1993). In poor rodent years fledglings do not survive, as in 1985 and 1989 at Utsjoki, Finland (L. Iso-Iivari, unpubl). In Finnish Forest-Lapland lower densities of 2–3 bp/100km² seem normal (Saurola 1985), but annual fluctuations are much smaller. Some pairs may breed annually (E. Pulliainen & L. Saari, unpubl). Between 100 and 2500 pairs breed in any one year in Finland (Saurola 1985). Since 1900, the range of the Rough-legged Buzzard apparently has contracted in S Finland (Lagerström 1993), but expanded in Norway (Gjershaug 1994). Sweden and Norway together hold at least 10 000bp, but European Russia perhaps as many as 120 000.

The Rough-legged Buzzard migrates mainly SSE for 2000–2500km to its wintering grounds between 45° and 55°N, mostly E of The Netherlands. Its main migratory route from Fennoscandia is along the Karelian isthmus. Some overwinter regularly in C and S Sweden.

Lasse Iso-Iivari (FIN) Lennart Saari (FIN)

Aquila nipalensis

Steppe Eagle

CZ	Orel stepní	I	Aquila rapace
D	Steppenadler	NL	Steppearend
E	Aguila Esteparia	P	Águia-rapace
F	Aigle des steppes	PL	Orzeł stepowy
FIN	Savannikotka	R	Степной орел
G	Στεπαετός	S	Stäppörn
H	Pusztai sas		

SPEC Cat 3, Threat status V

The large, migratory Steppe Eagle breeds only E of 42°E in European Russia from the Astrakhan to Stavropol regions, apparently recently having become extinct as a regular breeder in SE Ukraine. Its world distribution extends across C Asia to 110°E and S through China to the northern Himalayas. Its western decline accelerated in the early 1900s when it disappeared from Moldova and Romania, surviving in C and E Ukraine until the 1950s. The remaining S Ukraine population diminished rapidly in the 1970s. European birds belong to the subspecies *A.n. orientalis*, which occurs to C Asia, the nominate *nipalensis* breeding further E.

The Steppe Eagle has narrow habitat requirements in Europe: virgin plain or hill-steppes, semi-deserts and remote steppic valleys amongst mountains, preferably where feather-grass *Stipa pennata* or wormwood *Artemisia* are common, even in patches, but especially where rodents such as suslik *Citellus* spp are abundant (Zubarovsky 1977). Such habitat and prey disappeared under the plough, and the remaining populations were heavily persecuted, driving the Steppe Eagle's western limit 1000km eastwards in 100 years.

By the Sivash shores it nested on narrow sandspits and islands, elsewhere on the ground and also on haystacks, and where persecuted, in trees, bushes and artificial structures. In its core range where prey is abundant, nests can be only

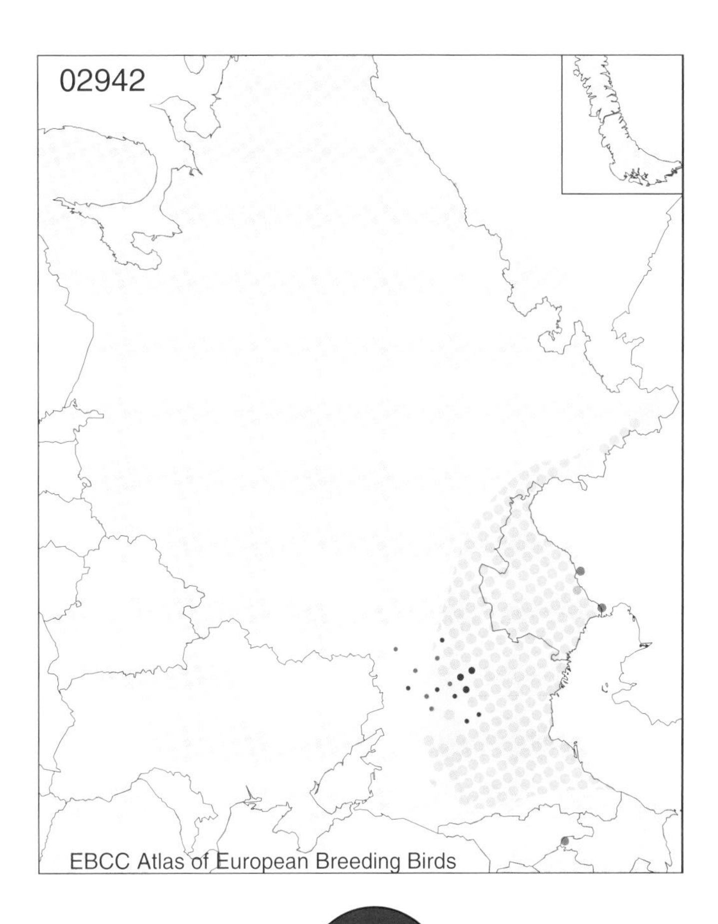

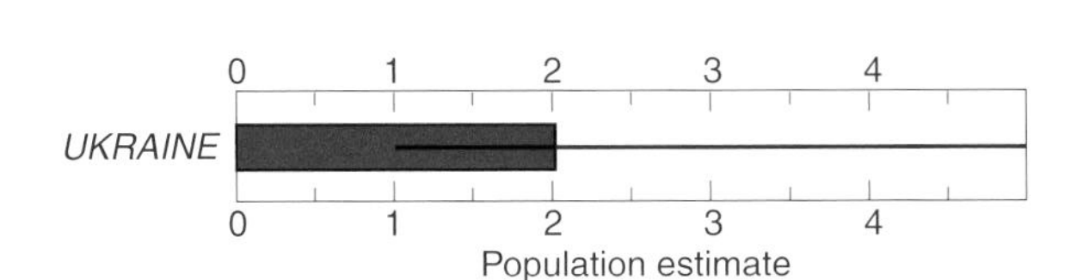

% in top 10 countries: 100
Total number of populated European countries: 1
Total European population 1–5 (2)
Russian population 15,000–25,000 (19,365)
Turkish population 1–10 (3)

500m apart, and here it is still numerous, judging by numbers recorded on migration (Génsbøl 1995), the majority of birds transiting Europe routing E of the Black Sea on both passages. Adult spring migration coincides with the end of ground squirrel hibernation, and egg-hatching with the emergence of young susliks (Agafonov *et al* 1957).

The European Steppe Eagle probably winters in Africa, its range in grassland and savanna overlapping with that of the resident Tawny Eagle *A. rapax*, from which it has only recently been separated. Some, mostly adults, wintering as far N as Israel, and rather more in Arabia survive by scavenging at abattoirs, refuse tips and Bedouin livestock casualties and by predation on rodent plagues in modern desert agriculture (Stagg 1985, pers obs). Eastern populations winter in the Indian subcontinent and Burma. The source of birds wintering in Mesopotamia is uncertain.

Igor Gorban (UKR) John Morgan (GB)
Hadoram Shirihai (ISR)

Aquila pomarina — Lesser Spotted Eagle

CZ	Orel křiklavý	I	Aquila anatraia minore
D	Schreiadler	NL	Schreeuwarend
E	Aguila Pomerana	P	Águia-pomarina
F	Aigle pomarin	PL	Orlik krzykliwy
FIN	Pikkukiljukotka	R	Малый подорлик
G	Κραυγαετός	S	Mindre skrikörn
H	Békászó sas		

SPEC Cat 3, Threat status R

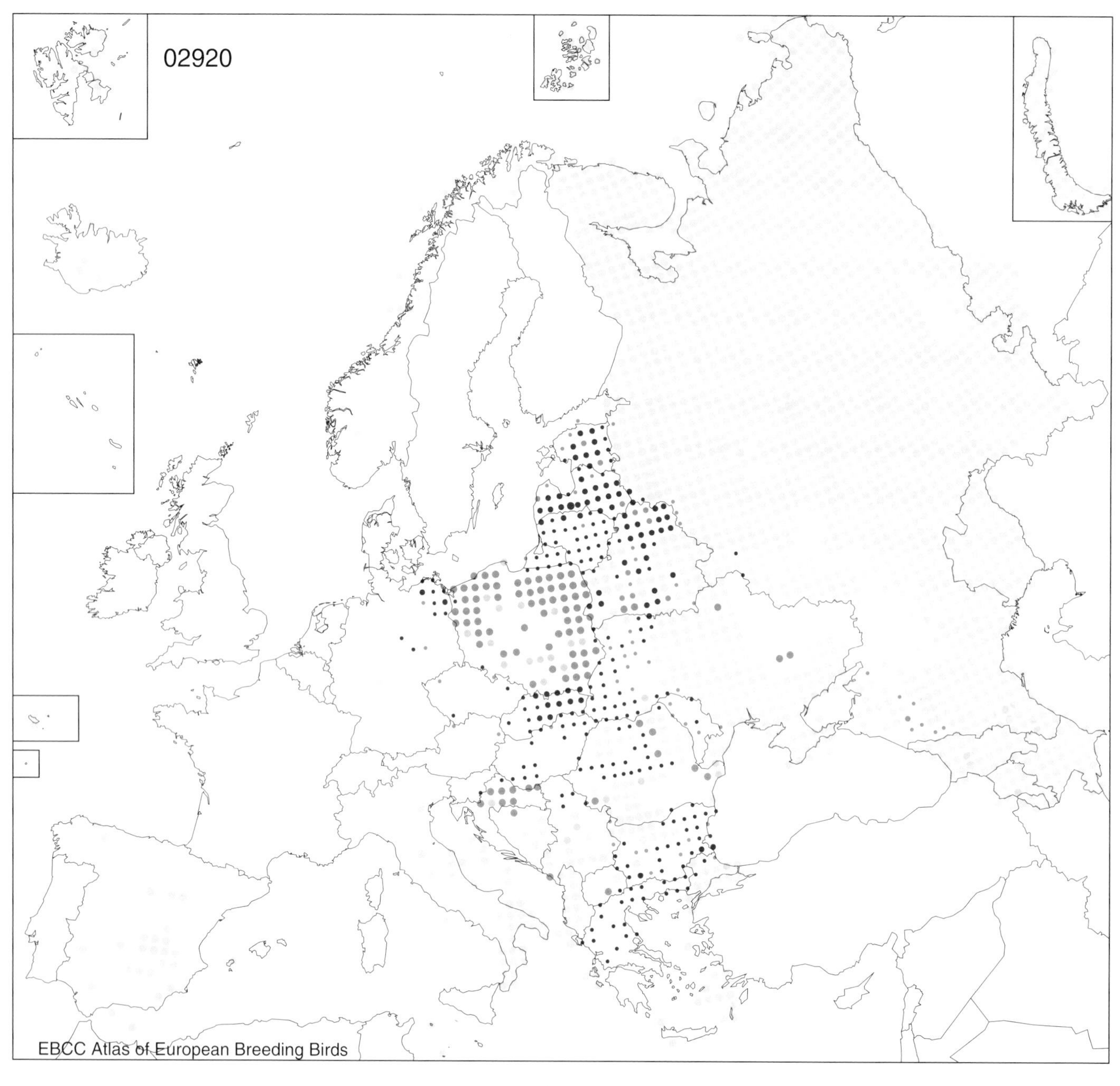

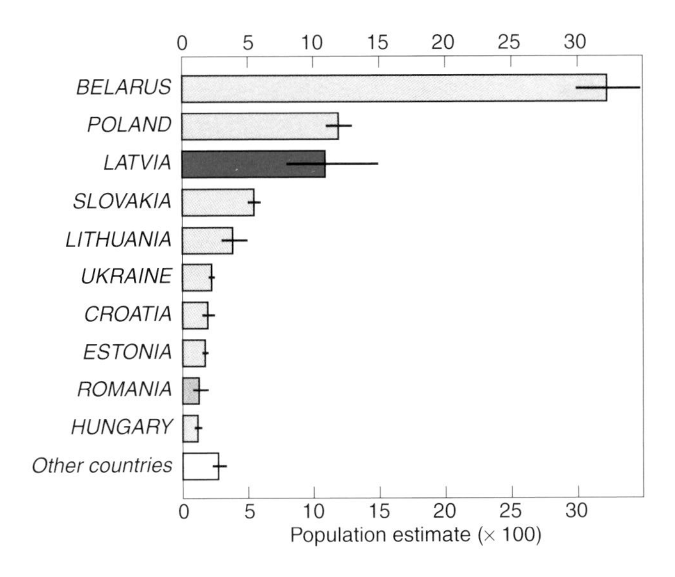

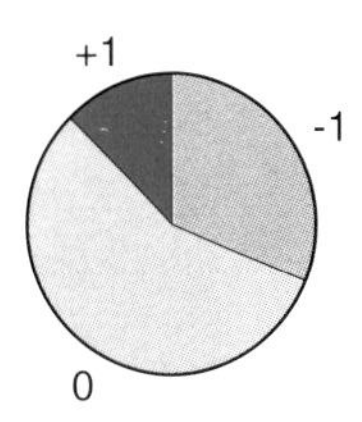

% in top 10 countries: 96.4
Total number of populated European countries: 16
Total European population 7158–8091 (7571)
Russian population 50–200 (100)
Turkish population 30–500 (122)

The Lesser Spotted Eagle is a medium-sized raptor with a disjunct distribution. The nominate *A.p. pomarina* occurs in C and most of E Europe, the Caucasus and Turkey, and is fully migratory. The other subspecies *hastata* inhabits E Pakistan, N India and Burma and is sedentary and somewhat smaller.

The European distribution stretches from the Balkan Peninsula in the S to the Baltic Sea in the N, its western limit extending irregularly from NE Germany across Poland, Slovakia and Hungary to the former Yugoslavia, Albania and N Greece. The delineation of the eastern limit is not yet clear, especially from W Russia to the Black Sea. To the S and SE, distribution is very patchy, as in Greece, the former Yugoslavia and through Turkey to the Caucasus and NW Iran.

Although a forest-dweller inhabiting coniferous, deciduous and mixed forests, whether in lowlands or hills, it prefers patchy woodland alternating with wet meadows, pastures, riverine valleys, marshes and peatbogs, usually below 400m asl, but in the Caucasus up to 2000m asl. It avoids unforested areas, high mountains and vast unbroken forests.

Densities in prime habitat of sufficient area (>100km^2) reach 9.7 bp/100km^2 in hilly country in Dolný Kubín (NW Slovakia) district, which is *c*40% afforested mainly with conifers at *c*500–900m asl (D. Karaska, pers obs), and 11.5 bp/100km^2 in mixed lowland forest (26% afforested) in Bukaisi district, C Latvia (U. Bergmanis, pers obs). Overall densities (in bp/100km^2) are highest in the E and NE of its range: Dolný Kubín, 6.0–7.0 (D. Karaska, pers obs); Stará Lubovňa district, N Slovakia, 6.4 (T. Bělka, pers comm); Humenné district, NE Slovakia, 4.2 (S. Pčola, Maderič *et al*, pers comm); Przemysl district (E Poland), 5.7–7.0 (Kunysz 1994); Susz district (NE Poland), 5.8 (Król 1985), Belarus and SW Latvia, 3.6–8.0 (Bergmanis *et al* 1990).

The European population is estimated at some 10 000bp. Apart from Belarus, Poland, Latvia and Slovakia, all other countries have 300bp or fewer. The European total, constituting almost the entire breeding population of the nominate subspecies, is greatly at variance with the claim of *c*141 000 seen transiting Israel during the autumn migration (Shirihai & Christie 1992). Given an average reproduction rate of 0.5–0.8 young/pair, the total European population may be *c*30 000 birds and even allowing for a probably substantial underestimate in eastern Europe, the discrepancy remains. It is conceivable that the breeding range is more extensive than hitherto known, and so a re-evaluation of counting methods in Israel would help gauge the strength of this hypothesis (Dovrat 1991).

Through persecution by man in the 19th and early 20th centuries, the Lesser Spotted Eagle suffered major population reductions and range contractions, mainly in the S, W and SW of its range, where today only residual populations remain. Drainage of meadows and pastures and felling of ancient forests probably have contributed to the declines. Since 1975, core populations appear to be stable, or are perhaps even increasing slowly (Latvia, Czech Republic). Declines, generally accompanied by slight range contractions, continue in the peripheral populations of Moldova, Romania, Bulgaria, Greece and Albania. The species' present distribution may not yet be limited by availability of suitable habitat; two adjacent areas in Slovakia, Dolný Kubín (1660km^2) andČadca (936km^2) with apparently identical habitat, hold 100–120 and 0bp respectively (D. Karaska, pers obs, J. Korňan, pers comm); such a high density at the western range limit suggests that further expansion may occur before the onset of intensification of forestry and agriculture in E Europe causes future declines.

The species winters S of the Equator in SE Africa, following rain-fronts in order to profit from swarming alate termites. Dependent on soaring during migration, it avoids long sea-crossings and therefore mostly travels via the Bosphorus and W Turkey, the eastern Mediterranean coast, Sinai and the Nile.

Ugis Bergmanis (LAT) Eugenijus Drobelis (LITH)
Dušan Karaska (SLK)

This species account is sponsored by Fachgruppe Ornithologie, Stralsund, D.

Aquila clanga

Spotted Eagle

CZ	Orel volavý	I	Aquila anatraia maggiore
D	Schelladler	NL	Bastaardarend
E	Aguila Moteada	P	Águia-gritadeira
F	Aigle criard	PL	Orlik grubodzioby
FIN	Kiljukotka	R	Большой подорлик
G	Στικταετός	S	Större skrikörn
H	Fekete sas		

SPEC Cat 1, Threat status E

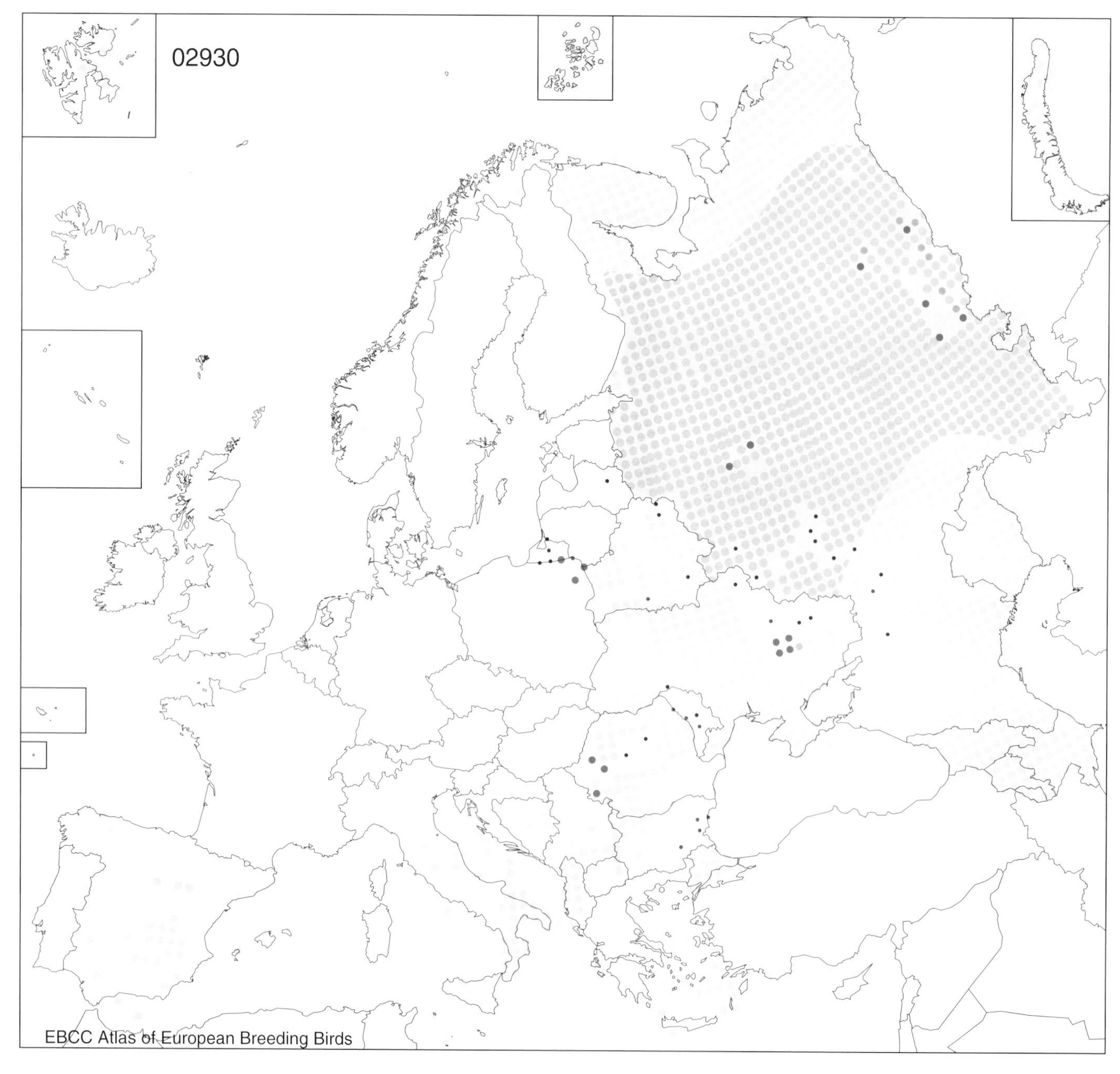

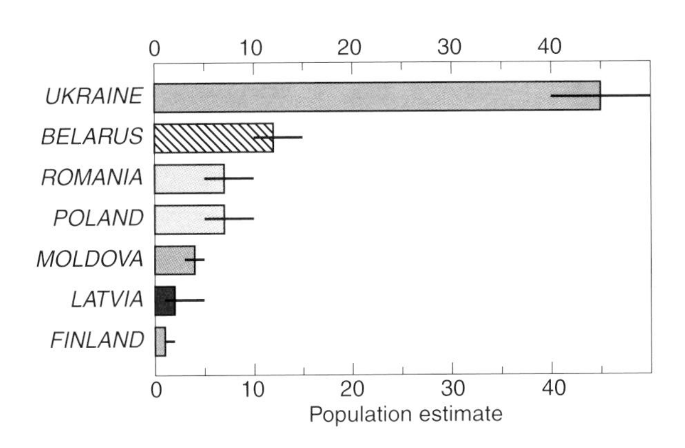

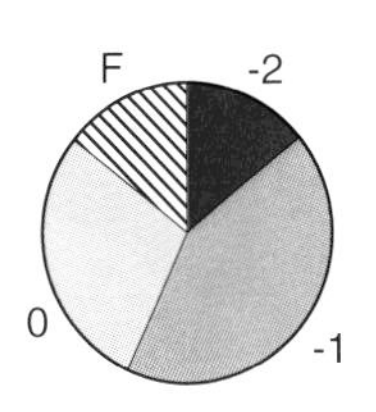

% in top 10 countries: 100.0
Total number of populated European countries: 7
Total European population 72–86 (79)
Russian population 800–800 (800)

The monotypic Spotted Eagle is distributed from the Baltic Kaliningrad region and eastern Poland, through European Russia in a broad swathe from the northernmost taiga (64–65°N) to the edge of the steppes (53–56°N), and into Siberia as far the Ussuriland and Manchurian coasts. Karelia holds the northernmost European breeding site at 65°45'N, 31°20'E.

Emphatically an inhabitant of wetland habitats, the Spotted Eagle favours flood forests for nesting. It hunts in adjacent humid meadows, bogs, swamps and lake and watercourse margins. Primarily a lowland breeder, it nevertheless nests up to 1000m asl in mountain forests.

The very patchy distribution of its specialist habitat governs its breeding range. Little is known of Asian numbers and trends, but in Europe fewer than 1000bp exist, the only substantial population being in Russia (several hundred bp). Until recently Ukraine held but 40–50bp (I. Gorban & V. Vetrov, pers comm), Moldova *c*3–5bp before 1990, Belarus 10–15bp (Ivanowsky 1963a,b, pers comm), Poland *c*30bp (only 10–15bp in 1993; Pugacewicz 1995) and Kaliningrad *c*10–14bp, but by 1995 it was almost extinct in Ukraine (V. Vetrov, pers comm). Even recently published population estimates are outdated. It is still declining in European Russia (V. Galushin, pers comm).

Breeding habitat destruction and direct persecution have caused the decline in numbers, making it one of Europe's rarest and most threatened raptors. It has disappeared from many regions and countries where formerly it bred regularly, such as Slovakia, Hungary, Romania, Bulgaria, the former Yugoslavia and Israel. Since 1985 it has declined almost to extinction in the Baltic States. At least one pair probably breeds most years in Latvia, perhaps more, but there is likely only one nest site in Lithuania. There is no reliable evidence of breeding in Estonia (V. Volke, pers comm). In southern Finland, despite rare but fairly regular sightings, it has not bred recently (P. Saurola, pers comm). The Spotted Eagle is probably also extinct in much of its former range between Bangladesh and Pakistan. It may still breed near the southern Caspian and in previous strongholds in Kazakhstan and China. Recent estimates of some European Russian populations provided densities of 20–30 bp/85 000km^2 or less in a number of regions. Only two known European population centres remain in 1995, one in the Oka Reserve in Ryazan region *c*200km SE of Moscow, where since the 1960s the population of 7–9bp has been stable (3–4bp in 230km^2) (Galushin 1962, pers comm), and the other on the Biebrza River in NE Poland, where the marshes held a maximum of 10 occupied territories during 1989–93 (Pugacewicz 1995) and where an ongoing research programme has located 11bp on *c*2000km^2 (B-U. Meyburg *et al* in prep).

The Spotted Eagle is a medium-distance migrant, wintering mostly in Asia Minor, the Middle East, Arabia, the Near East, India, and in eastern North Africa and scattered locations S to Kenya. Odd individuals also winter in southern Europe, and more recently in C Europe. There is a history of confusion with the very similar Lesser Spotted Eagle *A. pomarina*. At major migration concentration points such as the Bosphorus, Israel and Suez the Spotted Eagle is probably overlooked amongst flocks of its congener or even when there are mixed flocks. Even after advances in identification techniques (Forsman 1991), experienced field workers have problems, thus helping to under-record its occurrence in breeding areas.

The only Spotted Eagle so far tracked by satellite telemetry wintered in Yemen from late November to early February. It travelled 5526km (4516km in less than a month) to return to W Siberia. The longest daily stages, averaging 280km, occurred through Iraq and Iran (Meyburg *et al* 1995). Despite its enormous range, the species remains little-studied, partly because its nests are difficult to find, and there are few data relevant to its present status.

Bernd-U Meyburg (D) Marek Keller (PL)

Aquila heliaca

Imperial Eagle

CZ	Orel královský	I	Aquila imperiale
D	Kaiseradler	NL	Keizerarend
E	Aguila Imperial Oriental	P	Águia-imperial
F	Aigle impérial	PL	Orzeł cesarski
FIN	Keisarikotka	R	Могильник
G	Βασιλαετός	S	Kejsarörn
H	Parlagi sas		

SPEC Cat 1, Threat status E

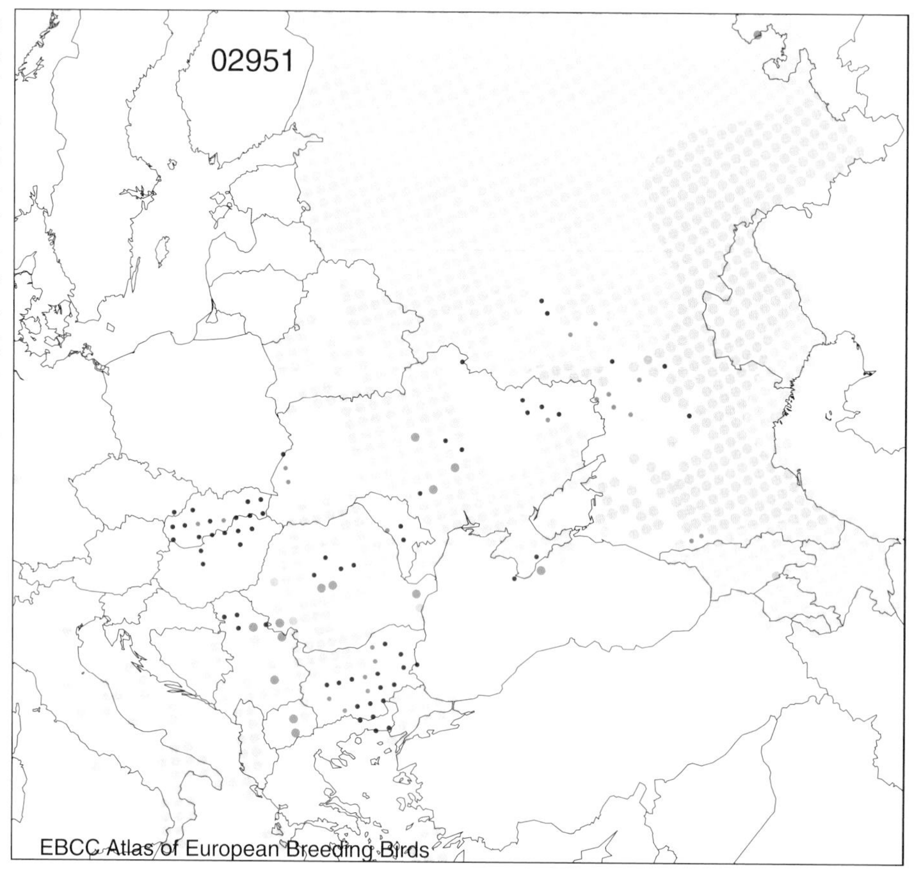

The rare and threatened Imperial Eagle occurs from 110°E (Lake Baykal) W to 17°E (western Slovakia), and from 55°N (Kyubyshev Reservoir) in Russia S to 35°N (Cyprus). Its European breeding range stretches from Slovakia and Hungary through Ukraine (hill-country and steppes) to SE Russia and the Caucasus, and includes the Carpathian basin through to the SE Balkan Peninsula. Its western breeding distribution recently became fragmented or very sparsely inhabited. D. Janossy (pers comm) suggests that the Imperial Eagle is a typical Asian species which reached the Carpathian basin as recently as the mid-1850s.

Formerly the Imperial Eagle bred solely in evergreen open country scattered with isolated trees or in river-fringed forests. As a consequence of persecution and the destruction of prime habitats or during range extension, it started to breed more often in deciduous and mixed forests or hilly areas (first the Carpathians, then the eastern Balkan Peninsula) up to 800m asl (Slovakia) and 1000m asl in Bulgaria (Petrov *et al* 1996b). At several Slovakian locations the breeding distributions of Imperial and Golden *A. chrysaetos* Eagles overlap. Since the mid-1980s, a part of the Slovakian and Hungarian lowland population reoccupied open agricultural country to breed in solitary trees, windbreaks and isolated patches of forest (Danko & Chavko 1996, Haraszthy *et al* 1996). In Europe the species occurs mostly in lowlands adjacent to foothills (as in the Great Danube basin), hilly country and river valleys (E Ukraine, Grishczenko 1993).

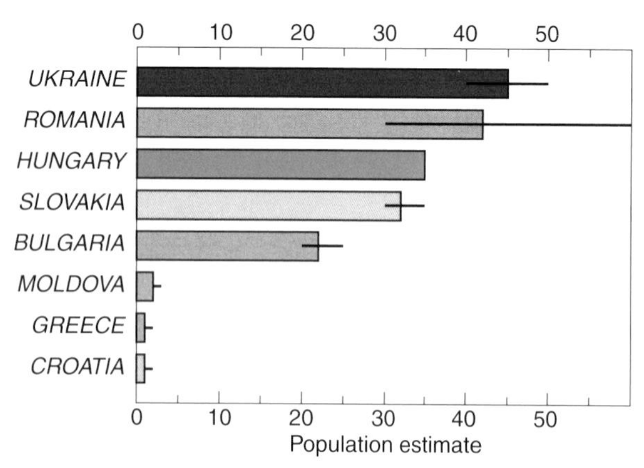

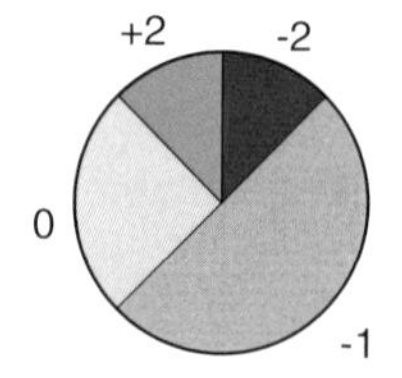

% in top 10 countries: 100.0
Total number of populated European countries: 8
Total European population 168–201 (182)
Russian population 150–300 (212)
Turkish population 10–50 (22)

Reliable census data are available from Slovakia and Hungary, but are lacking from Romania and European Russia. The recent Imperial Eagle Workshop held in Kirâlyrét, Hungary, led the participants to conclude that the European population size was 350–550bp in December 1993, but in our view Romania may have only 10–20bp. Not apparent from the map or from *BWP* maps is that Armenia and Azerbaijan hold breeding populations of 8–10 and 35–40bp respectively.

The species has declined considerably since the mid-1950s and remains in decline in most countries. Only in Slovakia and Hungary is there an evident steady increase in numbers since 1985, the result of consistent research, monitoring, management and sound conservation policies, all based on good co-operation between the countries. Consequently, in eastern Slovakia breeding productivity has improved from 1.0 to 1.4 young in newly occupied nests, and from 1.7 to 2.3 young in long-established sites. Population densities are also increasing, as in the Trebišov District: 4bp in 1991, 5 in 1992, 7 in 1993–94 and 8 in 1995 (4 in forests, 4 amongst cultivation), equivalent to 1 bp/146km^2. The shortest inter-nest distance between nests was only 1.6km, the range being 4–14km and the average 10km (Š. Danko, pers obs). Because of clear plumage differentiation between adults and young, the increase could be documented comprehensively. Young pairs may disperse to found new territories, hence extending the breeding range, or remain near their natal site, thus increasing local population density.

Immatures are almost exclusively migratory. Northwestern populations winter mostly in the southern Balkans (Greece, the Peloponnese Peninsula), some reaching western Turkey; a Slovakian bird wintered in southern Israel (Danko 1996). Adults are either sedentary or winter S or SE of their breeding grounds. Eastern European populations winter in NE Africa, Mesopotamia and the Middle East. Asian birds winter usually in N India and E China.

Štefan Danko (SLK) László Haraszthy (H)

Aquila adalberti

Spanish Imperial Eagle

CZ	Orel Adalbertův	I	Aquila imperiale occidentale
D	Spanischer Kaiseradler	NL	Spaanse Keizerarend
E	Aguila Imperial Ibérica	P	Águia-imperial
F	Aigle ibérique	PL	Orzeł hiszpański
FIN	Pyreneidenkeisarikotka	R	Испанский могильник
G	Ισπανικός Βασιλαετός	S	Spansk kejsarörn
H	Ibériai sas		

SPEC Cat 1, Threat status E

The total world population of *A. adalberti* until recently could be found only in Spain, occupying almost 150 breeding territories in 1994. It inhabits the central mountains, the plains of the Tagus and Tietar Rivers, Extremadura, the Toledo Mountains, the Sierra Morena and the Guadalquivir marshes (Doñana). In 1994 one pair probably nested in Morocco (B. Heredia, pers comm), perhaps a recolonization. In Portugal individuals have been observed but the species is not known to have bred recently (Rufino 1989). Between 1960 and 1970 it was near extinction, only 30bp being found, but a slow recovery, beginning in the 1980s, is producing 5 new bp each year (González 1995). Pairs are beginning to occupy marginal territories more prone to human disturbance. Pairs stay the

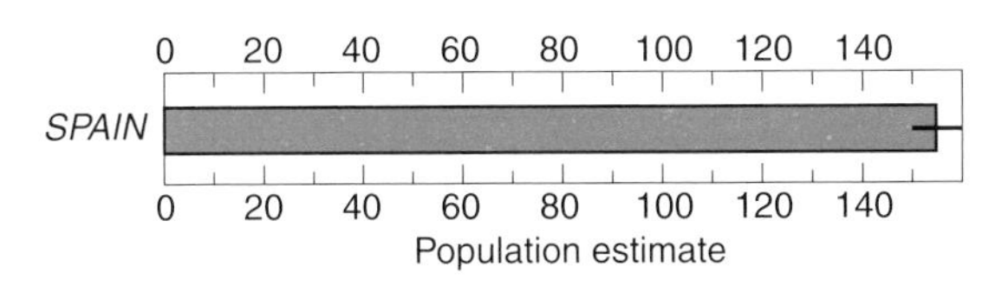

% in top 10 countries: 100.0
Total number of populated European countries: 1
Total European population 150–160 (155)

whole year in their territory, whereas the young disperse widely after reaching independence, travelling 350km on average. At this time immatures tend to congregate in a few favoured localities which have an extraordinary abundance of rabbits *Oryctolagus cuniculus*. Numbers using these localities are not constant, because individual birds move from one such site to another independently (González 1991, Ferrer 1993). The average nest-separation distance in prime habitat is 6.5km and the mean breeding density is 1.93 bp/100km^2 (González *et al* 1992). The Doñana subpopulation has the highest density and that in the Tagus Valley the lowest. Breeding density in protected areas is four times higher than in non-protected areas. The main breeding populations are in the Monfrague Natural Park (Cáceres), the Doñana National Park (Huelva) and the Royal State of 'Monte del Pardo' (Madrid). Some 35% of breeding territories lie in the Spanish network of Protected Areas and 62% in Important Bird Areas (González 1995). Perhaps the main factors influencing the range of the Spanish Imperial Eagle are the abundance and distribution of rabbits.

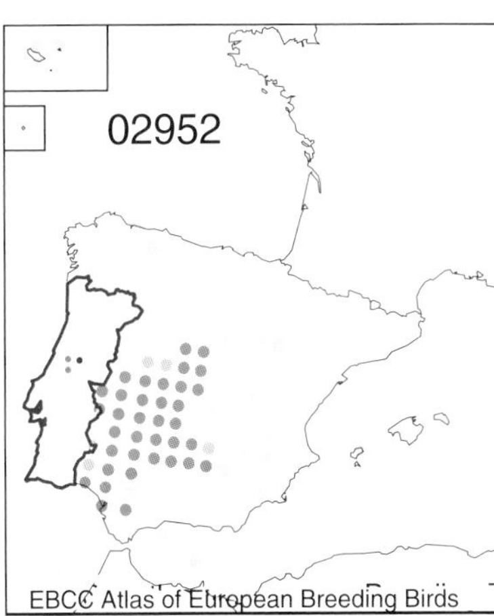

Luis Mariano González (E)

Aquila chrysaetos **Golden Eagle**

CZ	Orel skalní	I	Aquila reale
D	Steinadler	NL	Steenarend
E	Aguila Real	P	Águia-real
F	Aigle royal	PL	Orzeł przedni
FIN	Maakotka	R	Беркут
G	Χρυσαετός	S	Kungsörn
H	Szirti sas		

SPEC Cat 3, Threat status R

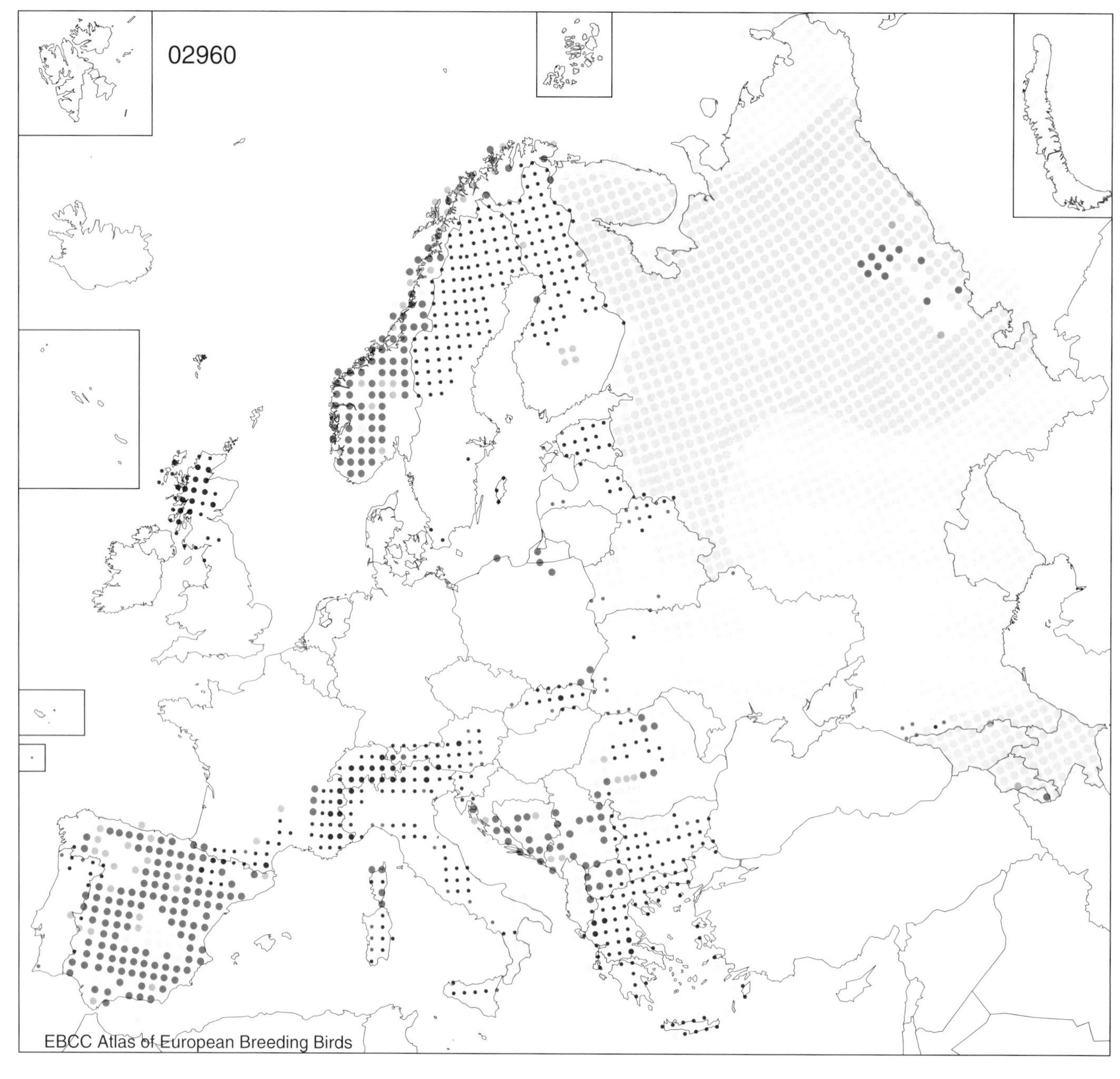

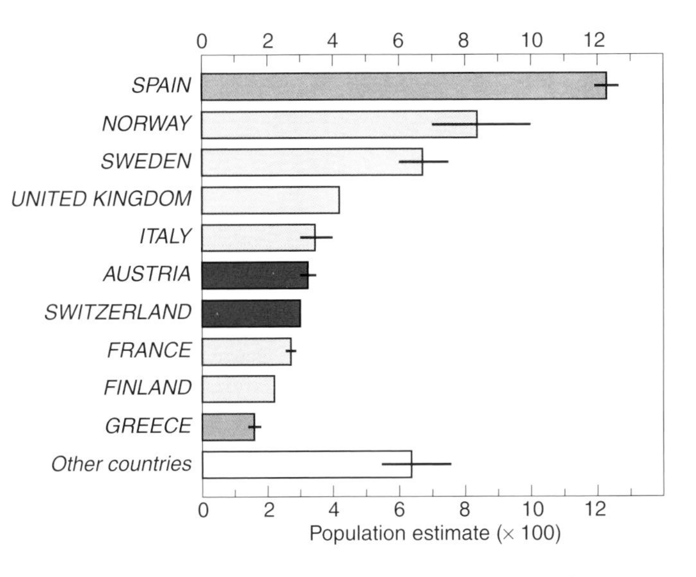

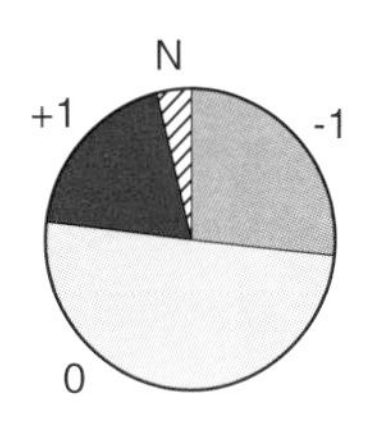

% in top 10 countries: 88.2
Total number of populated European countries: 26
Total European population 5239–5616 (5412)
Russian population 200–400 (283)
Turkish population 100–1000 (316)

The range of the Holarctic Golden Eagle extends across vast areas of the Northern Hemisphere from W Europe and North Africa to Kamchatka and Japan, across Alaska, Canada and the western USA to Mexico. The nominate subspecies *A.c. chrysaetos* inhabits Europe (except the Iberian Peninsula) eastwards to W Siberia. Iberia holds the subspecies *homeyeri*, whose distribution includes North Africa and the Middle East. The species' breeding habitats must contain at least the following elements: large-scale areas of open unwooded, or semi-open moderately wooded terrain, usually uncultivated or subject only to low-intensity pastoralism; the availability during the breeding season of living prey weighing 2–5kg; a similar prey supply or ungulate carrion during the non-breeding season, and secure nesting sites in cliffs or mature trees. It is the most abundant of large eagles within its distribution.

Throughout N Europe the Golden Eagle occurs from the mountains of the Scottish Highlands and Scandinavia through the forests of N Sweden and Finland to the peatland habitats of the Baltic lowlands. Its southern European range extends across the hilly country and mountain chains of the Iberian and Italian Peninsulas, over the Alps and Carpathians to the Balkans and includes the large Mediterranean islands. In the N, prime habitats comprise mountain tundra, blanket bogs, semi-open boreal woodland, peatland, heath and rocky seashores. Throughout C and S Europe it is confined to the subalpine and alpine zones of the higher mountain chains and the summer-dry scrublands of the Mediterranean. It nests on cliffs from near sea level in Scotland up to 2600m asl in the Alps. In high mountains, it usually breeds near the tree-line below its hunting grounds.

Except in the densest lowland forests, the species originally was distributed all over Europe, but following centuries of severe persecution and large-scale land-use changes, the species became extirpated from the northern lowlands and secondary mountain chains of C Europe and southern Britain. Long-term population levels for the Scottish Highlands and Fennoscandia, estimated at 1900–2400bp, are constant (Tjernberg 1983, Dennis *et al* 1984). S Sweden is experiencing a slow recolonization by isolated pairs. In the Alps better protection and an improved food supply through extensive management of ungulate game species has encouraged a population increase (1100–1200bp), in Switzerland almost to carrying capacity (Haller 1982, Jenny 1992), but so far expansion of the breeding population beyond the foothills of the Alps remains unconfirmed. Immigration from other Alpine regions explains the stable population in S Germany, where the recruitment rate is not self-sustaining (Bezzel 1995). In contrast, through persecution and habitat change, the Iberian population has decreased to 1200–1300bp since the mid-1960s (Arroyo *et al* 1990a). Throughout the Balkans (500–700bp), information on population trends differs by country, but in Greece and Albania negative trends are evident. The remaining European populations outside Russia comprise fewer than 500 bp.

The Golden Eagle's population dynamics are governed by longevity, low reproduction rates, territorial spacing of breeding pairs in a near-regular pattern in a seasonally predictable environment, and high fidelity to breeding areas. Its breeding densities therefore are relatively low, varying among the core populations across Europe from 50 to 200 km^2/bp. In sparsely populated areas, such as the Apennines, densities below 300 km^2/bp were recorded. In Europe outside Russia, pairs remain within their breeding territories year-round, while those in northern populations above *c*60°N are migratory. Dispersing juveniles and immatures from the Alpine populations usually remain within the Alps, reducing breeding success of resident pairs through intraspecific competition (Haller 1982, Jenny 1992), whereas young birds ringed in Finland were winter migrants to Belarus, Ukraine, and Hungary.

Heinrich Haller (CH) Peter Sackl (A)

This species account is sponsored by Schweizer Vogelschutz SVS – BirdLife Schweiz, CH.

Hieraaetus pennatus | Booted Eagle

CZ	Orel nejmenší	**I**	Aquila minore
D	Zwergadler	**NL**	Dwergarend
E	Aguililla Calzada	**P**	Águia-calçada
F	Aigle botté	**PL**	Orzełek włochaty
FIN	Pikkukotka	**R**	Орел-карлик
G	Σταυραετός	**S**	Dvärgörn
H	Törpesas		

SPEC Cat 3, Threat status R

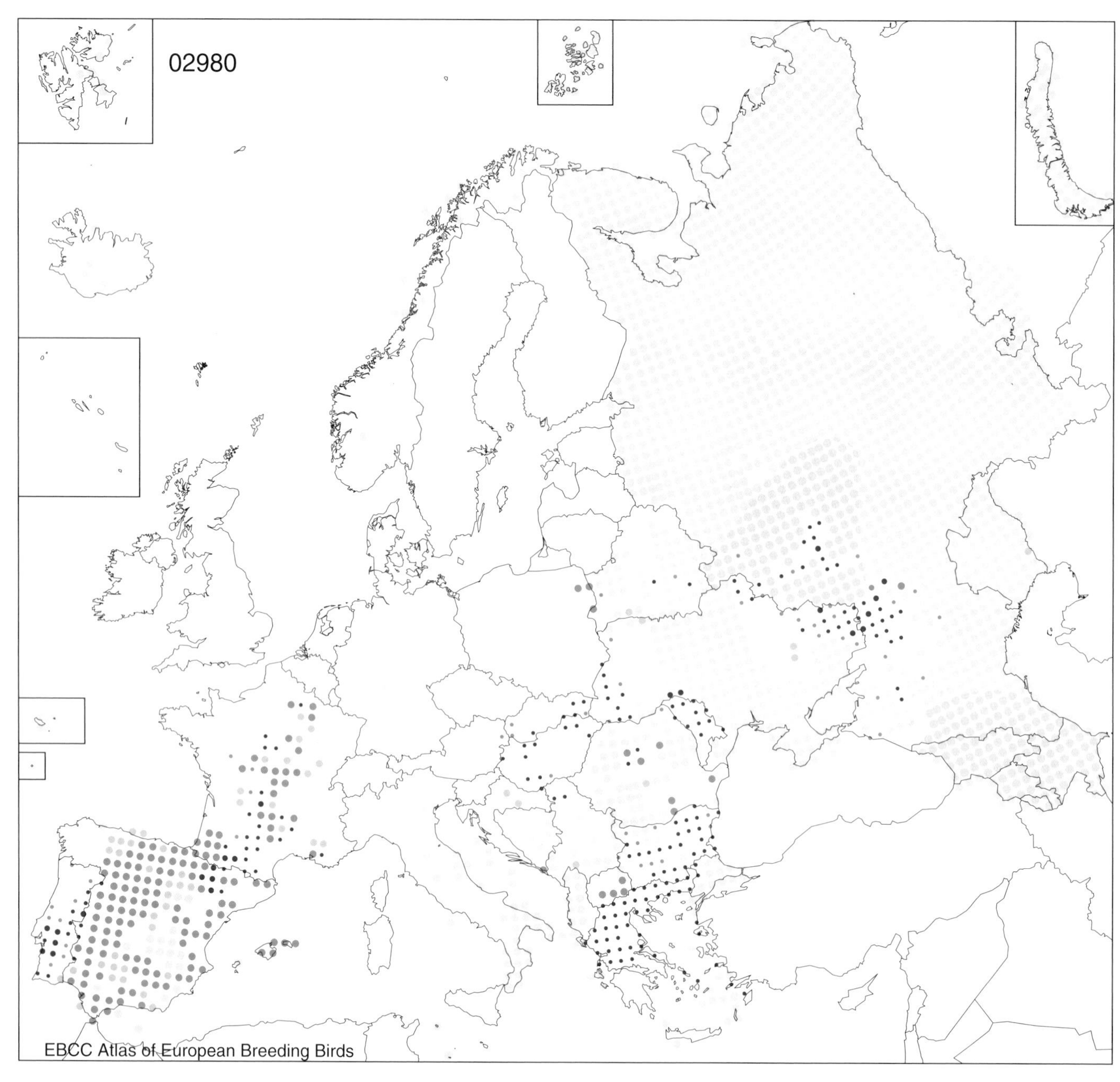

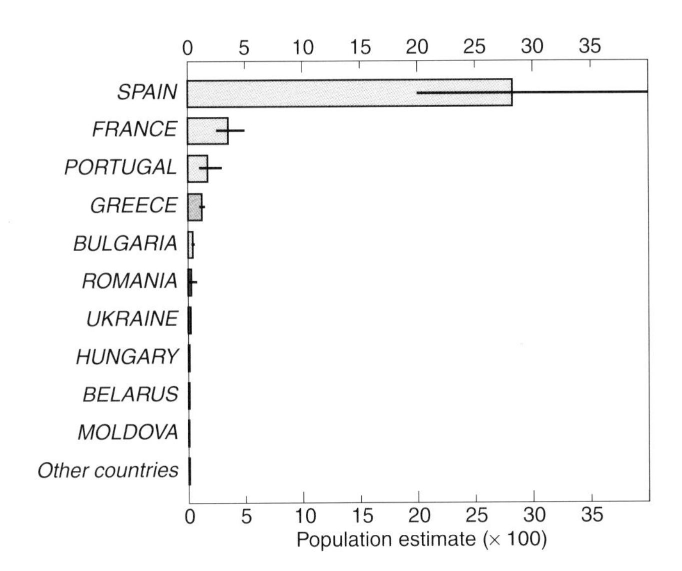

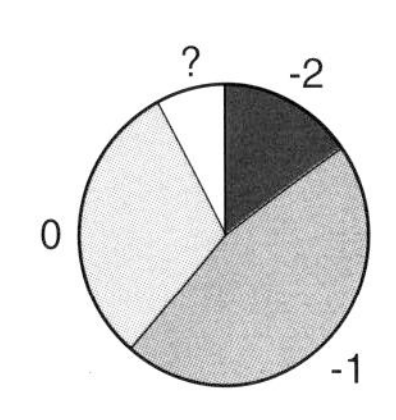

% in top 10 countries: 99.8
Total number of populated European countries: 13
Total European population 2765–4793 (3604)
Russian population 200–400 (283)
Turkish population 100–500 (224)

The Booted Eagle's distribution covers a rather narrow belt between 56°N and 30°N, stretching from Portugal and North Africa in the W through the Caucasus and W Kazakhstan to W Manchuria in the E. There is a resident population in southern Africa. The European population winters in wooded savanna in the Sahelian–Sudanese belt from the Atlantic coast to Ethiopia and S towards South Africa. Small numbers winter regularly in S Europe, on Mediterranean islands and in North Africa.

The smallest european eagle, it is a typical western Palearctic forest species, occurring on plains, hills and mountains, from sea level up to 1600m asl (Nore 1994), but occasionally in suitable habitat up to 2000m asl (Carlon 1987, Nankinov *et al* 1991). It breeds in dense or patchy forests interspersed with clearings and open areas of shrubland, grassland, fallows or cultivated land, but avoids continuous even-aged forest plantations. Nesting on cliffs is quite uncommon in Europe.

In S and W Iberia, the species nests in evergreen oak and pine woods and parkland, apparently preferring pines for nest-building. In N Spain, France and the Balkan countries its breeding habitat consists of mixed and pure stands of deciduous and coniferous trees, including evergreen oaks (Iribarren 1975, Nore 1994). In the plains of SE Europe it nests usually in floodplain poplar and oak forests, less commonly in ravine oak woods or arenicolous pine stands (Zubarovsky 1977).

The European population is estimated at some 5800bp and is concentrated (65%) in SW Europe, especially in Spain (3000bp). The French population has increased in Provence but elsewhere is reasonably stable. Its apparent range increase from the 1970s to the 1980s probably stems from better coverage (Nore 1994). The Iberian breeding numbers are also considered stable (L. Palma *et al,* in prep). In C Europe and the Balkans the Booted Eagle's distribution has become scattered, almost to the point of extinction. Albania, Moldova, Hungary, Slovakia, Poland and Belarus now each have fewer than 15bp and all report a decline in range and numbers during 1970–90. Bulgaria (50bp), Romania (10–80bp) and the former Yugoslavia (50bp in the early 1980s; Vasic *et al* 1985) have slightly higher numbers. The Bulgarian population is probably stable, but that in Romania has declined by >50% from 1970 to 1990. The populations furthest E in Europe, in our opinion and contrary to the graph, seem stable or even increasing, Ukraine holding 100–300bp, and European Russia 500–800bp at breeding densities ranging from 0.05 to 0.5 bp/100km^2 and averaging 0.1 bp/100km^2 in the forest-steppe zone (Belik 1990).

Habitat destruction, in both breeding and wintering habitats, is probably the most important factor responsible for the declining European populations. In the breeding areas, many ancient forests are replaced by even-aged plantations of fast-growing (often non-indigenous) trees. Human pressure is also increasing, resulting in disturbance and poisoning. Its main wintering grounds in the Sahelian zone are even more under threat, because the human population is far above the carrying capacity of the area, thus preventing any recovery of the vegetation (Thiollay 1989).

The Booted Eagle, being dependent on soaring flight when covering large distances, avoids long sea-crossings and therefore concentrates at both ends of the Mediterranean Sea during migration. Highest counts at Gibraltar totalled 14 000 birds (1972), which complies rather well with the known population in France and Iberia (3850bp) achieving an average fledgling production of 1.5/pair (Nore 1994). Numbers in the E Mediterranean are much smaller, with a maximum of 2000 in Israel in 1986 (Shirihai & Christie 1992). Given the population size in E Europe, many birds probably enter Africa via the Strait of Bab al Mandab, after having crossed Saudi Arabia, rather than via Israel and Egypt.

Victor Belik (R) Nuno Onofre (P)

Hieraaetus fasciatus

Bonelli's Eagle

CZ	Orel jestřábí	**I**	Aquila del Bonelli
D	Habichtsadler	**NL**	Havikarend
E	Aguila-azor Perdicera	**P**	Águia de Bonelli
F	Aigle de Bonelli	**PL**	Orzełek południowy
FIN	Vuorikotka	**R**	Ястребиный орел
G	Σπιζαετός	**S**	Hökörn
H	Héjasas		

SPEC Cat 3, Threat status E

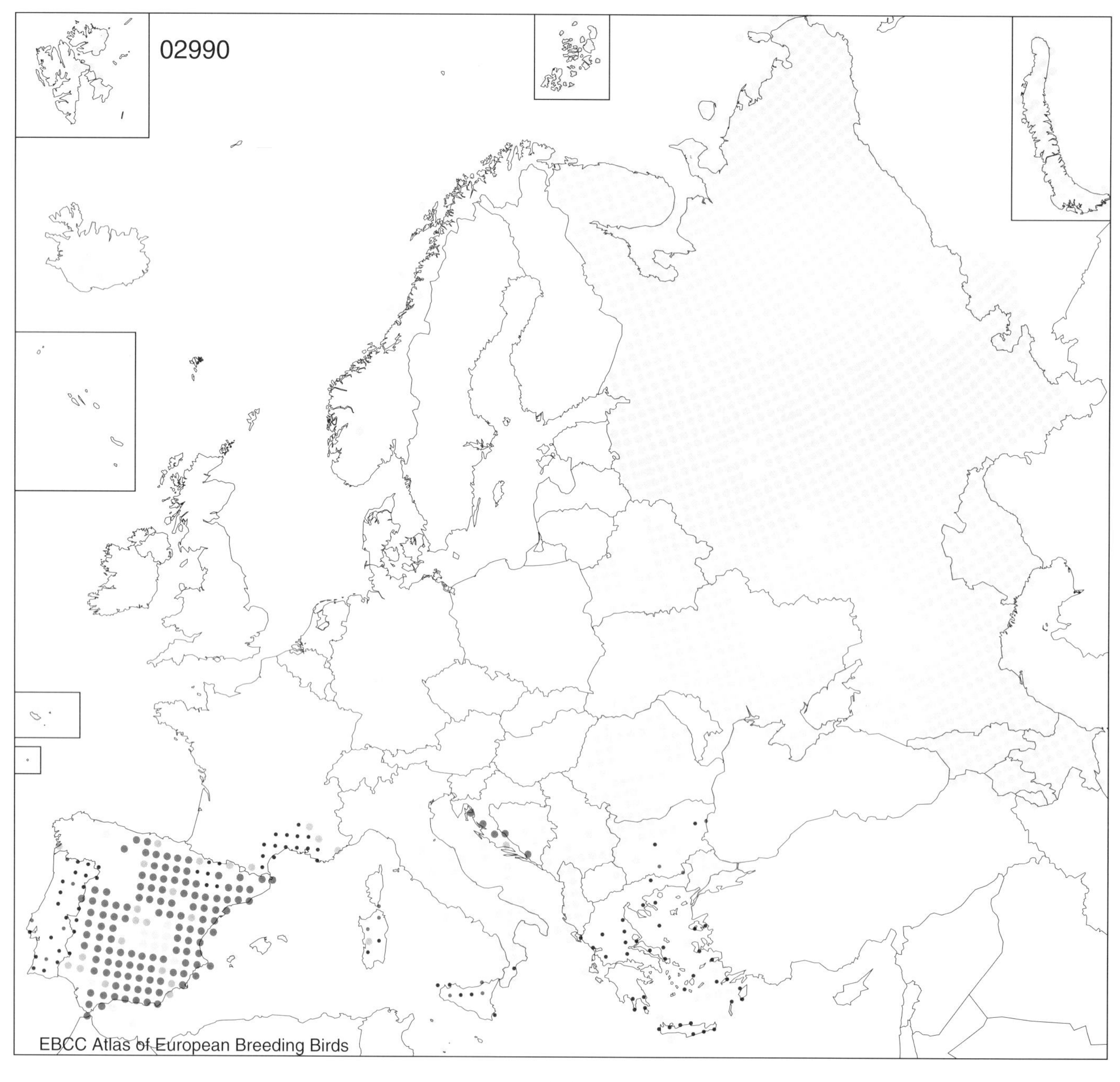

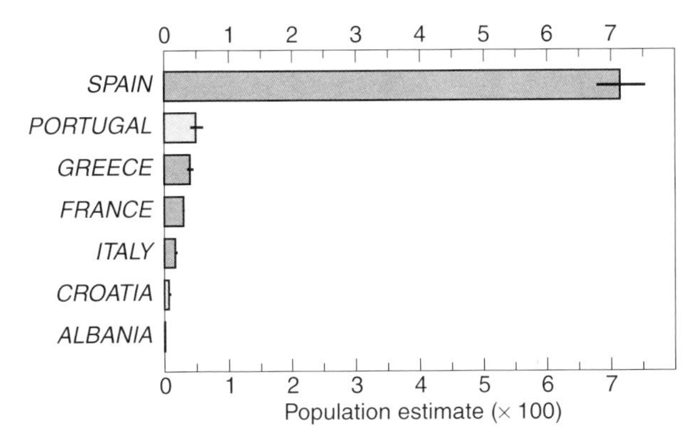

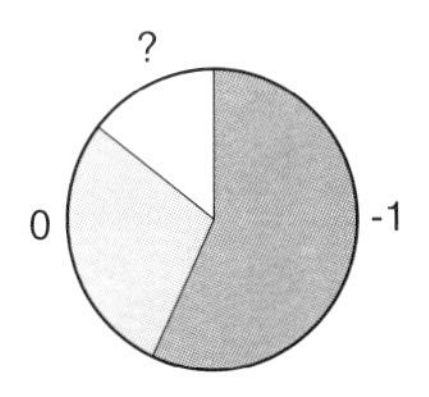

% in top 10 countries: 100.0
Total number of populated European countries: 7
Total European population 818–898 (856)
Turkish population 10–100 (32)

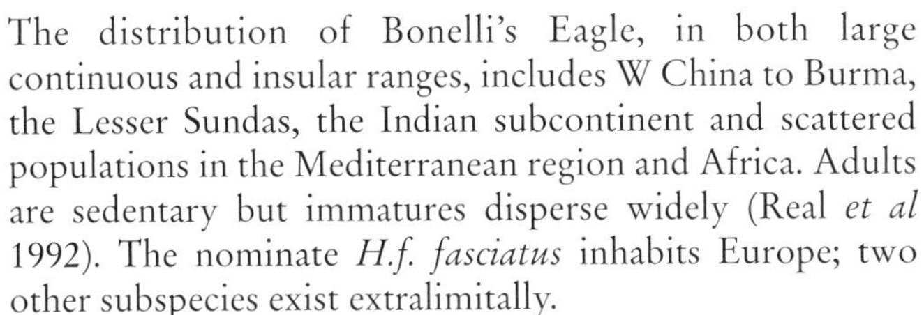

The distribution of Bonelli's Eagle, in both large continuous and insular ranges, includes W China to Burma, the Lesser Sundas, the Indian subcontinent and scattered populations in the Mediterranean region and Africa. Adults are sedentary but immatures disperse widely (Real *et al* 1992). The nominate *H.f. fasciatus* inhabits Europe; two other subspecies exist extralimitally.

In Europe, Bonelli's Eagle occupies arid to semi-humid areas within the mediterranean region from sea level to 1000m asl (occasionally to 1500m). It favours rough cliff-strewn sierras for nesting, although it also occupies foothills, river valleys containing small cliffs and even some plains. Some southern populations predominantly are tree-nesters, especially in tall cork oak *Quercus suber*, pine *Pinus* spp and eucalyptus *Eucalyptus* spp (Palma 1994).

The species generally hunts at altitudes where garrigue, maquis, rocky habitats, pine and evergreen oak forests alternate with the small dry fields of low-intensity farming. Immatures temporarily occupy low-altitude plains, where dry cultivated fields alternate with shrubby vegetation or wetlands, areas characterized by high prey densities (rabbits, partridges) and an absence of breeding adults.

Recent data indicate a European breeding population of 938–1039bp (Real *et al* in prep), *c*80% being in Spain. The Spanish non-breeding population comprises *c*1000–1500 individuals in autumn, 70% being first-summer birds.

Because European populations are not censused regularly, precise trends are not deducible. Nevertheless, national counts indicate clear decreases. The French population (60bp in 1975) comprised only 29bp in 1992 (Cheylan 1994a). In Spain the species has declined, or even disappeared in at least 27 out of 40 provinces since 1980, numbers reducing in northern and C provinces by >20% (Real *et al* 1995). In some regions like Andalucía and Extremadura the trend was stable (Real *et al* in prep). Portugal's population is poorly known; we estimate it at *c*75–90bp (L. Palma, pers obs). Apparently it remains stable overall (Palma 1994), but locally there have been extinctions along the coast, colonizations and recolonizations. The Sardinian population has decreased drastically since the 1960s. Sicily holds most of the Italian 15–20bp (Lo Valvo & Massa 1992), numbers remaining stable (Lo Valvo 1993). The Greek population numbered >200bp in the early 1980s (Hallmann 1985), but only 35–45bp ten years later. The status of the tiny Croatian and Macedonian populations is unknown.

All populations monitored in France (Provence, Languedoc) and Spain (Catalonia, Murcia, Alicante), from 1980 onwards have decreased, the northern populations (France, Catalonia) declining slightly and the southeastern (Iberia) sharply. These patterns are related to adult mortality, which is low or moderately high in the N and extremely high in the SE. A further complication is high immature mortality, which reduces the numbers of new recruits and undermines breeding population stability (Real *et al* in prep). Power-line accidents and direct persecution by hunters and pigeon fanciers are the main causes of mortality.

The highest known European densities of Bonelli's Eagle occur in the coastward sierras of Iberia, from Barcelona to Cádiz and S Portugal, where average densities of 1 bp/100–200km^2 prevail. During the 1970s in some Vallès district sierras (Catalonia), densities reached 1 bp/60km^2, some breeding pairs being separated by only 1–3km (5.1km on average). Since the recent dramatic decrease, pair-separation distance averages 17km, giving a density of 1 bp/192km^2 (Real 1991, pers obs). Some populations in S Catalonia (1 bp/84km^2; Real 1991) and in Cádiz (1 bp/85km^2; del Junco 1984) still maintain healthy densities, although by 1995 several pairs had been lost.

Known dispersal areas lie in La Crau–Camargue (France), C Catalonia, Alicante–Murcia, Albacete and Cádiz (Spain). Intensive agricultural methods, high hunting pressure and transformation of dry fields by irrigation could further reduce its numbers, as has already happened in Catalonia.

Joan Real (E) Luis Palma (P) Gérard Rocamora (F)

Pandion haliaetus — Osprey

CZ	Orlovec říční	I	Falco pescatore
D	Fischadler	NL	Visarend
E	Aguila Pescadora	P	Águia-pesqueira
F	Balbuzard pêcheur	PL	Rybołów
FIN	Kalasääski	R	Скопа
G	Ψαραετός	S	Fiskgjuse
H	Halászsas		

SPEC Cat 3, Threat status R

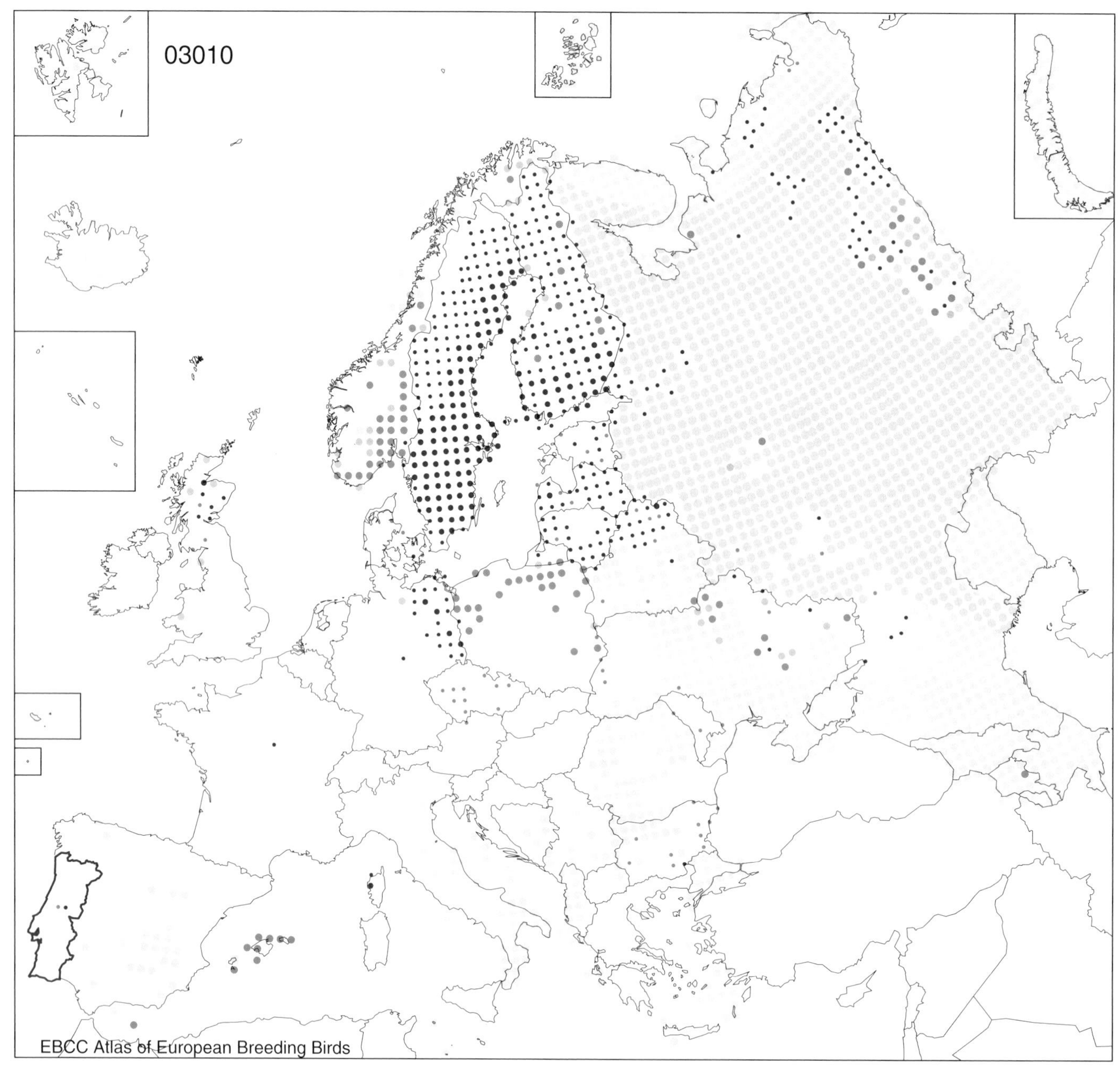

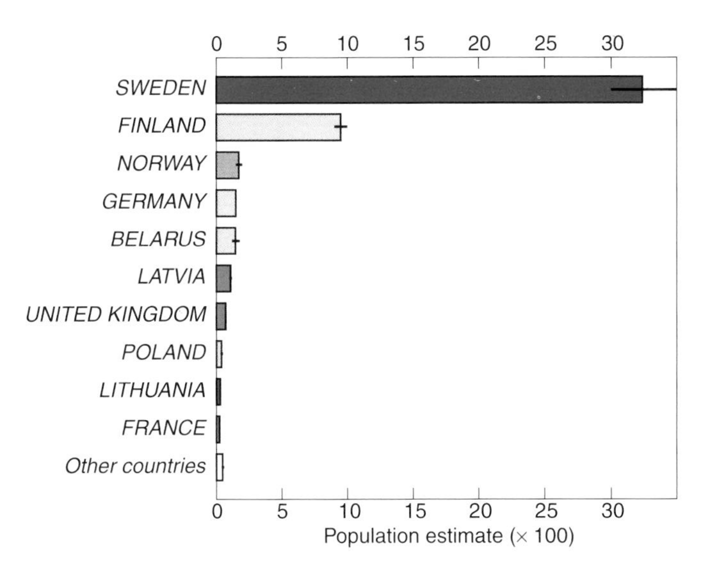

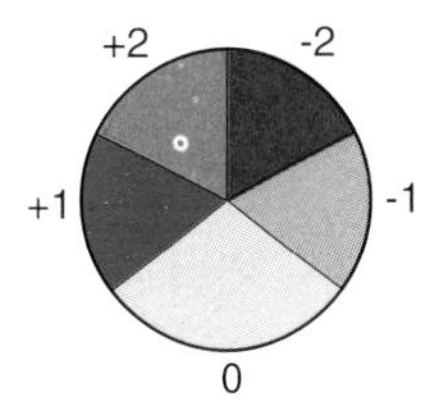

% in top 10 countries: 99.1
Total number of populated European countries: 17
Total European population 4732–5249 (4981)
Russian population 2500–3500 (2958)
Turkish population 1–10 (3)

The Osprey is a large, long-winged and easily identified cosmopolitan raptor. It can be found in every continent except the Antarctic, although it does not breed in South America nor in most of Africa. The total world population is probably 25 000–30 000bp (Poole 1989). The nominate *P.h. haliaetus* occupies the Palearctic, four other subspecies being recognized elsewhere.

Because the Osprey eats only fish it has caught, it is restricted to the vicinity of suitable fishing areas throughout the year. Furthermore, a stable and exposed base for its large eyrie is a prerequisite for successful breeding. Yet the breeding habitat may vary greatly, ranging from closed coniferous forest and pine bog to coastal cliff and even treeless desert. In Europe, the Osprey nests mostly in trees, mainly in forests, the only exceptions being the Mediterranean cliff-nesters and those German birds (60%) which nest on power-line pylons in rural areas (Schmidt 1994).

Formerly distributed throughout Europe, from the Mediterranean to northernmost Norway, and from Great Britain to the Urals, the Osprey now has 90% of its European breeding population in Sweden, Finland and Russia, most of the remainder being in Norway, Scotland, Germany, Poland, Belarus and the Baltic republics. Fewer than 50bp breed in southern Europe (24bp in 1992 on Corsica).

Nearly all Osprey populations worldwide have a similar 20th-century history; up to the 1920s, perhaps earlier, dramatic decreases and even extinctions occurred through heavy persecution. The subsequent recovery period lasted until another decrease from the 1950s to the mid-1970s, through the effects of organochlorines in the food chain. In the early 1980s a second recovery period began whose trend continues (Poole 1989, Dennis 1995, Saurola 1995).

The Osprey is fairly easy to monitor: displaying and fishing males are conspicuous and large exposed nests and noisy fledglings are easily detected. The most precise country-wide data on the recent population trends come from Scotland, Germany and Finland. In Scotland, the Osprey population was re-established in 1954, when the first pair bred after 38 years of extinction. By 1974, there were 15bp, but in 1994 the total exceeded 90bp (Dennis 1995). The much-reduced German population has increased rapidly since the mid-1980s, reaching *c*210 pairs in 1993 (Schmidt 1994). In Finland, all known occupied territories (961 in 1994) have been checked annually since 1971. During the 1970s the population first decreased and then stabilized, but since the early 1980s it has been increasing by 1% per year, the data suggesting this trend is due to decreased persecution during migration, a decrease in organochlorine concentrations in eggs, and the construction of artificial nests to compensate for nest losses caused by felling. In 1994, 42% of all known nests were artificial, thanks to voluntary work by bird ringers (Saurola 1995). Shortage of nest sites may restrict further increases, as probably in Sweden, where numbers remain largely stable despite the reproductive output allowing a potential annual increase of 11% (Ryttman 1994). Persecution may still be a problem locally (Mizera 1995).

In most favourable environments, as in North America, the Osprey is a colonial breeder. In Europe, the average density over large areas (>1000km^2) is not higher than 1–4 bp/100km^2. In small areas density can be much higher; in Mecklenburg in 1992 there were five active pylon nests along 1250m of power line and 12 nests within 50km^2 (D. Schmidt, pers comm).

Except for the resident Mediterranean birds, all European populations migrate to the tropics. The Sahel zone between 5° and 15°N in W and C Africa comprises the main wintering area of all age-classes of European populations, the eastern subpopulations spending their non-breeding periods further E than western subpopulations (Saurola 1994). Some Finnish (and perhaps some Russian) birds extend their migration as far as South Africa.

Pertti Saurola (FIN) Bronius Sablevicius (LITH)

This species account is sponsored by Raimund Waigmann, Wuppertal, D.

Falco naumanni Lesser Kestrel

CZ	Poštolka jižní	**I**	Grillaio
D	Rötelfalke	**NL**	Kleine Torenvalk
E	Cernícalo Primilla	**P**	Peneireiro-das-torres
F	Faucon crécerellette	**PL**	Pustułeczka
FIN	Pikkutuulihaukka	**R**	Степная пустельга
G	Κιρκινέζι	**S**	Rödfalk
H	Fehérkarmú vércse		

SPEC Cat 1, Threat status V (P)

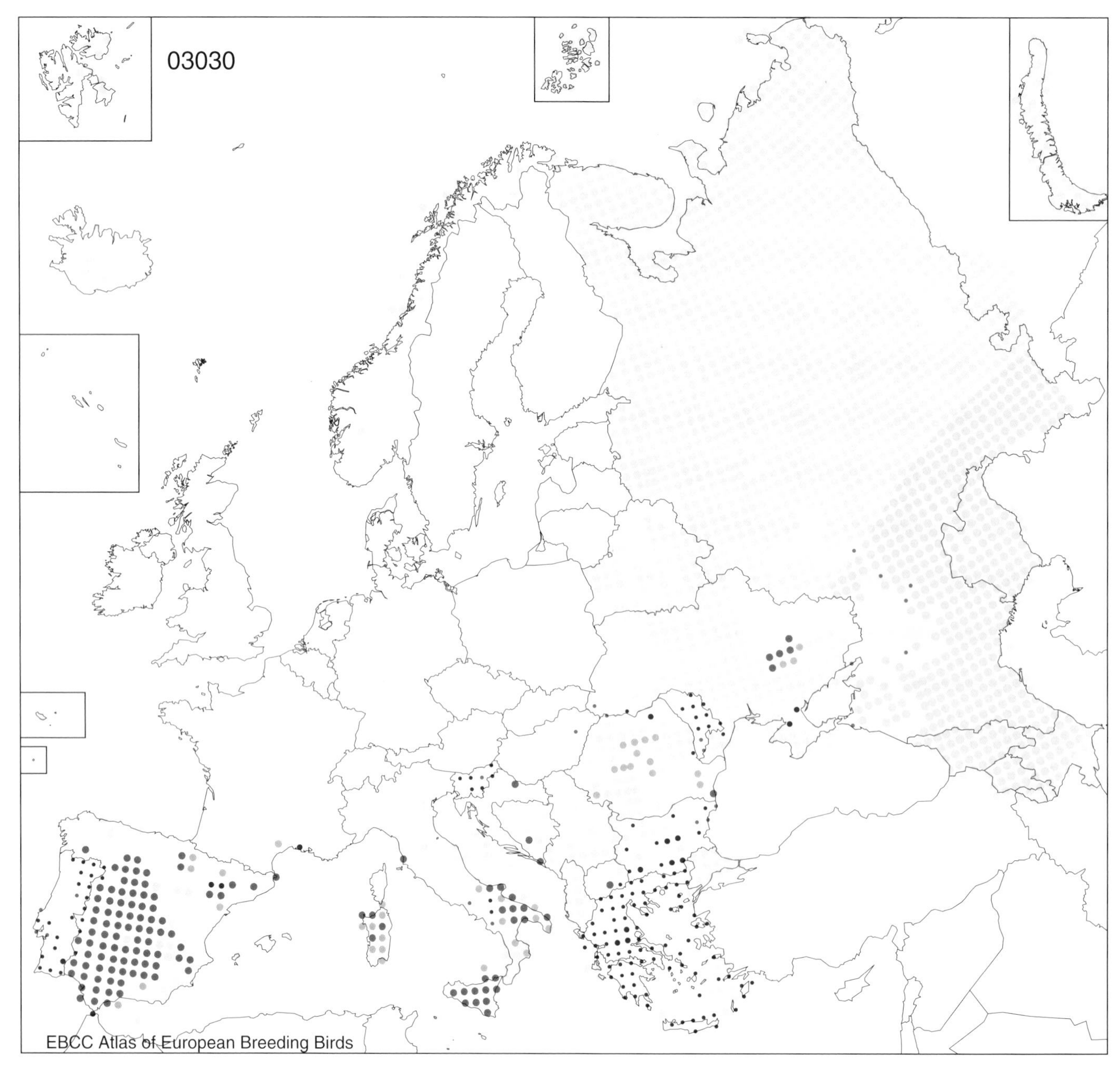

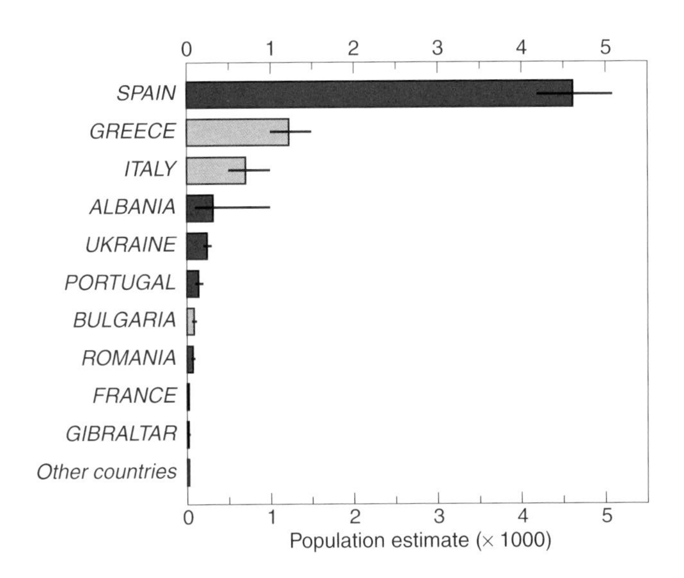

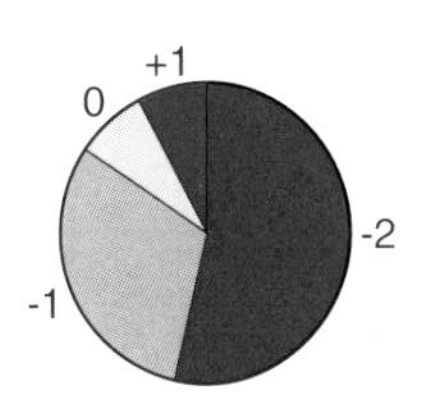

% in top 10 countries: 99.7
Total number of populated European countries: 13
Total European population 6911–8412 (7484)
Russian population 70–150 (102)
Turkish population 4000–7000 (5292)

The Lesser Kestrel is distributed from southern Europe, North Africa, Turkey and Asia E to China, mostly S of a line from N Slovenia to *c*55°N in the S Urals, narrowly extending to Israel and C Iran. Its European breeding range is mainly Mediterranean but continues N of the Black Sea.

The Lesser Kestrel is highly gregarious. It breeds in colonies, migrates and winters in flocks, and roosts communally (sometimes in thousands) in trees. It prefers open country, deserts, dry grassland, steppes and open, low-intensity cultivated plains, avoiding areas with scrub and trees (Donázar *et al* 1994). It nests mostly close to human settlements or on suitable rocky or sandy slopes. Some 96% of Spanish colonies larger than 20bp occur in old town or village buildings, or in small rural *fincas* and sheds. In Ukraine and Georgia it occupies primarily deserted corvid nests (Zollinger & Hagemeijer 1994).

Over much of its European range, the Lesser Kestrel has suffered massive declines. Recent estimates from more comprehensive coverage than achieved for the graph values (derived from the European Bird Database), are marginally higher in some places but leave the regression's scale unaffected. Declines include: Spain, >100 000bp (early 1960s) fell to *c*50 000bp (1970s) then to 8000bp by 1994 (J-P. Biber 1995) (the 1989 census had suggested <5100bp (González & Merino 1990), probably slightly too conservatively); France, numbers crashed to only 20–26bp (1992; Yeatman-Berthelot & Jarry 1994); Greece, 2980–3100bp (1995 census) representing an apparent increase from better coverage (B. Hallman, pers comm); Italy, 1300–1600bp (1994), vital areas being Sicily (stable), Sardinia (declining) and Puglia-Basilicata (increasing); the lower 1981–92 estimates had derived from incomplete information, but the Puglia-Basilicata increase is real, from 90–110bp (mid-1980s) to 777–1023bp (1994; Gallo Orsi, pers comm); and Hungary, extinct (formerly a regular breeder).

The apparently positive Romanian trend (120–130bp, 1970–90) contrasts with declines in the early 1900s (Zollinger & Hagemeijer 1994). The Bulgarian population totals *c*60bp (P. Iankov, pers obs). The declining W Ukraine population probably comprises a few hundred breeding pairs (I. Gorban, pers comm). A few hundred probably bred near the Sea of Azov in the early 1990s (J. van der Winden, pers comm). The Georgian estimated total is *c*650bp (early 1990s), slightly down from the 1980s, and the Armenian 50–100bp (A. Abuladze, pers comm). Fewer than 1000bp (probably several hundred) breed in Azerbaijan (A. Abuladze, pers comm; Zollinger & Hagemeijer 1994).

The declining trends include a reduction in overall colony size and an increase in solitary breeding pairs. Of 350 Spanish breeding sites known in 1989, only 50 colonies held more than 20bp, the largest, *c*175–200bp, being in Cáceres (González & Merino 1990); in 1987 it had held at least 225bp (E.J.M. Hagemeijer, unpubl). In Italy (1994) two colonies each of 200–250bp still remained in Puglia-Basilicata, but none in Sicily was larger than 16bp (Gallo Orsi, pers comm). In Greece, Thessaly alone accounts for 2680bp (26bp/colony). The largest colony at Nees Karies held *c*200bp (B. Hallman, pers comm).

The species' decline parallels huge changes in agricultural practice in its breeding and wintering areas. Breeding area habitat loss has reduced critically food availability; many traditional colony sites are now deserted (González & Merino 1990). Agricultural intensification (eg sunflower cultivation, Spain) and farmland abandonment (allowing encroachment, La Crau, France) are implicated (J-P. Biber 1995). Winter quarter and migration stop-over habitat loss, loss of nest sites and widespread pesticide usage are all likely contributing factors. Direct pesticide effects may be low (see Hagemeijer 1993); but indirectly, prey abundance probably is reduced (J-P. Biber 1995).

Western Palearctic populations winter mostly in sub-Saharan dry savanna regions. In South Africa (Orange Free State), in preferred pure grassland habitats, wintering numbers declined by >50% between 1966/67 and 1992/93 (McCann 1994).

Ward J M Hagemeijer (NL) Petar Iankov (BUL)

Falco tinnunculus **Kestrel**

CZ	Poštolka obecná	**I**	Gheppio
D	Turmfalke	**NL**	Torenvalk
E	Cernícalo Vulgar	**P**	Peneireiro-vulgar
F	Faucon crécerelle	**PL**	Pustułka
FIN	Tuulihaukka	**R**	Обыкновенная пустельга
G	Βραχοκιρκίνεζο	**S**	Tornfalk
H	Vörös vércse		

SPEC Cat 3, Threat status D

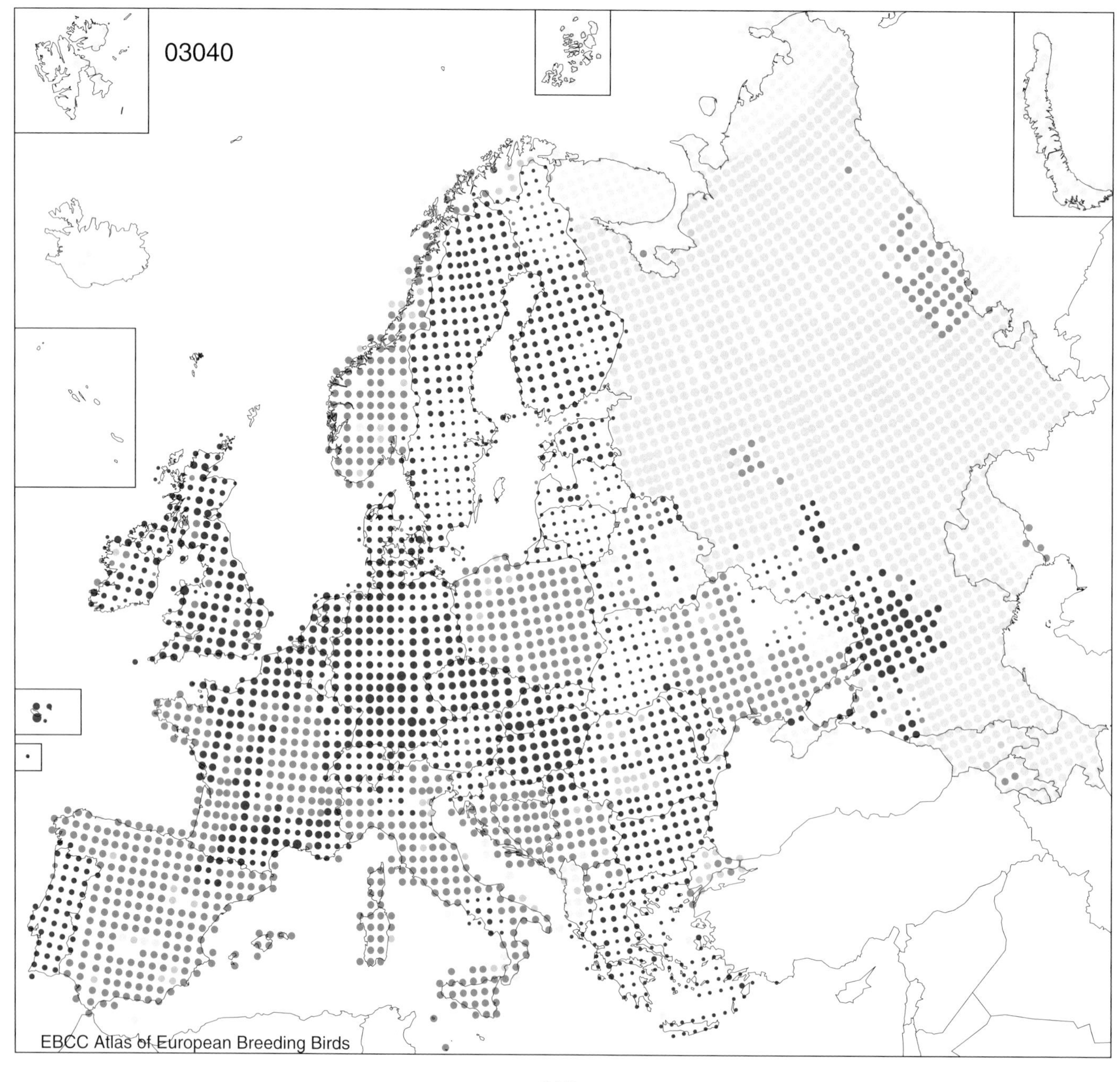

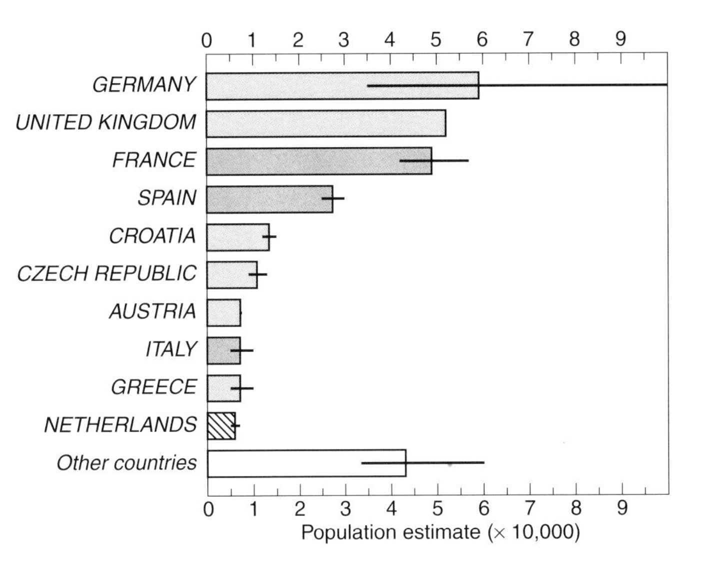

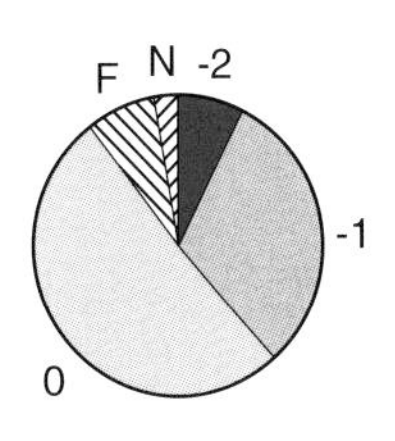

% in top 10 countries: 84.7
Total number of populated European countries: 39
Total European population 256,420–324,787 (282,127)
Russian population 50,000–90,000 (67,082)
Turkish population 5000–25,000 (11,180)

The Kestrel is widespread in Europe, breeding almost everywhere except Iceland and above *c*70°N in Siberia. Recently persecuted to extinction in Malta, it is attempting recolonization. *F. tinnunculus* also occurs as subspecies, or very similar species, in the Middle East, across Africa to South Africa, Asia E to *c*163°E and S to Hainan and Sri Lanka, and Indonesia (Moluccan Kestrel *F. moluccensis*) and Australasia (Australian Kestrel *F. cenchroides*).

The Kestrel breeds in most terrestrial habitats, but is largely an open-country species that avoids dense forest. It adapts relatively well to human activity and has colonized successfully many urban areas. Its wide distribution reflects its abilities to feed on a variety of prey and to breed in a range of different sites. Nests are usually on rock ledges, in tree-holes, or in disused stick-nests of other species. Although ground-nesting has been reported, the Kestrel generally does not breed in open areas if ground predators are present nor if safe nest sites are lacking, a limitation which can restrict its breeding distribution in such as polders, steppe or tundra. Experiments have shown that nestboxes can allow it to breed in open areas which are devoid of natural sites and are not part of another pair's territory (Village 1990, Korpimäki & Norrdahl 1991).

Northern populations that breed where there is permanent snow-cover in winter are entirely migratory, wintering in C or S Europe and in Africa. Elsewhere the breeding populations are partially migrant or sedentary.

Variations in Kestrel abundance largely parallel the abundance of their main prey, the microtine voles. Highest densities occur during vole peaks in northern Europe, when the Kestrel achieves over 40 bp/100km^2. Local densities may be even higher, especially where available nest sites are unevenly distributed (Village 1990, Korpimäki & Norrdahl 1991). In poor vole years densities can be as low as 5 bp/100km^2 because few birds settle during spring. Large annual variations in food supply result in a high turnover of the breeding population (Korpimäki 1984).

Further S, where vole numbers show less annual variation, Kestrel breeding populations are more stable, but densities rarely exceed 30 bp/100km^2. In intensive farmland, with little vole habitat, they can be as low as 10 bp/100km^2 (Schmid 1990, Village 1990). Where populations are sedentary, severe winter weather or poor winter food-supply can reduce breeding density in the following spring (Village 1990). There are few accurate density estimates for S Europe, but the Kestrel there can apparently breed at good densities by feeding on insects, reptiles and birds.

The large annual variations in breeding density in northern Europe make it difficult to record long-term trends in abundance. The available data suggest two counter-trends. Firstly, in areas where organochlorine pesticides were used heavily during the 1960s and 1970s, there were increases in range and in breeding density after these chemicals had been banned. For example, the Kestrel re-established itself in E England during the 1970s and present populations are not seriously affected by pesticides (Village 1990). Secondly, the Kestrel has declined in many other areas. Sixteen countries have reported overall declines in population (but not in range), and only one has reported an increase. Decreases in western Britain and The Netherlands since the 1970s seem to be associated with increased intensification of farming, and may reflect a decline in vole populations (Gibbons *et al* 1993, Bijlsma 1993). Changes in food supply due to farming practices may also account for declines in other areas across Europe. For example, in Spain and Switzerland, numbers have remained stable in mountainous areas, where farming is less intensive, but have declined in more intensively farmed lowlands (Schmid 1990).

Erkki Korpimäki (FIN) Hans Schmid (CH)
Andrew Village (GB)

This species account is sponsored by Natur- und Vogelschutzverein Pfäffikon, CH.

Falco vespertinus Red-footed Falcon

CZ	Poštolka rudonohá	**I**	Falco cuculo
D	Rotfußfalke	**NL**	Roodpootvalk
E	Cernícalo Patirrojo	**P**	Falcão-pés-vermelhos
F	Faucon kobez	**PL**	Kobczyk
FIN	Punajalkahaukka	**R**	Кобчик
G	Μαυροκιρκίνεζο	**S**	Aftonfalk
H	Kék vércse		

SPEC Cat 3, Threat status V

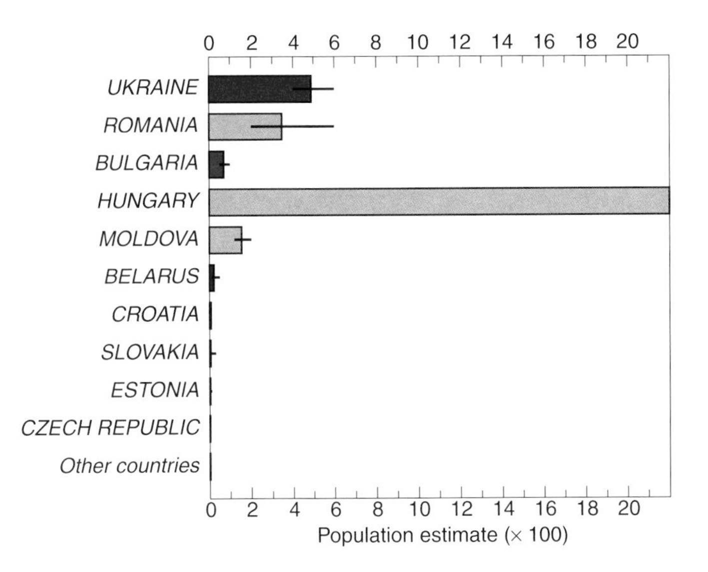

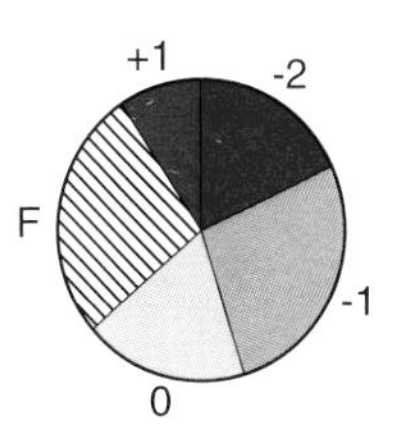

% in top 10 countries: 99.9
Total number of populated European countries: 11
Total European population 3127–3589 (3304)
Russian population 15,000–40,000 (24,495)

The graceful Red-footed Falcon is monotypic and forms a superspecies with the Amur Falcon *F. amurensis*. Its distribution is rather extensive, ranging from Hungary through N and C Asia to the eastern tributaries of the Yenisey and the upper Lena.

In Europe, breeding is confined mostly to the temperate continental limits of the western Palearctic, with marginal overlap into the boreal zone. Because it needs open terrain densely populated with insects, major breeding habitats comprise steppe and wood-steppe regions, lines of trees in cultivated land and riparian woodland transecting open country. A lowland species, it rarely breeds above 300m asl.

The Red-footed Falcon is gregarious throughout the year. It tends to breed in loose colonies of up to 200bp, often in rookeries, although solitary pairs also occur but suffer lower breeding success (Haraszthy & Bagyura 1993). Adults are mainly insectivorous, but the young consume a variety of vertebrates and insects.

In Europe, breeding nowadays is restricted mostly to Hungary (2200bp) and S Russia (15 000–40 000bp), smaller numbers inhabiting Romania (200–600bp), Moldova (120–200bp) and Ukraine (400–600bp). However, a 1992 survey in the Sivash region found the species fairly common in shelterbelts and copses in grazed steppes and farmland, either breeding solitarily or in small colonies (1–4bp), numbers being estimated at 250–500bp in an area of 4000km^2 (van der Winden 1995). The Red-footed Falcon breeds throughout Ukraine (*c*450 000km^2) and so I suggest the Ukrainian population has been seriously underestimated. Fewer than 100bp were recorded in E Bulgaria and Belarus; the N Serbian population possibly is of the same order.

Elsewhere in Europe, some *Atlas* records mislead, firstly because cumulative records may overemphasize numbers, and secondly because the species' tendency to appear beyond its normal range in spring has led to possible breeding records in many countries (Austria, the Czech Republic (Danko *et al* 1994), Finland, Poland, the Baltic States) which have not had confirmed breeding records for many years. Since the surveys, many breeding sites have been lost (E Slovakia, Danko *et al* 1994). Surprisingly, three pairs bred in France in 1993, one pair failing during incubation in the Crau (S France), the other two each rearing three young in Isère (E France) and Vendée (W France) respectively (de Sousa *et al* 1994).

The overall trends for European breeding birds have been decidedly negative during the late 20th century, probably following habitat destruction and widespread use of pesticides (such as large-scale DDT spraying against the *Eurigaster* spp shield bug group; Belik & Mihalevich 1994). Outlying breeding sites have been successively abandoned, leading to the breeding range retreating eastward. Strongholds, as in Russia, probably declined in range and numbers by >50% between 1970 and 1990, but substantiation is needed. Conversely, the present Hungarian total of 2200bp apparently differs little from the 2000bp of 1957 (Haraszthy & Bagyura 1993). The earlier figure is suspect, because known colonies have continued to decline (some well-documented as in the Ohat forest; 1953, 112 nests, Horváth 1955; 1973, 50bp, Haraszthy & Bagyura 1993) and improved survey methodology now prevails.

The species congregates in large flocks prior to migration, but is rarely seen migrating, probably because it travels long distances at high altitude. In its wintering range in southern Africa, it follows rain-fronts to profit from termites swarming over semi-arid grassland and savanna. It performs a loop-migration, spring movement being further W. Occasionally, when migrants utilize air-masses circulating round large, warm spring anticyclones, substantial numbers appear in S and W Europe. The largest such influx of the 20th century happened in May 1992, over 5000 birds crossing the Straits of Messina in just a few days (A. Giordano, pers comm), 1500–2000 reaching The Netherlands, 760 Denmark and >100 Great Britain and Sweden (Hagemeijer 1994).

Rob G Bijlsma (NL)

Falco columbarius

Merlin

CZ	Dřemlík tundrový	I	Smeriglio
D	Merlin	NL	Smelleken
E	Esmerejón	P	Esmerilhão
F	Faucon émerillon	PL	Drzemlik
FIN	Ampuhaukka	R	Дербник
G	Νανογέρακο	S	Stenfalk
H	Kis sólyom		

Non-SPEC, Threat status S

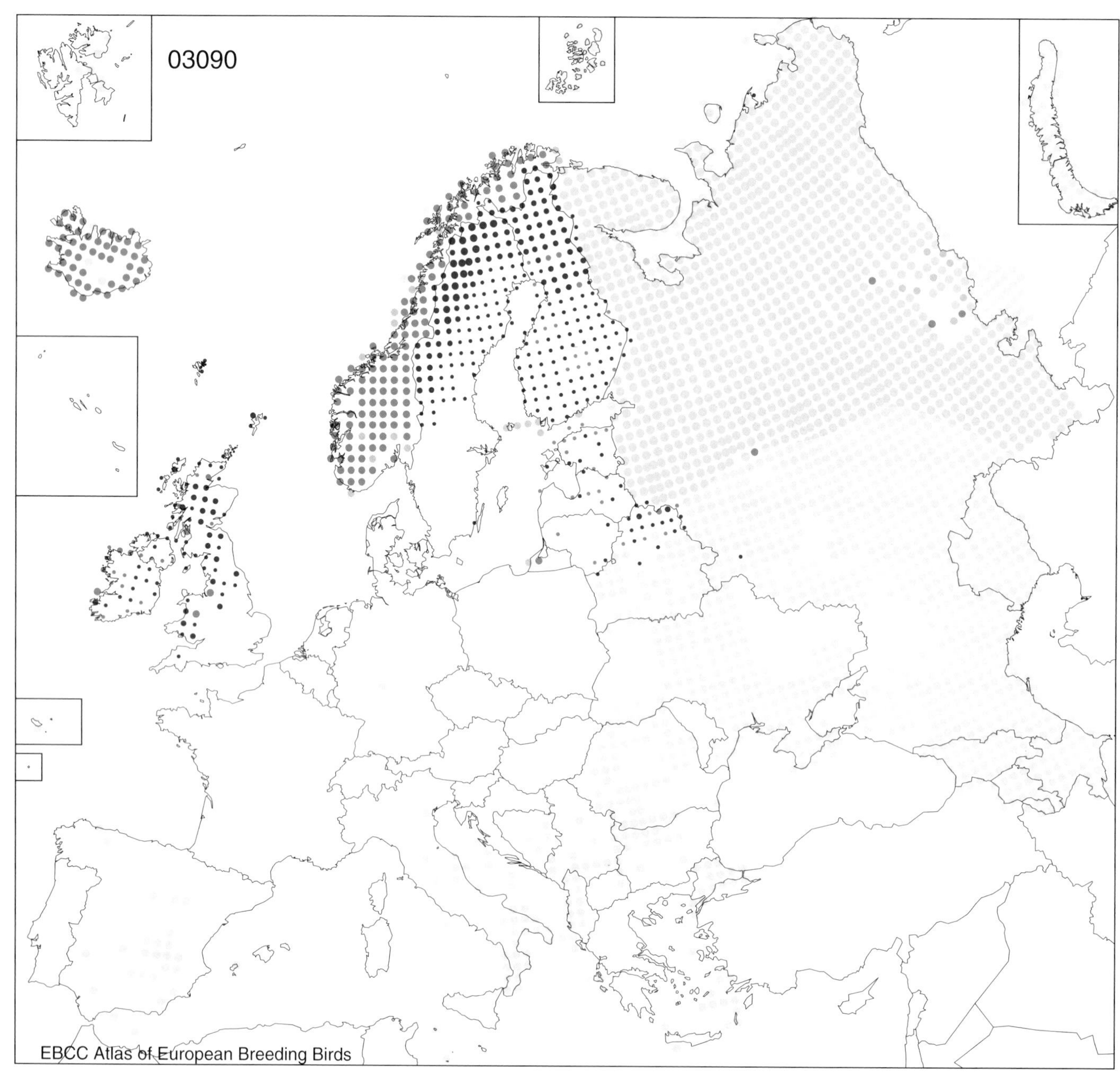

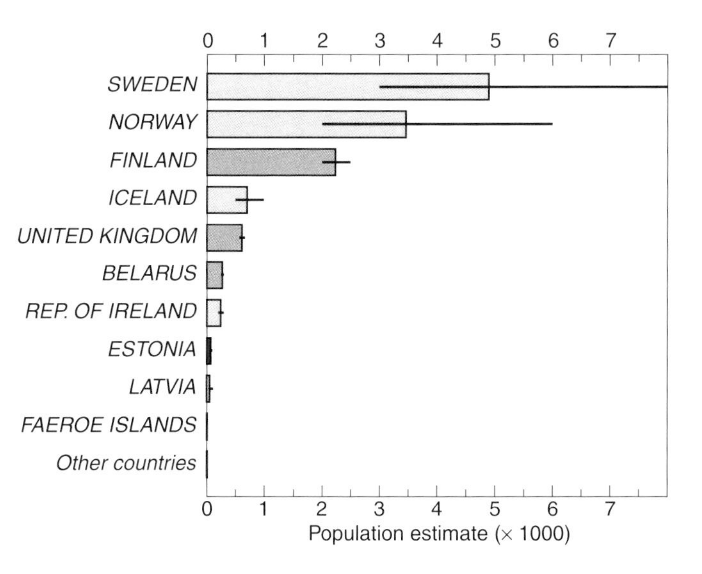

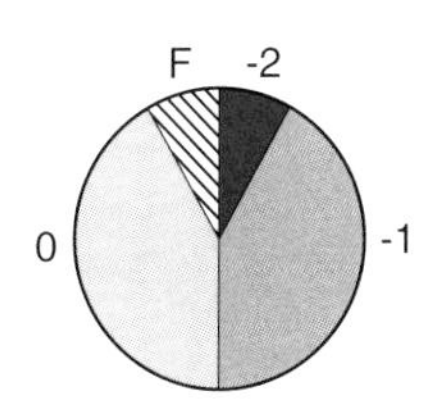

% in top 10 countries: 99.9
Total number of populated European countries: 12
Total European population 10,166–16,612 (12,586)
Russian population 25,000–35,000 (29,580)

The Merlin, the smallest falcon breeding in Europe, has a circumpolar distribution. Nine subspecies are recognized, of which *F.c. subaesalon* occurs in Iceland, the Faeroes, Ireland and Britain, *aesalon* is found from northern Europe to C Siberia, and *pallidus* inhabits E-C and SE European Russia. The remainder occur from C Siberia to North America.

It is a bird of upland and high-altitude moorland or open countryside, tending to avoid areas of dense forest or steep mountain ranges. Discriminant analysis of habitat occupancy in Britain has shown that the Merlin prefers heather *Erica* spp or bracken *Pteridium aquilinum* managed for Red Grouse *Lagopus lagopus scoticus* on moderate slopes to grass moors managed for sheep (Haworth & Fielding 1988). Throughout most of its range it breeds sometimes on rocky crags but usually in former Crow *Corvus corone* nests in trees. The British population is unusual in showing a high prevalence of ground-nesting, particularly among heather or bracken but with increasing afforestation of upland areas, birds appear to be switching to nest sites in trees on the edges of moorland as conifer plantations become sufficiently mature (S. J. Parr 1994). Nest success in tree sites is higher than on the ground because of lower predation rates (Newton *et al* 1978).

During breeding, Merlin pairs are territorial and use traditional nesting home-ranges. Although a shortage of suitable nest sites can lead to greater dispersion, they occur fairly evenly at a density of 5–16 bp/100km^2 in Great Britain, so long as there is an adequate supply of small passerines (especially Meadow Pipit *Anthus pratensis*) for food. In Fennoscandia, average densities are 2–4 bp/km^2 in open birch or coniferous forest and maximum densities of 2.7–7.5 bp/km^2 in N Russia have been recorded in forested tundra (Shubin 1984). Cyclicity in rodent numbers influences Merlin breeding density and breeding success; these are high during rodent peaks when rodents become a major prey item.

The *subaesalon* population of Iceland, Faeroes and Britain & Ireland comprises *c*1300–2000bp. The Fennoscandian (7000–16 500bp) and Russian (25 000–35 000bp) populations are the largest. Further S, only small numbers of breeding pairs occur, mainly in Belarus (250–300bp), Estonia (50–100bp) and Latvia (30–100bp).

As with most raptors, the Merlin suffered from the effects of organochlorine pesticides in the 1950s and 1960s but declines in its productivity thus caused now appear to have been reversed (Crick 1993). In Britain the Merlin is still the most heavily contaminated raptor, with organomercury being the apparent cause of decreased numbers of young fledged per nest (Newton & Haas 1988). It is likely that these pesticides were picked up by birds on their wintering grounds rather than in the relatively untouched northern breeding areas. It is not clear how populations on breeding grounds in N Europe were affected by organochlorines during the 1950s and 1960s nor is the extent known to which organomercury affects the Russian populations because there is little documentation available to chart significant changes which may have occurred in their pattern of distribution and abundance (but see Henny *et al* 1994).

There is no evidence that the Merlin in Scandinavia has been affected by pesticides since 1980. In the core of its range in Russia, Sweden and Norway, there is little current evidence of any population changes, although there is some for a population decline in Finland.

The Merlin is widespread throughout Europe in winter, generally occurring S of a line that takes in S Iceland, S Sweden, S Poland, Ukraine and S Russia. It winters throughout France, Germany, Iberia, W Turkey, along the N Mediterranean coasts and on its islands. Small numbers reach North Africa. Some western birds remain resident.

Humphrey Q P Crick (GB) Christer G Wiklund (S)

This species account is sponsored by Michael Kuhn, Erftstadt, D.

Falco subbuteo Hobby

CZ	Ostříž lesní	I	Lodolaio
D	Baumfalke	NL	Boomvalk
E	Alcotán Europeo	P	Ógea
F	Faucon hobereau	PL	Kobuz
FIN	Nuolihaukka	R	Чеглок
G	Δενδρογέρακο	S	Lärkfalk
H	Kabasólyom		

Non-SPEC, Threat status S

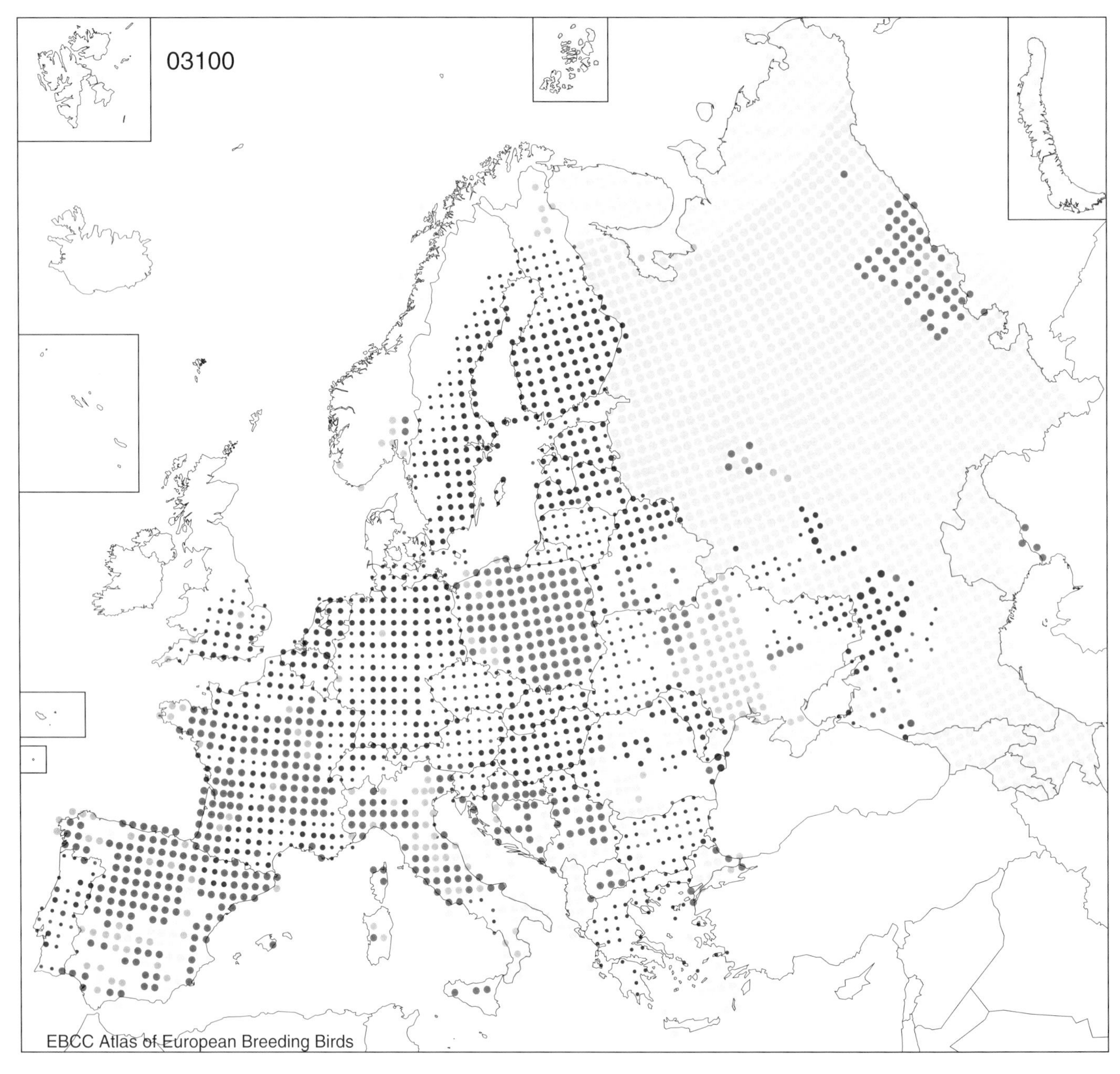

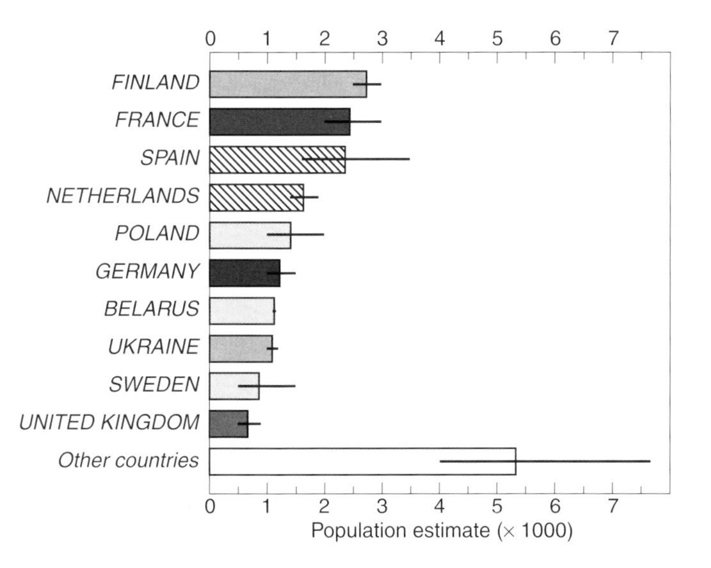

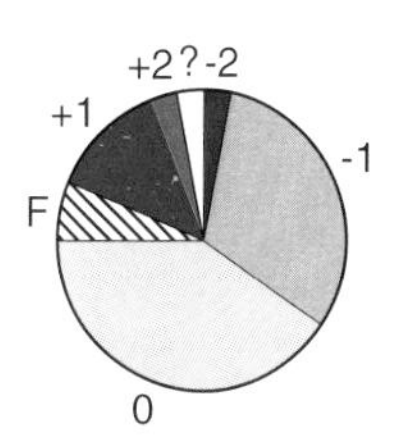

% in top 10 countries: 74.4
Total number of populated European countries: 33
Total European population 19,720–22,799 (20,942)
Russian population 40,000–70,000 (52,915)
Turkish population 1000–5000 (2236)

The Hobby has a huge breeding range, covering Eurasia from Portugal and S England through North Africa, Europe, C Asia and N China to Kamchatka, Sakhalin and N Japan, mostly between 67° and 35°N. It is markedly migratory. European birds winter in southern Africa.

The Hobby is essentially a lowland bird of temperate, continental and southern boreal climate zones, occasionally ranging beyond the Arctic Circle and in mountainous areas up to the timber-line. It avoids open treeless areas such as steppes and deserts. The Hobby occupies a wide range of habitats, provided a profusion of old nests (mostly crow and Magpie *Pica pica*) is available. It prefers forests interspersed with glades and clearings, cultivated land containing copses and lines of trees, heaths, moors and bogs sparsely overgrown with trees, parks and wetlands. During the breeding season, its main prey comprises highly aerial birds, hunted >5km away from the nest site. Insects, especially dragonflies, may become relatively more important as a food resource after fledging (Fiuczynski 1987, Bijlsma 1993, Prince & Clarke 1993).

The species is distributed sparsely over much of its range, especially towards its distribution margins in England, SE Norway, C Sweden, C Finland, S Iberia, S Italy, the Balkan States and Greece. It is absent as a breeding bird from Iceland, Ireland and Scotland (despite some attempts) and very rare in Denmark (10bp). Although the major reason may be high precipitation levels in summer, the very high overall density of 130 bp/50km square in the climatically maritime Netherlands (Bijlsma 1993) is an anomaly. Elsewhere in Europe, such high densities occur but locally, as in the Danube Delta (300bp on 4340km²; Th. Müller & Rohde 1991) and in poplar plantations along the River Po in N Italy (16–18bp on 62km²; Bogliani *et al* 1994). Across the European temperate and continental zones remarkably consistent densities of 11–33 bp/50km square prevail, declining to <10 bp/50km square in the Mediterranean region and in parts of E Europe. Apart from Russia's 40 000–70 000bp, the total European population is estimated conservatively at 18 000–28 000bp.

Detecting long-term trends is difficult because of the species' low overall densities, wide range of breeding habitats and low detectability during much of the breeding cycle (Bijlsma 1993, Guthmann *et al* 1996), a circumstance reflected in a confusing array of European trends. Some 50% of European countries registered stable populations during the *Atlas* survey, or fluctuations without apparent trend. Few countries recorded a positive trend, notably England (>50% increase in range and numbers) and France (probable and confirmed breeding in 239 and 602 squares respectively in 1970–75 and 1985–89; Dronneau & Wassmer 1994). Both countries, however, seriously under-recorded the Hobby during their first national atlas surveys and so the increases are probably (much) less pronounced (Prince & Clarke 1993, Dronneau & Wassmer 1994).

Germany recorded a marked decrease of >50%, but few reliable long-term trends are available and matters are further complicated by strong fluctuations. For example, the well-studied Berlin (480km²) population declined by >50% during 1956–88, smallest numbers occurring during the early 1970s and late 1980s (Fiuczynski 1991), yet the population in Nordrhein-Westfalen (34 066km²) was adjudged stable during 1972–94, with annual fluctuations of up to 25% (Guthmann *et al* 1996). The Netherlands also shows the pattern of rapidly declining strongholds, but stability or increase in peripheral populations (Bijlsma 1993, pers obs). Less clear-cut declines have been recorded in Finland, Estonia, Lithuania, Ukraine, Moldova and Greece, but the evidence is often circumstantial.

Some concern is warranted, because the Hobby's main prey populations have shown marked declines (hirundines, larks), PCB-contamination of eggs has been shown in Germany (probably causing the increase in hatching failure rate) and the impact of the Goshawk *Accipiter gentilis* on reproductive success (and possibly adult survival) is increasing (Fiuczynski 1991, Bijlsma 1993, pers obs).

Rob G Bijlsma (NL)

Falco eleonorae

Eleonora's Falcon

CZ	Ostříž jižní	I	Falco della regina
D	Eleonorenfalke	NL	Eleonora's Valk
E	Halcón de Eleonora	P	Falcão-da-rainha
F	Faucon d'Élénore	PL	Sokół skalny
FIN	Välimerenhaukka	R	Сокол Элеоноры
G	Μαυροπετρίτης	S	Eleonorafalk
H	Eleonóra-sólyom		

SPEC Cat 2, Threat status R

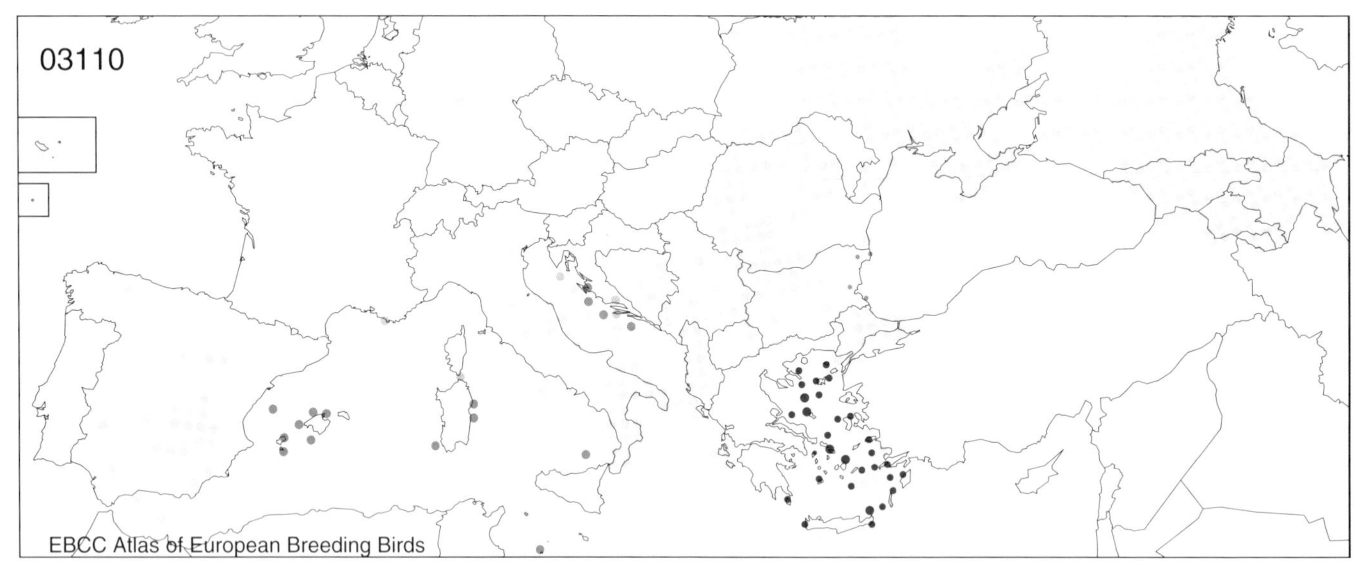

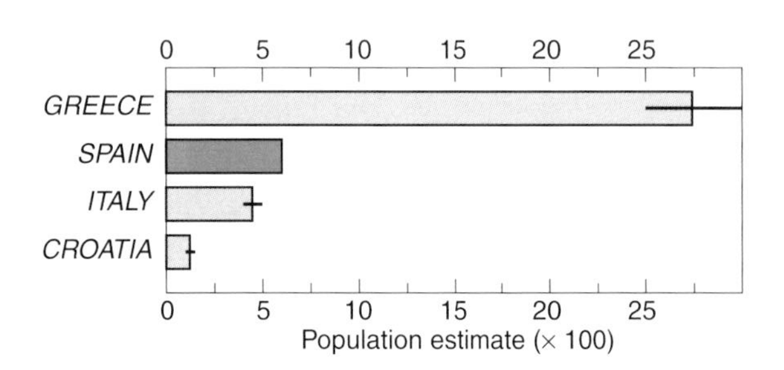

+2

0

% in top 10 countries: 100.0
Total number of populated European countries: 4
Total European population 3666–4178 (3910)
Turkish population 18–100 (42)

Eleonora's Falcon breeds on Mediterranean islands, on the Moroccan Atlantic coast and in the Canary Islands. It is monotypic, but may form a superspecies with Sooty Falcon *F. concolor*. Most birds winter in Madagascar, and smaller numbers in Kenya and the Mascarene Islands.

Eleonora's Falcon breeds on small rocky islands in colonies of up to 300bp. Breeding sites become occupied from May onwards, egg-laying commencing synchronously in late July and young hatching in late August (Wink *et al* 1993). Such late nesting is an adaptation to hunt prey amongst the European autumn migrants crossing the Mediterranean Sea in a broad front to winter in Africa. Eleonora's Falcon raises its young when the peak migration provides a rich food supply almost at the nest (Walter 1979).

The world population of the Eleonora's Falcon is confined almost completely to the Mediterranean, being distributed over some 100 colonies. Of the present maximum estimate of 4500bp, 90bp breed along the Moroccan Atlantic coast, 66bp on the Canary Islands (1991) and 160bp on islands off Algeria and Tunisia (Ristow & Wink 1985). The major colonies are found in Greece, where 2500–3000bp are scattered over the islands in the Aegean Sea, the Cyclades and the Dodecanese Islands. Smaller numbers are found in Cyprus (100–120bp), the Adriatic Sea (100–150bp in Croatia), the Tyrrhenian Sea and the Sicilian Channel (400–500bp) and the Balearics (600bp).

Overall the population is apparently largely stable, but decreases have been recorded in Morocco and Cyprus. Balearic numbers probably have increased by >50% during the 1980s. The average fledging rate of 1.2 young/bp would suffice to maintain a stable population (Ristow & Wink 1985), but most colonies are under threat from human activities; tourist developments, hunting, rat predation on islands and theft of eggs and young, but fortunately not pesticide contamination (Wink *et al* 1993). Protection of the 10–15 major colonies should therefore have priority.

Rob G Bijlsma (NL)

Falco biarmicus

Lanner

CZ	Raroh jižní	**I**	Lanario
D	Lanner	**NL**	Lannervalk
E	Halcón Borní	**P**	Alfaneque
F	Faucon lanier	**PL**	Raróg górski
FIN	Keltapäähaukka	**R**	Средиземноморский сокол
G	Χρυσογέρακο	**S**	Slagfalk
H	Feldegg-sólyom		

SPEC Cat 3, Threat status E (P)

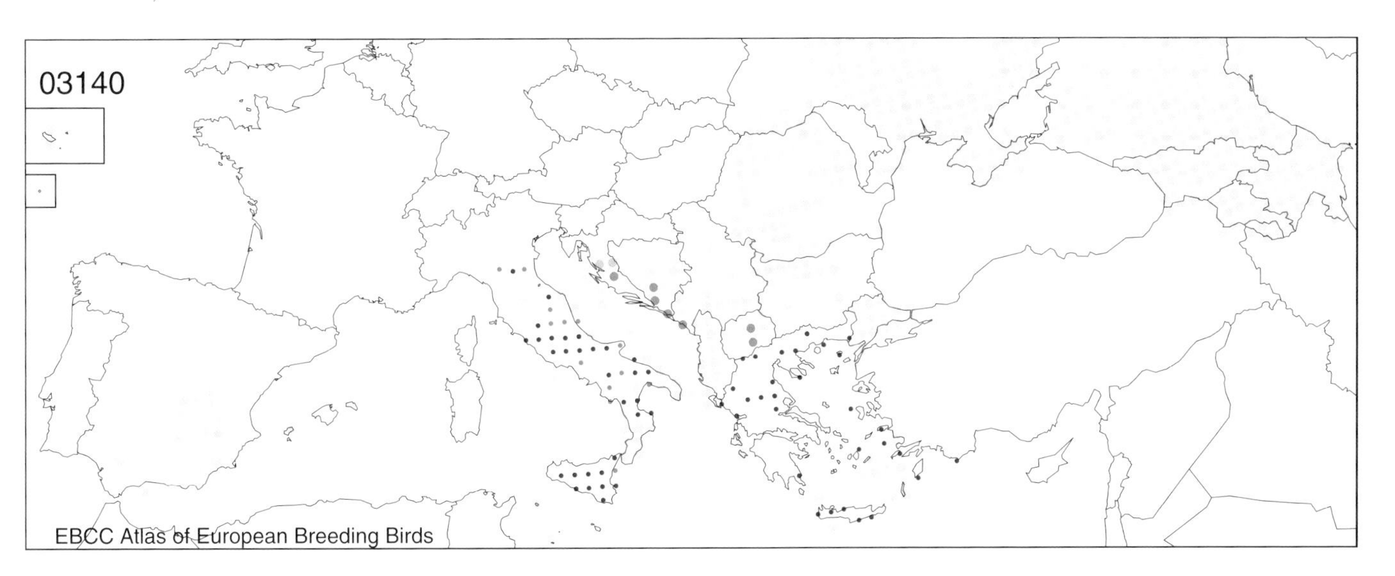

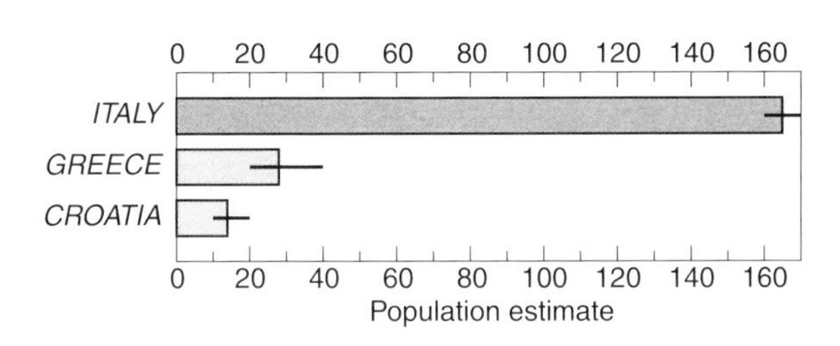

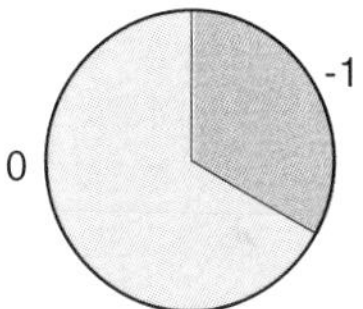

% in top 10 countries: 100.0
Total number of populated European countries: 3
Total European population 197–221 (207)
Turkish population 10–100 (32)

The Lanner is a large falcon whose global distribution comprises mainly the African continent apart from wet and forested areas. Its occurrence in southern Europe and the Middle East is therefore peripheral.

In Europe the Lanner typically frequents open dry grassland and steppe, whether natural or cultivated, but it requires suitable cliffs for nesting. It generally prefers a climate with less than 500mm of rainfall annually, breeding from sea level up to 1200m asl. The European population (subspecies *F.b. feldeggii*) is restricted to C-E Mediterranean regions below 45°N, such as peninsular Italy, Sicily, the former Yugoslavia (Dalmatia and Croatia), Albania, Greece and Turkey. Because its distribution is so limited in Europe, the Lanner is poorly known and its population probably has been underestimated. Even the sharp decline during 1950–70 (Chiavetta 1981) may have been less serious than suggested. In the 19th century the Lanner bred in southern Spain (McGowan & Massa 1990) and somewhat earlier probably in southern France (Cheylan 1981). Probably climatic factors were responsible for the range contraction.

Italy alone hosts *c*50–80% of the estimated European population of 140–360bp (Lambertini 1994), Sicily representing the stronghold of the species with *c*60–100bp (Massa *et al* 1991, LIPU 1995) at a maximum density of 1 bp/60km^2 (Massa *et al* 1991). In the former Yugoslavia and the Balkans the known population is fewer than 100bp, but is almost certainly underestimated. Albania lacks reliable data. The Lanner is mainly sedentary, there being few records from the Mediterranean migration bottlenecks, and most are of dispersive immatures.

The major threats suffered by the Lanner are human persecution and collecting eggs and nestlings for falconry. In northern Italy competition with Peregrine *F. peregrinus* for nest sites may occur (Chiavetta & Martelli 1991), but has not been recorded in Sicily (Massa *et al* 1991). There is no evidence that pesticides or pollutants are having serious effects on breeding performance.

Andrea Ciaccio (I) Marco Lambertini (I)

Falco cherrug

Saker Falcon

CZ	Raroh velký	I	Sacro
D	Saker	NL	Sakervalk
E	Halcón Sacre	P	Falcão-sacre
F	Faucon sacre	PL	Raróg
FIN	Aavikkohaukka	R	Балобан
G	Στεπογέρακο	S	Tatarfalk
H	Kerecsensólyom		

SPEC Cat 3, Threat status E

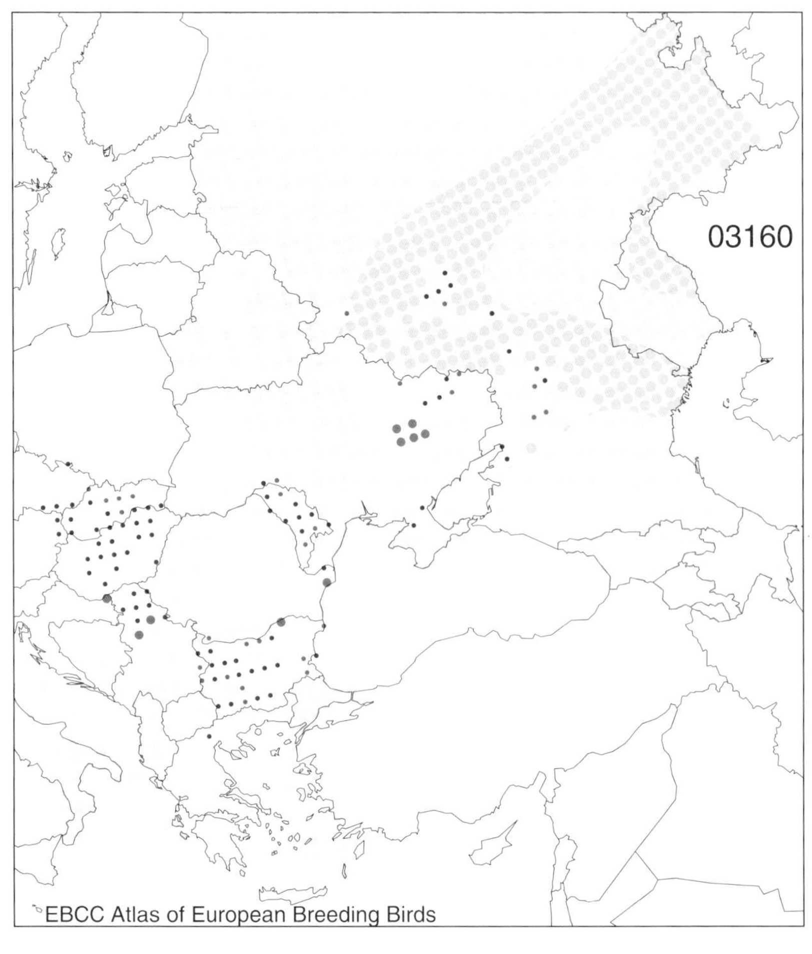

The large Saker Falcon is distributed in a broad swathe between 30° and 60°N from Mongolia and Tibet (*F.c. milvipes*) W to Iran, Turkey and the steppes and forest-steppes of southern Russia and Ukraine. The two isolated western populations are centred on Romania (Dobrogea, Danube Delta), Moldova and Bulgaria and on Hungary, Austria, the Czech Republic, Slovakia, Croatia and northern former Yugoslavia (the nominate *cherrug*) (where small numbers remain) (Baumgart 1991).

In Europe it occurs mainly in open steppe-like habitats and locally in agricultural and pasture land with short vegetation. It may occupy bare hillsides (Slovakia, N Hungary) or mountains (Bulgaria) up to 2000m asl. During the breeding season its distribution correlates strongly with ground squirrel (*Citellus* spp) colonies, the main food for the young. The Saker breeds on cliffs or uses former nests of corvids, herons or eagles in gallery forest. Recently it has taken to nesting on power-supply pylons in open areas.

In winter, C European adults remain resident or migrate as far as the Mediterranean. Juveniles are mainly migratory, C and E European birds wandering from the Balkans to Turkmenistan, Egypt and NW India. Before 1900 Europe held perhaps *c*5000–10 000bp but contemporary census data largely are lacking. The Saker population has declined markedly since 1945, to extinction in Austria and to fewer than 30bp in Hungary by 1975, where successful protection measures reversed the decline (Bagyura *et al* 1994) in the 1980s (92 nests surveyed; 1994, at least 120bp). Now the Saker is increasing in Slovakia and has recolonized Austria. It is thinly spread in European Russia (Baumgart *et al* 1992, Galushin 1992, Baumgart 1994), European birds forming *c*1% of the world population.

The Saker's past decline in lowland abundance correlates with breeding habitat destruction and associated prey reduction: nowadays it is targeted for falconry (extensive nest-robbing, trapping during migration). Its European natural strongholds remain in remoter hilly areas.

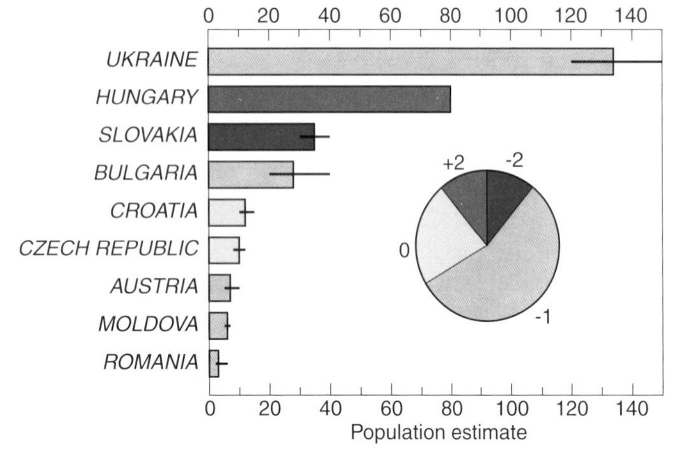

% in top 10 countries: 100.0
Total number of populated European countries: 9
Total European population 298–337 (316)
Russian population 80–150 (110)
Turkish population 10–100 (32)

Wolfgang Baumgart (D) László Haraszthy (H)

Falco rusticolus

Gyrfalcon

CZ	Raroh lovecký	I	Girfalco d'Islanda
D	Gerfalke	NL	Giervalk
E	Halcón Gerifalte	P	Falcão-gerifalte
F	Faucon gerfaut	PL	Białozór
FIN	Tunturihaukka	R	Кречет
G	Ασπρογέρακας	S	Jaktfalk
H	Sarki sólyom		

SPEC Cat 3, Threat status V

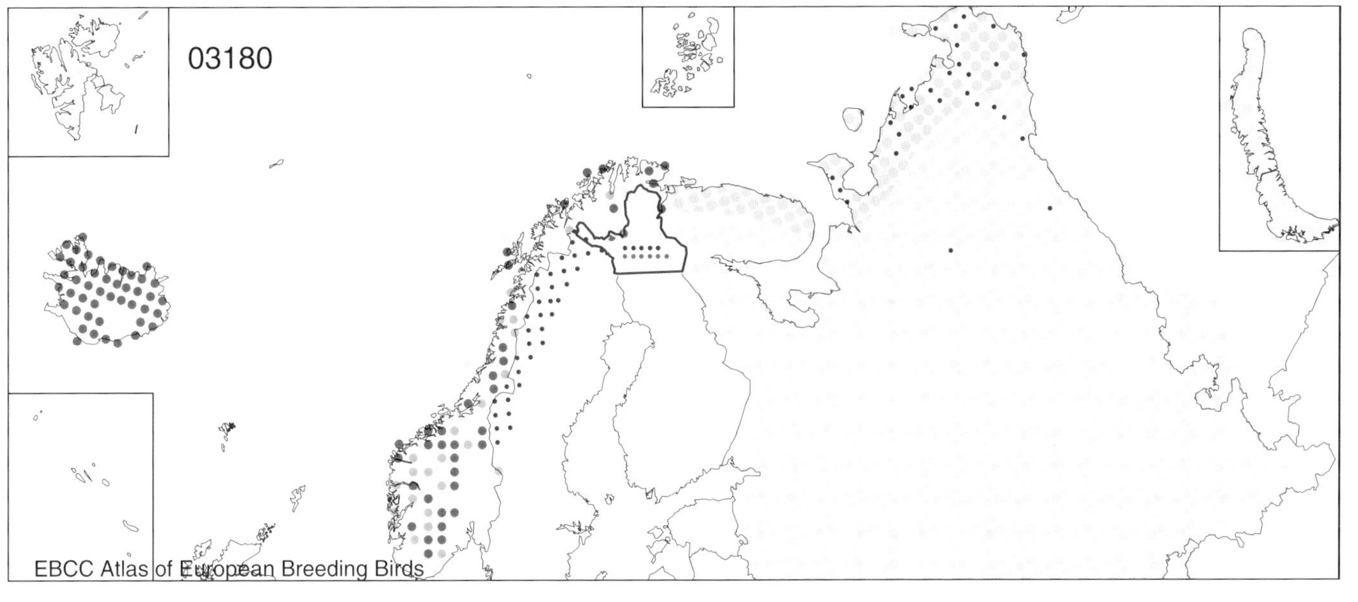

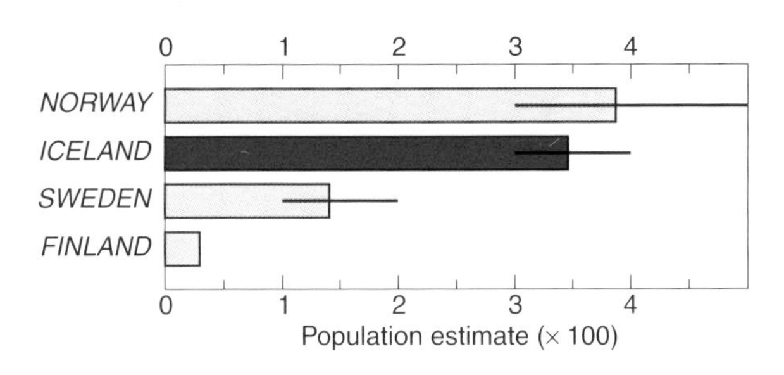

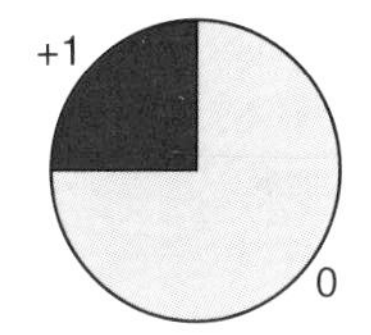

% in top 10 countries: 100.0
Total number of populated European countries: 4
Total European population 798–1043 (905)
Russian population 50–200 (100)

The Gyrfalcon is the world's largest falcon, and currently has four recognized morphs. It has a northern circumpolar breeding range which includes Alaska, Canada, Greenland, Iceland, Norway, Sweden, Finland and Russia. Within this extensive area the Gyrfalcon occurs in a variety of arctic and subarctic environments: mountainous terrain, open uplands, maritime and riverine, but sometimes also in the taiga.

In Europe, its main breeding habitats consist of mountainous heath, birch *Betula* or willow *Salix* scrub, and tundra. Its eyrie is usually situated on a precipice or crag ledge, preferably below an overhanging rock outcrop. Occasionally the Gyrfalcon will utilize other species' stick nests in trees. Usually, adults remain in the vicinity of their breeding territory the year round, whereas immature birds tend to move to areas where food is more plentiful in winter, such as open seacoasts and agricultural land.

The Icelandic population of Gyrfalcon (*F.r. islandus*-type) is estimated at 300–400bp (O.K. Nielsen, pers comm). Norway harbours 300–500bp (Tømmeraas 1994), Sweden *c*100bp (U. Falkdalen & S. Blomqvist, pers obs), Finland *c*30bp (Koskimies 1995) and NW Russia at least 50bp. Hence, the total population of Gyrfalcon in continental Europe (nominate *F.r. rusticolus*-type) is *c*500–700bp. Current trends in population numbers are but vaguely known. Reports from Lapland (Tømmeraas 1993) and NE Greenland (Elander & Blomqvist 1986) suggest considerable long-term decreases from the 1850s but also during the 20th century.

Threats to the Gyrfalcon generally relate to human actions, such as illegal taking of eggs and young, poaching, and disturbance through tourism and outdoor activities. There is also a risk that overhunting of their main prey, Ptarmigan *Lagopus mutus* and Willow Grouse *L. lagopus* will lead to winter food scarcity. Further studies of the effects of these threats are badly needed, as is intensified population monitoring.

Ulla Falkdalen (S) Sven Blomqvist (S)

Falco peregrinus **Peregrine Falcon**

CZ	Sokol stěhovavý	I	Pellegrino
D	Wanderfalke	NL	Slechtvalk
E	Halcón Peregrino	P	Falcão-peregrino
F	Faucon pèlerin	PL	Sokół wędrowny
FIN	Muuttohaukka	R	Сапсан
G	Πετρίτης	S	Pilgrimsfalk
H	Vándorsólyom		

SPEC Cat 3, Threat status R

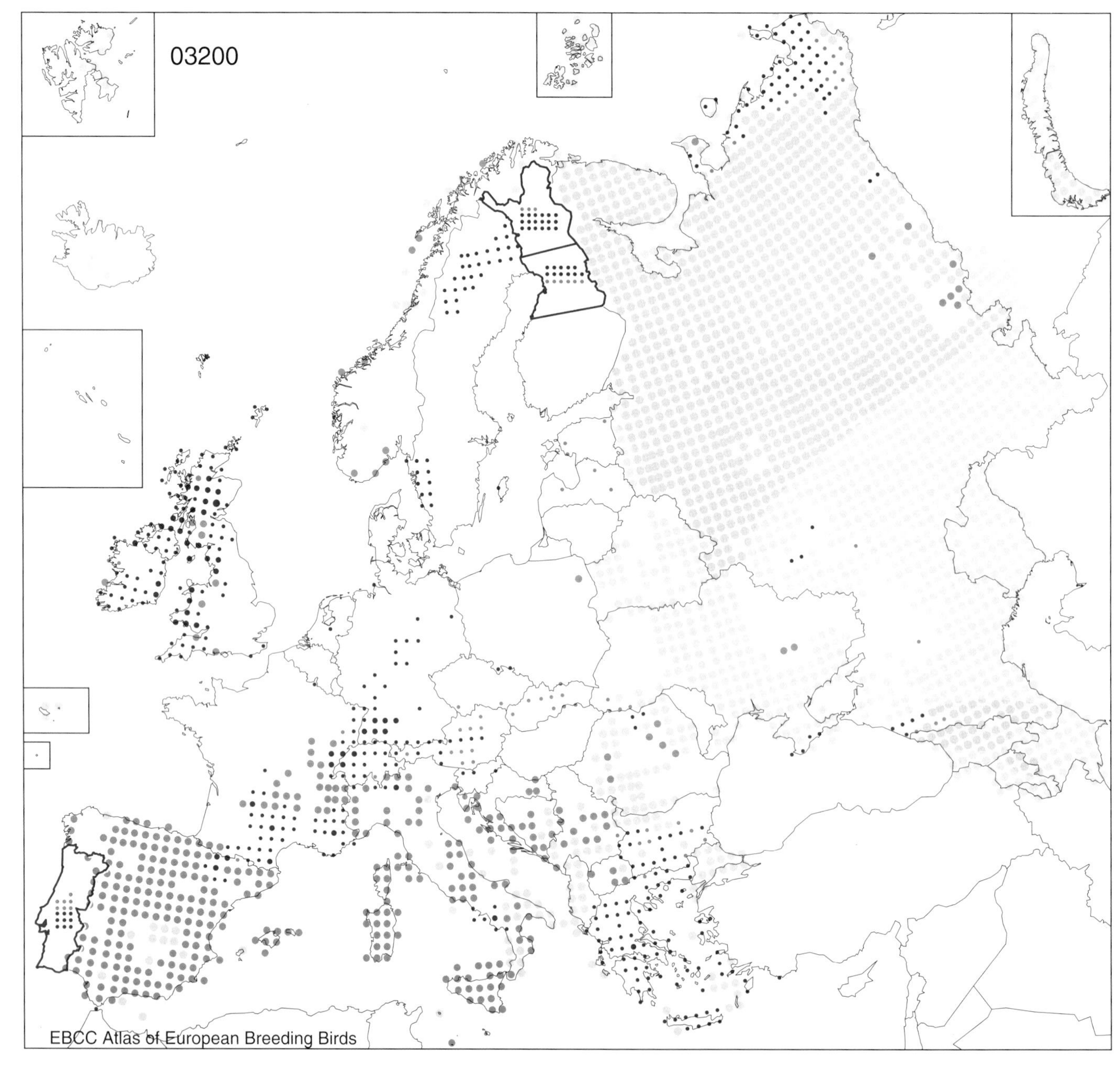

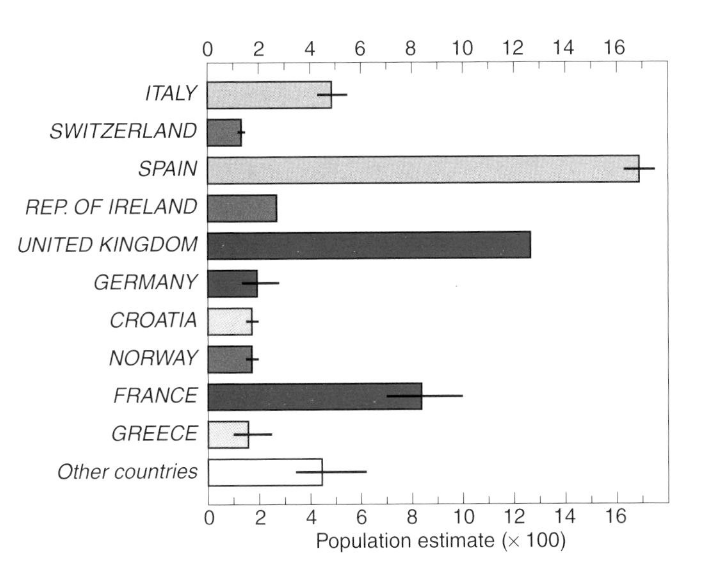

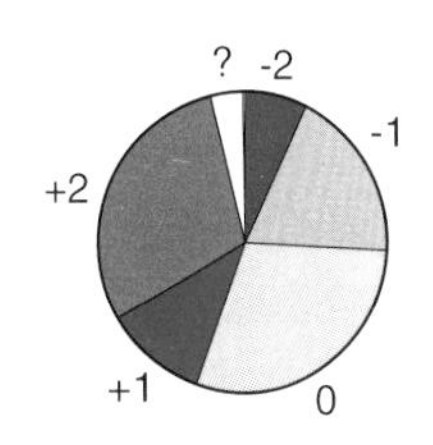

% in top 10 countries: 92.4
Total number of populated European countries: 27
Total European population 5633–6075 (5824)
Russian population 400–800 (566)
Turkish population 100–2000 (447)

The Peregrine is a cosmopolitan species with 19 currently recognized subspecies, of which four occur in Europe. As a breeding bird it is absent from few regions (such as Antarctica, parts of South America, New Zealand, Iceland), and in the Northern Hemisphere it occurs from the Equator to 77°N.

European habitats range from treeless to quite heavily wooded country, but the species has a general dependence for nest sites on cliffs, both coastal and inland. While often most numerous in mountainous areas, it is not a montane bird and most nesting places lie within the potential forest zone. In the Arctic it nevertheless breeds far N of the treeline. In N Fennoscandia about half the population nests on dry hummocks of large bogs within the taiga forests.

Tree-nesting in stick nests built by other species was formerly widespread around the Baltic. Nesting on buildings and other constructions is widespread and increasing. At least one tenth of the British and Irish populations nests in quarries, many of them actively worked. Use of ground or near-ground nests is increasing in Britain & Ireland and tree-nesting has been recorded recently (Ratcliffe 1993).

The Peregrine has a patchy breeding distribution across Europe, largely because of breeding habitat limitations. On coasts it is restricted to cliff sections, and inland mostly to rocky river valleys and hilly areas. Release programmes and adaptation to breeding in nestboxes and on artificial structures have allowed it to colonize the German lowlands (Wegner 1994). Few habitat types are unsuitable because of inadequate food supply, as is evidenced by the Peregrine's wider distribution outside the breeding season. The largest populations are in Spain (1650+bp), Great Britain (1280+bp; Crick & Ratcliffe 1994), Russia (400–800bp), France (650+bp), Italy (500bp) and Ireland (450bp). Where these differ from the graph, it is my opinion that the new estimates will be upheld. The total European population was estimated at 5720–7415bp in 1992.

Most European Peregrine populations N of the Mediterranean regions collapsed during 1956–65, through the toxic effects of persistent residues of agricultural organochlorine pesticides ingested from prey species. The declines were greatest in regions where the species was most exposed to such contamination by proximity to major agricultural (and especially arable) areas. Following phased withdrawals or banning of most organochlorine pesticide uses, there has been variable recovery in affected populations. Those in Britain & Ireland have now reached overall levels higher than ever known before. However, there is incomplete recovery in coastal N Scotland, probably through continuing adverse effects of marine pollutants (Ratcliffe 1993). Recovery appears to be proceeding apace in most C European countries (France, Germany, Switzerland; Cade *et al* 1988), but lags behind in Fennoscandia, suggesting a continuing problem for migratory populations wintering S of the Baltic (Lindberg *et al* 1988).

Highest breeding densities are reported from Great Britain (up to 8.5bp/100km^2 inland), Ireland (Rathlin Island, 8bp on island of 13.6km^2) and Gibraltar (5bp in 6.5km^2). Local concentrations on cliffs where there is ample food can produce unusually dense breeding clusters. Numbers are limited by availability of good nesting sites, but where cliffs are plentiful, territorial demands, evidently geared to food supply, impose an upper limit to breeding density and maintain population stability.

Northern populations of subspecies *peregrinus* and *calidus* in Fennoscandia and Siberia migrate S to winter in C Europe and the Middle East. There may be partial migration according to winter climate and movements of main prey species, for example, from high mountain areas to adjoining lowlands.

The Peregrine continues to recover from its threatened status, except in N Europe, where the once large populations are still depleted. Elsewhere, its numbers appear secure, though persecution remains a problem locally.

Derek A Ratcliffe (GB)

This species account is sponsored by Arbeitsgemeinschaft Wanderfalkenschutz, D.

Bonasa bonasia

Hazel Grouse

CZ	Jeřábek lesní	I	Francolino di monte
D	Haselhuhn	NL	Hazelhoen
E	Grévol Común	P	Galinha-do-mato
F	Gélinotte des bois	PL	Jarząbek
FIN	Pyy	R	Рябчик
G	Αγριόκοτα	S	Järpe
H	Császármadár		

Non-SPEC, Threat status S

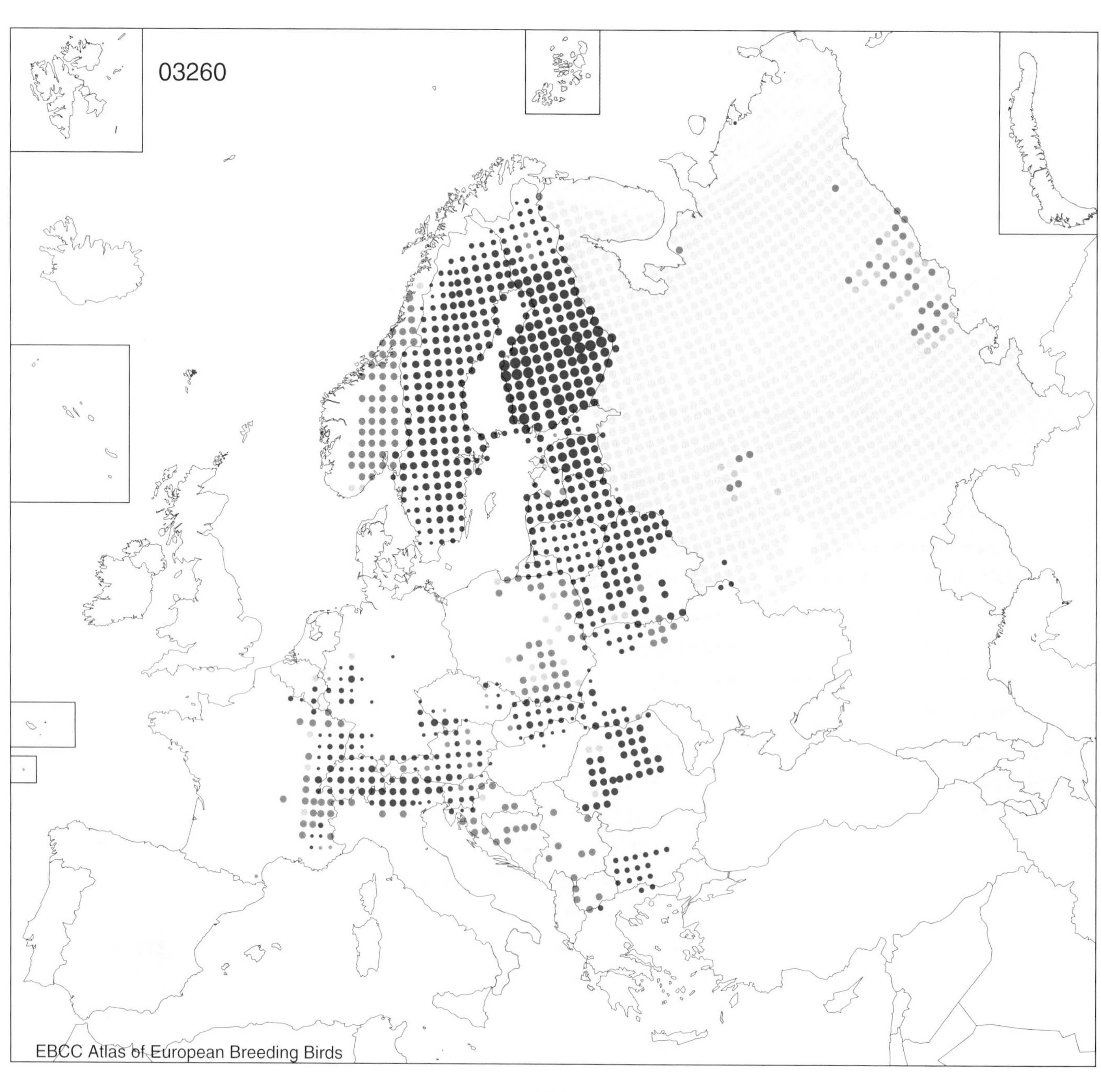

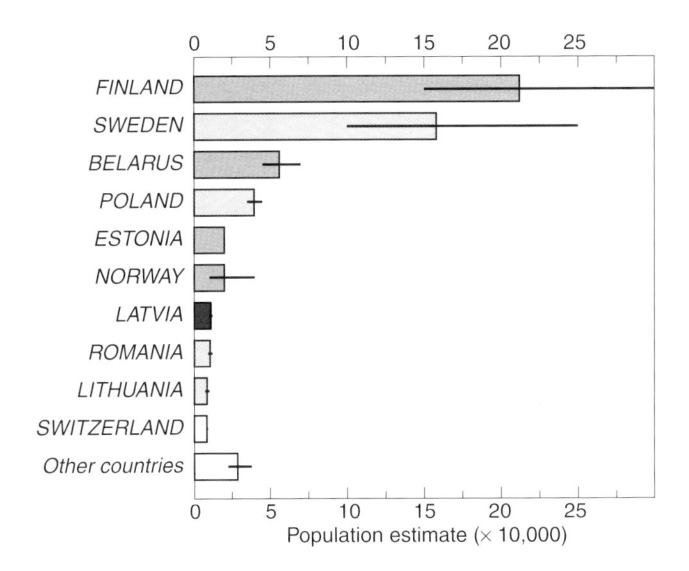

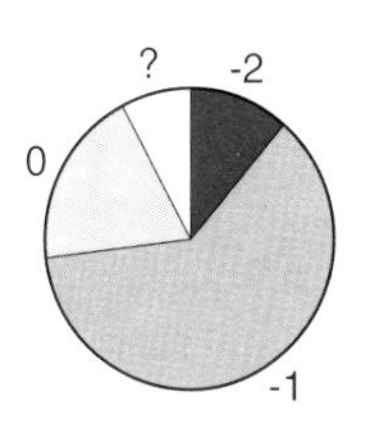

% in top 10 countries: 95.0
Total number of populated European countries: 26
Total European population 486,125–702,345 (572,704)
Russian population 1,000,000–10,000,000 (3,162,278)

The Hazel Grouse is a Palearctic species with a mainly Siberian distribution. In Europe, its range lies between 40° and 70°N. Its western border runs from E Norway to SE Belgium and E France. In the S it reaches the French–Italian Alps, the Balkans as far as Montenegro and northern Albania and Greece. Its distribution in C and W Europe is insular, individual populations usually being confined to higher altitudes and of a relict character. In European Russia and W Siberia the southern boundary of its range lies between 52° and 53°N. From the River Ob catchment it passes through Mongolia and Manchuria where it turns S to Korea and N Japan. In the far N it is absent only from the tundra regions.

The Hazel Grouse inhabits coniferous, mixed and broad-leaved woodland at high and medium altitudes, but it does not avoid lowlands. In mountains it reaches the subalpine zone, up to 1900m asl in the Swiss Alps. The Hazel Grouse prefers extensive mature stands of Norway spruce *Picea abies*, fir *Abies* or larch *Larix* with a lush shrub layer and a mixture of birch *Betula* and alder *Alnus* (Swenson 1993). The highest population densities are attained where old patches of successional stages have developed after windthrows or avalanches, and in boundary zones between various woodland types.

The species is notoriously difficult to census. Nevertheless, more than 95% of the European population breeds in the former Soviet Union and in Fennoscandia; European Russia alone contains from 1 to 10Mbp (*c*80% of the Russian total). The 20th century and particularly the decades since 1965 have been marked by a conspicuous decrease in numbers, especially in W and C Europe, but decreases have also occurred in Scandinavia and in E Europe. Only Sweden, Poland, Romania, Lithuania and Greece had stable populations during 1970–90, whereas the large Russian population was fluctuating. All other countries reported declines. This trend has resulted in the eastward retreat of its western range limit. It has been thought extinct in the Pyrenees since the mid-1970s, but the finding of a single tail-feather in February 1992 in Haute-Garonne may indicate that it still survives. Furthermore, a small population was rediscovered in the Massif Central (Dronneau 1994). In the Czech Republic numbers were stable until 1920, but dropped dramatically thereafter. Consequently, the Hazel Grouse has vanished from much of the interior, remaining preserved only in border mountain ranges, where numbers apparently show no clear fluctuations as yet (Hudec & Èerný 1977). The major causes of these decreases include hunting pressure and the negative impact of modern forestry management techniques, to which the highly sedentary Hazel Grouse is sensitive.

In Switzerland the Hazel Grouse breeding density varies from 2 to 5 bp/100ha (Zbinden 1979). The following peak densities have been ascertained in the Polish Carpathians: broad-leaved forest 2.5 birds/100ha, mixed forest 5.6 birds/100ha, coniferous forest 18 birds/100ha (Bonczar 1991). In Latvia, in a forest stand dominated by Scots pine with an admixture of Norway spruce and birch, Hazel Grouse density corresponded to 13.2 bp/100ha; in a mature mixed forest dominated by spruce and in a broad-leaved forest, from 1.9 to 11.8 bp/100ha (Priednieks *et al* 1989). Densities in Russia and Belarus are variable, depending on forest type and year and on average between 10 and 15 bp/km^2 (Potapov 1989a), matching Finnish densities of 10–15 bp/km^2 in suitable habitats (Koskimies 1989a).

The Hazel Grouse is a polytypic species showing considerable geographic variability which is clinal in character. The nominate subspecies, *bonasia*, inhabits northern Europe up to the Urals and to the Pechora River catchment where it encounters *sibirica*. The remainder of the European range is inhabited by *rupestris*. Some authors distinguish more subspecies in Europe.

Vladimír Bejćek (CZ)

Lagopus lagopus Willow Grouse

CZ	Bělokur rousný	I	Pernice bianca nordica
D	Moorschneehuhn	NL	Moerassneeuwhoen
E	Lagópodo Común	P	Lagópode (-escocês/ -escandinavo)
F	Lagopède des saules	PL	Pardwa
FIN	Riekko	R	Белая куропатка
G	Βαλτοχιονόκοτα	S	Dalripa
H	Sarki hófajd		

Non-SPEC, Threat status S

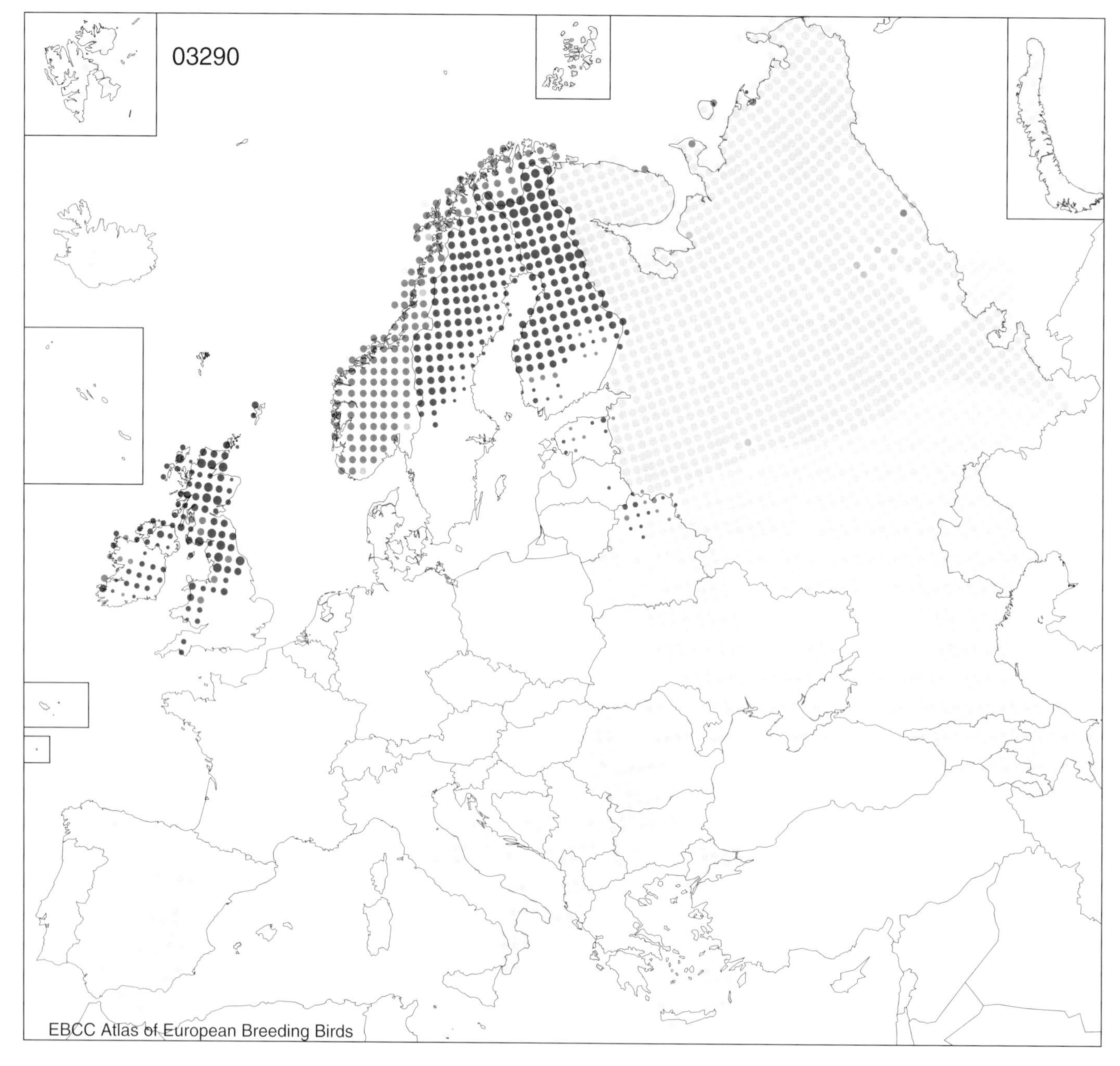

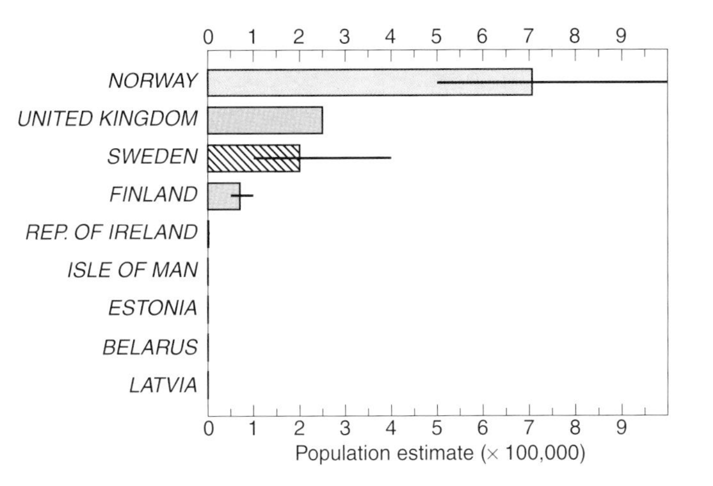

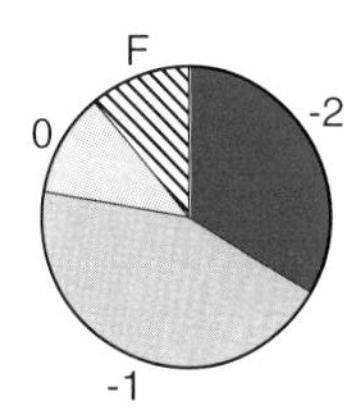

% in top 10 countries: 100.0
Total number of populated European countries: 9
Total European population 998,767–1,585,560 (1,229,684)
Russian population 100,000–6,000,000 (774,597)

The Willow Grouse has a circumpolar distribution and is an important component of the arctic–alpine ecosystem. It is an essential prey species of open-country predators, and once was a vital prey for human hunters. In North America its breeding range is confined almost exclusively to the arctic tundra, whereas in Eurasia other treeless habitats such as ling *Calluna vulgaris* heaths and moors are also favoured. In Finland, the Baltic states and many parts of Russia it also uses forested areas. It is absent from some large arctic islands like Greenland, Iceland and Novaya Zemlya. Both in North America and in Eurasia the southernmost populations breed between 50° and 55°N.

European breeding habitats fall roughly into two categories; the 'primary' open-country habitat supporting high densities, and the 'secondary' forested lowland habitat sustaining lower densities. Willow Grouse occurs mainly in the alpine and open areas of Fennoscandia and Russia. Red Grouse *L.l. scoticus*, which does not attain white winter plumage, breeds in high densities on mostly treeless heather moors in Britain & Ireland, although the Irish population is below 5000bp. On islands in northern Norway densities of 50–100 bp/km^2 (an exceptionally high figure) have been recorded (Myrberget 1988) and similar figures apply to Red Grouse on Scottish moors (Jenkins *et al* 1963), but the Red Grouse is a heavily managed species, numbers being highly dependent on the intensity of manipulative operations by gamekeepers. More representative Swedish densities of 5–10 bp/km^2 neatly match the average value for Norway. Willow Grouse in Finland and the Baltic states mostly inhabit bogs deep in forests, the birds and their broods utilizing the forest margins much as other 'forest grouse' do, but densities are moderate with respect to open habitats.

Willow Grouse populations are declining, as are those of other grouse species, but less seriously than for other tetraonids. In the main areas of occurrence no real decrease has been observed, but in the more marginal areas of Finland and especially Estonia, Latvia and Belarus decreases have been severe, perhaps to the extent of local extinctions. Up to *c*1895 the Willow Grouse was reasonably abundant in S and C Finland when forests were much more open due to extensive logging and slash-burning, but with the abandonment of such techniques and the introduction of large-scale bog drainage important habitat was lost. Willow Grouse distribution is heavily dependent on the presence of suitable open habitats.

In North America and Siberian Russia the Willow Grouse makes considerable long-distance seasonal migrations, remaining within its southern breeding range in the Palearctic, but reaching beyond it in North America. Elsewhere in Europe only local movements, usually within a radius of several dozen kilometres of the breeding areas, take place between summer and winter areas. Characteristic of the species is a cyclic fluctuation in numbers, an intensively studied phenomenon (Moss & Watson 1985, Bergerud & Gratson 1988, Hudson & Dobson 1988, Myrberget 1988). Cycle length varies greatly: in Scandinavia it is 3–4 years, in Britain 6 and in North America 10. Increases in peak years often exceed the lowest population levels fourfold, and occasionally tenfold. Predation, parasites and behavioural changes play important roles in population regulation.

In addition to Red Grouse, another 13–14 subspecies have been described of which those found in Europe are: *variegates* (which becomes partially white-plumaged in winter) on mid-Norwegian large offshore islands, *rossicus* in Russia S of the nominate, and *maior* in SW Siberia and N Kazakhstan. In North America, *alascensis* in Alaska, *alexandrae* in the Alaskan Peninsula and NW British Columbia, and *alleni* in Newfoundland, are the most-studied subspecies. Population trends for the different subspecies are unknown.

Harto Lindén (FIN) Hans Chr. Pedersen (N)

Lagopus mutus

Ptarmigan

CZ	Bělokur horský	**I**	Pernice bianca
D	Alpenschneehuhn	**NL**	Alpensneeuwhoen
E	Lagópodo Alpino	**P**	Lagópode-branco
F	Lagopède alpin	**PL**	Pardwa górska
FIN	Kiiruna	**R**	Тундряная куропатка
G	Βουνοχιονόκοτα	**S**	Fjällripa
H	Havasi hófajd		

Non-SPEC, Threat status S

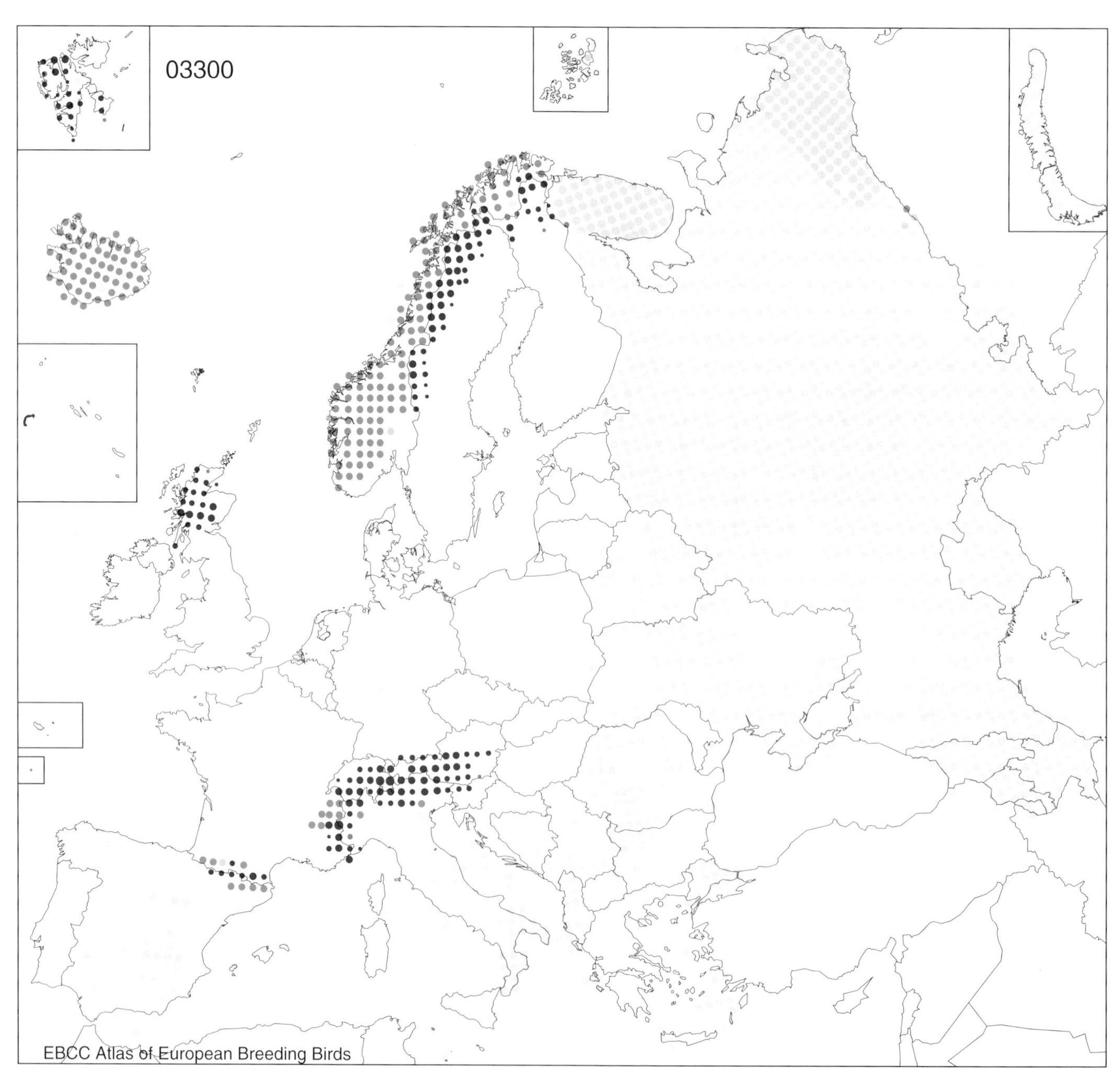

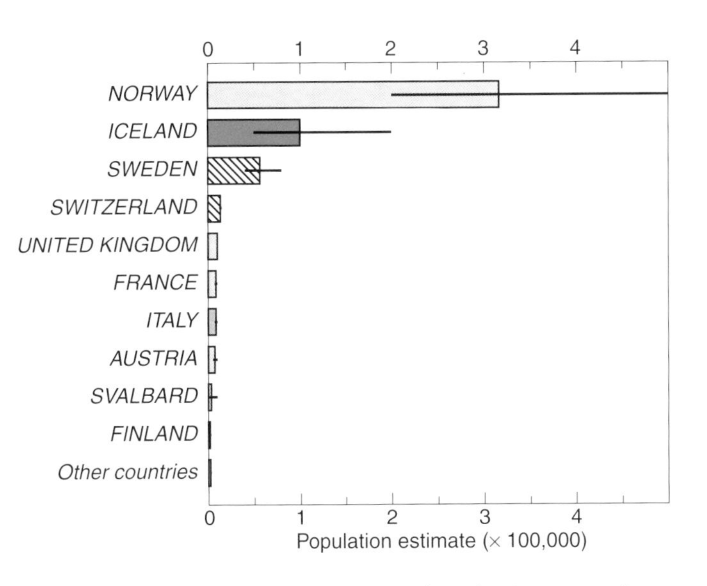

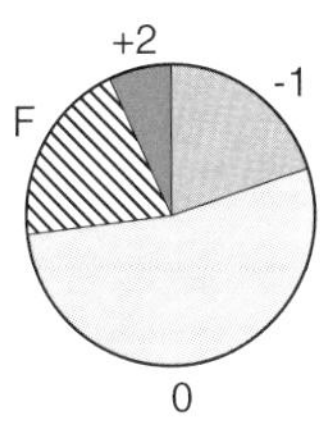

% in top 10 countries: 99.6
Total number of populated European countries: 15
Total European population 399,345–737,694 (527,012)
Russian population 100,000–600,000 (244,949)

The Ptarmigan's circumpolar arctic distribution extends to remote islands and mountain ranges. In the Palearctic, alpine populations (presumably glacial relicts) occur well S of the main range, in Scotland, the Pyrenees, the Alps and Japan. In the W Nearctic (Rocky Mountains) similar sites are occupied by the White-tailed Ptarmigan *L. leucurus*.

The Ptarmigan breeds mostly on upland tundra or mountains, where rocks and boulders often provide cover from aerial predators. In nesting areas the vegetation, continuous or patchy, is usually a heath with an assortment of dwarf shrubs (crowberry *Empetrum*, mountain avens *Dryas*, willow *Salix*, birch *Betula*, cranberry *Vaccinium*, ling *Calluna*, cassiope *Cassiope*). Broods occupy more mesic sites, such as meadows and snowbeds. Below the timberline the Ptarmigan generally is replaced by related species. Where the Willow Grouse *L. lagopus* is absent (Iceland, Greenland, the Alps) the Ptarmigan also breeds in scrubland (birch, willow, rhododendron *Rhododendron*).

Except for Willow Grouse on Kolguev, the Ptarmigan is the only gallinaceous bird inhabiting arctic islands, including Greenland (reaching 83°N), Iceland and Svalbard. In the Arctic it breeds from sea level up to the altitude limit of dwarf-shrub heath vegetation, but further S it is restricted to mountains above the treeline; in Iceland (*c*65°N) from 0 to 700m asl, in Scotland (57°N) from 200 to 1200m and in the Alps (47°N) from 1500 to 2500m (exceptionally 2800m).

Examples of European breeding densities (in bp/km^2) are: Iceland 1–34 (Gardarsson 1988), Scotland 3.1–9.0 (A. Watson 1965), Alps 1–6.6 (Bossert 1995). Density estimates usually are based on selected study areas and may therefore be biased toward good habitat.

In Iceland the Ptarmigan population is cyclic, fluctuating at a periodicity of *c*10 years (Gudmundsson 1960), a value which has also been suggested for Scotland and W Greenland; other populations are thought to show 3-year cycles (A. Watson & Moss 1979). Between cycle peaks and troughs, local densities show up to a ten-fold variation in Iceland and a three-fold variation in Scotland and Switzerland.

Annual movements vary regionally. Scottish birds are sedentary or nomadic. In the Swiss Alps the Ptarmigan move above 3000m asl in late summer, the males moving first and females and chicks later. They return to the breeding areas when the high-level snow-cover becomes heavy. Most Icelandic birds move to the high-alpine zone (above 600m asl) in autumn and gradually come down to the lowlands (below 300m asl) as snow-cover increases in early winter. Ringing recoveries have shown that they also undertake long-distance movements of up to *c*300km. In autumn, diurnal movements are conspicuous, birds seeking daytime cover between boulders and rocks but roosting on heaths, often several kilometres away. Old males are the least mobile segment of the population, females the most. Some high-arctic populations engage in long migrations, such as *L.m. captus* of E Greenland, which has repeatedly been taken in winter at sea and in Iceland. In snowy periods in winter the Ptarmigan selects wind-exposed slopes and ridges, where snow-cover is light and where there are evergreen dwarf shrubs or birch and willow scrub.

The numerous subspecies of Ptarmigan are often divided on plumage characteristics into two main groups: the *mutus* group of western Europe, including Fennoscandia–Kola, the Alps, the Pyrenees and Scotland; and the *rupestris* group from the Urals through Siberia, Japan, North America, Greenland, Iceland and Svalbard. High-arctic Ptarmigan, unlike other gallinaceous birds, have a layer of subcutaneous fat in autumn and winter, a condition which is especially pronounced in the Svalbard Ptarmigan *L.m. hyperboreus* which accumulates depot fat in autumn (up to 40% of body weight) for use when food is scarce in winter (Mortensen *et al* 1983).

Arnthor Gardarsson (ICE) Andreas Bossert (CH)

This species account is sponsored by Nos Oiseaux, Société romande pour l'étude et la protection des oiseaux, CH.

Tetrao tetrix

Black Grouse

CZ	Tetřívek obecný	**I**	Fagiano di monte
D	Birkhuhn	**NL**	Korhoen
E	Gallo-lira Común	**P**	Galo-lira
F	Tétras lyre	**PL**	Cietrzew
FIN	Teeri	**R**	Тетерев
G	Λυροπετεινός	**S**	Orre
H	Nyírfajd		

SPEC Cat 3, Threat status V

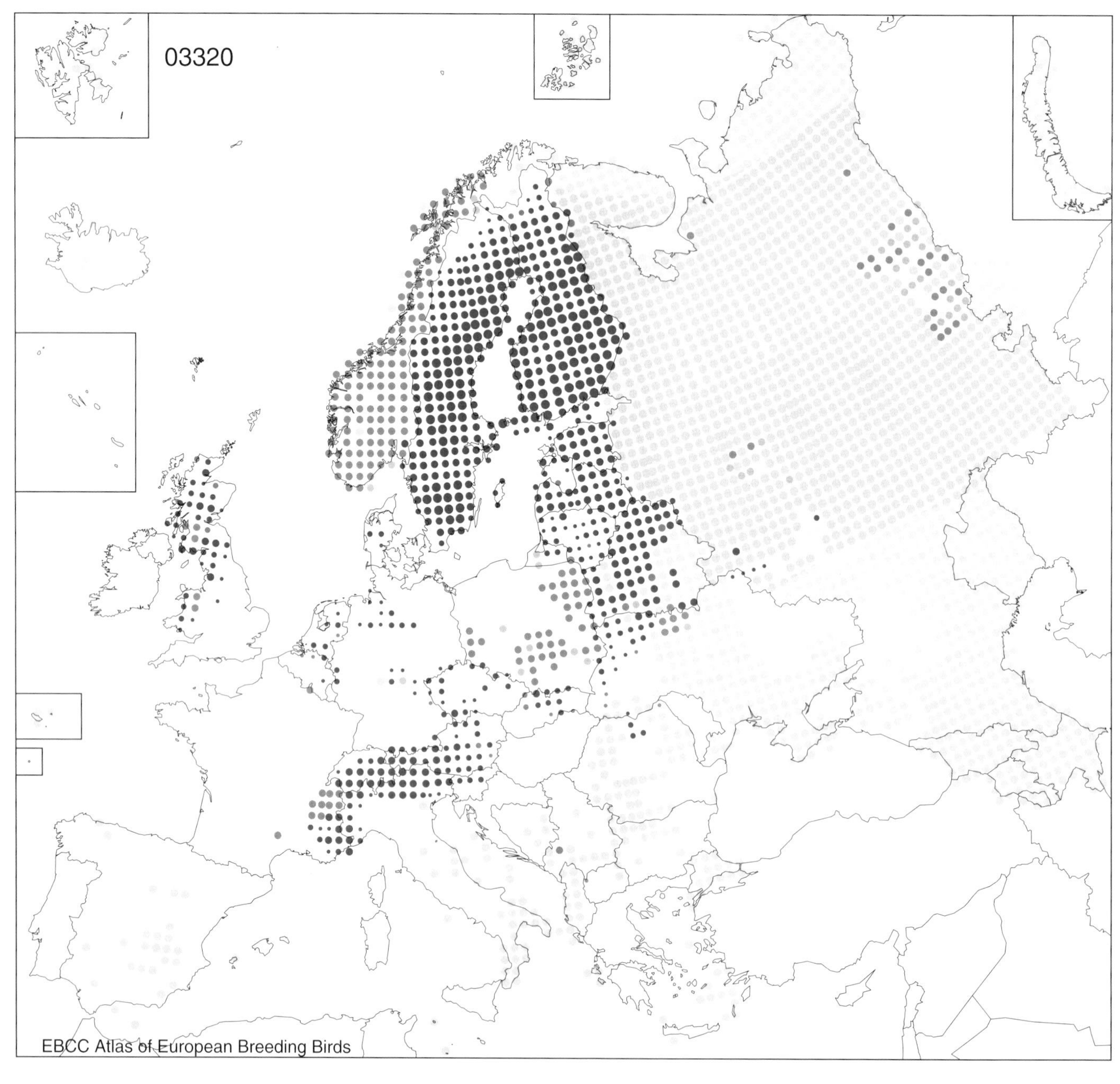

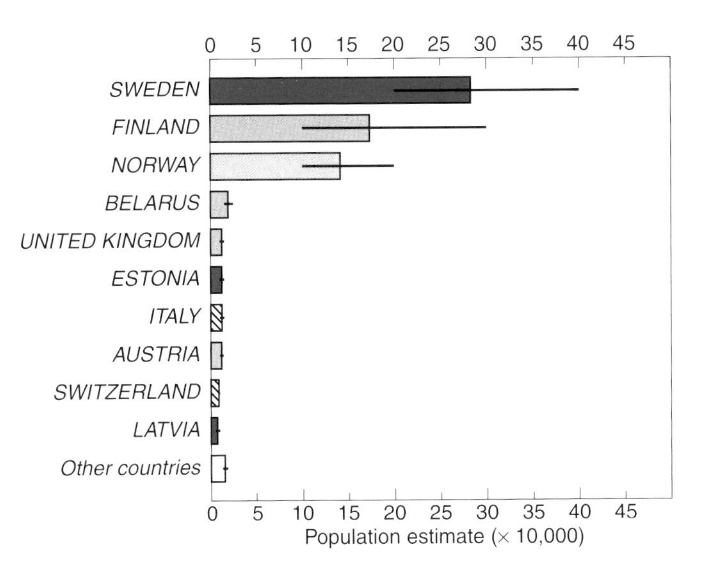

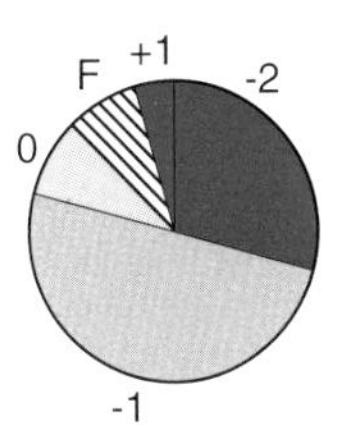

% in top 10 countries: 97.8
Total number of populated European countries: 24
Total European population 578,136–878,889 (696,385)
Russian population 100,000–1,000,000 (316,228)

The distribution of the Black Grouse covers almost the entire Palearctic forest belt, mainly in boreal, subarctic and alpine zones but locally spreading into the steppe zone. To the W and S, it splits into isolated areas corresponding to favourable relict habitats such as heaths, peat-bogs or mountain zones. Its occurrence in mid-latitude mountains such as the Alps and Carpathians is considered a glacial relict.

The Black Grouse has a preference for open, mixed habitats with a transitional character, such as alpine forest borders, raised bogs, heathland and young successional forest stages following clear-felling, burning, insect infestation or atmospheric pollution. Black Grouse habitats are normally patchily distributed, the size and position of which determines the distribution of breeding birds. The birds may wander considerably (up to several dozen kilometres in Belgium; L. Schmitz, pers obs), or even make long-distance movements after heavy snowfall (in the north), but high site fidelity is the rule. In E Russia very large movements have occurred (Potapov 1988).

The stronghold of the European population lies in Fennoscandia, Russia, Belarus and the Baltic States, where at least 1M 'pairs' inhabit the vast stretches of forest, fens, bogs and heaths. The C European population of the Alpine and Carpathian mountains and their foothills, comprises *c*43 000 males, the majority of which inhabit the Italian, Austrian and Swiss parts of the Alpine range. The British population is smaller, with a little over 25 000 displaying males in spring (Baines & Hudson 1995). Relatively insignificant numbers remain in the Danish–German–Dutch–Belgian lowlands, several hundred breeding pairs occurring in Germany and fewer than 50bp in each of the other countries.

The entire population is in a steady decline except in Sweden where specific conservation measures have been applied. This widespread decrease correlates with the species' range contraction in S, W and C Europe, a trend characterized by accelerated extinction of isolated populations, probably resulting from rapid habitat destruction and fragmentation. For example, following the disappearance of heaths in N Belgium the Black Grouse has become extinct, as it has in the W and C Ardennes. Only two isolated areas in E Belgium still hold the species, although numbers have crashed from over 200 males in 1971 to *c*50 in 1995 (Ruwet *et al* 1986, unpubl). Similar scenarios are typical for The Netherlands (36 cocks in 1992; SOVON), Britain (range contraction of 28% between 1968–72 and 1988–91; Baines & Hudson 1995), Denmark (only 7 displaying cocks in 3 localities in 1991; Sørensen 1995) and N Germany. Elsewhere, the decline may seem less dramatic because the remaining population remains large. Locally, the Black Grouse seems adaptable to some artificially altered habitats, such as *Ericacea*-deficient grasslands in Thüringia, Bohemia, the Rhône valley and S Denmark.

The reasons for the general decline are complex: changes in human exploitation of habitats (afforestation of open land, intensive agricultural and forestry practices; Baines & Hudson 1995), huge increases in the application of chemicals, use of artificial fertilizers, pollution of the atmosphere (acidic deposition, resulting in superabundant grass growth), increased disturbance of breeding grounds, spread of human settlement, increased tourism, hunting, and a succession of cool and moist summers affecting chick survival rates. The effects of these pressures must be superimposed on any natural short-term fluctuations (Klaus *et al* 1990). The long-term deterioration in the spatial and temporal distribution of habitat patches of the preferred successional stages of sufficient size is probably the main cause of decline, locally enhanced by predation pressure and reduced primary production (Angelstam 1988).

Within Europe there are three subspecies, the nominate *T.t. tetrix* occupying continental Europe apart from E-C Russia, where *viridanus* is found and Great Britain contains *britannicus*. Elsewhere there are up to four subspecies.

Luc Schmitz (B)

This species account is sponsored by Clement Agten, Peer, B.

Tetrao mlokosiewiczi

Caucasian Black Grouse

CZ	Tetřívek kavkazský	I	Fagiano di monte del Caucaso
D	Kaukasus-Birkhuhn	NL	Kaukasisch Korhoen
E	Gallo-lira Caucasiano	P	Galo-lira-caucásico
F	Tétras du Caucase	PL	Cietrzew kaukaski
FIN	Kaukasianteeri	R	Кавказский тетерев
G	Λυροπετεινός του Καυκάσου	S	Kaukasisk orre
H	Kaukázusi nyírfajd		

SPEC Cat 2, Threat status INS

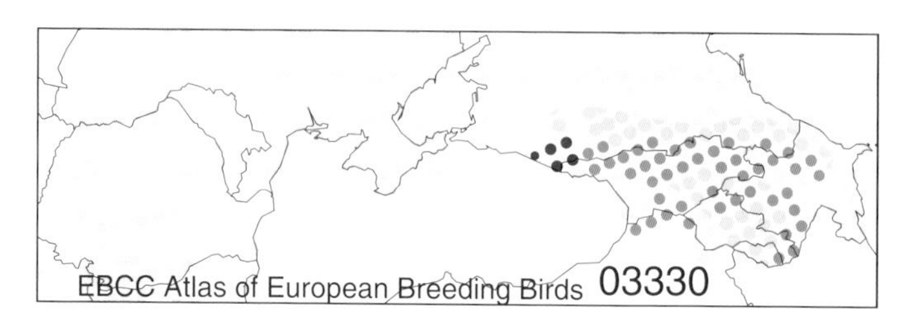

Breeding mostly between 2000 and 3000m asl, the Caucasian Black Grouse has a patchy world distribution, comprising four major components: the Great Caucasian Ridge, the Lesser Caucasus Mountains, the Pontian Ridge and 3–4 isolated mountain areas in E Turkey. It breeds in the subalpine and alpine zones and occupies a variety of habitats (usually on steep southern slopes, Potapov 1984, 1985), such as sparse pine forest, krummholz birch and beech on the timberline, subalpine scrub (shrub juniper, rhododendron), subalpine glades and subalpine and alpine meadows.

In general, the species' winter range coincides with its breeding range. Snowfall depth and plant-food availability determine the extent to which the Caucasian Black Grouse descends in winter from its breeding grounds.

Roughly 70 000 birds inhabit the Great Caucasus (Potapov 1984, 1985) and *c*8400 the Lesser Caucasus (Armenia 500; Airumian & Margarian 1974). Georgia holds *c*75 000 birds and Azerbaijan 400 (R.L. Potapov, unpubl). The Turkish population is little known, but comprises probably at least 2500 birds (R.L. Potapov, unpubl). Iran has *c*300 birds on the Azerbaijani border.

Numbers in the W Caucasus increase from SE to NW. At present, the density in the Teberda Nature Reserve is 3–4 birds/km^2 and in the Caucasian Nature Reserve 14 birds/km^2. Numbers have declined in some parts of the C Caucasus, as around the North Ossetian Nature Reserve, where data from 1977 revealed a density of 7–9 birds/km^2 (Komarov 1991). A decline has also occurred in Georgia. For 1967–69, census data from N Georgia indicated a density of up to 5 birds/km^2 (Sikharulidze 1974). The low-altitude range in the N began disappearing in the 1930s, retreating 50km S (Potapov 1978). A gradual range contraction, coinciding with a rapid population decrease, has been recorded to the E and S (Potapov 1982). Reports of a decreased range in the NW are erroneous (Til'ba 1994).

The principal causes of the decline in Caucasian Black Grouse numbers are increased grazing of livestock high in the mountains, and habitat changes resulting from road-building and the spread of human settlement. Historically, increases have occurred during wars, conflicts, when grazing has ceased for any reason, or after a series of warm springs (Vitovich 1977). The present political turmoil may provide a temporary reduction in the extent of habitat changes in some areas, but in the long term, continuing declines outside reserves are likely.

Peter Til'ba (R) Roald L Potapov (R)

Tetraogallus caucasicus

Caucasian Snowcock

CZ	Velekur kavkazský	H	Kaukázusi királyfogoly
D	Kaukasisches Königshuhn	I	Tetraogallo del Caucaso
E	Perdigallo Caucasiano	NL	Kaukasisch Berghoen
F	Tétraogalle du Caucase	P	Tetraogalo do Cáucaso
FIN	Kaukasianlumikana	PL	Ułar kaukaski
G	Χιονοπετεινός του Καυκάσου	R	Кавказский улар
		S	Kaukasisk snöhöna

SPEC Cat 4, Threat status S

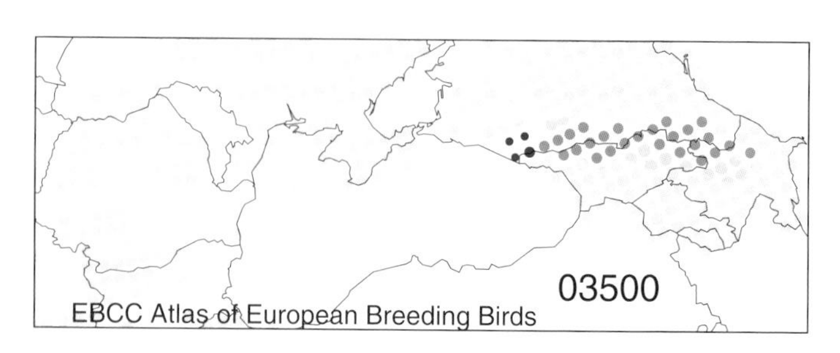

The range of the Caucasian Snowcock, a species similar to, but smaller than the Caspian Snowcock *T. caspius*, lies above 2600m asl in the Greater Caucasus Mountains in Russia, Georgia and Azerbaijan, where it is the only endemic species. It is resident in the alpine and subalpine mountain zones from Mount Oshsten (2808m) in the NW Caucasus to Mount Babadag (3632m) in the SE Great Caucasian Ridge. Its most characteristic habitat is a combination of scree, steep rocky precipices and patches of meadow at 1800–4000m asl. In winter, it keeps to the subalpine zone and lower edge of the alpine zone. It prefers south-facing slopes, usually nesting at the bases of rocks or cliffs, sheltered by large tussocks, or occasionally in cliff niches. Its range is divided into complexly-related micro-populations with varying degrees of isolation dependent on terrain relief, but no population is completely isolated.

Amongst its extreme adaptations to mountain habitats, the most striking is its inability to maintain horizontal flapping flight. Instead, it normally dives down mountain slopes. It therefore has to climb back up on foot (Potapov 1987). Such extreme morphological specialization confines this species to mountains, because it cannot escape from predators on flat terrain.

In the 1960s, the total population comprised *c*200 000 birds (Baziev 1978). The highest density, 11 birds/km^2, was recorded in the C Caucasus (Baziev 1978), where its favoured habitat is at its most extensive. Spring densities are lower than autumn densities, but otherwise there is no cyclicity, no changes having been recorded.

In the lower W Caucasus the Caucasian Snowcock's range is more fragmented and its density lower. In the Caucasian Nature Reserve in 1983, density was 6–8 birds/km^2, and in the Teberda Nature Reserve in the 1960s, 6.5 birds/km^2 (Tkachenko 1966). The pattern is similar in the eastern Great Caucasus where counts undertaken in the 1960s found that density does not exceed 1–4 birds/km^2 (Drozdov 1965).

Living as it does in remote and inaccessible places, the Caucasian Snowcock is much less vulnerable to the influence of human beings than are other high-mountain species. Nevertheless, in some areas which are experiencing intensive agricultural activity, it is under considerable pressure. For example, in the Russian mountains of the Stavropol' region where livestock graze density does not exceed 1.3 birds/km^2 (Tkachenko 1966), and in similar circumstances in Georgia, 11–12 birds/10km^2 is the maximum (Sikharulidze 1977).

Peter Til'ba (R) Roald Potapov (R)

Tetraogallus caspius

Caspian Snowcock

CZ	Velekur kaspický	I	Tetraogallo del Caspio
D	Kaspisches Koenigshühn	NL	Kaspisch Berghoen
E	Perdigallo del Caspio	P	Tetraogalo do Cáspio
F	Tétraogalle de Perse	PL	Ułar kaspijski
FIN	Kaspianlumikana	R	Каспийский улар
G	Χιονοπετεινός της Κασπίας	S	Kaspisk snöhöna
H	Kaspi királyfogoly		

SPEC Cat 3, Threat status INS

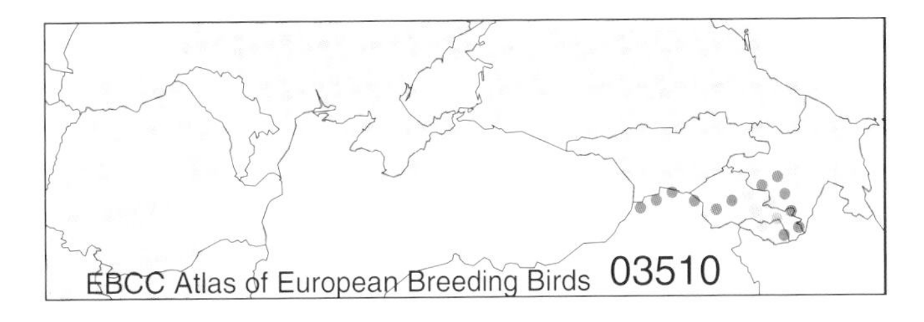

The Caspian Snowcock, a large member of the partridge family, is distributed across open grasslands and rocky slopes in the alpine zone of the Lesser Caucasus, E Turkey, W and N Iran and S Turkmenistan. About 7–10% of the species' range lies in the *Atlas*' coverage area, mainly in a set of isolated populations in Armenia, Azerbaijan and Georgia (Baziev 1978). A typical snowcock, extremely adapted to mountain habitats, it cannot maintain horizontal flapping flight. After diving along mountain slopes, it must regain altitude on foot (Potapov 1989b). Naturally such extreme morphological specialization compels it to live exclusively in mountains, because it cannot survive on flat terrain.

The species' preferred breeding habitat is steppe grassland in the alpine zone between 2400 and 4000m asl, usually on steep slopes possessing rocky outcrops and stony areas. In summer it favours north-facing slopes and in winter, south-facing. Wintering birds tend to avoid snow-cover to select open areas with steppe-like vegetation. The Caspian Snowcock normally nests on steep slopes beneath overhanging rocks, among stones, or in tussocks.

The extent of its alpine habitats predetermines its patchy distribution. The Lesser Caucasus holds *c*20 local populations of 10–277 birds, totalling in 1964 no more than 850 (Baziev 1978). Political turmoil since has prevented subsequent data-collection. The Turkish population of 200–2000bp is poorly known, as are trends. There are no data on the Iranian population. No reliable census information exists for any population.

The Caspian Snowcock declined in the Lesser Caucasus around 1900, when it disappeared from the Talysh Mountains in Azerbaijan (Satunin 1907). This decline continued, and in the 1960s the species almost reached local extinction on the Gegam and Aiozdor ridges in Armenia (Baziev 1978). No figures exist, but it is likely that populations inhabiting large continuous areas of the alpine zone reach higher densities than those in smaller areas.

Populations in Armenia, Georgia and Azerbaijan are highly threatened because of degradation of the high-mountain pastures through overgrazing, especially in early summer when sheep move up from their wintering refuges. Wandering sheep cause nest desertion. Herdsmen's dogs are known to destroy nests and broods. Foxes *Vulpes vulpes*, which have markedly increased in the 20th century, also take incubating females (Baziev 1978). Habitat losses due to increased aridity and global climate change may also be contributing to the decline of the species (Potapov 1989b).

Roald L Potapov (R)

Tetrao urogallus

Capercaillie

CZ	Tetřev hlušec	I	Gallo cedrone
D	Auerhuhn	NL	Auerhoen
E	Urogallo Común	P	Tetraz
F	Grand Tétras	PL	Głuszec
FIN	Metso	R	Глухарь
G	Αγριόκουρκος	S	Tjäder
H	Siketfajd		

Non-SPEC, Threat status S (P)

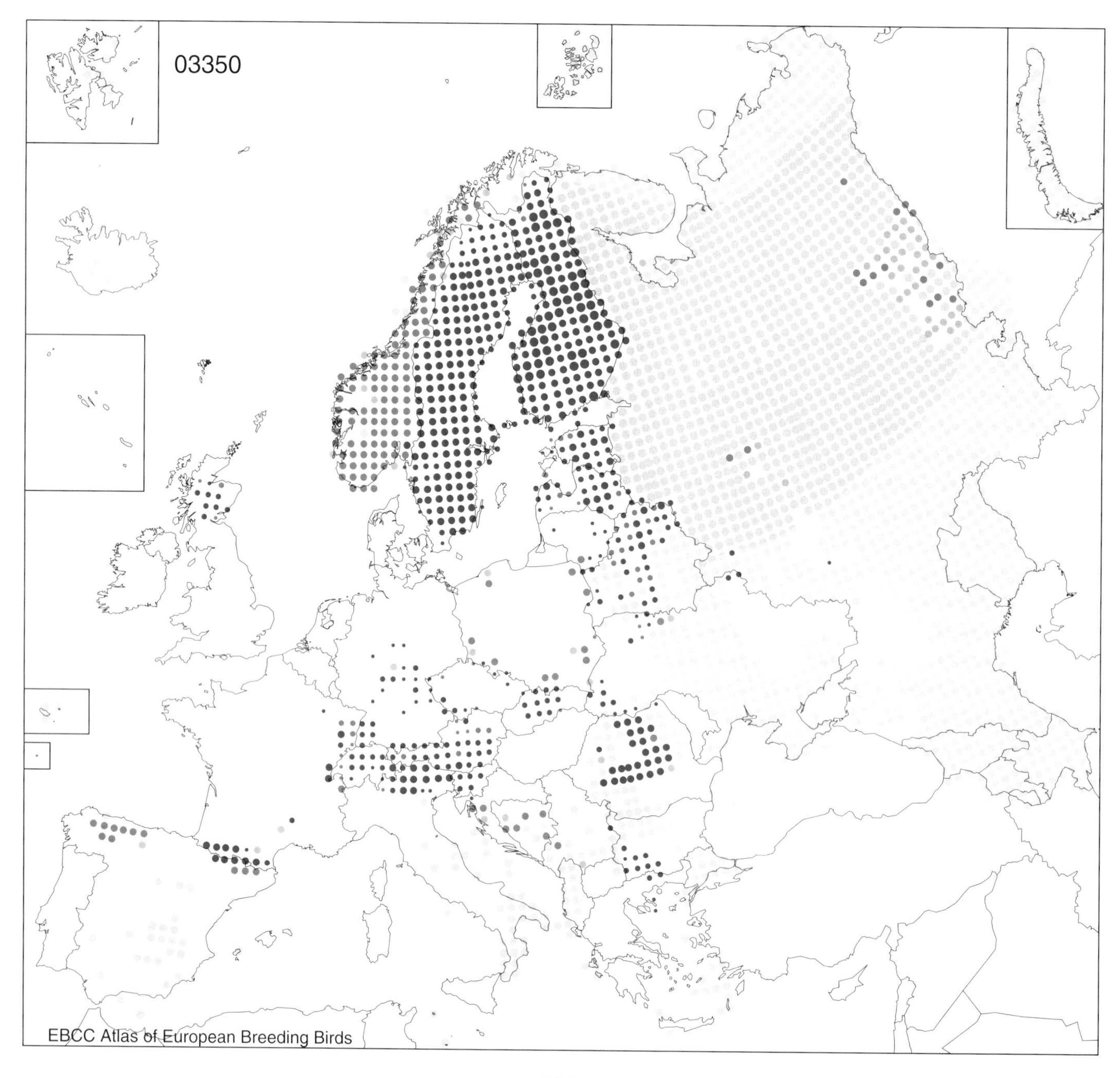

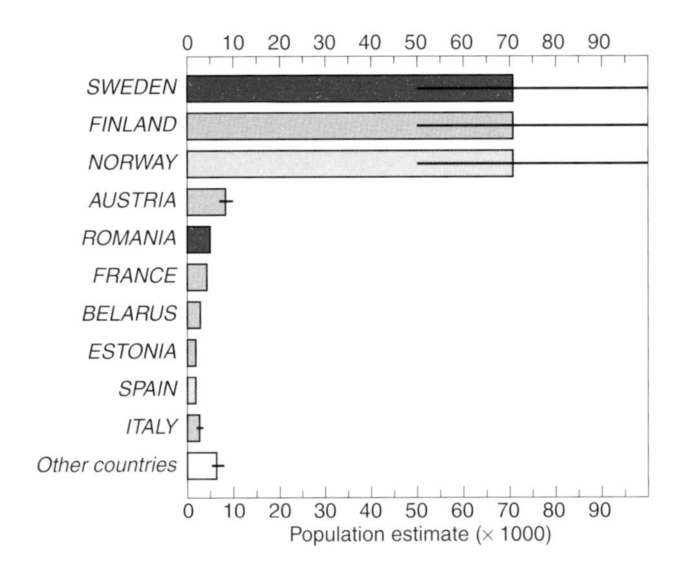

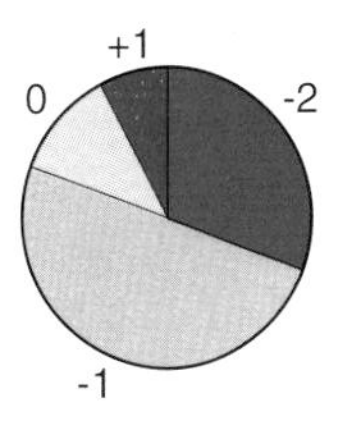

% in top 10 countries: 97.4
Total number of populated European countries: 26
Total European population 209,405–296,085 (245,313)
Russian population 400,000–800,000 (565,685)

The Capercaillie, largest and most sexually dimorphic of the tetraonids, is essentially a bird of the Old World boreal and temperate forests. Its range extends across the Northern Hemisphere between the July 13° and 21°C isotherms from Scandinavia eastwards to mid-Siberia, where there is some overlap with the Black-billed Capercaillie, *T. parvirostris*. This distribution is associated with that of the Scots pine *Pinus sylvestris*, and even more so with that of bilberry *Vaccinium myrtillus* (Klaus *et al* 1989). Bilberry is important, not only as food for adults and chicks (Storch 1993), but also for the variety of invertebrates it supports, especially lepidoptera larvae which are especially favoured by young chicks.

Some populations in Russia are migratory. In Europe, cocks are mainly sedentary but hens may move up to 20km or more (Moss & Picozzi 1994). Exceptional movements of more than 1000km S in autumn have been recorded in Sweden.

An isolated subspecies *cantabricus* is present in the Cantabrian Mountains of N Spain, where it inhabits hardwood forests, holly representing the evergreen element. Another subspecies *aquitanicus* is quite widespread in the Pyrenees. The nominate *urogallus* occurs as far S as Bulgaria and locally in Greece although distribution is patchy throughout Europe. The isolated Scottish population became extinct in the late 18th century. The first successful reintroductions in 1837–38 involved birds trapped in Sweden. Reintroduction projects are currently under way in C Europe where the Capercaillie is declining or extinct; Klaus & Bergmann (1994) refer to eight major programmes in Germany but it is too soon to know if self-sustaining populations will result from these attempts.

The structure of a woodland is the main factor influencing its suitability for Capercaillie (Picozzi *et al* 1993). Old, fairly open coniferous forest containing good ground flora of dwarf shrubs, especially bilberry, provides the typical habitat. Pine, particularly Scots pine, and white fir *Abies alba* are the preferred conifer species, but the Capercaillie also occurs in stands dominated by Norway spruce *Picea abies*. In southern Europe and parts of Russia, the Capercaillie inhabits mixed hardwood forests, especially those with oak. In Scotland, some live in non-native Sitka spruce *P. sitchensis* plantations (Moss & Picozzi 1994).

Spring densities usually range between 1 and 2 displaying cocks/100ha. In August, mean densities of 10–15 birds/100ha can be found throughout Scandinavia and northern Russia (Klaus *et al* 1989). Winter density in prime habitat in Scotland generally ranges from 10–15 birds/100ha in good habitat to 1–5 in poor habitat. However, in one semi-natural pine forest, 20–25 birds/100ha were recorded in November 1993 (R. Moss, pers comm).

Throughout its range a reduction in numbers, often considerable, is causing concern. The most consistent explanation for the decline is habitat loss resulting from the effects of modern forestry practice (review in Klaus & Bergmann 1994). Disturbance from forestry operations and recreation, and predation of eggs and young by fox *Vulpes vulpes*, marten *Martes* spp and wild boar *Sus scrofa*, and by birds such as Crow *Corvus corone* and Goshawk *Accipiter gentilis* may all have played a part in the decline. Furthermore, it has been shown in Sweden (Höglund 1955) and Scotland (Moss 1986) that chick survival is poor in wet weather and that Capercaillie distribution is confined to areas with relatively low rainfall. While this may apply throughout the birds' range, it is possible that climatic change (leading to wetter summers) could be affecting Capercaillie populations. The reduction presently recorded all over Europe will inevitably lead to further isolation of populations (already apparent from the map), and probably to local extinctions.

Christian Marti (CH) Nicholas Picozzi (GB)

Alectoris chukar

Chukar

CZ	Orebice čukar	I	Coturnice orientale
D	Chukarhuhn	NL	Aziatische Steenpatrijs
E	Perdiz Chucar	P	Perdiz-chukar
F	Perdrix choukar	PL	Kuropatwa górska
FIN	Vuoripyy	R	Азиатский кеклик
G	Νησιώτικη Πέρδικα	S	Berghöna
H	Csukár		

SPEC Cat 3, Threat status V

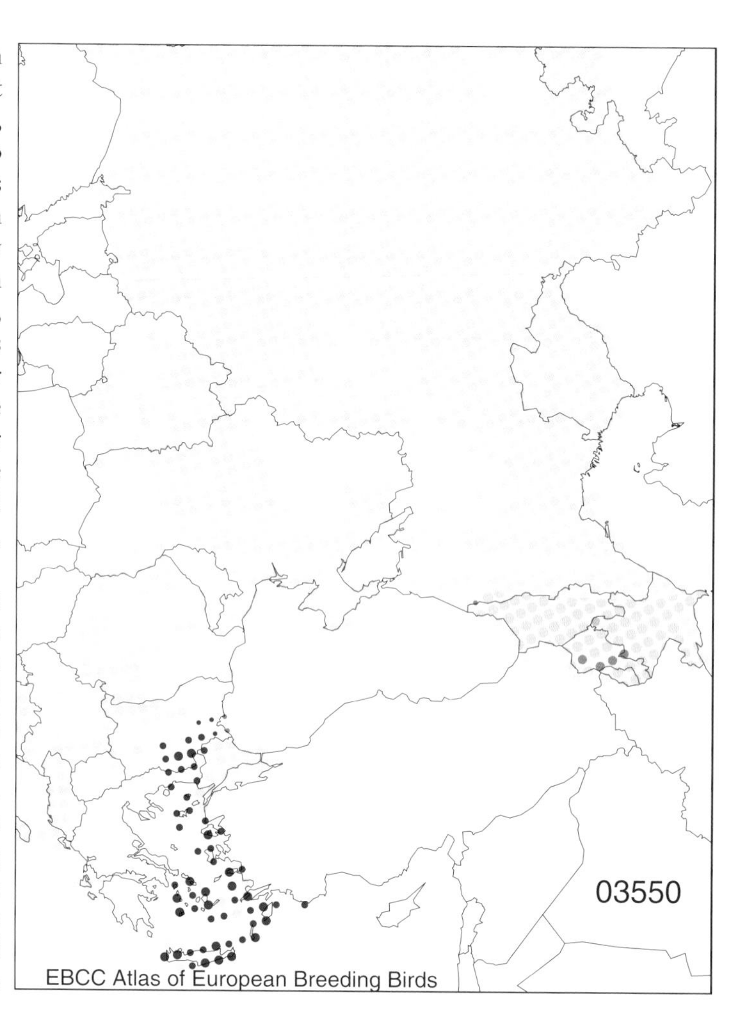

The natural range of this sedentary partridge extends from the E Balkans (Greek Thrace, SE Bulgaria), the adjacent Mediterranean islands (most Aegean islands, Crete, Cyprus) and Turkey through C Asia and the Himalayas to NE China. Of the six recognized subspecies, *kleini* occurs in mainland Europe while *cypriotes* is the Mediterranean island subspecies. It has been introduced locally in many countries, with particular success in western North America and New Zealand. Its presence in Great Britain, France, mainland Greece (Attica) and some Greek islands during the census period results from introductions for shooting (discontinued in Britain after 1992). Outside Greece, such nuclei are unlikely to persist because of poor breeding success. Nevertheless small populations have been reported from C France (S of Paris 10–100 pairs) and from 19 squares in Great Britain, mainly in SW England, N England and the Scottish Highlands (not mapped).

Typically it is a bird of barren arid or semi-arid hillsides covered in low grasses or herbs interspersed with occasional stunted trees and bushes. At low altitudes in Europe, it inhabits vineyards, olive groves, agricultural land and rocky slopes possessing xerophyllous bushes and shrubs. Elsewhere, it occupies forested mountain slopes up to 2800m asl in Turkey and 4000m asl in the Himalayas.

The Chukar has declined over most of its SE European range, partly at least through hunting and poaching (Watson 1962). Agricultural intensification, abandonment of terrace farming and increased predation mainly have been to blame (Papaevangelou 1980, Papaevangelou *et al* in press). Currently there are probably fewer than 10 000bp in Bulgaria but recent evidence suggests at least 11 000–16 000bp in Greece (at densities of 1.2–3.6/km²) and a wider distribution there than the map suggests (Papaevangelou *et al.* in press), and at least 100 000bp in Cyprus. Densities are lowest in the agricultural lowlands and in mountain areas without water, even though birds will travel several kilometres to drink (Watson 1962, Pantelis 1980). Increasing water availability can affect numbers dramatically, density rising from 1–5 bp/km² to 50 bp/km² locally following desert irrigation in Israel (Mendelssohn 1980). Outside the breeding season, the birds form into coveys of 5–40 individuals that, in the mountains, often move to lower altitudes over winter.

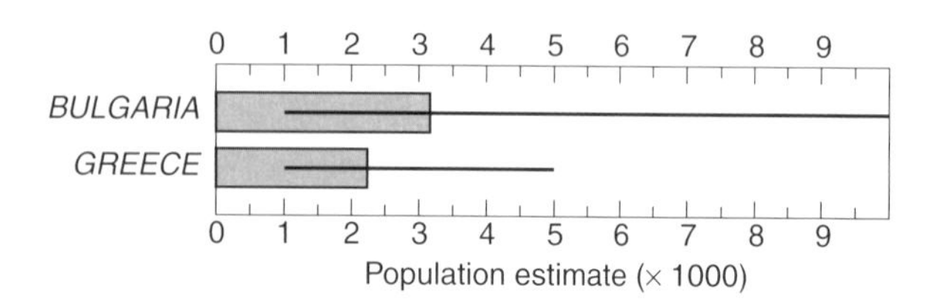

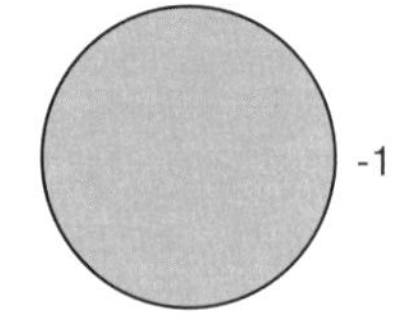

% in top 10 countries: 100.0
Total number of populated European countries: 2
Total European population 2908–12,774 (5398)
Russian population 1–1 (1)
Turkish population 50,000–200,000 (100,000)

Nicholas Aebischer (GB)

Alectoris graeca

Rock Partridge

CZ	Orebice horská	I	Coturnice
D	Steinhuhn	NL	Steenpatrijs
E	Perdiz Griega	P	Perdiz-grega
F	Perdrix bartavelle	PL	Kuropatwa skalna
FIN	Kivikkopyy	R	Европейский кеклик
G	Πετροπέρδικα	S	Stenhöna
H	Szirti fogoly		

SPEC Cat 2, Threat status V (P)

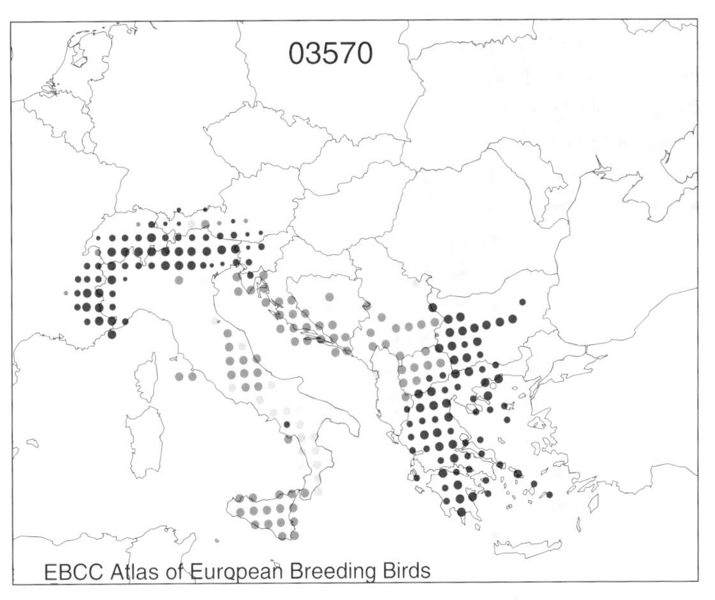

The sedentary Rock Partridge is found throughout the Alps, the C and southern Apennines, Sicily and the Balkan Peninsula as far E as C Bulgaria. It inhabits not only low-altitude rocky steppes containing scrub, but also steep mountain slopes which have grassy patches, low shrubs and sometimes scattered conifers. In the Alps it breeds between 1400 and 2500m asl, descending in winter to seek food and shelter on snow-free slopes. Outside Europe it occurs from 400 to 2700m asl.

Declines began over most of the range in the 1950s; in Italy numbers declined in the Alps, the Apennines and in Sicily (Priolo & Bocca 1992); some 13 000–20 000bp remain. In the other Alpine countries, the total population size is estimated at a few thousand breeding pairs. In the French Alps, the range contracted in the N and NW regions between the early 1960s and 1989. However, spring censuses made since the mid-1980s have revealed that populations in suitable habitats are stable overall

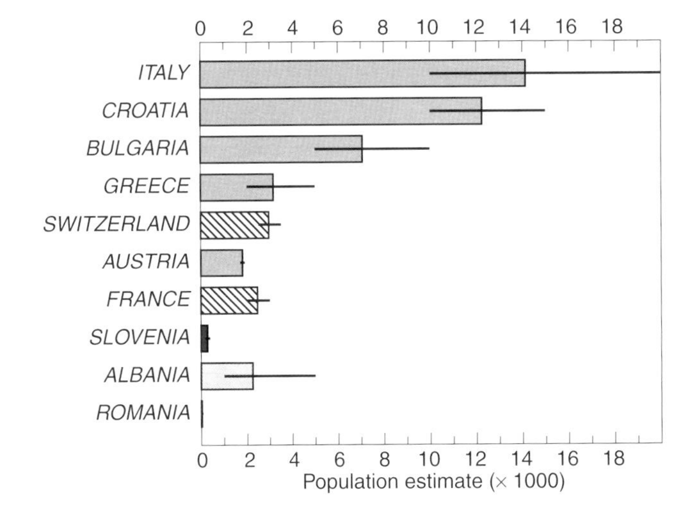

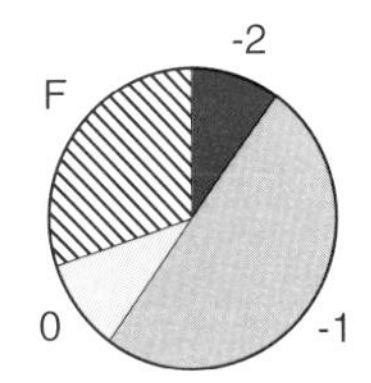

% in top 10 countries: 100.0
Total number of populated European countries: 10
Total European population 40,919–54,259 (46,378)

(Bernard-Laurent & de Franceschi 1994). In Austria, the Rock Partridge, which was widespread in the 1890s, now survives in Carinthia (Gossow *et al* 1992). In Albania, Croatia, Slovenia and Bulgaria, populations are believed to have decreased greatly, but recent quantitative data are not available. In Greece, Papaevangelou *et al* (in press) estimate that the population is *c*9500bp.

The main cause of decline in mountain areas is probably the loss of, and changes to, prime habitat associated with decreasing rural low-intensity activities, such as grazing and cereal farming. In Mediterranean regions, the decline seems due to increased human impact, especially poaching and intensive hunting.

Rock and Red-legged Partridge *A. rufa* are known to hybridize along the border of the Southern French Alps, where there is a narrow zone of phenotypical intergradation (Bernard-Laurent 1984). Another hybridization zone has been described between Chukar *A. chukar* and Rock Partridge in Bulgaria (P. Petrov *et al* 1969).

Ariane Bernard-Laurent (F) Zlatozar Boev (BUL)

Alectoris rufa Red-legged Partridge

CZ Orebice rudá
D Rothuhn
E Perdiz Roja
F Perdrix rouge
FIN Punapyy
G Κοκκινοπέρδικα
H Vörös fogoly
I Pernice rossa
NL Rode Patrijs
P Perdiz-comum
PL Kuropatwa czerwona
R Рыжая горная куропатка
S Rödhöna

SPEC Cat 2, Threat status V

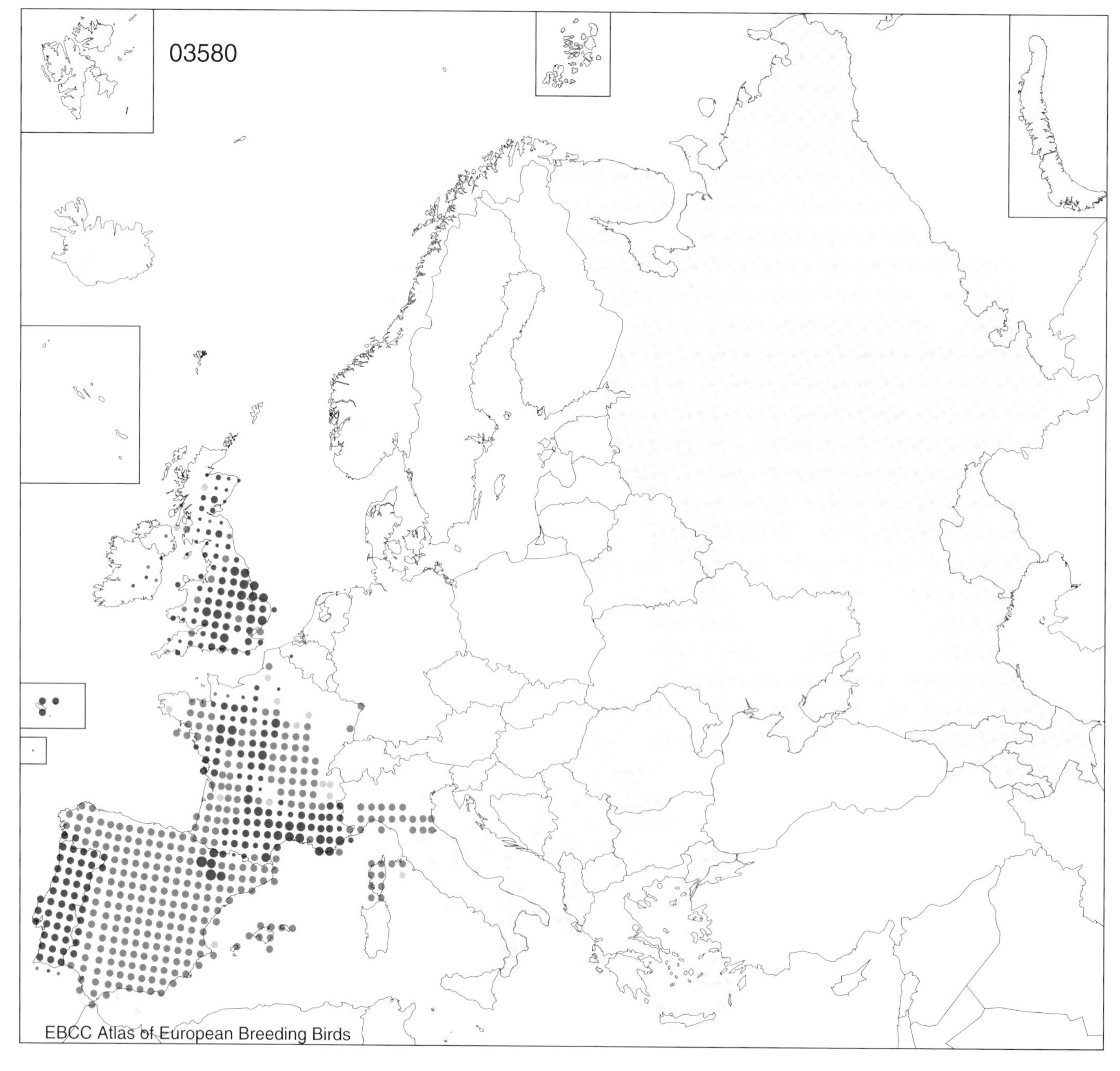

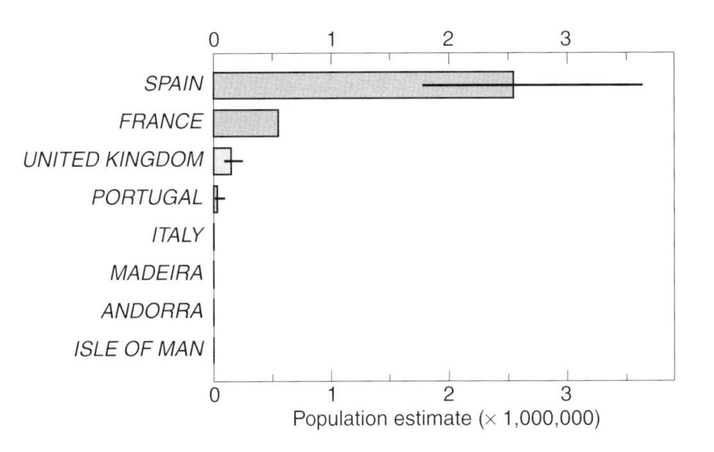

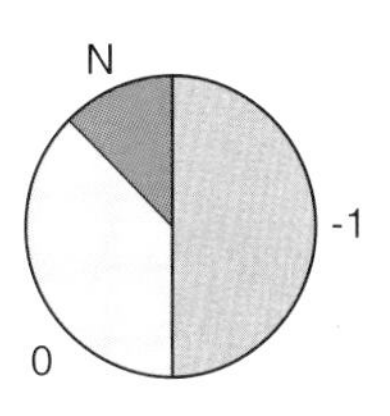

% in top 10 countries: 100.0
Total number of populated European countries: 8
Total European population 2,508,595–4,377,931 (3,276,546)

The Red-legged Partridge is a resident of SW Europe, occurring naturally in Portugal, Spain, France, Corsica, N Italy, Elba and the Balearics (where possibly it was introduced). Once it was present in W Germany, Switzerland, NE France and the Channel Islands, but these areas have been abandoned progressively over the past four centuries as its natural range retracted southwards, maybe as a result of climatic change. It was introduced to Great Britain two centuries ago and is now well-established throughout most of England, and parts of Scotland and Wales. Other successful historical introduction sites are the Azores, Gran Canaria and Madeira. Recently, releases of this species for shooting has resulted in small scattered nuclei outside its normal range, such as in Ireland, but these mostly are not self-sustaining.

Essentially a bird of open ground, the Red-legged Partridge prefers a warm dry climate, well-drained soil and a combination of low bushy vegetation for shelter and areas of short grass or bare ground for feeding. Over much of its range it is associated with arable farming, especially low-intensity cropping with a mixture of cultivated, fallow and uncultivated ground (Potts 1980, Lucio & Purroy 1992a). In the Iberian Peninsula and Italy it also occurs on rocky mountain slopes with alternating areas of open ground and low scrub up to 2000m asl. Intermediate habitats include vineyards, olive groves, unimproved pastures and marginal hill farmland. It avoids particularly arid or wet areas.

The species' world population now stands at *c*3.25Mbp, of which 2.5M are in Iberia and 0.5M in France. However, since the 1960s, wild partridge stocks have declined throughout the range. In France, they have fallen across the whole country so that in many areas density is below 1 bp/km^2 (Farthouat 1980). The declines have been patchier in Portugal and Spain, where the species is rare in the coastal plains but locally still common in its preferred altitudinal zone of 200–1000m asl. The best partridge areas are in Castilla-La Mancha, Extremadura, Castilla-Léon and E Portugal. In Britain, this species is encountered most frequently in eastern England between the Humber and the Thames; the decline in wild stocks has been masked by large-scale releases of reared birds, as in the small Italian population.

The reasons for the decline include the intensification of agriculture (heavy pesticide use, mechanization, irrigation, removal of hedges; Rands 1986), the abandonment of farming in the hills and subsequent scrub encroachment (Lucio & Purroy 1992a), and heavy shooting pressure exacerbated by the release of reared birds which encourages a level of exploitation that wild stocks cannot sustain. In many areas of Spain, releases of hybrids *A. rufa* × *A. chukar* (Chukar) and *A. rufa* × *A. graeca* (Rock Partridge) threaten the genetic purity of the wild stocks (Lucio & Purroy 1992b).

Outside the breeding season, birds form coveys of 10–40 individuals that are essentially family groups joined by failed breeders. Although sedentary, in mountain areas the birds will move to lower altitudes in hard winters. The coveys split up in early spring, and the males establish territories by calling from prominent positions. Under the managed conditions in Britain, breeding success depends strongly on the level of predation by mammalian and avian predators (Potts 1980). In optimal conditions, density can reach 35 bp/km^2 (Rands 1986). In areas of mixed farmland and scrub it averages 5–9 bp/km^2. In intensively cultivated regions it falls below 5 bp/km^2 (Rands 1986, Lucio & Purroy 1992b).

Three subspecies are recognized: the nominate *A.r. rufa* occurs throughout France, Italy and Great Britain, while *hispanica* and *intercedens* are found across N and W Iberia, and S and E Spain, respectively.

Nicholas Aebischer (GB) Antonio Lucio (E)

Alectoris barbara

Barbary Partridge

CZ	Orebice pouštní	I	Pernice sarda
D	Felsenhuhn	NL	Barbarijse Patrijs
E	Perdiz Moruna	P	Perdiz-moura
F	Perdrix gambra	PL	Kuropatwa berberyjska
FIN	Kalliopyy	R	Берберийская каменная куропатка
G	Βραχοπέρδικα		
H	Berber fogoly	S	Klipphöna

SPEC Cat 3, Threat status E (P)

The sedentary Barbary Partridge is widespread across North Africa, where it occurs from the coastal plains to the Atlas Mountains and edges of the Sahara. The bulk of the European population occurs on Sardinia, where it may have been introduced in Roman times, although Spanó (1975) believes that it colonized naturally in the late Miocene. It was also introduced to the Rock of Gibraltar in the late 19th century, and has spread to the adjacent Spanish mainland. There are four recognized subspecies, of which the nominate *A.b. barbara*, resident in the Maghreb, occurs in Sardinia and Gibraltar.

In Gibraltar, of the south-facing stony terraces, the birds favour the uppermost which is covered with sparse short vegetation and open scrub (Finlayson & Cortés 1987). The apparently stable population numbers about 50bp within 1.1km^2 of suitable habitat, with another 50bp in nearby Spain.

A much greater variety of habitat is occupied in Sardinia, ranging from steep mountain slopes in the interior to rocky hillsides, open or degraded maquis, unimproved agricultural land and vineyards. The species' basic requirements are open areas for feeding, thorny undergrowth or craggy outcrops offering safety from predators, and bushes, hedges or walls providing shade from the sun. Outside the breeding season, the Barbary Partridge gathers in coveys of 10–15 individuals, often moving to lower altitudes near farmland in winter (Mocci Demartis 1992). The species has declined markedly to fewer than 10 000bp, mainly through hunting and poaching but

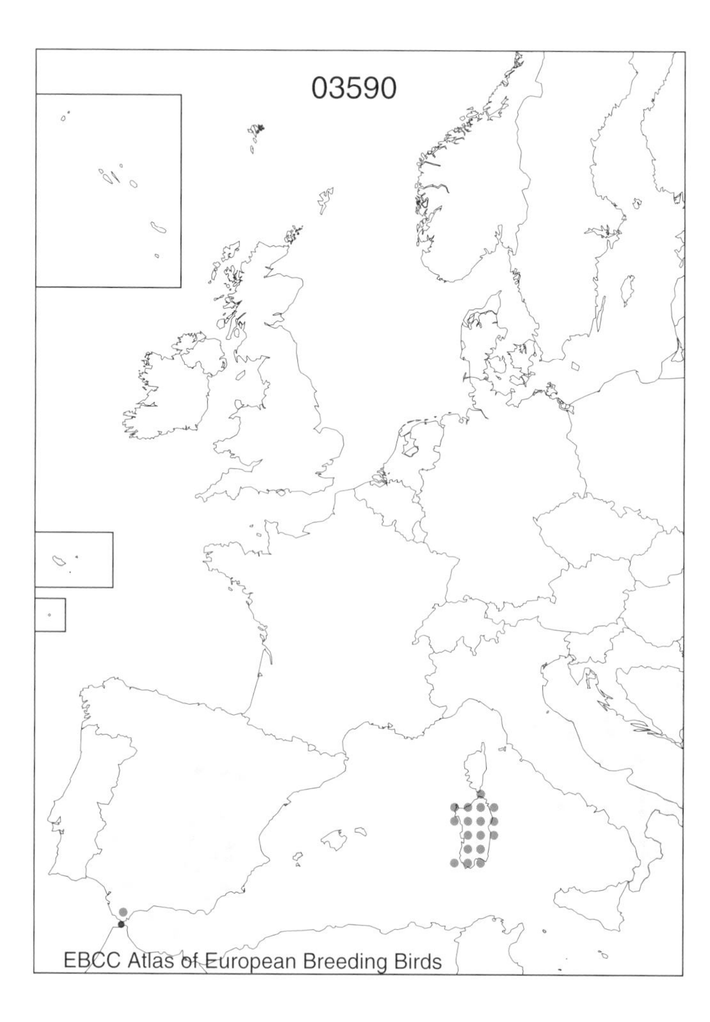

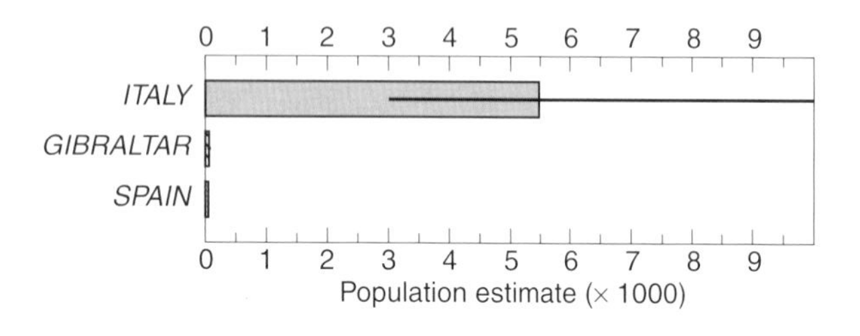

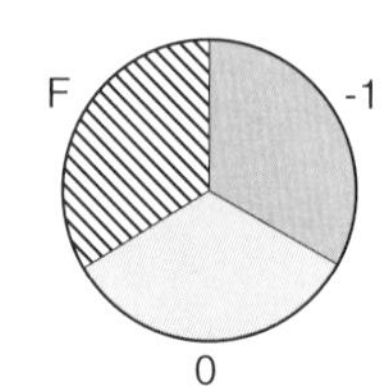

% in top 10 countries: 100.0
Total number of populated European countries: 3
Total European population 3111–10,111 (5588)

also because of intensive pesticide use in agriculture and habitat destruction by fire in summer (Mocci Demartis & Massoli-Novelli 1978). The difficult terrain between 250m and 650m asl is its main stronghold. Autumn densities exceeding 2 coveys/km^2 have been recorded in the provinces of Nuorno and Cagliari. The density drops rapidly at lower altitudes, to 0.6 coveys/km^2 or less (Spanó *et al* 1986).

Nicholas Aebischer (GB)

Francolinus francolinus

Black Francolin

CZ	Frankolín obecný	I	Francolino
D	Halsbandfrankolin	NL	Zwarte Frankolijn
E	Francolín Ventrinegro	P	Francolim-comum
F	Francolin noir	PL	Frankolin obrożny
FIN	Mustafrankoliini	R	Турач
G	Φρανκολίνος	S	Svart frankolin
H	Frankolin		

SPEC Cat 3, Threat status V

The main distribution of the Black Francolin stretches from Iraq E to Assam and Bangladesh. The resident subspecies in Transcaucasia is *F.f. francolinus*. Until the 19th century, its natural range reached the western Mediterranean. Now there are only isolated populations in southern Turkey and Cyprus (Charalambides 1994). The Transcaucasian range is restricted to the Caspian lowlands of Azerbaijan but may still branch out through river valleys of the Kura, Araks, Iory and Alazany into Georgia and Armenia. It disappeared as a regular breeder in Georgia in the early 1970s.

The Black Francolin inhabits generally open landscapes such as semi-natural grasslands, dunes, arable land containing cereals, lucerne or cotton, vineyards and garden. Open water and ample dense scrub, especially tamarisk thickets, are essential elements of its habitat. In Cyprus it occupies dense juniper forest (Flint & Stewart 1992). Its northern range limit is determined by winters whose average temperatures are below −5°C and which maintain snow-cover for longer than 20 days. Its habitat preferences force it into living close to human settlements. Its abundance in its wintering areas therefore depends entirely on human tolerance of its presence.

In Transcaucasia it is restricted by winter conditions to land below 800m asl. It abandons Azerbaijan farmland in autumn, switching to areas providing food and shelter during winter. After severe winters with snowfalls, the population usually crashes then re-establishes within 3 years (Litvinov 1977). For example the Kyzylagach Reserve population on the Caspian coast crashed to 350–400 individuals in spring 1972, doubled by spring 1974 and reached the optimum of 1210 in 1975. However, severe winter conditions in 1977/78 decimated the population again.

Until the 1950s, the species was common on the Azerbaijan plain and the valleys to Armenia and Georgia. At that time, the population density could vary significantly. For example, in Azerbaijan the maximum density found was 288 birds/km^2 whereas the minimum was 10 birds/km^2 (Litvinov 1977). In 1947–50 the population numbered *c*600 000 birds, by 1958–66 it had declined to *c*100 000 (Khanmamedov 1971), and in 1991 may have reached an unprecedented low of 4000 (Babayev 1991). Now the species seems restricted to Azerbaijan, and to the Kyzylagach Reserve in particular, where the 1987 density was 29.1 birds/100ha. This population centre continues to decline, and the reserve is threatened by the restoration of the Caspian Sea level. Elsewhere it is now known only from isolated locations along the Kura River (Babayev 1991).

The continuing decline is probably due to the loss of habitat, the collapse of the land-control infrastructure, habitat changes caused by intensive farming practices, and to excessive and barbarous uncontrolled hunting.

Iljas P Babayev (AZ) Vincent van den Berk (NL)
Roald L Potapov (R)

Perdix perdix

Grey Partridge

CZ	Koroptev polní	**I**	Starna
D	Rebhuhn	**NL**	Patrijs
E	Perdiz Pardilla	**P**	Perdiz-cinzenta
F	Perdrix grise	**PL**	Kuropatwa
FIN	Peltopyy	**R**	Серая куропатка
G	Καμπίσια Πέρδικα	**S**	Rapphöna
H	Fogoly		

SPEC Cat 3, Threat status V

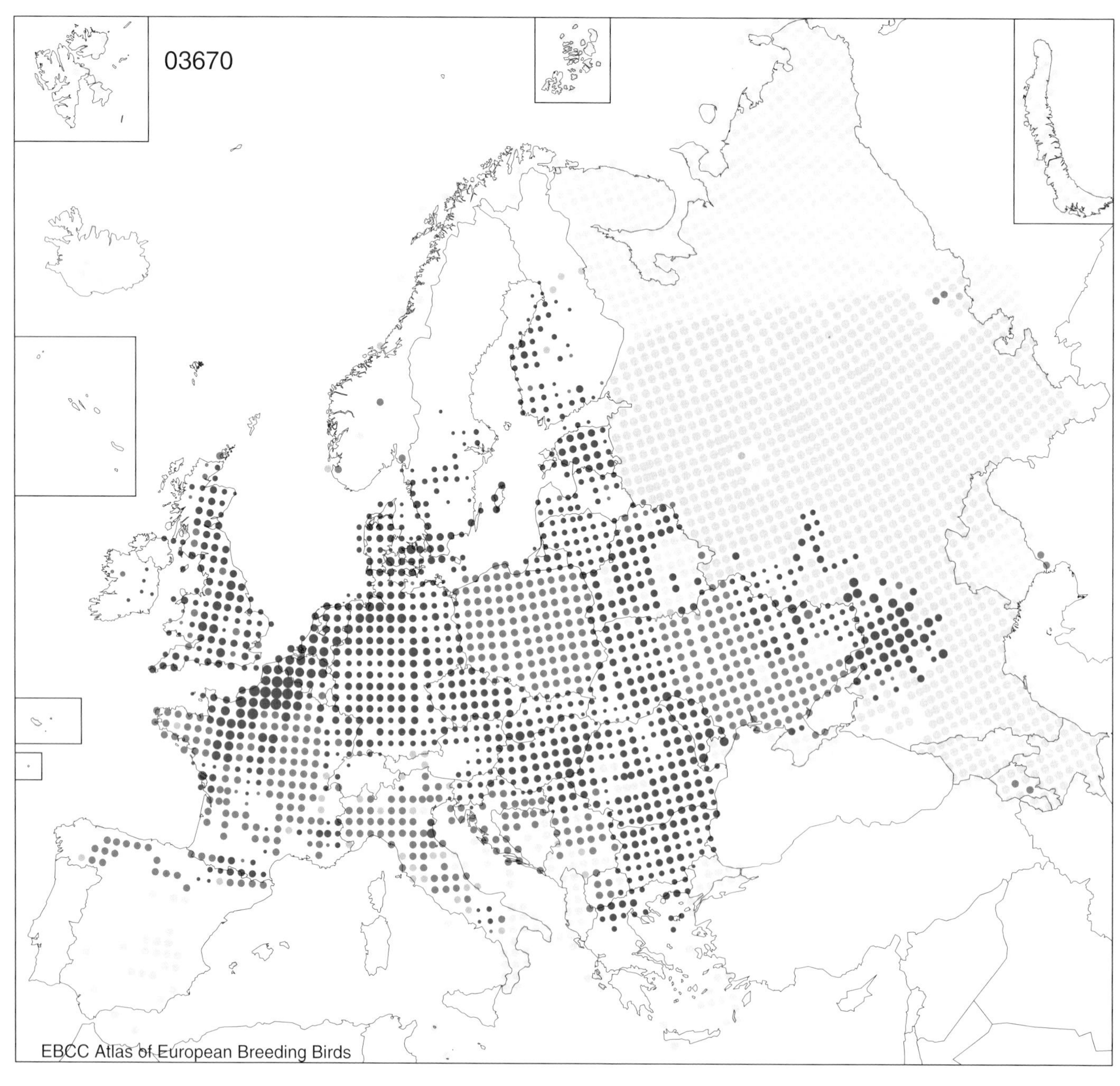

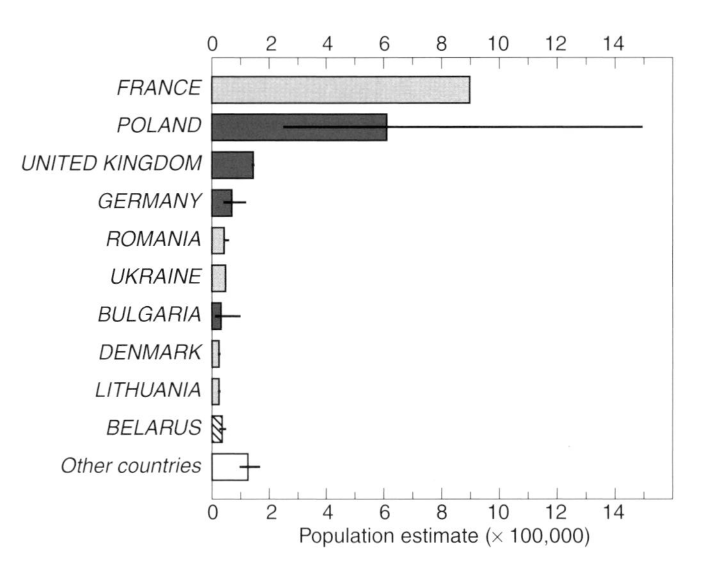

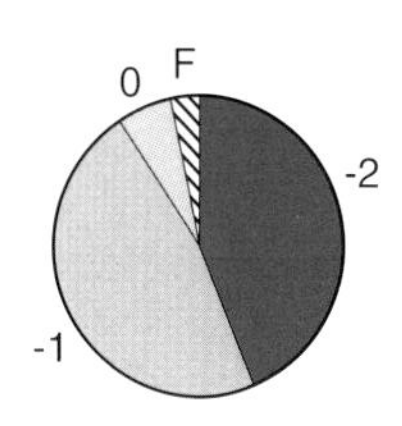

% in top 10 countries: 93.9
Total number of populated European countries: 32
Total European population 1,699,686–2,956,396 (2,064,354)
Russian population 1,000,000–2,000,000 (1,414,214)
Turkish population 5000–30,000 (12,247)

The Grey Partridge, originally a bird of short steppe and open grassland, has adapted to farmland as its main habitat. It is found across Europe from Ireland to the Urals and from northern Sweden to the Mediterranean, and in Asia it reaches eastern Mongolia. In the early 1900s it was introduced successfully to North America where it now occurs in the northern USA W of the Great Lakes and in Canada from Ontario to Alberta.

Its preferred habitat is open, low-intensity, mixed farmland (including tillage) comprising small fields bounded by hedges, grassy banks or grass strips. it avoids woodland and heavy cover. Despite an overall decline in most countries since the 1950s, it is still found in most 50km squares within its current range,

Grey Partridge numbers remain high (though not as high as formerly) in parts of Poland and northern France, but are at less than 10% of their pre-war level in many other countries such as Great Britain, The Netherlands, Germany, Italy, Austria and Hungary. The species is currently on the verge of extinction in Norway, Ireland and Switzerland. Further declines in density across Europe will most likely result in a marked contraction in range and an increasingly patchy distribution. The species has already withdrawn from much of its montane range in the Alps where once it nested regularly up to 1300m asl and now is unlikely to be encountered above 500m asl. Papaevangelou *et al* (in press) estimate numbers in Greece to be *c*3150bp.

Changes in farming practices in recent decades have altered its habitats adversely. The traditional mosaic of mixed farming has disappeared or has declined severely in many countries, causing a reduction in abundance of insect prey for chicks, loss of nesting cover and increased predation. These changes are underlying causes of the species' reduced breeding success; successful pairs have produced fewer fledged young in most areas (Potts 1986).

In prime habitats in France, breeding densities exceeding 30 bp/km² still occur in many areas (Reitz 1992), although how much this is due to released stock is unknown. In contrast densities as low as 0.19 bp/km² exist in countries such as the former East Germany (Nösel 1992). Local areas of suitable habitat can support intermediate densities. Densities of 0.2–1.7 bp/km² prevail over much of The Netherlands, probably one of the most intensively managed farmland areas in Europe (Bijlsma 1990a).

Over most of the range populations generally are resident, becoming partially migratory in severe winters (depending on snow depth; Potts 1986) from Belarus eastwards (Nikiforov 1992). Groups of 100–150 birds, presumed to be on migration, have been reported (Kuzmina 1977). Heavy mortality during extended periods of snow-cover is not unusual in E Europe and North America.

During autumn and winter the Grey Partridge forms coveys, which normally comprise a pair and their year's offspring, but sometimes they are joined by barren pairs and single unpaired males. In late winter, coveys break up and pair formation occurs. Pairs space themselves out for the nesting season. Differential sexual mortality results in a surplus of adult males after each breeding season.

Eight subspecies, all of which occur in Europe, are widely accepted though many others have been proposed. The nominate *P.p. perdix* occurs from Denmark to Britain & Ireland and across C Europe to the Alps and Balkans. Importation and release of stocks from several countries by game-farm breeders in the 20th century may have blurred the distinctions between subspecies locally, as in Italy. In general, individuals are more rufous-brown in W Europe, and paler and greyer in the E. The taxonomy of the subspecies needs revision by modern analytical methods.

Nicholas Aebischer (GB) Brendan Kavanagh (IRE)

This species account is sponsored by The Game Conservancy Trust, Hants, GB.

Coturnix coturnix **Quail**

CZ	Křepelka polní	**I**	Quaglia
D	Wachtel	**NL**	Kwartel
E	Codorniz Común	**P**	Codorniz
F	Caille des blés	**PL**	Przepiórka
FIN	Viiriäinen	**R**	Перепел
G	Ορτύκι	**S**	Vaktel
H	Fürj		

SPEC Cat 3, Threat status V

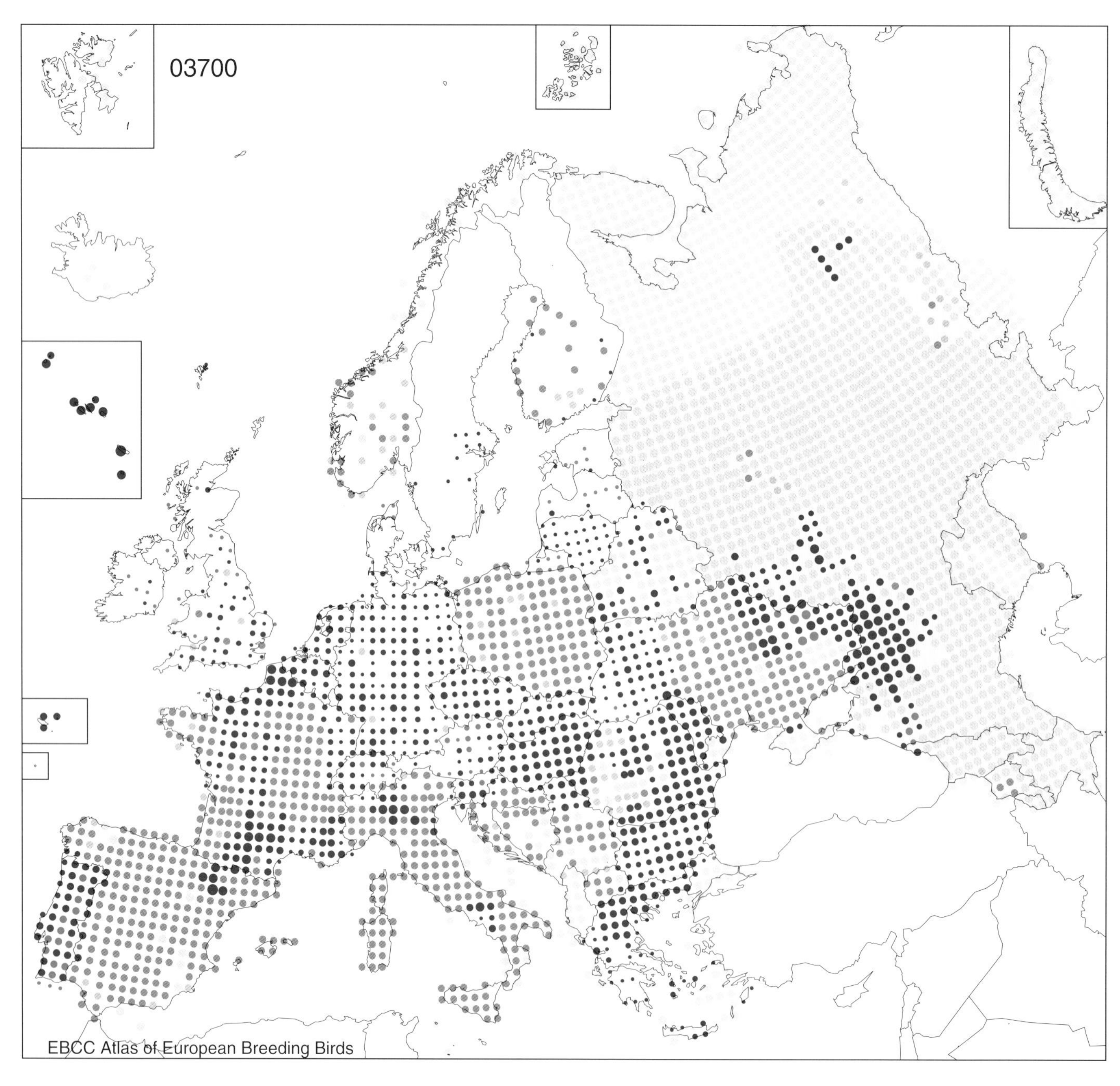

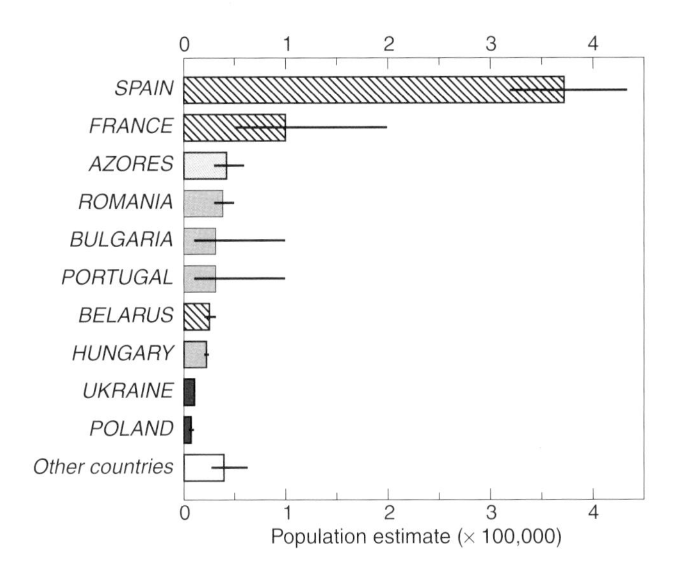

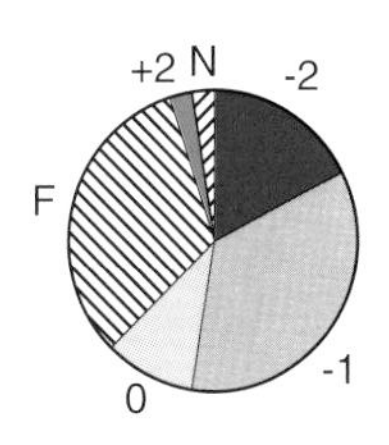

% in top 10 countries: 94.5
Total number of populated European countries: 40
Total European population 641,525–876,497 (722,404)
Russian population 100,000–1,000,000 (316,228)
Turkish population 50,000–350,000 (132,288)

This small galliforme is found in the western Palearctic and W and C Asia. Its European range normally excludes N Great Britain, Scandinavia and Iceland. In the E, its range extends to N China, and S to N India, Pakistan, Iran, Turkey and Africa, including the Mediterranean and the nearer Atlantic islands.

The Quail was recently separated from the Japanese Quail *C. japonica*, nowadays an allospecies, but the number of subspecies remains open to question. Five possible subspecies have been described, but the percentage of unequivocal diagnostics is low, suggesting that they should not be considered as subspecies (Puigcerver 1990); of the five proposed, three (*C.c. confisa*, Madeira; *conturbans*, Azores; and *coturnix*) occur in Europe.

The Quail breeds in open spaces, mainly in cereal crops, lucerne, vetches or clovers, and on grasslands where herbaceous cover provides protection. Its breeding range encompasses the western Palearctic as far as the boreal zone, and North Africa (Algeria, Morocco, Tunisia, Sahara). Its wintering ranges are located in Africa. The Equator is the southern boundary for the nominate subspecies. Sporadically, wintering individuals are reported from various European countries.

Quail populations have shown great fluctuations. Egypt exported more than 2M per annum at the end of the 19th century, dropping to 1.2M in 1908, and to 0.5M in 1926. This century, numbers in Europe continued to decline. During 1960–80, the decline in Russia has been catastrophic due to widespread use of fertilizers and pesticides, breeding ceasing in *c*46% of the districts and numbers stabilizing at low levels in the remainder. Numbers shot decreased from 2.5M in the 1960s to 1.6M in the mid-1970s (Mezhnev 1994). French hunting records show a decline beginning in the late 1960s, bottoming out in 1977 (Combreau 1992); since the mid-1980s populations have remained stable but at a lower density level than in the 1960s. In NE Spain, estimates of males calling throughout the breeding season have remained stable since 1983, with weak annual fluctuations and low-density populations (3 males/km^2; Puigcerver *et al* 1989). The abandonment of cereal crops before 1983 may explain the decrease in Spanish populations (authors' pers obs), while the increase in artificially irrigated areas in Morocco is associated with an increase in Quail abundance (Saint-Jalme & Guyomarc'h 1990).

Exceptionally, years of high Quail abundance may occur, without a clear pattern of regularity or distribution. For example, 1979 and 1987 were good Quail years in France (J.C. Guyomarc'h, pers comm), 1988 in Spain (Puigcerver *et al* 1989) and 1989 in NW Europe, including Sweden (high numbers; *Brit. Birds* 84: 229), Britain (>1655 calling males; Rare Breeding Birds Panel), The Netherlands (estimated total of 8000–12 000; Bijlsma 1990a) and Denmark (best summer for decades; *Brit. Birds* 83: 11). Such erratic fluctuations in at least 22 countries cannot hide the overall decline in Europe. Many of the 12 countries reporting fluctuating populations may soon show long-term declines. At present, the main threats are agricultural intensification (habitat destruction) and increasing use of pesticides (reducing chick food availability).

Quail movements are complex. A loop migration (North Africa to Italy and C Europe in spring, France to Spain and North Africa in autumn) has been described, but recent findings show that there is also an intense spring flow across the Iberian Peninsula (M. Puigcerver, pers obs). This may explain the high abundance of Quail in Spain. The high turnover rate found at two breeding sites in NE Spain throughout the breeding season (Rodriguez-Teijeiro *et al* 1992) suggests that males are highly mobile. Their migratory movements may overlap with nomadic ones in search of free females and suitable habitats. The Quail is an opportunist, exploiting suitable habitats in space (in latitude and altitude) and time, trying to breed before the vegetation is destroyed during harvesting or by droughts.

Secundino Gallego (E) Manuel Puigcerver (E)
José Rodriguez-Teijeiro (E)

Callipepla californica

California Quail

CZ	Křepel kalifornský	I	Colino della California
D	Schopfwachtel	NL	Californische Kuifkwartel
E	Colín de California	P	Perdiz da Califórnia
F	Colin de Californie	PL	Przepiór kalifornijski
FIN	Kaliforniantupsuviiriäinen	R	Калифорнийская зубчатоклювая куропатка
G	Ορτύκι της Καλιφόρνιας		
H	Búbos fürj	S	Kalifornisk tofsvaktel

Criteria not applied

Attempts to introduce the California Quail into Europe have been made since the 1840s. They seem to have been successful only in Corsica, where this Nearctic quail became established in the 1960s. The species has so far kept mainly to the eastern coastal strip, which holds the greatest area of arable land on the island.

The bulk of the population occurs where crops are closely interspersed with patches of tall cork-oak maquis. The bird is found to a much lesser extent in non-arable areas where human pastoral activities (grazing, woodcutting, burning) have created open grassy and scrubby clearings in the cork-oak forest. This pattern of habitat use is typical of other successful introductions outside Europe.

In Corsica, the California Quail is uncommon and extremely secretive; its density in 1990 averaged 0–2 bp/km² (maximum 9 bp/km² locally) within an area covering 600km² from sea level up to 900m asl (Pietri 1993).

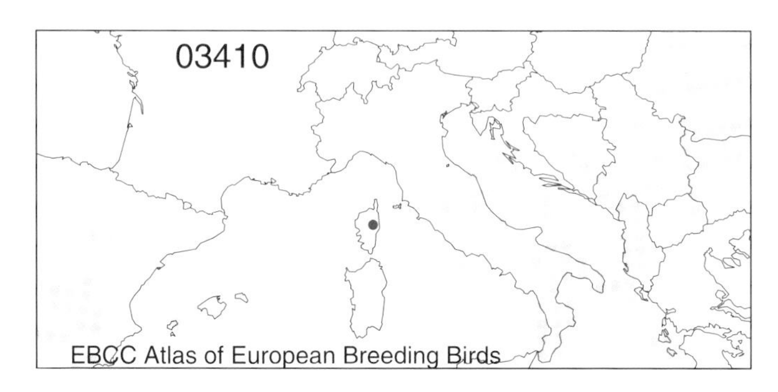

Nicholas Aebischer (GB) Christian Pietri (F)

Colinus virginianus

Northern Bobwhite

CZ	Křepel virginský	I	Colino della Virginia
D	Baumwachtel	NL	Boomkwartel
E	Colín de Virginia	P	Colino da Virgínia
F	Colin de Virginie	PL	Przepiór wirginijski
FIN	Peltoviiriäinen	R	Виргинский перепел (Виргинский бобуайт)
G	Δεντροπέρδικα		
H	Virginiai fürj	S	Vitstrupig vaktel

Criteria not applied

The Northern Bobwhite is a Nearctic species which was first introduced into Europe about 1813, starting in England and Ireland as an ornamental and quarry species, but with low success. Subsequent introductions, solely for hunting purposes, were made in France (1816 onwards), Sweden, Germany and Italy (1930s), Croatia, Slovenia and Spain (1960s). Although small populations existed or remain present in other European countries such as France (Voisin 1994), Spain (Calderon Rodriguez 1964) and Slovenia (A. Meriggi *et al*, unpubl), only in Italy has the species become self-sustaining. It has been added to the Checklist of Italian Birds, as a naturalized population (Brichetti & Massa 1984). Its present range is restricted to 960km² of the plains and the low hills of NW Italy, especially in the Ticino Valley. In this area a breeding

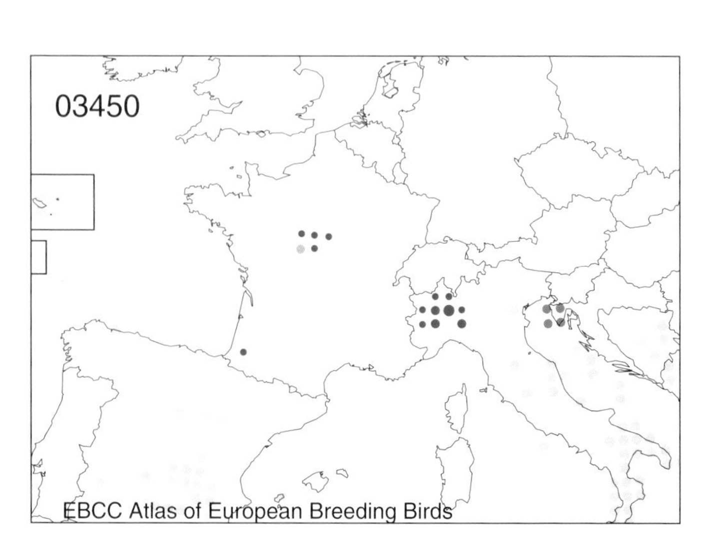

density of 7.3 males/km² and a winter density of 20.9 birds/km² have been recorded (Meriggi *et al* 1992). From its plumage the Northern Bobwhite in Italy can be attributed to the nominate subspecies *C.v. virginianus* (Fasola & Gariboldi 1985). The Croatian population may be self-sustaining, but it also recruits from releases (J. Kralj, pers comm); its presence is restricted to the vicinity of Istra. The French population is confined to surroundings of Sologne and Puisaye (C France, 200–400bp in the 1980s) and Les Landes (SW France, 1000–2000bp in 1975). This population may be partly self-sustaining, although it is still being augmented with releases. Its fortunes depend on favourable climatic conditions (mean temperature in April till August >17°C, >65mm of rainfall in summer, cold winters), releases and the interest of hunters (Voisin 1994).

Its preferred habitats are woodlands with a dense undergrowth of bushes and grass, clearings and fields (Fasola & Gariboldi 1987). In Italy the population has declined to 5000–8000bp. The Croatian population is estimated at 3000bp. Recent estimates for France are lacking.

Armando Gariboldi (I)

Syrmaticus reevesii — Reeves's Pheasant

CZ	Bažant královský	I	Fagiano venerato
D	Königsfasan	NL	Koningsfazant
E	Faisán Venerado	P	Faisão-venerado
F	Faisan Vénéré	PL	Bażant krówelski
FIN	Kuningasfasaani	R	Длиннохвостый фазан Рива
G	Βασιλικός Φασιανός	S	Kungsfasan
H	Királyfácán		

Criteria not applied

In ancient times Reeves's Pheasant was distributed in deciduous and mixed forests in mountainous regions of N and C China from SW Manchuria (40°N), S to Szechuan, the Chang Jian (Yangtze) River (30°N). Its actual distribution is now halved and it is limited to C China where only *c*1500 birds survive (Weishu 1989, Fen-Qi & Tai-Chun 1991).

Reeves's Pheasant has been introduced successfully into several European countries to afford hunters and sportsmen a game species which flies fast and high. This very attractive pheasant favours densely wooded areas which other gamebirds usually shun.

In Europe Reeves's Pheasant was first released in Great Britain in 1870–90, and subsequent introductions have met varying success. Although it breeds in the wild, it seems unable to establish viable naturalized populations.

The most successful acclimatization has been in France. In 1970–75 (Yeatman 1976), it occupied 22 sectors (2% of the total), coverage probably being incomplete. In 1987 it was found in 16 separate forest areas in populations which apparently were self-sustaining, and had persisted for at least 10 years, particularly in N and C France (Roobrouck 1994). During 1985–89 it occupied 51 sectors (4.7%), the population being estimated at 1000–1500bp.

In the Czech Republic the breeding distribution is concentrated in N and C Moravia, mostly close to pheasantries from which releases or escapes reinforce the wild birds. In the 1973–77 Czech Atlas eight l0km squares were occupied, breeding being confirmed in most, and in the new Czech Atlas (1985–89) nine squares were occupied (Šťastný *et al* 1995). It seems to be a prospective game-bird in non-flooded forests up to 400m asl, its present population containing 200–400 free-living birds.

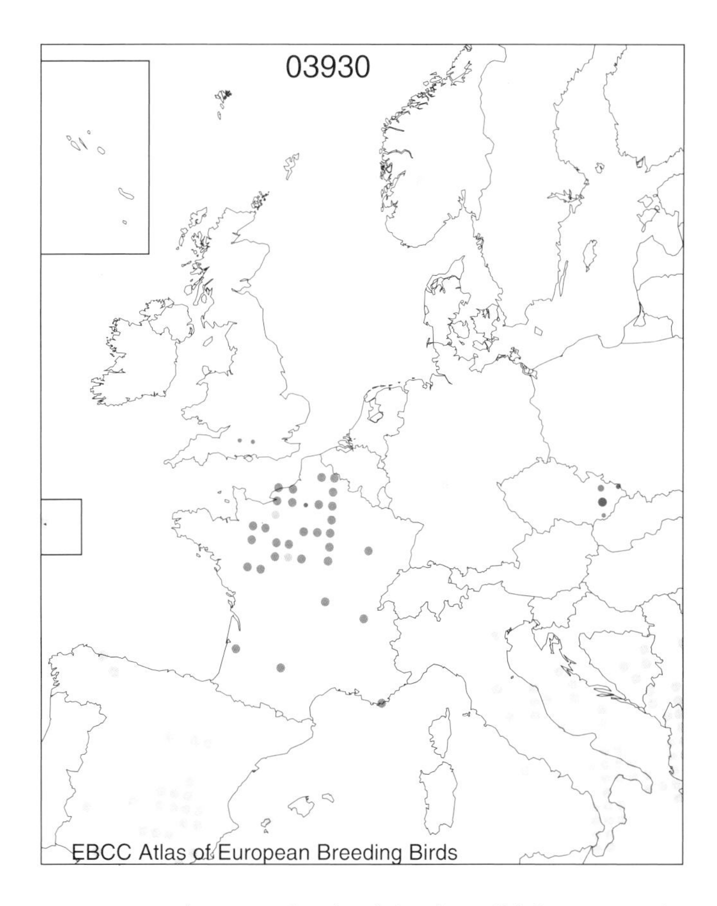

Reeves's Pheasant also bred in the wild in Europe in forested areas of Hungary, Austria and Germany (Lever 1987). From 1985 to 1989, the total European population of Reeves's Pheasant is estimated to have been 1100-1700bp.

Karel Šťastný (CZ)

Phasianus colchicus **Pheasant**

CZ	Bažant obecný	**I**	Fagiano comune
D	Fasan	**NL**	Fazant
E	Faisán Vulgar	**P**	Faisão
F	Faisan de Colchide	**PL**	Bażant
FIN	Fasaani	**R**	Фазан
G	Φασιανός	**S**	Fasan
H	Fácán		

Non-SPEC, Threat status S

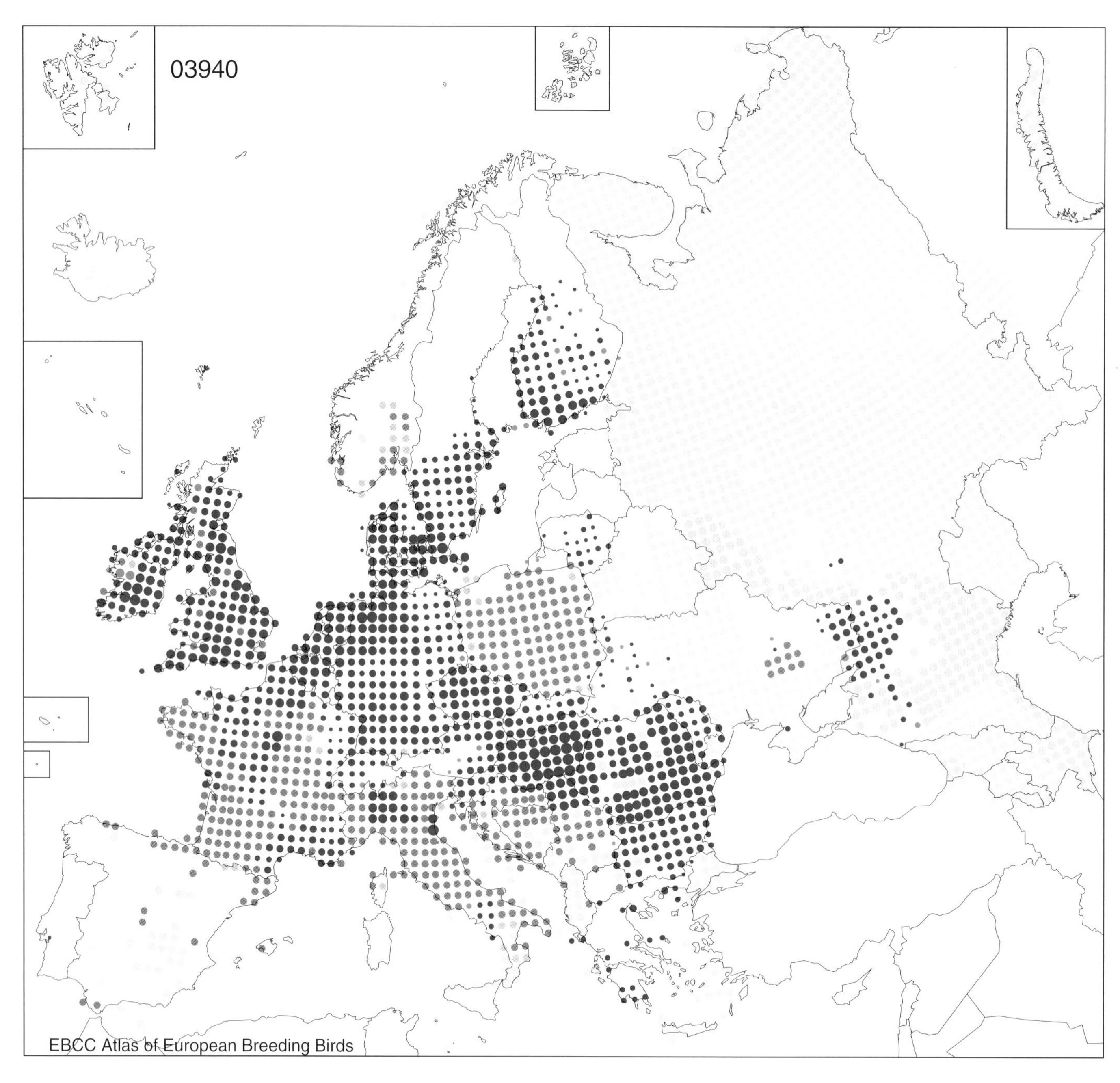

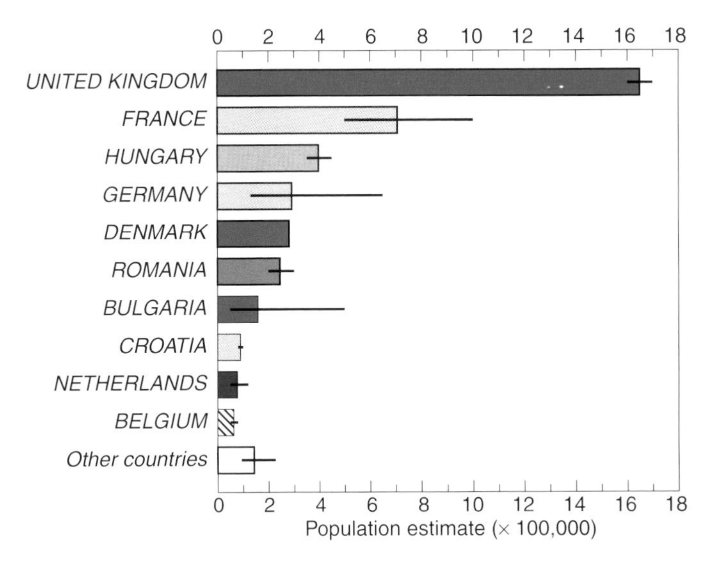

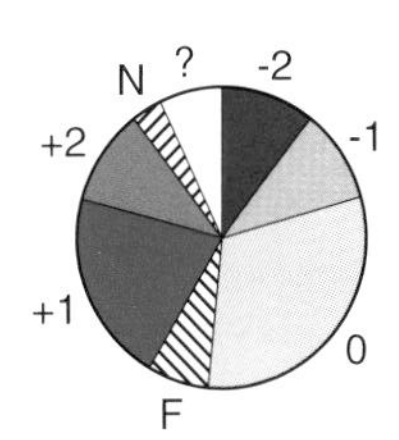

% in top 10 countries: 96.5
Total number of populated European countries: 29
Total European population 3,800,856–4,686,590 (4,098,950)
Russian population 5000–50,000 (15,811)
Turkish population 1000–10,000 (3162)

The Pheasant's native European range covers western Georgia, the W Caspian shore plain, Armenia and Azerbaijan. Its distribution then extends E along the northern slopes of the Himalayas, N into Manchuria and Korea and S towards Vietnam. It is also found on Taiwan and the Japanese archipelago. In Europe the Pheasant is therefore mostly an introduced species (Long 1981), not only as a game-bird, but also because it was valued as a gourmet food, being popular with the Romans who introduced it to Italy, Germany and France, although it may have reached Greece as early as 1300 BC. It was first released in Norway in 1875–76, in Finland about 1900 and in Transcaucasia around 1890. The Romans may have introduced it into Great Britain, although it is unlikely that it was well-known or feral before 1500. The Normans therefore probably introduced the stock which did not spread across the whole of Britain until the late 1700s.

The Pheasant is a bird of lowland wooded valleys, scrubland and thickets, but also frequents marshland and fens, foothills and dry uplands, although it is seldom found above 500–700m asl in the W Palearctic. It is now associated significantly with an arable farmland landscape possessing a mosaic of woods and copses (Hill & Robertson 1988a), although in W Europe, large areas of woodland and pasture have fewer birds than mixed farmland where the crops grown are cereals and vegetables (Robertson *et al* 1993). The curbing of pheasant releasing in The Netherlands has resulted in widespread population crashes and local extinctions in woodland, dunes, heaths and farmland (Bijlsma 1990a). Its nesting habitats are the ground below thin scrub in or at woodland rides and edges, or in grassy margins and cereal crops which also serve as brood-rearing habitat (Hill 1985).

Its distribution and abundance patterns follow that associated with relatively low-lying country and the slopes of hills. It becomes sparse in many Mediterranean areas although Italy has become populated since 1980. It is less common in Greece, the Italian Alps, parts of the S-C and E French highlands, and is almost totally absent from Portugal and Spain. Numbers and range decline in northern Scotland, Norway and Sweden, though there has been a significant numerical and range increase in Finland since the 1950s (Koskimies 1989a). The *Atlas* survey dates are quite widespread for some countries, but levels of abundance are apparently fairly well-known in most countries. (Because the species is polygynous the use of 'breeding pairs' is misleading.) It is likely that underestimates occur in those countries where the species is released in large numbers for shooting.

Great Britain has the highest population (though not necessarily the highest densities) of any European country as a consequence of the interest in game-shooting and the release of probably 15M pheasants each year for shooting (Hill & Robertson 1988a). The trend towards releasing increasing numbers of birds for sport since 1965 has led to an increase in breeding population size, despite modern agricultural techniques providing less food and hand-reared birds suffering much greater mortality (due to naivety about predators) than wild-reared birds (Hill & Robertson 1988b). The six countries holding the largest Pheasant populations – Britain, Hungary, France, Germany, Denmark and Romania – together possess 88% of the mean European population. The Romanian population has undergone very significant increases in abundance and range from 1970 to 1990. Declines of at least 50% are reported in The Netherlands and Sweden; in the former the decline is attributed to intensified agriculture and reduced game-rearing and releases (Bijlsma 1990a). The species is extending its range into Spain but in all countries its distribution limits are largely determined by man. It is largely resident and sedentary across its range.

Rob G Bijlsma (NL) David Hill (GB)

Chrysolophus pictus

Golden Pheasant

CZ	Bažant zlatý	FIN	Kultafasaani
D	Goldfasan	G	Χρυσός Φασιανός
E	Faisán Dorado	H	Aranyfácán
F	Faisan doré		

I	Fagiano dorato	PL	Bażant złocisty
NL	Goudfazant	R	Золотистый фазан
P	Faisão-dourado	S	Guldfasan

Criteria not applied

This pre-eminently terrestrial pheasant is native to the mountains of C China, in dense vegetation (Beebe 1936) in which it is remarkably elusive for a bird of such dramatic colours. In Europe, small feral populations occur in England around Breckland and Thetford Forest in Norfolk and Suffolk and on the South Downs in Hampshire and Sussex, in Scotland in Galloway, and in Wales on Anglesey (Lever 1977). Home ranges are less than 1km diameter (Balmer *et al* 1996) so this distribution may reflect strongly where introductions, beginning in the 19th century, were successful. In Britain, home ranges mainly centre around roosts in 10–20-year-old conifer plantations, sited to allow feeding in older, more open, plantations (Balmer *et al* 1996). Territories in deciduous woodland normally have a thick undergrowth of plants such as snowberry *Symphoricarpos*, box *Buxus sempervirens*, *Rhododendron* or blackthorn *Prunus spinosa*.

This elusive species is difficult to census accurately. Any estimates should be treated with caution. There is no hard evidence of a general decline in Britain (Gibbons *et al* 1993), where the population is estimated at 500–1000bp, but anecdotal evidence suggests that numbers are declining in one of its strongholds, Thetford Forest. This may result from the cessation of large-scale releases in the 1950s, inbreeding, and increased predation as gamekeepers become fewer. In China, the Golden Pheasant though rare is still trapped for meat and the animal trade. It is therefore doubly important to continue studying the Golden Pheasant in Britain, its only other viable population.

Mark Rehfisch (GB)

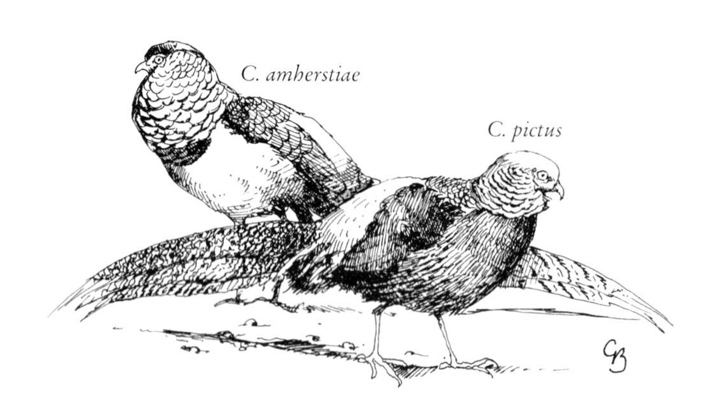

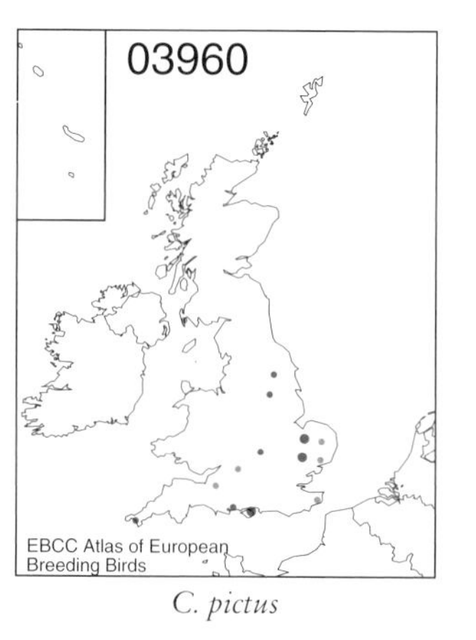

C. pictus

C. amherstiae

Chrysolophus amherstiae

Lady Amherst's Pheasant

CZ	Bažant diamantový	FIN	Platinafasaani
D	Diamantfasan	G	Φασιανός της Amherst
E	Faisán de Lady Amherst	H	Gyémántfácán
F	Faisan de Lady Amherst		

I	Fagiano di Lady Amherst	PL	Bażant diamentowy
NL	Amherstfazant	R	Алмазный фазан
P	Faisão Lady Amherst	S	Diamantfasan

Criteria not applied

This beautiful pheasant is native to E Tibet, SW China and NE Burma, in dense forest, bamboo scrub and bracken in broken mountainous country from 1800 to 4000m asl. In Europe, the species was introduced into Britain from the 1890s onwards in several widely separated areas. It is known to survive at only two locations: most in Bedfordshire and Buckinghamshire (S England) and a few close to the English border in Wales (Lever 1977, Long 1981).

In England it inhabits various wooded habitats, from conifer plantations with little undergrowth to mixed scrub and *Rhododendron* patches. In China, it appears to prefer evergreen coniferous forests, secondary deciduous forest containing scrub, and also *Pinus armandii* secondary forest (at lower densities) (Han *et al* 1989).

It is believed to have declined in Bedfordshire from 250 birds in 1979 to 100–200 birds in the early 1990s (Trodd & Kramer 1991). The much smaller population in Buckinghamshire is also believed to have contracted since the 1960s, with no recent records from two sites (Lack & Ferguson 1993). These population estimates should be treated with caution because it is difficult to survey this species reliably. Despite its extravagant plumage, the male is rarely seen, even in sites with little undergrowth. Calling males are the most readily detected; the dispersion suggests that birds are patchily distributed through available habitat in spring.

This is one of Europe's least known species. The introduced population has great value because not only does it provide quantitative data currently unobtainable in China, but it also can be the means by which Chinese ornithologists could receive technical training on a native species.

Philip J K McGowan (GB) Mark M Rehfisch (GB)

Meleagris gallopavo

Common Turkey

CZ	Krocan divoký	I	Tacchino
D	Truthuhn	NL	Kalkoen
E	Guajolote Gallipavo	P	Perú-bravo
F	Dindon sauvage	PL	Indyk
FIN	Kalkkuna	R	Индюк
G	Γάλλος	S	Kalkon
H	Pulyka		

Criteria not applied

Originally naturally distributed from SE Canada to S Mexico, the turkey's natural distribution is from the southern USA to N Mexico, all other populations being introduced or reintroduced. Outside North America, the species was introduced successfully into the Hawaiian Islands, Tasmania and New Zealand, and generally unsuccessfully elsewhere except for the Czech Republic, where the population (530 birds in 1988) has existed at least since 1927.

Natural habitats in North America range from mountain forests to coastal woodland. In the Czech Republic the species favours riverine forests that are not subject to extensive flooding, near Olomouc (Dřímal 1989). Its survival is dependent largely on supplementary feeding in winter.

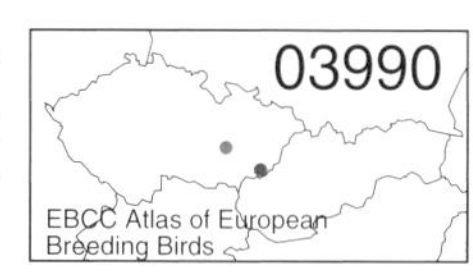

The first attempt, of many, to introduce the species in Europe was in the Lower Rhine area, as early as 1571. Others have occurred in Britain (since the 17th century), the Czech Republic (before 1781, but mainly since 1880), France (since 1875), Hungary (since 1930) and Austria (1880, 1947) (Niethammer 1963, *HVM*, Long 1981, Lever 1987).

Karel Hudec (CZ)

Turnix sylvatica

Andalusian Hemipode

CZ	Perepel evropský	I	Quaglia tridattila
D	Laufhühnchen	NL	Gestreepte Vechtkwartel
E	Torillo Andaluz	P	Toirão
F	Turnix d'Andalousie	PL	Przepiórnik
FIN	Viiriäispyyjuoksija	R	Малая трехперстка (Пятнистая трехперстка)
G	Ψευτόρτυγας		
H	Guvatfürj	S	Springhöna

SPEC Cat 3, Threat status E

The Andalusian Hemipode is extremely secretive and largely sedentary. It has a relict distribution in the Palearctic but is widely distributed in the Oriental and Ethiopian regions, occupying a variety of grassland and scrub habitats.

In Europe it is now known only from the Andalusian western Guadalquivir marshes (Doñana National Park) and is on the brink of extinction. It inhabits the mediterranean scrubland of rockrose *Halimium halimifolium* and the mosaic of grassy patches, mastic tree *Pistacia lentiscus* and cork oak *Quercus suber* open forest on coastal sands, which is probably suboptimal (Llandres & Urdiales 1991, Urdiales 1993). Formerly, its typical habitat was the palmetto *Chamaerops humilis* scrub that once dominated the Andalusian coastal area.

Some 150 years of steady decline have extirpated it from Portugal, Sicily and almost from Spain (Violani & Massa 1993, Urdiales 1994). A recent two-year thorough search in the Doñana area could establish only that the species was still present in extremely low numbers in two locations (Urdiales 1993), breeding density being impossible to assess (probably only 5–10 pairs). The decline is probably related to hunting pressure and to land reclamation and modern agriculture, which have destroyed much of its prime habitat (Urdiales 1994, Violani & Massa 1993).

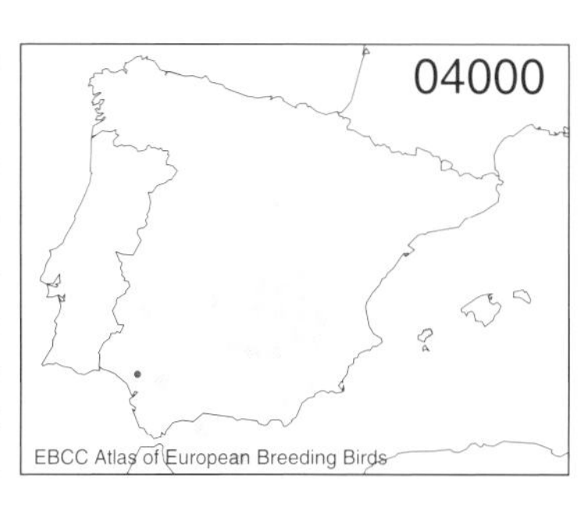

The severely threatened Mediterranean subspecies, *T.s. sylvatica*, is well-differentiated (Violani & Massa 1993). Although the nearly-extinct Iberian form is biometrically similar to other Mediterranean populations, it is distinctly darker than the light rufous birds of North Africa or formerly of Sicily (C. Urdiales, pers obs), so may even be of a different taxon.

Carlos Urdiales (E)

Rallus aquaticus

Water Rail

CZ	Chřástal vodní	I	Porciglione
D	Wasserralle	NL	Waterral
E	Rascón Europeo	P	Frango-d'água
F	Râle d'eau	PL	Wodnik
FIN	Luhtakana	R	Водяной пастушок
G	Νεροκοτσέλα	S	Vattenrall
H	Guvat		

Non-SPEC, Threat status S (P)

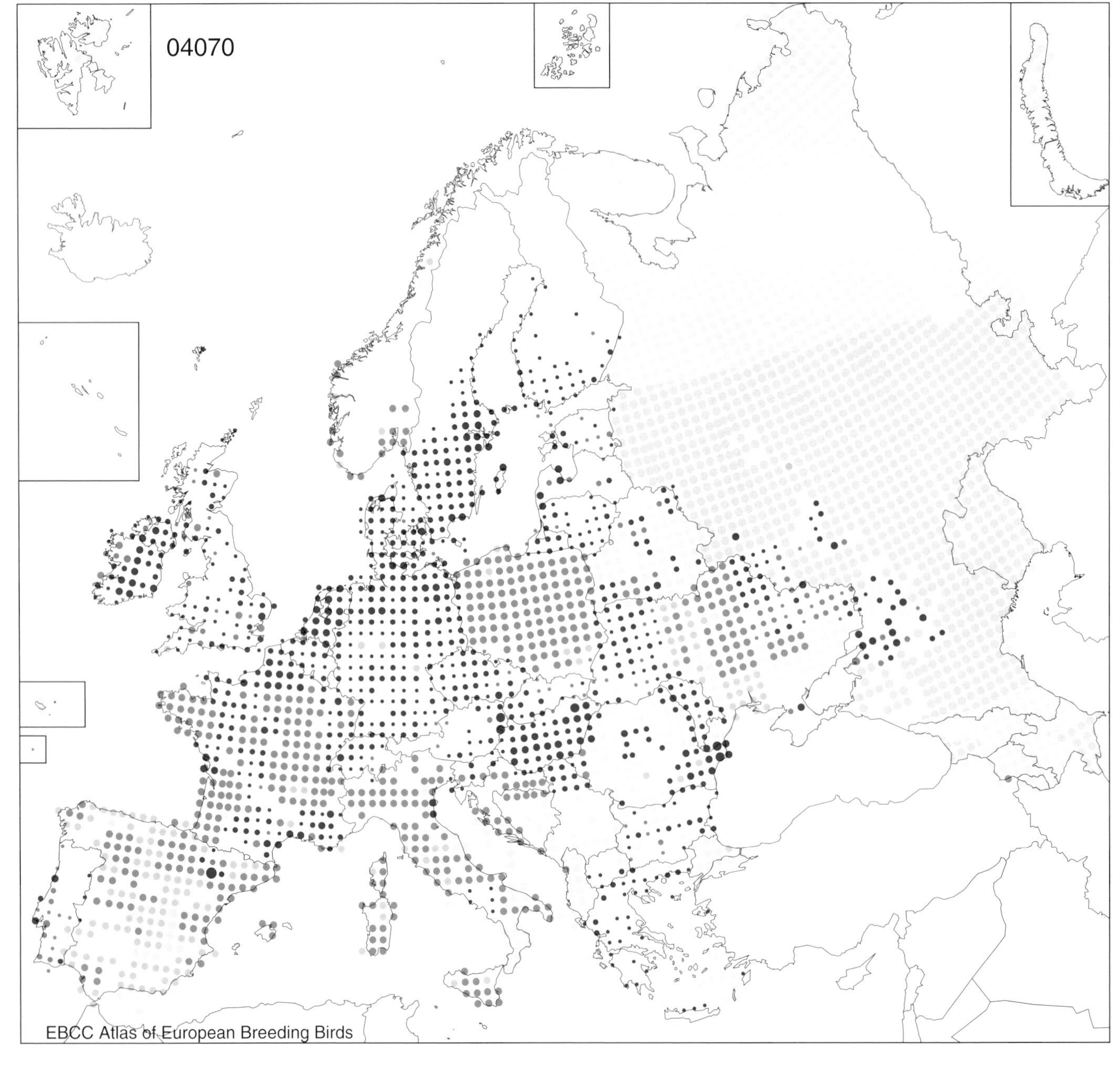

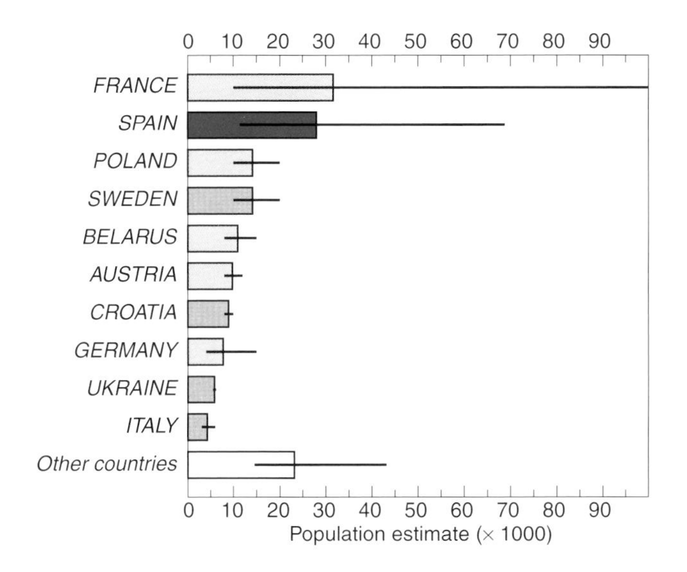

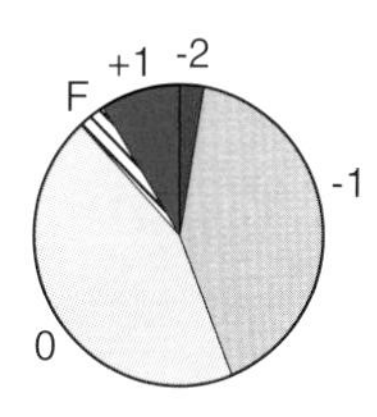

% in top 10 countries: 85.4
Total number of populated European countries: 34
Total European population 129,994–239,718 (158,578)
Russian population 10,000–100,000 (31,623)
Turkish population 10,000–30,000 (17,321)

An elusive bird of water-fringe vegetation and other permanent waterlogged densely overgrown habitats, the Water Rail breeds in Eurasia from Ireland and Portugal as far E as China, and from Iceland and C Finland S to North Africa and Iran. Whereas the southern and western populations are resident, the northern and northeastern populations are mostly migratory, wintering in W and SW Europe, mainly in Great Britain, France, Portugal and the Mediterranean and Black Sea regions.

Because of its secretive behaviour and vocalizations from dusk to dawn, the Water Rail is heard much more often than seen during the breeding period. In suitable, often inaccessible habitats the species may breed at very high densities, making it difficult to census accurately. Estimates of population sizes for large or remote wetlands are therefore prone to substantial underestimation where it has been impossible to employ appropriate field methods, such as tape-recorder use, nocturnal visits or special capture and ringing programmes.

The Water Rail's breeding habitats consist of brackish or freshwater (also waste water) habitats (up to 1700m asl, Bulgaria) which are shallow yet are permanently waterlogged and densely overgrown by reeds *Phragmites*, sedges *Carex*, rushes *Juncus*, reedmace *Typha* or willow *Salix* thickets. The preferred water depth is 5–30cm, the habitat structure normally being patchy with a mosaic of luxurious vegetation and exposed mudflats, pools or ditches. Such habitats exist mostly in the water-fringe vegetation of the still or slow-moving waters of marshes, swamps, rich fen and sewage lagoons, but sometimes also along ditches in wet meadows, or even in crops, the less dense alder carrs, poplar plantations and other thickly vegetated wet or boggy forests. The species clearly prefers base-rich and species-rich, eutrophic to polytrophic habitats.

Although the Water Rail may often breed as solitary pairs or in small clusters in tiny sites such as ponds, narrow reedbeds or overgrown ditches in farmland, large clusters of breeding birds can be found in extensive wetlands, like Neusiedlersee/Fertő in Austria and Hungary (8000–12 000bp estimated in 1993; Dvorak *et al* 1993), the Camargue, the Romanian Danube Delta (Weber *et al* 1994), the Polish Biebrza and Narew River valleys (>10 000bp; M. Flade & N. Schäffer, in prep), the Belarussian Pripyat marshes and the Bulgarian Lake Durankulak.

Its population and range size trends are influenced adversely by habitat destruction through the commonplace reclamation of marshes and drainage of wetlands, but may benefit in some regions from the eutrophication of reedbeds, mainly in C and W Europe, as evidence from several breeding grounds in Germany indicates (M. Flade, unpubl). Overall, the population is believed to be declining or stable rather than increasing or fluctuating. The declines seem strongest in E and SE European countries like Lithuania, Ukraine, Moldova, Romania, Czech Republic, Slovenia, Croatia and Albania, where the landscape is changing rapidly due to economic development and agricultural intensification. Only towards the range limits have increasing populations been recorded, mostly in Spain, Denmark and Finland. The Finnish population became established before 1920, increased rapidly in the 1950s and 1960s, but in the late 1980s contained no more than 350bp (Koskimies 1989a).

An analysis of 58 census plots in German reedbeds (Flade 1994) showed just how high breeding densities can be. For small breeding sites, typical values were 7.5 bp/ha (6bp in 0.8ha), for sites of 1–3ha, up to 3.6 bp/ha and for plots of 33–100ha, up to 13.4 bp/10ha (overall mean density 2.78 bp/10ha; median density value from 23 plots each larger than 10ha, 2.1 bp/10ha). Such densely populated habitats consisted mainly of eutrophic or polytrophic reedbeds.

Ventzeslav Delov (BUL) Martin Flade (D)

Porzana porzana

Spotted Crake

CZ	Chřástal kropenatý	I	Voltolino
D	Tüpfelsumpfhuhn	NL	Porseleinhoen
E	Polluela Pintoja	P	Franga-d'água-grande
F	Marouette ponctuée	PL	Kropiatka
FIN	Luhtahuitti	R	Погоныш
G	Στικτοπουλάδα	S	Småfläckig sumphöna
H	Pettyes vízicsibe		

SPEC Cat 4, Threat status S

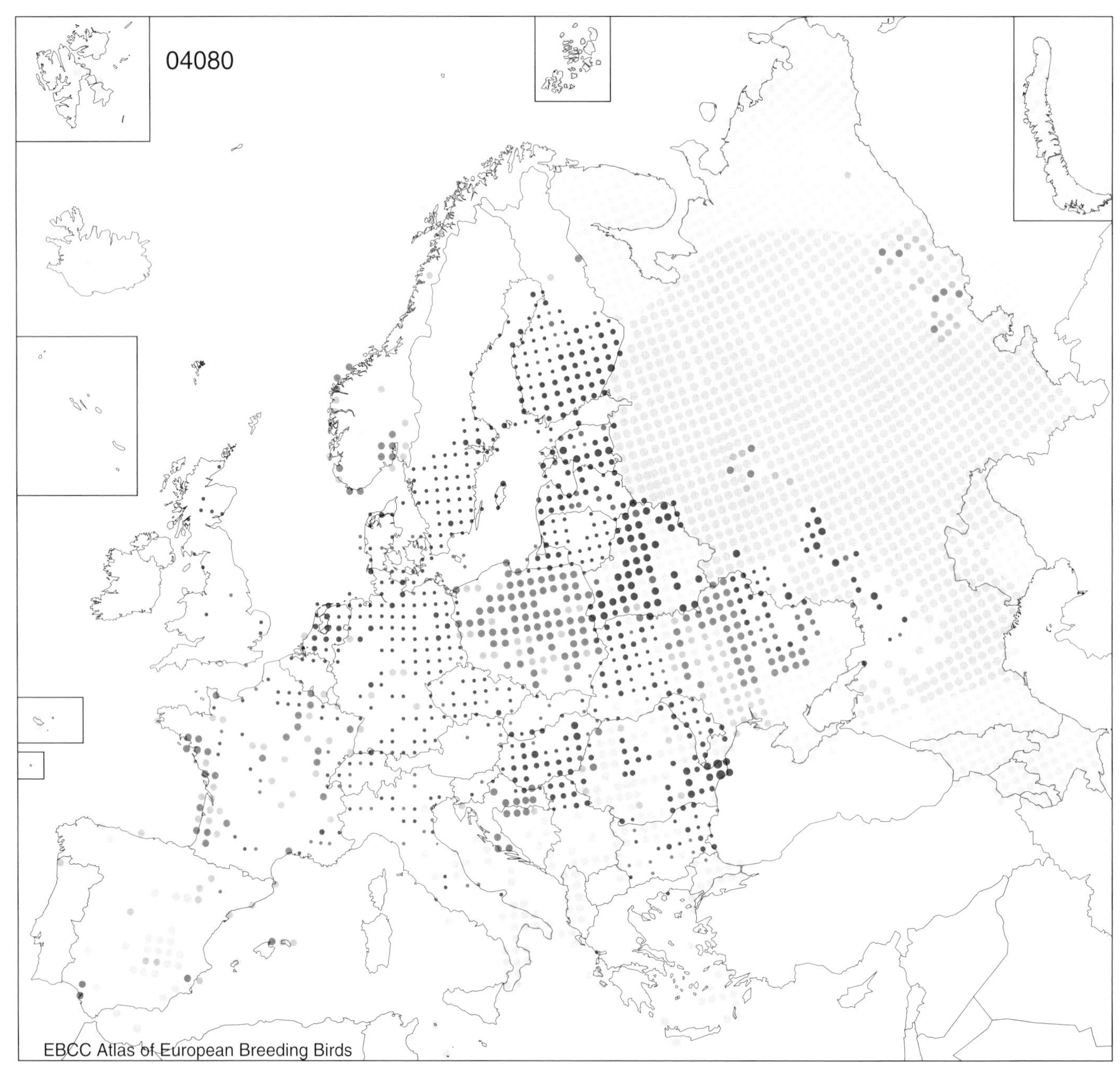

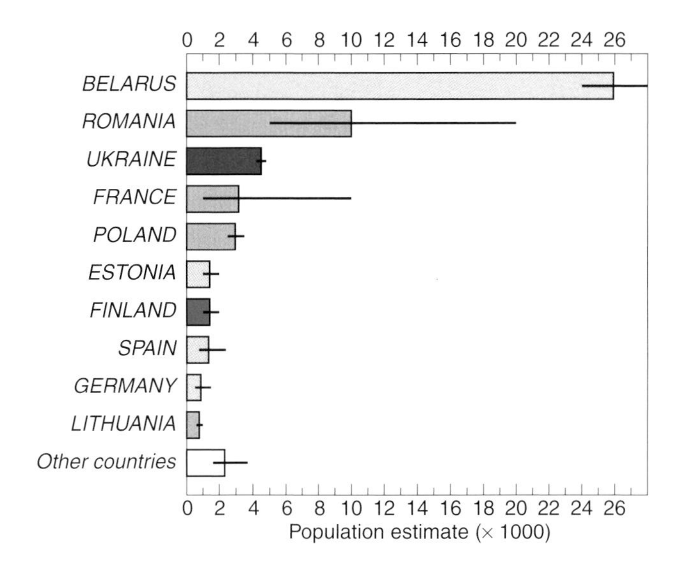

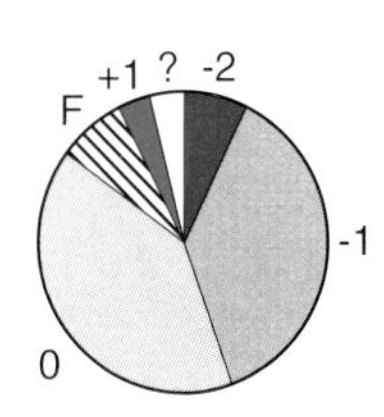

% in top 10 countries: 95.7
Total number of populated European countries: 27
Total European population 48,786–67,083 (54,669)
Russian population 10,000–100,000 (31,623)
Turkish population 1–100 (10)

The Spotted Crake's breeding distribution covers much of the W and C Palearctic from W Europe and S Fennoscandia to C Siberia (to 100°E). Its wintering range is poorly known, but most European birds cross the Sahara to reach E and SE Africa. Few remain in temperate Europe or the Mediterranean.

The Spotted Crake breeds mostly in continental lowlands, avoiding higher mountains, sea coasts and brackish waters where water levels vary too much for successful breeding. Its breeding habitat requirements are narrow; it needs open, inundated meadows, marshes or fens (dominated by various sedges *Carex* spp) whose water depth is <30cm. Sites which dry out during incubation are usually abandoned. It avoids pure reed *Phragmites* stands unless they possess a grassy soft-stemmed base layer. Such habitats in W and C Europe lie mostly on shallow lakes and pond margins, in low-lying, wide river valleys or in larger fens. Hence the species is distributed very patchily throughout Europe, something not apparent from the map's 50km resolution.

Population sizes and distributions are difficult to establish, even in a single year. The only means of censusing this skulking rail during the breeding season is to plot its loud, whistling calls, uttered almost entirely in late evening or at night. Calling ceases completely after pairing, confining the census 'window' to but a few weeks or even days. Additionally, local abundance can change drastically from year to year, from large numbers to a few or none, if water levels are unsuitable. In Finland and Denmark this variation shows some cyclicity (Koskimies 1982, 1989b, unpubl; Sørensen 1995). Shifts within a breeding season may also occur, some sites quickly becoming unsuitable and others being colonized very late (Vogel & van der Wal 1988).

The species breeds in some 29 European countries, but for the above reasons, we believe that in many cases the map deriving from several years' data gives an over-optimistic picture of a single year's distribution. The graph estimates should be treated with caution until better data become available, especially for the little-studied eastern areas.

Nevertheless, the breeding strongholds lie in eastern Europe, where the species remains relatively common because low-intensity agricultural is still practised, leaving large areas of wet meadows. The bulk of the European population (*c*50 000–180 000bp) inhabits Russia, Belarus, Romania and Ukraine, some 43 200–152 800bp (*c*85%). Other sizeable populations, each of a few thousand, occur in Poland, Estonia and Finland and probably also in Lithuania and Latvia. In W and C Europe only France, Spain (despite so few confirmed sites), Germany and Hungary seem to have >500bp each. All other national populations comprise a few hundred breeding pairs or fewer, and are therefore not significant in an European context.

Density data are difficult to obtain and are very scarce: in Neusiedlersee/Austria, a site with suitable habitat held up to 10 calling birds on 30ha (M. Dvorak, pers obs), an overgrown eutrophic lake (3.6km^2) in SE Finland contained 60–70 males or 5–21/km^2 of suitable habitat (Koskimies 1989) and the Kasari River mouth (western Estonia) has between 0.5 and 4.0 bp/km^2 (Leibak *et al* 1994).

Only in Finland have both range and population increased since 1970 (Koskimies 1993), a northward expansion which began probably in the 19th century, just when lowering of lake water levels (to create agricultural land) and eutrophication of waterbodies started to produce new habitats for the species. Populations most probably are fluctuating everywhere, making trends difficult to detect. However, a continuing declining trend has been reported in almost half of the European countries, and most strongly in W and C Europe, where the Spotted Crake has suffered from large-scale wetland drainage and agricultural intensification, a process likely to continue in E Europe.

Pertti Koskimies (FIN) Michael Dvorak (A)

Porzana parva

Little Crake

CZ	Chřástal malý	**I**	Schiribilla
D	Kleines Sumpfhuhn	**NL**	Klein Waterhoen
E	Polluela Bastarda	**P**	Franga-d'água-bastarda
F	Marouette poussin	**PL**	Zielonka
FIN	Pikkuhuitti	**R**	Малый погоныш
G	Μικροπουλάδα	**S**	Mindre sumphöna
H	Kis vízicsibe		

SPEC Cat 4, Threat status S (P)

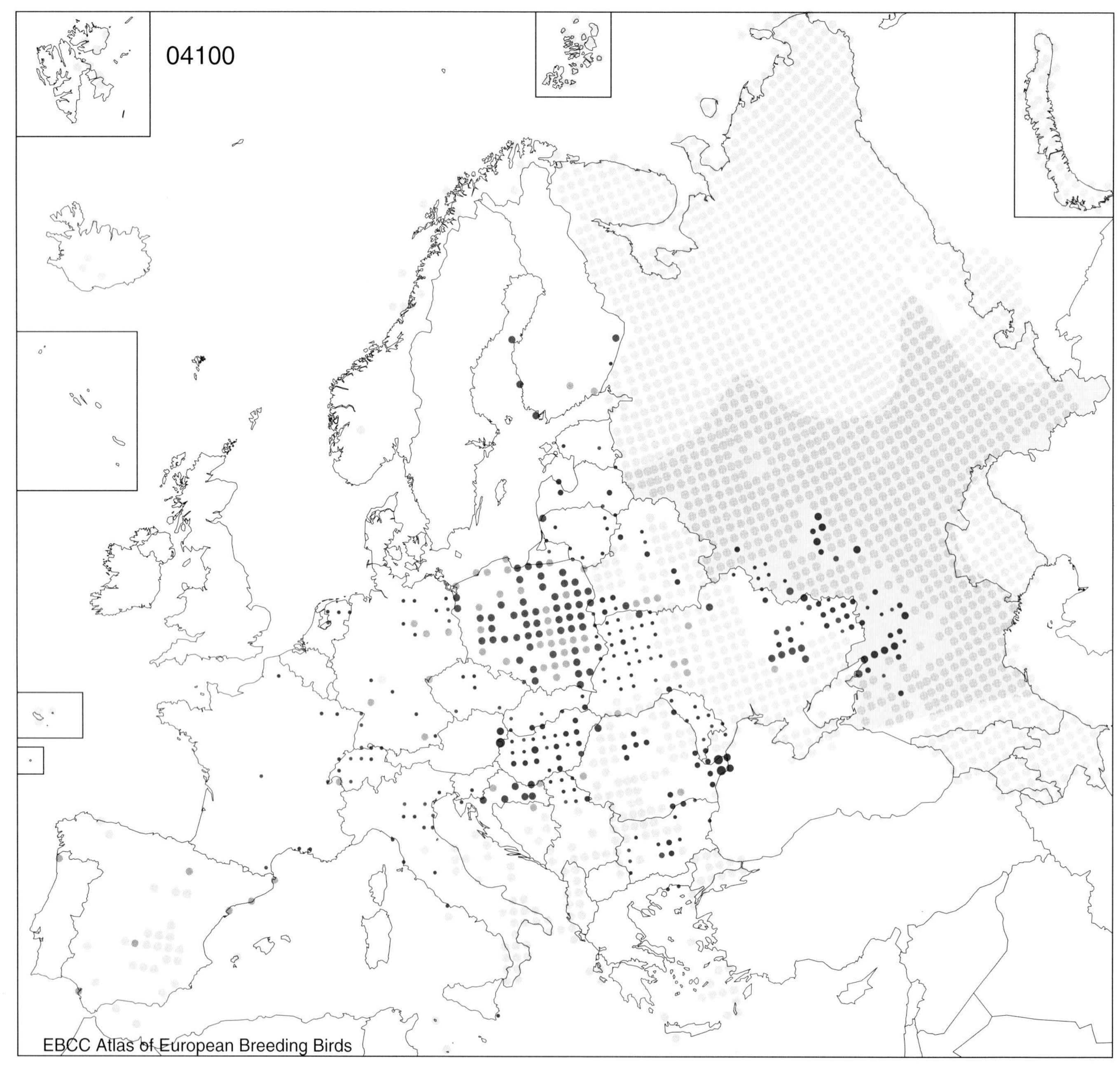

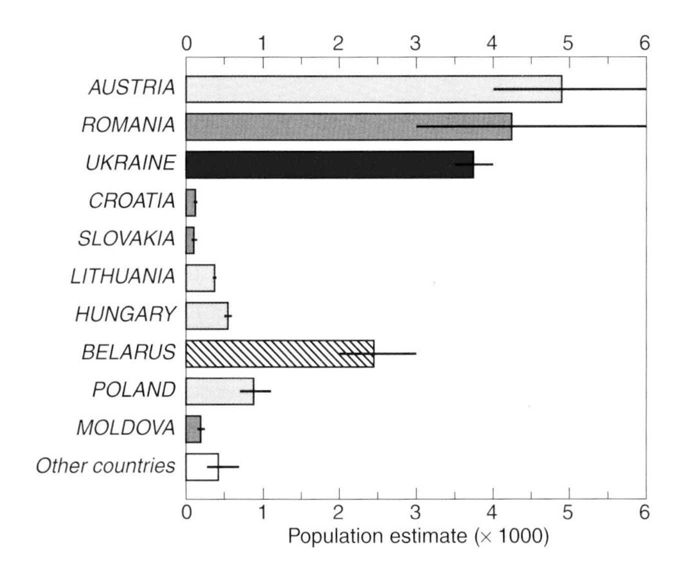

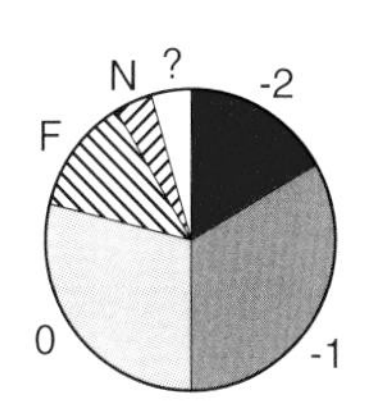

% in top 10 countries: 97.6
Total number of populated European countries: 24
Total European population 16,344–20,150 (17,973)
Russian population 10,000–100,000 (31,623)
Turkish population 1–100 (10)

The Little Crake is mainly a species of the steppe zone in the W and C Palearctic, reaching *c*85°E. In C Europe, its continuous range includes the Polish lowlands, the Great Hungarian Plain, Ukraine and southern Russia. As a long-distance migrant, the Little Crake probably winters mostly in East Africa, but odd records are known from Egypt, Arabia and West Africa.

The Little Crake breeds almost exclusively in reedbeds flooded to a depth of over 50cm and dominated by reed *Phragmites* or reedmace *Typha*. The most important habitat features are small stretches of open water and a thick layer of broken stalks at ground or water level. Both features are characteristic of old reedbeds, which have been neither harvested nor burnt for many years, and are rarely met elsewhere. In C Europe, this secretive rail normally occurs in reedbeds bordering eutrophic fishponds or shallow lakes. In regularly inundated floodplains it also inhabits smaller ponds or oxbows. Deltas of the larger rivers are coastal strongholds.

Like its relatives, the Little Crake is notoriously difficult to survey due to its skulking behaviour and its inaccessible habitat. Normally, the only method to record the species is by listening to their calls. The far-carrying (<1km) advertising calls of both male and female come only from unpaired birds. It is easy, although time-consuming, to stimulate territorial calls by using a tape-recorder, the only possible method of assessing the species' abundance.

Its European distribution is very patchy due to its specialized habitat requirements. Although regular breeding occurred in 24 countries during the *Atlas*' survey period, only 10 have estimated minimum populations of over 100bp. At its range limits the species is very scarce and local. In our opinion, in countries like The Netherlands, Switzerland and Italy the crakes are not so common as the maps suggest. Many sites probably were inhabited only temporarily, or held unpaired birds (which are relatively easy to record).

Its strongholds lie in C and SE Europe. Only Russia, Austria, Romania, Ukraine and Belarus reported more than 1000bp. In Hungary and Poland the species is relatively widespread, but most sites hold only small populations. Reasonably reliable data for countries with large populations are available only from Austria and Poland, but other estimates are (due to censusing difficulties) but rough indications of the true numbers. Excluding Russia, the European population total of *c*16 300–20 200bp is therefore very provisional and will require adjustment as better estimates become available.

Breeding densities in optimal habitats can be very high: at Neusiedlersee/Austria, the best-known European site, where the population is estimated at 4000–6000bp (Dvorak *et al* 1993), the long-term investigations over the vast reedbed area revealed average densities of 1–2 bp/ha of suitable habitat; optimum habitats can hold up to 5 pairs/ha (M. Dvorak, unpubl). At the northern range limits densities are much lower: in the Kasari River delta (W Estonia), the maximum mean density was 2.5 bp/km^2 (1957–60; Leibak *et al* 1994). On Lake Siikalahti (SE Finland) in 3.6km^2, the population fluctuated between 1–6bp, representing a density range of 0.3–2 territories/km^2 of marshy vegetation (Koskimies 1989b, unpubl).

The reported trends give cause for concern. Declines are occurring in 12 countries which together hold probably more than 25% of the European population. Wetland destruction or degradation and intensive reed-harvesting will affect the species adversely. However, in well-protected wetlands like Neusiedlersee in Austria populations have remained stable or increased locally at least since the early 1980s (M. Dvorak, unpubl). In spite of declines in some regions since the mid-1970s, the Little Crake has expanded its range northwards, colonizing Estonia during the 1930s (Leibak *et al* 1994), Sweden in the 1940s (Breife *et al* 1990) and Finland since the 1970s (Koskimies 1989).

Michael Dvorak (A) Pertti Koskimies (FIN)

Porzana pusilla — Baillon's Crake

CZ	Chřástal nejmenší	**I**	Schiribilla grigiata
D	Zwergsumpfhuhn	**NL**	Kleinst Waterhoen
E	Polluela Chica	**P**	Franga-d'água-pequena
F	Marouette de Baillon	**PL**	Karliczka
FIN	Kääpiöhuitti	**R**	Погоныш-крошка
G	Νανοπουλάδα	**S**	Dvärgsumphöna
H	Törpe vízicsibe		

SPEC Cat 3, Threat status R

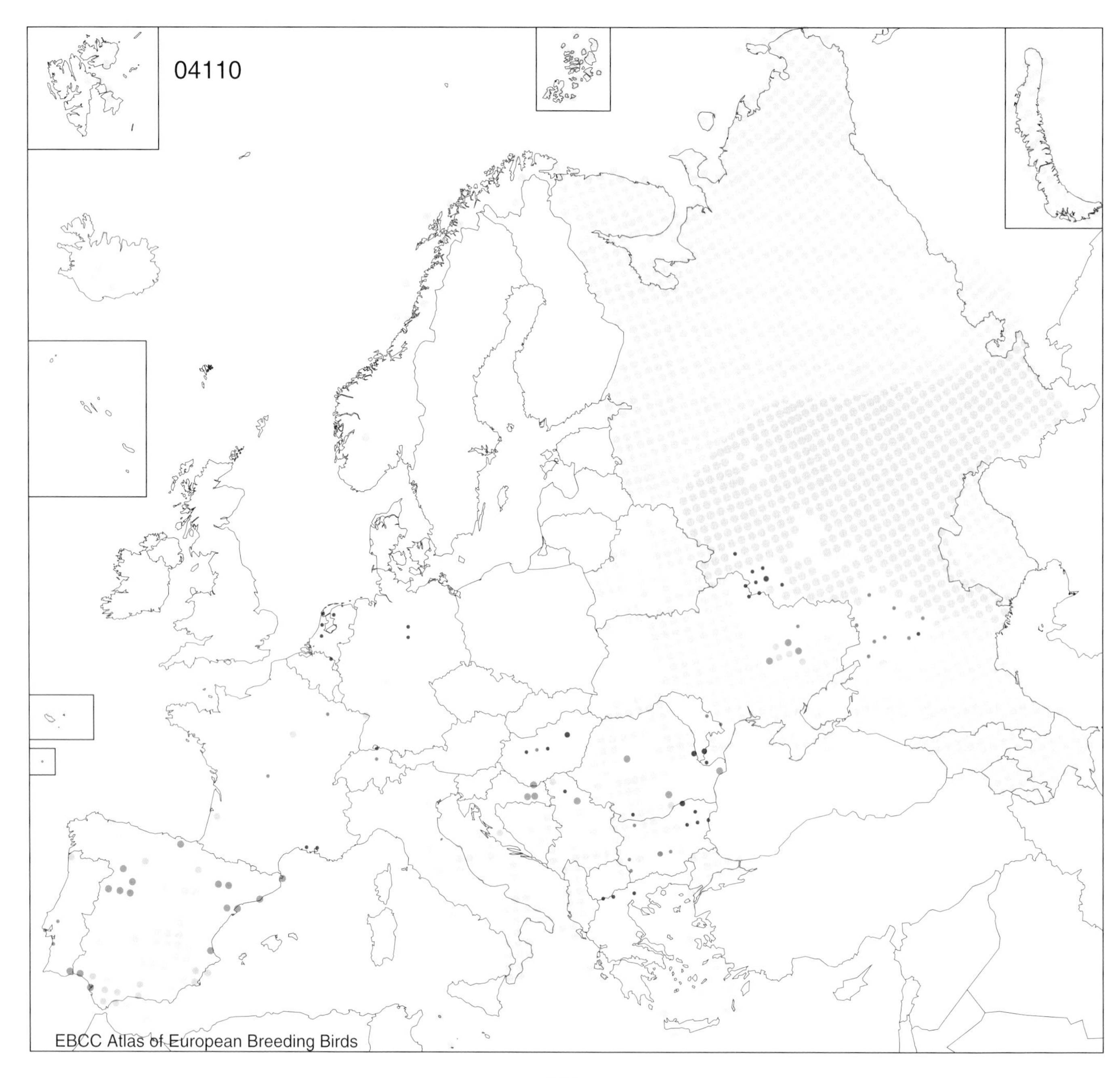

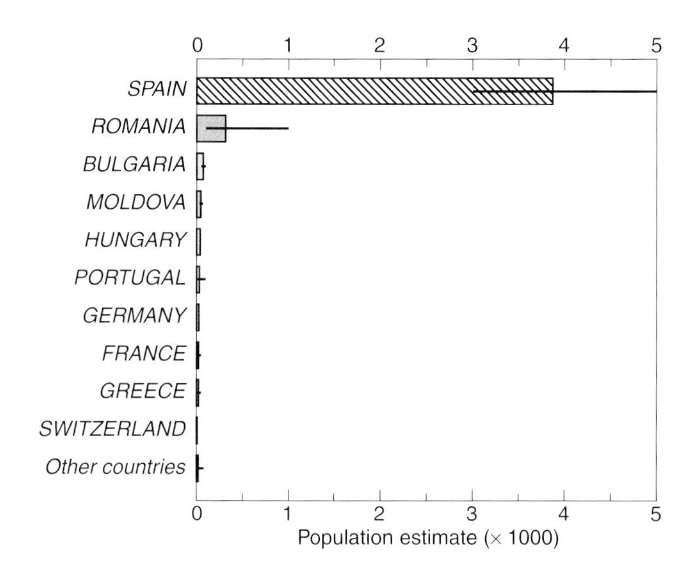

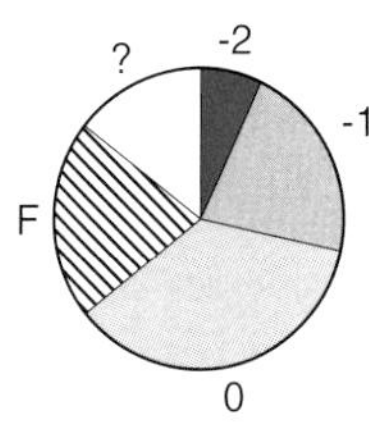

% in top 10 countries: 99.6
Total number of populated European countries: 14
Total European population 3574–5796 (4474)
Russian population 500–2000 (1000)
Turkish population 1–100 (10)

The secretive Baillon's Crake, the least-known Palearctic crake, is a breeding bird of Eurasia, Africa and Australasia. In the Palearctic it is a migrant, its distribution stretching from Portugal and Spain through C Siberia to Sakhalin and Japan. There are scattered populations of varying sizes, in Morocco, Jordan, Iran and the C Asian republics. A sizeable distribution arm encompasses the region from the Sea of Okhotsk to S China. The populations in Ethiopia and below the Equator are resident. Within the *Atlas*' coverage area, Baillon's Crake is confined mainly to the temperate, mediterranean and steppe climate zones below 55°N. Of the six recognized subspecies, *P.p. intermedia* occurs in Europe W from Romania, and the nominate *pusilla* largely E of Romania.

Baillon's Crake inhabits floodplains and flooded meadows with stagnant fresh water, overgrown with soft-stemmed sedge *Carex*, rush *Juncus*, spike-rush *Eleocharis*, reed sweet-grass *Phalaris arundinacea*, clubrush *S. lacustris* or sea club-rush *S. maritimus*. Somewhat drier habitats may contain purple loosestrife *Lythrum salicaria* or marsh mallow *Althaea*. Water depth is critical, not exceeding 30cm (Szabó 1976, Becker 1983). It is a very skulking crake, difficult to identify (Becker & Schmidt 1990), not necessarily vocal and if so, with a confusing and often barely audible repertoire. Reliable censuses are therefore scarce.

The distribution of Baillon's Crake throughout Europe is much patchier than the map depicts. Many breeding habitats characteristically are transient in nature, because flood-meadows vary in the extent of flooding between and within years, and may contain suitable breeding sites only occasionally. Baillon's Crake is a solitary nester, but little is known of the extent of any territoriality. The species' stronghold apparently lies in Spain (3000–5000bp), but its actual abundance is poorly understood and probably varies with changes in water level. In the Coto Doñana, probably thousands of birds nest in good rainfall years, but breeding is rare in dry years (Llandres & Urdiales 1991). Furthermore, extensive potential breeding areas like ricefields are rarely studied (Koshelev 1994), and so the occurrence of Baillon's Crake in Portugal and Spain possibly is under-recorded.

European Russia also holds a substantial population (rough estimate, 500–2000bp) and so may Ukraine (where no estimate is available), but the species seemingly has been little-studied, and so the likely totals are difficult to assess. Many principal breeding areas in the Don, Kuban, Dnepr, Dnestr and Danube River floodplains are threatened by drainage, reed-cutting and -burning and heavy grazing pressure, but a particular problem is the sudden, large water-level changes which are caused by discharges from dams on the rivers (Koshelev 1994). Nests can be swamped, if downstream of the dam, or left isolated from water if upstream; in either case with probable loss of clutches or young.

Elsewhere in Europe, breeding is at best irregular, depending on temporary floods lasting long enough for a brood to be raised, on the effects of reclamation projects or on the sympathetic management of nature reserves. At a very rough estimate, taking into account censusing difficulties and the limited coverage of southern habitats in particular, the European population of Baillon's Crake may total fewer than 10 000bp.

Baillon's Crake is migratory, but its wintering grounds are largely unknown. Apparently, many European birds cross the Mediterranean in a broad front and there are indications that many winter in wetlands S of the Sahara, from Senegal to Ethiopia, the latter possibly being the main centre of the wintering range. Most Asian populations probably winter in the Indian subcontinent, SE Asia and S China. Where there are resident populations in Africa, European birds are indistinguishable except in the hand.

Rob G Bijlsma (NL)

Crex crex

Corncrake

CZ	Chřástal polní	**I**	Re di quaglie
D	Wachtelkönig	**NL**	Kwartelkoning
E	Guión de Codornices	**P**	Codornizão
F	Râle des genêts	**PL**	Derkacz
FIN	Ruisrääkkä	**R**	Коростель
G	Ορτυκομάνα	**S**	Kornknarr
H	Haris		

SPEC Cat 1, Threat status V

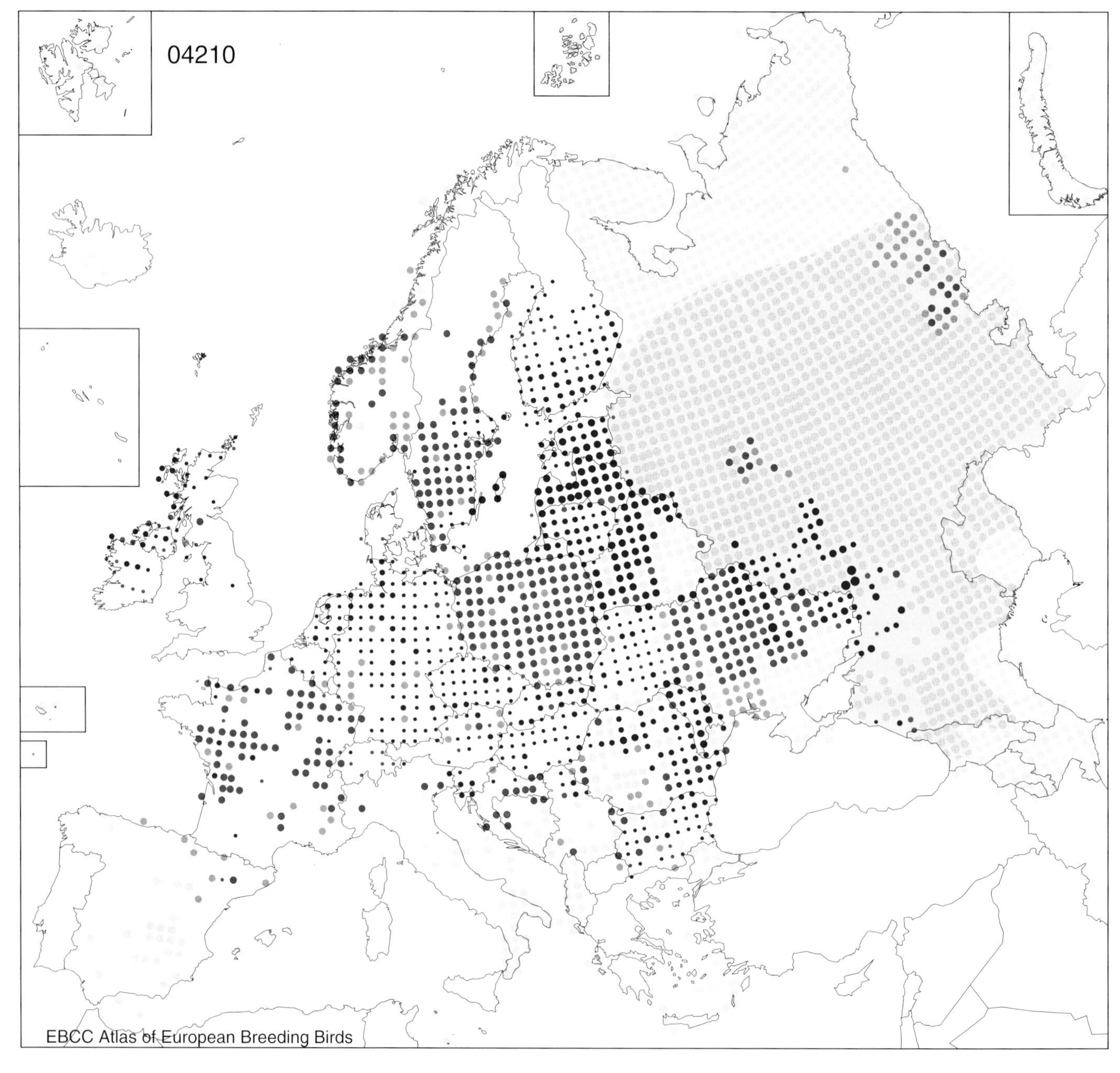

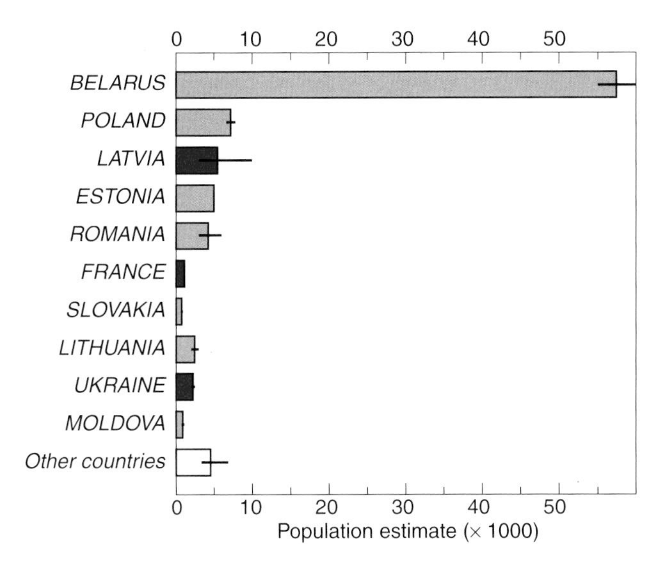

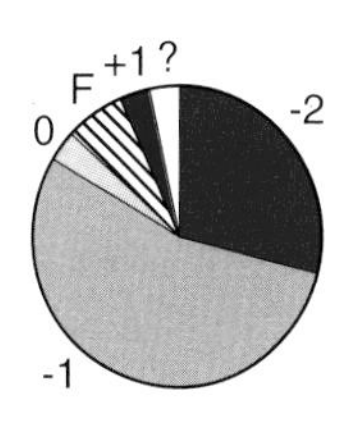

% in top 10 countries: 95.0
Total number of populated European countries: 31
Total European population 87,470–96,920 (91,277)
Russian population 10,000–100,000 (31,623)
Turkish population 1–10 (3)

In comparison with related species, this rail is less dependent on wetland habitats. The Corncrake is distributed from W Europe to C and E Europe, and as far as W Siberia (NW Lake Baykal). Its main wintering grounds lie in the savannas of South, C and SE Africa (Stowe & Becker 1992), although it is known from West Africa. In Egypt, where migration routes converge, large numbers are killed each year; 4600 in 1991 (S. Baha el Din, pers comm), 11 000 in 1992 and 1993 and 14 000 in 1994 (estimates made during detailed RSPB investigations; Rhys Green, pers comm).

Breeding occurs in open or semi-open landscapes, mainly in tall grass meadows. Suitable habitats include moist, unfertilized grassland or regularly cut meadows in wetlands along rivers or brooks, marshlands, the fringes of moorland (peatland, mires), silting-up meadows in the margins of standing waters, as well as cleared (deforested) grassy areas or mountain pastures. The species occupies abandoned land provided that the walking resistance caused by old, overgrowing vegetation is not too great. Dispersed solitary bushes, hedgerows or reed-margins are used as calling places and therefore are favoured in breeding areas. The Corncrake can also occur in fertilized meadows (unless drained) or arable land sown with cereals, rape and caraway, but here reproductive success is low. A concentration of >100 calling males was found in The Netherlands on arable land on clayish soils (Voslamber 1989).

Bordering herbaceous vegetation, embankments or fallow lands are of utmost importance as moulting sites when adults are temporarily flightless. These areas are also used as alternative habitats during the harvest. Without a doubt riverine meadows of the *Carex–Iris–Typhoides* type and other wet grasslands which lack natural arboreal vegetation and which exist in the planar, foothill and montane zones represent the Corncrake's original breeding grounds. In the Alps, breeding sites occur up to 1400m asl and in Russia up to 3000m asl.

In the past, most of C and W Europe presumably was inhabited by the Corncrake. Its distribution has become more discontinuous; it is absent from many formerly occupied areas in Great Britain, France and Germany. Dense populations still remain in the Baltic States (10 000–18 000bp), Belarus (55 000–60 000bp) and Russia (10 000–100 000bp), representing some 75–89% of the estimated world population of 100 000–200 000bp. The reliability of these figures remains uncertain, because the species is notoriously difficult to census (Schäffer 1994).

All countries with sizeable Corncrake populations experienced declines of >20% (17 countries) or >50% (10 countries) during 1970–90, except Sweden (stable at 250–1000bp) and Finland (fluctuating, 500–1000bp). Drainage, enabling advancement of mowing dates and expansion of the area of cultivation, and modernization and mechanization of farming practices are generally held responsible for the demise of the Corncrake. In Slovakia (A. Kristin, pers comm) and the Czech Republic (J. Pykal, pers comm) the Corncrake is now found largely at higher altitudes, where the harsher climatic conditions result in delayed vegetation growth and later mowing dates. Very wet areas also tend to be harvested later, allowing concentrations of Corncrake to form in these habitats. Declining populations were already apparent in many European countries in the early 1900s, but the rate of decline and range contraction has accelerated since the 1970s (Hashmi 1989, Stowe 1993, Broyer 1994).

To make matters worse, almost nothing is known about breeding success in any part of its distribution. Calling males are an unreliable basis of population estimates because they abandon the females on clutch completion. New techniques must be devised. It is plausible that the reproductive output must have declined as well, given the mechanized and fast farming practices of today and these circumstances will be aggravated in E European countries now that agricultural intensification techniques have been introduced there.

Robert Horváth (H) Norbert Schäffer (D)

Gallinula chloropus — Moorhen

CZ	Slípka zelenonohá	I	Gallinella d'acqua
D	Teichhuhn	NL	Waterhoen
E	Gallineta Común	P	Galinha-d'água
F	Gallinule poule-d'eau	PL	Kokoszka wodna
FIN	Liejukana	R	Камышница
G	Νερόκοτα	S	Rörhöna
H	Vízityúk		

Non-SPEC, Threat status S

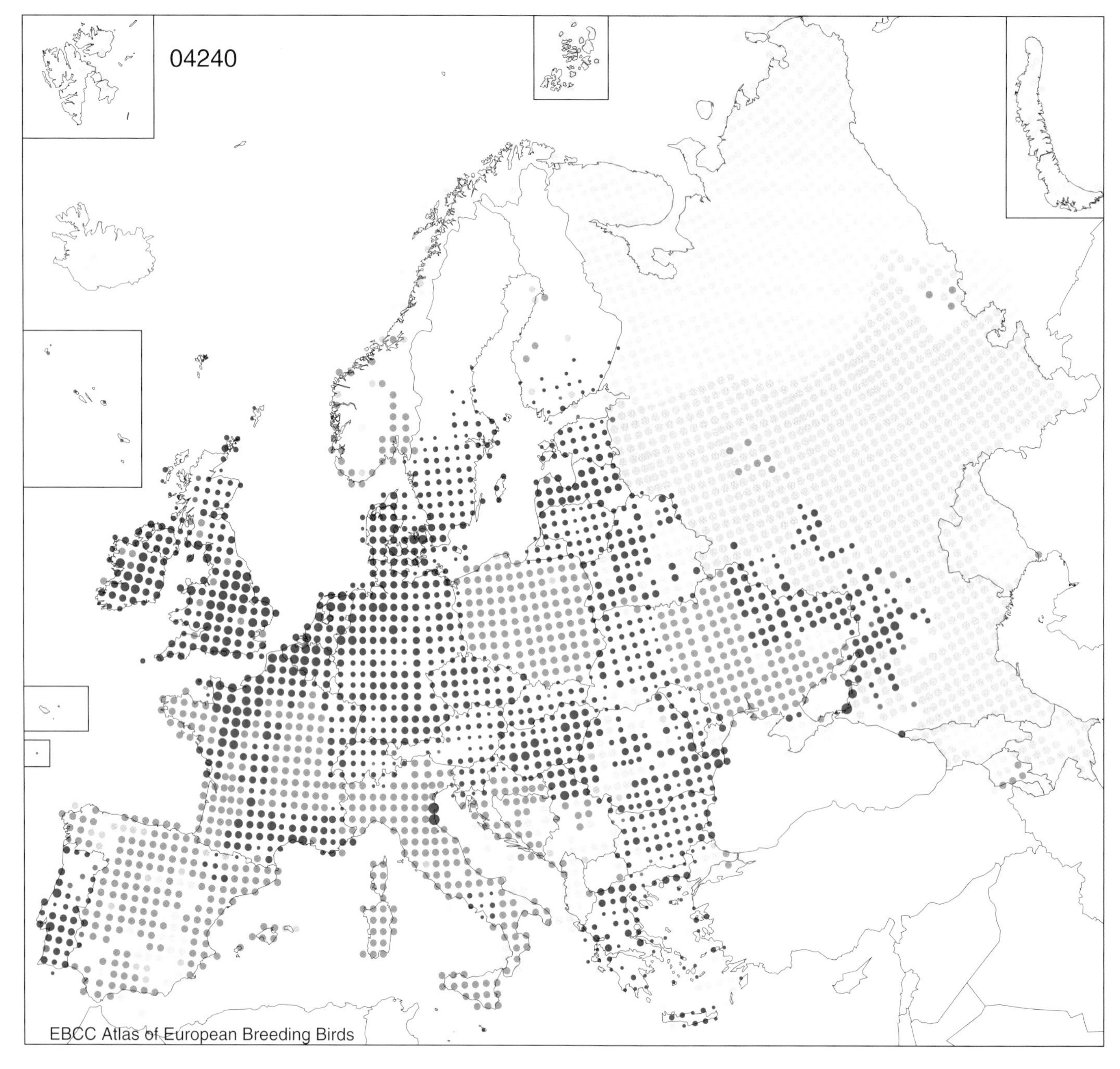

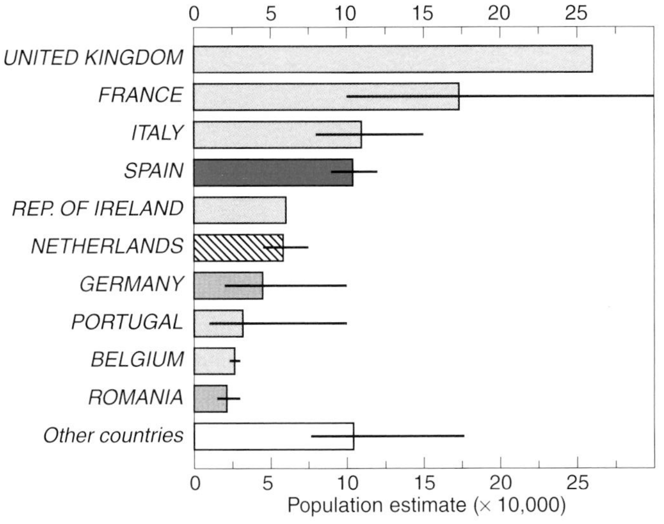

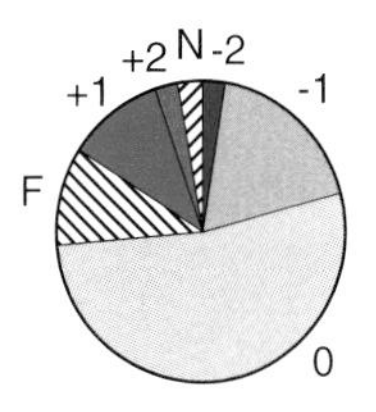

% in top 10 countries: 89.5
Total number of populated European countries: 38
Total European population 903,990–1,160,988 (992,774)
Russian population 10,000–100,000 (31,623)
Turkish population 5000–20,000 (10,000)

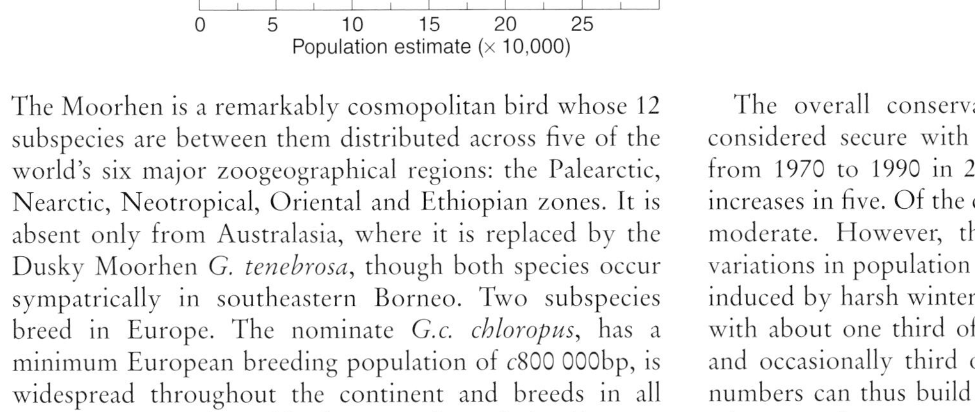

The Moorhen is a remarkably cosmopolitan bird whose 12 subspecies are between them distributed across five of the world's six major zoogeographical regions: the Palearctic, Nearctic, Neotropical, Oriental and Ethiopian zones. It is absent only from Australasia, where it is replaced by the Dusky Moorhen *G. tenebrosa*, though both species occur sympatrically in southeastern Borneo. Two subspecies breed in Europe. The nominate *G.c. chloropus*, has a minimum European breeding population of *c*800 000bp, is widespread throughout the continent and breeds in all European countries with the exception of the Faeroes, Iceland, Svalbard, Madeira and possibly the Azores. The second subspecies, *G.c. correiana*, has a tiny world population of 20–30bp, with a range restricted to the islands of Terceira and, possibly, Fayal and Sao Miguel, in the Azores (Bannerman & Bannerman 1966).

The Moorhen is a bird of wetlands and breeds anywhere where there is sufficient eutrophic fresh water with emergent vegetation providing the food and nesting cover necessary for successful breeding. Because it is so intimately linked to inland fresh water, periods of extreme cold can lead to temporary loss of habitat. As a consequence its distribution is bounded both altitudinally, with few birds breeding above 700m asl (Dvorak *et al* 1993), and latitudinally; hence its absence from the northernmost parts of Europe. Though it is a year-round resident throughout much of its range in Europe, it migrates away from the NE of its breeding range, from just N of the 0°C January isotherm and from much of NW Europe, particularly Sweden and Denmark. As a result the populations of southern and western Europe are boosted by an influx of immigrants during the winter months.

The map and population estimates both show that the Moorhen is not evenly distributed across its range in Europe. Rather the bulk of the population occurs in the W, with 70% of the European population in Britain & Ireland, The Netherlands, France and Spain. Great Britain in particular has a special responsibility for this species.

The overall conservation status of the Moorhen is considered secure with stable or fluctuating populations from 1970 to 1990 in 26 countries, declines in eight and increases in five. Of the changes registered, most were only moderate. However, there can be considerable annual variations in population size as a consequence of mortality induced by harsh winters. The Moorhen is multi-brooded, with about one third of pairs attempting a second brood and occasionally third or fourth broods (Gibbons 1989); numbers can thus build up rapidly again following severe winter weather.

The Moorhen's range extended northwards, especially into Fennoscandia, in the second half of the 19th century. Breeding was first recorded in Finland in 1850, in Norway in 1860, in Denmark in 1865 and in Shetland in 1890. It remains rare in Finland, where the population of about 150 pairs is restricted to a few dozen localities in southern and southeastern localities (Koskimies 1989a), less so in Norway, where most pairs are again found in the southeast of the country (Gjershaug *et al* 1994), while the population in Denmark has built up steadily and is now widely distributed across the country.

Population densities are highly variable and are often greatest in artificial habitats such as waterfowl collections where up to five territories/ha have been recorded (Gibbons 1986). Such densities are, however, uncommon and are restricted to areas of optimal habitat. In general, densities are much lower; across farmland in Britain, for example, mean densities are *c*0.03 territories/ha (Gibbons 1993). One of the largest reported populations of Moorhen at a single site was of 1000–1500bp in the 103km² of reedbelts at Neusiedlersee (Dvorak *et al* 1993).

David W Gibbons (GB)

This species account is sponsored by Helmuth Engler, Köln, D.

Porphyrio porphyrio Purple Gallinule

CZ	Slípka modrá	**I**	Pollo sultano
D	Purpurhuhn	**NL**	Purperkoet
E	Calamón Común	**P**	Caimão-comum
F	Talève sultane	**PL**	Modrzyk
FIN	Sulttaanikana	**R**	Султанка
G	Σουλτανοπουλάδα	**S**	Purpurhöna
H	Kék-fú		

SPEC Cat 3, Threat status R

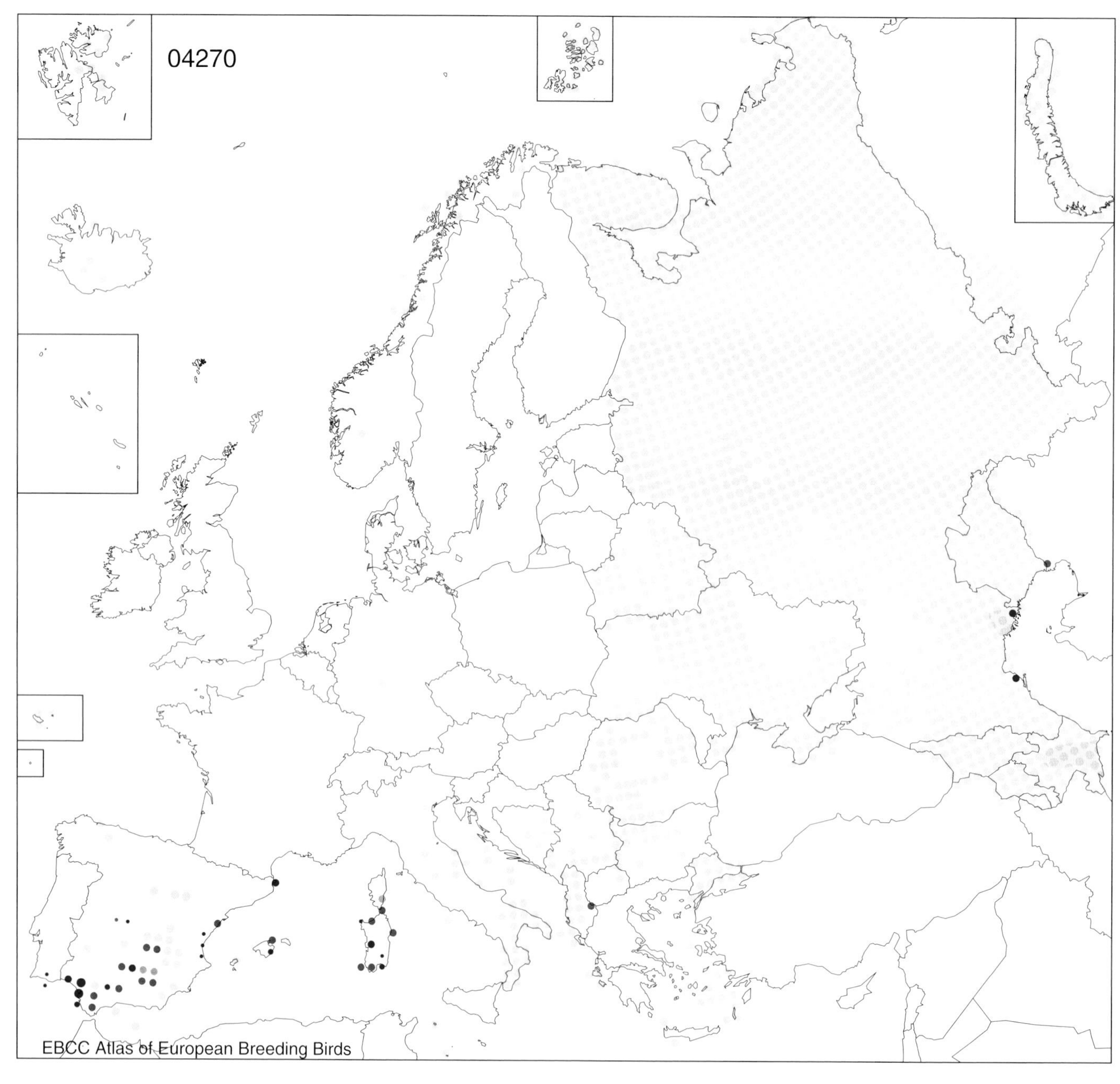

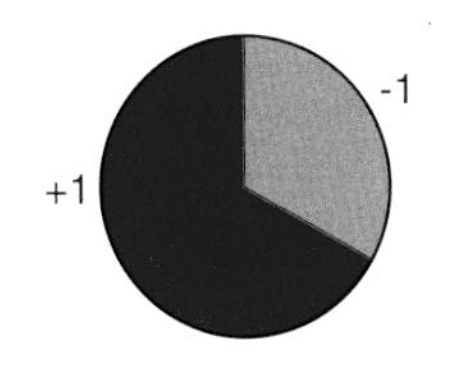

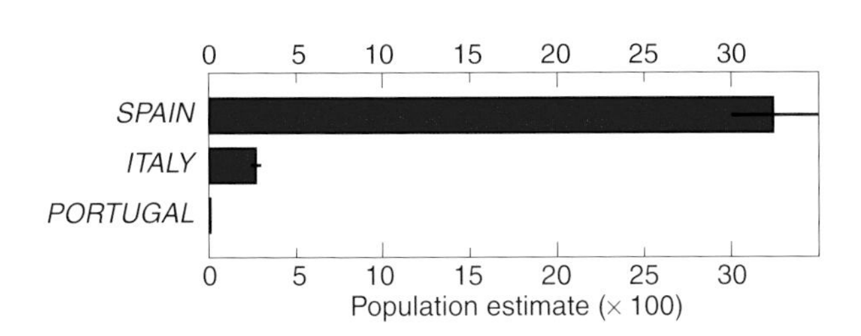

% in top 10 countries: 100.0
Total number of populated European countries: 3
Total European population 3274–3777 (3516)
Russian population 100–1000 (316)
Turkish population 100–200 (141)

The Purple Gallinule, a large rail, has a large distribution throughout many wetlands in the tropical and subtropical regions of West and South Africa, Madagascar, S Asia and Oceania. It occurs locally in temperate regions, as in New Zealand, SE Australia and widely separated parts of southern Europe.

It inhabits tideless marshes, lakes, lagoons and reservoirs (if water levels are stable) with dense areas of marshy vegetation (mainly reedmace *Typha* spp, rush *Scirpus* spp, reed *Phragmites* spp and sedge *Carex* spp). Typical breeding densities in natural habitats (Doñana National Park 1988) are 1.5 nests/ha in a 4ha sea club-rush *Scirpus maritimus* marsh and 3.3 nests/ha in an adjacent 4ha marsh which comprised a transition to shrubby glasswort *Arthrocnemum macrostachyum* (Máñez 1991).

Relatively small numbers breed in Europe, mainly in Spain, whose most important population (*c*3000bp; Blanco & González 1992) occupies the Marismas of the Guadalquivir River (comprising the Doñana National Park and neighbouring areas of varying protected status). A series of droughts in the region since 1992 have probably adversely affected the species.

Further W, the Purple Gallinule occurs mainly in four marshy areas in Huelva: the unspoilt Palos and Las Madres lagoons, the upper Domingo Rubio swamp, El Portil lagoon reserve and Prado de la Redondela lagoon (H. Garrido, pers comm). E of the Marismas, it usually breeds (except in drought years) on five groups of lagoons in Cádiz (Lebrero 1991), although it has bred elsewhere. S Córdoba holds a small population. In the upper Guadalquivir, in Jaén, the 1980s population of 62 individuals (Sánchez-Lafuente *et al* 1987) had grown to 300–350 by 1990 (A. M. Sánchez-Lafuente, pers comm). Its recent nesting on Castrejón reservoir (near the Tajo River) in 1992 and 1993 represents a notable range extension.

The Portuguese population is small and unstable (*c*6–9bp in two Algarve localities; Ramos 1989). The Sardinian population is thought to be recovering from decline, *c*240–300bp occupying several coastal wetlands. Although numbers are poorly known in Russia (100–1000bp), a small range expansion may have occurred in the N and W Caspian (the Volga Delta and the Terek River).

The disappearance and degradation of many Mediterranean and S Atlantic littoral wetlands and the species' vulnerability to hunting pressure (Consellería d'Agricultura i Pesca 1988) have led to a decline in Europe since the late 19th century. Once protection measures (initially in 1973, reinforced in 1989) were enforced, recovery was immediate, and the range contraction was reversed.

Reintroduction programmes, started in the Mediterranean littoral in three nature reserves, using individuals from the Marismas, have successfully produced populations in Cataluña since 1990 (Garrigós & Sargatal 1990), in S'Albufera (Mallorca) since 1992 (Vicens 1993) and since 1995 at Albufera (Valencia) (C. Gómez, pers comm). There is evidence (chicks seen) of further natural spread.

The species is basically resident, although it is often recorded beyond its normal breeding range, either through its tendency to wander or an initiation of a range expansion. Furthermore, because the Marismas characteristically dry out every summer, the local population moves to the nearest habitat which remain wet, such as those along channels, in lagoons and in areas which tend to retain marshy vegetation throughout the year (M. Mañez, pers obs). The Russian population moves S to escape the ice, boosting the numbers in Azerbaijan (Schuz 1959).

The Purple Gallinule has many subspecies worldwide, which comprise six subspecies-groups, each differentiated by marked colour variations. The main group consists of the nominate *P.p. porphyrio*, to which the W Mediterranean populations belong. The Russian population belongs to the largest subspecies of the *poliocephalus* group, namely *caspius*.

Manuel Mañez (E)

Fulica atra | Coot

CZ	Lyska černá	I	Folaga
D	Bläßhuhn	NL	Meerkoet
E	Focha Común	P	Galeirão-comum
F	Foulque macroule	PL	Łyska
FIN	Nokikana	R	Лысуха
G	Φαλαρίδα	S	Sothöna
H	Szárcsa		

Non-SPEC, Threat status S

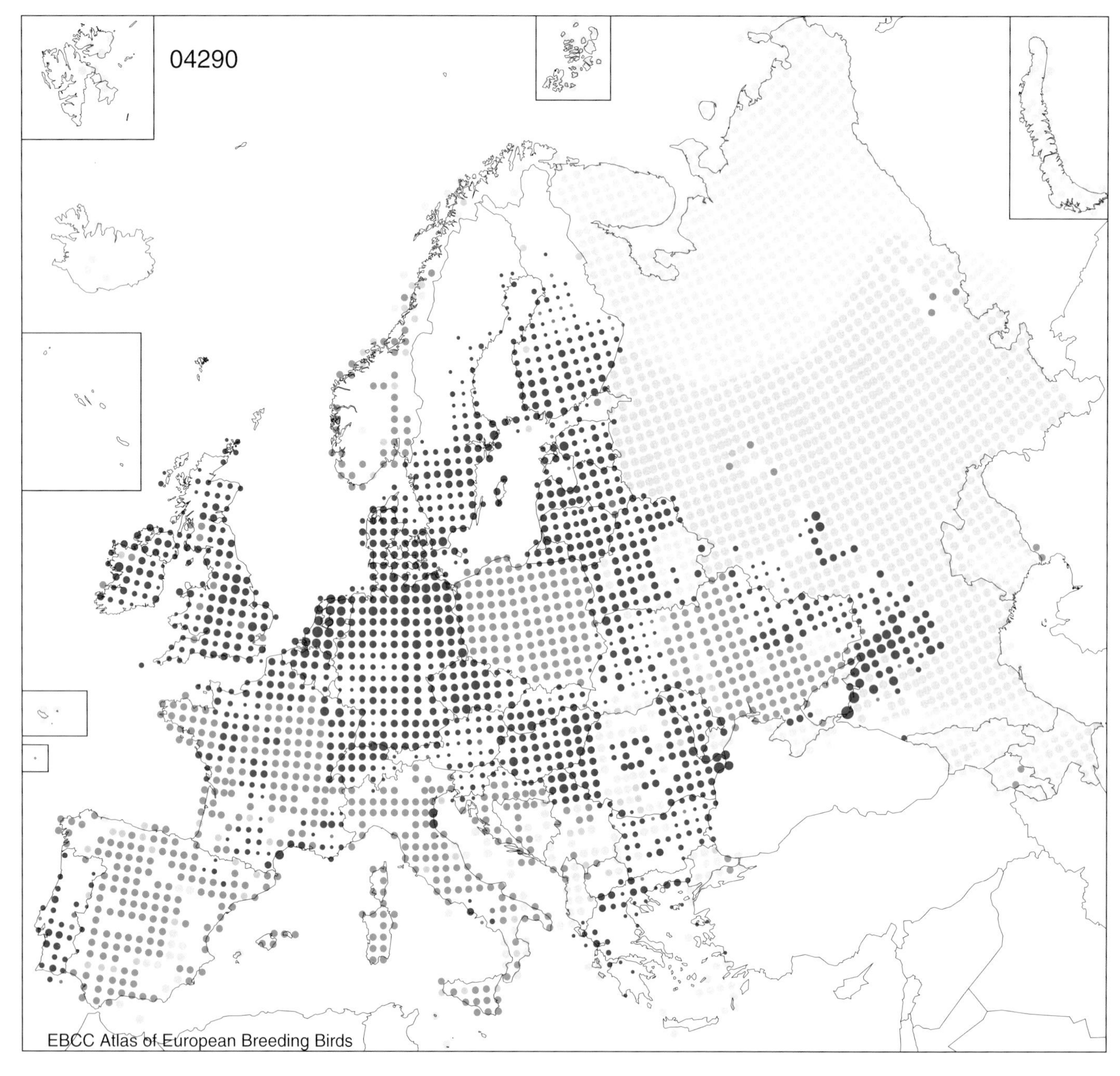

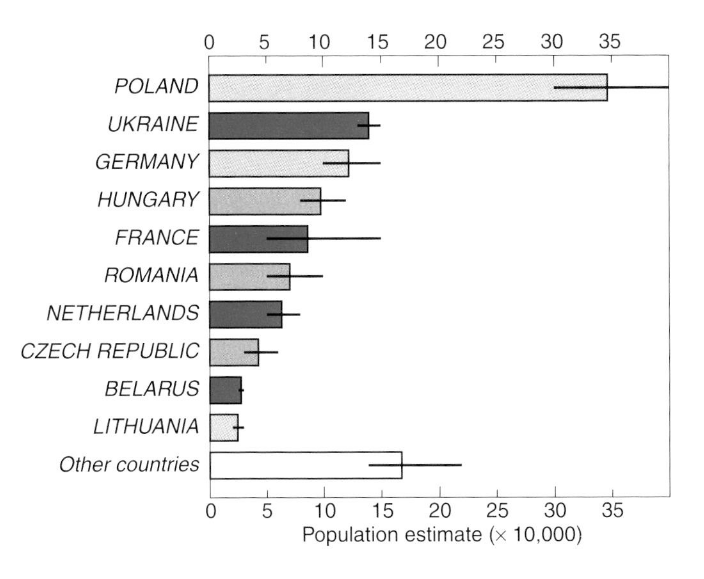

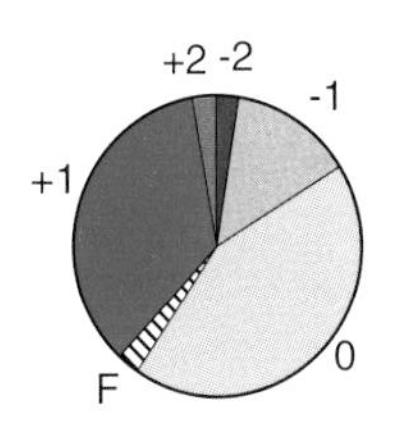

% in top 10 countries: 85.9
Total number of populated European countries: 37
Total European population 1,115,952–1,289,548 (1,188,657)
Russian population 130,000–230,000 (172,916)
Turkish population 5000–50,000 (15,811)

The Coot is widespread across Eurasia (below 66°N) to Sakhalin and S to China, India and Australia, except where deserts prevail. It occurs patchily in North Africa, Turkey, the Middle and Near East, the Sundas and New Guinea. Recently it has reached Burma and New Zealand.

The Coot will occupy almost any area of open water provided there is good cover amongst emergent and floating vegetation, a limiting factor during the breeding season. Among the most important habitats are eutrophic and mesotrophic lakes, fishponds, large artificial reservoirs and river deltas. The Coot breeds in a great variety of smaller freshwater or slightly saline ponds, creeks and wetlands, either in open areas or partially enclosed by riverine forest or carrs. It prefers mosaic biotopes where emergent vegetation is interspersed with wet grassy mounds, banks and islets with bushes or tree-clumps. It breeds up to 1000m asl and in the Swiss Alps to 1200–1400m, locally to 1800m (L. Schifferli pers comm to the Editors).

Breeding densities vary greatly: in the Volga Delta values of *c*13 bp/ha are attained; in Moldova 6 bp/ha; in Latvia 7 bp/ha (Kuročhkin & Košhelev 1989); on eutrophic Lithuanian lakes, 0.6–2.5 bp/ha of emergent vegetation (Stanevičius 1992) and in Poland from 1.8–10.6 bp/10ha on fishponds in Silesia (Dyrcz *et al* 1991) to 2.0–2.8 bp/10ha in the more elevated SE (Walasz & Mielczarek 1992).

The Coot's stronghold lies in a broad belt from The Netherlands to Poland and Lithuania, and S into Hungary, N Serbia, E Romania (Danube Delta), Ukraine and S Russia. In this area, average densities per 50km square exceed 500bp. Highest average densities (>2000 bp/50km square) occur in The Netherlands, Poland and Hungary. Densities rapidly decline in conjunction with latitude and altitude, as is evident in Fennoscandia and Great Britain. Towards the S, the distribution becomes patchier and overall densities decline to less than 100 bp/50km square in the Iberian Peninsula, Italy, Greece and much of the Balkans.

There was a considerable decrease in Coot numbers in many European countries during the 19th century, and a similar decline has taken place in the former USSR since the mid-1950s, an effect often attributed to severe winters. However, severe winters alone cannot be responsible and it is more likely the result of interacting effects of varying winter mortality and delayed density-dependence relative to territorial behaviour (Cavé & Visser 1985). Drainage or creation of water reservoirs can have a large impact on local densities, as in C Asia where its range has extended considerably due to the construction of many artificial reservoirs, which it colonizes once vegetation appears (Kuročhkin & Košhelev 1989).

Up to the 1930s, the Coot showed a clear tendency to expand its range northward (Kuročhkin & Košhelev 1989), Finland experiencing one of the more rapid avifaunal expansions (Koskimies 1989a). During 1970–90, at least 15 European countries recorded some increase in numbers and range, compared to only six having declining populations. In the long term, Coot numbers apparently have remained quite stable throughout Europe.

In much of Europe the Coot is sedentary or a partial migrant, but populations from Fennoscandia and from E of the Czech Republic are mostly migratory. Autumn migration occurs generally from mid-August until late November, but some remain in C Europe until January. Spring migration begins in late February, birds appearing in C Europe in early March. Major wintering areas for European populations lie in western Europe, Tunisia, the southern Balkan Peninsula, Asia Minor, Mesopotamia and around the southern Caspian Sea (Blums & Litzbarski 1982).

The Coot is a versatile and adaptable species and is unlikely to suffer any threat in the near future. Up to four subspecies are recognized, but only the nominate *F.a. atra* occurs in the *Atlas*' coverage area.

Igor Gorban (UKR) Vitas Stanevičius (LITH)

Fulica cristata

Crested Coot

CZ	Lyska hřebenatá	I	Folaga cornuta
D	Kammbläßhuhn	NL	Knobbelmeerkoet
E	Focha Moruna	P	Galeirão-de-crista
F	Foulque à crête	PL	Łyska czubata
FIN	Syylänokikana	R	Хохлатая лысуха
G	Λειροφαλαρίδα	S	Kamsothöna
H	Bütykös szárcsa		

SPEC Cat 3, Threat status E

The main centre of distribution of the Crested Coot is sub-Saharan Africa, especially the southern third of the continent, and Madagascar. A relict population exists in Iberia and North Africa. The Crested Coot occurs in lagoons, salinas, natural marshes, ricefields and reservoirs, but it appears to be very selective about its breeding requirements, needing deep and productive wetlands. Probably the quantity and quality of submerged macrophytes form the species' key requirement (Fernández Palacios & Raya 1991).

Around 1900, the majority of the abundant Iberian population was concentrated in two areas: the Guadalquivir marshes and their surrounding lagoons, and the wetland system of la Janda, both in Andalucía. After la Janda was destroyed in 1960, the species disappeared there. The Crested Coot remains in the Guadalquivir area, but in very low numbers, the population being estimated at 50 adults (Fernández Palacios & Raya 1991) and fewer than 20bp (J. A. Amat, in prep) in a favourable year. In such years, there are a maximum of 10–20bp in the marshes (Máñez 1991, L. García *et al*, in prep) and at most 14bp in the lagoons (in 1990 and 1991) (Fernández Palacios & Raya 1991, C. Raya, in prep). However, the drought in 1994 prevented breeding that year (L. García, pers comm). Between 1992 and 1994 a total of 51 captive-born individuals was released in the area (L. García *et al*, in prep). It is likely that the viability of the Andalucían population is reinforced by Moroccan recruits (J. A. Amat, in prep).

Recently breeding has been confirmed in a new location, Pantano del Hondo in Alicante, but numbers are not yet known (C. Raya, in prep). The species has also been recorded in several other localities; the Guadalhorce estuary and Pantano de Barbate in Andalucía, the Ebro Delta in Tarragona, the Estanca de Borja in Zaragoza, the Covadonga lakes in Asturias, the Castro Marim marshes and a littoral lagoon in the lower Alentejo in the Algarve, Portugal (C. Raya, in prep).

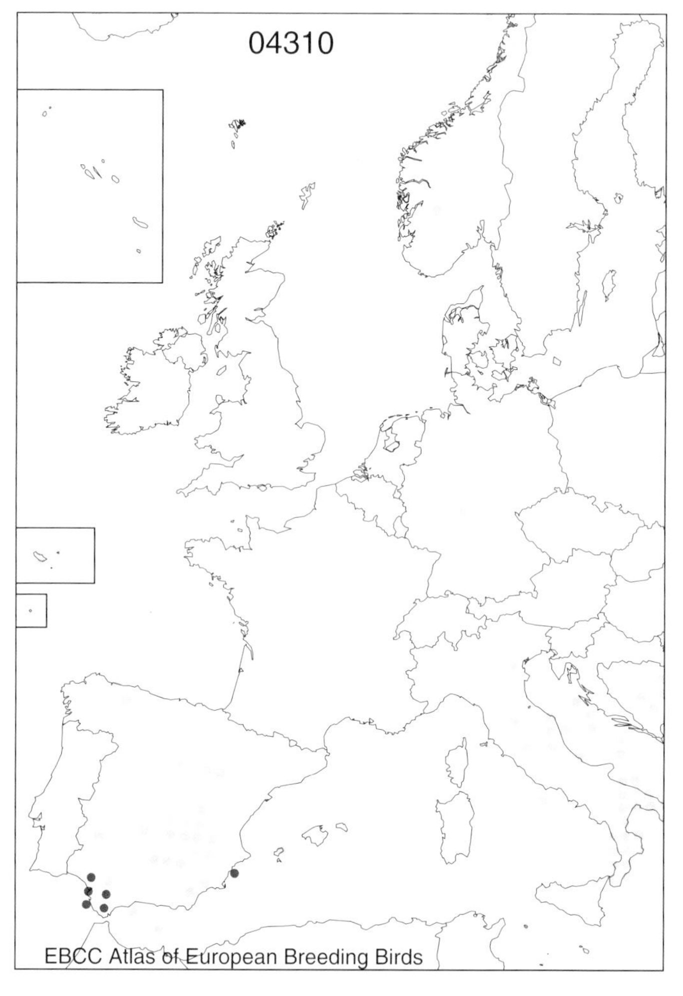

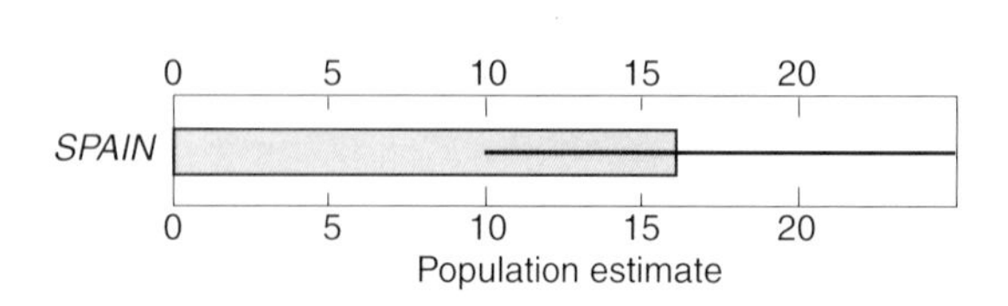

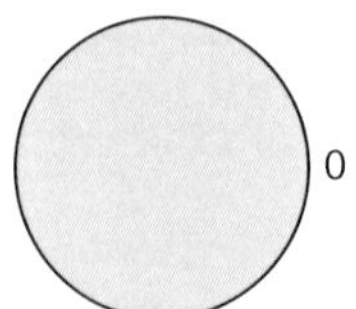

% in top 10 countries: 100.0
Total number of populated European countries: 1
Total European population 10–25 (16)

The main factor that limits the distribution of the Crested Coot in Europe is the lack of suitable habitat. The main cause of mortality is accidental hunting, because of confusion with the Coot *F. atra* (L. García *et al*, in prep; J. A. Amat, in prep).

Cristina Ramo (E)

Anthropoides virgo

Demoiselle Crane

CZ	Jeřáb panenský	I	Damigella di Numidia
D	Jungfernkranich	NL	Jufferkraan
E	Grulla Damisela	P	Grou-pequeno
F	Grue demoiselle	PL	Żuraw stepowy
FIN	Neitokurki	R	Журавль-красавка
G	Νυφογερανός	S	Jungfrutrana
H	Pártásdaru		

Non-SPEC, Threat status S

The Demoiselle Crane, one of the smallest members of the crane family, has a breeding range between 40°N and 50°N extending continuously from SE Ukraine through Kazakhstan to NW China and Mongolia. A separate small population exists in Turkey (20–30bp). It is a migratory species, wintering primarily in two separate areas: Sudan (the destination of Ukrainian birds) and the Indian subcontinent. Small numbers winter in Burma.

By the late 1920s it had become extinct in Romania and by 1985 in Morocco. Since the mid-1960s its breeding range has contracted, especially in Europe where its distribution has become increasingly patchy through the spreading cultivation of the steppes for agriculture, a process which still is a serious threat. However, since the 1980s in Ukraine, the Demoiselle Crane has begun to adapt to breeding in agricultural areas.

The species prefers dry and rolling topography and sparsely vegetated plateaus in the steppe and semi-desert zones. It is not dependent on open water, but tends to choose breeding sites no further than 1.5km from access to water. Sometimes it selects elevated sites, perhaps as high as 2300–2400m asl.

Except in the W of its continuous range, the population is showing a steady increase, but it is not yet clear if its range is beginning to expand again. The Ukrainian population is found in Crimea, the Sivash lagoon area, on the steppes close to the Sea of Azov and apparently is stable, though comprising only 150–170bp (Neufeldt & Kovshar 1991). In the territories of the former Soviet Union the Demoiselle Crane population is estimated at *c*80 000bp, out of a world total of perhaps 130 000bp, perhaps at least 25 000bp being in European Russia.

The European population remains vulnerable to agricultural and other human activities in the breeding areas, but its apparent adaptability may improve the chances of successful conservation action.

Valentin Serebryakov (UKR)

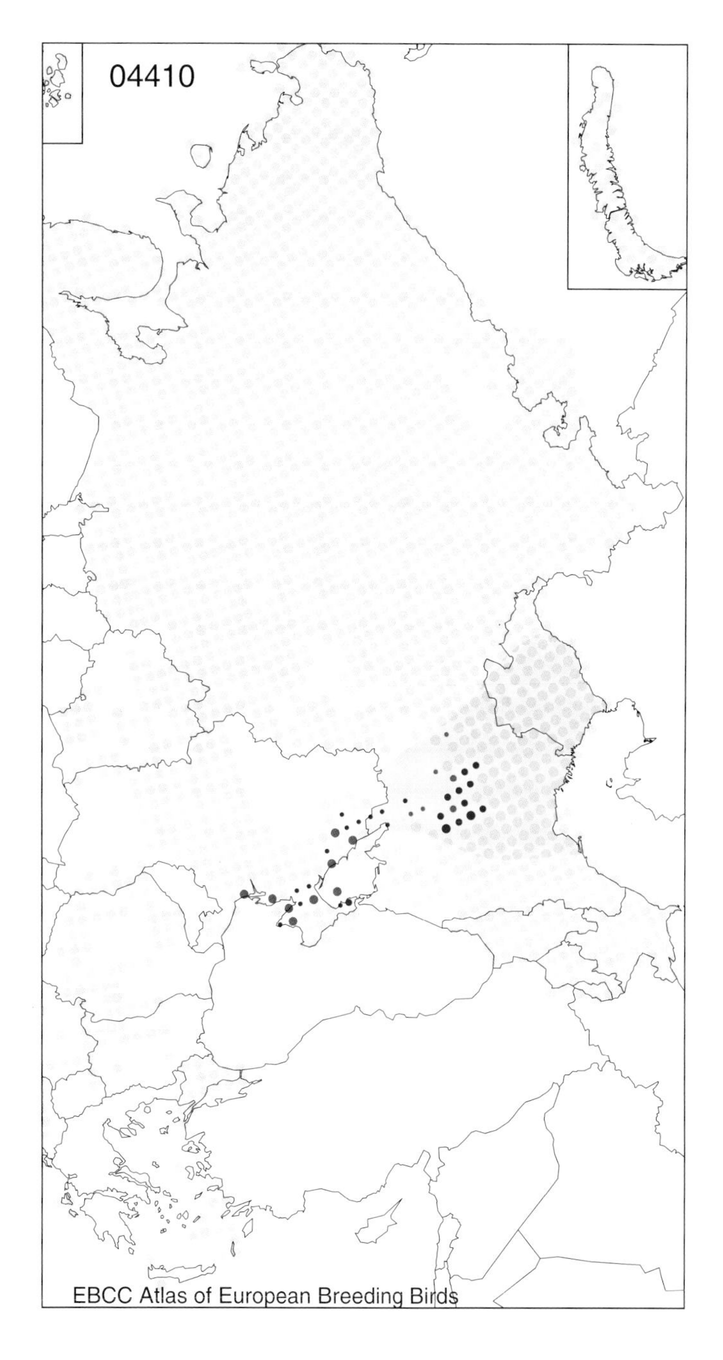

Grus grus

Crane

CZ	Jeřáb popelavý	**I**	Gru
D	Kranich	**NL**	Kraanvogel
E	Grulla Común	**P**	Grou-comum
F	Grue cendrée	**PL**	Żuraw
FIN	Kurki	**R**	Серый журавль
G	Γερανός	**S**	Trana
H	Daru		

SPEC Cat 3, Threat status V

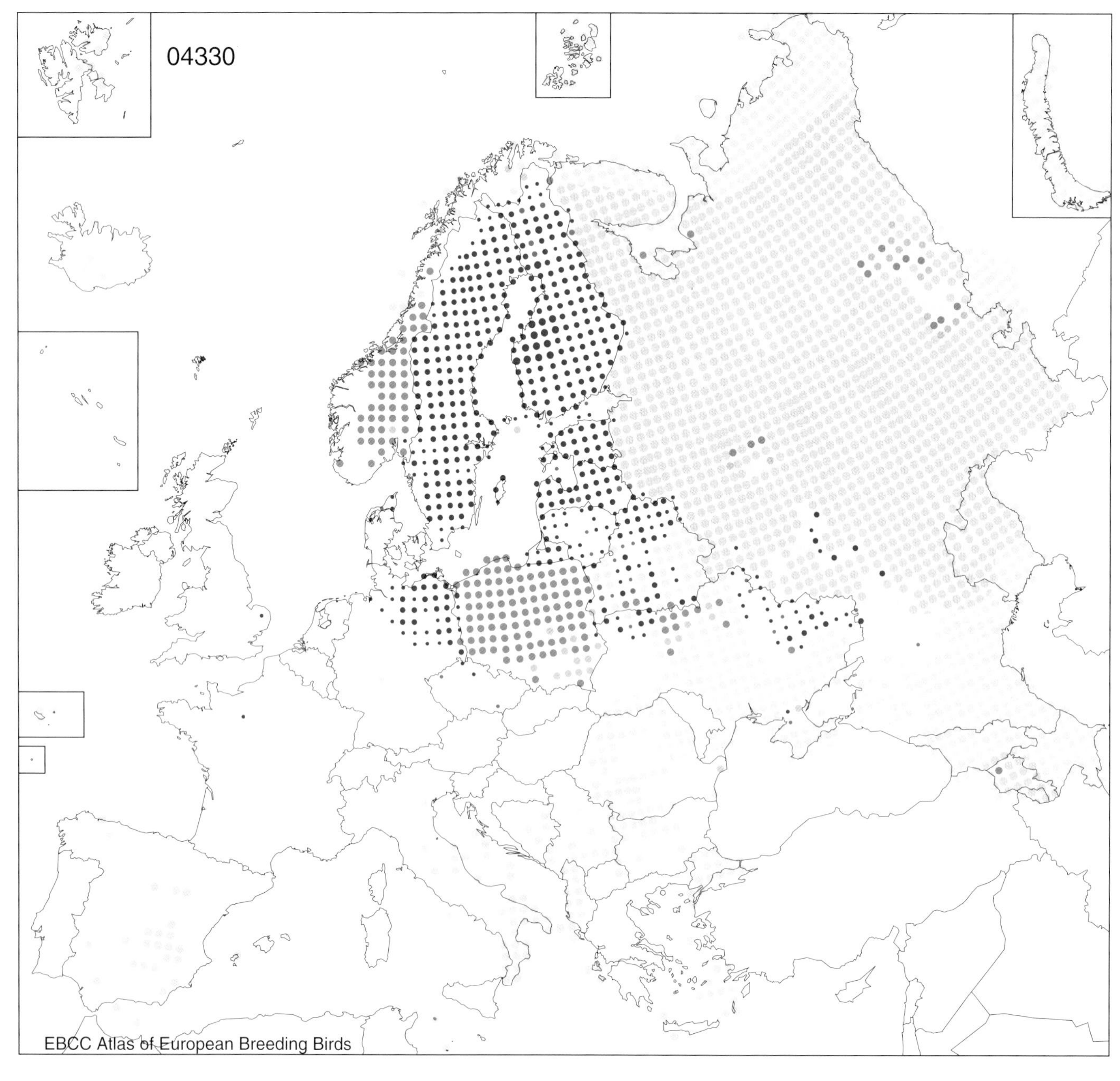

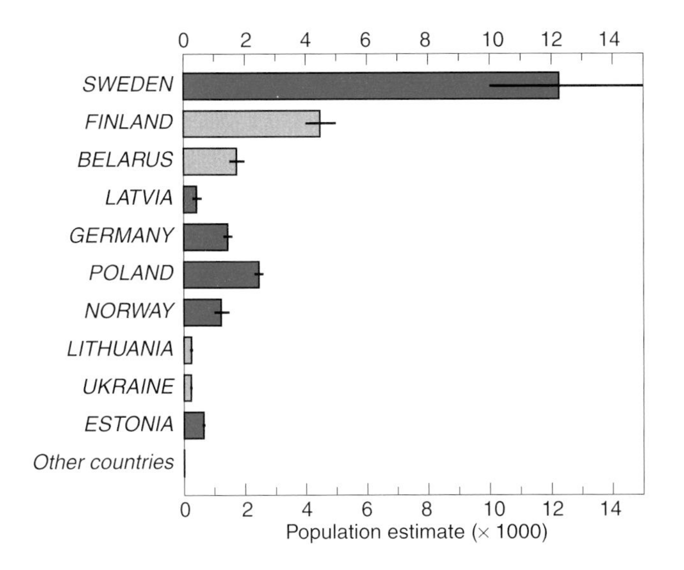

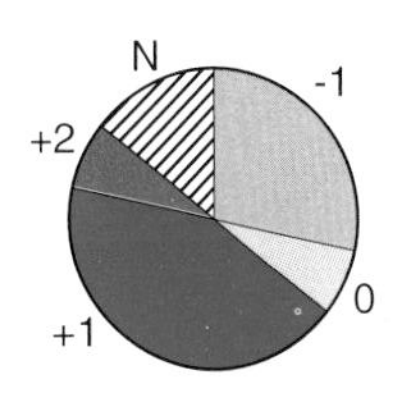

% in top 10 countries: 100.0
Total number of populated European countries: 14
Total European population 22,793–27,970 (25,126)
Russian population 30,000–50,000 (38,730)
Turkish population 100–300 (173)

The Crane's breeding distribution extends from C Europe to the Far East, from the northern taiga to the C Asian steppes. Turkey holds a small sedentary breeding population. The nominate *G.g. grus* inhabits most of the European range except for Georgia and Armenia where the other subspecies *lilfordi* occurs.

A Crane's breeding location comprises feeding and nesting sites naturally protected by water. The species prefers alder *Alnus* marshes, moors, and standing water in woods, meadows and fields, in areas possessing lakes, ponds and rivers. A gathering or resting place (which may be both) comprises feeding and sleeping sites, the latter being situated in lagoons in bogs and peatbogs, on lake-shores, at oxbows, in brackish waters near the Baltic, at fish and sewage ponds and in wet fields and meadows (Prange 1989).

Crane population density varies according to latitude (decreasing from the middle breeding latitudes towards the S and far N) and the landscape structure. Typical breeding densities (in bp/100km^2) are: N Poland, greater than 2.0; NE Germany, between 2.1 and 4.3 and up to 40 in smaller areas. Within C Europe, typical population breakdown is: 35–40% are adults which have attempted to breed, 14–16% (in autumn) are young fledged that year, 10–15% are adults which did not attempt to breed, and 30–35% are 2–4-year-old immatures. Therefore non-breeding adult and 2–4-year-old immatures together are present in a ratio of between 1.2:1 and 1.4:1 with adult breeders. The mean total of *c*40 000bp therefore represents a total European population of *c*200 000 birds (Prange 1994).

By the 17th century, the Crane had become extinct in much of W and S Europe, a trend which continued until the 1960s since when most national populations have experienced increasing trends: a continuous increase in breeding pairs, an increasing breeding density (through increased productivity in wet years) and a range expansion to the W and N (100km since 1964 in Germany) (Mewes 1995). The reported Finnish decrease is attributed to mire drainage for forestry (L. Saari, pers comm to the Editors).

The European Crane Working Group believe that the total Russian population now comprises 50 000–60 000bp, perhaps 20 000 being in European Russia, and that the graph totals for Finland, Poland, Germany, Norway, Estonia, Latvia and Lithuania generally should be higher (1995) by *c*10–25%.

The autumn migration in particular is interrupted (September to October/November) at traditional resting places, the largest on the western route being in Sweden (Lake Hornborga, up to 7000; Lundin *et al* 1993), in NE Germany (Rügen-Bock region, up to 40 000), NE France (Lake du Der-Chantecoq, up to 30 000) and in NE Spain (Laguna de Gallocanta, up to 50 000; Alonso & Alonso 1990); *c*75 000 birds from C, N and parts of NE Europe use this flyway. The central route resting places are mainly in Estonia (several; up to 30 000) and E Hungary (Hortobágy puszta, up to 60 000); *c*70 000 migrate from E Poland, Finland, the Baltic States and Belarus via this route. Further E, over 600 resting places (30–5000 birds each) exist in the vast Russian breeding areas and Ukraine, through which other N-S routes run, either crossing the Black Sea directly from Crimea or bypassing it to the E and W.

Some 75% of those using the western flyway winter in Spain, the remainder choosing France, Portugal and North Africa; a very few remain in C Europe. The other routes lead to North and East Africa (particularly Tunisia, Algeria, Ethiopia and Sudan), Turkey, Israel, the Near and Middle East, Iran, Afghanistan, Pakistan, and probably also India.

The present number of birds migrating on the western and the Baltic–Hungary routes is double that of the 1960s, largely because of improved protection measures not only at breeding sites (the species has become more confiding) and resting locations, but particularly at SW European wintering areas (Prange 1995).

Hartwig Prange (D)

This species account is sponsored by Dr S Athanasiadis, Duisburg, D.

Tetrax tetrax

Little Bustard

CZ	Drop malý	I	Gallina prataiola
D	Zwergtrappe	NL	Kleine Trap
E	Sisón Común	P	Sisão
F	Outarde canepetière	PL	Strepet
FIN	Pikkutrappi	R	Стрепет
G	Χαμωτίδα	S	Småtrapp
H	Reznek		

SPEC Cat 2, Threat status V

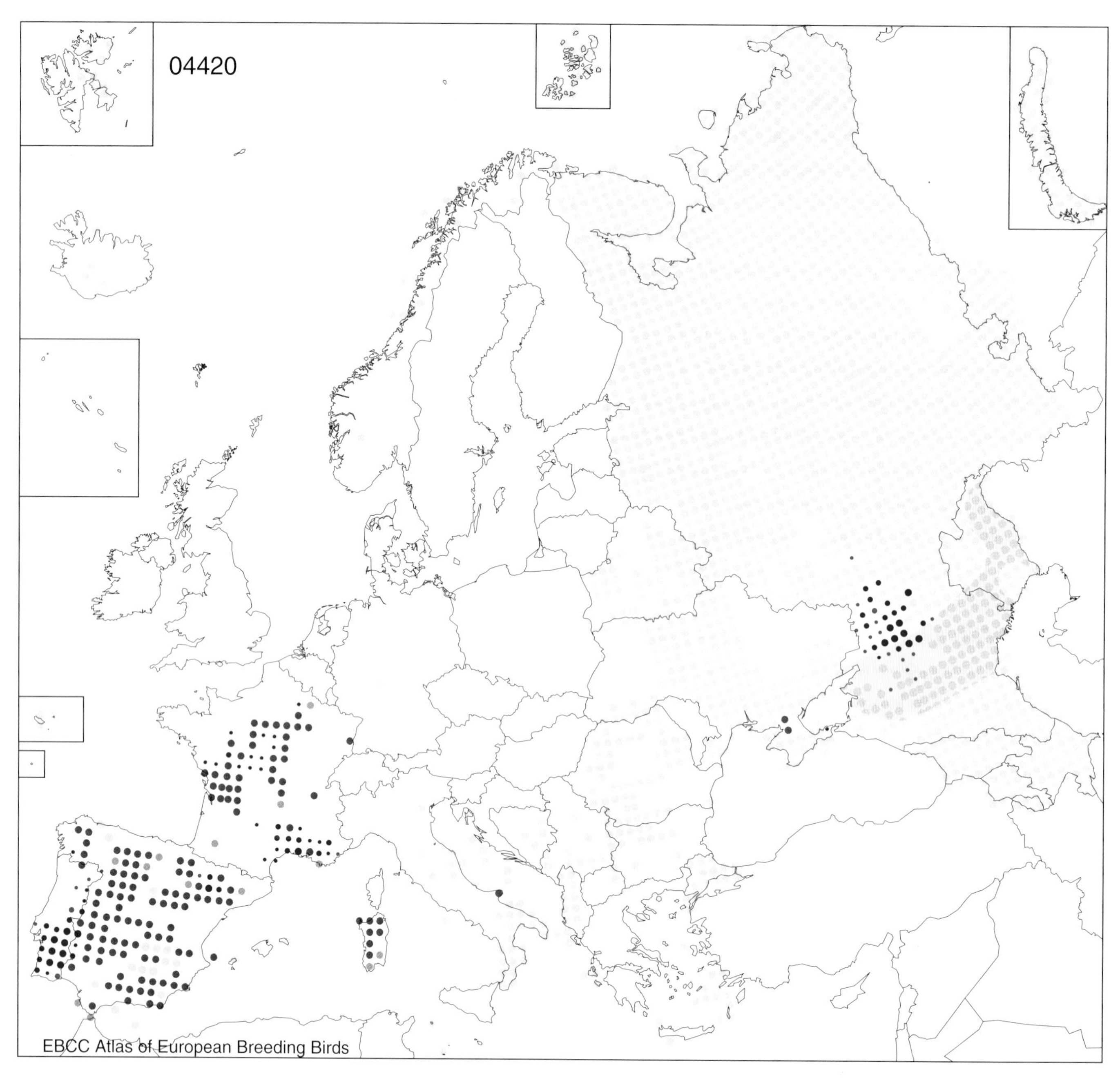

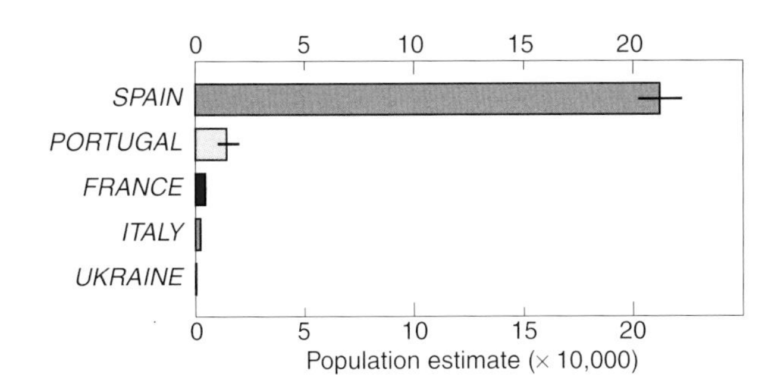

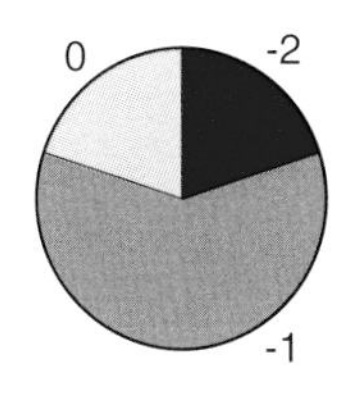

% in top 10 countries: 100.0
Total number of populated European countries: 5
Total European population 220,004–242,431 (230,621)
Russian population 18,000–20,000 (18,974)
Turkish population 1–50 (7)

The fragmented range of the Little Bustard covers the W Palearctic between 35°N and 55°N. There are two main nuclei: the Iberian Peninsula and a large area between Ukraine and W Siberia.

In western Europe, the breeding habitat includes agricultural areas, such as cereal cultivation, pastures and various types of steppe. In cultivated areas, the species shows a preference for fallow lands and legume crops. In Russia, however, the Little Bustard rarely nests in cereal crops, preferring alfalfa, and to a lesser extent, fallow lands. Lack of tall vegetation is an important limiting factor.

In the Iberian Peninsula, its stronghold lies in S Meseta over a wide area between the Portuguese region of Alentejo, to Madrid and the easternmost provinces of the Spanish region of Castilla–La Mancha. This is the largest known area of high population density and hence it offers the greatest guarantee of survival to the species. In Spain, other important population centres are located in N Meseta. Some more isolated populations are found in the Ebro Valley, in Andalucia and in Galicia. Present estimates of the Spanish population indicate that it exceeds 200 000 birds (C. Martínez & E. De Juana, pers obs). The Portuguese population is estimated at 13 000–18 000 individuals (M. Pinto, pers comm).

In France, the species is mainly distributed in two areas, one in C–W France (Deux-Sèvres: 900 males in 1985) and another in mediterranean France with 700–1000bp, of which Crau harbours 425–475 males (Bernard 1994). Italy holds 2000–2500 individuals distributed in two major zones, 1400–2000 on the island of Sardinia, and the rest in Apulia (Petretti 1991).

S Ukraine and Crimea have fewer than 10bp. In Russia, the Little Bustard is relatively common in the Don Basin and the Lower Volga region but is less frequent in the E Cis-Caucasus, where it is found mostly on sandy steppes. In the mid-1980s the Rostov region population was estimated at 1000–1500bp (Belik & Sidelnikov 1989), the Saratov region having 1300–1600 males (Moseykin 1992) and the E Cis-Caucasus 300–400bp (A.N. Khokhlov, pers comm). Since then, its numbers have increased in all eastern regions and by the early 1990s had reached an estimated 9000bp in European Russia (Belik in prep). The main wintering ground in the former USSR is located in the Kyzyl-Agach Reserve, on the SW coast of the Caspian Sea, where 9000 were recorded in 1980–81 (Vorobyova 1992), rising to 26 000 in 1986, and to an amazing 100 000 individuals in 1990 (Schadilov & Khakhin 1991).

Because the Little Bustard is polygamous and is wary of people, the only practical census method during the breeding seasons is to count territorial males. A sampling carried out in ten selected suitable areas in Spain during 1992–93, showed the average density to be 3.5/km^2 (C. Martínez & E. De Juana, in prep). In Portugal the highest density was found in N Alentejo, 9/km^2 (Schulz 1985), whereas S Alentejo held densities of 4/km^2 (M. Pinto, pers comm). In France, the density of the Crau population averaged 3.9/km^2 (Cheylan 1985). In Italy, from 1982 to 1990, the average density was 2.4/km^2 in Sardinia and 1.5/km^2 in Apulia (Petretti 1991). In Russia, on the sandy steppes which had the status of refuges in the Don Basin in the 1960s and 1970s, the average density ranged from 0.1 to 1/km^2 in different districts. Nowadays, in some places the density in alfalfa is as high as 10–20/km^2 (Belik & Sidelnikov 1989).

The migratory or resident character of populations varies across the species' distribution. In the N it is migratory, especially in eastern Europe. The breeding birds in France are mostly migratory. In Iberia the species is partially migratory, the main wintering grounds being in the SW of the Peninsula.

Carmen Martínez (E) Rui Rufino (P) Victor Belik (R)

Otis tarda

Great Bustard

CZ	Drop velký	**I**	Otarda
D	Großtrappe	**NL**	Grote Trap
E	Avutarda Común	**P**	Abetarda-comum
F	Grande Outarde	**PL**	Drop
FIN	Isotrappi	**R**	Дрофа
G	Αγριόγαλος	**S**	Stortrapp
H	Túzok		

SPEC Cat 1, Threat status D

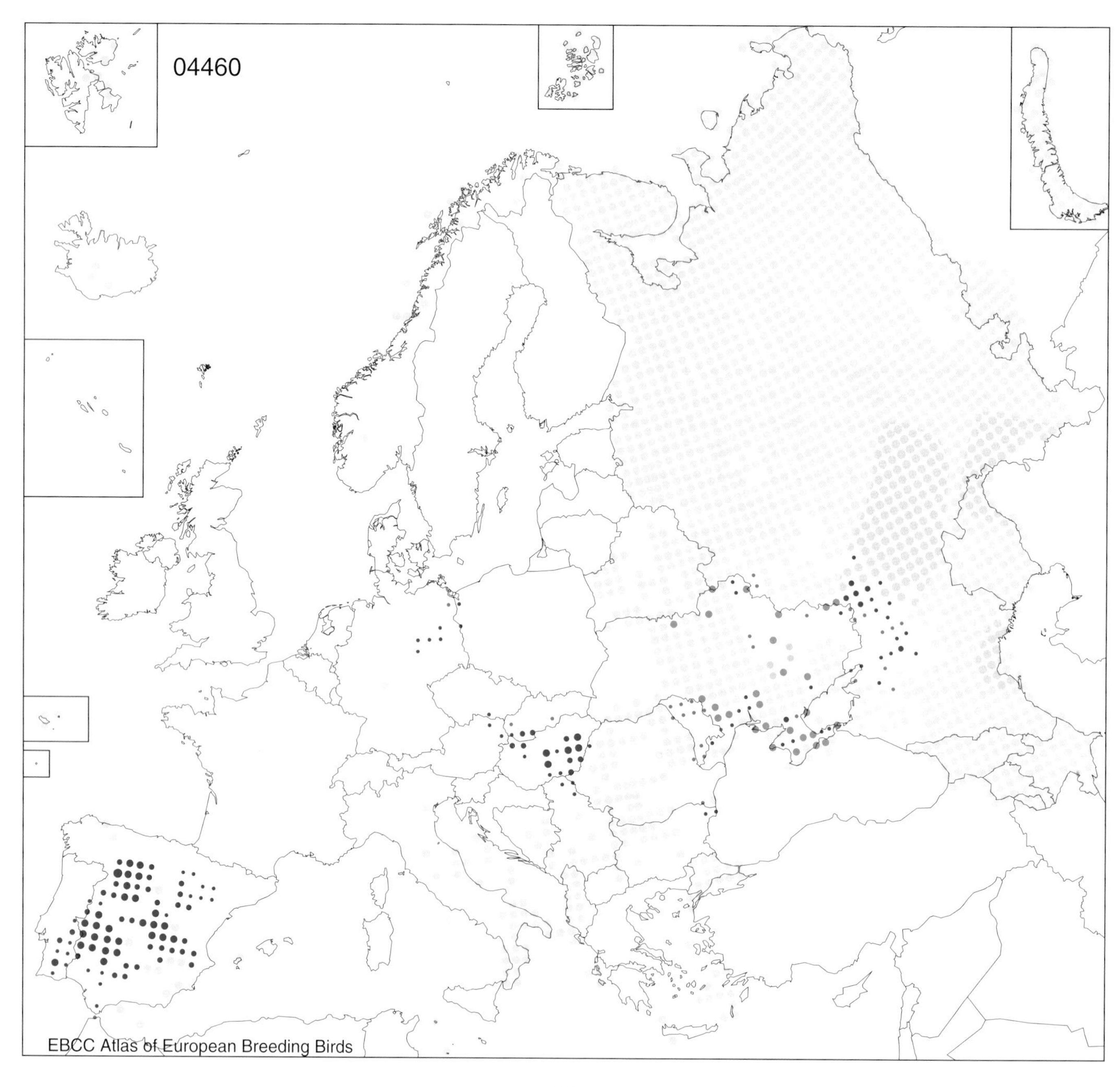

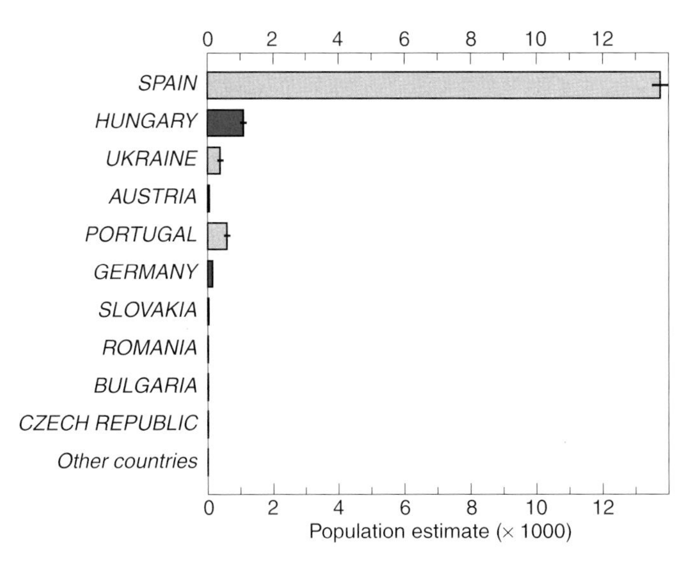

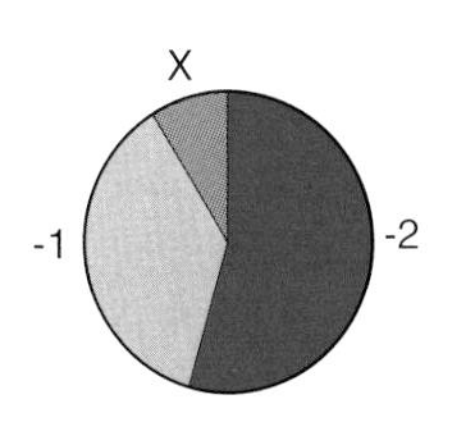

% in top 10 countries: 100.0
Total number of populated European countries: 11
Total European population 15,801–16,410 (16,095)
Russian population 10,000–11,000 (10,488)
Turkish population 145–4000 (762)

The globally threatened Great Bustard has a widespread Palearctic distribution range between 35° and 55°N. The nominate subspecies *O.t. tarda* breeds from Iberia and NW Morocco to C Siberia, and the other, *dybowskii*, from the eastern Altai and Lake Baykal to Mongolia. Across its distribution, the Great Bustard's breeding ranges lie in disjunct areas, in the W highly fragmented, in the E probably less so. However, easternmost birds seem separated from C Asian birds by 17° of longitude.

The species' distribution probably reached its maximum extension during the 18th century, when it benefited from extensive forest clearance in W and C Europe. Subsequently it began to retreat due to habitat changes caused by human population growth, increasingly intensive farming practices, and hunting pressure. Since the mid-1970s many C European populations have suffered dramatic decreases, some now being threatened with extinction. In Germany the 1970s total of 800 birds has plummeted to 130 (Litzbarski 1993). In Hungary annual counts have shown that the 3400 of the mid-1980s reduced to *c*1100 in 1995, levels significantly lower than estimates made by hunters (L. Farago, pers comm, G. Magyar, pers comm to the Editors).

Iberia holds the largest European population, comprising *c*50% of the world total. At the Villafáfila Reserve in NW Spain, the highest densities in Europe occur, 3 birds/km² in summer and 6 birds/km² in winter (Alonso & Alonso 1995). The Russian and Turkish populations also apparently are large, but remain very poorly known, their conservation status being much less secure than that of the Spanish population.

Iberian numbers probably have remained largely stable since legal protection was imposed in 1980, but hunting pressure in previous decades accounted for up to 2000 individuals annually, surely decimating many subpopulations. The present stability remains fragile because of the persistence of inappropriate land management in many areas and the uncertainty surrounding future changes in agricultural policy. These changes may increase ploughing-up of grasslands, spread afforestation, introduce widespread irrigation schemes and fragment habitat by building roads, erecting fences and digging drainage ditches. Of particular concern are the possible future changes in crops and their associated land management. Once again, subpopulations might become severely endangered. Indeed several marginal nuclei already have declined or become extinct due to excessive fragmentation of the original populations (H.P. Collar 1995).

The Great Bustard has adapted from its original steppe habitat to pseudo-steppes represented by the current long-established low-intensity farming mixed in a mosaic with pastures. It inhabits open, flat, and preferably treeless cereal farmland, reaching its highest densities where alfalfa (lucerne) or oilseed-rape is also grown and where fallow plots are left uncultivated (Demeter 1996).

In W and C Europe populations mostly are resident and make moderate seasonal movements to and from the sexual display arenas (Alonso *et al* 1995). Some C and E European (including European Russia) populations participate in migratory displacements of variable magnitude, wintering perhaps several hundred kilometres S of the breeding areas, particularly in severe winters. Some winter in the eastern Caucasus. Dispersing juvenile males may occupy sites up to 70km away from their natal areas and may remain for some time or establish themselves definitely as breeding adults, while females tend to return from shorter-distance juvenile dispersal displacements to their natal areas (Alonso *et al* 1995). C Asian populations probably move to N Iran in severe winters. The Far Eastern population winters in N China.

Conservation measure implementation in Hungary suffers because there is no compensation funding for farmers not to harvest crops (lucerne, wheat) containing breeding sites. Many sites being outside protected areas are liable to disturbance (recent construction, spring-harvested crops) (G. Magyar, pers comm to the Editors).

Juan C Alonso (E) Marcia Pinto (P)

Haematopus ostralegus **Oystercatcher**

CZ	Ústřičník velký	I	Beccaccia di mare
D	Austernfischer	NL	Scholekster
E	Ostrero Euroasiático	P	Ostraceiro
F	Huîtrier pie	PL	Ostrygojad
FIN	Meriharakka	R	Кулик-сорока
G	Στρειδοφάγος	S	Strandskata
H	Csigaforgató		

Non-SPEC, Threat status S

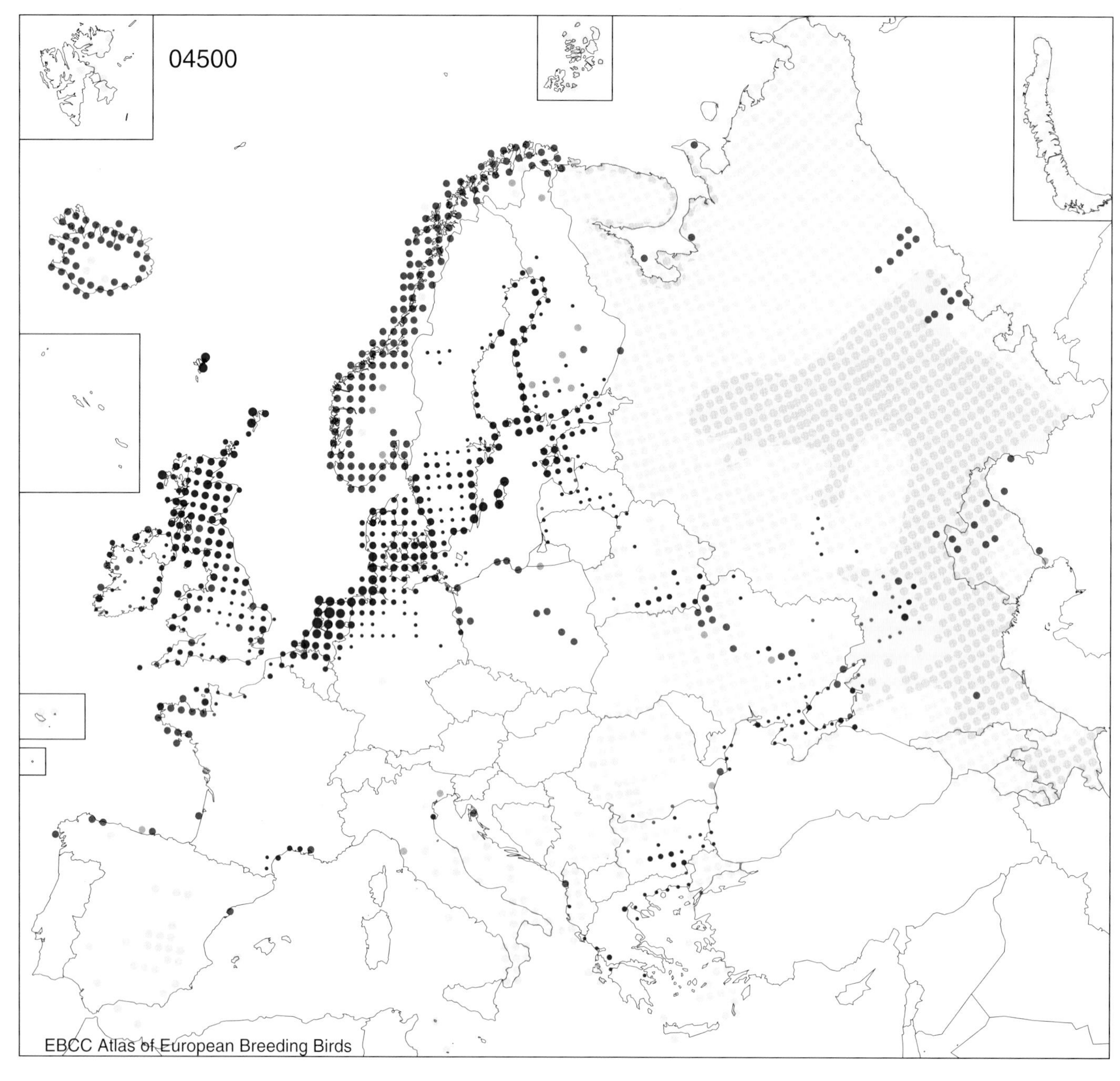

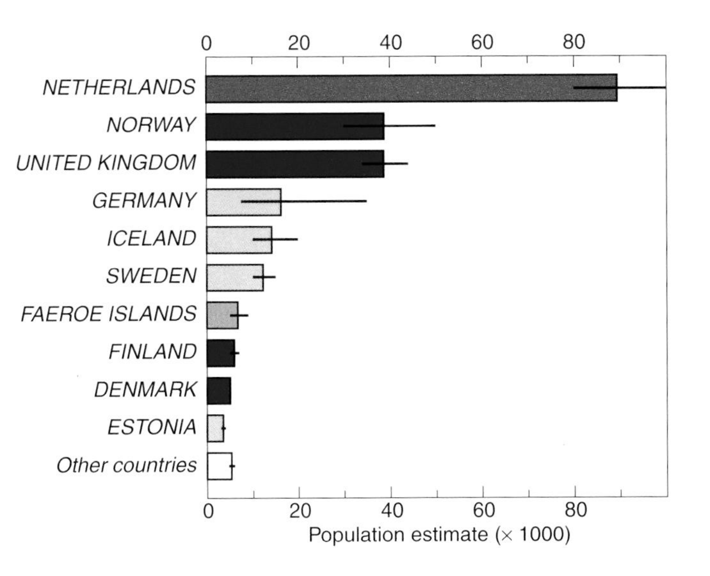

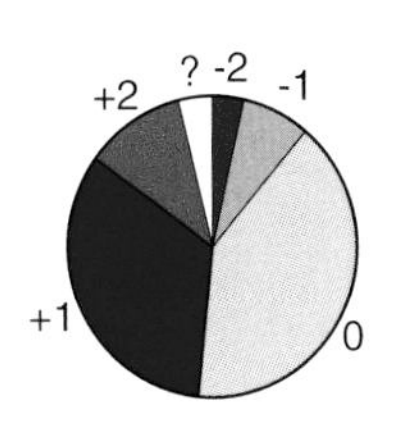

% in top 10 countries: 97.8
Total number of populated European countries: 27
Total European population 218,779–261,652 (235,788)
Russian population 10,000–30,000 (17,321)
Turkish population 100–1000 (316)

The Oystercatcher is a large polytypic Palearctic wader. The nominate *H.o. ostralegus* breeds mainly along the coasts of W Europe and the Mediterranean, *longipes* inland from Ukraine to W Siberia, and *osculans* along the coast of Kamchatka to S Korea.

Breeding is linked largely to two behavioural specializations. Firstly, the Oystercatcher can open large hard-shelled bivalves such as mussels with its strong bill. Secondly, when feeding chicks, the adults bring one item per visit, often from several hundred metres away. Successful breeding depends on the availability of high densities of large prey in order to cope with the high energy expended in transporting food (Ens *et al* 1992). Originally such conditions applied only along coasts possessing intertidal molluscs and large marine worms, but during the 20th century similar circumstances developed along riverbanks and on grasslands because in places earthworm and leatherjacket densities increased due to the first widespread usage of fertilizers, although later intensive applications are known to have decreased invertebrate densities.

The species breeds in coastal habitats, like rocky shores, sand-dunes, shingle and saltmarshes, inland (in W Europe up to 500km from the coast) along lakesides, in river valleys, and on farmland, heath and rough grazing up to 500m asl in Scotland and 2000m in Russia. It nests increasingly on shingle-covered roofs in suburban areas near food sources (playing-fields, parks).

Breeding is evenly distributed along most of the coastline of the White Sea, Barents Sea, Irish Sea, North Sea (S to Belgium), the Baltic (except for the SE Baltic from Poland to Latvia, where breeding is scarce) and NE Atlantic. Along the Atlantic coasts of France and Spain, in the Mediterranean and northern Black Sea its distribution is patchy and numbers are small. The European population totals 200 000–300 000bp.

Inland breeders are distributed fairly continuously in the coastal strip bordering the North Sea from Denmark to Belgium, densities decreasing with distance from the coast, distribution being very local in Sweden, Norway and Finland. In C and E Europe it is restricted to a few broad rivers (Rhine, Oder, Don, Dnieper).

A marked, and continuing inland breeding range expansion has occurred: Scotland (sharply in the 1700s), Iceland and The Netherlands (1920), England (1940) and then in Germany, Denmark, Sweden, Norway and Finland. The inland E European population seems stable. The inland breeding range expansion arises from a surplus of inland-born birds (Becker & Erdelen 1987). Range extensions and population increases possibly are linked to several factors; better protection (since *c*1920; Dare 1966), an increase of subsurface food in farmland (see above), eutrophication in the main wintering areas producing more food (Beukema 1991), and probably recent climatic improvement. Whether the climate change is part of a long-term process is not known.

In The Netherlands breeding density (bp/10ha) in the coastal prime habitat of saltmarshes adjacent to tidal flats in the Wadden Sea is as high as 45, in vast dune areas 1–3, on inland large grasslands between 1.4 and 2.2 within 30km of the coast, 0.3 at 100km and 0.015 (mainly arable land) at 160km.

The nominate subspecies breeding along coasts in Russia, Norway (above 64°N) and the Baltic and all inland breeding birds are fully migratory. The remaining coastal breeders are partially migratory, sedentariness increasing with decreasing latitude. French, Iberian and Mediterranean are probably resident. About 98% of the *c*875 000 birds of the nominate subspecies winter in large estuarine areas in Europe: 400 000 in the Wadden Sea, 100 000 in the Dutch delta and 150 000 around the Irish Sea. The remainder move to Africa, S to about 13°N in Gambia (Hulscher *et al* in press). The inland *longipes* subspecies winters in E Africa, Arabia and W India.

Jan B Hulscher (NL)

Himantopus himantopus **Black-winged Stilt**

CZ	Pisila čáponohá	**I**	Cavaliere d'Italia
D	Stelzenläufer	**NL**	Steltkluut
E	Cigüeñuela Común	**P**	Perna-longa
F	Échasse blanche	**PL**	Szczudłak
FIN	Pitkäjalka	**R**	Ходулочник
G	Καλαμοκανάς	**S**	Styltlöpare
H	Gólyatöcs		

Non-SPEC, Threat status S

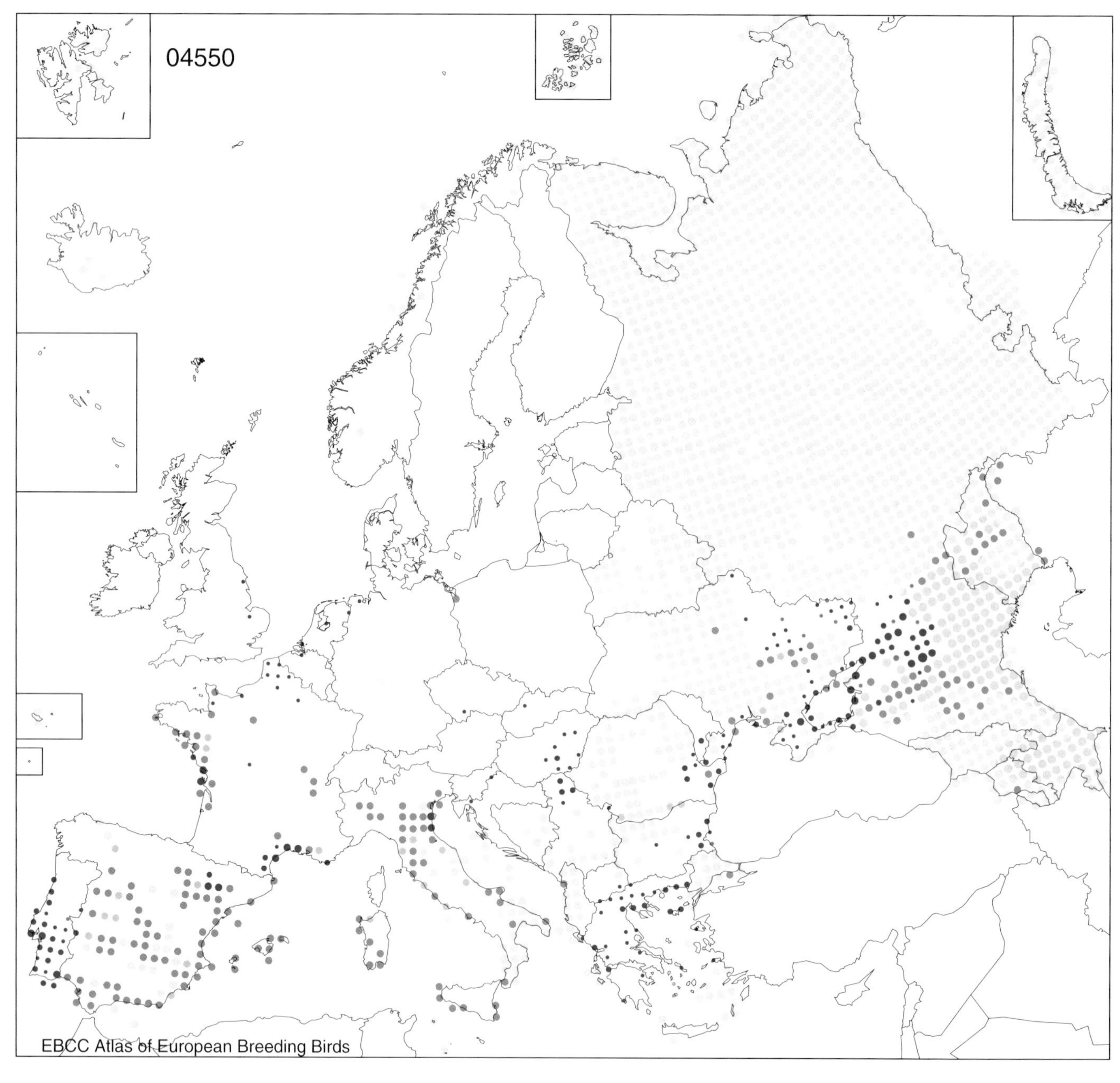

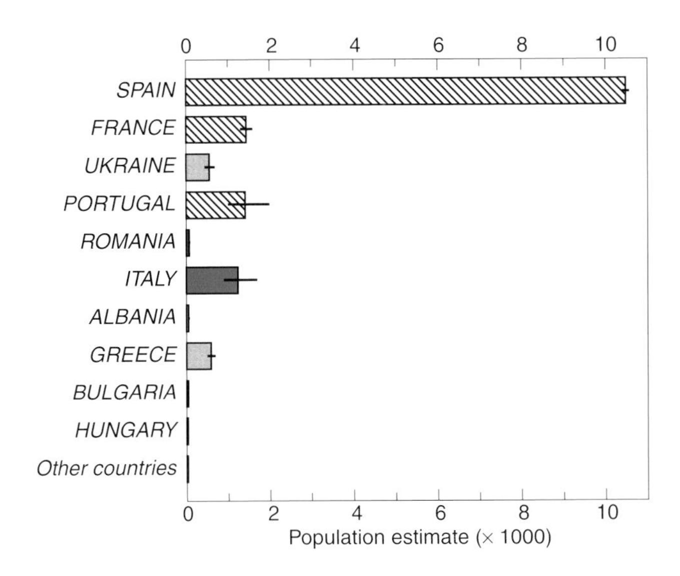

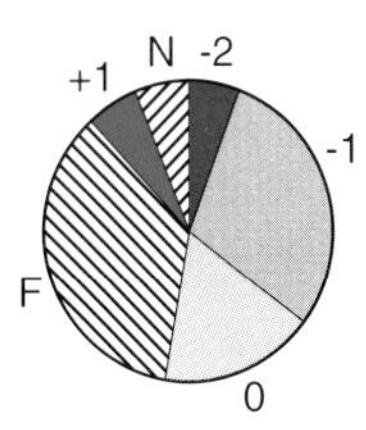

% in top 10 countries: 99.8
Total number of populated European countries: 17
Total European population 15,382–16,750 (15,960)
Russian population 1000–3000 (1732)
Turkish population 5000–15,000 (8660)

The evocative Black-winged Stilt is a member of a worldwide family distributed between 35°N and 40°S. Relationships between family members remain unclear; some argue for one species with five subspecies, and others for eight full species. All the birds are extremely long-legged and strikingly black and white or black. In the traditional view, *H.h. himantopus* occurs in Eurasia from SW Europe to Mongolia and S to South Africa. It is normally associated with a sunny climate, thus breeding in the temperate, mediterranean, steppe and desert zones.

Within its European range this opportunistic species uses mostly non-tidal habitats, provided that water depth does not exceed 20cm over a significant proportion of each site, apparently a determining factor during habitat selection (Neves & Rufino 1995). Although adults can forage up to such a depth, chicks in particular require adequate areas of very shallow water in which to feed. Breeding habitats include fresh, brackish and saltwater marshes, shallow lakes, inundation zones, ricefields, sewage farms, large fish farms, salinas (salt extraction pans) and even sugar factory decanting ponds. The species selects habitats according to availability and quality, choice varying between regions. Salinas hold 70% of the total Portuguese population (Rufino & Neves 1991) whereas at Emilia-Romana, they support only *c*25% of the Italian population (Tinarelli 1990).

Its patchy European breeding distribution largely matches suitable habitat, but the map cannot show that most breeding pairs are concentrated in relatively few sites. Emilia-Romana holds *c*40% of the Italian breeding population (Tinarelli 1990), and only four sites contain *c*70% of the Portuguese breeding birds (Rufino & Neves 1991). On a wider scale, Spain accounts for almost 60% of the European breeding population of 18 000bp. Over 80% of European breeding birds occur in Mediterranean countries from Portugal to Greece. None of the Balkan countries has over 100bp, but Ukraine (450–700bp) and Russia (1000–3000bp) hold sizeable populations. The map may suggest the Ukrainian and Russian populations to be larger than previously thought. The species breeds irregularly N of its normal range, most records coming from The Netherlands where 56 breeding attempts were registered from 1989 to 1993 inclusive; it attempted to breed in at least 36 of the 63 years preceding 1994 (Meininger 1993).

The dependence of the Black-winged Stilt upon unpredictable habitats results in significant regional breeding population fluctuations, particularly in SW Europe. At Portugal's major breeding site in the Sado estuary, numbers increased from 350bp to 750bp from 1990 to 1991, remaining stable since (Neves & Rufino 1995) whereas in Emilia-Romana, *c*900bp in 1983 decreased to only *c*450bp in 1984 (Tinarelli 1990). Some interchange between SW European populations occurs (Tinarelli 1990), probably indicating between-season movement according to habitat availability, but further substantiating evidence is required, particularly for the Spanish population. Asynchronous fluctuations mask any clear trends for the western European breeding population, contrary to eastern Europe, where breeding range contraction apparently has followed reductions in numbers.

The Black-winged Stilt breeds in loose colonies whose sizes are highly variable. Nests in Italy were spaced between 1m and 30m apart (Tinarelli 1990), but much lower colony breeding densities of 0.7–3bp/10ha were recorded on the Tejo (Tagus) estuary in Portugal (Rufino & Neves 1992).

The European population is mostly migratory, moving S to sub-Saharan wetlands during winter (Dubois 1992). However, SW Iberia supports an increasingly large wintering population, which in Portugal has risen from 164 in 1988 to 1300 in 1993. Apparently most of these birds breed locally, and thus have become resident, although the remainder continue to migrate S of the Sahara. The winter range has therefore become split, not shifted northwards, because the NW African wetlands do not contain overwintering birds. Whether this is a weather-driven short-term change or a longer-term consequence of climatic trends is not yet known.

Renato Neves (P) Rui Rufino (P)

Recurvirostra avosetta **Avocet**

CZ	Tenkozobec opačný	**I**	Avocetta
D	Säbelschnäbler	**NL**	Kluut
E	Avoceta Común	**P**	Alfaiate
F	Avocette élégante	**PL**	Szablodziób
FIN	Avosetti	**R**	Шилоклювка
G	Αβοκέτα	**S**	Skärfläcka
H	Gulipán		

*SPEC Cat 4/3*W, Threat status L*W*

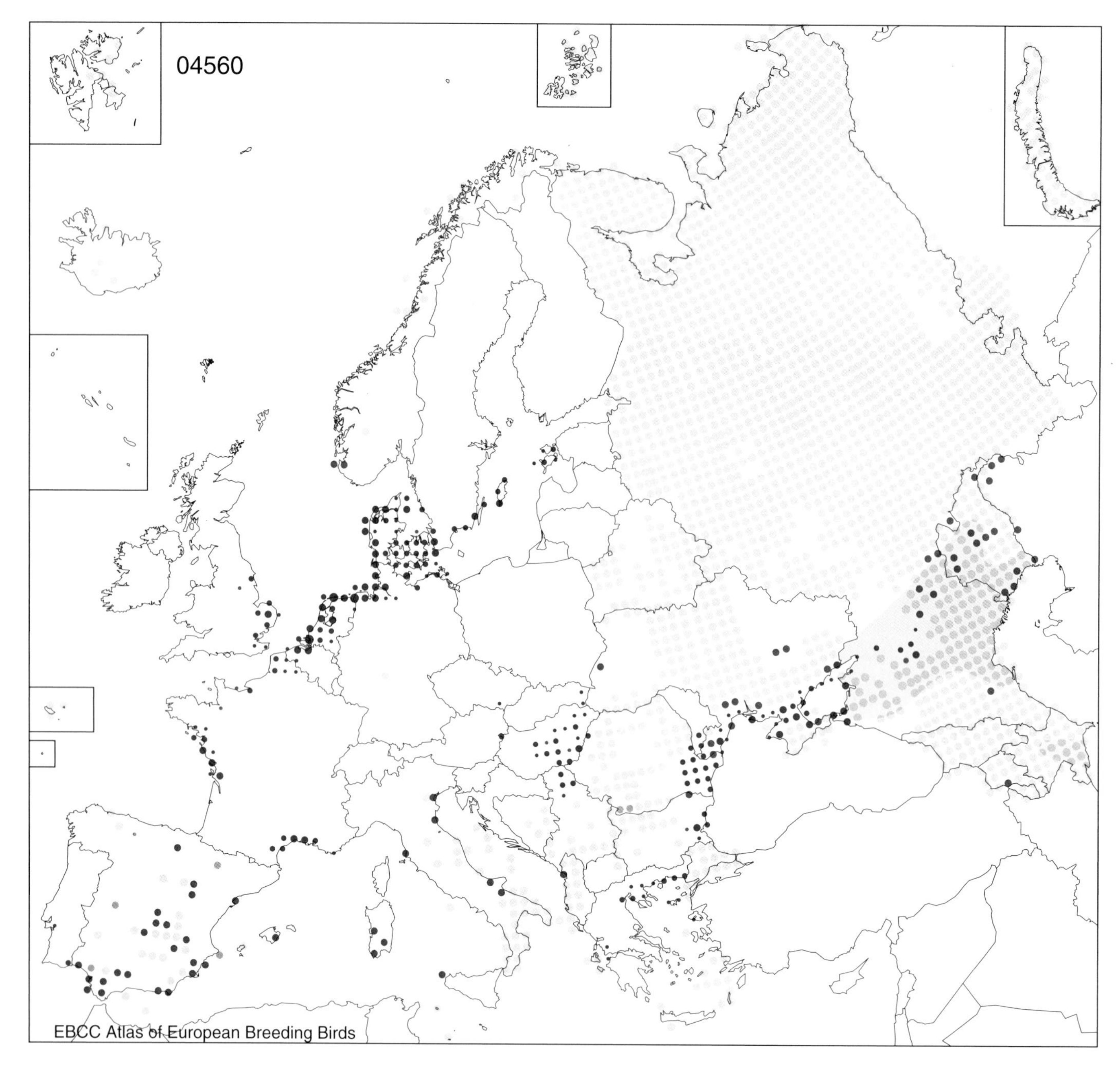

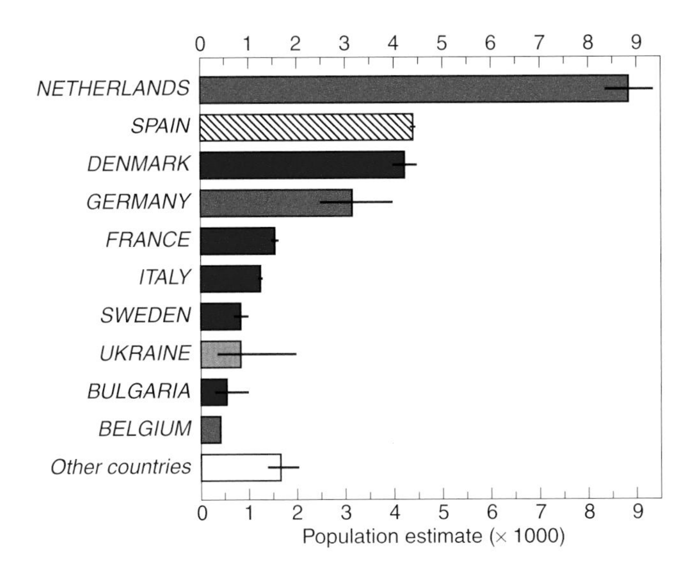

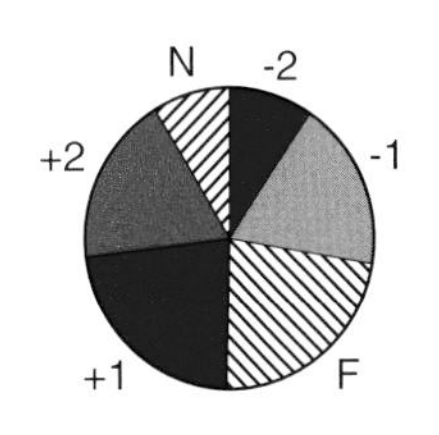

% in top 10 countries: 94.0
Total number of populated European countries: 27
Total European population 26,762–29,436 (27,802)
Russian population 1000–9000 (3000)
Turkish population 5000–15,000 (8660)

The Avocet breeds locally from southern Sweden to southern Spain and NW and North Africa, E to southern Ukraine and the Black Sea and across C Asia to Outer Mongolia. Other significant populations breed locally in E-C Africa and in southern Africa.

Through the temperate and tropical climatic zones, the species' main breeding habitat is relatively dry and inhospitable, comprising sandy or muddy shores of shallow saline and brackish waters in coastal lagoons, saltmarshes, or inland salt, saline or alkaline lakes, up to high altitude, even above 3000m asl in Afghanistan. In The Netherlands, it shows an increasing tendency to breed inland on arable land, alongside ditches in open farmland or muddy sections in meadows.

The Avocet's winter quarters lie along the East Atlantic coast from Britain to Ghana (Blomert *et al* 1991), the Nile Valley, tropical and southern Africa and western India, and for eastern populations mainly in E China and Burma in locations similar to their breeding habitat. In Europe, the spring migration begins in late February to early March, most birds arriving in April, except in European Russia, where arrival is still later. In autumn, the adults depart the breeding grounds from mid-July onwards. Many which breed N of the Dutch delta region use it as a moulting area, and later meet up with the juveniles and the southern European breeders on the wintering grounds further S. A recent unusual development has been the twenty-fold increase over ten years of numbers wintering in southern England where more than 2500 were counted in the winter of 1993/94. African populations are largely sedentary.

This monotypic species breeds in colonies which vary greatly in size from only a few breeding pairs to several hundred, with up to 400 bp/35ha on saline marshes along the French Atlantic coast (Girard & Yésou 1989) and 273, 277 and 389bp respectively on three sites in SW Netherlands in 1994. Of the Dutch 1994 total of 2684bp, 75% bred in colonies of more then 20bp (Meininger *et al* 1995). Location, size and breeding success of colonies may vary considerably from year to year, depending on flooding, rainfall, vegetation succession and access of sites to predators (Tchernitchko 1980, Goutner 1985, Hill 1988, Meininger *et al* 1995). Predation of eggs and young by gulls, corvids and foxes *Vulpes vulpes* at a colony at Chanteloup, France is now so severe that in a good year perhaps 10 young fledge from 400 nests (O. Girard, pers obs).

The European distribution of the Avocet has not changed recently, save perhaps in England where 135bp in two eastern locations in 1972 have increased to perhaps 500bp in ten sites in 1993. Over the whole area considered, the population estimate generally seems reliable, except for Russia where data are very imprecise, allowing only a rough estimate of 1000–9000bp. Only Russia and Bulgaria experienced significant decreases. For the majority of the other countries populations are stable or increasing. The Netherlands hold the largest population, 8400–9400bp, whose size and vicissitudes are very well defined. The Dutch population doubled during the last 15 years, mainly through eutrophication of the Wadden Sea (increasing food supply) and the creation of artificial breeding sites in the Delta area. Improvement of water quality, habitat destruction, increasing recreational demands and overgrowing of saltmarshes are future threats to the Dutch Avocet population and are unlikely to be offset by the switch to inland farmland breeding (Osieck & Hustings 1994). There are also important populations in Spain, Denmark and Germany of *c*4400, 4200 and 3200bp respectively, which have from time to time fluctuated but seem to show an increasing trend. The most recent estimate of the populations in the *Atlas*' coverage area amounts to some 40 000bp.

Olivier Girard (F)

This species account is sponsored by the Royal Society for the Protection of Birds, Sandy, Bedfordshire, GB.

Burhinus oedicnemus — Stone Curlew

CZ	Dytík úhorní	**I**	Occhione
D	Triel	**NL**	Griel
E	Alcaraván Común	**P**	Alcaravão
F	Oedicnème criard	**PL**	Kulon
FIN	Paksujalka	**R**	Авдотка
G	Πετροτριλίδα	**S**	Tjockfot
H	Ugartyúk		

SPEC Cat 3, Threat status V

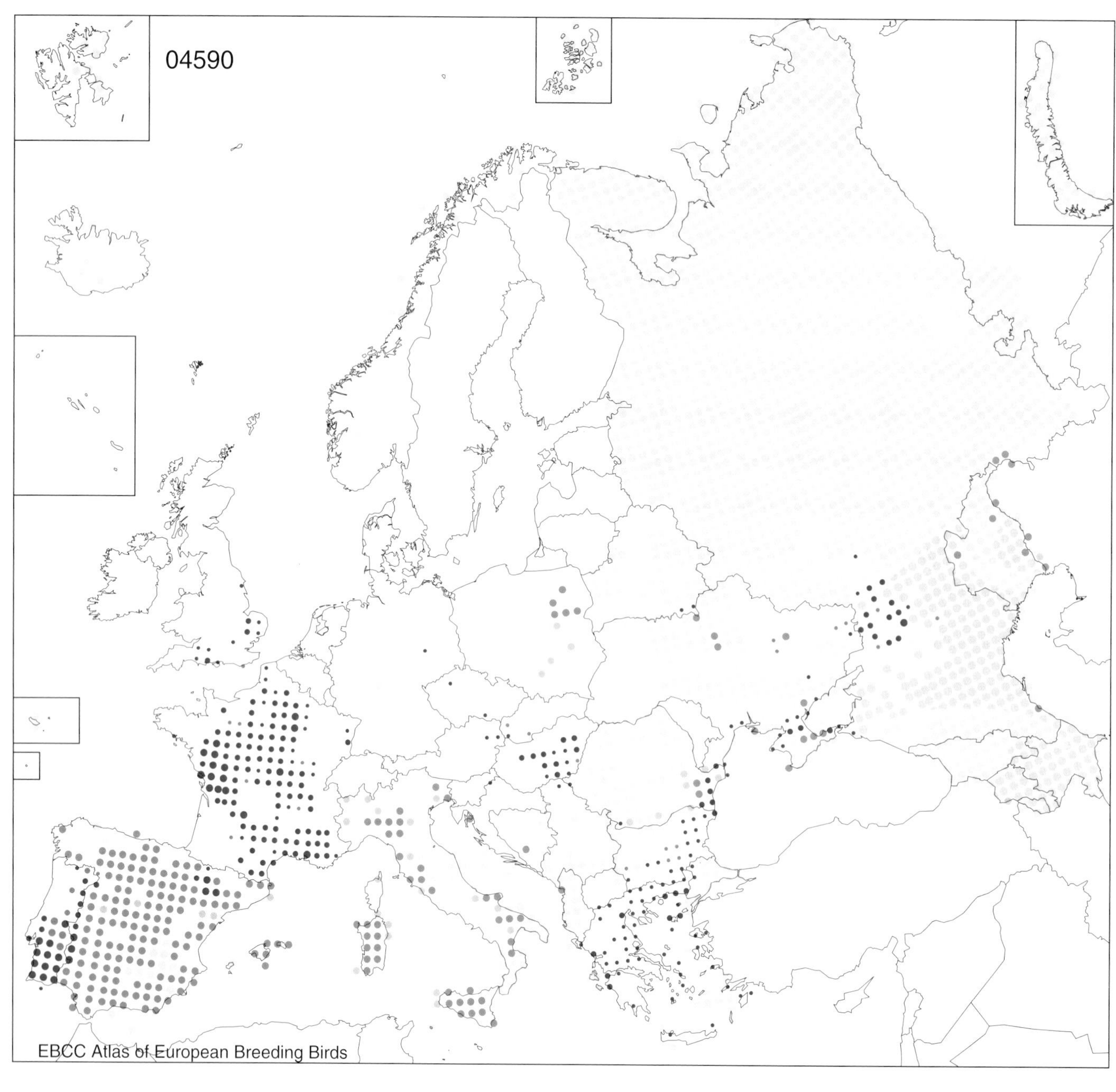

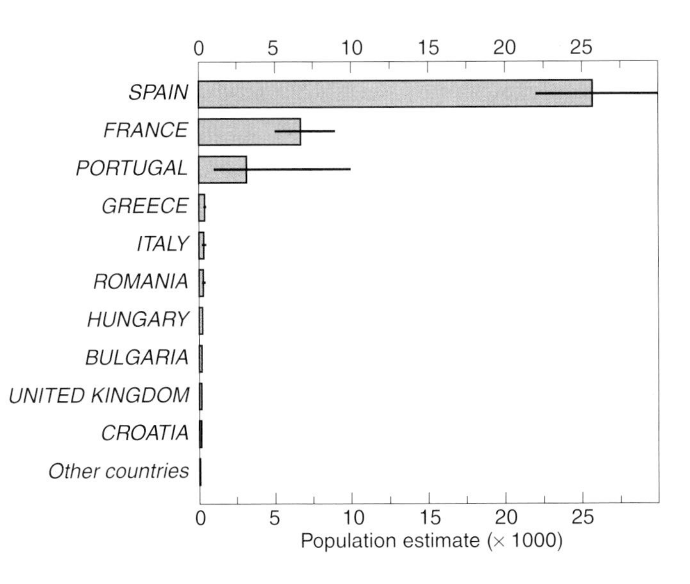

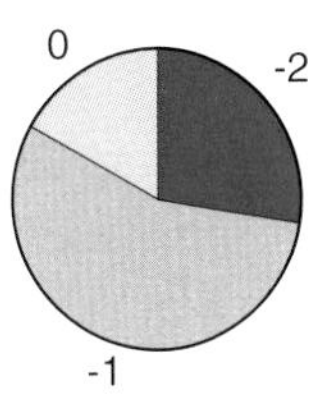

% in top 10 countries: 99.8
Total number of populated European countries: 18
Total European population 32,690–45,704 (37,299)
Russian population 10,000–100,000 (31,623)
Turkish population 1000–5000 (2236)

The world distribution of the Stone Curlew, a crepuscular and nocturnal wader, covers much of the SW Palearctic and the Mediterranean and Oriental regions. Within Europe the nominate *B.o. oedicnemus* is found from southern England E to Poland and S Russia, and from Iberia to Italy, the Balkans and the Caucasus. The subspecies *saharae* occurs on the smaller Mediterranean islands, in Greece and in most of Turkey. The Iberian Peninsula, France and Russia together hold *c*95% of the European population.

Breeding areas are characterized by low precipitation and many hours of sunshine. They are dry, even arid, with short or cropped vegetation allowing good all-round visibility. Consequently, the Stone Curlew's preferred habitat is limited to dry, sparsely vegetated heaths, calcareous or acid short grasslands, sand-dunes, boulder or stony deposits in streams, stony plains and tablelands. Recently, the species has begun to use well-drained, spring-sown tilled farmland, even vineyards (especially in the Vaucluse, France), orchards and young forest plantations, instead of traditional habitats (Nipkow 1994, Malvaud 1995).

Formerly more widespread, the species' geographical range decreased in most of C Europe as suitable breeding habitat was lost to human settlement, afforestation, intensified farming of marginal land and through the decline in sheep and goat grazing. Furthermore, disturbance often reduces reproductive success. This negative trend is apparent throughout Europe, except in Hungary (P. Bod, pers comm) and possibly Russia.

Although generally gregarious, the birds nest at well-spaced intervals, reaching densities of 1.5–3 bp/km^2 in prime habitat, such as the 'coussous' of Crau (*Asphodeletum fistulosi*). In the mixed cultivation of maize, cereal and rape in Alsace overall density was 1.1 bp/km^2 in 1986 and 1987 (Nipkow 1990), but less then half that on neighbouring maize monocultures. In the latter, breeding success was lower, first-clutch loss rates and repeat layings are higher, and overall recruitment rate is low (Nipkow 1988). Unlike spring-sown crops, maize grows quickly, preventing second clutches being laid in July and August and reducing the area available for birds to gather in autumn.

In Germany breeding was last proven in 1987 (Leipe 1990), although some of the abandoned military training areas in the former East Germany remain adequate habitats (Nipkow 1994). The lowland Polish population, once widespread, crashed to only a dozen. Two locations held the Austrian total of only 7–8bp in 1995 (H-M. Berg, pers comm). A few sporadic breeders remain in the Czech Republic and Slovakia. The Bulgarian population is in severe decline at a recently determined 150–200bp, remarkably few considering that half of the country's 110 912km^2 is potentially breeding habitat (Uhlig & Baumgart 1995). The present situation in Russia, Romania and Croatia is impossible to assess because of lack of data.

In Britain, the species has declined steadily since the mid-19th century. Local increases occurred during the 1920s and 1930s (1000–2000bp), when agriculture was in recession. Overall the species has been affected progressively by conversion of Breckland grass heath and chalk downland to arable farmland, by afforestation of heathland and by scrub growth after myxomatosis depressed rabbit numbers. It is now restricted to small areas in S and E England. Recent conservation management of cultivated areas and heaths has had a favourable effect, the population becoming stabilized at *c*150bp from 1985 onwards (Green & Griffiths 1994).

Southern birds are largely sedentary, or make short seasonal movements. After gathering in pre-migratory flocks at traditional sites, some N European birds depart to winter in Iberia, a few travel only as far as SW France, but substantial numbers cross the Mediterranean to reach North, West and East Africa. Occasionally a few may winter in southern England.

Markus Nipkow (D)

Glareola pratincola

Collared Pratincole

CZ	Ouhorlík stepní	I	Pernice di mare
D	Rotflügel-Brachschwalbe	NL	Vorkstaartplevier
E	Canastera Común	P	Perdiz-do-mar
F	Glaréole à collier	PL	Żwirowiec łąkowy
FIN	Pääskykahlaaja	R	Луговая тиркушка
G	Νεροχελίδονο	S	Rödvingad vadarsvala
H	Székicsér		

SPEC Cat 3, Threat status E

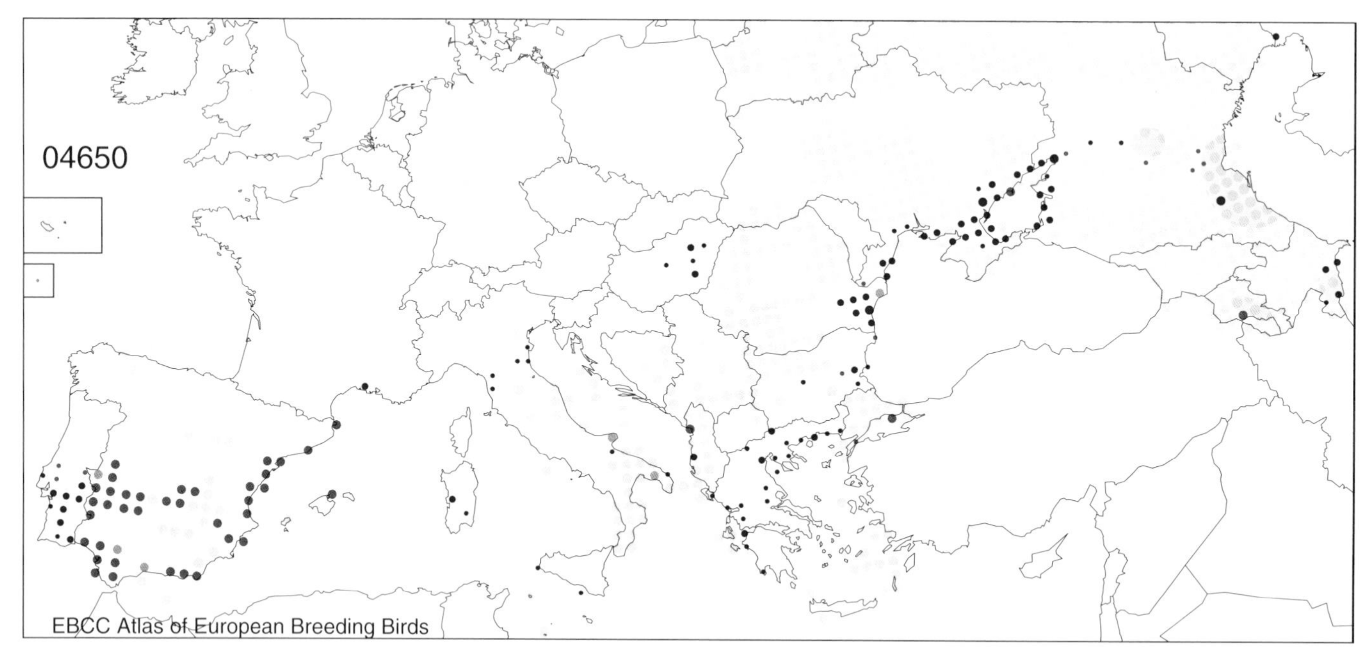

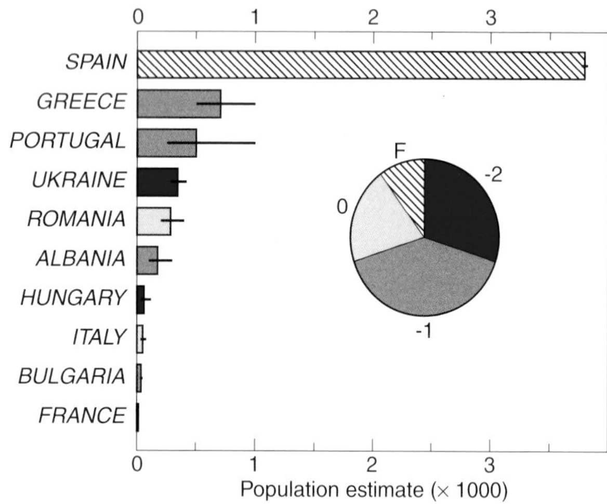

% in top 10 countries: 100.0
Total number of populated European countries: 10
Total European population 5601–6567 (5952)
Russian population 1000–10,000 (3162)
Turkish population 500–5000 (1581)

This species has an Afrotropical and SW Palearctic breeding distribution. In Europe it breeds around the Mediterranean, Black and Caspian Seas, and in Asia as far as E Kazakhstan. Palearctic populations winter in Africa. An aerial insectivore, its colonies are on flat open areas with sparse short vegetation and warm shallow water, as found on damp salines, in river valleys or near seas or alkaline lakes. Its European distribution therefore is mosaic-like, especially inland, as in E Hungary. Colonies hold from 3–50bp, often near terns or other waders, particularly Black-winged Pratincole *G. nordmanni* (Ukraine and Russia).

Since the 1970s, as natural habitats have declined, it has bred increasingly in cropless fields and sometimes in ricefields. Especially in the N, year-to-year fluctuations are characteristic. From the mid-1950s (Tomkovich 1992) to the mid-1980s (Molodan 1988), numbers increased considerably in Ukraine and Cis-Caucasus before declining again. Elsewhere in Europe, range and population have declined since the 1960s. The Spanish stronghold of the Guadalquivir marshes held >10 000bp (*c*80% of the European total) in the early 1960s but only 1260–1370bp in 1990 (Calvo *et al* 1993). In the Danube Delta (Ukraine), 3000bp (1960s) declined to <100bp (1980s). In 1984, Ukraine contained *c*600bp, mostly in the SE (Chernichko *et al* 1990). S Russia has 250–1000bp, concentrated near the Azov and Caspian Seas (V. Belik, pers obs). In the Hungarian Hortobágy, there were 500bp in the 1900s, 100–110bp in 1980, but only 50bp by 1992 (Kovács 1993).

Numbers depend on extreme continental climatic fluctuations. Droughts and agricultural intensification degrade breeding habitat and floods destroy nests (Széll 1993). In Ukraine and Russia predation by the large corvid populations is important (Kostin 1983, Molodan 1988), especially during droughts. Agrochemicals may be linked to the species' decline in SW Spain (Garcia *et al* in Calvo *et al* 1993).

Victor P Belik (R) Emil Boross (H)
Pavel S Tomkovich (R)

Glareola nordmanni

Black-winged Pratincole

CZ	Ouhorlík černokřídlý	I	Pernice di mare orientale
D	Schwarzflügel-Brachschwalbe	NL	Steppevorkstaartplevier
E	Canastera Alinegra	P	Perdiz-do-mar-d'asa-preta
F	Glaréole à ailes noires	PL	Żwirowiec stepowy
FIN	Aropääskykahlaaja	R	Степная тиркушка
G	Μαυρόφτερο Νεροχελίδονο	S	Svartvingad vadarsvala
H	Feketeszárnyú székicsér		

SPEC Cat 3, Threat status R

The Black-winged Pratincole has a Palearctic distribution, mainly in the steppe zone from Hungary and SE Romania eastward across S Ukraine and S Russia to E Kazakhstan. A colonial breeder, it penetrates sporadically along large river valleys northward to S Belarus, to the Lipetsk, Penza and Ul'yanovsk regions in Russia, and to the S Urals. It winters in sub-Saharan Africa. Breeding colonies vary from 2–3bp to 200–300bp or more, often amongst other waders and terns. Colonies are mainly located on alkaline soils and salines in river valleys, and on lake and sea shores, preferably on dry sites. The species breeds quite often on bare fields, but it requires nearby open fresh water for drinking.

It has declined throughout its European breeding range since the 1970s, especially in the W. Fewer than 10bp remain in Romania, and the 40–100bp in Ukraine represent a tenfold decline in 20 years, its range contracting considerably (Molodan 1988, Bulakhov *et al* 1990). Due to the irrigation of the dry and desert steppe of S Russia (Cis-Caucasus and Kalmykia) since the 1950s, numbers increased markedly to 5000–7000bp by the mid-1980s (Belik *et al* 1994), but now it has begun to decline. Simultaneously, small colonies formed briefly in Hungary, Germany, Belarus and C Russia, far from its main breeding range, where probably local drought had provoked these movements. The European population is *c*6000–11 000bp out of a world total of *c*15 000–45 000bp.

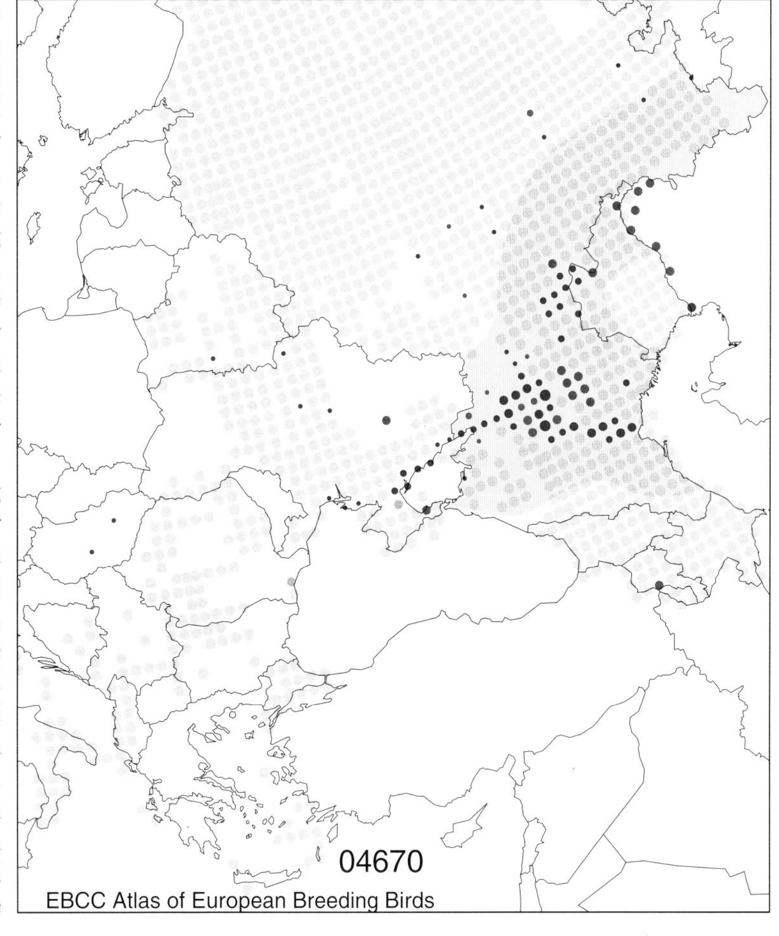

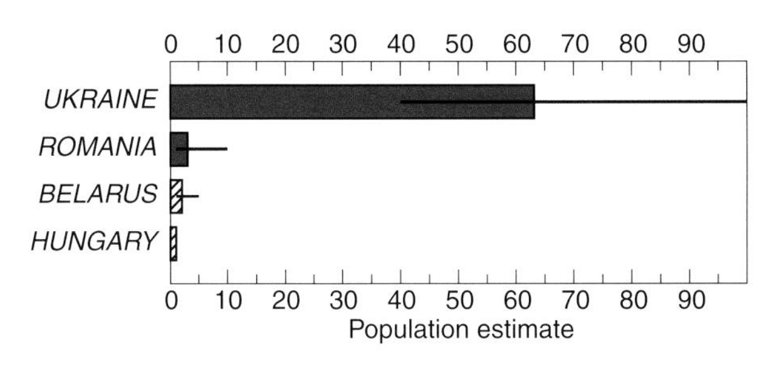

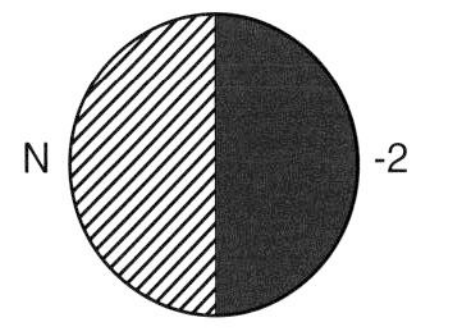

% in top 10 countries: 100.0
Total number of populated European countries: 4
Total European population 46–107 (70)
Russian population 6500–11,100 (8494)

The primary causes of its range contraction and decline in numbers are the cultivation of virgin steppes and intensive use of the remaining natural areas for grazing livestock. The large-scale planting of forest strips as shelter-belts across the steppes in S Russia and Ukraine led to dense corvid populations, primarily of Rook *Corvus frugilegus*. Ground-nesting birds such as Black-winged Pratincole suffer heavily now from corvid predation, although its effect on the population level is unknown.

Victor P Belik (R) Pavel S Tomkovich (R)

Charadrius dubius

Little Ringed Plover

CZ	Kulík říční	**I**	Corriere piccolo
D	Flußregenpfeifer	**NL**	Kleine Plevier
E	Chorlitejo Chico	**P**	Borrelho-pequeno-de-coleira
F	Petit Gravelot	**PL**	Sieweczka rzeczna
FIN	Pikkutylli	**R**	Малый зуек
G	Ποταμοσφυριχτής	**S**	Mindre strandpipare
H	Kis lile		

Non-SPEC, Threat status S (P)

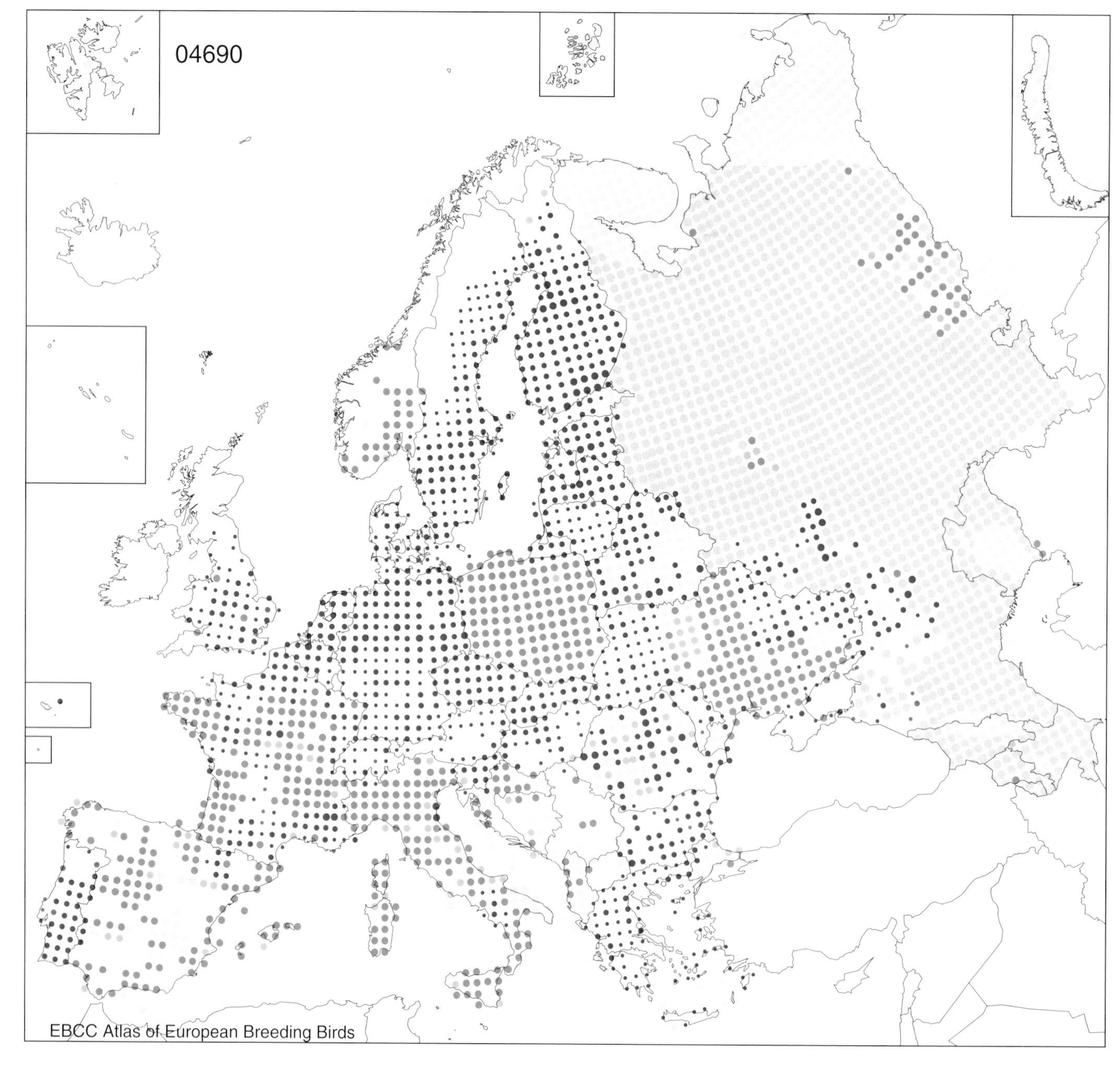

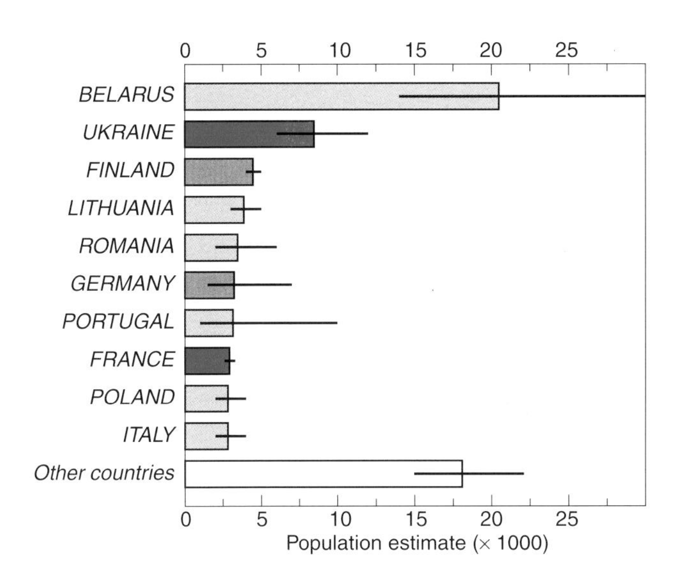

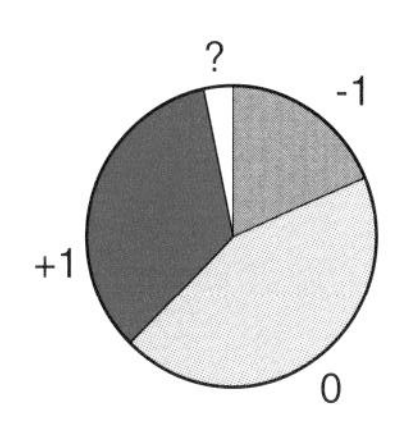

% in top 10 countries: 75.5
Total number of populated European countries: 32
Total European population 66,015–87,123 (73,859)
Russian population 50,000–500,000 (158,114)
Turkish population 3000–10,000 (5477)

As a trans-Palearctic species, the Little Ringed Plover occurs from western Europe to Japan, from the Sea of Okhotsk in the N to Pakistan in the S. Its European distribution covers Scandinavia to the Mediterranean. It breeds in every European country except Ireland and Iceland. The subspecies *C.d. curonicus* breeds in Europe; there are two other subspecies in the Orient.

In C Europe it inhabits lowlands, particularly river valley habitats below 600m asl. In N and S Europe it breeds also on coasts, especially river mouths. The original habitat of the Little Ringed Plover was shingle, richly structured and interspersed with gravel or sand and appropriate primary vegetation. To breed successfully it needs expanses of raised shingle, ideally on river islands, but to rear young it requires low banks with marshy ground and calm, shallow waters as often exist below shingly shores.

Nowadays its habitat choice has changed. Populations declined in the late 19th and early 20th centuries, attributed mainly to climate 'oceanization' (wet summers, high water levels, nest site overgrowth), not conducive to successful breeding. Simultaneously, human 'control' of nature through vast hydraulic engineering schemes took place. Consequently, many areas of bare, pebbly and sandy ground and similarly constituted banks and heaps were created. In the 1920s and 1930s the climate reverted to a more continental type (dry, hot summers). The Little Ringed Plover's population began to increase quickly, probably due mainly to its adaptation to and exploitation of these artificial secondary sites. A further surge in numbers was doubtless due to the widespread construction activities after World War II, when gravel extraction greatly increased.

The Little Ringed Plover has also learnt to exploit other artificially cleared areas which, although suitable because they contain rubble, sandy flat areas and shallow water (even puddles), may only exist for a season or two. It now nests in industrial sites, opencast mines, polders, rubbish dumps, spoil tailings, industrial refuse dumps, army training grounds, airfields, drained ponds and fields, if they are sandy enough. It is estimated that in C Europe only 6% of the Little Ringed Plover population still breeds in its natural habitat (*HVM*), and in Britain even less so (Parrinder 1989).

Overall population density estimation in such scattered secondary habitats is very difficult. In prime habitat, 31bp bred along 60km of the River Warta in Poland (Tomiałojć 1990). In Slovenia, 5bp occupied 5km along the River Sava. Given that 0.4ha may suffice for a pair in gravel-pits, a natural density of 1 bp/ha seems achievable. Around Ljubljana in 1991–92 the Little Ringed Plover bred at nine secondary localities, most of which achieved a breeding density of 1–2 bp/ha; in one industrial site, semi-colonial breeding produced 5bp in 0.5ha (Trontelj 1992).

Russia, Belarus and Ukraine hold 80% of the European population of 100 000–600 000bp. The remaining breeding pairs show a wide scattering throughout Europe up to the Arctic Circle in Finland, but nowhere reaching high densities over large stretches. Breeding is more localized than the present resolution of 50km squares reveals.

The proportion of natural habitats renewed through river dynamics continues to decrease as more watercourses come under control. Conversely, the number of suitable artificial sites, which are predominantly temporary, is increasing. This implies that breeding distribution changes yearly across much of the Little Ringed Plover's range. It is not known if the species' adaptability shown in the 20th century will persist if the rate of artificial site creation diminishes below a certain minimum. There remains, therefore, a potentially serious threat to the species. It is encouraging that modern flood-control entails less disruption of natural river dynamics than in the past, since this species is adapted to such conditions.

Iztok Geister (SLN)

This species account is sponsored by Gesellschaft Rheinischer Ornithologen, Düsseldorf, D.

Charadrius hiaticula Ringed Plover

CZ	Kulík písečný	**I**	Corriere grosso
D	Sandregenpfeifer	**NL**	Bontbekplevier
E	Chorlitejo Grande	**P**	Borrelho-grande-de-coleira
F	Grand Gravelot	**PL**	Sieweczka obrożna
FIN	Tylli	**R**	Галстучник
G	Αμμοσφυριχτής	**S**	Större strandpipare
H	Parti lile		

Non-SPEC, Threat status S

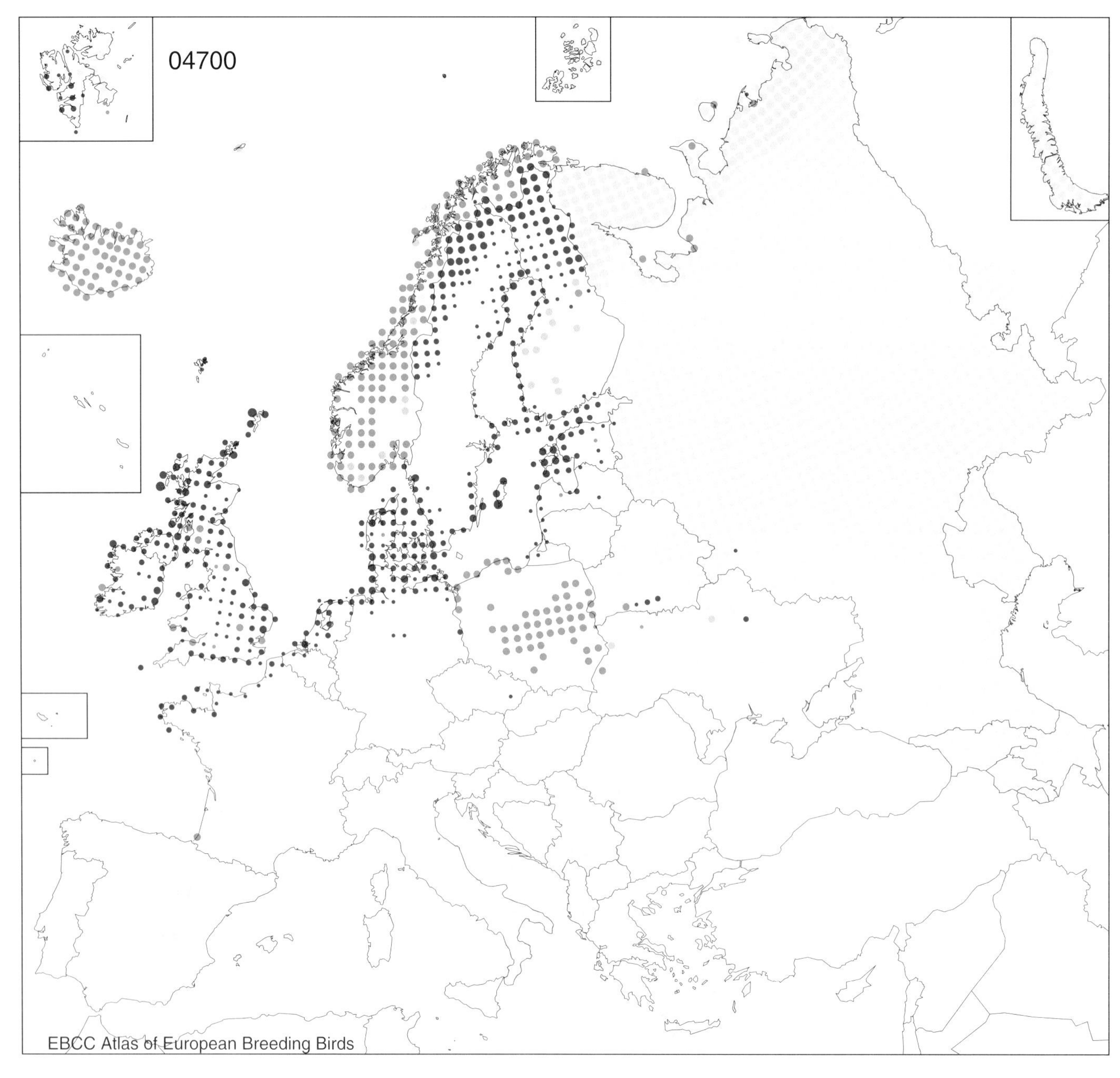

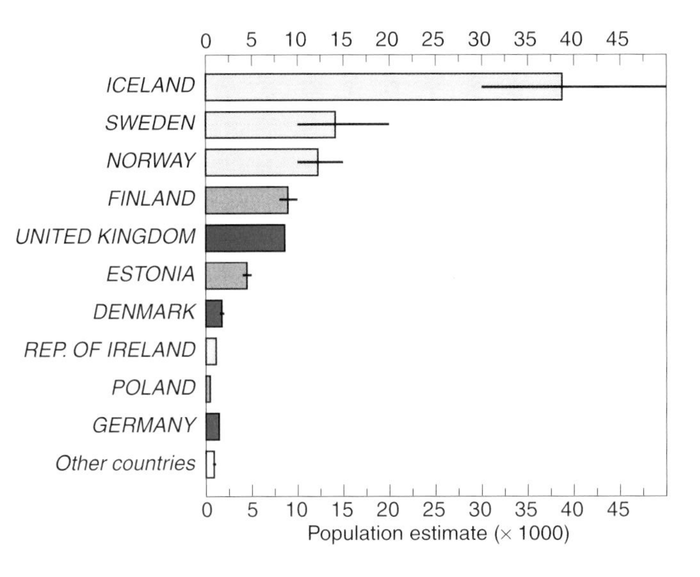

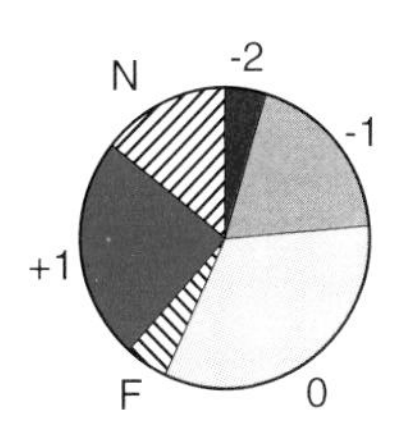

% in top 10 countries: 99.1
Total number of populated European countries: 21
Total European population 82,724–105,757 (92,703)
Russian population 1000–10,000 (3162)

The Ringed Plover breeds along coasts of the N Palearctic, its distribution extending E to the Chukotskiy Peninsula, and W to Greenland and Baffin and Ellesmere Islands. In North America it is replaced by the closely related Semipalmated Plover, *C. semipalmatus*.

It inhabits open, bare or sparsely vegetated areas adjacent to water, typically coastal beaches, and also a variety of inland habitats, including tundra heath, river valleys, lakeshores, farmland and bare industrial habitats.

In temperate Europe, the Ringed Plover is primarily a sea-coast species, the majority breeding on wide sand, gravel or shell beaches, or locally on adjacent sand-dunes. It frequently uses short-grazed coastal pastures and other agricultural habitats by the sea such as the Outer Hebrides machair (Fuller 1978), or arable fields in NE Germany and E England (Holz 1987, Prater 1989). It also breeds by natural rivers, nesting on flat sandy banks and islets, and on intensively grazed floodplain pastures. Both coastal and inland birds will readily colonize cleared or excavated habitats, like gravel-pits, sewage farms, drying-out fishponds, industrial gravel areas and reclaimed land (Prater 1989). In northern Europe inland breeding, more widespread than in the continental temperate zone, occurs widely across tundra habitats, mostly along rivers, on shingle banks and stony ground but also on sparsely vegetated montane moorland, lakeshores or palsa-bogs. In N Scandinavia it occurs also along forest roads, breeding on roadside gravel or in small gravel-pits spaced alongside.

Since the mid-1970s, the species increasingly has tended to colonize inland sites, mostly in Great Britain and N Germany (Holz 1987, Prater 1989), but many, being artificial and transitional in character, are occupied only briefly (Holz 1987). However, inland breeders can have higher reproductive success than coastal birds (Briggs 1983, Holz 1987). At the same time, in many coastal areas numbers declined, breeding productivity falling below self-sustaining levels, due to increasing human usage of beaches coupled with intense predation (Pienkowski 1984, Prater 1989). In the Baltic, loss of coastal pastures has worsened matters. The overall effect may reduce noticeably the species' breeding range in Europe, particularly at its SW limit (Pienkowski 1993).

Birds breeding in the shoreline habitat tend to be somewhat clustered, preferring islets, river mouths, peninsulas or spits in early stages of succession. At such sites, local densities can be very high (over 40 bp/13ha in Bessin, NE Germany; Siefke 1982). The species is extremely abundant on the Hebridean machair, at an average density of 16 bp/km^2 (representative over 50km^2; Fuller 1978). Large-scale coastal densities (>100km of shoreline) are *c*2–3 bp/10km in the S and E Baltic (Holz 1987, Hildén & Hario 1993) but tend to be 2–3 times higher further N and on shingle beaches. Figures are strongly influenced by local features such as geomorphology, substrate (shingle preferred over sand), area and human pressure.

Densities along larger rivers in Poland and England averaged 2–5 bp/10km (locally up to 15) (Bukaciński *et al* 1995, Briggs 1983). For inland populations in artificial habitats, large-scale densities were *c*5–15 bp/100km^2 for field-breeders in Mecklenburg (Holz 1987) and roadside-breeders in Kuusamo, N Finland (H. Seppänen, pers comm).

The species is migratory, only the British population being partially resident. European and Nearctic populations winter mostly along the coasts of West Africa, in the Mediterranean basin, and on the Atlantic coasts from SW Europe to Great Britain.

Two subspecies generally are recognized: *C.h. hiaticula* (W Europe, Greenland and Iceland) and *tundrae* (N Scandinavia, Russia). The complex clinal and discordant pattern of geographic variation within the described distinguishing features merits a review.

Przemek Chylarecki (PL) Mikko Ojanen (FIN)

Charadrius alexandrinus **Kentish Plover**

CZ	Kulík mořský	**I**	Fratino
D	Seeregenpfeifer	**NL**	Strandplevier
E	Chorlitejo Patinegro	**P**	Borrelho-de-coleira-interrompida
F	Gravelot à collier interrompu	**PL**	Sieweczka morska
FIN	Mustajalkatylli	**R**	Морской зуек
G	Θαλασσοσφυριχτής	**S**	Svartbent strandpipare
H	Széki lile		

SPEC Cat 3, Threat status D

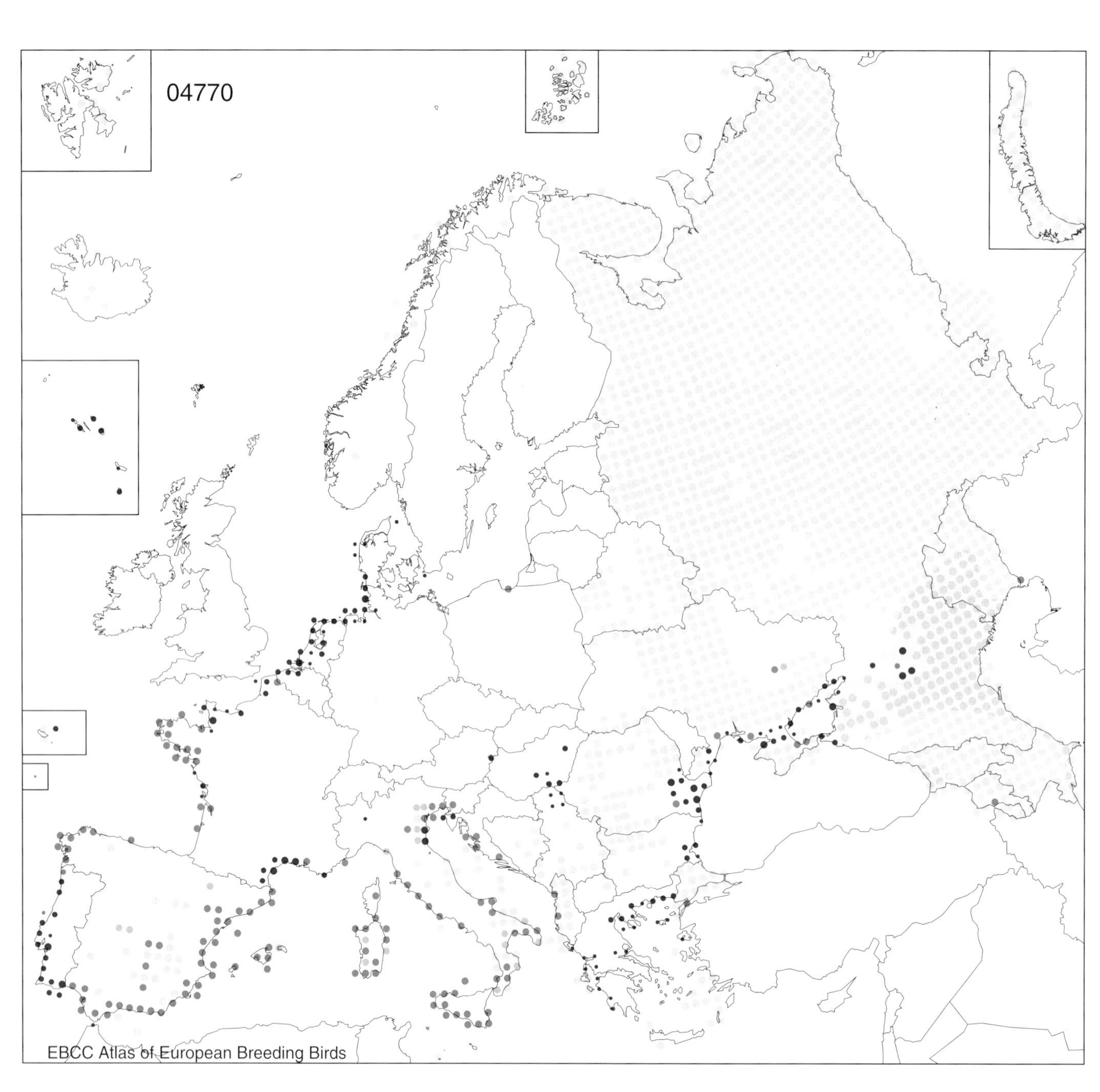

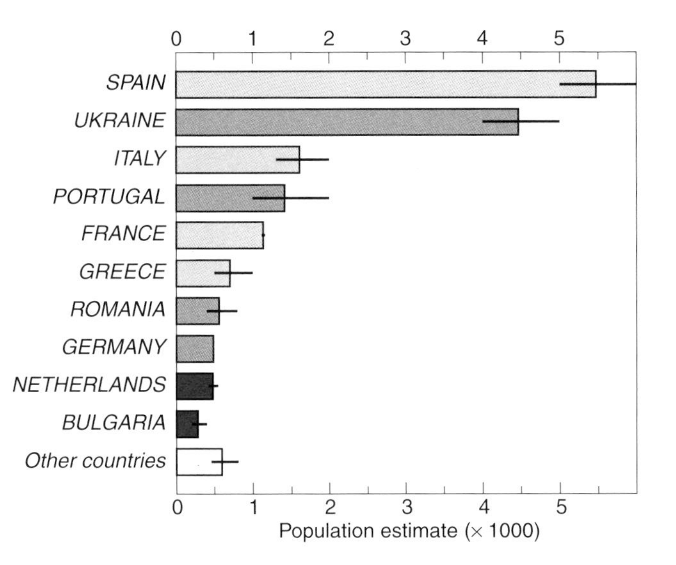

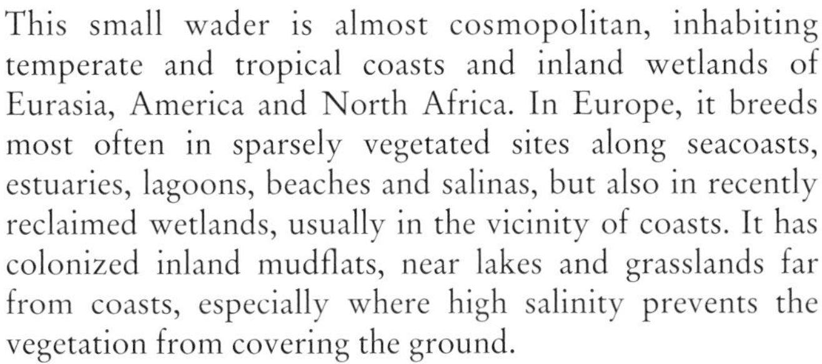

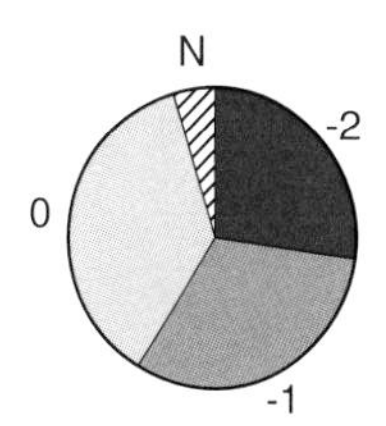

% in top 10 countries: 96.5
Total number of populated European countries: 22
Total European population 16,342–18,347 (17,241)
Russian population 1000–10,000 (3162)
Turkish population 5000–15,000 (8660)

This small wader is almost cosmopolitan, inhabiting temperate and tropical coasts and inland wetlands of Eurasia, America and North Africa. In Europe, it breeds most often in sparsely vegetated sites along seacoasts, estuaries, lagoons, beaches and salinas, but also in recently reclaimed wetlands, usually in the vicinity of coasts. It has colonized inland mudflats, near lakes and grasslands far from coasts, especially where high salinity prevents the vegetation from covering the ground.

The distribution of the Kentish Plover in Europe, predominantly coastal, includes the western Baltic, North Sea, Atlantic Ocean, Mediterranean Sea and Black Sea. Relatively small inland populations, which could be considered relicts, are found mostly in Spain, E Austria, Hungary and Vojvodina (former Yugoslavia). It avoids high altitudes.

Most populations clearly are in the process of decline, resulting in a contraction of the range in NW and C Europe. This decline can be attributed mainly to human activities; disturbance, especially on coasts, destruction of breeding habitat and predation by scavengers attracted by garbage. The Kentish Plover disappeared as a regular breeder from Norway in the late 19th century and from England in the 1930s. By 1992 the Swedish population consisted of only 20 adult birds in the extreme south (Jönsson 1993). In Denmark, the population has shown a marked decrease since the 1940s; 136bp in 1969, 75bp in 1975 and only 28–33bp in 1990 (Dybbro 1970, 1978, K. Fisher, pers comm). The German population, virtually confined to the Wadden Sea area, held 567bp in 1990 and 469bp in 1991 (Hälterlein & Behm-Berkelmann 1991, Hälterlein & Steinhardt 1993). In The Netherlands, between 1900 and 1940 there still were at least 1000bp, after which a steady decline resulted in a population of 435bp in 1992 (P.L. Meininger & F. Arts, pers obs). In Belgium there were 130bp in 1981 and 55–60bp in 1990 (Voet *et al* 1982, Devos *et al* 1991). In S Hungary, 110bp were found in 1950, 50bp in 1960 and 35–41bp in 1990 (T. Székely, pers obs).

The largest populations are found in Spain (5000–6000bp, of which *c*10% are at inland temporary saline lakes; Amat 1993), Italy (1500–2000bp; Tinarelli & Baccetti 1989) and Ukraine (4000–5000bp; Korzyukov & Potapov 1992). The C European population (120–175bp) breeds in saline marshes attached to lakes or in alkaline grasslands away from permanent water and since the 1970s also on the bottom of drained fishponds. In The Netherlands and Belgium, breeding is now confined to artificial habitats, dammed estuaries and recently reclaimed polders. Two essential factors seem to limit its distribution; flat and barren ground and an insufficiently high density of invertebrate food. Adequate food density may occur on coastal mudflats or on grassland (insects).

The Kentish Plover may breed in lone pairs or in loose colonies. In Ukraine, colonies of up to 300–400bp are known (Korzyukov & Potapov 1992). Typically the breeding density is lower inland (0.2–1.2 bp/ha; Székely 1992) than on the coast (5–16 bp/ha in Portugal; T. Székely, pers obs).

The populations breeding above *c*40°N are mainly migratory, those further S are dispersive. The most important wintering areas for W European breeders are in the W Mediterranean (Spain and Tunisia) and in West Africa (Mauritania and Guinea-Bissau). The C European breeders migrate through Italy, some overwintering in N Italy. There appears to be a wide overlap of various populations in wintering areas.

Peter L Meininger (NL) Támas Székely (H)

Charadrius leschenaultii

Greater Sand Plover

CZ	Kulík pouštní	**I**	Corriere di Leschenault
D	Wüstenregenpfeifer	**NL**	Woestijnplevier
E	Chorlitejo Mongol Grande	**P**	Borrelho-mongol-grande
		PL	Sieweczka pustynna
F	Gravelot de Leschenault	**R**	Тонкоклювый зуек
FIN	Aavikkotylli	**S**	Ökenpipare
G	Ερημοσφυριχτής		
H	Sivatagi lile		

SPEC Cat 3, Threat status E (P)

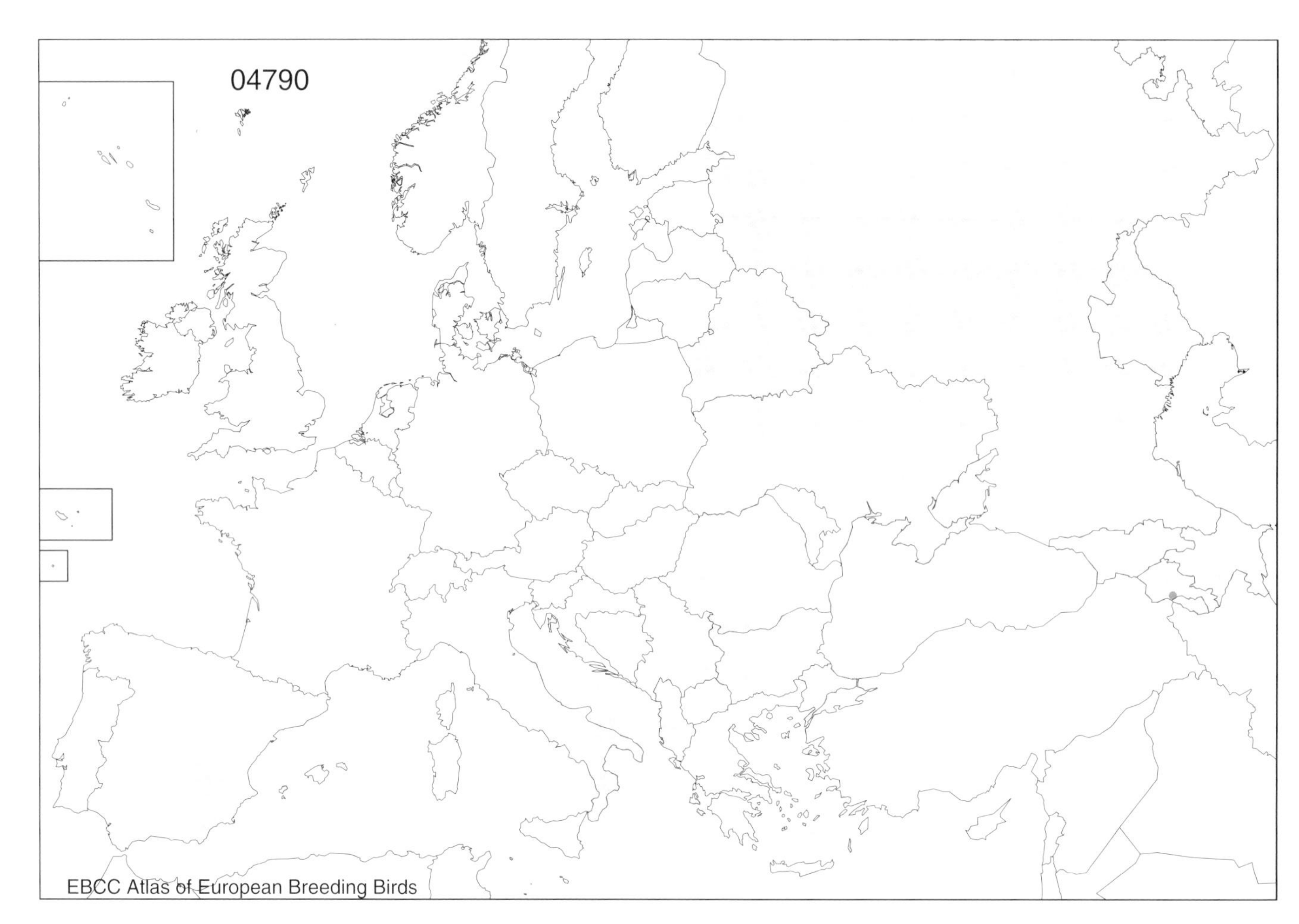

The breeding range of the Greater Sand Plover stretches from the eastern Caspian Sea through the continental middle latitudes E to *c*110°E. In the *Atlas*' coverage area it occurs only in southernmost Armenia, other known isolated W Palearctic breeding sites being in C Turkey and Jordan. The Armenia breeders occur just within the range understood to belong to the western subspecies *C.l. columbinus* (*BWP*), but Armenian records at present are ascribed to *crassirostris* (P. Saenger, pers comm to the Editors), whose main range stretches eastwards from the Caspian. The results from the 1995 fieldwork for *The Birds of Armenia* project may resolve this issue. The nominate *leschenaultii* occurs in the Far East.

The Greater Sand Plover is a lowland species (occasionally up to 1000m asl in Turkey), breeding in saltpans and mud-caked, sparsely-vegetated plains in steppes, semi-deserts and deserts. Densities normally are low, but droughts may reduce the available area of suitable breeding habitat, thus causing some clustering of breeding pairs. Armenian quantitative data are lacking. In C Anatolia, at least 10bp bred in the saltpans of the Sultan marshes in the mid-1970s (Kasparek 1985). Occupation of such sites probably depends upon floods in good rainfall years, as at Qa Hanna and Azraq Oasis in Jordan (Evans 1994). Long-term trends are therefore not discernible from so few data.

The Greater Sand Plover is migratory, spending the winter along the shorelines of Asia, Australia and Africa over much the same vast range as the very similar Lesser Sand Plover *C. mongolus*, although some Caspian breeders remain on the southern Caspian shores (Hayman *et al* 1986). The small-billed, morphologically separable western *columbinus* population is thought to winter along the Red Sea and the Gulf of Aden (*BWP*).

Rob G Bijlsma (NL)

Charadrius asiaticus

Caspian Plover

CZ	Kulík kaspický	I	Corriere asiatico
D	Wermutregenpfeifer	NL	Kaspische Plevier
E	Chorlito Asiático Chico	P	Borrelho-asiático
F	Pluvier asiatique	PL	Sieweczka długonoga
FIN	Kaspiantylli	R	Каспийский зуек
G	Αψινθοσφυριχτής	S	Kaspisk pipare
H	Kaspi lile		

SPEC Cat 3, Threat status V (P)

A typical desert species, the Caspian Plover breeds mainly in the continental parts of C Asia (Kazakhstan, Uzbekistan, Turkmenistan), wintering in river valleys and lake depressions of the Middle East, East and South Africa. Its breeding range extends just into Europe where it inhabits the desert and semi-desert area between the Volga and Ural Rivers, in the Caspian lowlands and the Manych River valley.

The Caspian Plover is a common but unevenly distributed inhabitant of clay and stone deserts containing sparse, low herbage and patches of loose saline soil (solonchak) in depressions and by rivers or lakes. It usually breeds in loose colonies. Outside the breeding season it forms small flocks which may frequent waterholes used by cattle, or move on to grassland occupied by cattle, probably to feed on insects attracted to cattle dung (Dolgushin 1962). In Europe near its range limit, the Caspian Plover is rare and its distribution very sporadic. It nests mainly on solonchak adjacent to larger waterbodies.

The species' range limits and population are relatively stable or show a slight tendency to decrease. Provided that traditional cattle-rearing practices do not change, it will continue to benefit. However, as tree shelter-belts, plantations and their predatory corvid inhabitants become more widespread in the steppe and semi-desert regions, breeding conditions will become detrimental to ground-nesting birds (as has happened further W) such as the Caspian Plover. There are practically no data on the size of the European breeding population, though a very approximate estimate (in Dagestan, Kalmykiya, the Astrakhan region, and eastern parts of the Volgograd and Saratov regions) would be 200–500bp (Belik in press). After breeding, birds assemble in loose flocks whose movements gradually turn into migration during August. Return migration is altogether a more purposeful affair, birds leaving their wintering grounds in late March and early April, to take up territories by mid-April (Kozlova 1961, Dolgushin 1962).

Victor Belik (R)

Charadrius morinellus — Dotterel

CZ	Kulík hnědý	**I**	Piviere tortolino
D	Mornell-Regenpfeifer	**NL**	Morinelplevier
E	Chorlito Carambolo	**P**	Tarambola-carambola
F	Pluvier guignard	**PL**	Mornel
FIN	Keräkurmitsa	**R**	Хрустан
G	Βουνοσφυριχτής	**S**	Fjällpipare
H	Havasi lile		

Non-SPEC, Threat status S (P)

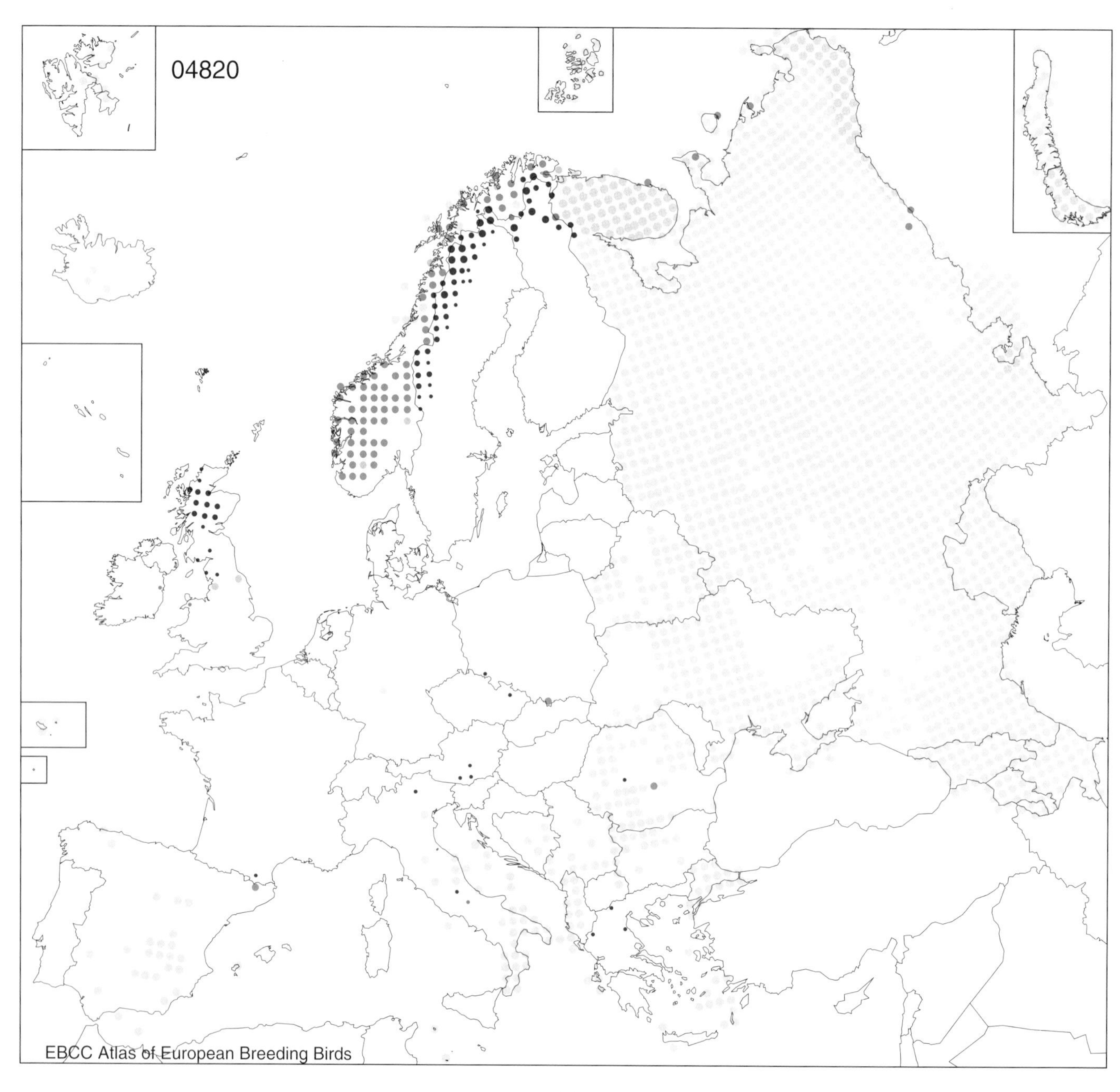

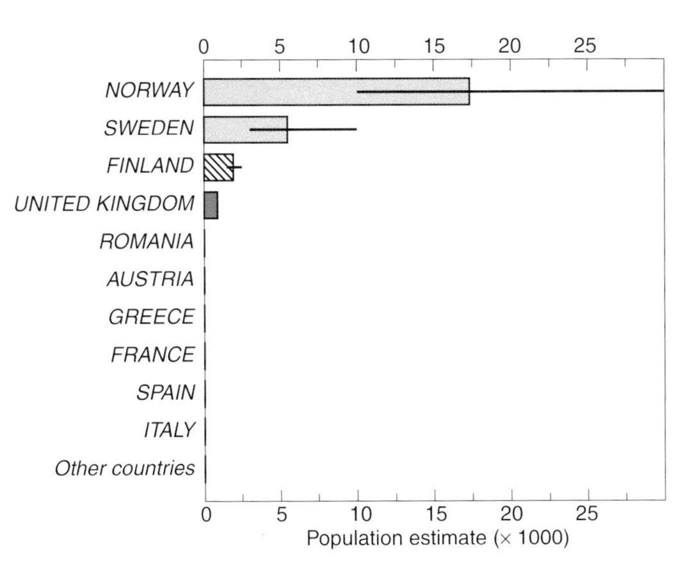

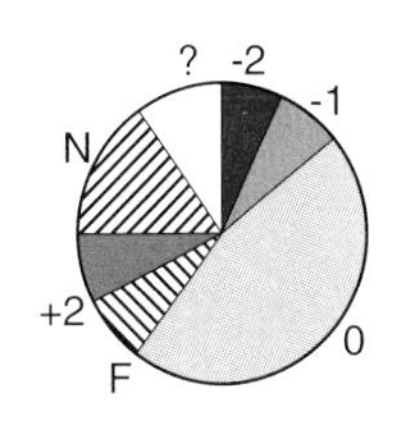

% in top 10 countries: 100.0
Total number of populated European countries: 13
Total European population 17,922–39,136 (25,663)
Russian population 10,000–50,000 (22,361)

The Dotterel is an arctic–alpine wader, occasionally polyandrous, of restricted European distribution. Sizeable European populations occur only in N Russia, Fennoscandia and Great Britain. There are small populations on some S and C European mountains. The Dotterel occasionally has bred on lowlands along its W European migration routes. Its world range extends along the northern shores of E Siberia to the Bering Strait, and to mountain chains in Mongolia and C Siberia.

Its winter range is confined to a narrow zone between Morocco and W Iran, imposing a migration route of at least 10 000km on the easternmost populations. The different populations probably mix in winter because chicks ringed in Finland and Scotland were found in E Siberia and Mongolia respectively, during the breeding season, and a migrant ringed in Ireland appeared in W Siberia.

Since 1850, the Dotterel has declined dramatically in Europe. Historically, overhunting was a major threat and may still be so in North Africa. In spring 1884 5200 Dotterel were shot in Ringköping, Denmark, whereas today, records of more than 100 are few (Meltofte 1993). Recent declines are probably due to the indirect effects of anti-locust pesticides in the wintering areas. The Dotterel has decreased severely in Finland, probably to about 1–10% of its original level, although its range appears to have remained constant since the 19th century (Saari 1995). Similar declines in the Austrian Alps and S Finnish Lapland (Sackl 1993) since the early 1970s indicate that the species is most at risk during migration or in its wintering areas. Conversely, the increase in the British population has been attributed to a cooling of spring climate since the early 1960s. Because some Dotterel breed in both Great Britain and Norway in different years (sometimes in the same year; Galbraith *et al* 1993), this is plausible. There are also some newly formed populations in mountains in S Europe.

The breeding habitat of the Dotterel is dry, flat or gently sloping, sparsely vegetated alpine heath or tundra above or beyond the treeline. In Norway it nests down to about 100m asl, in S Finnish Lapland down to under 500m. In S Scandinavia and Great Britain it breeds at *c*1000m, in the Austrian Alps at *c*2000m, and in Mongolia up to *c*3000m. On the Dutch polders it has nested below sea level!

Most Dotterel in Europe breed in N Russia, whose population is *c*10 000–50 000bp. Elsewhere, Norway has 5000–20 000bp, Sweden 3000–10 000bp, Finland 1500–2500bp and Great Britain 840–950bp. Other European populations are tiny; *c*10bp in Austria, France and Greece, and *c*5bp in each of Spain, Italy, Andorra, Czech Republic and Poland.

The highest recorded breeding density was on 58ha of alpine heath at Värriö, Finland (17 bp/km^2, 1969), not a regular breeding area (Saari 1995). In Britain a density of 10 bp/km^2 was exceeded in mountain areas (Galbraith *et al* 1993) but these densities are not typical of larger areas.

The Dotterel probably migrates non-stop from its wintering areas to its breeding grounds in N Europe (Maumary & Duflon 1989). Except for its traditional spring resting sites in The Netherlands and Denmark, it is usually recorded elsewhere only when bad weather affects the breeding grounds. In Finland it is recorded S of its breeding range only when its arrival dates (21–30 May) coincide with unseasonal cold weather (L. Saari, in prep). During autumn it is scarce on the coasts of W Europe, the main concentration occurring on the Hungarian steppes. The first arrivals in Hungary apparently are contemporaneous with those leaving N Fennoscandia (Saari 1995), but the migration period in the puszta is long, indicating that the more easterly populations arrive later.

Erich Hable (A) Lennart Saari (FIN)

Pluvialis apricaria **Golden Plover**

CZ	Kulík zlatý	**I**	Piviere dorato
D	Goldregenpfeifer	**NL**	Goudplevier
E	Chorlito Dorado Europeo	**P**	Tarambola-dourada
F	Pluvier doré	**PL**	Siewka złota
FIN	Kapustarinta	**R**	Золотистая ржанка
G	Βροχοπούλι	**S**	Ljungpipare
H	Aranylile		

SPEC Cat 4, Threat status S

04850

EBCC Atlas of European Breeding Birds

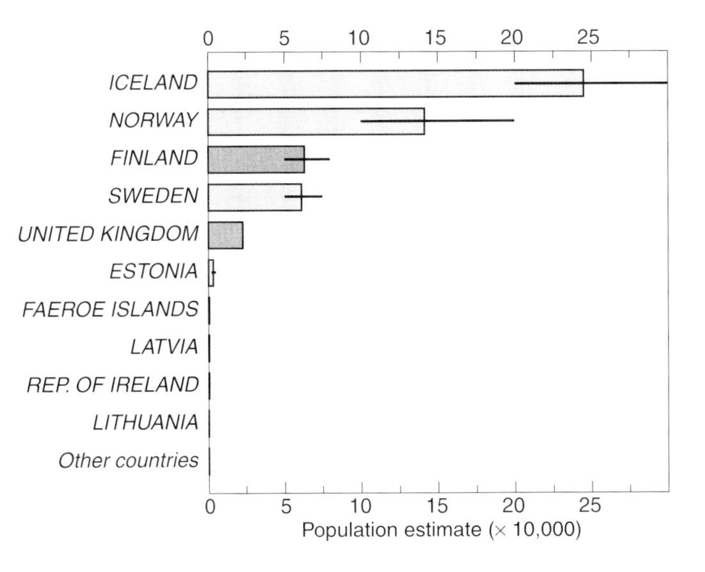

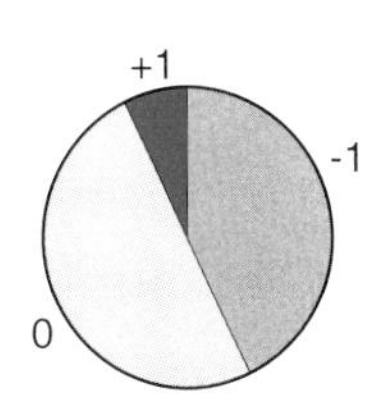

% in top 10 countries: 100.0
Total number of populated European countries: 14
Total European population 474,920–621,757 (538,476)
Russian population 10,000–100,000 (31,623)

The Golden Plover is a characteristic species of tundra, boreal grassland, upland grass, heather and bog moors and, in the S of its range, some drier heaths. It is a Palaearctic species that occurs from Iceland in the W to as far E as C Siberia (*c*122°E), but small numbers (*c*100bp) breed in Greenland and Ellesmere Island in the Nearctic (Boobyer 1992).

Approximately 50% of its European population of 440 000–785 000bp breeds in Iceland, with a further 25% in Norway and the bulk of the remainder in Finland, Sweden, Russia and Great Britain. It tends to avoid tall or dense moorland vegetation and prefers flat, sloping ground covered by low vegetation. There is some evidence that breeding success may be greater on heather moorland and bog than grass moorland (Crick 1992). Population densities tend to be related to the productivity of the land, being higher on base-rich soils, near pastures or regularly burned moorland, and being lower on acid soils. The highest recorded population density was 16.4 bp/km^2 on upland limestone grassland (Ratcliffe 1976), but more typical high population densities are 10 bp/km^2, moderate densities are 1.5–4 bp/km^2 and low densities are <0.5 bp/km^2. In some areas breeding space may be limiting requiring sequential use of territories: in a colour-marked population second pairs occupied nesting territories once the brood of the original territory holders had hatched and dispersed away from the nest site (Parr 1979). In N Europe, densities of 2–5 bp/km^2 prevail over much of the low-lying peatlands and mires (Koskimies 1989a, Leibak *et al* 1994).

Since the 19th century there has been a marked contraction of its range at the southern limits of its distribution in NW Europe. An important factor has been the loss of heathland areas to agricultural improvement and afforestation. Previously extensive populations in Denmark, Belgium, Luxembourg, Germany and Poland have gone extinct or are near extinction and there have been some declines in southern Swedish and Norwegian populations. In contrast, the Finnish population has increased since the mid-1960s, perhaps due to drainage of peatlands and clearfelling of forests (Koskimies 1989a). The Estonian population also increased in the 1960s (Leibak *et al* 1994). The British and Irish populations are considered distinct and relatively isolated from the populations of Scandinavian and Icelandic birds that visit in winter (Ratcliffe 1976). A population decline of *c*20% in Britain has been attributed to loss of habitat due to afforestation (Stroud *et al* 1987), a decline in the management of Red Grouse *Lagopus lagopus scoticus* moors (Ratcliffe 1976) and an increase in sheep-grazing that may increase nest losses (Crick 1992).

The populations of Iceland, Scandinavia and Russia are wholly migratory and winter in Britain & Ireland, W Netherlands, W Belgium, W France and on northern and southern Mediterranean coasts. There are three principal migration routes (Boobyer 1992): a western 'Atlantic route' from Iceland and the Faeroes, through the Western Isles of Scotland, Ireland and reaching down to western Iberia; the 'North Sea route' from northern Scandinavia and Svalbard through Denmark, The Netherlands, Eastern Britain, ending in northern France, and an 'East–West route' from NE Russia through C Europe to Iberia. Birds from Iceland are rarely encountered on the North Sea coast, but populations may mix when severe weather forces birds from all three routes to Iberia and North Africa. Wintering flocks tend to occur inland on fields of mown grass, closely cropped pasture, stubbles and fallow. It is a popular quarry species among hunters and is hunted extensively in France, but also in Denmark, Germany, Italy, Spain and Portugal. Azerbaijan and the southern Caspian littoral hold a significant wintering population whose origin and scale are uncertain.

Humphrey QP Crick (GB)

This species account is sponsored by Dr Gerhard Heyl, Leverkusen, D.

Pluvialis squatarola

Grey Plover

CZ	Kulík bledý	I	Pivieressa
D	Kiebitzregenpfeifer	NL	Zilverplevier
E	Chorlito Gris	P	Tarambola-cinzenta
F	Pluvier argenté	PL	Siewnica
FIN	Tundrakurmitsa	R	Тулес
G	Αργυροπούλι	S	Kustpipare
H	Ezüstlile		

Non-SPEC, Threat status S (P)

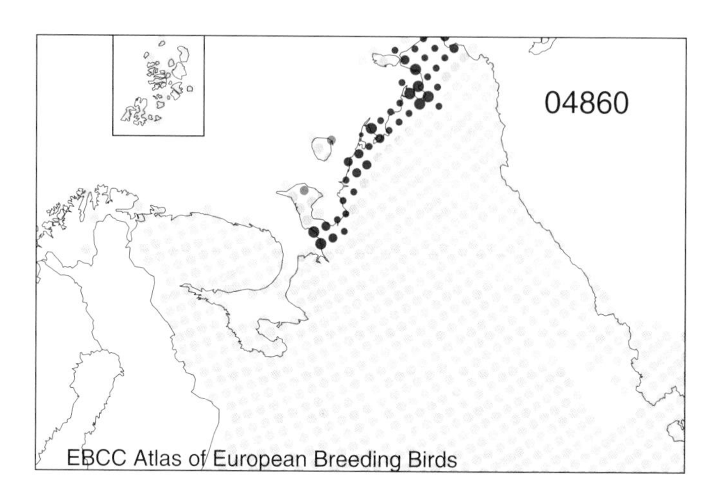

The Grey Plover has a circumpolar distribution and breeds over the whole Eurasian high-arctic mainland and on most offshore islands, from the Kanin Peninsula in the W to Chukotskiy Peninsula and Anadyr Bay in the E.

In Europe, it nests in several types of tundra. In the Kanin Peninsula, the habitat is mainly undulating heath tundra, whereas the mosses and lichens of bare tundra predominate further E, as in the Malozemel'skaya tundra (the River Indiga to the lower reaches of the Pechora) and the Bol'shezemel'skaya tundra (the Pechora to Prince Yugorskiy Peninsula). Poorly developed grasses (*Luzula confusa*, *Poa arctica*, *Calamagrostis holmii*) and a few higher taxa (purple saxifrage *Saxifraga oppositifolia*, mountain avens *Dryas octopetala*, bog rosemary *Andromeda polifolia*, Labrador tea *Ledum palustre*) comprise the vegetation. Inadequately drained soils and bogs are less favoured for breeding (Seebohm & Harvie-Brown 1876, Estafiev 1991, Yu. Mineyev, pers obs).

The Grey Plover nests on littoral tundras, within 20km of the coast, generally in clusters. E of the Pechora mouth, such areas are larger and breeding may occur 20–50km inland, even within the northern limits of the forest tundra (Estafiev 1991, Morozov 1992, Yu. Mineyev, pers obs). On the Timan coast (Malozemel'skaya), the Grey Plover prefers dryer soils with adjacent bare sandy patches, unlike the Golden Plover *P. apricaria*.

Like other Arctic breeding waders, breeding densities fluctuate considerably from year to year not only because of variable weather conditions, but also because of predator pressure in poor lemming (*Lemmus sibiricus*, *Dicrostonyx torquatus*) years. From long-term (1976–91) summer research over vast areas, densities of birds/km² are as in Table A. However, densities of nests/km² were much lower (Table B) over much of the same area (Estafiev 1991). Vaygach Island may be a stronghold (Karpovich & Khokhanov 1967).

Table A Densities of Grey Plovers

Area	Birds/km²
Malozemel'skaya tundra	0.68–2.53; mean (1986–91) 1.57 (Yu. Mineyev, in prep)
Bol'shezemel'skaya tundra	0.39–1.95; mean (1976–79) 1.01. Divided into:
Littoral tundra	1.73–1.95; mean (1976–77) 1.84
Central tundra	0.00–0.39; mean (1978–9) 0.2 (Estafiev 1991)
Yugorskiy Peninsula	0.18–4.07; mean (1981–4) 1.52 (Estafiev 1991)
Vaygach Island	2.4 (1965)

Table B Densities of Grey Plover nests

Area	Nests/km²
Bol'shezemel'skaya tundra (two vast areas)	
Littoral tundra	0.8 (1976) and 0.7 (1977)
Central tundra	0.0 (1978 and 1979)
Yugorskiy Peninsula	0.0, 0.49, 0.0 and 1.1, 1981–84
Vaygach Island	1.0, 1965

The Table B averages are higher than for long-term (1982–91) nest counts in Central Yamal (0.00–0.04) but considerably lower than for N Yamal (2.2–3.6) (Ryabitsev & Alekseeva 1992).

A minimum estimate of 10 000bp in Europe is probably extremely conservative (10 000–100 000), yet in the early 1950s it was considered comparatively rare. Its western expansion and population increase are therefore very significant. The recent sharp increase in wintering numbers reported in some areas in W Europe (Kirby *et al* 1991) may reflect its changing breeding distribution.

Long-term investigations by Yu. Mineyev (in prep) and Estafiev (1991) established that the highest densities (in birds/km²) in N European Russia were restricted to four prime habitats: the W coast of the Kanin Peninsula, between the Rivers Shemza and Kiya, *c*3.0; the Russkiy Zavorot Peninsula, 1.6; the coast of Khaypudirskaya Bay, 1.8; the W coast of Yugorskiy Peninsula, between the Rivers Bolshaya and Belkovskaya, 2.7, and the River Lymbadaykha, 4.0.

Grey Plover populations migrating through or wintering in W Europe are known to breed as far E as the Taymyr Peninsula. Recoveries of birds ringed in Sweden, Denmark and Great Britain indicate that some of these migrants winter as far S as the Gulf of Guinea. Strong evidence supports a smaller movement via the Mediterranean Flyway, probably of birds wintering in South Africa (Branson & Minton 1976).

Yuri N Mineyev (R) Jacques Van Impe (B)

Hoplopterus spinosus

Spur-winged Plover

CZ	Čejka trnitá	I	Pavoncella armata
D	Spornkiebitz	NL	Spoorkievit
E	Avefría Espinosa	P	Abibe-esporado
F	Vanneau éperonné	PL	Czajka szponiasta
FIN	Kynsihyyppä	R	Шпорцевый чибис
G	Αγκαθοκαλημάνα	S	Sporrvipa
H	Tüskés bíbic		

SPEC Cat 3, Threat status E (P)

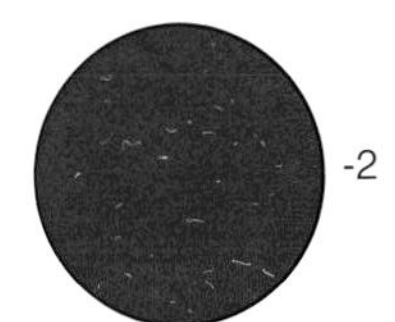

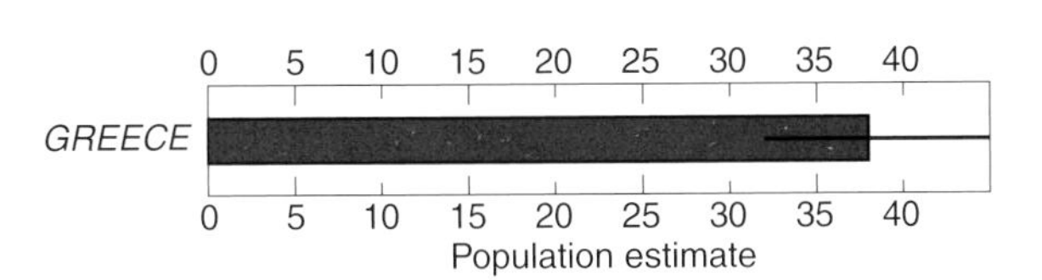

% in top 10 countries: 100.0
Total number of populated European countries: 1
Total European population 32–45 (38)
Turkish population 1000–5000 (2236)

The medium-sized Spur-winged Plover inhabits warm dry latitudes in mediterranean, subtropical and tropical zones. Its main distribution lies across sub-Saharan Africa and along the length of the Nile Valley, other centres being in Asia Minor and the Levant. Within the *Atlas*' area of coverage, it is a summer migrant to Greece and Turkish Thrace. Possibly these birds winter along the lower Nile. Elsewhere, it is a partial migrant or resident. The species generally favours mainly low-lying, flat coastal areas providing good all-round visibility.

It usually is found close to open water, from fresh to very saline. In Israel it occupies a variety of saline habitats (Shirihai 1996), in Greece islands in river-mouths (Jerrentrup 1994), coastal brackish marshes (Raines 1962), saltmarshes, coastal dunes and sandbanks in the Nestos Delta, and sandbanks near Lake Vistonis (de Nobel *et al* 1990) and in Turkey it prefers saltpans (Kasparek 1992). Increasingly it is colonizing irrigated habitats in Israel, being found in almost any habitat with moist ground (H. Shirihai, pers obs).

In Turkey, it breeds locally in the Marmara region and locally to very locally elsewhere (Kasparek 1992). It has bred locally in NE Greece in the Nestos area, Porto Lago and in the Evros Delta (Raines 1962). The drier sections in the Nestos marshes near Keramoti and the Evros Delta still held territorial pairs in 1987 (de Nobel *et al* 1990). Population trends in Greece have declined since the mid-1970s through habitat destruction, land reclamation, intensified lagoon fisheries and clutch predation by feral dogs, golden jackal *Canis aureus* and increasing numbers of Yellow-legged Gull *Larus cachinnans*. The 60–90bp of 1970–90 had declined to 32–45bp by 1993. The trends in Turkey are not known.

In summer, pairs are very territorial, but nevertheless often congregate semi-colonially. Two nests only 40m apart have been noted in Israel where 100–150m is quite usual (Shirihai 1996). Yet, apparently suitable nearby areas remain unoccupied. In winter, it is less gregarious than many plovers, such as Sociable Plover *Chettusia gregaria* or Lapwing *Vanellus vanellus*, but occasionally small groups up to 15 are seen. However, on passage in Israel flocks of hundreds have been reported from wetland areas.

John Morgan (GB) Hadoram Shirihai (ISR)
Hans Jerrentrup (DK)

Chettusia gregaria

Sociable Plover

CZ	Keptuška stepní	I	Pavoncella gregaria
D	Steppenkiebitz	NL	Steppekievit
E	Avefría Sociable	P	Abibe-gregário
F	Vanneau sociable	PL	Czajka towarzyska
FIN	Arohyyppä	R	Кречетка
G	Αγελοκαλημάνα	S	Stäppvipa
H	Lilebíbic		

SPEC Cat 1, Threat status E

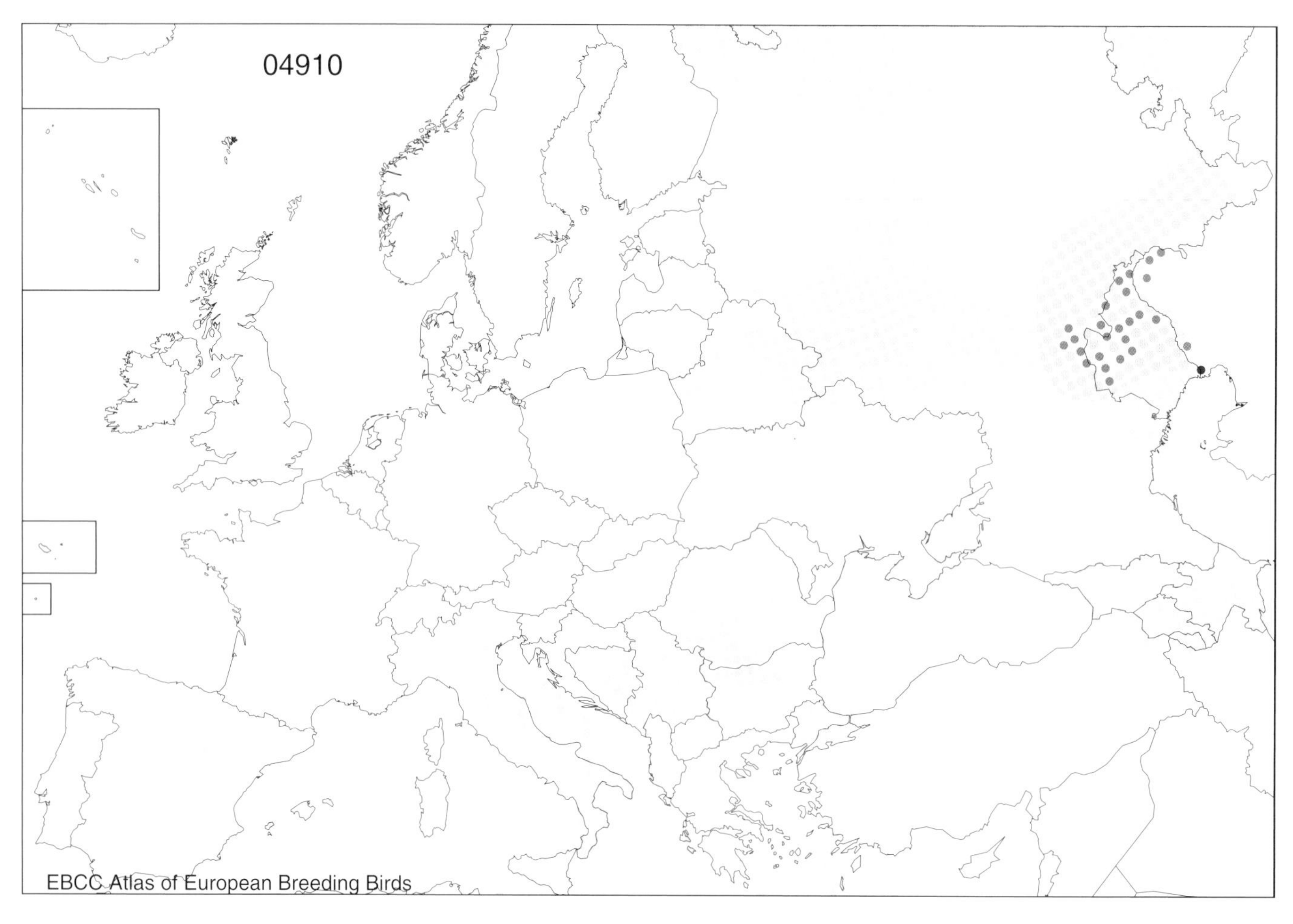

The Sociable Plover, a large member of its family, breeds on the steppes from the Volga River to E Kazakhstan. In Europe, it occupies the area between the Volga and Ural Rivers well inland from the Caspian Sea, between 47° and 53°N, breeding mainly on the original dry steppes containing feather grass *Stipa pennata* or wormwood *Artemisia* spp, usually in a saltmarsh area.

Its breeding range reached as far as Ukraine in the early 20th century (Borovikov 1907, Zarudni 1911, Sharleman 1938), but it has declined steadily since. The maximum European population, all in Russia, is estimated at *c*2000bp (1000–2100). It is possible that a population of that order occurs within the *Atlas*' coverage area between the Volga and Ural Rivers, a region which belongs mostly to Kazakhstan (Belik 1994a). The reason for the decline is probably habitat loss through agriculture, drainage and irrigation schemes. The spread of cattle into the species breeding areas renders the nests vulnerable to trampling. Predation by the increasing number of corvids occupying the maturing shelter-belts is also a threat.

Densities between the Volga and Ural Rivers probably average 1 bp/10–20km² of suitable steppe habitat, but in semi-desert areas adjoining the lower Volga in Russia, values are probably very much lower (Belik 1994a).

It is migratory, wintering in widely separated locations in Africa (Sudan, Kenya) and NW India, small numbers probably occurring at suitable locations in between. Its migration patterns are poorly known, but may still be indicative of much wider original breeding and winter distributions. It is now a very rare vagrant to western Europe and eastern Europe outside Russia, although as recently as the 19th century it was a common migrant in SE Europe (Kistyakivski 1957).

Valentin Serebryakov (UKR)

Chettusia leucura

White-tailed Plover

CZ	Keptuška běloocasá	I	Pavoncella codabianca
D	Weißschwanzkiebitz	NL	Witstaartkievit
E	Avefría Coliblanca	P	Abibe-de-cauda-branca
F	Vanneau à queue blanche	PL	Czajka stepowa
FIN	Suohyyppä	R	Белохвостая кречетка
G	Λεύκουρος	S	Sumpvipa
H	Fehérfarkú lilebíbic		

Non-SPEC, Threat status S (P)

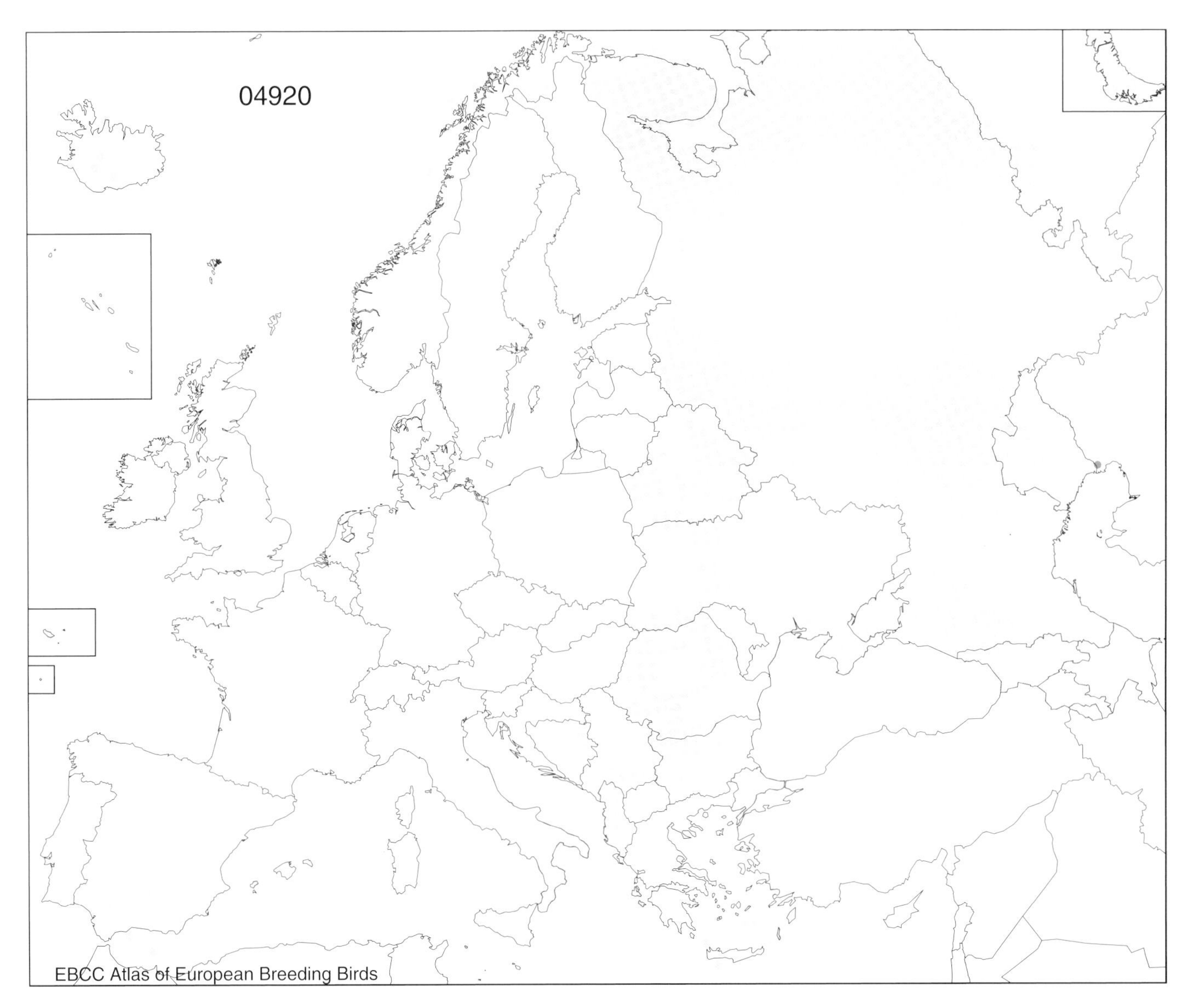

The present distribution of the White-tailed Plover has two main centres in the desert steppe zone, one in Iraq and Iran, where it is partly resident, and the other in Turkmenistan and Uzbekistan. It tends to nest in semi-colonial groups or in loose association with other colonial waders, usually being found near slow-flowing water.

Since the mid-1960s it has expanded its range N and W, but the extent to which this was due to droughts is uncertain. There seems to be a more permanent expansion associated with irrigation schemes and there may also have been an increase in numbers (Tomkovich 1992). In the area of *Atlas* coverage, it has bred near the N Caspian coast (Belik 1989), in Armenia (P. Saenger, pers comm to the Editors) and in Azerbaijan (Tomkovich 1992). The total number breeding in the *Atlas*' coverage area is unknown, but is likely to be low, perhaps only a few dozen breeding pairs.

The C Asian breeding population migrates in winter to Sudan, the Middle East or the northern Indian subcontinent, remaining from September to March. The Mesopotamian population is largely sedentary, but the northernmost birds move southwards in winter.

Philip Jackson (GB)

Vanellus vanellus **Lapwing**

CZ	Čejka chocholatá	**I**	Pavoncella
D	Kiebitz	**NL**	Kievit
E	Avefría Europea	**P**	Abibe-comum
F	Vanneau huppé	**PL**	Czajka
FIN	Töyhtöhyyppä	**R**	Чибис
G	Καλημάνα	**S**	Tofsvipa
H	Bíbic		

Non-SPEC, Threat status S (P)

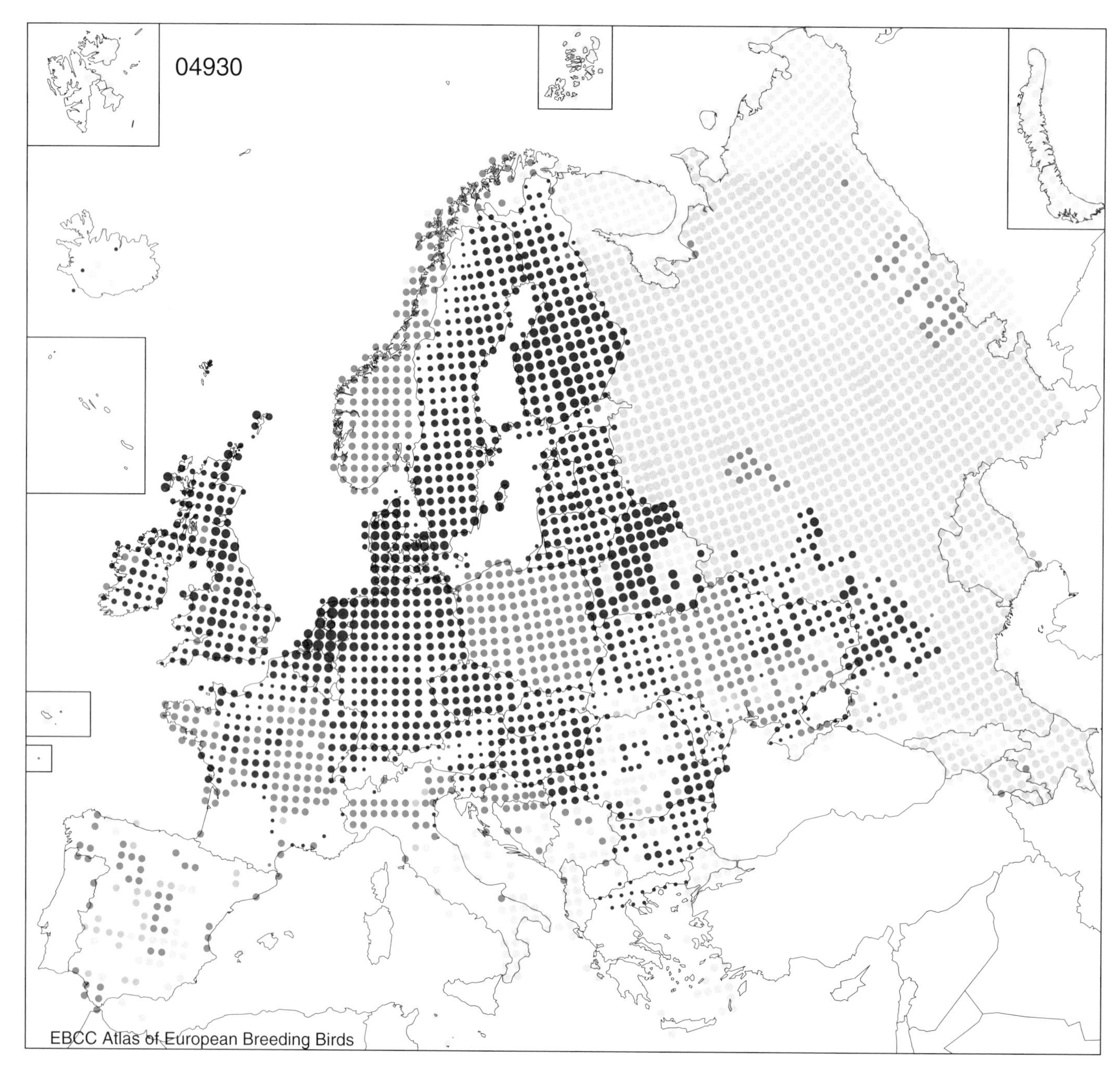

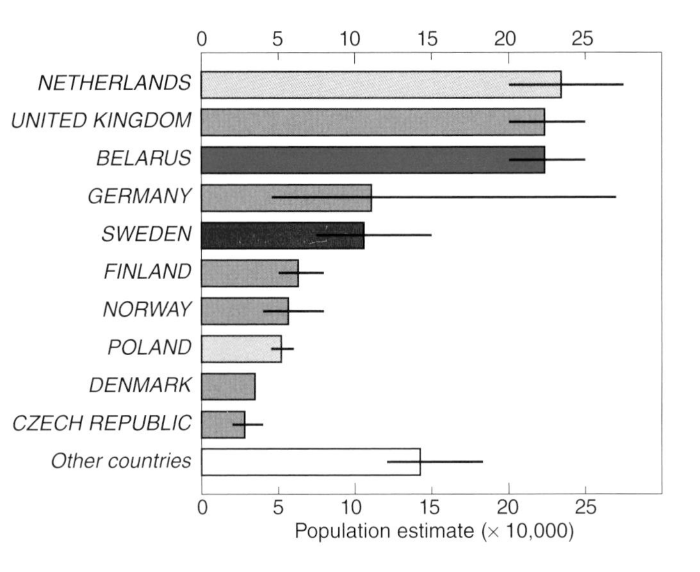

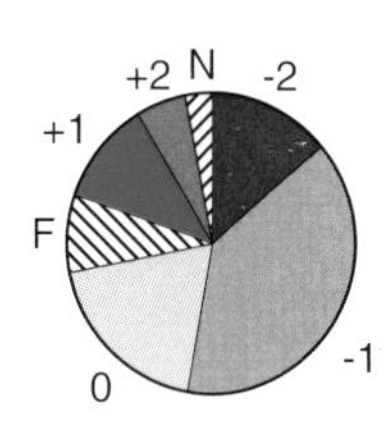

% in top 10 countries: 88.8
Total number of populated European countries: 36
Total European population 1,185,967–1,454,357 (1,276,324)
Russian population 1,000,000–10,000,000 (3,162,278)
Turkish population 5000–50,000 (15,811)

The Lapwing, a widespread, monotypic Palearctic wader, breeds in most of Europe including Iceland, but more sparsely through North Africa (Morocco) across S Russia and N China to Ussuriland. Its unbroken wintering area stretches from the Atlantic littoral (Ireland to Iberia) from the coastal plains of NW Africa through the Mediterranean basin to Mesopotamia. Eastwards, it winters in discrete areas to the Oriental region.

It inhabits a large variety of open landscapes, preferring lowlands. It avoids undulating ground, small open patches devoid of adequate all-round visibility, and plots densely covered by tall vegetation. The shift from its original habitats of marshes, bogs and coastal grasslands to farmland began when these habitats began to be drained for conversion to farmland. The changing agricultural landscape in Fennoscandia from the late 19th century onwards resulted in a rapid northward range expansion to Lapland (von Haartman 1973) and a concomitant population growth. Regionally, there were also expansions from long-established farmland and grazed meadow habitats to natural mire habitats.

Russia, The Netherlands, Belarus and Great Britain, each with >200 000bp, hold 80–90% of the total European breeding population. From 1984 to 1987 in mainland Britain, there was a decline of 40% to *c*208 000bp, 90% being on farmland. Perhaps three successive cold winters, after a long period of comparative stability, played their part, but the quality and area of suitable nesting habitat had also declined drastically with the increase in autumn tillage and a reduction in lowland pasture. Areas where spring tillage remains predominant retain high densities (Shrubb & Lack 1993). Upland pastures may have received more birds. The link between agricultural changes and decreasing breeding numbers is particularly evident in S and E England, where the population has suffered most (Shrubb & Lack 1991). Some 50% of European countries experienced range contractions and decreasing numbers during 1970–1990, mostly by 20–50%. The vicissitudes of the dense Dutch population are complex, with apparently stable numbers on arable land since 1985 (when numbers crashed probably because of the 1984/85 severe winter) and a slow, long-term decline on grassland (van Dijk 1995). E European countries, such as Russia, Poland, Ukraine, Romania, Lithuania and Croatia, all regions where farming practices are not yet fully industrialized, report mostly stable numbers. Increases occurred in Belarus (200 000–250 000bp) and in the small Slovenian and Italian populations.

Over its entire range, the principal causes of population decline are drainage, more intensive use of grasslands and greater use of artificial chemicals. The first reduces the availability of wet habitats essential for chick survival (Shrubb 1990), the second causes high nest and fledgling losses through mowing or cattle trampling, and the third reduces the availability of invertebrates in cultivated fields and creates a highly productive single-species environment, thus reducing the Lapwing's foraging and breeding opportunities. In The Netherlands, the species adapted partly to these adverse changes by increased breeding on arable land (especially maize) and by breeding two weeks earlier than in the early 1900s. The latter change is probably an adaptation to changing agricultural activities (Beintema *et al* 1985). Its effect on breeding success is not yet quantified but British populations are known to have difficulty in producing sufficient fledglings to maintain the population (Peach *et al* 1994). A population increase in NW Germany possibly arose through immigration, rather than through increased reproductive success locally (Kooiker 1990).

C European breeding densities fluctuate between 1 and 10 bp/km^2 of agricultural land, but on prime Dutch grassland habitats reach 35–40 bp/km^2 (Friesland and Noord-Holland peat districts) and in eastern Netherlands, up to 25 bp/km^2 (SOVON). On the damp pastures (machair) and fens of the Outer Hebrides, NW Scotland 42 bp/km^2 were found (Fuller *et al* 1986). In Finland, density varied in the mid-1980s between 5 and 13 bp/km^2 on agricultural land (Piiroinen *et al* 1985).

Timo Pakkala (FIN) Miroslav Šálek (CZ) Juha Tiainen (FIN)

This species account is sponsored by Ala, Schweizerische Gesellschaft für Vogelkunde und Vogelschutz, CH.

Calidris canutus

Knot

CZ	Jespák rezavý	I	Piovanello maggiore
D	Knutt	NL	Kanoetstrandloper
E	Correlimos Gordo	P	Seixoeira
F	Bécasseau maubèche	PL	Biegus rdzawy
FIN	Isosirri	R	Исландский песочник
G	Χοντροσκαλίδρα	S	Kustsnäppa
H	Sarki partfutó		

*SPEC Cat 3*W, Threat status L*W*

The Knot is a circumpolar tundra species and only an occasional breeder in the western Palearctic. Most of the world population breeds in North America, Greenland and eastern Siberia. In Eurasia breeding occurs only on the Taymyr Peninsula, the Novosibirskiye Islands, on Chukotka (Rogacheva 1992) and on Svalbard. It breeds up to 300m asl near the coasts of peninsulas and large islands N of the continental mainland. Suitable habitats include dry rocky plateaus containing tufts of mountain avens *Dryas octopetala* (*BWP*).

There are five subspecies worldwide, two of which, the nominate *C.c. canutus* and *islandica* are encountered in the western Palearctic, the former breeding on Svalbard (and the Taymyr Peninsula) and wintering in Africa, and the latter inhabiting Greenland and NE Canada and wintering in NW Europe (Piersma & Davidson 1992).

Few reliable demographic data are available on high-arctic waders and the Knot is no exception. The Svalbard population currently numbers *c*5–10bp, probably breeding beside the Sassen River in Sassendalen (V. Bakken, pers comm). On Ellesmere Island breeding density was relatively low at 1.09 bp/km² (Nettleship 1974), as it was in the northeastern Taymyr Peninsula (0.07–0.21 nests/km² in

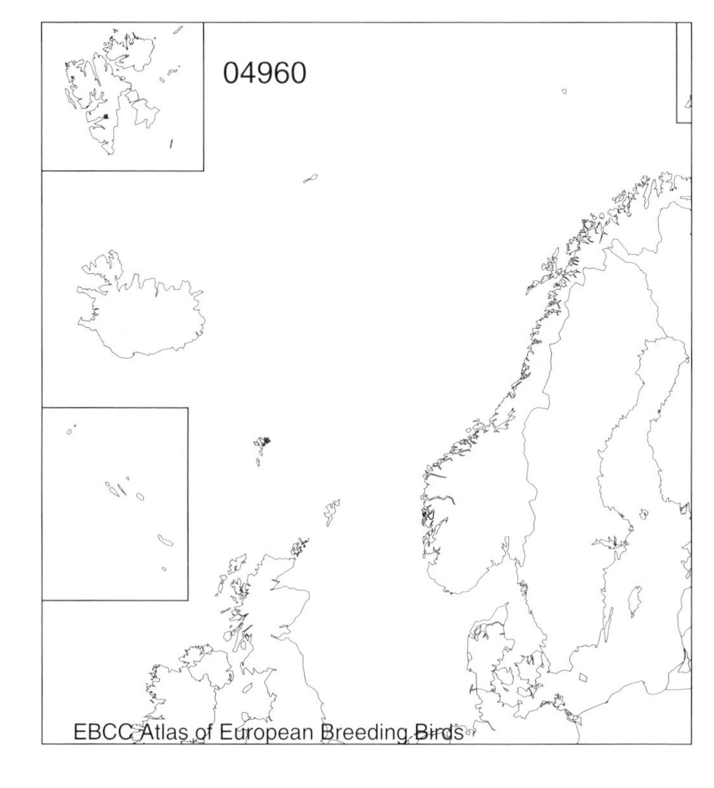

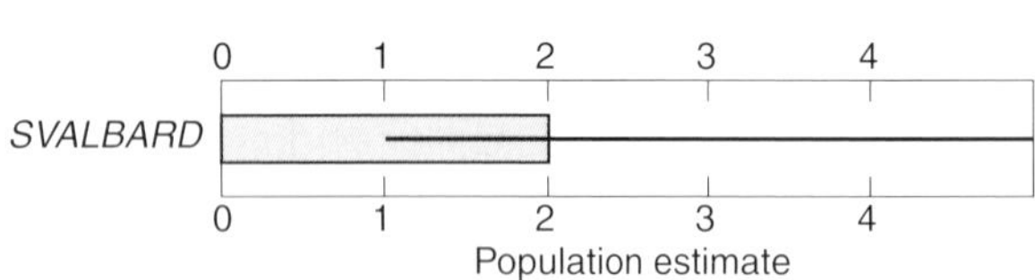

% in top 10 countries: 100.0
Total number of populated European countries: 1
Total European population 1–5 (2)

1991; Underhill *et al* 1993). Well over half of the European wintering population is found in British and Irish estuaries, smaller numbers occurring in The Netherlands and France. In 1972, 1974 and 1979 the number of Knot wintering in Britain fell sharply. In 1972 for instance, the winter total was almost half that of the previous year. High adult mortality and low reproductive success on their breeding grounds in the Queen Elizabeth Islands and northern Greenland were probably caused by cold arctic summers (Boyd 1992). Though there are small annual fluctuations, wintering numbers in Britain & Ireland have now more or less stabilized. During the winter of 1993–94 there were peaks of 257 800 and 7627 individuals in Britain and Ireland respectively (Cranswick *et al* 1995).

Populations of *islandica* and *canutus* have been estimated at 345 000 and 516 000 birds, respectively (Piersma & Davidson 1992). Both subspecies depend on a precariously small number of intertidal coastal areas along their migration routes. Recent research implies that the tropically wintering *canutus* has a 10% higher survival rate than the temperate wintering *islandica* (Boyd 1992), suggesting differences in age of first breeding and recruitment.

Simon Gillings (GB)

Calidris alba

Sanderling

CZ	Jespák písečný	I	Piovanello tridattilo
D	Sanderling	NL	Drieteenstrandloper
E	Correlimos Tridáctilo	P	Pilrito-sanderlingo
F	Bécasseau sanderling	PL	Piaskowiec
FIN	Pulmussirri	R	Песчанка
G	Λευκοσκαλίδρα	S	Sandlöpare
H	Fenyérfutó		

Non-SPEC, Threat status S

This high-arctic species has a discontinuous circumpolar breeding range (arctic Canada, northern Greenland, Svalbard and N-C Siberia) but a very wide winter distribution (most temperate and tropical coasts). It occurs in Europe in winter and on migration, but breeding in the region is restricted to Svalbard. The Sanderling is monotypic. The migration system is complex and poorly understood, because the wintering ranges of different breeding populations seem to overlap to a large degree. Individuals migrating through Europe may be members of Greenland or Siberian breeding populations, but those wintering in Europe are probably mainly of Greenland origin (Gudmundsson & Lindström 1992).

The Svalbard population seems to be very small, given the handful of breeding records (Løvenskiold 1963, Kålås & Byrkjedal 1981). The population in Greenland has been estimated at 17 000bp (Meltofte 1985). A total of 27 000 Sanderling have been reported wintering on European coasts (Smit & Piersma 1989). The Siberian breeding population, which to some extent migrates through Europe is probably large, as judged by the numbers wintering in West Africa (43 000, Smit & Piersma 1989) and southern Africa (78 000, Summers *et al* 1987a).

The breeding phenology and habitat descriptions below derive from studies of the Greenland population (Meltofte 1985 and references therein). The Sanderling appears on the breeding grounds in late May to early June, laying its eggs mainly in the 2nd and 3rd weeks in June. It nests in a variety of tundra habitats ranging from the immediate surroundings of well-vegetated moist sites to drier arctic heaths and even gravel slopes and flats with little vegetation cover apart from lichens. Hatching peaks in the second week of July. After the first week of August, the adult birds leave the breeding grounds and by the end of August the young of the year have all started their migration to their wintering quarters.

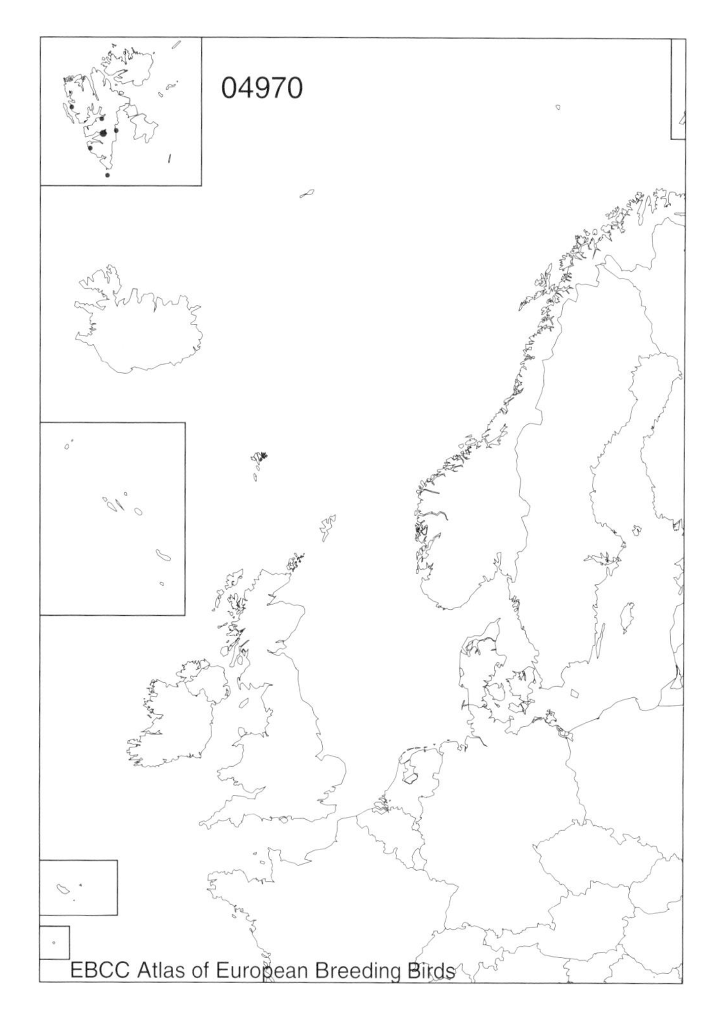

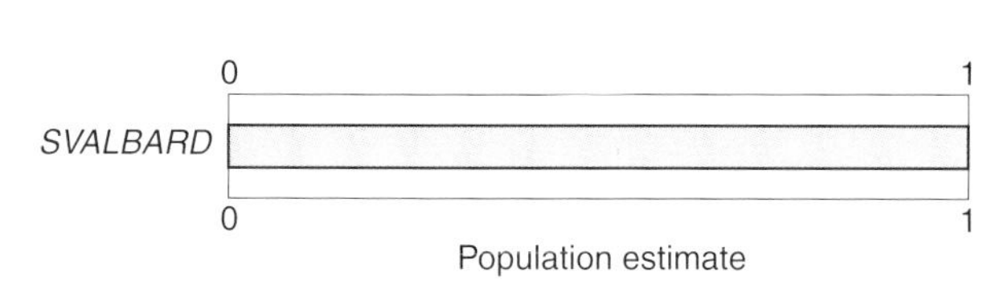

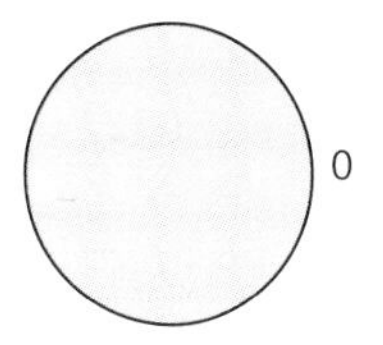

% in top 10 countries: 100.0
Total number of populated European countries: 1
Total European population 1

Gudmundur A Gudmundsson (ICE)

Calidris minuta

Little Stint

CZ	Jespák malý	I	Gambecchio
D	Zwergstrandläufer	NL	Kleine Strandloper
E	Correlimos Menudo	P	Pilrito-pequeno
F	Bécasseau minute	PL	Biegus malutki
FIN	Pikkusirri	R	Кулик-воробей
G	Νανοσκαλίδρα	S	Småsnäppa
H	Apró partfutó		

Non-SPEC, Threat status S (P)

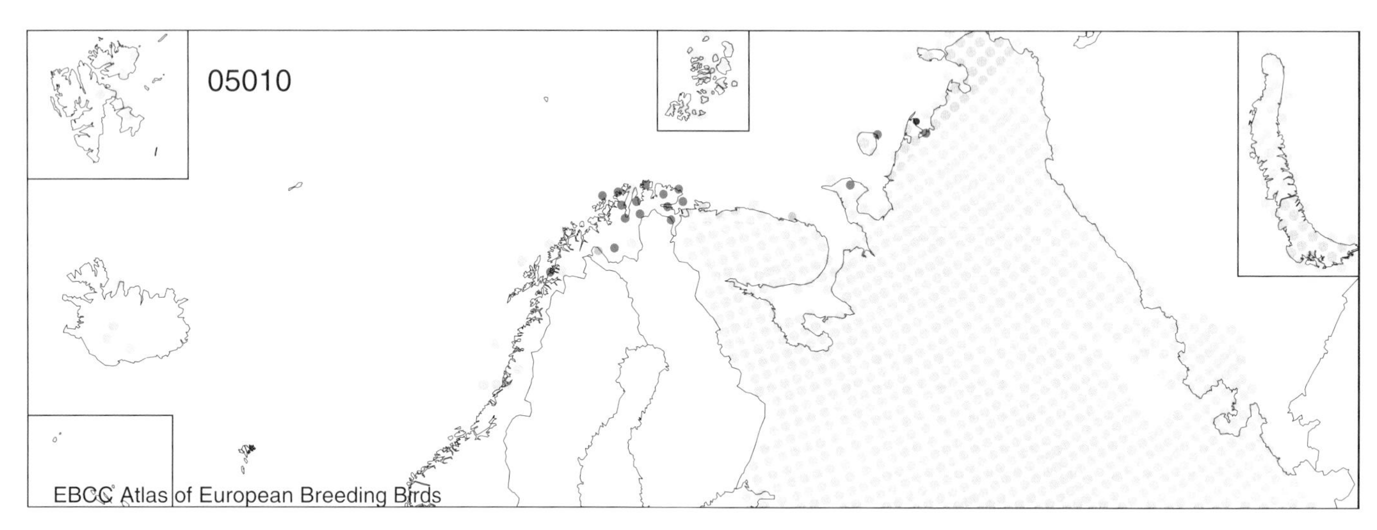

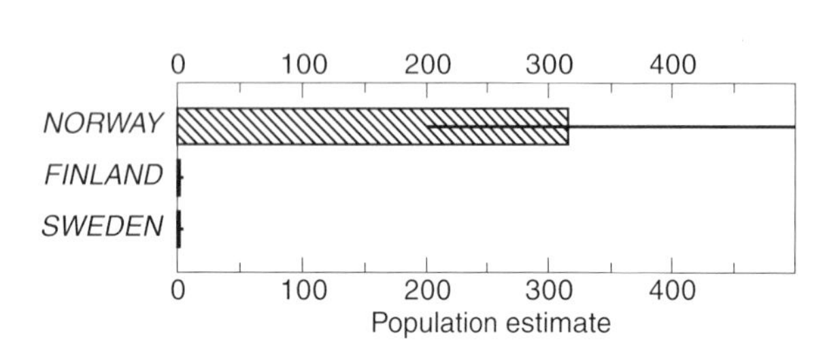

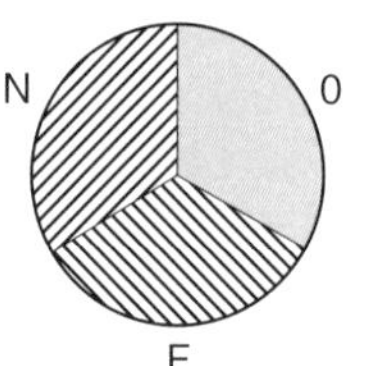

% in top 10 countries: 100.0
Total number of populated European countries: 3
Total European population 204–505 (321)
Russian population 100,000–1,000,000 (316,228)

The Little Stint, a tiny Palearctic wader, breeds in Siberia, from the River Lena in the E to northern Norway in the W, being distributed mainly along the northernmost tundra zone. Russia holds the main breeding population (>100 000bp), the Norwegian population being of marginal importance (200–500bp). The European breeding population has remained stable in numbers, exhibiting no trend.

The Little Stint's main breeding habitats in Europe are coastal tundra and islands with shallow freshwater pools. In Russia it now breeds on inland areas of tundra containing reindeer mosses *Cladonia* spp, low sedges and dwarf shrubs. The highly fluctuating Norwegian breeding population is patchily distributed in over 30 different localities (Hildén 1978a, Schmidt 1988, Sæter 1994) in Finnmark mainly in the uplands at *c*300m asl and along the coastline. Small numbers breed inland in upland habitats (300m asl) near the Finnish border, nesting sometimes near the birch *Betula* treeline limit (Sæter 1994). The species requires a particular combination of suitable feeding grounds and nesting terrain as its breeding habitat. In coastal areas it feeds partly on muddy shores whose extensive areas of seaweed are exposed at low tide, and partly on flat, sparsely vegetated freshwater shores of lakes, pools and river deltas (Hildén 1988). However, it usually nests near tundra freshwater pools in dry tundra low-vegetation heath, fresh water apparently being an important nesting habitat element (Hildén 1988, T. Breiehagen & K-B. Strann, unpubl). Although there have been very few studies in Europe, breeding densities do seem to fluctuate, but for reasons yet unknown (Hildén 1988). Over a 5-year study period (1989–93) near Gamvik in Norwegian Finnmark, breeding densities in a 10km^2 coastal study plot varied greatly between years (1–59 nesting individuals), breeders showing little site fidelity (T. Breiehagen & K-B. Strann, unpubl, Hildén 1988).

Migrating birds flock on European marine shores in spring and autumn, but they also appear at inland wetlands. Most W Palearctic birds probably migrate through tropical Africa to South Africa.

Torgrim Breiehagen (N) the late Olavi Hildén (FIN)

Calidris temminckii

Temminck's Stint

CZ	Jespák šedý	I	Gambecchio nano
D	Temminckstrandläufer	NL	Temmincks Strandloper
E	Correlimos de Temminck	P	Pilrito de Temminck
F	Bécasseau de Temminck	PL	Biegus Temmincka
FIN	Lapinsirri	R	Белохвостый песочник
G	Σταχτοσκαλίδρα	S	Mosnäppa
H	Temminck-partfutó		

Non-SPEC, Threat status S (P)

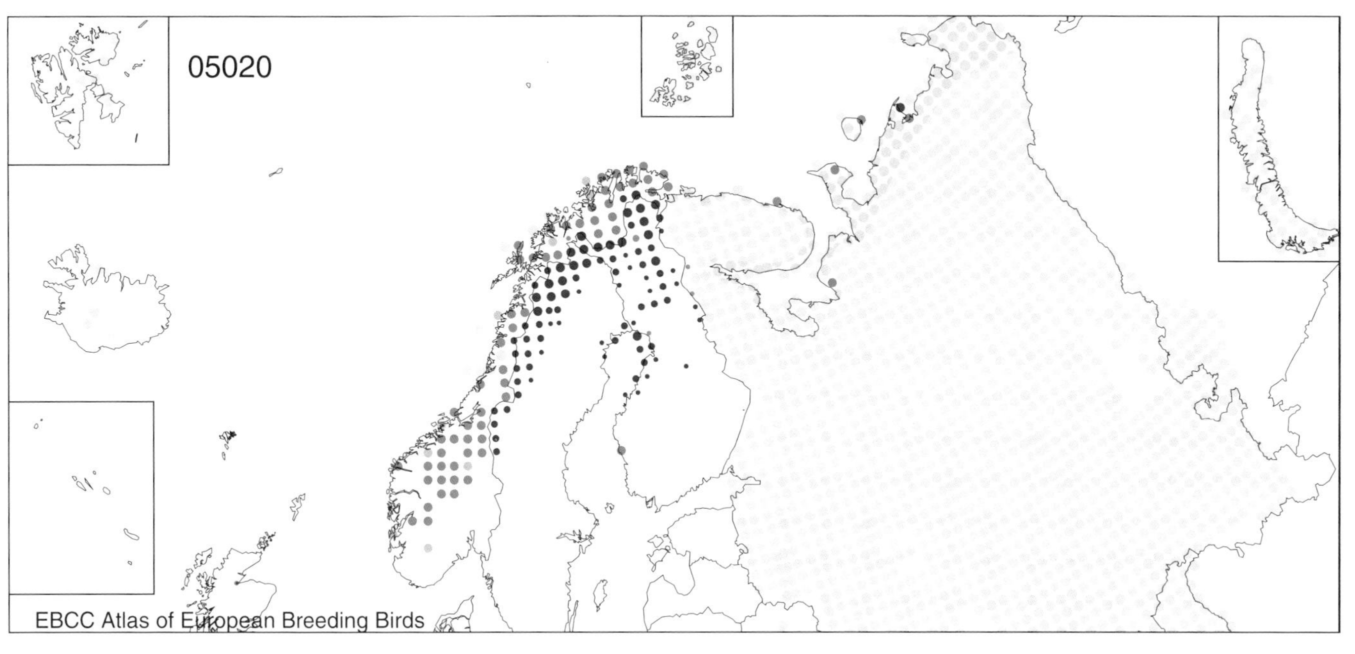

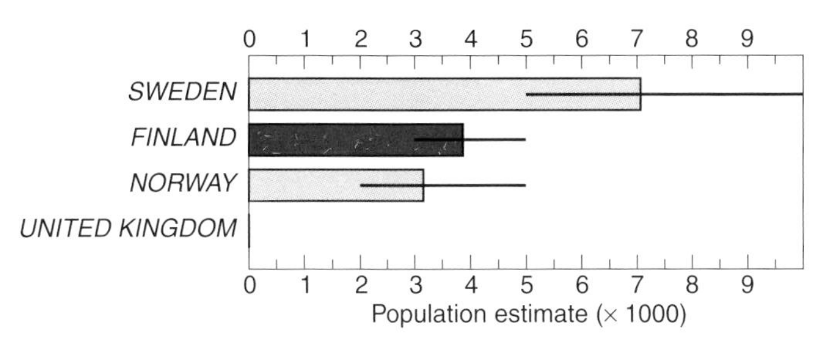

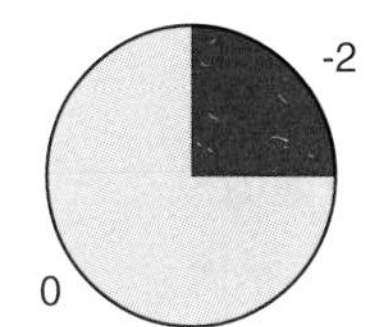

% in top 10 countries: 100.0
Total number of populated European countries: 4
Total European population 11,579–17,746 (14,109)
Russian population 1,000,000–10,000,000 (3,162,278)

Temminck's Stint is a tiny Palearctic wader breeding mainly in the tundra zone from E Siberia to Scandinavia, where it is also extending its range into the boreal zone. A few breed annually in Scotland. Russia holds the main European breeding population, at least 1Mbp, mainly N of the taiga zone, where it nests either on tundra and uplands (from 200 to 1300m asl) or in coastal areas, including fjords. In the former case, the species prefers low and scattered willow scrub or grasses near deltas, lakes or meandering rivers, and in the latter, breeds on the mainland or islands where low vegetation predominates. Because of its very specific habitat requirements, its breeding populations are patchily distributed, but, through the movement of 'vagrant' females in the egg-laying period, are not entirely isolated (Hildén 1975, Breiehagen 1989).

There are no data about overall population trends in Russia or in Scandinavia. The Scandinavian coastal breeding population has declined markedly since 1970, especially in Finland, probably due to habitat changes arising from reduced livestock grazing (Hildén 1978b, Hildén & Hario 1993) or to habitat destruction in fjords (deltas) (Breiehagen 1994). However, Temminck's Stint has bred quite close to habitation and industry.

Breeding densities are probably highest overall in tundra areas, varying enormously within known areas and from year to year, weather and food availability being major factors in tundra and montane regions. In S Norway, an alpine (1200–1250m asl) population achieved an average density of 15.8 nesting individuals/km^2 over three years, but local variation of snow conditions produced an inter-year density variation of 5.6–83.3/km^2 (Breiehagen 1989). In prime coastal habitat in Finland, Hildén (1975) recorded an exceptional 25–42 territorial males/10ha, but elsewhere densities were very much lower.

Migrating birds occur singly or in small groups in spring and autumn on marine shores and inland wetlands over most of Europe. Western Palearctic birds winter mainly in the African savanna zone wetlands.

Torgrim Breiehagen (N) the late Olavi Hildén (FIN)

Calidris melanotos

Pectoral Sandpiper

CZ	Jespák skvrnitý	**I**	Piro-piro pettorale
D	Graubruststrandläufer	**NL**	Gestreepte Strandloper
E	Correlimos Pectoral	**P**	Pilrito-peitoral
F	Bécasseau à poitrine cendrée	**PL**	Biegus arktyczny
FIN	Palsasirri	**R**	Дутыш
G	Θωρακωτή Σκαλίδρα	**S**	Tuvsnäppa
H	Vándorpartfutó		

Criteria not applied

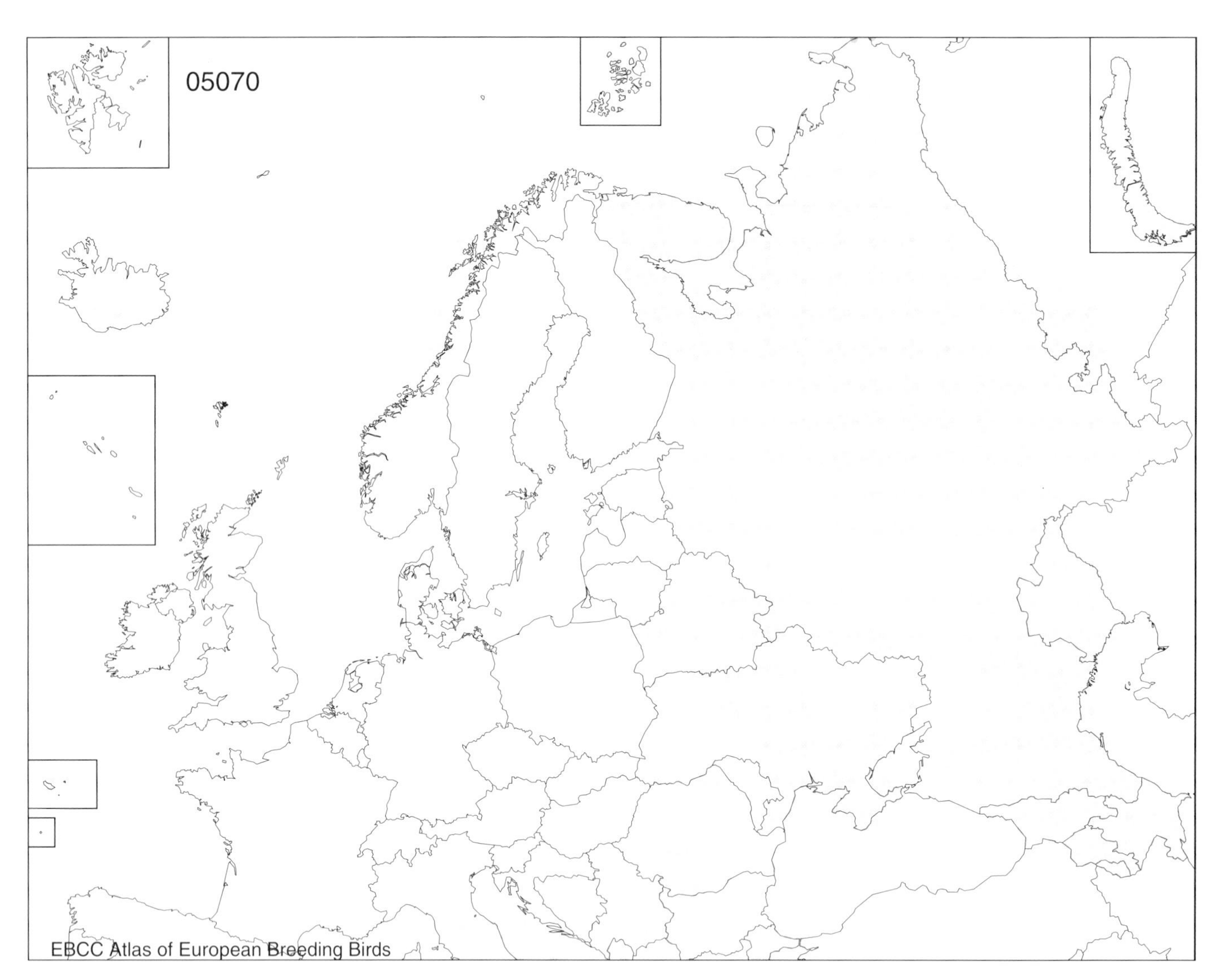

The breeding distribution of the Pectoral Sandpiper stretches from Alaska and northern Canada in the Nearctic across the eastern and C Siberian subarctic, traditionally as far W as the Taymyr Peninsula, but there has been an apparent westward expansion recently. Since 1980 there have been irregular sightings of displaying males in summer on the west side of Karskaya Inlet, just inside the *Atlas*' area of coverage (Estafiev 1991), thus meeting the criteria for assessment as a possible breeder. A summer visitor to the Siberian tundra, nesting usually on the dry margins of tundra wetlands, often in grasses or sedges close to pools, this species requires a well-drained site with ample plant cover.

The migratory pattern of all Pectoral Sandpiper populations is not entirely clear. Nearctic populations winter in South America and it seems likely that most of the Siberian populations join them after a journey of 16 000km. The intriguing possibility arises that some Pectoral Sandpipers encountered on migration in Europe may have an Asian and not North American origin. Breeding birds return from their winter quarters before the end of May. On arrival the males begin their distinctive vocal displays, sounding like a miniature fog-horn. The inflated throat sac producing the sound also displays the contrasting shape of breast and belly. Males may mate with several females, while females visit the territories of different males.

Philip Jackson (GB)

Calidris maritima

Purple Sandpiper

CZ	Jespák mořský	I	Piovanello violetto
D	Meerstrandläufer	NL	Paarse Strandloper
E	Correlimos Oscuro	P	Pilrito-escuro
F	Bécasseau violet	PL	Biegus morski
FIN	Merisirri	R	Морской песочник
G	Βραχοσκαλίδρα	S	Skärsnäppa
H	Tengeri partfutó		

SPEC Cat 4, Threat status S (P)

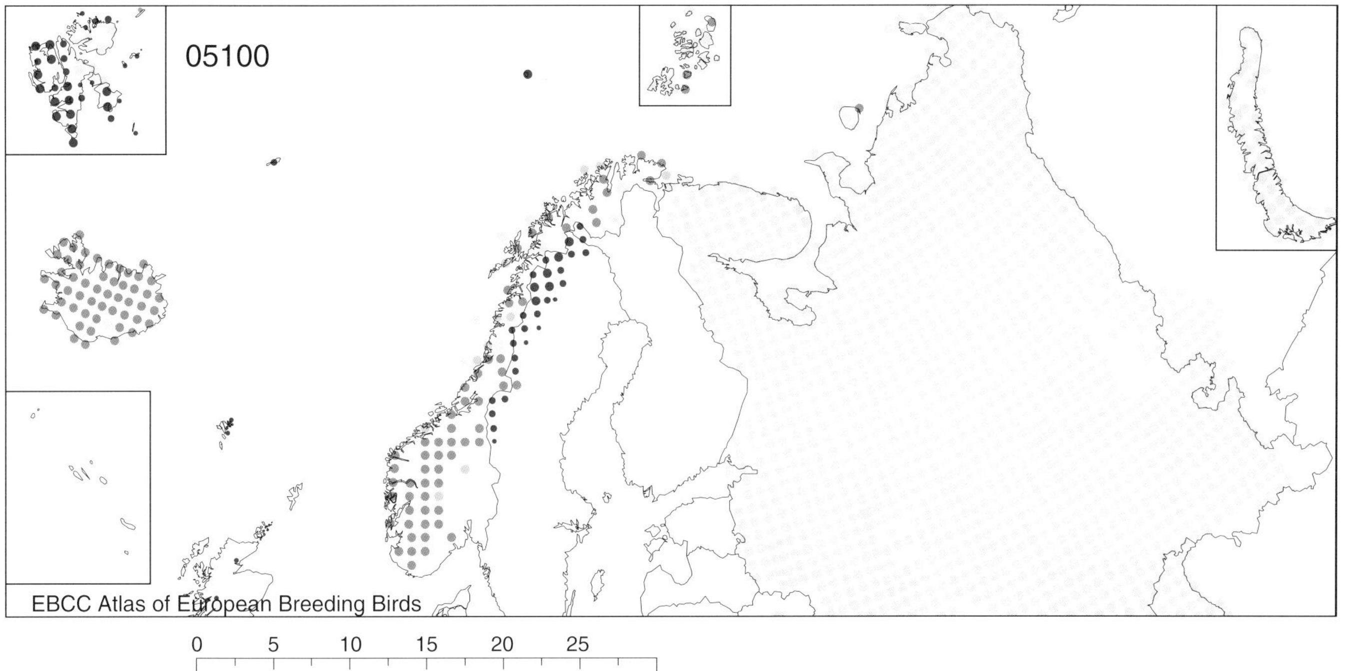

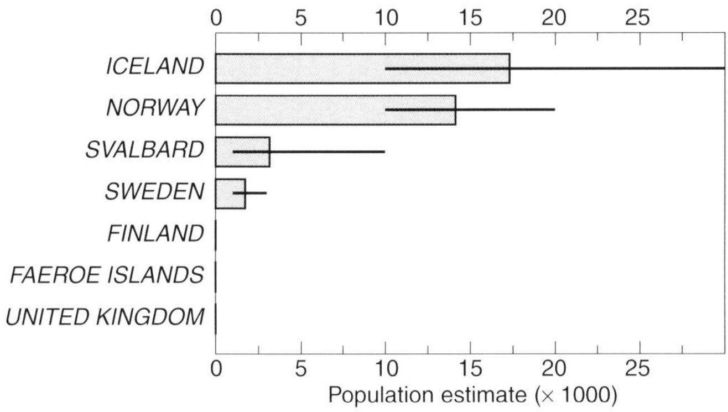

-2

0

% in top 10 countries: 100.0
Total number of populated European countries: 7
Total European population 27,658–51,976 (36,373)
Russian population 1000–10,000 (3162)

The Purple Sandpiper breeds in mid- and high-alpine and arctic areas from the eastern Canadian high arctic, through Greenland, Iceland, Scandinavia and eastwards to Severnaya Zemlya and the Taymyr Peninsula in Siberia. It is replaced in the N Pacific by the closely related Rock Sandpiper *C. ptilocnemis*. Birds from different Purple Sandpiper populations vary in size, the smallest birds breeding in Greenland and in southern Scandinavia, those from Russia, arctic Canada and Iceland being larger (Boere *et al* 1984).

The Icelandic breeding population appears to winter there while the Russian and Scandinavian populations winter along rocky shores from the Kola Peninsula southwards to Spain. Canadian populations winter along ice-free shores S to Maryland. The species has more northerly wintering areas than any other wader, large numbers occurring along the coast even N of the Arctic Circle (Summers *et al* 1990).

The Purple Sandpiper breeds in alpine and tundra habitats containing short, often patchy vegetation cover. It is the most arctic breeding wader species in Europe, being a relatively common bird as far as 80°N in Svalbard and Franz Josef Land. The southern limits of its breeding range lie in the Faeroes and in Scotland, the latter having a tiny population.

In the S of its range, the Purple Sandpiper breeds only in alpine habitats whereas in Iceland and the arctic areas of northern Norway and Russia it nests down to sea level. It is territorial while breeding and so densities usually are low (1 bp/km^2) (Alendal *et al* 1982), but in optimal habitats in coastal areas in Iceland and in its arctic European range, it may form aggregations, nests being separated by only 20–30m (10–30 bp/km^2) (Summers *et al* 1987b).

There are no data available from breeding areas about population changes, but its breeding range in Europe seems to be stable and counts of birds wintering in Great Britain between 1960 and 1990 indicate no dramatic changes in those populations (Bell 1989, Summers & Rogers 1991).

John Atle Kålås (N)

Calidris alpina Dunlin

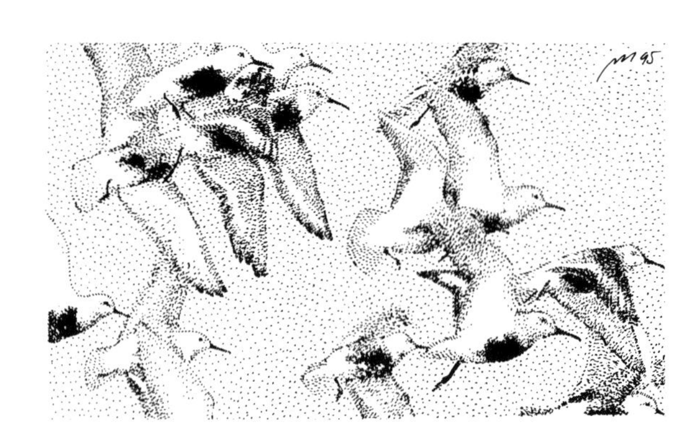

CZ	Jespák obecný	**I**	Piovanello pancianera
D	Alpenstrandläufer	**NL**	Bonte Strandloper
E	Correlimos Común	**P**	Pilrito-comum
F	Bécasseau variable	**PL**	Biegus zmienny
FIN	Suosirri	**R**	Чернозобик
G	Λασποσκαλίδρα	**S**	Kärrsnäppa
H	Havasi partfutó		

*SPEC Cat 3*W, Threat status V*W*

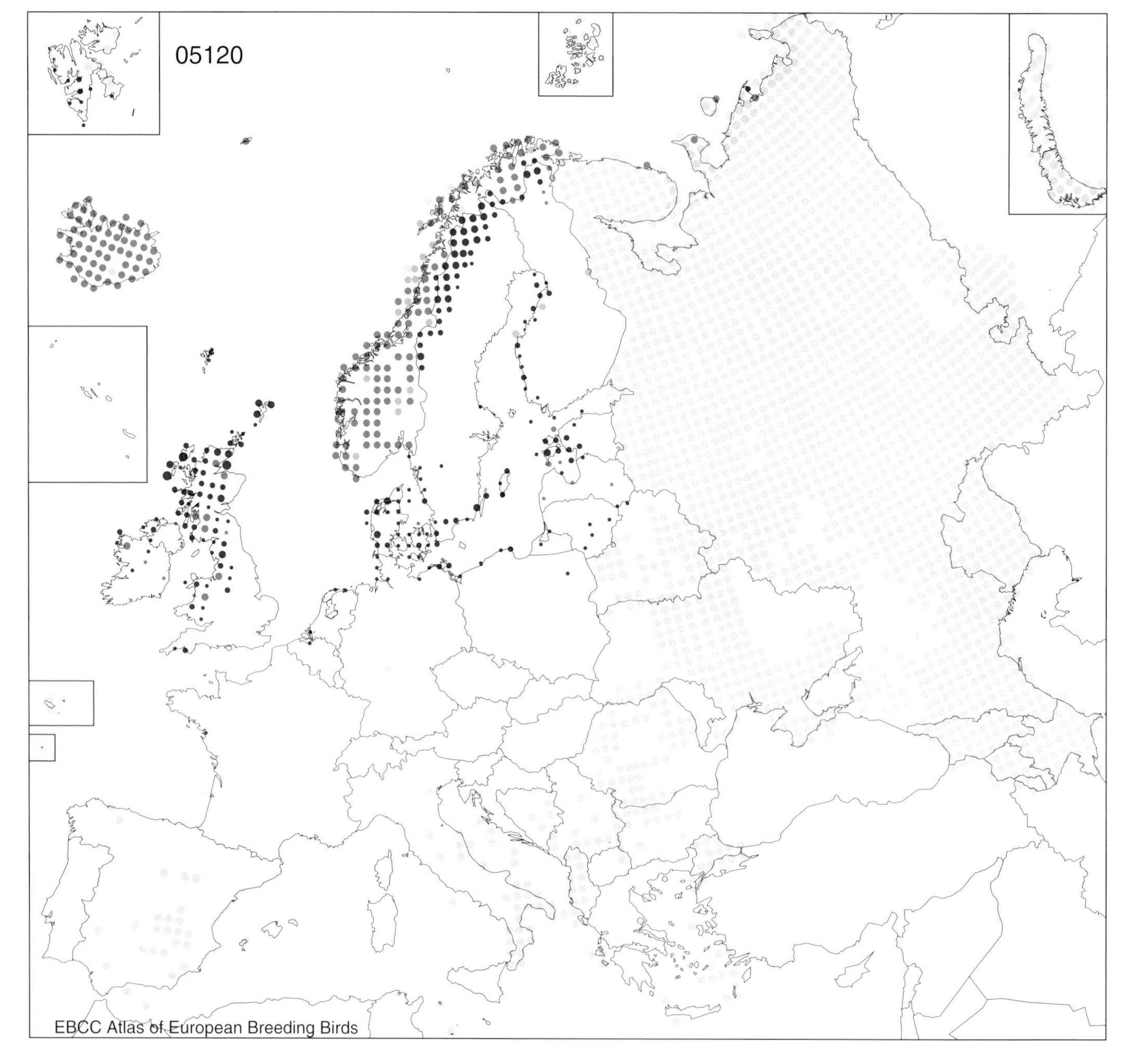

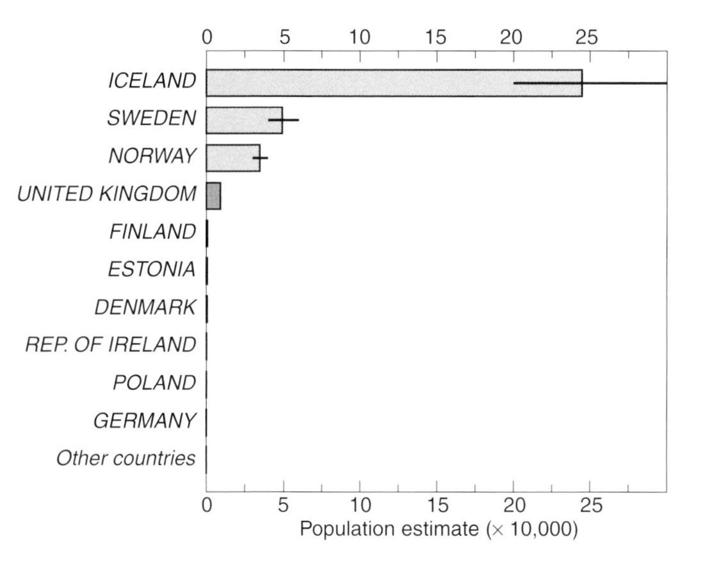

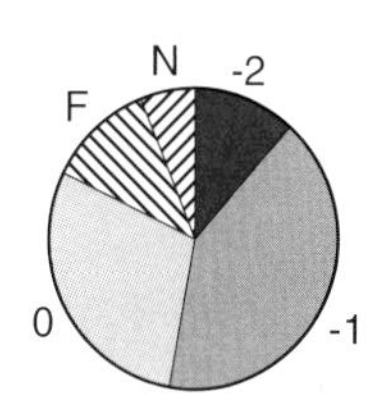

% in top 10 countries: 100.0
Total number of populated European countries: 17
Total European population 293,873–396,344 (339,947)
Russian population 100,000–1,000,000 (316,228)

The Dunlin breeds in northern temperate and arctic latitudes throughout a circumpolar distribution. Two subspecies breed within Europe and a third (*arctica*), breeding in Greenland, appears in western Iceland and on the European Atlantic coasts as a passage migrant. The stronghold of *schinzii* is in Iceland and a substantial population also breeds in Great Britain. It winters mainly in West Africa although the very small Baltic breeding populations possibly winter in France and in the Mediterranean (Jönsson 1988). The nominate *alpina* breeds across northern Fennoscandia and Russia and winters in western Europe and around the Mediterranean. Its breeding range's eastern limit is not clear, but lies the E of the Urals. Nor are the exact Norwegian and Swedish southern breeding limits known; southern Norway's inland breeding population may consist of *schinzii* (H-U. Rösner, pers comm).

The Dunlin always breeds in open wet habitats, occupying alpine tundra, meadows, pastures and heaths. In upland bogs and mires, its habit of associating with the Golden Plover *Pluvialis apricaria* has given it the name of 'plover's page'. The small Baltic remnant *schinzii* population (Estonia, 500–700bp: Latvia and Lithuania, 10–15bp) is restricted mainly to wet coastal meadows and river-mouth floodplains (Leibak *et al* 1994). In northern Russia the Dunlin breeds on moss-sedge tundra.

Coastal breeding populations may reach extremely high densities; for instance in Britain densities equivalent to more than 300 bp/km^2 were found in some places on South Uist (Fuller *et al* 1986), some nests being less than 10m apart (Etheridge 1982). Around the Baltic densities of up to 50 bp/km^2 occurred, but there, the breeding habitat became less attractive to the Dunlin as coastal grazing declined. Densities away from the coast tend to be rather lower, as in the flow country of northern Scotland where densities average 1–3 bp/km^2, square, but sometimes reach 25 bp/km^2. In Northern Russia (Kolguyev Island) in natural tundra habitats, within the breeding range of *alpina*, densities of 80 bp/km^2 have recently been recorded (E. Syroechkovski Jr, pers comm).

Iceland's *schinzii* population is stable, but that in Britain is declining mainly as a result of upland afforestation although there has been some corresponding increase in NW Scotland, especially on islands (Thompson & Boobyer 1993). The Baltic breeding population is also in decline as a result of agricultural intensification and the decrease or cessation of coastal grazing (Jönsson 1988).

Monitoring breeding populations of Dunlin is difficult, especially in the sparsely populated Russian tundra regions forming the heart of *alpina*'s breeding range. The fortunes of this subspecies have been monitored in the main part of its wintering range through the BTO's Birds of Estuaries Enquiry (now subsumed into the Wetlands Bird Survey, or WeBS, run by the BTO, WWT, RSPB and the JNCC). The results reveal that the high numbers of the mid-1970s suffered a lengthy decline, the population halving between 1975 and 1987. However, subsequently there has been some recovery (Prŷs-Jones *et al* 1994).

On autumn passage adults are largely restricted to intertidal habitats, feeding on seaweed beds in the Baltic or on estuarine flats in other areas, but juveniles migrate on a broad front and occur at many inland sites where there is exposed mud or very shallow water. On spring passage *schinzii* are confined to the extreme W coast of Europe with large numbers concentrating in the estuaries around the Irish Sea, whereas the *alpina* populations which winter on the European Atlantic coasts congregate mainly in the northern Wadden Sea and then overfly the Baltic on their way to the breeding grounds. Some *alpina* migrate through C and eastern Europe to winter around the Mediterranean, and in spring congregate by the Black Sea en route to their eastern breeding areas.

Nigel Clark (GB) Jaga Gromadzka (PL)

Limicola falcinellus **Broad-billed Sandpiper**

CZ	Jespáček ploskozobý	I	Gambecchio frullino
D	Sumpfläufer	NL	Breedbekstrandloper
E	Correlimos Falcinelo	P	Pilrito-falcinelo
F	Bécasseau falcinelle	PL	Biegus płaskodzioby
FIN	Jänkäsirriäinen	R	Грязовик
G	Μπεκατσινοσκαλίδρα	S	Myrsnäppa
H	Sárjáró		

SPEC Cat 3, Threat status V (P)

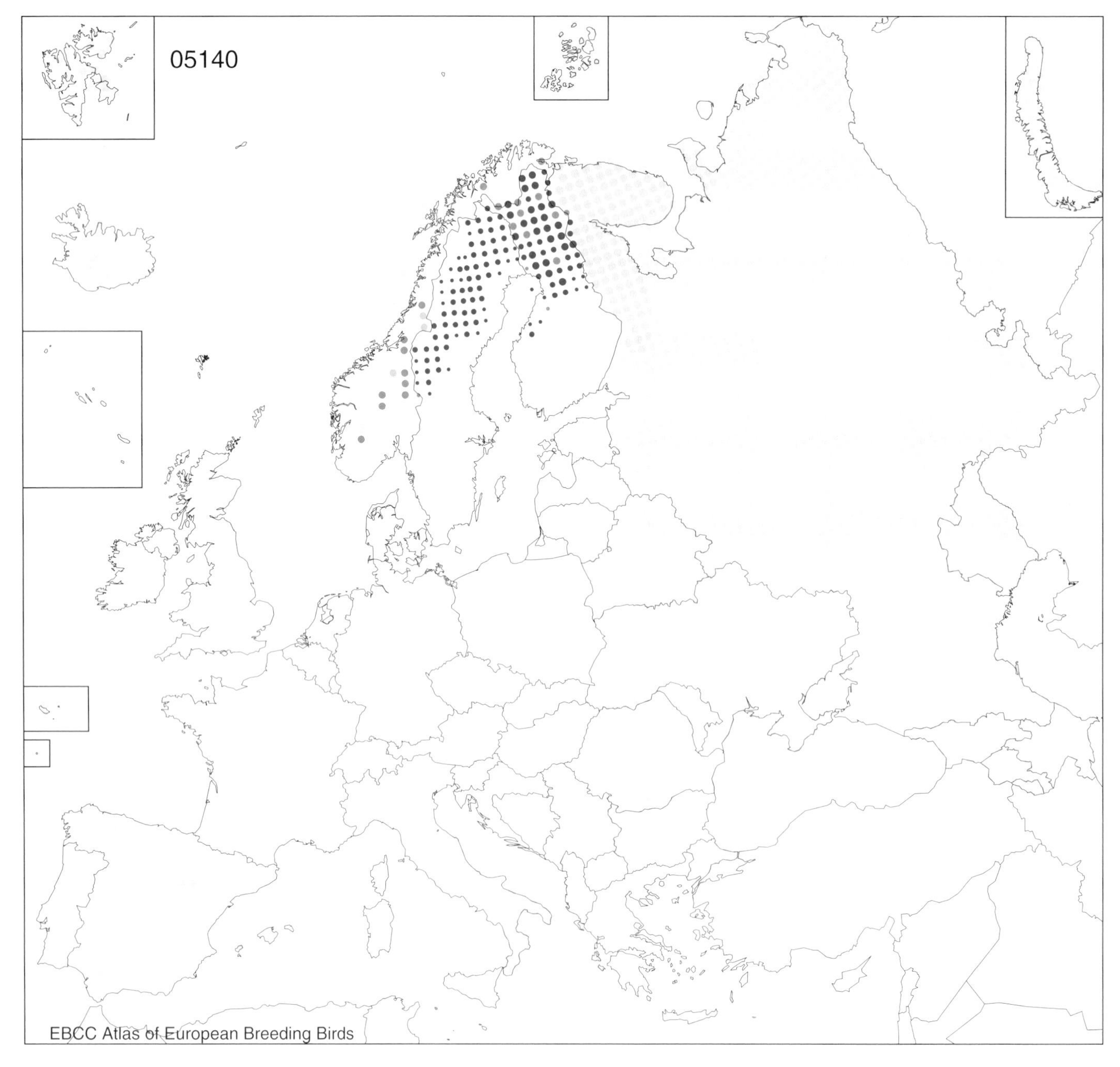

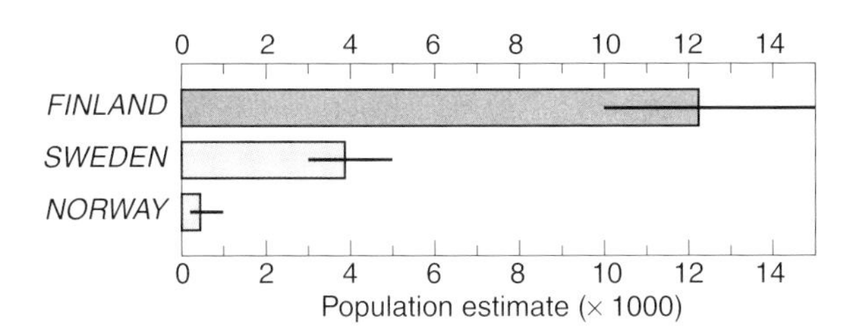

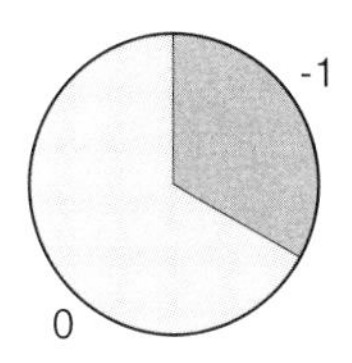

% in top 10 countries: 100.0
Total number of populated European countries: 3
Total European population 14,144–19,593 (16,568)
Russian population 100–1000 (316)

The Broad-billed Sandpiper is a secretive, rare or scarce boreal–subarctic wader which has three separate breeding populations: in the bogs of Fennoscandia including (old records only) the Kola and Kanin Peninsulas, in the bogs of W Siberia (both comprised of the nominate *L.f. falcinellus*), and in the Siberian tundras from the Taymyr Peninsula to the Kolyma River delta (*sibirica*).

The patchy breeding distribution of the Broad-billed Sandpiper results from its habitat requirements. In N–C Fennoscandia it is confined to the wettest parts of open *Sphagnum* moss bogs, especially where areas of open water have isolated sloughs of thin peat mud lightly overgrown with such plants as sedges *Carex*, cotton-grass *Eriophorum* and bog rosemary *Andromeda*. It sometimes inhabits bogs no larger than 1–2ha. In one locality in the Kanin Peninsula it nested on the *Sphagnum* bog banks of a small river whose peat sediments came from tiny underground streams (Spangenberg & Leonovich 1960). The Broad-billed Sandpiper may breed in loose colonies which may result in high local densities; 8bp on 3ha on the Kanin Peninsula, 6–10bp in 20ha Finnish Lapland bogs (over a 6-year period, indicating small inter-year fluctuations) and locally up to 20 bp/km^2 (Koskimies 1989a).

In Sweden and Finland it is mostly a lowland species, but it also breeds in mountain areas up to or slightly above the timberline, as in Norway (1000m asl). We believe that the main European Broad-billed Sandpiper population, in Finland, comprises at most *c*12 000bp, rather than 15 000 indicated in the graph. The Norwegian population, only a few hundred breeding pairs, seems recently to have expanded slightly southward. The species is poorly known in NW Russia, but there are at most probably only a few hundred breeding pairs in the Kola region. Using only data from its wintering grounds, the European population can be estimated roughly at *c*25 000 birds (Rose & Scott 1994). The size of the W Siberian population is unknown.

The Broad-billed Sandpiper's great dependence on its specialized breeding habitat would make it very vulnerable to habitat change, but fortunately in Sweden, the difficulties of access to its breeding areas coupled with the enforcement of the present regulations largely protect it against human impact. The populations in Norway and Sweden are more or less stable, but the species possibly has declined since 1970 in Finland (Koskimies 1994). It disappeared from S Sweden in the late 19th century because of drainage projects and a decline in the usage of extensive grazing areas.

On migration, the autumn passage of the Fennoscandian population flows largely southeastwards through the Sea of Azov and Black Sea region, but also encompasses the eastern Mediterranean and Caspian Seas. An important resting area is the Black Sea Sivash lagoon (van der Winden *et al* 1993). There are less pronounced southerly and southwesterly movements through Europe. The migration route of the easternmost European birds possibly overlaps in Kazakhstan with that of the W Siberian population. Ringing recoveries are few, but probably their bias overestimates the southerly to southwesterly component. The main wintering areas are the Arabian Gulf, India and Sri Lanka. Small numbers have been recorded in Kenya, Eritrea, Djibouti, Sudan and Uganda; some reach Namibia, Natal and Cape Province. Some *c*16 000 birds from the E Siberian population migrate through the Far East and overwinter in SE Asia, Indonesia and Australia (Watkins 1993). Rose & Scott (1994) suggest that this population is much larger, perhaps of the same order as the European population. Further studies are required to determine more accurately the sizes of the species' breeding populations. Its skulking nature in inaccessible boggy habitat will make that difficult.

Bo W Svensson (S) Pavel Tomkovich (R)

This species account is sponsored by Limicola – Zeitschrift für Feldornithologie, D.

Philomachus pugnax **Ruff**

CZ	Jespák bojovný	**I**	Combattente
D	Kampfläufer	**NL**	Kemphaan
E	Combatiente	**P**	Combatente
F	Combattant varié	**PL**	Batalion
FIN	Suokukko	**R**	Турухтан
G	Μαχητής	**S**	Brushane
H	Pajzsoscankó		

SPEC Cat 4, Threat status S (P)

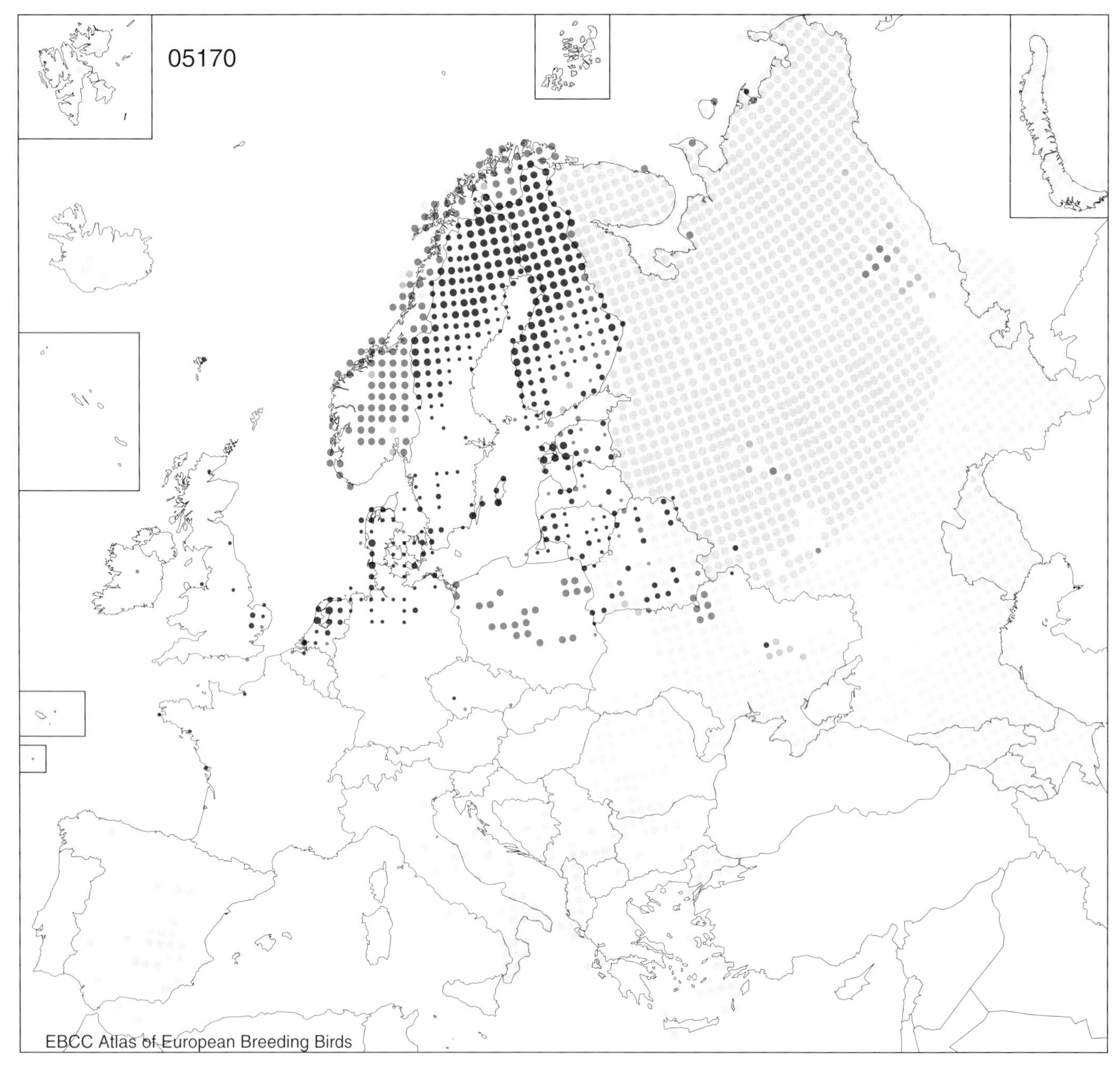

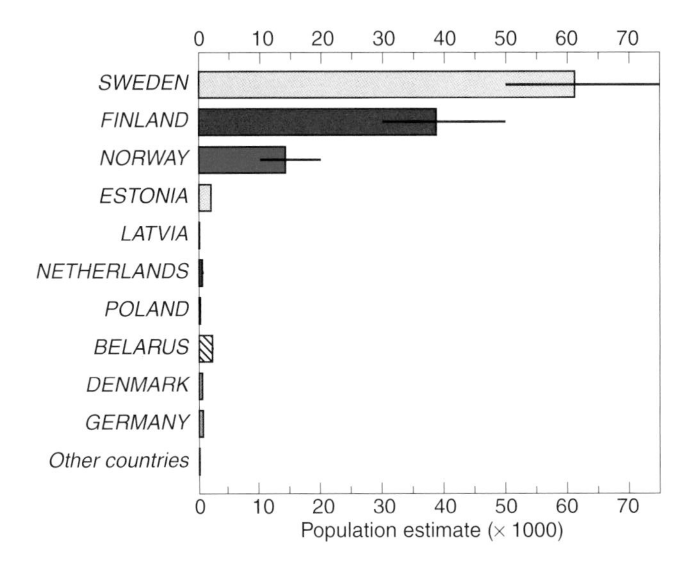

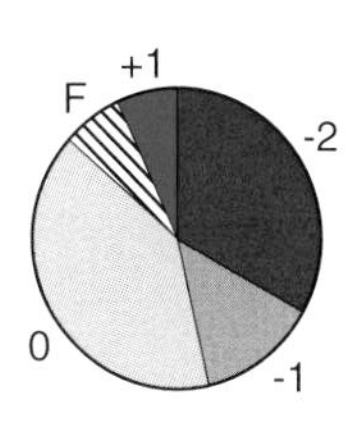

% in top 10 countries: 99.9
Total number of populated European countries: 15
Total European population 105,655–139,209 (120,477)
Russian population 1,000,000–10,000,000 (3,162,278)

The Ruff breeds from Scandinavia and Great Britain to the Bering Strait, mainly above 60°N. In the temperate zone, the main breeding habitat is wet, low-lying, grassy terrain at sea level or below (as on polders in The Netherlands). Further N, it breeds on moorland bounded by pine forest, and further N still or above the mountain timberline, it occupies the tundra.

The bulk of the population, including E Siberian breeders, winters in sub-Saharan Africa on flooded or dry plains, marshes or ricefields. Small numbers winter in NW Europe in coastal areas or on inland floodplains in S Germany, The Netherlands and Great Britain. On migration the Ruff also frequents lake margins, sewage farms and other inland waters (OAG Münster 1989). Along the coast it prefers muddy creeks in saltmarshes, but rarely uses intertidal habitats.

During the breeding season, the spectacular and energetic males display to the females on traditional lek sites, activity peaking shortly after sunrise, but although males are therefore easy to count, their numbers may not necessarily reflect population size. Females, often outnumbering males, visit leks only for copulation, and are extremely skulking; they may nest some considerable distance from the leks and care for the offspring without male help, either alone or gregariously at densities of up to 5–10 females/10ha (Dubois & Maheo 1986).

Assessing breeding group and population size is therefore difficult, the term 'breeding pair' (bp) not being quite appropriate. In waterlogged open meadows in the Polish Biebrza River valley, prime habitat, densities of 7–9 bp/10ha were recorded (Dyrcz *et al* 1985). The highest densities attained in suitable habitat in Finland may reach 10–15 females/km^2 (Koskimies 1989a).

This monotypic species has a scattered breeding distribution. Since 1980, a serious decline has taken place in most countries. Some increase was recorded in Norway, mostly as a result of a range extension in the S (Kålås & Byrkjedal 1981). In Russia and Sweden, which have the largest breeding populations, numbers and trends are very difficult to estimate but are considered stable. Massive declines (>50% in 1970–90) have occurred in Finland (the third largest breeding population), The Netherlands (90% decline since the 1950s, only 400–800bp left in early 1990s; Osieck & Hustings 1994), Poland and Latvia. Smaller but still significant decreases were recorded in Germany and Denmark. There is no clear trend for Belarus. In other countries whose populations generally are small and towards the main breeding range limits, there have been either small declines or no significant changes.

Over the *Atlas*' area of coverage, the most recent estimates suggest a population of 3.28M 'bp', of which 96% occurs in Russia alone. Sizeable populations also occur in Sweden (61 000), Finland (39 000) and Norway (14 000), all other national populations comprising 2000bp or fewer.

The declines seem due to several factors, especially drainage of breeding and feeding areas, increased fertilizer use (depletion of insect stocks) and encroachment on previously mown or grazed breeding sites. Hunting has also had an effect (van Rhijn 1991, Kirby 1993). Consequently, in areas with intensive farming the Ruff has disappeared completely as a breeding bird, and now is confined to nature reserves which are specifically managed for it and other species unable to adapt to rapid changes in farming practices. Whether this will halt the decline or help recolonize lost breeding grounds, is subject to debate. The findings in The Netherlands are not promising in this respect.

In Europe (and Africa), males initiate the spring migration as early as mid-February; females follow later. Spring counts often reveal two peaks, one in late March (perhaps mostly males) and the other in late April (perhaps mostly females). Breeding areas are occupied from mid-April around the North Sea, but progressively later to the north and east: mid-June or even later in Siberia. During the autumn migration, the Ruff traverses temperate Europe from late July to October, males again migrating first, followed by females and juveniles (Girard 1992), but over a more westerly route.

Olivier Girard (F) Jeff Kirby (GB)

Lymnocryptes minimus　　Jack Snipe

CZ	Slučka malá	I	Frullino
D	Zwergschnepfe	NL	Bokje
E	Agachadiza Chica	P	Narceja-galega
F	Bécassine sourde	PL	Bekasik
FIN	Jänkäkurppa	R	Гаршнеп
G	Κουφομπεκάτσινο	S	Dvärgbeckasin
H	Kis sárszalonka		

*SPEC Cat 3*W, Threat status V*W (P)*

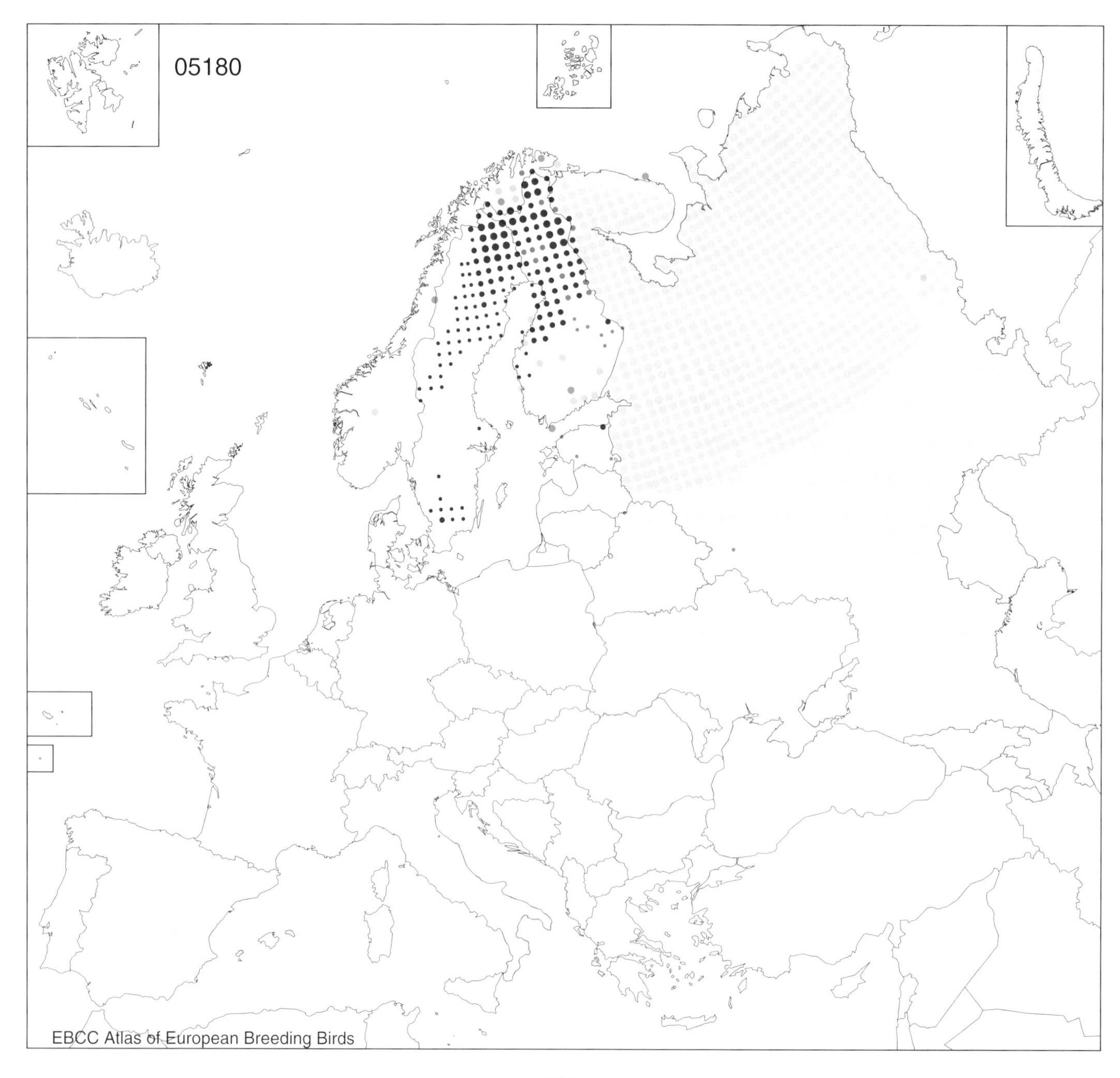

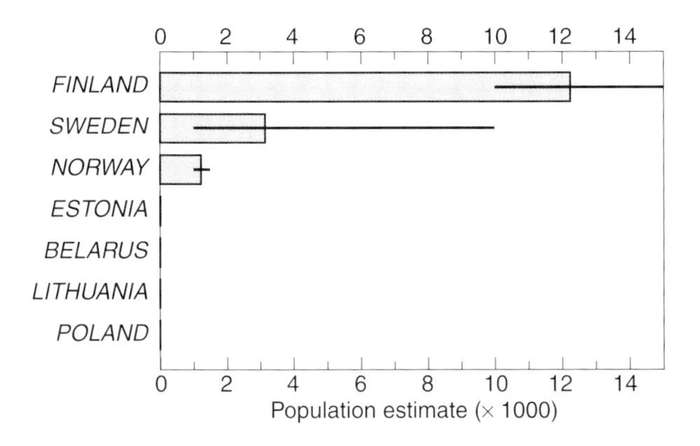

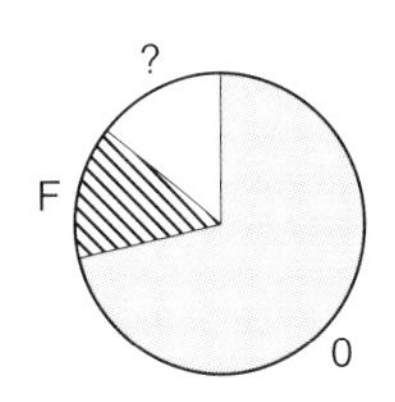

% in top 10 countries: 100.0
Total number of populated European countries: 7
Total European population 13,530–24,033 (16,657)
Russian population 10,000–100,000 (31,623)

A diminutive and highly crepuscular wader, the Jack Snipe prefers open and swampy mires, floodplain meadows and transition bogs in its distribution from N Scandinavia and N Russia E to C Siberia. The extent of its range in Russia, its stronghold, is not known, but apparently is less evenly distributed in the tundra and taiga than commonly assumed (P.S. Tomkovich, pers comm). The species was presumed to have withdrawn from its SW range boundary of S Sweden and the SE Baltic region in the early 1900s, being classed as only an accidental and sporadic breeder, but recent surveys have confirmed its range still extends E of the line drawn from S Sweden to NE Poland.

Its southwesterly breeding range coincides with its northeasterly wintering range. N and W Europe (including Britain & Ireland) and North and West Africa form the (probably) equally-favoured major wintering areas for the pan-European population. Presumably birds from C Siberia and Asian Russia winter from East Africa to eastern India.

Russia may possess up to 100 000bp, but the species appears much commoner in European Russia than E of the Urals (Rogacheva 1992). Although poorly studied, its annual fluctuations apparently can be predicted in relation to severe weather conditions and cyclic abundance of predators.

The Scandinavian peninsula holds *c*25 000bp, the majority being in N Finland and N Sweden, and in my opinion, fewer than 500bp breed elsewhere in Scandinavia, mostly in N Norway and S Sweden. Poland, Lithuania, Belarus and Estonia probably share fewer than 100bp. A very few breed in Latvia (M. Strazds, pers comm).

In Småland, S Sweden, a recent census of *c*9000km^2 of lowlands revealed 86bp in 43 different sites (Pedersen 1990), giving an extrapolated estimated population of 120bp (0.01 bp/km^2). Sites of less than 50ha held nearly half of the population, and with the smallest breeding site being 15ha, the importance of relatively small mires is clear. Following fluctuations, the population decreased by 47% between 1991 and 1992, but the overall population trend, based on census results from the 1970s and 1980s, is stable over a 20-year period. A similar trend over the same period applies at one of the main Estonian breeding sites (A. Leivits, pers comm).

Due to the shortcomings of the census techniques used, breeding densities are often poorly known, some published figures being 1.6 bp/km^2 in N Russian taiga (survey), 1.9 bp/km^2 in a S Swedish transition bog (survey) and 0.07 bp/km^2 in N Norwegian mires (transects). A recent study in S Sweden demonstrated that reliable data on population size can be obtained through nocturnal surveys of displaying males whereas diurnal transects heavily underestimate the abundance of breeding pairs (M.B. Pedersen, unpubl).

The total pan-European population is estimated as fewer than 130 000bp, which figure must suffice until better censusing methods are employed more widely. We must therefore recognize that the status of the Jack Snipe remains relatively unknown, and consequently it is not yet possible to determine long-term population trends. However, amongst others, Tuck (1972) assumed that during the 19th century the breeding population of C and E Europe had declined significantly. It is likely that it has continued to do so since 1900 (probably less rapidly), because agricultural intensification, industrialized peat extraction and land-use changes and drainage brought about by afforestation inevitably have had a deleterious effect on Jack Snipe populations. This conjecture is supported by the apparent decline in wintering populations (Pedersen 1994).

Further studies, especially in Russia, are needed to determine the current population status and trends so that appropriate conservation measures may be defined for this vulnerable species.

Michael Brinch Pedersen (DK)

Gallinago gallinago **Snipe**

CZ	Bekasina otavní	I	Beccaccino
D	Bekassine	NL	Watersnip
E	Agachadiza Común	P	Narceja-comum
F	Bécassine des marais	PL	Kszyk
FIN	Taivaanvuohi	R	Бекас
G	Μπεκατσίνι	S	Enkelbeckasin
H	Sárszalonka		

Non-SPEC, Threat status S (P)

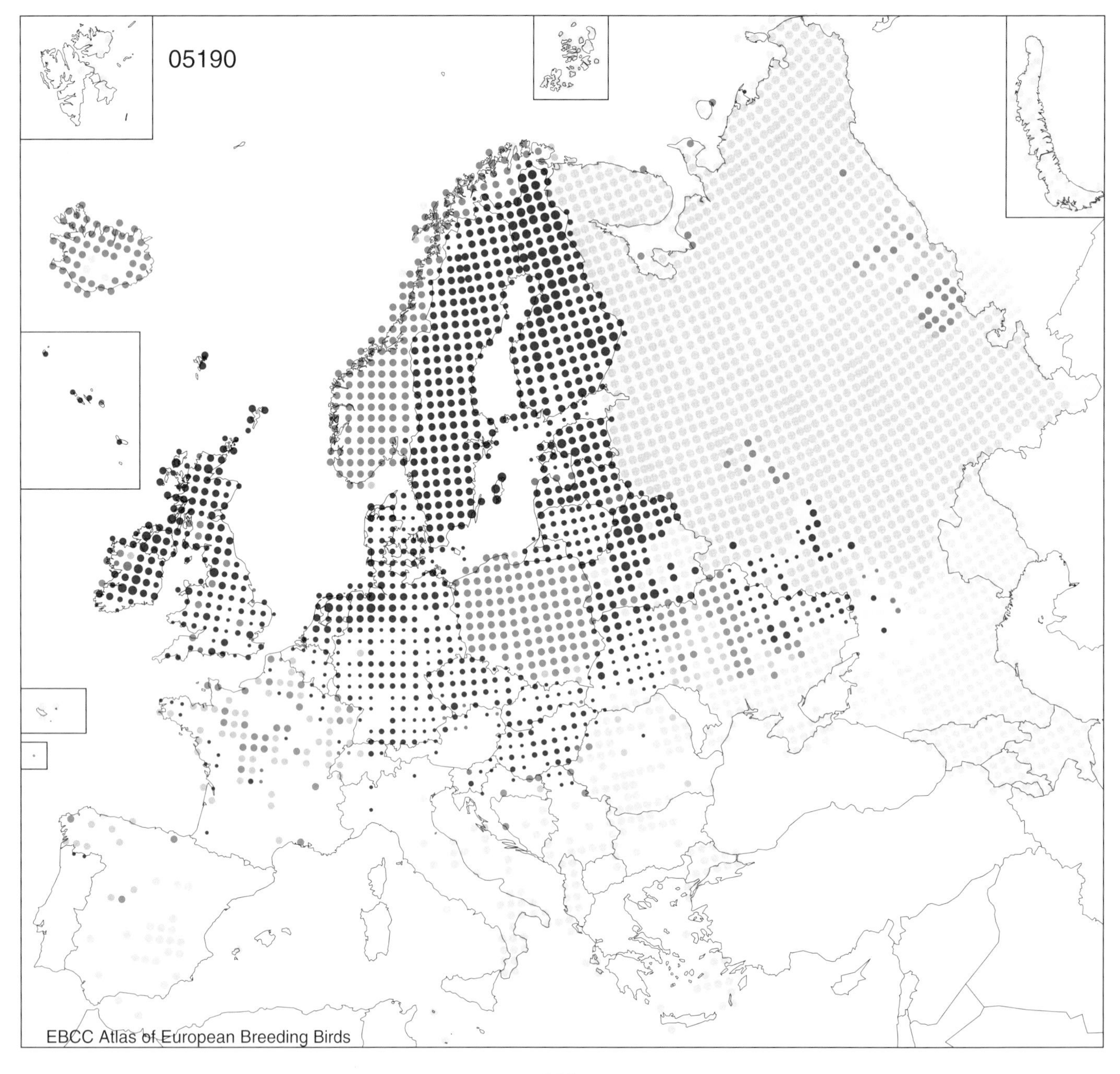

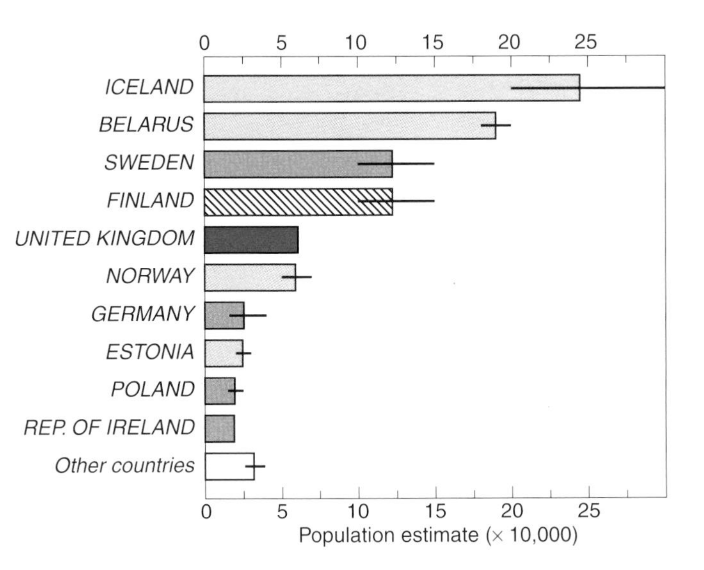

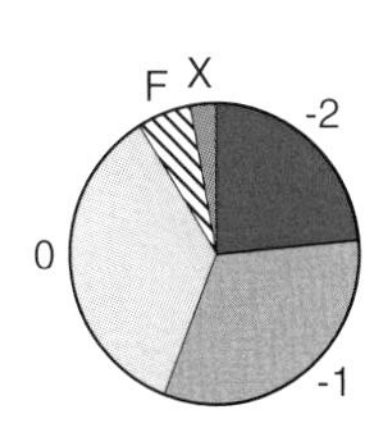

% in top 10 countries: 96.6
Total number of populated European countries: 34
Total European population 861,593–990,503 (919,393)
Russian population 1,000,000–10,000,000 (3,162,278)

The Snipe, a Holarctic wader, has an extensive range in N and C Eurasia from Iceland to the Bering Strait (nominate *G.g. gallinago*, except for *faeroeensis* on Atlantic islands). The Nearctic subspecies is widespread within Canada and the USA. Additional subspecies breed in Africa and South America. Eurasian birds winter in any part of the breeding range which remain unfrozen (Tuck 1972), in small numbers in S Scandinavia, but principally in Britain & Ireland, the Low Countries and S to the Mediterranean basin. Considerable numbers winter in Africa below the Sahara.

The Snipe breeds from the arctic tundra of Russia, through the fens and raised bogs of N and S Fennoscandia, the Baltic coast shore meadows, the C European marshy meadows and uncultivated grasslands, to the British and Irish blanket bogs. It has a very catholic choice of habitat, the basic requirement being soft organic soil rich in subsurface invertebrates.

In Fennoscandia the Snipe is widespread, probably breeding in every 50km square; empty squares probably reflect the level of survey coverage. It is one of the most abundant waders in Fennoscandia, densities being high in the N (up to 6–7 bp/km^2 on the best fens) but much lower in the S. However, on S Finnish shore meadows densities locally may reach 20–40 bp/km^2. The overall density exceeds 0.5 bp/km^2 in C Lapland, diminishing northwards and southwards, sometimes to 0.05 bp/km^2. Throughout large Dutch study areas, maximum densities reached 10 bp/km^2 and locally even 50–80 bp/km^2 in small favourable plots (Beintema 1995). In the raised bog zone of the Biebrza marshes (NE Poland) similar densities (59–80 bp/km^2) occur in very wet open fens dominated by sedges *Carex paradoxa* and *C. limosa* amid an extensive moss layer (Dyrcz *et al* 1985).

In several countries Snipe populations have declined recently, probably through loss of breeding habitat. The loss of suitable moulting grounds in The Netherlands due to agricultural development and drainage (Beintema & Müskens 1983) probably also affects N European populations. Finland has the most precise data: the population more than doubled from the 1940s to the 1970s (200 000bp), but decreased by 33% in the 1980s (120 000bp), the low level of the 1940s probably arising from a series of extremely hard winters, and the high of the 1970s from mild winters. However, the decline has been continuous since the hard winters of the mid-1980s despite a subsequent succession of extremely mild winters. A sample study in the SW Finnish archipelago charted a population increase from 1975 to an overall density of *c*3 bp/km^2 in 1982, a steady decrease to *c*0.1 bp/km^2 in 1993 and total disappearance in 1994 (L. Saari, unpubl), probably the consequence of habitat loss through the cessation in the late 1970s of cattle-grazing on shore meadows allowing encroachment by reeds and shrubs.

Russia, not unexpectedly, holds the largest population, guesstimated at 1M–10Mbp. Iceland, Belarus, Finland and Sweden each have between 100 000 and 300 000bp, Great Britain, Norway, Germany, Estonia, Poland, Ireland and Lithuania, more than 10 000bp, and Ukraine, Latvia, Denmark, The Netherlands, the Czech Republic and Faeroes more than 1000bp. The remaining countries with breeding Snipe share a few hundred breeding pairs.

The British and C European populations respectively are mainly and partially sedentary. The Russian, Fennoscandian and Icelandic populations are mainly migratory. Spring migration starts in C Europe in March, reaching the SW Finnish coast in late March. The peak occurs in April, and the northernmost breeding areas are occupied in May. The autumn migration begins in July and peaks in September–October in W Europe. Birds reach their wintering grounds in November (*eg* Reddig 1981).

Albert Beintema (NL) Lennart Saari (FIN)

Gallinago media

Great Snipe

CZ	Bekasina větší	**I**	Croccolone
D	Doppelschnepfe	**NL**	Poelsnip
E	Agachadiza Real	**P**	Narceja-real
F	Bécassine double	**PL**	Dubelt
FIN	Heinäkurppa	**R**	Дупель
G	Διπλομπεκάτσινο	**S**	Dubbelbeckasin
H	Nagy sárszalonka		

SPEC Cat 2, Threat status V (P)

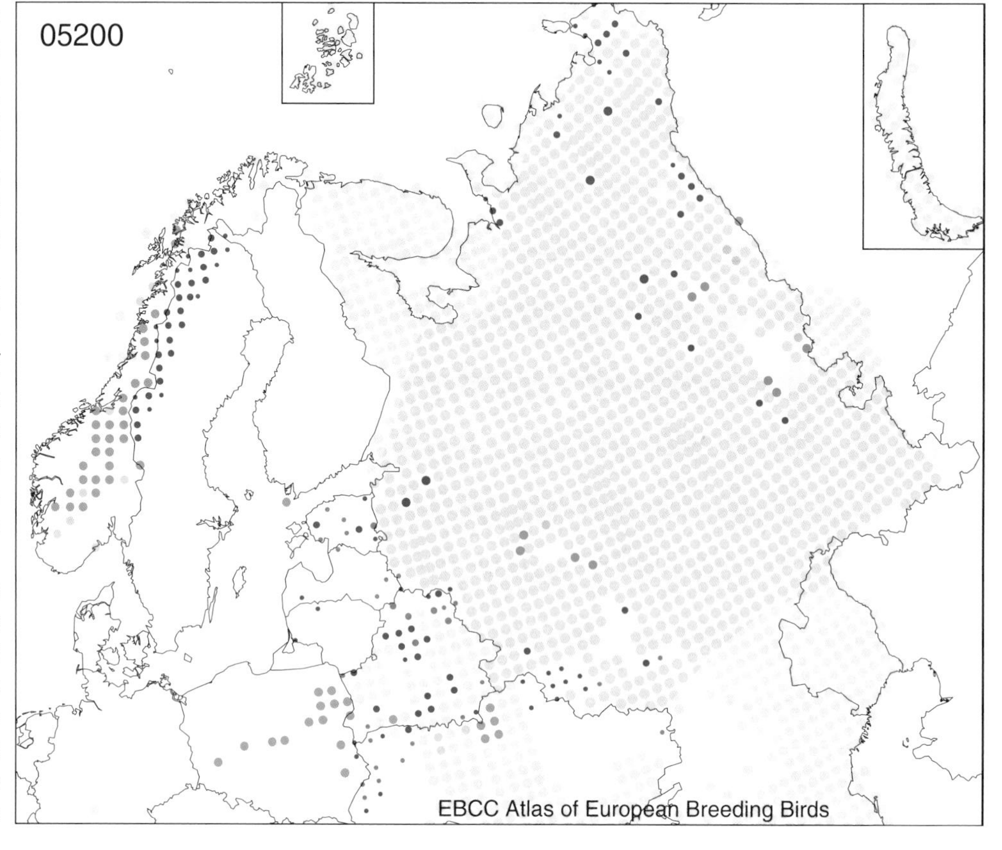

Nowadays, the Great Snipe, a lek-breeding wader which prefers slightly damp and base-rich areas, is distributed in the C Scandinavian mountains, and from Poland E through the St Petersburg region and Komi Republic to the Yenisey. It winters in Africa S of the Sahara. Large numbers have occurred both high in Ethiopia and in low-lying wetlands near the Gulf of Guinea. Observations indicate movements southward from Sudan and Ethiopia through Kenya, Uganda and Zaire to Zambia from November to January (Massoli-Novelli 1987).

In Scandinavia the Great Snipe breeds in rich fen and shrub areas along the timberline (Løfaldli *et al* 1992). In the N of its eastern range, it inhabits fen and shrub areas northwards into the bush tundra whereas in the S it breeds mainly in river valley meadows (Estafiev 1991, Tomkovich 1992). Because the species breeds only in the rich habitats nurtured by high-quality soil, its distribution is often scattered (Kålås *et al* in prep).

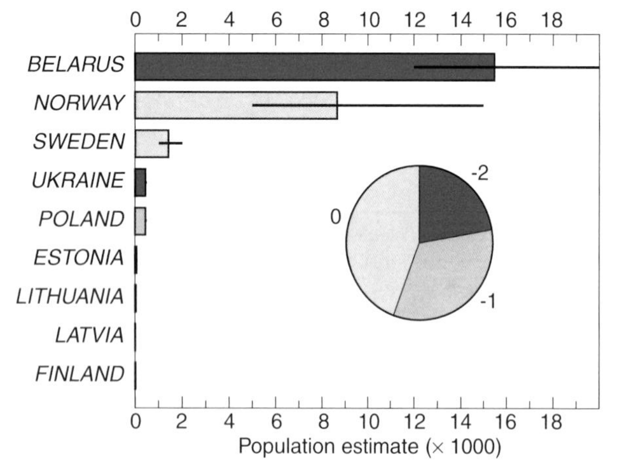

% in top 10 countries: 100.0
Total number of populated European countries: 9
Total European population 21,506–34,384 (26,583)
Russian population 150,000–250,000 (193,649)

During a dramatic range contraction from 1850 to 1900 the species disappeared from Germany, Denmark, Finland, the lowlands of S Norway and Sweden, much of Poland and the southern former Soviet Union. Its dependency on rich habitats in open surroundings makes it vulnerable to human activity. The decline may be explained by the concurrent extent of industrial development and changes in agricultural practices adding to the toll from traditional harvesting of Great Snipe on lekking arenas. The Scandinavian population apparently has remained stable since 1945, but S Russia is experiencing a continued decline (Tomkovich 1992).

In optimal habitats Great Snipe may breed at very high densities. Over the period 1986–94 from 70 to 130 lekking males were observed within a 6km² area at the centre of the Scandinavian breeding population. In optimal habitats in the taiga zone in the Pechora Valley densities may reach 6 individuals/km² (Estafiev 1991), but overall density is usually 0.4 (S.K. Kotchanov, pers obs).

John Atle Kålås (N) Alexei A Estafiev (R)
Sergei K Kotchanov (R)

Gallinago stenura

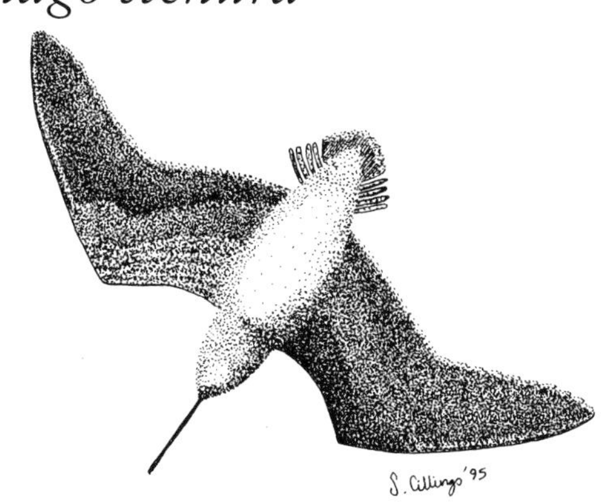

Pintail Snipe

CZ	Bekasina asijská	I	Beccaccino stenuro
D	Stiftbekassine	NL	Stekelstaartsnip
E	Agachadiza Colirrara	P	Narceja-siberiana
F	Bécassine à queue pointue	PL	Bekas syberyjski
FIN	Suippopyrstökurppa	R	Азиатский бекас
G	Οξύουρο Μπεκατσίνι	S	Sibirisk beckasin
H	Ázsiai sárszalonka		

Non-SPEC, Threat status S

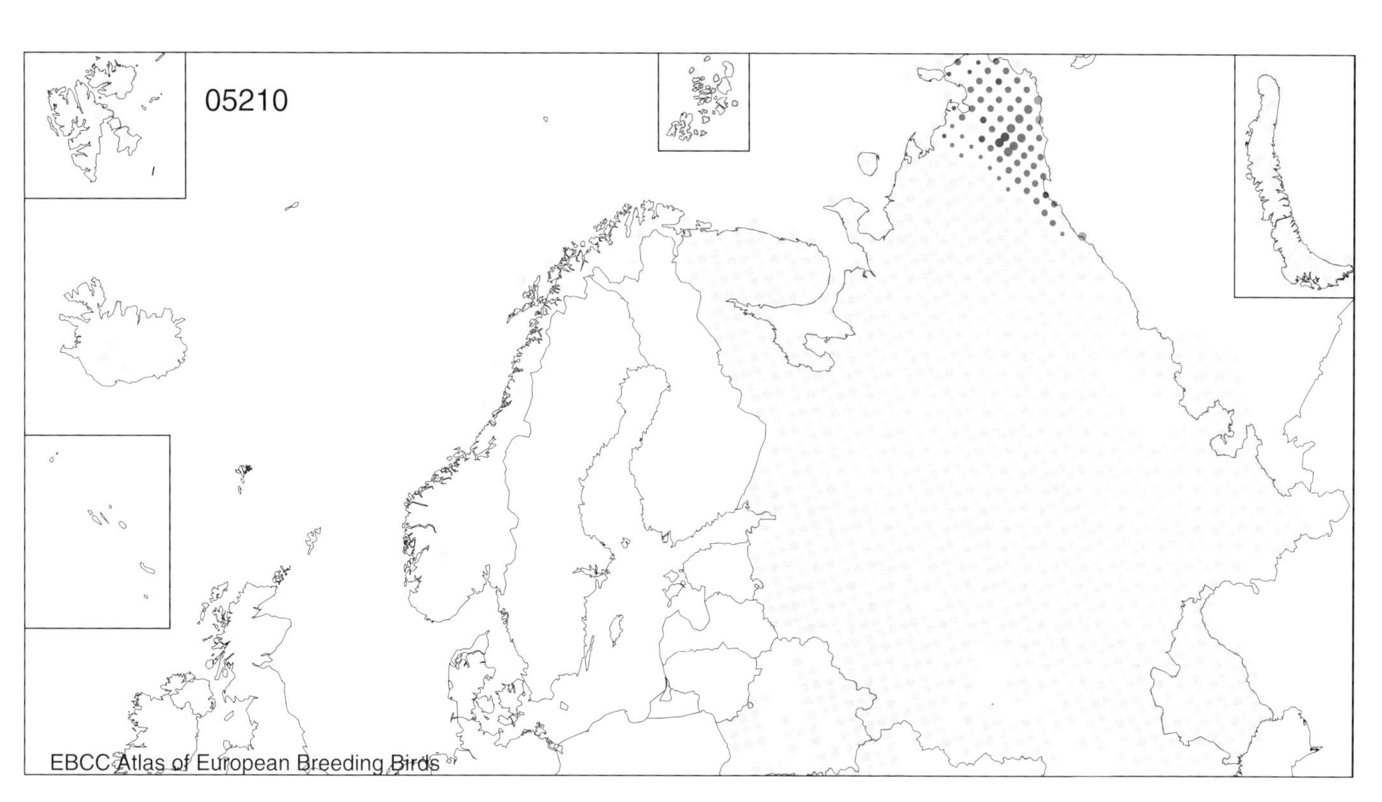

The Pintail Snipe is distributed in Europe from the Pechora River basin in the forest zone and the Chornaya River basin in the Bol'shezemel'skaya tundra in the W to the Urals, occurring from the upper River Chornaya and the Yugorskiy Peninsula coasts (Estafiev 1991, Morozov 1993), S along the Urals to 62°N, 60°E. In Asia it occurs from the Urals across the eastern Palearctic to the Kolyma Delta, the Neitlin foothills (Kondratiev 1982) and the upper Kanchalan River (Kistchinskiy *et al* 1983), the Nurmayakha River in the Yamal Peninsula (Danilov *et al* 1984), the Taz and the Yenisey (to 67–68°N) and the Lena (to 71°N) to the Kolyma mouth. Its southern breeding limits are the Stanovoy Range, the upper Zeya River, southernmost Baikal, Sayan the Altai, near Tomsk and Kansk (Kozlova 1962), Lake Hubsugul (Mongolia) (Sumya & Skryabin 1989), and in western Siberia reaching the northern limit of the taiga zone (Morozov 1996). It winters in Burma, India, Sri Lanka, probably in the Philippines, and in small numbers in S China.

In the European tundra it inhabits shrub and moss tundras and wetland habitats and in the forest zone, sparse forests containing shrubby river valleys and forest-edge bogs. In the Urals it prefers shrub meadows and swamps scattered with stands of trees, various dwarf birch and willow tundras and mossy bogs. The breeding density of Pintail Snipe in the western Bol'shezemel'skaya tundra (Chornaya River) is *c*0.1 bp/km^2, in the centre (More-Yu River) 0.3, in sedge and moss swamps 0.7 and in shrub tundras up to 1.2. On the Yugorsky Peninsula density is 0.03–0.3 bp/km^2 in small willow-shrub tundras (Estafiev 1991), but reaches 1.0–1.7 in other shrub habitats. In the eastern Bol'shezemel'skaya tundra and the polar Urals, breeding density varied from 0.5 to 7.8 bp/km^2 in dwarf birch tundras to 6.0 in shrubby river valleys, reaching 18.0 locally in some years (Morozov 1996). In the sub-polar Urals at the Bolshaya Synya River basin, density was 0.7 bp/km^2 and 0.6 near the city of Inta (Estafiev 1991, S.K. Kotchanov, pers obs).

The species is tending to expand its range westwards. Displaying males have been recorded on the Russkiy Zavorot Peninsula (*c*53°E) and near Lake Don-Ty in the Vychegda River basin. The total European population is estimated as at least 3000bp, but is liable to annual fluctuations.

Alexey A Estafiev (R) Sergey K Kotchanov (R)
Vladimir V Morozov (R)

Scolopax rusticola **Woodcock**

CZ	Sluka lesní	I	Beccaccia
D	Waldschnepfe	NL	Houtsnip
E	Chocha Perdiz	P	Galinhola
F	Bécasse des bois	PL	Słonka
FIN	Lehtokurppa	R	Вальдшнеп
G	Μπεκάτσα	S	Morkulla
H	Erdei szalonka		

*SPEC Cat 3*W, Threat status V*W*

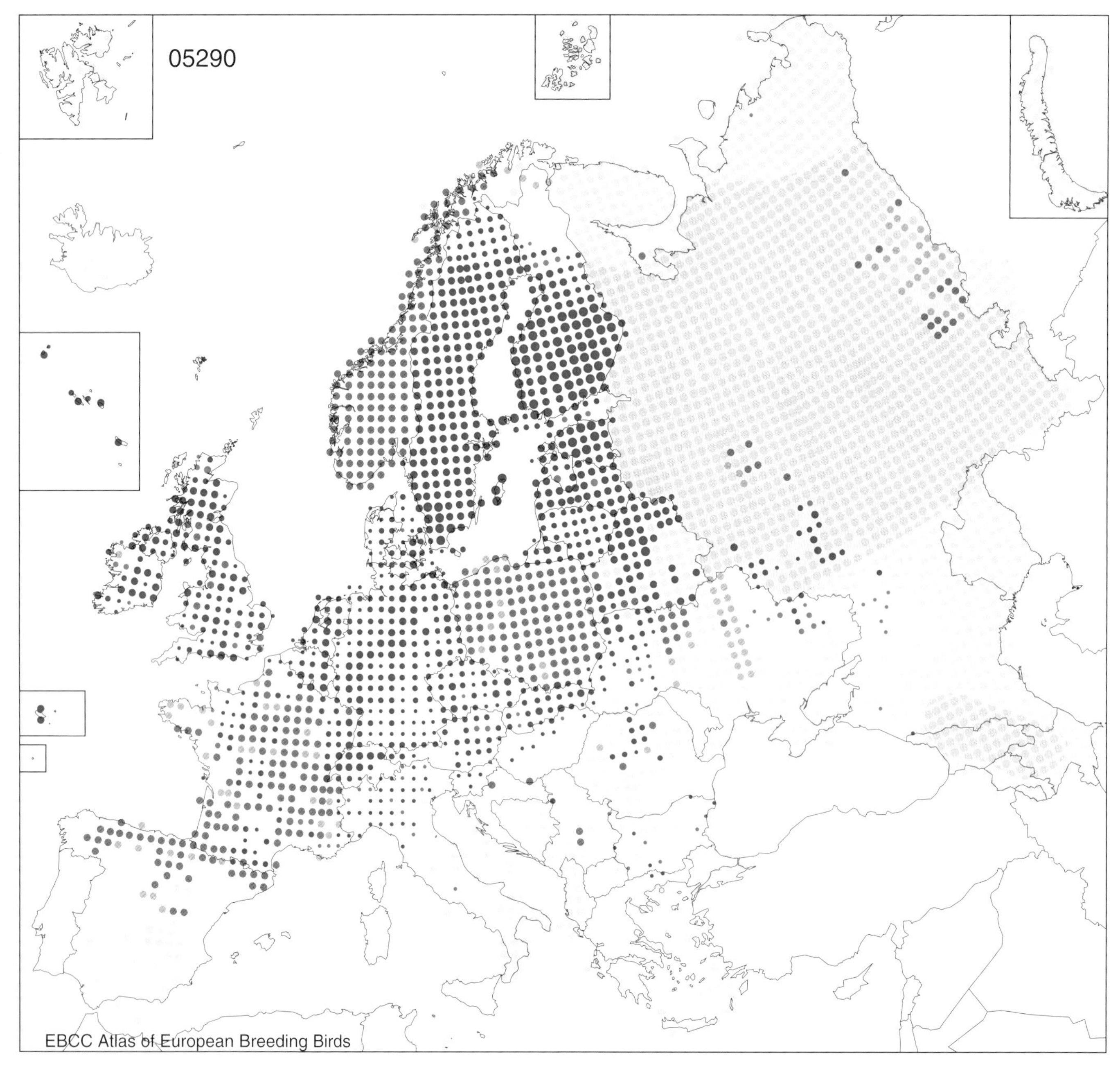

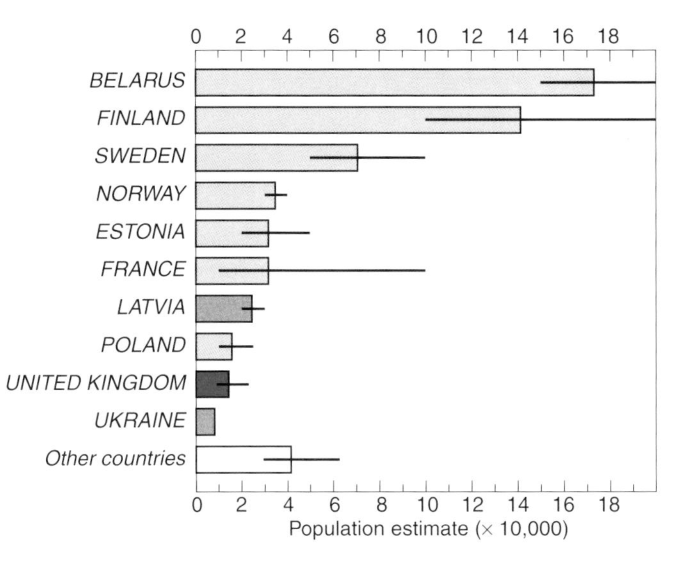

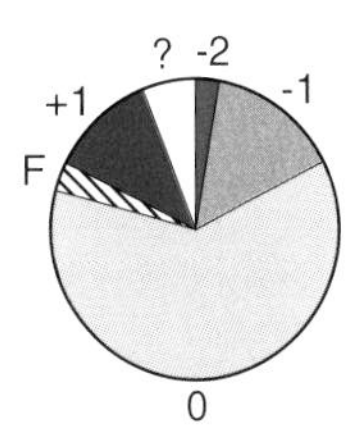

% in top 10 countries: 92.9
Total number of populated European countries: 34
Total European population 529,282–689,418 (587,741)
Russian population 1,000,000–10,000,000 (3,162,278)

The Woodcock, a secretive and solitary wader, breeds in forests, woodland and scrub throughout the entire temperate and boreal Palearctic. Its preferred breeding habitat in Europe is deciduous or mixed woodland, but it often uses conifer plantations, up to the thicket stage. In Fennoscandia it breeds in mature coniferous forests, particularly those of moist spruce *Picea* spp. It requires an understorey of brambles *Rubus* spp, hazel *Corylus avellana*, holly *Ilex aquifolium*, bracken *Pteridium maculinum* or bilberry *Vaccinium myrtillus* as cover from avian predators (Hirons & Johnson 1987) and earthworm-rich soils in which to feed. Wide rides and clearings (2–4ha) in forests provide easy access and flight paths.

Roughly 30% of the global Woodcock population breeds in Europe, where its range extends from Fennoscandia S towards the Mediterranean zone, and from western Europe E to most of Russia. In S Europe, the Woodcock breeds only at higher altitudes, its mainland southern distribution limit traversing the Cantabrian Mountains, the Pyrenees and the French–Italian Alps. Over 90% of the European population breeds in Russia, Belarus, Finland, Sweden and Norway. The absence of semi-quantitative data from Norway, France, Spain and Poland distorts their mapped distribution patterns, particularly where lower densities exist. Because the male Woodcock may mate with several females during the breeding season, it is not valid to express the population in terms of 'breeding pairs' (bp). In prime breeding habitat in Great Britain, breeding density may reach 12 'pairs' per km^2 of woodland, whereas in the more extensive forests of Fennoscandia a density of about 1 'pair' per km^2 is probably more typical.

The Woodcock's European range and population size appear to have remained stable since the mid-1970s. However, there are few reliable quantitative data upon which to assess population size trends in most countries, due to the difficulty in counting Woodcock. The largest decline in population has occurred in the UK, probably due to closure of the forest canopy in the conifer plantations created during the 1960s (Lewis & Roberts 1993). The conversion of pasture fields to cereal production has probably contributed to the decline because the Woodcock relies on pastures for feeding.

Population declines of between 20% and 50% have occurred in Latvia, Ukraine and Germany. Fluctuations in the size of the Russian breeding population give cause for concern because it comprises such a large proportion of the European population. Its breeding range and population size in Russia are poorly documented and clearly require more research. A substantial decline in the French wintering population in recent years (Fadat 1991) is also indicative of problems on the Woodcock's eastern European breeding grounds. Small increases in breeding range and population size have occurred in Denmark, The Netherlands, Ireland and Spain since 1974. Recent line transect counts in Finland indicate a range extension N of the Arctic Circle. At present, the Woodcock's breeding distribution is very patchy in France, relatively few birds being found in parts of NW and S France. In Britain it is most abundant in Scotland and northern England.

The large Fennoscandian and Russian breeding populations are migratory, wintering throughout S and W Europe, but particularly in France, Spain, Italy, Britain and Ireland. Ringing recoveries indicate that Norwegian birds winter further W than those from Sweden and Finland, a higher proportion occurring in Britain & Ireland (Clausager 1974, Hoodless & Coulson 1994). The breeding populations of NW Europe are largely sedentary.

The Woodcock is a difficult bird to count accurately. Populations can be estimated roughly from numbers of roding males, but some males rode more than others and birds do not occupy discrete areas (Hirons 1983). Because nests are difficult to find, breeding is rarely confirmed. The problem can be overcome to some extent by examining breeding and wintering population trends in combination.

Andrew Hoodless (GB) Lennart Saari (FIN)

This species account is sponsored by NV PWN Waterleidingbedrijf Noord-Holland, Castricum, NL.

Limosa limosa

Black-tailed Godwit

CZ	Břehouš černoocasý	**I**	Pittima reale
D	Uferschnepfe	**NL**	Grutto
E	Aguja Colinegra	**P**	Maçarico-de-bico-direito
F	Barge à queue noire	**PL**	Rycyk
FIN	Mustapyrstökuiri	**R**	Большой веретенник
G	Λιμόζα	**S**	Rödspov
H	Nagy goda		

SPEC Cat 2, Threat status V

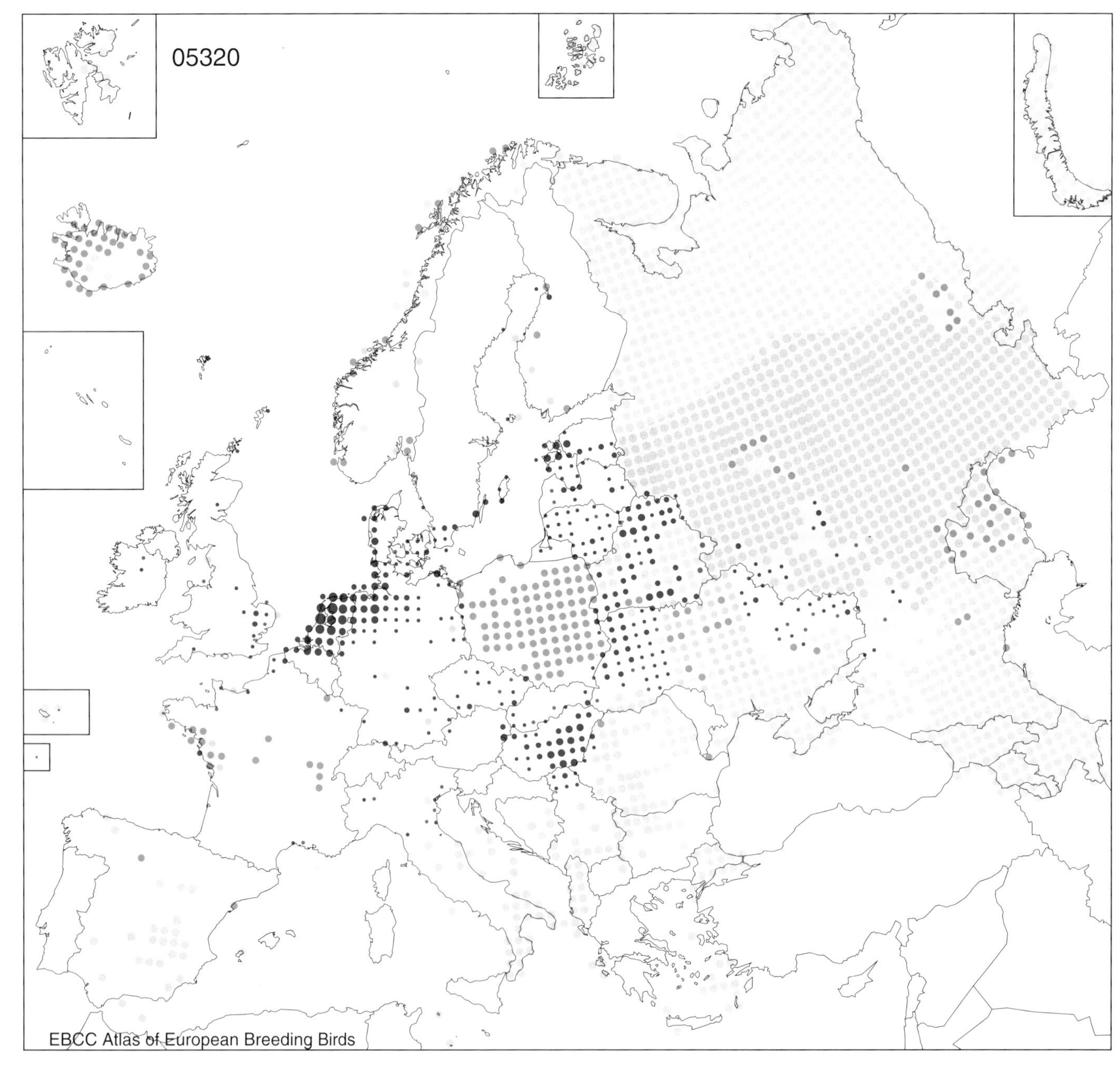

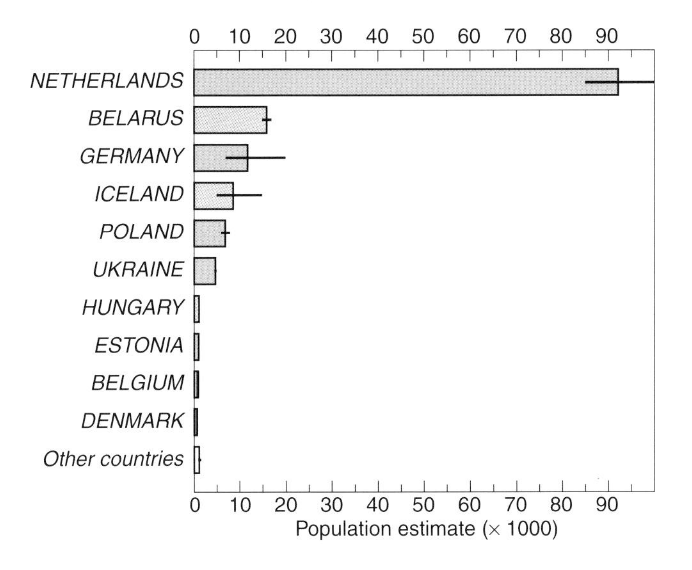

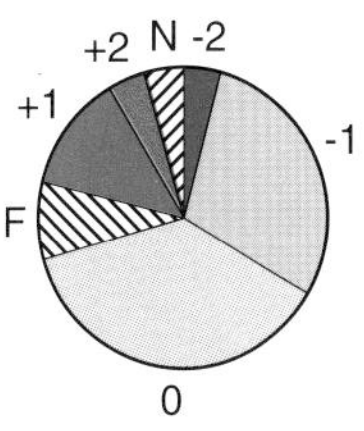

% in top 10 countries: 99.2
Total number of populated European countries: 24
Total European population 135,594–158,147 (145,102)
Russian population 10,000–100,000 (31,623)

The Black-tailed Godwit is confined to the Palearctic, where it occurs in three discrete subspecies: two from Europe, the third from E Siberia. The two European subspecies differ little in appearance, but very much so in breeding habitat and wintering habits. The Icelandic Black-tailed Godwit *L.l.islandica* nests in subarctic tundra and moorland and winters in estuarine habitats along the Atlantic coast from Britain S to Morocco. The continental Black-tailed Godwit *L.l.limosa* is a bird of temperate grasslands and moorlands, wintering predominantly in freshwater habitats S of the Sahara. *L.l.limosa* has to a greater extent adapted to the agricultural environment, and together with the Lapwing *Vanellus vanellus*, they form the heart of the characteristic Dutch meadow bird community. About half the European population of 130 000–255 000bp is concentrated in the Dutch agricultural grasslands, used for dairy farming. These low-lying wet grasslands have a high water table, were subject to winter flooding in the past and suffer a high degree of fertilization. Here *limosa* nests typically in densities of 20–100 bp/km^2, but in prime habitat (nowadays invariably reserves) up to 300 bp/km^2 (Beintema 1995). Populations in adjacent Belgium, Germany (Klinner 1991) and Denmark live under similar conditions. The populations in E Europe inhabit more natural habitats, like steppe in Hungary and Ukraine, or flooded river meadows in Poland, Belarus and Estonia. Open fens and meadows along rivers may hold densities of 55–160 bp/km^2, such as in the Biebrza Valley in NE Poland (Dyrcz *et al* 1985). All these habitats are used for agriculture, but at a much lower intensity than in western Europe.

Population trends are negative over most of the species' range. In western Europe, the decrease results from improved drainage and over-intensification of grasslands, mainly affecting reproductive success. In eastern Europe the decrease results from rapid changes in semi-natural habitats, which either are drained and used for intensive agriculture, or are abandoned and suffer encroachment by tall vegetation and bushes. Range expansion or population growth has occurred in peripheral areas; in western Europe in Britain, Norway, Denmark and Belgium, and in eastern Europe in Latvia and Romania. Improved protection has led to the re-establishment of small populations in S Europe, or even the formation of new populations (Italy). However, these positive developments affect only a very small proportion of the population and do not compensate for the heavy losses in the core areas. The Icelandic population is considered to be stable (5000–15 000bp). However, the British wintering population (*islandica*) is increasing.

Post-breeding, the continental Black-tailed Godwit concentrates in large flocks in shallow flooded areas, such as Oostvaardersplassen in The Netherlands or the Danube Delta in Romania, prior to migration. The birds fly non-stop from W Europe to Morocco, and from there non-stop to wetlands in Senegal and Guinea-Bissau. Birds from eastern Europe pass through Tunisia and Algeria to sub-Saharan Mali and Chad; a small proportion migrates E to East Africa. The easternmost Siberian populations overwinter in India, SE Asia and Australasia.

Typical winter habitats in W Africa are shallow floodplains in the large sahelian river systems. Many birds have taken to ricefields, especially the Dutch population, which has thus become very much an agricultural bird all year round, wintering largely in the rice-growing areas of Senegal and Guinea-Bissau. During spring migration, large concentrations stop-over in ricefields in Portugal and on wet grasslands in France and Italy. Spring migrants in Italy mostly are third calendar-year birds, going N for their first breeding season (Beintema & Drost 1986). In its second year the *limosa* subspecies summers in Africa, where its distribution is poorly known. Some *islandica* birds oversummer in Great Britain.

Albert J Beintema (NL) Johannes Melter (D)

This species account is sponsored by the Netherlands Ornithological Union, Culemborg, NL.

Limosa lapponica — Bar-tailed Godwit

CZ	Břehouš rudý	I	Pittima minore
D	Pfuhlschnepfe	NL	Rosse Grutto
E	Aguja Colipinta	P	Fuselo
F	Barge rousse	PL	Szlamnik
FIN	Punakuiri	R	Лапландский веретенник
G	Ακτοτούρλι	S	Myrspov
H	Kis goda		

*SPEC Cat 3*W, Threat status L*W*

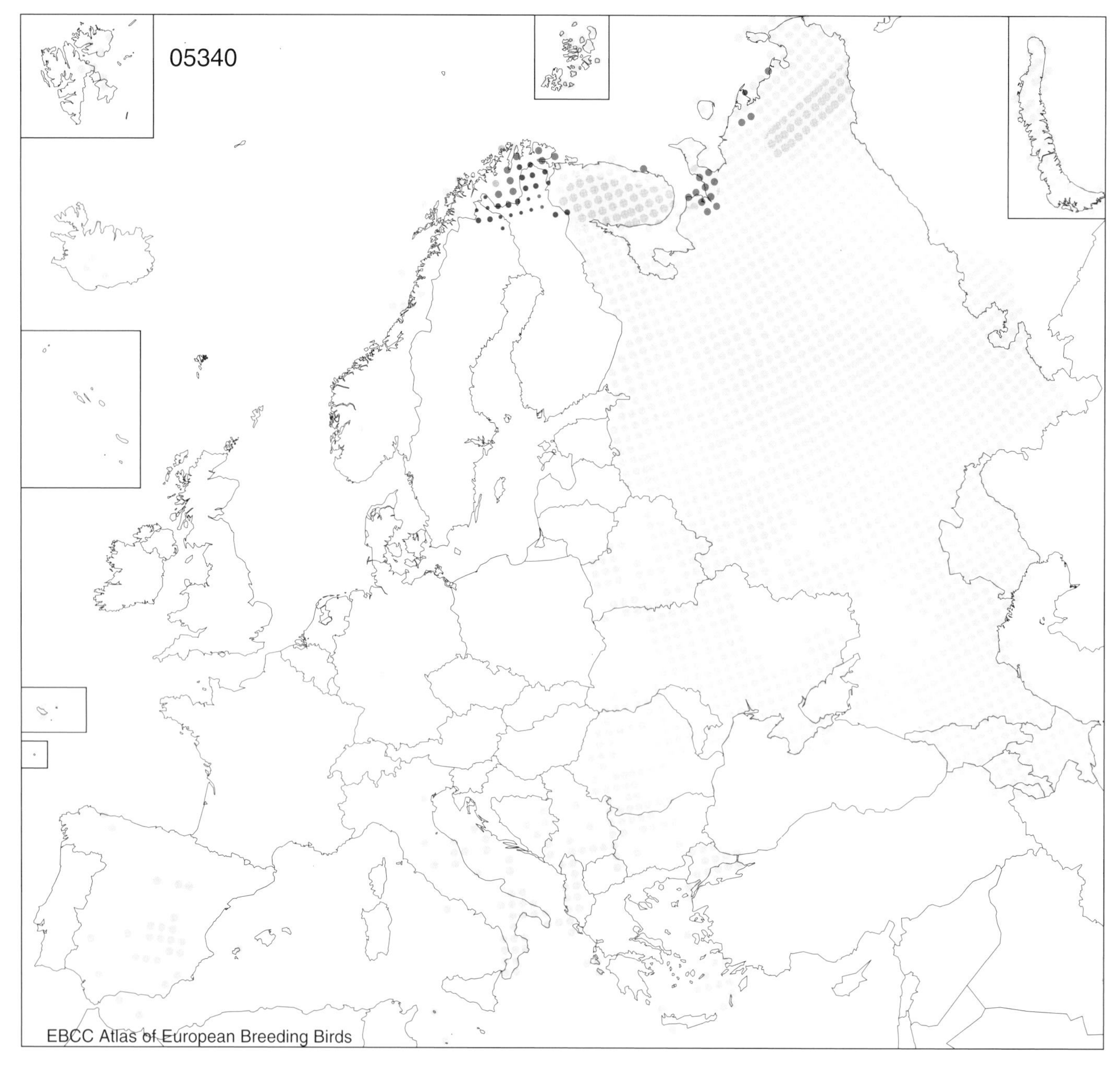

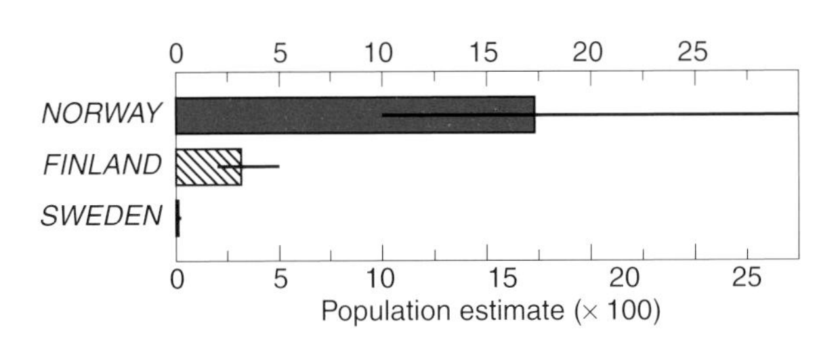

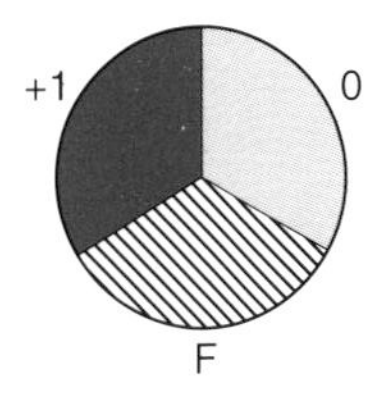

% in top 10 countries: 100.0
Total number of populated European countries: 3
Total European population 1318–3341 (2059)
Russian population 1000–10,000 (3162)

A large wader, the Bar-tailed Godwit breeds in a discontinuous belt in the high-arctic and subarctic climatic zones from Norway and European Russia through to Asia and westernmost Alaska, replacing the Black-tailed Godwit *L. limosa* ecologically in more northerly habitats. Breeding habitats, usually above the tree-limit, include sedge marshes (Bianki 1977), marshy sites in moss and shrub tundra, swampy heathlands in the willow and birch zones (near the tree-limit), dry hillock or moss-lichen tundras, wet river valleys and open larch woodlands near waterbodies. Alaskan birds may occupy the lower slopes of mountains, preferring grassy terrain (*BWP*). The Bar-tailed Godwit occurs in low densities in the forest-tundra (Rogacheva 1992).

In general two populations are distinguished, the nominate form breeding from Lapland to the eastern Taymyr Peninsula, and *L.l. baueri* breeding in NE Siberia and W Alaska. In northern Siberia between the Khatanga River and the Kolyma Delta birds are intermediate between *lapponica* and *baueri*, and often considered (as discussed in *HVM* and *BWP*) to be a separate population, *L.l. menzbieri*.

The Bar-tailed Godwit occurs rather patchily within its range. Although it may be encountered quite commonly on the Kola Peninsula, there are relatively few birds, and it is absent from the Murmansk coast and from the adjacent islands of the Barents Sea. It is locally abundant on the eastern side of the White Sea, although smaller numbers are found in the tundra proper (Bianki 1977). Annual numbers may vary strongly and the areas occupied may shift (Rogacheva 1992). Densities range from 15 nests in 15km^2 in areas near the White Sea (*HVM*) to 0.1 bp/km^2 on the Yamal Peninsula. Elsewhere on Yamal 2.6, 1.0 and 0.6 bp/km^2 were found in 1970–72, respectively (*HVM*). In easternmost Finnish Lapland, densities of up to 0.7 bp/km^2 were achieved on mires or vast clearfells in the coniferous forest. Here, line transects indicate that the overall density of the core area is 6 bp/100km^2, a value representing a much larger population than previously calculated (L. Saari *et al*, in prep). On the Kola Peninsula where there were high breeding densities, the shortest distance between occupied nests was only 270m (*HVM*).

Koskimies (1992a) estimates that 1000–3000 pairs breed in Norway, 5–25 in Sweden and 200–500 in Finland (but see above). The estimated total for European Russia of 1000–10 000 is very approximate, and for 1995 is probably an overestimate. The populations of Norway and Finland apparently are increasing, but trends for European Russian and Sweden are not known (Koskimies 1992a). In Finland the species was more widespread in the 19th century and early 20th century (*BWP*); recent estimates indicate some expansion.

Unlike the Black-tailed Godwit, the Bar-tailed Godwit rarely occurs inland except in the breeding season, remaining strongly associated with coasts during migration and when wintering. Ringing recoveries, phenological observations and data on fat accumulation indicate that birds from Scandinavia, European Russia and W Siberia winter mainly in western Europe and constitute one population (Smit & Piersma 1989, Meltofte 1993). Birds breeding further E winter in West Africa and use W European coastal wetlands only as stop-over and refuelling sites. Birds from E Taymyr are believed to migrate southwards to India, Iran, the Arabian Gulf and the Red Sea (Rogacheva 1992). East Siberian and Alaskan breeding birds winter over a vast range from E China to Malaysia, the Philippines, the East Indies, western Polynesia to Australasia. The population wintering in western Europe amounts to 125 000 birds (Smit & Piersma 1989), a figure which greatly surpasses the total numbers breeding in Europe and must be comprised partly of Asian breeding birds.

Cor Smit (NL) Lennart Saari (FIN)

Numenius phaeopus **Whimbrel**

CZ	Koliha malá	**I**	Chiurlo piccolo
D	Regenbrachvogel	**NL**	Regenwulp
E	Zarapito Trinador	**P**	Maçarico-galego
F	Courlis corlieu	**PL**	Kulik mniejszy
FIN	Pikkukuovi	**R**	Средний кроншнеп
G	Σιγλίγουρος	**S**	Småspov
H	Kis póling		

SPEC Cat 4, Threat status S (P)

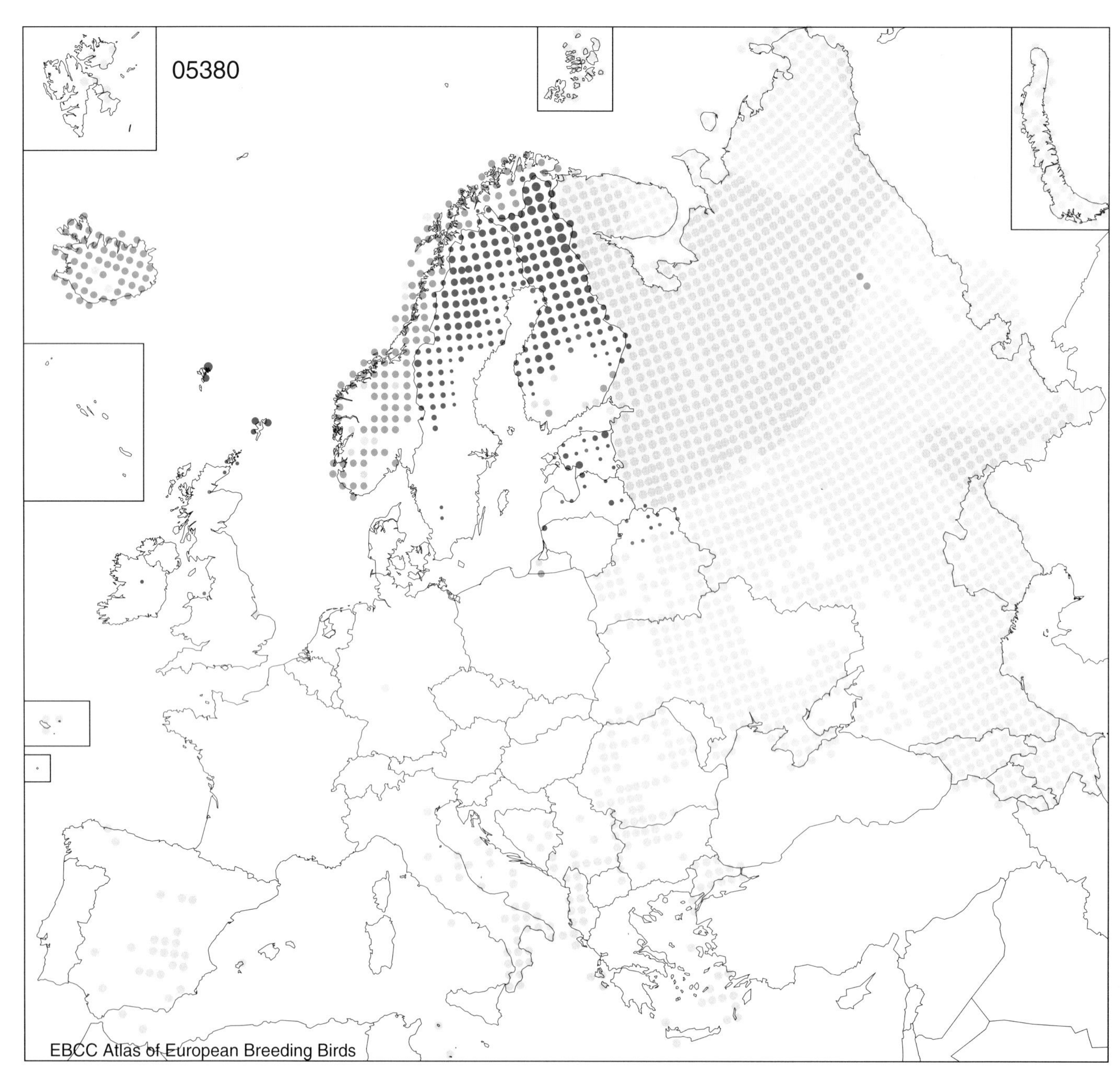

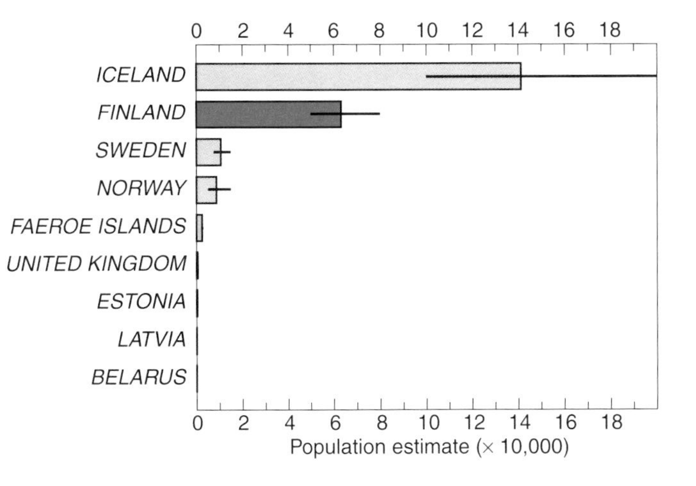

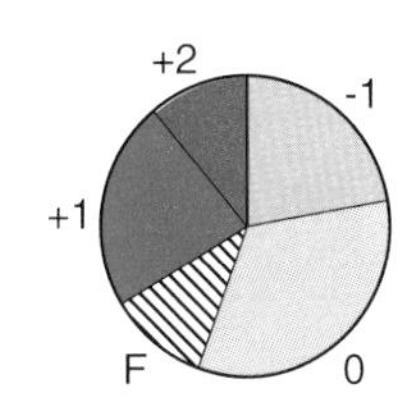

% in top 10 countries: 100.0
Total number of populated European countries: 9
Total European population 183,554–288,724 (227,308)
Russian population 10,000–30,000 (17,321)

The Whimbrel is a monogamous and highly territorial wader whose Holarctic breeding area lies primarily in the boreal, subarctic and low-arctic zones of Eurasia and America. Within Europe its breeding range extends from Iceland and northern Great Britain in the W to the Urals in the E, reaching N to *c*70°N in Norway and S to 50–55°N, E of the Volga. Atlantic and N European populations belong to the nominate *N.p. phaeopus*, which also occurs in W Siberia. The Siberian distribution appears to be relatively continuous (Rogacheva 1992) contrary to earlier distribution maps, but the racial differentiation of the Whimbrel in Asia is under discussion. Species status has sometimes been given for the American *N.p. hudsonicus*.

The Whimbrel tends to breed in conspicuous, loose aggregations in open, exposed habitats containing short vegetation. It nests mainly on wet moorlands in Iceland, although it also uses dry, dwarf-shrub heaths and overgrown lava flows. In subalpine areas in N Fennoscandia nesting often occurs on alpine heaths and mires and also in sparse mountain birch forests. In boreal Fennoscandia the species occupies extensive wet peatlands, clearfelled forests, less often farmland and rarely sparse conifer forests. Shetland Isles nesting habitats range from wet moorlands to relatively dry heathlands. Nesting areas are at low to moderate altitudes though they occur up to 700m asl in Iceland.

With 100 000–200 000bp Iceland probably holds *c*50% of the total European population. Fennoscandia holds a further 50 000–70 000bp, but we believe the 10 000–30 000bp for Russia is probably an underestimate given the vast extent of potentially suitable breeding habitat there. In maritime Iceland, the Faeroes (2000–3000bp) and Shetland, breeding densities are notably higher than at equivalent latitudes elsewhere. Within Belarus, Latvia, Estonia, Finland and Sweden, overall breeding densities increase towards the N, and are highest in N boreal and subarctic Lapland (0.5–0.7 bp/km^2; R.A. Väisänen *et al*, in prep). Densities on suitable habitat in Shetland range from 10 to 20 bp/km^2 (Grant 1991), whereas up to 30 bp/km^2 occur in parts of the Faeroes (M.G. Richardson, pers comm). Densities on the continent are much lower: in NE Finland 8 bp/km^2 on ploughed clearfells and 1–2 bp/km^2 on alpine heaths and mires (Pulliainen & Saari 1993); 1–3 bp/km^2 on large open Finnish mires (R.A. Väisänen *et al*, in prep) and 0.4 bp/km^2 in N Sweden (Arvidsson *et al* 1992).

Recent changes in Whimbrel distribution and population within Europe suggest an overall increase. The Estonian population has increased by 20–50%, and the Finnish by over 50% since the late 1960s; in C Finland the Whimbrel has also begun to breed in farmland habitats, behaviour not recorded previously. In Great Britain numbers increased from *c*200bp in 1969/70 (Sharrock 1976) to 434–495bp by the mid-1980s (Richardson 1993), more than 90% of which bred in the Shetland Isles (Richardson 1990). The Whimbrel has bred in Greenland since 1970. Although declines of 20–50% are indicated in Belarus and the Faeroes, the Belarus population comprises only 20–50bp and evidence for a decline in the Faeroes has not been quantified.

The causes of these changes are not known, although the increase in Shetland has coincided with a period of relatively cool, wet summers. Furthermore, recent studies suggest that the production of Whimbrel fledglings in Shetland is in excess of that required to balance adult mortality (Grant 1991). Moreover, the increase in the Fennoscandian population has coincided with substantial declines in populations of Peregrine *Falco peregrinus* and Gyrfalcon *F. rusticolus*, both of which are potentially important predators of adult and fledgling Whimbrel (Pulliainen & Saari 1993).

Birds from the European breeding population winter mainly in West Africa. There are important spring passage staging sites in Hungary and inland in the Low Countries, especially The Netherlands.

Murray Grant (GB) Risto A Väisänen (FIN)

Numenius arquata — Curlew

CZ	Koliha velká	**I**	Chiurlo maggiore
D	Großer Brachvogel	**NL**	Wulp
E	Zarapito Real	**P**	Maçarico-real
F	Courlis cendré	**PL**	Kulik wielki
FIN	Isokuovi	**R**	Большой кроншнеп
G	Τουρλίδα	**S**	Storspov
H	Nagy póling		

*SPEC Cat 3*W, Threat status D*W*

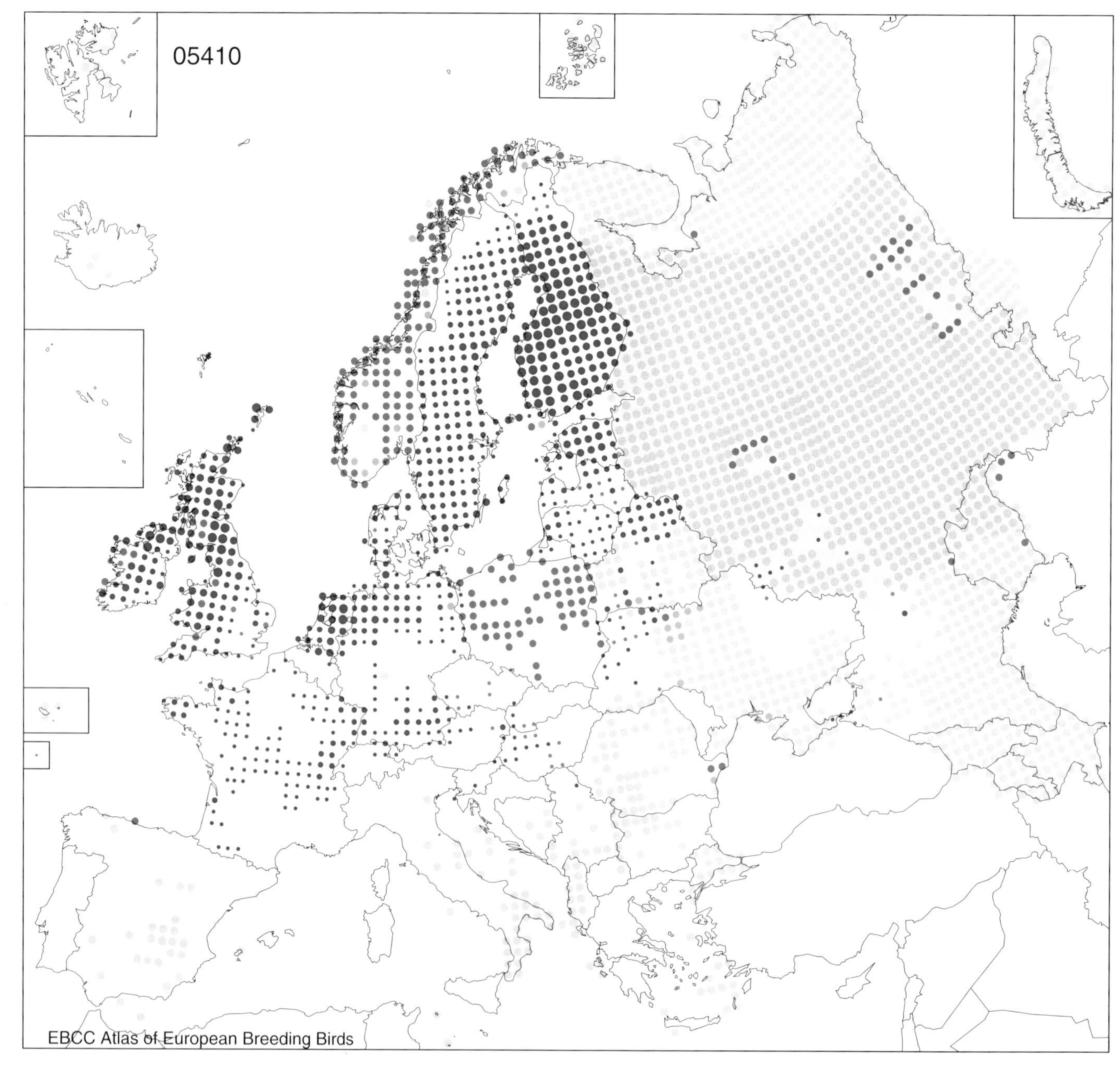

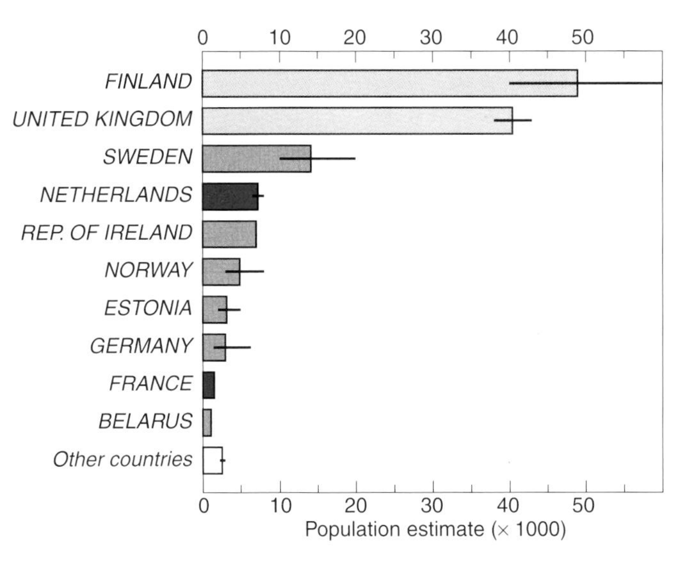

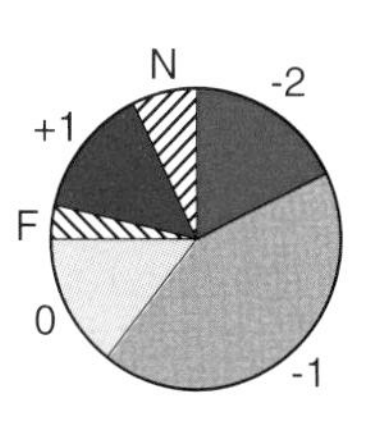

% in top 10 countries: 98.1
Total number of populated European countries: 28
Total European population 123,312–147,559 (133,886)
Russian population 10,000–100,000 (31,623)

The Curlew, a Palearctic species, occurs in the temperate and boreal climatic zones of Europe and Asia. The nominate *N.a. arquata* breeds in Europe, but grades into the Asiatic *orientalis* in SE Europe and European Russia. Its triangular range in Asia narrows eastwards from the Urals through the boreal zone, to reach the upper Amur River. It occurs as often in lowlands as in extensive, flat uplands, in general up to 600m asl. It rarely breeds in mountains.

Bogs (sedges *Carex* spp) and moorlands with cross-leaved heath *Erica tetralix*, ling *Calluna vulgaris*, purple moor-grass *Molinia caerulea*, and cottongrass *Eriophorus* spp were once the Curlew's traditional breeding habitat (Peitzmeier 1952), much of which is nowadays degraded. Most probably now nest in other habitats such as rough marginal grasslands, wet meadows, saltmarshes and even arable fields (increasingly so on sandy soils in The Netherlands; van Klinken 1994) or coastal dunes. However, an essential nesting requirement is all-round unhindered visibility of large open areas.

Generally, Curlew distribution and numbers in Europe depend on the availability of suitable breeding habitat. The species is most evenly distributed and abundant in Fennoscandia, but accurate censusing is often difficult, especially where abundance is high. Consequently population estimates vary widely. In our opinion, reliable estimates made since the graph data were compiled indicate that breeding numbers are higher than previously thought in Finland (70 000–90 000bp), Great Britain (possibly 80 000+bp), Sweden (20 000–25 000bp) and Ireland (12 000bp). Norway holds 3000–8000bp. These figures represent over 60% of the European breeding total.

The only significant increases at present are occurring in France (from 700–1200bp in 1960–70 to 1400–1600bp in 1985–89, Sigwalt 1994) and on the coastal plains of Belgium (*c*460bp), The Netherlands (7200bp), Germany (*c*3000bp) and Denmark (270bp). However, the Dutch grassland population is presently declining (van Dijk 1995). Declines have occurred in Finland, Sweden and Norway (Henrikson 1991) and evidence exists for a slight decline in Great Britain and a greater decline in Ireland (Grant 1993, J.K. Partridge, pers comm). In S Germany, Curlew numbers are also decreasing (Ranftl 1982, Opitz 1982), as is the case in the S and SE of its range where it is already very rare (Switzerland 3–5bp; Liechtenstein 2–3bp; Austria 70–90bp; Czech Republic 5–15bp; Slovakia 15–30bp; Slovenia 10–20bp; Hungary 20–50bp; Romania 20–80bp and Ukraine 160bp).

The breeding population in the SW is declining towards the North Sea centre, only 6–12 remaining in N Spain. A similar tendency exists in eastern Europe. The population centre of Poland (*c*500bp) and Belarus (*c*1050bp) is stable, but declines are apparent in Latvia (*c*280bp) and Lithuania (*c*170bp). The stability in Estonia (*c*3200 bp) is an exception, possibly because its habitat spectrum resembles that of Finland. The wide limits of the Russian estimate (10 000–100 000bp) arise from lack of data; the upper limit is more likely given the vast extent of potentially suitable habitat.

It is difficult to derive meaningful European population density estimates because most published studies tend to relate to small areas. Moreover, because the species is liable to occur in aggregations, overestimates will result if extrapolations assume all suitable habitat is similarly occupied. In extensive European moorlands, breeding density rarely exceeds 1–2 bp/km^2 (*HVM*), whilst in agricultural meadows and remnant bogs, values range from 0.2 bp/km^2 in an 865km^2 area in the Notea River valley in W Poland (J. Bednorz, unpubl) to 0.8 bp/km^2 in a 200km^2 area in the Danube Valley in Germany (*HVM*). Exceptional densities occur in the Orkney Isles, averaging 14 bp/km^2 over extensive moorland areas (13–100km^2) and 60 bp/km^2 on small fragments of semi-natural habitat (up to 3km^2) amid improved grasslands (M. Grant, unpubl).

European populations winter in western Europe, in the Mediterranean, and in many parts of Africa, but other populations winter from Japan to Africa.

Jan Bednorz (PL) and Murray Grant (GB)

Tringa totanus

Redshank

CZ	Vodouš rudonohý	I	Pettegola
D	Rotschenkel	NL	Tureluur
E	Archibebe Común	P	Perna-vermelha-comum
F	Chevalier gambette	PL	Krwawodziób
FIN	Punajalkaviklo	R	Травник
G	Κοκκινοσκέλης	S	Rödbena
H	Piroslábú cankó		

SPEC Cat 2, Threat status D

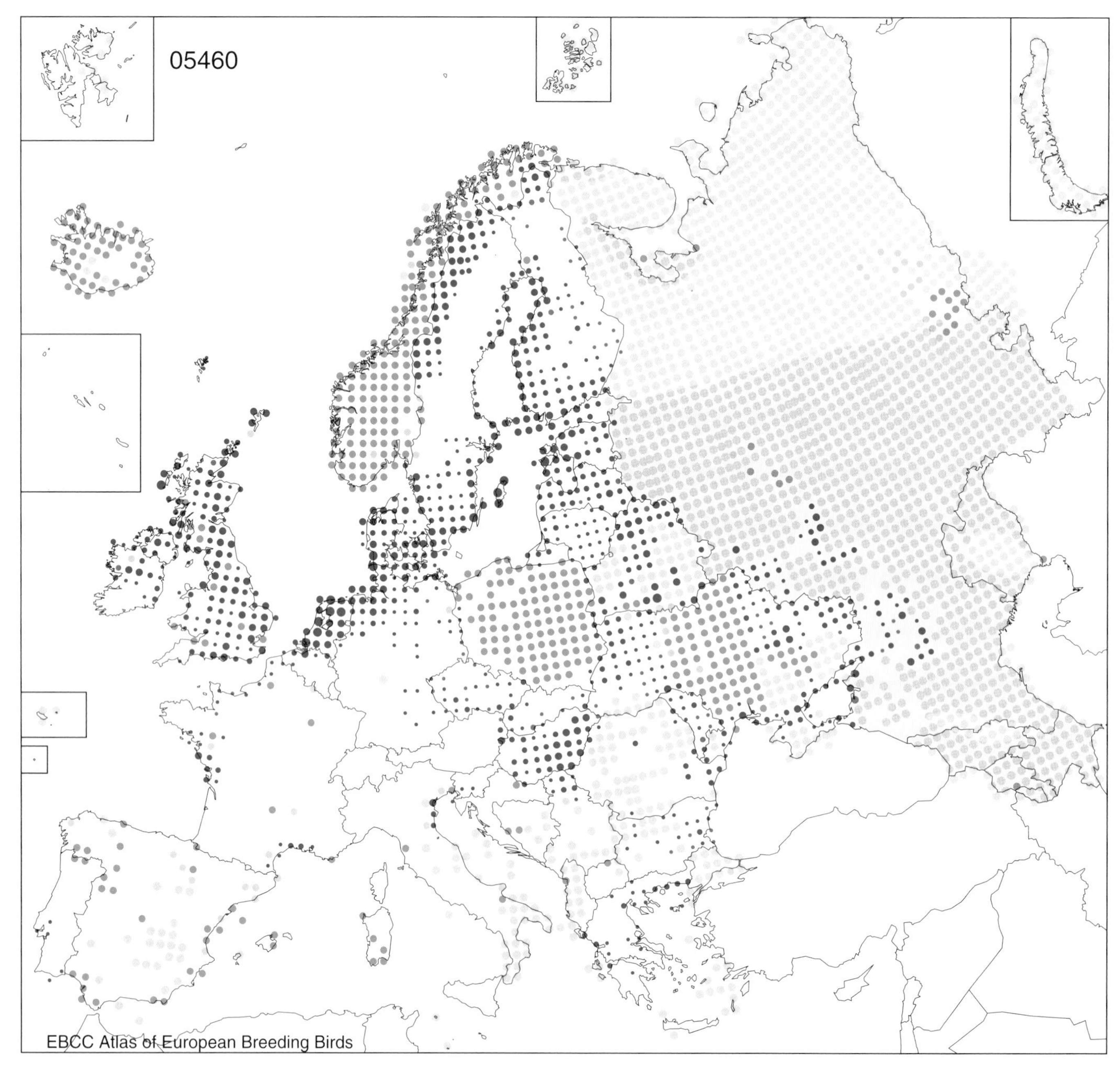

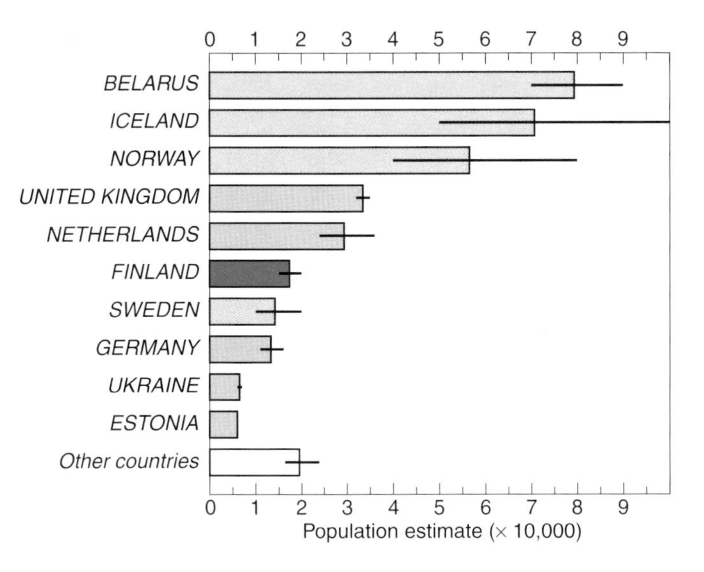

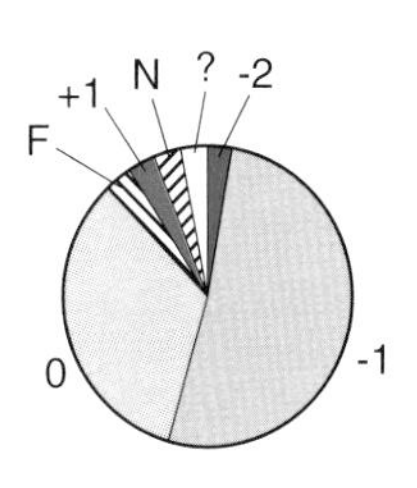

% in top 10 countries: 94.4
Total number of populated European countries: 33
Total European population 317,008–386,417 (346,192)
Russian population 10,000–100,000 (31,623)
Turkish population 10,000–100,000 (31,623)

The Redshank has an extensive Palearctic distribution, breeding from Iceland to E China, mainly in the temperate and boreal zones. In the W of its range, it also breeds in the subarctic and mediterranean zones. Its distribution centres are further S than those of similar species such as Greenshank *T. nebularia*, and Spotted Redshank *T. erythropus* but there are zones of sympatry. In the western Palearctic its northern distribution limit seems coincident with the 9°C July isotherm. Of the six subspecies, two, the nominate *T.t. totanus* (Ireland to European Russia) and *robusta* (Iceland, Faeroes), occur in Europe.

In Europe the Redshank breeds in a great variety of habitats, panoramic views and the presence of shallow water being common denominators. Suitable habitats are sedge-bogs, brackish or saltmarshes, damp or saline meadows and wet heathland. Its specific breeding habitat requirements are unclear; apparently ideal sites may be empty or nearly so.

In S Europe, the Redshank is mostly a coastal breeder, being almost exclusively confined to lagoons and brackish marshes, making its distribution very localized (Tinarelli & Baccetti 1989). Yet it can form impressive breeding colonies, as in Crimea, reaching densities of up to 600bp on 15ha of islets (Zhmud 1992). Elsewhere in Europe, its distribution is less localized, but remains predominantly coastal. Densities can reach 122–285 bp/km^2 on grazed saltmarshes in Britain (Thompson & Hale 1993), 107 on Dutch saline meadows (Beintema & Timmerman 1976), 80 in Iceland and 10–15 in the Finnish archipelago (Koskimies 1989a). On its breeding grounds, breeding pairs distribution is determined by habitat characteristics, the species' social organization (generally semi-colonial), and its predilection for extant colonies of other waders, in particular Lapwing *Vanellus vanellus*, and Bar-tailed Godwit *Limosa lapponica*, which breed earlier and are aggressive towards potential predators (Ibañez & Trolliet 1990).

The European distribution has not changed recently. Local changes may influence both distribution and population size. However, even in censused areas, precise breeding numbers are difficult to obtain, due to the Redshank's low territoriality and to the presence of non-breeding birds in spring. Numbers and trends quoted may be only rough estimates.

In Great Britain, Redshank numbers declined in the early 1800s, but the subsequent range extension and steady population increase lasted until the 1950s. Since then, numbers decreased inland, and the population is now only *c*33 000bp. In Ireland too, a decline is apparent. The large populations in Iceland (50 000–100 000bp), Norway (40 000–80 000bp), Sweden (*c*16 000bp) and Belarus (70 000–90 000bp) seem stable. Long-term trends in The Netherlands vary according to habitat. Grassland and heath populations have declined strongly since the 1950s. Numbers breeding on saltmarshes have increased. Overall, since the 1960s a decline of >50% has occurred, down to 24 000–36 000 bp by 1989–91, and is attributed to drainage work and agricultural intensification reducing habitat (Osieck & Hustings 1994). In Finland (10 000–20 000bp), an inland range extension apparently accompanied by a general population increase has occurred, despite local decreases (Koskimies 1989a). S and C European countries hold less significant populations which are stable or experiencing slight decreases which locally are attributed to wetland reclamation and intensified agriculture.

Outside the breeding season, the Redshank usually occurs on coastal mudflats. The Icelandic population winters mainly in NW Europe, where it may suffer high mortality during severe winters, as in the mid-1980s (Meininger *et al* 1991). The British population is partially migratory, with some movement between Denmark and Portugal. W European populations may remain close to their breeding sites or winter in North Africa. Those from Scandinavia and the Baltic States have a wintering range stretching from the North Sea to the Gulf of Guinea. C European populations shift to the Mediterranean. E European breeders winter mainly in the E Mediterranean and Asia Minor.

Bertrand Trolliet (F)

Tringa erythropus

Spotted Redshank

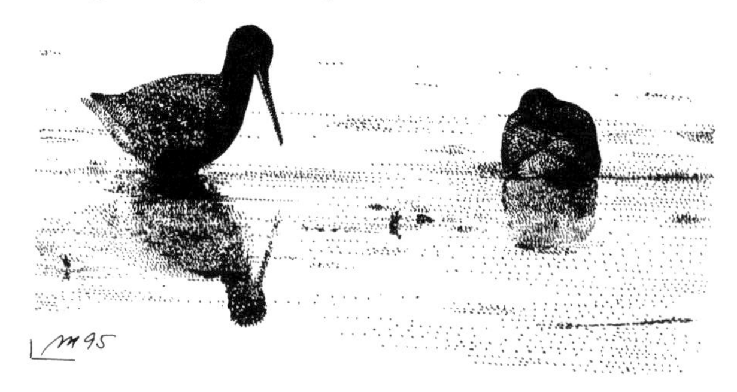

CZ	Vodouš tmavý	I	Totano moro
D	Dunkelwasserläufer	NL	Zwarte Ruiter
E	Archibebe Oscuro	P	Perna-vermelha-escuro
F	Chevalier arlequin	PL	Brodziec śniady
FIN	Mustaviklo	R	Щеголь
G	Μαυρότρυγγας	S	Svartsnäppa
H	Füstös cankó		

Non-SPEC, Threat status S

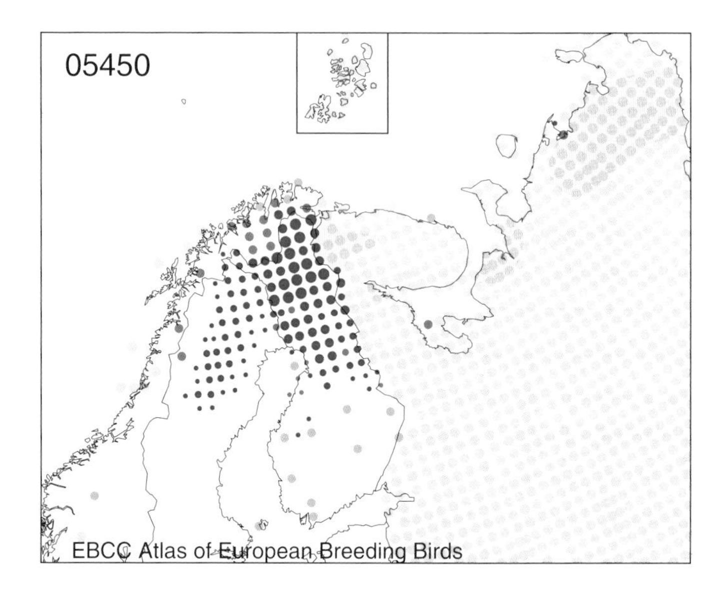

The monotypic Spotted Redshank occupies a rather narrow zone N of the closed taiga, along the N coast of Russia from the Chukotskiy Peninsula, except for N Taymyr, W at least as far as the Pechora River. An apparent distribution gap from the Pechora to the Finnish border probably reflects lack of coverage.

This graceful wader is a bird of bogs and wetlands in the taiga, especially thinly wooded or forest-bog mosaic taiga. It breeds further N and at higher elevations in the N Fennoscandian birch *Betula* zone whereas in the C Swedish birch zone it is rare because the usually rather steep slopes have few mires. It may breed N of or above the treeline, but it avoids mountainous areas. It occupies dry habitats if wetter areas are near enough to allow the young to walk there after hatching. Some pairs breed on clearfells, burnt areas or very small bogs surrounded by deep forest, flying to wetter areas to feed.

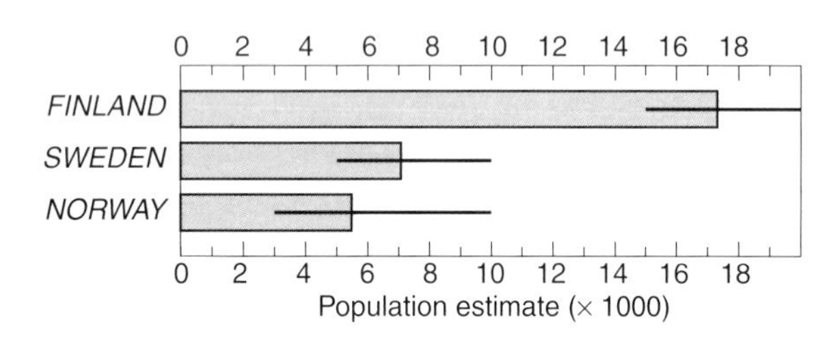

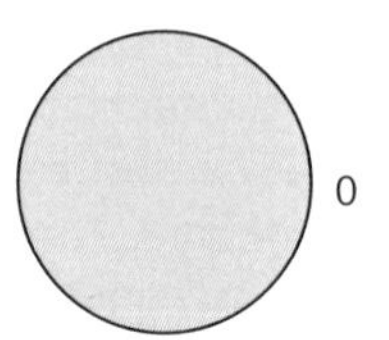

% in top 10 countries: 100.0
Total number of populated European countries: 3
Total European population 25,893–35,887 (29,869)
Russian population 1000–10,000 (3162)

Its distribution is patchy but in suitable habitats the Spotted Redshank is a fairly common bird. Except during the incubation period, it is vigorous in defence of its nest or young. Provided its breeding area is accessible, it is relatively straightforward to census in the breeding season. In areas with much preferred habitat its density may reach 1–3 bp/km^2. In Sweden, it has expanded its range to the S since the mid-1960s and now breeds regularly in Vilhelmina and Lycksele, some 150–200km further S than in the early 20th century (Curry-Lindahl 1960). In all three Nordic countries there were a few scattered records during the breeding period S of its continuous breeding range.

The Finnish population is the best-known, and apparently the largest, but the Russian estimate is very approximate and perhaps reflects the likely population of European Russia alone; however, until density estimates are available across its vast Asian Russian distribution, the puzzle of its apparently very sparse occurrence in northern Siberia must remain unsolved. In C Siberian forest tundra it is locally common, reaching 4–5 bp/km of river-shore (Norilskiy Lakes) and 15 birds/km^2 in swampy, open larch *Larix* woodlands (Rogacheva 1992).

Apart from its range expansion in Sweden, little is known about population trends (Mjelstad & Sætersdal 1986). The reason for the expansion is unknown. The possibility that it might have benefited from the numerous recent clearfells in the expansion region can be ruled out because most new pairs have settled on natural mires where formerly the species did not breed. Apparently suitable habitats exist much further S and hence the potential for further expansion remains.

The Spotted Redshank migrates on a broad front. Females begin to leave the breeding grounds in June, the males follow in July and August and the juveniles soon after. En route in autumn it is often seen in small parties at inland localities. In spring several hundred birds may assemble at stop-overs close to the main breeding grounds. European populations winter mainly S of the Sahara but N of the equator but small numbers remain in W Europe and in the Mediterranean region.

Pertti Koskimies (FIN) Sören Svensson (S)

Tringa stagnatilis

Marsh Sandpiper

CZ	Vodouš štíhlý	I	Albastrello
D	Teichwasserläufer	NL	Poelruiter
E	Archibebe Fino	P	Perna-verde-fino
F	Chevalier stagnatile	PL	Brodziec pławny
FIN	Lampiviklo	R	Поручейник
G	Βαλτότρυγγας	S	Dammsnäppa
H	Tavi cankó		

Non-SPEC, Threat status S (P)

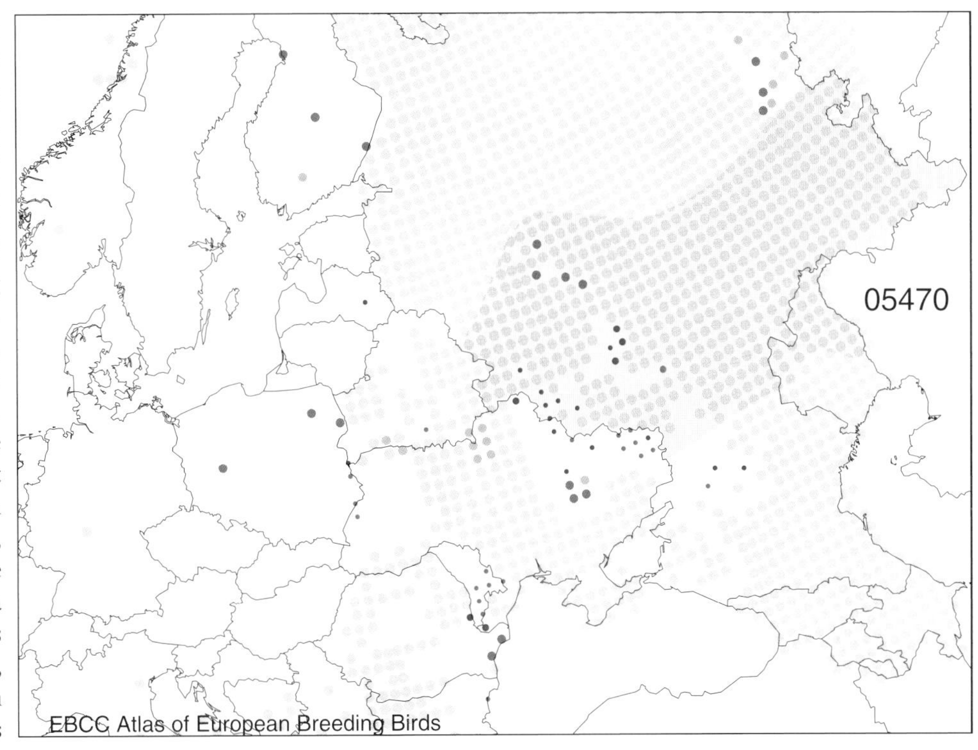

The Marsh Sandpiper breeds in Europe in steppe, forest-steppe and the southern forest zones from the Black Sea, Poland and Finland through C Ukraine, S Russia then extralimitally to N Kazakhstan and the northern and western foothills of the Altai range. Further E its breeding distribution is discontinuous, reaching as far as Khanka Lake, but mainly in large river valleys (Amur, Agrun', Olyokma, Vilui). In Europe its northern limits are at Botnik Bay (65°N), from St Petersburg to the Kirov region (59°N) and in Asia to Tyumen', Ishim, Novosibirsk, to N Lake Baykal and the upper Angara River. The southern limit runs from 47–49°N through Ukraine, S Russia and Kazakhstan (Stepanyan 1990). The species winters mainly on seacoasts, lakeshores and along larger rivers in South and East Africa, the Nile Delta, Sri Lanka, the Indian subcontinent, Indonesia, tropical SE Asia and Australia.

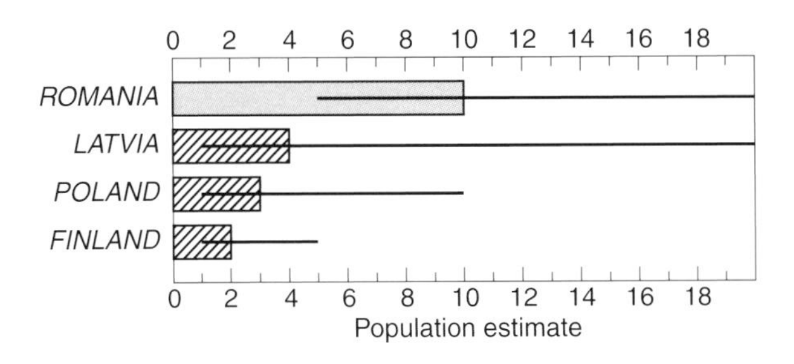

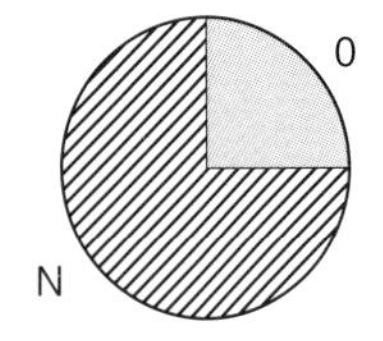

% in top 10 countries: 100.0
Total number of populated European countries: 4
Total European population 13–40 (20)
Russian population 10,000–100,000 (31,623)

The Marsh Sandpiper prefers open country, river and lake floodplain meadows, steppe grasslands and pastoral areas in river valleys, but also uses artificial habitats such as fishponds and sewage-farms. Its main habitat requirements are short grasses and small shallow pools or lakes.

In Europe the distribution is patchy, matching the distribution of suitable breeding habitats. Core areas lie in N Ukraine, S and C Russia (Volga, Don, Dnepr, Desna, Kama, Oka, Ural and smaller river valleys), and from the Ural Mountains to 30°E. To the W, breeding is irregular and numbers fluctuate between years (V.V. Morozov, unpubl). An expansion to the W and N has been recorded in recent years, such as in Poland, Belarus, Finland and the Leningrad region in Russia (Kuźniak & Pugachevich 1992, Doropheev 1993, A.M. Sokolov, pers comm). Breeding density in prime habitats reaches 5.5 bp/km^2 (Morozov 1990).

Although not under immediate threat, the species' low overall population increases its vulnerability to reclamation of its habitat.

Vladimir V Morozov (R)

Tringa nebularia Greenshank

CZ	Vodouš šedý	**I**	Pantana
D	Grünschenkel	**NL**	Groenpootruiter
E	Archibebe Claro	**P**	Perna-verde-comum
F	Chevalier aboyeur	**PL**	Kwokacz
FIN	Valkoviklo	**R**	Большой улит
G	Πρασινοσκέλης	**S**	Gluttsnäppa
H	Szürke cankó		

Non-SPEC, Threat status S

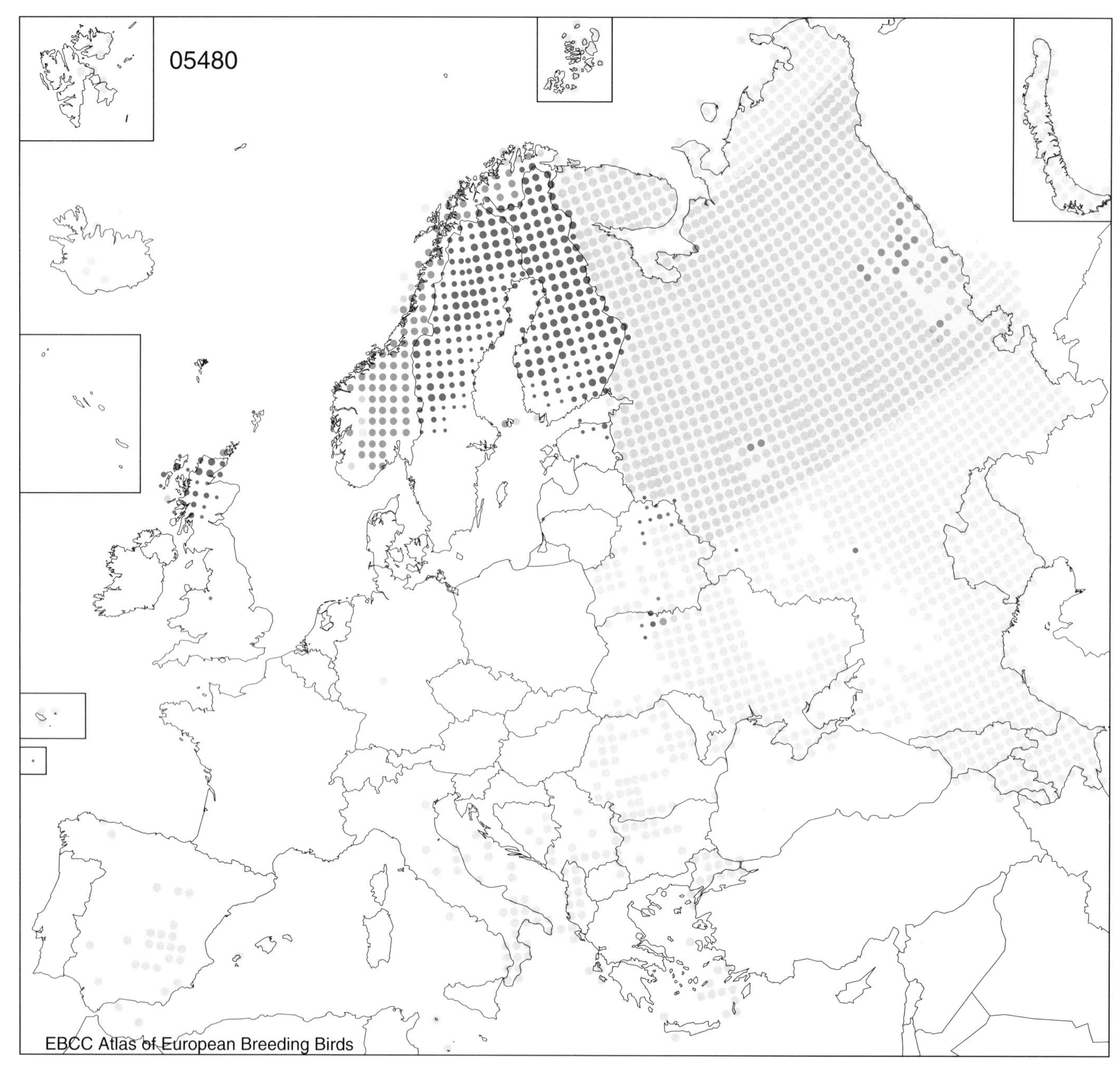

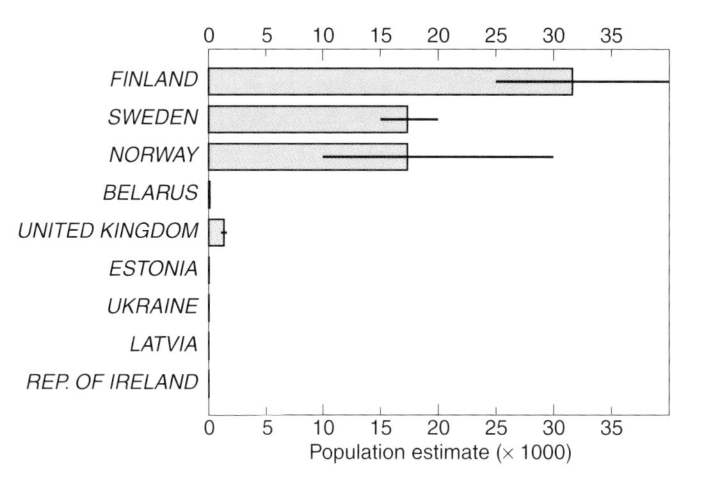

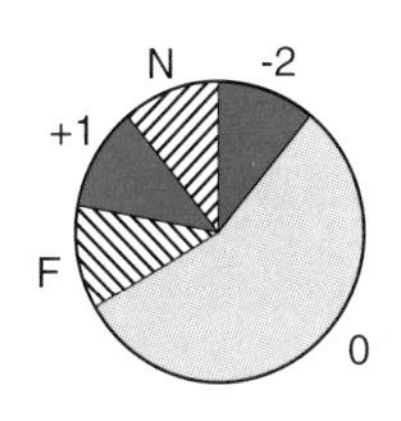

% in top 10 countries: 100.0
Total number of populated European countries: 9
Total European population 57,612–83,189 (67,756)
Russian population 10,000–100,000 (31,623)

Throughout its breeding range, the Greenshank is confined largely to the Palearctic boreal forests (taiga) N of the steppes and S of the tundra. It breeds from Great Britain in the W (rarely in Ireland) to the Kamchatka Peninsula in the E. In northern Europe, it breeds as far S as Latvia and in Russia between *c*55° and 67°N. There are no recognized subspecies.

The Greenshank nests on the ground, typically beside a piece of dead wood or at the base of a tree, in the forest marshes and boggy or dwarf-shrub dominated clearings found throughout its breeding range. In NW Scotland, in the extreme W of its range, it behaves contrarily, usually nesting beside a rock in open areas of wet blanket mire and heath, now devoid of trees. It is absent from the coastal fringes of Norway and from the more fertile lowlands of Sweden and Finland. In Fennoscandia, the species breeds up to 1200m asl although towards its northern range limits, it may nest near sea level; in Scotland it normally breeds below 550m asl.

Save for three studies in Scotland, there is no information available on recent changes in numbers or distribution: in the C Highlands, a forest-breeding population declined and contracted in range as the breeding habitat dried out and the ground vegetation became rank (Nethersole-Thompson & Nethersole-Thompson 1979); in NW Sutherland, the number of breeding pairs declined from the early 1980s onwards through damage inflicted on valley-bottom breeding sites by off-road vehicles (Thompson & Thompson 1991, unpubl), and the third study (Whitfield 1996) found that breeding numbers had declined in Caithness and Sutherland (3% per annum, 1979–94) and the Western Isles of Lewis and Harris (1% per annum 1987–95). Tucker & Heath (1994) assess that overall the European breeding population is stable although a tenth of the winter population apparently has declined by >20%. The graph generally gives rough approximations of national totals.

Throughout its range, Greenshank breeding densities are highest in areas where there is ample standing or running water (rivers, lochs or pools) in boglands. Such wet areas hold essential feeding sites for adult and young birds, although adults may feed several kilometres from the nest and broods can travel similar distances prior to fledging. Generally the species avoids dense, mature pine *Pinus* spp, birch *Betula* spp or other forests which have few natural openings.

Overall annual breeding densities ranged from 0.2 to 0.7 bp/km^2 in prime habitat in NW Scotland, some parts holding up to 2 bp/km^2 (Nethersole-Thompson & Nethersole-Thompson 1986). Whitfield (1996) more recently calculated 0.14 bp/km^2 in the blanket peatlands (the Flow Country) of Caithness and Sutherland and 0.22 bp/km^2 in Lewis and Harris. In Norway, densities ranged from 1.0 bp/km^2 in the S to 0.5 bp/km^2 in the N (Kålås & Byrkjedal 1981). No other breeding density estimates are available.

Outside the breeding season the Greenshank, a long-distance migrant, generally is confined to coastal and inland wetlands. N European breeders winter S and W of their breeding grounds in the Mediterranean and Africa (particularly SW Africa). N and E Eurasian populations migrate S to the wetlands and coasts of Asia, Malaysia, Indonesia and Australasia.

Because of the Greenshank's secretive nature (nests are difficult to find; off-duty birds may feed remotely from the breeding site) and its generally low breeding density, it is extremely difficult to census accurately. Like many wader species, it may suffer considerable fluctuations in breeding numbers from year to year. One study area revealed a fluctuation in breeding numbers which related in part to the levels of breeding success attained in the previous two years (Thompson & Thompson 1991), with threefold differences recorded over 30 years.

Patrick S Thompson (GB) Des BA Thompson (GB)

Tringa ochropus

Green Sandpiper

CZ	Vodouš kropenatý	I	Piro-piro culbianco
D	Waldwasserläufer	NL	Witgatje
E	Andarríos Grande	P	Pássaro-bique-bique
F	Chevalier culblanc	PL	Samotnik
FIN	Metsäviklo	R	Черныш
G	Δασότρυγγας	S	Skogssnäppa
H	Erdei cankó		

Non-SPEC, Threat status S (P)

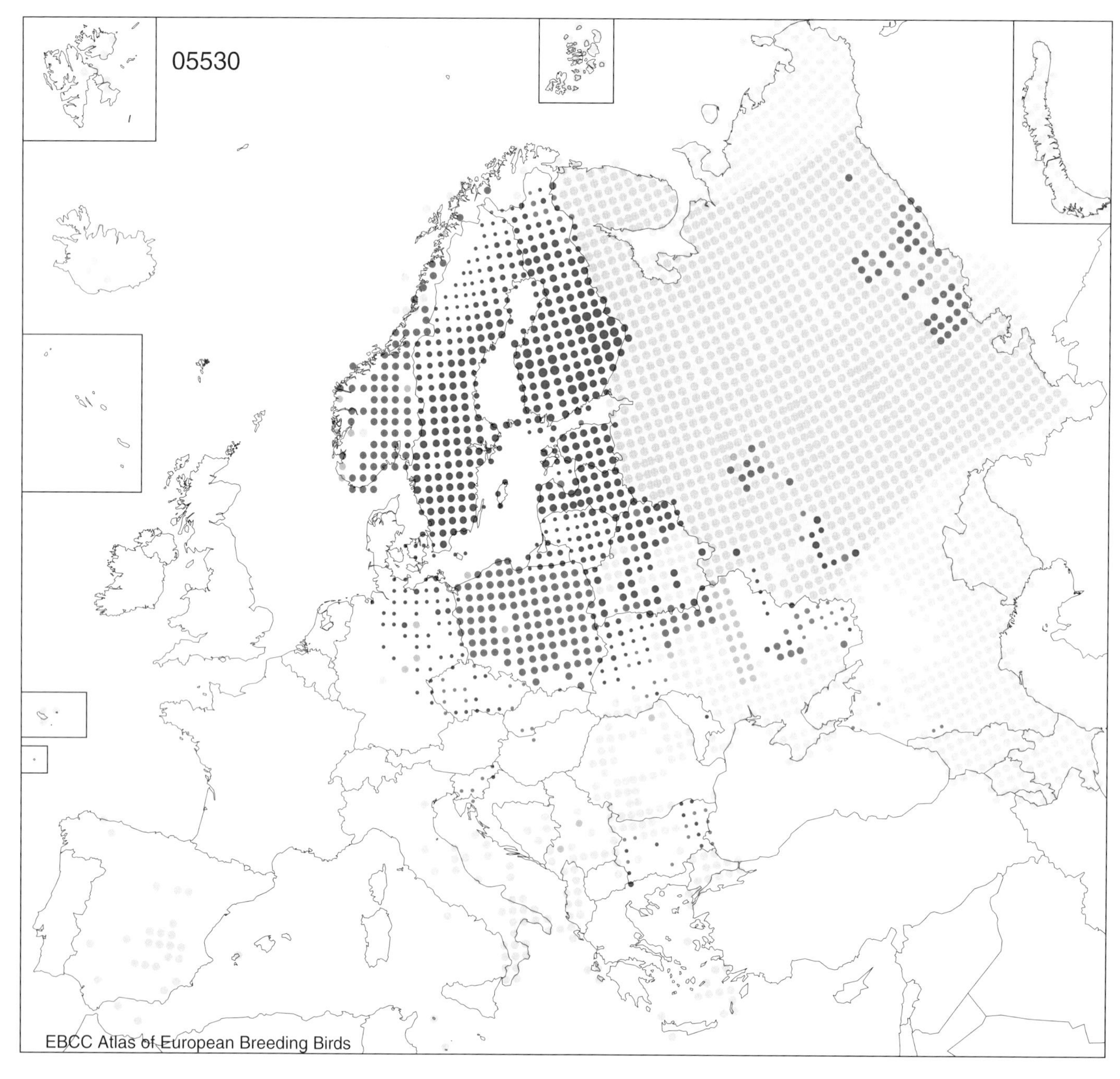

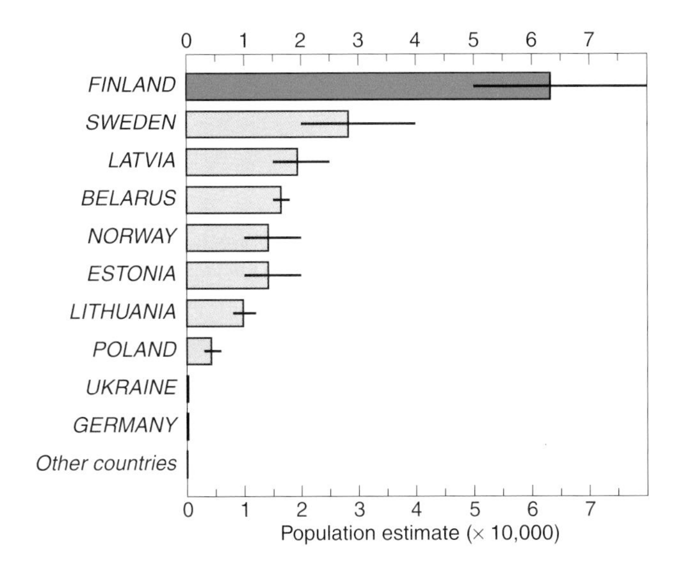

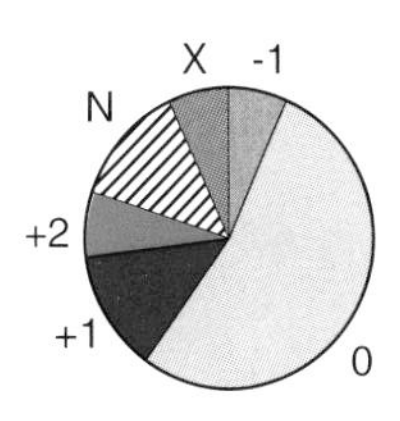

% in top 10 countries: 100.0
Total number of populated European countries: 15
Total European population 152,786–193,224 (170,229)
Russian population 100,000–1,000,000 (316,228)

The monotypic Green Sandpiper is a trans-Palearctic species, mostly confined to the boreal zone. In the western parts of its range it penetrates locally into the temperate zone, and to the N into the subarctic zone. Most of its range lies between the Arctic Circle in the N and the steppe zone in the S, stretching from Scandinavia and the countries around the Baltic Sea in the W to the Sea of Okhotsk in the E. The Green Sandpiper is a rare breeder in much of eastern Europe, only occurring regularly from Poland eastwards. There are no subspecies.

The southwestern limit of breeding is difficult to confirm, because some non-breeding birds may remain in their wintering areas and display there. The species also displays on passage (sometimes up to several days at the same site without breeding). Because the interval between the end of the spring migration and the start of the autumn migration is exceptionally short, further confusion may ensue. This problem exists as far N as SW Finland, where the autumn migration may start very early in June (L. Saari, pers obs).

The various populations seem mostly to be stable or increasing, despite drainage of its favoured habitats, certainly in Finland (*cf* Hildén & Hyytiä 1981). Since the mid-1970s increases have been documented both in the N (Finland and Norway) and S (Germany, Denmark, Czech Republic and Austria) of its range. The only conflicting evidence is of decreases in Ukraine and also in Slovenia, where the species last bred in 1991 (Geister 1995). The Finnish range has probably expanded N throughout the 20th century; from the 1950s onwards the northern range limit has shifted from *c*67° to 69°N, and it has now reached, or even locally gone beyond, the limit of Norway spruce *Picea abies* (see Hildén & Hyytiä 1981). The recent spread into Lapland has also been repeated in the Kola Peninsula: the first record in the Lapland preserve dates from 1981 and the species has been recorded annually since (Semyonov-Tyan-Shansky & Guylyazov 1991). Breeding in Denmark was first recorded in the 1950s and the spread has continued (Sørensen 1995).

Excluding the population estimates for Russia because of their very broad limits (100 000–1Mbp) the highest populations (maximum estimates) are found in Finland (80 000bp), Sweden (40 000), Latvia (25 000), Estonia and Norway (both 20 000), Belarus (18 000), Lithuania (12 000) and Poland (6000). The total for all remaining populations in Europe is less than 100bp. Density data are scarce in the literature; the only figure given for overall density of an extensive area is 0.4–0.5 bp/km^2 over 91km^2. The density in spruce-dominated grove-like forests in E Estonia varies between 0 and 6.0 (usually 2–3) bp/km^2 (Leibak *et al* 1994).

The Green Sandpiper is decidedly a bird of coniferous or mixed forests, and it thrives in moist spruce or pine *Pinus* woods which have adjacent small bodies of water: ponds, springs, brooks and ditches usually far from human habitation. At its northern range limit, as in Finnish Lapland, it prefers the favourable microclimate of spruce-dominated canyons of the upper reaches of rivers, avoiding fens and pine-peat bogs (L. Saari *et al*, in prep). The Green Sandpiper lays its eggs in nests of other species, usually thrushes, and is thus confined to wooded habitats.

In Fennoscandia spring migration starts usually in April and ends around mid-May. Females leave their mates from early June onwards. The autumn migration peaks in July and ends in August. The European Green Sandpiper populations winter in W and C Europe, the Mediterranean basin, Turkey, sub-Saharan and tropical Africa, and possibly Iran. Eastern populations winter in India and throughout SE Asia.

Lennart Saari (FIN)

Tringa glareola

Wood Sandpiper

CZ	Vodouš bahenní	**I**	Piro-piro boschereccio
D	Bruchwasserläufer	**NL**	Bosruiter
E	Andarríos Bastardo	**P**	Maçarico-bastardo
F	Chevalier sylvain	**PL**	Łęczak
FIN	Liro	**R**	Фифи
G	Λασπότρυγγας	**S**	Grönbena
H	Réti cankó		

SPEC Cat 3, Threat status D

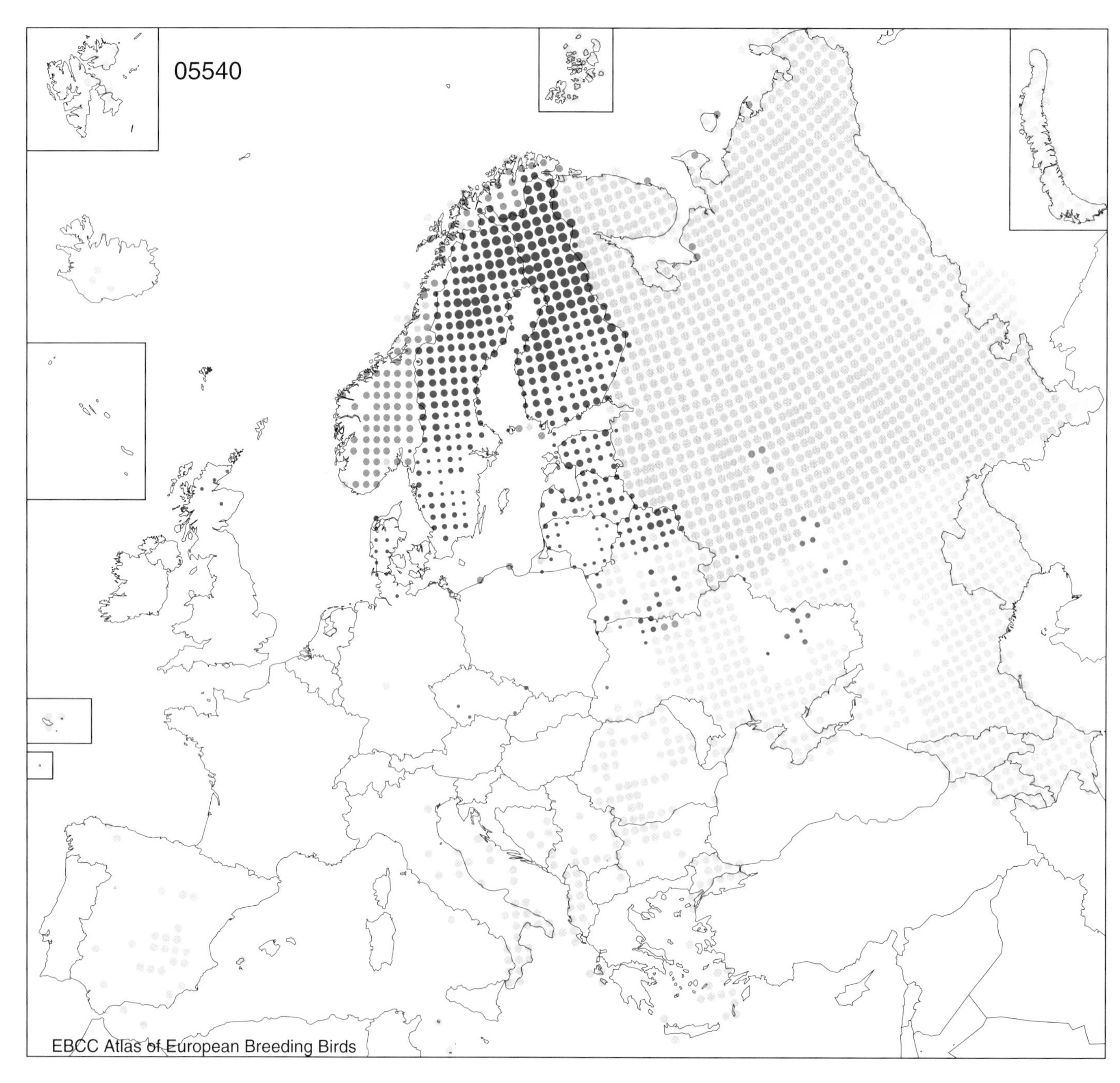

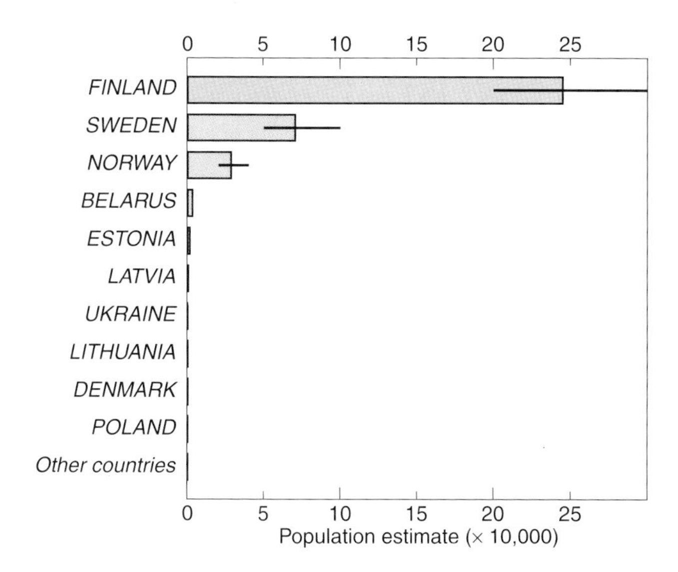

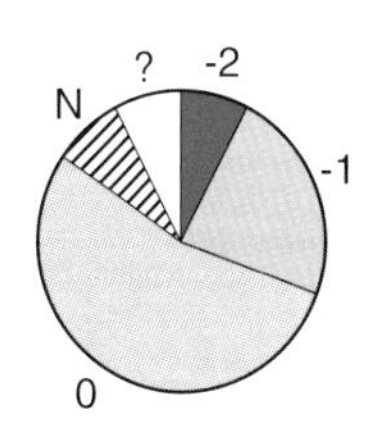

% in top 10 countries: 100.0
Total number of populated European countries: 13
Total European population 298,842–412,474 (349,023)
Russian population 100,000–1,000,000 (316,228)

The Wood Sandpiper is a medium-sized wader whose numerous population is distributed extensively throughout the Palearctic, occupying a wide variety of habitats. The main population breeds in the northern boreal and subarctic zones, from Fennoscandia to E Siberia, regions where waders are most abundant (Järvinen & Väisänen 1978c). The Wood Sandpiper becomes scarcer through the southern boreal zone, only marginal populations being found in temperate areas. It winters in a wide range of climatic zones ranging from temperate to tropical in SE Asia, Australia and Africa.

Wader diversity is highest in the most important habitat of the Wood Sandpiper, on open, wet and productive flark fens (fens having a complex habitat structure of numerous ponds and pools, *Sphagnum* strings [hummock banks] and hummocks). On flark fens in N Finland breeding density is generally 7–12 bp/km^2 (Järvinen *et al* 1987) and in pine bogs 3–4.5 bp/km^2, but on the open mires of S Sweden, only 0.3 bp/km^2 (Arvidsson *et al* 1992). The species prefers a thin scattering of trees which provide suitable take-off points for its song flight. The Wood Sandpiper often breeds in pine bogs, at the boundary of open mire and forest, but may also choose smaller bogs more enclosed by forest, if these contain sufficient muddy margins or small, shallow pools. Where there are trees nearby, the female may lay her eggs in old thrush nests instead of on the ground (Pulliainen & Saari 1991).

Further S, where mires become more impoverished, too small, or too enclosed, the Wood Sandpiper may breed on large, open and damp lakeshore meadows. In C Europe, it is not uncommon to find pairs breeding by lakeshores and shallow riverbanks in heather moorlands (Kirchner 1978).

The species becomes scarcer towards the S and W coasts of Fennoscandia, occurring only sporadically in Denmark. In continental Europe, distribution gaps increase in size below 58°N, S of Estonia. In boreal Finland its density increases about 50-fold from <0.1 bp/km^2 in a large area of the southern coastal region to about 3 bp/km^2 in C Lapland (R.A. Väisänen, unpubl), some 900km further N where peatlands predominate. Further N still on the Norwegian Arctic Ocean coast its density decreases again to <0.1 bp/km^2.

Extensive line transect census data show that the Finnish population remained reasonably constant through the 1940s and 1950s, increased temporarily by about 20% by the 1970s, but then decreased to the previous level during the 1980s (R.A. Väisänen, unpubl). As shown in the Finnish bird atlases of 1974–79 and 1986–89, the Wood Sandpiper's distribution contracted, corresponding to a declining trend revealed by the annual monitoring of land birds from 1979 to 1994.

Since 1965 in S Finland the decline possibly has been caused by the large-scale drainage of peatlands for forestry. The Danish population also has declined due to habitat changes. The species' breeding range has contracted in Latvia, Ukraine and Great Britain. Furthermore, local decreases have been observed in several other countries.

It seems that wetland reclamation is a serious threat to the southern European populations of Wood Sandpiper, but not to the main northern European population, because the vast majority of wet mires in Finland, Sweden and Russia remain in pristine condition. It is therefore more likely that the reasons for the current decline of the main population will be found in Africa, where European birds winter.

The largest breeding populations are in Russia (100 000–1Mbp), Finland (250 000; annual range 200 000–300 000), Sweden (50 000–100 000) and Norway (20 000–40 000). In comparison, other populations are insignificant, Belarus having 3000–3200bp and Estonia 1000–2000. When Finnish breeding densities are applied to the corresponding botanical zones elsewhere, a crude estimate of 1.2Mbp is obtained for Europe, the Russian and Nordic populations being in the rough proportion of 2:1.

Risto A Väisänen (FIN)

Actitis hypoleucos **Common Sandpiper**

CZ Pisík obecný
D Flußuferläufer
E Andarríos Chico
F Chevalier guignette
FIN Rantasipi
G Ποταμότρυγγας
H Billegetőcankó
I Piro-piro piccolo
NL Oeverloper
P Maçarico-das-rochas
PL Brodziec piskliwy
R Перевозчик
S Drillsnäppa

Non-SPEC, Threat status S

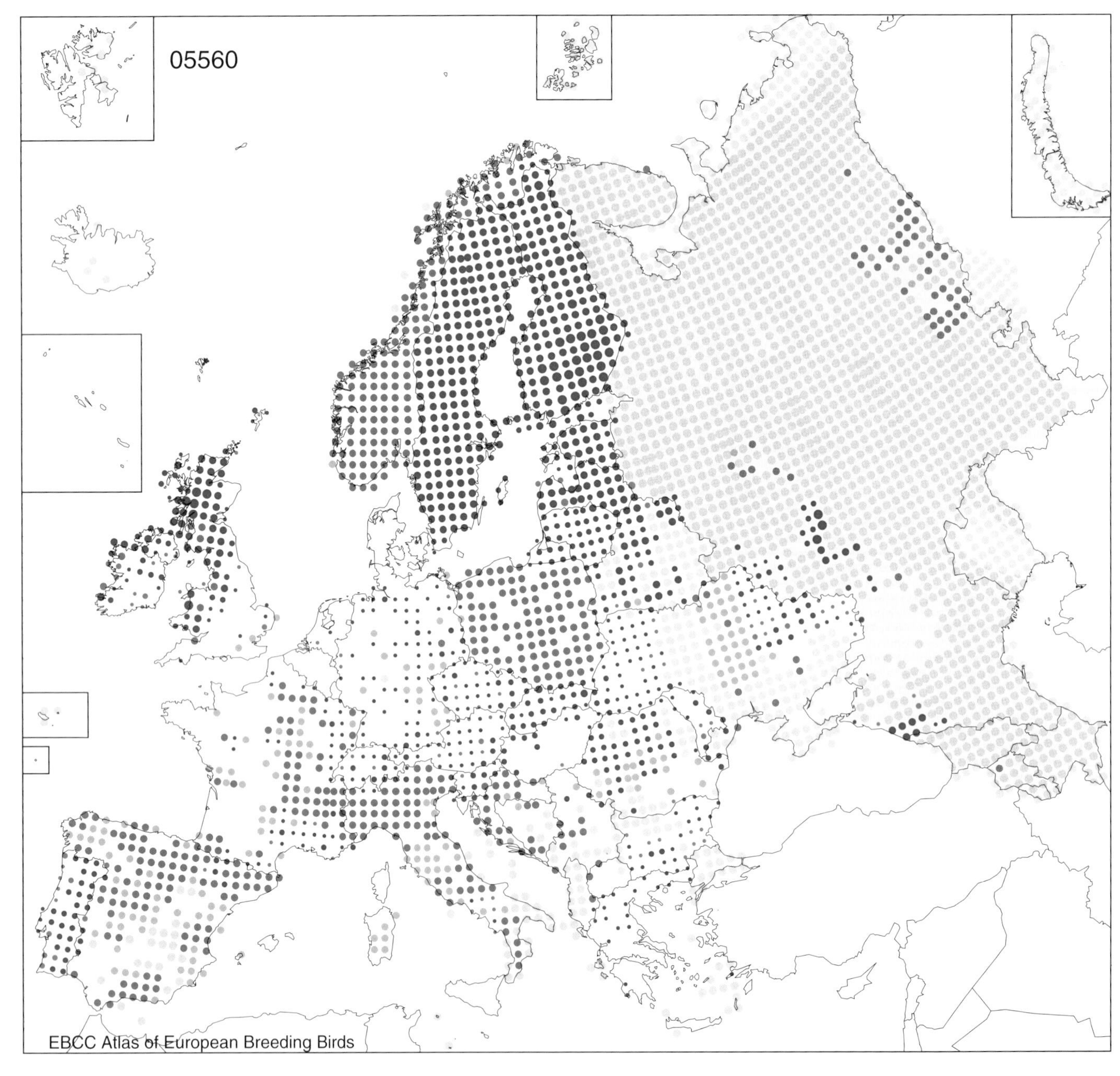

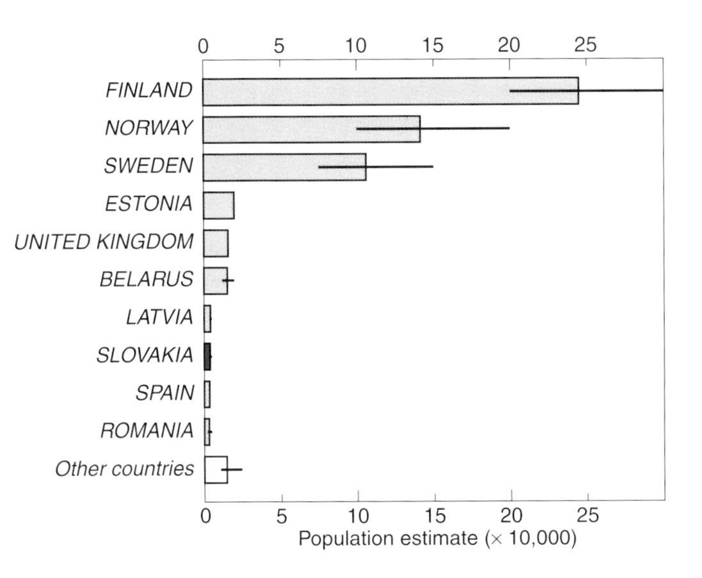

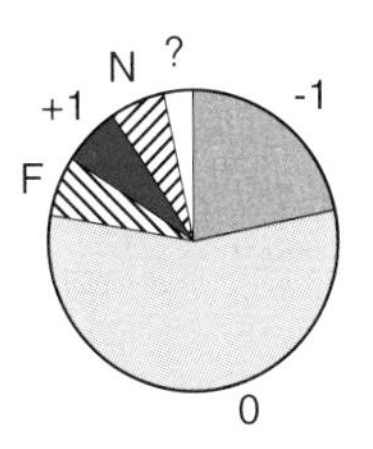

% in top 10 countries: 97.4
Total number of populated European countries: 32
Total European population 504,611–665,336 (573,324)
Russian population 50,000–500,000(158,114)
Turkish population 2000–10,000 (4472)

The Common Sandpiper is distributed across the whole Palaearctic region, except for Iceland. It is replaced by its congener, the Spotted Sandpiper *Actitis macularia*, in the Nearctic. As the most widespread of the *Scolopacidae* in Europe, the Common Sandpiper provides an interesting example of adaptation to, and high occupancy of, a distinctive habitat found almost everywhere, geography and rainfall permitting.

The Common Sandpiper is found in open freshwater areas. When it arrives in spring on its breeding grounds its display flights are mainly over water, sometimes skimming low almost touching the water before rising to a height to display in higher air space. For the chicks, a pair will need a length of water's edge where under normal conditions the flow is low. The Common Sandpiper also requires *c*1000m^2 of shingle or stony habitat to cope with changes in water level following high rainfall. Ground vegetation is essential, not only for nesting, but also for cover for the chicks, which, because they run to concealment from threats rather than relying on cryptic behaviour, also benefit from the presence of roots or stones to provide hiding places. Such habitat is associated most commonly with upland rivers whose flood conditions provide it, but the species also breeds at sea level, and includes coastal sites near mountains. Because the chicks eat terrestrial and freshwater food, the Common Sandpiper's territory will have freshwater inflow. Even on migration, the Common Sandpiper makes relatively little use of seashore or salty estuarine sites.

The main European population breeds above 55°N from the northern half of Great Britain through Scandinavia into Russia. The remaining European populations occur mainly in upland areas where high rainfall sustains the necessary habitat. Along rivers in C Europe it breeds on gravel banks overgrown with early successional vegetation (willow *Salix*, alder *Alnus*, poplar *Populus*) or ash *Fraxinus* woodland.

Only in Hungary and Slovakia are small populations judged to be increasing. Minor populations elsewhere S of 55°N are either stable or gauged to be decreasing. A clear indication of a gradual contraction in range is given by Yalden (1993) where a 30% contraction is shown for Ireland since 1968. This is probably a continuation of a trend with a mainly climatic basis but made worse by agricultural and recreational pressures and by waterway regulation and increased gravel extraction. However, the huge Fennoscandian, Russian, Belarussian and Baltic population of *c*700 000bp is considered to be stable (except for a decline in Lithuania), indicating that the decline is confined mostly to peripheral populations in W and C Europe (>20 000bp) and E Europe (>9400bp). There is a good population in Portugal and NW Spain (4000–14 000bp), perhaps aided by recruitment from passing migrant flocks, a mechanism which would help maximize the occupation of all suitable habitat. The Common Sandpiper does not show high philopatry to its natal area, but does to an established breeding territory (Holland & Yalden 1991).

A summary of 19 surveys from all over Europe of breeding density (Nethersole-Thompson & Nethersole-Thompson 1986) showed that in appropriate habitat typically there was 1 bp/km of riverbank or lakeshore. Locally in prime habitat, nests have been found only *c*50m apart.

A few European birds overwinter, but nearly all migrate on a broad front in small groups typically of 5–10 individuals to S of the Sahara. They return in April to S Europe and in May to N Europe. The Common Sandpiper has a short breeding cycle. Females start autumn migration in mid-June, increasing their weight by about 50% beforehand. Ringing recoveries indicate a fairly rapid migration over long stages back to Africa. Asian birds winter in India, China, SE Asia and Australasia.

Philip Holland (GB) Iztok Geister (SLN)

Arenaria interpres **Turnstone**

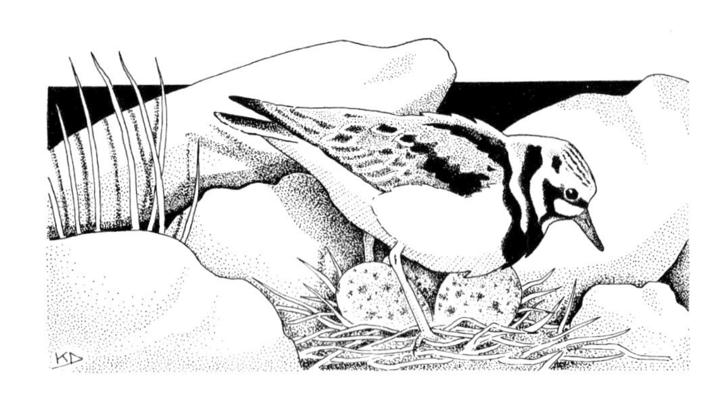

CZ	Kameňáček pestrý	**I**	Voltapietre
D	Steinwälzer	**NL**	Steenloper
E	Vuelvepiedras Común	**P**	Rola-do-mar
F	Tournepierre à collier	**PL**	Kamusznik
FIN	Karikukko	**R**	Камнешарка
G	Χαλικοκυλιστής	**S**	Roskarl
H	Kőforgató		

Non-SPEC, Threat status S

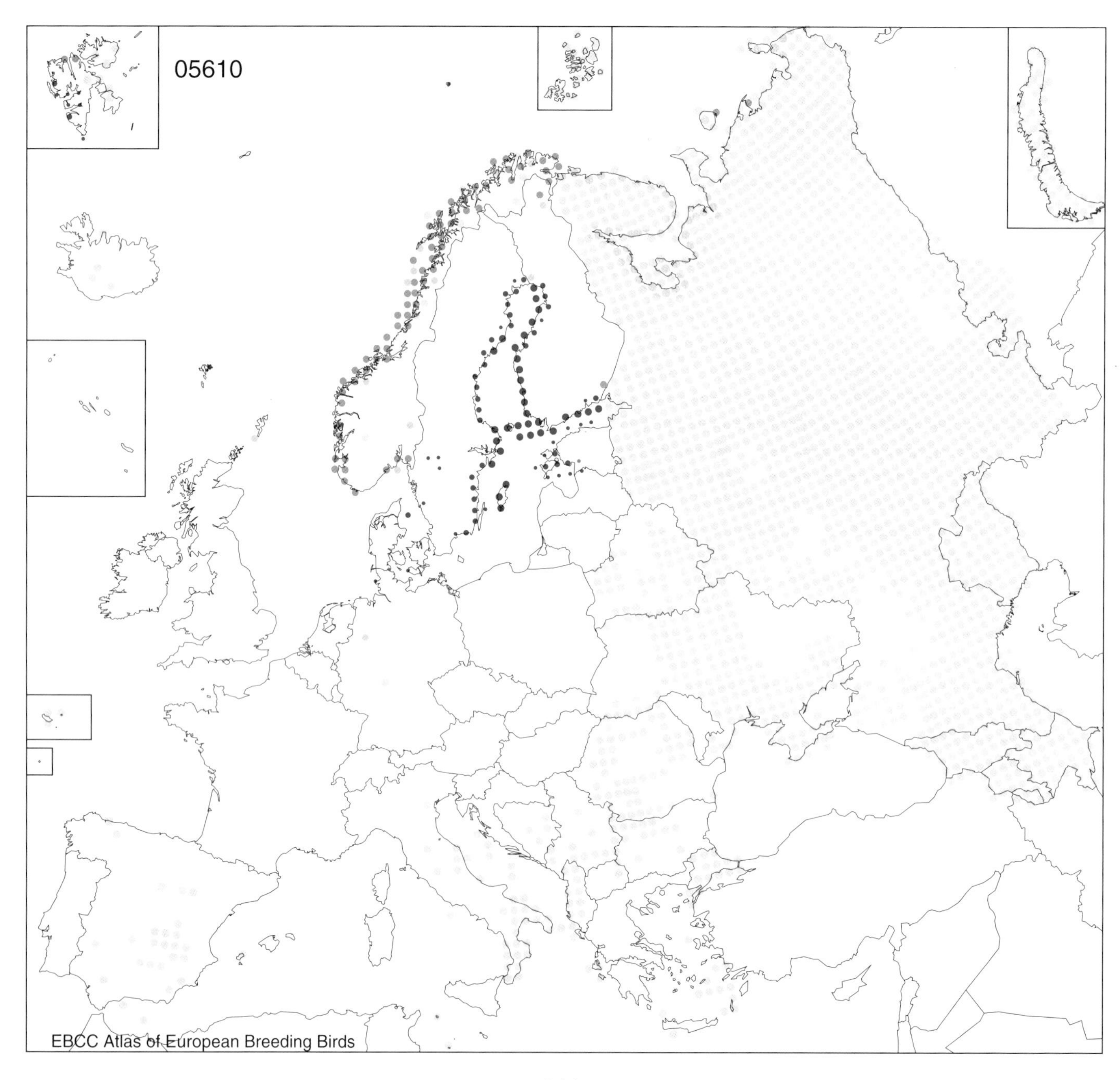

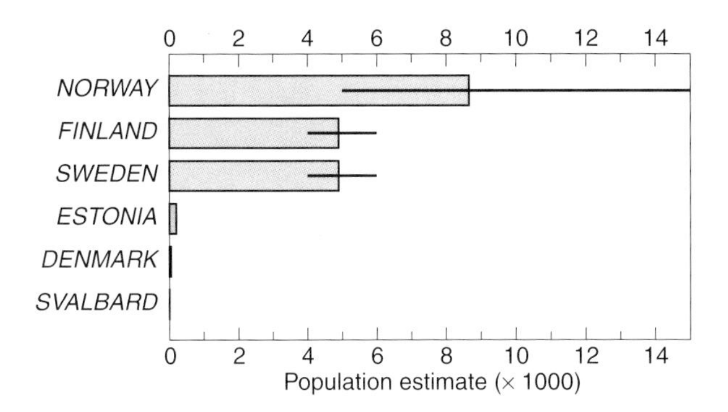

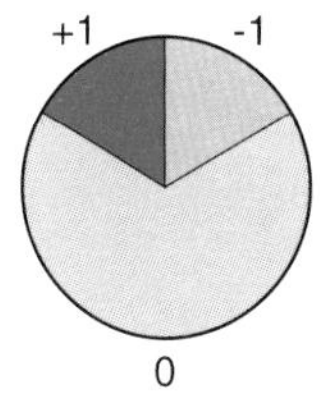

% in top 10 countries: 100.0
Total number of populated European countries: 6
Total European population 14,830–25,233 (18,705)
Russian population 3000–10,000 (5477)

This long-lived, brightly coloured wader breeds mainly in the marine tundra climatic zone. It is one of the northernmost breeding landbirds in the world, being 'an arctic dweller of frozen or snowclad terrain'. It has bred up to 83°N in Greenland and above 80°N in Svalbard. Its circumpolar Holarctic distribution also includes the boreal and even the temperate marine zones. It breeds as far S as the Baltic, where it may be a relict of early post-glacial times (von Haartman *et al* 1963–72).

Its breeding habitat varies: bare rock, stony, gravel and sandy seashores with patchy heath, grass, moss, lichen and other low-lying vegetation preferably in combination with moist depressions and small pools, up to 100m asl. Its breeding area feeding localities are largely littoral inlets, estuaries and lagoons on rocky, muddy, sandy or shingle coasts.

Along arctic coasts, it may breed several kilometres inland, beside lakes, estuaries and similar habitats, and occasionally much further inland on rocky or pebble tundra ridges remote from watercourses. A few also breed 'inland' on islets and the smaller islands in the largest lakes of Finland and S Sweden (Hildén & Hario 1993). Others occupy the northern archipelago of Lake Ladoga in Russia (Pakarinen & Siikavirta 1993).

In the N Baltic, the Turnstone is the commonest wader species on small treeless islets in the outermost archipelago. The highest population densities occur in the Gulf of Bothnia; two islands off Norrskär, Finland, 0.2 and 0.6km^2 in area, held 40 and 60bp respectively (Hildén & Hario 1993). Here, the land has risen almost 1m in 100 years, creating a new open moraine archipelago with many low islets and extensive areas of shallow waters which are especially rich in chironomid flies, the Turnstone's main food. In other Baltic countries, the density remains 1–5bp per treeless islet. The average breeding density on larger-scale archipelagos with a greater depths of water and variety of island types is 0.15–1.5 bp/km^2. The Turnstone shows a strong breeding association with larids, especially small gulls and terns, reaching high densities in their colonies; 10–20bp are typical in Arctic Tern *Sterna paradisaea* colonies on islets smaller than 0.05km^2 (Vuolanto 1968). Elsewhere the Turnstone breeds in solitary pairs.

In the Eurasian tundra, the Turnstone is scarce on the White Sea and Murmansk coast. Further E it breeds only on Kolguyev, Vaygach, Novaya Zemlya and a few smaller islands, and at two coastal sites on the Yugorskiy Peninsula mainland. There are no mainland breeding records inland (P. Tomkovich, pers comm).

The southern Baltic population has declined throughout the 20th century in Denmark. The species last bred in Germany in 1916. In the N Baltic, in contrast, a slow population increase occurred up to the 1950s and 1960s. Since then some decline has been reported from several areas, such as the Gulf of Finland. In the Arctic breeding areas very little is known of population trends.

The Turnstone is a cosmopolitan migrant. It can be found along continental coastlines and on islands in the Southern Hemisphere. Palearctic breeders migrate S to tropical and subtropical coasts. Most Nearctic breeders migrate to the Pacific islands and South America. Birds from Greenland and NE Canada winter in W Europe and NW Africa. The Turnstone can be found on its wintering grounds in summer. It does not breed until 3–6 years old (S. Vuolanto, pers obs). Some non-breeding age classes may not leave southern latitudes until their first breeding season, but non-breeding birds and pairs occur throughout the breeding season in the Baltic (S. Vuolanto, pers obs), thus giving the impression of breeding. Birds in nuptial or near-nuptial plumage found S of known breeding areas may be sub-adults.

the late Olavi Hildén (FIN) Seppo Vuolanto (FIN)

Xenus cinereus

Terek Sandpiper

CZ	Vodouš malý	**I**	Piro-piro Terek
D	Terekwasserläufer	**NL**	Terekruiter
E	Andarríos del Terek	**P**	Maçarico-sovela
F	Chevalier bargette	**PL**	Terekia
FIN	Rantakurvi	**R**	Мородунка
G	Τερεκότρυγγας	**S**	Tereksnäppa
H	Terekcankó		

Non-SPEC, Threat status S (P)

The Terek Sandpiper is a Siberian faunal-type species, whose world distribution extends from Finland and Latvia in the W through the taiga into the Russian Far East, mostly above 55°N. It prefers forest marshes, but also occupies tundra and steppe marshes, nesting on marshy riverbanks or lakeshores overgrown with such as willow *Salix* and horsetail *Equisetum*. It also uses overgrown shrubby wet grassland, flooded meadows, lakesides, and marshy stream banks in the taiga. Silty, muddy banks are indispensable for feeding and other activities. At its westernmost limits it uses landfills, dredged sludge or refuse tips, fishponds or other open artificial sites which may have an ample bark and wood-residue bottom layer. Older locations are often sparsely vegetated.

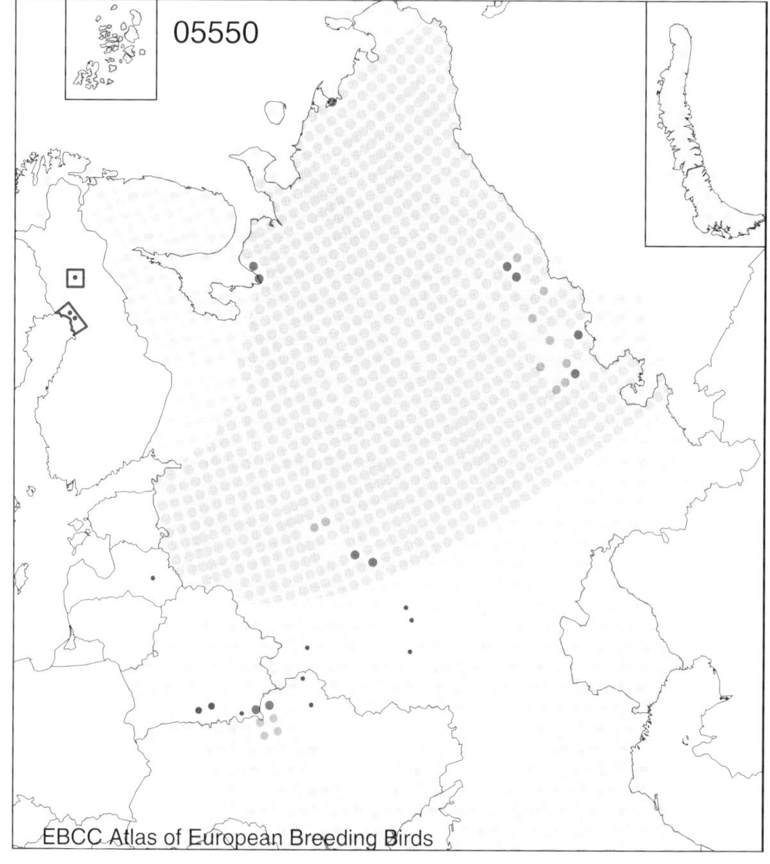

Russia holds the main European population, far fewer occupying Finland, Latvia, Belarus and Ukraine (Dolbik 1959). Finland had *c*20bp in the early 1990s. Latvia held 1–2bp in 1990 and *c*10bp in 1993 (J. Baumanis, pers comm). Belarus (in 1995) may hold several dozen breeding pairs more than previously estimated (A. Tishechkin & M. Flade, pers comm to the Editors). In the 20th century the species has spread westwards into Finland (since the 1950s; it bred from 1880 to 1910) and into Latvia (1980s). The Belarussian and Ukrainian populations are of older origin. Finnish numbers peaked at *c*30bp in the 1980s (Fritzen, pers comm, M. Ojanen, pers obs).

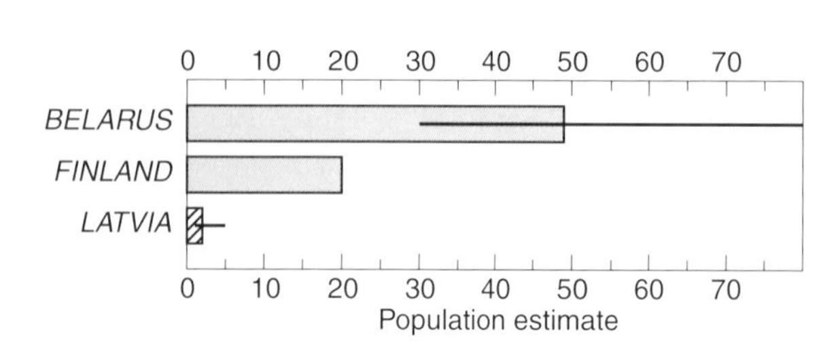

% in top 10 countries: 100.0
Total number of populated European countries: 3
Total European population 52–102 (71)
Russian population 10,000–100,000 (31,623)

In Russia densities may reach 10 nests/km² in prime habitat (Ivanov 1976). It may breed solitarily, but usually forms small colonies (in Finland up to 5bp), but colony area may be as small as 1–2ha, because adults fly far to feed during incubation.

Birds depart soon after breeding to winter widely dispersed from the sub-equatorial W African coast to Australasia; females leave very soon after the eggs hatch (late June), the males following mid-July when the young are independent.

Mikko Ojanen (FIN) Pentti Rauhala (FIN)

Phalaropus lobatus

Red-necked Phalarope

CZ	Lyskonoh úzkozobý	I	Falaropo beccosottile
D	Odinshühnchen	NL	Grauwe Franjepoot
E	Falaropo Picofino	P	Falaropo-de-bico-fino
F	Phalarope à bec étroit	PL	Płatkonóg szydłodzioby
FIN	Vesipääsky	R	Круглоносый плавунчик
G	Κολυμπότρυγγας	S	Smalnäbbad simsnäppa
H	Vékonycsõrû víztaposó		

Non-SPEC, Threat status S (P)

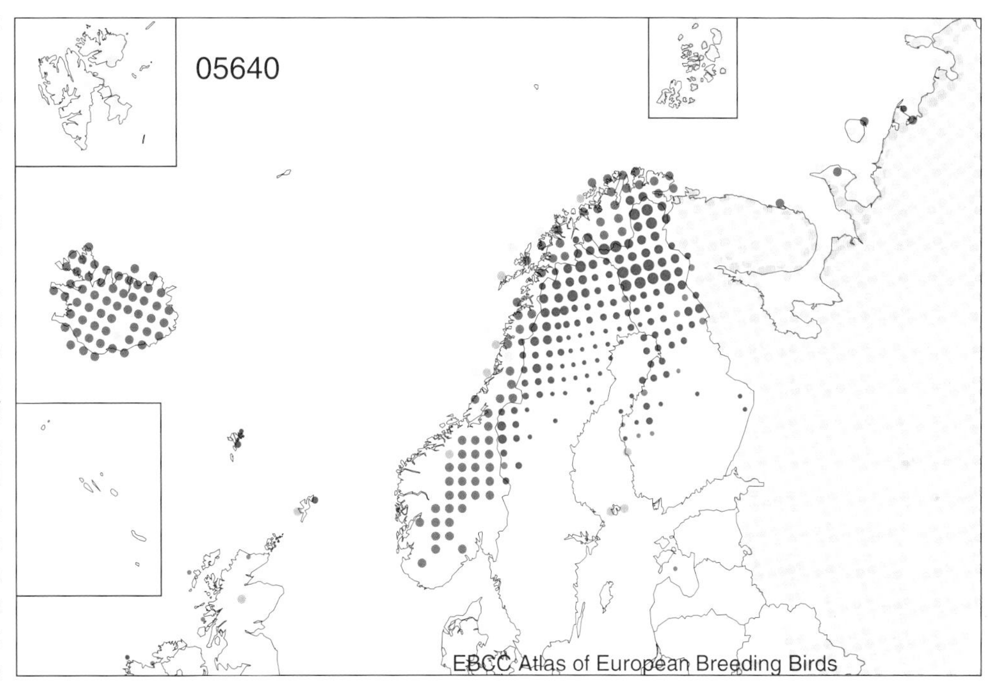

The cicumpolar distribution of this species mainly encompasses tundra wetlands in the low-arctic and subarctic. Small numbers breed in the temperate zone. Most of the European mainland population passes through the Caspian and Black Seas to winter pelagically in the Arabian Sea. The small populations on the Atlantic and Baltic coasts may be relicts from early post-glacial times (von Haartman *et al* 1963–72). Typical habitats are marshy depressions with small pools and watercourses with rich, tussocky vegetation. In Fennoscandia and the Kola Peninsula the species is found in the birch and alpine zones, at 600–1300m asl, and in lowlands in bogs in the coniferous zone. It breeds in small colonies, suitable habitat permitting. Solitary breeding is the norm in tundra. Densities of 1–5 bp/km^2 occur in Finland and Sweden (Koskimies 1989a). In Iceland's central highlands, it inhabits sparsely vegetated lava deserts, in Scotland rough damp grazing pasture or margins of shallow pools and in Estonia (Matsalu Bay) and some Finnish localities (Gulf of Bothnia) grazing pasture. In the 1990s, the most southerly Russian sites were rough damp pastures at Lake Ilmen and on the Volkov floodplain. On the N Baltic and White Sea coasts, the species nests also on islets with low vegetation and small freshwater pools, often with Arctic Tern *Sterna paradisaea* colonies.

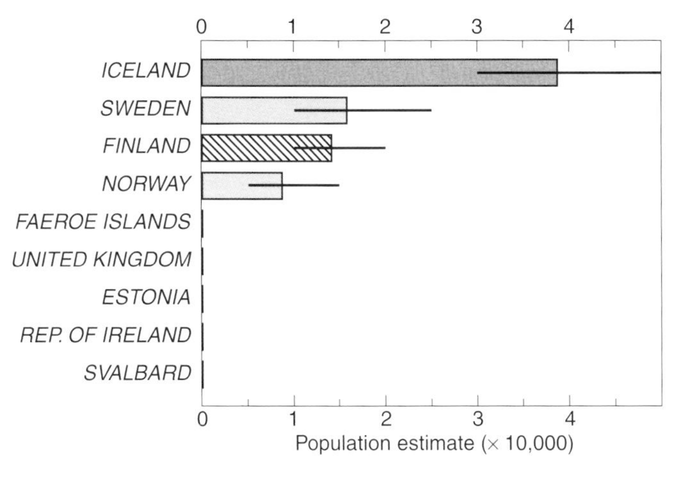

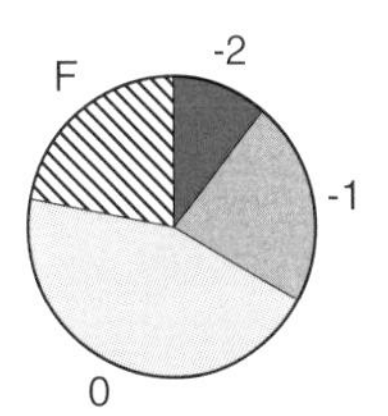

% in top 10 countries: 100.0
Total number of populated European countries: 9
Total European population 65,536–94,301 (77,391)
Russian population 100,000–1,000,000 (316,228)

The tiny European maritime populations show signs of decline (Nethersole-Thompson & Nethersole-Thompson 1986). Possibly they are not truly separate populations, but recruit more northerly breeders on passage. Finnish coastal populations fluctuate greatly (Grenquist 1965), making it difficult to identify long-term trends. In Norway, there is some evidence of southward expansion. In Finland new censuses in the 1980s revealed formerly unknown breeding sites in southern marshes (Hyytiä *et al* 1983). There may be similar sites in N Russia.

Pavel S Tomkovich (R) Seppo Vuolanto (FIN)
Vladimir V. Morozov (R)

Phalaropus fulicarius

Grey Phalarope

CZ	Lyskonoh ploskozobý	I	Falaropo beccolargo
D	Thorshühnchen	NL	Rosse Franjepoot
E	Falaropo Picogrueso	P	Falaropo-de-bico-grosso
F	Phalarope à bec large	PL	Płatkonóg płaskodzioby
FIN	Isovesipääsky	R	Плосконосый плавунчик
G	Σταχτής Κολυμπότρυγγας	S	Brednäbbad simsnäppa
H	Laposcsõrû víztaposó		

Non-SPEC, Threat status S (P)

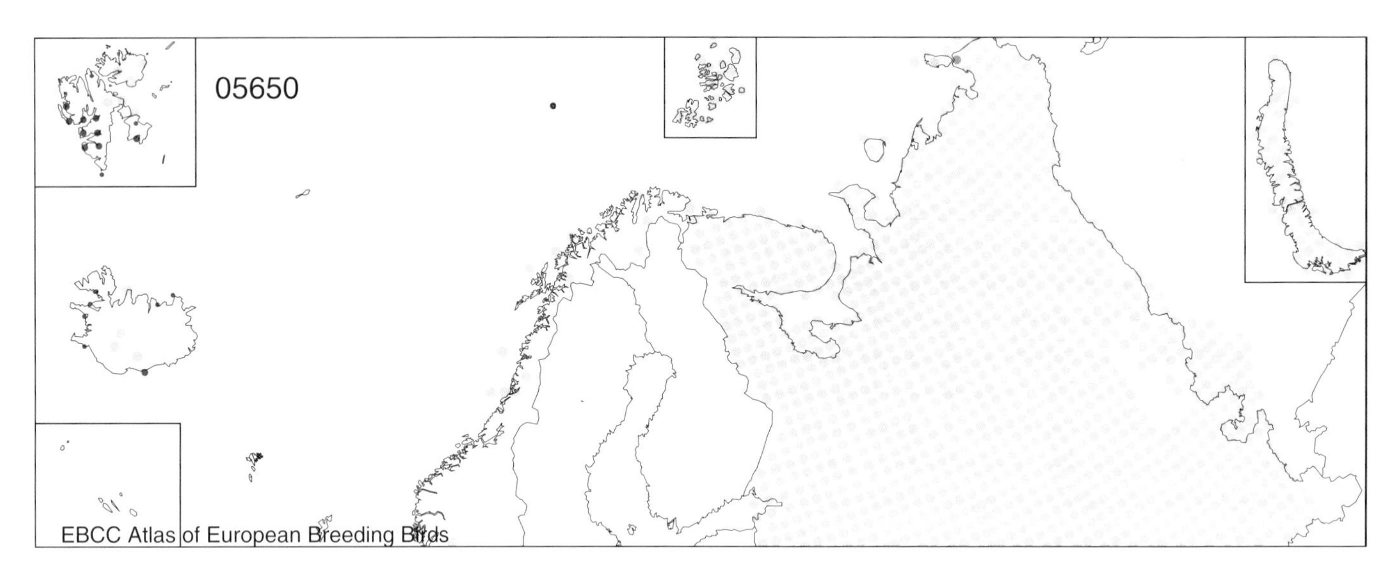

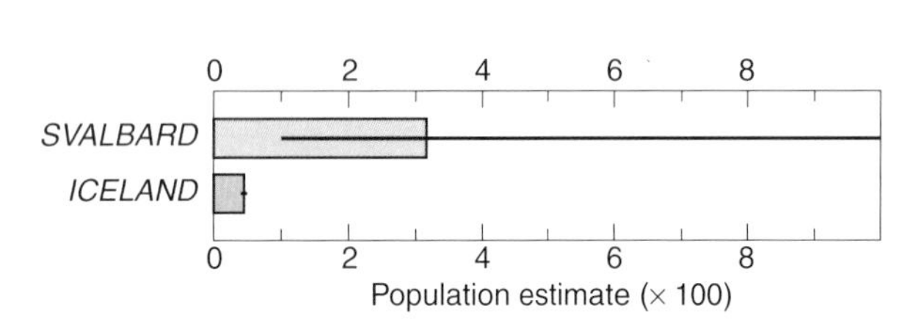

0 -1

% in top 10 countries: 100.0
Total number of populated European countries: 2
Total European population 145–1045 (361)

The Grey Phalarope has a circumpolar breeding range with an almost continuous distribution outside Europe and Greenland in low- and high-arctic zones. It occupies lowland boggy and marshy tundra where mosses, sedges and grasses prevail amongst pools, ponds or other shallow freshwater bodies. Unusually, the breeding populations in Europe and in Hudson Bay, Canada, are partly dependent more on coastal rather than inland habitats, and forage amongst the seaweed.

The main European populations are insular (Iceland and Svalbard) and are patchily distributed (sometimes semi-colonially) near coasts because of the mountains. There are two recent mainland breeding records on the Yugorskiy Peninsula close to the *Atlas*' coverage area limit (V.V. Morozov, pers obs). Breeding numbers are highly variable, due to low site fidelity and to the incidence of new pairs forming during migration; long-term population trends are difficult to evaluate. In Iceland numbers apparently are declining, possibly through pesticide or other marine pollutant effects (Gillandt 1974).

Large regular post-breeding concentrations occur in E Canada (Orr *et al* 1982, Brown & Gaskin 1988). The highest known Canadian arctic breeding densities are 7–20 bp/km² (Meltofte 1985). Therefore the core breeding area of this geographic population probably lies in the Nearctic, the European insular part in this case being marginal. Most European, Greenlandic and Canadian populations probably winter offshore from West Africa.

Birds wintering in areas of upwelling oceanic currents off western South America are from a population which breeds in Alaska and Siberia at densities of up to 200 bp/km² (Kistchinski 1975). The breeding density of the Siberian population W of the Lena Delta decreases gradually westwards to the Yamal Peninsula (E.G. Lappo, pers obs). Records from Novaya Zemlya and the Yugorskiy Peninsula reflect the fluctuating westernmost boundary of the Pacific wintering population's breeding range, and so both geographic populations of Grey Phalarope probably occur in Europe.

Pavel S Tomkovich (R)

Stercorarius pomarinus

Pomarine Skua

CZ	Chaluha pomořanská	I	Stercorario mezzano
D	Spatelraubmöwe	NL	Middelste Jager
E	Págalo Pomarino	P	Moleiro-pomarino
F	Labbe pomarin	PL	Wydrzyk tęposterny
FIN	Leveäpyrstökihu	R	Средний поморник
G	Ληστόγλαρος	S	Bredstjärtad labb
H	Szélesfarkú halfarkas		

Non-SPEC, Threat status S (P)

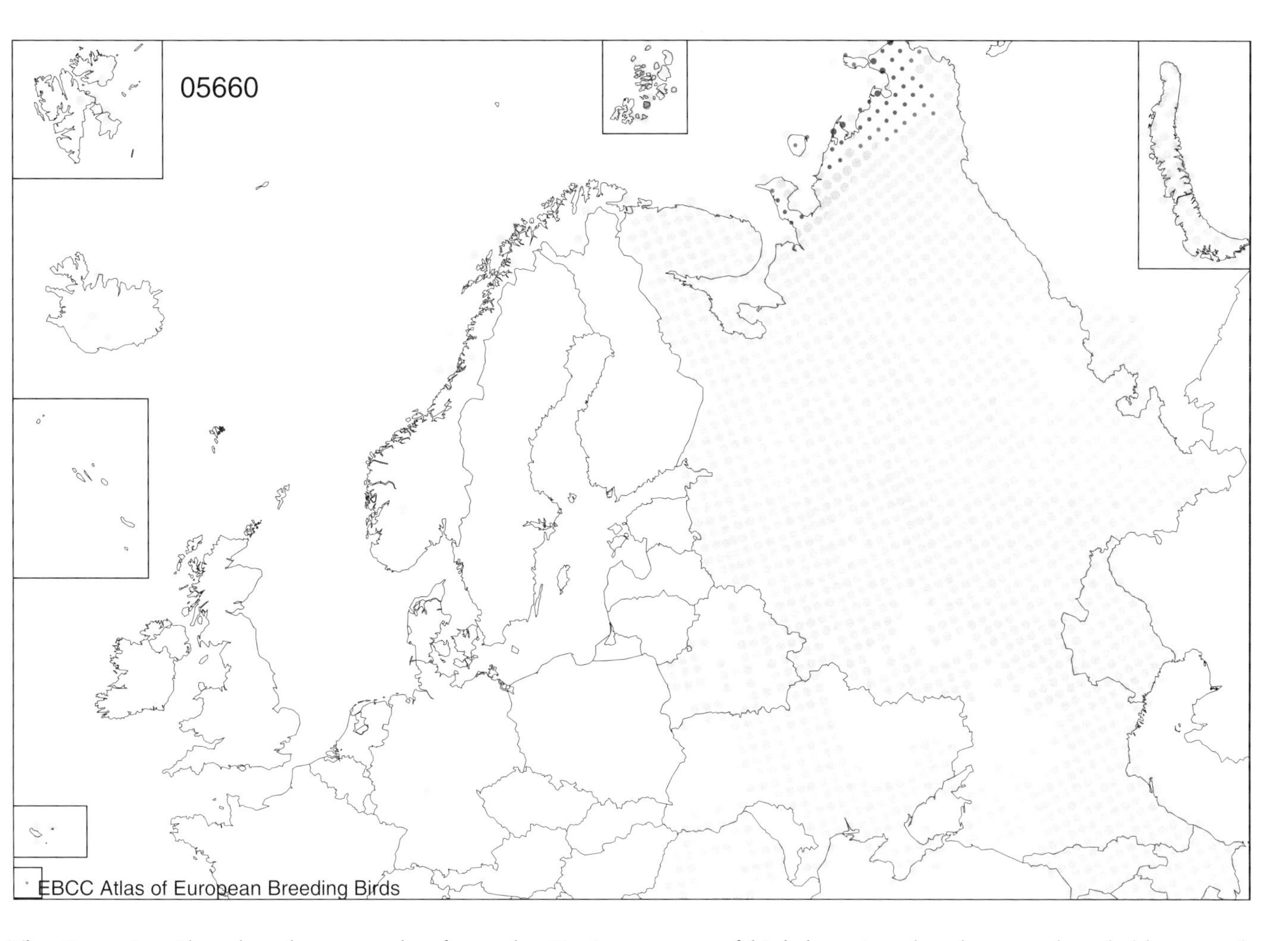

The Pomarine Skua breeds on tundra from the Kanin Peninsula in Russia E to Siberia, Alaska and arctic Canada. It does not breed anywhere from W Greenland to NE Norway or in the Kola Peninsula in NW Russia. Thus within the *Atlas*' coverage area this species is found breeding only in N Russia from the Kanin Peninsula to the Yugorskiy Peninsula, and on Novaya Zemlya.

Nesting is sporadic in years when lemmings, the primary food during breeding, are scarce (Maher 1974). In years when small mammals are abundant, the Pomarine Skua breeds at densities of up to 2 bp/km^2 on the Yugorskiy Peninsula, and up to 0.7 bp/km^2 in the Bol'shezemel'skaya and Malozemel'skaya tundras (Mineyev 1982). Highest nesting densities occur on hillocky wet moss or grass tundras, and moss or sedge bogs containing sparse low bushes, in particular close to the coast.

The total population size within the *Atlas*' area is not known, but is thought to be between 1000 and 10 000bp in years of high lemming abundance, and probably towards the lower limit. There are no data on long-term changes in abundance or distribution, but it seems likely that little change has occurred over recent decades.

The Pomarine Skua migrates from its breeding grounds to wintering areas that are generally coastal and at low latitudes such as the SE Atlantic and Australasia. Migrations are often by slow coastal progression. Although generally pelagic, the species migrates overland, probably in small numbers, to reach Middle Eastern waters. Failed breeders or birds choosing not to nest during years of low food supply may move S in July or August. Peak migration occurs in October. The return to the breeding areas occurs early in June, so that birds can be seen at sea in Europe in almost any month, although few are in European waters in February or March (Furness 1987).

Robert W Furness (GB) Yuri N Mineyev (R)

Stercorarius parasiticus

Arctic Skua

CZ	Chaluha příživná	I	Labbo
D	Schmarotzerraubmöwe	NL	Kleine Jager
E	Págalo Parásito	P	Moleiro-parasítico
F	Labbe parasite	PL	Wydrzyk ostrosterny
FIN	Merikihu	R	Короткохвостый поморник
G	Στερκοράριος		
H	Ékfarkú halfarkas	S	Labb

Non-SPEC, Threat status S (P)

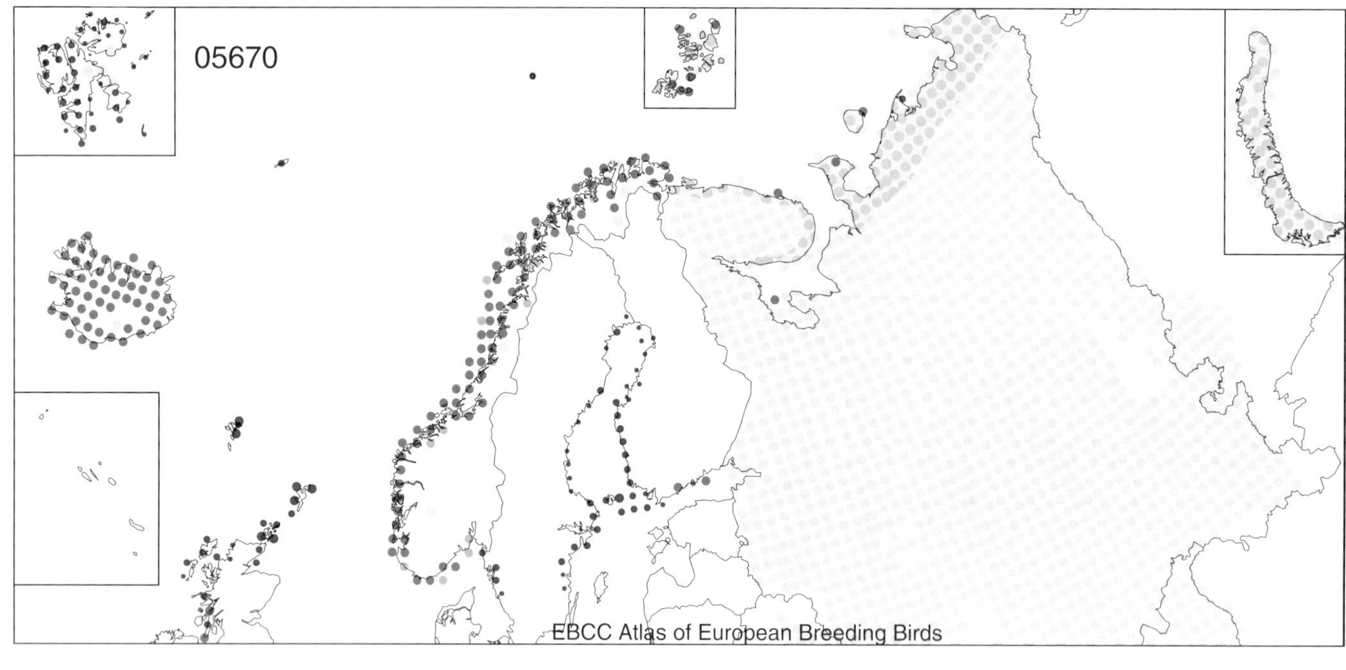

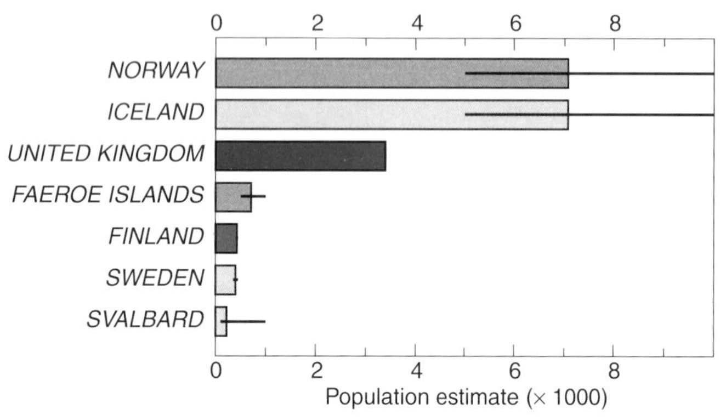

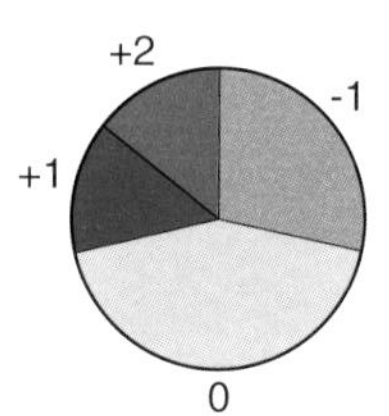

% in top 10 countries: 100.0
Total number of populated European countries: 7
Total European population 16,442–23,595 (19,387)
Russian population 10,000–100,000 (31,623)

The Arctic Skua breeds in a circumpolar band between 82°N and 56°N. It breeds on tundra and on coastal moors, the latter being most important at lower latitudes. It prefers nesting on vegetated ground but avoids growth taller than 10cm. In Europe it breeds near most coasts N of 59° and on inland tundra in Russia, Iceland, Svalbard, Norway and Sweden.

Russia, Iceland and Norway hold the largest populations. Numbers breeding in Scotland (3400bp) have increased over the 20th century, partly in response to reduced persecution and probably also to increases in populations of the seabirds they rob of fish (Ewins *et al* 1988). Numbers and breeding range have increased respectively in Finland by more than 50% and 20% during 1970–90, but numbers have fallen in the Faeroes and Norway. The northern breeding limit is probably set by climate (summer maximum temperatures below 0°C in Russia) affecting food supplies and energy demands of breeding birds. The southern limit lies close to the 14°C July mean isotherm and may represent a thermal limit for this cold-adapted species (Furness 1990).

Arctic Skua population density is highly variable. On the tundra where it feeds on birds, insects, berries and occasional small mammals within its territory, it holds territories 0.3–1.0km in diameter (Maher 1974). Where it breeds in association with colonial seabirds which it robs of fish, it nests colonially, up to 200 bp/km^2 (Furness 1987).

The Arctic Skua winters off southern coasts of Africa, South America and Australasia. Most migrate along coasts, often associating with and robbing terns and small gulls. Some migrate overland, probably especially the Russian tundra breeders, and may appear in any European country in autumn.

Robert W Furness (GB)

Stercorarius longicaudus

Long-tailed Skua

CZ	Chaluha malá	I	Labbo codalunga
D	Falkenraubmöwe	NL	Kleinste Jager
E	Págalo Rabero	P	Moleiro-de-cauda-comprida
F	Labbe à longue queue	PL	Wydrzyk długosterny
FIN	Tunturikihu	R	Длиннохвостый поморник
G	Γερακοληστόγλαρος	S	Fjällabb
H	Nyílfarkú halfarkas		

Non-SPEC, Threat status S (P)

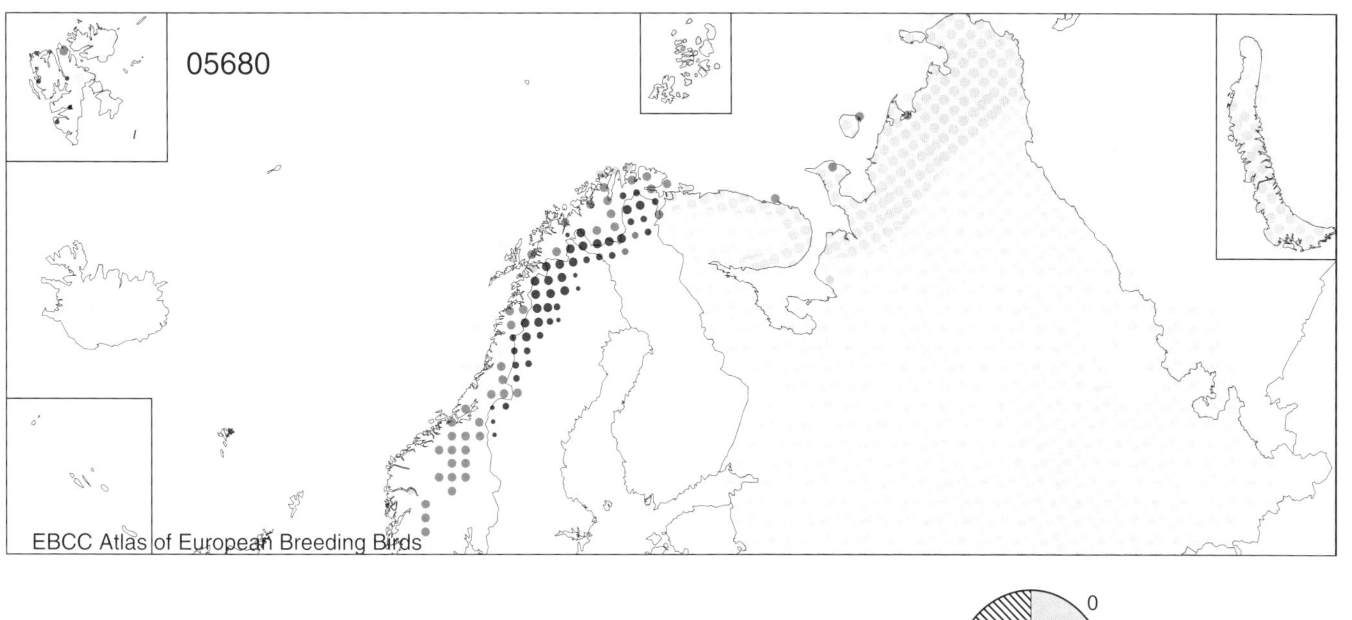

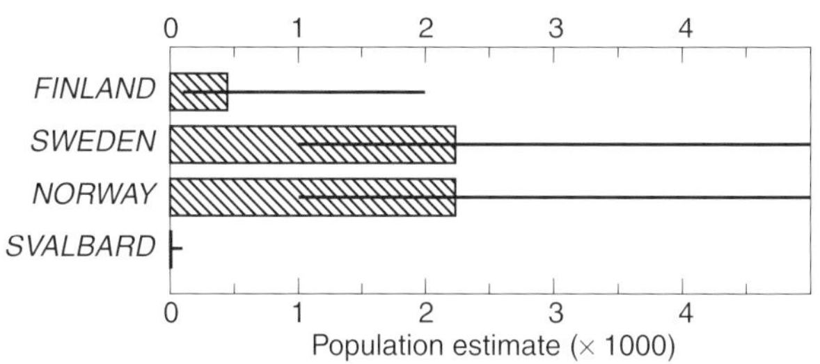

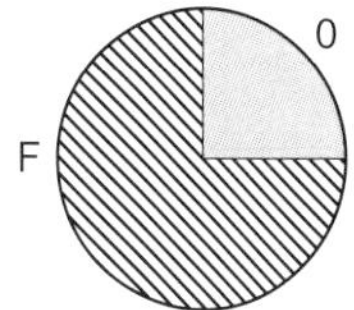

% in top 10 countries: 100.0
Total number of populated European countries: 4
Total European population 3147–9136 (4929)
Russian population 10,000–100,000 (31,623)

The Long-tailed Skua, the smallest skua, has a circumpolar and predominantly arctic breeding distribution. It breeds mostly on the arctic tundra, but further S nests on mountain plateaus in tundra-like habitat. Thus the species' breeding distribution in Europe includes the Norwegian and Swedish uplands as well as the N coast tundra of Norway, Finland and Russia.

Russia holds the largest European population (>10 000bp). There is no evidence of long-term changes in numbers or breeding range but census data are poor. Breeding numbers fluctuate, following lemming population cycles because lemmings are the main food during breeding (Andersson 1981). In its main breeding areas the species nests fairly thinly but uniformly over suitable habitat, territories being *c*1km in diameter. Nesting densities vary between about 0.01 and 1.7 bp/km^2.

Not infrequently, the Long-tailed Skua shows interest in colonizing new breeding areas; in Scotland birds have held territory on the Cairngorms mountain plateau and have probably nested in at least two years. Several pairs have held territory on coastal moors in the Northern and Western Isles of Scotland. Although its breeding range is largely dictated by the lemming distribution, it is less dependent on lemmings than is the Pomarine Skua *S. pomarinus*, and can nest successfully on tundra lacking lemmings, feeding instead on plentiful small birds and insects (Kampp 1982, de Korte 1986).

The European Long-tailed Skua population (the nominate *S.l. longicaudus*, which occurs E to at least the Lena) winters probably mostly between Antarctica and the southern parts of Africa and South America (Furness 1987). Migrations between the arctic tundra and its wintering areas are generally pelagic, avoiding overland travel or coastlines. Occasionally spring weather conditions push large migratory flocks close to the W coasts of Britain & Ireland. The other subspecies, *pallescens*, occurs in the Nearctic and W to Siberia beyond the Kolyma.

Robert W Furness (GB)

Stercorarius skua

Great Skua

CZ	Chaluha velká	I	Stercorario maggiore
D	Skua	NL	Grote Jager
E	Págalo Grande	P	Moleiro-grande
F	Grand Labbe	PL	Wydrzyk wielki
FIN	Isokihu	R	Большой поморник
G	Πειρατής	S	Storlabb
H	Nagy halfarkas		

SPEC Cat 4, Threat status S

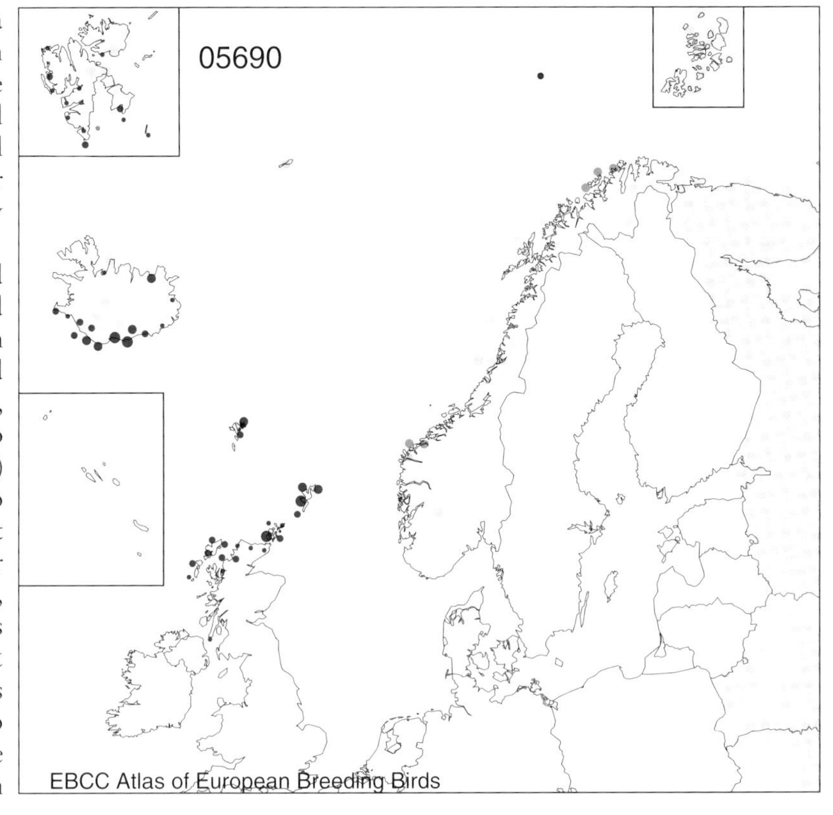

The Great Skua is endemic to Europe and has a very restricted breeding distribution, more than half the population (*c*7900bp) breeding in the northern isles of Scotland. It breeds on coastal moorland, preferring vegetation about 10cm tall around its nest. It tends to nest close to major seabird colonies, feeding extensively by predation, piracy and scavenging.

It was reduced close to extinction in Scotland and the Faeroes around 1900 but has increased since receiving protection from human persecution. The Scottish population, reduced to two small colonies in Shetland in the 1890s, spread slowly to almost all the Shetland Isles, to Orkney (1914), Lewis (1945), St Kilda (1962) and Handa (1964). Further range expansion to the S did not occur (perhaps climate-limited) but the species began a N and E spread to Bear Island (1970), Svalbard (1970), Norway (1975), Jan Mayen (1984) and N Russia (1989). There is no evidence of Icelandic (Lund-Hansen & Lange 1991) or Faeroese Great Skua populations (which are roughly stable at 5400bp and *c*275bp respectively) being involved in these range expansions, but Shetland-ringed birds have been found in every newly colonized area (Klomp & Furness 1992a). The range extension has reached the most northeasterly part of Europe: although not mapped, breeding records were received from 10 squares in NE and E Russia. Confirmed breeding was reported from S Vaygach Island and 2 squares on Novaya Zemlya near M. Vkhodnov and M. Bol'shevik. Furthermore there are 7 squares with possible breeding on Novaya Zemlya: near Rusanova, M. Sakhanina, M. Yuzh. Gusiny Nos, M. Sev. Gusiny Nos, E of Stolbovoy, near Fod'Kino and near Russkaya Gavan.

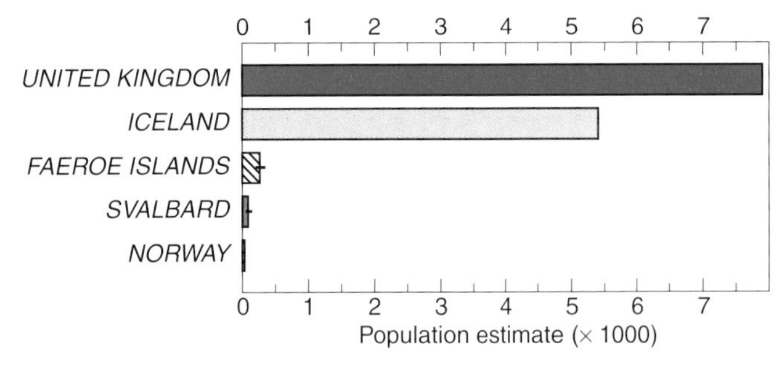

N 0 F +1 +2

% in top 10 countries: 100.0
Total number of populated European countries: 5
Total European population 13,611–13,792 (13,686)

The Svalbard population (100–200bp) is probably still increasing (Isaksen & Bakken 1995). Numbers in Shetland appear to have increased partly as a consequence of the abundance of sandeels, and of whitefish discarded by fishermen as undersized catches (Hudson & Furness 1988). A recent period of recruitment failures of Shetland sandeels led to a considerable reduction in Great Skua breeding numbers. The numbers of potential recruits on Foula were particularly reduced (Hamer *et al* 1991, Klomp & Furness 1992b).

Mean inter-nest distances in larger colonies are 30–50m. Concentration of this species in a few major colonies is partly a consequence of high natal philopatry, the largest Scottish colonies also being the oldest. Newly colonized areas such as Russia and Norway can probably support increased numbers of the Great Skua.

Robert W Furness (GB)

Larus ichthyaetus

Great Black-headed Gull

CZ	Racek velký	I	Gabbiano del Pallas
D	Fischmöwe	NL	Reuzenzwartkopmeeuw
E	Gavión Cabecinegro	P	Alcatraz-de-cabeça-preta
F	Goéland ichthyaète	PL	Mewa orlica
FIN	Mustapäälokki	R	Черноголовый хохотун
G	Ψαρόγλαρος	S	Svarthuvad trut
H	Halászsirály		

Non-SPEC, Threat status S

The Great Black-headed Gull breeds on the shores of large (mainly saline) lakes, seas, and sometimes on reservoirs in the steppe, semi-desert and desert zones from the N Black Sea in Ukraine to Lake Kukunor in China, and from Lake Chany, SW Siberia, to S of the Caspian Sea where it forms dense colonies on islands. Its main winter range includes the Caspian Sea and inland waterbodies of the Middle East and C Asia, but some reach the N Indian Ocean.

Characteristically, each year it experiences rapid asynchronous changes in numbers, extensive redistribution of individuals and colonies within its breeding range, and the appearance of temporary colonies adjacent to the permanent colonies. Conversely, colonies may form more than 100km apart. The largest European breeding colony is in the N Caspian, on the Maly Zhemchuzhny Islands (*c*42 000bp in 1987) (Gavrilov 1993). In the late 1980s, there were also colonies in the Lake Sapra region (*c*1000bp), on the Kumo-Manych depression lakes (*c*1000bp) and on the limans (brackish lagoons) of the Sea of Azov (300bp) (Kukish 1990, Khokhlov 1989, Til'ba *et al* 1990). In Ukraine colonies exist in W and E Sivash and in Dzharylgach and Karkinitski Bays on the Black Sea (250bp in 1986, 419bp in 1987; Ardamatskaya *et al* 1989).

The European population increased by 150–200% throughout the 1980s and was estimated at 45 000–50 000bp. An especially rapid increase was recorded in Ukraine where in 1993 there were 42 000bp (I. Chernichko, pers comm), far in excess of the estimate in the *Atlas* database.

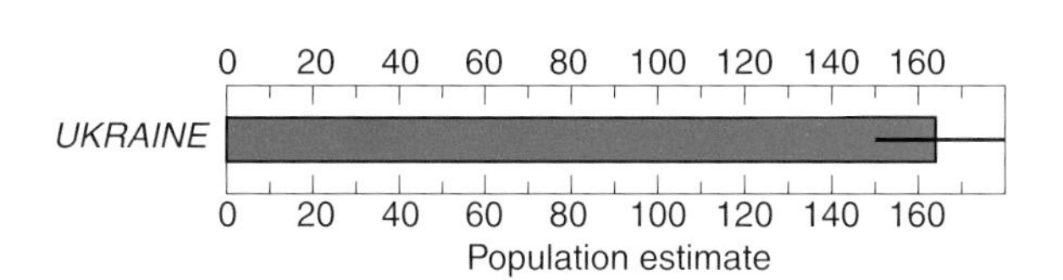

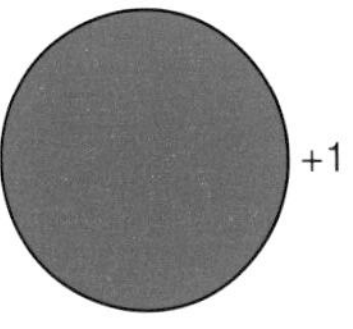

% in top 10 countries: 100.0
Total number of populated European countries: 1
Total European population 150–180 (164)
Russian population 24,000–40,000 (30,984)

The Russian increase occurred within the breeding range; in Ukraine the range extended over 100km westwards, a new colony appearing in Yagorlitski Bay (Rudenko 1992). The general increase is partly due to successful conservation measures but probably also reflects a redistribution of Asian and European populations, mainly across the Caspian Sea.

In the future some decrease in numbers should occur in Europe as a result of the forthcoming partial restoration of the reduced Caspian Sea water level: flooding the Zhemchuzhny Islands will encourage the birds to found new colonies on islands further E.

Valentin Serebryakov (UKR) Victor Zubakin (R)

Larus melanocephalus **Mediterranean Gull**

CZ	Racek černohlavý	I	Gabbiano corallino
D	Schwarzkopfmöwe	NL	Zwartkopmeeuw
E	Gaviota Cabecinegra	P	Gaivota-de-cabeça-preta
F	Mouette mélanocéphale	PL	Mewa czarnogłowa
FIN	Mustanmerenlokki	R	Черноголовая чайка
G	Μαυροκέφαλος Γλάρος	S	Svarthuvad mås
H	Szerecsensirály		

SPEC Cat 4, Threat status S

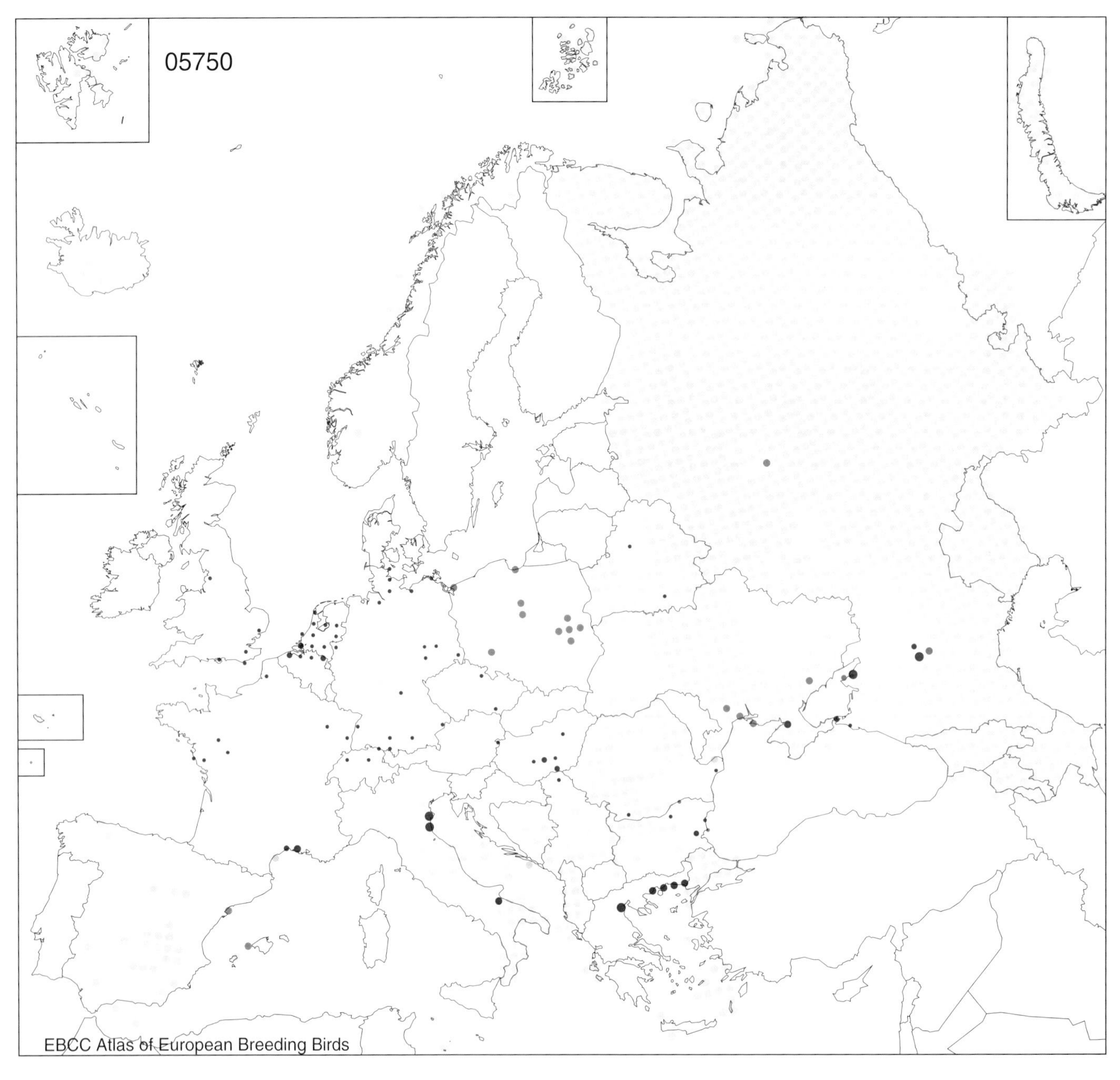

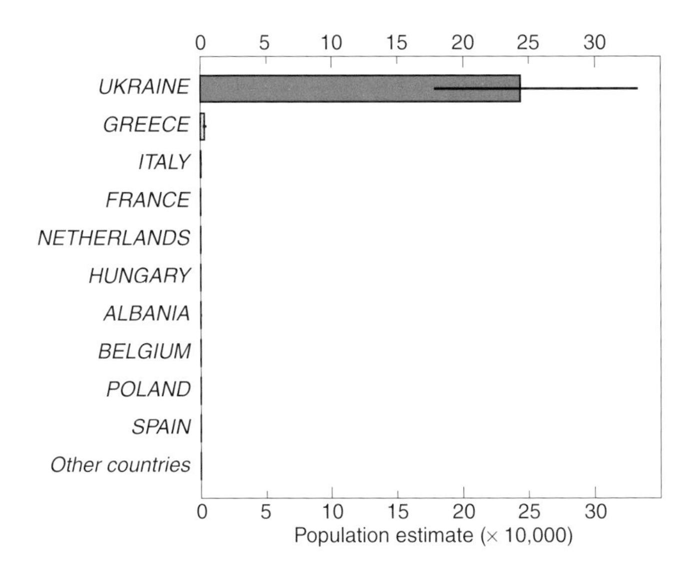

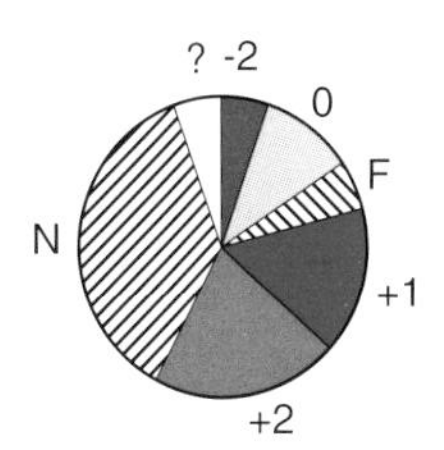

% in top 10 countries: 100.0
Total number of populated European countries: 19
Total European population 183,925–339,963 (249,862)
Russian population 100–13,300 (1153)
Turkish population 500–5000 (1581)

The Mediterranean Gull has a W Palearctic distribution. Its main breeding grounds are on the warm and dry N coast of the Black Sea. In recent decades its breeding range has expanded and the population has increased. Most birds winter in coastal waters of the Black Sea and the Mediterranean, and along the Atlantic coast of SW Europe.

Its favoured breeding habitat is coastal terrain with low vegetation or small islands. Originally it bred solely in salty or brackish areas, where it tends to form huge colonies. About 99% of the population breeds at coastal sites. Its breeding distribution is patchy and ranges from the Caspian Sea in the E to the Atlantic and North Sea coasts in the W, and from the Mediterranean in the S to the Baltic coast in the N. Its breeding distribution is highly biased towards the Black Sea and Mediterranean areas. In W and C Europe, the breeding population consists of comparatively few birds.

In the 1940s and early 1950s its breeding range was restricted mainly to the NW Black Sea coast of Ukraine, and especially on offshore islands in Tendra Bay. The population was then estimated at fewer than 40 000bp, but there have been considerable fluctuations since (Chernichko 1993): an increase from 1953 to 1966 (peak, 1966: *c*155 000bp); a decline from 1967 to 1974 (nadir, 1974: *c*17 000bp); a large increase from 1975 to 1983 (peak, 1983: *c*335 000bp), and since then a decline (nadir, 1993: fewer than 20 000bp). In 1994 60 000bp nested at Golaya Pristan alone (A.G. Rudenko, pers comm), the highest total in the last six years.

The Mediterranean Gull bred in Romania and Greece in the early 1900s, but then declined, although at present Greece still holds several substantial colonies. In the Mediterranean basin, the late 1970s saw new colonies founded and the population increase. The Mediterranean Gull was firmly established in NE Italy by 1978. The Camargue population, established in the early 1980s, had increased to 470bp by 1995 (P. Isenmann, pers comm). The Mediterranean population consists of several thousand breeding pairs, mostly at only a few sites (Goutner & Isenmann 1993), but fluctuates considerably.

Range expansion eastwards was first observed in 1972, when the species started to breed in Dzarilgatsky Bay on the Black Sea, on the Azov coast and on Lake Manych-Gudilo. The expansion reached the Caspian Sea by the late 1980s. Population fluctuations also occur in this area, numbers probably exceeding 10 000bp in good years.

A westward range expansion in C Europe was noticeable by the early 1950s, starting in Hungary (incidental breeding since 1940 (1940i), regular since 1953 (1953r) and later spreading to adjacent countries, then to Germany (1951i, 1963r), The Netherlands (1959i, 1970r), Belgium (1964i, 1969r), France and Great Britain (1968i, 1976r). The temperate climatic zone population is characterized by low numbers distributed over a great variety of breeding sites (mainly Black-headed Gull *L. ridibundus* colonies). W and C Europe held *c*200bp in 1990. More than half of this population is concentrated in NW Belgium and SW Netherlands, where the significant increase in the 1980s was paralleled by high nesting success (Meininger & Bekhuis 1990). This population is still increasing, with 210bp in 1994 (P. Meininger, pers obs). Although the very strong and more or less cyclic fluctuations of its core NW Black Sea population coincided with impressive range expansions, the majority of the Mediterranean Gull population remains restricted to its traditional range.

Ringing programmes have revealed that individual birds may breed at widely separated sites in successive years, for example moving from the Black Sea to the Mediterranean, or from the Mediterranean to the North Sea (Boldreghini *et al* 1992). Its recent breeding history in Europe underlines the species' ability to explore and occupy new breeding grounds, a subject of continuing interest.

Johan Bekhuis (NL) Peter Meininger (NL)
Antonia G Rudenko (UKR)

Larus minutus

Little Gull

CZ	Racek malý	**I**	Gabbianello
D	Zwergmöwe	**NL**	Dwergmeeuw
E	Gaviota Enana	**P**	Gaivota-pequena
F	Mouette pygmée	**PL**	Mewa mała
FIN	Pikkulokki	**R**	Малая чайка
G	Νανόγλαρος	**S**	Dvärgmås
H	Kis sirály		

SPEC Cat 3, Threat status D

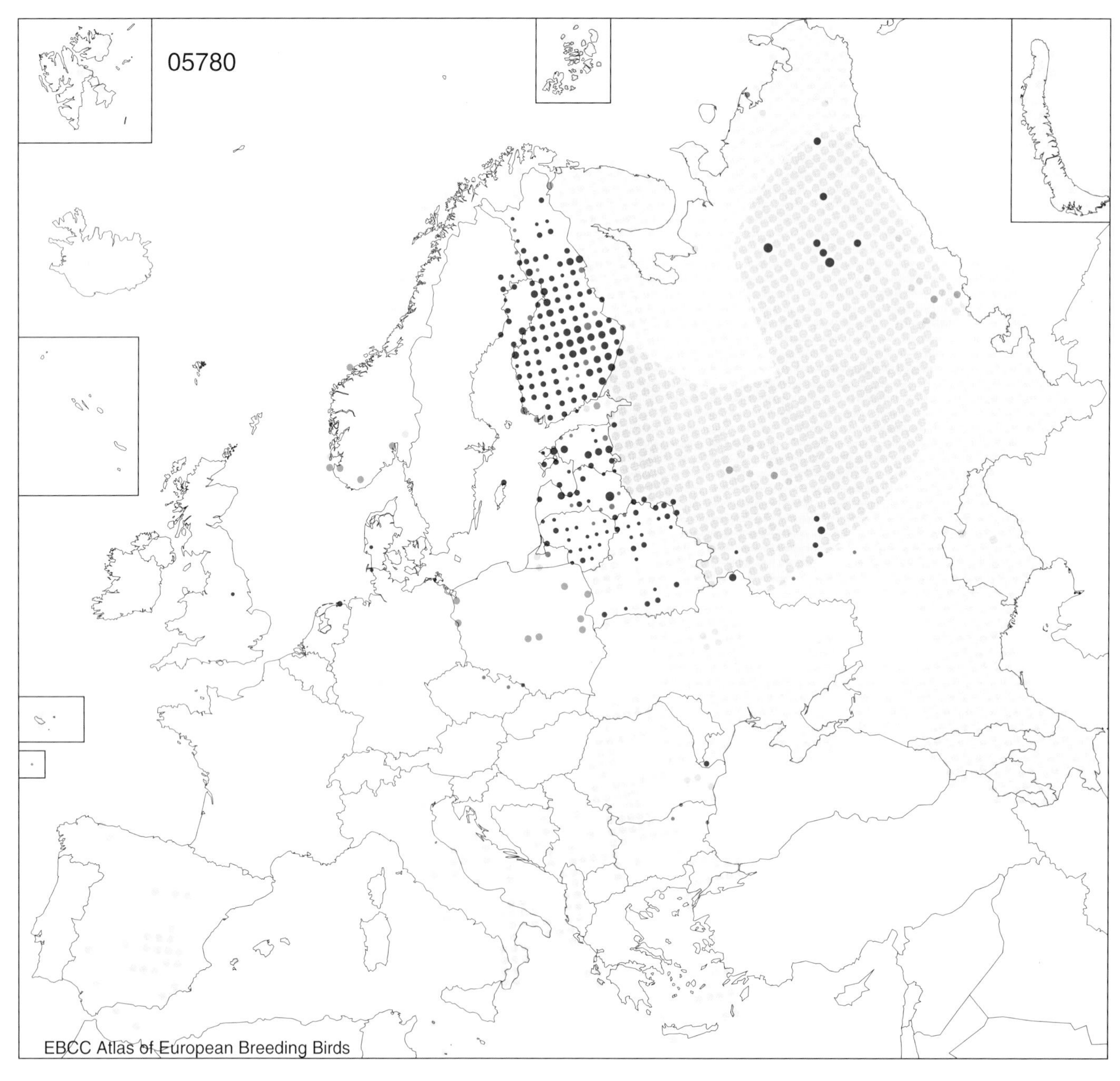

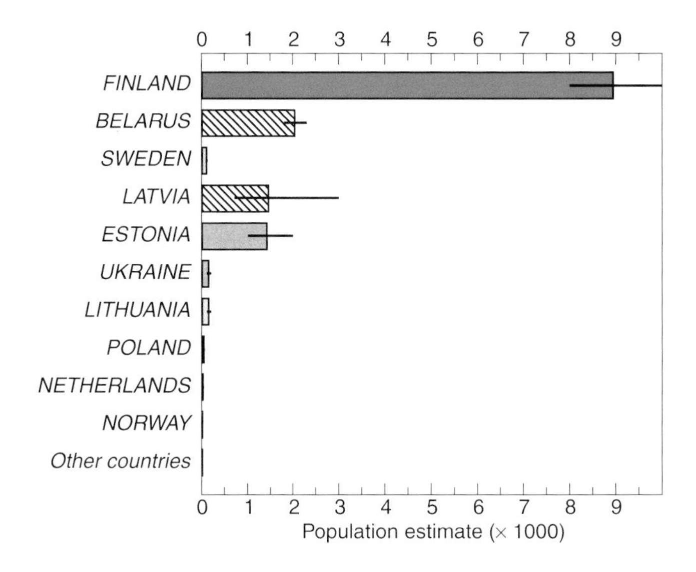

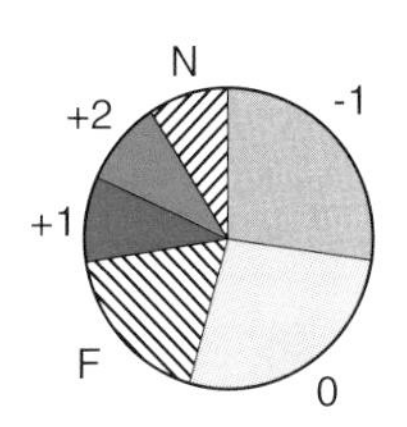

% in top 10 countries: 100.0
Total number of populated European countries: 11
Total European population 12,979–16,262 (14,276)
Russian population 11,000–14,000(12,410)

The Little Gull, the smallest gull, frequents inland marshes in the breeding season and winters offshore. Most breed in SW Siberia and N Kazakhstan, with an uninterrupted breeding range from the Ob basin in the E, to the E and S coasts of the Baltic Sea in the W, including the middle and upper Volga basin, the upper Dnepr basin, Lake Ladoga, C and S Finland, the Baltic States, Belarus and Poland. It also breeds in E Siberia in the vicinity of Lake Baykal, and the middle Lena and Vilui valleys. It is prone to nest sporadically hundreds, even thousands of kilometres beyond its main breeding range, especially northwards to the Arctic Circle, occasionally W to Britain and France, S to Bulgaria, and since 1962 as far W as North America. Despite the Little Gull's vast range, no subspecies have been described.

The Little Gull breeds in areas rich in emergent vegetation on grassy islets in shallow freshwater lowland lakes, oxbows, marshes and fishponds, and in brackish water in the E Baltic. It prefers to associate with other larids such as the Common *Sterna hirundo*, Black *Chlidonias niger* and White-winged Black *C. leucopterus* Terns and Black-headed Gull *L. ridibundus*, in more or less isolated groups on the periphery of mixed colonies, avoiding the larger colonies of the predatory Black-headed Gull (Veen 1980). They change their breeding sites more often than other gulls and these temporary colonies may be very large; for example, 2000bp bred on 150ha at the highest recorded density of 13.3 bp/ha in the Gomelis wetland in Latvia in 1987, where normally there are only a few dozen breeding pairs or even none. They also have bred in what are normally only feeding areas, such as the adjoining Lake Lubana and the Nagli fishponds at densities of 0.7 bp/ha and 0.3 bp/ha respectively.

The Little Gull's distribution is very patchy in Europe, so that it is difficult to estimate population sizes or changes in trends but the European population may total between 23 000 and 32 000bp, almost half of which breeds in Russia (at least 11 000–14 000bp, which may be a considerable underestimate), including *c*2000bp in the Leningrad region (Mal'chevski and Pukinski 1983), and 300–400bp in the Moscow region (Ilyichev & Zubakin 1988). Finland holds about a third of the total, some 8000–10 000bp. Smaller numbers were recorded in Estonia (1000–2000bp), Latvia (700–3000bp) and Belarus (1800– 2300bp) and fewer still in Lithuania (100–200), Ukraine (100–200), Sweden (75–125), Poland (20–60) and The Netherlands (5–40; breeding was first recorded in the SW delta in 1992–94; Meininger 1995). A handful breed in each of Norway and Romania. The Little Gull population is evidently increasing and expanding in its northernmost European range in Finland (>50% in 1970–90) and in the Leningrad and neighbouring Russian regions (Mal'chevski & Pukinski 1983). There is a more or less stable population in the E Baltic countries and probably a decrease further S, but which involves insignificant numbers.

The western Palearctic populations disperse gradually westward and southward, often along river valleys, to winter offshore from the Baltic Sea, Britain & Ireland S to West and exceptionally equatorial Africa, and throughout the Mediterranean to the Black and Caspian Seas. They frequent areas of tidal turbulence off the mouths of inlets and headlands, resting on the shore and visiting coastal waters in bad weather (Hutchinson & Neath 1978). Over 50 000 have recently been recorded in the lagoons of the Nile Delta (Meininger & Sørensen 1993). Wintering birds have also recently extended markedly the northern limits of their wintering range. The origin of all the birds wintering in North America has not yet been established. In spring the Little Gull populations may return more rapidly overland to their breeding grounds (Messenger 1993).

Janis Viksne (LAT) WRP Bourne (GB)

Larus ridibundus

Black-headed Gull

CZ	Racek chechtavý	**I**	Gabbiano comune
D	Lachmöwe	**NL**	Kokmeeuw
E	Gaviota Reidora	**P**	Guincho-comum
F	Mouette rieuse	**PL**	Śmieszka
FIN	Naurulokki	**R**	Озерная чайка
G	Καστανοκέφαλος Γλάρος	**S**	Skrattmås
H	Dankasirály		

Non-SPEC, Threat status S

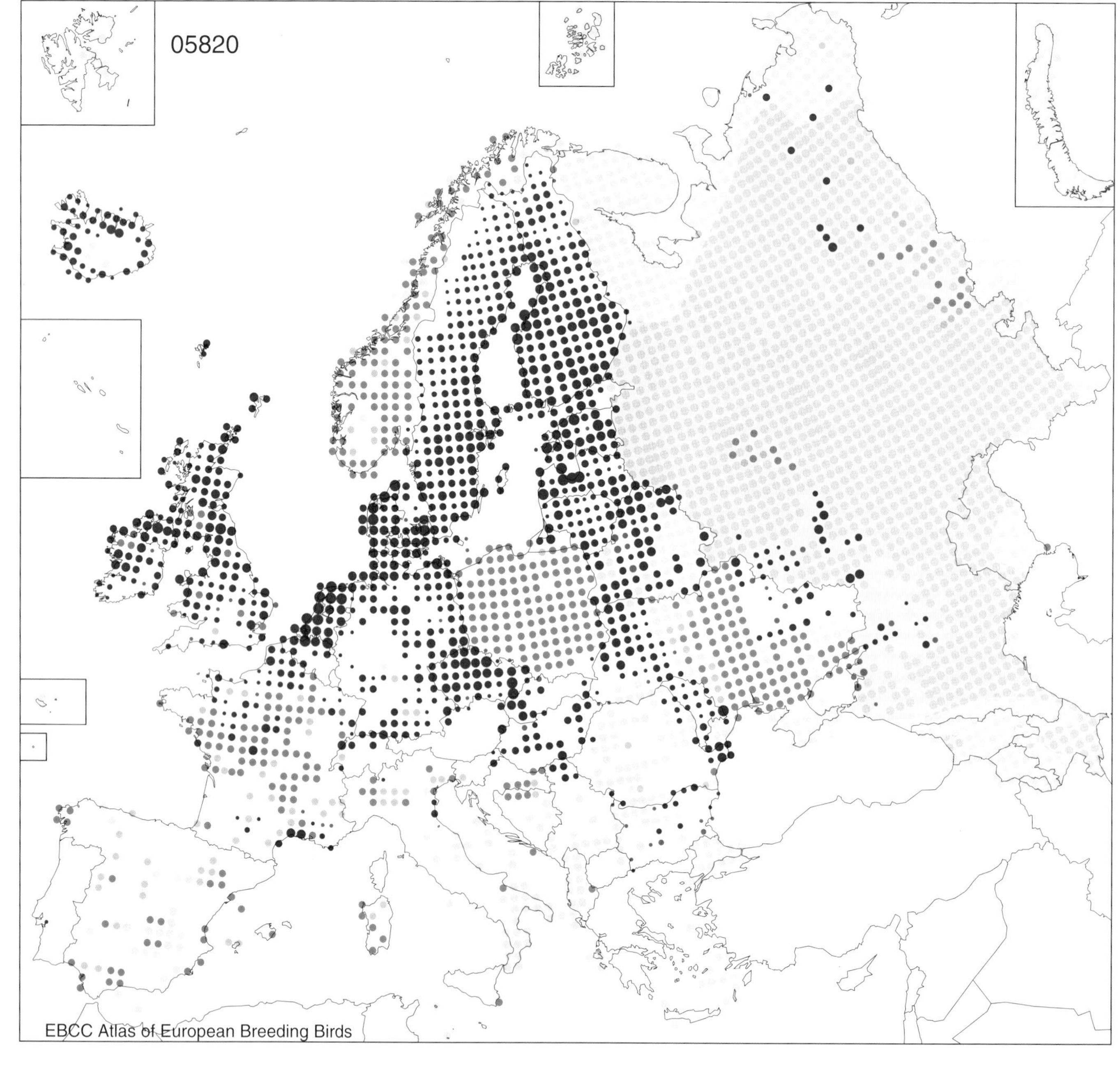

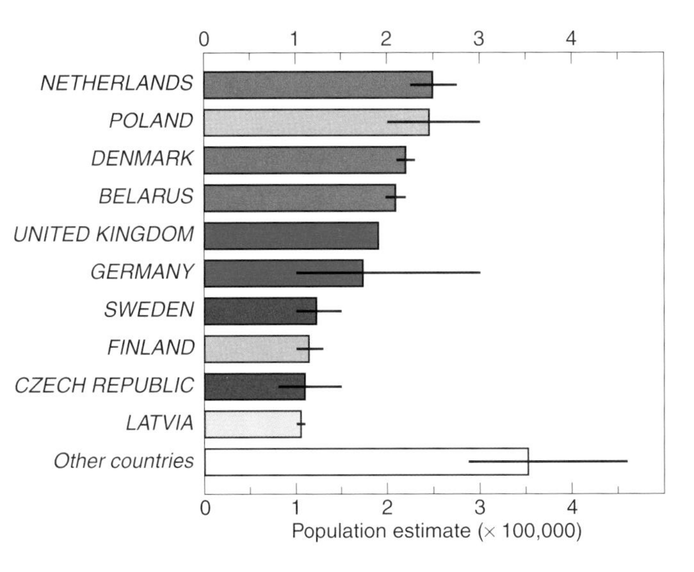

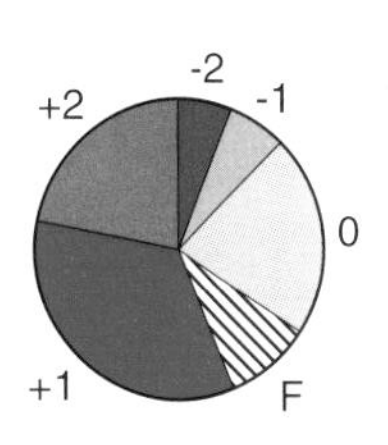

% in top 10 countries: 83.2
Total number of populated European countries: 32
Total European population 1,985,158–2,246,547 (2,087,768)
Russian population 400,000–500,000 (447,214)
Turkish population 2000–10,000 (4472)

The Black-headed Gull breeds throughout the Palearctic from Kamchatka to the Atlantic, mostly between 45° and 65°N (in N Norway reaching *c*70°N), but the status of Siberian populations is poorly known. It colonized Greenland and Newfoundland in 1969 and 1977 respectively. It avoids low latitudes (southern limit 37°N) and high altitudes (up to 700m asl in Scotland, 1000m in the Massif Central). Its Palearctic distribution is the largest of the 15 'hooded' gulls, and so, despite a short breeding season, it is exposed to a variety of climates. There are no subspecies.

Black-headed Gull colony size varies from under 10bp up to 30 000bp. Typical breeding habitats comprise a variety of continental wetlands, bogs, marshes and artificial ponds, but dry sites close to water are also used (coastal sand-dunes, heather moors, industrial waste dumps, rocky islets). Invariably, the species' feeding habits require adjacent open land such as farmland and coastal zones. This combination of habitat requirements and coloniality produces a patchy distribution on a small scale. Density in prime habitat is largely unknown, but it varies dependent on the proportion of suitable waterbodies in any area.

Numbers have increased and its range has expanded probably since the late 19th century and it first bred in Iceland in 1911 and in Spain in 1960. The increase followed a decline in egg-collecting and is probably due largely to improved survival rates brought about by the species' increased exploitation of human activities: fishing industry waste and refuse tips. The pattern in Sweden is representative of northern Europe. Until the early 20th century, when a slow colonization in S Sweden began, it occupied only a few sites in the S. Population growth and range expansion accelerated after World War II, producing *c*270 000bp in the early 1970s (Fredriksson 1979). Although northward expansion may still be continuing, numbers started decreasing in the late 1970s, especially in the S, stabilizing at under 20% of the peak level. The Latvian decrease was from 110 000bp in 1986 to 40 000 in 1994, probably because of changes in food availability (Viksne *et al* in press). The reduced, largely stable levels reached since the 1970s (apparent also in parts of C France), may be more widespread than previously thought, because of underestimates in many early counts. In the Mediterranean zone the Black-headed Gull is sparsely distributed in small numbers (only *c*2000bp altogether in Spain and Italy and 35 000bp in France, yet >100 000bp in Great Britain). Overall, western Europe holds *c*1Mbp, or 3M individuals in autumn (Isenmann *et al* 1991).

Natural threats include late-season heat and drought which reduce food availability (earthworms) for chicks, water level variation, predators (especially mink) and disturbance. Colonies may move to a new site following breeding failure.

Inter-nuptial moult sees the Black-headed Gull returning to its ancestral larid habitat, seacoasts. However, numbers wintering inland in association with human activity have increased considerably since the mid-1960s. Except for the Irish population which shows only limited dispersal, the general pattern in Europe is a southerly to southwesterly shift of all populations. Individuals from southerly populations (C France) reach coastal western and northern Africa whereas birds from Fennoscandia and the Baltic countries winter in western Europe. Young birds in immature or adult plumage tend to summer in their wintering zone, although apparently there is limited exchange between local populations. However, only a slight gene-flow would already explain the striking morphological and plumage homogeneity over the species' entire range.

Many species nest in association with Black-headed Gull colonies, such as Whiskered Tern *Chlidonias hybridus* and grebes. In some regions, the Black-necked Grebe *Podiceps nigricollis* breeds successfully only in such colonies (Trouvilliez 1988).

Hans Källander (S) Jean-Dominique Lebreton (F)

Larus sabini

Sabine's Gull

CZ	Racek Sabinův	**I**	Gabbiano di Sabine
D	Schwalbenmöwe	**NL**	Vorkstaartmeeuw
E	Gaviota de Sabine	**P**	Gaivota de Sabine
F	Mouette de Sabine	**PL**	Mewa obrożna
FIN	Tiiralokki	**R**	Вилохвостая чайка
G	Χελιδονόγλαρος	**S**	Tärnmås
H	Fecskesirály		

Non-SPEC, Threat status S

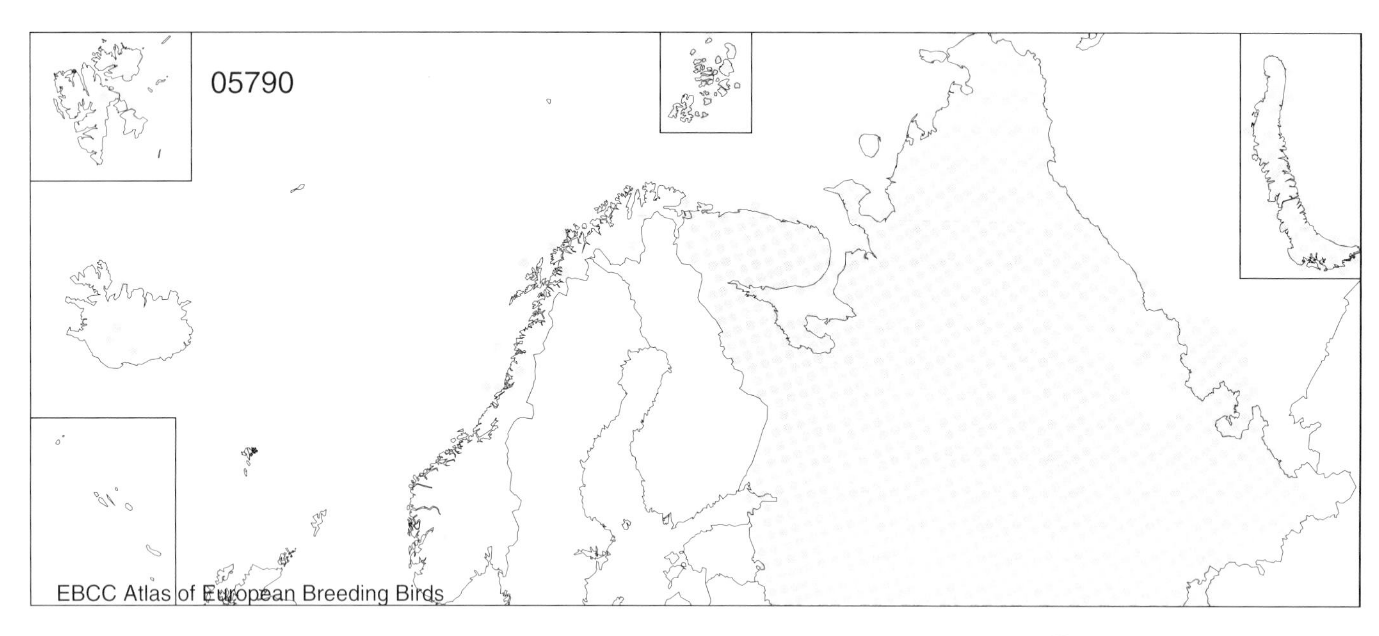

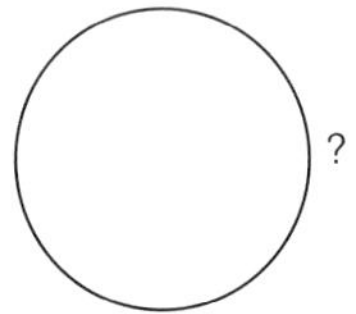

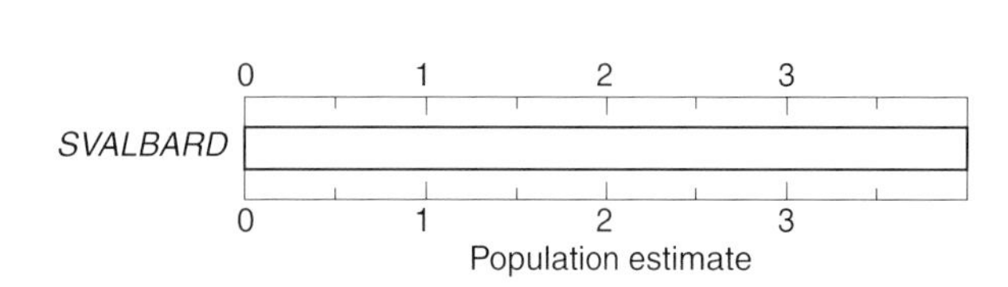

% in top 10 countries: 100.0
Total number of populated European countries: 1
Total European population 4–4 (4)

Sabine's Gull is a small, hooded gull which breeds in marshy tundra near the coasts or rivers in the high arctic (Sutton 1962), and migrates to the areas of upwelling along the eastern boundary currents of the Southern Hemisphere. The only regular breeding place in the western Palearctic may be N Svalbard, where there were 31 records of up to 4 birds during 1963–84. It probably bred at Sørkappøya (76°30'N, 16°33'E) in 1986 and at least 4 pairs bred at Moffen Island (80°02'N, 14°30'E) in 1993, breeding also being known to occur in 1986 and 1994 (Isaksen & Bakken 1995). These birds may be outliers of the E Canadian and Greenland population which migrates S in the eastern Atlantic to winter off South Africa, whereas those from Alaska to N Russia migrate S in the eastern Pacific to winter off western South America.

The location of the small, scattered colonies, and indeed whether the birds breed at all, may be determined by the weather, which may also cause 'wrecks' of migrants (Hume & Christie 1989). The nests are located in swampy tundra or on islands; in N Greenland they are normally in colonies of Arctic Tern *Sterna paradisaea*, which aggressively repulse Arctic fox *Alopex lagopus*, and whose eggs the gulls may eat (Salomonsen 1950), though this is not necessarily the case in lower latitudes in Alaska (R.G.B. Brown *et al* 1967) nor on the Taymyr Peninsula (Yésou 1991a).

Little is known about the birds' numbers or welfare. Apparently colonies seldom exceed tens of pairs, but assemblies of over a thousand birds have been seen on migration and in the winter quarters. They seem sensitive to disturbance when breeding, and might be affected by the development of the Arctic and the associated proliferation of predators. Fortunately the Svalbard colony is in a strict nature reserve. Despite there being two well-separated wintering populations, Sabine's Gull is regarded generally as monotypic.

WRP Bourne (GB)

Larus genei

Slender-billed Gull

CZ	Racek tenkozobý	I	Gabbiano roseo
D	Dünnschnabelmöwe	NL	Dunbekmeeuw
E	Gaviota Picofina	P	Gaivota-de-bico-fino
F	Goéland railleur	PL	Mewa cienkodzioba
FIN	Kaitanokkalokki	R	Морской голубок
G	Λεπτόρραμφος Γλάρος	S	Långnäbbad mås
H	Vékonycsőrű sirály		

Non-SPEC, Threat status S (P)

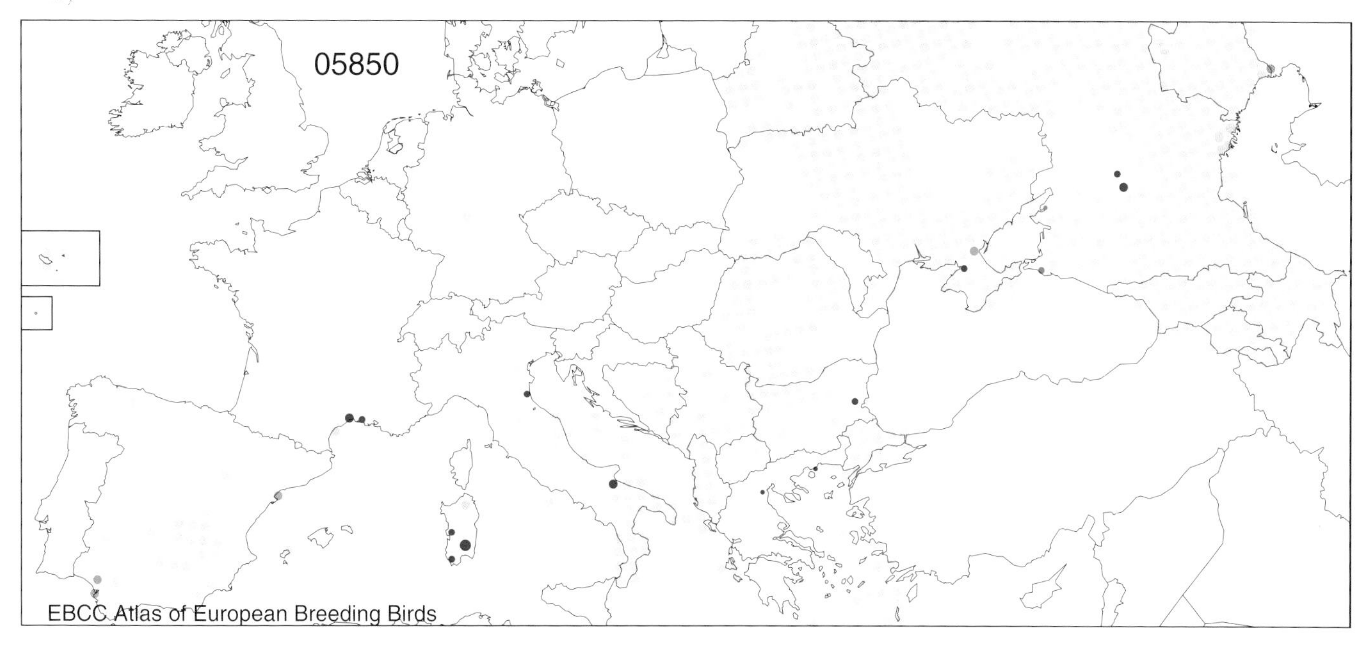

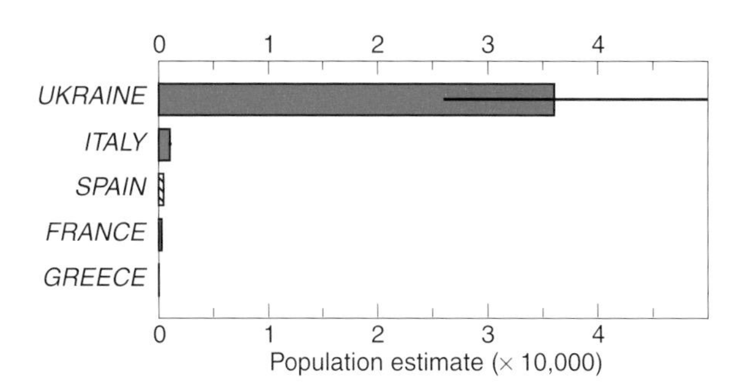

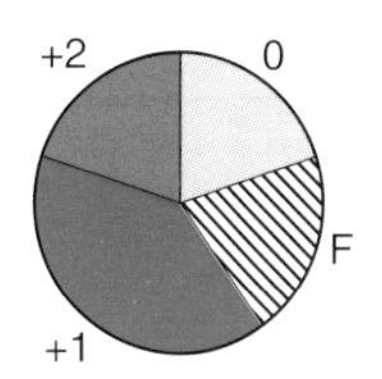

% in top 10 countries: 100.0
Total number of populated European countries: 5
Total European population 27,787–51,789 (37,844)
Russian population 10,000–20,000 (14,142)
Turkish population 3100–10,000 (5568)

In the *Atlas* coverage area, the medium-sized Slender-billed Gull breeds colonially in the Mediterranean, Black and Caspian Seas, in the Sea of Azov, locally in Romania, S France, S Spain, Greece and Italy, and extralimitally on several inland wetlands in Egypt, Turkey, Iran, other parts of Asia Minor, and also Tunisia and in W Africa as far S as 17°N. Its main breeding sites are in Ukraine's Black Sea region. The largest colonies in Ukraine are now on Tendra Island (37 450bp) and the Crimean Kerch Peninsula (18 000–20 000bp in 1984; Siokhin *et al* 1988). Its numbers overall are increasing. Since the 1960s it has bred in the W Mediterranean, evidently having spread through the E Mediterranean from the Black Sea. However, the Romanian population has diminished from abundant to scarce since the 19th century (Vasiliu 1968).

For breeding, the Slender-billed Gull has a preference for low-lying islands in salt or saline shallow waters, rarely choosing freshwater bodies (Nile Delta, NE Tunisia, Malta, Italy, Greece).

The Black Sea and E Mediterranean populations are mostly migratory, but the more southerly populations tend largely to be resident. Individuals tend to be dispersive and vagrant. Its wintering grounds are usually in the Mediterranean and Caspian Seas and in the Arabian Gulf. A few sometimes winter in the northern Black Sea and in the Sea of Azov.

Due to its dispersive nature, its numbers tend to fluctuate from year to year both at its established breeding locations and on its wintering grounds. Its total European population is therefore difficult to estimate and is probably between 41 000 and 82 000bp. Vagrants occur well beyond the species' normal wintering range and have been recorded in the Canary Islands, Belarus and western India. The Slender-billed Gull is not under any apparent threat at present.

Valentin Serebryakov (UKR) Victor Zubakin (R)

Larus canus

Common Gull

CZ	Racek bouřní	**I**	Gavina
D	Sturmmöwe	**NL**	Stormmeeuw
E	Gaviota Cana	**P**	Alcatraz-pardo
F	Goéland cendré	**PL**	Mewa pospolita
FIN	Kalalokki	**R**	Сизая чайка
G	Θυελλόγλαρος	**S**	Fiskmås
H	Viharsirály		

SPEC Cat 2, Threat status D

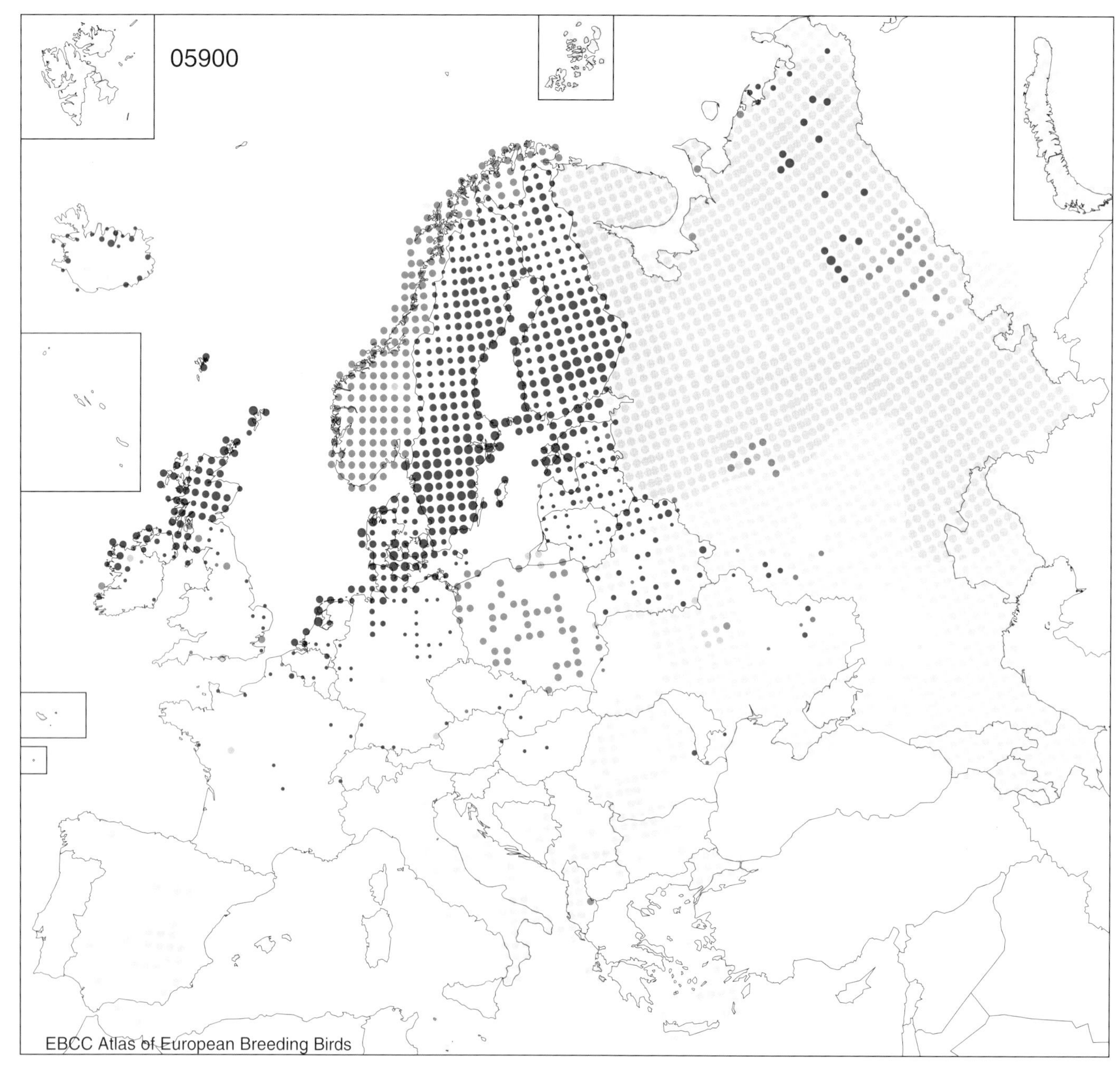

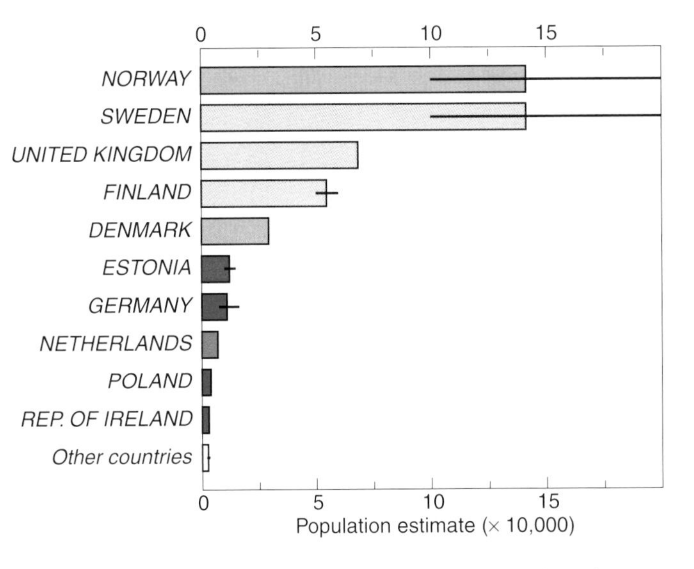

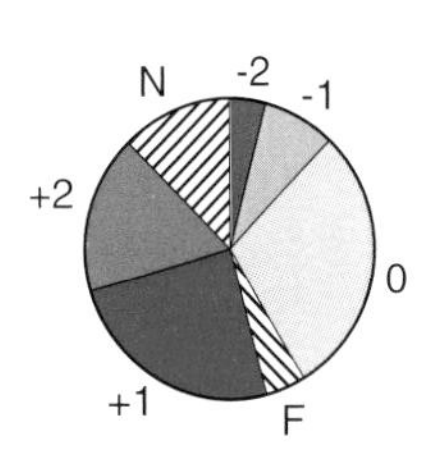

% in top 10 countries: 99.5
Total number of populated European countries: 24
Total European population 416,157–558,316 (475,087)
Russian population 40,000–60,000 (48,990)

The Common Gull has an almost circumpolar distribution in the Northern Hemisphere: *L.c. canus*, the most numerous subspecies, breeds from Iceland S to France and E to the White Sea, *heinei* from the Kanin Peninsula, Dvina and Moscow region E to the Lena, *kamtschatschensis* in NE Siberia and *brachyrhynchus* in NW North America.

The species breeds usually near to but sometimes far from water along sheltered parts of the coast, and widely inland, on lake islands, marshes and bogs up to 1400m asl in Norway. Most nest in small groups, though isolated pairs are common on islets, beaches, dunes, rocky, grassy or heathery slopes and moorland, but rare on cliffs or in trees. Colonies running into thousands of breeding pairs developed in Denmark (Møller 1978), Scotland (Tasker *et al* 1991) and The Netherlands (Woutersen 1992) when rabbits *Oryctolagus cuniculus* and therefore foxes *Vulpes vulpes* were reduced after the introduction of myxomatosis. Since the resurgence of foxes the birds have dispersed and started to move to buildings in both Scotland (Sullivan 1978, W.R.P. Bourne, pers obs) and The Netherlands (Costers 1992), also occupying Dutch enclosed industrial areas.

Over 50% of the European population of 524 000bp breeds in Norway and Sweden, 38% in Great Britain, Finland, Russia and Denmark and 12% in 19 other European states. Scarce and patchily distributed S of 52°N (Géroudet 1995) and in Iceland (300–400bp), the species elsewhere is numerous and widespread. The European population possibly accounts for 80–90% of the world population.

Marked and widespread population increases have occurred since 1890, when breeding was first reported in the Faeroes. The year 1908 saw the species breeding in The Netherlands (having occurred before 1870), 1924 Belgium, 1955 Iceland, 1956 Poland, 1957 Germany, 1958 Austria and 1966 Switzerland. It spread and increased in Britain & Ireland from the 19th century onwards. It is likely that climatic trends, cessation of persecution, eutrophication of inland waters and increased foraging on human refuse contributed to the increases (Goethe 1983). It is now declining in the range core (Norway, Denmark, Estonia, NE Scotland) and inland in Ireland. British and Irish populations apparently have concentrated into fewer and larger colonies; one group in NE Scotland increased up to fivefold from 5000bp from 1976 to the late 1980s (Tasker *et al* 1991), but is now declining again (W.R.P. Bourne, pers obs). Reasons other than foxes for some local declines are: in former East Germany, culling, and a reduction of human refuse availability (Hartwig & Prüter 1990); in Scotland the spread of feral American mink *Mustela vison*, and poor weather (W.R.P. Bourne, pers obs), and in Ireland feral American mink, inter-colony movement, disturbance, habitat loss and possible climatic change (Whilde *et al* 1993). In Poland, dam construction will eliminate island breeding sites in rivers such as the Vistula (Wesołowski 1986). Changes in dispersed populations may go unnoticed.

The Common Gull generally is migratory but distances vary. However, northern populations tend to winter N of southern populations after migration. Scandinavian flocks fly low WSW past the North Sea oil installations, presumably to join moulting birds in Scotland (W.R.P. Bourne, pers obs). Most European birds winter on the western seaboard from the Baltic to Brittany, but a few reach Iberia and the Mediterranean. Scandinavian and Estonian birds move S, some remaining within the Baltic, but most reach the Wadden Sea, Britain & Ireland (Kilpi & Saurola 1985). Danish and German birds move S and W to the southern North Sea, birds of Baltic origin tending to remain on the continent. Colour-ringing in W Ireland indicates a dispersal eastwards, sometimes to W England, occasionally The Netherlands, and southwards mainly to the S Irish coast, and infrequently to France and Spain. There is a fast, high return movement in spring.

WRP Bourne (GB) the late Tony Whilde (IRE)

Larus audouinii

Audouin's Gull

CZ	Racek Audouinův	I	Gabbiano corso
D	Korallenmöwe	NL	Audouins Meeuw
E	Gaviota de Audouin	P	Alcatraz de Audouin
F	Goéland d'Audouin	PL	Mewa śródziemnomorska
FIN	Välimerenlokki	R	Средиземноморская чайка
G	Αιγαιόγλαρος	S	Rödnäbbad trut
H	Korallsirály		

SPEC Cat 1, Threat status L

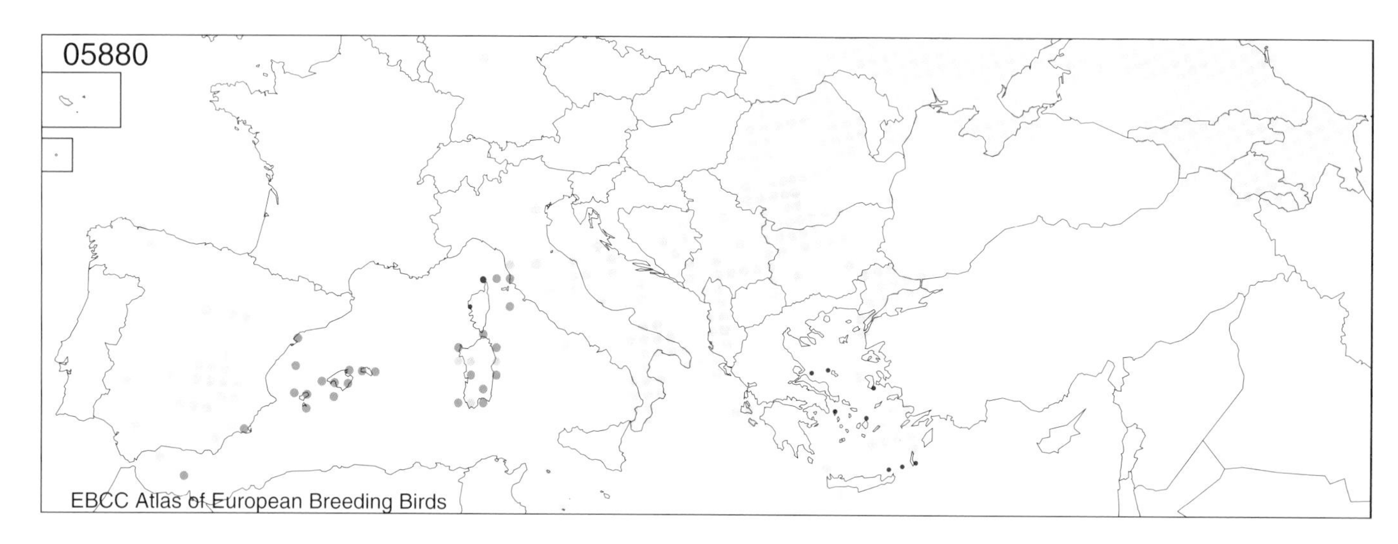

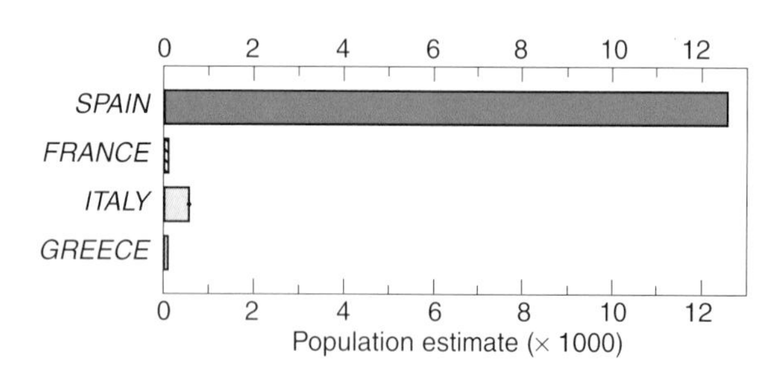

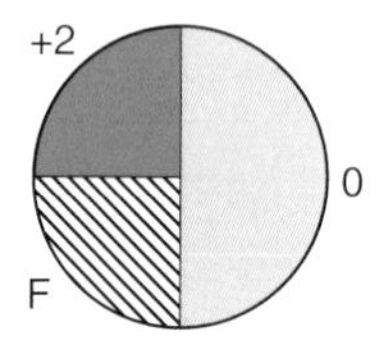

% in top 10 countries: 100.0
Total number of populated European countries: 4
Total European population 13,304–13,410 (13,355)
Turkish population 50–50 (50)

As a breeding species the medium-sized Audouin's Gull is confined to the Mediterranean Sea, where its colonies are found mainly on islets or small, uninhabited rocky islands, not far from the coast.

The distribution and relative size of the breeding colonies are extremely uneven, perhaps due to differences in food availability (H-H. Witt 1982). While for the E Mediterranean (Lebanon, Turkey, Cyprus and Greece) the few known colonies are very small and scattered, in the W Mediterranean there are important populations in Spain (the Ebro Delta and the Columbretes, Balearics, Grosa, Alboran and Chafarinas Islands), in Corsica, in Italy (the Tuscan archipelago and Sardinia), Morocco, Algeria and Tunisia. In 1989 over 80% of the world breeding population lived in Spanish territory and some 70% in just two colonies, those of the Chafarinas Islands (off the Moroccan coast), and in the Ebro Delta, the latter exceptionally being sited at the tip of a long sandy peninsula (de Juana & Varela 1993).

The world breeding population has grown considerably since 1965, from the 800–1000bp estimated in 1966 to 9000–9500bp in 1989, and although improved monitoring doubtless boosted the known total, there has been a real average increase of *c*10–11% per annum (de Juana & Varela 1993). As for other gulls, the increase could be attributed, at least in part, not only to the protection of its principal breeding colonies, but also to its ability to exploit discarded waste from fishing vessels. By 1993 there were some 14 000bp on Spanish territory, 9373 being in the Ebro Delta and 3540 in the Chafarinas Islands (Plan Coordinado de Actuaciones de la Gaviota de Audouin 1994). The development of the Ebro Delta colony, established with 36bp in 1981 and reaching 4200bp in 1989 (Oró & Martínez Vilalta 1992) has been especially impressive.

The majority of the population winters outside the Mediterranean, on the Atlantic coasts of Africa between Morocco and Senegal. Passage takes place through the Straits of Gibraltar, mainly during July–October and March–April (de Juana *et al* 1987).

Eduardo de Juana (E)

This species account is sponsored by Dr Hans Hinrich Witt, Körle, D.

Larus armenicus

Armenian Gull

CZ Racek arménský
D Armeniermöwe
E Gaviota Armenia
F Goéland d'Arménie
FIN Armenianlokki
G Γλάρος της Αρμενίας
H Örmény sirály
I Gabbiano di Armenia
NL Armeense Meeuw
P Gaivota da Arménia
PL Mewa armeńska
R Армянская серебристая чайка
S Armenisk trut

Non-SPEC, Threat status S (P)

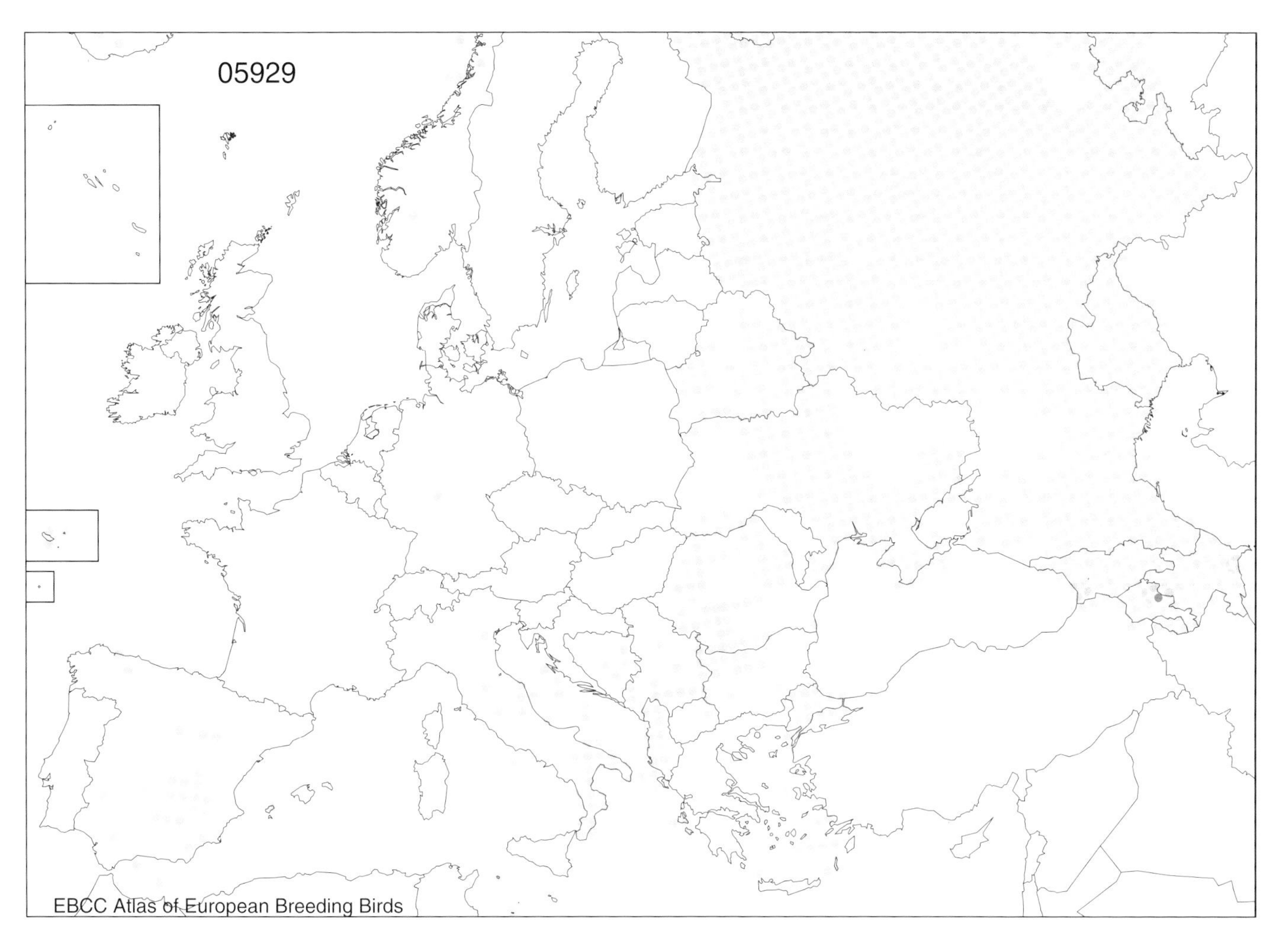

The relationships between various groups, subspecies, and populations of many Palearctic gulls are not yet clear, but gradually are being teased out. The *Atlas*' treatment of the Armenian Gull as a full species separated from *L. argentatus* reflects the present general assessment of that work. The feature which distinguishes the Armenian Gull from similar members of the *Larus* complex is its characteristic, if variable, black band on a yellow bill (Grant 1986).

Its present known distribution is limited to Armenia. It breeds at Lake Sevan in Armenia where it was first described, there being an estimated 4000bp on two islands (Filchagov 1993). A second colony, which was formed between 1970 and 1980 on Lake Arpilich, may be even larger (Filchagov 1993). Such high concentrations may be linked to a lack of sufficient suitable breeding sites protected from terrestrial predation, both animal and human. It is not clear whether other colonies exist in the region. Clearly, such a limited choice of nest sites makes the population vulnerable to chance factors.

The Armenian Gull population was in decline until the 1960s, which perhaps has contributed to the delay in recognizing its status as a full species (Grant 1987). A large proportion of the population winters in marine habitats along the Mediterranean coast of Egypt and Israel (Meininger & Sørensen 1992).

Although a versatile and opportunistic species, well-adapted to take advantage of favourable circumstances, the apparent lack of suitable breeding habitat within its restricted range and its tendency to suffer population fluctuations make the Armenian Gull a vulnerable species.

Philip Jackson (GB)

Larus fuscus

Lesser Black-backed Gull

CZ	Racek žlutonohý	I	Zafferano
D	Heringsmöwe	NL	Kleine Mantelmeeuw
E	Gaviota Sombría	P	Gaivota-d'asa-escura
F	Goéland brun	PL	Mewa żółtonoga
FIN	Selkälokki	R	Клуша
G	Μελανόγλαρος	S	Silltrut
H	Heringsirály		

SPEC Cat 4, Threat status S

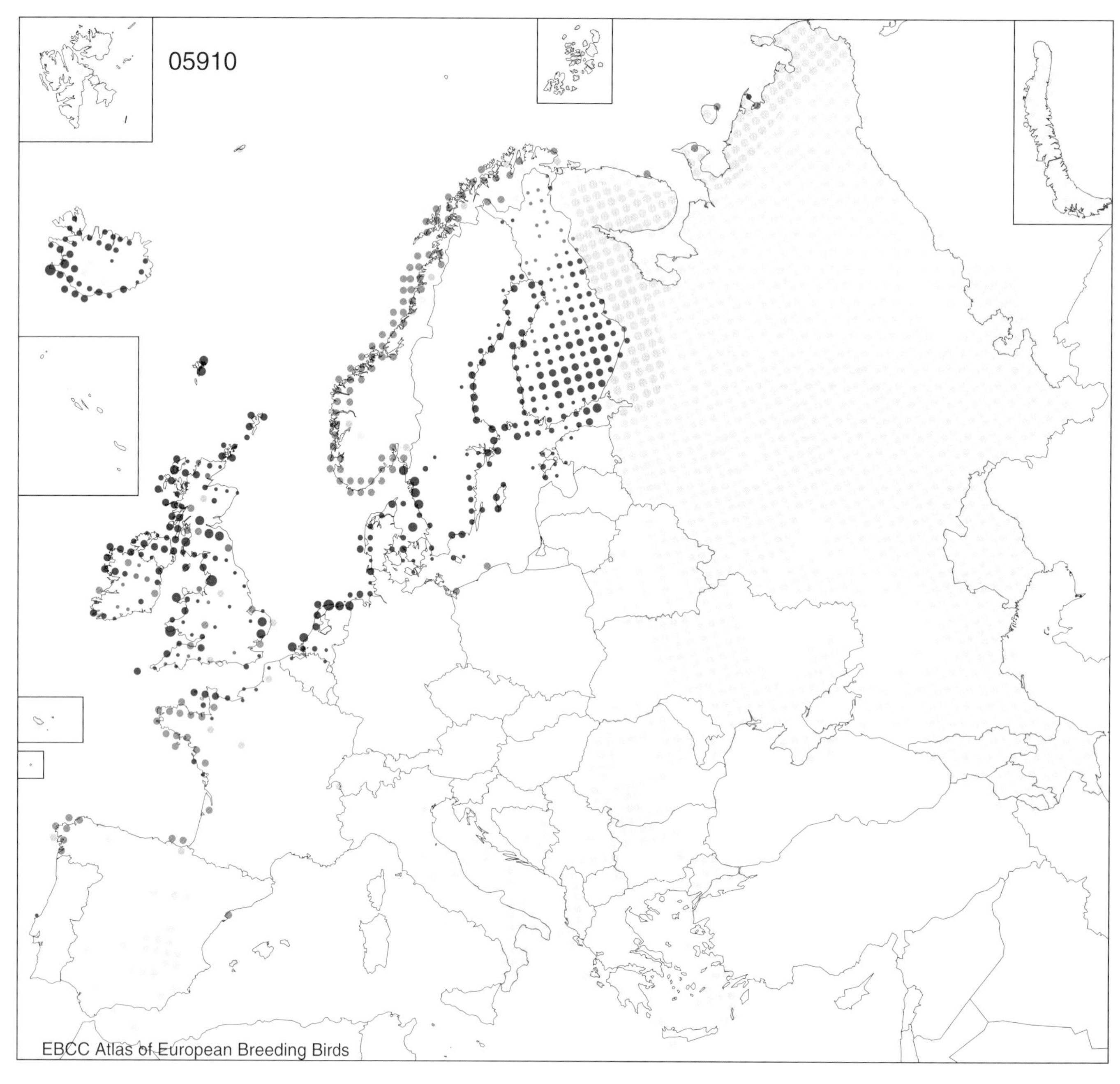

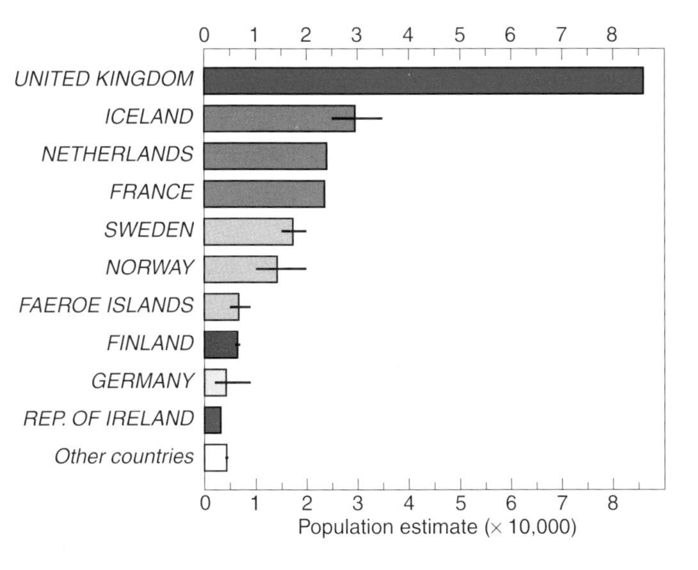

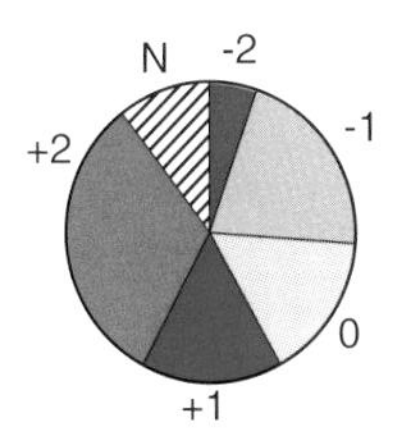

% in top 10 countries: 98.0
Total number of populated European countries: 19
Total European population 212,377–229,522 (219,569)
Russian population 700–2300 (1269)

The Lesser Black-backed Gull breeds only in N and W Europe from the White Sea to Iceland and S to the Iberian Peninsula. Populations from N Norway eastwards belong to the nominate *L.f. fuscus*. Variations between *intermedius* (S Scandinavia) and *graellsii* (remaining range) are mainly clinal. More specialized in its feeding ecology than other subspecies, *fuscus* shows important differences in demography, moult timing and migration route. Gulls breeding in N Russia and Siberia, E to the Taymyr, sometimes have been considered conspecific, sometimes as a subspecies of Herring Gull *L. argentatus*, but recent studies suggest that they form a separate species, Heuglin's Gull *L. heuglini* (Filchagov *et al* 1992).

The Lesser Black-backed Gull will occupy cliffs, but prefers less rugged habitats, including islets or coasts possessing dunes. In its northern range from Finland to Iceland it also breeds inland regularly. Colonies then occur in wetlands of various kinds, from moors to shingle pits. About 20 000bp in Great Britain breed inland (23% of the country's population), an incidental habit further S. Since the 1940s, roof-nesting in towns has increased, mostly in Britain, The Netherlands and France. Some urban colonies total several hundred breeding pairs.

The species' distribution is rather even on Finnish bogs and lakes and along the rocky coasts of Scandinavia, Shetlands and western Scotland, the relatively high breeding density indicating almost continuous favourable habitats. Conversely, its distribution is patchier to the S where good habitats become scarcer and breeding density lower.

The population size has increased markedly since the early 20th century in the species' western range, as far as Denmark and S Norway in the E. Iceland was colonized in the 1920s, Portugal and Spain in the 1970s. This extension may be explained by a decrease in human disturbance, including shooting and egg-taking, combined with an increase in food availability through commercial fishing activities, and at rubbish tips. Dutch birds nowadays mainly feed on fishing-boat discards, having out-competed the Herring Gull *L. argentatus* through greater manoeuvrability (Noordhuis & Spaans 1992). However, this overall increase masks some local misfortunes, such as in the Faeroes, and the negative effect of culling on some colonies, especially in Britain & Ireland (Lloyd *et al* 1991).

A contrasting situation arises in N Norway, Sweden, Finland, Estonia and Russia, where *fuscus* numbers have fallen dramatically since the mid-1960s (Strann & Vader 1992) to the point where the species may be threatened in some areas. In Russia, the species has disappeared from all its inland breeding sites and only a few hundred breeding pairs are left on the White Sea archipelago (A.V. Filchagov, pers comm). Reasons for this decline include food shortage following decreasing fish stocks, and locally, human disturbance and competition with the Herring Gull *L. argentatus* (Strann & Vader 1992).

The overall population size was 210 000–250 000bp during the *Atlas* census, Great Britain holding some 86 000bp, Iceland 25 000–35 000bp, The Netherlands and France 24 000bp each, Sweden 15 000–20 000bp and Norway 10 000–20 000bp. No other country has more than 7000bp. Only 250–300bp exist in Estonia and Spain, and fewer than 10bp in Belgium or Portugal. Britain holds the largest (>10 000bp) colonies, other sizeable colonies being found in W France and The Netherlands. Breeding density reaches 120 bp/ha in Brittany (J-M. Pons & P. Yésou, pers obs).

The Lesser Black-backed Gull migrates S outside the breeding season, deserting its northern breeding range. Immature birds tend to move further than adults. Birds from W Europe migrate SW towards the Iberian Peninsula and NW Africa, some reaching the Gulf of Guinea. Increasing numbers overwinter in the North Sea or along the Biscay coast. Eastern *fuscus* populations migrate SE to the E Mediterranean, the Red Sea, the Arabian Gulf and particularly E Africa.

Jean-Marc Pons (F) Pierre Yésou (F)

Larus argentatus

Herring Gull

CZ	Racek stříbřitý	**I**	Gabbiano reale
D	Silbermöwe	**NL**	Zilvermeeuw
E	Gaviota Argéntea	**P**	Gaivota-argêntea
F	Goéland argenté	**PL**	Mewa srebrzysta
FIN	Harmaalokki	**R**	Серебристая чайка
G	Ασημόγλαρος	**S**	Gråtrut
H	Ezüstsirály		

Non-SPEC, Threat status S

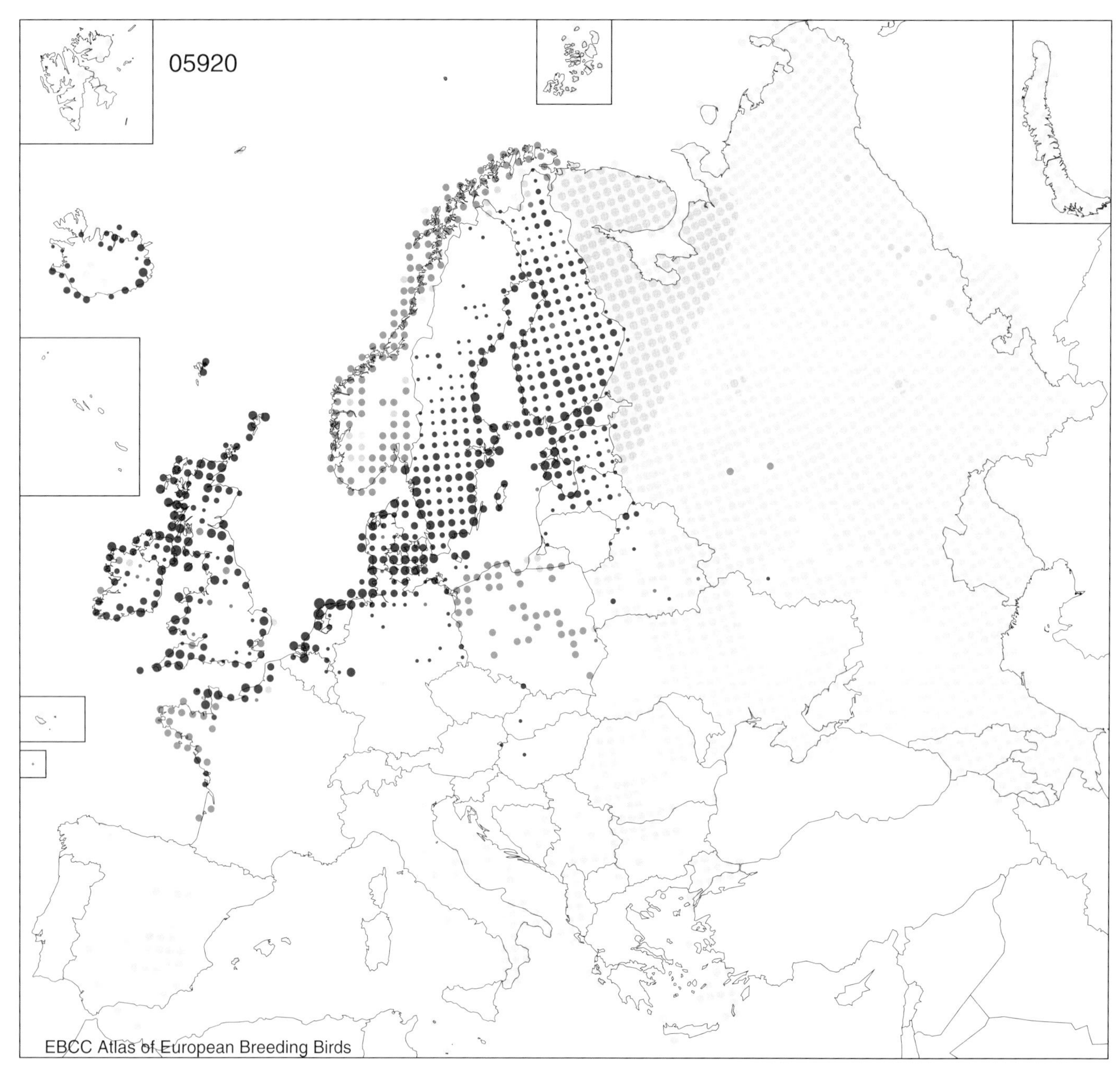

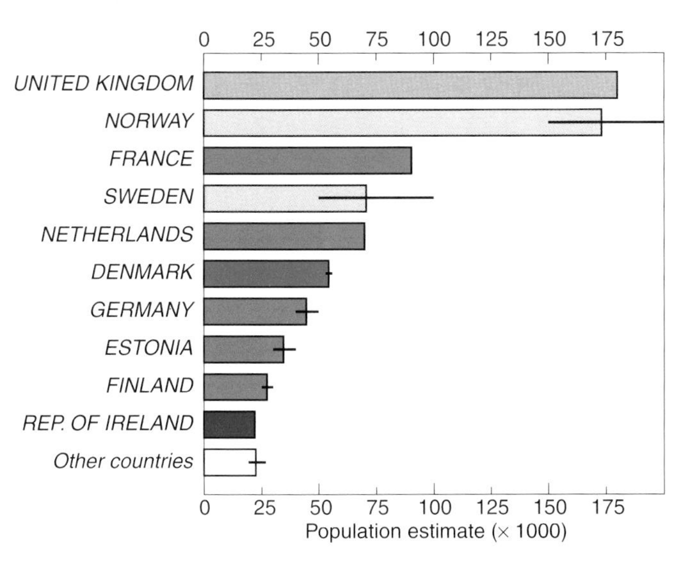

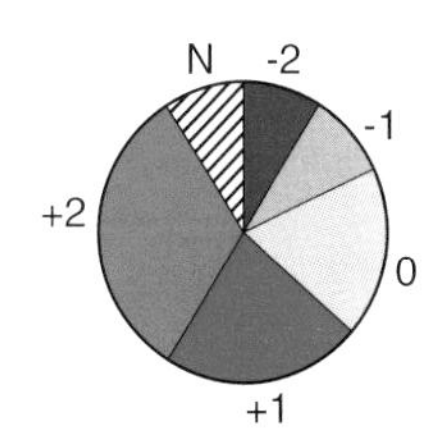

% in top 10 countries: 97.2
Total number of populated European countries: 22
Total European population 757,945–830,567 (789,940)

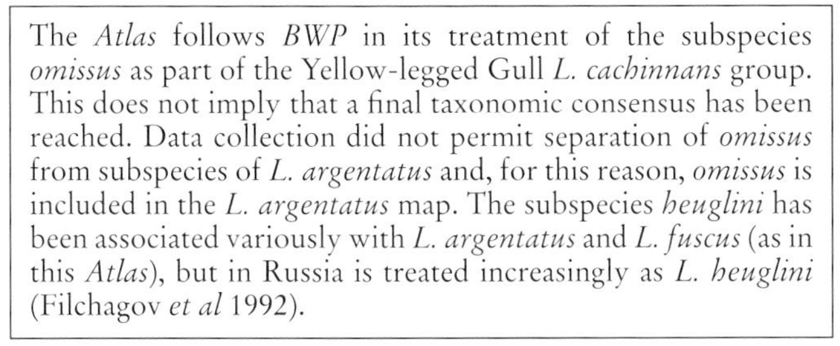
The *Atlas* follows *BWP* in its treatment of the subspecies *omissus* as part of the Yellow-legged Gull *L. cachinnans* group. This does not imply that a final taxonomic consensus has been reached. Data collection did not permit separation of *omissus* from subspecies of *L. argentatus* and, for this reason, *omissus* is included in the *L. argentatus* map. The subspecies *heuglini* has been associated variously with *L. argentatus* and *L. fuscus* (as in this *Atlas*), but in Russia is treated increasingly as *L. heuglini* (Filchagov *et al* 1992).

This species, until recently embracing the Yellow-legged Gull *L. cachinnans*, has a Holarctic distribution, breeding mainly in mid- to high latitudes (below the high arctic). It is separated into a number of subspecies, the nominate *L.a. argentatus*, occurring in the *Atlas*' area of coverage, as does *argenteus*, others being *smithsonianus* of North America and *vegae* of N Siberia.

In Europe the species breeds in Iceland (hybridizing freely with the Glaucous Gull *L. hyperboreus*), the Faeroes, Britain & Ireland, Norway, Sweden, Finland, NW Russia, the Baltic States, Poland, Germany, Denmark, The Netherlands, Belgium and W France. Throughout its range it breeds mainly on the coast, though in Sweden, Finland and NW Russia it also breeds on low tundra, high moorland and even on mountain lakes at altitudes over 2000m asl. Elsewhere, inland breeding (mainly on lake islands) is much rarer. The preferred coastal habitats for breeding colonies are rocky coasts, with cliffs, stacks, islands and skerries. On 'soft' coasts the Herring Gull often breeds on sand-dunes, shingle banks and saltmarshes. Recently in The Netherlands it has used cabbage fields. Increasingly it is establishing colonies in towns, both coastal and inland. Colonies can range from a few pairs to many thousands at some sites.

Away from the colonies and outside the breeding season the Herring Gull is usually found on the coast and in inshore waters, but increasingly it is occurring inland, especially in areas where the winter climate is mild. It is generally resident or dispersive, with only the northern populations (N Norway, Finland, NW Russia) migrating SW to the Baltic and North Sea.

The Herring Gull's European population is estimated at between 739 000 and 835 000bp. The 'centre of gravity' of the breeding population lies in Great Britain, Norway, Sweden, Denmark, Germany, The Netherlands and France, where 81–84% of the birds breed. Outside this core area national populations are mostly small, ranging from under 100bp in Belgium to a maximum of 40 000bp in Estonia. Some areas where the Herring Gull is still found in small numbers have been colonized only relatively recently.

During the 20th century the Herring Gull population has undergone a marked increase over its entire NW European range. Iceland was colonized as recently as the 1920s. In Denmark there has been a 20-fold increase, while in Germany it has been 15-fold. The Netherlands' population has increased fivefold in spite of systematic culling between 1930 and the 1960s (Lloyd *et al* 1991). Such dramatic increases in Herring Gull numbers, exemplified by a rate of 13% per annum in Britain up to the mid-1970s (Chabrzyk & Coulson 1976), is attributed to a combination of increased protection (including a decline in commercial egg-collecting) and the species' opportunistic adaptation to new sources of year-round food supplies. It utilizes waste at refuse-tips, from fishery discards, abattoir and fish factory offal, and sewage outfalls. More recently, it has taken to following farm machinery during tillage. These increases have been accompanied by a northward range expansion.

In some areas, recent declines such as the halving of the British population between 1969 and 1987 (Lloyd *et al* 1991) are considered to be due to a combination of culling (as public health or safety measures, or towards the conservation of more vulnerable species such as terns), outbreaks of diseases such as botulism and salmonella, a reduction in food availability through better refuse disposal management, improved utilization of commercial fish catches and possibly (in The Netherlands) interspecific competition with Lesser Black-backed Gull *L. fuscus* (Noordhuis & Spaans 1992).

Oscar J Merne (IRE)

Larus cachinnans **Yellow-legged Gull**

CZ	Racek bělohlavý	**I**	Gabbiano reale mediterraneo
D	Weißkopfmöwe	**NL**	Geelpootmeeuw
E	Gaviota Patiamarilla	**P**	Gaivota-de-patas-amarelas
F	Goéland leucophée	**PL**	Mewa białogłowa
FIN	[Valkopäälokki]	**R**	Хохотунья
G	Ασημόγλαρος	**S**	[Gråtrut]
H	Sárgalábú sirály		

Non-SPEC, Threat status S (P)

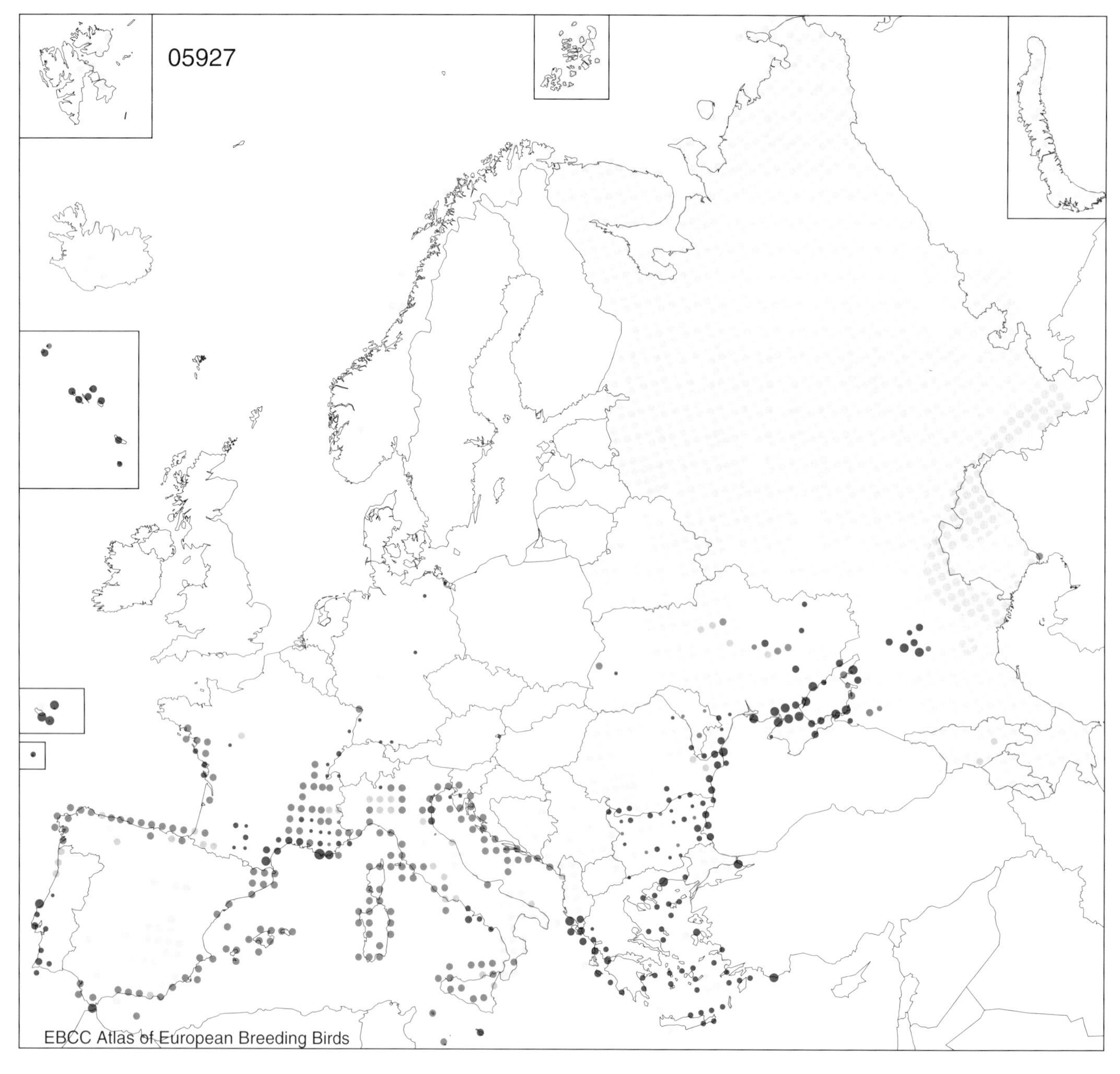

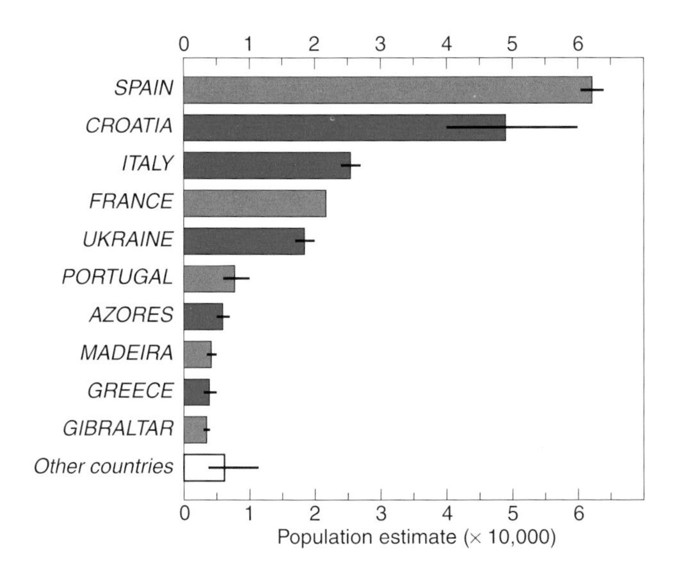

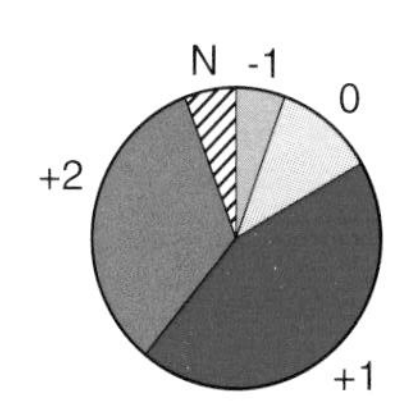

% in top 10 countries: 97.0
Total number of populated European countries: 18
Total European population 198,341–220,323 (208,122)
Russian population 25,000–35,000 (29,580)
Turkish population 1–1 (1)

The *Atlas* follows *BWP* in its treatment of the subspecies *omissus* as part of the Yellow-legged Gull *L. cachinnans* group. This does not imply that a final taxonomic consensus has been reached. Data collection did not permit separation of *omissus* from subspecies of *L. argentatus* and, for this reason, *omissus* is included in the *L. argentatus* map.

Large, and possessing a powerful hooked bill and rather long and broad wings, the Yellow-legged Gull prefers rocky coasts comprising cliffs and outlying stacks, skerries and islets, but also breeds on sand-dunes, beaches, salinas and occasionally saltmarshes. Its distribution covers the Mediterranean countries (including North Africa), the Black Sea, the Atlantic coast of the Iberian Peninsula through to France, scattered pairs being found inland in Austria and Switzerland. It also breeds in the Azores and on Madeira. In the Mediterranean basin, many adults are resident or even sedentary, being present near the colony-site all year, although immatures participate in movements whose patterns have still to be clarified. However, immatures apparently tend to move to C Europe (Hungary, Poland, Denmark, Austria, Slovakia; K. Kravos, pers comm), a post-fledging tendency, mainly in August.

Since 1895, the population of Yellow-legged Gulls, like many other gull species worldwide, has been increasing rapidly (especially since 1975), mainly through the species' increased role as an urban scavenger, but also as a consequence of greater protection, in that egg-harvesting and culling by man have dwindled. Due to the scale of its population increase, the Yellow-legged Gull has had a significant effect on human beings, in terms of a risk to public health, and to other species through predation, such as Storm Petrel *Hydrobates pelagicus* and Audouin's Gull *L. audouinii* (Paterson 1994).

The largest populations are in the Adriatic basin (probably more than 50 000bp, the low accuracy of the estimates reflecting the lack of observations), in Spain (more than 30 000bp), S France (*c*16 000bp), Ukraine (more than 20 000bp) and Portugal. There are significant populations in the Azores (at least 2000bp; L. Monteiro, pers comm to the Editors), breeding on all the islands in the group, and on Madeira and the Desertas, possibly *c*6000bp (P. Oliveira, pers comm to the Editors), but the apparent increasing numbers (le Grand *et al* 1984) cannot be verified because quantitative data are lacking. The small population in Malta, seemingly stable, does not exhibit the characteristic overall increase of 7–12% per year of the Mediterranean basin. In some areas the rate of increase on inaccessible island breeding grounds is above 20%. Recently the species has taken to breeding on roofs (in Bulgaria over 50%; Paterson 1994), especially in ports, or in colonies close to human settlements. This behavioural change is attributable to the increased availability of food at adjacent refuse dumps. In turn, the Yellow-legged Gull is exposed to infection from pathogenic microbes which may represent a public health risk to human beings because of the bird's new feeding and nesting habits (Mudge 1978, Skornik 1992).

The taxonomy of various populations of Yellow-legged Gull is not wholly consistent in their degree of separation from other species, but it is now generally recognized that the *L. cachinnans* group is separable (Yésou 1991b). Three subspecies, the nominate *cachinnans*, *michahellis* and *atlantis*, have received more or less general acceptance, but the fourth, *omissus*, is still subject to debate. On the Atlantic coast of Spain, birds exhibit characteristics intermediate between *L. cachinnans* and *L. argentatus*, a circumstance repeated to greater or lesser degree in some other locations. The relationships between the various populations of Yellow-legged Gull, Herring Gull, Lesser Black-backed Gull and other large gulls are exceedingly complex, and uncertainties will remain in the foreseeable future.

Iztok Skornik (SLV)

This species account is sponsored by Arbeitsgemeinschaft Möwen, Nordrhein-Westfälische Ornithologen, D.

Larus glaucoides

Iceland Gull

CZ	Racek polární	I	Gabbiano d'Islanda
D	Polarmöwe	NL	Kleine Burgemeester
E	Gaviota Groenlandesa	P	Gaivota-polar
F	Goéland à ailes blanches	PL	Mewa polarna
FIN	Grönlanninlokki	R	Малая полярная чайка
G	Γλάρος της Ισλανδίας	S	Vitvingad trut
H	Sarki sirály		

Non-SPEC, Threat status S (P)

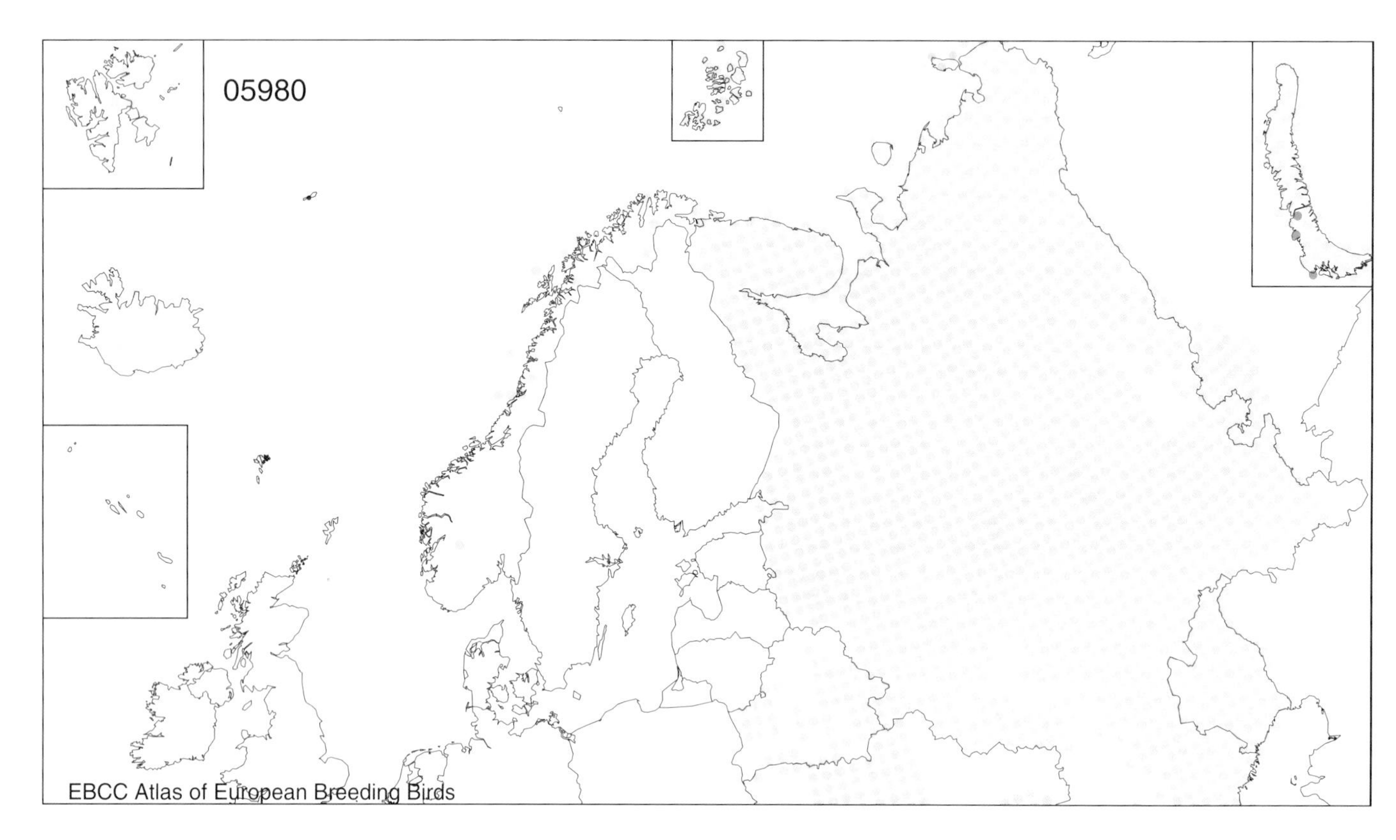

The Iceland Gull resembles a small Glaucous Gull *L. hyperboreus* with longer wings, a rounder head, shorter bill, and a darker ring round the eye in the breeding season. It feeds largely on marine animals caught along the shore. Greenland holds a mostly sedentary population which possesses white wingtips; some reach Iceland and variable numbers appear off NW Europe in winter (Salomonsen 1950). The form *kumlieni*, with grey in the wingtips, breeds N of Hudson's Bay and disperses down the E coast of North America to Long Island in winter, and may also reach Europe (Bannerman 1962, Weir *et al* 1995). Another form, *thayeri*, with black in the wingtips, breeds in NW Greenland and along the N Canadian coasts and winters down the W coast of North America to California and may also be a subspecies of the Iceland Gull. Their numbers are not large, of the order of 100 000bp.

Reports of a few breeding on Jan Mayen Island in 1883–85 (Fischer & von Pelzeln 1886) are nowadays treated with caution. Subsequent reports of their occurrence around the Barents Sea have been treated as records of small Glaucous Gulls (Dementiev 1951). Until recently, it was considered a vagrant in the former Soviet Union, with two birds shot at Novaya Zemlya (Judin & Firsova 1990). In August 1993 moulting Glaucous Gulls along the W coast of Novaya Zemlya were accompanied by a minority of smaller, tamer adult birds which were not yet in moult, had a brighter eye-ring and yellower iris, and were accompanied by smaller, greyer immatures (V.N. Kalyakin, pers obs). In 1994 a pair of these birds, with distinctive calls, was found with a nest and chicks near the top of a low cliff in Pukhovaya Bay 1–15km E of Cape Zhuravlev (V.N. Kalyakin, pers obs). The female, which was collected, had a bright lemon-yellow iris, orange eye-ring, and measurements similar to a large Iceland Gull. Small numbers of similar birds were observed nesting in five separate localities in western Novaya Zemlya, four of which were S of the narrow strait between the two main islands (V.N. Kalyakin, pers obs). The birds were not present in the same locations in 1995. The status of the Iceland Gull in the Palearctic clearly needs reassessment. In Russia it is now treated as an occasional breeder (A. Filchagov, pers comm), hence its provisional categorization in the *Atlas* as a confirmed breeder on Novaya Zemlya, pending publication of DNA analysis.

VN Kalyakin (R) WRP Bourne (GB)

Larus hyperboreus — Glaucous Gull

CZ	Racek šedý	I	Gabbiano glauco
D	Eismöwe	NL	Grote Burgemeester
E	Gavión Hiperbóreo	P	Gaivota-hiperbórea
F	Goéland bourgmestre	PL	Mewa blada
FIN	Isolokki	R	Бургомистр
G	Παγόγλαρος	S	Vittrut
H	Jeges sirály		

Non-SPEC, Threat status S

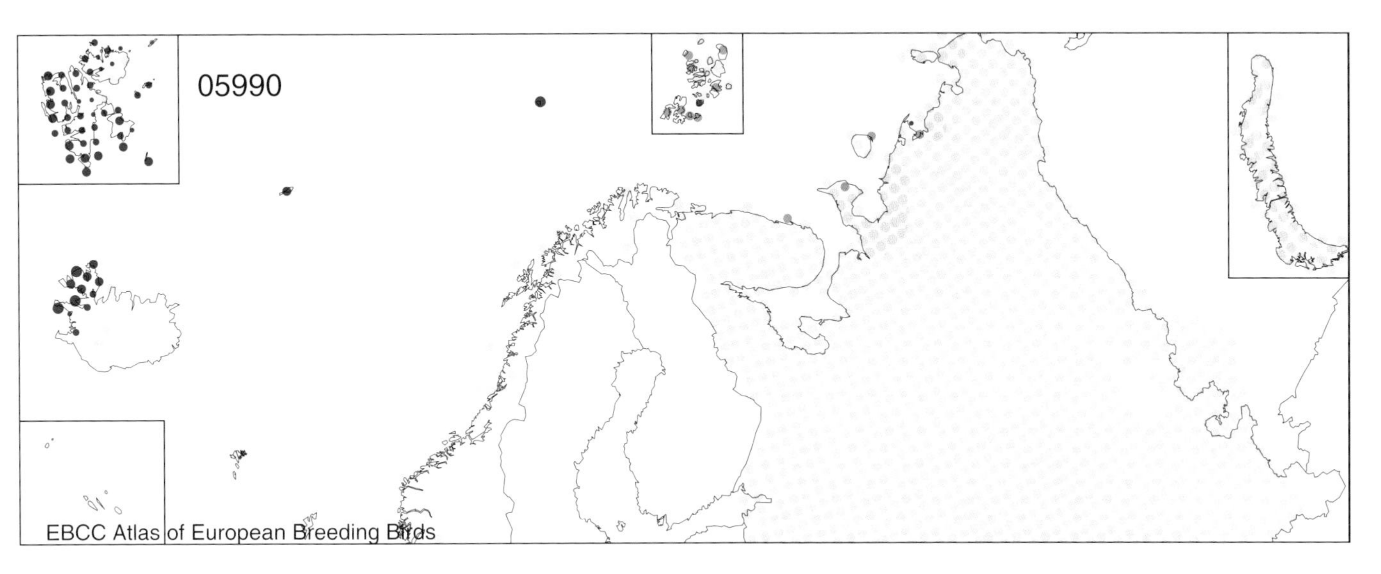

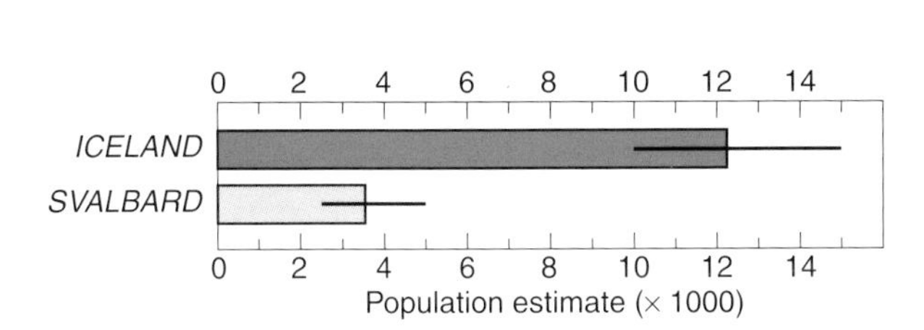

% in top 10 countries: 100.0
Total number of populated European countries: 2
Total European population 13,308–18,901 (15,783)
Russian population 4000–7000 (5292)

The Glaucous Gull is the large predatory gull of the Arctic. The nominate subspecies *L.h. hyperboreus* breeds along the N coast of Canada from the Mackenzie River to Labrador, in Greenland, N Iceland, the Arctic islands and the N coast of Russia from the Kanin to the Taymyr Peninsulas, and disperses S into the Atlantic. The subspecies *pallidissimus*, breeding further E in Russia, and *barrovianus*, breeding further W in North America, disperse S on opposite sides of the North Pacific.

The species may nest singly but usually forms groups of tens or exceptionally hundreds near colonies of other seabirds on which they prey. Normally it nests in fairly sheltered places inaccessible to the polar bear *Ursus maritimus*, wolf *Canis lupus* and arctic fox *Alopex lagopus* on islets, pinnacles or cliffs, often at a considerable altitude, reaching 600m asl in Greenland (Salomonsen 1950). Gull guano causes a local increase in the vegetation.

While breeding, the Glaucous Gull feeds mainly on smaller seabirds and the eggs and young of larger seabirds. At other times it preys upon and parasitizes other seabirds and forages along shores and out at sea, where the species comprises the most northerly component of the gulls which scavenge human offal and refuse jettisoned from ships and at dumps, a tendency which may have led to a population increase. The population in Iceland (now between 10 000 and 15 000bp) increased by >50% during 1970–90. Numbers in European Russia (4000–7000bp) may be stable, but locations are not well-studied. The latest estimate for Svalbard, approximate because of inaccessibility and widespread breeding groups, is 1000–10 000bp (Mehlum & Bakken 1994).

The species' main natural predators appear to be the arctic fox (Larson 1960) and man, but a more recent threat in Svalbard is chemical contamination. Being a top predator, the Glaucous Gull, feeding on mildly contaminated seabirds, appears to be accumulating lethal levels of toxic chemicals (Gabrielson *et al* 1995); a considerable number of highly contaminated dead birds have been found on Bjørnøya (Isaksen & Bakken 1995).

WRP Bourne (GB)

Larus marinus

Great Black-backed Gull

CZ	Racek mořský	I	Mugnaiaccio
D	Mantelmöwe	NL	Grote Mantelmeeuw
E	Gavión Atlántico	P	Alcatraz-comum
F	Goéland marin	PL	Mewa siodłata
FIN	Merilokki	R	Большая морская чайка
G	Γιγαντόγλαρος	S	Havstrut
H	Dolmányos sirály		

SPEC Cat 4, Threat status S

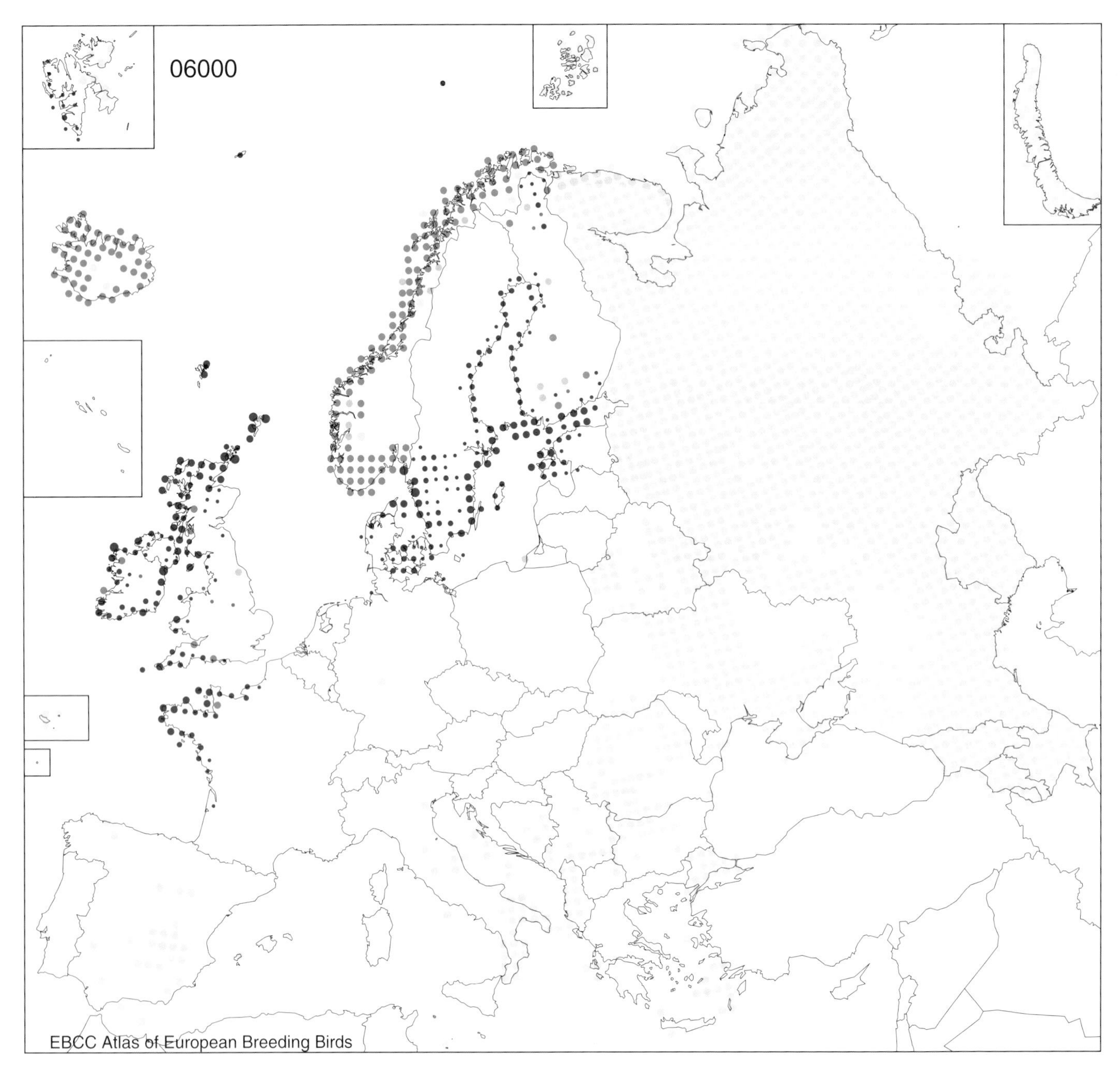

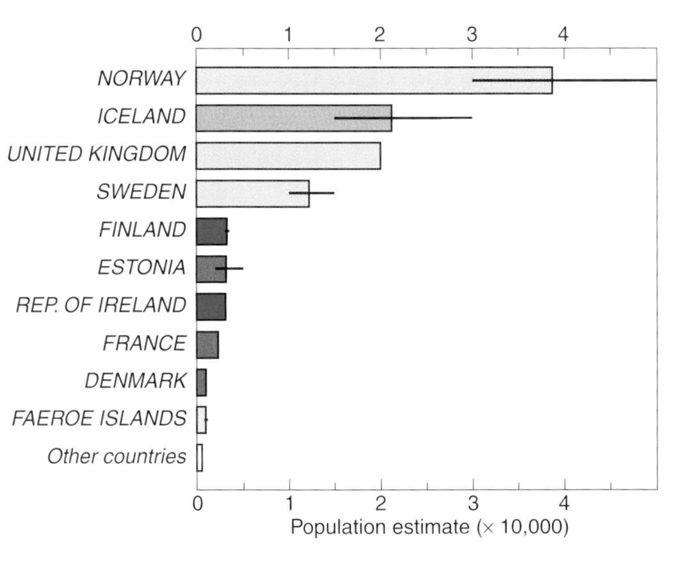

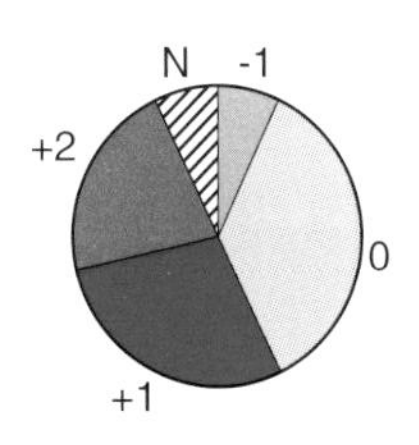

% in top 10 countries: 99.5
Total number of populated European countries: 14
Total European population 95,546–121,233 (106,560)
Russian population 8200–10,000 (9055)

The largest of the European gulls, the monotypic Great Black-backed Gull breeds on the maritime coasts of the North Atlantic and in the Baltic Sea. It sustains itself on a variety of foods, but is more closely associated with the open sea than are the related Herring *L. argentatus* and Lesser Black-backed *L. fuscus* Gulls. Only birds from the northernmost parts of the breeding range move far in winter (Coulson *et al* 1984, Kilpi & Saurola 1984), the rest disperse for short distances, generally southward.

On the Atlantic coast, the species breeds on islands and on top of rocky stacks. Colonies as large as a few thousands of pairs are scarce (Lloyd *et al* 1991). The Great Black-backed Gull maintains larger inter-nest distances than does the Herring Gull, making colonies looser. Cannibalism in colonies is frequent. A sizeable fraction of the population breeds as solitary pairs, to a predominant extent in the Baltic, where the species nests on very small islets and also in colonies of other gulls. Throughout the range, some pairs breed in inland habitats on lakes and on moorland. Good feeding opportunities at sea, in the intertidal zone and at fish-processing plants probably promote colonial nesting, but the species seems less influenced by rubbish-tip distribution than the Herring Gull (Greig *et al* 1986), and therefore is more restricted in its habitat use.

Most of the *c*120 000 European pairs of Great Black-backed Gull breed in Norway (32%), Great Britain (predominantly in Scotland, 17%), Ireland and Iceland (17%). The Baltic holds probably less than 10% of the total population. The apparent absence of the species on the North Sea coasts of Denmark, Germany and The Netherlands is interesting. It may reflect the fact that it avoids open sandy habitats even in areas occupied by both Herring and Lesser Black-backed Gulls. However, it has colonized successfully rocky islets on the Brittany coast.

Great Black-backed Gull numbers have increased over large areas, in Denmark and France accompanied by a range expansion. and it colonized Germany in 1984 (a single breeding attempt, scattered breeding thereafter; Goethe 1991) and The Netherlands in 1993 (first breeding, a single pair; 4bp in 1994; Vercruijsse & Spaans 1994, SOVON). Svalbard, colonized in 1921, holds probably fewer than 100bp, mostly on islets colonized by Eider *Somateria mollissima* (Isaksen & Bakken 1995). The evidence from the 1980s suggests that populations in Norway, Britain & Ireland, Iceland and W Sweden have remained stable or even declined slightly, paralleling the Herring Gull widespread trend on the Atlantic coasts (Lloyd *et al* 1991). The Baltic populations have increased by at least 20% since the 1970s. An increase of >50% in numbers was recorded in Denmark and France. In Brittany, the population increased from 260bp in 1970 to 801bp (1978) and 1824bp (1988), accompanied by a habitat shift, from the preferred rocky islets to large, flat islands and human constructions (Linard 1994).

Where increases have occurred, they have been attributed to increasing availability of rubbish, discarded fish and fish offal, but the recent development in its strongholds may indicate that food availability is now reducing. However, persecution and culling have also affected populations, although to what extent is unclear. Where the Great Black-back Gull nests in mixed colonies, predation upon other species may be perceived as significant. Consequently, for many years it has been culled systematically on a large scale. Lloyd *et al* (1991) considered culling in Britain & Ireland in the 1970s and 1980s had prevented any increase in that period. Traditional persecution in the Baltic has probably decreased, which may have contributed to the population growth since the 1950s, but few quantitative data are available. The prospects for a further population increase seem poor, but a serious decline seems equally unlikely.

Mikael Kilpi (FIN)

Rissa tridactyla

Kittiwake

CZ	Racek tříprstý	I	Gabbiano tridattilo
D	Dreizehenmöwe	NL	Drieteenmeeuw
E	Gaviota Tridáctila	P	Gaivota-tridáctila
F	Mouette tridactyle	PL	Mewa trójpalczasta
FIN	Pikkukajava	R	Моевка
G	Ρίσσα	S	Tretåig mås
H	Csüllő		

Non-SPEC, Threat status S

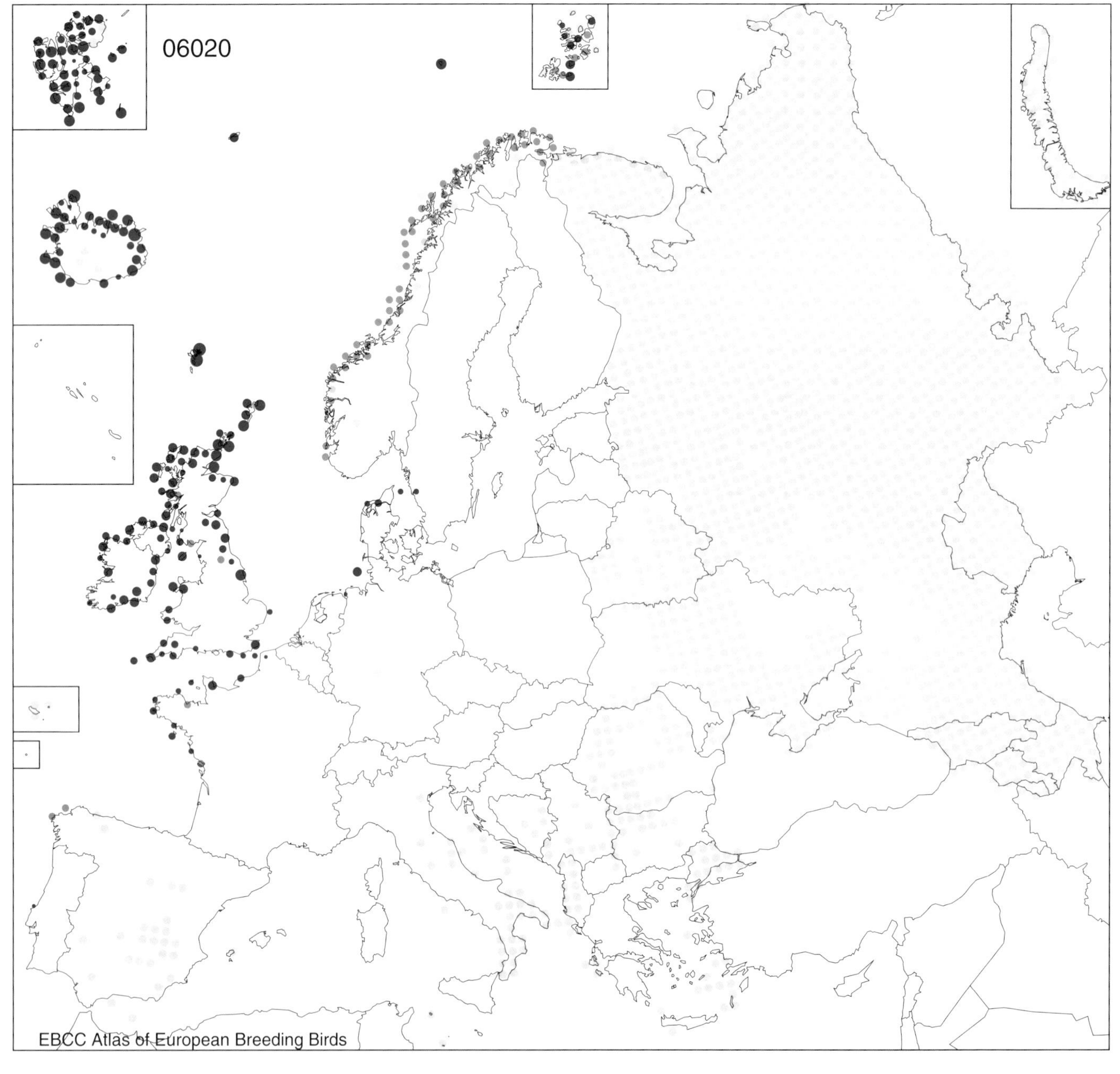

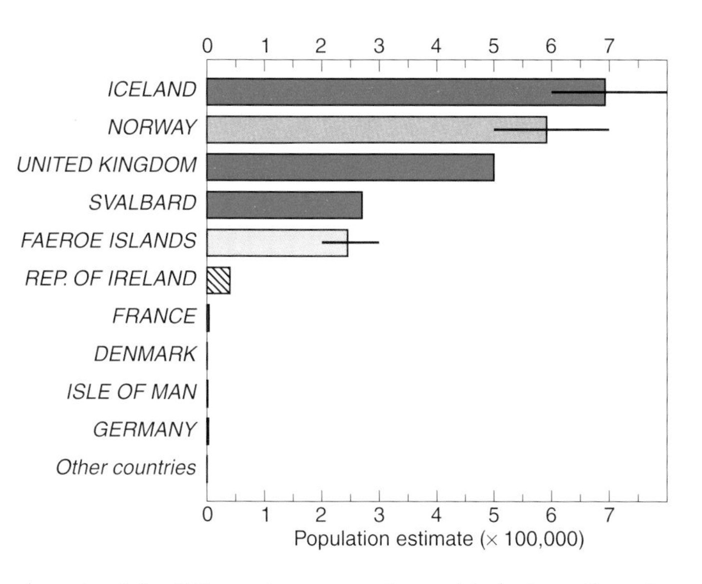

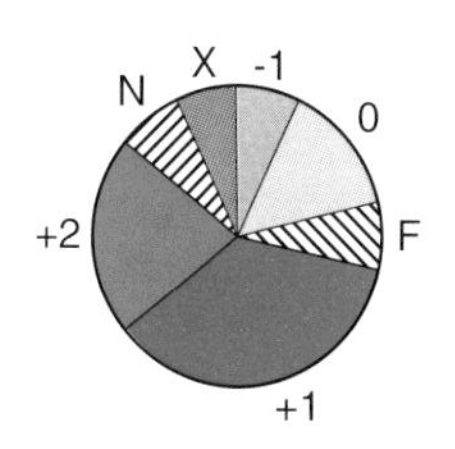

% in top 10 countries: 100.0
Total number of populated European countries: 14
Total European population 2,209,777–2,509,790 (2,347,719)
Russian population 60,000–70,000 (64,807)

A colonial cliff-nesting oceanic seabird, breeding in temperate, boreal and subarctic climatic zones in the Atlantic (the nominate subspecies *R.t. tridactyla*) and Pacific (*pollicaris*) oceans above 40°N along coasts, the Kittiwake often forms joint, multi-species colonies with Fulmar *Fulmarus glacialis*, auks and shags, nesting on the narrowest ledges. It breeds mainly where the sea summer temperature is below 10°C, except in the North Sea, France and Iberia. In Europe, colonies occur from Portugal to Russia, but breeding numbers are concentrated mostly in Iceland, Norway, Great Britain, Svalbard and the Faeroes. Even though Kittiwake colonies are relatively easy to census, the huge size of some remote colonies makes the estimation of population sizes difficult. In Iceland for instance, the estimates are of between 600 000 and 800 000bp (Lloyd *et al* 1991). Little is known of the status of the Kittiwake in Arctic areas where there are large numbers, but where little detailed census work has been undertaken save in Norway. Monitoring changes in breeding numbers has been suggested as a reliable method of indicating changes to the marine environment (Aebischer *et al* 1990). Around the North Sea, where it is not persecuted it nests readily on buildings and marine constructions such as breakwaters and piers.

During winter, European populations disperse mainly westward to the northern Atlantic, significant numbers crossing to the eastern seaboard of Canada and the USA. Birds from more northerly areas tend to winter north of birds from more southerly colonies. Ringing has shown that immature Kittiwakes may cross the Atlantic, even in the breeding season, in under six weeks.

The populations of European Kittiwakes have been increasing steadily from 1900 to the 1970s, when numbers started to level off. During this long period of consolidation, first extant colonies became larger and then many new colonies were established, sometimes on low cliffs. The breeding range extended southward to Portugal and Spain, although there numbers have never been high. The Swedish population has also remained small.

Since 1985 there have been periods where breeding success has been very low, and where this has occurred in Norway, Russia, and Scotland, it has been associated with a shortage of food, possibly the effect of commercial overfishing. The ability of breeding pairs to attend to the chicks' needs is clearly influenced by the availability of food, but is also dependent on clutch size and differences in competence between pairs (Coulson & Hohnson 1993). In the extreme N, the late arrival of spring will sometimes result in many birds failing to breed.

The current stable situation hides important variations in the dynamics of local populations, where in some regions they are still increasing rapidly while in others they are declining so rapidly that it must imply significant emigration of breeders. Furthermore, the demographic status of a given local breeding colony may vary rapidly in time when previously increasing populations start to decline or vice versa. This is explained mainly by the relationship between breeding success and natal dispersal. When breeding success is consistently high, there is no movement of breeding birds away from the colony to which they first were recruited. In contrast, where breeding success is low because of local variations in predation risks (mainly from crows [including Raven, *Corvus corax*], gulls and skuas), ectoparasite load (of soft and hard ticks) and food supplies, the adults behave differently from those at stable colonies and tend to desert their previous breeding area. First breeders and deserting adults preferentially tend to settle in areas which currently are the most productive (Danchin *et al* 1991, Danchin & Monnat 1992).

John Coulson (GB) Etienne Danchin (F)

Pagophila eburnea

Ivory Gull

CZ	Racek sněžní	I	Gabbiano eburneo
D	Elfenbeinmöwe	NL	Ivoormeeuw
E	Gaviota Marfileña	P	Gaivota-marfim
F	Mouette ivoire	PL	Mewa modrodzioba
FIN	Jäälokki	R	Белая чайка
G	Αρκτικόγλαρος	S	Ismås
H	Hósirály		

SPEC Cat 3, Threat status E (P)

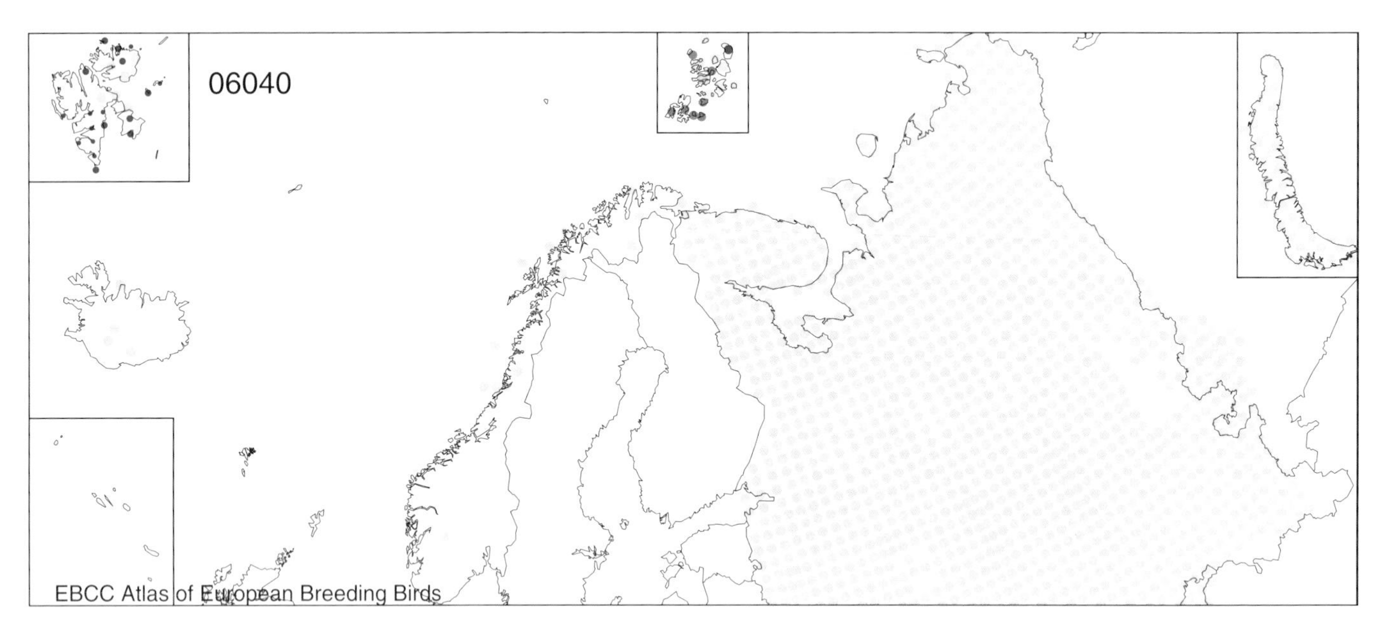

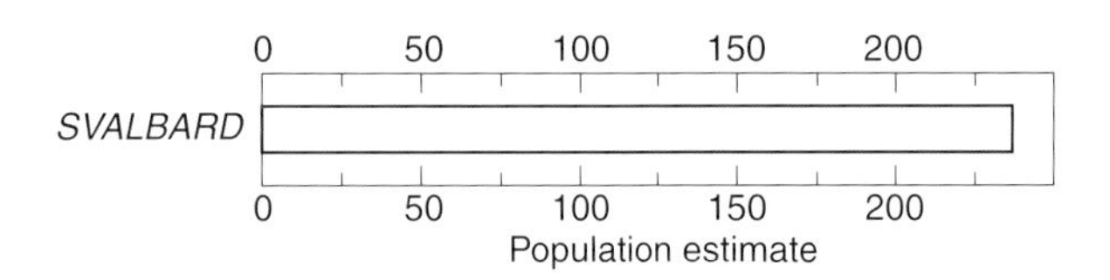

?

% in top 10 countries: 100.0
Total number of populated European countries: 1
Total European population 237–237 (237)
Russian population 1000–1500 (1225)

The Ivory Gull is a medium-sized, snowy-white gull which breeds in small colonies on tundra or in mountains in the arctic zone between Franz Josef Land, E Siberia (Severnaya Zemlya) and arctic Canada. Small numbers breed in N and SE Greenland, but substantial populations are found in E Siberia and in Franz Josef Land. The Ivory Gull is one of the most northerly species, rarely leaving the ice-covered arctic seas even in winter. Its ice-connected distribution may relate to the likely availability of good food supplies (Polar Cod *Boreogadus saida* and seal carcases) in the drift-ice zone (Isaksen & Bakken 1995). Stragglers occur in most European countries above 50°N.

In Europe, breeding is confined to Svalbard and Franz Josef Land. In Svalbard, most colonies are small and found on nunataks, but others are situated on flat ground. The Ivory Gull often breeds in association with Kittiwake *Rissa tridactyla* colonies, but also forms solitary pairs (Isaksen & Bakken 1995). In the 20th century, 29 colonies have been found in the archipelago, the total population now numbering fewer than 500bp (Løvenskiold 1964, Mehlum & Bakken 1994, V. Bakken, pers comm). Most colonies were found in remote parts of the Svalbard archipelago (Nordaustlandet, Kongsøya and Kvitøya) and on isolated nunataks on the S and E of the island of West Spitsbergen.

In Franz Josef Land, where Ivory Gulls are common breeding birds, nesting on flat ground is more frequent and at least 14 small colonies are known (Węsławski & Malinga 1993). Recent population estimates are not available. The Ivory Gull displays low site fidelity, and many breeding colonies are deserted within few years (Løvenskiold 1964, Volkov & de Korte 1995). Because of these frequent changes in breeding sites, coupled with the fact that most breeding colonies are on remote islands or highly inaccessible cliffs, population trends are notoriously difficult to assess. Reported declines in Svalbard are poorly documented (Camphuysen 1994).

Kees Camphuysen (NL)

Gelochelidon nilotica

Gull-billed Tern

CZ	Rybák černozobý	I	Sterna zampenere
D	Lachseeschwalbe	NL	Lachstern
E	Pagaza Piconegra	P	Gaivina-de-bico-preto
F	Sterne hansel	PL	Rybitwa krótkodzioba
FIN	Hietatiira	R	Чайконосая крачка
G	Γελογλάρονο	S	Sandtärna
H	Kacagócsér		

SPEC Cat 3, Threat status E (P)

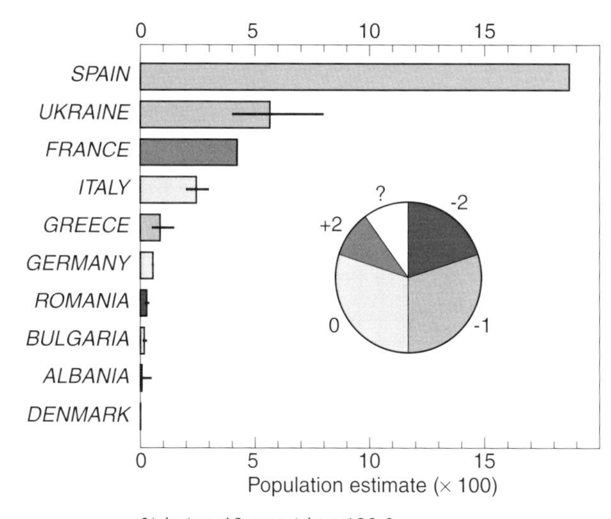

% in top 10 countries: 100.0
Total number of populated European countries: 10
Total European population 3122–3551 (3298)
Russian population 1800–5000 (3000)
Turkish population 2000–7000 (3742)

The Gull-billed Tern has a cosmopolitan but very discontinuous distribution encompassing the Neotropical, Nearctic, Australian, Oriental, Palearctic and Afrotropical regions. The nominate subspecies *nilotica* breeds in Europe, NW Africa and the Middle East, E to Kazakhstan, Manchuria, Pakistan and perhaps Sri Lanka.

Sand-dunes, islands, coastal and inland wetland shores and short-grass pastures on polders are preferred breeding habitats (Goutner 1987, J-P. Biber 1993). Vegetation is apparently important; nests are often built beside a vegetation tuft. Breeding is often in mixed tern and gull colonies. It forages over beaches, dunes, freshly irrigated or cereal and vegetable fields, orchards, ditches separating ploughed fields and in freshwater or brackish wetlands (Lévêque 1956).

In Europe it breeds mainly in the Mediterranean and Black Sea regions. It may still breed in Albania (Lamani & Puzanov 1962), but recent data are lacking. A colony remains in N Germany but the Danish colonies dwindled to a single site with only 0–2bp by 1991 (Sørensen 1995) and most European colonies have decreased since the 1900s and many continue to do so in Greece, Romania, Russia and Ukraine (J-P. Biber 1993). Some 95% of the European population occurs in countries where numbers have declined since the 1970s (J-P. Biber 1994a). The main threats are destruction of foraging habitats and colony sites, predation and disturbance in the colonies, drought and pesticides in its winter quarters (J-P. Biber 1993).

European populations winter in Africa, western birds probably from Mauritania E to Nigeria and Chad, and eastern birds probably from Sudan S to Botswana.

Jean-Pierre Biber (CH)

Sterna caspia **Caspian Tern**

CZ	Rybák velkozobý	I	Sterna maggiore
D	Raubseeschwalbe	NL	Reuzenstern
E	Pagaza Piquirroja	P	Gaivina-de-bico-vermelho
F	Sterne caspienne	PL	Rybitwa wielkodzioba
FIN	Räyskä	R	Чеграва
G	Καρατζάς	S	Skräntärna
H	Lócsér		

SPEC Cat 3, Threat status E (P)

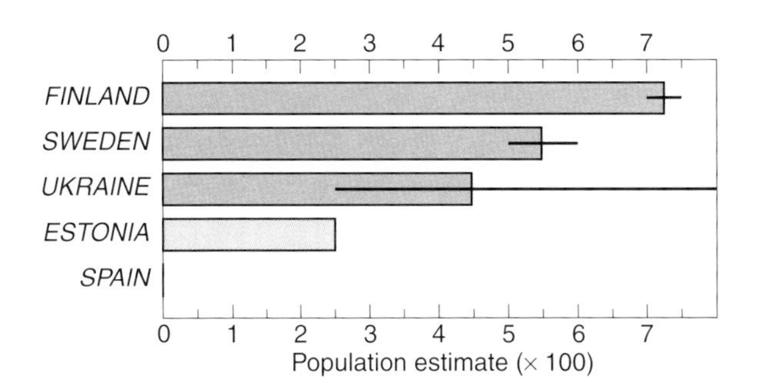

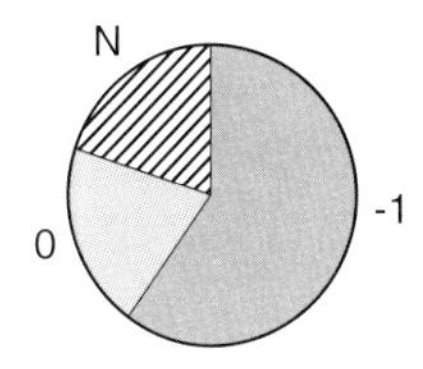

% in top 10 countries: 100.0
Total number of populated European countries: 5
Total European population 1766–2328 (1971)
Russian population 3000–5500 (4062)
Turkish population 50–200 (100)

The Caspian Tern has a cosmopolitan, highly scattered breeding distribution across every continent except South America and Antarctica. Both migratory and resident populations breed in several biogeographical and climatic regions. Palearctic populations occupy coastal and inland sites from the northern Red Sea and Arabian Gulf through C Asia centred around 50°N to Ussuriland. In Europe there are three separate migratory populations, in the Baltic basin, on the northern Black Sea and in the N Caspian region, the last-named being part of a larger Caspian population. Occasionally, isolated pairs will breed elsewhere in Europe, such as the first breeding record for the Ebro Delta in 1988. Despite the existence of sedentary populations, no subspecies are recognized.

The distribution pattern of the Caspian Tern is patchy. It is a strictly coastal species, breeding on small isolated skerries and flat sandy islands at extremities of archipelagos, or along coastlines. Almost all the N European birds breed in brackish-water habitats, only a few favouring freshwater areas. The majority (*c*90%) in the Baltic form breeding colonies, sizes varying from two to over 100bp. The remainder breed as solitary pairs. Precisely the same breeding site may be used for decades, but a site can be abandoned for no apparent reason, breeding in that general locality becoming a rare event.

In Sweden the Caspian Tern has been recorded since the late 1700s, but has always had the status of a rare and rather local species. The Baltic population, which is somewhat isolated in N Europe, has experienced great fluctuations. In recent years it has decreased considerably, and colonies in Sweden, Finland and Estonia are now monitored annually. Colonies have decreased from 44 with 2200bp in 1971, to 36 with 1816bp in 1984 and only 25 with 1500bp in 1992 (Hario *et al* 1987, and authors' notes). In 1992, 7 colonies contained over 100bp (the largest had 155 nests), 3 held 50–99bp, 6 had 20–49bp, and 9 consisted of 2–19bp.

That the Caspian Tern bred at Lake Ladoga in Russia had been known for some time, but not until 1993 was a colony and two solitary pairs located on its NW shore, thus adding to the known Baltic population (Pakarinen & Siikavirta 1993).

The decrease is due to several factors, but human disturbance is not amongst them, because most of the Baltic colonies are protected bird reserves which people are not allowed to enter during the breeding season. The Caspian Tern has a low productive capacity, because it is a long-lived species and does not breed until it is between three and five years old, and so regular losses are not easily overcome. Consequently, the prevalence in recent years of American mink *Mustela vison* on several breeding grounds probably has led to the extirpation of colonies. Another major cause of the decline may be hunting during migration and in the winter areas. The Caspian Tern is killed either to prevent the birds taking fish, especially from fishponds, or for food or sport.

The main wintering area for both the Baltic and the Black Sea populations is the inundation area of the River Niger in Mali, tropical West Africa. In dry years in the Sahel, the fish-stocks are reduced, which not only affects the people and fish-eating birds directly, but also leads to greater persecution of the birds by local fisherman. There is a strong correlation between drought in the Sahel and the size of the Baltic population of Caspian Tern. A few from the Black Sea overwinter in the Mediterranean. Caspian birds, together with much of the C Asian population, winter from the Arabian Gulf to India and Bangladesh (*BWP*).

Taivo Kastepõld (EST) Roland Staav (S)
Torsten Stjernberg (FIN)

Sterna sandvicensis

Sandwich Tern

CZ	Rybák severní	**I**	Beccapesci
D	Brandseeschwalbe	**NL**	Grote Stern
E	Charrán Patinegro	**P**	Garajau-comum
F	Sterne caugek	**PL**	Rybitwa czubata
FIN	Riuttatiira	**R**	Пестроносая крачка
G	Χειμωνογλάρονο	**S**	Kentsk tärna
H	Kenti csér		

SPEC Cat 2, Threat status D

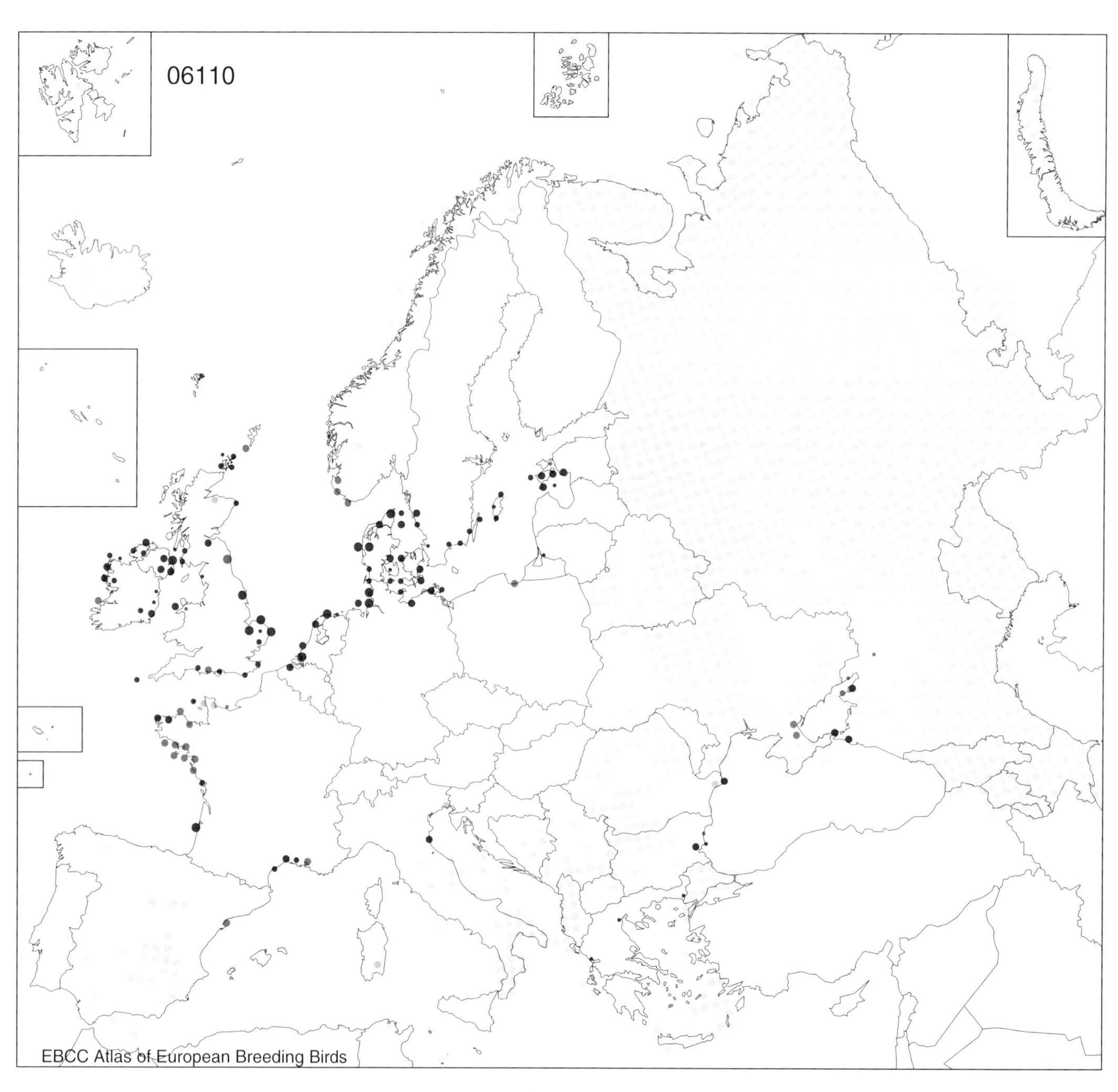

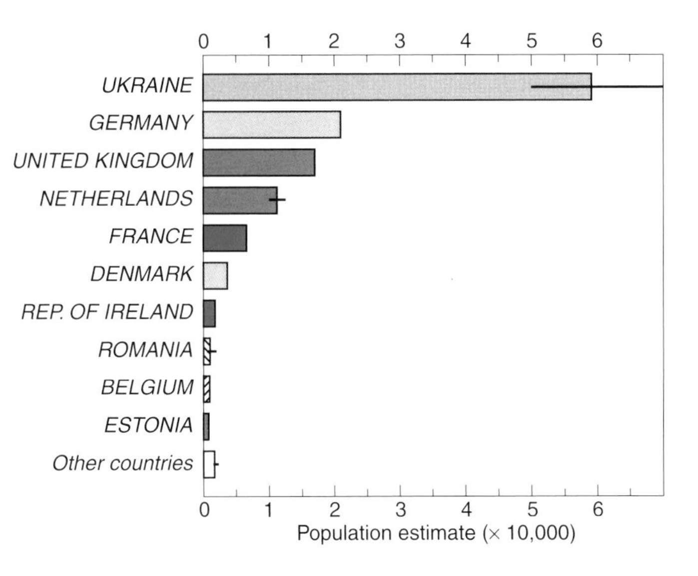

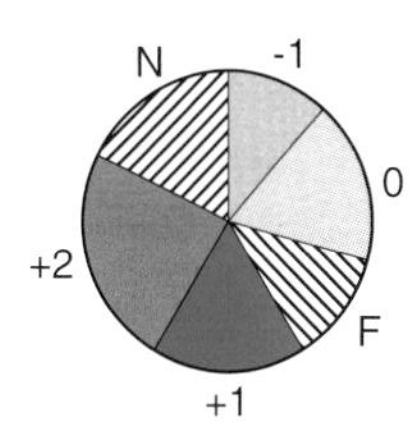

% in top 10 countries: 98.7
Total number of populated European countries: 17
Total European population 115,561–135,784 (124,812)
Russian population 4000–6000 (4899)

The nominate subspecies, *S.s. sandvicensis*, of the Sandwich Tern breeds along the Atlantic coasts of Europe, around the North Sea, in the Baltic, the W Mediterranean, the Black Sea, the Sea of Azov and the Caspian Sea. In the New World there are two subspecies, one found on the E coast of the USA and in the Caribbean (*acuflavida*), and the other on the N and E coasts of South America south to Patagonia (*eurygnatha*).

Sandwich Tern colonies in Europe are usually located in low-lying areas on coasts, often in sheltered loughs, bays, lagoons and deltas, but sometimes on exposed coasts. Generally, islands are preferred, but mainland spits and dunes are also used (Lloyd *et al* 1991). In Ireland there are colonies on freshwater lakes, but the terns fly to the nearby sea to feed (Whilde 1985). Areas of short vegetation are preferred, but the birds are capable of arresting summer growth through trampling.

The breeding population in Europe is currently estimated at 70 000–95 000bp, with two main centres of population, the Atlantic/North Sea coasts of Europe with 45 000–50 000bp and the Black Sea/Sea of Azov with 22 000–41 000bp. There are smaller populations in the Mediterranean (E Spain, S France, N Italy and Greece) which has *c*850–1500bp, and the Baltic (mainly Poland, Estonia and Sweden) with *c*1375–1800bp.

Instability of breeding habitats, disruption of colonies by human disturbance or predation and a major kill in The Netherlands in the 1960s due to pesticide pollution, have resulted in large fluctuations in numbers and frequent changes of sites, making it difficult to establish population trends. However, in many areas in the 20th century numbers have been increasing, sometimes dramatically, after declines in the 19th century. For example, the British & Irish population increased from *c*6000bp in 1962 to 18 400bp by 1987 (Lloyd *et al* 1991). Conversely, The Netherlands population was 25 000–40 000bp in the 1940s and 1950s before it crashed to 650bp in 1965 due to pesticides (Rooth 1989). In recovery, it now stands at 10 000–12 500bp. Colonization near Zeebrugge, Belgium, in 1988 and the subsequent increase to 1000–1650 in 1992–94 coincided with a severe decline in the main colony at Lake Grevelingen, SW Netherlands (Meininger *et al* 1995). Most of the Baltic colonies have become established since 1965.

Sandwich Tern colonies often are associated closely with those of the earlier-nesting Black-headed Gull *Larus ridibundus*, so that the terns benefit from the gulls' aggressiveness towards predators and intruders (Veen 1977). This benefit appears to outweigh the disadvantages of risking egg predation by the gulls, although much of the egg-robbing is directed at deserted clutches. Many Sandwich Tern colonies are also in nature reserves, so that disturbance and predation are further limited. Nesting attempts in other locations are usually less successful (or unsuccessful) suggesting that protective measures and the presence of Black-headed Gull colonies largely account for the current distribution of the Sandwich Tern.

The Sandwich Tern tends to nest at a very high density, with up to 12 nests/m^2 being quite common (pers obs). Most birds on Griend Island, The Netherlands, nested 31–40cm apart (Veen 1977).

The Atlantic, North Sea, Baltic and W Mediterranean populations migrate S along the W coast of Africa to overwinter between Mauritania and South Africa (Cape of Good Hope). The Black Sea and Sea of Azov populations spend the winter principally in the E Black Sea, C and SE Mediterranean, with some moving W to Iberia and occasionally W Africa. Usually the first tern to return to breed, its early presence may encourage other tern species to nest nearby.

Like other terns, it is vulnerable to the effects of industrial overfishing and to marine pollution.

Oscar J Merne (IRE)

Sterna bengalensis

Lesser Crested Tern

CZ	Rybák bengálský	I	Sterna di Rüppell
D	Rüppellseeschwalbe	NL	Bengaalse Stern
E	Charrán Bengalí	P	Garajau-bengalense
F	Sterne voyageuse	PL	Rybitwa bengalska
FIN	Pikkutöyhtötiira	R	Малая хохлатая чайка
G	Ταξιδογλάρονο	S	Iltärna
H	Bengáli csér		

Criteria not applied

This tern has a highly fragmented distribution from Australia to the Mediterranean. The Mediterranean subspecies (*torresii*) is migratory, wintering mainly in the E Atlantic Ocean along the coasts of Senegal, The Gambia and Guinea-Bissau. Passage through the Strait of Gibraltar occurs regularly during March to May and from late July to early November.

In the Mediterranean, the only known breeding colonies are on two small islands off the Libyan coast, Geziret al Elba and Geziret Garah. The latter held over 2000 adults, chicks and young in 1937 (Moltoni 1938) and c1700bp in 1993 (Meininger *et al.* 1994). In S Europe the only regular breeding localities are in the Comacchio Lagoon (Po Delta, Italy), where from 1985 to 1993 one pair bred successfully amongst a Sandwich Tern *S. sandvicensis* colony and a third adult paired with a Sandwich Tern female in 1990 (Brichetti & Foschi 1987, unpub), and in the Ebro Delta (Spain), where there have been 1–2bp regularly from 1978 to date (Blanco & Gonzalez 1993). In Greece, in the Evros Delta, a single bird, probably paired with a Sandwich Tern, was recorded in June 1987 (Goutner 1988). In Britain, on the Farne Islands, a single bird frequented a Sandwich Tern colony from 1984 to date and bred successfully in mixed pairs in 1989 and 1992 (Spencer and RBBP 1993). In France an adult was recorded in 1971 in a Sandwich Tern colony in the Camargue. Single birds, previously identified as *S. bengalensis*, which formed mixed pairs with *S. sandvicensis* on Banc d'Arguin, are now regarded as Elegant Tern *S. elegans*. There have been further sight records in Italy, France, Austria, Switzerland and Great Britain.

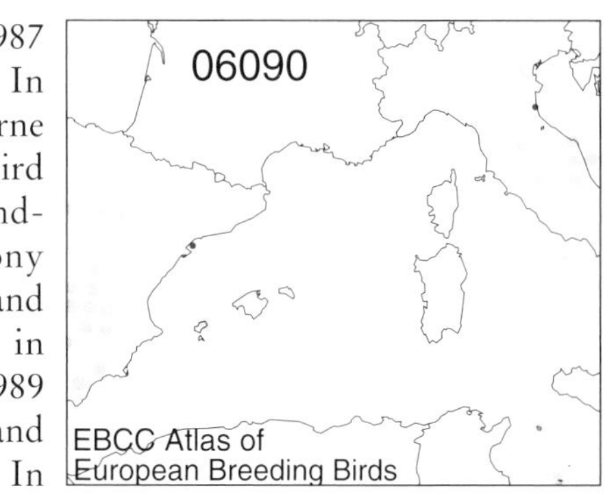

Pierandrea Brichetti (I) Ugo Foschi (I)

Sterna dougallii

Roseate Tern

CZ	Rybák rajský	I	Sterna di Dougall
D	Rosenseeschwalbe	NL	Dougalls Stern
E	Charrán Rosado	P	Andorinha-do-mar-rósea
F	Sterne de Dougall	PL	Rybitwa różowa
FIN	Ruusutiira	R	Розовая крачка
G	Ροδογλάρονο	S	Rosentärna
H	Rózsás csér		

SPEC Cat 3, Threat status E

Outside Europe the Roseate Tern breeds in the W Atlantic and Caribbean (the nominate *S.d. dougallii*), the Indian Ocean, SE Asia, Japan, China (*bangsi* and *korustes*), Australia and Melanesia (*gracilis*). In Europe the species' preferred habitat is small (often rocky) islands, in sheltered bays and lagoons. It also uses sand and shingle banks. It

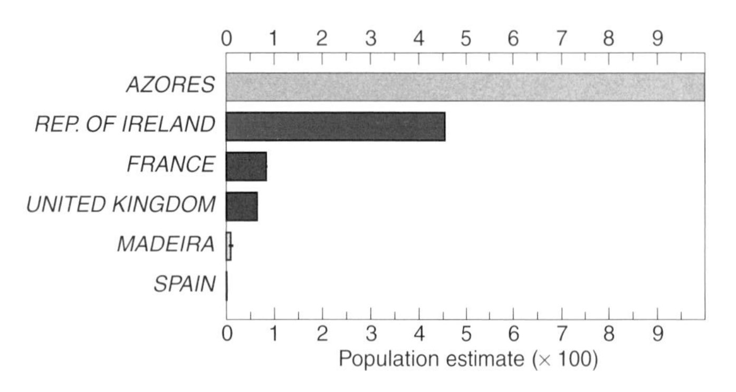

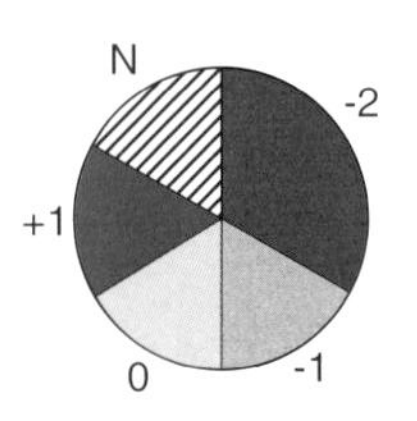

% in top 10 countries: 100.0
Total number of populated European countries: 6
Total European population 1607–1618 (1612)

prefers more cover than do other terns and usually nests in thick vegetation or rock crevices (Lloyd *et al* 1991). Recently it has started using artificial nest sites (O.J. Merne, pers obs). It usually breeds in association with other terns, benefiting from the extra protection they provide.

Within the *Atlas*' coverage area, the Azores population recently declined from 1120 to 750bp (Wynde 1993), but elsewhere there are currently *c*650bp (1993; A. del Nevo, pers comm), the great majority of which (427bp) are on Rockabill, a tiny islet on the Irish E coast. Lady's Island Lake, SE Ireland, holds *c*140bp (1994) and Baie de Morlaix, Brittany, held 107–110bp in 1989 (A. Thomas 1994). Other outposts are much smaller. In the 19th century Roseate Terns were exterminated in Ireland and nearly so in Great Britain, but numbers increased this century, peaking at *c*3500bp in the 1960s (Avery & del Nevo 1991). Outside the present range small numbers bred in Germany, Belgium and southern France. Until the 1970s *c*2000bp nested on sand and shingle banks in E Ireland, but these were eroded by storms. Loss of habitat and high mortality on the wintering grounds (casual persecution and hunting for sport) probably contributed heavily to the decline of the NW European population to *c*450bp by the late 1980s (R.E. Green *et al* 1990). Subsequent conservation measures, especially at Rockabill where the species breeds very successfully, have reversed the decline. The Azores population is sensitive to disturbance but several tourist developments adjacent to colonies are planned (L. Monteiro, pers comm to the Editors).

The NW European population migrates along the West African coast to the Gulf of Guinea (especially Ghana) in winter, where it meets the population from the Azores. The W Azores population may winter in the W Atlantic.

Oscar J Merne (IRE)

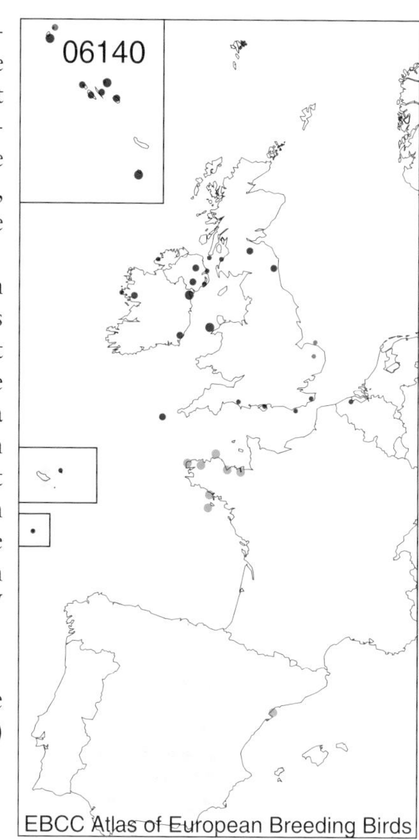

Sterna fuscata

Sooty Tern

CZ	Rybák černohřbetý	I	Sterna scura
D	Rußseeschwalbe	NL	Bonte stern
E	Charrán Sombrío	P	Andorinha-do-mar-escura
F	Sterne fuligineuse	PL	Rybitwa czarnogrzbieta
FIN	Nokitiira	R	Темная крачка
G	Καρβουνογλάρονο	S	Sottärna
H	Füstös csér		

Criteria not applied

This species is widespread in tropical oceans but the very rare European breeding records are confined to Portuguese Atlantic islands. A pair probably bred on Ilhéu de Fora, Selvagens, in 1982 (F. Roux, pers comm). Up to 2bp regularly have attempted to breed on the rocky, grass-topped Isla da Vila near Santa Maria, the Azores archipelago's easternmost extremity: one egg was laid in 1989 and 1990, but was broken each time; a bird held territory in 1992 and 1993; one chick was raised in both 1994 and 1995 (L. Monteiro, N. Ratcliffe, pers comm). The pairs nested on the edge of a Roseate Tern *S. dougallii* subcolony, part of a Common Tern *S. hirundo* colony (L. Monteiro, pers comm).

Apart from other recent Azores sightings, vagrants to Europe have been recorded widely in European seas. These birds are attributed to the nominate *fuscata* which breeds on islands from Yucatan to the Florida Gulf coast (occasionally up to North Carolina), in the Bahamas, West Indies, Fernando Noronha, Ascension, St Helena, the Tenhosas and the Gulf of Guinea. Juveniles ringed on the Dry Tortugas (off southern Florida) have dispersed to the Gulf of Guinea (Robertson 1969).

Euan Dunn (GB)

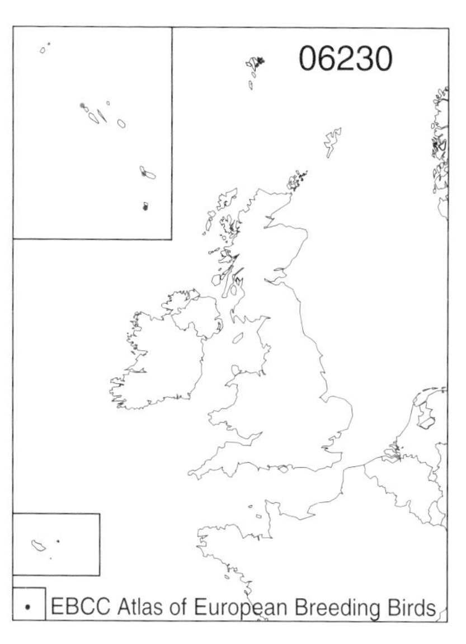

Sterna hirundo

Common Tern

CZ	Rybák obecný	**I**	Sterna comune
D	Flußseeschwalbe	**NL**	Visdief
E	Charrán Común	**P**	Andorinha-do-mar-comum
F	Sterne pierregarin	**PL**	Rybitwa rzeczna
FIN	Kalatiira	**R**	Речная крачка
G	Ποταμογλάρονο	**S**	Fisktärna
H	Küszvágó csér		

Non-SPEC, Threat status S

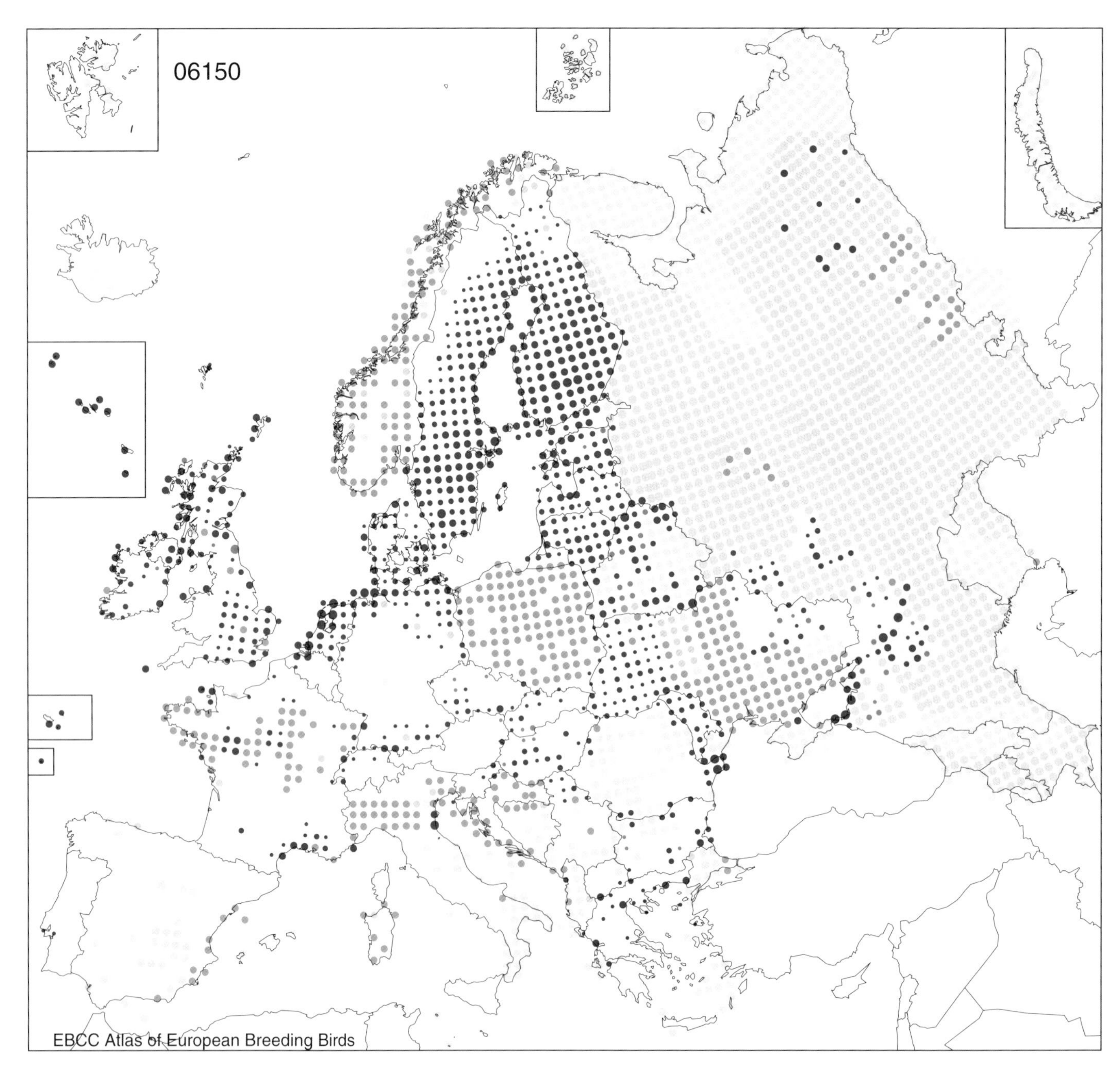

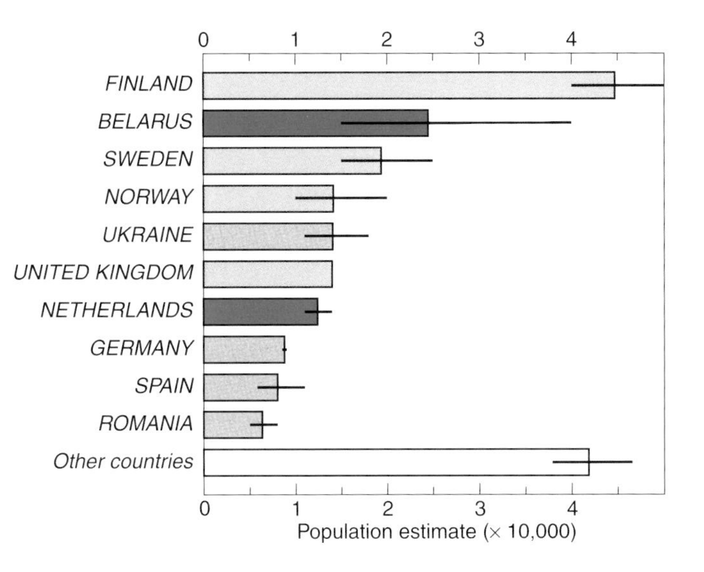

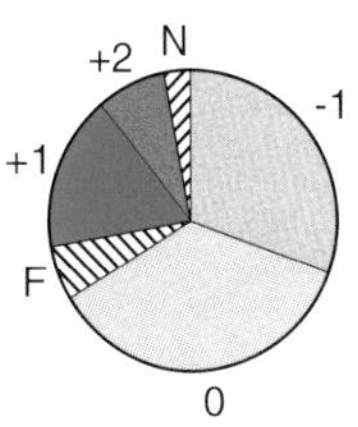

% in top 10 countries: 79.9
Total number of populated European countries: 36
Total European population 195,105–227,250 (208,091)
Russian population 30,000–60,000 (42,426)
Turkish population 1000–10,000 (3162)

The most widespread of the *Sterna* terns, with the greatest penetration into continental land masses, in places the Common Tern is typically a coastal species. It occurs widely from the Arctic fringe S through the boreal and temperate zones, in eastern North America and from western Europe continuously E to Kamchatka. Its breeding range extends S to Tibet and N China and erratically to the Gulf of Mexico, the Arabian Gulf and North Africa, with a few isolated outposts.

The species winters S to Argentina, around the entire African coast and to E Australia. N European breeding birds tend to winter offshore in sub-equatorial Africa, further S than S European birds. First-year individuals usually remain in the wintering areas (Hume 1993).

In Europe, the species usually nests colonially on marine and freshwater shores and islands, often in association with Arctic Tern *S. paradisaea* and Black-headed Gull *Larus ridibundus*. On marine coasts, it occupies rocky islets and headlands, sand-dunes, beaches, islets in lagoons and drier parts of saltmarsh. It avoids sheer cliffs and wave-swept platforms beneath them. Inland, it frequents riverine shingle, open spaces with short vegetation in freshwater marshes and islands in flooded sand and gravel quarries. Artificial sites include specially provided rafts, wrecks, piers and, increasingly, building roofs (Groen *et al* 1995). It breeds in Asia up to 4800m asl, but in Europe is chiefly a lowland species.

The European distribution has a northerly bias. It becomes scattered S to Mediterranean shores but penetrates along major river systems, especially the Loire, Rhine and Danube. The northernmost population in Finnmark is very sparse on both sea and inland shores. In the NW, it is largely a coastal breeder, its recent colonization, in small numbers, of inland sites having been helped by new, artificial habitats (chiefly islets in shallow flooded pits). In the N (especially Sweden and Finland), regular breeding on stony islands in a multitude of freshwater lakes allowed a more comprehensive spread inland (Koskimies 1989a).

The European breeding distribution has changed little recently, save for range contractions since 1900 in some inland areas and on Mediterranean islands. Russia, Belarus and Ukraine clearly are important for the species, as previously suspected from less complete data. Finnish populations have declined greatly since the late 1920s, sufficiently for the Arctic Tern to be more numerous in shared Baltic coast nesting areas. Inland populations probably have increased slightly recently through lake eutrophication (Koskimies 1989a). The present Swedish estimate is markedly lower than the 40 000bp of the 1970s. The Norwegian population appears stable. The numbers breeding in Britain & Ireland remain remarkably stable after a decline (through persecution and disturbance) in the 19th century and a recovery (through protection) by the 1930s (Lloyd *et al* 1991). Increases in Scotland balance a decline in southern Britain. Many small Scottish colonies have disappeared as the larger have thrived on remote islands (Cramp *et al* 1974, Thomas 1980, Lloyd *et al* 1991). The Netherlands once was a stronghold of 50 000bp before persecution (plumage trade) around 1900; near extinction, the species' decline was reversed by protection measures, recovering to 42 000–48 000bp by 1954, but declining further in the 1960s, partly because of organochlorine pollution of the Rhine. Present numbers range between 14 000 and 19 000bp.

Disturbance of beaches and lagoons favoured by nesting terns is a serious problem in places. Local reserves (or temporary protection) are often vital in maintaining its viability, as in France. Declines continue in Spain and Greece. Some recovery is evident in Italy. Newer problems for the Common Tern include local overfishing by man of staple prey, and increasing contamination in the Wadden Sea, especially by PCBs and mercury (which affect reproduction adversely; Becker *et al* 1992).

Rob Hume (GB) Risto Lemmetyinen (FIN)

This species account is sponsored by Barbara C. Meyer and Stefan R. Sudmann, Köln, D.

Sterna paradisaea

Arctic Tern

CZ	Rybák dlouhoocasý	**I**	Sterna codalunga
D	Küstenseeschwalbe	**NL**	Noordse Stern
E	Charrán Artico	**P**	Andorinha-do-mar-árctica
F	Sterne arctique	**PL**	Rybitwa popielata
FIN	Lapintiira	**R**	Полярная крачка
G	Χιονογλάρονο	**S**	Silvertärna
H	Sarki csér		

Non-SPEC, Threat status S

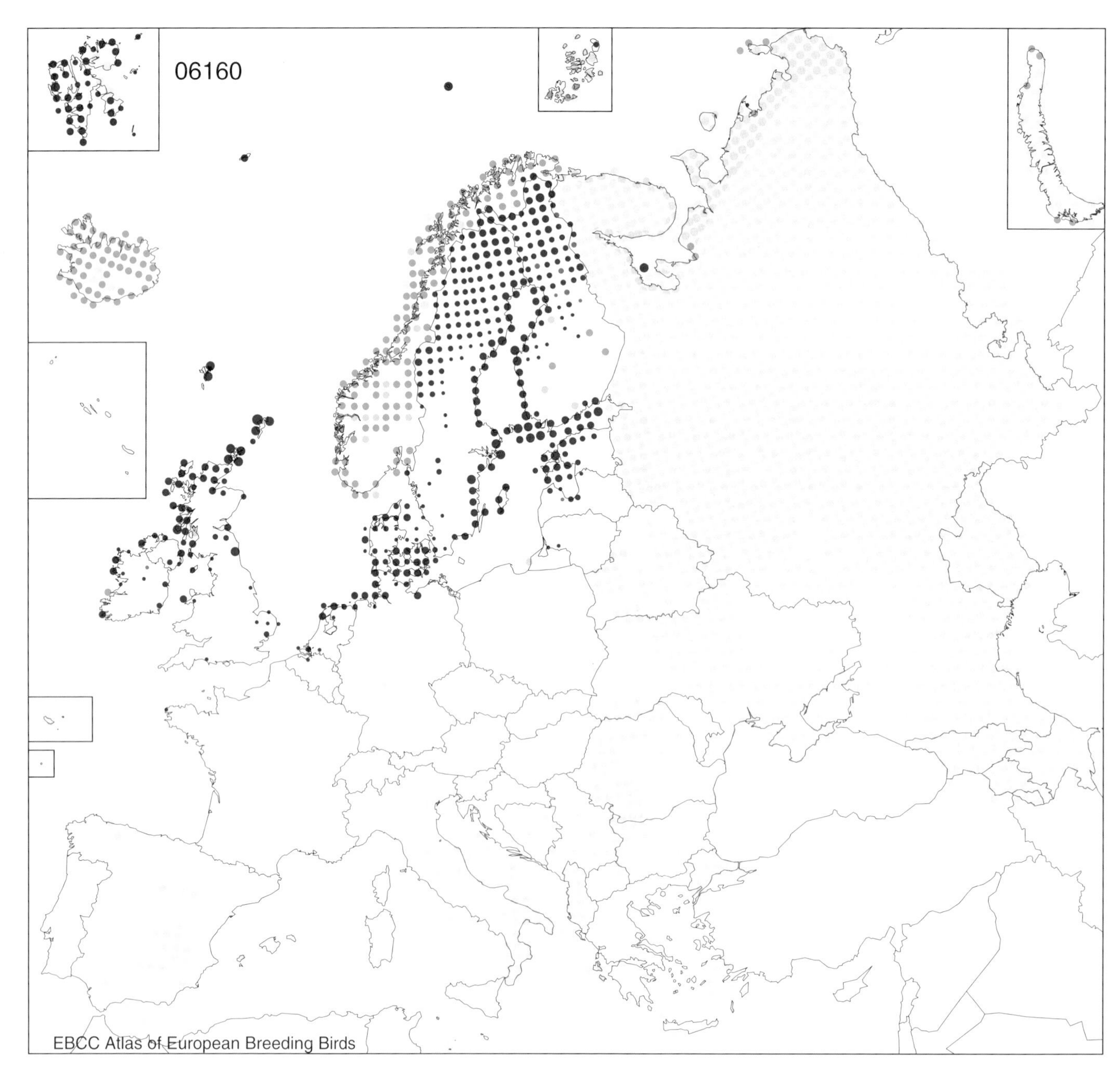

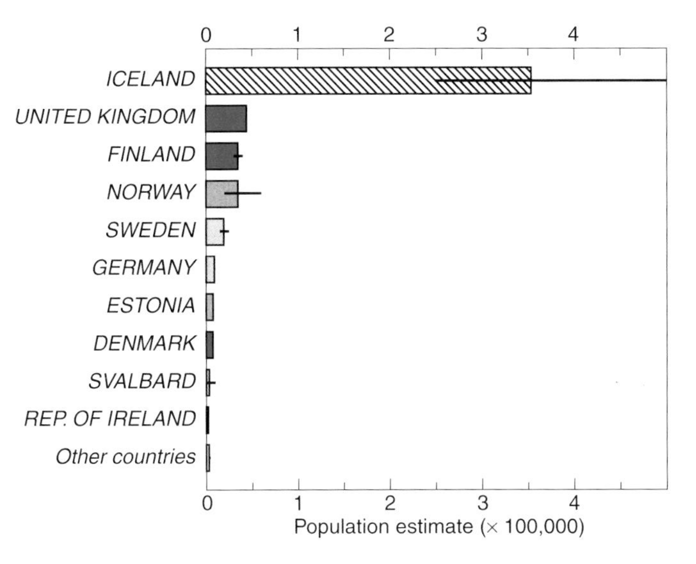

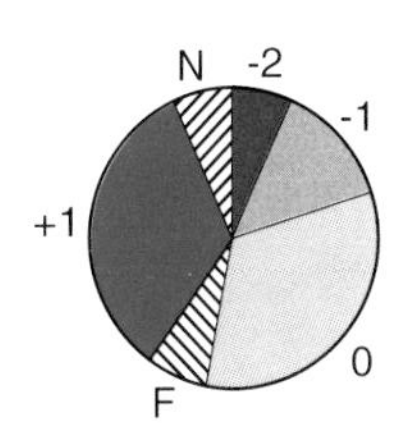

% in top 10 countries: 99.4
Total number of populated European countries: 15
Total European population 413,092–666,896 (517,900)
Russian population 25,000–30,000 (27,386)

As correctly denoted by its English name, the Arctic Tern is a truly arctic breeding bird, its circumpolar distribution extending into the boreal zone. It is therefore the most northerly of all Northern Hemisphere terns, breeding extensively N of the timberline. In North America the Arctic Tern breeds from Alaska S to British Columbia on the W coast and Massachusetts on the E coast. In Europe it breeds in Britain & Ireland and Scandinavia, The Netherlands, N Germany and the Baltic States. From there its distribution runs along the coast of Siberia to the Bering Strait. It also breeds along the coasts of Iceland, Greenland and Svalbard and on other Arctic Ocean islands.

The Arctic Tern occupies mainly marine coastal areas, but locally can be found further inland along oligotrophic lakes and rivers of the tundra and northern coniferous zone. It often nests colonially, showing a preference for small islands in an attempt to avoid disturbance by ground predators. In the high arctic it breeds on rolling tundra, marsh or shingle (Frantzen *et al* 1991). In the Baltic Sea and other areas in its southern breeding range, the species prefers low, sparsely vegetated rocky or sandy islets where it usually breeds in colonies of 5–50bp. About 10% of breeding pairs are solitary. When overlapping with the Common Tern *S. hirundo*, it tends to concentrate on barer breeding sites.

Its distribution centre lies in the subarctic, Iceland having by far the largest Arctic Tern population in Europe, 250 000–500 000bp (*c*60% of the European total). Since the mid-1960s the species has extended its range in the Baltic archipelagos into the inner zones whose sole representative of the family had been *S. hirundo* (Koskimies 1989a). The cause of the expansion may be the increase of insect food, especially chironomid flies, due to coastal water eutrophication. In some areas in C Finland, the species has begun to nest at artificial inland lakes (Frantzen *et al* 1991). However, its most southerly breeding range has contracted in recent years.

Although the species has suffered local population fluctuations, its overall numbers have not changed dramatically since the early 1970s. On the coasts of Finland from 1940 to 1970, there was an increase, but recently there has been a decline due to American mink *Mustela vison* predation and to disturbance by yachting and other leisure activities. The Estonian population also has decreased. In the mid-1960s along Dutch and German coasts widespread chemical pollution was linked to considerable local Arctic Tern population decreases (Becker & Erdelen 1987). These populations have not yet recovered completely. Pollution is probably still a major factor in preventing full recovery, whether directly or indirectly. The decreases in numbers on the Faeroes and on Shetland are thought to be due to foodstock declines, possibly related to intensive fishing. Yet potential foodstocks in coastal waters of Germany and The Netherlands are believed to be high from increased eutrophication (Becker & Erdelen 1987). However, eutrophication may have contributed to increasing water turbidity making it more difficult for seabirds who hunt by sight to catch sufficient prey. The relationship between water turbidity and prey catching performance remains poorly understood. In much of its breeding range population declines are correlated with increases in gull abundance, but the causality of this relationship is very much under debate.

The migration routes of the Arctic Tern are the longest known for birds, extending from the Arctic areas down to the Antarctic pack ice. Joined by eastern North American terns, European and W Siberian terns travel southwards along the coasts of Europe and Africa. Some young birds may stop over in South Africa, but most individuals continue on their journey to the Antarctic.

Marcel Klaasen (NL) Risto Lemmetyinen (SF)

Sterna albifrons **Little Tern**

CZ	Rybák malý	**I**	Fraticello
D	Zwergseeschwalbe	**NL**	Dwergstern
E	Charrancito Común	**P**	Andorinha-do-mar-anã
F	Sterne naine	**PL**	Rybitwa białoczelna
FIN	Pikkutiira	**R**	Малая крачка
G	Νανογλάρονο	**S**	Småtärna
H	Kis csér		

SPEC Cat 3, Threat status D

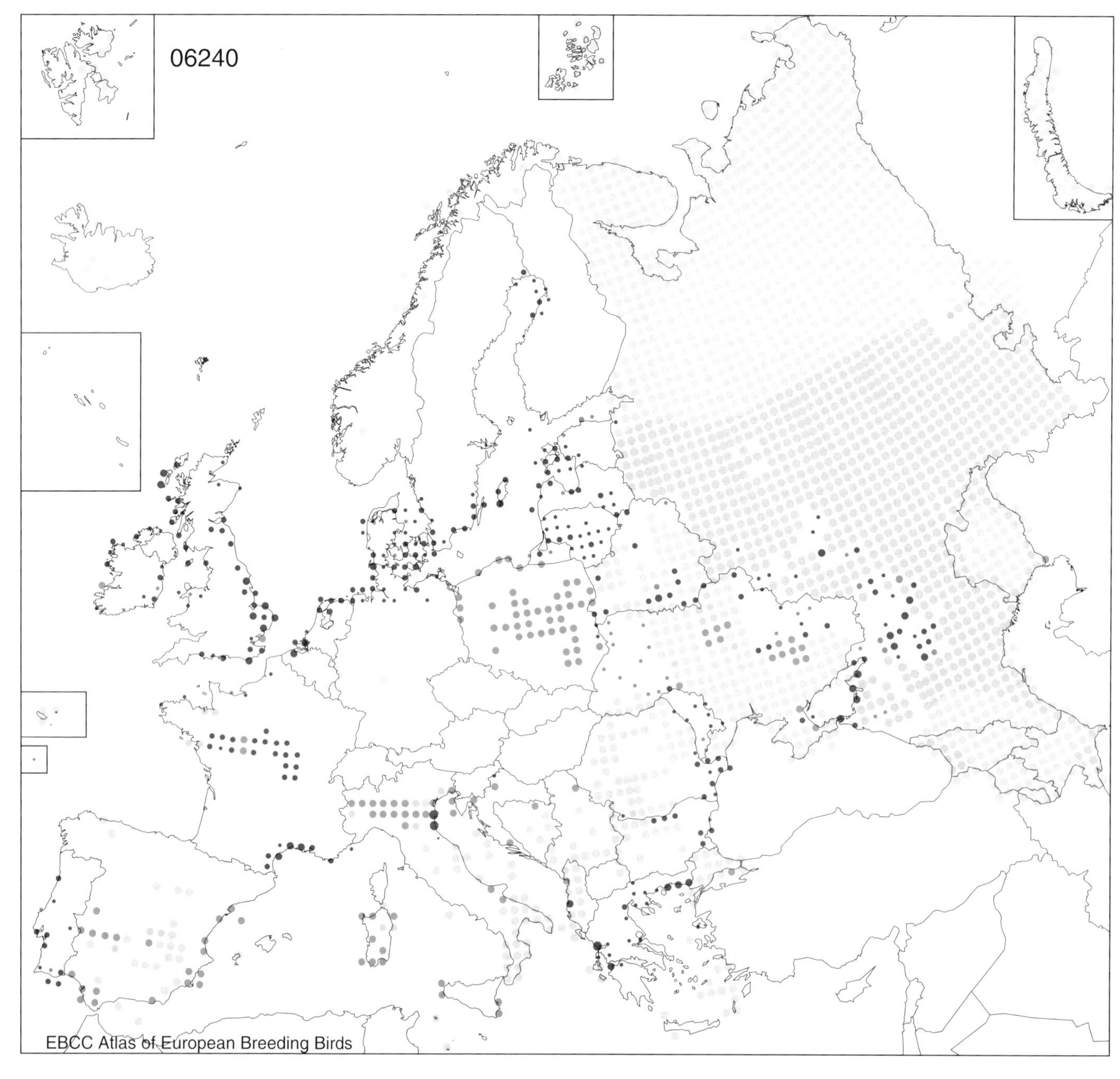

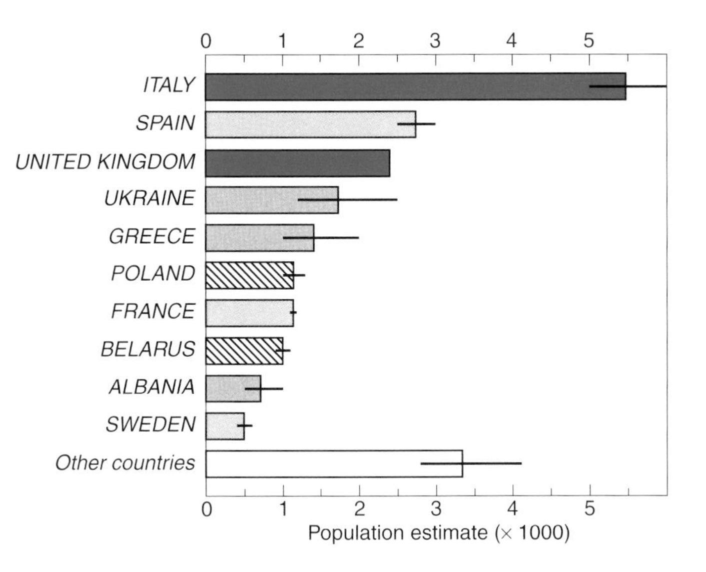

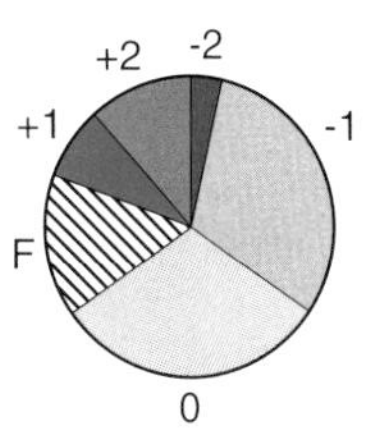

% in top 10 countries: 84.5
Total number of populated European countries: 26
Total European population 20,643–22,799 (21,571)
Russian population 5000–9000 (6708)
Turkish population 5000–15,000 (8660)

The Little Tern, the smallest European tern, is a colonial breeder, inhabiting marine and lakeshores, and sand or gravel islands along inland rivers, often far from the sea. It has a scattered distribution over temperate and tropical regions from Tasmania to Finland and, if the closely related *S. antillarum* is included, from the USA to Japan. Between the two, eight subspecies have been proposed, with nominate *albifrons* in Europe. Most European birds winter between Guinea and Cameroon (Muselet 1985). Others reach South Africa, and perhaps the Red Sea.

The European population amounts to *c*37 000bp, the world total being 70 000–100 000bp. After having decreased for several decades, the number of European birds has increased since the mid-1970s. Excluding the populations in the former USSR, there were 11 000bp in 1975–79, but 18 000bp in 1985–88. The carefully monitored British population decreased during the 19th century, but recovered somewhat to a peak in the late 1920s and again in the 1970s, with a decrease in between. This population has been largely stable in the 1980s, although colony locations have shown many changes. France also experienced an increasing trend, from *c*600bp in the mid-1960s to 1100bp in the late 1980s. Over the last 20 years, the Little Tern has made a comeback on certain river sections (Muselet 1987) and has also colonized others sites such as gravel-pits in Seine-et-Marne (Siblet 1994).

Its coastal breeding distribution has changed little apart from the northern Gulf of Bothnia being colonized in the early 1960s. In Belgium, whose population disappeared in 1964, new colonies appeared in 1984 (de Schuyter & de Schutter 1989). In contrast, following river-canalization, inland breeding birds have forsaken some large rivers like the Rhine, Danube, Oder and Elbe. The species has always occupied some well-preserved natural river areas throughout Europe, particularly the Loire, Tagus, Po, Vistula, Bug, Dnepr, Don and Volga. However, these populations' survival is dependent on the extent of habitat protection achieved. Indeed, the populations nesting on bare islands of the Loire/Allier and Vistula Rivers are at risk from hydraulic engineering works both to control flooding and to minimize the effects of droughts. French and Polish birds therefore face similar threats.

The main factor limiting inland distribution is construction and development, whereas coastal populations are at risk from natural tidal extremes, tourism and similar disturbance (Haddon & Knight 1983). Consequently, many colonies have disappeared, often to re-establish themselves in remoter or protected areas. Because most Little Tern breeding colonies are now in such areas, the colony size trend is known for 70% of the European population, decreases being recorded in 48% of these colonies, stability in 16%, and increases in 36%. The significance of these trends is difficult to assess because of the limited philopatry of the species (Meininger *et al* 1987). Decreases are confined mainly to N and E Europe in a swathe through The Netherlands, Germany, Denmark to the former USSR. Greece is the only S European country where the population has decreased. However, stable populations are also to be found in parts of N Europe, such as Sweden and Estonia. Bulgaria, Moldova and Croatia too have retained stable populations, as have Spain and Ireland.

In addition to the increases in Great Britain, Belgium and France, a similar trend has occurred in Italy, whereas Finland has been colonized. Overall, the increases in most of the larger populations probably exceed the losses from decreases, but two important trends, from Poland, and outside the *Atlas* area from Turkey, are unavailable, giving rise to some uncertainty about the species' long-term future. At present, it appears to be quite resilient to local threats at colony sites.

Daniel Muselet (F)

This species account is sponsored by AVES, Société d'études ornithologiques, B.

Chlidonias hybridus

Whiskered Tern

CZ	Rybák bahenní	I	Mignattino piombato
D	Weißbart-Seeschwalbe	NL	Witwangstern
E	Fumarel Cariblanco	P	Gaivina-de-faces-brancas
F	Guifette moustac	PL	Rybitwa białowąsa
FIN	Valkoposkitiira	R	Белощекая крачка
G	Μουστακογλάρονο	S	Skäggtärna
H	Fattyúszerkő		

SPEC Cat 3, Threat status D

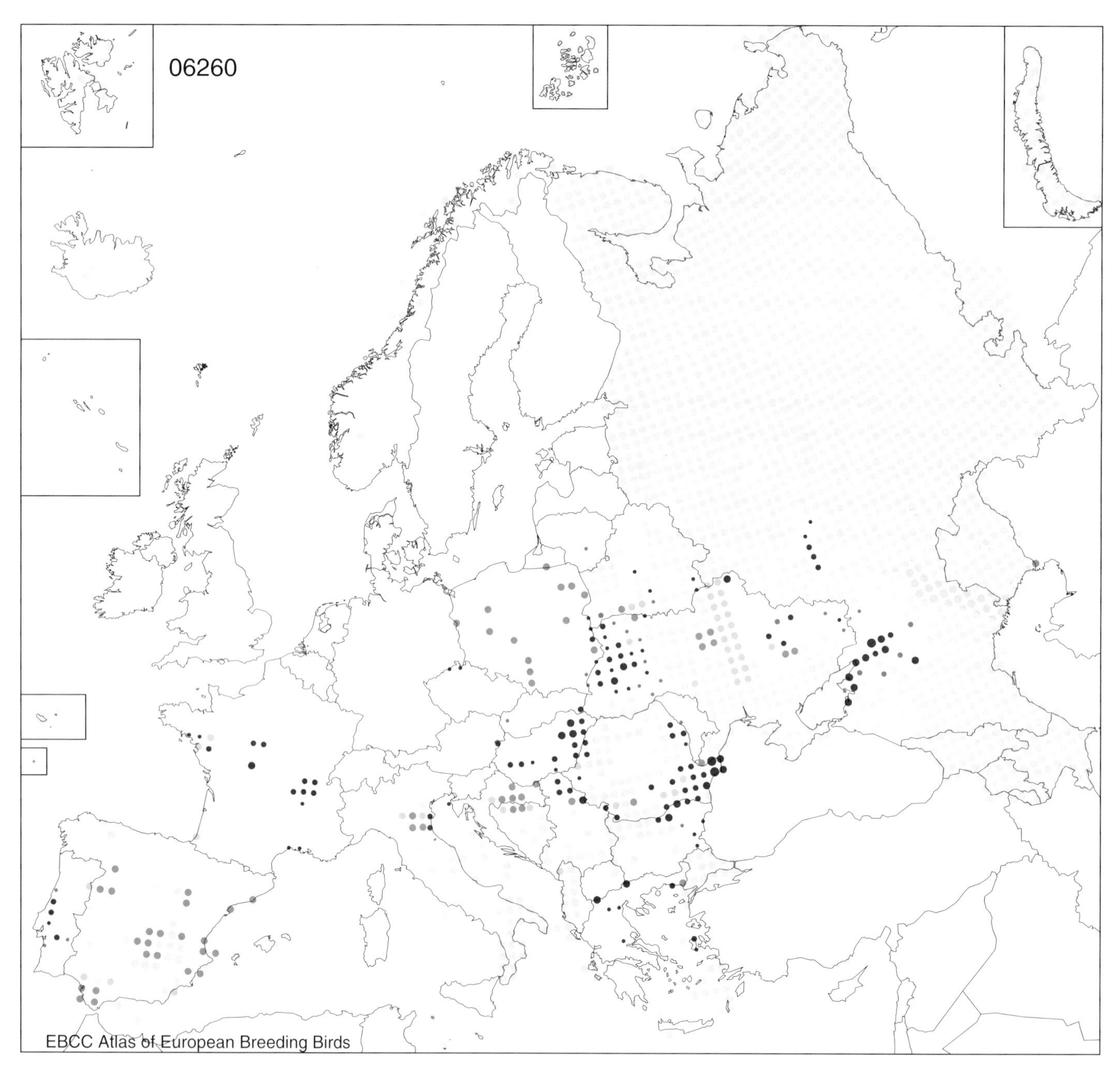

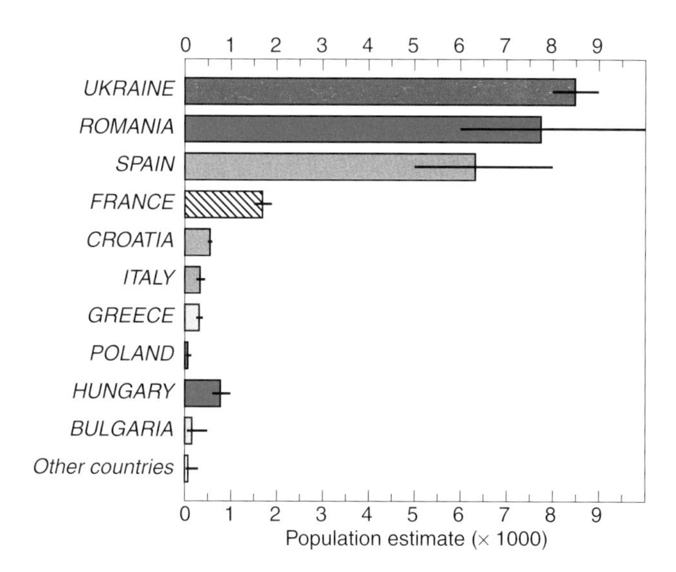

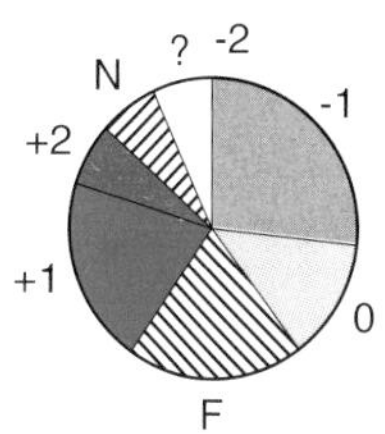

% in top 10 countries: 99.7
Total number of populated European countries: 15
Total European population 24,252–29,418 (26,517)
Russian population 10,000–13,000 (11,402)
Turkish population 1000–5000 (2236)

The Whiskered Tern has a scattered breeding distribution throughout S and E Europe, C and S Asia (the nominate *C.h. hybridus*), South and East Africa (*delalandii*), and SE Australia (*javanicus*). In Europe it breeds predominantly in the steppe and mediterranean zones, and especially in C and E Europe in the continental temperate zone. Its prime habitat is fresh, stagnant or slowly flowing water rich with floating vegetation. Apart from these natural habitats, it can breed in fishponds and ricefields which possess emergent vegetation. The European population is almost completely migratory. A few birds winter in S Europe, particularly in Spain or France. The SW European populations winter mostly in tropical West Africa. E European birds winter in Lakes Burullus and Manzala in the Nile Delta (45 000 in winter 1989/90; Meininger & Atta 1994) and East and South Africa.

Its distribution in E Europe is mostly patchy. Although parts of Ukraine and Russia (W of the Caspian Sea) were not fully covered by the present survey, there is no reason to suppose that in much of this area its distribution pattern is any different from elsewhere in Europe. The Volga–Ural steppes and the Volga Delta probably contain the largest single European population. In the mediterranean and steppe zones, the species' patchy distribution relates to the year-to-year distribution of available breeding habitat. Here, the core breeding areas are situated along large riverine systems and deltas, but elsewhere in these regions, the Whiskered Tern reacts opportunistically to suitable, albeit temporary, wetlands (Mees 1979).

The Guadalquivir, Rhône, Danube (Hungary to the Black Sea) and the Volga hold the majority of regular colonies. Outside these core areas, in S and E Europe the Whiskered Tern can be regarded as an accidental breeder, for breeding success depends on whether warm weather and lack of rainfall cause the more regular breeding sites to dry out (Mees 1979). The map shows the distribution over the whole survey period, but not which sites were regularly occupied, nor those which were used occasionally, thus presenting a more optimistic impression than exists in reality.

In Europe colonies are usually rather small, rarely exceeding 50bp. Along the N Mediterranean, totals are low, although numbers can be rather high locally. Colonies of more than 100bp can occur in deltas or along large riverine systems. The Volga Delta holds several thousand breeding pairs (Mees 1979), probably scattered over a large number of small colonies (Kapocsy 1979). Most colonies are usually divided into several subcolonies.

From 1930 to 1970, the population in the Mediterranean declined (Mees 1979). Recently another slight decrease has occurred in places. However, due to the species' tendency to breed opportunistically in response to local conditions, large natural fluctuations in numbers may occur in most colonies, sometimes within a single season, and trends are difficult to verify (Trotignon *et al* 1994). In the E European steppe zone the population has recently declined (L. Tomiałojć, pers comm). Simultaneously, there has been an apparent increase to the N and W of this zone.

In S Europe, habitat destruction is probably the major reason for the species' decline. In the E European steppes, a succession of dry seasons and the increase in drainage schemes are likely to be the main causes of a significant decline. Locally, the species can increase when it occupies artificial habitats such as ricefields, fishponds or shallow drainage sumps. In Italy, for instance, the entire population of *c*400bp uses artificial sites (Fasola 1986). Although the Whiskered Tern is able to colonize such artificial habitats, it is unlikely this will ever happen on a large enough scale to compensate for the losses due to reclamation of natural wetlands.

Jan van der Winden (NL)

Chlidonias niger

Black Tern

CZ	Rybák černý	**I**	Mignattino
D	Trauerseeschwalbe	**NL**	Zwarte Stern
E	Fumarel Común	**P**	Gaivina-preta
F	Guifette noire	**PL**	Rybitwa czarna
FIN	Mustatiira	**R**	Черная крачка
G	Μαυρογλάρονο	**S**	Svarttärna
H	Kormos szerkő		

SPEC Cat 3, Threat status D

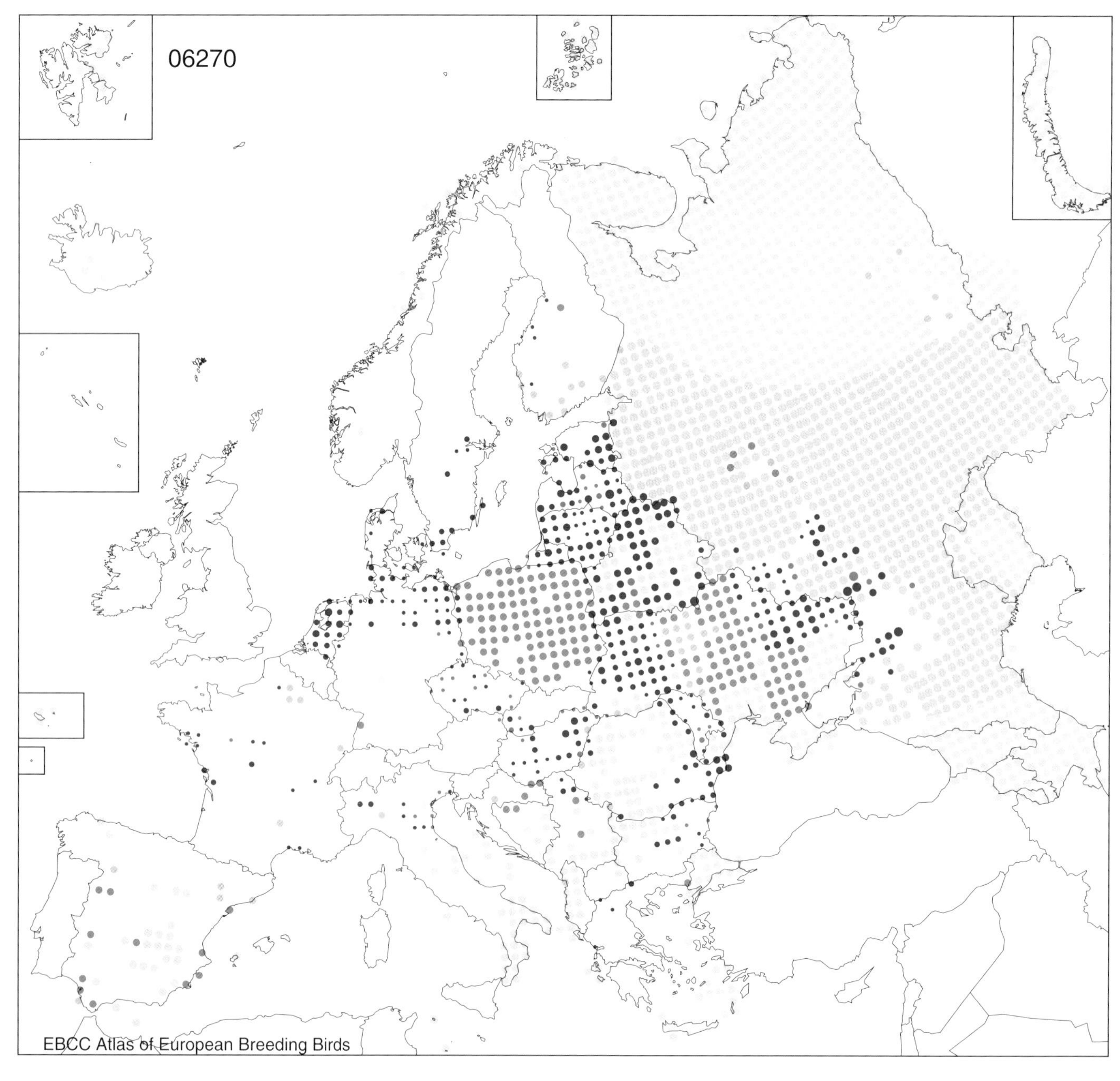

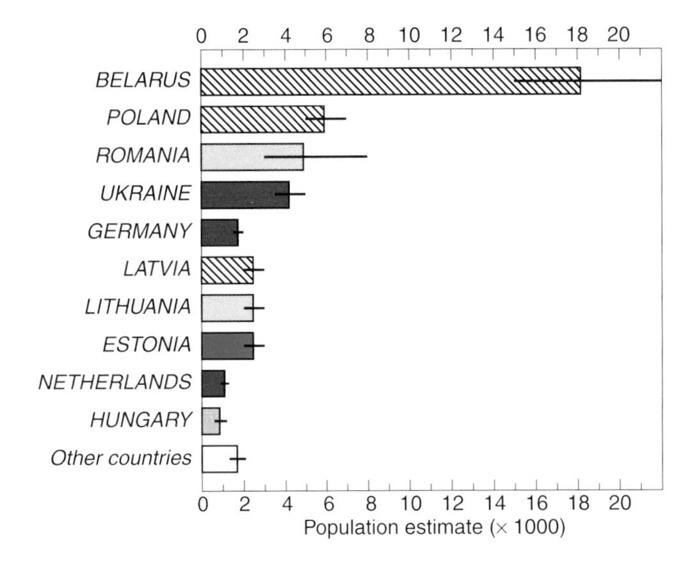

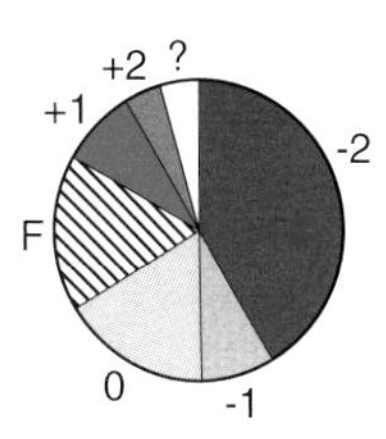

% in top 10 countries: 96.4
Total number of populated European countries: 24
Total European population 41,884–51,075 (45,846)
Russian population 20,000–30,000 (24,495)
Turkish population 50–500 (158)

The Black Tern breeds in North America (subspecies *C.n. surinamensis*) and from western Europe (the nominate *niger*) eastwards to the Yenisey in Asiatic Russia. In Europe the northernmost breeding places are in W Russia and Finland, and the southernmost in the Mediterranean.

The species breeds in a broad range of wetland habitats, but predominantly so in eutrophic natural freshwater marshes with stagnant shallow pools rich in floating aquatic vegetation. It will also colonize more cultivated areas such as open grasslands divided by well-vegetated broad ditches. Indeed, part of the Italian population breeds in ricefields. It nests regularly on floating aquatic vegetation, but it also uses grassland or muddy banks. Primarily a lowland breeder, it nevertheless breeds locally in the former USSR at mountain lakes up to 2000m asl. The European population winters mostly off the W African coast from 20°N to South Africa, some entering the Indian Ocean. Others winter in the Nile Valley.

The distribution of the Black Tern is biased towards the temperate and steppe climatic zones, across the N European plain from The Netherlands to C Russia. Because of insufficient survey data, the map may not adequately depict the probable homogeneous distribution in parts of Ukraine and Russia. The Black Tern has a patchy distribution in Sweden, Finland and the Mediterranean. Because of unstable breeding conditions in the N and S of its range, the Black Tern does not breed in the same locations every year. Nowadays, the patchy distribution in W Europe and the Mediterranean can be considered a relict of a formerly more even distribution (Fasola 1986).

The largest colonies can be found in E Europe. In W Europe, only NE Germany and The Netherlands contain significant colonies, whose size ranges from 5 to 30bp, exceptionally >50bp (Dittberner & Dittberner 1993). Over 40% of Dutch colonies contained fewer than 10bp, and only three (4%) colonies had more than 50bp (J. van der Winden, pers obs). In E Europe, the average colony size is similar. In Poland most colonies consist of 20–50bp, only 2% containing >50bp (Tomiałojć 1990). In the Baltic States and Russia, exceptionally large colonies of 1000–2000bp occur, such as that at Lake Lubana, E Latvia, in 1986–87 (Viksne & Janaus 1989). In the Mediterranean colony size invariably is small.

The European population, including European Russia, is estimated at 57 000–110 000bp, which matches remarkably the estimate of 150 000–200 000 birds from the August counts at roosting sites around the IJsselmeer in The Netherlands, representing 60 000–75 000bp plus immatures (Schouten 1985). The entire N and E European population probably remains at the IJsselmeer for 2–3 weeks, partly to moult, before departing on autumn migration.

Since the 1970s, the population of the Black Tern has decreased by more than 50% in most countries in W Europe and the Mediterranean, colonies becoming smaller and distribution patchier. In The Netherlands, large colonies of up to 1000bp (1930s) have been reduced to 30bp at most (J. van der Winden, pers obs). In the E of the Black Tern's range, the population is relatively stable, despite pronounced fluctuations. Because almost the entire European breeding population winters together, the difference in population changes between W and E Europe probably is due to changes experienced in the respective breeding areas. In W Europe, the causes of the declines are probably linked to extensive land reclamation, widespread introduction of intensive farming methods and the direct and indirect effects of environmental pollution. It is likely that the same problems have reduced the Mediterranean populations. The population in W Europe seems to have stabilized recently, but this is a local and small-scale success restricted to nature reserves, often enhanced by providing artificial nest sites.

Jan van der Winden (NL) Janis Viksne (LAT)

Chlidonias leucopterus White-winged Black Tern

CZ	Rybák bělokřídlý	**I**	Mignattino alibianche
D	Weißflügel-Seeschwalbe	**NL**	Witvleugelstern
E	Fumarel Aliblanco	**P**	Gaivina-d'asa-branca
F	Guifette leucoptère	**PL**	Rybitwa białoskrzydła
FIN	Valkosiipitiira	**R**	Белокрылая крачка
G	Αργυρογλάρονο	**S**	Vitvingad tärna
H	Fehérszárnyú szerkő		

Non-SPEC, Threat status S

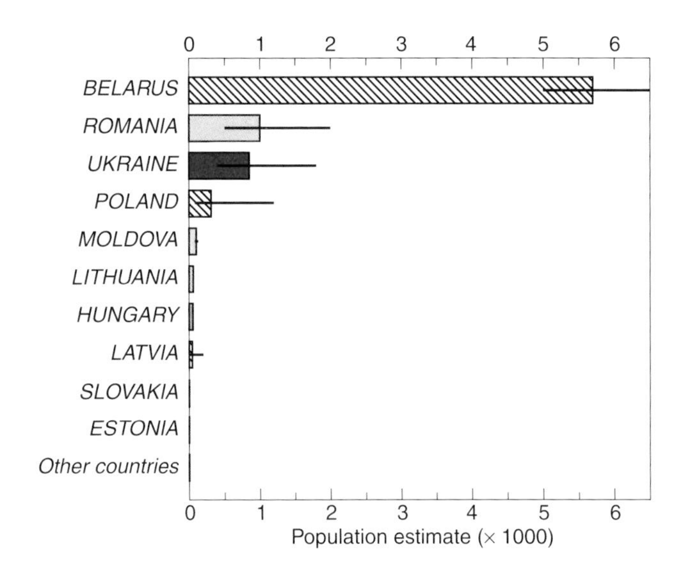

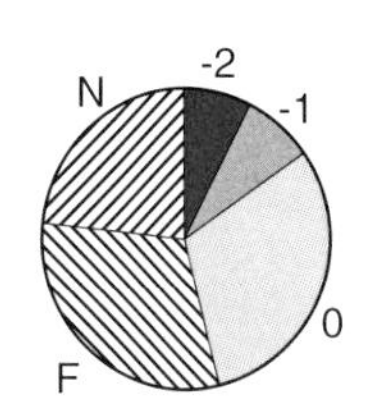

% in top 10 countries: 100.0
Total number of populated European countries: 13
Total European population 7129–9961 (8128)
Russian population 13,000–17,000 (14,866)
Turkish population 1–50 (7)

The White-winged Black Tern is restricted in its occurrence to the Old World. Its westernmost regular breeding sites are found in E–C Europe, and its distribution stretches E to C Asia and (a separate population) to N China and Ussuriland. To the S it occurs in the Caucasus and Mesopotamia. No subspecies are recognized. It breeds predominantly in natural extensive freshwater marshlands, and favours floodplains and temporarily flooded grasslands beside permanent waterbodies, such as lakes, large reservoirs or major rivers. In wet meadows it nests in shallow water overgrown with sedges (*Carex*) or similar vegetation.

European populations of the White-winged Black Tern winter in continental Africa south of the Sahara. They are possibly joined by C Asian populations (*BWP*). In spring, most migrate through E Mediterranean countries to the breeding grounds in E Europe. Smaller numbers participate in autumn in a loop migration from their breeding areas SW through Italy, France and E Spain. In autumn large concentrations gather in the N Black Sea, whereas in spring, in late April and early May, concentrations regularly appear in E Mediterranean countries (WIWO 1990). Eastern populations winter along the Chinese coasts, the Sundas, Melanesia and northern Australia.

In E Europe the bulk of the population favours the temperate continental lowlands and steppe climatic zones, where the species is fairly evenly distributed. Significant parts of its probable distribution area (E Ukraine and NW of the Caspian Sea) were not fully covered by the *Atlas* surveys, and so the map does not clearly indicate its supposedly even distribution in these areas. The northernmost breeding sites lie in the Baltic states, where breeding occurrence is irregular. The White-winged Black Tern is an uncommon and sporadic breeder in small numbers in Mediterranean countries, the westernmost regular (1979–85) breeding site being in Italian ricefields (Fasola 1986). Due to annual fluctuations of wetland water levels, the suitability of breeding sites can vary. Like all marsh terns, the White-winged Black Tern will adjust quickly to differing annual breeding conditions, colonizing whatever area has become prime habitat each spring. The mapped distribution density is therefore probably more optimistic in places than would be the case for a single year's results, although it is likely that a few colonies have been overlooked.

In the W of its range (Hungary, Ukraine), the White-winged Black Tern is in decline. Former more westerly breeding sites in Germany and Austria on the floodplains of the Danube were abandoned in the 1960s. The primary reason for the decline is the reclamation of wetlands. Recently a major decline has occurred in the southern (steppe) regions of Ukraine and Russia, due to a combination of dry breeding seasons and a multiplication of drainage schemes (Ilyichev & Zubakin 1988). However, there has been a simultaneous increase in the northern and western breeding range. In Poland, numbers increased and new colonies formed, in the Biebrza marshes, the population increasing from *c*20 to 1000bp from 1967 to 1994. Similar trends are evident in Belarus, the Baltic states and towards its northern limit in Russia. In the W of its breeding range, colony size is usually 1–20bp, but larger colonies may form, especially during a wet spring. To the E, colonies of 20–40bp are the norm, exceptionally more than 100bp. Extralimitally, large concentrations of over 1000bp can occur in a single marsh system. Most colonies are not heterogeneous, but consist of several subcolonies. The species appears to be heavily dependent on natural breeding habitats, cultivated habitats like fishponds or ricefields being less favoured. Consequently, habitat destruction and water regulation in wetlands form the greatest threat to the species' survival.

Ludwik Tomiałojć (PL) Jan van der Winden (NL)

Uria aalge **Guillemot**

CZ	Alkoun úzkozobý	**I**	Uria
D	Trottellumme	**NL**	Zeekoet
E	Arao Común	**P**	Arau-comum
F	Guillemot de Troïl	**PL**	Nurzyk
FIN	Etelänkiisla	**R**	Тонкоклювая кайра
G	Λεπτοραμφόκεπφος	**S**	Sillgrissla
H	Vékonycsőrű lumma		

Non-SPEC, Threat status S

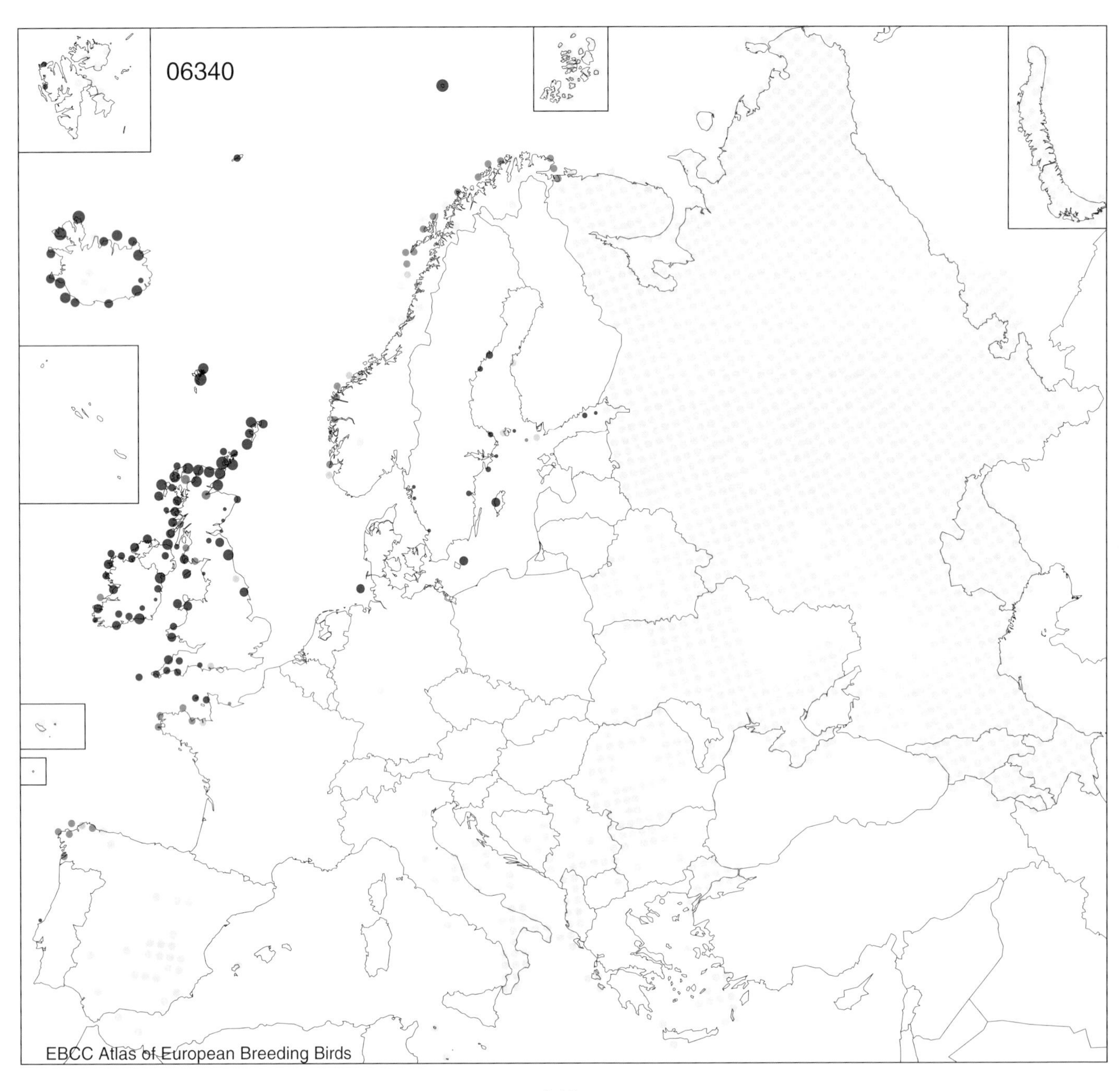

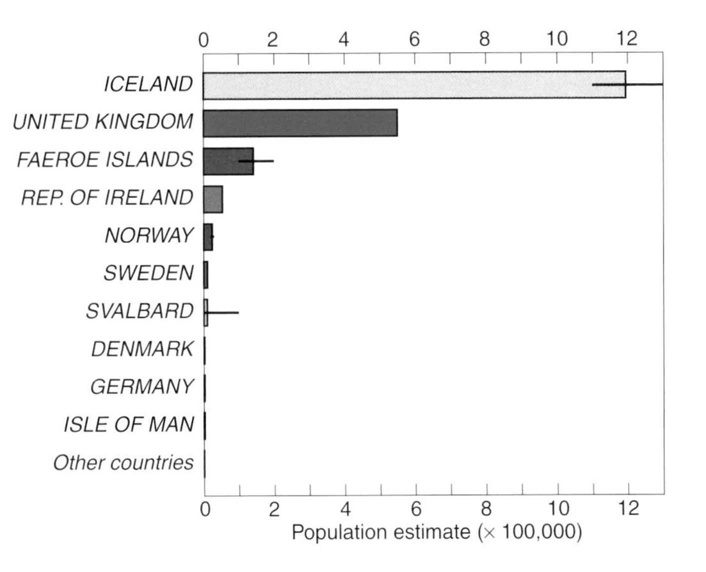

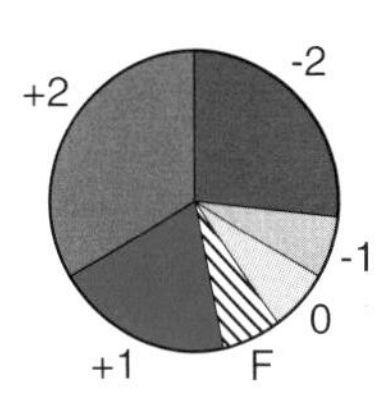

% in top 10 countries: 100.0
Total number of populated European countries: 15
Total European population 1,888,693–2,143,287 (1,993,573)
Russian population 70,000–70,000 (70,000)

The Guillemot is the most widespread of all the auks. It has a circumpolar breeding distribution on northern boreal and low-arctic coasts of the Atlantic and Pacific Oceans. In the high arctic it is replaced by Brünnich's Guillemot *U. lomvia*, except for a small number on Svalbard. Its southern European limit reaches the Berlengas Islands off Portugal. A colonial species, it requires ledges on sheer cliffs, isolated sea stacks or islands free from ground predators. Birds usually nest in the open, commonly at densities of 20 bp/m^2, sometimes up to 50 bp/m^2. Less commonly, it nests under boulders. Some southern birds visit their colonies for much of the year but generally most populations disperse southwards, a few reaching Gibraltar, to winter offshore. Three subspecies occur in Europe, the nominate *U.a. aalge*, *albionis*, and *hyperborea*; the other two inhabit the Nearctic.

The Guillemot is an adaptable species when not molested by man or other predators, but its breeding distribution is governed by the availability of potential breeding sites, the lack of which probably explains the small numbers breeding in the eastern North Sea. Individual colonies may contain up to 600 000bp, but where habitat is limited or fragmented, there may be many small adjacent colonies.

About 85% of the total Atlantic population of 2.0–2.5Mbp is in Europe. Despite a generally accepted method for estimating Guillemot breeding pairs from counts, for various reasons many estimates are inaccurate. The largest concentration is in Iceland (1.2Mbp), three colonies in the NW comprising 90% of this total; the status of the species in Iceland, critical to its status overall, is poorly known but there is no compelling evidence of any recent large change (Nettleship & Evans 1985). Britain & Ireland together have 0.6Mbp, mostly in N Scotland, which follows a doubling of numbers since 1969 (Lloyd *et al* 1991).

Annual monitoring of some British colonies indicates that increases continue in the Irish Sea but that trends have been reversed in the N and E. The reversal in the North Sea began in the far N (Shetland in the 1970s) and spread S by the mid-1980s (Harris 1991). The Faeroes population declined by two-thirds, to 141 000bp, between 1972 and 1987 (Nettleship & Evans 1985). Numbers in many parts of Norway have declined during the last 30–40 years, a 90% decrease occurring in the large colony on Vedøy from 1963 to 1988. A spectacular crash in numbers in E Finnmark and Bear Island occurred between 1986 and 1987 when 80% of birds disappeared, apparently through the collapse of the Barents Sea capelin *Mallotus villosus* stock (Anker-Nilssen & Barrett 1991). The Bear Island population declined from 245 000bp in 1986 to 36 000bp in 1987, recovering to 95 000bp in 1989. The few available data for Russia suggest that the Murmansk population (70 000bp) may be declining. Protection during the breeding season has allowed the Baltic population to increase substantially in the 20th century; there were 8800bp in the mid-1970s and 13 000bp in the mid-1980s (Lyngs 1992). The single German colony (Helgoland, 2400bp) has increased in the last two decades, whereas the small colonies in France, Spain and Portugal have all declined to the point of becoming endangered.

The Guillemot is peculiarly susceptible to a wide range of disasters, whether the result of human error or action (disturbance, hunting, widespread netting for both cod *Gadus morhua* and salmon *Salmo salar*, oil and toxic chemical spillage) or simply natural (food shortages, severe weather) (Evans & Nettleship 1985). It is difficult to interpret the interplay of these factors which confuse the understanding of changes in populations in recent years, but although the species is more adaptable than some about the food it will take, on balance, its vulnerability to relatively local catastrophic events puts it at long-term risk.

Michael P Harris (GB)

Uria lomvia

Brünnich's Guillemot

CZ	Alkoun tlustozobý	I	Uria di Brünnich
D	Dickschnabellumme	NL	Dikbekzeekoet
E	Arao de Brünnich	P	Arau de Brünnich
F	Guillemot de Brünnich	PL	Nurzyk polarny
FIN	Pohjankiisla	R	Толстоклювая кайра
G	Ισλανδόκεπφος	S	Spetsbergsgrissla
H	Vastagcsőrű lumma		

Non-SPEC, Threat status S

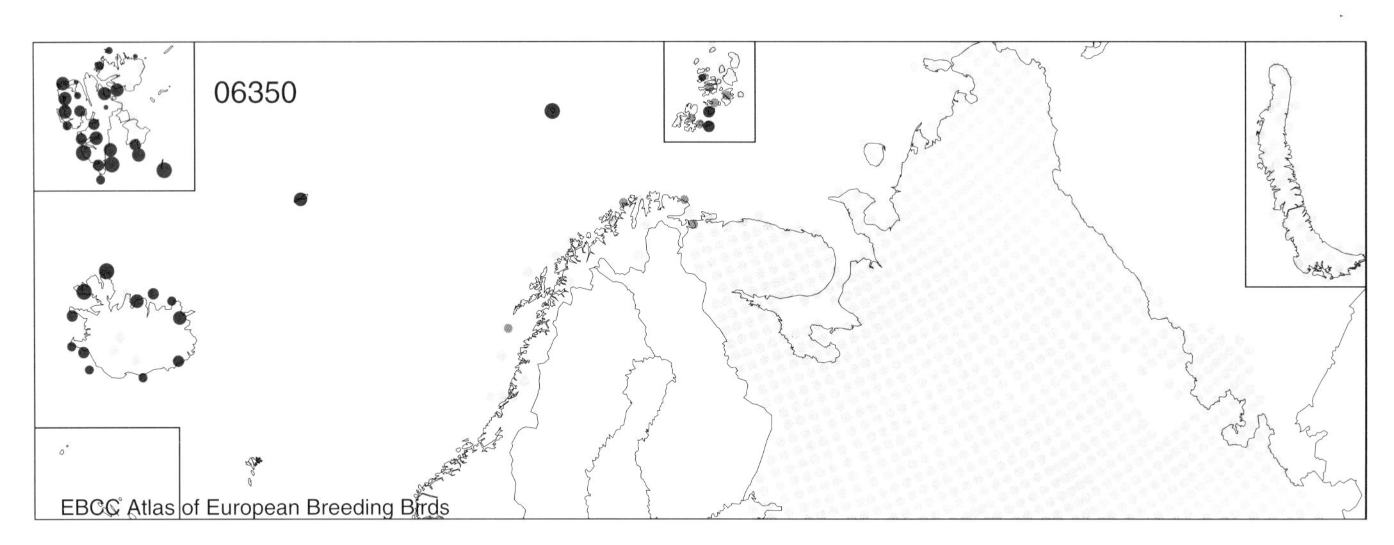

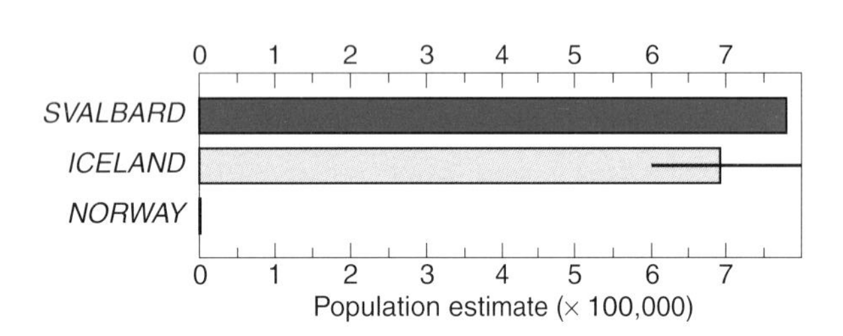

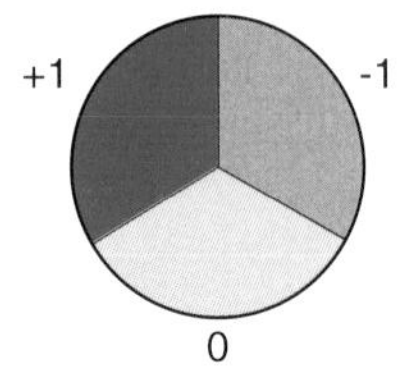

% in top 10 countries: 100.0
Total number of populated European countries: 3
Total European population 1,381,413–1,581,416 (1,474,235)
Russian population 950,000–1,000,000 (974,679)

Brünnich's Guillemot, a large auk, is a circumpolar panarctic species. It overlaps with the Guillemot, *U. aalge*, in the southern low-arctic regions. The nominate *U.l. lomvia* occurs in Europe and eastern Canada; three other subspecies inhabit arctic waters E of the Taymyr to the N Pacific. Throughout its range it breeds in dense and sometimes vast colonies on coastal cliffs.

In Europe the majority breeds in large colonies on Iceland, Bear Island, Svalbard, Franz Josef Land and Novaya Zemlya. Their size and inaccessibility makes these colonies notoriously difficult to census. Comprehensive population data for Europe therefore are lacking. Over 90% of the Icelandic population breeds in three colonies on the NW coast. In the southern Svalbard archipelago a few colonies (each over 100 000bp) contain the majority of birds, although colonies occur along the coasts which are ice-free in summer. The European Russian population breeds mainly on Franz Josef Land (only in the SW sector) and Novaya Zemlya (along the whole W coast). The European mainland population, a few thousand breeding pairs, is restricted to mixed auk colonies along the N Norwegian and Kola Peninsula coastlines.

The status of the European population is little known. On Novaya Zemlya, huge declines occurred in the largest colonies, such as in Bezymyannaya Bay, from 1933 to 1951 due to over-exploitation by man (Uspenski 1958). A 1992 survey revealed a further 60% drop (Krasnov & Barrett 1995). A second, independent survey in 1994 showed that numbers may have increased very slightly since the 1950s (Strøm *et al* 1994), but may have overestimated the population.

Outside the breeding season, some European birds move SW towards Greenland and Newfoundland, others gather along the pack-ice limit in the Barents Sea. In early spring, large flocks follow the capelin *Mallotus villosus* migrating to the spawning grounds off N Norway and the Kola Peninsula, then assemble at their breeding colonies in late April or early May (Nikolaeva *et al* in press). Other populations winter in the N Pacific.

Rob T Barrett (GB)

Alle alle

Little Auk

CZ	Alkoun malý	I	Gazza marina minore
D	Krabbentaucher	NL	Kleine Alk
E	Mérgulo Atlántico	P	Torda-anã
F	Mergule nain	PL	Alczyk
FIN	Pikkuruokki	R	Люрик
G	Νανόκεπφος	S	Alkekung
H	Alkabukó		

Non-SPEC, Threat status S (P)

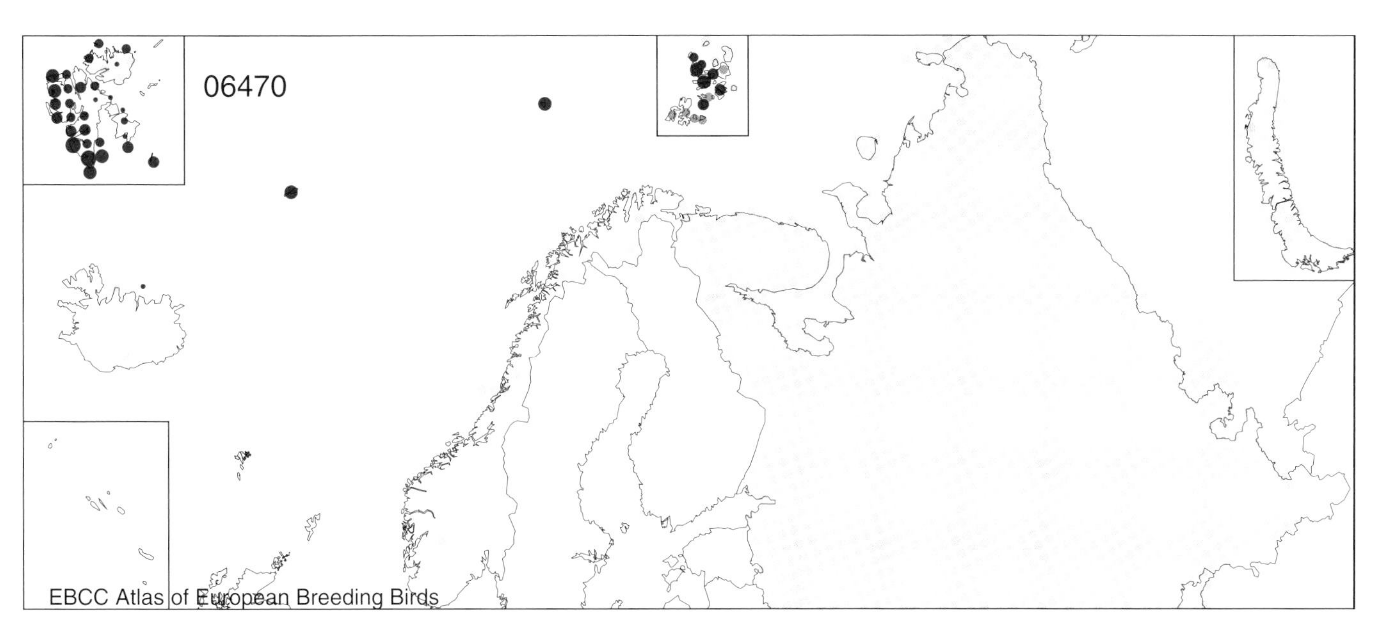

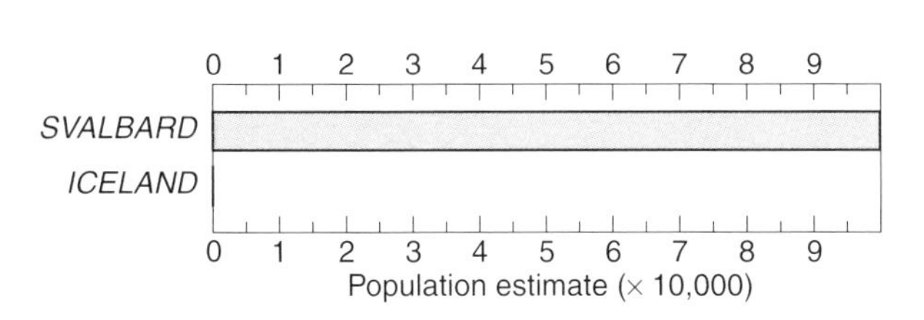

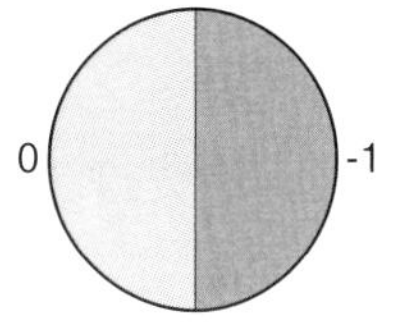

% in top 10 countries: 100.0
Total number of populated European countries: 2
Total European population 100,002–100,002 (100,002)
Russian population 260,000–260,000 (260,000)

The Little Auk, a small alcid, feeds on crustaceans at sea in the high arctic. There may be *c*12Mbp (range 8–18) (Nettleship & Birkhead 1985) altogether, 10Mbp in the Thule district and fewer elsewhere in Greenland, at least 1Mbp in Svalbard (Mehlum & Bakken 1994), 250 000 in Franz Joseph Land, 75 000 in Severnaya Zemlya and the New Siberian Islands, 50 000 on Jan Mayen, 10 000 on Bear Island, and a few on Grimsey off N Iceland and the islands off NE Canada and in the Bering Strait (Divoky & Springer 1988). Apart from *A. a. polaris* of Franz Joseph Land, all belong to the nominate subspecies *A. a. alle*. The Little Auk is replaced by ten other small alcids in the North Pacific, and by the unrelated diving-petrels in the Southern Hemisphere.

It feeds by diving, often to considerable depths, mainly in the region where convection currents occur around ice. It breeds colonially in crevices in cliffs and especially on the surrounding boulder-slopes (though it avoids the vegetation induced by its droppings) near adjacent coasts. Here it forms one of the main prey of Eskimos, the arctic fox *Alopex lagopus*, the Glaucous Gull *Larus hyperboreus* and the Raven *Corvus corax*. Humans and foxes may store bodies for the winter. Apparently such predation has little effect on Little Auk numbers, although some of the smaller southern colonies, notably on Grimsey, have been declining, possibly through climatic warming.

In the winter some disperse, especially along the Labrador current and to a lesser extent around NW Europe. Much of the Svalbard population may overwinter off SW Greenland (Isaksen & Bakken 1995). At intervals of years more marked northward movements may occur, punctuated by exhausted birds 'wrecked' ashore, associated usually with gales. Possibly there may also be some other predisposing factor such as overpopulation or food-supply failure.

WRP Bourne (GB)

Alca torda **Razorbill**

CZ	Alka malá	**I**	Gazza marina
D	Tordalk	**NL**	Alk
E	Alca Común	**P**	Torda-mergulheira
F	Pingouin torda	**PL**	Alka
FIN	Ruokki	**R**	Гагарка
G	Αλκα	**S**	Tordmule
H	Alka		

SPEC Cat 4, Threat status S

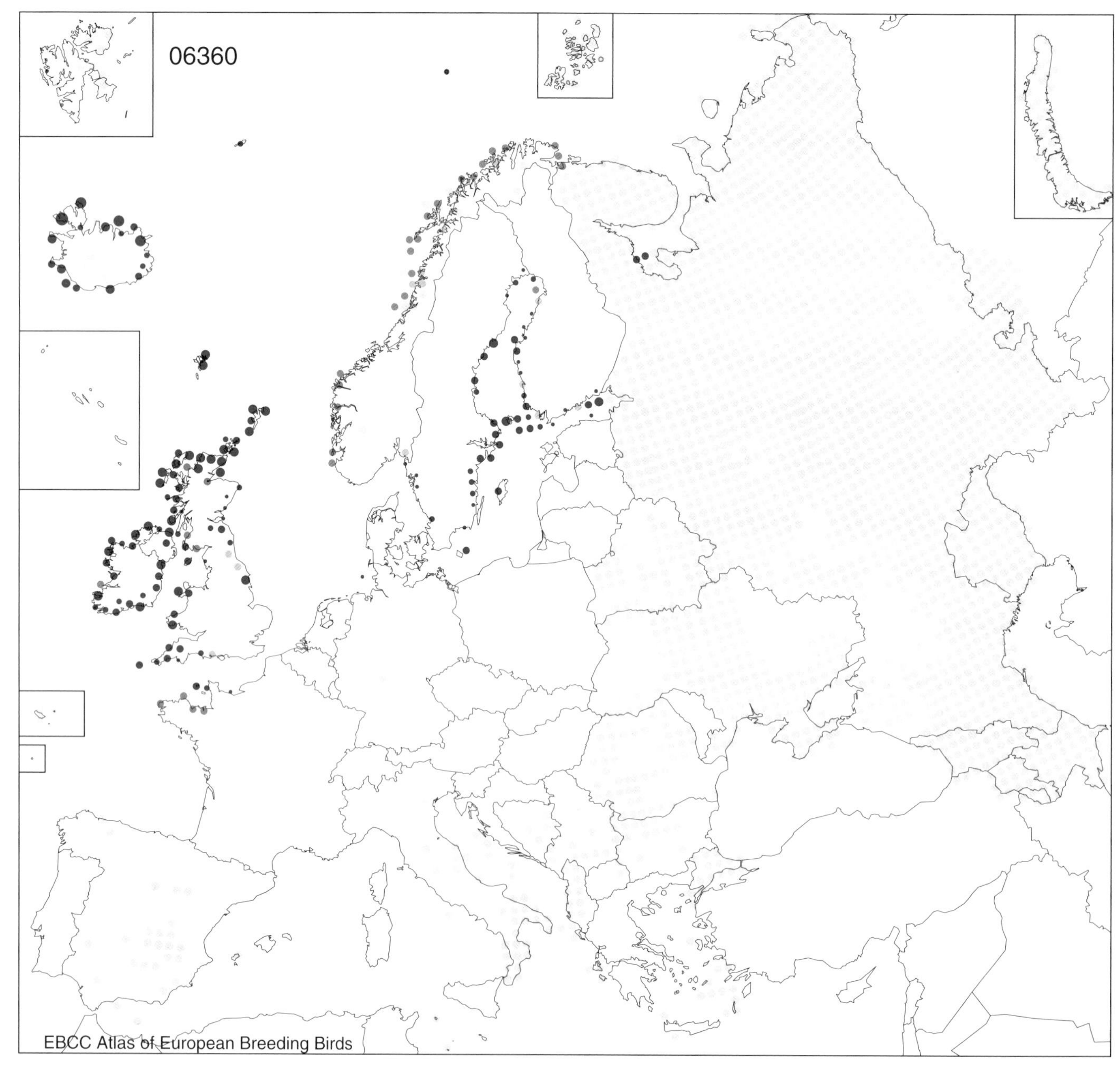

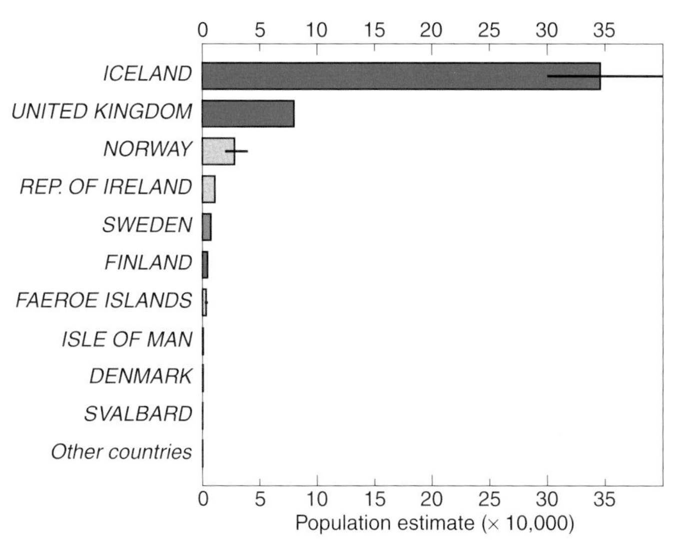

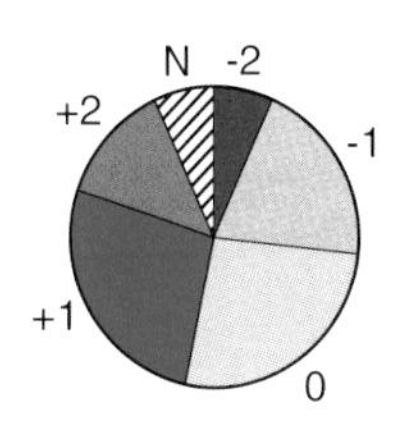

% in top 10 countries: 100.0
Total number of populated European countries: 15
Total European population 434,940–536,994 (482,103)
Russian population 2000–2000 (2000)

The Razorbill is endemic to the North Atlantic and associated seas. It breeds from the White Sea in the E to Maine in the W. Its European northern distribution limit reaches Bear Island and Svalbard (Isaksen & Bakken 1995); Brittany represents the southern limit of its range in the E Atlantic. Despite an extensive range in Greenland and E Canada, the W Atlantic population is relatively small. The nominate subspecies *A.t. torda* occurs in the W Atlantic, on Bear Island, and from Murmansk around the coast to the Baltic, and *islandica* in Iceland, Faeroes, Britain, Ireland and Brittany.

The Razorbill breeds typically in colonies on cliffs and islands with the Guillemot *Uria aalge*, but tends to nest on wider ledges or in small cavities and is somewhat more dispersed. In the Baltic, most colonies are on low rocky islands, with nests in rock crevices or under big boulders. The species requires good feeding grounds nearby, usually in shallow shelf seas. Most colonies are contained within the 4°C and 15°C summer marine isotherms.

The core of Razorbill distribution is Iceland (300–400 000bp), where over 50% of the world population nests. Elsewhere in Europe, the majority of the population nests in Britain, Ireland and Norway. A relatively small (*c*15 000bp) but widely dispersed population breeds in the Baltic. Bear Island, Jan Mayen Island, Svalbard and France hold small populations.

In Iceland the population size apparently has been increasing recently. Numbers have been very poorly known in the past; population estimates have varied greatly through the physical difficulties of monitoring large colonies. The cliffs at Latrabjarg, Haelavikarbjarg and Hornbjarg each hold more or less uncounted numbers, certainly many tens of thousands and maybe even over 100 000. These vast numbers must be supported by prime offshore feeding habitat. Numbers in Britain have increased, but here too, monitoring problems beset many colonies (Lloyd *et al* 1991). Great Britain holds the largest colonies outside Iceland, several in NW Scotland exceeding 10 000bp (Lloyd *et al* 1991), a figure unmatched in the rest of the Razorbill's range, because elsewhere the largest colonies are only a few thousand breeding pairs strong.

The Baltic population has undergone considerable change; large colonies in the northern Gulf of Bothnia were almost totally destroyed by egg-collecting and hunting around 1900 and have never recovered. Elsewhere in the Baltic, populations were reduced by severe winters and wartime oil spills in the 1940s, but since then steady increases have allowed levels to surpass those of the 1930s (Hildén & Pahtamaa 1992).

Decreases have been noted in Norway and Ireland, both perhaps related to entanglement of birds in fishing nets. In the English Channel, oil spills may have caused decreases in France. On the Faeroes, the population appears to have stabilized following large decreases earlier in the 20th century. Despite the difficulties of monitoring Razorbill colonies, a critical examination of past records, both ornithological and general, can provide a relatively good understanding of past trends in the status and distribution of the species (Nettleship & Evans 1985). There have been no apparent recent large-scale changes in range.

The Razorbill is partially migratory. Most birds from northern colonies move southwards for the winter (Mead 1974). Large numbers occur in the Skagerrak and Kattegat later in the winter. Young birds from more southerly populations may move to the Bay of Biscay or to Iberian and Mediterranean waters for winter. Large concentrations occur immediately after the breeding season in British and Irish waters, in particular off the E coasts of Scotland and Ireland, and in distinct localities off western Scotland (Tasker *et al* 1987, Webb *et al* 1990). Detailed information is lacking for more distant waters.

the late Olavi Hildén (FIN) Mark Tasker (GB)

Cepphus grylle — Black Guillemot

CZ	Alkoun obecný	I	Uria nera
D	Gryllteiste	NL	Zwarte Zeekoet
E	Arao Aliblanco	P	Arau-d'asa-branca
F	Guillemot à miroir	PL	Nurnik
FIN	Riskilä	R	Чистик
G	Κέπφος	S	Tobisgrissla
H	Fekete lumma		

SPEC Cat 2, Threat status D

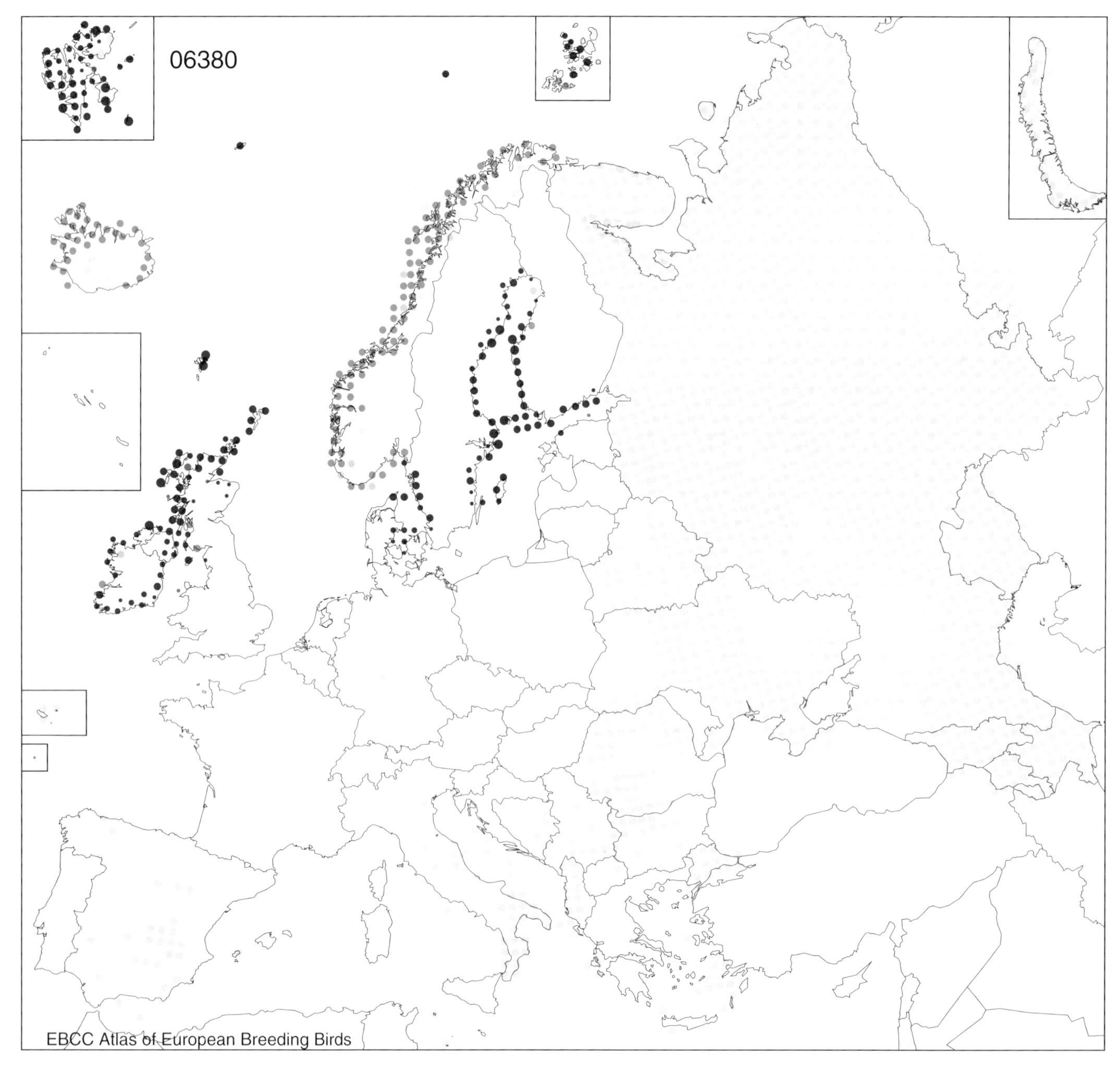

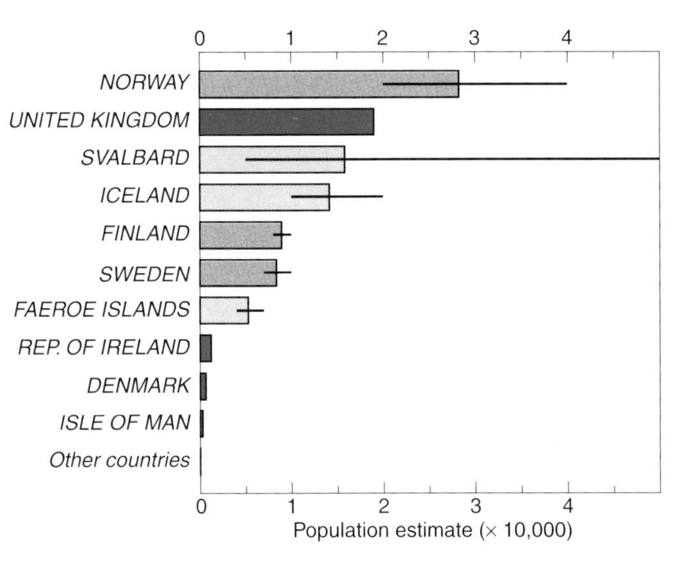

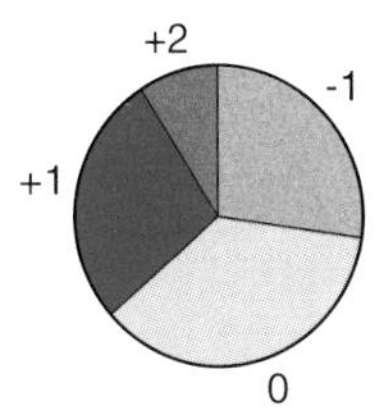

% in top 10 countries: 100.0
Total number of populated European countries: 11
Total European population 87,552–138,647 (101,943)
Russian population 23,500–23,500 (23,500)

The Black Guillemot, a relatively sedentary, inshore diving seabird, has a Holarctic breeding distribution along Arctic and North Atlantic coasts. By far the greatest numbers breed in the Arctic, where some colonies hold thousands of breeding pairs. All five subspecies breed in Europe: *grylle* (Baltic coasts), *arcticus* (the rest of Scandinavia, Russia, Britain & Ireland), *faeroensis* (Faeroes), *islandicus* (Iceland) and *mandtii* (Svalbard, Jan Mayen and Bear Island).

The nests are always in cavities, but in a wide range of habitats along marine shorelines. On islands lacking mammalian predators many nests are on boulder beaches, in burrows, or under driftwood or vegetation, as well as in cliff crevices. Along mainland coasts and on large islands infested with rats *Rattus* spp, mink *Mustela vison*, stoats *M. ermina*, feral cats *Felis catus* or hedgehogs *Erinaceus europaea*, most nests are found in inaccessible cliff crevices or caves. In recent years small colonies have become established in some areas in holes of harbour walls, buildings and even in wooden nest boxes.

Most colonies hold 1–20bp, dispersed fairly evenly along coastlines having suitable nesting sites and a vegetated rocky seabed. In Europe this species breeds mostly in areas with a mean August sea surface temperature below *c*16°C. It is the least numerous of European alcids (auks).

Changes in status and distribution are difficult to assess precisely, due to unsystematic previous surveys. Overall, numbers have probably remained fairly stable in the 20th century. Local decreases and extirpation of breeding colonies have been attributed to various factors: cold winters (Baltic), oil pollution (Shetland, Scandinavia), spread of mink and rats (Iceland, Scotland, Scandinavia), human disturbance, hunting, harvesting of eggs and chicks, and entanglement in fishing nets (Scandinavia, Scotland) (Asbirk 1978, Ewins & Tasker 1985, Hildén & Hario 1993). The spread of introduced mink has had the most dramatic effect on breeding distributions, particularly in the Baltic, western Norway and Iceland. Recent increases in Denmark are likely due to immigration from mink-infested Swedish colonies, and enforcement of new legislation restricting hunting and egg-collecting (Asbirk 1978). The single Estonian colony decreased from 100bp in 1936 to 25bp in 1960 and only 6bp in 1983, due mainly to continued hunting and entanglement in fishing nets (J.E. Shergalin, pers comm).

The most recent estimates suggest a European breeding population of *c*100 000–200 000bp. Highest breeding densities occur in more productive cold-water areas (Iceland, Svalbard, N Scotland, Norway). The Svalbard population has recently been estimated at roughly 20 000bp (Mehlum & Bakken 1994). Smaller populations, at lower density, occur in the Baltic, Denmark and Ireland. Mean breeding density is similar in Orkney and Shetland, at 3.8 bp/km of coastline (Ewins & Tasker 1985). Breeding distribution is limited primarily by food availability (inshore benthic fish and invertebrates) and suitable nest cavities.

Many birds move to more sheltered, inshore waters in winter, but adults often remain within 15km of the breeding colony (Ewins & Kirk 1988). Ice forces Baltic and northern birds S in winter, although this species occurs frequently among ice leads. Some Icelandic birds winter in Greenland. There is a general southerly movement of immatures in autumn and winter, but only as far S as northern France, although feeding movements also occur up the Norwegian coast.

Black Guillemot nests are very difficult to locate and colony attendance varies greatly, both diurnally and seasonally (Ewins 1985). Recent surveys have used systematic early-morning counts of adults associating with breeding areas 1–2 months prior to breeding to obtain realistic population estimates. Previous surveys used unsystematic counts later in the breeding season, making assessment of population trends difficult in many areas, unless detailed breeding studies had been conducted.

Peter J Ewins (GB) the late Olavi Hildén (FIN)

Fratercula arctica **Puffin**

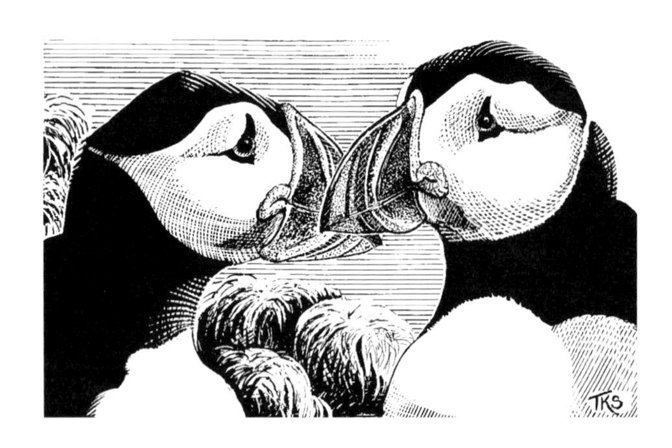

CZ	Papuchalk ploskozobý	**I**	Pulcinella di mare
D	Papageitaucher	**NL**	Papegaaiduiker
E	Frailecillo Atlántico	**P**	Papagaio-do-mar
F	Macareux moine	**PL**	Maskonur
FIN	Lunni	**R**	Тупик
G	Θαλασσοψιττακός	**S**	Lunnefågel
H	Lunda		

SPEC Cat 2, Threat status V

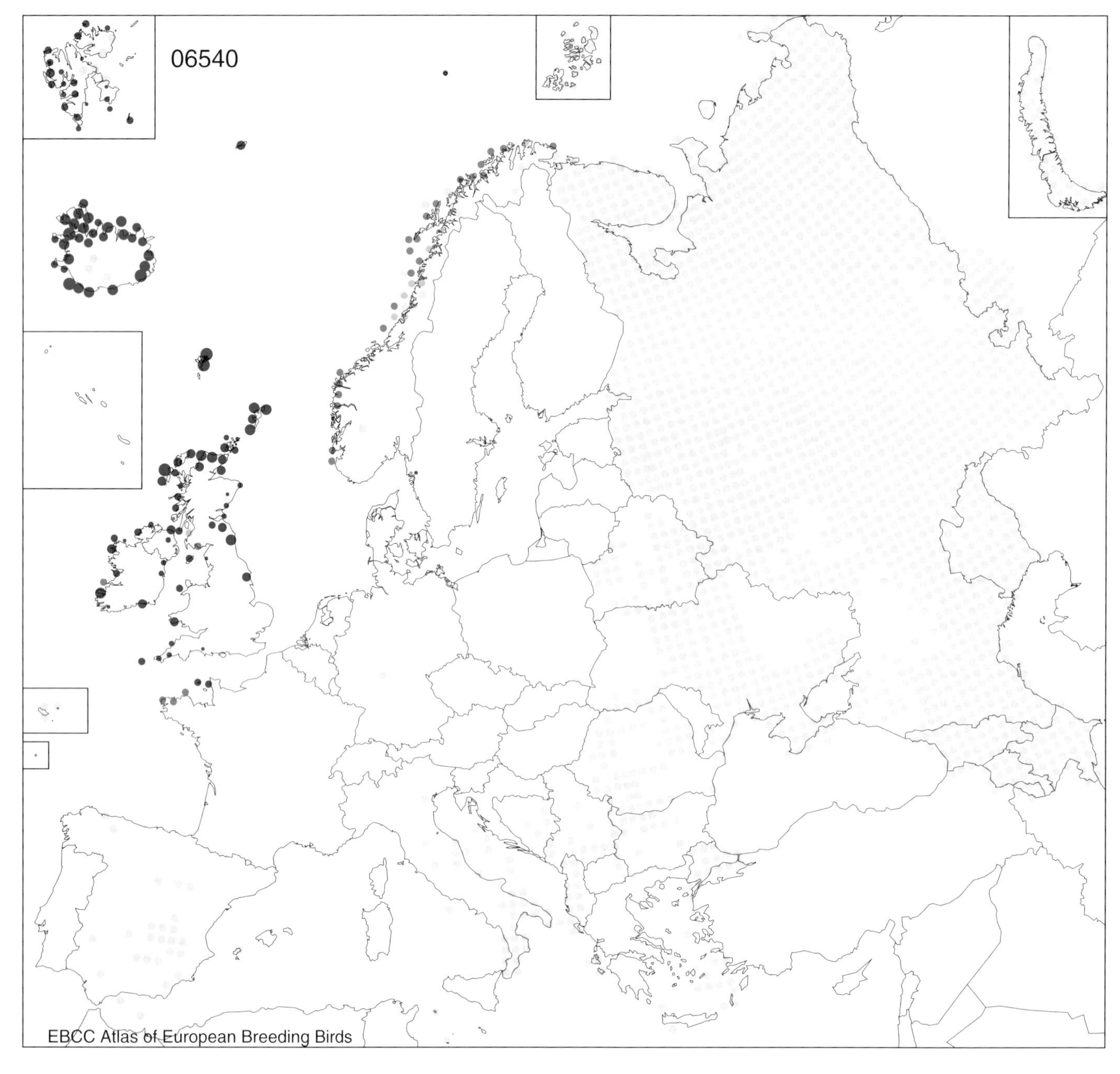

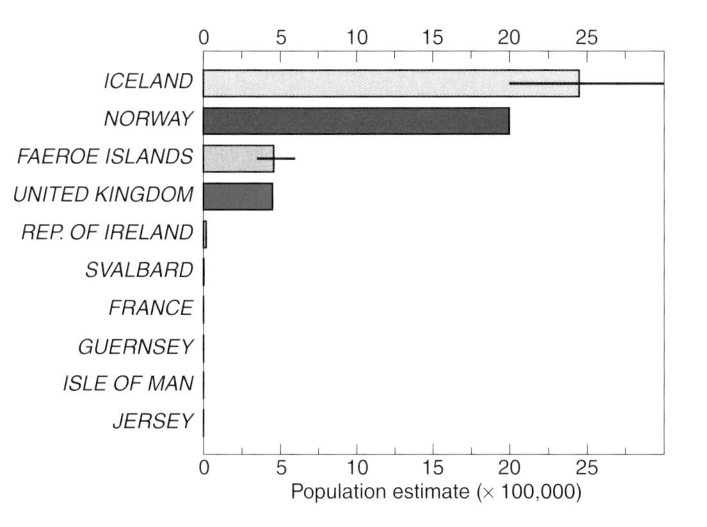

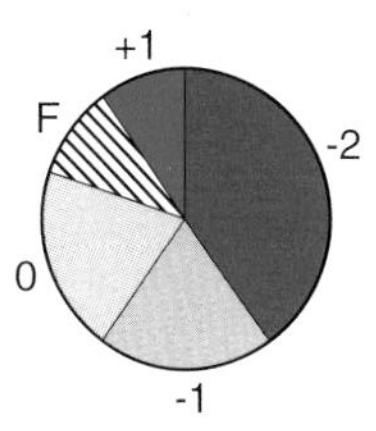

% in top 10 countries: 100.0
Total number of populated European countries: 10
Total European population 4,917,162–5,948,015 (5,379,509)
Russian population 20,000–20,000 (20,000)

The instantly recognizable Puffin is restricted to the colder parts of the North Atlantic and the adjoining areas of the Arctic Ocean. It breeds on maritime coasts from N Svalbard, N Greenland and Novaya Zemlya (subspecies *F.a. naumanni*, except for S Novaya Zemlya) as far N as there are ice-free coasts, and S to Brittany, France and Maine, USA. The nominate *arctica* occurs from North America via Iceland, Bear Island to northern Norway and southern Novaya Zemlya, and *grabae* from the Faeroes, Britain & Ireland to France and southern Norway.

Over 90% of the world population occurs in Europe. Occasionally, small numbers breed in amongst other species. However, the Puffin breeds mostly in colonies on isolated islands lacking mammalian predators but possessing sufficient soil for burrows to be dug, or boulder screes with ample nest cavities. Less commonly, colonies occur on steep mainland cliffs. In its range core, colonies are sometimes very large (100 000bp or many times larger) nesting at densities of up to 1–2 bp/m^2, but in the far N and S they may contain only dozens or hundreds of breeding pairs.

When not breeding, birds disperse widely at very low densities over vast areas of ocean from the ice-edge S to the Azores, Canary Islands and SE USA. Many northern birds move S but others, especially first-winter birds, appear off Newfoundland. Some birds of all ages from the west coasts of Britain & Ireland winter in the W Mediterranean whereas breeders from the east coast remain in the North Sea (Harris 1984).

Breeding distribution is fragmented, due to the availability of suitable safe breeding areas. Except for minor alterations at the southern range limit, and for the extinctions of the Helgoland population in 1830 and the Swedish population (on Soteskär) in 1970 there has been remarkably little long-term change in distribution. Young unfledged birds were introduced to Soteskär from 1981 to 1985, a pair probably breeding in 1988 (Ahlén & Tjernberg 1992).

Estimates of Puffin numbers should be treated with healthy scepticism, as they are often based on rough counts of large numbers of birds. The largest populations occur in Iceland (2–3Mbp), Norway (2M), Great Britain (0.5M) and the Faeroes (0.5M). By comparison, numbers in other countries are trivial. The total population is some 6Mbp. The large size and inaccessibility of colonies makes the assessment of change both difficult and speculative. However, without doubt the European population has declined substantially in the 20th century, as on St Kilda, Scotland, crashing from 'millions' to 300 000bp (Harris 1984). Many declines have now slowed or even reversed.

Puffin numbers in much of Norway have decreased since the 1960s. The Røst Archipelago population declined by 60–70% between 1969 and 1988 but then increased by 20% (Anker-Nilssen & Barrett 1991, pers comm). Declines occurred in the Faeroes, Russia, France and the Channel Islands, but again some recent increases have been noted. The main French population on Sept Îles declined from 10 000bp in 1912 to 250bp in 1982, but since has remained stable or possibly has increased very slightly (Siorat 1992). Numbers in Great Britain remained approximately constant during the 1970s and 1980s whereas those in Ireland declined slightly (Lloyd *et al* 1991). The population on the British North Sea coast increased at 15–20% *per annum* during the 1960–70s but the rate has now reduced. Unfortunately recent information on changes in the Icelandic population is lacking.

The reasons for the past declines are unclear. Those in Britain & Ireland appear to have been a result of oceanographic change, sometimes augmented by local factors such as oiling or mammalian predation. That on Røst followed a long run of breeding failures resulting from a dramatic decline in herring *Clupea harengus*, possibly due to overfishing (Anker-Nilssen 1987, Harris 1984).

Michael P Harris (GB)

Pterocles orientalis

Black-bellied Sandgrouse

CZ Stepokur písečný
D Sandflughuhn
E Ortega
F Ganga unibande
FIN Hietakyyhky
G Ερημοπεριστερόκοτα
H Feketehasú pusztaityúk
I Ganga
NL Zwartbuikzandhoen
P Cortiçol-de-barriga-preta
PL Stepówka czarnobrzucha
R Чернобрюхий рябок
S Svartbukig flyghöna

SPEC Cat 3, Threat status V

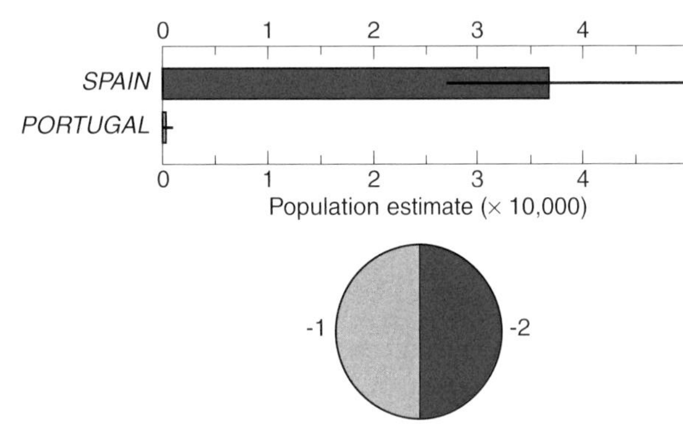

% in top 10 countries: 100.0
Total number of populated European countries: 2
Total European population 27,314–50,334 (37,059)
Russian population 100–1000 (316)
Turkish population 5000–50,000 (15,811)

The Black-bellied Sandgrouse is the largest of the *Pterocles* genus. The nominate subspecies is resident in W Europe, the other, *arenarius*, occurs in Europe in the area between the Volga and Ural Rivers and is migratory. A typical steppe bird, the Black-bellied Sandgrouse inhabits treeless plains, grassland, shrub-steppes or semi-arid (annual precipitation 200–500mm) cultivated land. Its breeding range stretches from the Iberian Peninsula and Fuerteventura (Canary Islands) in the W, through North Africa, Israel, Turkey, Iraq and Iran to Afghanistan, Kazakhstan and N China in the E. It is resident and sedentary over most of its range, but the Asiatic population is mostly migratory, wintering in N India and Asia Minor, some reaching Saudi Arabia.

In winter, the species tends to be gregarious, flocks usually smaller than 50 individuals. Now a scarce bird in the Iberian Peninsula, its distribution though extensive is limited to favourable habitats, such as flat or slightly rolling plains, rough pastures, eroded slopes, grassy steppes scattered with vegetation but lacking trees, or cereal farming areas, up to an altitude of 1300m asl. It shows a clear preference for fallow land, which illustrates its dependence on traditional, low-intensity farming.

In Spain, the largest populations are found in the Ebro Valley (Navarre and Aragón) and in Extremadura. In Catalonia it is now limited to two small nuclei of no more than 15bp (Muntaner *et al* 1984a, Estrada & Curco 1991). It is a regular but scarce breeder in Castilla-León, but slightly greater numbers can be found in C and SW Castilla-La Mancha. Andalucía retains only a few flocks in the provinces of Almeria, Granada (Pleguezuelos 1992) and Jaén (Yanes 1993), as does an area near Coto de Doñana, Sevilla. In Portugal it breeds in three areas, each representing the western limits of the Spanish populations of Salamanca, Caceres and Badajoz (Rufino 1989).

The Black-bellied Sandgrouse shows a decline in most of its range apparently due to the spread of intensive agriculture, the increase in irrigated land and the afforestation of prime habitat. As a European species, its long-term survival looks bleak.

Maria Nièves de Borbon (E) Cristina Barros (E)

Pterocles alchata

Pin-tailed Sandgrouse

CZ	Stepokur krásný	I	Grandule
D	Spießflughuhn	NL	Witbuikzandhoen
E	Ganga Común	P	Cortiçol-de-barriga-branca
F	Ganga cata	PL	Stepówka białobrzucha
FIN	Jouhihietakyyhky	R	Белобрюхий рябок
G	Περιστερόκοτα	S	Vitbukig flyghöna
H	Nyílfarkú pusztaityúk		

SPEC Cat 3, Threat status E

Like every species of the genus *Pterocles*, this handsome bird is strongly tied to steppe environments with an arid or semi-arid climate. Its distribution stretches from the Iberian Peninsula and SE France through North Africa, Israel, Turkey, Syria, Iran and Iraq to Afghanistan, Turkmenistan, Uzbekistan and S Kazakhstan. Although largely sedentary, the eastern populations are partially migratory and irregularly irruptive, reaching N Saudi Arabia, Pakistan and W India, but the species can be erratic in occurrence over most of its range. In winter, residents are liable to disperse to the southern parts of the breeding range or beyond. Gregarious all year round, in winter it can form flocks of 1000 birds or more.

In Europe, except for a relict population of 165–175bp at La Crau in SW France (Cheylan 1994b), fairly good numbers of birds can be found in the extensive steppe regions of the Iberian Peninsula. Common in the Ebro Valley (Aragón) and areas of Extremadura like Llanos de Caceres and La Serena (1650bp; M.N. de Borbon & C. Barros, pers obs), it has almost disappeared in Catalonia, with only one nucleus of about 100bp left (Estrada & Curco 1991). It has suffered a massive decline in Navarra (Elosegui 1985). Local and scarce in Castilla-León, it can be relatively abundant in some areas of Castilla-La Mancha. Although extinct in Almería and Granada (Pleguezuelos 1992), it is common on the mudflats of Coto de Doñana (García *et al* 1987), but decreasingly so to the W along the Huelva coast to Portugal (<100bp), where it can be found only in two separate ranges which are diminishing (Rufino 1989).

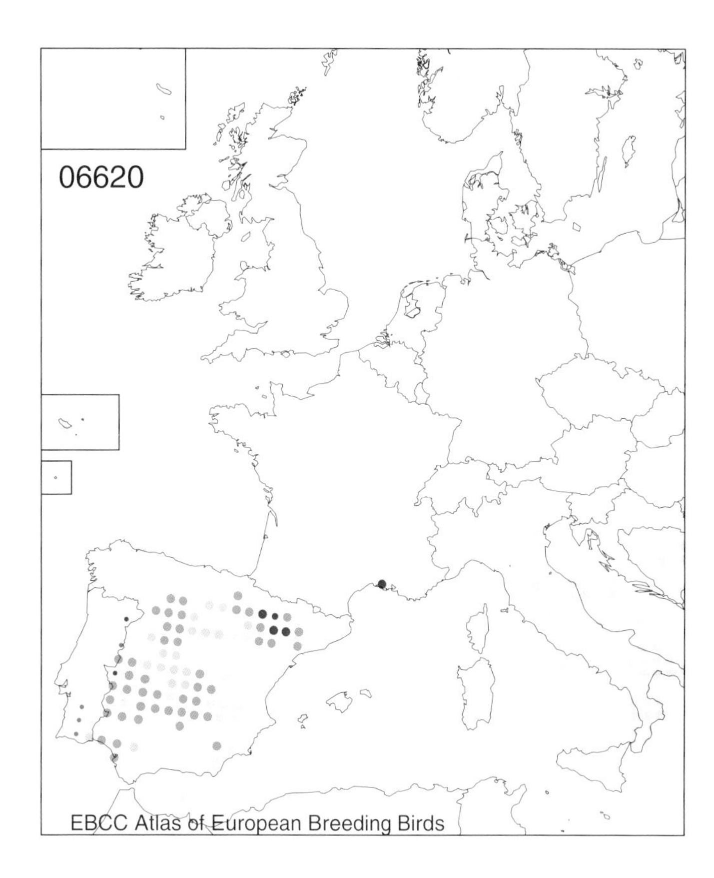

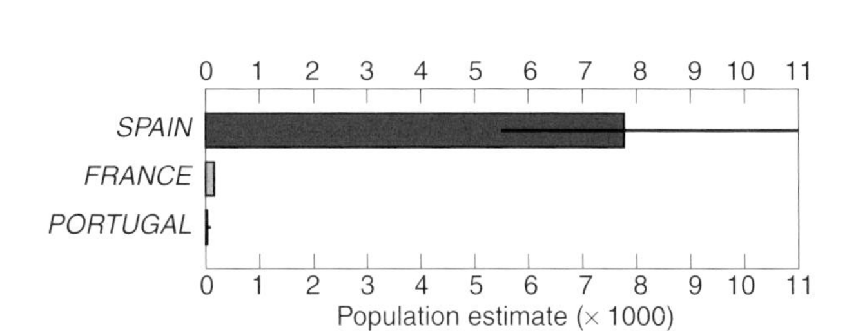

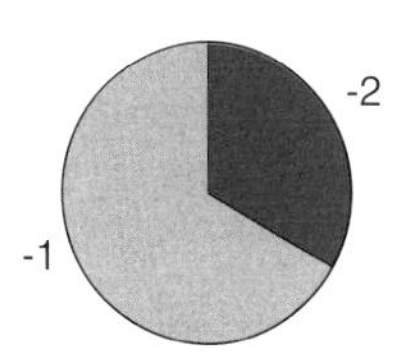

% in top 10 countries: 100.0
Total number of populated European countries: 3
Total European population 5691–11,192 (7969)
Turkish population 1000–10,000 (3162)

In Spain, its habitat is limited to treeless plains up to 1000m asl, mainly dry grasslands, uncultivated ground, dry and sparsely vegetated mudflats above the tideline, and more rarely, fallows. In its prime habitat of dry grassland the population density is *c*4 bp/100ha (M.N. de Borbon & C. Barros, pers obs).

The W European Pin-tailed Sandgrouse population is in clear decline over most of its range due to irrigation of natural habitats, agricultural intensification and locally, overgrazing of dry grasslands; it must be considered as under long-term threat.

Maria Nièves de Borbon (E) Cristina Barros (E)

Columba livia

Rock Dove

CZ	Holub skalní	I	Piccione selvatico
D	Felsentaube	NL	Rotsduif
E	Paloma Bravía	P	Pombo-das-rochas
F	Pigeon biset	PL	Gołąb skalny
FIN	Kalliokyyhky	R	Скалистый голубь
G	Αγριοπερίστερο	S	Klippduva
H	Szirti galamb		

Non-SPEC, Threat status S

Originally, the Rock Dove was confined to coastal and inland cliffs from the western Palearctic and northern Afrotropical regions to the Indian subcontinent, between 7° and 62°N, the exact limits being obscure. Its present distribution limits are obscure where widespread hybridization with feral stock has caused range extensions which largely form intergradation zones. The Feral Pigeon nests in urban areas worldwide.

Unfortunately feral Rock Dove populations have usually been considered scientifically uninteresting, making our knowledge of their past (and present) distribution incomplete and unsatisfactory. Of all the species in this

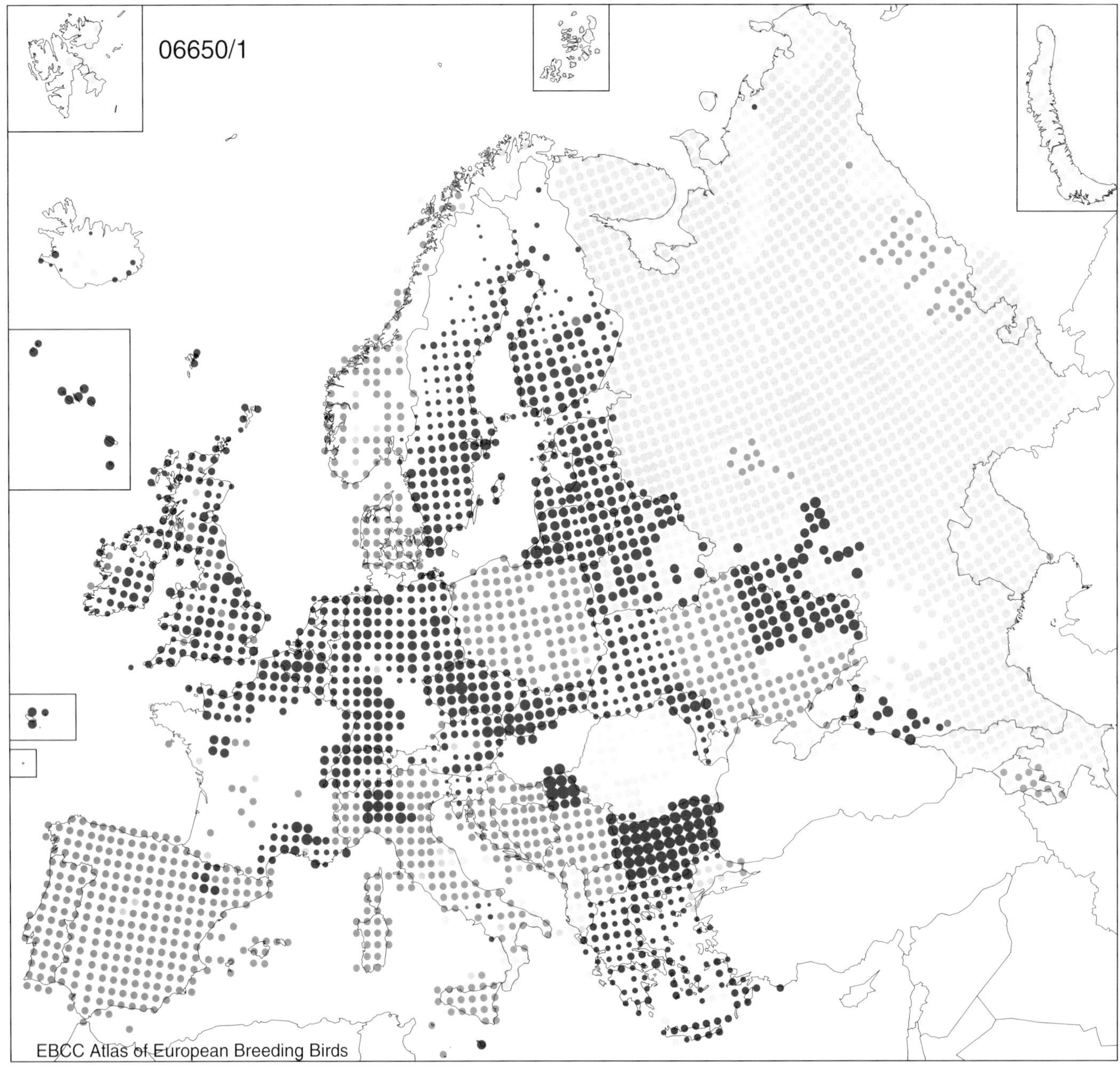

Note: Data for Feral Pigeons were not supplied for (all squares in) France, Germany, Hungary, Romania and Austria which accounts for the apparent gaps in the distribution of this species in these countries.

Feral Pigeon

CZ	Holub domácí	**I**	Piccione torraiolo
D	Straßentaube	**NL**	Tamme Duïf
E	Paloma Doméstica	**P**	Pombo-doméstico
F	Pigeon domestique	**PL**	Gołąb miejski
FIN	Kesykyyhky	**R**	Сизый голубь
G	Ημερο Περιστέρι	**S**	Tamduva
H	Parlagi galamb		

Atlas, few, if any, are as poorly known as the Rock Dove/Feral Pigeon. The maps and population data therefore had to be combined.

Finnish feral birds are descended from courier pigeons imported in the 19th century, feral populations becoming established in the larger cities in S Finland in the 1880s. Around 1900 the Feral Pigeon was introduced at several Lapland locations (Alapulli 1964). Only the Rovanimi population has become permanent, the northerly sites, Kemijarvi (lasted until World War II), Pelhosennimi, Sodentyta and Ivalo being occupied more briefly. Stray courier or racing pigeons may be encountered almost anywhere in Lapland. This same pattern of occupation, with courier or domesticated pigeon escapes, has occurred across the rest of the world, starting in Europe probably about the 11th century.

In the NW, the Rock Dove occurs in the Faeroes and northern Britain. It breeds along the coasts of Scotland, including Shetland, and also Ireland. It formerly bred on the Norwegian coast, the only Fennoscandian sites. A colony existed in the 18th century in Sør-Trøndelag, and the Rogaland colony of *c*100bp was destroyed by American Mink *Mustela vison* in the 1940s (Ree 1994). The Feral Pigeon's northern range limit crosses 70°N in Norway and 66°N in Finland, but in Russia (except for outlying populations, like Murmansk, 69°N) it lies along the St Petersburg–Kalinin–Gorki axis (*HVM*).

Feral populations breed in all European countries, although not all have been censused for the *Atlas.* Several countries provided population data only for Rock Dove. Recorded populations exceeding 1Mbp exist in Russia, Spain and Belarus. In much of Europe, numbers increased considerably after World War II (Lever 1987), apparently the consequence of people's higher living standards producing greater waste. However, in very dense populations, reproduction rate declines below that needed to compensate for adult mortality (Haag 1988).

The Rock Dove breeds naturally in Britain & Ireland on seacliffs, preferring those possessing undisturbed caves or deep fissures. In continental Europe it also uses inland cliffs (Simms 1979). Some feral populations have reverted to cliff-breeding. The Feral Pigeon usually prefers buildings and other human constructions, especially those with cavities and ledges, like churches, museums, theatres and railway stations (Simms 1979). In Finland it seemingly prefers urban centres with old buildings, largely avoiding later suburbs with modern architecture (L. Saari, pers obs). Small towns or villages may contain only a few birds, but large cities may hold well over 100 000, as in Zagreb, where *c*129 000 birds were counted in 1984–87 (Poljak *et al* 1990). In city centres densities of up to 250 bp/km² have been reported, although much higher values are likely given the censusing difficulties. Using stratified sampling, an average of 2849 birds/km² was calculated for Barcelona, almost four times the figure derived from mapping studies (Senar & Sol 1991). Such numbers may well be a major factor in the increase of Peregrine *Falco peregrinus* and Goshawk *Accipiter gentilis* breeding in some European cities (Würfels 1994).

Despite the pronounced long-distance homing ability of domesticated birds, free-living populations (wild and feral) are resident or even sedentary, although (apart from ubiquitous stray racing pigeons) Finnish bird observatories record some seasonal movement.

Lennart Saari (FIN)

0 5 10 15 20

SPAIN
BELARUS
GERMANY
UKRAINE
LATVIA
AUSTRIA
UNITED KINGDOM
ESTONIA
SWEDEN
AZORES
Other countries

0 5 10 15 20
Population estimate (× 100,000)

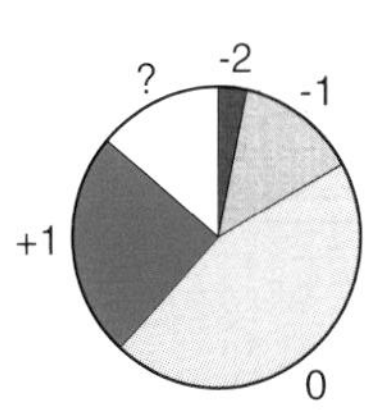

% in top 10 countries: 97.9
Total number of populated European countries: 28
Total European population 5,094,035–5,974,424 (5,420,033)
Russian population 1,000,000–10,000,000 (3,162,278)
Turkish population 50,000–500,000 (158,114)

Columba oenas **Stock Dove**

CZ	Holub doupňák	I	Colombella
D	Hohltaube	NL	Holeduif
E	Paloma Zurita	P	Pombo-bravo
F	Pigeon colombin	PL	Siniak
FIN	Uuttukyyhky	R	Клинтух
G	Φασσοπερίστερο	S	Skogsduva
H	Kék galamb		

SPEC Cat 4, Threat status S

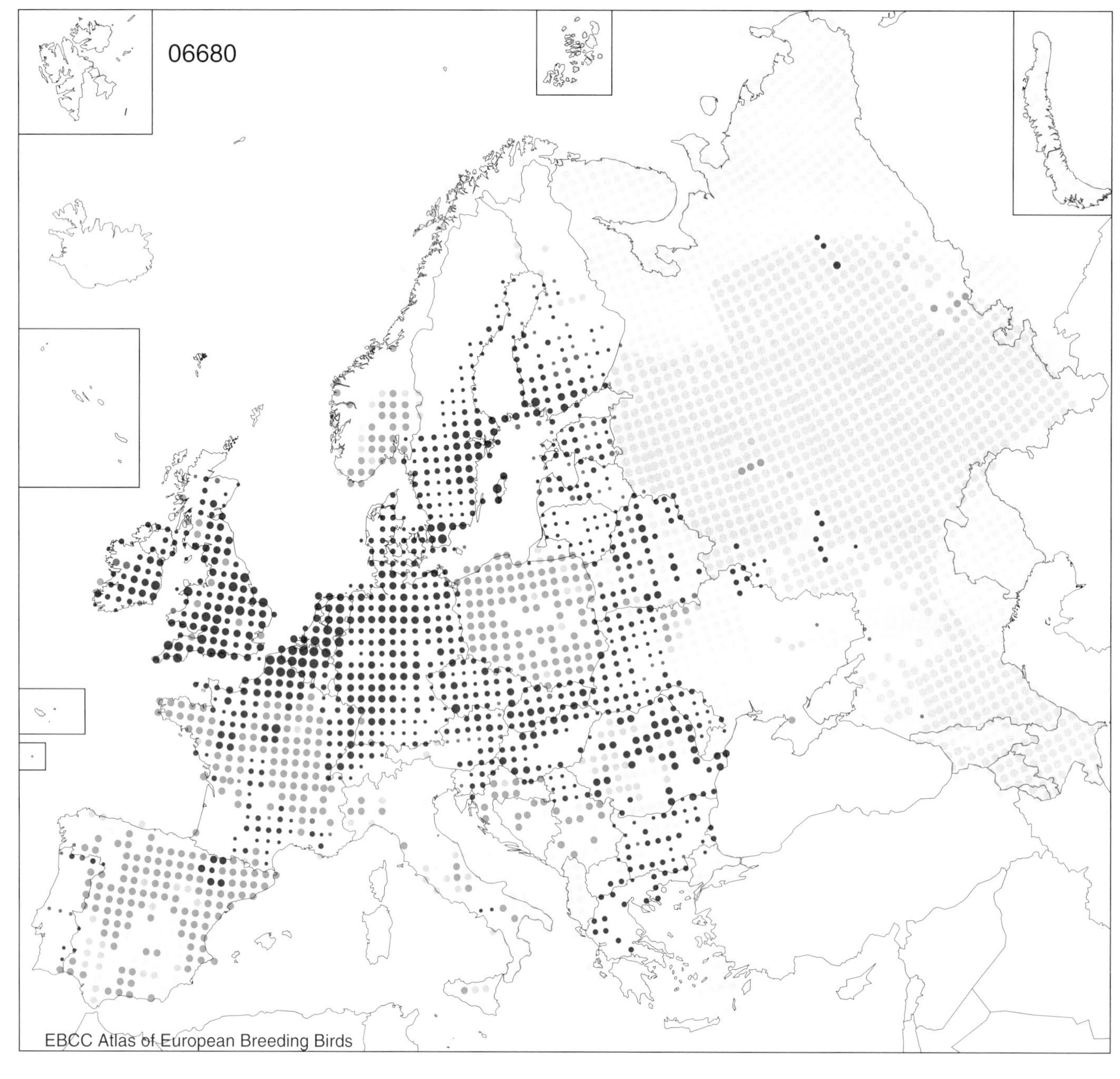

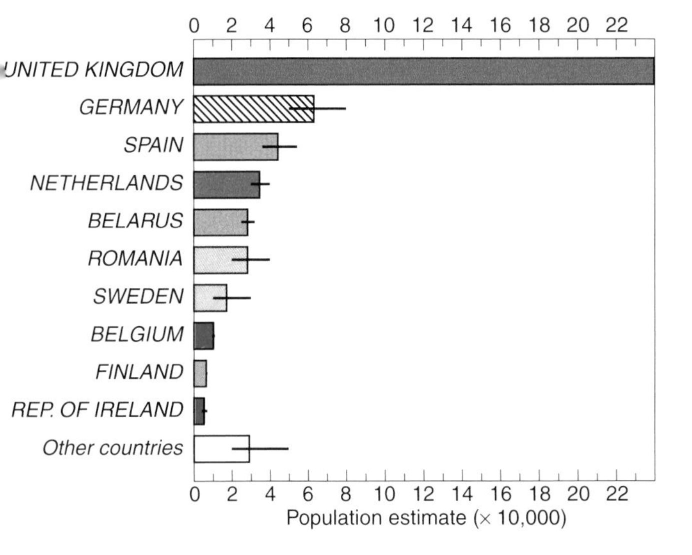

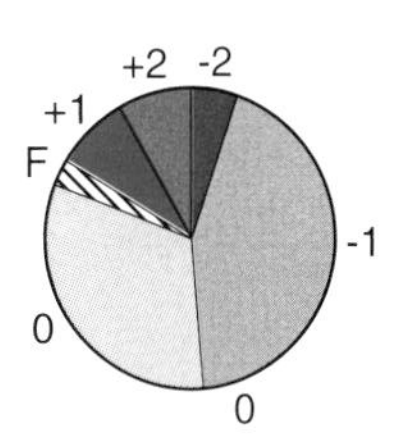

% in top 10 countries: 94.3
Total number of populated European countries: 37
Total European population 486,800–535,906 (507,128)
Russian population 10,000–100,000 (31,623)
Turkish population 1000–10,000 (3162)

The Stock Dove belongs to the European–Turkestan fauna type and has a W and C Palearctic distribution. The nominate subspecies' distribution extends from the Atlantic coast to W Siberia and from the Mediterranean (including Morocco) through Asiatic Turkey to the Caspian Sea and into N Kazakhstan. The other subspecies breeds eastwards from S Kazakhstan.

The Stock Dove breeds in the boreal, temperate and mediterranean zones, in montane regions and in small numbers in the steppe zone. It requires two different habitats for successful colonization, not necessarily adjacent, in which to feed and nest. It feeds on open areas with short growth or lacking vegetation and avoids dense grassland. It has a strong preference for mature woodland containing ample nesting holes, particularly where Black Woodpecker *Dryocopus martius* is prevalent and has excavated many cavities. Stands of European beech *Fagus sylvatica*, 120 or more years old and lacking undergrowth, are especially favoured, as are mature woodlands of pine *Pinus*, oak *Quercus* and alder *Alnus* regionally. Provided there are nest holes, the species will colonize city parks. It nests in holes in the ground (mostly rabbit burrows) on the Friesian Islands, increasing in number locally since 1965 (Plaisier 1992). It has formed colonies locally where it has discovered concentrations of holes in rocks or buildings.

The Stock Dove will breed at high altitude if the trees are sufficiently tall. In the low mountain ranges of C Europe it breeds up to *c*850m asl, in the Alps rarely above 1000m asl, but in Greece and Bulgaria almost up to 2000m asl (Möckel 1988).

The Stock Dove's northern limit matches the 13°C July isotherm, and apart from some small gaps, particularly towards the Mediterranean, achieves almost blanket coverage within its distribution area. The Nordic populations, mainly in low-lying southern regions, nevertheless spread quite far N, breeding up to 65°N, and exceptionally at 66°N.

There are prominent distribution gaps, usually near coasts, in SW France, N Spain, Portugal, Italy, Slovenia, Croatia and Greece, where the species frequents mainly mountain woodland. It is absent from Iceland, the Faeroes, the Orkney and Shetland Islands and most Mediterranean islands, but may breed in Sicily. The Stock Dove's European population comprises *c*550 000bp, liable locally to conflicting trends. Great Britain and The Netherlands recorded population increases of more than 50% between 1970 and 1990 (O'Connor & Mead 1984, SOVON 1987), other increases occurring in Ireland, Belgium and Denmark. Their total of *c*290 000bp represents over 50% of the European population. The populations in Poland, Germany, Sweden, Romania, Hungary and Greece appear stable. Some countries, however, report a population decrease of between 20% and 50%, particularly on the northern distribution limit (Norway, Finland and Estonia) and around the Mediterranean (Spain, France, Croatia and Bulgaria). Local decreases are occurring in Switzerland and Austria.

Two factors determine local abundance: the availability of food and the existence of sufficient nest holes. Intensive agriculture may be reducing the former, especially because it affects the herbaceous flora (Saari 1984), and loss of woodlands and the application of modern forest management techniques may be reducing the latter (Möckel 1988). Perhaps less important are predation and hunting pressure. Climatic variations may limit its breeding distribution and population density. However, where nest holes are plentiful, breeding can assume colony-like proportions. Densities of 6–11 bp/ha have occurred in stands of European beech, reaching 18–20 bp/240m^2 on a small island. In the sand-dunes of the Friesian Islands, the density reaches 5 bp/10ha. However, overall breeding density varies between 0.2 and 4.0 bp/10km^2, averaging *c*1.5 (Möckel 1988).

Stock Dove populations from NE and C Europe winter in the mediterranean zone, especially in C Spain. Populations in Britain, W Europe and the Mediterranean remain largely resident.

Reinhard Möckel (D)

Columba palumbus

Woodpigeon

CZ	Holub hřivnáč	**I**	Colombaccio
D	Ringeltaube	**NL**	Houtduif
E	Paloma Torcaz	**P**	Pombo-torcaz
F	Pigeon ramier	**PL**	Grzywacz
FIN	Sepelkyyhky	**R**	Вяхирь
G	Φάσσα	**S**	Ringduva
H	Örvös galamb		

SPEC Cat 4, Threat status S

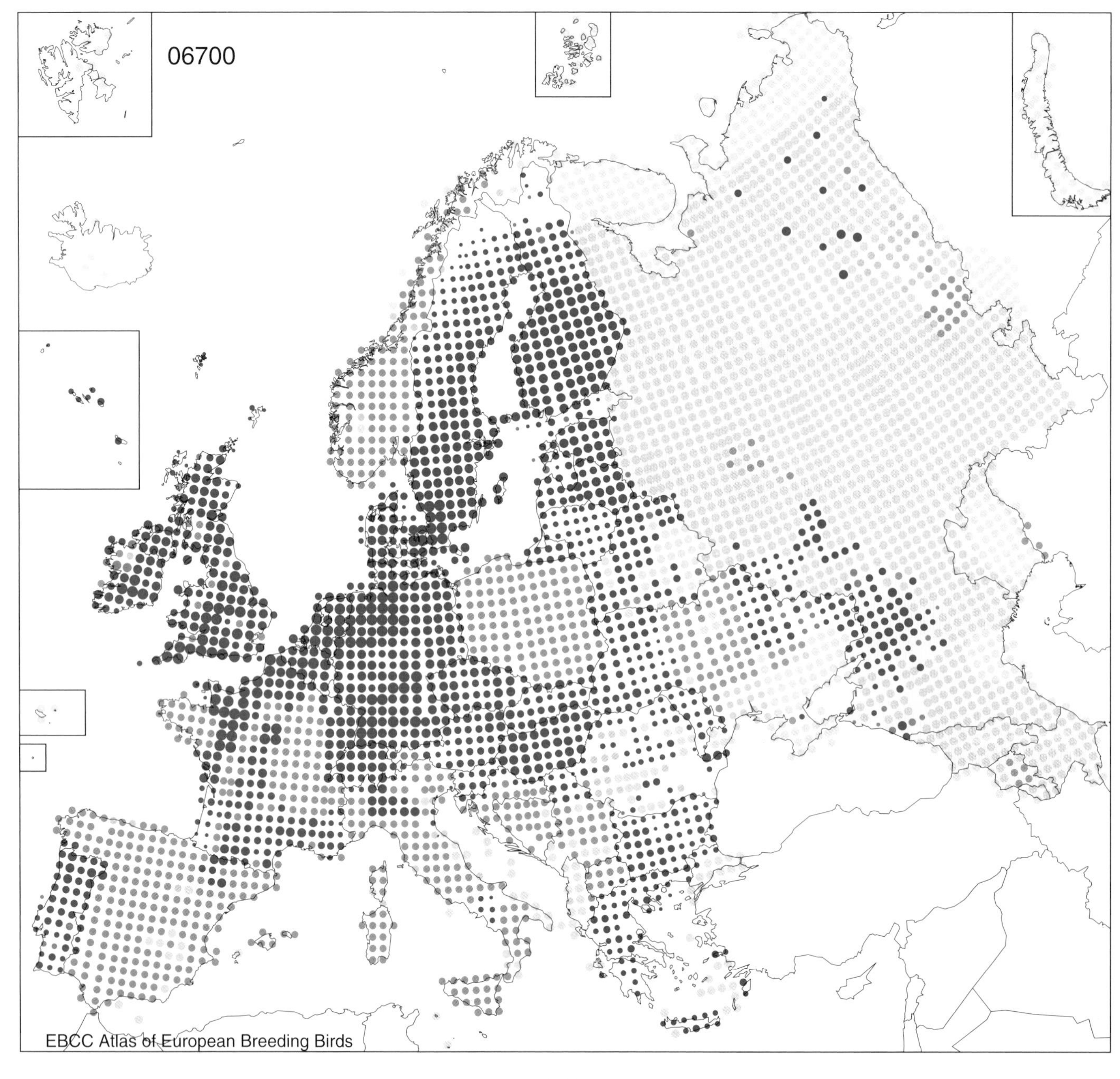

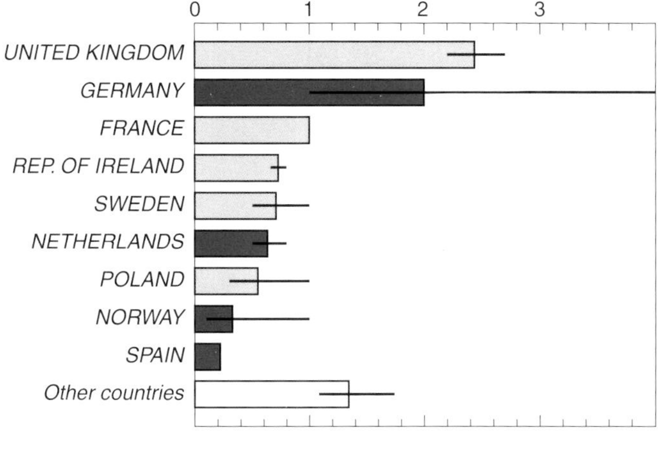

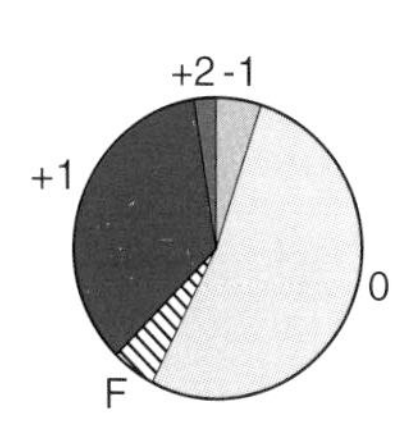

% in top 10 countries: 88.4
Total number of populated European countries: 40
Total European population 8,816,463–12,137,934 (9,928,646)
Russian population 100,000–1,000,000 (316,228)
Turkish population 5000–20,000 (10,000)

The Woodpigeon, a Palearctic species, has a predominantly European distribution, reaching 70°N in Norway, and breeding in all countries, although irregularly in Iceland. Outside Europe it occurs in North Africa, C–W Asia, W Siberia and occasionally reaches C Siberia (Rogacheva 1992). The island subspecies *C.p. madeirensis* and *azorica* occupy the respective archipelagos, and *palumbus* occurs over most of Europe, intergrading into *iranica* around the Caucasus; *casiotis* occurs E of Europe.

Once a typical woodland species, it can now maintain a high population level only in close association with arable farming (Murton 1965). Since the early 19th century it has steadily increased to take advantage of farming practice changes. Mechanized cereal harvesting in particular favoured successful reproduction and rearing additional broods, partly by enabling the main breeding season to shift towards late summer when food supplies (ripening cereals and harvest waste) peaked. The Woodpigeon further adapted to human activities by colonizing cities from the early 1800s onwards (Tomiałojć 1976), probably because predation risk was lower, allowing surplus birds from densely populated habitats to survive.

Its main breeding habitats remain dense coniferous stands, preferably spruce *Picea* and fir *Abies*, 5–10m high, close to arable land. The Woodpigeon may breed solitarily or semi-colonially, at densities of up to 30 bp/km^2 in Finland (Saari 1984), 1800 bp/km^2 in Dutch woodlands (Bijlsma 1980) and *c*1500 bp/km^2 in Polish urban parks (Tomiałojć 1976).

Owing to the difficulties of censusing the species (Saari 1984) the population figures are only rough estimates, the European total being between 7.7M and 15.5Mbp. Densities of 10 000–43 000 bp/50km square occur in Britain & Ireland, The Netherlands, Belgium, Germany and Denmark, all relatively sparsely wooded but intensively farmed countries. Intermediate densities of 1000–4500 bp/50km square are typical of France, C and E Europe and Fennoscandia, generally decreasing towards the S, E and N. Lower values (usually <500 bp/50km square) obtain in Ukraine, Portugal, Slovenia, Italy, Albania, Greece, Bulgaria, Romania and Moldova.

European populations increased markedly in range and numbers throughout the 20th century (Murton 1965). In Finland the range extended considerably in the warm 1930s and again in the 1960s and 1970s, advancing 700km northwards since 1900 (Saari 1984), and also in Norway (since the 1970s), some birds now nesting in Finnmark. These changes probably arose through increased cereal production (the Woodpigeon's northernmost limit in Finland in the 1970s matched that of barley *Hordeum* spp) and to increased plantation acreage of Norway spruce *P. abies* (Viker 1994), but the underlying reason is the gradual increase in mean annual temperature in NW Europe (Murton 1965). European stronghold populations seemingly have been stable or slightly increasing since 1970, but why this should be so is unclear. Drastic changes in farmland management largely determine the vicissitudes of the species (O'Connor & Shrubb 1986), locally and temporarily enhanced by severe winters and shooting. In The Netherlands, the upsurge of maize-growing since the 1970s and the simultaneous decrease in cereal acreage more than halved the population during the 1980s and decreased the reproductive rate (R.G. Bijlsma, pers comm). Indirect evidence for decreases elsewhere in Europe comes from autumn migration systematic counts, as in SW Germany (Gatter *et al* 1990).

Most Fennoscandian birds are migratory, leapfrogging the mainly sedentary W European populations (W of the 0°C January isotherm). Finnish birds start and finish migrating before their Scandinavian counterparts (Saari 1984). Fennoscandian birds winter mainly in France and Iberia, in Portugal and Spain exploiting the open oak-woodlands which harbour crops or pasture pigs (Purroy *et al* 1987).

In Europe, the Woodpigeon is subject to high hunting pressure, at least 9.5M birds being shot annually while the scale of hunting increases (Purroy *et al* 1987), a circumstance which may yet threaten the species' numbers if productivity drops for any reason.

Lennart Saari (FIN)

This species account is sponsored by Peter Herkenrath, Bonn, D.

Columba trocaz

Long-toed Pigeon

CZ	Holub dlouhoprstý	I	Colomba di Madera
D	Silberhalstaube	NL	Trocazduif
E	Paloma de Madeira	P	Pombo-dos-loureiros da Madeira
F	Pigeon trocaz	PL	Gołąb maderski
FIN	Madeirankyyhky	R	Серебристый голубь
G	Μακροδάχτυλο Περιστέρι	S	Madeiraduva
H	Madeira galamb		

SPEC Cat 1, Threat status V

The Long-toed Pigeon, also known as Madeira Laurel Pigeon, is resident on the island of Madeira. An endemic species, its main habitat is the native laurel forest, although it also uses a considerable area of non-native forest throughout the year. The laurel forest is restricted to the mountainous northern slopes, except for a few isolated pockets in the S, and covers an area of *c*15 000ha. (Costa Neves, pers comm).

The Long-toed Pigeon was probably exceptionally plentiful before the island was first settled, but overhunting and major habitat loss probably have led to a significant decrease in numbers and range. This decline may not have ceased until 1986, the year after its inclusion in the *EU Wild Birds Directive*. At that time its population was estimated to be over 2700 birds (M.J. Jones 1990). There now appears to have been a strong recovery, the most recent published estimate (1991–92) placing lower and upper limits of 3500 and 4900 individuals (Oliveira & Jones in press). The current population probably approaches that upper limit.

Its distribution and density within the laurel forest and surrounding areas changes throughout the year and there is strong evidence that the birds move from valley to valley and use different types of habitat (Oliveira 1992). Although the species occurs throughout the altitudinal range of the laurel forest (300–1200m asl), it shows a strong preference for forest below 850m asl (Oliveira & Jones in press).

The Long-toed Pigeon breeds in the most inaccessible areas of its habitat and builds its nest in trees in the forest or in cliff cavities (F.J.A. Zino & Zino 1986). This probably has contributed to the relative lack of knowledge about its breeding biology.

Now that the Long-toed Pigeon is a protected species, the only known factor limiting distribution is habitat area, which if diminished would pose a serious risk to the survival of the species.

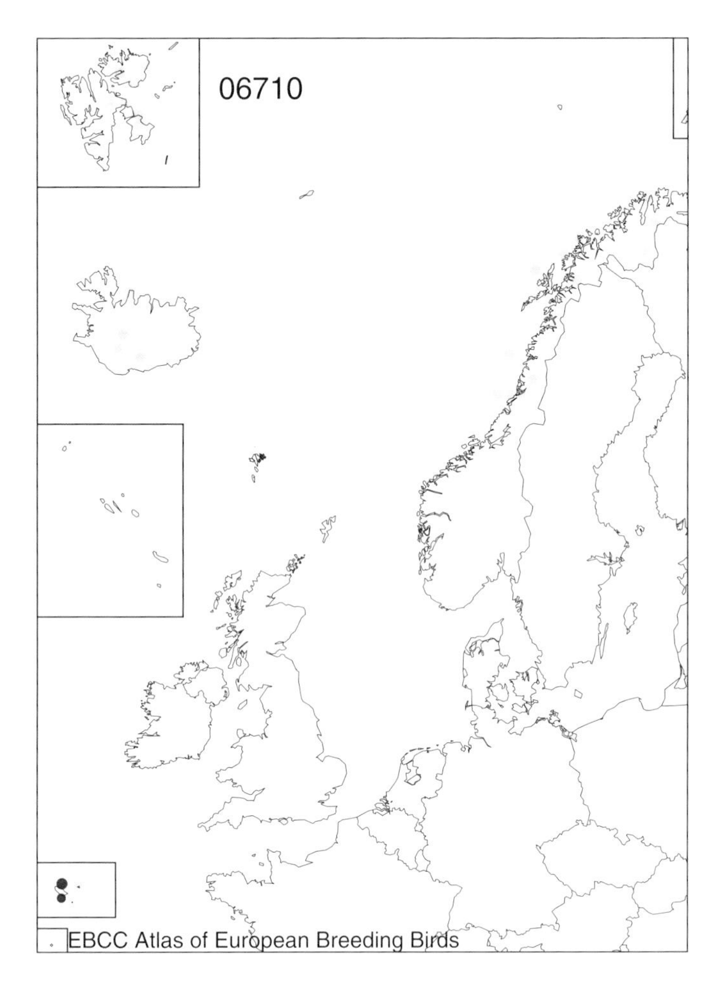

0

% in top 10 countries: 100.0
Total number of populated European countries: 1
Total European population 3500–4900 (4141)

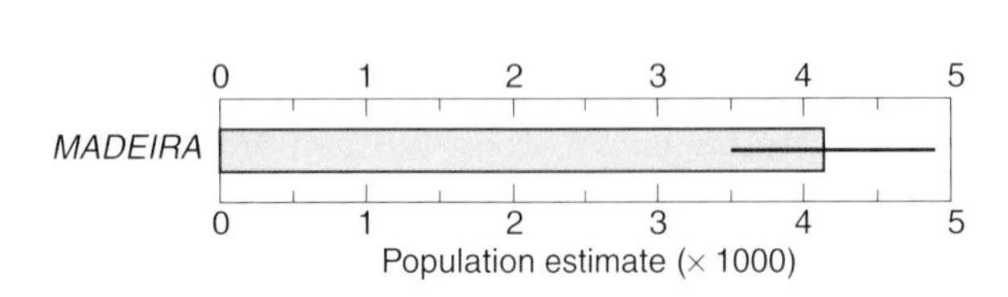

Paulo Oliveira (P)

Streptopelia senegalensis

Laughing Dove

CZ	Hrdlička senegalská	I	Tortora delle palme
D	Palmtaube	NL	Palmtortel
E	Tórtola Reidora	P	Rola do Senegal
F	Tourterelle maillée	PL	Synogarlica senegalska
FIN	Palmukyyhky	R	Большая горлица
G	Φοινικοπερίστερο	S	Palmduva
H	Pálmagerle		

Non-SPEC, Threat status S (P)

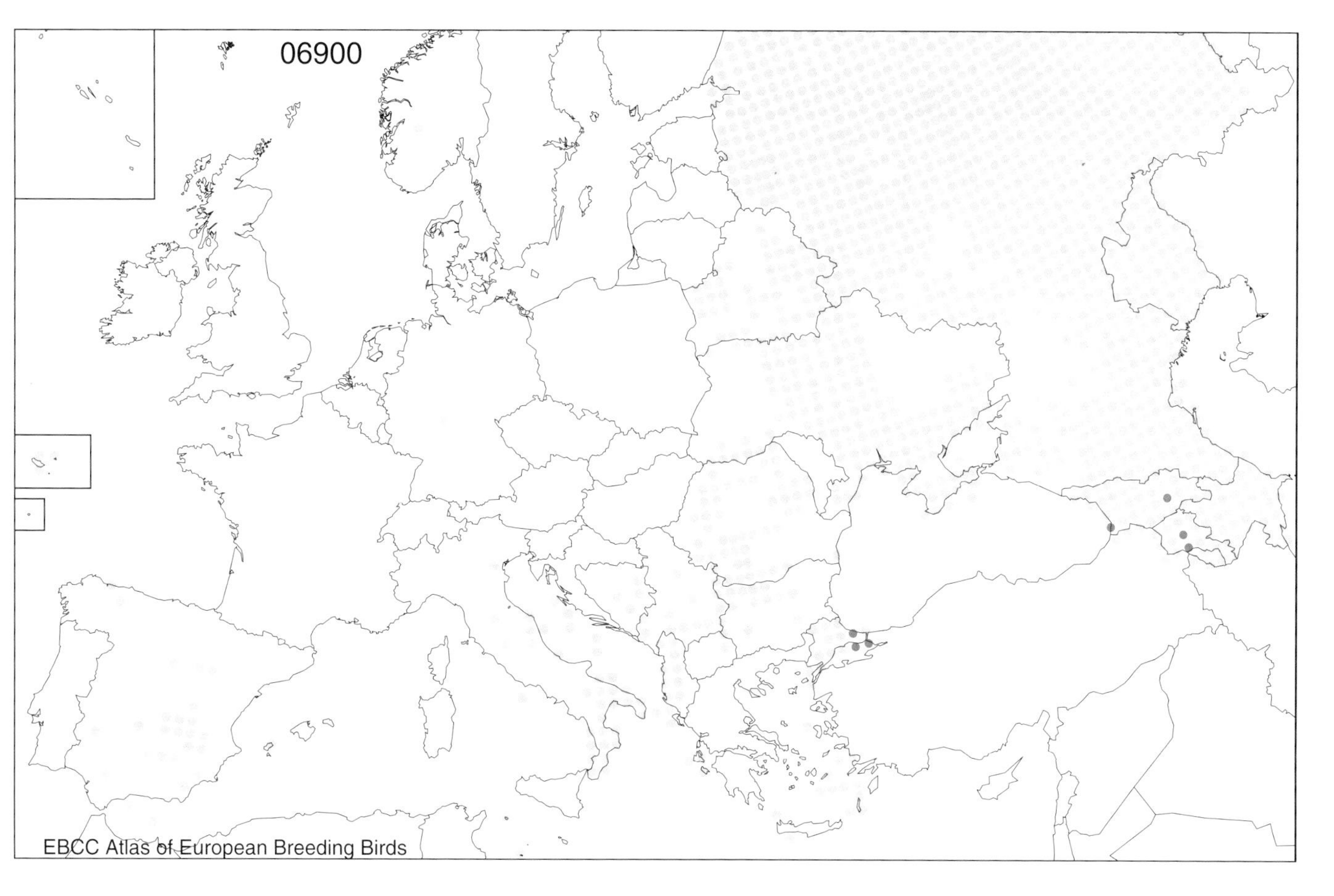

The Laughing Dove, similar to the Turtle Dove *S. turtur* in size and appearance, is distributed throughout Africa and SW Asia, but its occurrence is patchier in North Africa and the Middle East. It has been recorded in the *Atlas*' coverage area only in Georgia, Armenia and Istanbul (it also occurs in Asian Istanbul). It is more widespread in Turkey than generally stated (*cf* Kasparek 1991); breeding populations exist in most major cities. Birdwatchers visiting Istanbul typically record it only in the old city centre, but this reflects more the movements of birdwatchers; the species occurs throughout the city, including vast estates constructed in the late 1980s. It is absent from villages near Istanbul where Collared Dove *S. decaocto* is common, but within the city limits both species occur, Collared Dove occupying the more suburban park and garden habitats and Laughing Dove preferring densely built-up areas normally devoid of herbage.

Population trend data are not available but the species seemed scarcer in the past and is now expanding its range, at least in Asian Turkey (Kasparek 1991, Kirwan & Martins 1994). The Armenian and Georgian populations are probably of relatively recent origin, because the first records were in 1977 and 1981 respectively.

Detailed population density information is lacking, but possibly the Laughing Dove is commonest in older Istanbul: an estimated 20 singing males were noted in the Arnavutköy area alone (*c*1km^2), and the total Istanbul population could easily total several thousand breeding pairs (pers obs). The species has not been found anywhere else in Turkish Thrace despite searches during 1995.

The Laughing Dove is basically resident but stragglers have reached Malta, Italy, Greece and Cyprus. Istanbul birds, recorded first in 1836 (Kasparek 1991), are of the North African subspecies *phoenicophila* and probably originate from introductions; the nominate *senegalensis* breeds in SE Turkey (*BWP*), but the Armenian population is attributed to the C Asian *ermanni* subspecies (P. Saenger, pers comm to the Editors).

Gernant Magnin (TUR)

Streptopelia decaocto

Collared Dove

CZ	Hrdlička zahradní	I	Tortora dal collare
D	Türkentaube	NL	Turkse Tortel
E	Tórtola Turca	P	Rola-turca
F	Tourterelle turque	PL	Sierpówka
FIN	Turkinkyyhky	R	Кольчатая горлица
G	Δεκαοχτούρα	S	Turkduva
H	Balkáni gerle		

Non-SPEC, Threat status S (P)

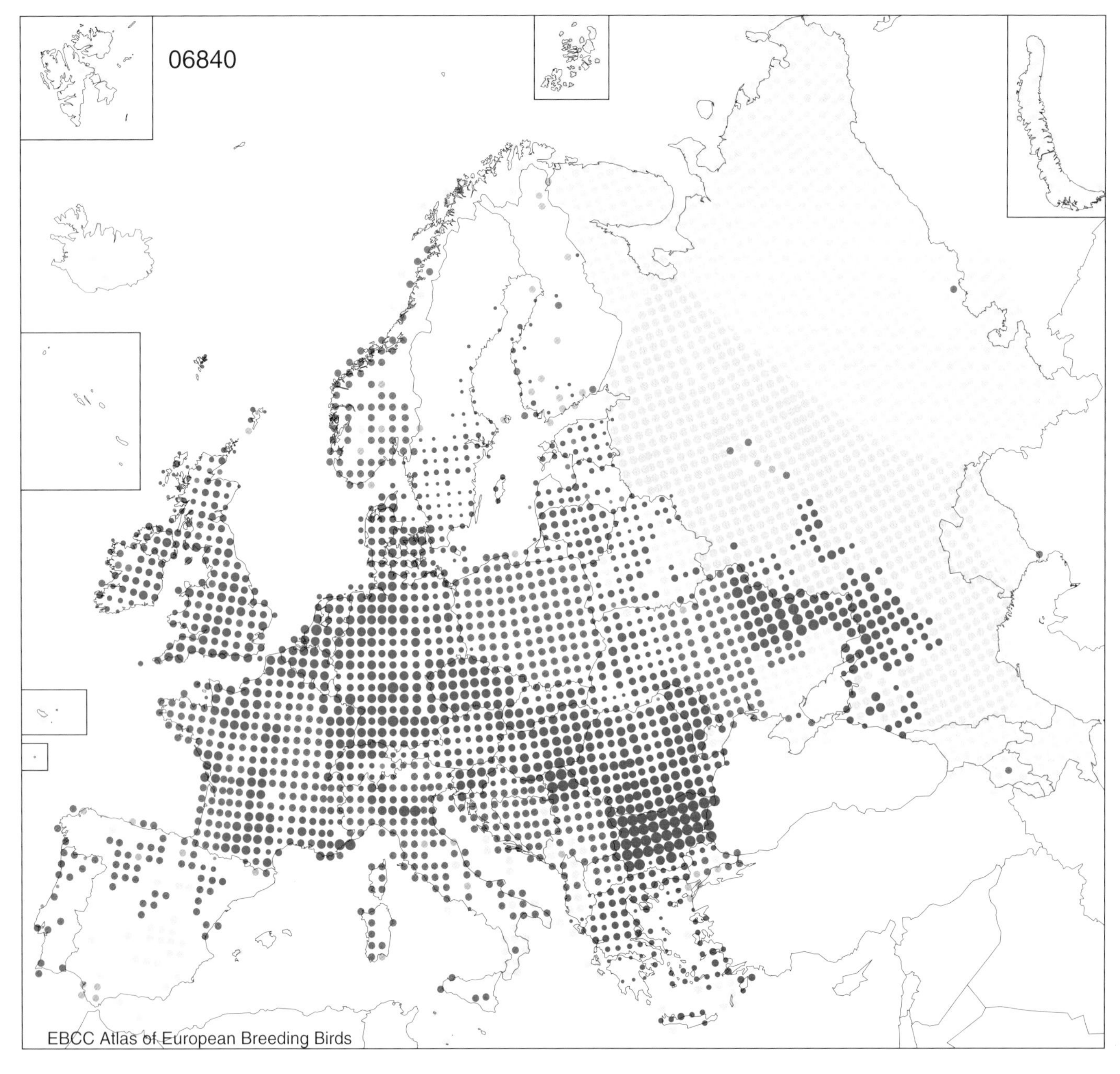

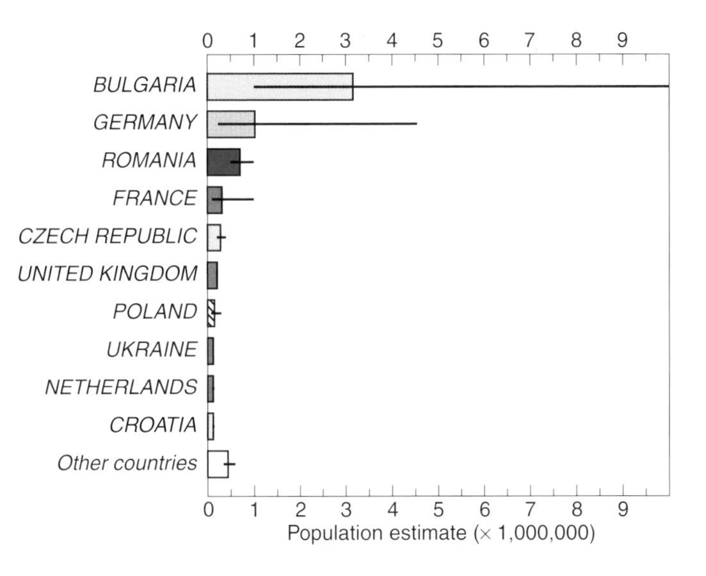

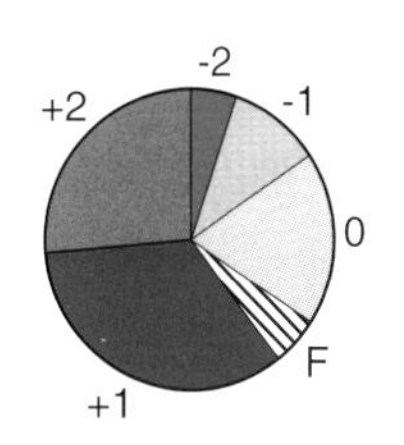

% in top 10 countries: 93.4
Total number of populated European countries: 38
Total European population 4,332,752–14,390,868 (6,658,482)
Russian population 10,000–100,000 (31,623)
Turkish population 100,000–1,000,000 (316,228)

The Collared Dove is now found almost throughout Europe, numbering some 7Mbp, yet it first bred on the continent around 1900. It spread from Turkey into the Balkan Peninsula, which it had filled, save for Greece, by 1928. Since then, it has progressed steadily northwestwards, its initial penetration sideways into Italy and Moldova being abortive. Confined to lower altitudinal levels, it squeezed into the alpine valleys and between the Alps and the Carpathians. The topography of the region first invaded therefore determined the shape of the invasion core, about which it spread equally forward and sideways. At present, it is saturating the Iberian Peninsula and spreading into North Africa on one side, and filling the entire Russian plain and crossing the Ural Mountains, penetrating western Siberia on the other (Nowak 1989). The diagrammatic map shows the pattern of the spread of the Collared Dove in Europe.

Apart from invading Europe so dramatically, it has also extended its range into Kazakhstan, Turkmenistan, and possibly Iran. Furthermore, this species of Indian origin has expanded W of the Jordan Valley via Palestine into Egypt and Saudi Arabia. Moreover, it also occurs in Japan and E China. Since its introduction into Florida around 1980, the Collared Dove is expected to fan out rapidly across the North American subcontinent (Hengeveld 1993).

The causes of the rapid spread are not known. One suggestion, that the species has altered genetically in a peripheral population (Mayr 1951), has not been substantiated. Another, that food conditions had improved, would not explain its expansion into Kazakhstan, Egypt, nor the Far East. Since it reached Britain, the proportion of long-range dispersers has declined; why it should have been relatively high during the invasion and whether that phenomenon would alone explain the speed and scale of the invasion is not known.

Additionally, the net rate of reproduction was greater than unity (Robertson 1990, van den Bosch *et al* 1992), which might also explain the range expansion; why and for how long the net rate should be so is not known. Curiously, the mean number of eggs per clutch (1.89) is too low to replace the two parents, particularly because the overall breeding success rate is only 39–41% (Górski 1989). Clearly, the number of clutches per year (3.8 in England, up to 6 in Poland) compensates for these low rates (Górski 1989, Robertson 1990). On the other hand the reproductive life of breeding birds cannot offer such compensation, because of the small proportion of birds which survive and reproduce to and beyond their second year.

It is clear from British monitoring data (Marchant *et al* 1990) that population size on farmland and in woodland there has stabilized since *c*1980. However, the main populations in suburban habitat have not been monitored. Trends amongst the longer established populations within the expanding invasion core may stabilize with time, and may contain fewer long-range dispersers. Populations at increasing distances from this core towards newly colonized areas show progressively more pronounced increases in numbers.

Rob Hengeveld (NL)

Pattern of spread of Collared Dove in Europe.

Streptopelia turtur

Turtle Dove

CZ	Hrdlička divoká	**I**	Tortora
D	Turteltaube	**NL**	Zomertortel
E	Tórtola Común	**P**	Rola-comum
F	Tourterelle des bois	**PL**	Turkawka
FIN	Turturikyyhky	**R**	Обыкновенная горлица
G	Τρυγόνι	**S**	Turturduva
H	Vadgerle		

SPEC Cat 3, Threat status D

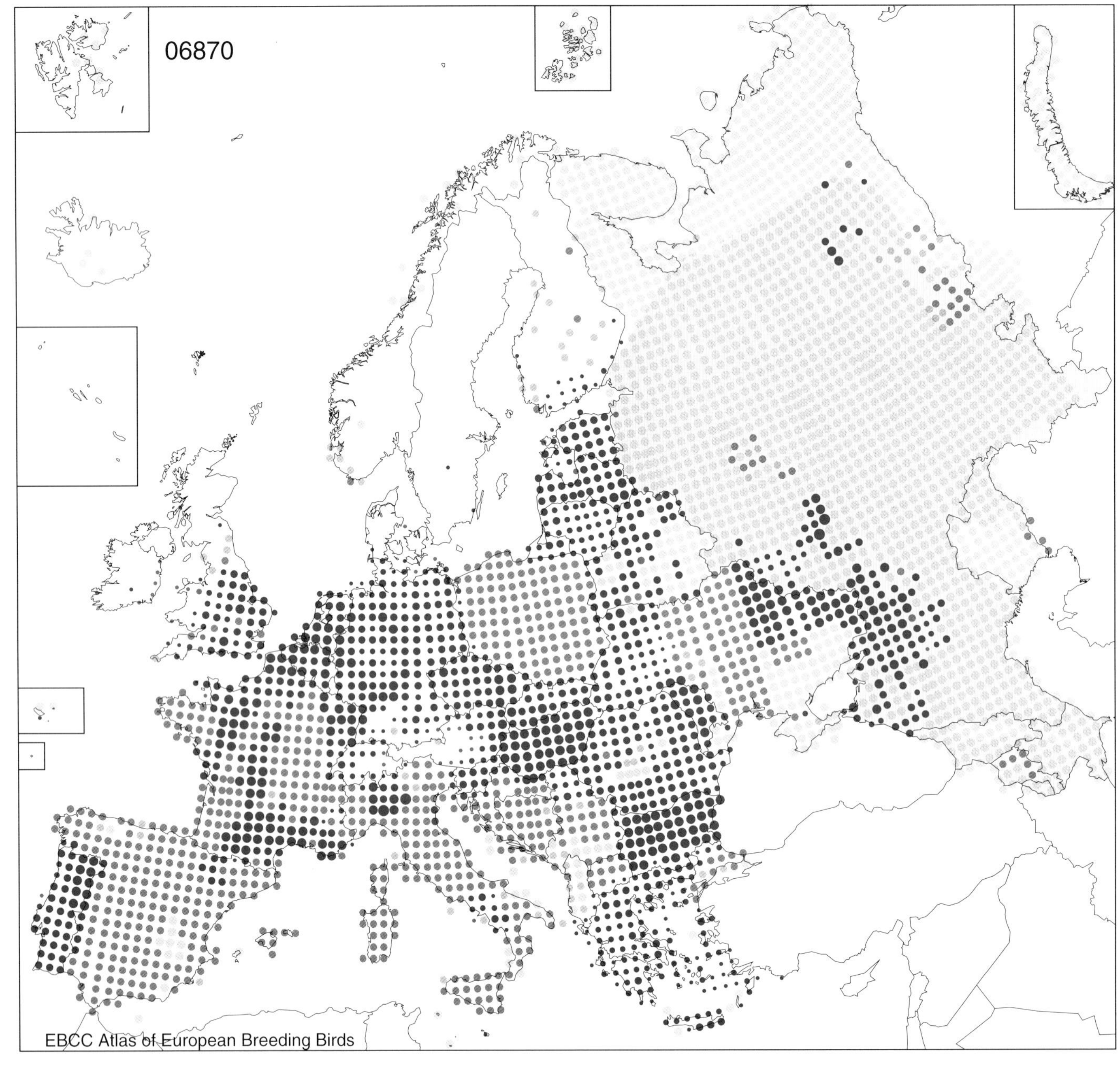

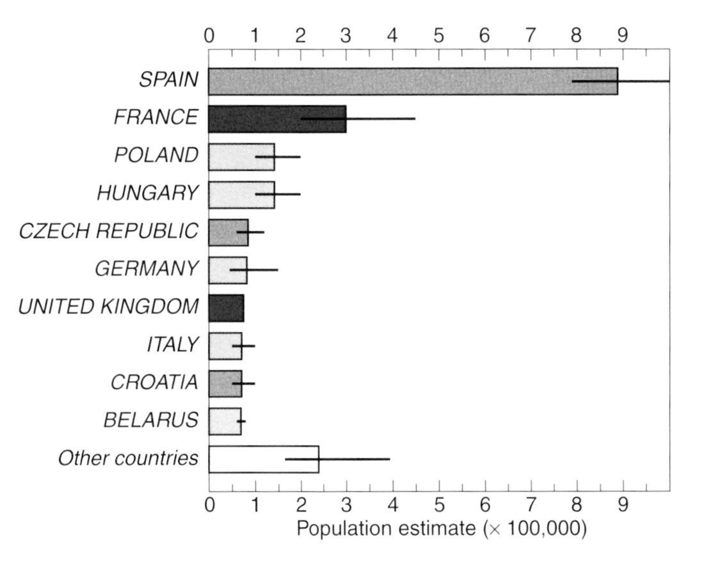

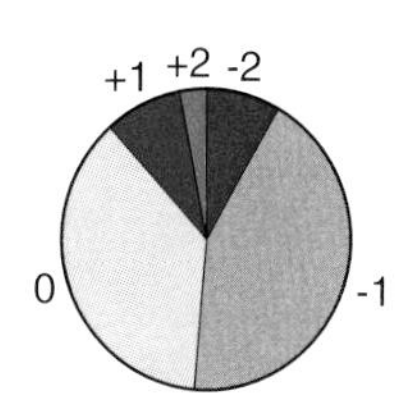

% in top 10 countries: 88.9
Total number of populated European countries: 35
Total European population 1,999,845–2,398,629 (2,164,089)
Russian population 500,000–5,000,000 (1,581,139)
Turkish population 500,000–5,000,000 (1,581,139)

Among the pigeons the Turtle Dove is an exception. It is the only species of *Columbidae* which is a long-distance migrant and which is typically granivorous throughout the year, even when wintering in tropical Africa. Its world range covers most of Europe, the Canary Islands, much of North Africa, Transcaspia, and stretches from the Near East to the western Altaï and Sinkiang. The nominate *turtur* is largely confined to Europe except for Kazakhstan; *arenicola* (S of the Mediterranean to the eastern Caspian) occupies the Balearics. There are two other subspecies.

In Europe the Turtle Dove inhabits areas of fragmented woodlands and shrubs (hedges, woodland fringes, orchards, wooded marshland, scrubby wasteland and garrigue) adjacent to farmland, which provides an essential food source. Preferring warmer regions with regular sunshine, the Turtle Dove is absent from much of northern Europe. It is rare in Ireland, absent from northern Britain and most of Denmark and is also rare in Sweden and Finland. It shows a preference for lower altitudes, generally occurring below 700m asl, but in southern Europe it may occur up to 1300m or 1500m asl (Jarry 1994, Nankinov 1994).

The entire European population winters in subtropical Africa, within the Sahelian and Sudanese regions from Senegambia to the Red Sea shores. Its patchy distribution over this vast area is explained by its highly gregarious behaviour and its need to use the relatively scarce acacia woodlands for roosting; several hundred thousand individuals may gather at a single location.

Since the mid-1970s and especially since 1985, a serious decline has occurred throughout most of its European breeding range. A decrease of more than 50% has been noted in Britain, France and Romania, but elsewhere the decreases have been less marked. In Austria, Belarus, Hungary, Italy, Poland, Russia, Slovakia and Slovenia populations are considered stable. However, the increases observed in Denmark (*c*20bp), Finland (50–100bp) and Latvia (3000–5000bp) are insignificant in relation to the total population; this trend may also relate to its occasional occurrence in Norway and Sweden as shown on the map. Its status in NW Russia is not known, but in the NE it apparently occurs in the Komi Republic further N than any previously mapped range (A.A. Estafiev, pers comm to the Editors). With an estimated European breeding population of some 2.2M–8Mbp (including Russia), the Turtle Dove remains widespread and reasonably common, even if it is less abundant than before. France, Hungary, Poland, Spain and Russia hold at least 100 000bp each; their total population comprises between 1.69M and 6.85Mbp (roughly 80% of the European population), Spain and Russia possessing the most important populations, although the latter is poorly known.

The probable causes of the decrease in the European population size are manifold. Habitat destruction, such as the disappearance of hedges, means fewer breeding sites. The widespread use of herbicides has destroyed food resources (Marchant *et al* 1990). Hunting pressure, especially upon the westernmost European population in the Gironde, is now significant, given the other threats. However, changes on its wintering grounds form the major reason for its decline.

The long drought period in the Sahelian and Sudanese regions since the early 1970s led not only to a reduction in food supply (reduced flooding prevented wild rice from fruiting; Skinner 1987) but also to an overall scarcity of water, and the Turtle Dove must drink at least once a day. Compounding these difficulties of natural origin is the diminution of the acacia forest through felling by people affected by the drought, and so the number of safe roosting sites for the species has been reduced. Overall, the quality of the Turtle Dove's wintering areas has been much reduced (Jarry & Baillon 1991, Jarry 1992).

Guy Jarry (F)

This species account is sponsored by Ms Margarete Klinkmüller, Neukirchen-Vluyn, D.

Myiopsitta monachus

Monk Parakeet

CZ	Papoušek mniší	**I**	Parrocchetto monaco
D	Mönchssittich	**NL**	Monniksparkiet
E	Cotorra Argentina	**P**	Caturra-da-Argentina
F	Conure veuve	**PL**	Mniszka
FIN	Munkkiaratti	**R**	Попугай-монах
G	Παπαγάλος–Μοναχός	**S**	Munkparakit
H	Barátpapagáj		

Criteria not applied

The natural range of the Monk Parakeet in South America covers C Bolivia, S Brazil, southwards to C Argentina. The present wild-breeding populations in Europe originated from escapes and releases. The species' high ecological adaptability enables it to live in urban or suburban areas (mainly parks and gardens) but also in more natural conditions. The species builds communal nests in palm trees and in a variety of deciduous and coniferous trees, in bushes (often hazel *Corylus avellana*) and on buildings and electrical pylons.

The Monk Parakeet has been recorded in Spain (Barcelona) as free-flying since 1975. In 1985, 97 birds were counted in Catalonia, mainly in coastal localities centred on Barcelona. In 1990–91 182 nests were found at 13 sites and isolated individuals were recorded at 13 other locations (Clavel *et al* 1991). Since 1978 the species has bred in Málaga (1989, 5–8bp) (Rodriguez Mariscal 1990). Madrid records date from 1985, but have not exceeded 12 birds (Pascual & Aparicio 1990).

In Italy the first wild breeding was in the 1930s in Milan (zoo escapes), but rats destroyed the colony. The Genoa colony probably started in 1970 from escaped birds and has grown to *c*20–30 individuals. Another population in Friuli (Udine) has been present since the early 1980s, 10 birds being recorded in 1988. At least 30 pairs have bred regularly since 1985 in the Pastrengo zoo-park (S. Spanó & G. Truffi, in prep). The present population at Lake Maggiore is not self-sustaining.

Released and escaped birds formed a feral population in Brussels, Belgium, increasing from one (1975) to 30–35bp (1989) (Rabosee *et al* 1995). In the Czech Republic one pair with four young escaped in Sázava town (C Bohemia) in 1985. After several other birds had been released, the population in the Sázava River valley grew to 42 birds in 1989 and 87 in 1990 (Žoha 1993). The Monk Parakeet has also bred in the wild in Great Britain, Germany and The Netherlands, but these instances have not resulted in viable populations.

Giorgio Truffi (I) Karel Šťastný (CZ)

Psittacula krameri

Ring-necked Parakeet

CZ	Aleksandr malý	I	Parrocchetto dal collare
D	Halsbandsittich	NL	Halsbandparkiet
E	Cotorra de Kramer	P	Piriquito-de-colar
F	Perruche à collier	PL	Aleksandretta obrożna
FIN	Aleksanterinkaija	R	Ожерелоголовый попугай Крамера
G	Δακτυλιωτός Παπαγάλος		
H	Kis sándor-papagáj	S	Halsbandsparakit

Criteria not applied

The Ring-necked Parakeet is widely distributed throughout much of the Afrotropical and Oriental regions. In Africa it frequents semi-arid country interspersed with patches of dense thorn-scrub. In Asia it lives in cultivated grounds and gardens, and is habitually found in villages and towns. In Europe, where it is very patchily distributed, principally in cities, the Ring-necked Parakeet nests in holes in trees in gardens, parks and orchards, where it competes with such native species as Jackdaw *Corvus monedula*, owls and woodpeckers.

In Great Britain, which supports the largest naturalized European population, the Ring-necked Parakeet has increased considerably in numbers and has extended its range since 1975 (Lever 1993c), although some subpopulations in NW England seem to have died out. It first appeared in the wild in England in 1969 (R. Hudson 1974), and by 1983 the population of this generally under-recorded bird was estimated at between 500 and 1000 birds. A similar trend is recorded for The Netherlands, starting in 1969, with over 60bp in the urbanized W of the country by 1992 (van Dijk *et al* 1994c).

Three sources have been suggested as the origin of the naturalized European population: it may derive from free-flying 'homing' birds that failed to return; it may come from birds which escaped from captivity; or it may originate in unwanted birds deliberately released by returning sailors. In all probability, each of these sources has contributed to the European population, the success of which is due at least in part to the species' ready acceptance of artificial feeding in winter (Lever 1977), which enables the birds to survive the harshest weather (Hawkes 1986).

In parts of its native range, where it is mainly sedentary, the Ring-necked Parakeet is a serious crop pest. It has the potential to become so in Europe, where it seems to have no predators apart from man. The Ring-necked Parakeet has become widely naturalized elsewhere throughout the world outside its natural range (Lever 1987).

Sir Christopher Lever (GB)

Clamator glandarius

Great Spotted Cuckoo

CZ	Kukačka chocholatá	I	Cuculo dal ciuffo
D	Häherkuckuck	NL	Kuifkoekoek
E	Críalo	P	Cuco-rabilongo
F	Coucou geai	PL	Kukułka czubata
FIN	Töyhtökäki	R	Хохлатая кукушка (большая кукушка)
G	Κισσόκουκος		
H	Szajkókakkuk	S	Skatgök

Non-SPEC, Threat status S

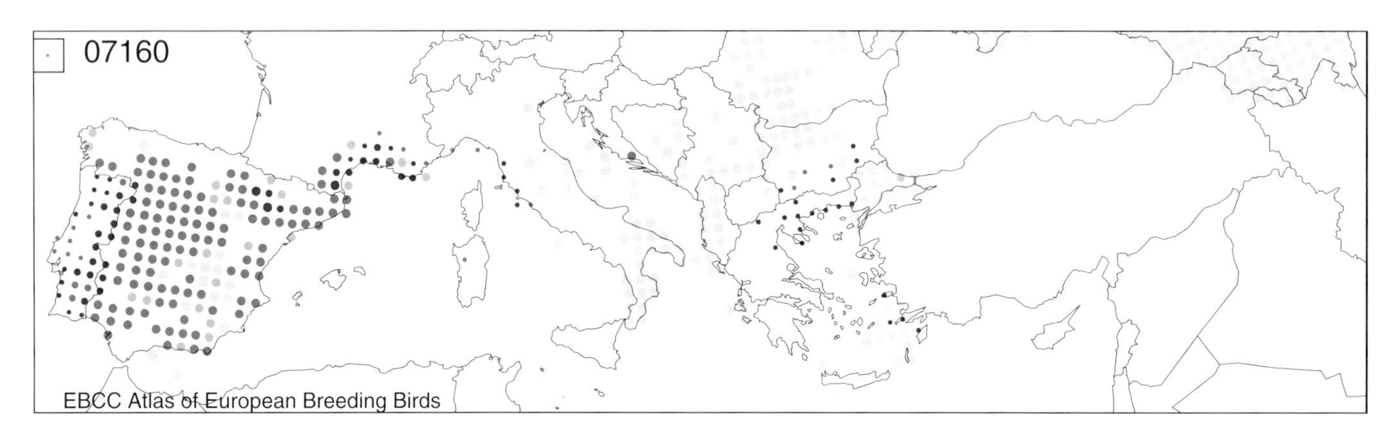

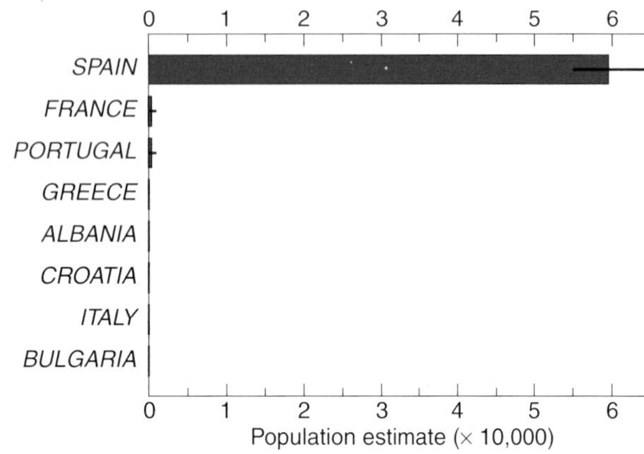

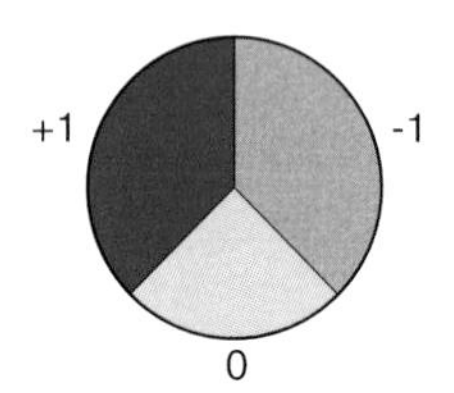

% in top 10 countries: 100.0
Total number of populated European countries: 8
Total European population 55,651–65,255 (60,222)
Turkish population 1000–5000 (2236)

The Great Spotted Cuckoo is an obligate brood parasite; it lays its eggs in other birds' nests. In the Palearctic it parasitizes mainly the Magpie *Pica pica*. Its distribution stretches from S Europe through C Africa to southern Africa. Palearctic birds (the nominate *C. g. glandarius*) winter mostly S of the Sahara, a few overwintering in S Iberia. Adults leave in June; juveniles may delay migration until November. African populations of the subspecies *choragium* are mainly resident. A migratory population (probably *glandarius*) in southern Africa, breeds during the northern winter, migrating to C Africa during the northern spring.

In Europe the species prefers open oak *Quercus* and pine *Pinus* woodland and in cultivated areas frequents mainly almond groves and open country scattered with trees. It generally avoids forests and mountains above 600m asl (Soler 1990). It is uncommon but widespread in S France, scarce but not yet a proven breeder in Italy, rather localized in Greece and Bulgaria, and common only in Spain which holds *c*98% (55 000–64 500bp) of the population.

The species is increasing and expanding its range (Soler 1990), mostly in Spain, France, Portugal and Italy. In France numbers have increased from 100bp in the 1940s to 1000bp in the 1970s (Yeatman 1976). Breeding was first proved in Greece in 1978 and in Bulgaria in 1988 (Milchev 1992). The species is numerous in Spain, mainly in the S. Large regional variations in abundance are linked with the distribution and abundance of the Magpie, the abundance of gregarious caterpillars (its main spring food), especially the hairy larvae of the processionary moth *Thaumetopoea pityocampa*, and the development of Magpie defence tactics against brood parasitism (M. Soler *et al,* in prep).

In Guadix, where the species is very abundant, 14 adults were caught and ringed in 5km², representing an estimated population density of 4/km² in prime habitat (M. Soler *et al*, in prep).

Manuel Soler (E) Bojan Milchev (BUL)

Cuculus saturatus

Oriental Cuckoo

CZ	Kukačka prostřední	I	Cuculo orientale
D	Hopfkuckuck	NL	Boskoekoek
E	Cuco Oriental	P	Cuco-oriental
F	Coucou oriental	PL	Kukułka wschodnia
FIN	Idänkäki	R	Глухая кукушка
G	Κούκος της Σιβηρίας	S	Taigagök
H	Tajgakakukk		

Non-SPEC, Threat status S (P)

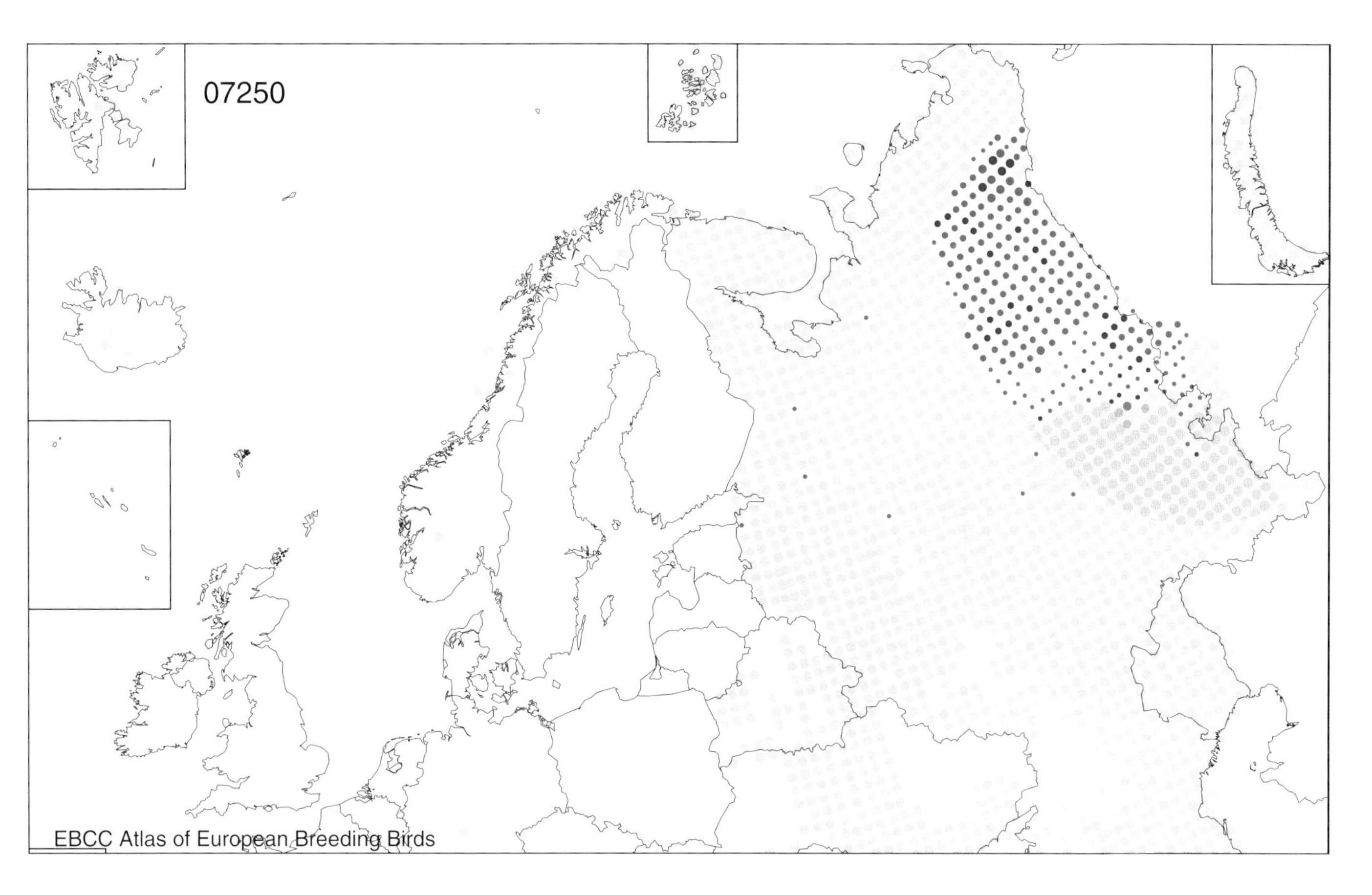

The present distribution of the Oriental Cuckoo covers primarily the Eurasian forest zone from NE European Russia through Siberia and N Mongolia to the Pacific Ocean coast, and includes the Kamchatka Peninsula, the Kurile Isles and Japan (over which area *C. s. horsfieldi* occurs). It is then continuous to the SE to cover Korea, merging into the nominate *saturatus* through NE and S China and in a narrow arm W to the eastern Himalayas (Nechayev 1993). The species winters in the Sundas (probably encountering *lepidus*, the main resident subspecies, and *insulindae* of Borneo), SW New Guinea and NE Australia (Blakers *et al* 1984).

Its distribution in Europe is wedge-shaped, being determined N and S by the limit of distribution of extensive continuous coniferous forests. The most westerly point of regular occurrence is at the Vychegda River mouth. Further W, there are scattered records of single singing males (Ilyichev & Fomin 1988) (Nechayev 1993, see map).

Its main habitats in Europe are various types of coniferous and coniferous-dominant mixed forests. Less commonly, it uses purely deciduous or coniferous–broad-leaved forests. In the S Urals it is found in habitats comprising small woodlands and shrubs. Breeding density is higher in the northern pre-Urals, where in a mosaic of primarily coniferous and deciduous forests it is 0.5–1.2 bp/km². Further W and SW, where human impact on the environment is large, breeding density decreases; in forest habitats between the Pechora and Vychegda Rivers in different years it varied from 0.1 to 0.9 bp/km², and in the Perm and Kirov regions from 0.05 to 0.4 (Garanin 1977). In primary forests in the Pechoro–Ilych Reserve, density in pine *Pinus* was 0.4 bp/km² and in spruce *Picea* 0.5, whereas in the primary spruce–aspen (*Populus tremula*) forests of the lower reaches of the Vychegda it is 0.1. We would now estimate the European population to be between 5000 and 10 000bp.

Vladimir N Anufriev (R), Alexey A Estafiev (R)
Sergey K Kotchanov (R)

Cuculus canorus

Cuckoo

CZ	Kukačka obecná	I	Cuculo
D	Kuckuck	NL	Koekoek
E	Cuco	P	Cuco-canoro
F	Coucou gris	PL	Kukułka
FIN	Käki	R	Обыкновенная кукушка
G	Κούκος	S	Gök
H	Kakukk		

Non-SPEC, Threat status S

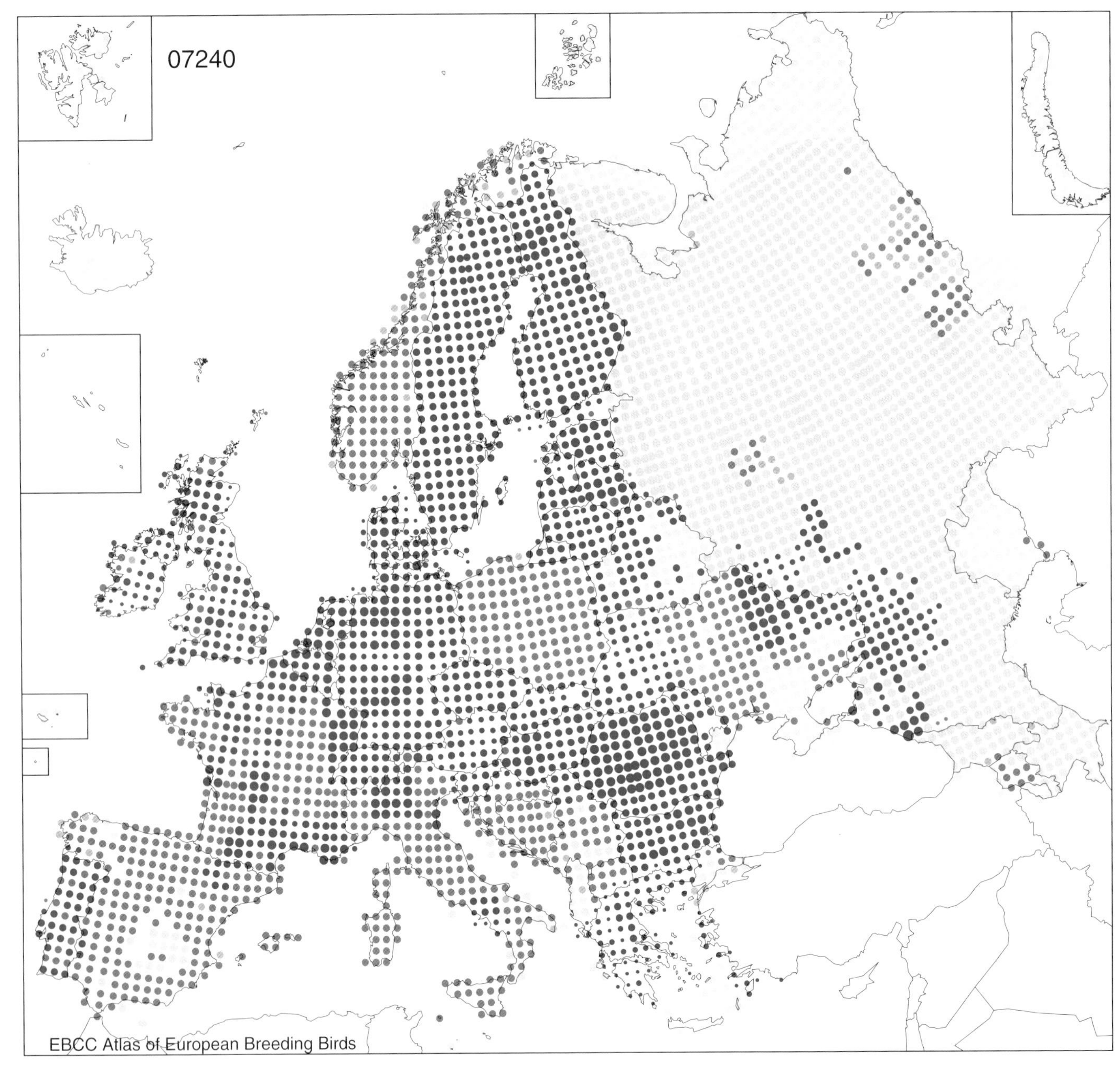

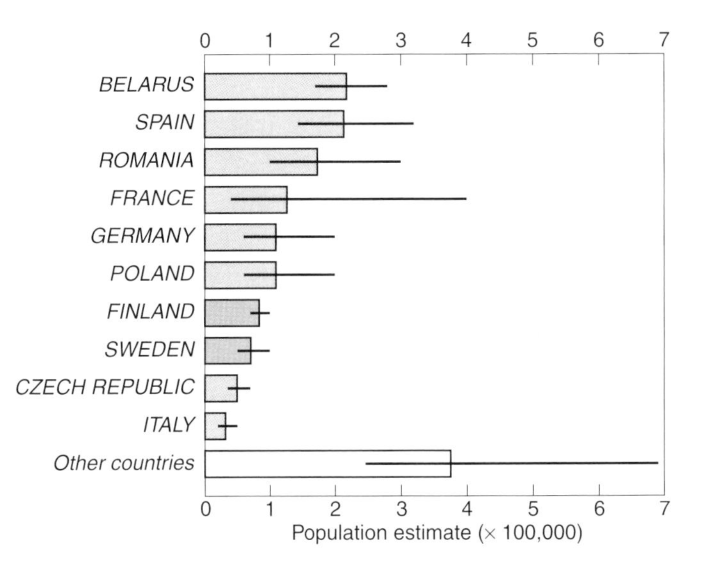

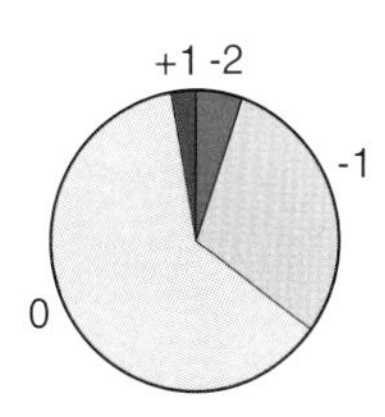

% in top 10 countries: 76.0
Total number of populated European countries: 37
Total European population 1,394,869–1,935,705 (1,561,640)
Russian population 500,000–1,000,000 (707,107)
Turkish population 50,000–500,000 (158,114)

The distribution and abundance of the Cuckoo, a brood parasite, are influenced by its two main requirements: nests of potential host species (of which there are several) and a diet of hairy caterpillars. Its extensive breeding range covers Europe and most of Asia from the Arctic tree-limit S as far as NW Africa and E across Russia and China to Japan.

European populations winter in Africa S of the Sahara, but the precise winter range is poorly known, the birds probably following the seasonal rains and associated outbreaks of caterpillars, especially armyworms *Spodoptera exempta* (Prins 1986). Some Asiatic birds also winter in southern Africa, while others migrate to SE Asia as far as New Guinea.

European birds migrate S in August and September, adults about one month before juveniles, and cross the Mediterranean and Sahara along a broad front to arrive in equatorial Africa as the rains start. They return in April and May, reaching the breeding range northern limits by early June.

In Europe most habitats are occupied except those lacking suitable hosts; large conurbations, extensive dense forests, extreme deserts, bare mountains (above *c*2500m asl) and a few islands. The Cuckoo is as ubiquitous in cover-deficient open habitats such as grassy areas or rocky shores, as it is in farmland, woodland (broad-leaved or coniferous), heathland or marshland. It particularly prefers habitats containing suitable vantage points, especially trees or bushes from which the female can reconnoitre potential hosts.

Its European distribution is fairly even across the habitat range, but it can reach higher densities where preferred host species such as *Acrocephalus* warblers form local concentrations. A typical home range in Great Britain of a Cuckoo parasitizing the Reed Warbler *A. scirpaceus*, is *c*30ha, whereas one using the Meadow Pipit *Anthus pratensis*, may require 300ha. The Cuckoo becomes less common at higher altitudes and in suburban areas as hosts and food thin out (Wyllie 1981); calling stations of males may be 5km apart (Dröscher 1988). Despite the male's conspicuous song, it remains difficult to assess numbers or to prove breeding. The Cuckoo's distribution in Europe, and elsewhere, has remained unchanged, but numbers have probably declined in many areas since 1965, possibly from loss of habitat through agricultural intensification. Declines are recorded mainly for Fennoscandia, the Baltic States and W through northern Europe to Britain. In Ireland numbers are thought to have decreased since 1900, particularly between 1968–71 (Sharrock 1976) and 1988–92 (Wyllie 1994).

Although the Cuckoo parasitizes a range of different host species, each female is thought to parasitize only one species. Therefore each different Cuckoo clan or 'gens' uses a different species. Throughout Europe the pattern of host use, and associated egg-mimicry, varies according to the degree either of isolation of each host-specific Cuckoo gens, or of egg-discrimination by the various hosts (Krebs & Davies 1993). Over 100 species, mainly small insectivores, have acted as Cuckoo hosts but in any one area only two or three are regularly victimized (Wyllie 1981). Thus in Scandinavia, the Redstart *Phoenicurus phoenicurus*, and Brambling *Fringilla montifringilla*, receive highly mimetic Cuckoo eggs, as does the Great Reed Warbler *A. arundinaceus*, and White Wagtail *Motacilla alba*, in E Europe. Other examples of good mimicry, mainly in E and C Europe, include Robin *Erithacus rubecula*, Garden Warbler *Sylvia borin*, Blackcap *S. atricapilla* and Red-backed Shrike *Lanius collurio*. Elsewhere, and with different host species, mimicry is less accurate perhaps because a host such as the Reed Warbler *A. scirpaceus* itself lays variably marked eggs, or because Cuckoo–host interactions are at different evolutionary stages.

The nominate subspecies *C.c. canorus* and the smaller *bangsi* (Iberian Peninsula and Balearics) occur in Europe. There are several Asiatic subspecies.

Ian Wyllie (GB)

Tyto alba — Barn Owl

CZ	Sova pálená	**I**	Barbagianni
D	Schleiereule	**NL**	Kerkuil
E	Lechuza Común	**P**	Coruja-das-torres
F	Effraie des clochers	**PL**	Płomykówka
FIN	Tornipöllö	**R**	Сипуха
G	Τυτώ	**S**	Tornuggla
H	Gyöngybagoly		

SPEC Cat 3, Threat status D

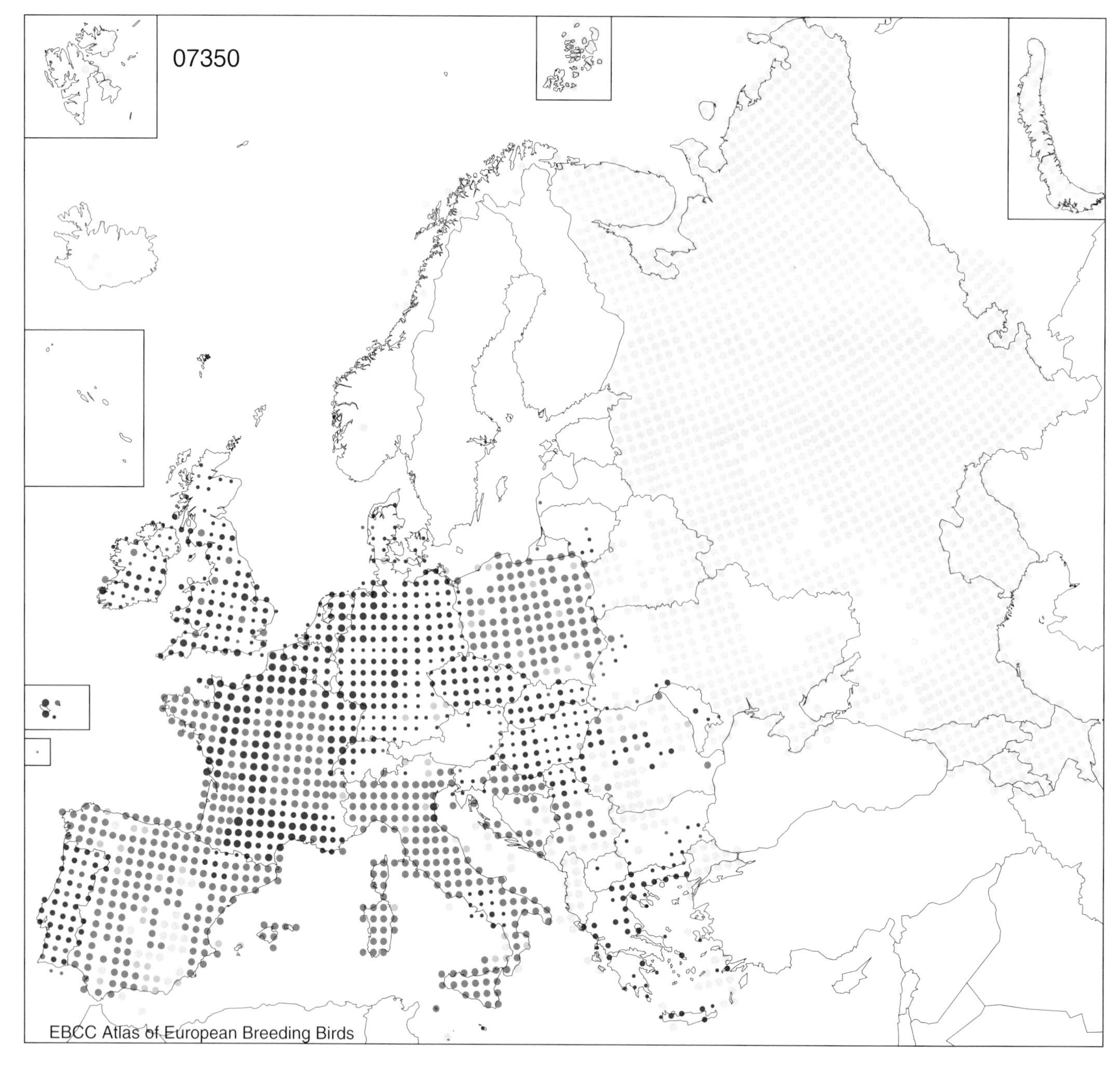

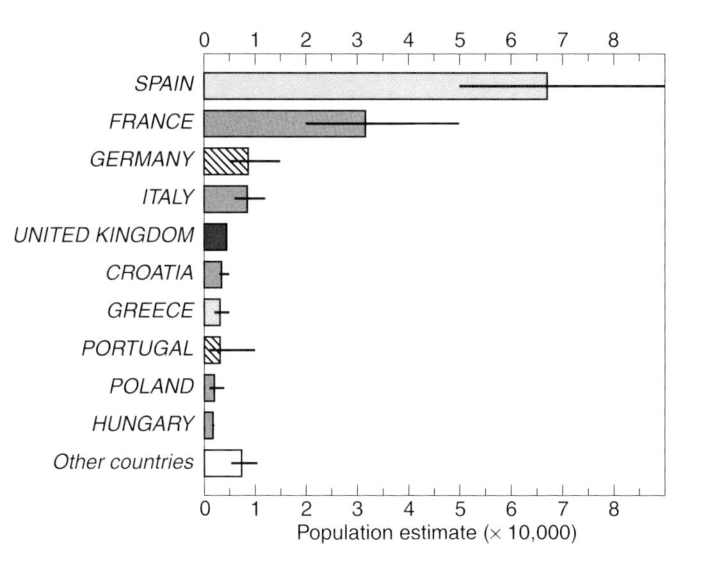

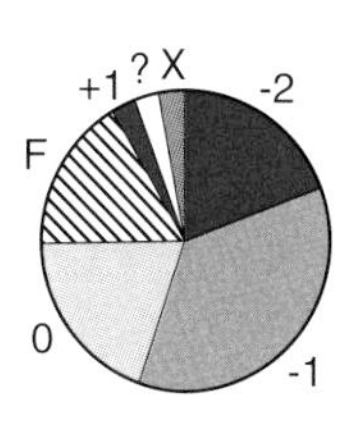

% in top 10 countries: 94.8
Total number of populated European countries: 36
Total European population 119,899–172,394 (141,218)
Turkish population 50–500 (158)

The Barn Owl's 35 subspecies breed in every continent except Antarctica. It is absent from Russia save the western edge, all of N and C Asia to Japan, much of the East Indies, Iran, Afghanistan, Greenland, Iceland, Fennoscandia, New Zealand and all of Canada except the southern fringe. In Europe two widespread subspecies and four island subspecies occur. The few in S Finland originated from reintroduced stock.

The 3°C January isotherm following the British E coast, the French eastern border, crossing N Italy through to Bulgaria, broadly marks the division between the two continental subspecies, *T.a. alba* to the W and *guttata* to the E. Of the *c*110 000–230 000bp in Europe, 90% occur to the W and S of this line, highlighting the Barn Owl's dependence on mild winters (its plumage retains warmth poorly; Taylor 1994).

Throughout most of Europe, the Barn Owl favours rank open grassland habitats, particularly those associated with the banks of drainage ditches, rivers and hedgerows, where stocks of its principal small-mammal prey, voles *Microtidae*, mice *Muridae* and shrews *Soricidae*, usually are adequate to maintain its high food requirements during the breeding season (Shawyer 1987, de Bruijn 1994). It avoids dune, heath, forest and all but the edges of mature woodland but exploits young tree plantations during their early years when small mammals (especially voles) are abundant. Though the Barn Owl basically is sedentary, Dutch-ringed young have travelled 1500km to Spain and Ukraine.

In much of NW and C Europe the Barn Owl favours low-lying regions because they not only provide the most dependable food supply in harsh winters, but also hold a wide diversity of prey species, thus offering a buffer against the cyclic fluctuations in vole numbers. These cycles are more significant at higher altitudes and where homogeneous grassland habitats are commonest (Shawyer 1994), breeding numbers and performance varying markedly with vole abundance (Baudvin 1986).

Ultimately, the scarcity of suitable breeding and roosting sites in old buildings, churches, hollow trees and in cliff and quarry crevices places limits on population size in many areas, even near optimal habitat (Taylor 1994). However, providing nestboxes in farm buildings, cavity-deficient trees or on wooden poles will often increase both population density and breeding productivity.

In western Europe, where grassland habitats tend to be fragmented, average breeding densities of between 1 and 10 bp/50km^2 are the norm; they rarely exceed 12–25 bp/50km^2. Such values are 50–100 times lower than those attained on nestbox-rich oil-palm estates in Malaysia where prey-saturated habitats are continuous and vast (Taylor 1994). In eastern Europe densities are much lower than in the W. Spain apparently has the highest Barn Owl density in Europe, and together with Great Britain, Germany and Italy holds *c*80% of the overall population.

The species is now extinct in Malta and has declined by 20% or more in over half of the countries of Europe. This decline is attributed mainly to modern agricultural practices which bring about the decline and fragmentation of rough grassland. Another significant factor in the bird's decline between 1940 and 1980, when severe winters were commonplace, was the steady reduction in farmyard foraging opportunities due to the increasing volume of grain being stored in rodent-proof bins and silos; corn ricks disappeared from farmyards as grain harvesting swiftly became more mechanized from the 1940s onwards (de Bruijn 1994, Taylor 1994). Organochlorine pesticide poisoning has also been implicated in the decline (Newton *et al* 1991).

Extensive road development not only fragmented prime habitat but also contributed to increased traffic speed, both of which have increased mortality locally probably to the extent that immigration of birds seeking their first territories is insufficient to offset the losses (de Bruijn 1994).

Eduard Osieck (NL) Colin Shawyer (GB)

This species account is sponsored by Deutscher Rat für Vogelschutz, D.

Otus scops

Scops Owl

CZ	Výreček malý	**I**	Assiolo
D	Zwergohreule	**NL**	Dwergooruil
E	Autillo	**P**	Mocho-d'orelhas
F	Petit-Duc scops	**PL**	Syczek
FIN	Kyläpöllönen	**R**	Сплюшка
G	Γκιώνης	**S**	Dvärguv
H	Füleskuvik		

SPEC Cat 2, Threat status D (P)

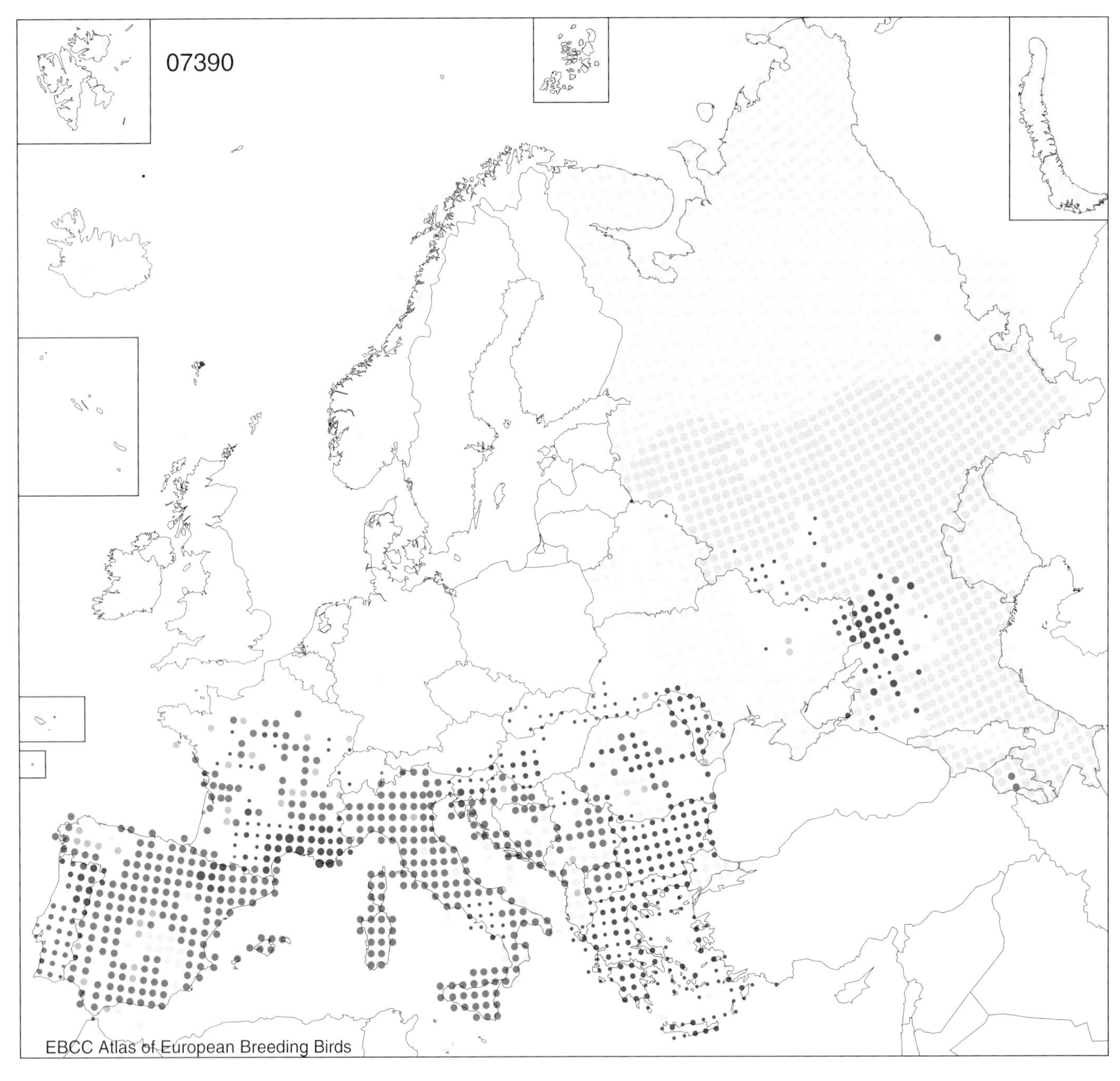

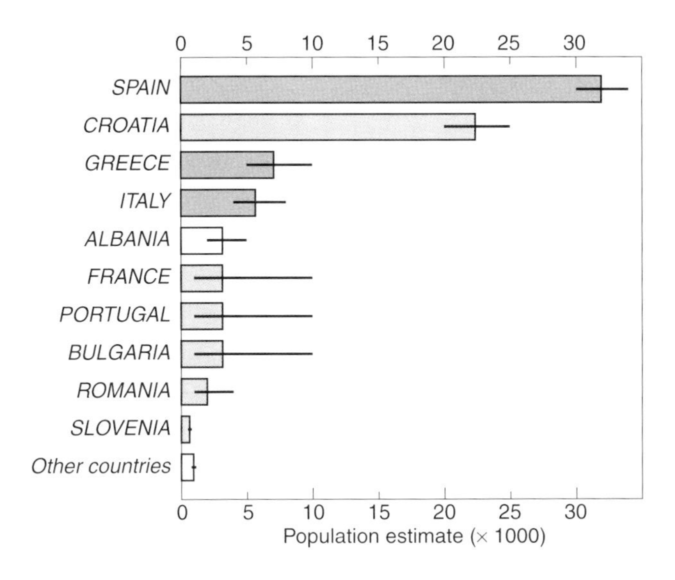

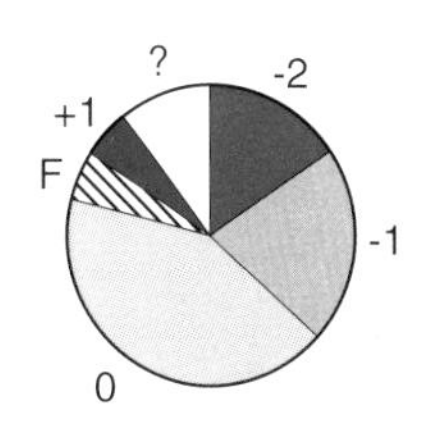

% in top 10 countries: 98.9
Total number of populated European countries: 19
Total European population 77,514–96,390 (83,238)
Russian population 5000–50,000 (15,811)
Turkish population 5000–30,000 (12,247)

The world distribution of the Scops Owl, a small nocturnal raptor, encompasses largely the Palearctic region and extends from Portugal in the W to C Asia, and from Lake Baykal, S of the Altai up to the Tian Shan. In the W of its breeding distribution, the Scops Owl is present in the meridional zones up to 50°N. Its southern limit is North Africa from Morocco to Tunisia. Further E, it reaches 58°N.

In Europe, the northernmost populations are fully migratory, their wintering area ranging from the Mediterranean to the Equator, but most remain in the savanna zone between 0° and 15°N. The more southerly breeding populations are partial migrants or sedentary. Wintering populations occur in S Spain, the Balearics, Corsica (Thibault & Patrimonio 1991), Sicily, S Italy and Greece.

The Scops Owl prefers climatic zones whose summers are warm and rich in insects, over an altitudinal range from sea level to 2000m asl. It occupies mostly semi-open areas which contain a mosaic of fallow land and copses and include old trees to provide daytime shelter and a breeding site. It uses other habitats too, such as riverine forests, olive and almond groves, old fruit plantations, parks, gardens, tree-lined village streets, even town centres. It avoids dense forests (especially conifers) and open panoramas, like fields. Typical nesting sites are holes in trees or walls. Occasionally it will use Bee-eater *Merops apiaster* burrows. It adapts easily to nestboxes, and also uses former corvid or raptors' nests.

Although it is easy to census singing males (not necessarily representative of breeding pairs), there are few long-term studies of population dynamics on a wider scale. In France, Bavoux *et al* (1991) recorded 46–60 singing males on Île d'Oleron (175 km^2) during five surveys between 1981 and 1990. High densities are known from small study plots: on the French island of Port Cros, 28 singing males on 620ha (Vidal 1986); in Romania, 5bp on 0.6ha in isolated copses surrounded by fields (Kalabér 1973), and in the former Yugoslavia, 10 singing males in *c*2ha of park and avenue environs (Böck & Walter 1976). An intermediate value was obtained in NE Italy (1991); 10–15 territories on 400ha (Galeotti & Garibaldi 1994).

The reliability of national population estimates probably varies considerably. Nevertheless, in general, southern Balkan and Mediterranean countries each hold *c*3000–6000bp, sometimes more. Slightly further N in C Europe and the Balkans, numbers fall off to *c*1000 or less. Spain, and probably Croatia (whose accuracy of estimate is not known), are particularly important with *c*32 000 and 21 000bp respectively. The Russian estimate (5000–50 000bp) and its low degree of precision reflect the country's large surface area.

For nine of the 19 countries in the *Atlas*' coverage area where the species has been counted, numbers remain generally stable (although quantitative information is incomplete), but they have decreased elsewhere, especially in the tiny populations at the range limits (reductions of >50% in numbers, range, or both in Ukraine (100–120bp), Austria (20–30bp) and Switzerland (12–15bp) and of 20–50% in Moldova, Spain, Greece and Italy). Only Hungary shows the Scops Owl increasing its range and numbers from 1970 to 1990 (300–400bp).

The causes of the declines are largely unknown, but amongst those cited are the disappearance of large insects and habitat destruction. The latter, from the 1950s onwards, was the main factor in Switzerland. Scops Owl habitat became fragmented by the spread of vineyards and agricultural intensification. The species now experiences a recruitment rate too low to replace losses, which cannot be balanced by immigration because of insufficient continuous habitat. Other factors, such as prey contamination, prey abundance changes, nest site shortages, catastrophes, long-term weather changes or degradation of wintering habitat in Africa were not significant in their effects (Arlettaz *et al* 1991).

Christian Bavoux (F) Guy Burneleau (F)
Pierre Nicolau-Guillaumet (F)

This species account is sponsored by Saxifraga foundation, Tilburg, NL.

Bubo bubo

Eagle Owl

CZ	Výr velký	**I**	Gufo reale
D	Uhu	**NL**	Oehoe
E	Búho Real	**P**	Bufo-real
F	Grand-Duc d'Europe	**PL**	Puchacz
FIN	Huuhkaja	**R**	Филин
G	Μπούφος	**S**	Berguv
H	Uhu		

SPEC Cat 3, Threat status V

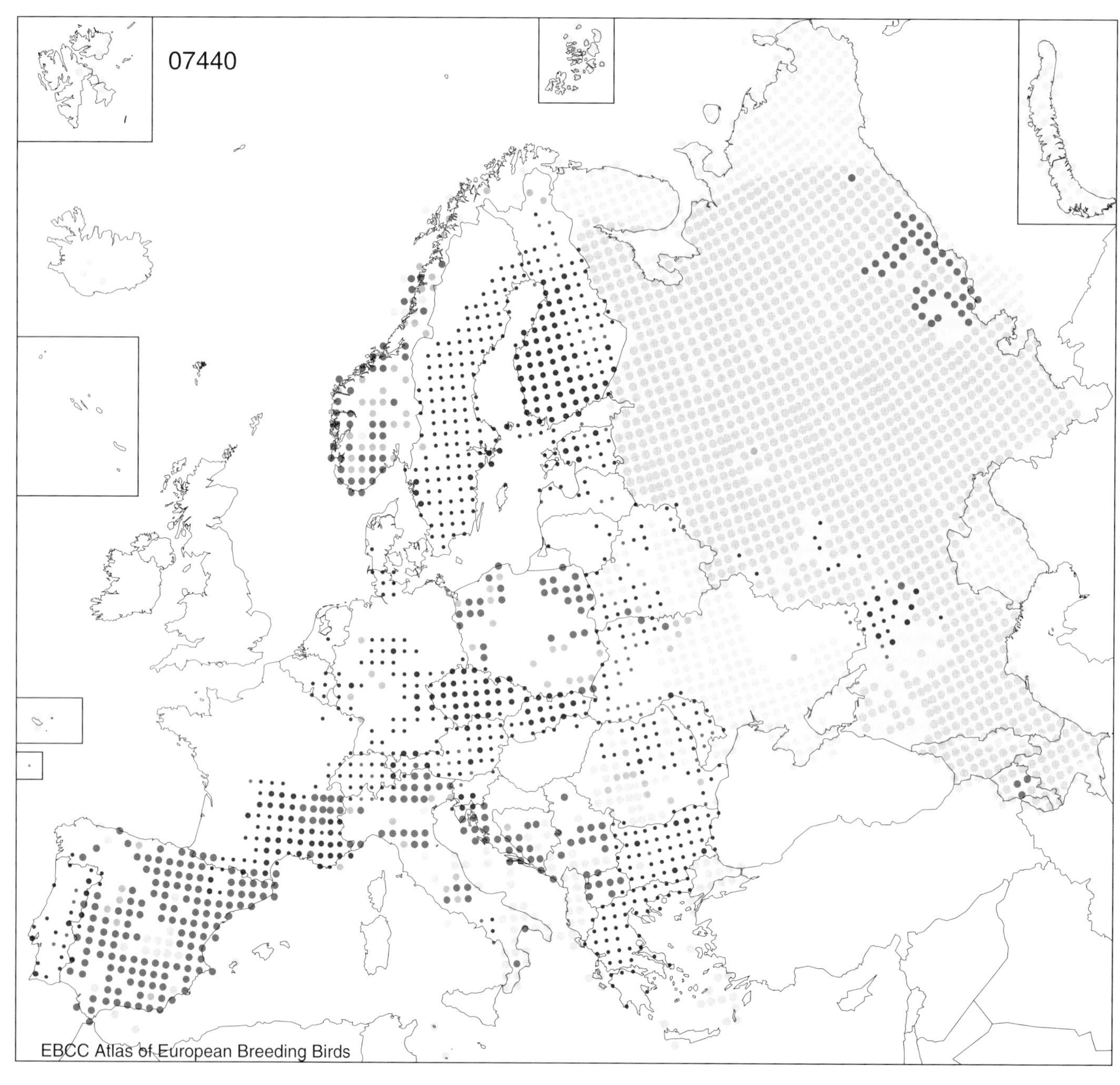

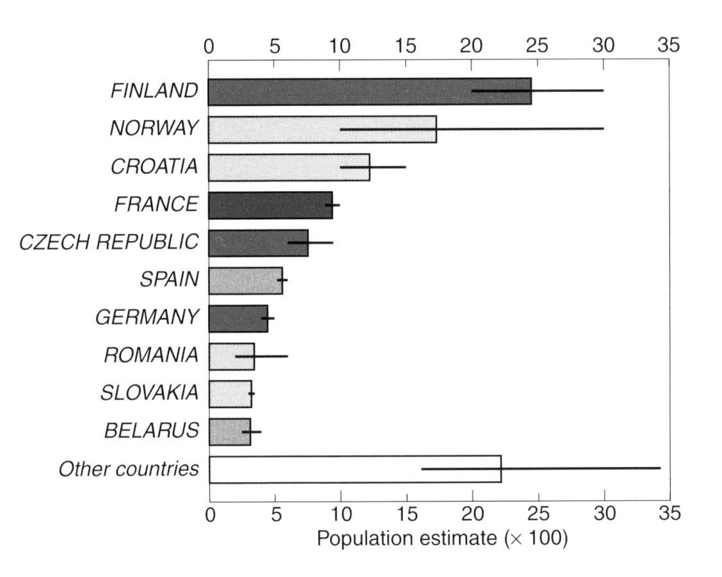

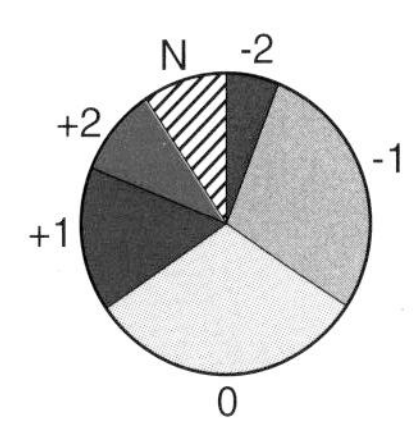

% in top 10 countries: 80.4
Total number of populated European countries: 32
Total European population 10,353–12,926 (11,308)
Russian population 2000–20,000 (6325)
Turkish population 500–5000 (1581)

The Eagle Owl, a powerful predator, has a world distribution in the subarctic to the sub-tropical climatic zones from Mauritania in the W to Ussuriland in the E, reaching sub-Saharan Africa, southern India and China to the S. It occurs throughout Europe except for Iceland, Britain & Ireland, western France, much of the C and E European lowlands and the Mediterranean islands. It is sedentary except at high latitudes, where southward movements in winter may occur. Of the many subspecies, probably six occur in Europe, of which *B.b. hispanus* (Iberia) and the nominate *bubo* (the remainder of Europe except C European Russia eastwards and Moldova E to the Caucasus) are best-known.

The Eagle Owl requires a large territory and despite its large size can be unobtrusive. The situation in Spain exemplifies the difficulties. In Murcia, Tarragona and Navarra alone (10% of the suitable territory) some 700bp have been calculated from survey work. Moreover, the species seems very common in some unsurveyed areas, such as the Andalusian ranges (F. Hiraldo, pers comm). In our opinion the Spanish population should be estimated at several thousand breeding pairs, many more than the graph suggests (520–600bp). Similar circumstances may apply in Russia and several E European countries.

The present Eagle Owl European population is *c*25 000bp, of which *c*50% resides in Russia and Fennoscandia. The C European mountain ranges, S France, Spain and the Balkan countries also hold important populations. The species occurs from sea level up to 1600–1800m asl in the Alps and 2000m in the Pyrenees. It frequents both mountains and plains, provided prey is ample and there are suitable nesting sites on undisturbed cliffs or steep vegetated slopes. It tolerates human activities well but its absence from some Spanish areas is due to harassment (Donázar 1988). In SW Europe, rabbit *Oryctolagus cuniculus* availability determines much of the Eagle Owl's range and abundance (Donázar 1988, Bergier & Badan 1991) and hence high densities occur in the mountains of E Spain (5.9 bp/100km^2; Donázar 1988) and in Provence, France, where 43–50bp occupied a study plot of 200km^2 of mediterranean mountains (Bergier & Badan 1991). Densities in Scandinavia are related to the abundance of small mammals, hares *Lepus* spp and waterbirds (Mysterud & Dunker 1982). Finnish densities are normally in the range of 2–4bp/100km^2, but can be as high as 8–13 bp/100km^2 in prime habitat (Koskimies 1989a). In C Europe, densities usually are much lower, but high overall values occur in the Czech Republic (1.1 bp/100km^2) and Slovakia (0.8 bp/100km^2) (Danko *et al* 1994).

European populations have decreased generally during the 20th century, mainly due to human persecution (Mikkola 1983). In Spain and S France the effects of myxomatosis led to significant Eagle Owl population declines along the Mediterranean (Donázar 1988). From 1970 onwards, many populations recovered rapidly, increases being detected in at least nine countries; numbers more than doubled in Finland, the Czech Republic and Germany. Simultaneously its range has expanded, and it has even re-appeared in Belgium, The Netherlands and Luxembourg, albeit in very small numbers. Recuperation seems linked to decreasing persecution and exploitation of new food sources like extensive clearfells (Epple 1987, Danko *et al* 1994) and also rubbish dumps containing abundant rats *Rattus* spp.

Large reintroduction programmes in Bayern and Baden-Württemberg (Germany), Belgium, France, Switzerland, Norway and Sweden may have assisted the recovery, but these birds suffer high mortality and comparatively low reproductive success (Epple 1987). Declining populations during 1970–90 were evident in Russia (>50% decline in numbers, but no range contraction), Belarus and several Mediterranean and C European countries. Altogether, some 60% of the European population is apparently in decline, but the present situation is much improved over that around 1900.

José A Donázar (E) Pertti Kalinainen (FIN)

This species account is sponsored by Förderkreis Museum Heineanum, Halberstadt, D.

Nyctea scandiaca

Snowy Owl

CZ	Sovice sněžní	I	Gufo delle nevi
D	Schnee-Eule	NL	Sneeuwuil
E	Búho Nival	P	Bufo-branco
F	Harfang des neiges	PL	Sowa śnieżna
FIN	Tunturipöllö	R	Белая сова
G	Χιονόγλαυκα	S	Fjälluggla
H	Hóbagoly		

SPEC Cat 3, Threat status V

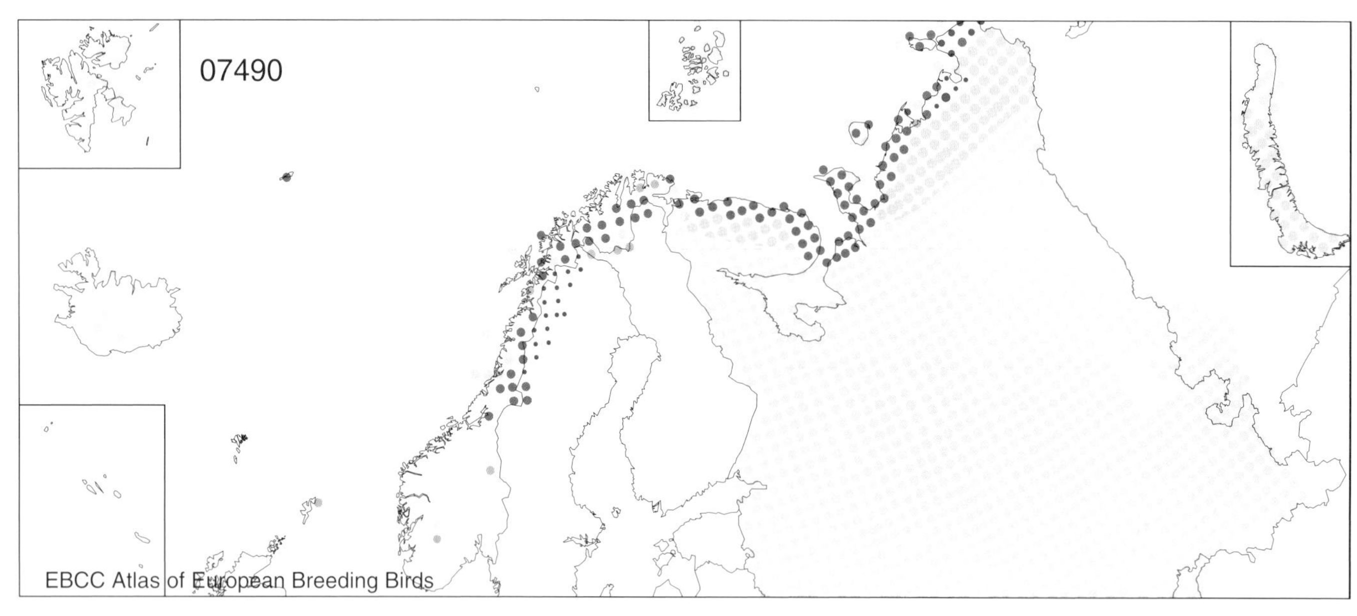

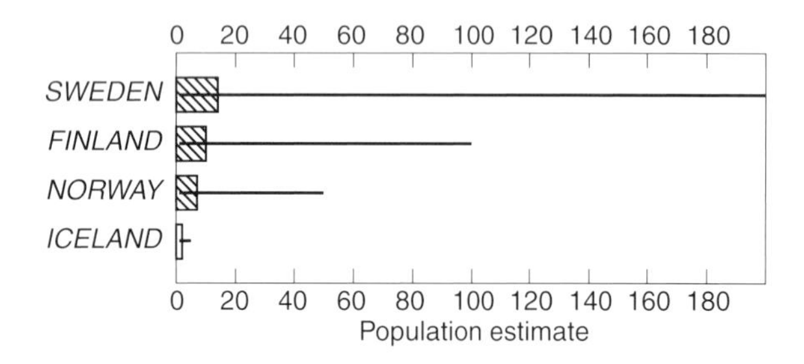

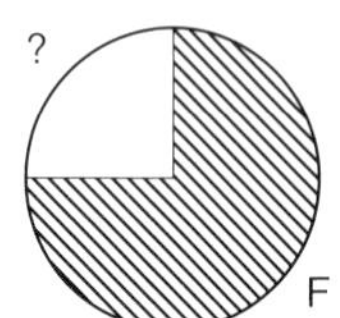

% in top 10 countries: 100.0
Total number of populated European countries: 4
Total European population 16–244 (33)
Russian population 1–1000 (32)

The Snowy Owl is a large, predominantly white owl whose fully feathered legs and toes are adaptations to the exposed and cold areas of the Arctic. It has a circumpolar distribution occurring between 60° and 83°N in open, treeless areas in Fennoscandia, Siberia and North America, and on Greenland and Iceland.

In summer its preferred habitat is tundra or quasi-tundra near the sea up to 1500m asl (Hagen 1959), whereas in winter it moves to plains and similar open country (Kerlinger & Ross Lein 1986, 1988). The Snowy Owl breeds where there is 24-hour daylight, where hillocks and boulders are frequent, providing perches as well as suitable nesting sites (Wiklund & Stigh 1983, 1986). The nest is a shallow hollow, often on top of a hillock.

The Snowy Owl is territorial and predominantly monogamous, rarely polygynous. For breeding it is dependent on a sufficiency of lemmings and voles, although its food spectrum is wide and includes prey ranging in size from hares and geese to passerines (Wiklund & Stigh 1986). Breeding numbers and the density of its regularly distributed nests vary greatly between rodent peak years. In N Sweden, the distance between the nearest nests varied from 600 to 3300m in one peak lemming year when Snowy Owl breeding density was 40–55 bp/100km^2, and from 2500 and 3200m in the next peak year when density was 15 bp/100km^2 (Wiklund & Stigh 1983, 1986). The large fluctuations in breeding density are not fully understood but are probably influenced by several factors, including weather.

In North America, there is N–S migration in autumn and winter (Kerlinger & Ross Lein 1986, 1988). Here, the Snowy Owl's abundance varies from year to year but is not synchronized over areas (including small areas of 40–60km^2) nor over time. Wintering areas of adults lie N of those of juveniles, adult females being furthest N and immature males furthest S. Immature birds migrate also to the SW and SE (Kerlinger & Ross Lein 1986, 1988). In Europe, birds sometimes move as far S as northern C Europe.

Christer G. Wiklund (S)

Surnia ulula

Hawk Owl

CZ	Sovice krahujová	I	Ulula
D	Sperbereule	NL	Sperweruil
E	Búho Gavilán	P	Coruja-gavião
F	Chouette épervière	PL	Sowa jarzębata
FIN	Hiiripöllö	R	Ястребиная сова
G	Σαϊνόγλαυκα	S	Hökuggla
H	Karvalybagoly		

Non-SPEC, Threat status S (P)

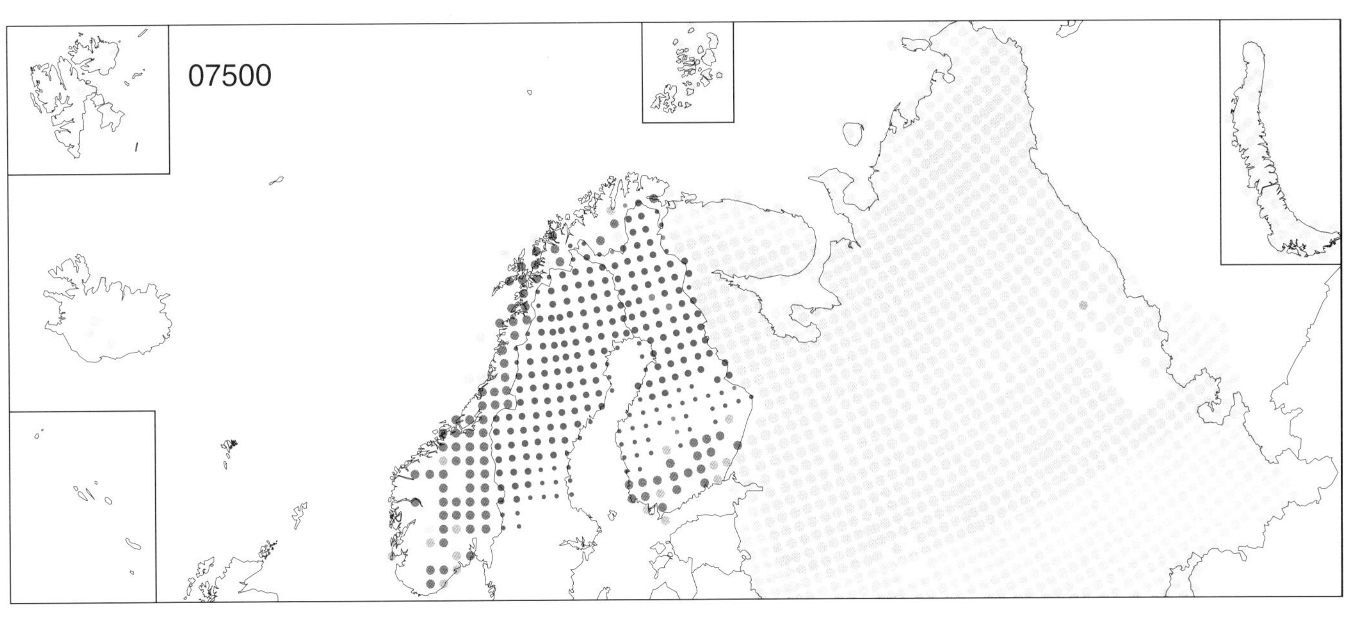

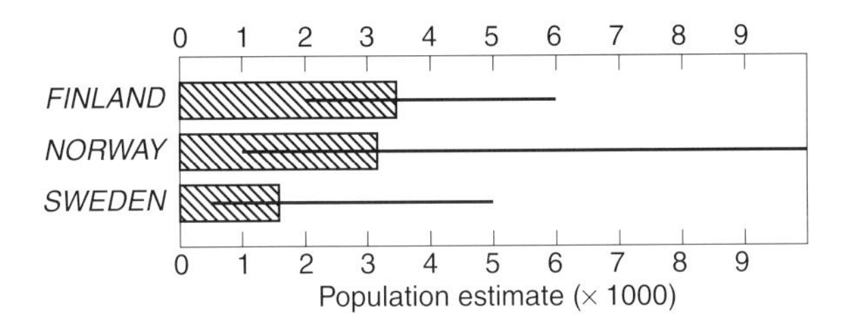

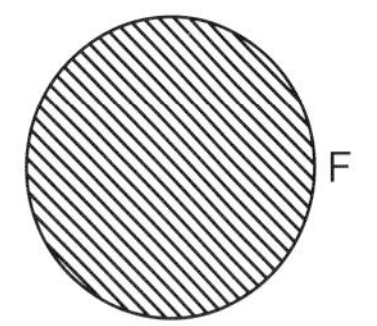

% in top 10 countries: 100.0
Total number of populated European countries: 3
Total European population 5381–16,262 (8208)
Russian population 10,000–100,000 (31,623)

The Hawk Owl breeds throughout the Holarctic in northern coniferous forests, the most southerly population being in the Tian Shan. In Europe it is a regular breeder only in the northern half of Norway, Sweden, Finland and Russia. It is an occasional breeder further S and it is rare in Estonia. Its distribution has long been reasonably stable, but in C parts (occasionally further S) of the Nordic countries it breeds only in vole-rich years. Of the three subspecies, only the nominate *S.u. ulula* occurs in Europe.

Its breeding habitats are forest edges or sparse forests, but it is a hole-nester, preferring suitable semi-open tree holes or nestboxes. Prime habitat for the Hawk Owl comprises of a forest edge beside an open bog, but nowadays it favours clearing edges. It is important for the bird to have an adjacent meadow or wet bog occupied by its main prey, voles. It is diurnal, usually occupying a high vantage-point, but is aggressive and noisy at the nest.

Even in good years, nests are usually several kilometres apart. In Norway in a good vole year, a breeding density of 1 bp/50km² is typical, but in Sweden it increases to 1 bp/5km² (Hagen 1956). After the 1920s, the Hawk Owl population seems to have decreased, but it has recovered somewhat since the 1960s (Saurola 1985). Recent peak breeding years in Finland were 1974, 1978, 1983 and 1988–89 (Saurola 1983, Haapala *et al* 1992).

In southern Finland, Norway and Sweden, the Hawk Owl is an irruptive species following vole peaks in Lapland. The irruptions begin in late August, peaking in October–November. The most recent major irruptions in the Nordic countries were recorded in 1950, 1957, 1964, 1976 and 1983 (Hildén 1977). Seldom do they reach Denmark and C Europe, as happened in 1914, 1920, 1927, 1957 and 1983.

It is difficult to estimate the total population, not only because it fluctuates from year to year, but also because the breeding areas are so remote. In the immense area of N European Russia, there are perhaps 10 000–100 000bp, whereas in Finland, Sweden and Norway perhaps 3500–21 000bp. Its habitat is secure at least in the medium-term, and so the European population is not at risk.

Seppo Sulkava (FIN)

Glaucidium passerinum **Pygmy Owl**

CZ	Kulíšek nejmenší	**I**	Civetta nana
D	Sperlingskauz	**NL**	Dwerguil
E	Mochuelo Chico	**P**	Mocho-pigmeu
F	Chevêchette d'Europe	**PL**	Sóweczka
FIN	Varpuspöllö	**R**	Воробьиный сыч
G	Σπουργιτόγλαυκα	**S**	Sparvuggla
H	Törpekuvik		

Non-SPEC, Threat status S (P)

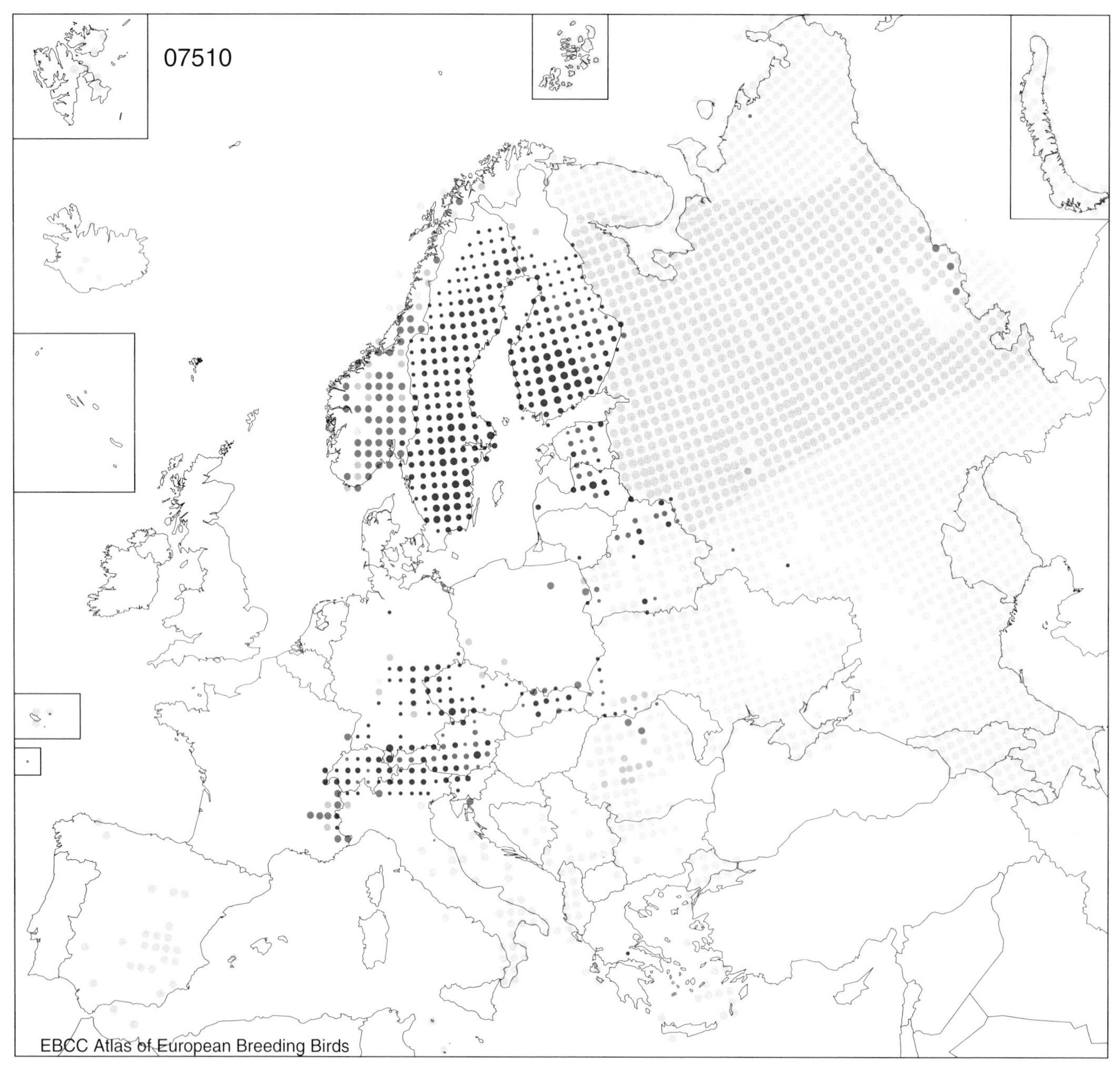

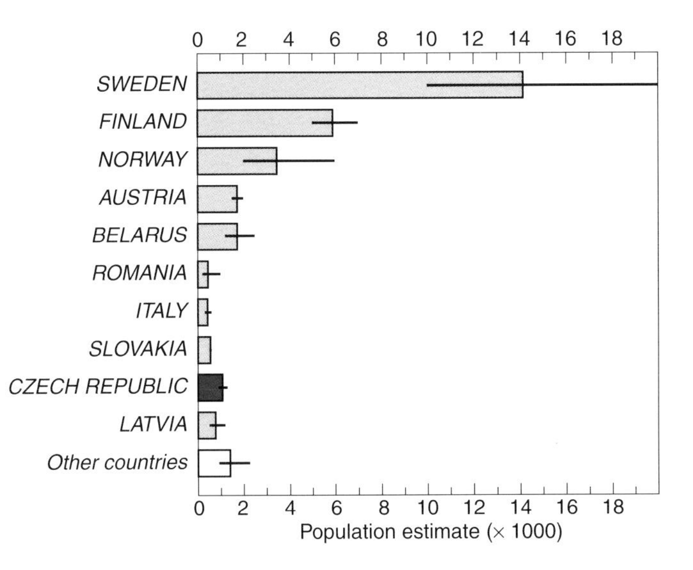

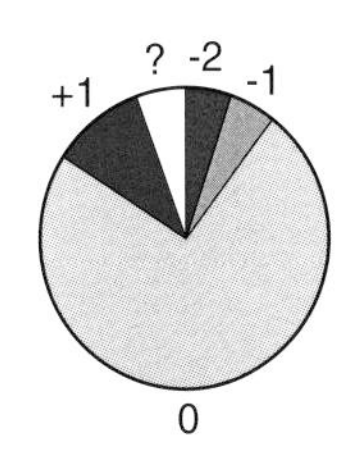

% in top 10 countries: 95.6
Total number of populated European countries: 19
Total European population 27,120–38,252 (31,671)
Russian population 10,000–100,000 (31,623)

The Pygmy Owl is the smallest Palearctic owl, but nevertheless is robust. It occupies the entire 600–1000km wide belt of the boreal coniferous forest (taiga) from Norway across N Eurasia to E Siberia and Sakhalin, including the Altai and Sayan Mountains of C Asia. Isolated and presumably post-glacial relict populations inhabit the cold montane zone of C Europe. Geographical variation throughout the range is slight, the European subspecies being *G.p. passerinum*, but the other subspecies *orientale*, of E Siberia, Manchuria and Sakhalin, tends to be larger and somewhat paler and greyer.

Like Tengmalm's Owl *Aegolius funereus*, the Pygmy Owl is a taiga element of the Siberian–Canadian faunal type. In Europe it is widespread throughout the Fennoscandian coniferous forests, which hold 17 700–34 700bp. The Scandinavian population occurs from the transition zone between the mixed temperate and boreal forests of S Sweden and the Baltic states to 67–68°N in Swedish Lapland. In the N European plain lowlands, where perhaps it was more widespread formerly, it is confined to scattered breeding sites, the most important being in the E Polish Białowieża Forest and in Belarus (1300–2600bp). The C European breeding populations are confined to the boreal altitudinal zones of the higher Alpine, Jura and Vosges ridges, to secondary ranges in S Germany and the Czech Republic and to the Slovak, S Polish, Ukrainian and Romanian Carpathians. Isolated populations exist in the Bulgarian Balkan and Rhodopes Mountains. In 1986 the species was first found nesting in Greece at 1230m asl in the Vardoussia Mountains (J. Hölzinger, pers comm). Throughout the Alps the Pygmy Owl inhabits the forests above the highest nesting territories of the Tawny Owl *Strix aluco* (from 700–1000m asl to the treeline at 1800–2100m), whereas breeding in the Ore Mountains and the Thuringian and Bohemian Forests usually occurs from 350–400m up to 900m asl (Scherzinger 1970, S. Schönn 1980). In C Europe, reliable population data are often lacking, but numbers probably are between 4100 and 7200bp.

The Pygmy Owl inhabits a variety of forest habitats, ranging from virgin coniferous through naturally managed to highly cultivated forests containing artificial clearings, completely deforested sections and scattered uncut island-stands. Richly structured, lighter and more open stands of climax coniferous forests dominated by common spruce *Picea abies* comprise prime habitat, where there is low interspecific competition from the larger Tawny and Ural *S. uralensis* Owls. Here, mature trees have holes, usually excavated by woodpeckers such as Great Spotted *Dendrocopos major*, Three-toed *Picoides tridactylus* or Grey-headed *Picus canus*, suitable for nesting and for catching and caching prey. Throughout the lowlands of Fennoscandia and the Baltic States the Pygmy Owl also nests in oak *Quercus* or barren pine *Pinus* forests, and in moist alder *Alnus*, birch *Betula* and aspen *Populus* woodlands interspersed with dense spruce stands.

The Pygmy Owl is a crepuscular hunter of rather open or unwooded terrain at forest edges and in clearings, over avalanche tracks, pastures, boglands and in young semi-open forests. Across Scandinavia population densities vary between 0.15 and 20–30 bp/10km^2, probably fluctuating according to weather conditions and rodent cycles, whereas in the C European mountains densities are between 0.7 and 4.2 bp/10km^2 (Scherzinger 1970, 1974), reaching in N Austria (very locally) 3–4 bp/1.5km^2 (Nadler 1994).

During winter, the Pygmy Owl hunts selectively a mixture of small rodents and birds and stores prey for later consumption, thus enabling it to withstand most boreal winter conditions. Throughout C Europe breeding birds are highly resident, moving lower after bad weather, but dispersing juveniles may occur more regularly further afield. Cold weather and very poor rodent years trigger large-scale, more cyclical southward movements of the northernmost populations. Remarkable irruptions have been recorded since 1903 (reviewed in Mikkola 1983).

Heimo Mikkola (FIN) Peter Sackl (A)

This species account is sponsored by Verein Sächsischer Ornithologen, D.

Athene noctua

Little Owl

CZ	Sýček obecný	**I**	Civetta
D	Steinkauz	**NL**	Steenuil
E	Mochuelo Común	**P**	Mocho-galego
F	Chevêche d'Athéna	**PL**	Pójdźka
FIN	Minervanpöllö	**R**	Домовой сыч
G	Κουκουβάγια	**S**	Minervauggla
H	Kuvik		

SPEC Cat 3, Threat status D

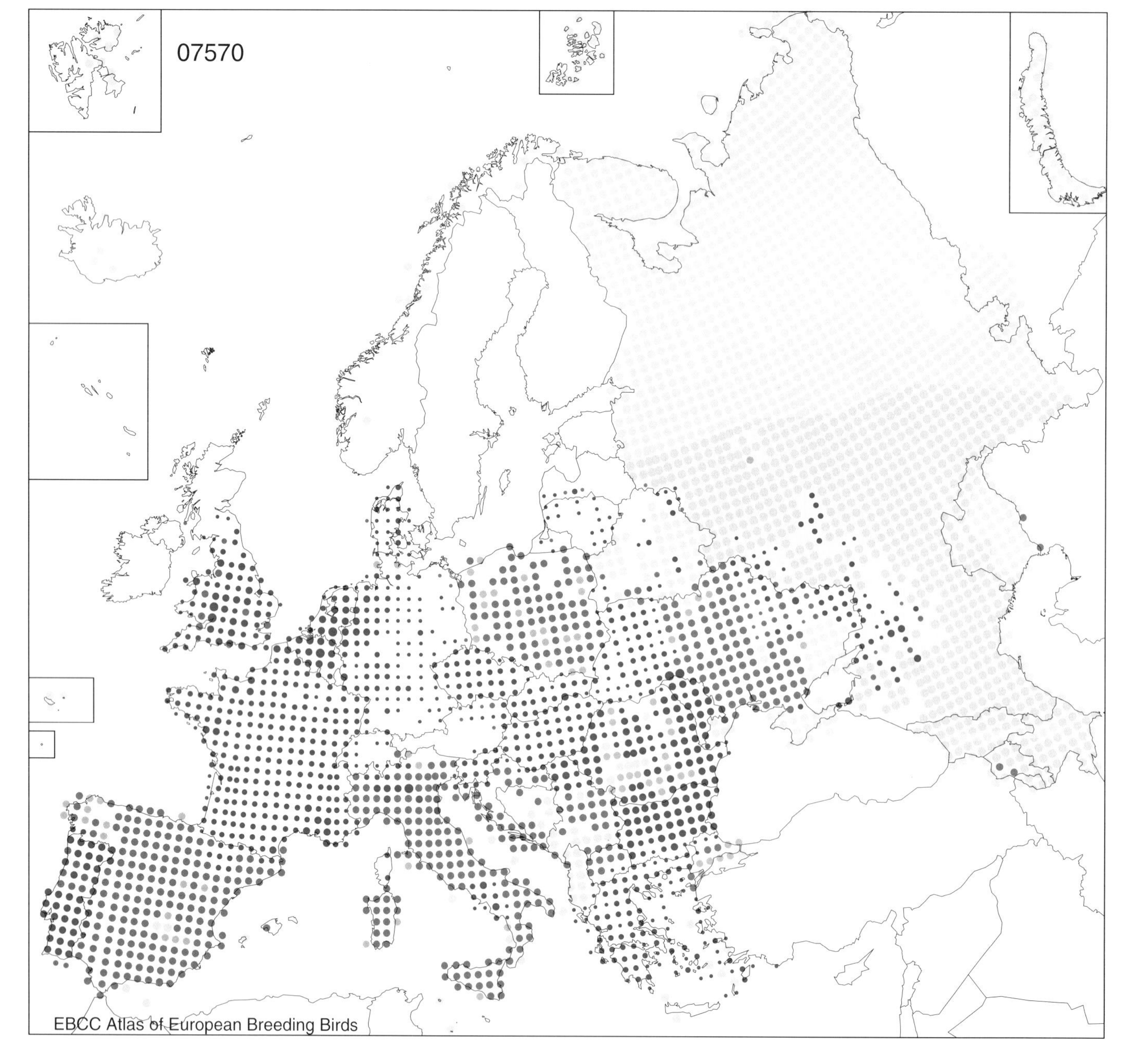

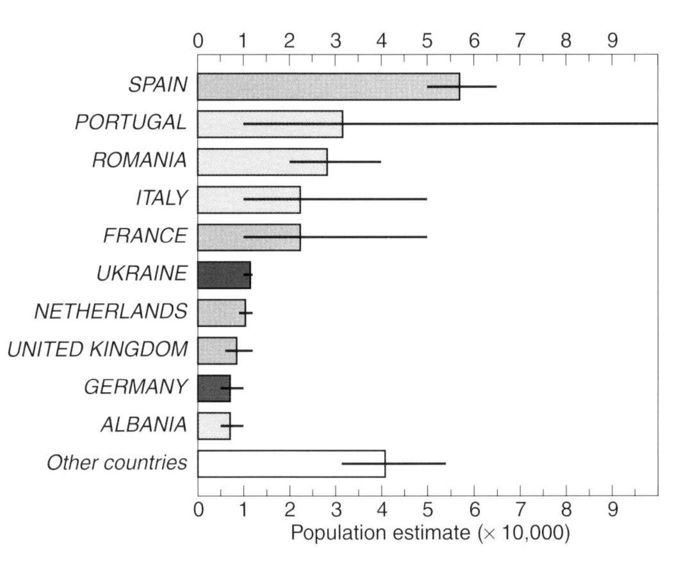

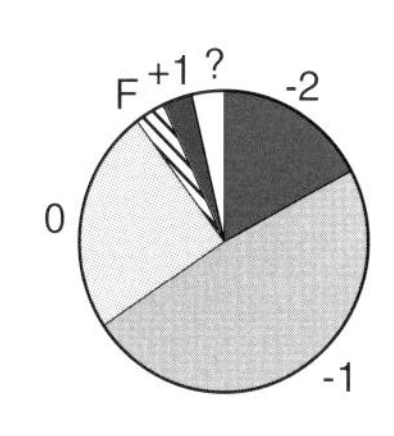

% in top 10 countries: 83.5
Total number of populated European countries: 29
Total European population 216,566–327,330 (246,921)
Russian population 10,000–100,000 (31,623)
Turkish population 5000–50,000 (15,811)

The Little Owl has a trans-Palearctic distribution from the Mediterranean basin to China. It also occurs in the Afrotropical region, in Ethiopia and S of the Arabian Gulf. It was introduced successfully into England in the 1870s and to New Zealand in 1906. The northern limit of its distribution is determined mainly by average winter temperatures. It avoids regions characterized by lengthy periods of snow-cover. The species is sedentary (71% of 322 British recaptures were within 10km of the ringing site), but large displacements do occur.

The species occupies a wide range of open agricultural landscapes; traditional orchards, meadows with pollarded willows, the environs of isolated farms and villages, parks, cemeteries, quarries, coastal zones, cork oak *Quercus suber* forests, olive plantations, dunes and pastures with ruins and stone aggregations. In Mediterranean mountainous areas it inhabits biotopes which feature sparse vegetation and rocky screes. Such primary habitat is rare in Europe, although it is typical of the deserts and steppes the Little Owl inhabits elsewhere.

The species is common and widespread in Italy, Portugal, Spain and Greece. Elsewhere in Europe it occurs in clusters in favourable zones. Generally it is found between 20° and 55°N, but does not occur in Sweden, northern Russia, Ireland nor most of Scotland. It is accidental on Corsica, Malta and Crete and absent from all the Atlantic islands except Île d'Oléron. Its breeding altitude limit depends on snow-cover, usually being between 600 and 1100m asl, but exceptionally reaching 4000m in the former Soviet Union.

In the N numbers are low and mostly declining. Dense populations remain in milder climatic zones and where low-intensity agriculture is practised. Where intensive agriculture predominates, populations generally are in decline, as in Great Britain, The Netherlands and Germany. In Great Britain the pattern of change shows a loss in the E and Midlands (intensive agriculture) and the SW (loss of habitat?) and a gain in the W, but overall 11% of the 10km squares with breeding evidence in 1968–72 had none in 1988–91 (Glue 1993a). In The Netherlands, numbers declined by probably over 50% between 1970 and 1990, thus qualifying the species for the Red List (Osieck & Hustings 1994). Habitat destruction was an important factor; industrialized farming practices, including over-application of manure, decimated foodstocks, especially voles and earthworms. Similarly, in C Europe increasing agricultural intensification prevents the sedentary populations from recovering from the effects of severe winters, especially in mountainous regions, forcing them into sharp decline.

In Switzerland the population of *c*185bp in 1980 (Juillard 1984) dropped to 30–40 in 1990. In Luxembourg numbers declined to 80–150bp from 3400–4200 in the 1960s. In Austria there were only 60bp in 1992 (Berg 1992). The pattern in Germany varies. In former East Germany, numbers reduced from 250–300bp in 1985–86 to 110–160 in 1987–88 (S. Schönn *et al* 1991). In Bavaria the Little Owl is very rare and limited by climate to the milder plains below 700m asl. However, there were increases in Saarland and beside Lake Constance following successful nestbox schemes. A Belgian scheme has achieved similar results. In our opinion, the French population has decreased from *c*100 000bp in 1976 to 5000–50 000 (Génot 1994). Overall, the regression is probably due to a combination of loss of breeding and hunting habitat through agricultural intensification, loss of nest holes, traffic casualties and severe winters. In SE Europe, the species remains abundant around the Black Sea because of ample prime habitat. In prime habitat, such as in the S Massif Central where dry pastures are grazed by sheep and contain many ruins and stone aggregations, the species reaches a maximum breeding density of 2.2 bp/km^2 (Lovaty 1990b).

Up to four subspecies occur in Europe: *A.n. vidalii* from Iberia through the Low Countries to the Baltic States, *noctua* C Mediterranean to Carpathians, *indigena* southern Balkans to S European Russia, and arguably *sarda* on Sardinia.

Jean-Claude Génot (F) Michel Juillard (CH)
Dries van Nieuwenhuyse (B)

This species account is sponsored by Natur- und Vogelschutzverein Kestenholz, CH.

Strix aluco

Tawny Owl

CZ	Puštík obecný	**I**	Allocco
D	Waldkauz	**NL**	Bosuil
E	Cárabo Común	**P**	Coruja-do-mato
F	Chouette hulotte	**PL**	Puszczyk
FIN	Lehtopöllö	**R**	Обыкновенная неясыть
G	Χουχουριστής	**S**	Kattuggla
H	Macskabagoly		

SPEC Cat 4, Threat status S

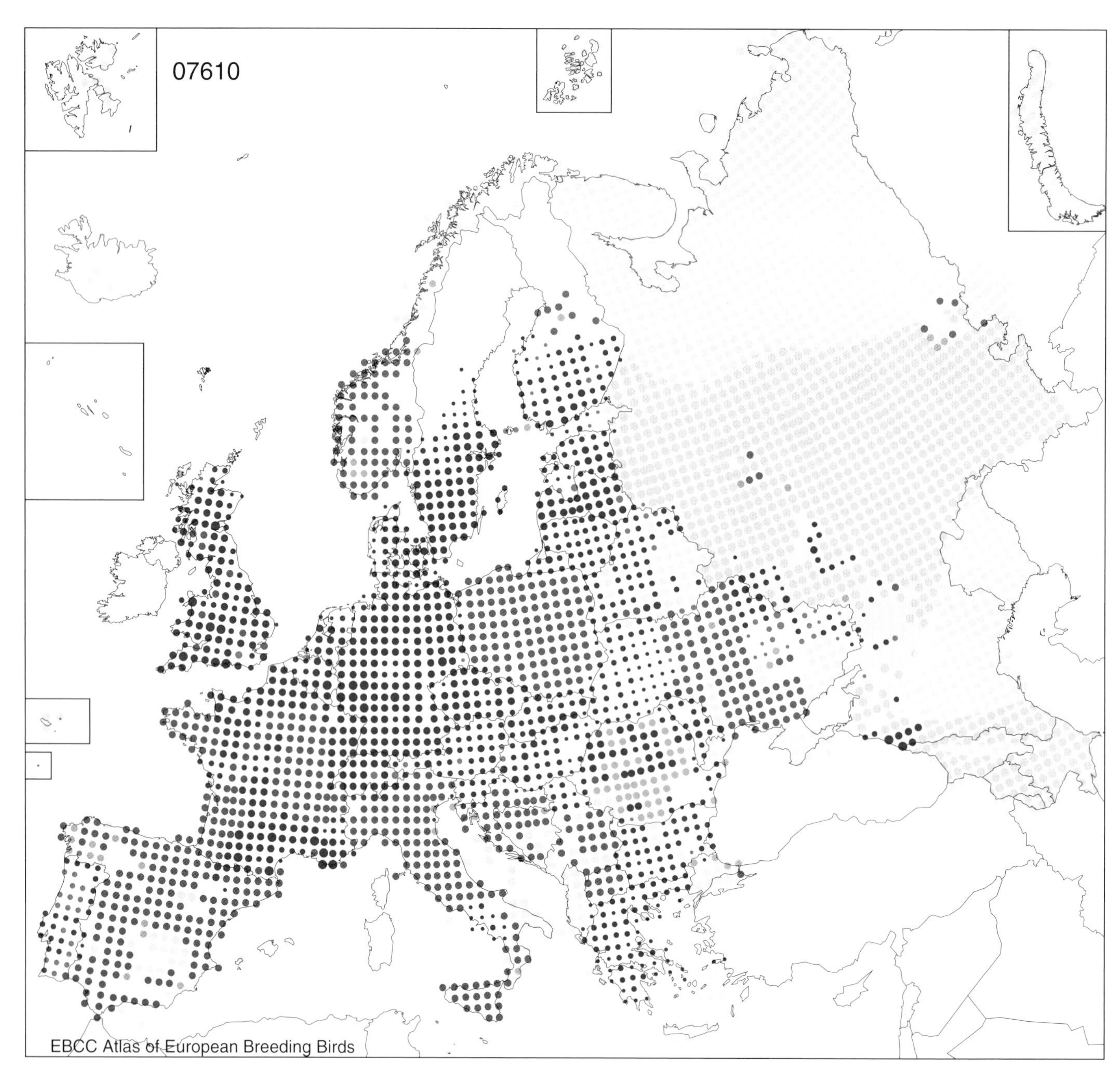

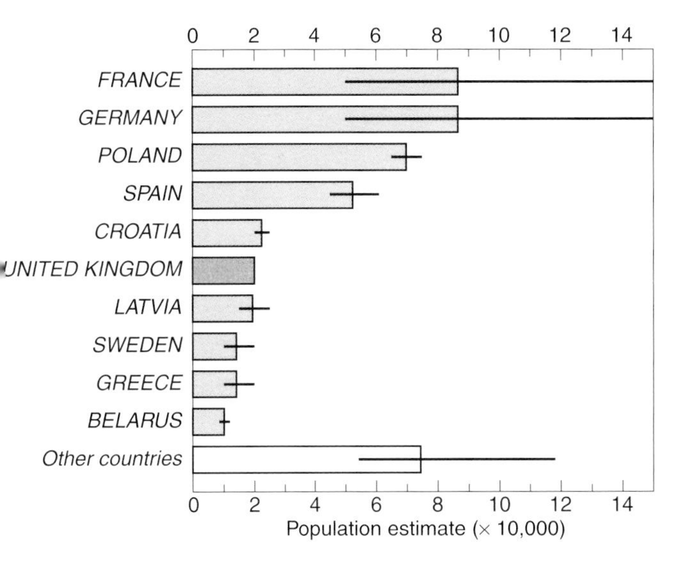

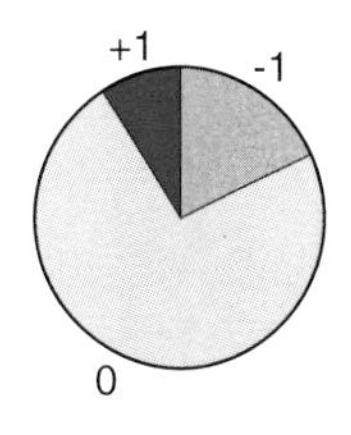

% in top 10 countries: 84.2
Total number of populated European countries: 33
Total European population 416,561–562,013 (469,968)
Russian population 10,000–100,000 (31,623)
Turkish population 5000–20,000 (10,000)

The Tawny Owl, a medium-sized wood owl, has separate European and Asiatic populations. Its Palearctic range extends from Portugal in the W to Korea in the E. Its main distribution lies within the temperate forest zone, and extends into boreal and mediterranean habitats. In many boreal and some alpine forests it is replaced by the closely related but larger Ural Owl *S. uralensis*. Four of the *c*10 subspecies occur in the *Atlas*' coverage area.

While its primary habitat is undoubtedly broad-leaved forest (Southern 1970, Delmée *et al* 1978), it has shown a remarkable ability to adapt to habitats made or altered by human beings (Galeotti 1990, Petty 1992). It has colonized many urban areas and has adapted to live in virtually treeless tracts created by deforestation and the rise of intensive agriculture. It is found in many woodland habitats including mixed conifer and broad-leaved forests, subalpine conifer forests and conifer plantations.

The Tawny Owl is widely distributed in Great Britain and mainland Europe and but is absent or scarce on other large islands in the Atlantic and Mediterranean. It extended its range northwards in the 1920s and 1930s. In Finland this expansion occurred in broad-leaved forests along coastal and riparian zones, and in arable areas from which the Ural Owl was absent (Lundberg 1980). In hilly terrain, territories are often distributed along valley bottoms, but absent or scarce on higher ground. The Tawny Owl is most abundant in C Europe, corresponding to the distribution of temperate broad-leaved forest. The European population is *c*360 000–800 000bp, of which some 30% occurs in Germany and France.

The few recent changes reported in either range or abundance are generally of increases in C Europe and decreases in the N and S. Climatic fluctuations may be involved, but increases in The Netherlands and Belgium are related to the maturation of forests planted since the 1890s. It should be noted that atlas techniques in many countries do not record accurately changes in distribution and abundance of this nocturnal species. For instance, the Tawny Owl has increased its range and density in Britain as a result of upland area reforestation (Petty 1992), but this was not shown in Britain's latest breeding bird atlas (1988–91).

Woodland structure, and its influence on food availability, is probably the main factor limiting Tawny Owl distribution (Southern 1970, Petty 1992). The abundance and distribution of small mammals (particularly voles and mice) are of prime importance, especially throughout winter and early spring. The Tawny Owl is a 'sit and wait' hunter, not well-adapted to exploit alternative prey at these crucial times of year. Thus, low numbers of small mammals result in few owl pairs breeding. It may exploit alternative prey such as recently fledged birds, amphibians, arthropods and other mammals, but later in spring and summer.

Although it prefers to breed in tree cavities, the Tawny Owl is extremely adaptable and will use a wide range of alternative nest sites, including buildings, crag ledges, and other species' stick nests. It will even nest on the ground, usually at the base of a tree. Therefore, nest-site availability is unlikely to limit distribution in otherwise suitable habitats. Competition with the Ural Owl, though, may limit the northern expansion of the Tawny Owl into the coniferous forest zone (Lundberg 1980).

The Tawny Owl is highly territorial and sedentary. Post-fledging movements are small, with most juveniles eventually settling to breed within 20km of where they hatched, but avoiding their natal territory (Petty 1992). Once established, most adults retain a territory for life. In prime habitats, average territory size can be as small as 10–12ha, but in poorer habitats as much as 60–70ha (see reviews in Galeotti 1990, Petty 1992).

Steve J Petty (GB) Pertti Saurola (FIN)

This species account is sponsored by Edouard Delmee, Paul Dachy and Paul Simon, Gaurain-Ramecroix, B.

Strix uralensis — Ural Owl

CZ	Puštík bělavý	I	Allocco degli Urali
D	Habichtskauz	NL	Oeraluil
E	Cárabo Uralense	P	Coruja-uralense
F	Chouette de l'Oural	PL	Puszczyk uralski
FIN	Viirupöllö	R	Длиннохвостая неясыть
G	Ουραλοχούχουλας	S	Slaguggla
H	Uráli bagoly		

Non-SPEC, Threat status S (P)

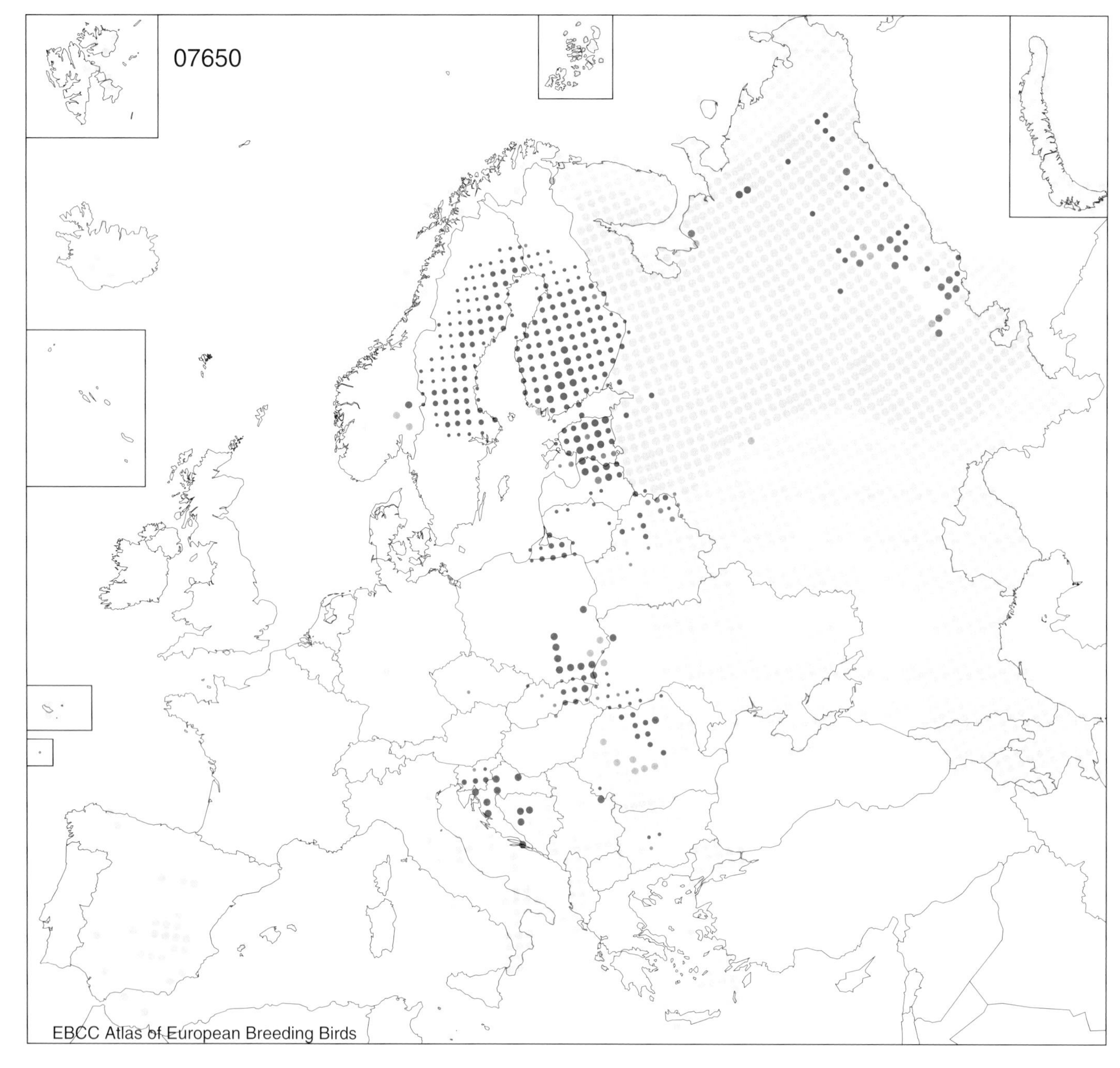

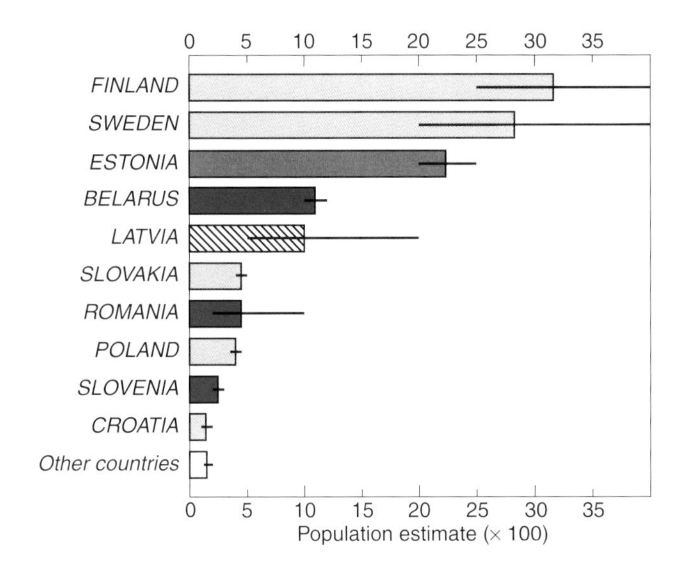

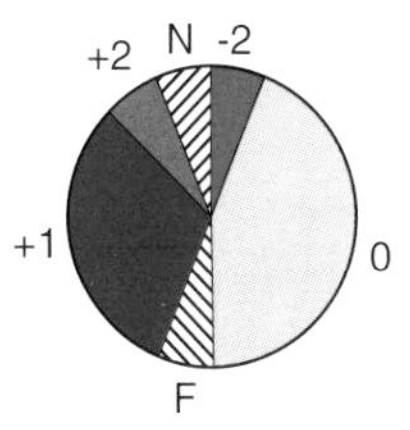

% in top 10 countries: 98.8
Total number of populated European countries: 16
Total European population 10,919–14,011 (12,147)
Russian population 100,000–1,000,000 (316,228)

The Ural Owl, a medium-sized inhabitant of the boreal forest or taiga, has a wide Palearctic distribution from Norway in the W to Japan in the E. In Europe, the bulk of the population lives in the coniferous forests of Sweden, Finland, Estonia and Russia. Isolated C European populations are restricted to mountain areas. In the Carpathians, and in the Slovenian, Croatian and Bosnian uplands, the Ural Owl's main habitat is deciduous forest.

The Ural Owl's distribution lies between two other members of the genus, the Great Grey Owl *S. nebulosa* being more northerly and the Tawny Owl *S. aluco* more southerly. In Finland and Sweden the Ural and Tawny Owls have a sympatric distribution, but occupy different main habitats, the former preferring coniferous forests and the latter, deciduous.

Ural Owl populations have been relatively stable in Fennoscandia. Slight changes in abundance are difficult to verify, because the Ural Owl exemplifies the category of species whose local population estimates depend largely on the intensity of research. In Finland and the Baltic States the recent increase in the number of known territories and active nests are therefore more an outcome of enthusiastic fieldwork than a reflection of a population increase; most Ural Owl breeding pairs occupy in nestboxes, especially in Finland. The provision of nestboxes has increased local populations, but we lack comparative information on populations inhabiting areas without boxes. Furthermore, the Ural Owl is not easy to census, being much harder to detect than the Tawny Owl; established pairs are fairly silent but unpaired males call more actively.

The proportion of breeding pairs varies in accordance vole numbers, which follow a 3–4-year cycle (Pietiäinen 1989, Saurola 1989). Because of a shortage of suitable nest sites, pairs are resident and territorial year-round (Lundberg 1979, Saurola 1987). Site tenacity is rendered possible because outside the breeding season the Ural Owl is a generalist feeder. The fluctuations of breeding pairs may result in inaccurate population estimates in less well-studied areas, because the species is easy to overlook beyond the immediate vicinity of the nest site; hence the results of successive surveys may be confusing.

In Finland and Sweden, where the species has been intensively studied, maximum population sizes have been estimated at 4000bp each. In comparison, the maxima given for Estonia (2500), Belarus (1200), Latvia (2000) and Romania (1000) are surprisingly high. At present, there is no realistic way of estimating the Russian population size.

In areas where the landscape composition is dominated by open areas such as fields and clearfells, the Eagle Owl *Bubo bubo* has a competitive advantage over the Ural Owl. Thus in SW Finland there are dense Eagle Owl populations over large areas from which the Ural Owl is absent. From the commencement of egg-laying to the dispersal of the young takes about five months for the Ural Owl, and so its northern distribution is limited to the latitude where the favourable season equals that period. Furthermore, the Ural Owl is not so well adapted to hunting in thick snow as is the Great Grey Owl.

In intensively studied areas in southern Finland, Ural Owl density may reach up to 8–10 bp/100km^2. From radio-tracking, home range size in optimal habitat in southern Finland has been estimated at about 10km^2. More often breeding density is 6–7 bp/km^2 or lower. These figures could not have been obtained if thousands of nestboxes had not been erected, because in much of Finland and Sweden modern forestry practices have eliminated chimney-like stumps or old trees with cavities large enough for the Ural Owl. Accordingly, nestboxes have real conservational value for this species' status in the future.

Hannu Pietiäinen (FIN) Pertti Saurola (FIN)

Strix nebulosa **Great Grey Owl**

CZ	Puštík vousatý	**I**	Allocco di Lapponia
D	Bartkauz	**NL**	Laplanduil
E	Cárabo Lapón	**P**	Coruja-lapónica
F	Chouette lapone	**PL**	Puszczyk mszarny
FIN	Lapinpöllö	**R**	Бородатая неясыть
G	Σταχτοχούχουλας	**S**	Lappuggla
H	Szakállas bagoly		

Non-SPEC, Threat status S

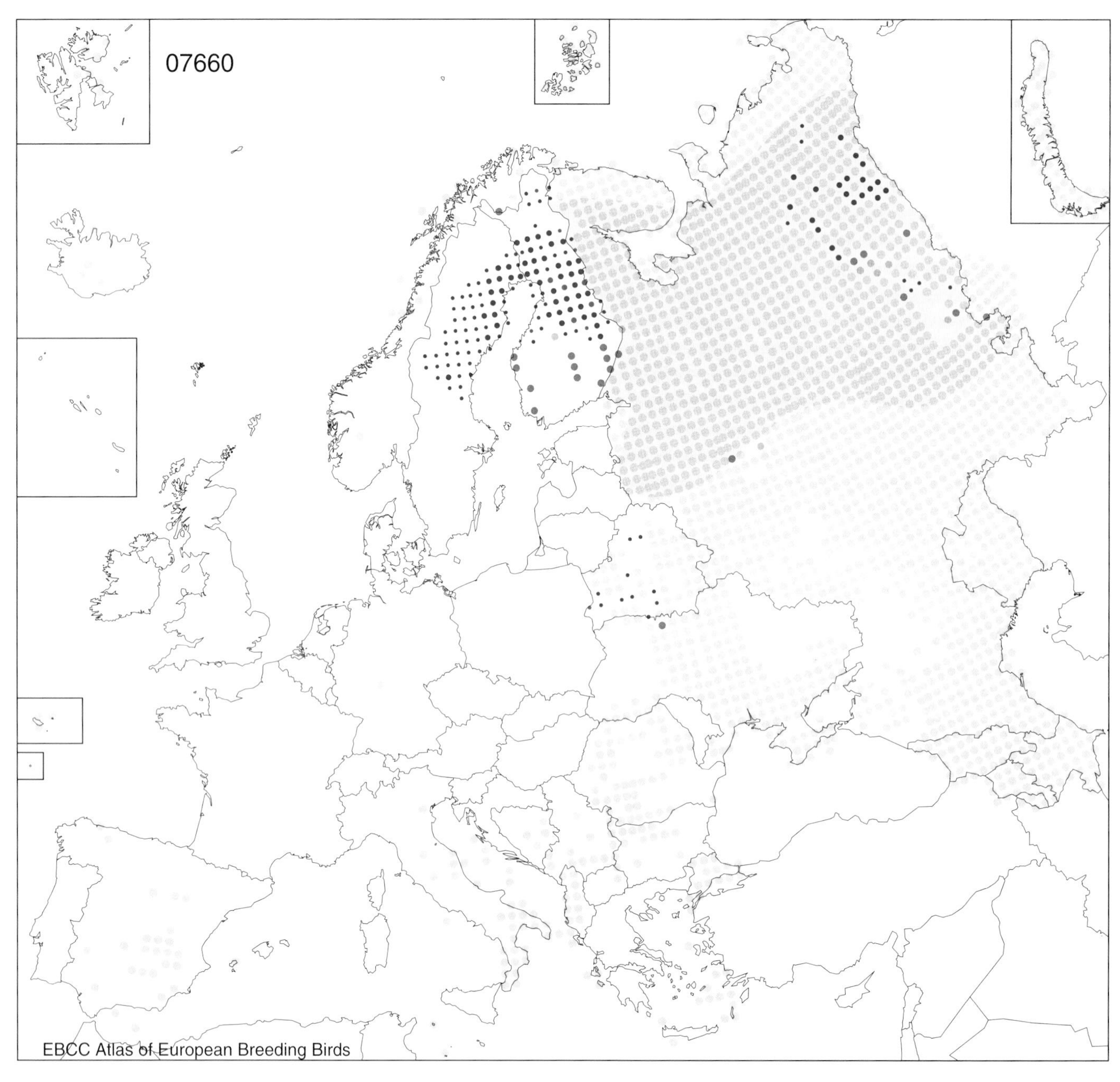

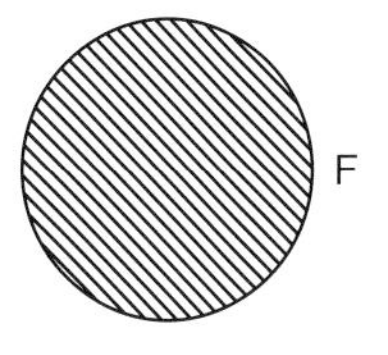

% in top 10 countries: 100.0
Total number of populated European countries: 1
Total European population 500–1500 (866)

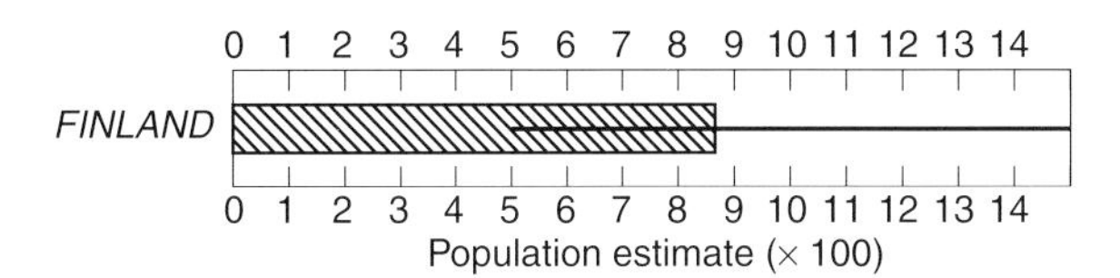

When it fluffs out its feathers, giving itself a heavy-headed and long-tailed outline, the Great Grey Owl can appear to be the largest and most massive of the northern forest owls, although it is only half the weight of the Eagle Owl *Bubo bubo*. It ranges further N than any other wood owl species, almost reaching the northern forest limits. Its most preferred habitats are lichen-covered spruce and pine forests, often intermixed with birch, and always adjacent to marshes, clearings, abandoned fields and other open hunting grounds. It is the only Holarctic *Strix* species, occupying a vast circumpolar range and breeding in boreal and boreal mountain climatic zones.

In the mountains of the United States it breeds as far S as 37°N (Sierra Nevada), but in NE Mongolia only to 54°N. The most southerly European nesting occurred at Zhytomyr in W Ukraine at *c*50°N (I. Gorban, pers comm), and the most northerly at *c*70°N in Finland and Norway, whereas in Siberia it has not bred above 68°N, and in Alaska only to 67°N.

When the vole population is at a normal level most birds winter in their nesting habitats, but concentrate at forest edges, swamps and cultivated fields, sometimes near farms. Following a vole crash, Great Grey Owl irruptions may occur to the S and W, and occasionally also the N. Irruptive pairs remaining to nest form the southerly breeding records.

The world status and distribution of this owl is poorly known, but it has been estimated that there may be upwards of 50 000 birds in North America. Allegedly, it is also common in E Siberia (Yakutia). In Europe the most westerly breeding occurs in Norway where the maximum of 14 nests was found in 1904. In Sweden there are more than 100bp in good vole years, 1984 seeing 70 confirmed and 60 possible breeding records (Stefansson 1986). Mikkola (1983, pers obs) suggested that C and S Finland contained more than 1000bp in good vole years, and according to Solonen (1986) probably as many as 1600bp in 1985.

The distribution and status of the Great Grey Owl in Russia and C Europe are poorly known, but a linear density (1976) of 1 bp/30km for the Archangel area in W Russia is in contrast with its rarity in the St Petersburg region (Mal'chevski & Pukinski 1983) and apparent absence from the Moscow area and the Ufa region. In mature forest in the Komi Republic densities reached 0.3 individuals/km^2 in a good vole year, but more typically are 0.05–0.1 ind/km^2 (Estafiev 1981, S.K. Kotchanov, unpubl). The mean overall density in the Perm region forests was 0.3 bp/1000km^2. It may still breed in Belarus and Lithuania near the Polish border. The species breeds from northern Ukraine southwards, three nests being found in 1985 in the Polessje Nature Reserve (A. Peklo, pers comm), and it was estimated that there were about 10bp in W Ukraine in the Rivne and Zhytomyr regions in 1991 (I. Gorban, pers comm).

Despite its scarcity over much of its Russian range, large irruptions still occur towards the normal range limits. It is clear that much must be learnt about the Great Grey Owl to begin to resolve these apparent anomalies. Because this species shifts its breeding areas according to food availability and to climatic conditions, it is difficult to estimate the European population size. The peak years in Finland and Sweden derived mostly from Russian emigrants. Should global warming persist, the Great Grey Owl's distribution will most likely move northwards. Only if the northern forests remain mainly undisturbed and unaffected by clearfelling, acid rain, mining and other developments will this species have a good chance of survival.

Heimo Mikkola (FIN) Alexey A Estafiev (R)
Sergei K Kotchanov (R)

Asio otus **Long-eared Owl**

CZ	Kalous ušatý	I	Gufo comune
D	Waldohreule	NL	Ransuil
E	Búho Chico	P	Bufo-pequeno
F	Hibou moyen-duc	PL	Uszatka
FIN	Sarvipöllö	R	Ушастая сова
G	Νανόμπουφος	S	Hornuggla
H	Erdei fülesbagoly		

Non-SPEC, Threat status S

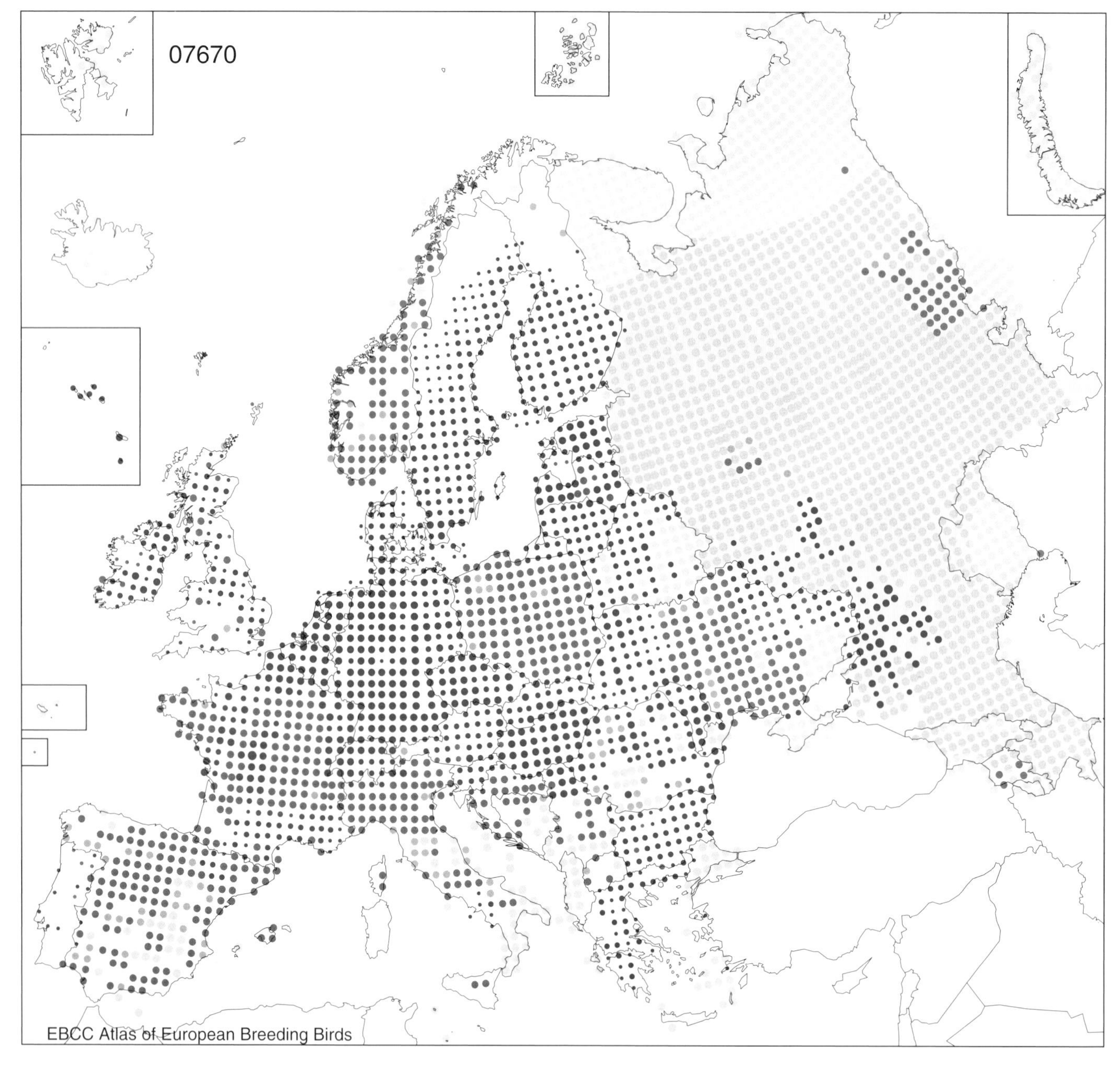

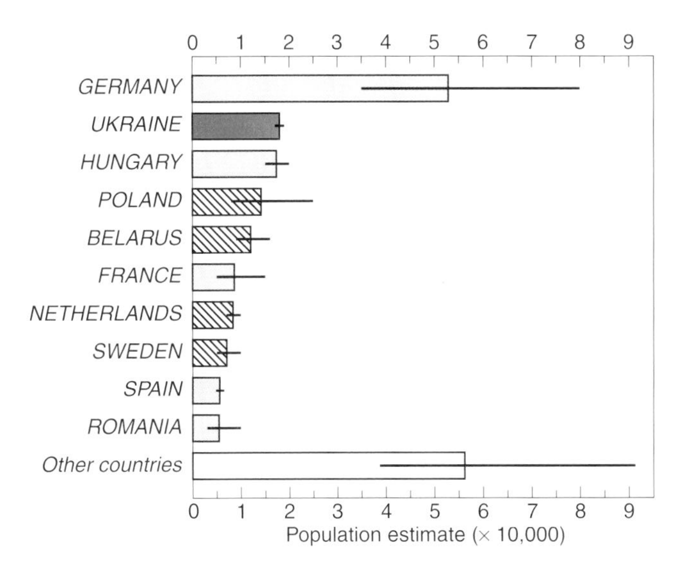

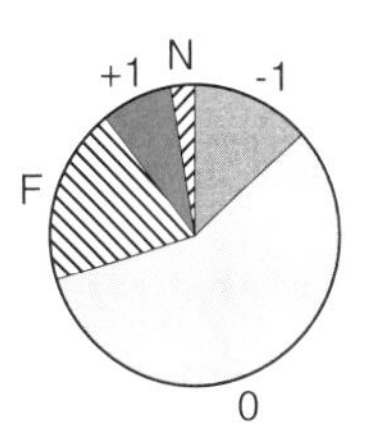

% in top 10 countries: 72.7
Total number of populated European countries: 37
Total European population 185,115–238,749 (205,741)
Russian population 50,000–500,000 (158,114)
Turkish population 100–1000 (316)

The Long-eared Owl has a circumpolar Holarctic breeding range, covering much of the boreal, temperate and also the wooded mediterranean and steppe zones. It breeds across Eurasia, S to Morocco and the Canaries, the Levant and Japan. The New World population extends from southern Canada to the southern USA. As a migrant in its northern range, respective elements of its populations winter S to Egypt, northern India, southern China and Mexico. This species is part of a cosmopolitan group, closely related species occurring further S in Central and South America and Africa.

In Europe the Long-eared Owl frequents a wide range of mainly arboreal habitats up to 2750m asl (S Armenia), notably coniferous forest, light broad-leaved woodland, timbered riverine tracts, copses, thickets and tree clumps. It also inhabits sand-dunes, marshes, natural steppe, thick hedges, hill pasture shelterbelts, heaths and moors, and to a lesser extent cultivated farmland, parks, orchards, large gardens and just occasionally, undisturbed areas in towns. Its basic nesting requirements usually comprise a sturdy nest platform (made by a corvid), scrub or tree cover, adjacent to open ground containing thick herbage supporting a substantial population of potential small mammal prey, notably microtine rodents (voles).

This primarily nocturnal owl is easily overlooked, its range in Europe and its relative regional abundance meriting cautious interpretation. Densities of >100–500 bp/50km square occur in the temperate zone from N France and the Low Countries in the W through C Europe to Russia, Belarus, the Balkans, Romania and Ukraine. Although the range extends to the Arctic Circle, densities decline rapidly with increasing latitude and altitude, especially in N Fennoscandia (almost absent from the alpine zone). In the countries fringing the Mediterranean, Adriatic and Black Seas, densities consistently are below 100 bp/50km square, distribution becoming patchier. Substantial island populations exist in Britain & Ireland and the Canaries, but densities are lower on the Azores, Balearics, Corsica, Cyprus and Sicily.

Most European Long-eared Owl populations have been stable or fluctuating since 1970. In Britain and continental W Europe pairs are often site-faithful (Glue & Hammond 1974, Wijnandts 1984), but are usually nomadic in Fennoscandia (Korpimäki 1992), and probably also in C Europe above 600–800m asl (Rockenbauch 1978). The Long-eared Owl is dependent on nocturnal quartering of open country for microtine rodents. Its breeding numbers, clutch sizes and fledging success fluctuate markedly where rodent populations change annually, peaking usually every 3–5 years. In good lemming *Lemmus lemmus* years it may extend its range northward (*BWP*).

In Great Britain the perceived decrease since 1990 has been attributed partly to competition for space, food and nest sites with the expanding population of the Tawny Owl *Strix aluco* which is physically dominant (I.N. Nilsson 1984). More recently, increases in Ireland (which lacks the Tawny Owl), and locally in Great Britain and The Netherlands have derived from the creation of suitable foraging and nesting habitat through afforestation, especially of heath and moor. Vegetational succession may render such habitats unsuitable in the long term (Koning & Baeyens 1990). However, long-term decreases through agricultural intensification and declining vole populations (in Westfalen, Germany, down 80% in a 125km^2 plot, 1974–86; Illner 1988), probably typify much of agricultural Europe, but large-scale quantification is probably impossible through the lack of reliable census data over sufficient area and time.

The Long-eared Owl is mainly migratory in Fennoscandia and Russia, mostly above 50°N. Ringed owls from these latitudes move S and SW in winter to countries fringing the North Sea, exceptionally as far as Spain. Further S in Europe, populations are mainly sedentary, staying on or close to territories throughout the year, although first-winter young tend to disperse widely, often joining assemblages where food is abundant (Wijnandts 1984).

David Glue (GB) Ingvar N Nilsson (S)

This species account is sponsored by Johannes Schwerdt, Rheinberg, D.

Asio flammeus

Short-eared Owl

CZ	Kalous pustovka	I	Gufo di palude
D	Sumpfohreule	NL	Velduil
E	Lechuza Campestre	P	Coruja-do-nabal
F	Hibou des marais	PL	Sowa błotna
FIN	Suopöllö	R	Болотная сова
G	Βαλτόμπουφος	S	Jorduggla
H	Réti fülesbagoly		

SPEC Cat 3, Threat status V (P)

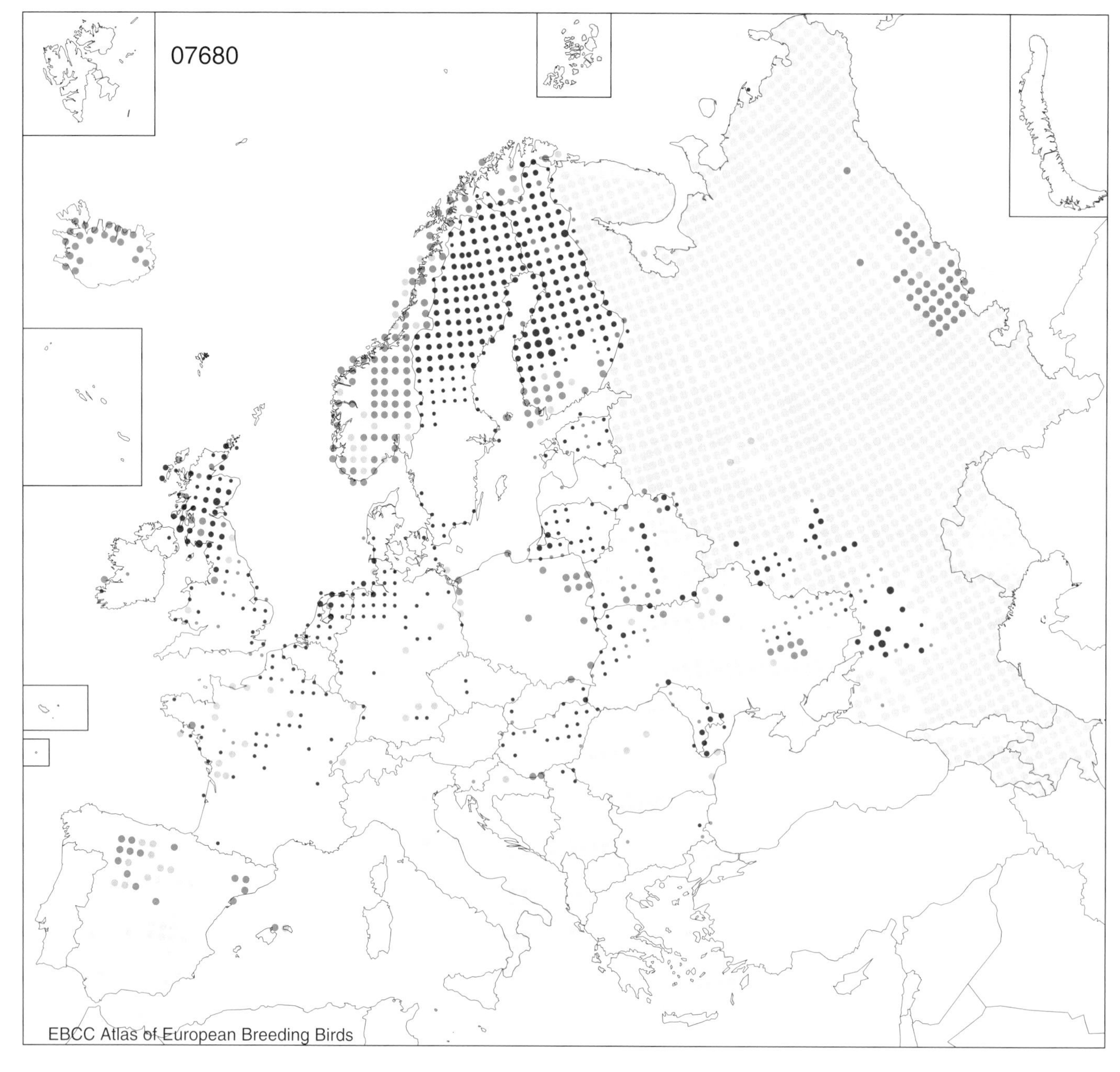

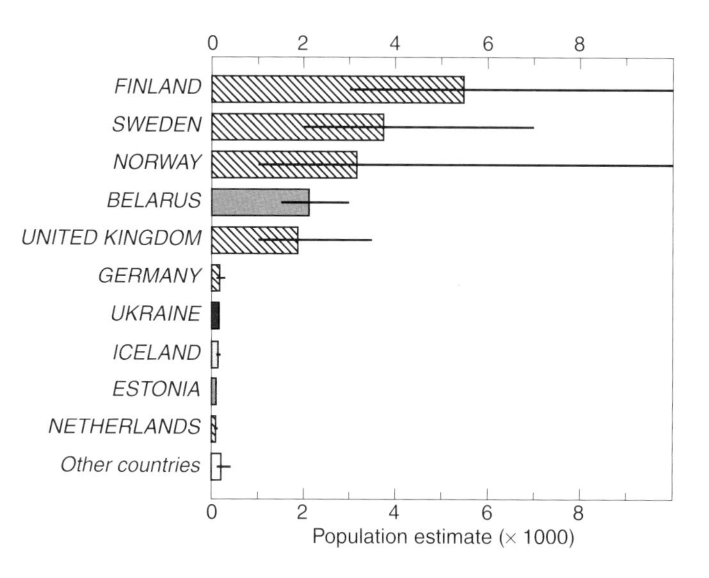

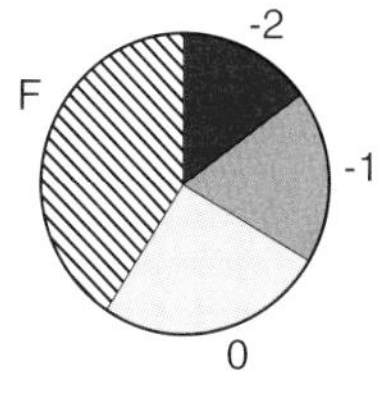

% in top 10 countries: 98.8
Total number of populated European countries: 26
Total European population 13,376–26,265 (17,249)
Russian population 10,000–100,000 (31,623)
Turkish population 1–50 (7)

The Short-eared Owl principally is a Holarctic species exhibiting a circumpolar range. There is a discontinuous South American distribution reaching the Neotropics. Populations occurring on outlying islands such as Hawaii and the Galapagos probably derive from the long-distance migrations and dispersion movements, typical of this nomadic owl, undertaken by individuals outside the breeding season.

In Europe the Short-eared Owl occupies chiefly tundra, boreal and temperate faunal types, and also some northern mountainous regions. For breeding grounds it favours swampy moss tundra, marshes and bogs, clearfells and damp woodland, wet or dry grassland, moorland and dry bush steppe, generally avoiding cultivated land in the breeding season.

Russia holds the largest (10 000–100 000bp) European population which breeds from the arctic tundra S to the temperate steppes. Elsewhere, the next-largest populations occupy Finland (3000–10 000bp), Sweden (2000–7000bp), Norway (1000–10 000bp), Belarus (1500–3000bp) and Great Britain (1000–3500bp). Iceland's small, regularly breeding population became established in low-lying areas in 1958. Over much of C and S Europe this owl's range becomes progressively patchier and nesting attempts more erratic. Here, breeding may occur only when microtine rodent (*Microtus* spp) populations reach high levels, or when birds from the northern strongholds are driven S by food shortages, causing a temporary increase in local owl numbers (Hölzinger *et al* 1973, Hölzinger 1987). Such sharp short-term fluctuations are typical across the European range. The species is an opportunistic feeder, but is heavily reliant upon small rodent prey, around which its spatial distribution and nesting success tend to revolve (Korpimäki & Norrdahl 1991). Territory size may be as small as 10ha, but it can vary by sevenfold or more as prey density reduces (Mikkola 1983, Körpimaki 1984). In Britain, moorland afforestation has provided ideal nesting habitat for owls because microtine rodents achieve high densities in the early stages of tree growth (Village 1987). Similar circumstances apply elsewhere in northern Europe. In The Netherlands, land reclamation, especially the creation of large polders in the IJsselmeer in 1943, 1957 and 1968 also increased vole numbers, the Short-eared Owl population comprising 2000–3000 birds in 1948/49 (Hagemeijer & Hustings 1994). However, neither afforestation nor land reclamation result in systematic restocking of owl populations.

The Short-eared Owl has declined or disappeared over much of C Europe, probably mainly through habitat degradation, most notably by drainage of coastal and inland wetlands and marshes and development of permanent pastures and semi-permanent meadows for arable cultivation, as in The Netherlands (Hagemeijer & Hustings 1994) and Germany (Hölzinger 1987). Shooting, rodenticide poisoning, and rail- and road-traffic casualties probably have had a lesser impact. Relatively few regular breeding areas now remain in C Europe, while in much of E Europe the species is now an erratic, scarce or rare breeder. Small populations exist in Austria, Croatia, Latvia, Romania and Greece, a few breeding pairs nesting as far S as the Balearics. The present European population (excluding Russia) is estimated at 9000–34 800bp, of which 50–75% breeds in Fennoscandia. The >50% decline in numbers in Russia (no range contraction, apparently) from 1970 to 1990 is of particular concern, because it affects by far the most important population.

After breeding, the species may disperse widely, especially from arctic and subarctic regions where populations of small microtine rodents tend to fluctuate sharply in a 3–4-year cycle (S. Ikola and E. Körpimaki, pers obs). Individual owls ringed in W Europe have later summered in Russia and Fennoscandia, birds from Britain travelling to Portugal and Spain, and even Gozo.

The European Short-eared Owl population comprises a substantial proportion of the total number of the nominate subspecies *A.f. flammeus*, which also occurs over the more northerly regions of Asia and North America. Seven other subspecies have been described elsewhere.

David Glue (GB) Erkki Korpimäki (FIN)

This species account is sponsored by Dr Walter Gehlhoff, Königswinter, D.

Aegolius funereus Tengmalm's Owl

CZ	Sýc rousný	I	Civetta capogrosso
D	Rauhfußkauz	NL	Ruigpootuil
E	Lechuza de Tengmalm	P	Mocho de Tengmalm
F	Chouette de Tengmalm	PL	Włochatka
FIN	Helmipöllö	R	Мохноногий сыч
G	Ελατόμπουφος	S	Pärluggla
H	Gatyáskuvik		

Non-SPEC, Threat status S (P)

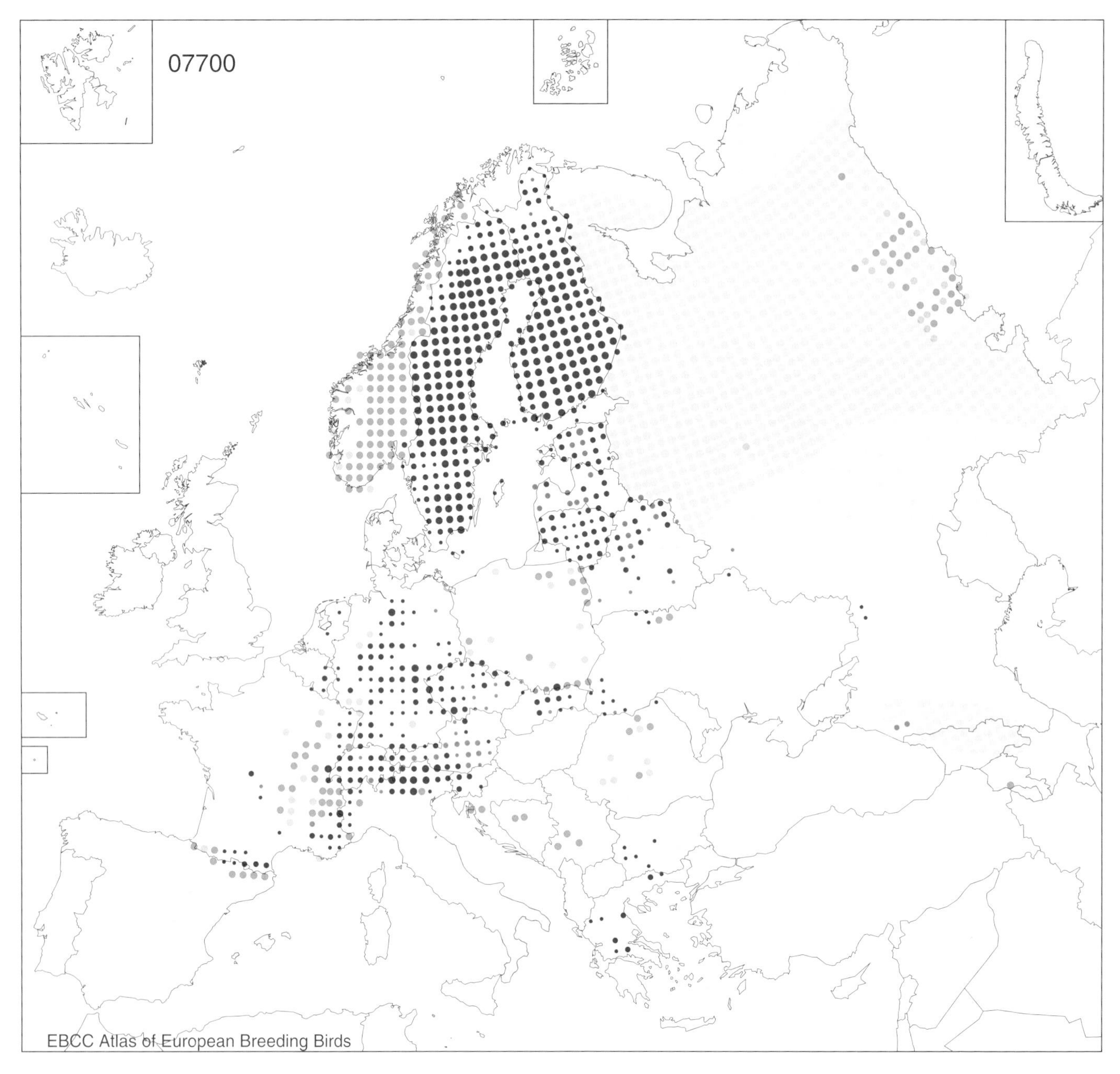

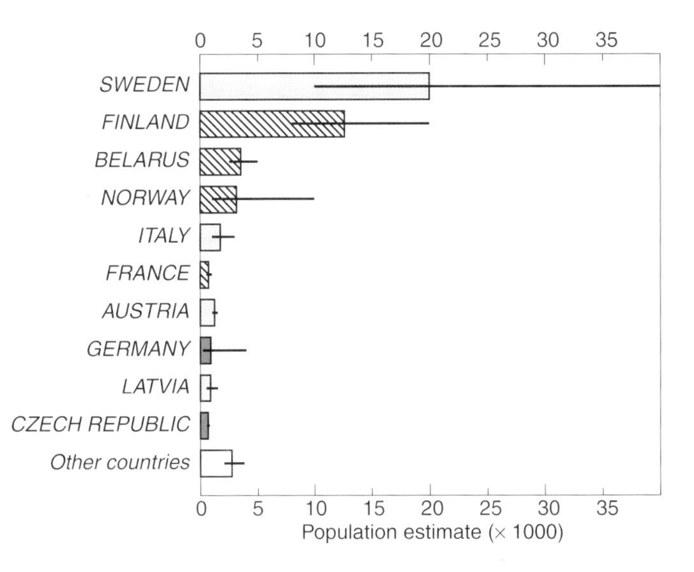

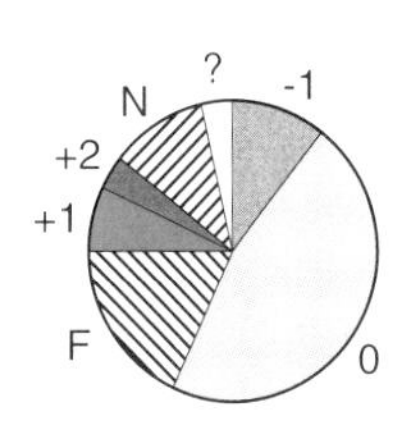

% in top 10 countries: 94.3
Total number of populated European countries: 28
Total European population 36,814–70,854 (48,159)
Russian population 10,000–100,000 (31,623)
Turkish population 5–50 (16)

Tengmalm's Owl, small and nocturnal, has a circumpolar Holarctic distribution, occupying North American and Eurasian coniferous (taiga) forests (Mikkola 1983). It breeds mainly in spruce *Picea* forests, but usually also occurs in mixed forests of pine *Pinus*, birch *Betula* and aspen *Populus tremula* and even in pure pine forests. However, breeding densities are much higher in spruce than in pine forests. In Finland, occupancy of breeding territories and reproductive success are higher in areas with high proportions of spruce forest and agricultural land and low proportions of pine forest and peatland bog (Korpimäki 1988).

In Europe the Tengmalm's Owl originally bred in natural cavities made mostly by the Black Woodpecker *Dryocopus martius*, and occasionally also in cavities made by smaller woodpeckers. Natural cavities are scarce in modern commercial forests, but it readily accepts nestboxes, which form a significant proportion of nest sites in many European countries. For example, Finnish birdwatchers have erected *c*11 000 owl nestboxes from which fledglings are ringed annually, and the scheme has much reduced the adverse effects of modern forestry techniques on owl populations. This may be why there are no major declines recorded.

Tengmalm's Owl feeds mostly on small mammals, especially *Microtus* and *Clethrionomys* voles, but it also takes shrews and small passerines in Fennoscandia, and wood mice and small birds in C Europe (Korpimäki 1981, 1986). Vole population densities fluctuate in three- to five-year cycles in Fennoscandia whereas in C and S Europe they remain relatively stable. Dietary diversity of European Tengmalm's Owl populations decreases northward (Korpimäki 1986). The probable reason for reduced dietary diversity in northern owl populations is that there owls feed almost exclusively on voles, whereas in the S there is an ample supply of alternative prey.

In Fennoscandia, as in much of Eurasia, it apparently is the commonest predatory bird. The largest European breeding populations occur in Russia, Sweden, Finland, Belarus and Norway, but numbers are also reasonably high in the Baltic States. Scattered and quite large local populations breed in the high-altitude forests of C Europe, especially in Austria, Germany, France, Switzerland and the Czech Republic. Recently, small local breeding populations have been found as far W as The Netherlands (Hasper & van Manen 1994) and as far S as northern Spain and Italy, Bulgaria and Greece. The S European populations may be relict populations from the post-glacial epoch (Mikkola 1983).

Tengmalm's Owl breeding pairs have been studied by similar methods for at least four years in 30 European populations in Germany, Norway and Sweden but mostly in Finland, and cyclicity indices estimating the amplitude of fluctuations in the yearly number of breeding pairs have been established. These indices increase from S to N and from W to E within C Europe and Fennoscandia (Korpimäki 1986). In Fennoscandia they are more closely related to snow conditions than to geographical location, being higher in areas with deep snow-cover than in areas with shallow snow-cover. Tengmalm's Owl is unable to penetrate deep snow-cover to reach prey living below it, and is forced to move where snow-cover is thinner, thus promoting population instability.

Northern Tengmalm's Owl populations are mostly nomadic, but further S adult males show greater year-round site tenacity than females (Korpimäki 1986), whereas in C Europe residency of both sexes year-round is high (Schwerdtfeger 1984). Nomadic females from western Finland disperse up to 500–600km annually. The intersexual differences are probably associated with conflicting selective forces between periodic winter food scarcity promoting mobility in females, and the need to guard nest holes promoting residency in males (Korpimäki *et al* 1987). The geographical variation probably is due to the climate becoming milder and snow-cover less with increasing latitude, thus reducing enforced nomadism.

Erkki Korpimäki (FIN)

This species account is sponsored by Adalbert Schlemmer, Wuppertal, D.

Caprimulgus europaeus **Nightjar**

CZ	Lelek lesní	**I**	Succiacapre
D	Ziegenmelker	**NL**	Nachtzwaluw
E	Chotacabras Gris	**P**	Noitibó da Europa
F	Engoulevent d'Europe	**PL**	Lelek
FIN	Kehrääjä	**R**	Обыкновенный козодой
G	Γιδοβυζάστρα	**S**	Nattskärra
H	Lappantyú		

SPEC Cat 2, Threat status D (P)

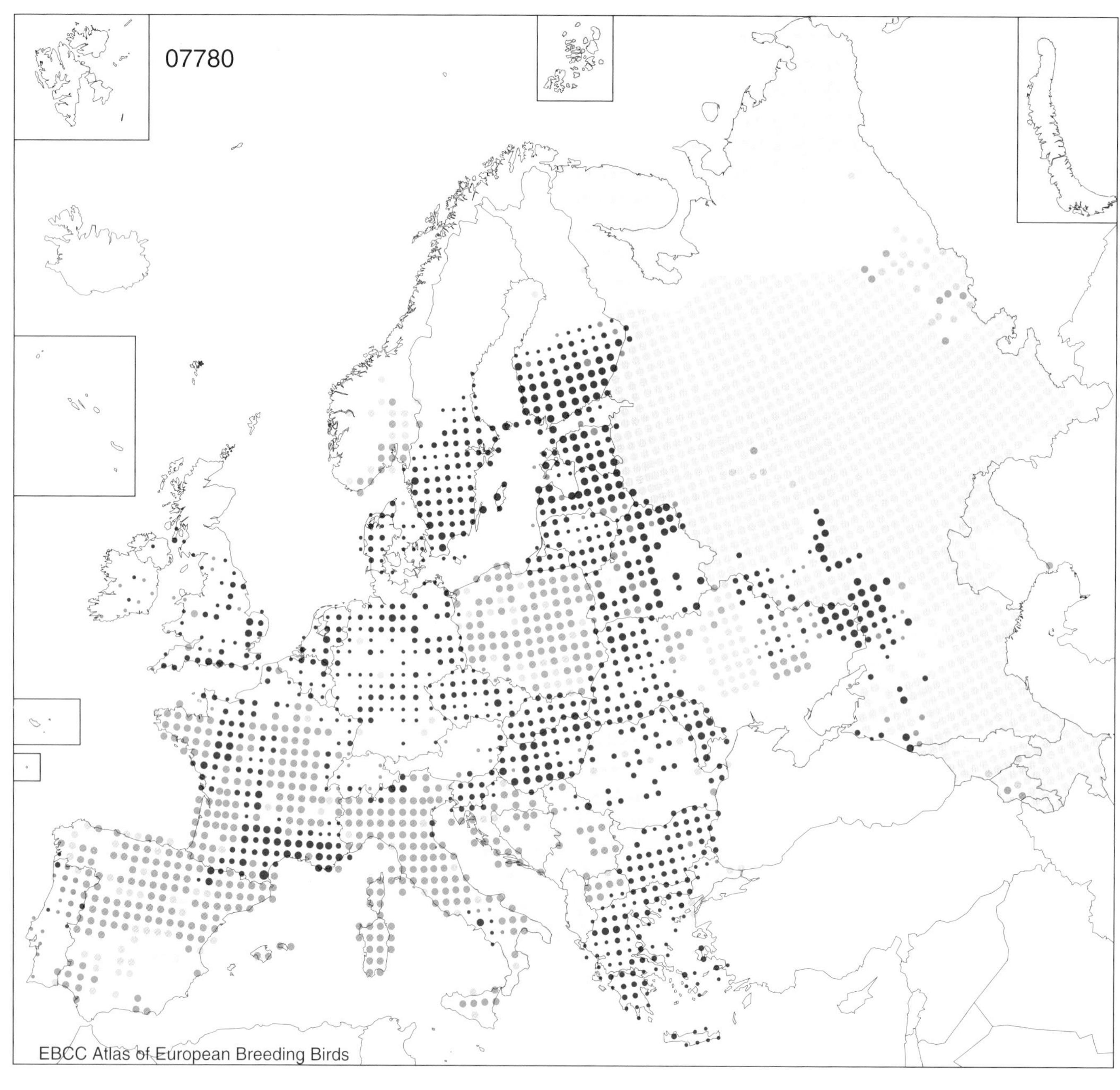

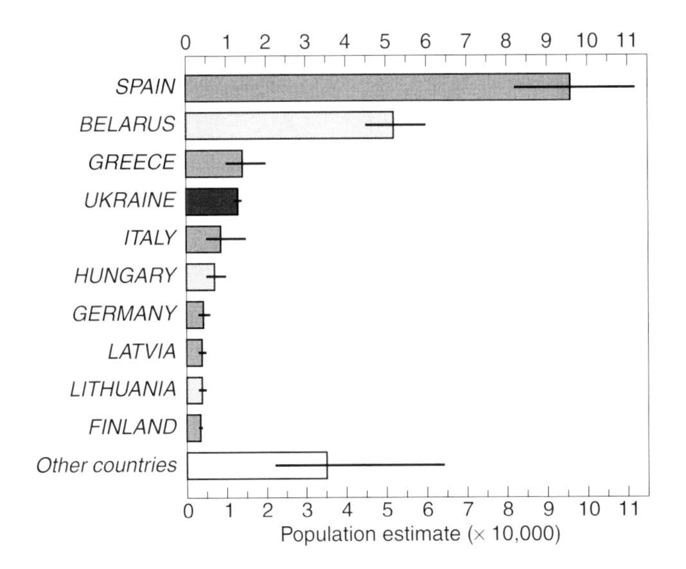

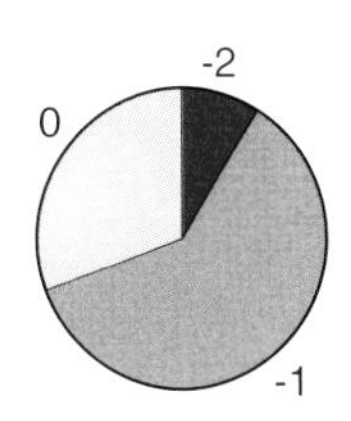

% in top 10 countries: 85.5
Total number of populated European countries: 33
Total European population 223,921–264,419 (241,165)
Russian population 100,000–500,000 (223,607)
Turkish population 1000–10,000 (3162)

The Nightjar, a mainly crepuscular and nocturnal species, ranges widely over much of Europe into NW Africa, the Near East and across C Asia as far as China. The European distribution encompasses a variety of zones from mediterranean to boreal and from oceanic to continental steppe. Two of the six subspecies occur in Europe: *C.e. europaeus* (N and C) and *meridionalis* (S).

All populations are migratory, wintering in sub-Saharan Africa. It is primarily a species of sparsely forested areas, such as open woodland, margins and clearings of mature woods, scrub, heathland and shrubby steppe, but avoids dense forests. It tolerates high altitudes if cover and adequate drainage exist. In parts of its range, clearfelled restocked woodland is frequently utilized (Sierro 1991).

Occurring over most of continental Europe, the Nightjar is absent mainly from treeless regions such as N Scotland, Iceland and Svalbard, the exposed highlands and tundra of N and W Scandinavia, Russia and the Alps and intensive farmland. It is most widespread and abundant in the Mediterranean countries, the Balkans, E Europe from Hungary eastwards into Russia and N to S Finland. These areas hold *c*95% of the European population, estimated at 295 000–809 000bp. Its thin distribution in the S Iberian open grasslands is possibly due to competition with the Red-necked Nightjar, *C. ruficollis*). In W Europe its distribution is patchier, population levels being lower than in E and S Europe, although localized pockets of comparable abundance occur. It is absent locally from intensively farmed and urban areas, like the English Midlands, NW France and the upper Rhine Valley.

Since the 1950s the Nightjar has experienced a reduction in range and numbers over much of Europe, especially W Europe. Of the countries bordering the Mediterranean and the former Eastern Bloc states, *c*50% reported a reduction in range or abundance, the remainder recording no change. The apparent reduction in range and numbers of >50% in Ukraine between 1970 and 1990 may have arisen from incomplete data.

In NW Europe the decline has been more general; first noted in Britain & Ireland in the early 1900s, it became widespread and still continues in many areas. In The Netherlands, the Nightjar has decreased by 80–95% since the 1950s, only 450–650bp remaining by 1992 (Maréchal & Taapken 1989, van Dijk *et al* 1994c). Ireland also experienced a decline of >50%. Since 1970 only Sweden has reported stability in range and numbers. In Britain numbers seemingly are recovering but the occupied range remains less than 50% of that of the early 1970s (Leslie 1993, Morris *et al* 1994). Only Germany in NW Europe has more than 3500bp.

There is no obvious link between the general decline of the Nightjar and climatic factors, although effects on productivity possibly contributed to the disappearance of small, isolated populations on the northwestern range periphery (Kemp 1983). Most declines are probably linked to habitat changes. Former prime habitat is now covered by commercial even-aged woodland. Areas of suitable tree cover are no longer coppiced or cleared of scrub (Maréchal & Taapken 1989, Morris *et al* 1994). The Nightjar remains common only in the less intensively farmed E and S Europe where prey is probably more readily available (low pesticide use?) and breeding habitat less disturbed.

Where favoured habitat is limited Nightjar populations may reach quite high densities. A mean of one male/7.7ha has been recorded from young plantations in S England, 1/17.3ha being the mean on nearby heathland (Morris *et al* 1994). Values of 1.0–1.5 males/km^2 (Luneberger Heide, *HVM*) are more representative of extensive areas.

Despite males being easy to locate through their distinctive song, the species' crepuscular and nocturnal nature makes the collection of reliable data difficult. Further monitoring is essential to assess the impact of agricultural intensification in Europe.

Ron Hoblyn (GB) Tony Morris (GB)

This species account is sponsored by Forest Enterprise, part of the Forestry Commission, Hexham, Northumberland, GB.

Caprimulgus ruficollis

Red-necked Nightjar

CZ	Lelek rudokrký	I	Succiacapre collorosso
D	Rothals-Nachtschwalbe	NL	Moorse Nachtzwaluw
E	Chotacabras Pardo	P	Noitibó-de-nuca-vermelha
F	Engoulevent à collier roux	PL	Lelek rdzawoszyi
FIN	Ruosteniskakehrääjä	R	Красношейный козодой
G	Κοκκινογιδοβυζάστρα	S	Rödhalsad nattskärra
H	Rozsdástorkú lappantyú		

Non-SPEC, Threat status S

The Red-necked Nightjar occurs widely as a breeding species over most of the Iberian Peninsula, except the Eurosiberian N. The nominate *C.r. ruficollis* occurs in Europe, *desertorum* occupying the non-desert areas of Morocco, Algeria and Tunisia.

In mediterranean forests, it prefers open areas containing bushes and pastures. In the Doñana, its preferred habitat is the open bushes of rockrose *Halimium halimifolium* at the edge of umbrella pine *Pinus pinea* woods and cork oak *Quercus suber* forests, close to marshland (Valverde 1960). The Iberian population breeds from the supramediterranean holm oak *Q. ilex* forests at 1500m asl (Sierra Nevada, Granada province) to the *Juniperus phoenicea* termo-mediterranean coastland bushes. In North Africa it even breeds in the pre-desert, remote from any forest. The Red-necked Nightjar is a common bird of the 'dehesas', the open forests of holm oak, cork oak or umbrella pine in Spain and Portugal.

In areas of sympatry with Nightjar *C. europaeus* in NW Spain (Salamanca province), the Red-necked Nightjar occurs lower down in valleys, the Nightjar occupying the higher plains (Carnero & Peris 1988).

Its range is continuous over the Iberian mediterranean biogeographic region, except for the highest inland mountains areas (Sistema Ibérico, Central and Penibético), the majority of pairs breeding below 1000m asl. The most northerly breeding area is in the upper Ebro Valley, at Bardenas Reales (Navarra province) (De Juana 1980).

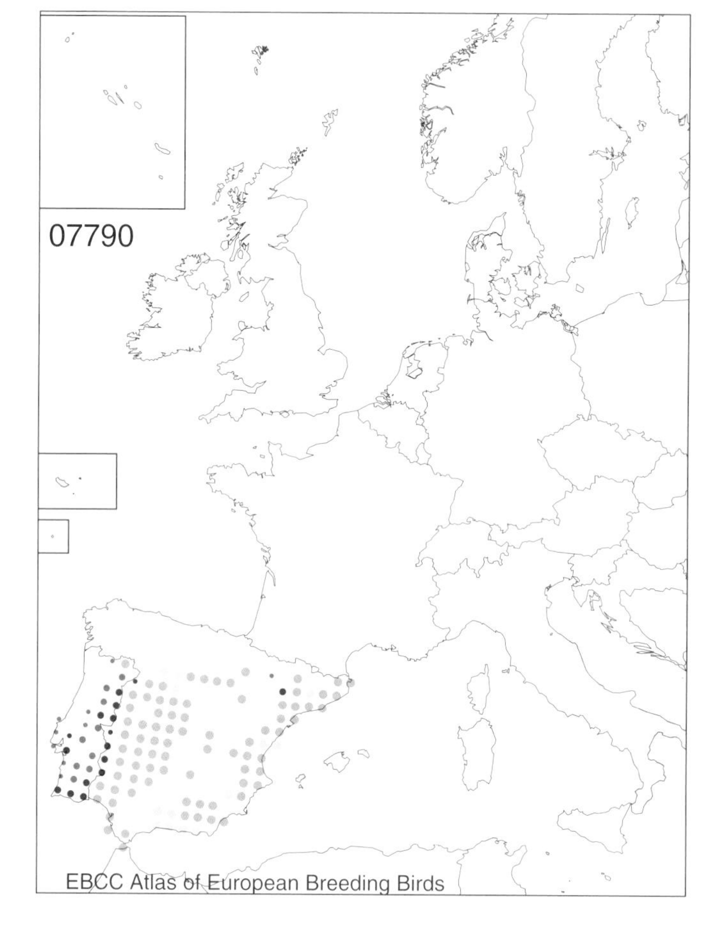

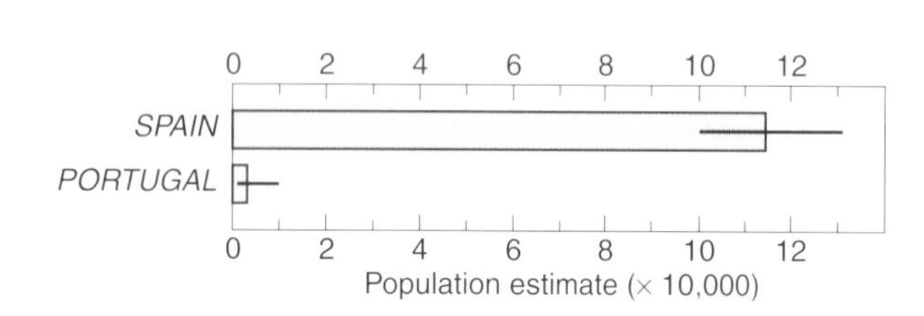

0

% in top 10 countries: 100.0
Total number of populated European countries: 2
Total European population 103,001–135,520 (117,618)

In *J. phoenicea* and mastic tree *Pistacia lentiscus* bushes, in the coastal steppe-land of Almería province (SE Spain) an overall breeding density of 1 bp/18ha was recorded (García & Purroy 1973).

The Red-necked Nightjar, after wintering in tropical western Africa, arrives in mid-April in the Iberian Peninsula on spring migration and departs in September, these dates being earlier than for the Nightjar (Bernis 1970).

Ramón Martí (E) Francisco Purroy (E)

Apus unicolor

Plain Swift

CZ	Rorýs jednobarvý	I	Rondone unicolore
D	Einfarbsegler	NL	Eilandgierzwaluw
E	Vencejo Unicolor	P	Andorinhão-unicolor
F	Martinet unicolore	PL	Jerzyk jednobarwny
FIN	Madeirankiitäjä	R	Тусклый стриж
G	Μονόχρωμη Σταχτάρα	S	Enfärgad seglare
H	Egyszínű sarlósfecske		

SPEC Cat 4, Threat status S

As a breeding species the Plain Swift is restricted to the archipelagos of Madeira and the Canaries. Recently, it has been recorded visiting holes and crevices in seacliffs in Morocco (Chantler & Driessens 1995).

Little is known about the Canaries population, but it has been recorded from all the large islands except Hierro and Lanzarote (Bannerman 1963). In the Madeiran archipelago it is present all year round (Bannerman & Bannerman 1965) but the population reduces in winter when large numbers migrate. It is known to breed on the main island of Madeira from sea level all the way up to Pico Ruivo, the island's highest point.

Its preferred breeding habitat is rocky cliffs where it constructs its nest in cracks. It also breeds on the small rocky islets surrounding Madeira. On Porto Santo and the Desertas, no nests have been found yet, but large numbers of birds have been observed entering crevices in the rockface and it is almost certain that they are breeding. The species possibly raises two broods in some locations.

The population is thought to be stable, with perhaps 1000–2000bp on Madeira and unknown but possibly large (Bannerman 1963) numbers on the Canary Islands. In summer it is common throughout the latter but a large proportion of the population leaves in winter. Large winter concentrations may be found in certain areas, presumably related to food availability. Wintering grounds are unknown, but recent records seem to suggest that many birds stay in NW Africa, rather than further S (Chantler & Driessens 1995).

Paulo Oliveira (P) Francis Zino (P)

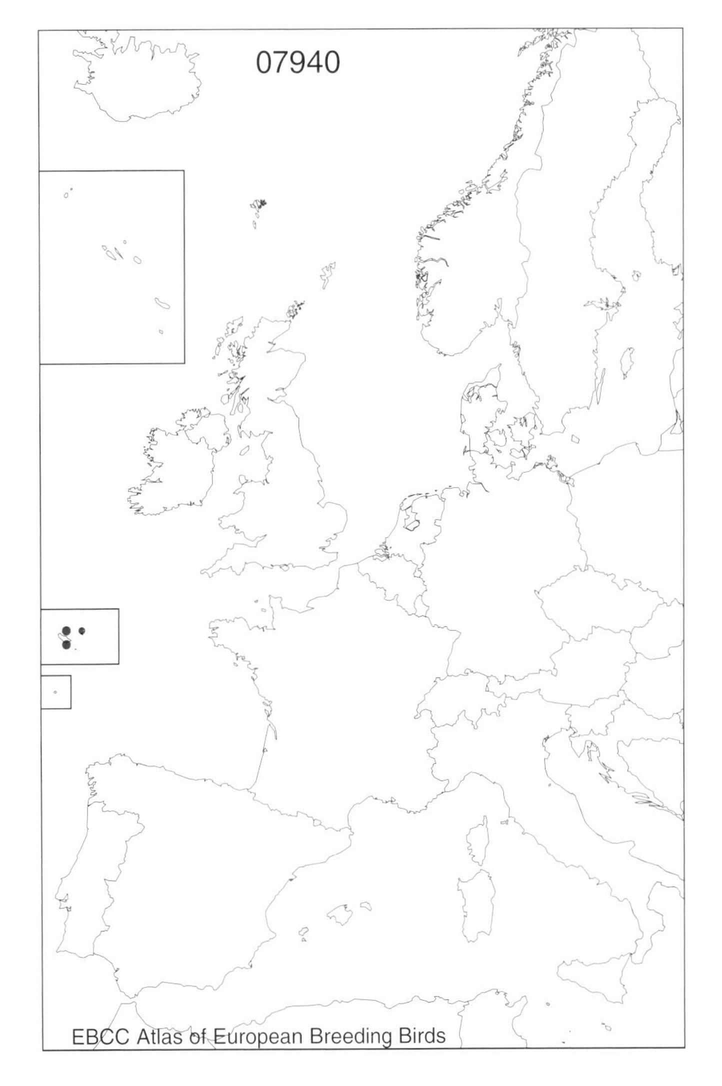

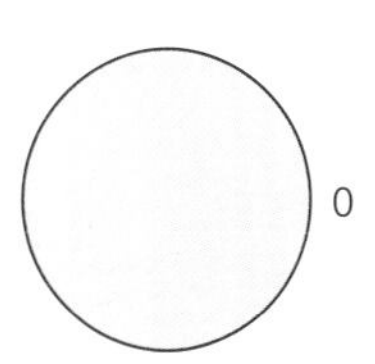

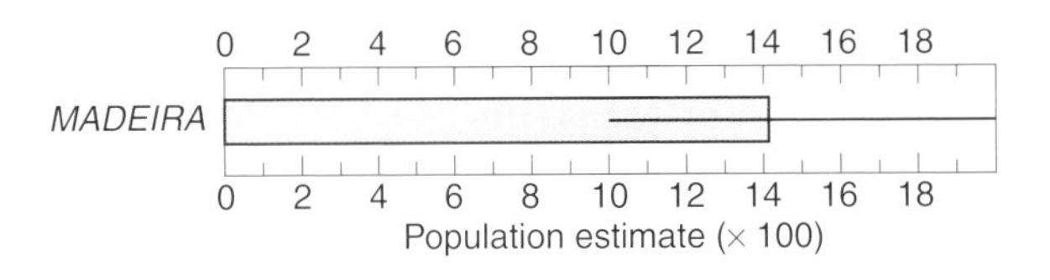

% in top 10 countries: 100.0
Total number of populated European countries: 1
Total European population 1000–2000 (1414)

Apus apus **Swift**

CZ	Rorýs obecný	I	Rondone
D	Mauersegler	NL	Gierzwaluw
E	Vencejo Común	P	Andorinhão-preto
F	Martinet noir	PL	Jerzyk
FIN	Tervapääsky	R	Черный стриж
G	Σταχτάρα	S	Tornseglare
H	Sarlósfecske		

Non-SPEC, Threat status S

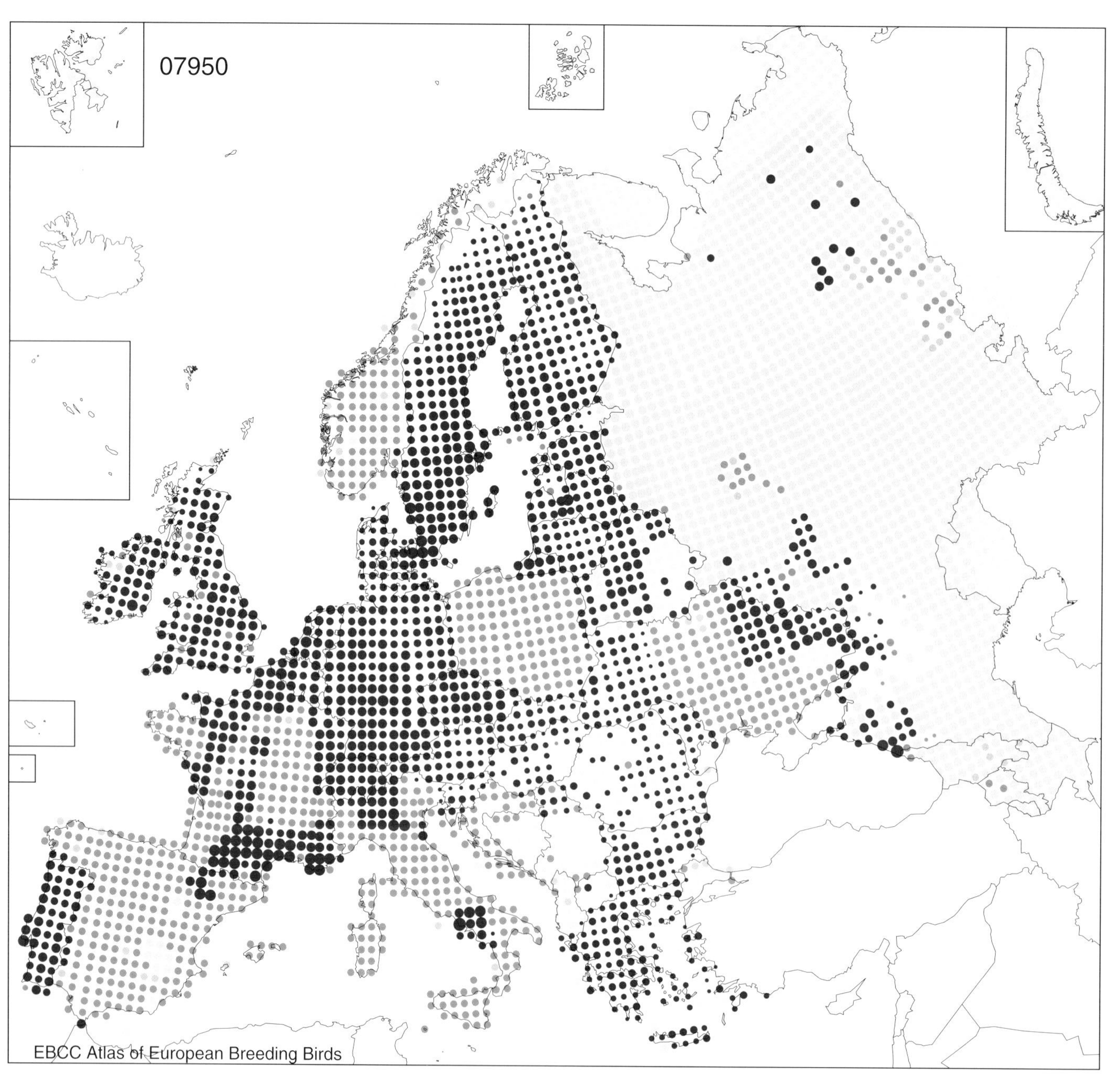

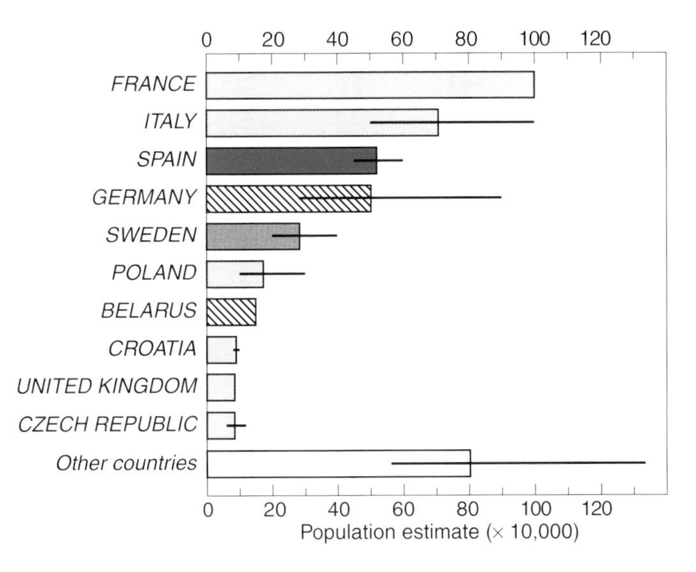

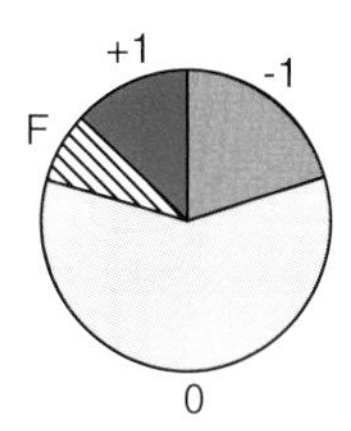

% in top 10 countries: 83.4
Total number of populated European countries: 38
Total European population 3,973,943–4,872,619 (4,311,588)
Russian population 1,000,000–5,000,000 (2,236,068)
Turkish population 50,000–500,000 (158,114)

The Swift is a widely distributed Palearctic species which spends most of its life in the air. Its breeding area covers the whole of the temperate zone from North Africa E to *c*122°E in Asia. Its northern limit reaches 70°N in Norway and 68°N in Russia. The nominate *A.a. apus* occurs in Europe, the only other subspecies *pekinensis* occupying the remainder of the range.

Although the Swift population remains large, it does not seem to be increasing. It is stable in most of Europe, but downward fluctuations have been reported in 12 countries. For this colonial species to be able to maintain its numbers in the long-term, changes in the availability of nesting sites would have to balance. The species nested originally mainly in crevices in cliffs and in old trees in remote areas, but it profited as soon as monuments and buildings were raised above 5m. These structures offered a new source of nests to which access and from which departure were safe. Old town centres whose buildings by design or through age had many cavities and cracks are now favourite sites. However, modern building techniques and materials proliferate and are also applied when renovating historic buildings in towns and villages, thus reducing the number of nesting sites suitable for the Swift. In the longer term, this process will be a significant problem for the species, because with the exception of known cases of nesting in trees in E European forests and in N Fennoscandia and Russia, nesting distribution correlates with human habitation. The species has a tendency to breed in large numbers in preferred towns, villages and sometimes even on isolated houses.

The 50km resolution of the map indicates a continuity of occurrence which is not matched in reality, because large proportions of any 50km square may be devoid of suitable breeding habitat. Nevertheless, most squares hold vast numbers of breeding pairs, showing the omnipresence of human settlements. Because the Swift performs long foraging flights, it can be encountered hunting in large numbers far away from breeding sites, even in remote upland.

The nesting ecology of the Swift depends to a considerable extent on the prevailing meteorological conditions which control the abundance of insect fauna, its main food (Gory 1987). Nesting is certainly much more weather-sensitive than for most other bird species, a factor which should be taken into account when local or national year-to-year distribution and population variation is considered. For example in Britain & Ireland the number of 10km squares in which there was evidence of breeding reduced by 11% (mostly in Scotland) and 48% respectively between 1972–76 and 1988–91, but because there is no reliable method of making quantitative estimates, how these populations were affected is unknown (Perrins 1993). However, these declines occurred in areas of sparse human habitation and may be linked more to weather fluctuations. In Britain and France the Swift seems to be more abundant in the drier and warmer S and E regions than elsewhere.

The Swift is strictly migratory, all populations wintering in tropical and southern Africa, mostly below the Equator. It arrives in S Europe in late March or early April, but at least a month later in N Europe. Established breeders display high site fidelity, and pairs tend to establish lasting bonds (Weitnauer 1975, Leys 1988). In the S of France, 80% of the nesting population leaves the nest site in the last third of July and most embark on post-nuptial passage in late July or the first third of August, late observations in September and October notwithstanding.

Some authorities regard the Plain Swift, *A. unicolor*, from Madeira and the western Canary Islands as being conspecific.

Gérard Gory (F)

This species account is sponsored by Naturschutzbund Deutschland, Bonn, D.

Apus pallidus

Pallid Swift

CZ	Rorýs šedohnědý	I	Rondone pallido
D	Fahlsegler	NL	Vale Gierzwaluw
E	Vencejo Pálido	P	Andorinhão-pálido
F	Martinet pâle	PL	Jerzyk blady
FIN	Vaaleakiitäjä	R	Бледный стриж
G	Ωχροσταχτάρα	S	Blek tornseglare
H	Halvány sarlósfecske		

Non-SPEC, Threat status S (P)

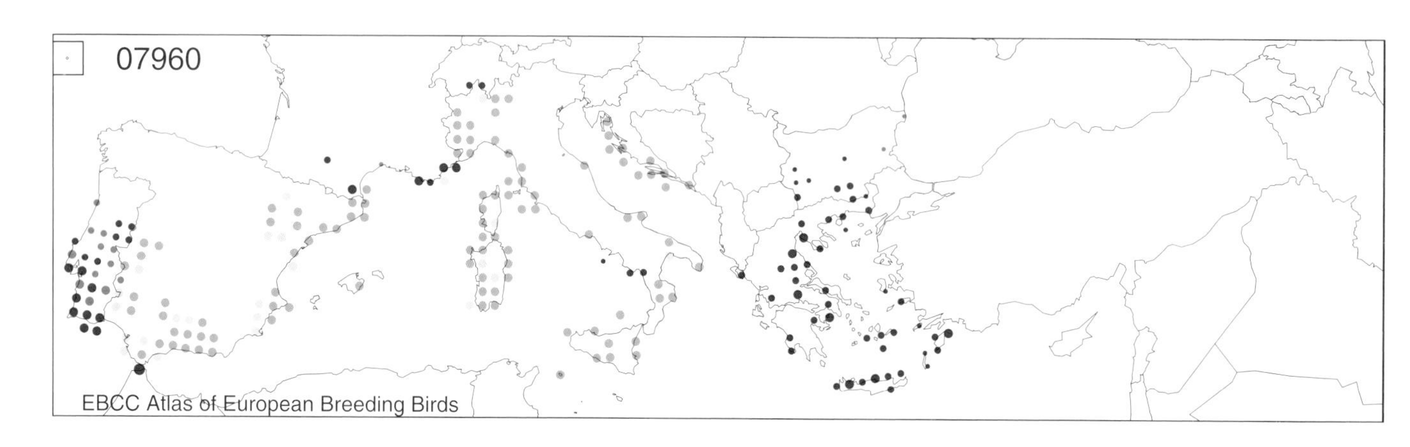

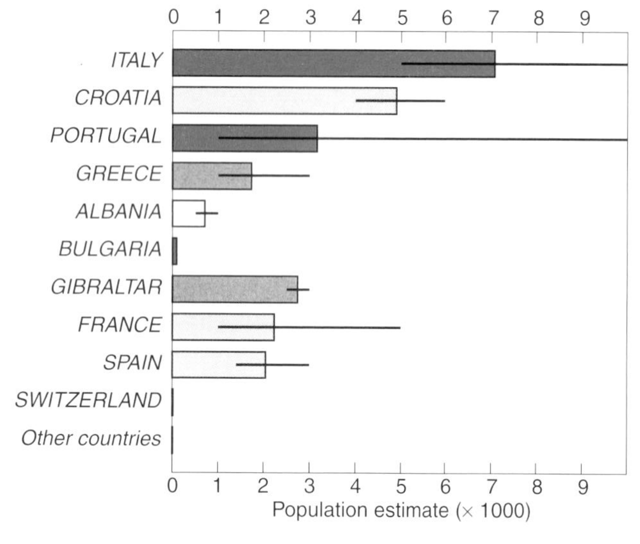

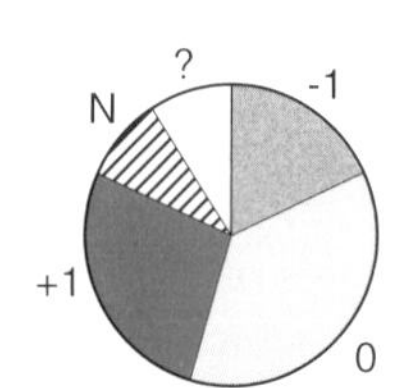

% in top 10 countries: 100.0
Total number of populated European countries: 11
Total European population 21,202–32,893 (24,717)
Turkish population 10–1000 (100)

The Pallid Swift breeds on the coasts and islands of the Mediterranean Sea, inland in southern Europe, in the Arabian Peninsula, North Africa, the Canary Islands, S of the Sahara and E to Pakistan. Due to lack of studies and its similarity to the Swift *A. apus*, its distribution remains imperfectly known. Two of the three subspecies, *A.p. illyricus* and *brehmorum*, occur in Europe.

Its preferred breeding habitats are islets (Thibault *et al* 1987) and seacliffs, especially where there are caves (Brichetti *et al* 1988), but it nests far inland in urban areas, often in towns below hills and mountains or, as is common in the W and centre of its European range, in towns with adjacent lakes. In southern Italy it breeds up to 1250m asl on a mountain plateau (Moltoni 1964), but in SW Bulgaria, *c*42% of the population breeds from 1200 to 1600m asl (some as high as 2700m), mainly at ski resorts in coniferous forests; only 38% breed at low altitude between 200 and 500m asl, in rural and suburban habitats (Iankov 1991).

The majority of the population inhabits the Iberian and Italian peninsulas, Sardinia, Corsica, S France, Croatia and Greece. In 1986 a single colony in Seville held *c*8000 individuals (Rodriguez de Los Santos & Rubio Garcia 1986). Elsewhere in Europe populations are rather low, perhaps due to a northward spread, but some recently discovered populations apparently reflect long-established colonies (Boano & Cucco 1989, Duquet & Frémont 1995). Overall, the population seems stable or slightly increasing. Local decreases may be due to the removal of suitable nest sites during the restoration of old buildings. In Gibraltar and Greece it is slightly declining and range contraction is reported for Albania.

Its main wintering area lies in the northern Afrotropics, but it has been observed further S. Small numbers from the Seville colony have overwintered at least to February, on occasion (Cuadrado *et al* 1985).

Giovanni Boano (I) Petar Iankov (BUL)

Apus melba — Alpine Swift

CZ	Rorýs velký	I	Rondone maggiore
D	Alpensegler	NL	Alpengierzwaluw
E	Vencejo Real	P	Andorinhão-real
F	Martinet à ventre blanc	PL	Jerzyk alpejski
FIN	Alppikiitäjä	R	Белобрюхий стриж
G	Σκεπαρνάς	S	Alpseglare
H	Havasi sarlósfecske		

Non-SPEC, Threat status S (P)

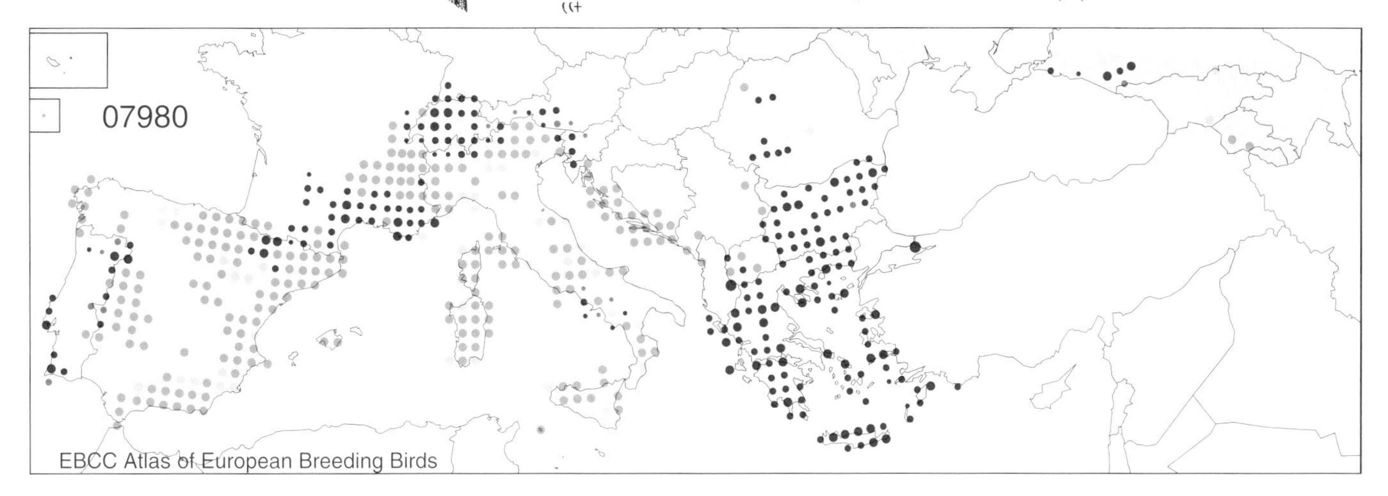

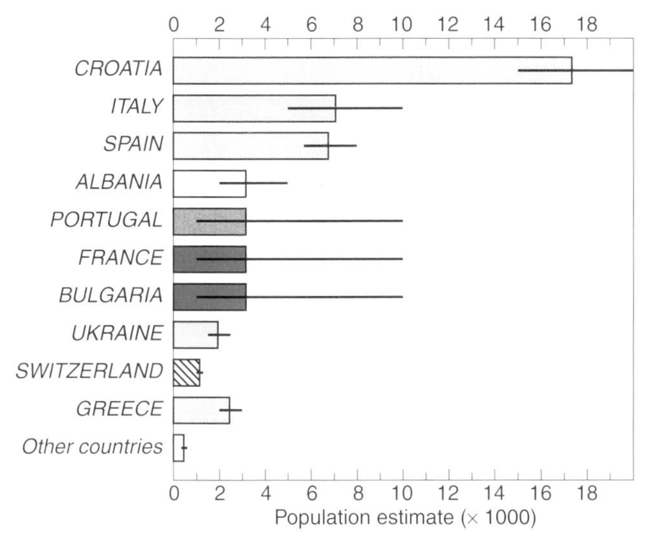

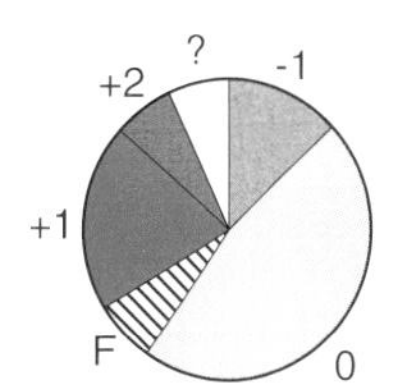

% in top 10 countries: 99.1
Total number of populated European countries: 15
Total European population 44,614–62,482 (49,770)
Turkish population 10,000–200,000 (44,721)

The Alpine Swift has a scattered distribution across the Old World, from southern and eastern Africa and Madagascar, to the Mediterranean, extending N to the northern edges of the Alps and E through Asia Minor to the Himalayas, India and Sri Lanka. Its main wintering areas include India and the Afrotropics. It breeds colonially along the rocky coasts of the Mediterranean and in mountainous regions usually below 1500m asl, occasionally up to 2200–2300m asl (Meschini & Frugis 1993). The nests, often glued to vertical surfaces, are in holes and crevices. It also commonly breeds in human settlements, especially in the foothills of the Alps. The northernmost colonies are at Freiburg in Germany (since 1955) and at Mulhouse in France (since 1990).

The population level seems stable in most European countries, local increases and range extensions occurring at the northern and eastern limits, as in France (Balluet 1993) and Bulgaria. From 1979 to 1994 the numbers in Sofia increased from 3–4 to 30bp (G. Gerasimov, pers comm). Switzerland has experienced a considerable increase since 1900, probably because many nestboxes were placed on tall structures (Engler 1994). However, severe weather during the autumn of 1974 more than halved the urban population from 760 to 320bp. The subsequent recovery seems to have stabilized around 1200–1300bp (1994, H. Schmid, pers comm). Similar decreases occurred in Bulgaria in prime habitat, the largest colony reducing from 300–500bp to *c*100 (Nankinov *et al* 1995). In NW Italy some intra-alpine colonies were deserted after a very rainy and cold spring (Mingozzi *et al* 1988).

Palearctic birds migrate between mid-September and mid-October: the spring vanguards reach the breeding colonies in late March or early April (*HVM*, Simeonov & Delov 1989).

Giovanni Boano (I) Ventzeslav Delov (BUL)

This species account is sponsored by Ornithologische Gesellschaft der Stadt Luzern, CH.

Apus caffer

White-rumped Swift

CZ	Rorýs kaferský	I	Rondone cafro
D	Kaffernsegler	NL	Kaffergierzwaluw
E	Vencejo Cafre	P	Andorinhão-cafre
F	Martinet cafre	PL	Jerzyk widłosterny
FIN	Kafferikiitäjä	R	Кафский стриж
G	Καφροσταχτάρα	S	Kafferseglare
H	Kaffer sarlósfecske		

Non-SPEC, Threat status S

The smallest of the European swifts, the White-rumped Swift is irregularly distributed across much of Africa, from Sudan to South Africa, from Angola to Gabon, and N of the Equator in the Ivory Coast, Upper Volta, S Nigeria and Chad. A small population was discovered in 1968 in Morocco close to the High Atlas. It has been known to breed in Europe since 1965 (del Junco & Gonzalez 1966) in rural areas, close to woodland adjacent to meadows and fields, and in general, in the same areas as Red-rumped Swallow *Hirundo daurica*. Although the European population is expanding its range gradually, breeding information is available only from S Spain. The total breeding population, in my opinion, is an estimated 50–100bp.

The available data, based on relatively few sightings, indicate that the White-rumped Swift breeds at isolated nest sites. The main nucleus of the known European population is centred in the Strait of Gibraltar where there are in excess of 30bp (pers obs). The highest density, within that zone, within a radius of 3km, is of 10bp (pers obs).

What separates the White-rumped Swift from other swifts is that it utilizes the nests of Red-rumped Swallow *H. daurica* for breeding. In all probability, this dependence is a limiting factor in the expansion of the species to other parts of Europe.

Most pairs arrive in the breeding areas during early May, with some birds continuing to arrive until mid-June (pers

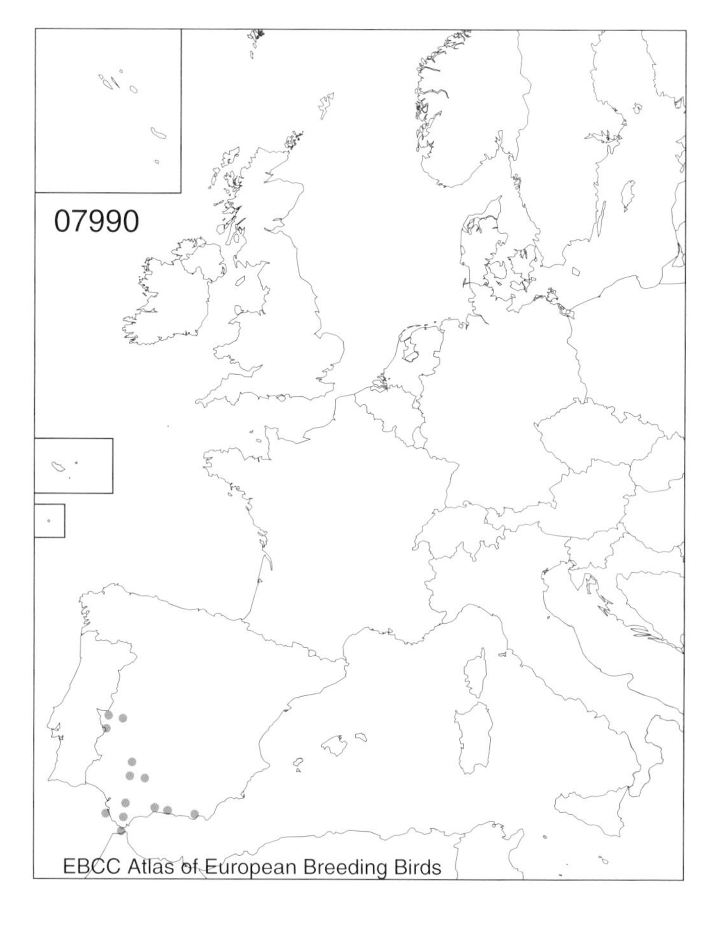

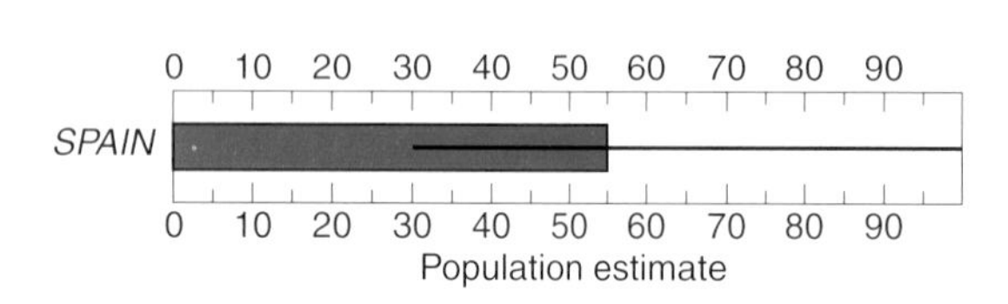

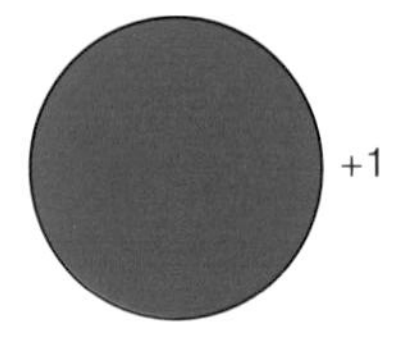

% in top 10 countries: 100.0
Total number of populated European countries: 1
Total European population 30–100 (55)

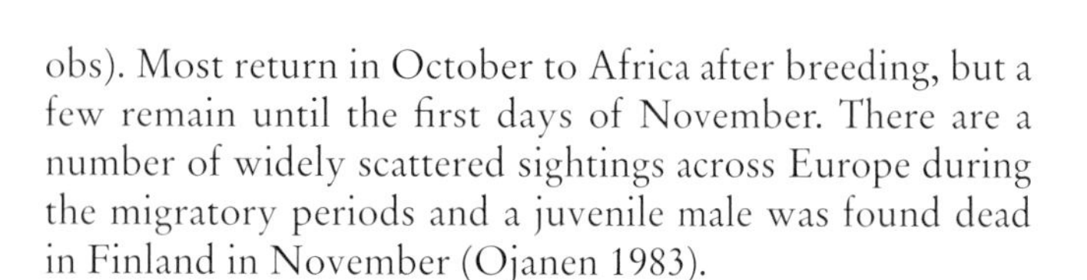

obs). Most return in October to Africa after breeding, but a few remain until the first days of November. There are a number of widely scattered sightings across Europe during the migratory periods and a juvenile male was found dead in Finland in November (Ojanen 1983).

It is not known to which of the two subspecies European birds belong.

Fernando Barrios (E)

Merops superciliosus

Blue-cheeked Bee-eater

CZ	Vlha zelená	I	Gruccione egiziano
D	Blauwangenspint	NL	Groene Bijeneter
E	Abejaruco Papirrojo	P	Abelharuco-de-garganta-vermelha
F	Guêpier de Madagascar	PL	Żołna zielona
FIN	Vihermehiläissyöjä	R	Зеленая щурка
G	Πρασινομέροπας	S	Grön biätare
H	Zöld gyurgyalag		

Non-SPEC, Threat status S (P)

The Blue-cheeked Bee-eater subspecies *M.s. persicus*, whose range includes the Middle East and Africa and just extends into Europe along the W Caspian and its feeder rivers, is almost fully migratory. The other three subspecies occur wholly in Africa, the W Saharan *chrysocercus* being a partial migrant, the eastern and South African *superciliosus* and western *alternans* being resident. The winter range of *persicus* in the Afrotropics overlaps the resident range of *superciliosus* in East Africa.

The species breeds in dry, very warm continental areas in habitats ranging from steppe and desert to mediterranean. In Europe, it is found on the lower reaches of the Ural, Volga, Kuma and Terek Rivers (Dementiev & Gladkov 1951). It usually prefers to breed in sand deserts close to waterbodies fringed with common reed *Phragmites australis* or tamarisk *Tamarix* spp, nesting in colonies or, less frequently, as solitary pairs (Dolgushin & Korelov 1970). It excavates burrows in gully banks formed in a variety of dry soils or on declivity faces and sandhill slopes and sometimes digs burrows in flat ground on clay plains.

In suitable habitat, the Blue-cheeked Bee-eater is common, but near its distribution limit, sporadically so. Range limits and population size apparently are stable, but *persicus* in particular is little studied and so there is no quantitative information on the size of the European breeding population (Fry 1984).

Departure from the breeding grounds is complete by the end of August, but it may not arrive in its wintering areas until mid-November, from which it sets out in late March or early April (Walker 1981) to arrive on its breeding grounds usually in early May. As far as is known, the habitats it occupies throughout the year are not under major threat. The Blue-cheeked Bee-eater population therefore seems relatively secure in the immediate future.

Victor Belik (R)

Merops apiaster Bee-eater

CZ	Vlha pestrá	I	Gruccione
D	Bienenfresser	NL	Bijeneter
E	Abejaruco Común	P	Abelharuco-comum
F	Guêpier d'Europe	PL	Żołna
FIN	Mehiläissyöjä	R	Золотистая щурка
G	Μελισσοφάγος	S	Biätare
H	Gyurgyalag		

SPEC Cat 3, Threat status D

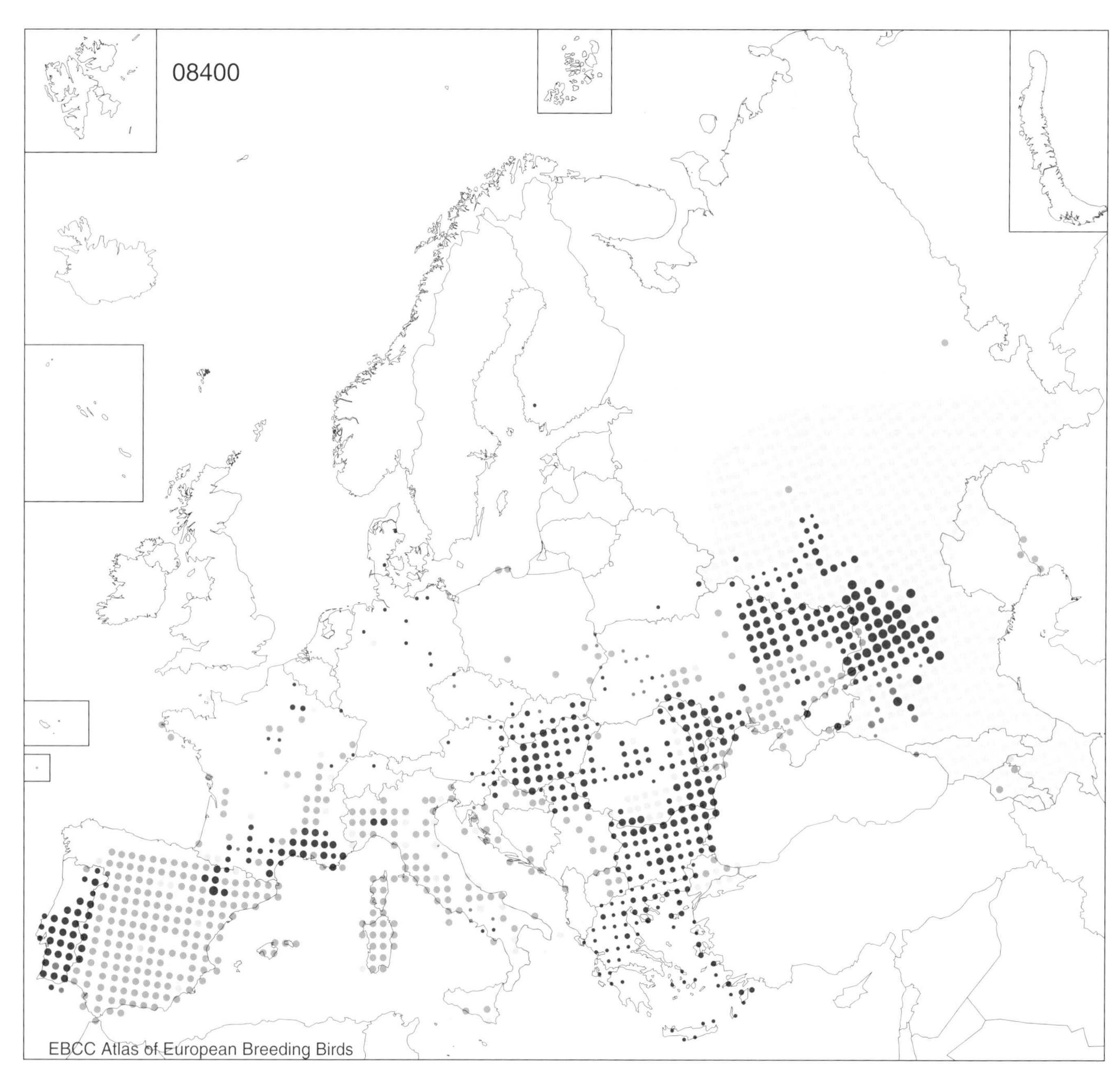

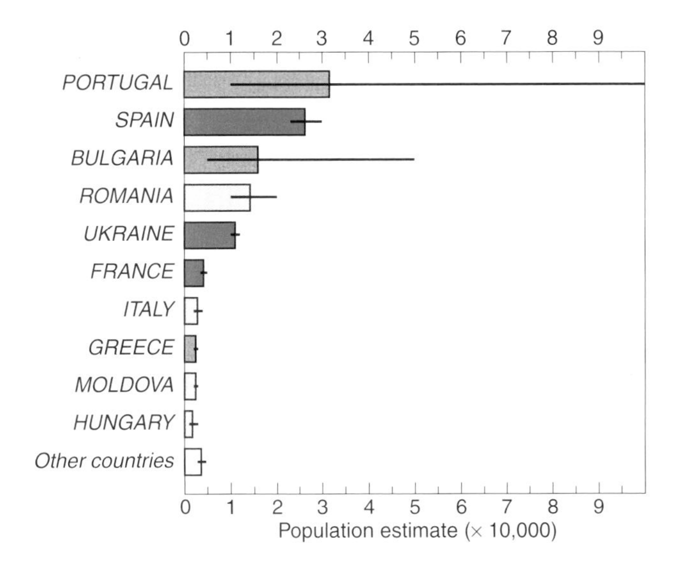

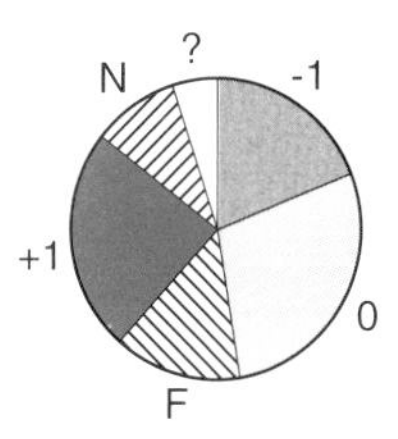

% in top 10 countries: 96.9
Total number of populated European countries: 21
Total European population 91,243–192,853 (116,052)
Russian population 5000–50,000 (15,811)
Turkish population 10,000–100,000 (31,623)

The Bee-eater breeds in SW, C and E Europe, E-C Asia and Asia Minor, and NW Africa. Although the discrete small resident South African breeding population is geographically isolated, it is not a separate subspecies, breeding during the northern winter, and perhaps encountering wintering birds from the Northern Hemisphere's eastern population.

The northern populations winter exclusively in Africa, but in two geographically separate regions. One population (probably birds from Iberia, France and NW Africa) winters in West Africa (N of the Equator), the other (birds from elsewhere in Europe, EC Asia and Asia Minor) in East and southern Africa (mostly far S of the Equator). Small numbers winter in W India and S Arabia.

The Bee-eater prefers valleys with vertical river-banks, open areas containing bushes or isolated trees, steppes, marshy terrain, rice-paddies and ponds, wherever insect life is abundant.

It excavates its burrows in sandy, loess or clayish slopes, river-banks and sand quarries, sometimes quite close to human settlements possessing bee-hives. It breeds in colonies, lone breeding pairs being rare. The largest colony in Bulgaria, inhabiting a sand quarry, numbered 125bp (Darakchiev *et al* 1986), but colony size is normally much smaller in S and SW Europe (Fry 1984). During the breeding season, the species occurs from sea level to about 2500m asl.

European population estimates indicate that the largest proportion of Bee-eater numbers occurs in the Iberian (44%) and Balkan (26%) Peninsulas and in E Europe (23%); only an insignificant 5% and 2% are to be found in C Europe and the Apennines respectively. However, the population size figures comprising the latter proportions are based on poor and incomplete data. The estimate in Fry (1984) of 1M birds for the Iberian Peninsula seems a little optimistic.

The Bee-eater is very common in Europe up to the 21°C July isotherm, with pronounced regional and short-term fluctuations in numbers for reasons unknown, but which may be vital for its long-term survival. It was first recorded in N Europe about 150 years ago, its range having contracted and expanded several times since. Small numbers of pairs occasionally reach Great Britain, The Netherlands, Belgium, Denmark, Finland, Sweden and Latvia.

Population studies by the authors in 1992 (Bulgaria) and 1993 (Slovakia) revealed densities of 73 bp/100km^2 and 51 bp/100km^2 respectively in areas containing prime habitat. Considering the patchy distribution of potential colony sites, a more meaningful figure is obtained when using data from nest counts in concentrations of prime habitat. Along 189km of the middle and lower reaches of five rivers in the Bulgarian district of Plovdiv, an average of two occupied nests per linear km was obtained (Darakchiev *et al* 1986).

Countries in Europe with large populations show contradicting trends, with apparently stable figures in Russia and Romania, an increase in Spain, Ukraine and France and a decline in Portugal, Bulgaria and Greece. These discrepancies may not be real because of the lack of quantitative data. Locally, decreases follow habitat destruction caused by river canalization and dredging, construction of concrete or stone reinforcing revetments and counter-erosion defences, commercial exploitation of aggregates (which can provide long-term benefits) or by nest and bird destruction (Krištín 1992). Massive application of insecticides may threaten the species' food supply or cause mortality, both on its breeding grounds and in its winter quarters (Mullié & Keith 1993).

Spring and autumn migration occur over a broad front over land, flocks being 7–40 strong (Petrov 1973). Large-scale migration occurs along the Black Sea coast (T. Michev, pers comm) and across the Strait of Gibraltar. The species crosses the Mediterranean in several places; SE Europe via Cyprus to NE Africa, Italy to Tunisia and SW Europe to NW Africa.

Anton Krištín (SLK) Tzeno Petrov (BUL)

This species account is sponsored by Prof. Dr H. Witschel, Freiburg, D.

Alcedo atthis

Kingfisher

CZ	Ledňáček říční	I	Martin pescatore
D	Eisvogel	NL	IJsvogel
E	Martín Pescador	P	Guarda-rios-comum
F	Martin-pêcheur d'Europe	PL	Zimorodek
FIN	Kuningaskalastaja	R	Зимородок
G	Αλκυόνα	S	Kungsfiskare
H	Jégmadár		

SPEC Cat 3, Threat status D

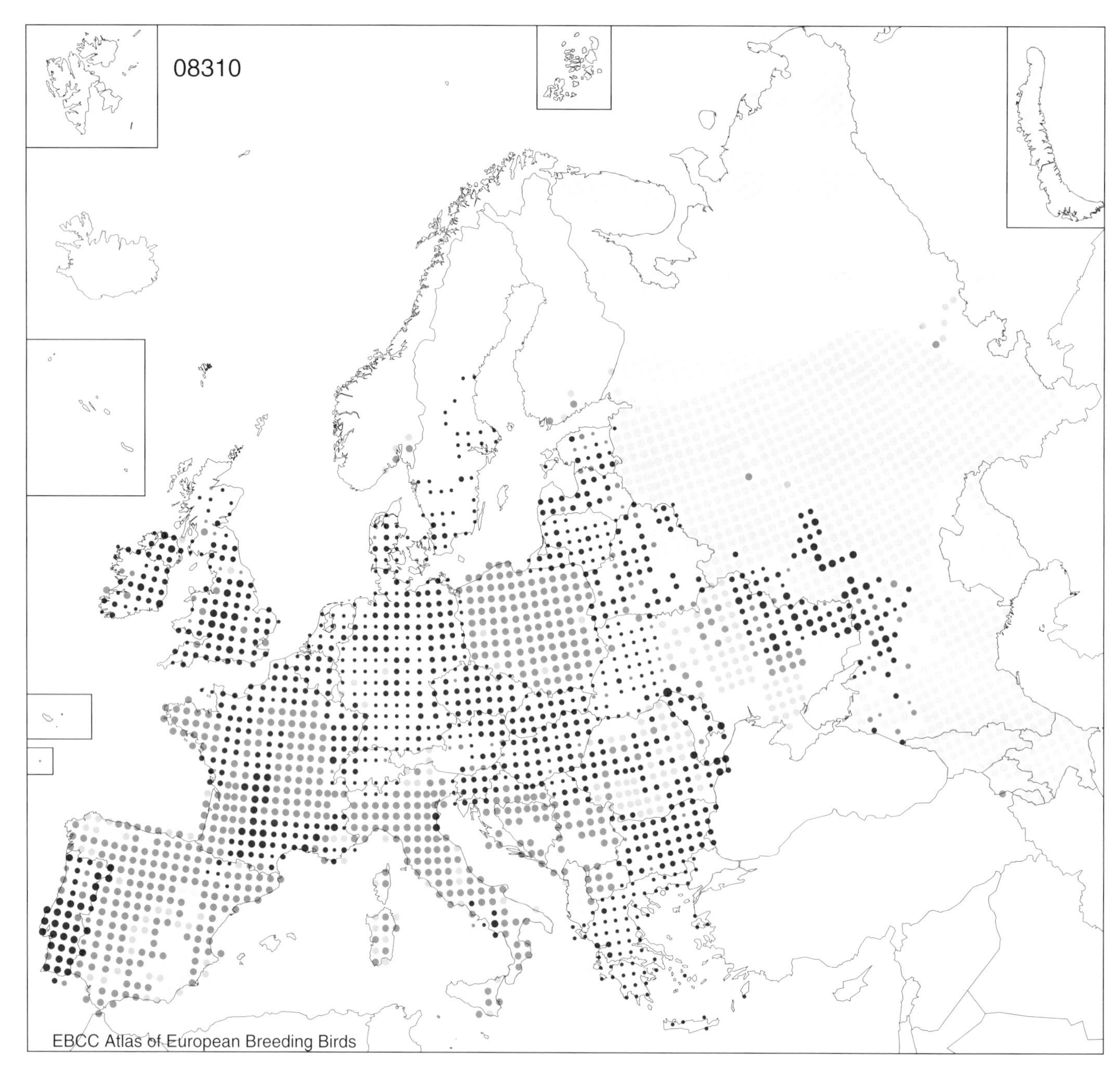

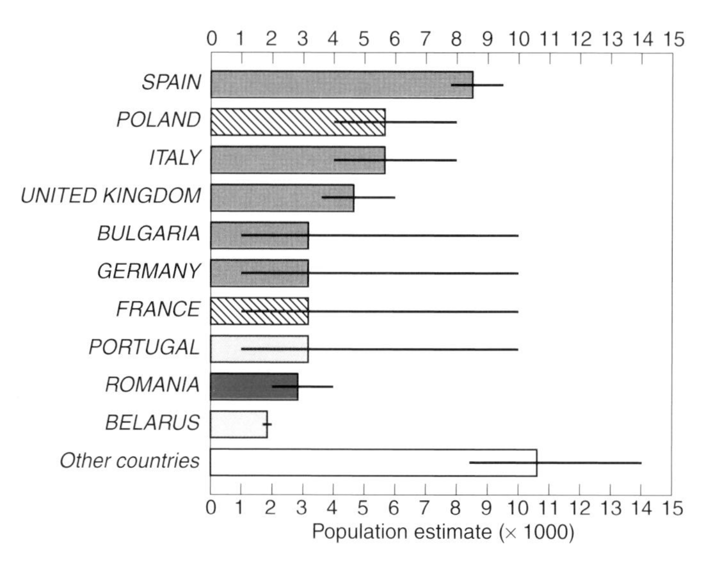

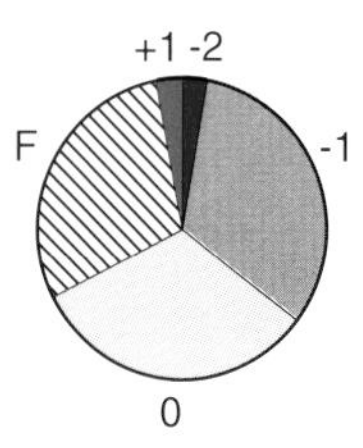

% in top 10 countries: 79.8
Total number of populated European countries: 34
Total European population 47,302–66,752 (52,500)
Russian population 10,000–100,000 (31,623)
Turkish population 100–1000 (316)

The Kingfisher inhabits the whole Indo-Malayan region, New Guinea and the Palearctic from Japan to the Atlantic coast, including North Africa. It avoids steppe, desert and high-altitude or -latitude (tundra, taiga) ecosystems. As a European breeder, it is absent only from Iceland, some Mediterranean islands like Malta and the Balearics, and above *c*900m asl, save perhaps in the Caucasus. It is very scarce in N Scotland and in Scandinavia occurs only below 61°N except in a few Swedish lowland Baltic areas. Only two subspecies, the nominate *atthis* and *ispida* occur in Europe.

Its basic habitat requirement is the availability of clear ice-free water rich in fish shorter than 10cm (Hallet-Libois 1985). Furthermore, it rarely catches fish from the hover, and so needs overhanging perches and branches from which to search and dive for prey. It therefore occurs along the banks of streams, rivers, canals, ditches, lakes, ponds and reservoirs and even in bays, estuaries or along the seashore. In the breeding season, the Kingfisher requires suitable banks in which to excavate a nesting chamber close to water. It prefers sandy or clay banks, more than 1m high and possessing a vertical or concave aspect. Occasionally its burrow is between the roots of fallen trees.

Breeding pairs generally are well-spaced along rivers at an average density of *c*1–3 bp/10km stretch in favourable years. Circumstances may make several pairs crowd together: in 1989, 4bp were recorded on a 650m-long islet in the River Meuse (France) (Libois & Hallet-Libois 1994) (5bp in 1995). In contrast, breeding holes more than 1km apart can belong to one pair or to a bigamous male (pers obs). Territory size is highly variable, depending not only on food and nest-site availability, but also on the general population level and probably on individual behavioural traits. As determined by radio-tracking in Belgium, the home range sizes of three nesting birds were respectively 0.6 (male 1, 45 days of survey), 1.4 (mate of male 1, 15 days) and 13.8km long (male 2, 70 days) (pers obs, A. Loncin, pers comm). Consequently, densities are low everywhere, never reaching 1000 bp/50km grid square and probably not exceeding a few hundred per square at best.

Numbers fluctuate heavily from year to year according to the climatic conditions (rainfall, temperature) prevailing in the preceding breeding season (Libois & Hallet-Libois 1989), as far as they influence reproductive success (Libois 1994). Numbers also depend on the severity of winter frosts. It is therefore difficult to assess actual numbers precisely on a large scale. Similarly, accurate population trends are elusive unless determined over a long period of time. In one Belgian census area, the 8bp remaining after the severe 1984/85 winter increased to 43 in 1990 but reduced to 25 in 1991 (pers obs). Large fluctuations therefore seem characteristic. Winter losses can be offset by an annual production of 2–3 broods and the female's mean lifetime reproduction rate of 9.7 fledglings, even given a mean annual mortality of 71–73% (Bunzel & Drüke 1989).

Loss of suitable feeding and nesting habitat through water pollution, drainage and irrigation schemes is the main threat to the species; it causes sharp local declines which may be significant, depending on the scale of change.

Eastern and continental populations are mainly migratory, moving southwards after the breeding season. C European birds are partially migratory, whereas western populations are dispersive or sedentary. Immatures disperse in all directions; exceptionally, some return to breed where they hatched (pers obs). In W Europe, dispersion distance usually is under 200km. Long-distance movements are well-oriented to the S or W (Euring databank). British populations appear to be relatively isolated because very few have been recorded on the Continent (Morgan & Glue 1977).

Roland Libois (B)

This species account is sponsored by Vogelbescherming Nederland, Zeist, NL.

Coracias garrulus Roller

CZ	Mandelík hajní	**I**	Ghiandaia marina
D	Blauracke	**NL**	Scharrelaar
E	Carraca	**P**	Rolieiro-comum
F	Rollier d'Europe	**PL**	Kraska
FIN	Sininärhi	**R**	Сизоворонка
G	Χαλκοκουρούνα	**S**	Blåråka
H	Szalakóta		

SPEC Cat 2, Threat status D (P)

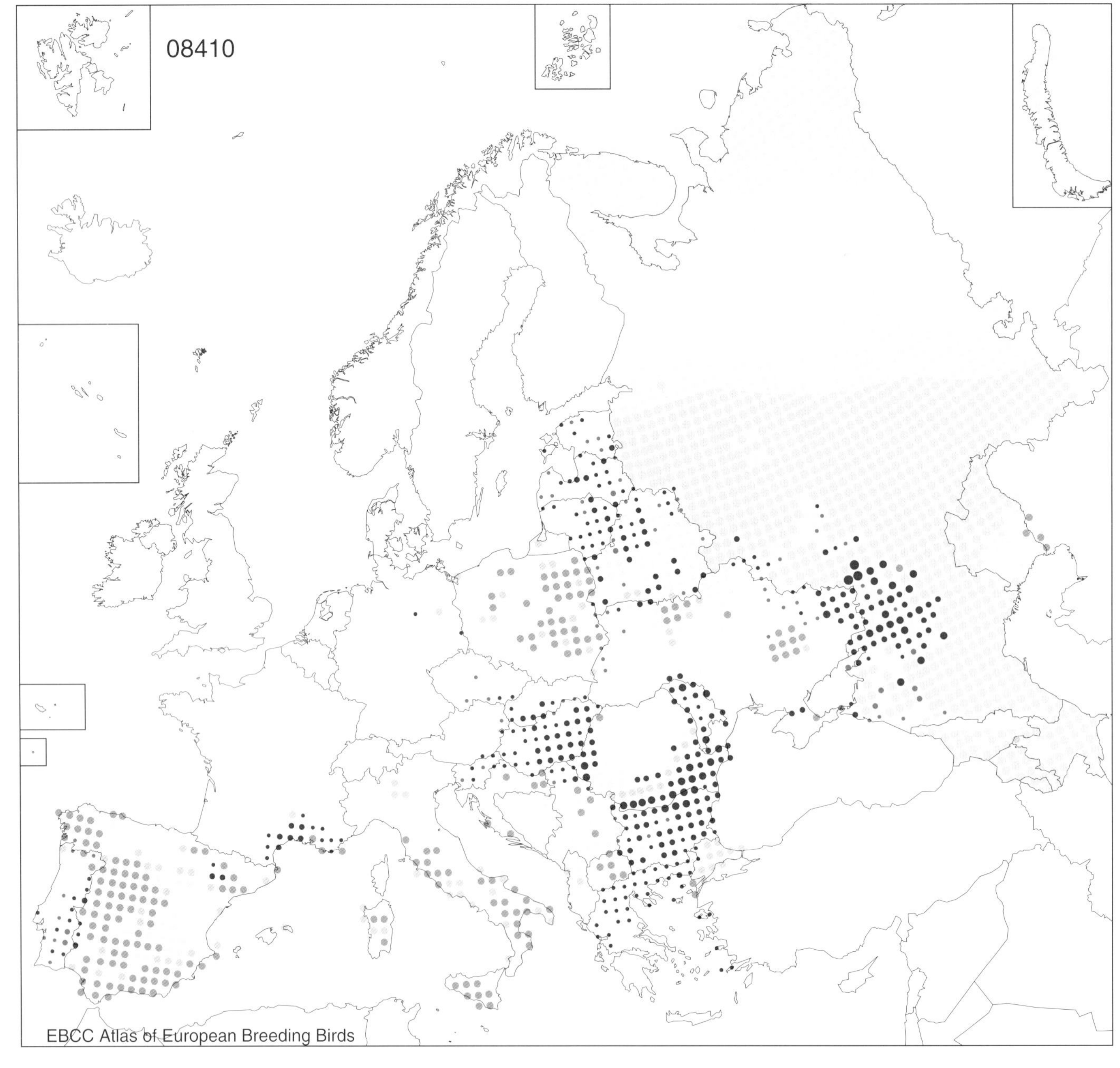

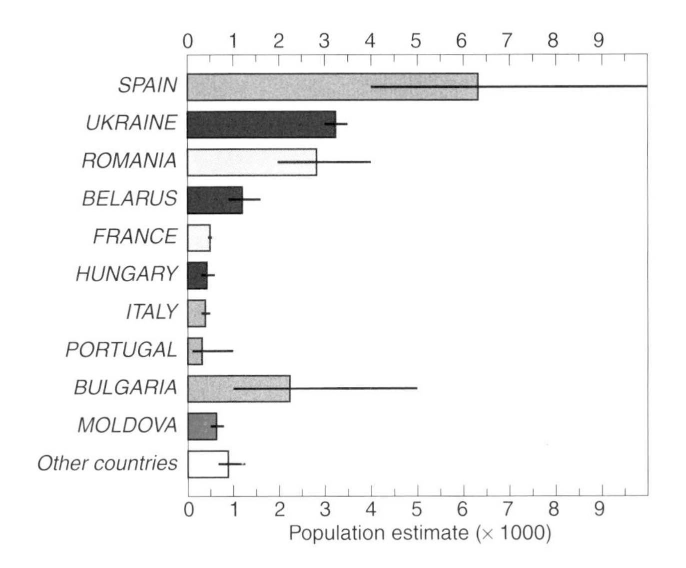

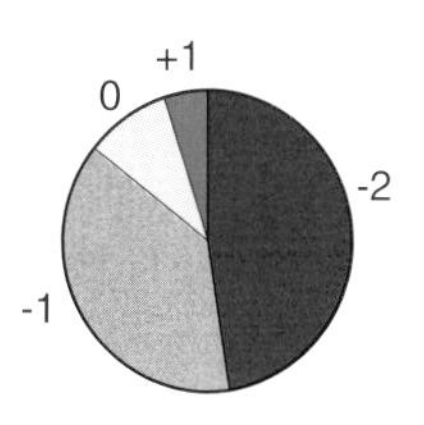

% in top 10 countries: 95.3
Total number of populated European countries: 21
Total European population 16,166–23,798 (18,969)
Russian population 10,000–100,000 (31,623)
Turkish population 5000–50,000 (15,811)

The size of a small crow, the insectivorous Roller breeds throughout temperate, steppe and mediterranean climate zones, the nominate *C.g. garrulus* from Iberia and North Africa to NW Iran and SW Siberia and *semenowi* eastwards to Kashmir and N Turkmenistan. The species' main distribution lies in Europe W of the Urals.

The Roller winters S of the Sahara, predominantly in the savanna region of East Africa, where it outnumbers other *Coracias* species. Brown & Brown (1973) estimated a total of 2M–3M birds in the eastern Kenyan thornbush alone, but numbers fluctuate within and between seasons. The SW African thornbush is of minor importance, contrary to previous belief, wintering numbers being 50–100 times smaller than in East Africa (Herremans *et al* 1994).

The Roller's breeding habitats usually lie below 600m asl in lowland areas whose summers are warm. It favours steppe, open forests, grassland, pastures and low-intensity cultivation. On its breeding grounds it is aggressively territorial, breeding solitarily, although nest-separation distances can be small (70–200m, exceptionally 5–10m). In Slovenia a loose colony of 15–18 bp/7km^2 existed up to 1978 (B. Štumberger, pers obs). The species nests mainly in tree-holes, but in its southern range also uses sandy banks and walls. In Steiermark, Austria, the majority (84%) breed in small woods and along tree-lined rivers, the remainder utilizing old orchards and solitary trees in open country, always adjacent to traditionally managed grassland (Samwald & Samwald 1989). The Roller is widespread but uncommon in Hungary, occurring mainly in the Danube–Tisza plain.

In Europe the Roller has two strongholds, the Iberian Peninsula (6600bp) and in eastern Europe, from the Balkans to Ukraine, Belarus and Russia (very approximately 42 000bp). Intervening populations are distributed rather more patchily in southern France (450–540bp), Sardinia and S Italy (300–500bp), N Greece (100bp), C Europe (700bp) and the Baltic States (380bp). The Turkish population of 5000–50 000bp occurs mostly beyond the *Atlas* coverage.

Since the 19th and early 20th centuries, the species' range has contracted markedly to the S and E. Breeding in Denmark and Sweden ceased in 1868 and 1967 respectively. Since the 1970s the decline has accelerated and includes much of S and E Europe. A range contraction of 20–50% during 1970–90 occurred in Iberia, Italy, Bulgaria (Brehme 1991) and parts of C Europe and the former Soviet Union, and a parallel range contraction of >50% has brought the populations of Latvia, Austria, Slovakia, the Czech Republic and Slovenia almost to extinction. In eastern Germany, the 150–200bp of 1961 declined to 30bp in 1976, the last known breeding pairs being recorded in 1990 (Robel 1991). A similar trend is obvious in Poland, where the Roller was once widespread in the lowlands (Tomiałojć 1990). It last bred in Silesia in 1982 (Dyrcz *et al* 1991). In Września district, N Poland, the 13–15bp of 1971–72 diminished to only 4bp by 1982–84 (Lewartowski 1986). The Polish population size declined by >50% from 1970 to 1990 and is confined to eastern Poland. Austrian birds have declined similarly from *c*300 to 400bp in Steiermark (1950) to 180bp in 1969 and only 8bp in the early 1990s (Samwald, & Samwald 1989, O. Samwald, pers obs). This decrease parallels widespread changes in agricultural practice, especially the replacement of meadows by maize cultivation. Neighbouring Slovenia duplicates that trend, the probable 600–700bp of 1950 reducing to but 7bp annually from 1989 to 1993 (B. Štumberger, pers obs). It commonly is assumed that range contractions are climatically induced, but habitat changes may play their part.

Apparently stable numbers remain only in Russia and Romania. Despite a slight recent increase in France, the *c*450–540bp total of 1990 is probably less than in the 1970s (Centre Ornithologique du Gard 1994).

Despite the Roller being an attractive and conspicuous bird, the scarcity of quantitative data on its population dynamics in its strongholds is remarkable.

Otto Samwald (A) Borut Štumberger (SLN)

Upupa epops

Hoopoe

CZ	Dudek chocholatý	**I**	Upupa
D	Wiedehopf	**NL**	Hop
E	Abubilla	**P**	Poupa
F	Huppe fasciée	**PL**	Dudek
FIN	Harjalintu	**R**	Удод
G	Τσαλαπετεινός	**S**	Härfågel
H	Búbosbanka		

Non-SPEC, Threat status S

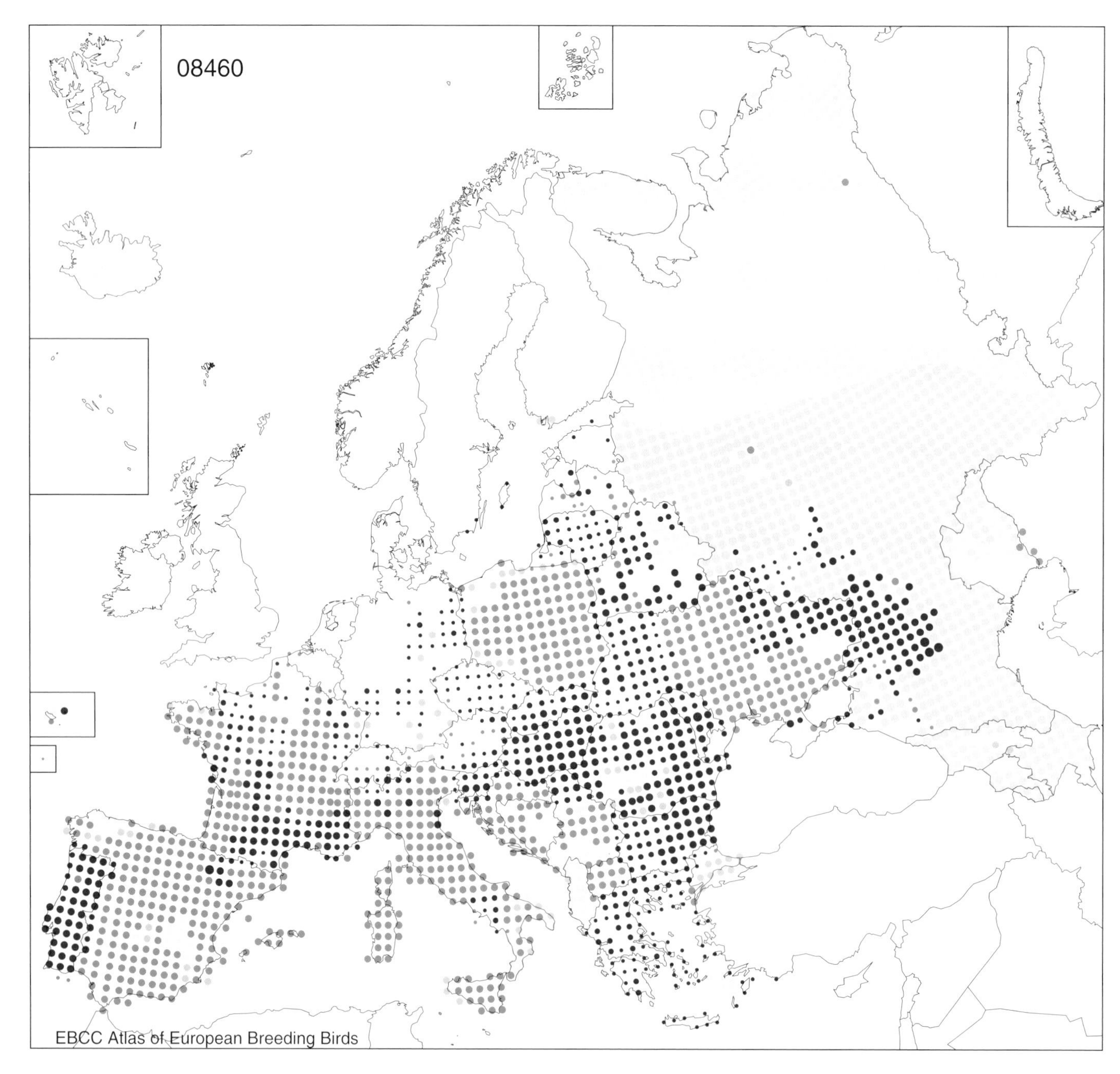

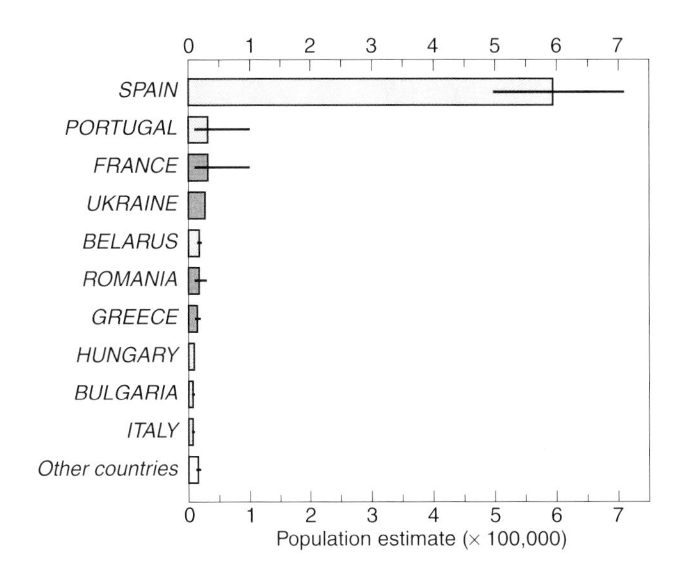

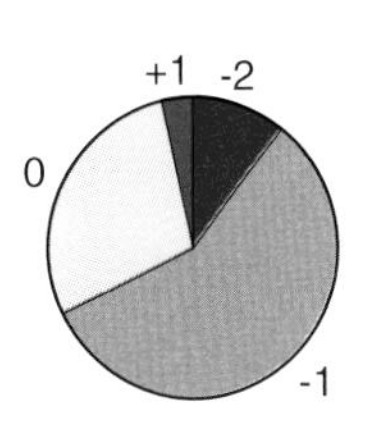

% in top 10 countries: 98.0
Total number of populated European countries: 28
Total European population 669,508–923,503 (771,714)
Russian population 50,000–500,000 (158,114)
Turkish population 10,000–100,000 (31,623)

The colourful Hoopoe is a breeding bird of the temperate and subtropical zones from the Canary Islands in the W to the Pacific coast of China and Siberia in the E. In Europe its range is biased to the S and SE, the northern breeding limit running S of a line from N France through NE Germany to Estonia. Breeding further N has become irregular.

In Europe the Hoopoe breeds in lowlands or uplands up to 1300m asl and prefers low-intensity farmland (pastures containing old trees, orchards and olive groves), woodland edges and very open woodland. Bare or sparsely vegetated soil is essential so that it can feed on large insects and their larvae and pupae which develop in the ground. It also requires large cavities in trees, stone walls or banks for nesting (Arlettaz 1984). The Hoopoe avoids wetlands and areas with high precipitation.

Hoopoe densities are by far the highest in the Iberian Peninsula, averaging some 2600 bp/50km square. In S and SE Europe, average densities between 100 and 300 bp/50km square are typical, as they are in S France, Greece, Slovenia, Croatia, Bulgaria, Moldova, Ukraine and Belarus. Exceptions in this region are Hungary (614) and Italy (58). Poland and the former Czechoslovakia have average densities of 25 and 17 respectively. All other W, C and E European countries have fewer than 10 bp/50km square on average. The species therefore thrives in the mediterranean and continental climate zones, but in the latter less successfully with increasing latitude. It has disappeared almost completely from areas of maritime climate, perhaps explaining its absence from NW Spain.

Decreasing trends have been reported throughout Europe, especially in peripheral populations but also in some strongholds such as France, Ukraine, Romania and Greece. The range contraction towards the S and the declining numbers in most European countries fit a longer term trend, which has been apparent since the late 19th and early 20th centuries. For instance, the Hoopoe ceased to breed regularly in Sweden (Risberg 1979) and in much of Germany (Hölzinger 1987) around 1920. A temporary reversal occurred from 1940 to 1955, when a partial recovery of locally depleted or extinct populations was recorded in the Low Countries and parts of Germany. Since 1955–60, an even stronger declining trend has ensued, leading to the extinction of the Hoopoe as a breeding bird in The Netherlands (last bred 1974), Belgium (1980) and Denmark (from 1976 to 1991, bred only 1977 and 1983; Sørensen 1995).

These long-term declining trends bear striking resemblances to those of Wryneck *Jynx torquilla*, Roller *Coracias garrulus* and Lesser Grey Shrike *Lanius minor*, which partly share the same habitats (Tucker & Heath 1994). Climatic changes are often held responsible for population fluctuations in these species (Burton 1995), but the revolutionary changes in farmland usage since the 1950s probably account for the present trends affecting the Hoopoe. In particular, removal of trees and hedges (loss of nest sites), large-scale application of insecticides (reducing numbers of prey such as mole-cricket *Gryllotalpa gryllotalpa* and cockchafers *Melolontha melolontha* and *M. hippocastani*) and the reduction of low-intensity, small-scale farming must have had a great impact. The relatively recent entry of Portugal and Spain into the European Community (EC) could be crucial to the species, because this event implies the end of low-intensity farming (Tellería *et al* 1995). A similar effect is likely in eastern Europe following the political changes of the late 1980s. Moreover, unfavourable developments in the wintering areas, including increased pesticide use and perhaps desertification, may have contributed to the decline.

Although small numbers winter in North Africa and the Mediterranean basin (occasionally up to southern France) the European breeding population winters mostly S of the Sahara.

Fred Hustings (NL)

This species account is sponsored by Société pour l'étude et la protection des Oiseaux en Limousin, Limoges, F.

Jynx torquilla

Wryneck

CZ	Krutihlav obecný	I	Torcicollo
D	Wendehals	NL	Draaihals
E	Torcecuello	P	Torcicolo
F	Torcol fourmilier	PL	Krętogłow
FIN	Käenpiika	R	Вертишейка
G	Στραβολαίμης	S	Göktyta
H	Nyaktekercs		

SPEC Cat 3, Threat status D

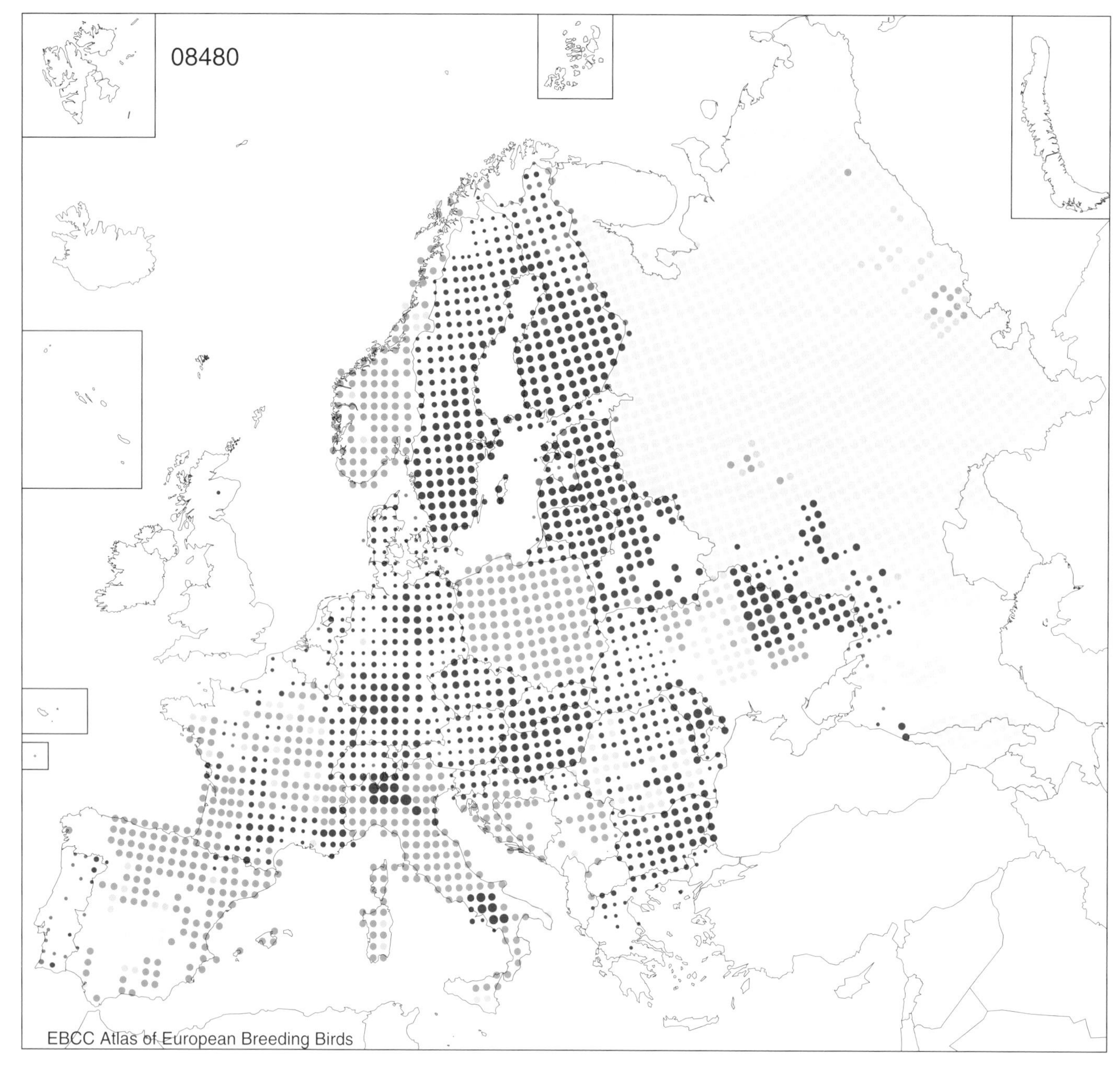

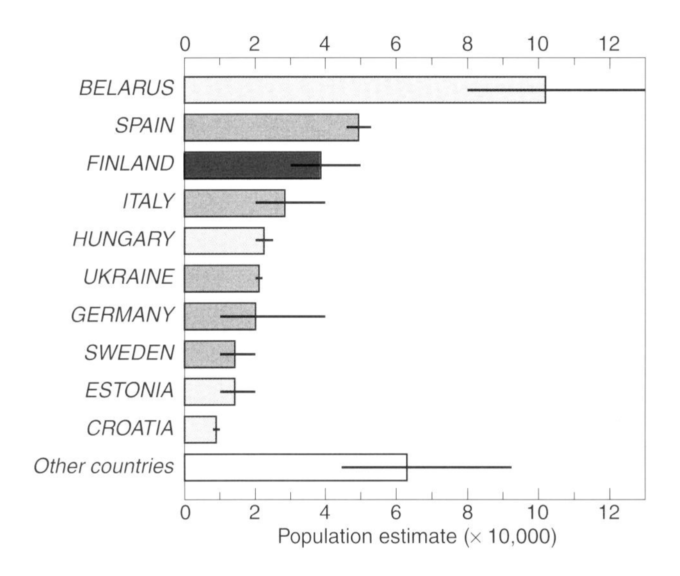

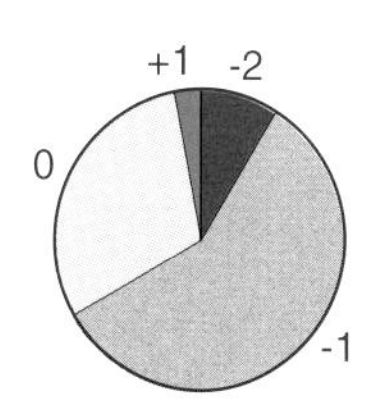

% in top 10 countries: 83.5
Total number of populated European countries: 33
Total European population 353,427–422,511 (382,005)
Russian population 50,000–500,000 (158,114)
Turkish population 100–1000 (316)

The Wryneck inhabits the boreal, temperate and subtropical zones in Europe and most of Asia, E to Sakhalin and Hokkaido. In most of its breeding range it is fully migratory, wintering mainly in Africa S of the Sahara and occasionally in the Mediterranean basin.

The Wryneck feeds mostly on the ground almost exclusively on ants (adults and larvae) and requires bare ground or short-sward vegetation in which to forage. It breeds in deciduous woodland and margins, such as fragmented forests, clearfells, parks, gardens or orchards, provided there are ample cavities or nestboxes, but is also attracted to low-intensity farmland scattered with trees. Such habitats must be dry and sunny. It avoids intensive agriculture and maritime climates. Breeding above 1000m asl is unusual except in the Caucasus.

It occupies a surprisingly wide range of climate zones and habitats within the *Atlas* coverage area, from N Lapland to Sicily. It is absent from Iceland and Ireland. It is almost extinct in Great Britain, a very few breeding pairs remaining in the Scottish Highlands (first bred late 1960s).

Most of the European population occurs in the E, especially in Russia and Belarus (>1000 bp/50km square). Densities reduce progressively towards the W and S, from 100 to 400 bp/50km square in Finland, E and C Europe and France to fewer than 50 bp/50km square in Greece, Portugal, Denmark and the Low Countries. This pattern suggests that a continental, rather than mediterranean or maritime, climate is preferred, which the map well-illustrates in France and Iberia (near-absence from the Atlantic zone) and in Fennoscandia (density increasing from Norway through Sweden to Finland, averaging 35, 80 and 300 bp/50km square respectively).

Stable populations exist in its E European stronghold – the Baltic, Russia and Belarus. However, in NW Europe the Wryneck has contracted its breeding range gradually southwards and eastwards, paralleled by declining numbers in most cases. The British fringe-population is typical: the probable high numbers of the mid-19th century tumbled to 150–400bp by 1954, 20–30bp by 1966 and fewer than 10bp in the 1980s (Taylor 1993). In the early 1900s, the Wryneck was still numerous in Dutch sandy soil habitats, even being considered a pest because it tended to disturb tits' nests. Since the 1960s, numbers have dropped considerably, although local increases did occur in the warm summers of the mid-1970s (van Dijk *et al* 1994c). In Germany, the decline apparent in the 19th century accelerated in the early 20th century. The increases of the 1940s and 1950s were superseded by an even stronger decline which continues (Epple 1992, Winkel 1992). In France, the species disappeared from the N, its coastal range retreating southwards to La Rochelle. Populations in the Touraine, Anjou and Champagne districts are seriously depleted (Goy 1994). Finland also suffered depletions (>50% decrease in 1970–90), but apparently not a range contraction (Koskimies 1989a).

The dramatic decline, especially in NW Europe, has been attributed mainly to long-term changes in temperature and rainfall. Certainly, the climatic improvement between 1890 and 1920 did not favour the Wryneck in continental Europe (Epple 1992), nor in Britain, presumably because of wetter summers (Burton 1995). However, since the 1950s, such factors as habitat destruction, modern forestry management techniques (which remove dead and dying trees, and plant densely packed fast-growing conifers), intensive fruit and cereal production (massive use of pesticides and herbicides, hedge and tree removal), eutrophication (causing overgrowth of formerly sparsely vegetated areas) and declining ant populations probably have also played a part in the species' misfortunes. Despite these relationships being strongly correlative, the causal links remain unclear. Given the similarity of trends in NW Europe since the 19th century, climatic change may have initiated the decline, which the subsequent detrimental habitat changes only reinforced.

Rob Vogel (NL)

This species account is sponsored by Natur- und Vogelschutzverein Liestal, CH.

Picus canus

Grey-headed Woodpecker

CZ	Žluna šedá	**I**	Picchio cenerino
D	Grauspecht	**NL**	Grijskopspecht
E	Pito Cano	**P**	Peto-de-cabeça-cinzenta
F	Pic cendré	**PL**	Dzięcioł zielonosiwy
FIN	Harmaapäätikka	**R**	Седой дятел
G	Σταχτοτσικλιτάρα	**S**	Gråspett
H	Hamvas küllő		

SPEC Cat 3, Threat status D

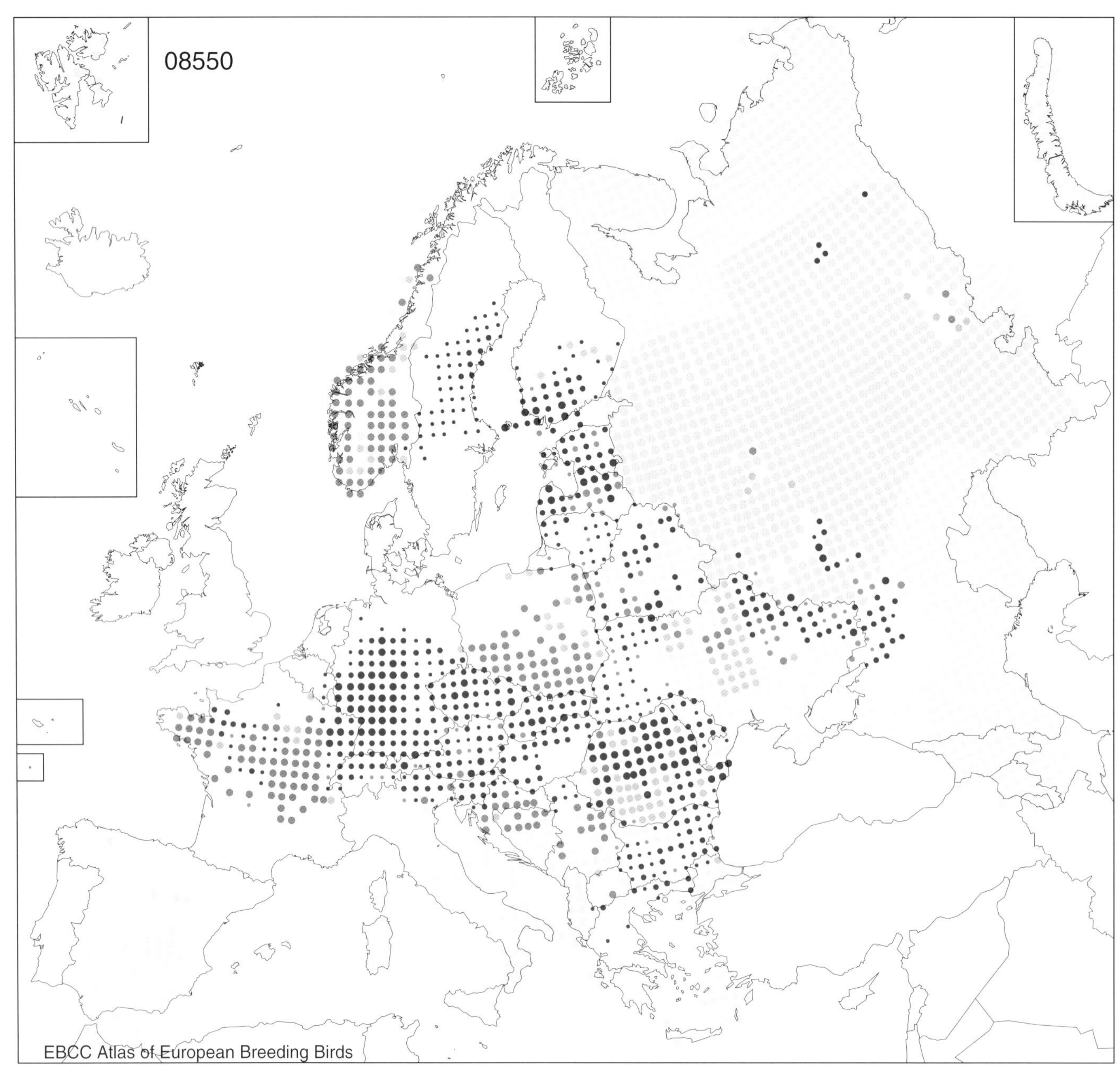

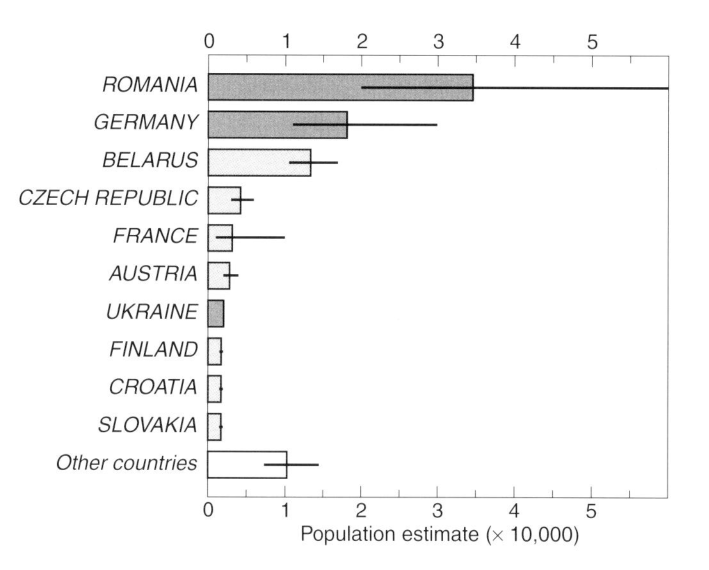

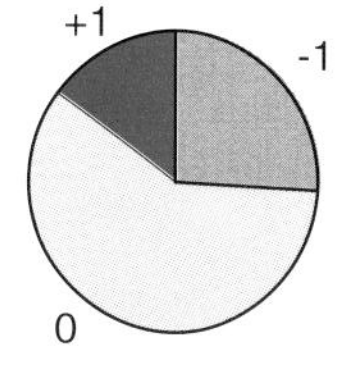

% in top 10 countries: 89.1
Total number of populated European countries: 27
Total European population 77,137–123,087 (93,931)
Russian population 10,000–100,000 (31,623)
Turkish population 100–1000 (316)

The world range of the Grey-headed Woodpecker extends at mid-latitudes across the whole Eurasian continent from the Atlantic to the Pacific Ocean (Hokkaido/Japan), and then turns S through China to Sumatra. The nominate subspecies *P.c. canus* occurs in Europe; there are up to 12 subspecies elsewhere. The European range is concentrated in the mountainous parts of the C and E. Its centre of altitudinal distribution is 700m asl, but it may breed up to 1700m asl; outside the breeding season it may appear above 2000m asl. It is absent from SW Europe, Britain & Ireland and N Fennoscandia. Breeding populations are absent from the lowlands of NW Europe and Hungary because suitable woodlands are lacking. It reaches coastal areas in the Baltic States, Fennoscandia (its northern limit, because of the relatively mild winters) and W France.

The species is a typical forest woodpecker preferring highly structured montane forests. Its nesting and feeding habitats differ, but have to be reasonably adjacent. It excavates nest-holes in old, damaged deciduous trees, mostly aspen *Populus tremula* and alder *Alnus* in N Europe, and beech *Fagus* and oak *Quercus* in C Europe (L. Saari, P. Südbeck, unpubl), but where population density is high it also uses apparently healthy pines *Pinus* (L. Saari, pers obs). It feeds mainly at ant colonies in glades, meadows, forest edges and seedling stands, but also in species-poor mountain (coniferous) forests. Because of its habitat requirements, the Grey-headed Woodpecker is a good indicator of natural climax forests (Scherzinger 1982). Secondary habitats include orchards, parks or riverine forests.

In winter it occurs in oak woods or riverine forests whose bark contains insects, vital food when anthills are snow-covered. Winter mortality is apparently an important population regulation mechanism, especially in the N, where a close association with the Black Woodpecker, *Dryocopus martius* probably helps the species to survive heavy snow-cover through the former's superior ability to dig out ants. The Grey-headed Woodpecker also visits bird feeders regularly.

It has decreased in Romania and Germany, but due to monitoring difficulties the information is scanty (Spitznagel 1993). Causes of decline are related to intensified forestry (clearfells of old deciduous stands, short rotation periods, overall propagation of conifer stands) and to nitrogen emissions (ant colonies avoid very dense vegetation).

The Grey-headed Woodpecker is distributed fairly evenly throughout its European range. Areas of high population densities are not delineated clearly, whereas decreases are apparent at the range limits, as in Sweden, Greece and N Germany. In Fennoscandia climatic influences and perhaps competition limit its range, but in S Europe the reasons remain obscure. There are no known adverse climatic influences, and its distribution is sympatric with Green Woodpecker *P. viridis*. Zoogeographical factors may explain the present distribution, which may not be fully developed. The Grey-headed Woodpecker is very sedentary, allowing a slow rate of expansion, as recorded since 1900 in the Finnish archipelago, W France and NW Germany.

Typical C European densities are *c*0.1 bp/km^2 over 215km^2 (Imhof 1984) and 0.25 bp/km^2 over 200km^2 (Ruge 1982). Locally, density may reach 10 bp/km^2. In N Germany the closest occupied nests were separated by 700m (P. Südbeck, pers obs), whereas in SW Finland (exceptionally) by only 150m (L. Saari, pers obs).

Except on the Pacific coast (Panov 1973) the Grey-headed Woodpecker is strictly resident. Altitudinal movements occur regularly (Scherzinger 1982) but post-breeding dispersal is slight. In C Europe individuals have been recorded some 150km from the nearest breeding site. The further N, the greater the post-breeding dispersal. Birds are often recorded N of their range, occasionally even N of the Arctic Circle (700km beyond their breeding range).

Lennart Saari (FIN) Peter Südbeck (D)

Picus viridis

Green Woodpecker

CZ	Žluna zelená	I	Picchio verde
D	Grünspecht	NL	Groene Specht
E	Pito Real	P	Peto-verde
F	Pic vert	PL	Dzięcioł zielony
FIN	Vihertikka	R	Зеленый дятел
G	Δρυοκολάπτης	S	Gröngöling
H	Zöld küllő		

SPEC Cat 2, Threat status D

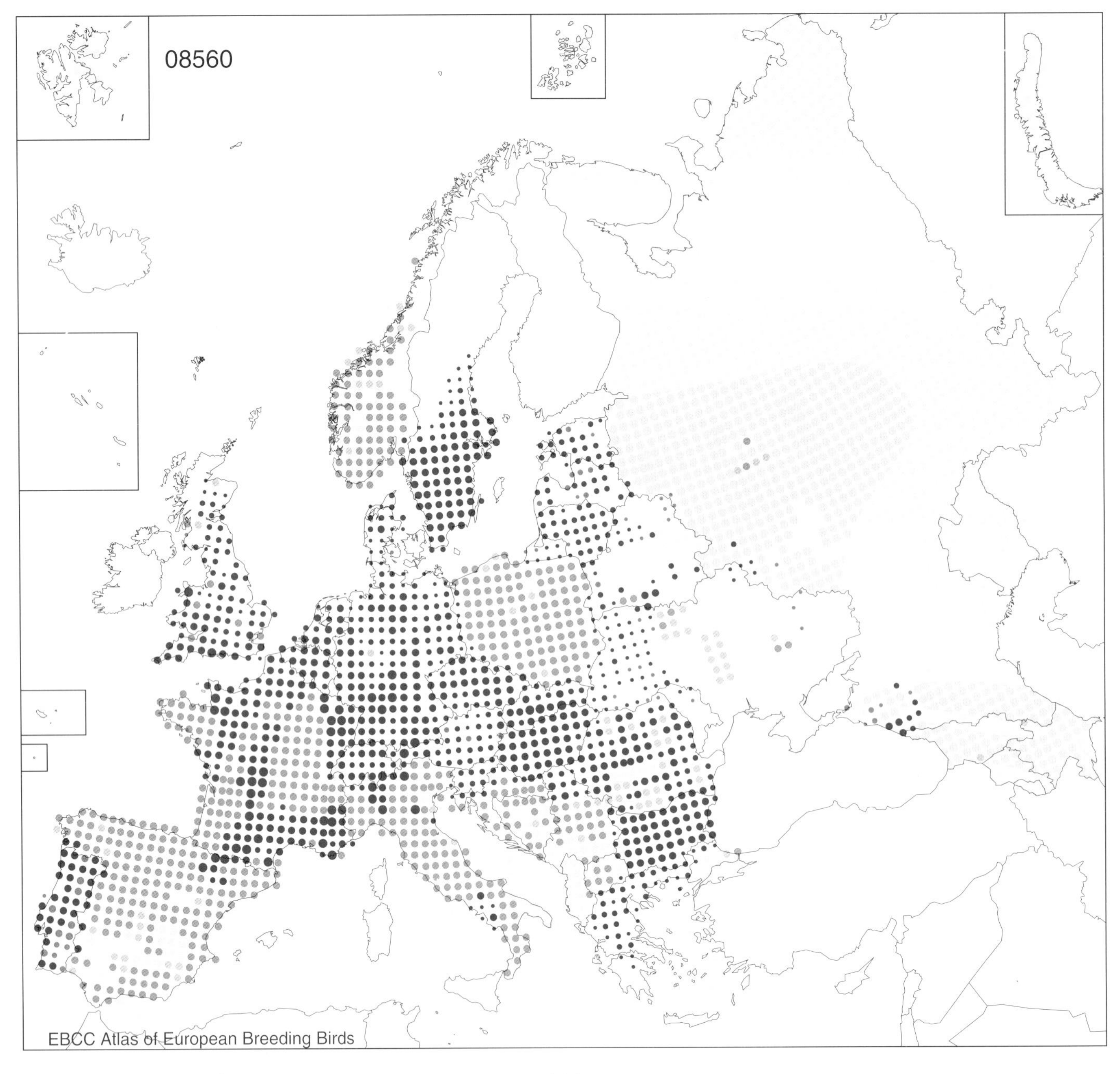

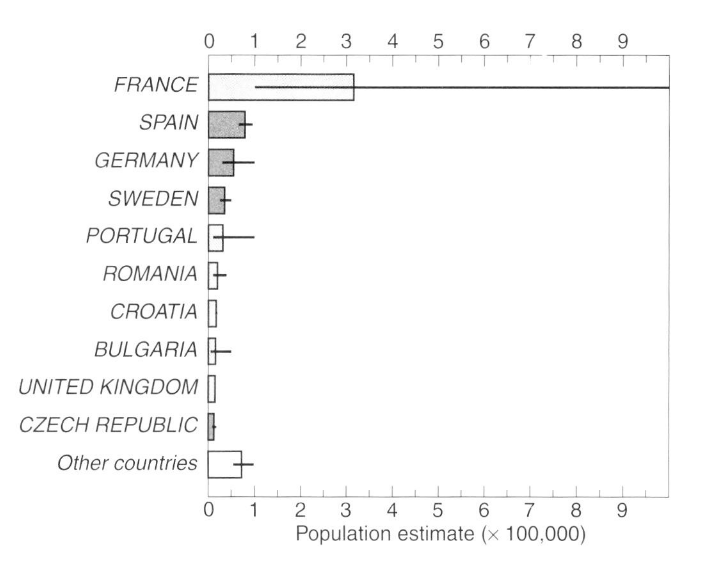

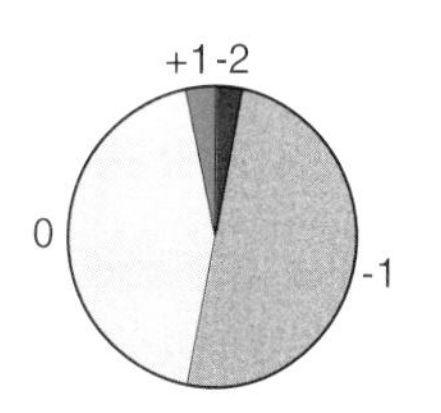

% in top 10 countries: 89.2
Total number of populated European countries: 32
Total European population 450,417–1,360,649 (670,409)
Russian population 10,000–100,000 (31,623)
Turkish population 1000–10,000 (3162)

The large, chiefly ground-feeding Green Woodpecker is restricted mainly to the boreal, temperate and mediterranean climatic zones of the western Palearctic. The nominate *P.v. viridis* occupies most of C Europe, N to Great Britain and S Fennoscandia, being absent only from parts of easternmost Russia. The range extends through much of Turkey, the Caucasus to N Iran where *innominatus* takes over. The Iberian population *sharpei* is distinctive, while birds from North Africa are normally separated as Levaillant's Woodpecker *P. vaillantii*.

The species occupies a wide variety of habitats, most often open wooded country rather than densely forested tracts, but always where mature and over-mature broad-leaved trees offer nest sites near grassy areas containing ground-living insects, especially all stages of ants which comprise the main constituents of its highly specialized diet. It adapts well to orchards, groves and large gardens, but less so in intensively cultivated areas, heath and moor. It rarely uses coniferous forests except in its northern range where a deciduous shrub layer exists, and more recently in open forests containing both broad-leaved standards and young conifers (Keßler 1986, Glue & Boswell 1994). Sparsely wooded marshland is marginal habitat, often remaining unoccupied (Tomiałojć 1990). It usually breeds below 400m asl, exceptionally up to 2000m asl in the Alps.

The Green Woodpecker's northern breeding limit extends SW from the Arctic Circle in W Norway, through C Sweden to the Estonian Baltic coast, except for the intervening montane regions. In Scotland the boundary now lies at 58°30'. The eastern limit is fragmentary and its status unclear, Russian data being unavailable (Blume 1981). Some islands, such as Sicily, Corsica and Ireland are uninhabited, perhaps because they lie beyond the effective flight range of the species to become and remain colonized.

The species reaches its highest abundance in France (average of 1450 bp/50km square). In its western distribution, from S Sweden, Benelux, Germany, much of C Europe and the Balkans to Iberia, values average 200–500 bp/50km square, but decline towards the N, E and SE, to under 60 bp/50km square in Norway, the Baltic States, Poland, Ukraine, Italy and Greece. Intermediate values, some 150 bp/50km square, obtain in Great Britain.

Most European populations of Green Woodpecker are stable, experiencing short-term fluctuations, or declining. Distribution gaps and local losses in Sweden (20–30% decline, 1974–90; S.G. Nilsson *et al* 1992), Spain, The Netherlands (50–75% decline since the 1960s; Osieck & Hustings 1994), Switzerland, Italy and elsewhere are attributed chiefly to suitable nest sites and foraging grounds being lost. Foremost among reasons are the intensification of many agricultural and forestry practices (Havelka & Ruge 1993), notably grassland improvement from increased nutrient input, conversion from permanent pasture to arable land and the disappearance of close-grazing (fewer sheep and rabbits). Similarly, grubbing-out woodlots, hedges, scattered old trees and removing decaying timber from woodlands has eliminated key nesting places and distanced birds from food supplies (S.G. Nilsson *et al* 1992, Glue & Boswell 1994).

A key factor limiting Green Woodpecker distribution is winter severity. Thick snow-cover and prolonged penetrating ground frosts render prey unavailable and reduces winter survival prospects, contributing to the population oscillations along the northern and eastern range fringes, although apparently not in Sweden (S.G. Nilsson *et al* 1992). The species shows great site-fidelity, which in extreme weather may add to winter mortality, unlike its much more versatile forest-dwelling congener, the Grey-headed Woodpecker *P. canus*. Movements of >20km are unusual and invariably involve immatures outside the breeding season. Some altitudinal movements occur but birds may winter at 1800m asl. In suboptimal habitats and at range extremes, losses caused by severe winters may have an impact lasting for a decade or more.

David Glue (GB) Peter Südbeck (D)

This species account is sponsored by Ornithologische Arbeitsgemeinschaft Bonn/Rhein-Sieg, D.

Dryocopus martius **Black Woodpecker**

CZ	Datel černý	I	Picchio nero
D	Schwarzspecht	NL	Zwarte Specht
E	Pito Negro	P	Peto-preto
F	Pic noir	PL	Dzięcioł czarny
FIN	Palokärki	R	Желна
G	Μαυροτσικλιτάρα	S	Spillkråka
H	Fekete harkály		

Non-SPEC, Threat status S

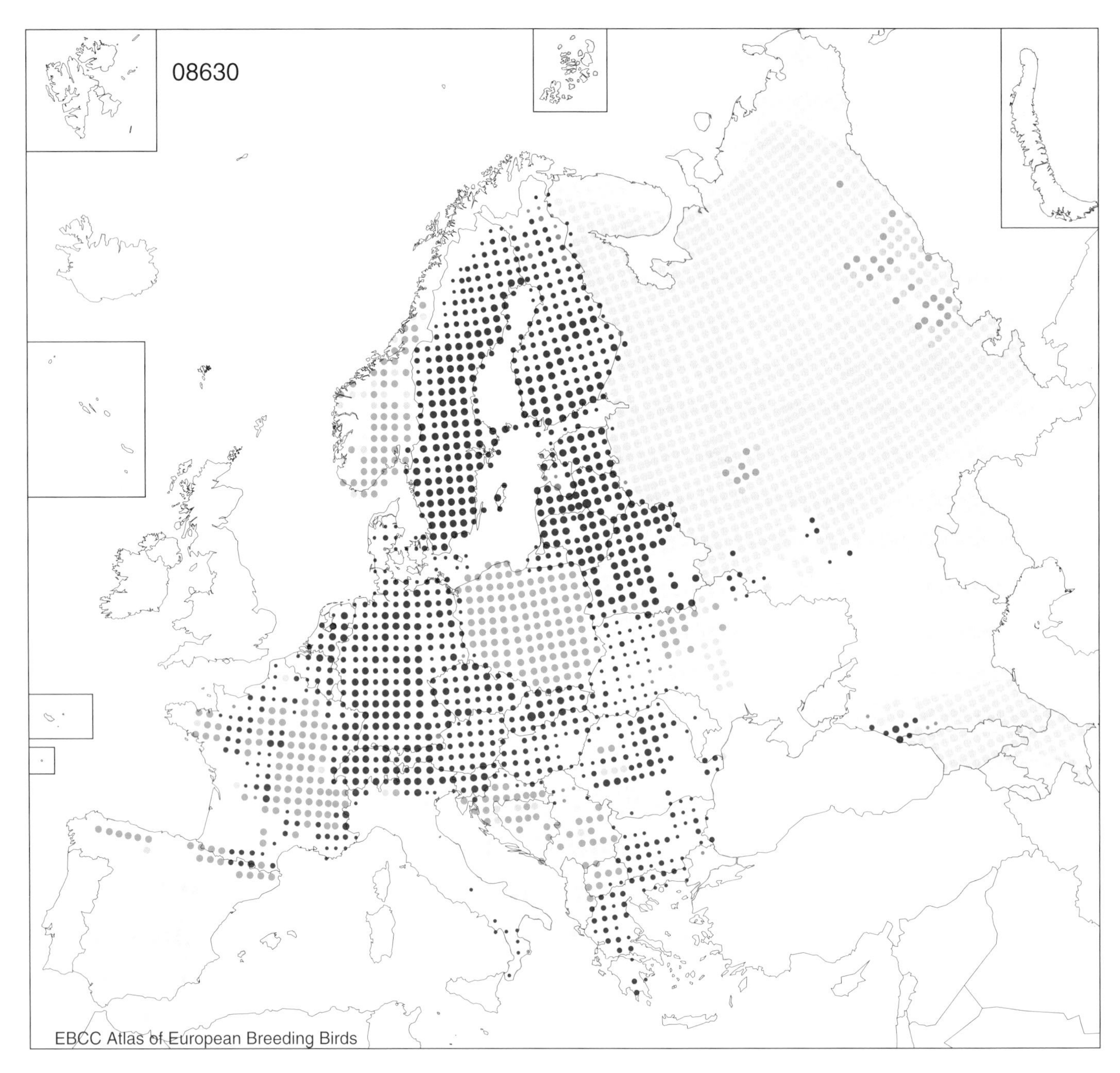

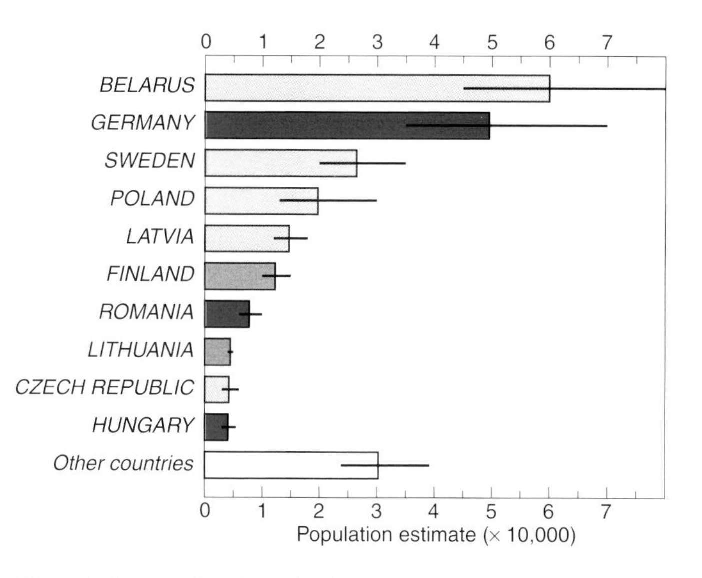

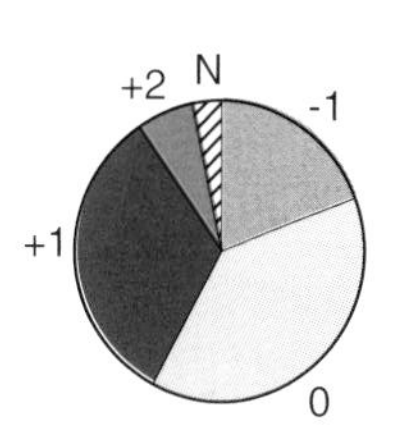

% in top 10 countries: 87.0
Total number of populated European countries: 31
Total European population 210,119–265,642 (233,458)
Russian population 100,000–1,000,000 (316,228)
Turkish population 50–500 (158)

The Black Woodpecker, the largest European woodpecker, has a wide distribution across the Palearctic region, largely below 66°N, from Spain in the W to Kamchatka and Sakhalin in the E. An isolated population, comprising the subspecies *D.m. khamensis*, occurs in SW China, reaching S to *c*29°N; all other populations consist of the nominate *martius*. In Europe it inhabits coniferous, mixed coniferous and deciduous forests from northern Finland and Russia in the N to Spain (Asturia and Pyrenees only) and Greece in the S. In the Mediterranean area it occurs mainly in mountain forests. In the Alps it breeds up to and above 2000m asl, and may nest at higher altitudes in the Great Caucasus. It is absent from Britain & Ireland and the Mediterranean islands. Following afforestation, mainly with conifers, considerable areas have been colonized since the mid-1960s in western Europe. Outside the breeding season, it exploits clearfells.

The Black Woodpecker is continuously distributed in the taiga forest, up to 600m asl in southern Norway but is absent from the Scandinavian mountain birch *Betula* forest and also from western Norway where spruce *Picea* is lacking. The absence of the species from Britain & Ireland is difficult to explain in terms of the amount of habitat available, but there are no authenticated records. The fact that the Black Woodpecker breeds on Åland, Gotland, Bornholm and Sjælland (Johansen 1989) implies that it is capable of colonizing isolated islands.

The Black Woodpecker can breed successfully in highly fragmented forest landscapes provided that the forest types are suitable (Tjernberg *et al* 1993). Its recent spread in western Europe is probably more a consequence of the increase in the amount of old and cut coniferous forest rather than of any increase of the total area of high forest. The expansion was most spectacular in France, where before 1950 the Black Woodpecker bred only in mountainous areas (Cuisin 1985). In modern times it has colonized Belgium (first breeding reported 1908, now *c*1000bp), The Netherlands (first breeding 1913, now *c*2900bp in forests mostly planted from 1890 to 1940) and Denmark (first breeding 1961, now *c*150bp). In marked contrast to the situation in C and W Europe, the Black Woodpecker has decreased considerably in northernmost Europe due to considerable felling of the ancient taiga forest (Järvinen *et al* 1977). In southern Sweden, the population trend was stable during the period 1975–91 (S.G. Nilsson *et al* 1992). However, in Germany, one of the core populations (35 000–70 000bp) shows an increasing trend, most other core populations at least being stable. The vast Russian population is poorly known, and there are no trend data. There is little information on the Caucasus population, but the map indicates it may be sizeable.

The highest densities and smallest home-ranges (*c*1 bp/100ha) have been reported from mixed beech *Fagus* and coniferous forests in C Europe (Ruge & Bretzendorfer 1981). Whether such densities occur over larger areas is unknown. A more representative density range in C Europe is 1 bp/300–1000ha. In Fennoscandia densities decrease northwards from >0.2 bp/100ha of forest in the S to below 0.1 bp/100ha in the N (Tjernberg *et al* 1993).

The Black Woodpecker is a key species in European forests because it is the only woodpecker which constructs breeding holes which other large hole-nesters, such as Goldeneye *Bucephala clangula*, Stock Dove *Columba oenas*, Tengmalm's Owl *Aegolius funereus* and Jackdaw *Corvus monedula* use (Johnsson *et al* 1993). This role is most important in the taiga forests, where rot-holes created by branches falling off trunks are scarce.

All populations are basically sedentary, but dispersal movements in August to October may give rise to eruptive movements in the N in exceptional years.

Sven G Nilsson (S)

Dendrocopos major

Great Spotted Woodpecker

CZ	Strakapoud velký	I	Picchio rosso maggiore
D	Buntspecht	NL	Grote Bonte Specht
E	Pico Picapinos	P	Pica-pau-malhado-grande
F	Pic épeiche	PL	Dzięcioł duży
FIN	Käpytikka	R	Большой пестрый дятел
G	Παρδαλοτσικλιτάρα	S	Större hackspett
H	Nagy fakopáncs		

Non-SPEC, Threat status S

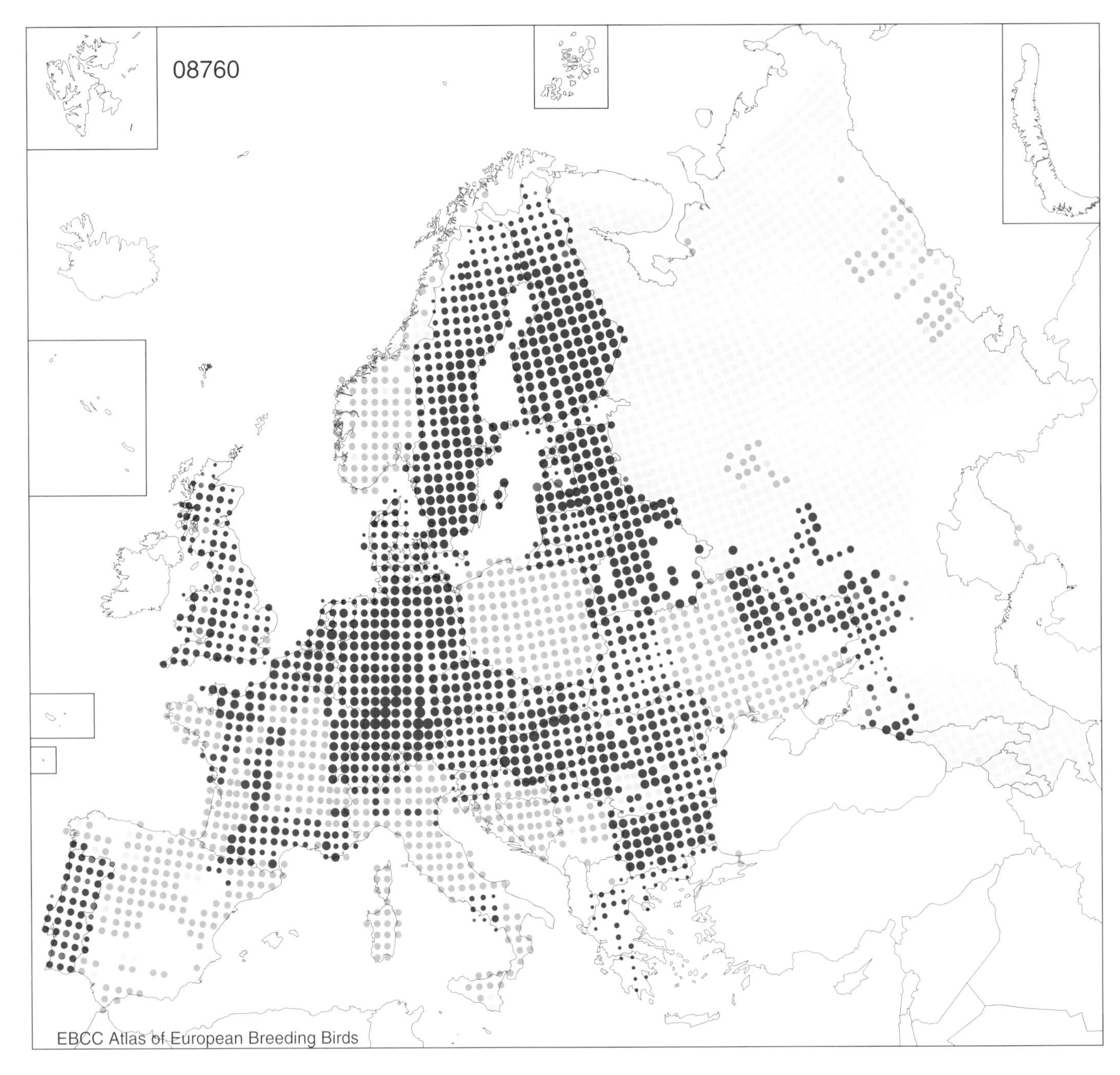

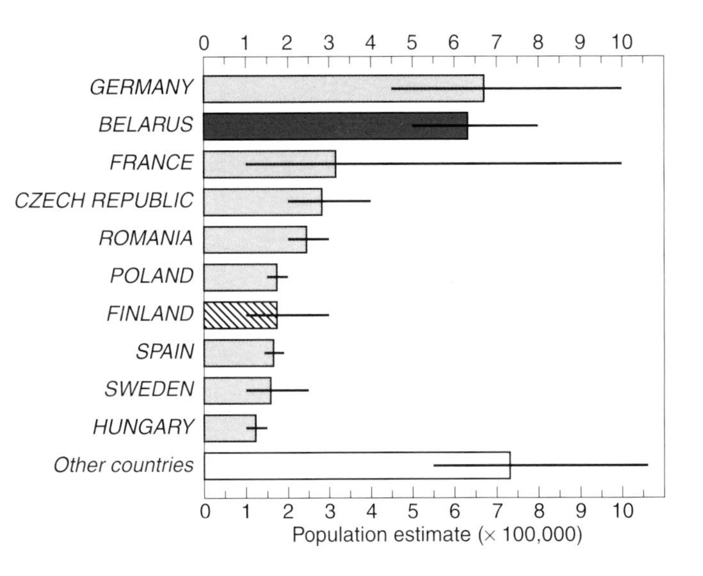

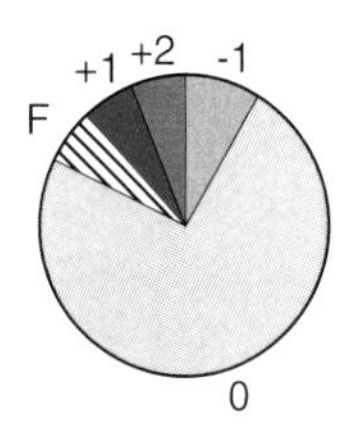

% in top 10 countries: 80.1
Total number of populated European countries: 34
Total European population 3,303,029–4,483,320 (3,671,076)
Russian population 1,000,000–10,000,000 (3,162,278)
Turkish population 1000–10,000 (3162)

The Great Spotted Woodpecker is distributed in trans-Palearctic coniferous and broad-leaved forests between the northern taiga zone and the Mediterranean (Maghreb, Atlas), N Anatolia and N Iran, from N Mongolia to Great Britain. Some ten subspecies breed in the *Atlas*' coverage area, *c*17 others occurring elsewhere.

The commonest woodpecker in Europe, within the temperate zone being absent only from Ireland, Iceland, the smaller islands in the Baltic and North Seas, and in the Mediterranean, from the Balearics, Malta and Crete. It avoids competition with other woodpecker species by foraging mostly near the tops of trees (others preferring the lower parts) or amongst thinner twigs. The C, western and southern European populations are mostly resident, whereas the boreal and eastern populations are short-distance irruptive migrants, their wintering numbers fluctuating strongly in C and W Europe. Irruptions depend mainly on the availability of seed-bearing spruce *Picea abies* and Scots pine *Pinus sylvestris* cones. In the Caucasus, birds move to lower altitudes in winter.

Overall density seems highest throughout the C European belt, from northern France through Germany, the Czech Republic, Poland, Belarus and Romania. Numerous and widespread in the Fennoscandian and Russian taiga, the species becomes more patchily distributed towards the northern forest limit. In S Europe, especially Spain, Italy and Greece, it remains widespread in forests, but at lower overall densities. It breeds up to 1000m asl in the Vysoké Tatry, Erzgebirge and Fichtelgebirge Mountains and up to 1700–2000m asl in the Swiss–Austrian Alps.

Range and population size trends seem stable overall, but some population increases have occurred in Britain, The Netherlands, Germany (evidence at least from C and N Germany; Flade 1994), Belarus and Ukraine. In Britain, the 1970s increase was thought to be the consequence of Dutch elm disease providing so many dead trees, but why the levels should remain high after the trees had been removed is not known (Smith 1993). The increase in The Netherlands is caused by afforestation, the maturation and diversification of woods planted in the early 1900s and the introduction of more liberal forestry practices since the 1980s.

The medium-term effects of air pollution in C and E European forests (causing 'Waldsterben'; extensive die-back) appear to be mixed. Where damage is heavy, especially in coniferous and higher-altitude forests, nesting possibilities, food supply and food quality deteriorate and the abundance of woodpeckers decreases with increasing damage (Flousek *et al* 1993). Where damage is slight, particularly in lowland deciduous forests, the species clearly has benefited from a continued increased food supply and improved nesting opportunities (M. Flade, pers obs). The long-term overall effects of 'Waldsterben' remain uncertain. The extent of any 'Waldsterben'-induced declines is not yet quantified. Slight declines in numbers have occurred in Croatia, Italy and Albania.

The species inhabits all types of forests, but also takes to well-timbered farmland, parks, gardens and isolated copses. Breeding densities are highest in mature alluvial forests of ash–elm–cherry *Fraxinus–Ulmus–Prunus* (mean 2.0, maximum 6.6 bp/10ha), hornbeam–oak *Carpinus betulus–Quercus* (mean 1.1, maximum 5.5), oak–beech (*–Fagus*) and lowland beech (mean 2.0, maximum 5.3), based on 538 German forest plots (Flade 1994).

Although the Great Spotted Woodpecker favours a high proportion of dead wood, densities are not necessarily higher in primeval temperate forests, such as in Białowieża National Park, Poland (0.1–1.9bp/10ha, being highest in ash–alder (*Fraxinus-Alnus)* and lowest in coniferous; Wesolowski & Tomiałojć 1986).

The Great Spotted Woodpecker hybridizes with Syrian Woodpecker *D. syriacus* in a narrow zone at the edge of the latter's steady spread northwestwards through Austria and the Czech Republic, but once sufficient Syrian Woodpecker females have colonized the hybridization zone, the extent of hybridization becomes insignificant.

Martin Flade (D)

Dendrocopos syriacus **Syrian Woodpecker**

CZ	Strakapoud jižní	**I**	Picchio rosso di Siria
D	Blutspecht	**NL**	Syrische Bonte Specht
E	Pico Sirio	**P**	Pica-pau-sírio
F	Pic syriaque	**PL**	Dzięcioł białosyzi
FIN	Syyriantikka	**R**	Сирийский дятел
G	Βαλκανοτσικλιτάρα	**S**	Balkanspett
H	Balkáni fakopáncs		

SPEC Cat 4, Threat status S (P)

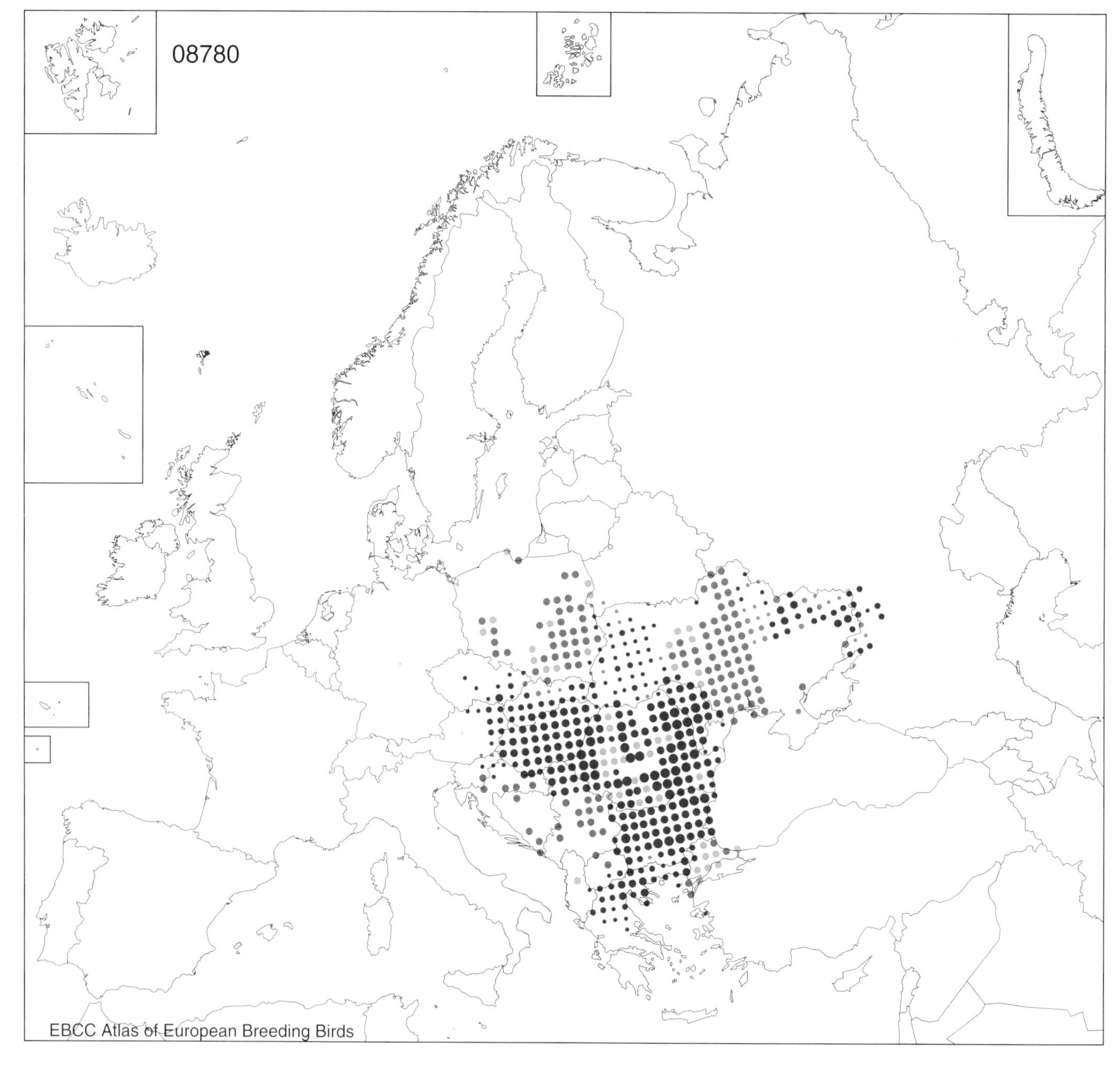

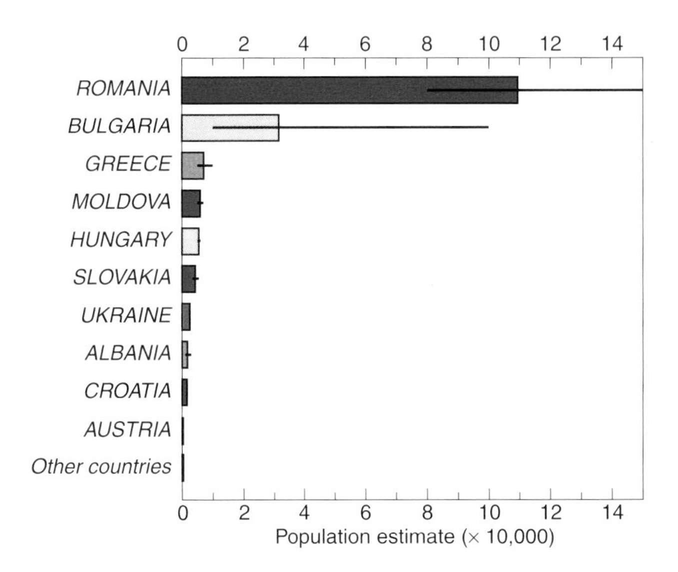

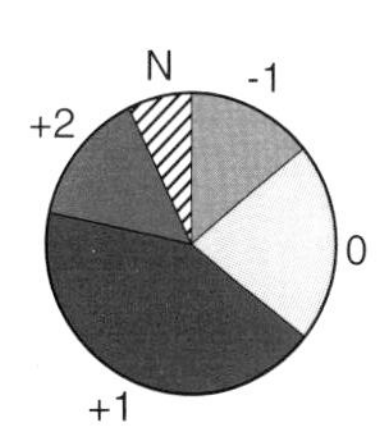

% in top 10 countries: 99.7
Total number of populated European countries: 14
Total European population 133,912–250,148 (170,617)
Turkish population 10,000–100,000 (31,623)

The Syrian Woodpecker is a resident species whose continuous breeding range in Europe covers the eastern Czech Republic, S Poland and E Austria to Greece, European Turkey, Ukraine and S–C Russia, a separate population inhabiting the E Caucasus. Elsewhere it breeds from Iran to Asian Turkey, Syria and Israel. Since *c*1890, it has spread rapidly from its original Turkish breeding areas into the Levant, Israel, the Balkans and C Europe. The subspecies *D.s. transcaucasicus* occurs in the Caucasus and the nominate *syriacus* in the remainder of the European range. There is one other subspecies.

The Syrian Woodpecker occupies the mediterranean, continental, temperate, steppe and boreal–montane climate zones, preferring the lower and mid-latitudes, up to 1000m asl in Bulgaria. In SE Europe it inhabits oak *Quercus* and riparian woodland, cultivated areas, parks and avenues. In C Europe it colonized open country containing solitary trees, avenues, orchards, gardens, parks, cemeteries and vineyards.

During its initially rapid range extension, the Syrian Woodpecker colonized much of the Balkan Peninsula, firstly in Bulgaria, Romania and Ukraine and in the NW in Hungary, Austria, the Czech Republic and Poland. By the 1970s it had possibly encountered a climatic barrier in C Europe, E German records referring to isolated birds. Since 1979, Bavarian observations have concerned hybrids with the Great Spotted Woodpecker *D. major*. Hybrids and mixed pairs are also frequent in Steiermark, Austria (O. Samwald, pers obs). The hybridization zone tends to be narrow, existing mostly where Syrian Woodpecker females are scarce. Both in the hybridization zone and in areas of sympatry, the Syrian Woodpecker appears dominant.

The first Bulgarian record was in 1890. Now it is widespread, its population being estimated at 10 000–100 000bp. The first Romanian record (1931) probably post-dates its actual arrival. It probably entered Transylvania from the SW, perhaps from Serbia and Banat, in the 1940s. By 1959, the species was widely distributed in Romania in suitable habitats (Munteanu 1968) and reached *c*80 000–150 000bp in 1970–90. In the former Yugoslavia it occurs sparsely in eastern Croatia (1400–1800bp) and Slovenia (10–50bp), but presumably is more numerous in Serbia. It is largely absent along the Mediterranean coast and in adjacent wooded mountains. The range expansion reached Hungary in 1937, becoming widespread by 1954, some 5000–6000bp now occupying all suitable habitats. Although there are sizeable concentrations in gardens or parks, the species' overall density is low in the scattered trees of the puszta.

In 1949 it reached eastern Slovakia whose population is now 3400–5500bp. The Czech Republic's 70–120bp lie at the periphery of the breeding range. Although the first record for Austria occurred in 1951 (K.M. Bauer 1952), by then the environs of Neusiedlersee were already occupied. By 1970 it had colonized the climatically favourable eastern Austrian lowlands whose population is stable at 320–400bp. The species attains its highest breeding density in vineyards and orchards, at 0.5–1.0 bp/100ha (Dvorak *et al* 1993).

In Poland the Syrian Woodpecker was first recorded in 1978 (possibly in 1977) and has since then spread slowly northwards (Tomiałojć 1990). Presently, it is most abundant in the Małopolska region in the SE, particularly in forests along the Rivers Vistula and San (Walasz & Mielczarek 1992). It is widely distributed in Moldova, but is commoner in the N (D. Munteanu, unpubl). In Ukraine the species was found in 1948 at Hotin (Czernowitz district), having spread eastwards from Romania and Moldova. It subsequently occupied C Ukraine, then crossed the eastern border eventually to reach the Don Valley in Russia (D. Munteanu, unpubl).

It is not known whether the range extension in Europe was caused by population changes in Asia Minor. The western range limit coincides with the July isotherm of 18°C, perhaps indicative of a climatically induced barrier towards further westward expansion.

Dan Munteanu (ROM) Otto Samwald (A)

Dendrocopos medius — Middle Spotted Woodpecker

CZ Strakapoud prostřední
D Mittelspecht
E Pico Mediano
F Pic mar
FIN Tammitikka
G Μεσοτσικλιτάρα
H Közép fakopáncs
I Picchio rosso mezzano
NL Middelste Bonte Specht
P Pica-pau-mediano
PL Dzięcioł średni
R Средний дятел
S Mellanspett

SPEC Cat 4, Threat status S

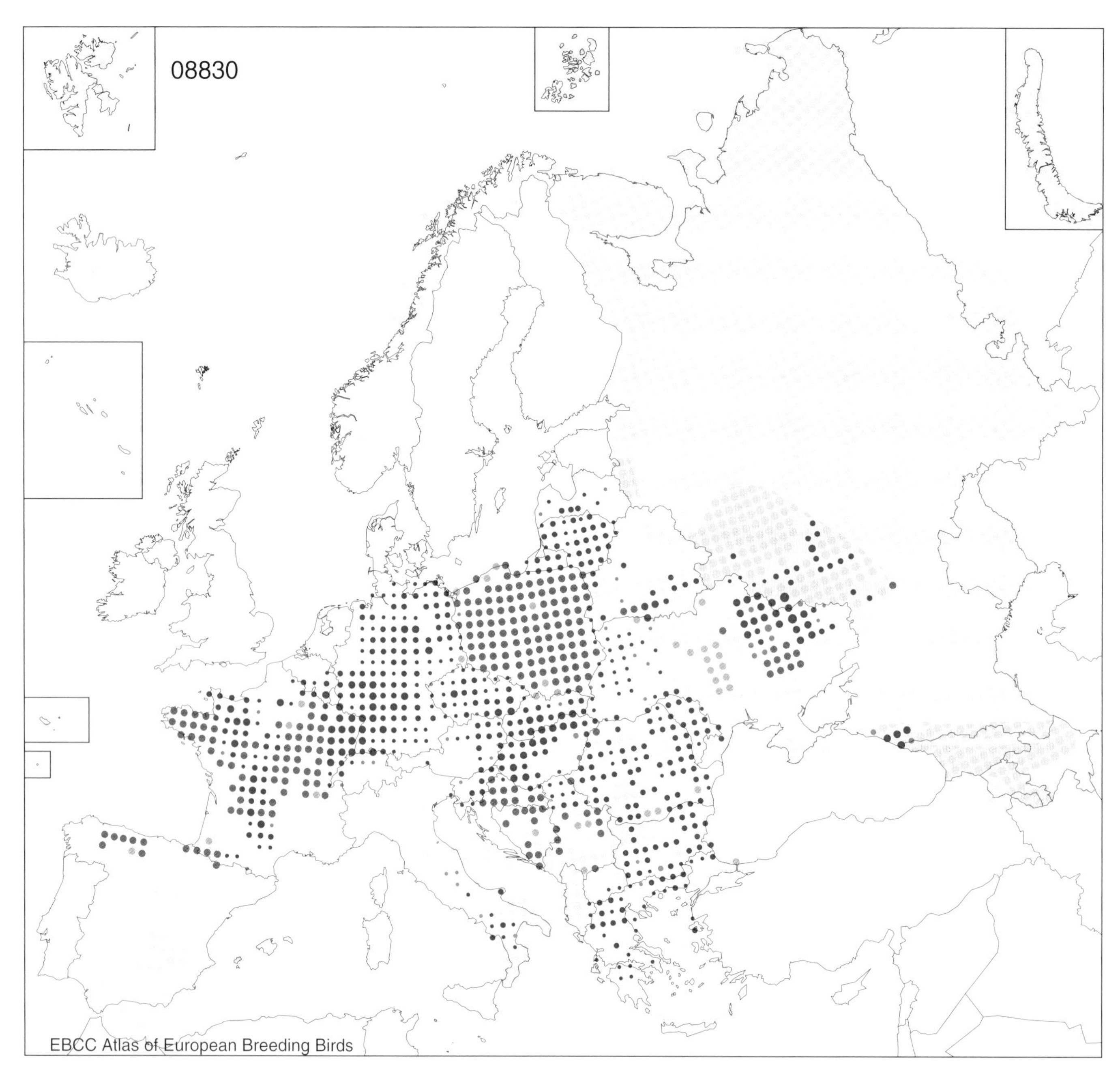

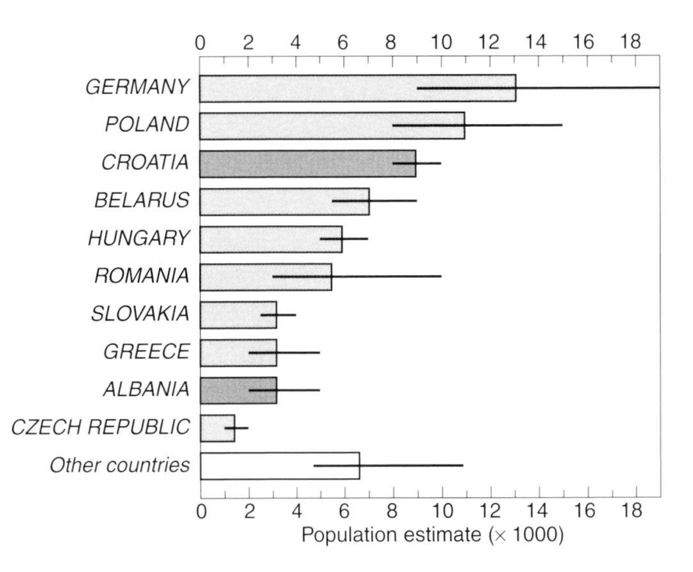

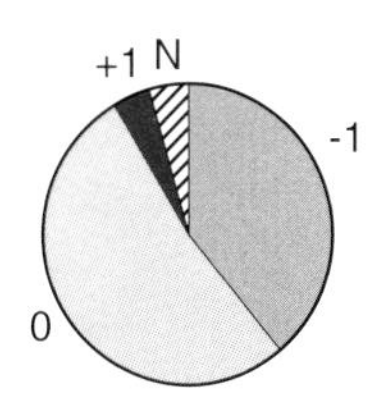

% in top 10 countries: 90.4
Total number of populated European countries: 23
Total European population 62,629–78,446 (68,913)
Russian population 1000–10,000 (3162)
Turkish population 1000–10,000 (3162)

The Middle Spotted Woodpecker is a non-migratory resident of the dense forests of the W Palearctic. Its range is bordered by the Zagros Mountains (Iran) to the E and by the Cantabrian Mountains (Spain) to the W. Its distribution is typically confined to the temperate continental climatic zone, from the Russian/Latvian border at 58°N southwards to just reach the western Mediterranean at Mersin, SE Turkey. The nominate subspecies *D.m. medius* occurs throughout Europe except in SE Russia and the Caucasus which hold *caucasicus*. Two other subspecies occur elsewhere.

The species' distribution generally corresponds with that of hornbeam *Carpinus betulus*. The breeding habitat may include other tree species (beech *Fagus*, elm *Ulmus*, ash *Fraxinus*, spruce *Picea*) in mixed woodland, but it is primarily a specialist of mature oak *Quercus* forests. As an insectivorous species which forages by gleaning, the Middle Spotted Woodpecker's life cycle is strongly tied to oak trees which provide it with abundant prey, particularly in winter.

Its geographic distribution is somewhat discontinuous, being mainly fragmented W of 15°E (from the German–Polish border S to Slovenia which the 50km map resolution cannot discriminate sufficiently clearly). Further E, its distribution becomes more continuous and uniform, reflecting the fragmentation pattern of dense forests across Europe. The total woodland area, the density of ancient oak trees, altitude (optimum 300–600m asl), a warm microclimate and the degree of isolation from neighbouring oak forests are all key factors affecting its distribution. Its habitat requirements are very specific, and in order to thrive, it requires relatively large areas of suitable habitat, >40ha in Switzerland (Müller 1982), 70–75ha in Sweden (Pettersson 1984) and 150–200ha in northern Spain (Purroy *et al* 1984).

The species' population in Europe (excluding Russia), is estimated at 53 000–97 000bp. The Russian population estimate of 1000–10 000bp is very broad, but better data are lacking. The optimum zone of high overall breeding density comprises the temperate lowland forests of C Europe, between the Rhine and Don catchments, and 52% of all breeding pairs occur in Germany, Poland, Hungary and Croatia. The breeding density in C Europe varies between 0.3 and 2.4 bp/10ha, but in most oak woodlands averages *c*1 bp/10ha (Bühler 1976). In the Polish Białowieża National Park densities were significantly higher in oak–hornbeam (1.0 bp/10ha, range 0.8–1.2) than in ash–alder forests (0.7 bp/10ha, range 0.5–1.0) (Wesołowski & Tomiałojć 1986). Oak-dominated forests in the Cantabrians (1300–1600m asl) contained <0.2 bp/10ha (Purroy *et al* 1984), home-range separation distances averaging 14km.

Slight declines in numbers have occurred in parts of W and C Europe, including Spain, France, Italy, Austria, Albania, Croatia, the Czech Republic, Moldova, and Ukraine. Major populations (>1000bp) have recorded declining numbers but rarely. Only in Belgium was some increase noted, both in numbers and range (Schmitz 1993). Suggested causes of the recent extinction (last bred successfully in 1980) of Sweden's relict Östergötland population were a low reproductive rate, inadequate food resources in the limited extent of suitable habitat (adequate only for *c*20bp) and severe winter weather. The long-term survival of this small population was unlikely because of its degree of isolation (Pettersson 1984), the species being highly sedentary. The Lithuanian population of *c*100bp may also be vulnerable. The last Dutch breeding record was in 1973, but several observations in the early 1990s suggest some influx from neighbouring breeding sites in Germany and Belgium (van Dijk *et al* 1994c). Elsewhere in Europe, regional declines have been caused by forest management activities, especially fragmentation of oak forests, elimination of old and decaying trees though intensive felling and replacement of indigenous deciduous forests by fast-growing conifers. The effect of atmospheric pollution on the availability and abundance of its main arthropod prey needs further research.

Francisco J Purroy (E) Frans J Schepers (NL)

This species account is sponsored by Ornithologische Gesellschaft Zürich, CH.

Dendrocopos leucotos **White-backed Woodpecker**

CZ	Strakapoud bělohřbetý	**I**	Picchio dorsobianco
D	Weißrückenspecht	**NL**	Witrugspecht
E	Pico Dorsiblanco	**P**	Pica-pau-de-dorso-branco
F	Pic à dos blanc	**PL**	Dzięcioł białogrzbiety
FIN	Valkoselkätikka	**R**	Белоспинный дятел
G	Λευκονώτης	**S**	Vitryggig hackspett
H	Fehérhátú fakopáncs		

Non-SPEC, Threat status S

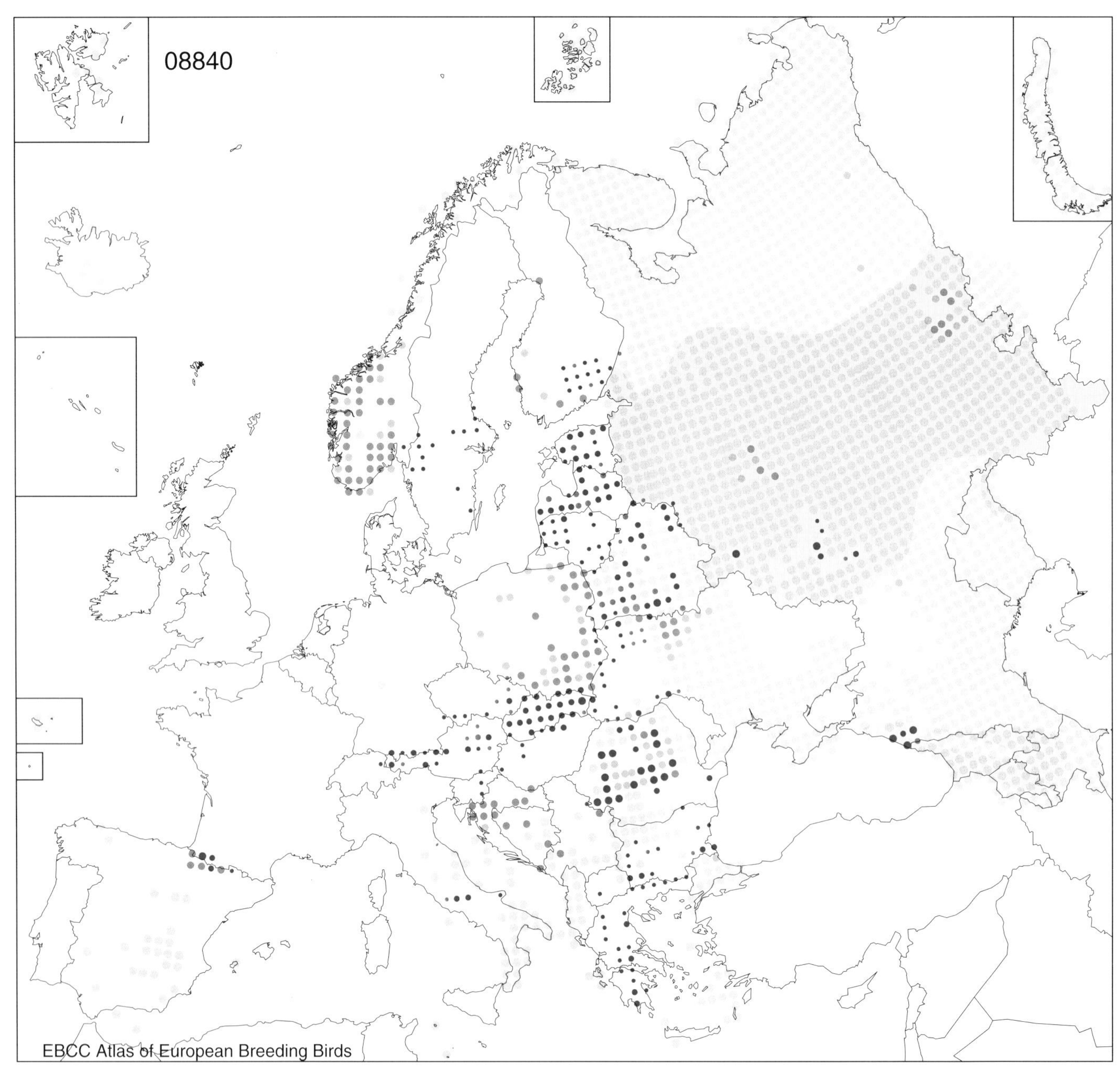

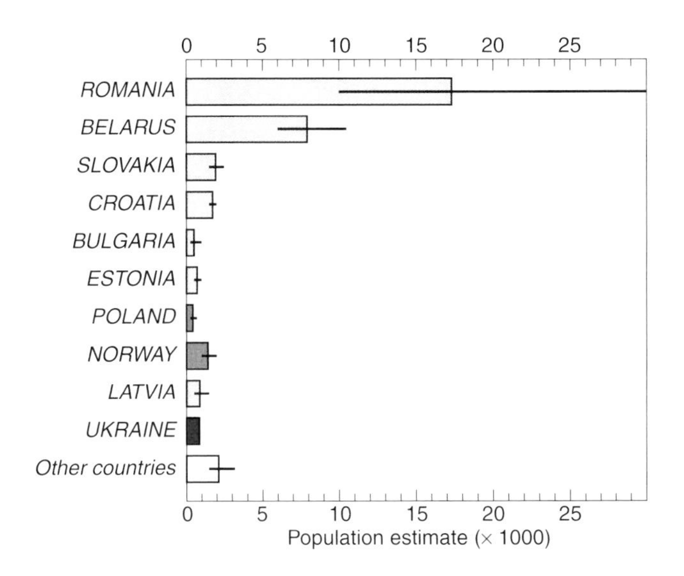

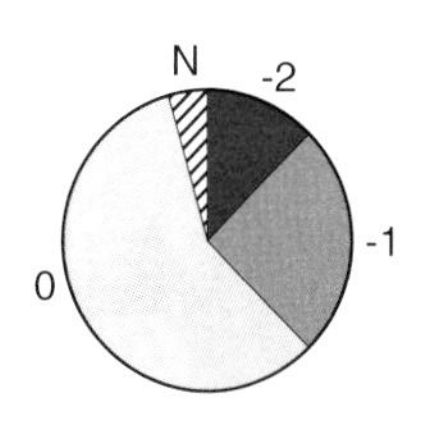

% in top 10 countries: 94.1
Total number of populated European countries: 24
Total European population 28,175–48,799 (35,796)
Russian population 10,000–100,000 (31,623)
Turkish population 50–500 (158)

The White-backed Woodpecker, a broad-leaved forest species, has a Palearctic distribution in the temperate and southern boreal deciduous zones. It occurs in C and S Europe in forests dominated by beech *Fagus* spp, hornbeam *Carpinus betulus*, and oak *Quercus* spp, and in N and E Europe in forests dominated by birch *Betula* spp and aspen *Populus tremula*. The mapped area may contain three subspecies: the nominate *D.l. leucotos* occupies C, N and E Europe, S to Austria, N Serbia and Ukraine and E to the Urals, *lilfordi* occurring S of *leucotos* and *uralensis* possibly near Chelyabinsk. At least 10 other subspecies exist elsewhere.

The White-backed Woodpecker feeds on wood-boring and bark-living insect larvae, mainly of beetles and moths, in deciduous trees, breeding up to 1300m asl in much of Europe and up to 1700m in the Caucasus. The species is strongly dependent on the occurrence of dead and dying trees (Aulén 1988), and is very sensitive to modern forestry management practice, which generally is to remove them as detritus.

Maximum densities of the White-backed Woodpecker in optimal deciduous forests are 1.0 bp/km^2 in N and C Europe (Stenberg 1990, Wesołowski 1995a) and 2.0 bp/km^2 in Italy (Bernoni 1994). Home-range sizes are normally quite large, from at least 50–100ha in Sweden (Aulén 1988), to 75–150ha in Norway (Stenberg 1990) and 100ha in E Poland (Wesołowski 1995a). White-backed Woodpecker adults are sedentary and show high site fidelity, but juveniles may migrate in autumn (Virkkala *et al* 1993). Studies in Białowieża National Park, Poland, indicate that some adults may switch home ranges from year to year (Wesołowski 1995a).

As a result of forest management, the White-backed Woodpecker has become an endangered species in Sweden (Aulén 1988) and Finland (Virkkala *et al* 1993). It has also decreased in many other European countries, such as Poland, Norway, Lithuania, Latvia, Ukraine, Austria and Spain. In Finland the population has collapsed from the estimated 1000bp of the early 1950s to the present 30–40bp as a consequence of large-scale industrial forestry which began in the 1950s (Virkkala *et al* 1993).

In the 15th century, the species' distribution probably covered large areas of western Europe but due to the initial clearance and subsequent intensified management of the deciduous lowland forests, it has disappeared from much of this area. At present only small isolated populations remain in the Pyrenees, in the Apennines and in the German and Austrian Alps.

In eastern Europe, the Balkans, Belarus and Russia, the White-backed Woodpecker apparently still thrives in deciduous lowland forests and mountain forests where some 90% of the European population of 67 000bp resides. In SE Europe it remains relatively common in the mountains of the former Yugoslavia and in the Slovakian and Romanian Carpathians. In Bulgaria (50–150bp), where the species has been stable during 1970–90, it is most abundant in deciduous mountain forests at an altitude of 1000m asl (Spiridinov 1985).

In E and SE Europe, clearing and managing of deciduous forests potentially suitable for the White-backed Woodpecker has not been as intensive as in W Europe, or in Finland and Sweden, but these circumstances may change dramatically once more modern forestry management techniques begin to be applied, a scenario only too likely as eastern European economies develop. Should that be the case, eastern White-backed Woodpecker populations would probably also collapse. In Poland, for example, the species' fortunes are dictated by the preservation of the primeval Białowieża Forest. Although the species may breed in swampy stands (alder and ash) in managed forests, its survival very much depends on the strict protection of unmanaged deciduous stands (Wesołowski 1995b).

Jeko Spiridinov (BUL) Raimo Virkkala (FIN)

This species account is sponsored by STORA Forest and Timber, Falun, S.

Dendrocopos minor — Lesser Spotted Woodpecker

CZ	Strakapoud malý	I	Picchio rosso minore
D	Kleinspecht	NL	Kleine Bonte Specht
E	Pico Menor	P	Pica-pau-malhado-pequeno
F	Pic épeichette	PL	Dzięciołek
FIN	Pikkutikka	R	Малый пестрый дятел
G	Νανοτσικλιτάρα	S	Mindre hackspett
H	Kis fakopáncs		

Non-SPEC, Threat status S

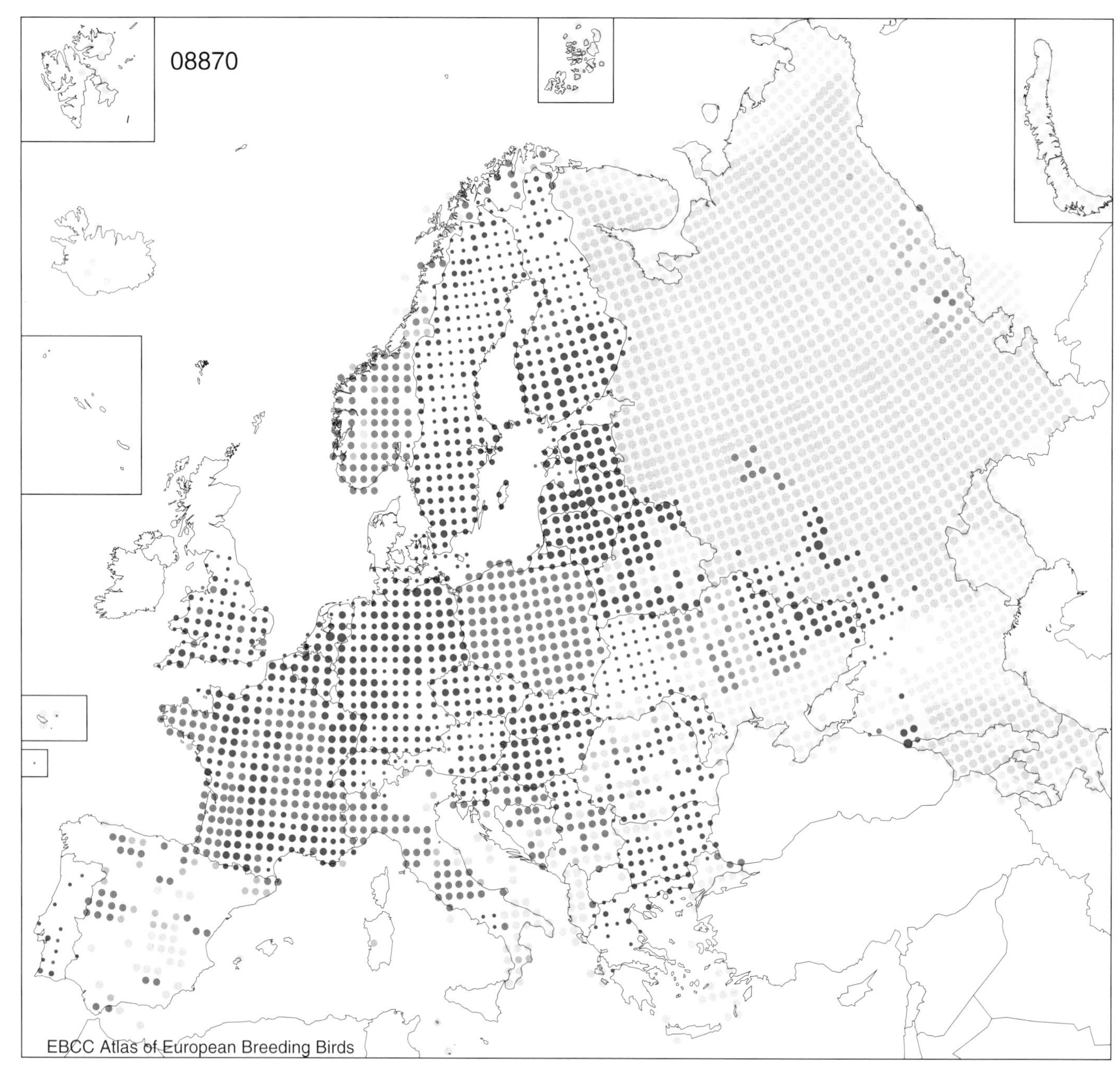

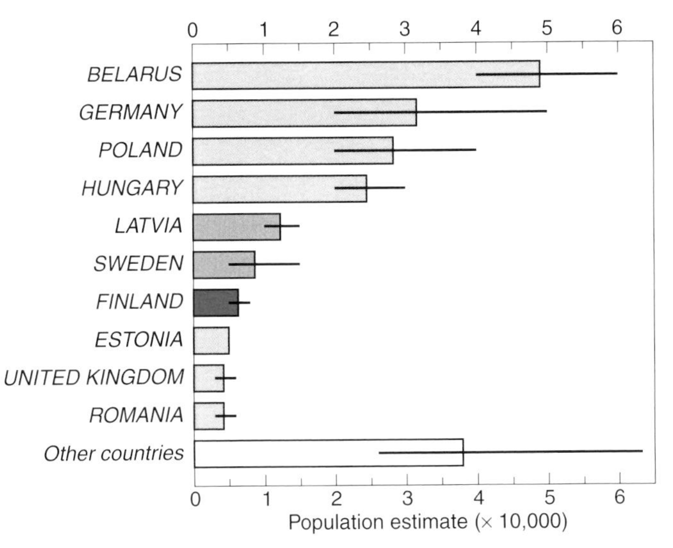

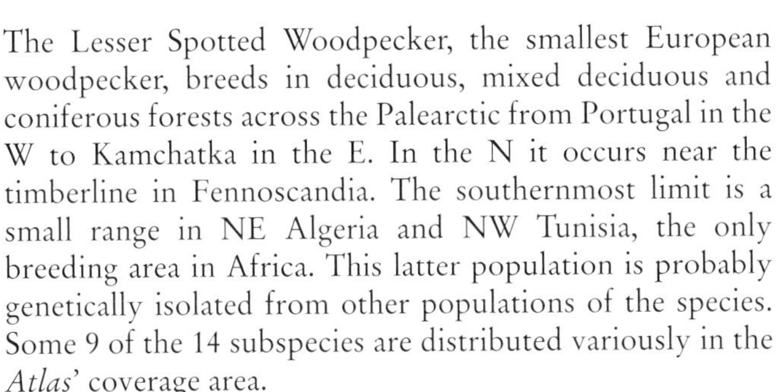

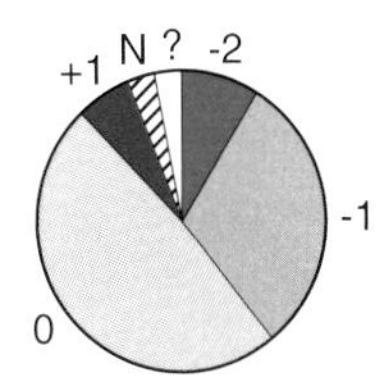

% in top 10 countries: 82.1
Total number of populated European countries: 33
Total European population 193,510–240,161 (212,023)
Russian population 10,000–100,000 (31,623)
Turkish population 1000–10,000 (3162)

The Lesser Spotted Woodpecker, the smallest European woodpecker, breeds in deciduous, mixed deciduous and coniferous forests across the Palearctic from Portugal in the W to Kamchatka in the E. In the N it occurs near the timberline in Fennoscandia. The southernmost limit is a small range in NE Algeria and NW Tunisia, the only breeding area in Africa. This latter population is probably genetically isolated from other populations of the species. Some 9 of the 14 subspecies are distributed variously in the *Atlas*' coverage area.

The species prefers unmanaged forests which have old trees and a high proportion of standing dead trees (Spitznagel 1990, Olsson *et al* 1992). The highest densities occur in riparian forest (often with alder *Alnus*) and broad-leaved deciduous forest (often with oak *Quercus*) (Wesołowski & Tomiałojć 1986, Spitznagel 1990, Wiktander *et al* 1992). In areas in western Europe with intensive forestry, the species' ability to survive in orchards, gardens and parks containing many deciduous trees gives a biased impression of its prime habitats.

The Lesser Spotted Woodpecker breeds over most of Europe where there are deciduous forests, reaching its highest densities in C Europe and the Baltic States. It is absent from Ireland, Scotland, most of Denmark (colonized the E in the 1960s) and the Mediterranean islands. The mapped occurrence in Sardinia may not represent a breeding population. Because it has a large home range (>50ha, pers obs) it is sensitive to fragmentation of forests possessing a high proportion of deciduous trees, a circumstance which may explain its absence from some regions within its main range in Europe. Wet weather depresses its breeding success (Wiktander *et al* 1994), a possible additional reason for its absence in some oceanic-climate regions. Absence from some Fennoscandian taiga squares may be due to its disappearance from extensive tracts of forests burnt since the mid-1970s or because forest management eliminated old deciduous trees. Cold winters apparently seem less of a problem, because the species inhabits Scandinavian mountain birch *Betula* forests.

Monitoring of Lesser Spotted Woodpecker populations is generally poor, with a few exceptions. A strong and continuous decrease has been documented in Finland for over 30 years (Väisänen & Koskimies 1989); in Sweden there was a decrease of about 4% per year during 1975–91 (S.G. Nilsson *et al* 1992). The species has also decreased between 1972 and 1991 in England, although there was a temporary increase up to about 1980 due to Dutch elm disease (Smith 1993). It is also suspected that recent decreases in other countries were due to forestry practices. The species colonized Denmark in the early 1960s, probably from Sweden, the population now being *c*20bp.

Generally, the highest densities occur in lowland areas in C Europe and in the Baltic States. Probably many of the density variations are attributable to the varying quality of forest management. The species' large home range constrains density calculations to large plots. Its behaviour can result in density overestimates if the mapping method is applied uncritically. Population estimates are therefore more uncertain than for other woodpeckers. In primeval deciduous forest in Poland breeding density is 2–3 bp/100ha (Wesołowski & Tomiałojć 1986). Even in large plots with much unmanaged deciduous forest densities are lower: 1.6 territories/km^2 in floodplain forest in SW Germany (Spitznagel 1990), 0.2–0.4 bp/km^2 in 60km^2 of mixed forest around Lake Möckeln, southern Sweden (S.G. Nilsson, pers obs) and 0.06 in W Norway (Stenberg & Hogstad 1992). The species tolerates only those coniferous forests containing a considerable proportion of deciduous trees; in W Norway in unmanaged pine-dominated forest its density was 0.01 territories/100ha of forest.

All populations are basically sedentary, but dispersal movements in August to November exceptionally may give rise to eruptive movements in the N.

Sven G Nilsson (S)

This species account is sponsored by Armin Deutsch, Bielefeld, D.

Picoides tridactylus

Three-toed Woodpecker

CZ	Datlík tříprstý	I	Picchio tridattilo
D	Dreizehenspecht	NL	Drieteenspecht
E	Pico Tridáctilo	P	Pica-pau-tridáctilo
F	Pic tridactyle	PL	Dzięcioł trójpalczasty
FIN	Pohjantikka	R	Трехпалый дятел
G	Τριδάχτυλος	S	Tretåig hackspett
H	Háromujjú hőcsik		

SPEC Cat 3, Threat status D

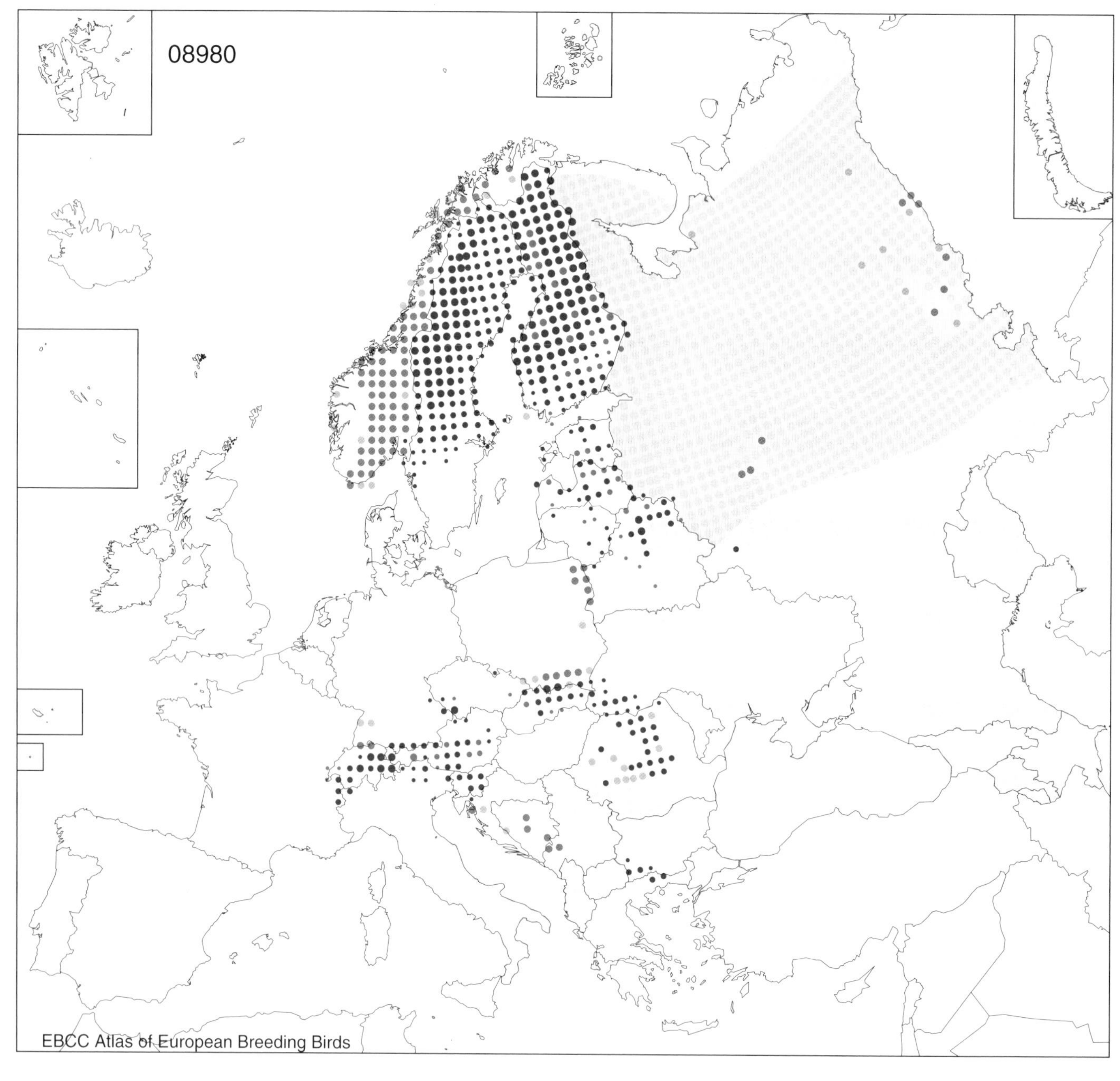

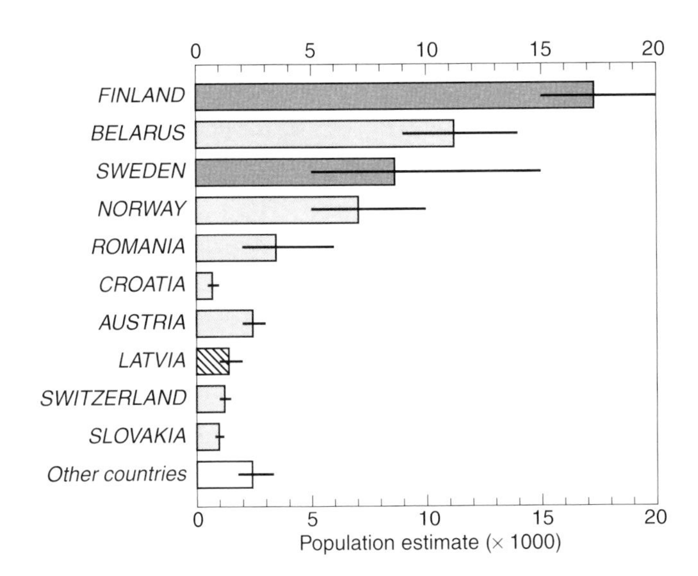

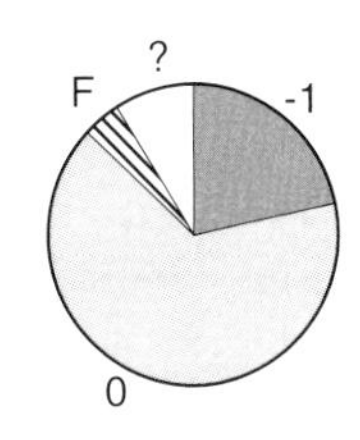

% in top 10 countries: 95.8
Total number of populated European countries: 23
Total European population 51,373–65,344 (56,915)
Russian population 10,000–100,000 (31,623)

The Three-toed Woodpecker, a conspicuous element of the taiga avifauna, has a circumpolar distribution. Several rather isolated breeding populations occur in southern mountain forests. It occupies the boreal coniferous forests of Europe, Asia and North America, northern Europe holding the nominate *P.t. tridactylus*, which occurs in Scandinavia, Finland, up to NE Poland (the Polish–Russian lowlands, Białowicza) and from the northern timberline to the Urals. The darker, more strongly marked *alpinus* inhabits C and southern Europe. Authorities variously recognize 7–9 other subspecies worldwide.

The Three-toed Woodpecker's distribution corresponds largely with that of Norway spruce *Picea abies* and certainly that of the genus *Picea*. It breeds in pine *Pinus* and spruce-dominated forests, and also in larch *Larix* and stone pine *P. cembra* forests. In low-lying areas it inhabits fir–beech *Abies–Fagus* forests and N of the taiga the birch *Betula* forest zone, which contains a high proportion of dead wood.

P.t. alpinus seems more restricted to spruce, most known breeding pairs occurring in generally sparse spruce or spruce–stone pine forest and those in the Black Forest in spruce–fir forest. The protected whip moss–spruce (*Bazzanio–Piceetum*) forests and the berrybush–spruce (*Vaccinio–Piceetum*) forests are particularly important. Although *alpinus*' distribution is biased strongly towards the alpine areas of Switzerland, Germany, Austria, Poland and Slovakia, generally it is not limited by altitude, rather to suitable forest types. Hence it is absent from the dry southern valleys of Graubünden, Switzerland but present in the higher Polish Beskiden Massif, the Bohemian, Bavarian (Scherzinger 1982), Bregenz, Adelegg and Black Forests. However, in alpine regions the species occurs mostly above 1000m asl, the majority between 1400 and 1500m asl (Hess 1983).

Population density depends strongly on forest structure. High densities are found in the Bavarian Forest in almost natural pure spruce stands; 1 bp/59–89ha (Scherzinger 1982). In favoured areas of inner Switzerland, the density was 1 bp/108ha (overall 1 bp/42–200ha; *HVM*), in the eastern Austrian Alps (for 5bp found) 1 bp/228ha (Ruge & Weber 1974), in the Engadine (E Switzerland) a pair occupied 20ha from May to July, but year-round the same pair required >100ha of spruce–stone pine forest (Bürkli *et al* 1975).

The Three-toed Woodpecker's population history is largely unknown. Modern forestry's practice of removing old and dead trees caused a decline in Finland (Väisänen *et al* 1986) and Sweden. Probably, clearfelling in the Dinaric Alps diminished numbers there (*HVM*). However, the species has colonized vigorously older spruce afforestations, which replaced old natural montane mixed forests, such that densities now are higher than for the Great Spotted Woodpecker *Dendrocopos major*, a circumstance applying also in Berchtesgaden district (Pechacek, pers comm).

The species became extinct in the Black Forest in 1924, but recolonized from 1982 onwards (first breeding proved 1990) to reach *c*15–20bp (1994), an event probably related to forest die-back caused by pollution emissions. This process leads, at least temporarily, to an increasing supply of favourite Three-toed Woodpecker food; longhorn *Cerambycidae* (especially the larvae) and bark *Scolytidae* beetles. Such forests may also be attractive because the canopy becomes more open; the earlier disappearance of forest pasture and subsequent planting of dense tree-stands may have driven away the species originally. In many areas, these processes may explain the species' isolated distribution which, when mapped, often resembles pearls on a string (Scherzinger 1982). Although obviously in expansion, the species is not yet established in the Fichtelgebirge, Erzgebirge or the Vosges Mountains, despite apparently ample habitat. A small population was detected in the Swiss Jura in 1993 (Chabloz & Wegmüller 1994).

Further research is required to establish whether the species' expansion tendency continues. Overall, it is not threatened at present.

Klaus Ruge (D)

Chersophilus duponti

Dupont's Lark

CZ	Skřivan Dupontův	I	Allodola del Dupont
D	Dupont lerche	NL	Duponts Leeuwerik
E	Alondra de Dupont	P	Calhandra de Dupont
F	Sirli de Dupont	PL	Skowronek sierpodzioby
FIN	Kaitanokkakiuru	R	Толстоклювый жаворонок
G	Χερσόφιλος	S	Dupontlärka
H	Vékonycsőrű pacsirta		

SPEC Cat 3, Threat status V

The scarce and elusive Dupont's Lark has a very restricted distribution, breeding only in a few countries round the Mediterranean. Populations are scattered from Morocco and Algeria to Egypt, but in Europe it now breeds only in Spain. Around 1887, it might have been a scarce and occasional breeder in Portugal (Irby 1895).

The Spanish distribution is concentrated in certain C and NE regions (the 'páramos' and the Ebro Valley, respectively), which hold *c*95% of the total of 13 000 birds (Garza & Suárez 1990). The remainder is patchily distributed in isolated zones in the SE and N. This scattered pattern, also detected locally within the main populations, results from its choice of breeding habitat, shrub-steppes on flat terrain. Unlike some other larks, Dupont's Lark will

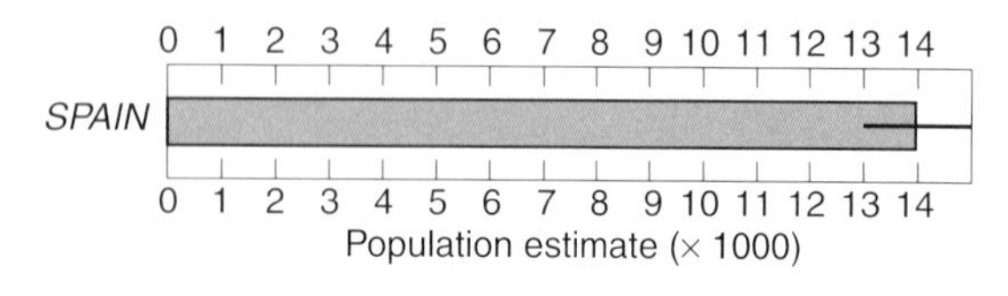

% in top 10 countries: 100.0
Total number of populated European countries: 1
Total European population 13,000–15,000 (13,964)

not occupy land totally converted to arable use. Typical habitat comprises low and dispersed scrub, averaging 20–-40cm high, with limited grass cover and a high proportion of bare ground (Tellería *et al* 1988a, Garza & Suárez 1990). Altitude or climate are less important, as suggested by it breeding from sea level up to 1600m, not only in semi-deserts and warm habitats, but also in colder areas subject to greater rainfall. Contrary to common belief, most of the Spanish population occupies cooler regions at 1000m asl.

Breeding density of Dupont's Lark is between 0.2 and 5.7 birds/10ha (Tellería *et al* 1988b, Garza & Suárez 1990), usually being highest in the breeding range core and lowest

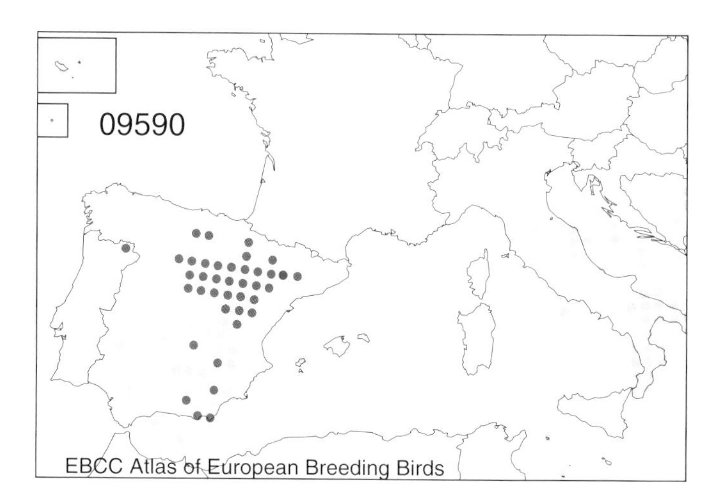

in isolated populations. Although density appears lower almost everywhere in winter, this is probably a more function of detectability than a real decrease. Nevertheless, some birds may leave the breeding grounds in severe winters (Garza & Suárez 1989).

A general trend can be discerned from changes in habitat. Dupont's Lark probably had an even patchier distribution and perhaps a lower population in the 1940s and 1950s, when much of its current breeding range was under cultivation. Subsequent population trends have differed between regions. As the area of arable land in the Ebro Valley has increased, the species' population has gradually decreased, whereas the inland 'páramos' population has increased and expanded over abandoned previously cultivated fields subject to shrub-steppe encroachment. It has recently colonized some new areas, but other isolated populations have disappeared simultaneously. Dupont's Lark is currently in decline, because the amount of arable land in the 'páramos' is increasing again, a trend set to continue.

Vicente Garza (E)

Melanocorypha calandra – continued

The species' range and population size are apparently decreasing throughout most of its range, phenomena seemingly related mainly to land-use changes such as agricultural intensification and reafforestation, although further data are needed urgently to understand these trends fully.

Mario Díaz Esteban (E)

Melanocorypha calandra

Calandra Lark

CZ	Kalandra zpěvná	I	Calandra
D	Kalanderlerche	NL	Kalanderleeuwerik
E	Calandria	P	Calhandra-comum
F	Alouette calandre	PL	Kalandra szara
FIN	Arokiuru	R	Степной жаворонок
G	Γαλιάντρα	S	Kalanderlärka
H	Kalandrapacsirta		

SPEC Cat 3, Threat status D (P)

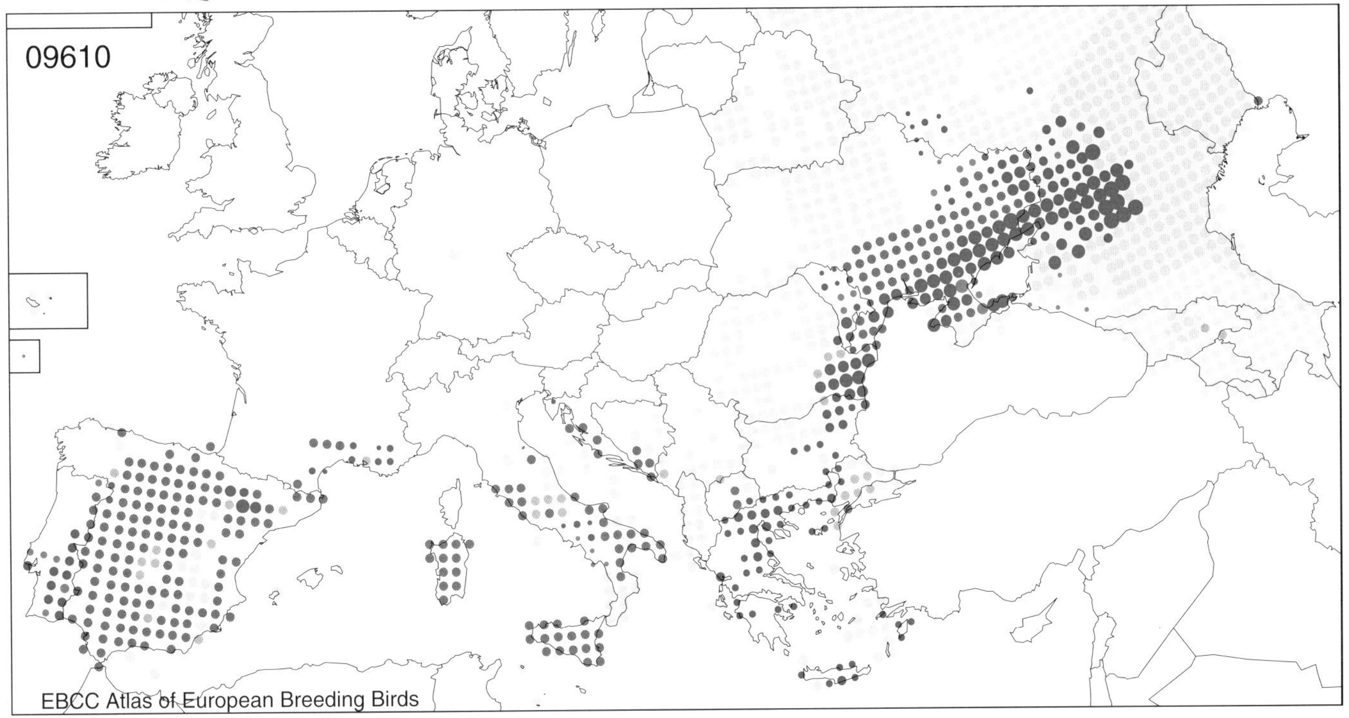

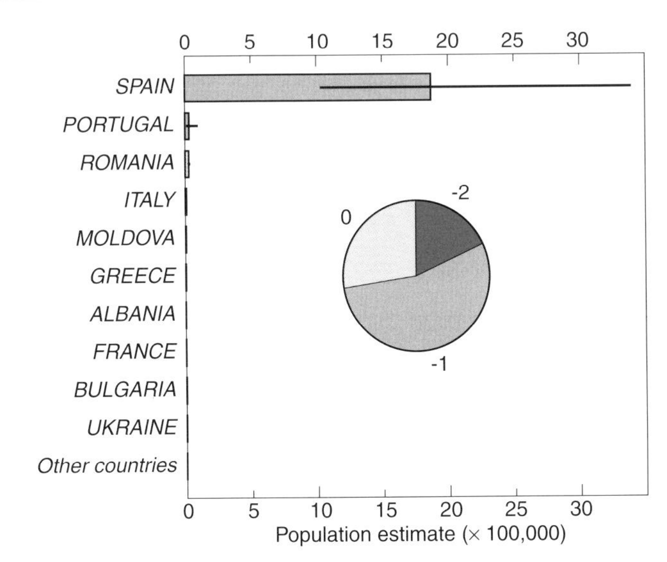

% in top 10 countries: 100.0
Total number of populated European countries: 11
Total European population 1,109,490–3,481,409 (1,951,182)
Russian population 1,000,000–10,000,000 (3,162,278)
Turkish population 100,000–1,000,000 (316,228)

The large, little-studied Calandra Lark is distributed around the Mediterranean basin, including Sardinia, Sicily and Crete, and eastwards to the steppes of C Asia. Most of the European population breeds in Russia and Iberia, minor but sizeable populations occurring elsewhere in S and SE Europe.

It occupies open lowland plains and upland plateaux (up to 1600m asl in Spain; Peris & Carnero 1988), tending to avoid coastal areas (de Juana *et al* 1988). It prefers to breed on grasslands, ranging from virgin steppe to cereal cultivation. In its NE European range sometimes it breeds in scrubby areas, whereas in the W and S it is found mainly in open habitats. In Spanish patchy cereal cropland it prefers growing cereal fields to grassland and low scrub (Tellería *et al* 1988a). The highest densities occur in saline steppes in the Spanish Ebro Valley (20–25 birds/10ha; Hernández & Pela 1987).

Southwestern and southern populations (the nominate subspecies *M.c. calandra* of Europe and *hebraica* of the Near East) appear to be mainly resident, whereas northeastern populations (*psammochroa* southwards from southern Russia) migrate S in winter. However, components of the western European population probably also perform migratory movements: in Spain winter densities decrease in the breeding areas without concomitant changes in habitat preferences nor latitudinal distribution shifts (J.L. Tellería, unpubl); some spring and autumn passage occurs through Gibraltar (Tellería 1981, Finlayson 1992) and Malta; the species appears in winter in the southern Algerian Atlas (Heim de Balsac & Mayaud 1962); and some Mediterranean islands (such as Sardinia) are occupied only during the breeding season.

(continued opposite)

Melanocorypha leucoptera

White-winged Lark

CZ	Kalandra bělokřídlá	I	Calandra siberiana
D	Weißflügellerche	NL	Witvleugelleeuwerik
E	Calandria Aliblanca	P	Calhandra-d'asa-branca
F	Alouette leucoptère	PL	Kalandra białoskrzydła
FIN	Valkosiipikiuru	R	Белокрылый жаворонок
G	Λευκόφτερη Γαλιάντρα	S	Vitvingad lärka
H	Szibériai pacsirta		

*SPEC Cat 4*W, Threat status S (P)*

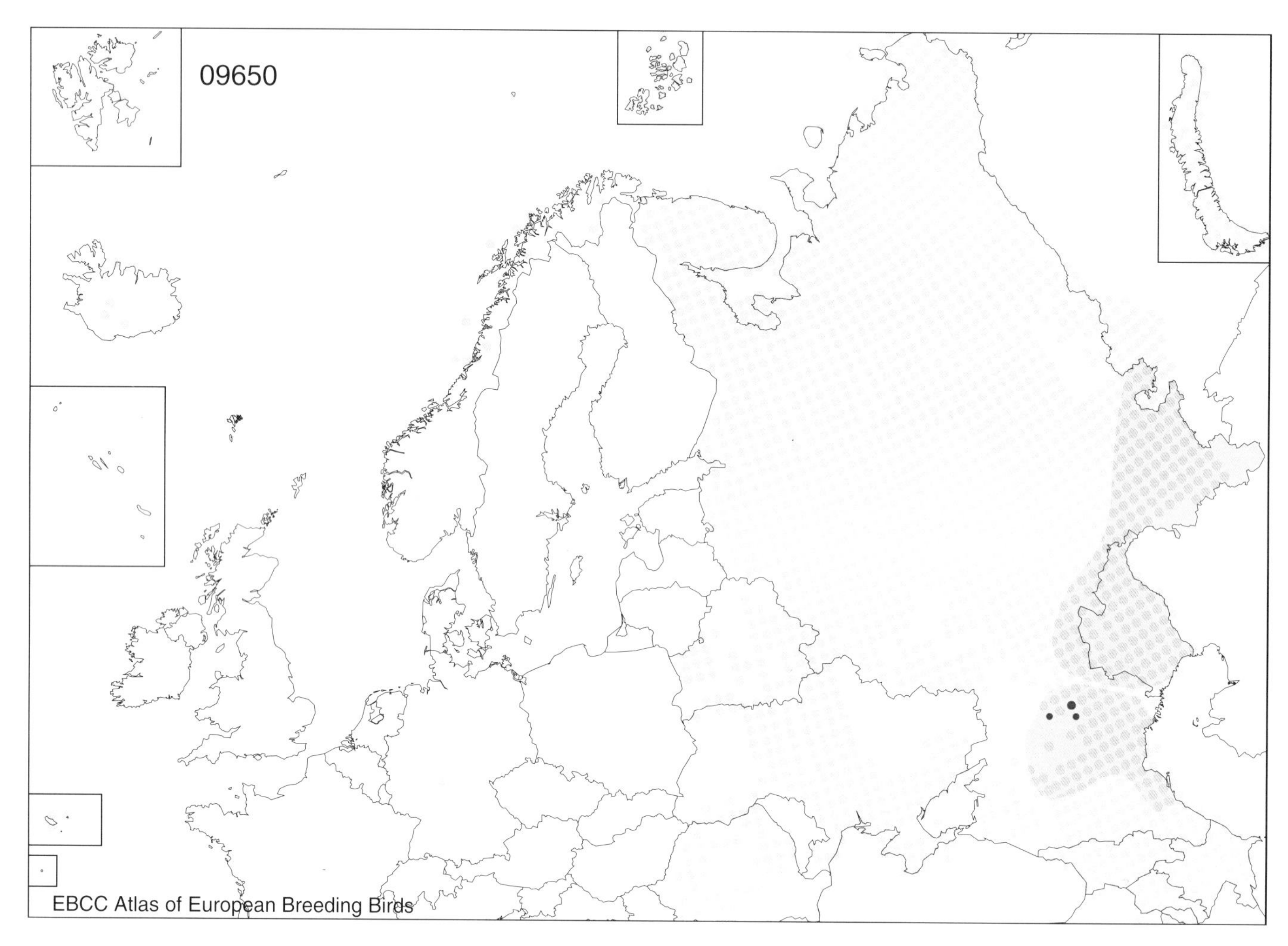

The White-winged Lark, an inhabitant of the temperate zone, has a world distribution which is limited to the C Palearctic. It breeds between the July 22°C and 25°C isotherms. Both it and the closely related Black Lark *M. yeltoniensis* breed in the Lower Volga area and in Kazakhstan, though the White-winged Lark's range extends further S into the C Caucasus. Both species breed in high salinity terrain (solonchaks) and wormwood *Artemisia* and feather-grass *Stipa* steppe, though the White-winged Lark usually tolerates aridity rather better than the Black Lark, often occupying patches of bare earth (C. Harrison 1982, V.E. Flint *et al* 1984).

Few population data exist but a crude estimate of 10 000–100 000bp has been made for European Russia. The species is not common anywhere within its range. Shishkin (1976) found that the White-winged Lark, along with several other lark species, had declined in the region between the Volga and Ural Rivers. Generally its range has decreased since the 1920s as a result of ploughing up the steppes and the creation of shelter-belts (*BWP*). The former destroyed much habitat, and the latter aided the spread of corvids which prey on the eggs and young of ground-nesting birds. Europe holds half the total world wintering population. The spread of agricultural intensification probably will cause the species to decrease further.

Both White-winged and Black Lark are short-distance migrants, autumn migration taking birds W and WSW, some reaching Romania (Dunn 1994). The White-winged Lark forms flocks in midsummer after breeding and migrates from mid-August to October. Return passage begins in March and southerly breeding areas are occupied from mid-April onwards (*BWP*).

Simon Gillings (GB) Philip Jackson (GB)

Galerida theklae

Thekla Lark

CZ	Chocholouš vavřínový	I	Cappellaccia di Tekla
D	Theklalerche	NL	Theklaleeuwerik
E	Cogujada Montesina	P	Cotovia-montesina
F	Cochevis de Thékla	PL	Dzierlatka iberyjska
FIN	Kivikkokiuru	R	Короткоклювый хохлатый жаворонок
G	Κατσουλιέρης της Θέκλας		
H	Kövi pacsirta	S	Lagerlärka

SPEC Cat 3, Threat status V

The world distribution of the Thekla Lark lies in two disjunct areas, the larger comprising Iberia, the Balearics, southern France, NW Africa and isolated groups in Libya, and the smaller in Somalia, Eritrea and Ethiopia. The nominate subspecies *G.t. theklae* is confined to Europe. At least 12 subspecies occur elsewhere in the distribution.

The Thekla Lark is eclectic in its choice of nesting habitat. It occupies steppe areas such as coastal dunes, stands of esparto grass or thyme, and even maquis, dehesas (open woodlands) and pine forests, on both flat and rugged land, although it tends to prefer slopes and higher altitudes than its closely related congener, the Crested Lark *G. cristata* where they overlap. It avoids dense coppices and large expanses of arable land.

The species is widely distributed on the Iberian Peninsula, from sea level to alpine areas, the further S the higher the altitude. In Andalucía it reaches 2200m asl in the Sierra Nevada (Pleguezuelos 1992). The highest known spring densities (*c*30 individuals/10ha), are reached in the arid southeastern steppes (Garza *et al* 1989).

There is no evidence of recent changes in its distribution. On a local scale, however, a decline in numbers has been detected in recent years, linked to changes in land management (Suárez *et al* 1993). This is the case in the Las Amoladeras Bird Reserve (Spain), where studies since the reserve was established have revealed density decreases of 25–80% in various reserve sections (Yanes *et al* in press). The small French population of 10–100bp is considered to be stable, although it has been little studied and has experienced severe winters (Prodon 1994).

The species is very sedentary and does not disperse far, although it may make altitudinal movements in winter, when it becomes somewhat gregarious, but never forms large flocks.

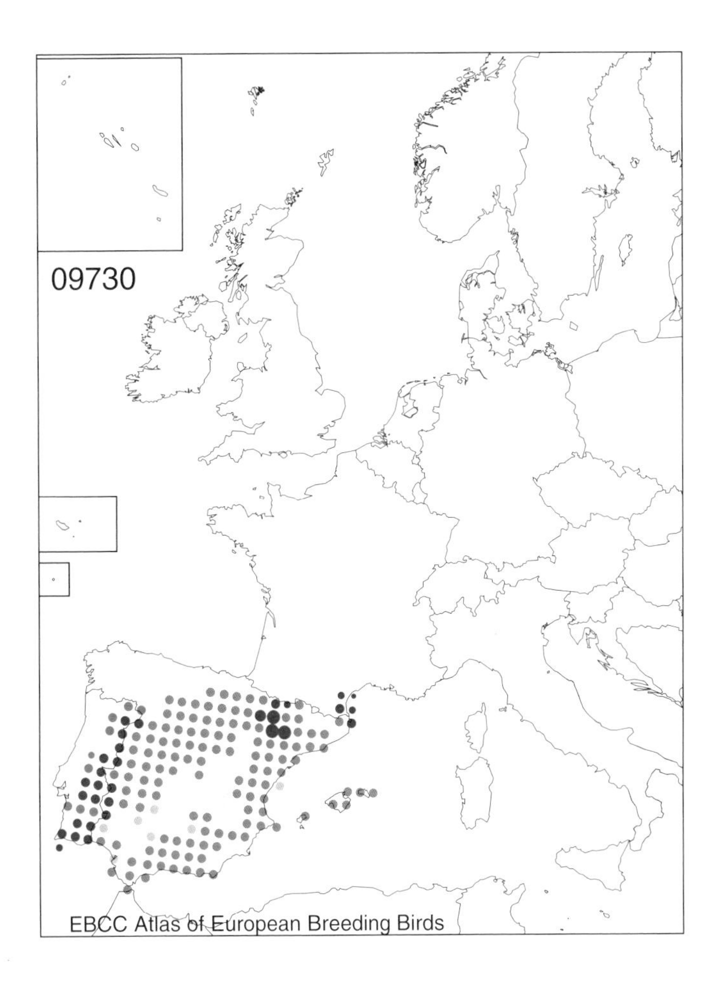

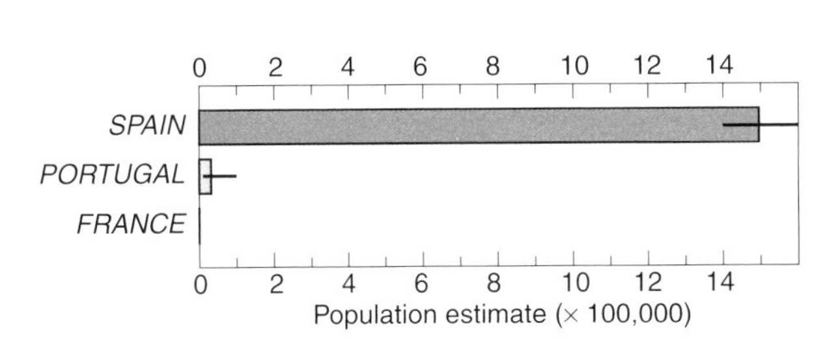

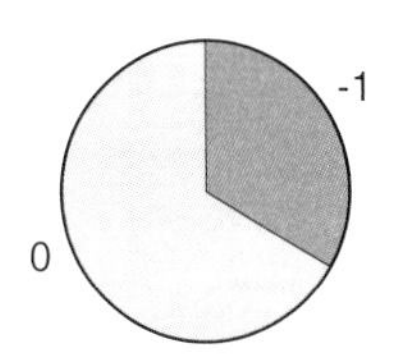

% in top 10 countries: 100.0
Total number of populated European countries: 3
Total European population 1,429,265–1,652,229 (1,528,317)

Juan Manrique (E) Miguel Yanes (E)

Galerida cristata Crested Lark

CZ Chocholouš obecný
D Haubenlerche
E Cogujada Común
F Cochevis huppé
FIN Töyhtökiuru
G Κατσουλιέρης
H Búbospacsirta
I Cappellaccia
NL Kuifleeuwerik
P Cotovia-de-poupa
PL Dzierlatka
R Хохлатый жаворонок
S Tofslärka

SPEC Cat 3, Threat status D (P)

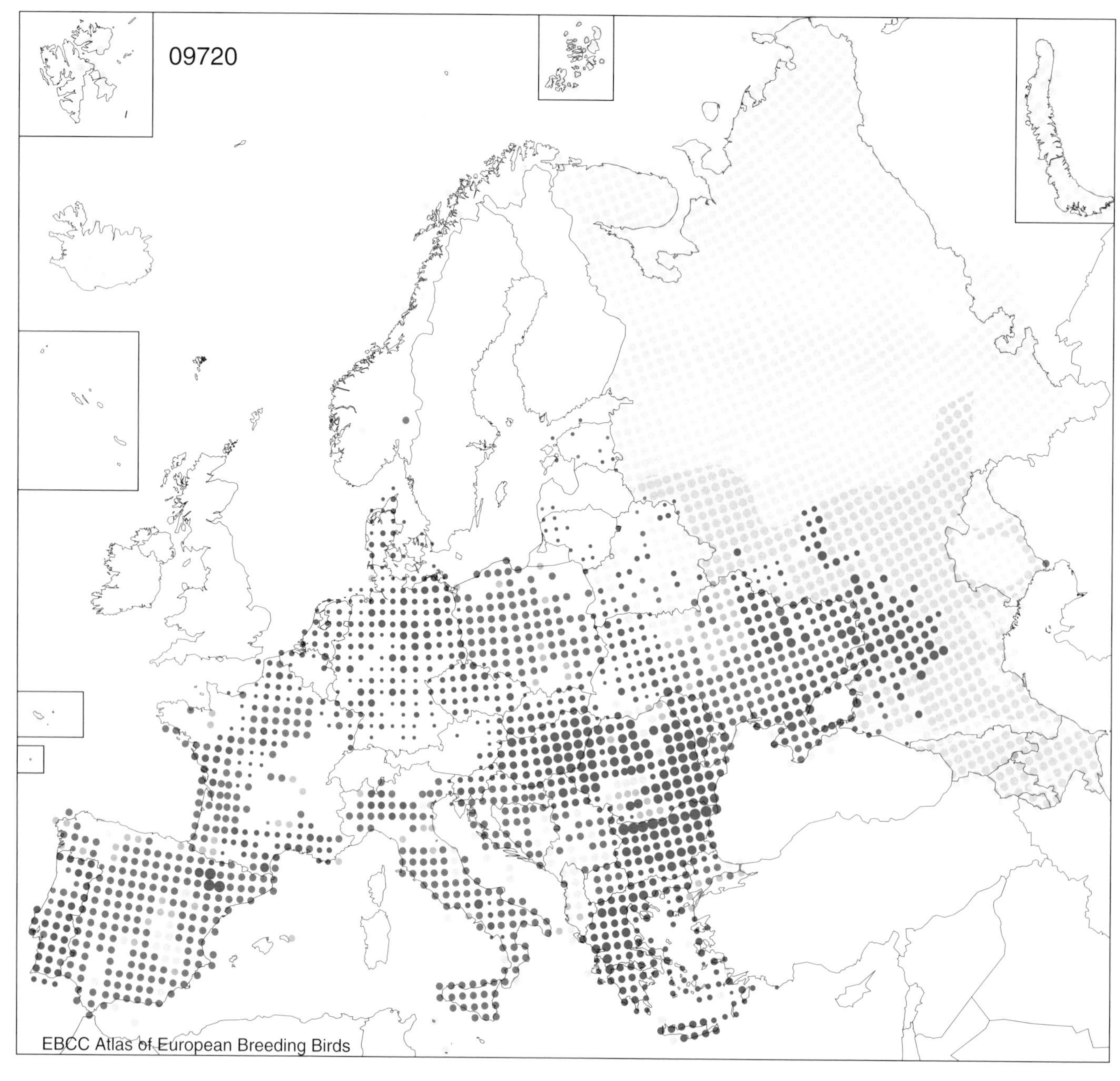

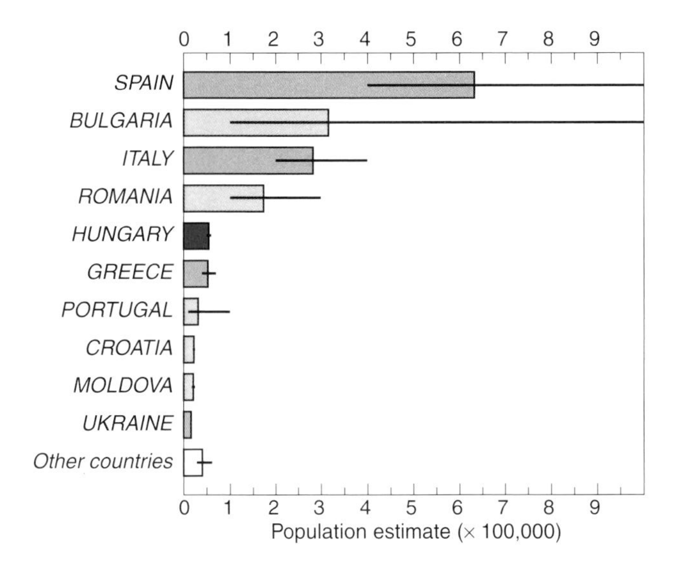

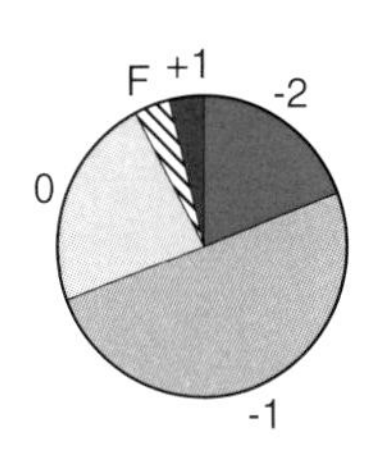

% in top 10 countries: 97.5
Total number of populated European countries: 26
Total European population 1,307,583–2,443,284 (1,644,809)
Russian population 100,000–1,000,000 (316,228)
Turkish population 1,000,000–10,000,000 (3,162,278)

The breeding range of the Crested Lark spans the southern Palearctic regions, and extends into the Afrotropical and Oriental regions. It occurs across much of Europe south of 58°N, exclusive of Britain, Ireland, large mountain ranges (Alps, Carpathians), NW France, extensively forested areas and the Balearics, Corsica and Sardinia. Generally it breeds below 600m asl. Of the *c*40 subspecies, perhaps 9 occur in the *Atlas*' coverage area.

A semi-desert species, the Crested Lark inhabits warm dry plains possessing only sparse low vegetation. It prefers steppes, barren areas, sand-dunes, arid pastures, low-intensity farmland and vineyards. It has adapted increasingly to rural, suburban and even urban habitats, and often may be seen on fallow land near villages, along roads, at railway stations, rubbish dumps, gravel-pits or even on grass between apartment blocks. The species has taken to nesting on the flat roofs of buildings in suburban areas.

Its present distribution is limited by its preference for drier climates and by the spread of modern agriculture, resulting in a marked SE-NW decreasing cline of abundance. It remains a common and familiar bird in the S and E, with >100 000bp each in Spain, Italy, Bulgaria, Romania and Russia. The distribution in E and C Europe is becoming increasingly patchy towards the N and NW, densities averaging considerably lower than in prime southern habitats. Low numbers in localized patches are characteristic over much of western Europe and in the Baltic; Estonia, Lithuania and Latvia each have fewer than 100bp.

Except in Spain, Italy and Greece, where slight decreases since the mid-1970s have occurred following large-scale agricultural changes, populations seem stable in prime habitats in its southern European range. However, further N, its last known breeding in Norway was in the 1970s (Hagen 1994), only 3bp remained by 1989 in S Sweden, and in the late 1980s it had become extinct in Switzerland. In Austria the population has retreated to lowland areas within the July 20°C isotherm (Dvorak *et al* 1993), only 150–200bp remaining in the 1980s. The Dutch population declined from >3000–5000bp in 1973–77 to 1000–2000bp in 1985–86, then crashed to only 400–450bp in 1991; the species had been widespread on sandy soil and in urban areas in the 1970s, but by the 1980s its range had contracted by some 75% (Hustings *et al* 1992). Similar declines have occurred all over W, C and E Europe, usually including range contractions of 20–50%. The anomalous slight increase in Hungarian numbers merits further investigation, but apparently it remains widespread near human settlements and in rural, cattle-grazing areas.

From the mid-19th century onwards, the Crested Lark underwent a marked range expansion, apparently supported by its ability to spread quickly along the newly constructed road and rail networks in W and C Europe. It reached its peak in the early 1900s, when S Fennoscandia became patchily colonized. From the 1930s onwards it began to decline, especially in the N. The declining trends (numbers and range) remain evident, even at its S European range core, where further deterioration is forecast (Tellería *et al* 1995). Undoubtedly, such large-scale changes have a climatic undertone, but the exact relationships remain to be unravelled. Whatever the initial causes, agricultural intensification has accelerated the pace of decline in reducing livestock grazing on drier pastures and developing former fallow land. Although urbanization initially favoured the species through creation of unsurfaced sites, modern increasingly dense conurbations are unattractive to this former steppe species.

Breeding densities in suburban and urban habitats mostly range from 0.4 to 3 bp/10ha (Varadinov & Nankinov 1978, Dvorak *et al* 1993, *HVM*). In open agricultural land densities mostly are lower at 0.1–0.6 bp/10ha (Varadinov & Nankinov 1978, Šťastny *et al* 1987, Dyrcz *et al* 1991). The Crested Lark is usually sedentary, but some move to S Europe in winter.

Igor Gorbán (UKR) Andreas Ranner (A)

This species account is sponsored by Dr Achim Neuheuser, Bonn, D.

Calandrella brachydactyla

Short-toed Lark

CZ	Skřivánek krátkoprstý	I	Calandrella
D	Kurzzehenlerche	NL	Kortteenleeuwerik
E	Terrera Común	P	Calhandrinha-comum
F	Alouette calandrelle	PL	Skowrończyk krótkopalcowy
FIN	Lyhytvarvaskiuru	R	Малый жаворонок
G	Μικρογαλιάντρα	S	Korttålärka
H	Szikipacsirta		

SPEC Cat 3, Threat status V

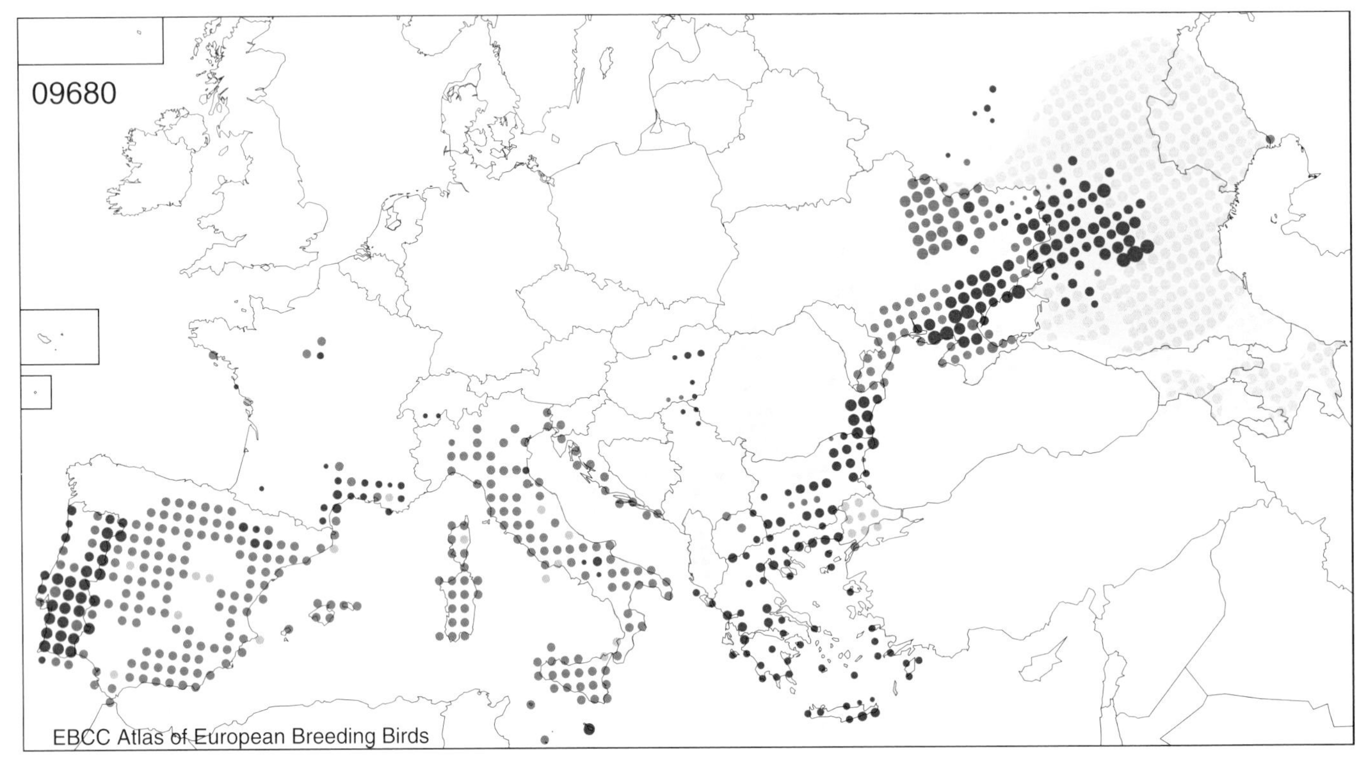

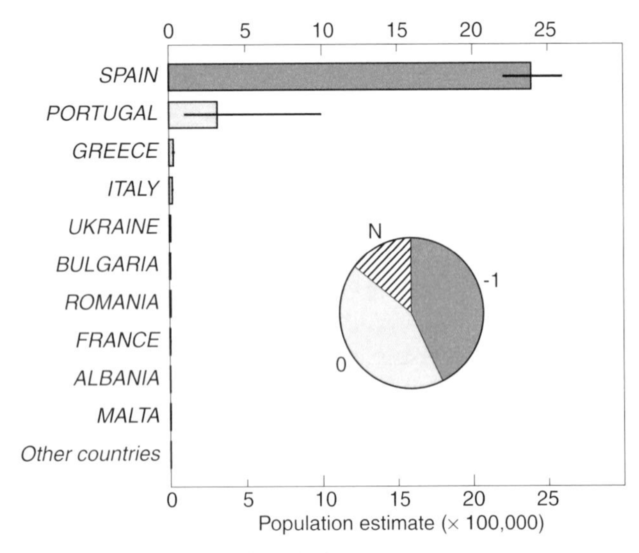

% in top 10 countries: 100.0
Total number of populated European countries: 14
Total European population 2,499,727–3,503,889 (2,788,879)
Russian population 100,000–1,000,000 (316,228)
Turkish population 10,000–100,000 (31,623)

The Short-toed Lark has an extensive range throughout the S Palearctic, from Portugal and Morocco to C China, in arid grasslands of steppe and semi-desert zones. It breeds mostly on plains; also on plateaux or gently sloping hills. It prefers dry grasslands, alkali flats scattered with herbs, abandoned farmland, fallows, dunes or sandy shores with low vegetation, salt steppes and arid agricultural fields with low crops. Such habitats and (except in C France; Olioso 1994) the 20°C July isotherm determine the distribution of the species.

The species' spread in Europe was favoured by the expansion of low-intensity farming and pastures, and then by the land degradation which followed in the plains and low hills. Agricultural intensification bringing marginal land into production has caused local range contractions.

The species is most numerous in the Iberian (*c*85% of the European population), Italian and Balkan Peninsulas. Since 1975, numbers have decreased and ranges contracted in Spain, France and Ukraine by at least 20%. *C.b. hungarica* occurs in Hungary and Vojvodina in low numbers, *rubiginosa* in Malta (2000–3000bp) and *brachydactyla* elsewhere in Europe.

The Short-toed Lark is migratory. European populations winter in Africa between 10° and 20°N, and Asian populations in the N of the Indian subcontinent.

Juan Manrique (E) Dan Munteanu (ROM)

Calandrella rufescens

Lesser Short-toed Lark

CZ	Skřivánek menší	NL	Kleine Kortteenleeuwerik
D	Stummellerche	P	Calhandrinha-das-marismas
E	Terrera Marismeña	PL	Skowrończyk mały
F	Alouette pispolette	R	Серый жаворонок
FIN	Pikkukiuru	S	Dvärglärka
G	Ρηγογαλιάντρα		
H	Vörhenyes pacsirta		
I	Pispoletta		

SPEC Cat 3, Threat status V

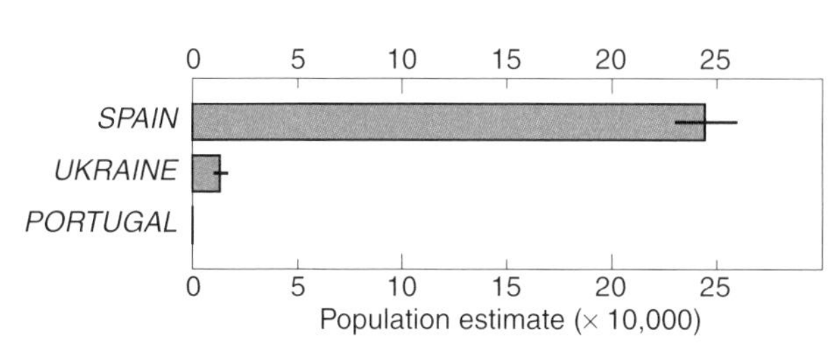

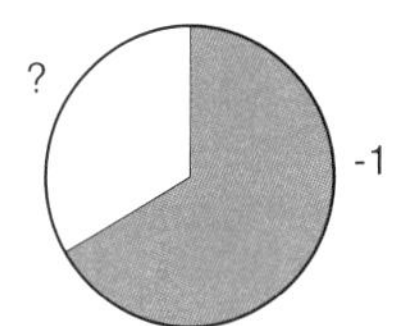

% in top 10 countries: 100.0
Total number of populated European countries: 3
Total European population 242,756–273,570 (257,610)
Russian population 100,000–1,000,000 (316,228)
Turkish population 10,000–100,000 (31,623)

The Lesser Short-toed Lark has a broad distribution within the Palearctic region, breeding in the Canary Islands, North Africa, Iberia, the Levant, Turkey, Saudi Arabia, Iran, Iraq and the Sea of Azov and Caspian region E to Korea and Mongolia. In Europe, its distribution is disjunct, western populations inhabiting peninsular Spain and the Portuguese Algarve, and eastern groups occupying Ukraine, Russia and the Caucasus. Throughout its range, it occupies steppe-type habitats such as coastal dunes, salt-flats, grasslands and low shrub-steppes. It generally avoids croplands.

On the Iberian Peninsula, it is distributed mainly in the coastal Mediterranean provinces, penetrating inland only along the Ebro River valley and very occasionally to other areas. During 1970–90, slight range contractions and numerical declines were recorded in the Canary Islands (Martín 1987), the Iberian Peninsula (Yanes 1994) and probably in Ukraine.

The most important nuclei of the Lesser Short-toed Lark populations are in Russia and the Iberian Peninsula, which together hold *c*90% of the European population (*c*600 000bp). Quantitative information is lacking from the former area, while in the latter it can reach densities of 25–50 birds/10ha in favourable zones (Garza *et al* 1989, Sánchez 1991). It is extremely rare, however, in large parts of its range, and suffers considerable local variations in abundance, probably linked to habitat quality.

The Iberian population is sedentary, although in the post-nuptial period it groups into medium-sized flocks that move erratically in the most favourable zones. The eastern populations behave similarly, although they can abandon completely large parts of Russia in winter.

The Lesser Short-toed Lark is polytypic. Three subspecies occur in the *Atlas*' coverage area; *C.r. apetzii* in Iberia, *heinei* from NE Romania E to the northern Caucasus and *pseudobatica* in the southern Caucasus. Many other subspecies occur elsewhere in the distribution area.

Juan Manrique (E) Miguel Yanes (E)

Lullula arborea

Woodlark

CZ	Skřivan lesní	**I**	Tottavilla
D	Heidelerche	**NL**	Boomleeuwerik
E	Totovía	**P**	Cotovia-pequena
F	Alouette lulu	**PL**	Lerka
FIN	Kangaskiuru	**R**	Юла (Лесной жаворонок)
G	Δενδροσταρήθρα	**S**	Trädlärka
H	Erdei pacsirta		

SPEC Cat 2, Threat status V

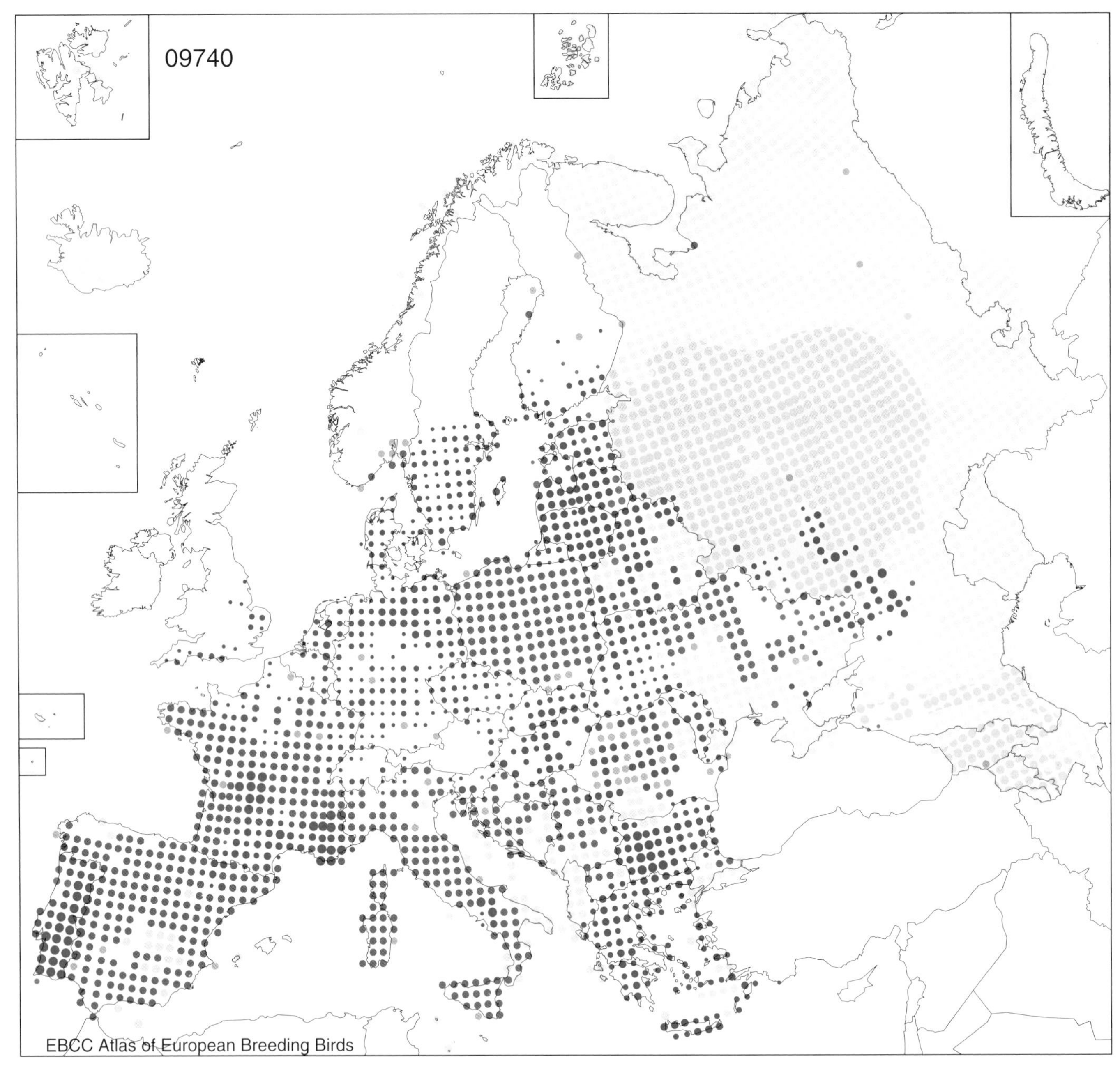

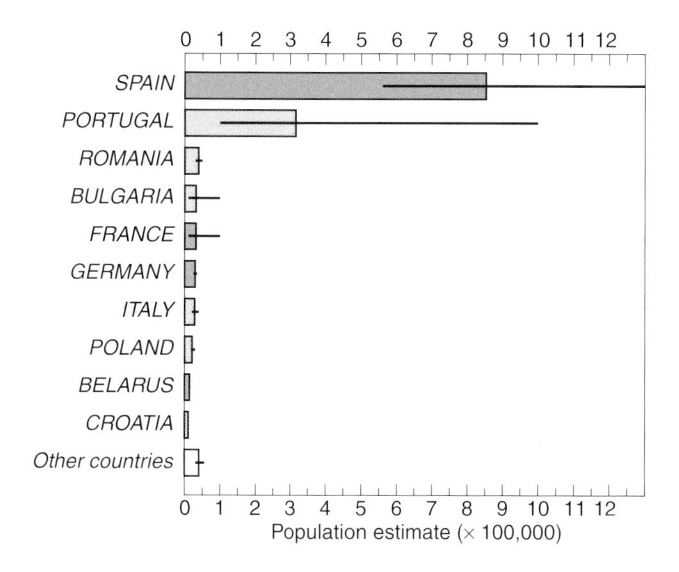

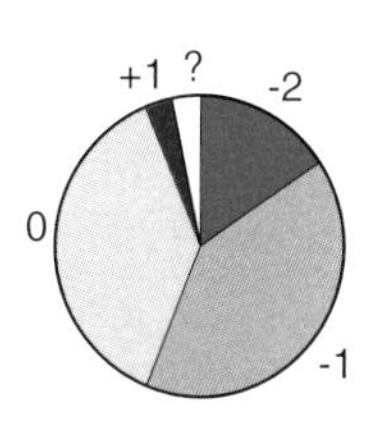

% in top 10 countries: 97.1
Total number of populated European countries: 32
Total European population 1,050,376–2,239,048 (1,416,296)
Russian population 10,000–100,000 (31,623)
Turkish population 10,000–100,000 (31,623)

The Woodlark, predominantly a European breeding bird, occurs mostly below 60°N, and elsewhere only in NW Africa, the Levant, Iran and S Turkmenistan. Breeding and wintering ranges overlap almost completely, northerly populations moving S mostly to mix with resident populations. The nominate *L.a. arborea* occupies most of Europe, *pallida* inhabiting S Spain, much of Italy, the Mediterranean islands, the southern Balkans, Crimea and the Caucasus.

The Woodlark prefers temperate and mediterranean rather than boreal and arid conditions. Its distribution is constrained by climate (warm summers and mild winters), both on a European scale and locally. It breeds in open, often unstable habitats which have a marked (micro-)relief, a sunny aspect and are sparsely vegetated. It requires scattered perches, and its feeding sites must have short-sward vegetation. Heaths, low-lying moors, open oak *Quercus* and pine *Pinus* woods and forestry plantations are prime habitats, the last-named only for 4–5 years after planting (Bowden & Hoblyn 1990).

Woodlark distribution is rather patchy, a pattern not fully apparent from the 50km resolution of the map. However, many gaps are visible along the Atlantic coast, in the German lowlands, mountainous C Europe (the Alps, Carpathians) and arid Spanish regions, where its absence is caused by climatically adverse conditions or unsuitable habitat.

Of the European population (0.9–3.0Mbp) some 75% breeds in Iberia, which possesses the optimum conditions of a mediterranean climate, widespread semi-natural habitats (dehesas, shrubland) and relict woodland interspersed with extensive cereal farming. The average Iberian breeding density of 6000 bp/50km square are exceptional. In E Europe and some Balkan areas whose landscape remains largely semi-natural and farming low-intensity, the Woodlark reaches 400–700 bp/50km square. Similar values occur locally over much of C and W Europe, but the scarcity of suitable habitats leads to lower overall densities.

Since the mid-1960s, the Woodlark has experienced marked population fluctuations through rapid changes in habitat availability and harsh weather conditions in its main wintering area in SW Europe (Bijlsma *et al* 1988). Long-term trend figures suggesting stable or declining European trends mask the species' vicissitudes from 1970 to 1990, as in England, where the population was probably much reduced in the 1960s, but increased throughout the 1970s into the early 1980s (Sitters 1986), and after some decline in the mid-1980s increased again after 1987 (Hoblyn 1992). Similar trends were recorded in Sweden, The Netherlands and locally in Germany, where, after the gales of November 1972 and April 1973 had devastated woodlands, the subsequent extensive forest clearing and restocking provided prime breeding conditions for a number of years (Südbeck 1981, Gustafsson & Wahlén 1985, Bijlsma *et al* 1988). Simultaneously, declines occurred in N Germany and locally in E Germany, mainly because of habitat destruction and encroachment of heaths (Gnielka 1985, Daunicht 1985). Three successive severe winters after 1985 depleted most European populations, but the Woodlark is a prolific breeder, conditions permitting, raising two and sometimes three broods annually (Virtanen 1991, R.G. Bijlsma, pers obs). Subsequent mild winters permitted populations in W, C and N Europe to proliferate in the late 1980s and early 1990s, examples being The Netherlands (850–1000bp in 1986, 3500bp in 1991; Bijlsma *et al* 1988, R.G. Bijlsma, unpubl) and England (*c*150% increase in Thetford Forest from the mid-1980s to 1992 (Hoblyn 1992). Such marked increases are curbed ultimately by habitat availability.

The Woodlark winters mainly in S Europe, especially in SW France and Iberia. British populations, once considered resident, may be partly migratory (Sitters 1986). Normally, the Woodlark is largely unaffected by severe winters because conditions in its wintering grounds remain relatively mild. Successive mild winters may induce W European populations to winter closer to their breeding areas, rendering them vulnerable in a severe winter.

Rob G Bijlsma (NL) Ron Hoblyn (GB)

Alauda arvensis Skylark

CZ	Skřivan polní	I	Allodola
D	Feldlerche	NL	Veldleeuwerik
E	Alondra Común	P	Laverca
F	Alouette des champs	PL	Skowronek
FIN	Kiuru	R	Полевой жаворонок
G	Σταρήθρα	S	Sånglärka
H	Mezei pacsirta		

SPEC Cat 3, Threat status V

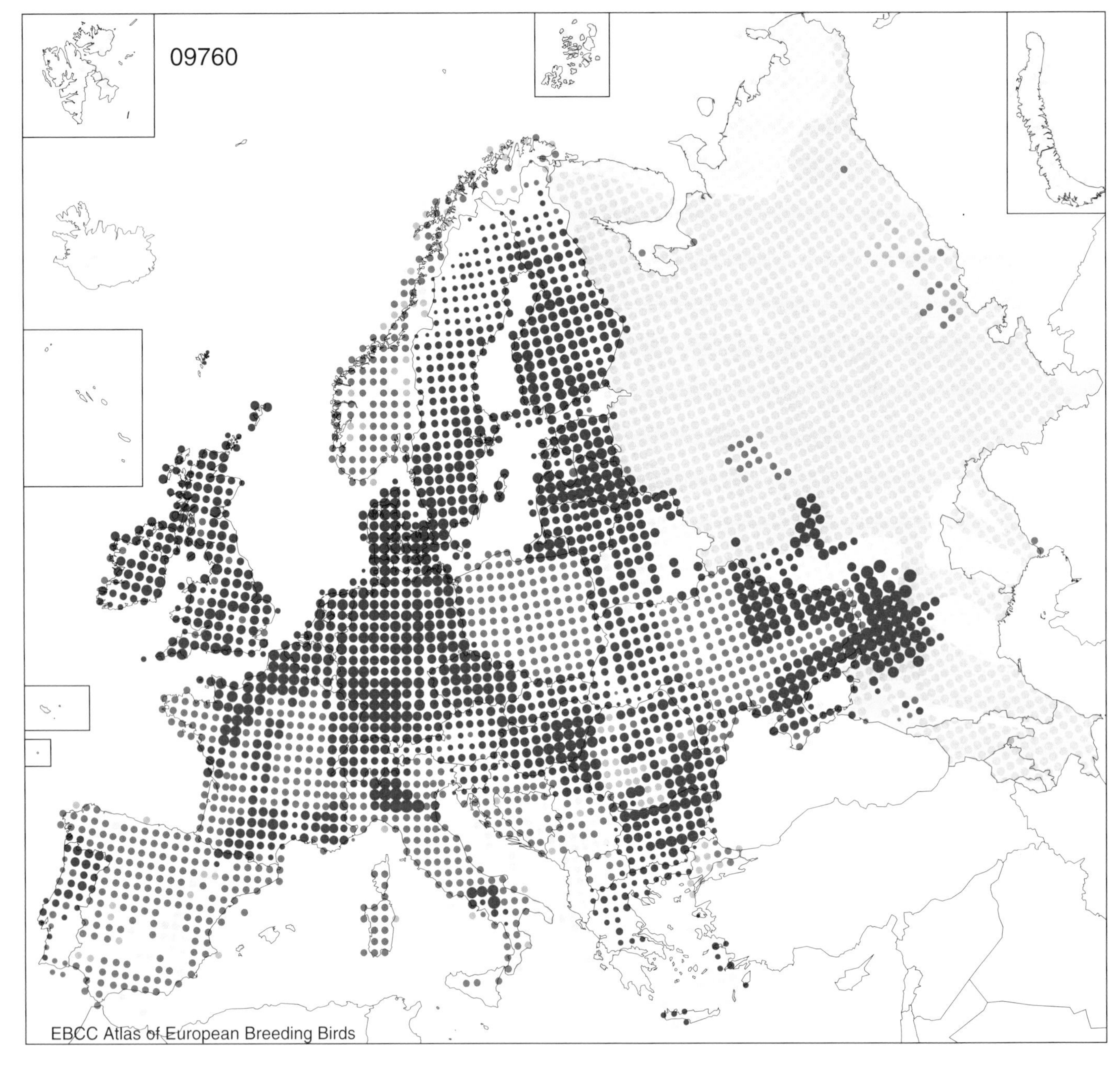

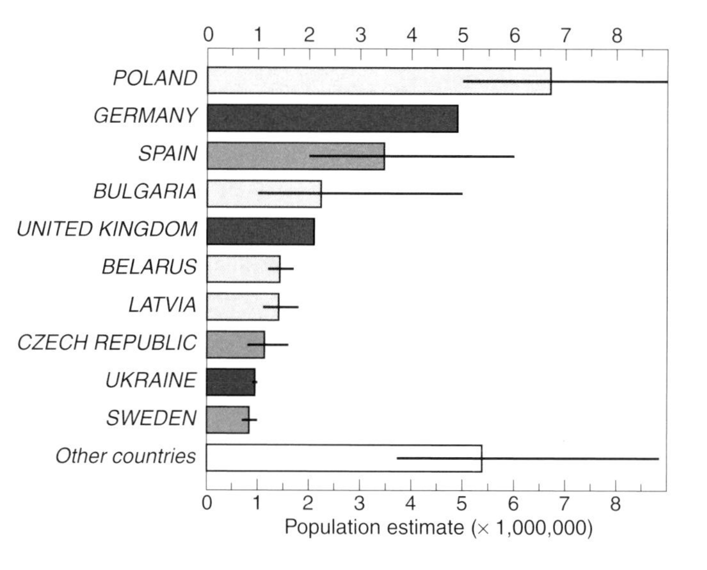

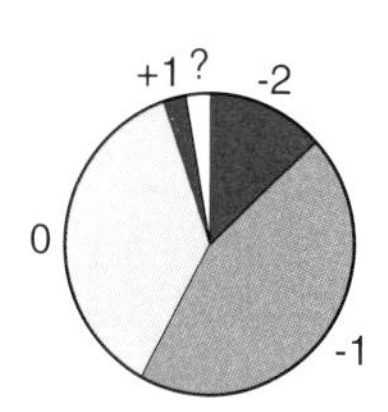

% in top 10 countries: 82.4
Total number of populated European countries: 38
Total European population 27,858,777–35,206,958 (30,542,570)
Russian population 1,000,000–10,000,000 (3,162,278)
Turkish population 50,000–500,000 (158,114)

The Skylark breeds throughout the Palearctic between *c*35° and 65°N both in the oceanic and continental climatic zones. It is absent only from Iceland. In Fennoscandia it avoids high altitudes and latitudes. Its southern distribution is patchy. Introduced populations are established in S Australia, Tasmania, New Zealand and Vancouver Island.

The Skylark nests on the surface of firm, partially vegetated soils, and will tolerate taller and denser plant cover (up to 50%; M. Jenny 1990a) than most other larks. It will occupy almost any open landscape, but at a local scale avoids the immediate vicinity of tall, vertical structures. Consequently, the Skylark occupies a wide variety of habitats including natural steppe grasslands, farmland, amenity grasslands, sand-dunes, saltmarsh, rough upland pasture, moorland, bog, tundra, heathland and forest clearings, a characteristic which makes it one of Europe's most widespread breeding species, occurring up to 2750m asl (Armenia) and avoiding only the arctic–alpine zone.

Population densities vary both with altitude and latitude, tending to be highest in high-latitude lowland areas and at high altitudes in the southern range. Densities exceed 10 000 bp/50km square from Britain & Ireland to Russia, Belarus and Bulgaria. Such high values probably are typical of extensive steppes and low-lying, largely agricultural countries. Towards the range limits, densities tend to decrease sharply, as in Fennoscandia, southern Iberia (whose population nevertheless is large), Italy and Greece. Alpine regions experience a similar pattern, but with increasing altitude.

The Skylark's wide distribution probably results from the natural steppe-grassland breeding range expanding into the great variety of open landscapes which provided suitable habitat following deforestation and agricultural development. Although evidence is lacking for any recent range changes, most European countries have experienced declining populations since the mid-1960s (Nordahl 1990). These changes may reflect reduced habitat diversity, nesting or foraging opportunities (Schläpfer 1988) and invertebrate and seed food resources (M. Jenny 1990a, Potts 1991), all because of progressive agricultural intensification. In Britain, lowland farmland populations declined by >54% from 1969 to 1991, reflecting a loss of >1.5Mbp (Fuller *et al* 1995). Similar declines occurred elsewhere, especially in Germany (locally 26–100%, mean 60%, in the 1970s and 1980s; Büsche 1989a) and The Netherlands (probably >75% in the 1960s to 1980s, still continuing; Osieck & Hustings 1994).

Local breeding densities vary greatly with habitat and landscape structure. Pre-decline values commonly reflected a minimum territory size of 0.5ha (Delius 1963), according well with larger-scale densities of 100–200 bp/km² in grassland and low-intensity farming (Klafs & Stübs 1977). Mean territory size in modern farmland varies between 2.0 and 8.3ha in Swiss lowlands (Schläpfer 1988, M. Jenny 1990b), probably representative of W and C Europe, where massive herbicide and pesticide use produces impoverished monocultures possessing limited arthropod numbers and diversity (M. Jenny 1990a).

The Skylark is totally migratory in N and E Europe, but generally makes no more than local movements in its southern range and in temperate W Europe. It largely vacates Scandinavia and continental regions N of 45°N and E of 15°E in winter, most birds moving S and W to winter in Britain, Ireland, the Low Countries, France, Iberia and perhaps North Africa. A large autumn passage S across the Strait of Gibraltar may include Iberian breeding birds. Elsewhere in Europe, the species is largely sedentary, populations being augmented by winter immigrants. In Britain, the Skylark leaves high-altitude areas in winter, but lowland populations probably make no more than local movements (Hardman 1974).

Six subspecies occur in Europe; the nominate *A.a. arvensis* (England, Wales; N Europe to the Urals); *scotica* (Ireland, Scotland, Faeroes); *guillelmi* (N Portugal, NW Spain); *sierrae* (C, S Portugal, S Spain); *cantarella* (Mediterranean seaboard; E Spain to the Black Sea) and *armenicus* (Caucasus). Perhaps eight subspecies occur elsewhere.

Jeremy Wilson (GB)

This species account is sponsored by David Bird, coordinator of the Arable Farmers' Conservation Group, Hants, GB.

Eremophila alpestris Shore Lark

CZ	Skřivan ouškatý	I	Allodola golagialla
D	Ohrenlerche	NL	Strandleeuwerik
E	Alondra Cornuda Lapona	P	Cotovia-cornuda
F	Alouette hausse-col	PL	Górniczek
FIN	Tunturikiuru	R	Рогатый жаворонок
G	Χιονάδα	S	Berglärka
H	Havasi fülespacsirta		

Non-SPEC, Threat status S (P)

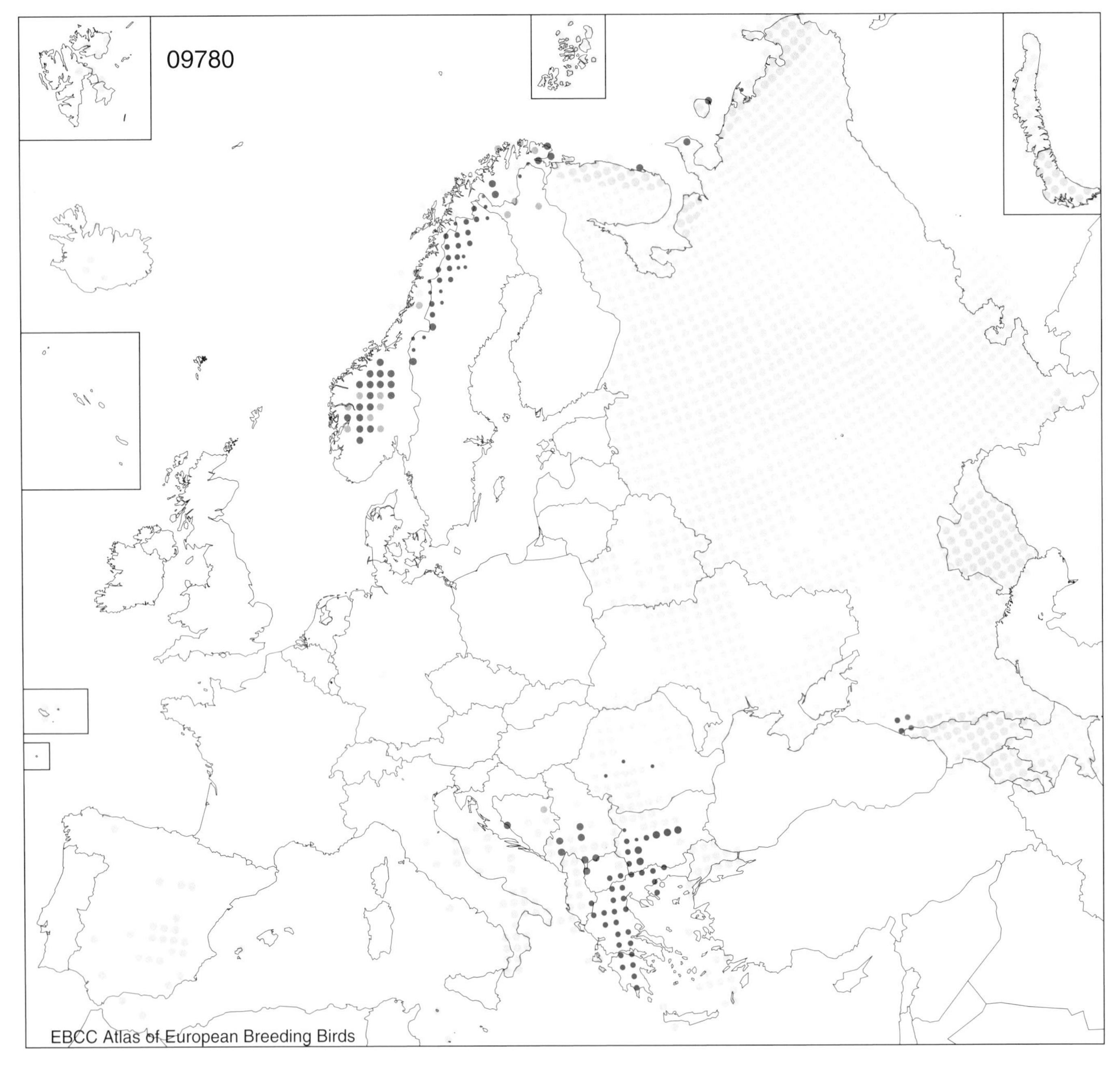

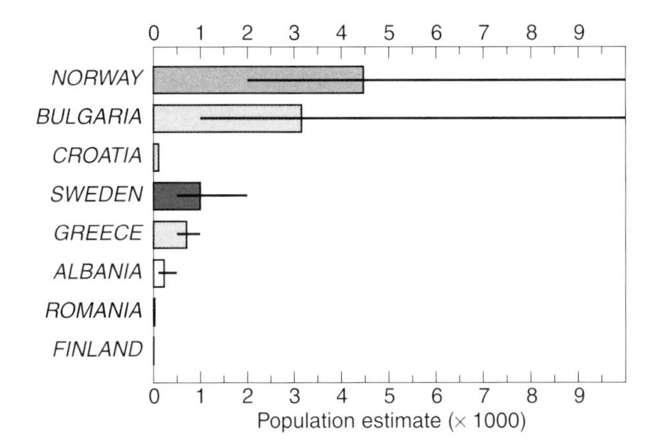

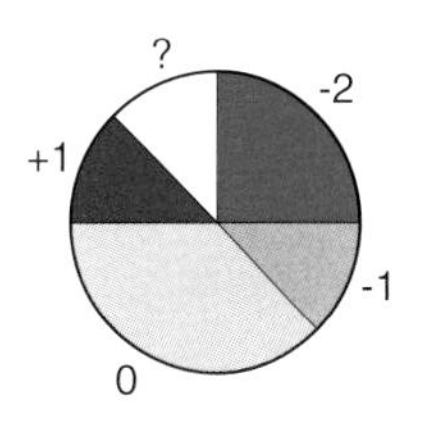

% in top 10 countries: 100.0
Total number of populated European countries: 8
Total European population 6371–18,561 (9702)
Russian population 100,000–1,000,000 (316,228)
Turkish population 10,000–100,000 (31,623)

The colourful Shore Lark is a widely distributed Holarctic species with a small Neotropic outpost in the Andes near Bogotá. In Eurasia the range is divided: subspecies *E.a. flava* breeds along the Arctic coast westwards from the Kolyma River and in the Fennoscandian mountains, *brandti* in the Volga steppes eastwards, *balcanica* mainly at high elevations in the S Carpathians, the Balkans (almost to the Adriatic coast) and Greece, and *penicillata* in Transcaucasia and the Caucasus. The isolated Moroccan population *atlasi*, although separated by habitat, is connected geographically to the more easterly subspecies through the lowland Temminck's Horned Lark *E. bilopha* of North Africa and Arabia, sometimes considered conspecific. There are several other Asian subspecies, and many in the Americas. In North America the Shore Lark (Horned Lark) breeds not only in the N and in mountains but also in grassland and prairies, possibly through lacking lark competitors.

Most Europeans know the Shore Lark as a wintering bird, when Scandinavian or Russian birds forage on farmland and seashores of W and C Europe respectively. The Carpathian population is migratory, but that of the Balkans is partly sedentary, making only short, vertical migrations. The Caucasus population is migratory and moves to the foothills and adjacent valleys in winter, assembling in flocks up to 100 strong (Molamusov 1967).

In Fennoscandia the Shore Lark is a rather recent immigrant, expanding its range rapidly during the 19th century, an expansion mirrored by increasing numbers on migration and at wintering sites. The population size apparently peaked around 1900, but particularly from 1950 onwards there has been a drastic decline, most pronounced in Finland (Hildén 1987), N Sweden (Svensson 1990a, Svensson & Berglund 1995) and N Norway, but less so in S Norway (Stueflotten 1994). Only a handful of pairs now remains in Finland, where thousands of pairs formerly bred, and (author's opinion, S. Svensson) it is unlikely that more than 1000bp remain in Sweden. The population in Norway is estimated at 2000–10 000bp (Stueflotten 1994). The cause of this decline is unknown, the only major habitat change in the Fennoscandian mountains being the elimination of the formerly characteristic thick lichen-cover by reindeer overgrazing. In N Russia and Siberia the Shore Lark prefers as breeding habitat dry lichen tundra on well-drained sandy and gravelly soils, a habitat particularly sensitive to reindeer grazing. The numbers wintering in W Europe have declined in parallel with those in the breeding areas.

However, data on C European wintering populations do not indicate similar declines in the more easterly breeding populations, but rather the contrary. A. Schmidt (1983) even reports an 'explosive' increase since 1950 in Brandenburg. The Balkan Peninsula population also appears to be increasing in numbers and expanding its range, a similar pattern emerging in Romania (D. Munteanu, pers obs) where breeding was first recorded in the Carpathians only in 1960. In the Caucasus high-alpine meadows the species is common, reaching 4.5–6.0 birds/km^2 (P. Til'ba, pers comm).

There are few ringing recoveries. A recent study of colour-ringed birds in southern Lapland produced seven recoveries from the Swedish W coast, southern Norway, Jutland, and Jersey (S. Svensson, pers obs). Birds on passage through, or which winter in, C and E Europe probably originate in N Russia. In the past in western Europe when birds were more abundant on passage or during winter, inland observations on farmland were much commoner. Their winter haunts essentially are restricted now to coastal areas. The virtual disappearance of winter stubbles through autumn sowing probably has created wintering habitats unsuited to the Shore Lark. Hence it is possible that the decline of the Fennoscandian population may also be related to changes in agricultural methods.

Dan Munteanu (ROM) Sören Svensson (S)

Riparia riparia — Sand Martin

CZ	Břehule říční	I	Topino
D	Uferschwalbe	NL	Oeverzwaluw
E	Avión Zapador	P	Andorinha-das-barreiras
F	Hirondelle de rivage	PL	Brzegówka
FIN	Törmäpääsky	R	Береговушка
G	Οχθοχελίδονο	S	Backsvala
H	Partifecske		

SPEC Cat 3, Threat status D

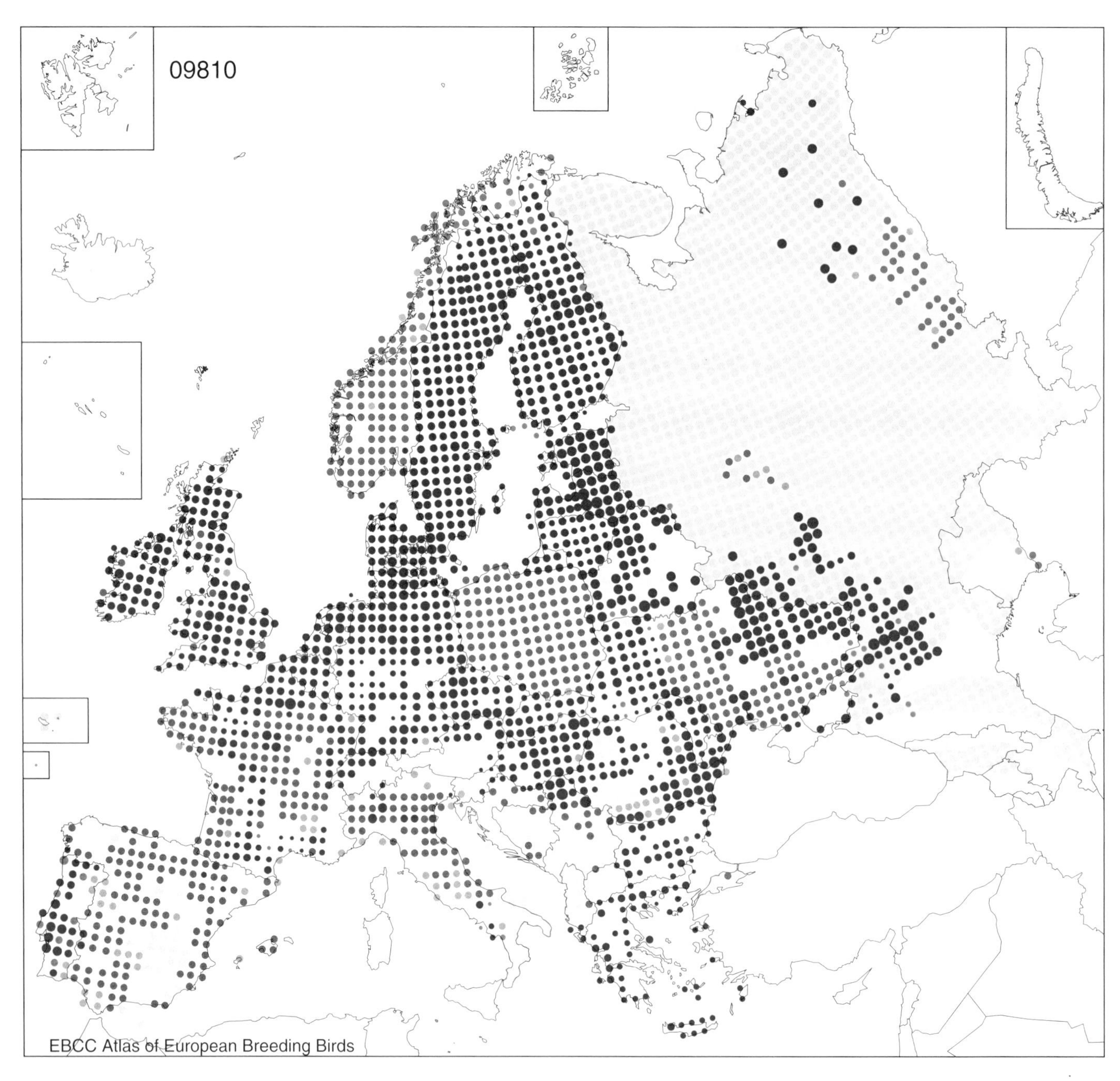

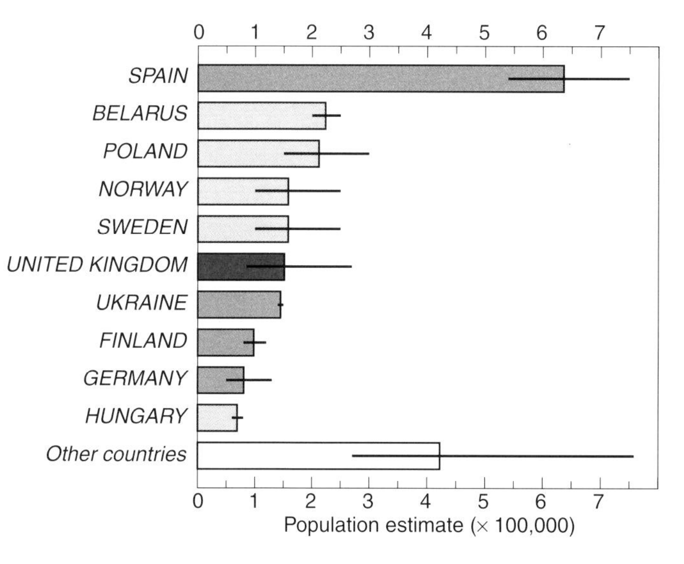

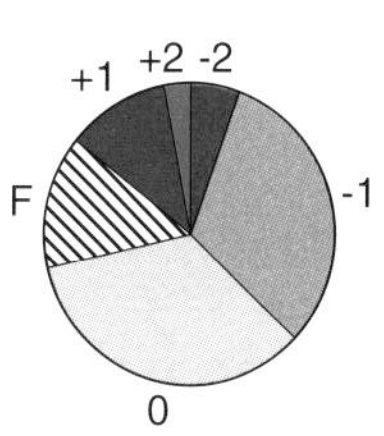

% in top 10 countries: 82.1
Total number of populated European countries: 35
Total European population 2,185,866–2,624,102 (2,355,277)
Russian population 1,000,000–10,000,000 (3,162,278)
Turkish population 10,000–100,000 (31,623)

This migrant hirundine is distributed very widely through the Palearctic and Nearctic: it is a common breeding bird of Europe, Asia to N India, SE China, the Pacific coastal islands and much of North America. European populations breed from Mediterranean regions through steppe, temperate and boreal habitats up to 70°N in the subarctic zone. The subspecies *R.r. diluta* occurs S of the lower Ural River, the nominate *riparia* occupying the remainder of Europe; two other subspecies occur elsewhere.

Apart from the eastern populations, which winter in E and SE Africa, European breeding birds winter in the Sahel zone immediately S of the Sahara. The autumn migrations are mainly to the W through Spain and Morocco and to the E via Greece and Turkey, even across Arabia. The Sand Martin is gregarious at all times, even on passage. Generally, it is associated with wetlands for feeding and roosting. Wintering birds are nomadic and some of the western populations gradually drift E during the winter. The spring migrations are rather further E, traversing the C Mediterranean via Tunisia, Malta and Italy.

The Sand Martin is common throughout Europe where suitable nesting substrates are exposed in vertical faces. Densities range between 1000 and 3000 bp/50km square in Britain & Ireland, the C and eastern European lowlands and parts of N Europe. Forested, dry or mountainous countries in W, C and S Europe exhibit lower densities, normally averaging 300–800 bp/50km square.

Erosion renews natural nesting sites each winter but in intensively managed river systems such sites may be very rare. It is then that artificial sites provided unknowingly by man in sand- and gravel-pits become increasingly important, particularly in highly developed areas of W and C Europe (G. Jones 1986). As an aerial feeder the species forages over any habitat where food organisms may arise or have drifted. Wetlands are particularly important in times of cold weather.

In most European countries where populations have been studied, numbers are subject to wide fluctuations which probably are associated with the transitory nature of most breeding sites and with drought problems in wintering areas. Investigations in Germany, The Netherlands, Great Britain, Sweden and Hungary have demonstrated severe effects of drought on survival over winters in 1968/69 and 1983/84 (Kuhnen 1975, Cowley 1979, C. Persson 1987, G. Jones 1993, Leys 1993, Szép 1995). The population size, related to drought in the Sahel, may decrease drastically over a single winter. A 1990 population of 33 300bp in E Hungary diminished by 50% in 1991 (Szép 1995). In general, breeding success is crucial in compensating for an annual mortality of 50–80%.

The population distribution has become more restricted and numbers have declined in areas of S and W Europe where it has been studied. In Britain & Ireland, occupied 10km squares dropped by 25% between 1968–72 and 1988–91 (G. Jones 1993). At the nadir, British Sand Martin populations may have comprised only 16% of the mid-1960s peak, but the early 1990s have seen a modest recovery. Similarly, the Dutch population size bottomed out in 1984, when numbers dropped to 14% of the high 1964 level (Leys 1993). These decreases were associated with an increasing frequency of drought conditions in the Sahel and degradation of the environment there through overgrazing. However there may also have been effects associated with the breeding season (site stability, disturbance, availability and food abundance).

Between 1990 and 1992 the average population density in primary breeding habitat along a 560km section of the River Tisza in E Hungary varied between 31 and 59 bp/km, even exceeding 200 bp/km in places (Szép 1995). The detailed distribution along the river is strongly related to the presence of new vertical banks, renewed by erosion. Almost 66% of the local population bred in large colonies of between 300 and 2500bp.

Chris Mead (GB) Tibor Szép (H)

This species account is sponsored by Karl-Heinz Gaßling, Rheinberg, D.

Ptyonoprogne rupestris

Crag Martin

CZ	Břehule skalní	I	Rondine montana
D	Felsenschwalbe	NL	Rotszwaluw
E	Avión Roquero	P	Andorinha-das-rochas
F	Hirondelle de rochers	PL	Jaskółka skalna
FIN	Kalliopääsky	R	Скалистая ласточка
G	Βραχοχελίδονο	S	Klippsvala
H	Szirti fecske		

Non-SPEC, Threat status S

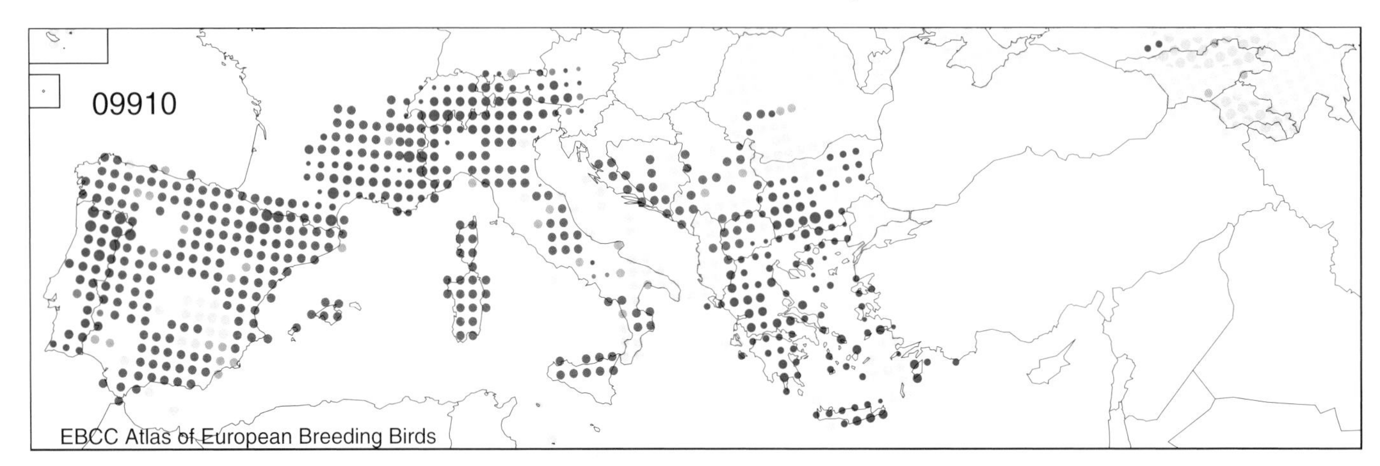

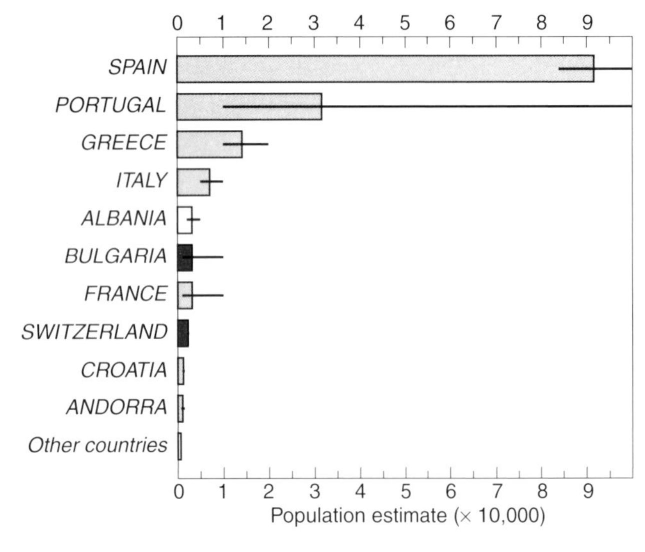

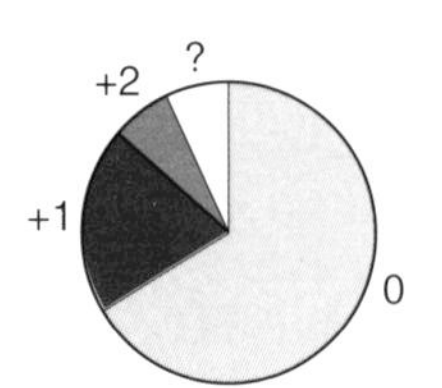

% in top 10 countries: 99.6
Total number of populated European countries: 15
Total European population 135,513–229,040 (159,145)
Turkish population 10,000–100,000 (31,623)

The monotypic Crag Martin inhabits the warm temperate mountains of the S Palearctic from the Iberian Peninsula and the Atlas, throughout the Mediterranean and the Middle East, to the Himalayas and the Chinese Tian Shan and Altai Mountains. Small resident populations exist on the Arabian Peninsula.

Throughout Europe the Crag Martin is widespread in the dry mountains of the Mediterranean, nesting solitarily or in loose colonies of 2–20bp on vertical surfaces of rocky outcrops, steep mountain-slope crags and precipices, river gorges and coastal cliffs. To the N the species is more patchily distributed in the Massif Central and throughout the Alps, breeding irregularly N to the Allgäu and Bavarian Alps. Nesting occurs at varying altitudes from sea level in the Mediterranean up to 2300m asl in the Alps and 2500m in the Sierra Nevada. Most breeding sites are situated on NE/SW slopes of the broader alpine valleys between 500 and 1000m asl.

Since the 1960s a gradual breeding expansion has occurred along the northern range limit from the Balkans to the Transylvanian Alps (Vasic 1985). During the late 1970s and 1980s the small Alpine population expanded its range to the Jura and the E Alps of Slovenia and Austria, increasingly nesting on viaducts, bridges and buildings (Šere 1989, Hable *et al* 1991, Kery 1991). Of the European population (*c* 160 000bp), 75% breeds in Portugal and Spain, its status remaining stable throughout 1970–1990.

Apart from local post-breeding movements, most Mediterranean coastal breeders are resident, but inland populations of the Iberian and Balkan Peninsulas move to lower ground or coastal areas after breeding. From November to March, Gibraltar holds a large wintering population (2000–3000 birds), probably from inland breeding sites (Elkins & Etheridge 1974). Northern birds are migratory, wintering mainly in the Mediterranean and North Africa, but some reach Senegal, the Nile Valley, the Red Sea coast and Ethiopia.

Peter Sackl (A) Dare Šere (SLN)

Hirundo daurica

Red-rumped Swallow

CZ	Vlaštovka skalní	I	Rondine rossiccia
D	Rötelschwalbe	NL	Roodstuitzwaluw
E	Golondrina Daúrica	P	Andorinha-dáurica
F	Hirondelle rousseline	PL	Jaskółka rudawa
FIN	Ruostepääsky	R	Рыжепоясничная ласточка
G	Δενδροχελίδονο	S	Rostgumpsvala
H	Vörhenyes fecske		

Non-SPEC, Threat status S

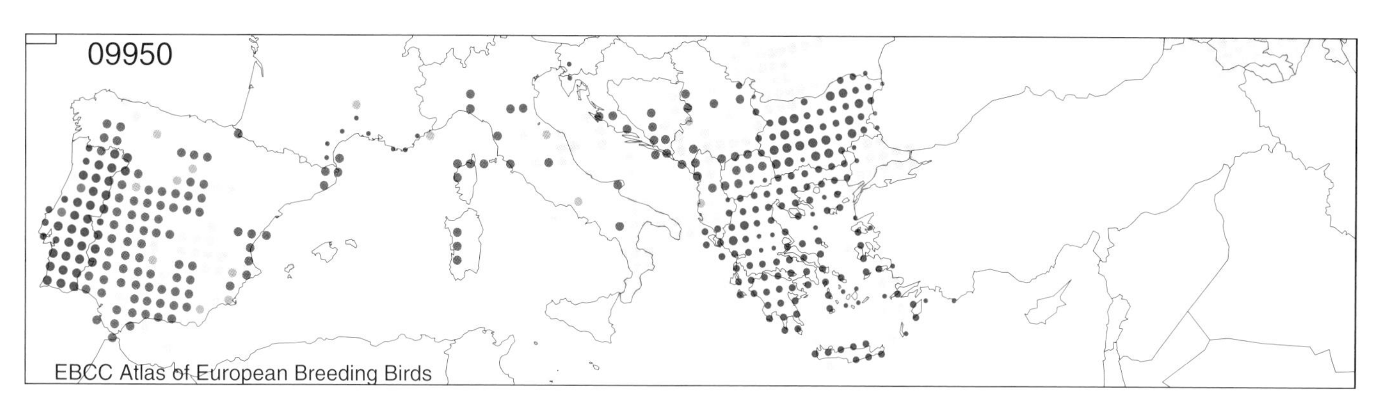

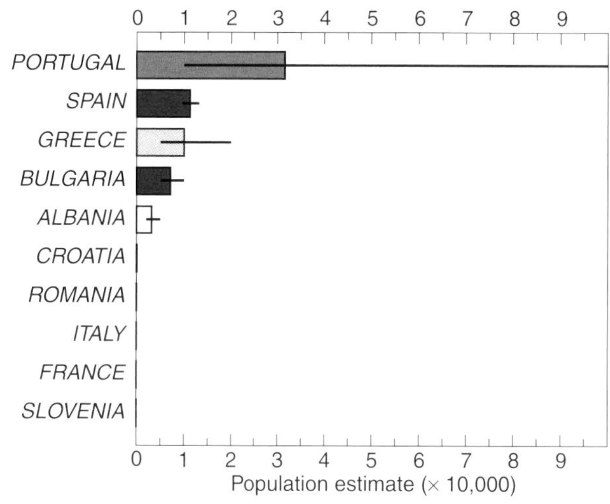

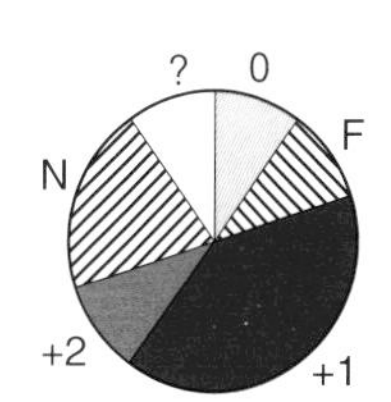

% in top 10 countries: 100.0
Total number of populated European countries: 10
Total European population 40,915–132,515 (63,297)
Turkish population 10,000–100,000 (31,623)

The Red-rumped Swallow breeds in southern Europe, C and NW Africa and Asia (Asia Minor, the Middle East, C Asia, India, China and Japan). The winter range of the migratory European and SW Asian populations lies presumably in the savanna zone of the northern Afrotropics. Some Asian populations are resident, others winter in SE Asia. Of 12 subspecies, only *H.d. rufula* breeds in Europe.

In Europe the Red-rumped Swallow breeds, singly or in small colonies, in dry and rocky habitats of the Mediterranean region including coastal cliffs, low mountain and rural areas. It builds its nest under overhangs in caves, hollows, cracks in rocks, and under bridges, culverts, in abandoned buildings and ruins, from sea level to 800m asl, rarely up to 1600m asl (Simeonov & Michev 1980) and exceptionally up to 1950m asl (L. Profirov, pers comm).

The Iberian Peninsula (*c*64%) and the Balkan Peninsula (*c*36%) hold almost the entire European population, only minor breeding numbers residing in Romania (20–50bp), Italy (15–30bp), France (5–10bp) and Slovenia (1bp). Population sizes are poorly known.

The European breeding range expanded northwards into colder and wetter regions, from the 1920s in Iberia and from the 1950s in the Balkans (Dontchev 1963, Simeonov 1965), becoming particularly noticeable during 1970–90 (>50% range expansion) in Portugal (Santos Jr. 1960, Rufino 1989), Bulgaria and Romania. Smaller range expansions of 20–50% have occurred in Spain and Croatia. Range size apparently is stable in Greece, but France (including Corsica) experienced some expansion during the 1980s (Nicolau-Guillaumet & Prodon 1994). Recently, the species first bred in Slovenia. Increases in breeding numbers were large in Portugal, but smaller in Spain, France, Croatia and Bulgaria. Greece holds a stable population, as probably does Italy. Climatic changes have been invoked as the major cause of the northward spread but other, yet unknown, factors may be involved.

Tanu Michev (BUL) Rui Rufino (P)

Hirundo rustica Swallow

CZ	Vlaštovka obecná	**I**	Rondine
D	Rauchschwalbe	**NL**	Boerenzwaluw
E	Golondrina Común	**P**	Andorinha-das-chaminés
F	Hirondelle rustique	**PL**	Dymówka
FIN	Haarapääsky	**R**	Деревенская ласточка (Ласточка-касатка)
G	Χελιδόνι	**S**	Ladusvala
H	Füsti fecske		

SPEC Cat 3, Threat status D

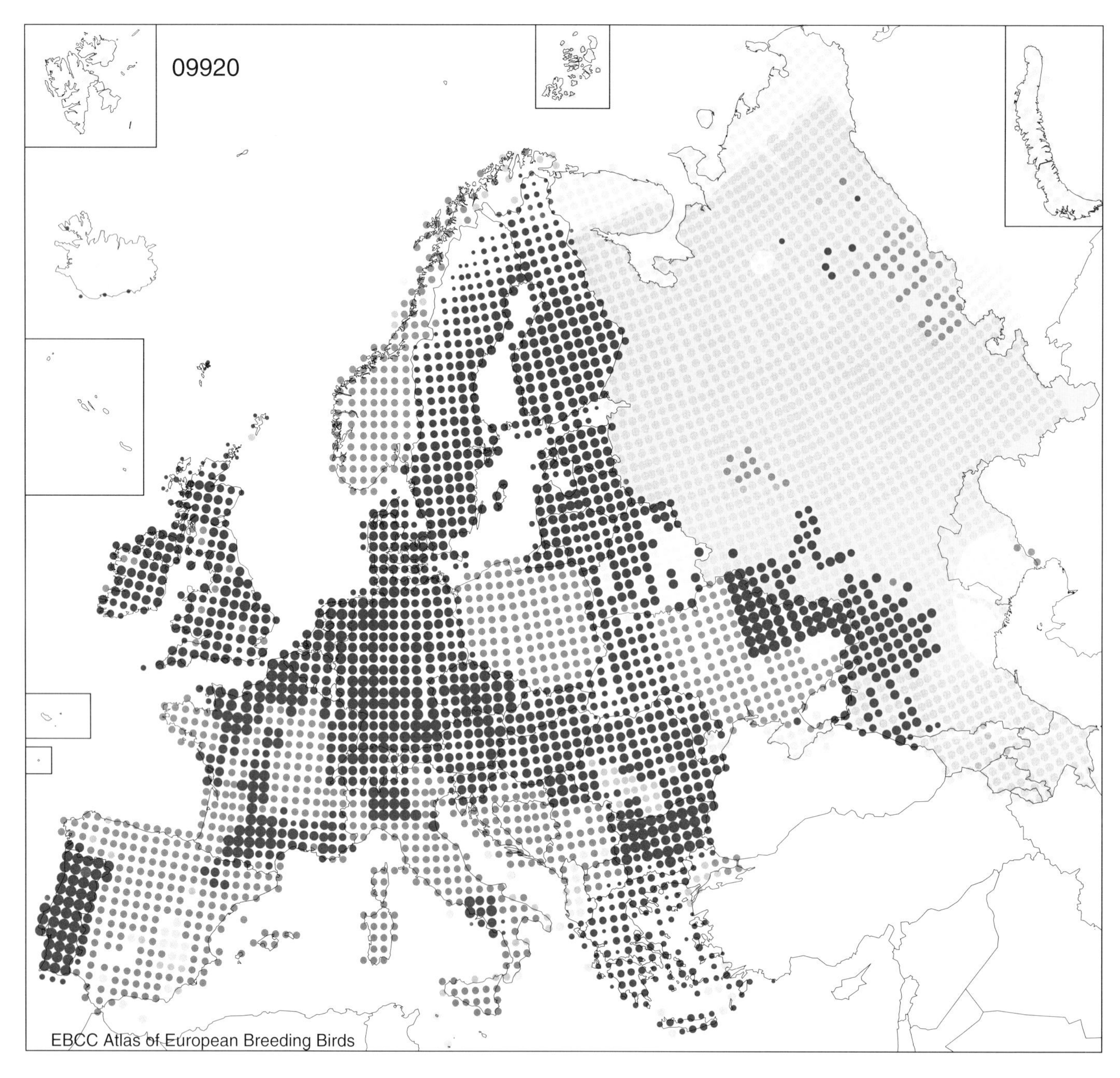

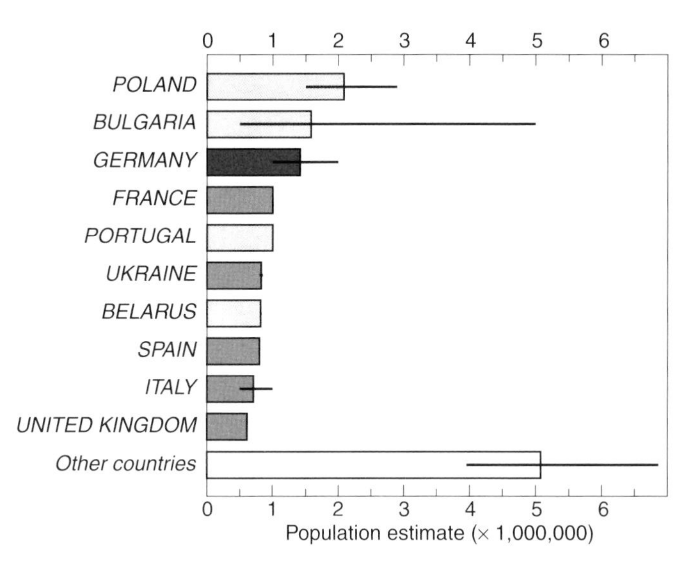

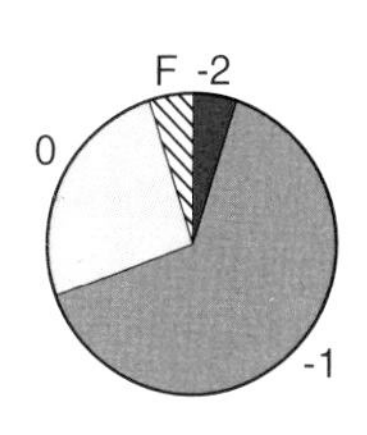

% in top 10 countries: 70.8
Total number of populated European countries: 39
Total European population 13,950,805–18,922,379 (15,304,550)
Russian population 1,000,000–10,000,000 (3,162,278)
Turkish population 100,000–1,000,000 (316,228)

The Swallow is a Holarctic species occurring throughout Europe with the exception of Iceland, where it breeds sporadically, and mountainous regions of northern Norway (Troms). Apparent distributional gaps in Castilla and southern Extremadura, Spain, arise through lack of coverage. It breeds at low altitudes, rarely above 1000m asl, but R. Garcin (pers comm) noted nesting in 5 consecutive years in the Queyras (Alps) at 1820m asl. Only the nominate *rustica* breeds in Europe, five other subspecies occurring elsewhere.

The Swallow is dependent entirely on a constant supply of small insects taken in flight over vegetation or shallow water. It builds its nest in any permanently open building, nowadays less commonly in buildings occupied by people, preferring barns, cowsheds and various outhouses. It breeds regularly under bridges and culverts, but rarely in cliff-cavities.

The Swallow is a semi-colonial species. Single pairs are not uncommon, but the majority of pairs breed in colonies, which form not because suitable sites are concentrated, but because food is abundant, especially in villages amid low-intensity agriculture. In C and N Europe, the presence of large domestic animals favours the choice of breeding sites. Large colonies occur occasionally; Bavaria, 120bp (von Vietinghoff-Riesch 1955) and recently Ukraine (>100bp; A.P. Møller, pers obs). In N Europe and at high altitudes most pairs nest singly. The Swallow generally avoids large city centres but occurs in the suburbs.

Population density in prime habitat in W and C Europe reaches a maximum of 34 bp/km^2 (usually 1–15 bp/km^2). Densities tend to decrease N of the temperate zone, probably reflecting the human population's distribution pattern. The overall density in Fennoscandia is *c*1300–1700 bp/50km square, but in predominantly agricultural states which retain much low-intensity farming (Russia, Belarus, Poland, the Balkans, the Czech Republic, Slovakia, Portugal) it may exceed 10 000 bp/50×50km square. Similar values attained in Germany, Denmark and The Netherlands derive from the abundance of nest sites amongst the large human population, partly offsetting the effects of widespread agricultural intensification. Intermediate densities of 4000–8000 bp/50×50km square prevail over much of W, C and S Europe, including Britain, Ireland, France, Spain, Italy and the Baltic States.

The Swallow probably has been associated with artificial habitats since Neolithic times. In small populations, numbers fluctuate greatly. Many national and local monitoring programmes confirm declining numbers throughout Europe during 1970–90. In NW Germany, population declines of >50% occurred during 1977–87 in several well-studied plots, especially from 1982 onwards (Loske 1993). A similar local decrease of >50% also occurred during 1970–88 in Denmark, where the trend started in the late 1970s (Møller 1989). Declining numbers (by 20–50%) affected most W and C European countries during 1970–90, and Spain, Austria, Albania, Romania, Moldova and Ukraine recently also noted range contractions. Populations have suffered through pesticide use affecting insect numbers. Altered farming practices have affected breeding habitats and closed off many potential breeding sites (Møller 1983). Overwinter mortality is governed by food availability through the effects of precipitation in the winter quarters. Recent decreases in population size are caused apparently by an increase in density-independent winter mortality in South Africa (Møller 1989).

European populations winter mainly in Africa S of the Sahara, those from N and E Europe, Britain and Ireland mostly leapfrogging more southerly populations to reach southern Africa (mainly Botswana and South Africa), and those from C (including Germany and Switzerland), W and SW Europe occupying the equatorial forest zone (from Guinea to Zaire), where the species inhabits mainly forest clearings containing dense *Pennisetum* grass. Here, or along rivers, local people in SE Nigeria trap 100 000 birds annually (J. Ash, pers comm). Small numbers winter regularly in the Mediterranean region.

Anders Pape Møller (DK) Christian Vansteenwegen (B)

This species account is sponsored by Peter Barran, Duisburg, D.

Delichon urbica — House Martin

CZ	Jiřička obecná	**I**	Balestruccio
D	Mehlschwalbe	**NL**	Huiszwaluw
E	Avión Común	**P**	Andorinha-dos-beirais
F	Hirondelle de fenêtre	**PL**	Oknówka
FIN	Räystäspääsky	**R**	Городская ласточка
G	Σπιτοχελίδονο	**S**	Hussvala
H	Molnárfecske		

Non-SPEC, Threat status S

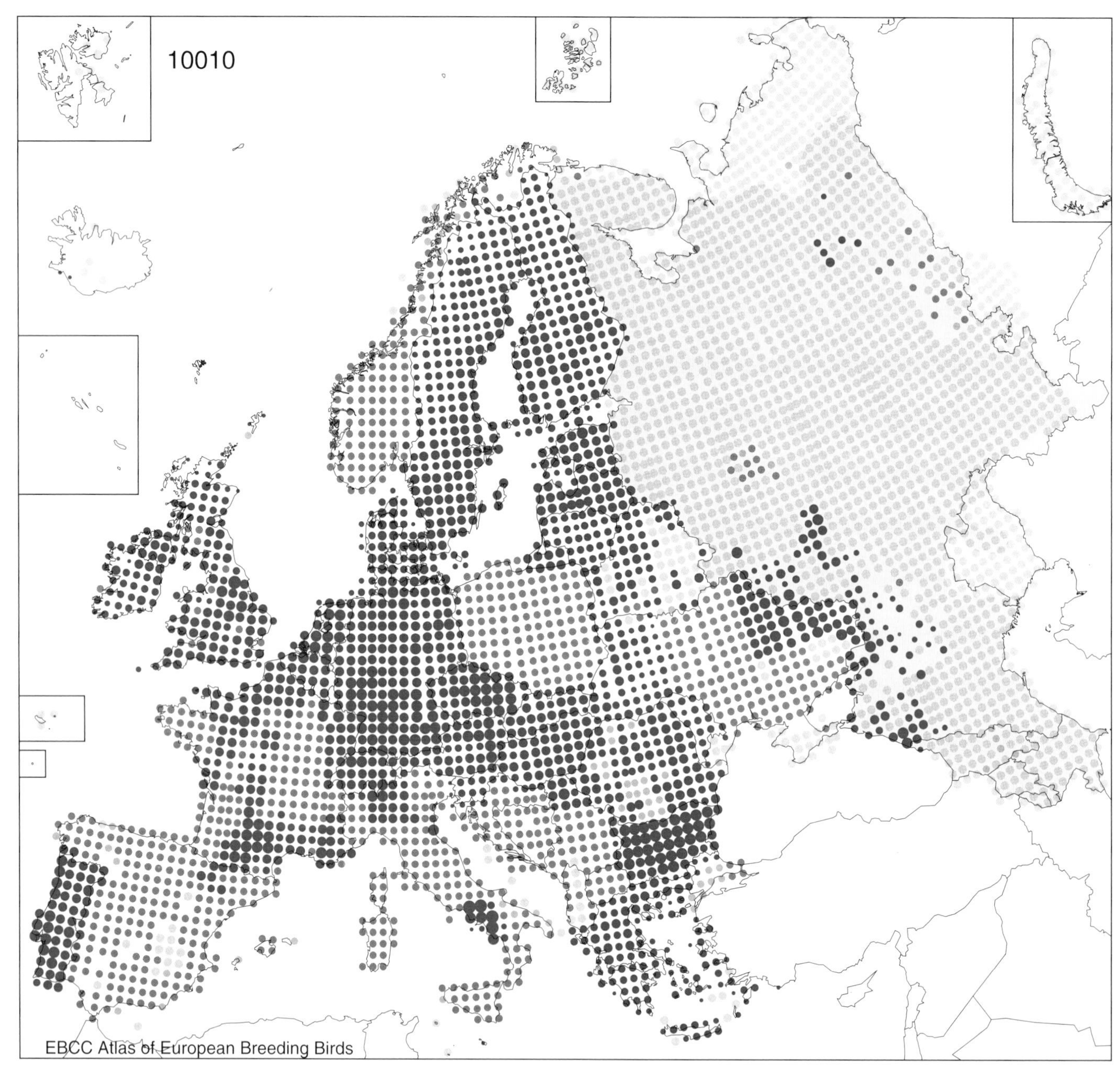

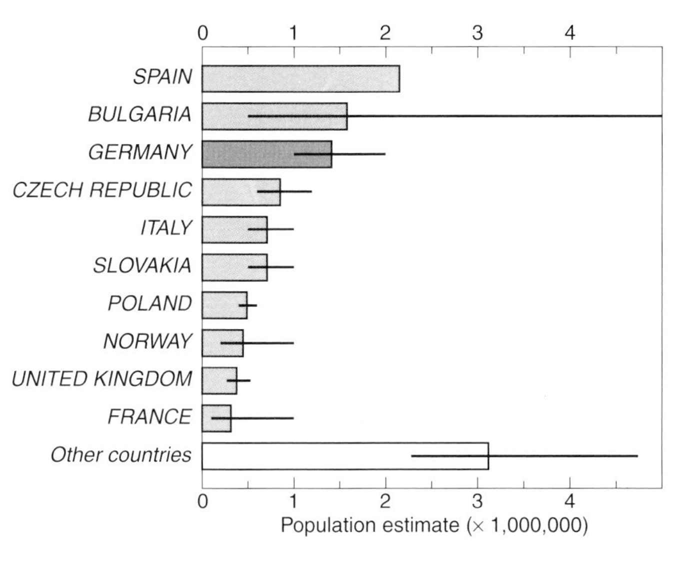

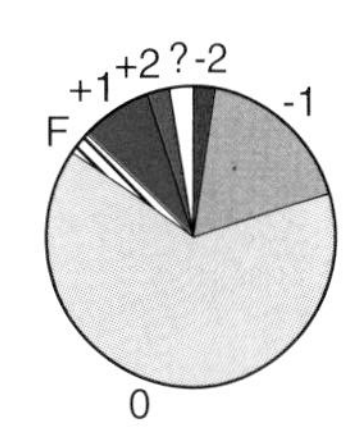

% in top 10 countries: 74.3
Total number of populated European countries: 39
Total European population 10,860,472–15,857,690 (12,160,002)
Russian population 1,000,000–10,000,000 (3,162,278)
Turkish population 100,000–1,000,000 (316,228)

The House Martin inhabits almost the entire Palearctic, from Britain and Ireland in the W to Japan and China in the E. Of five subspecies, only the nominate *D.u. urbica* breeds in Europe. In the N it normally is absent from the Faeroes, Iceland and Svalbard, which lie beyond the July 12°C isotherm. Although it breeds in subarctic and boreal regions, it is more typical of temperate, steppe and mediterranean climate zones where it tolerates both maritime and continental conditions provided that insect supplies and hawking opportunities abound.

Traditional breeding sites, such as inland rock-faces and seacliffs, are nowadays occupied but locally, and almost only in S Europe. Elsewhere, the species has shifted to nest on all kinds of artificial structures in villages, towns and cities, a process which began in the 19th century, becoming complete in the early 1900s. Generally, nests are built under eaves on outer walls, but since the mid-1970s the species increasingly has bred inside cattle-sheds and barns in Belgium and N France, sometimes simultaneously excluding the Swallow *Hirundo rustica*. The House Martin feeds usually at greater heights than the Swallow. Colonies normally form from sea level to 2000m asl close to forests or large waterbodies which attract large numbers of flying insects.

In the C European mountains, but not in alpine Scandinavia, the House Martin remains abundant in villages in high valleys (J-P. Fouarge, pers obs), the typical habitat of the *Delichon* genus outside Europe. It flourishes (>5000 bp/50×50km square) in the temperate and mediterranean zones, partly reflecting dense human populations, as in The Netherlands, Germany, the Czech Republic and Switzerland, and partly the extent of predominantly rural environments (Iberia, Bulgaria, Russia, the Baltic States). Mean colony size tends to be largest in S Europe (sometimes exceeding 1000 nests/colony), rural colonies being larger than urban. Northwards in Europe, including Scotland, densities decline rapidly as suitable nesting sites become scarcer and poor weather more frequent.

The distribution has remained largely unchanged since the 1960s, most countries reporting stable numbers. Locally, breeding numbers may show large annual fluctuations in response to adverse weather (Stoepel 1984). Some indications of a decline arose during 1970–90 from Finland and Sweden through Denmark and Germany to the Low Countries. Although the Dutch population did not change significantly during 1989–93, the level in the early 1990s was only 35% of that in 1965 (Jonkers & Leys 1994). Uppsala in Sweden experienced a worse decrease, average 1957–59 densities of 657 bp/100km² reducing to 92 bp/km² in 1983 (Frycklund 1984). Between 1982 and 1992, numbers in Brussels declined by 75%, mainly in highly urbanized areas (Fouarge 1992). Modern greening of urban environments, by encouraging increases in insect numbers, allows House Martin numbers to increase in some cities. Some British cities saw increases, as in London, Birmingham and Manchester when implementation of the Clean Air Act reduced air pollution (Marchant *et al* 1990). Berlin experienced a 36% rise from 1979 to 1983/84 (K. Witt 1985). Madrid holds the highest European densities (*c*5000 bp/100km²). The negative trend in N and W Europe does not have a single cause, given the variety of strength and timing of declines in different regions and years. Locally at least, mud for nest-building has been scarce, as in Puglia, Italy (May–October precipitation >25cm; Meschini & Frugis 1993) but air pollution also seems to play a role.

European birds probably winter in Africa S of the Sahara but the few sightings mostly are from highland areas (W Zimbabwe, Kenya, N Tanzania), presumably of birds foraging high above forested areas. Migration occurs on a broad front, concentrating neither at narrow Mediterranean sea-crossings nor along the Atlantic coast.

Andon Darakchiev (BUL) Jean-Paul Fouarge (F)

This species account is sponsored by Vogelfreunde Rheinbach/NABU Rhein-Sieg, D.

Anthus campestris

Tawny Pipit

CZ	Linduška úhorní	I	Calandro
D	Brachpieper	NL	Duinpieper
E	Bisbita Campestre	P	Petinha-dos-campos
F	Pipit rousseline	PL	Świergotek polny
FIN	Nummikirvinen	R	Полевой конек
G	Χαμοκελάδα	S	Fältpiplärka
H	Parlagi pityer		

SPEC Cat 3, Threat status V

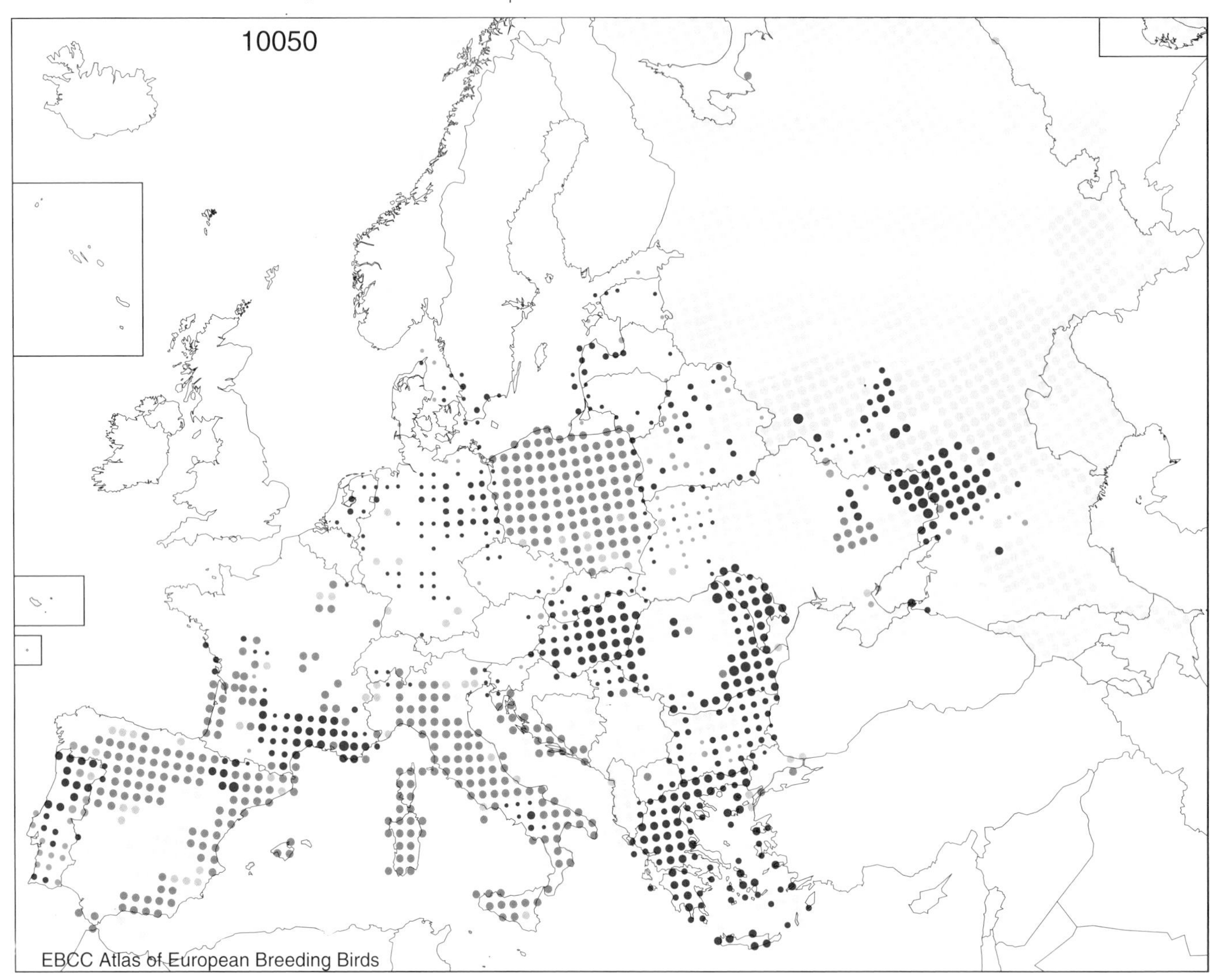

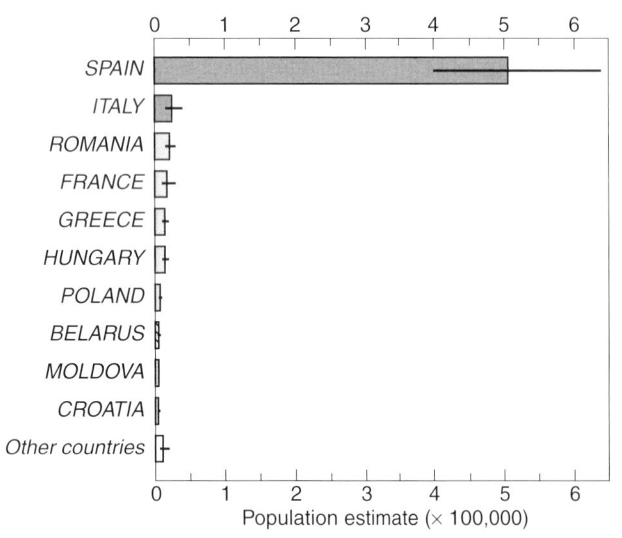

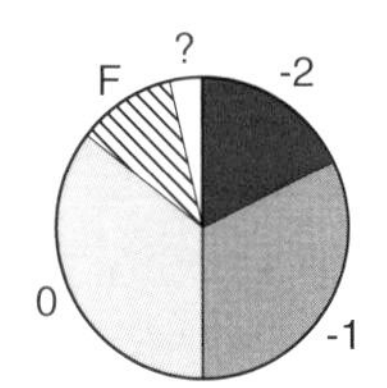

% in top 10 countries: 98.4
Total number of populated European countries: 28
Total European population 521,417–764,801 (628,474)
Russian population 10,000–100,000 (31,623)
Turkish population 50,000–500,000 (158,114)

The Tawny Pipit has a Palearctic world distribution which extends from Morocco to Inner Mongolia (*c*117°E), and from *c*55°N (except in Estonia where it reaches 59°N) to *c*35°N in the S. Of the three subspecies, only the nominate *campestris* breeds in Europe.

In dry and warm habitats, typical breeding locations comprise a mosaic of the following elements: open, sandy areas with sparse plant growth (preferred feeding sites) and taller grasses, dwarf shrubs and low-growing trees (nesting sites and song-posts). It avoids pure deserts and poorly textured steppes.

The main breeding population centres lie in the Mediterranean area (high densities in maquis and garrigue), and the steppe and semi-deserts of SE European Russia and Asia. The W and C European distribution is patchy and restricted to sand-dunes (The Netherlands: 4.6 bp/100ha, mean territory size 6.5ha; Bijlsma 1990b), dry grassland, clearfells, military training areas and gravel-pits. In the N the species breeds principally in low-lying areas, but up to 2000m asl in the Mediterranean (Sierra de Gredos, Spain). Wholly migratory, it winters in the Sahel zone E to the Arabian peninsula and the Indian subcontinent.

Over much of W and C Europe the Tawny Pipit has decreased sharply since the mid-1960s, mainly through habitat loss from intensive agriculture, afforestation, shrub encroachment on nutrient-poor land and eutrophication of cultivated land, although climatic causes have also been implied (Krüger 1989). In C Europe only isolated breeding sites remain, except on open expanses of inland sand-dunes, clearings and open-cast mines (Lausitz, Germany) on sandy soil. Such sites, if left unforested, remain occupied for decades. Even in population strongholds like Spain, Italy and Ukraine negative population trends have followed agricultural intensification in previously low-intensity farming or steppe areas. Nowhere have increases been reported.

Frank Neuschulz (D)

Anthus berthelotii — Berthelot's Pipit

CZ	Linduška kanárská	I	Calandro di Berthelot
D	Kanarenpieper	NL	Berthelots Pieper
E	Bisbita Caminero	P	Corre-caminhos
F	Pipit de Berthelot	PL	Świergotek kanaryjski
FIN	Kanariankirvinen	R	Конек Бертелота
G	Κελάδα του Berthelot	S	Kanariepiplärka
H	Kanári pityer		

SPEC Cat 4, Threat status S

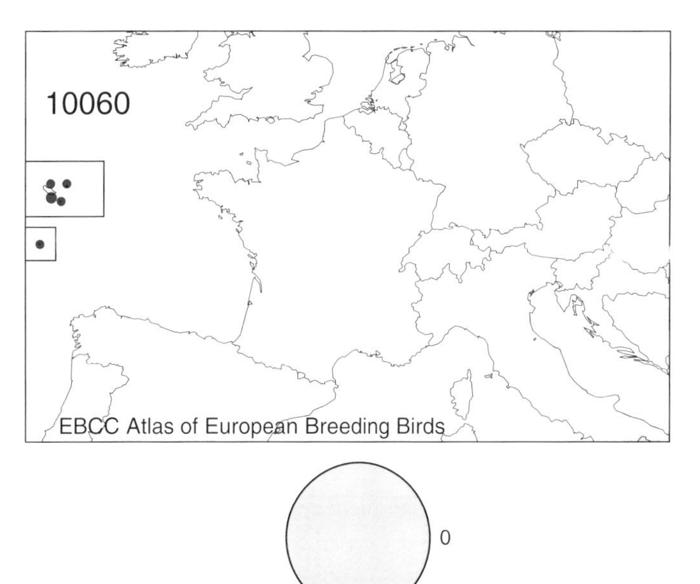

% in top 10 countries: 100.0
Total number of populated European countries: 1
Total European population 1000–1500 (1225)

Berthelot's Pipit is confined to the archipelagos of Madeira and the Canaries, where it is common within its preferred habitat. The nominate subspecies *A.b. berthelotii* is found in the Canaries and in the *Atlas*' area of coverage in the Selvagens (Salvage Islands) whereas *madeirensis* occupies Madeira, Porto Santo and the Desertas. The species is sedentary.

Within the archipelago of Madeira and the Selvagens Berthelot's Pipit occupies rocky, open and scrubby terrain at all altitudes where such habitat is available (at least up to 1600m asl). The Canaries population is thought to comprise 15 000–20 000 birds. On Lanzarote, it was considered the most ubiquitous bird species in open habitats, with 10bp on a plot of *c*2.7ha following exceptional cool and rainy weather in 1990 (Hildén & Hildén 1995). The population on Selvagem Grande varies considerably according to climatic conditions, and probably has a core breeding population of *c*50bp. Madeira probably holds 500–1000bp (F. Zino, pers comm to the Editors).

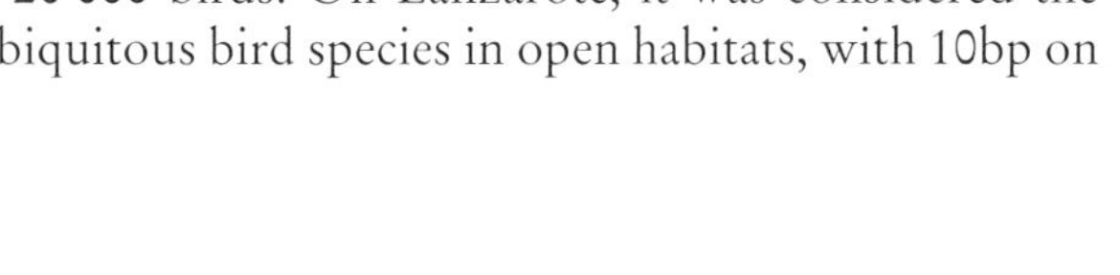

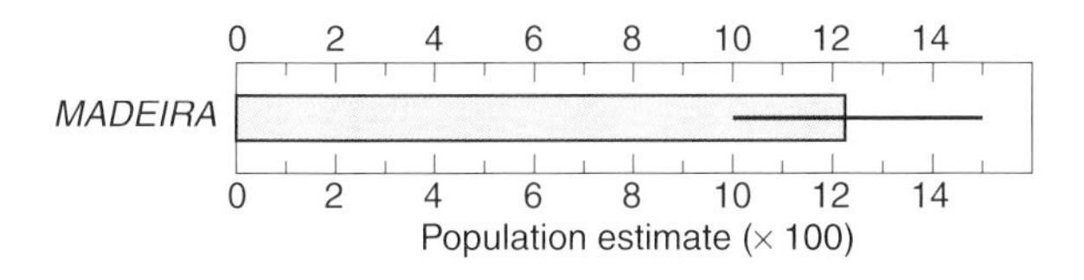

There is no evidence that Berthelot's Pipit moves any significant distance and it is strictly territorial (Hildén & Hildén 1995). The population is considered stable, subject to variations depending on environmental conditions preceding and during the breeding season. Natural predation by raptors does not have a significant impact on the population, and at present suitable habitat is plentiful. Depending upon local development projects, Berthelot's Pipit could suffer future habitat loss, but is not threatened at present.

Paulo Oliveira (P) Francis Zino (P)

Anthus hodgsoni

Olive-backed Pipit

CZ	Linduška zelená	I	Prispolone indiano
D	Waldpieper	NL	Siberische Boompieper
E	Bisbita de Hodgson	P	Petinha-silvestre
F	Pipit à dos olive	PL	Świergotek tajgowy
FIN	Intiankirvinen	R	Пятнистый конек
G	Δασοκελάδα	S	Sibirisk piplärka
H	Tajga pityer		

Non-SPEC, Threat status S (P)

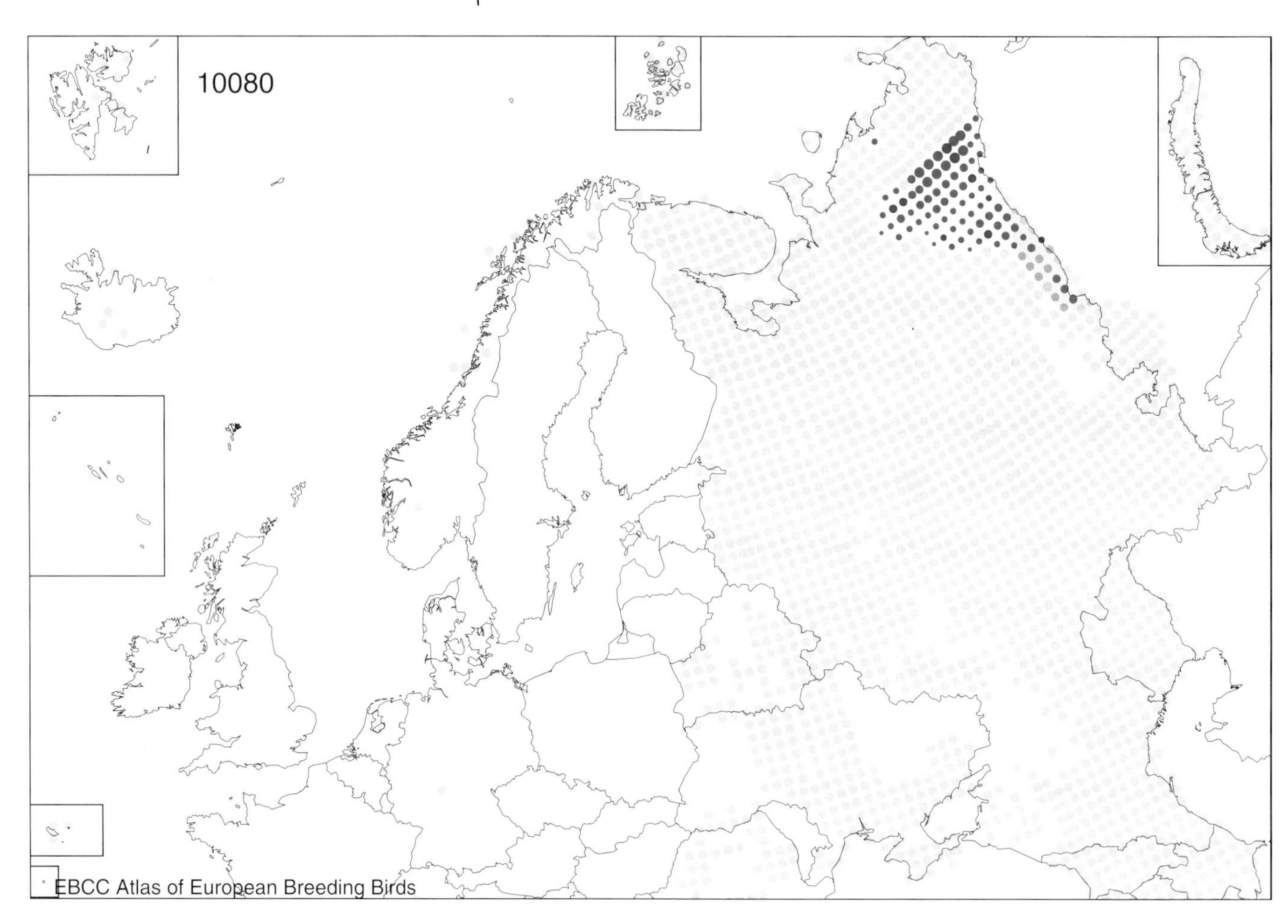

The Olive-backed Pipit occupies the Eurasian forest zone from the western macroslope of the Urals in NE European Russia E through C and eastern Siberia and Mongolia, to the Kurile Isles and Japan. A separate range stretches from NW and S China, W to E Afghanistan and S to N Burma. The species' wintering areas lie in SW Japan, S China, SE Asia, the Philippines and the Indian subcontinent. Regular migration through Israel indicates that some birds winter in Arabia or Africa (Helbig 1987).

Over much of its range it overlaps with Tree Pipit *A. trivialis*, but the ecological separation factors are not yet known (*BWP*). The Olive-backed Pipit is replaced N of the Eurasian forest zone by Pechora Pipit *A. gustavi* (*BWP*), whose present breeding occurrence in Europe is doubtful. The Olive-backed Pipit subspecies which breeds in Europe is *A.h. yunnanensis* whose distribution stretches to Kamchatka, Japan and Mongolia. The only other subspecies described is the nominate *hodgsoni*.

In Europe the Olive-backed Pipit breeds from the northern limit of the continuous coniferous forests in the lower reaches of the Pechora River S to the upper reaches of the Rivers Mezen, Vychegda and Pechora. Its main European habitats are various types of old coniferous forests. Sometimes it uses mixed and deciduous forests.

The highest breeding densities occur in the northernmost taiga subzone, where in primary forest habitats 2–4 bp/km² is representative, compared with 0.3–2.0 bp/km² in the primary coniferous and deciduous forests of the northern Urals. In the S and SW of the European range, density values are lower: 0.6 bp/km² in primary pine *Pinus* forests of the Pechora–Ilych Reserve and 0.2 bp/km² in mixed forests near Ukhta city. The present European population is estimated to be between 35 000 and 45 000bp.

Vladimir N Anufriev (R) Alexey A Estafiev (R)
Sergey K Kotchanov (R)

Anthus cervinus

Red-throated Pipit

CZ	Linduška rudokrká	I	Pispola golarossa
D	Rotkehlpieper	NL	Roodkeelpieper
E	Bisbita Gorgirrojo	P	Petinha-de-garganta-ruiva
F	Pipit à gorge rousse	PL	Świergotek rdzawogardły
FIN	Lapinkirvinen	R	Краснозобый конек
G	Κοκκινοκελάδα	S	Rödstrupig piplärka
H	Rozsdástorkú pityer		

Non-SPEC, Threat status S (P)

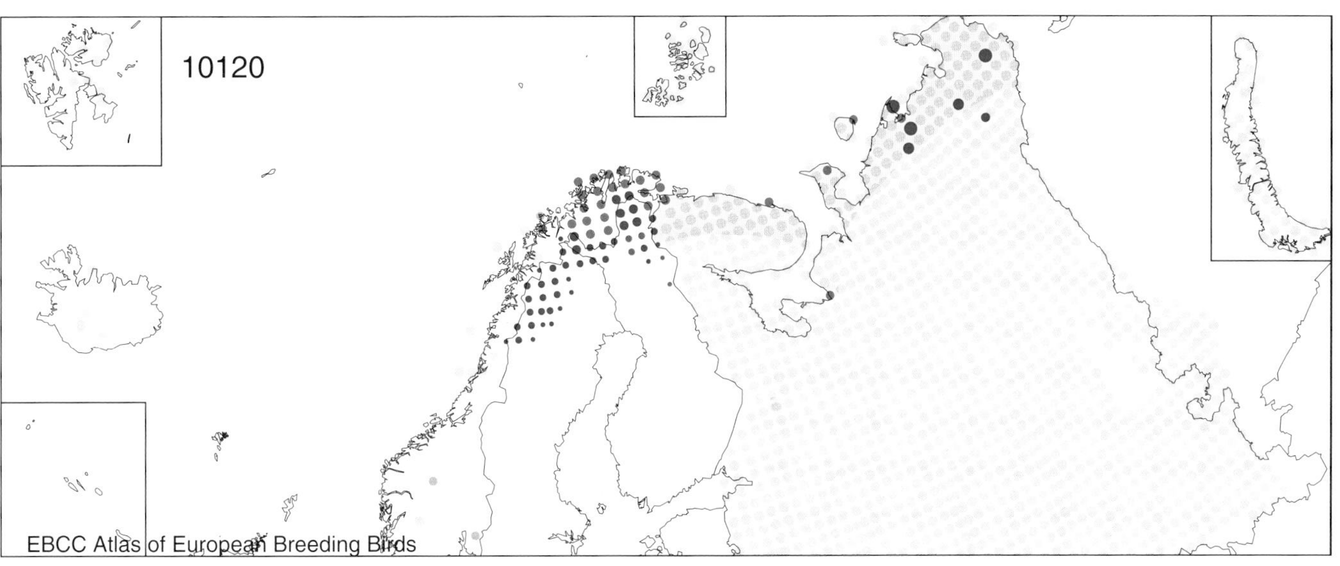

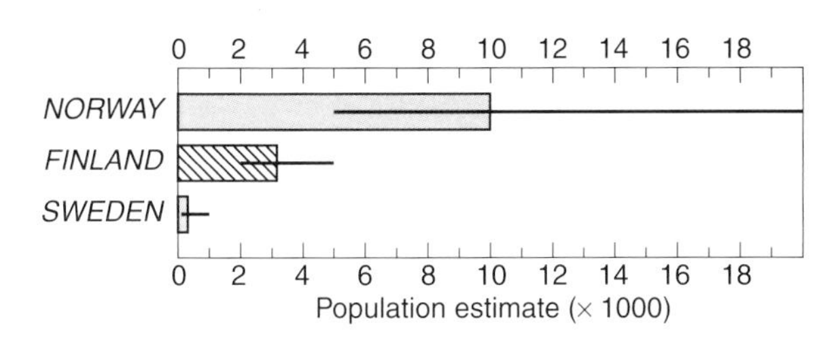

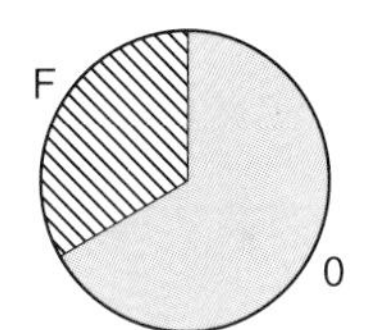

% in top 10 countries: 100.0
Total number of populated European countries: 3
Total European population 8341–23,669 (13,479)
Russian population 10,000–100,000 (31,623)

The breeding distribution of the monotypic Red-throated Pipit covers the arctic and subarctic zones from Fennoscandia to western Alaska. One of the most numerous species breeding in the arctic tundra, its optimal habitat comprises lush willow *Salix* mires amid small creeks, sedge *Carex* marshes and peat mounds both above the treeline and in the mountain birch *Betula* forest zone. In the past it has occupied the northern parts of Forest Lapland.

Its westernmost continuous range reaches S to 66°N in the Scandinavian mountains, but occasionally it breeds or attempts to breed S as far as 62°N in the Norwegian mountains. Large-scale line-transect censuses since the mid-1960s suggest there are 5000–20 000bp in Norway, 3000bp in Finland and 100–1000bp in Sweden (R.A. Väisänen, pers comm). The European Russian population is estimated roughly at 10 000–100 000bp. In the subarctic, abundance varies irregularly.

The Finnish distribution contracted between 1974–78 and 1986–89, the species disappearing from Forest Lapland and the number of occupied 100km² squares decreasing by 30% between surveys for the two Finnish bird atlases. Line-transect censuses in Fjell-Lapland and Finnmark revealed a 15% population size decrease over the same period (R.A. Väisänen, pers comm). The reasons for the changes are unclear. In a well-studied area in N Finland the population increased from the early 1950s to the 1960s, but in the early 1970s it disappeared for no obvious reason.

Finnmark breeding densities are: *c*4 bp/km² on maritime fjell heaths, 8 bp/km² in wet mires, but only 0.6 bp/km² on dry fjell habitats (Järvinen & Väisänen 1978b, R.A. Väisänen, pers comm). Regional density for arctic Lapland is *c*1 bp/km² and 0.3 bp/km² for Forest Lapland (R.A. Väisänen, pers comm). In optimal habitats in Finland densities can reach 13–21 bp/km² over several years (Jaakkola 1972) and 30–40 bp/km² in the Bol'shezemel'skaya tundra (Pulyakh 1977).

European populations migrate mainly to sub-Saharan Africa but scattered wintering sites exist in SE Italy, Turkey and North Africa.

Juha Tiainen (FIN)

Anthus trivialis

Tree Pipit

CZ	Linduška lesní	I	Prispolone
D	Baumpieper	NL	Boompieper
E	Bisbita Arbóreo	P	Petinha-das-árvores
F	Pipit des arbres	PL	Świergotek drzewny
FIN	Metsäkirvinen	R	Лесной конек
G	Δενδροκελάδα	S	Trädpiplärka
H	Erdei pityer		

Non-SPEC, Threat status S

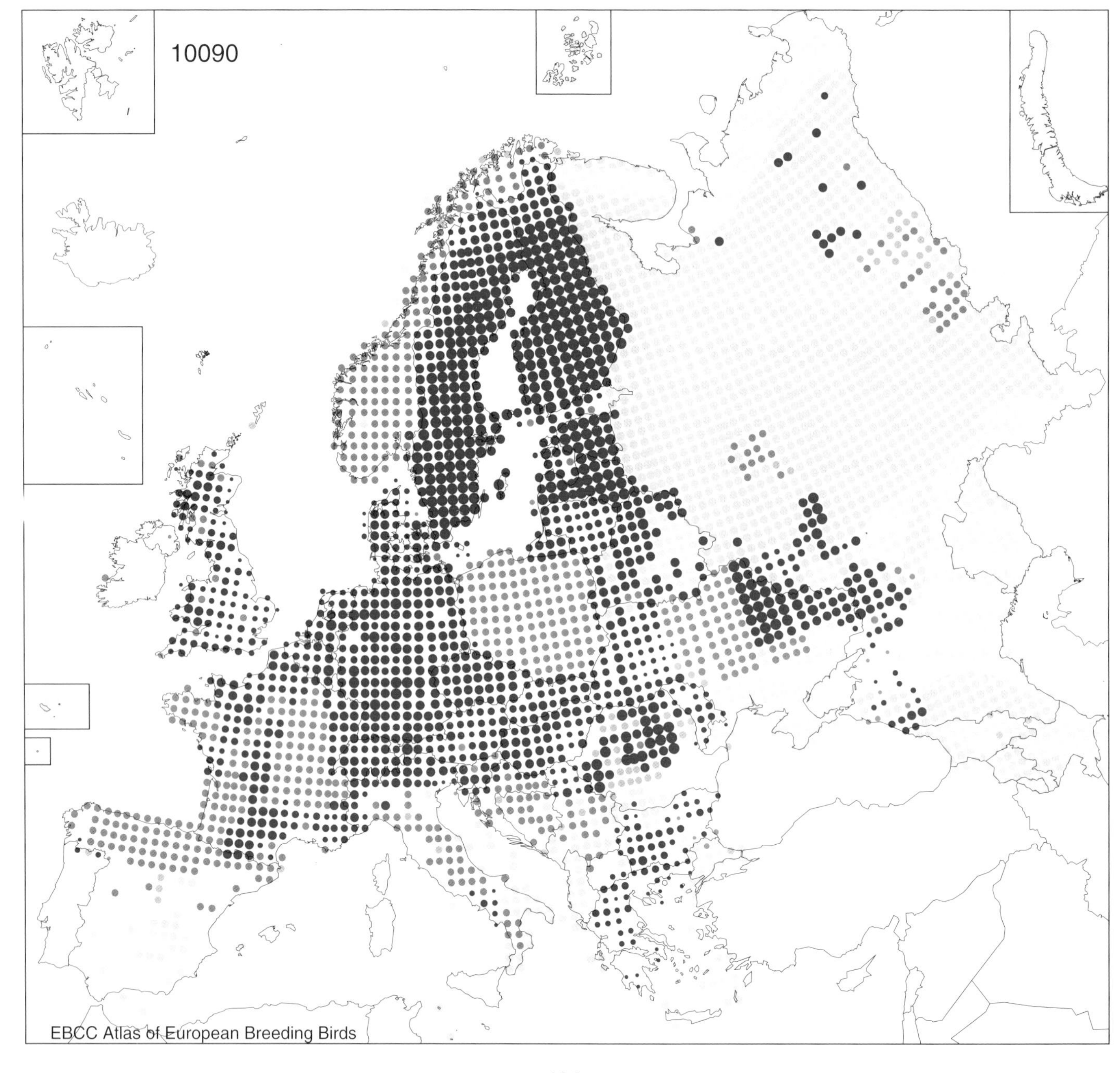

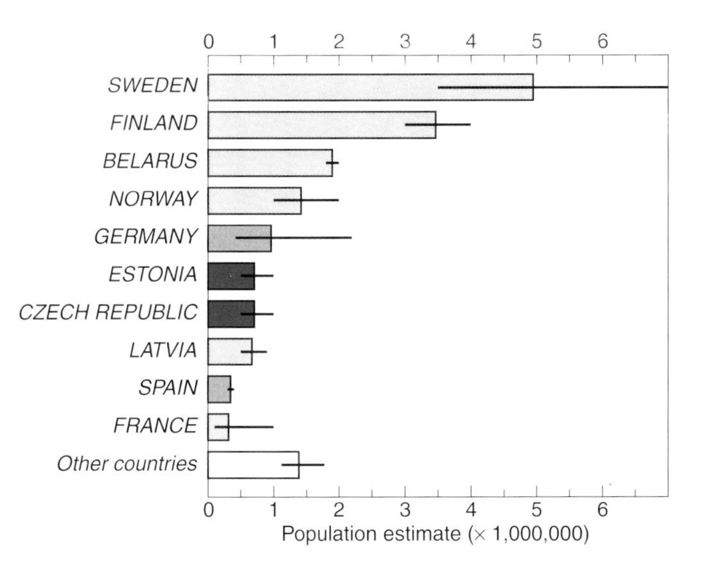

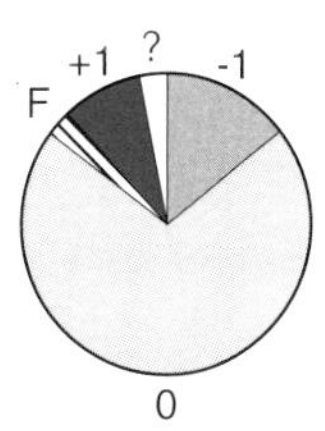

% in top 10 countries: 91.8
Total number of populated European countries: 34
Total European population 15,092,519–19,479,044 (16,814,671)
Russian population 10,000,000–10,000,000 (10,000,000)
Turkish population 10,000–100,000 (31,623)

The Tree Pipit breeds throughout most of Europe but is absent from Iceland, S Iberia and most Mediterranean islands, and is scarce in Ireland and Portugal. Its breeding range extends E through Siberia past Lake Baykal to Yakutskaya, and S in two distinct arms to the southern shore of the Caspian and to the Himalayas. Of the three subspecies, only the nominate subspecies *A.t. trivialis* occurs in Europe, the other two being *schluteri* and *haringtoni* from the distribution arm towards the Himalayas.

The Tree Pipit is a long-distance migrant, *trivialis* wintering mainly in Africa and the Indian subcontinent, and in small numbers also in the Middle East, on Crete and on Aegean islands. The sub-Saharan wintering grounds extend from the Guinea coast to Ethiopia, then S to Transvaal between the eastern edge of the C rainforest belt and the forests bordering the Indian Ocean. The other two subspecies migrate to C India.

The Tree Pipit breeds from sea level to just above the treeline in the Alps (2300m asl), and probably even higher in its southeastern range. Its breeding habitat normally comprises open, sparsely vegetated country, scattered with trees or bushes for song-posts. Suitable habitats, normally dry, include heaths and grasslands in early stages of tree colonization, open woodland, scrub and low-intensity farmland. Marshland may also be used. The species avoids treeless and shrubless habitats, intensively cultivated land and suburban areas, and usually is absent from closed-canopy forest, although it does occur along forest edges. In Germany, a Tree Pipit population would tolerate no more than 80% canopy-cover (Loske 1987).

Young conifer plantations have provided additional breeding habitat in much of N and C Europe. However, in the lowlands, such plantations become increasingly unsuitable as the trees mature and the canopy closes over and are abandoned as early as the fourth year of growth. The Tree Pipit colonizes upland plantations at a later stage, when trees are about nine years old (Sykes *et al* 1989), and in Fennoscandia it prefers to breed in mature conifer stands (Helle 1985). Clearfelling mature trees recreates suitable habitat which the Tree Pipit will recolonize quickly (M. Shepherd, pers obs). Coppiced woodlands in the first few years of growth have also provided additional Tree Pipit breeding habitat (Fuller & Moreton 1987).

The highest recorded breeding densities come from Swiss low-intensity farming areas; up to 126 bp/km^2 (Fuchs 1979). More typical are values of 2–20 bp/km^2, up to 26% of males remaining unpaired (Meury 1989). In Europe, Tree Pipit abundance, while locally even, decreases towards the S. Optimal breeding conditions in the vast northern coniferous forests of Russia, Fennoscandia, Belarus and the Baltic States allow overall representative densities of *c*11 000–40 000 bp/50km square. Just S of this belt, forests remain mainly coniferous but cultivation is widespread; typical densities are *c*2500–7000 bp/50km square, especially in Hungary and from Poland westwards across the lowlands to France. Further S, values reduce to less than 500 bp/50km square in Greece, Italy, Slovenia and Bulgaria.

The European population size and range has remained very stable since 1970, only a few countries experiencing small increases or decreases. In W Germany from 1977 to 1986 fluctuations in numbers from the previous year ranged from +27% to −33%, apparently reflecting the occupation or avoidance of suboptimal habitats (Loske & Lederer 1987). With the virtual cessation of commercial planting of conifers in southern Britain, older plantations, unsuitable for the species, predominate, probably accounting for the local declines experienced. However, in the northern British uplands new conifer plantations continue to be established, permitting the possibility of local density increases, although there is to date little evidence of a range expansion.

Karl-Heinz Loske (D) Michael Shepherd (GB)

This species account is sponsored by the Swiss Ornithological Institute, CH.

Anthus pratensis **Meadow Pipit**

CZ Linduška luční
D Wiesenpieper
E Bisbita Común
F Pipit farlouse
FIN Niittykirvinen
G Λιβαδοκελάδα
H Réti pityer
I Pispola
NL Graspieper
P Petinha-dos-prados
PL Świergotek łąkowy
R Луговой конек
S Ängspiplärka

SPEC Cat 4, Threat status S

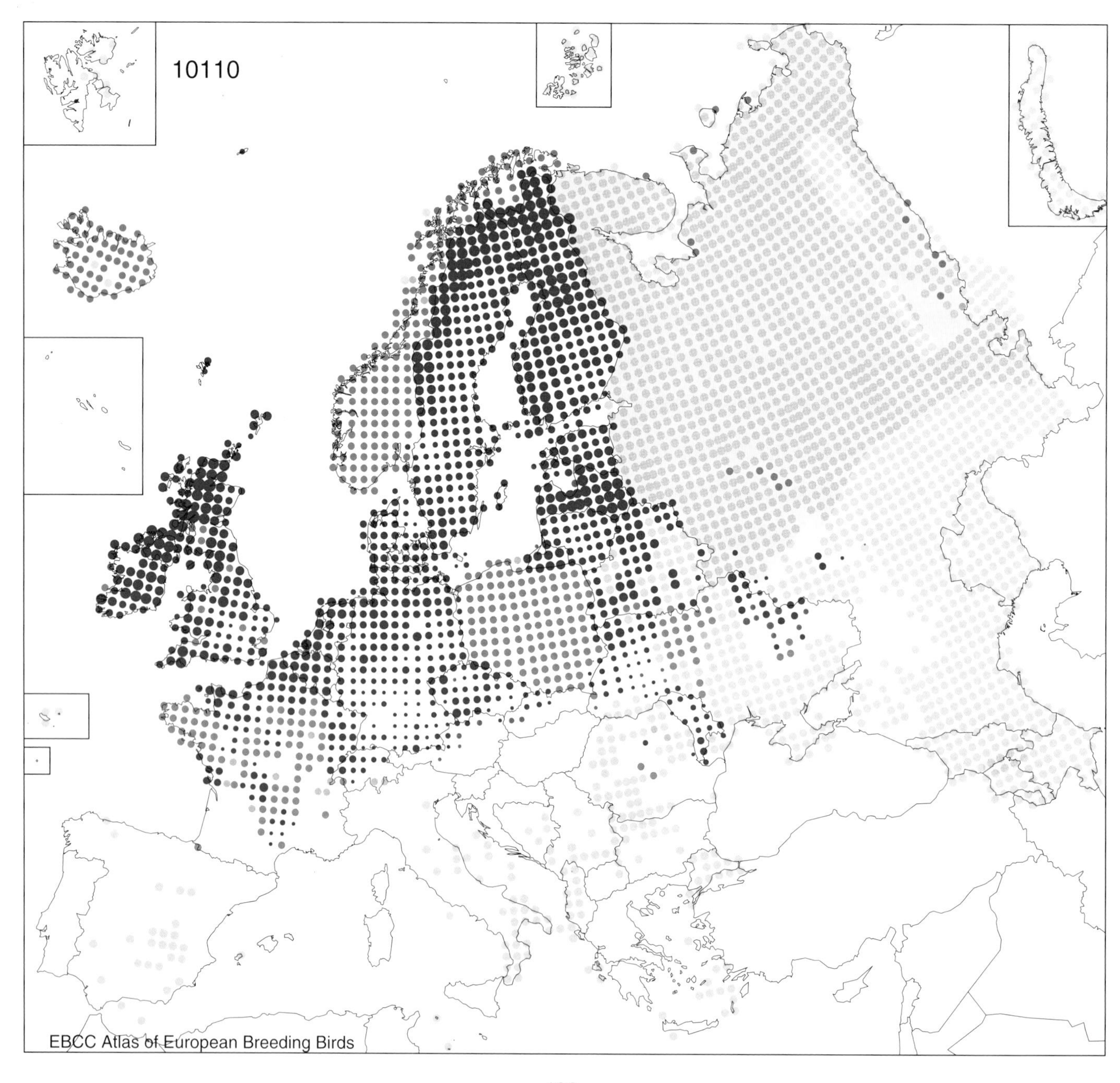

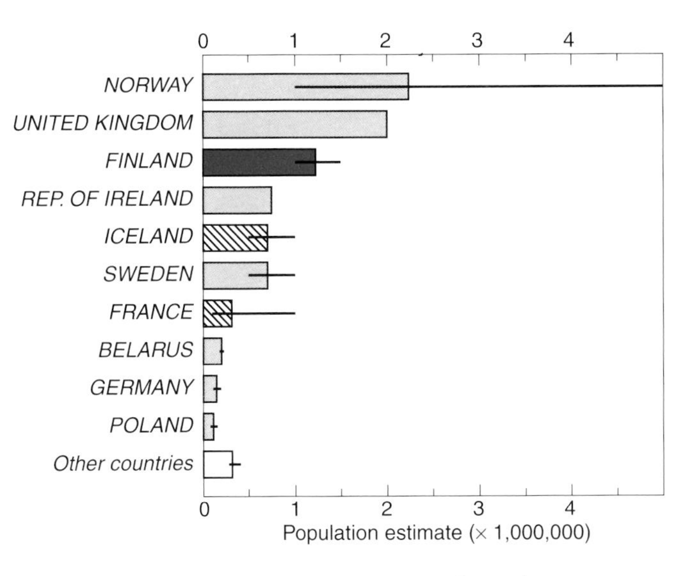

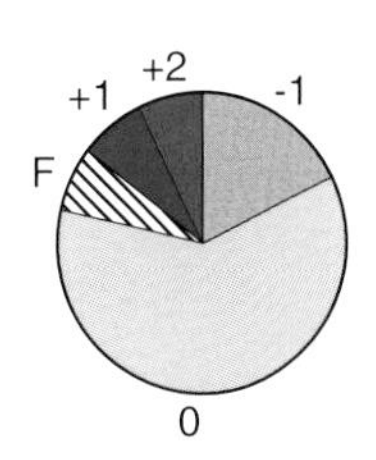

% in top 10 countries: 96.3
Total number of populated European countries: 28
Total European population 7,415,051–11,616,649 (8,724,890)
Russian population 1,000,000–10,000,000 (3,162,278)

The Meadow Pipit is almost an exclusively European species. It is a common breeder in most open habitats in C and N Europe, its range extending from E Greenland in the W, across northern Europe to the high mountains of C and northernmost S Europe and to the lowlands of the River Ob E of the Urals. Isolated populations exist in the C Appennines in Italy and in the border mountains of Georgia and Armenia.

Across its extensive distribution the Meadow Pipit inhabits tundras, moorlands, fells, all types of grasslands, heaths, saltmarshes, dunes, forest clearings, fallow land and, in some parts of the range, arable land. Along its southern range border, the distribution of breeding areas becomes patchy, isolated and confined to higher altitudes (usually from 800m to 1600m asl), whereas in the centre and N of the range, the species occupies all altitudes, breeding distribution being more or less even, depending only on the availability of suitable habitats.

The Meadow Pipit prefers breeding habitats which are open but not too dry and contain areas of low vegetation whose composition is suitable for nesting sites. The species usually constructs its nest in taller vegetation, like tussocks, or where the terrain has low ridges, shallow vegetated gullies or contains small sections which slope slightly more steeply than average (such as depressions and ditches) (Hötker & Sudfeldt 1982). However, the Meadow Pipit also requires areas of vegetation no taller than 10cm in which to forage (straw-stubbles are a good equivalent), because if it is unable to adopt its normal running gait, it will move elsewhere. Consequently, the extent of foraging areas containing low vegetation strongly influences breeding density (Hötker 1989). Breeding densities vary between a low value of 0.1 bp/10ha on arable land to more a representative 15.5 bp/10ha in prime habitat (Hötker 1989). In the N, densities are highest (up to 80 bp/km^2) in the alpine and *palsa* peatlands in Lapland, compared to 5–20 bp/km^2 in suitable southern habitats (Koskimies 1989a).

In general, the rainy, sea-exposed western areas of Britain & Ireland, continental Europe and Scandinavia seem to be the most densely populated parts of its breeding range. Together, Russia, Norway, Britain & Ireland, Finland and Iceland hold approximately 90% of the European population of *c*12Mbp.

Meadow Pipit breeding populations show large annual fluctuations which partly are attributable to the severity of the weather in its winter quarters and during the spring migration (Hötker 1989, Marchant *et al* 1990). In western Europe, the Meadow Pipit is mostly sedentary. Elsewhere only the northernmost populations migrate annually, some others moving only if the weather becomes severe, and then often as short-distance migrants (*BWP*). Migrant birds move to C, W and S Europe where the greatest numbers congregate in the W Mediterranean region. Others winter in North Africa and the Middle East, some as far E as Iran and E Kazakhstan.

Apart from the irregular, weather-dependent population fluctuations, no long-term trends are discernible at present. There have been some range expansions in Finland, the Czech Republic (Hudec & Šťastný 1979) and in France (Isenmann 1987), but these are counteracted, at least in part and especially in the Low Countries, Denmark and C Europe, by declines in numbers brought about by intensification of farming practices. In some of the C European mountains, forest degradation by acid rain has provided new breeding habitats for the Meadow Pipit, but this change may be as temporary as for other species whose food supply declined after initial expansion.

Of the two subspecies, *A.p. whistleri* occurs only in Ireland and western Scotland, the nominate *pratensis* occupying the bulk of the distribution.

Herman Hötker (D) Karel Šťastný (CZ)

This species account is sponsored by Manfred Reinhardt, Rheinberg, D.

Anthus spinoletta **Water Pipit**

CZ	Linduška horská	**I**	Spioncello Alpino
D	Wasserpieper	**NL**	Waterpieper
E	Bisbita Alpino	**P**	Petinha-ribeirinha
F	Pipit spioncelle	**PL**	Siwerniak
FIN	Vuorikirvinen	**R**	Горный конек
G	Νεροκελάδα	**S**	Vattenpiplärka
H	Havasi pityer		

Non-SPEC, Threat status S

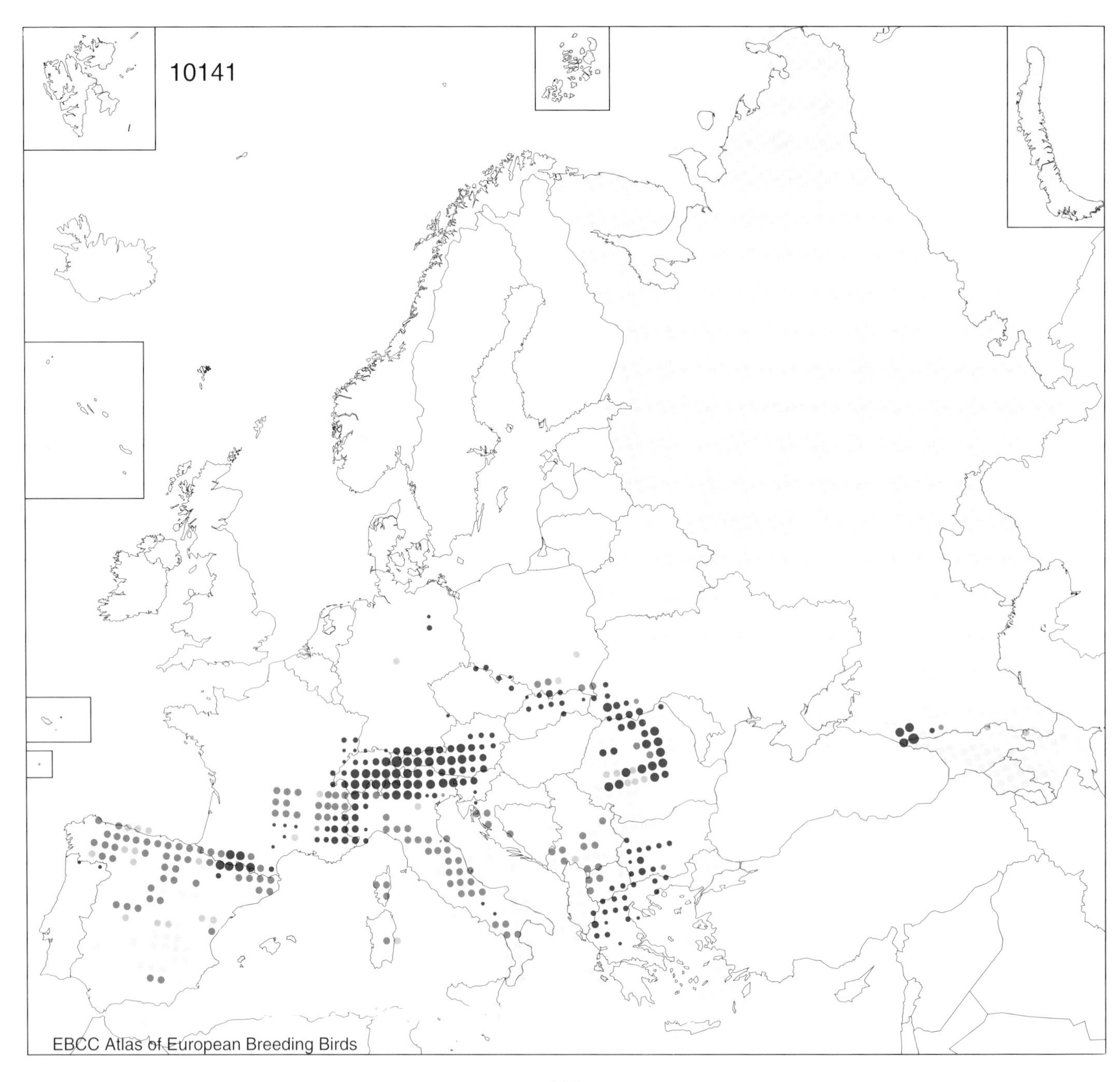

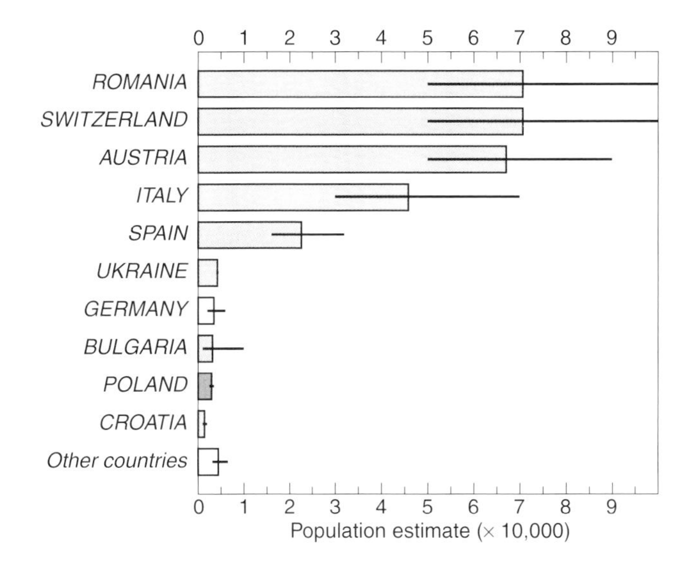

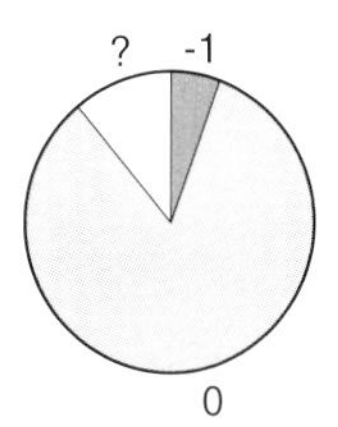

% in top 10 countries: 98.5
Total number of populated European countries: 18
Total European population 258,531–351,115 (296,632)

The *spinoletta/petrosus* pipit group (the systematic position of Asian and American birds has yet to reach a consensus since the split of the previous single European species into two) has a discontinuous Holarctic distribution. In North America (the split proposes Buff-bellied Pipit, *Anthus rubescens*) these pipits breed in Alaska, N Canada and the Rocky Mountains. In Eurasia the group's breeding distribution stretches from Spain to the Caucasus and the mountains S of the Caspian Sea, then through C Asia, from NE Afghanistan to the Okhotsk Sea, Kamchatka and the Chukotskiy Peninsula. In northern Europe populations breed along the coasts of NW and N France, the Channel Islands, Britain & Ireland, and Fennoscandia. The systematics of the *spinoletta/petrosus* group are in constant revolution, the number of species and subspecies varying considerably from one author to another.

In Europe the Water Pipit *A.s. spinoletta* breeds in mountainous areas of the Pyrenees, the Cévennes, the Massif Central, the Vosges, the Jura, the Black Forest, the Apennines, the Alps and the Carpathians. The species occurs at altitudes ranging from *c*615m to almost 3000m asl, but the highest breeding densities are found between 1400m and 2500m asl (J-P. Biber 1982, 1994b). It is widespread in Cis-Caucasus and Transcaucasia. In the Alps, the highest densities were 3.0–3.5 bp/10ha (Catzeflis 1978), between 1950m and 2350m asl. In the Swiss Jura values were rather lower, averaging 2.4 bp/10ha (J-P. Biber 1982), between 1400m and 1600m asl. In prime habitats in the Polish Tatra Mountains, densities of up to 4.5 bp/10ha were found between 1250 and 2200m asl (Walasz & Mielczarek 1992).

The Water Pipit prefers open habitats containing short grassy vegetation, such as mountain or alpine pastures and high mountain meadows. It needs scattered rocks, bushes or trees as lookout posts. Most territories are on slopes which provide sheltered nesting-places (cavities under rocks or gouged by cattle hooves); level areas are often left uncolonized or may be used for foraging. In areas where the Water Pipit and the Meadow Pipit *A. pratensis* cohabit, their territories often overlap. Both species use the same type of nest sites, but their foraging habitats differ. The Water Pipit rarely feeds in tall and dense vegetation, which is the preferred milieu of the Meadow Pipit (J-P. Biber 1982).

The species' distribution in Europe is very patchy due to its altitude requirement and its habitat preferences, a circumstance which accounts for very small isolated populations (perhaps a dozen breeding pairs) being separated by 24km or more from the nearest population.

For some time now there have been no important changes, neither in distribution nor in population. The relatively high numbers of low-altitude breeding locations simply may reflect the increased ornithological activity arising from the development of atlas work in many countries. Since the mid-1960s several mixed populations of Water and Meadow Pipits have been found, and often territories have overlapped (J-P. Biber 1982), but so far there is no discernible negative effect on the Water Pipit.

The Water Pipit is migratory or partially migratory. Many birds simply leave the mountains to winter in the valleys below, others move to larger rivers and lakes or to the seashores of the North Sea (some winter in Britain & Ireland), the Atlantic and the Mediterranean. A few birds travel as far as North Africa. At many wintering sites in NW Europe, the Water Pipit shows marked site fidelity, although numbers fluctuate in response to low temperatures (K. Witt 1982). Birds wintering in Mesopotamia and C Arabia are presumed to come from Turkish and Transcaucasian breeding populations, although the latter are partly resident.

Jean-Pierre Biber (CH)

Anthus petrosus

Rock Pipit

CZ	Linduška skalní	I	Spioncello marino
D	Strandpieper	NL	Oeverpieper
E	Bisbita Costero	P	Petinha-maritima
F	Pipit maritime	PL	Świergotek nadmorski
FIN	Luotokirvinen	R	Горный конек
G	Ακτοκελάδα	S	Skärpiplärka
H	Parti pityer		

SPEC Cat 4, Threat status S

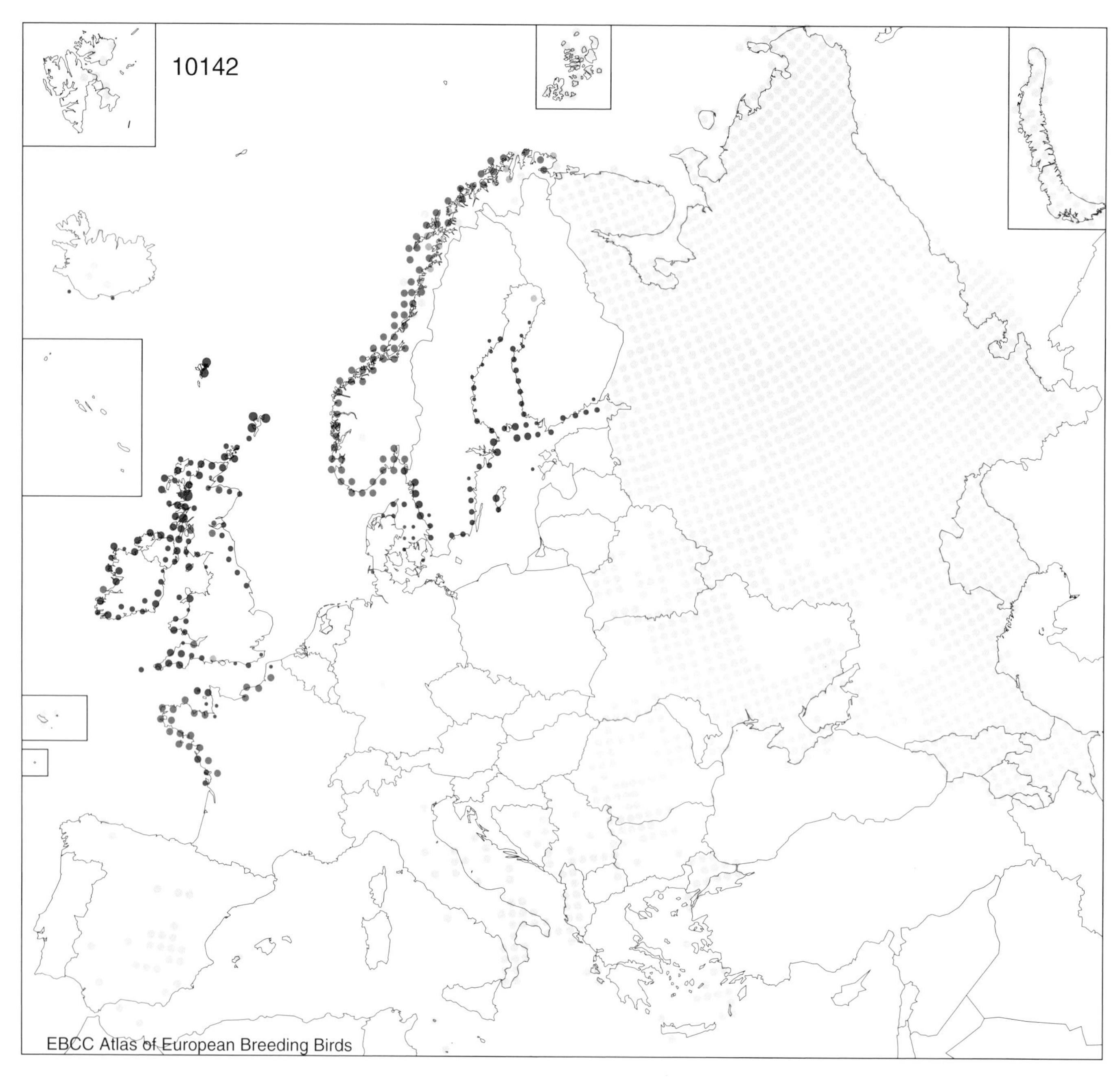

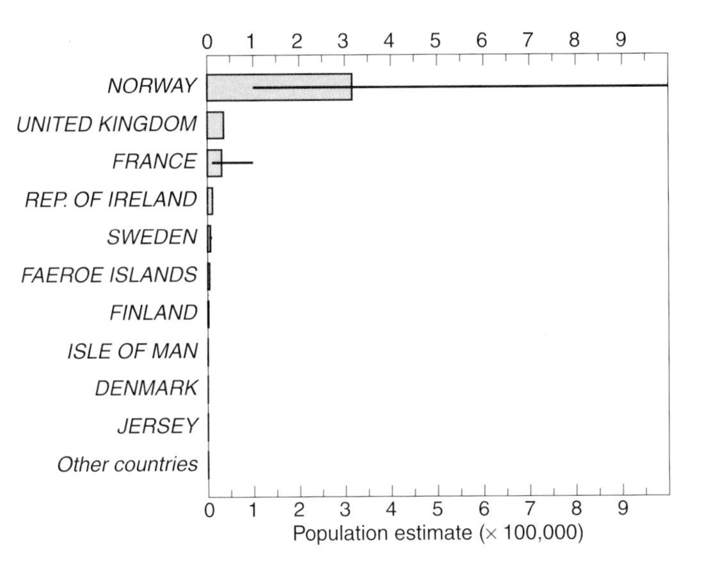

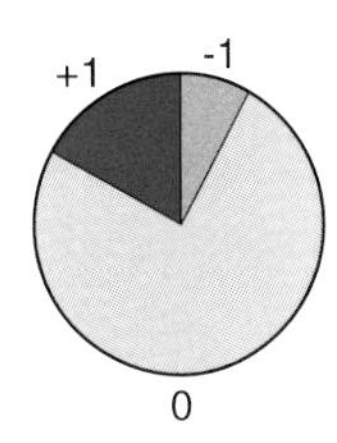

% in top 10 countries: 100.0
Total number of populated European countries: 12
Total European population 190,226–1,094,743 (407,549)

The *spinoletta/petrosus* pipit group (the systematic position of Asian and American birds has yet to reach a consensus since the split of the previous single European species into two) has a discontinuous Holarctic distribution. In North America (the split proposes Buff-bellied Pipit, *Anthus rubescens*) these pipits breed in Alaska, N Canada and the Rocky Mountains. In Eurasia the group's breeding distribution stretches from Spain to the Caucasus and the mountains S of the Caspian Sea, then through C Asia, from NE Afghanistan to the Okhotsk Sea, Kamchatka and the Chukotskiy Peninsula. In northern Europe populations breed along the coasts of NW and N France, the Channel Islands, Britain & Ireland, and Fennoscandia. The systematics of the *spinoletta/petrosus* group are in constant revolution, the number of species and subspecies varying considerably from one author to another.

The Rock Pipit *A. petrosus* now comprises all former coastal subspecies of Water Pipit *A. spinoletta* (*petrosus* from Britain & Ireland, the Channel Islands and N and NW France, *kleinschmidti* from the Faeroes, Shetland, Orkney, Fair Isle and St Kilda and *littoralis* from Fennoscandia) and breeds only in Europe. During the breeding season, the Rock Pipit lives almost solely on rocky coasts. It may nest just 2m above the high-tide mark, but rarely does it breed above 100m asl. The Rock Pipit is relatively evenly distributed along the rocky shorelines of its distribution area; breeding densities vary from 0.9 to 6 bp/km of coast (Glue 1993b).

Most Rock Pipit territories include coastal strips of cliff or large rocks several metres high, but sometimes they are located on sandy shores (Gibb 1956) when there are slopes or cliffs further inland. Its nest resembles that of the Water Pipit and is made in sheltered small cavities on grassy slopes, under rocks or even in crevices in cliffs. The Rock Pipit habitat usually allows it to forage for roughly equal periods on the intertidal zone and on land; in the grass, on slopes above the sea and on short-grass terrain on the cliff-tops (pers obs). A similar ecological isolation seems to exist between Rock Pipit and Meadow Pipit *A. pratensis* in areas of cohabitation as between the latter and the Water Pipit: the Rock Pipit does not seek to feed on heather-moors which are much favoured foraging habitats for the Meadow Pipit (pers obs).

Since the mid-1970s, the Rock Pipit population in Britain & Ireland seems to have declined slightly (Glue 1993b), whereas most other populations appear to be stable. A northward range extension occurred in Finland in 1970–90, but did not proceed beyond Quark, probably due to a lack of rockweed (prime foraging substrate) in the Gulf of Bothnia (Koskimies 1989a).

The Rock Pipit may be resident or migratory. Mainland Irish and British populations are largely resident, with some local dispersion. Populations of *kleinschmidti* are strongly tied to the breeding range, although first-year birds may wander. Outside the breeding season, most remain on the coasts, although some move to sandy shores which are unsuitable for breeding. Many birds winter by rivers and lakes, as far as 20km inland. Fennoscandian birds are mostly migratory. Concentrated wintering has been recorded on saltmarshes in the SW Netherlands, with up to 5300 ± 1100 birds on 2450ha in the winter of 1992/93, feeding almost exclusively on the mollusc *Asiminea grayana* (Bourgonje 1994). Individuals (*petrosus* as well as *littoralis*) can be found as far S as Sicily, Malta, southern France, Portugal and Spain. There are also records from NW Africa. The subspecies *littoralis* is encountered regularly in Scotland during the spring migration (J-P. Biber 1986).

Jean-Pierre Biber (CH)

Motacilla flava

Yellow Wagtail

CZ	Konipas luční	I	Cutrettola
D	Schafstelze	NL	Gele Kwikstaart
E	Lavandera Boyera	P	Alvéola-amarela
F	Bergeronnette printanière	PL	Pliszka żółta
FIN	Keltavästäräkki	R	Желтая трясогузка
G	Κιτρινοσουσουράδα	S	Gulärla
H	Sárga billegető		

Non-SPEC, Threat status S

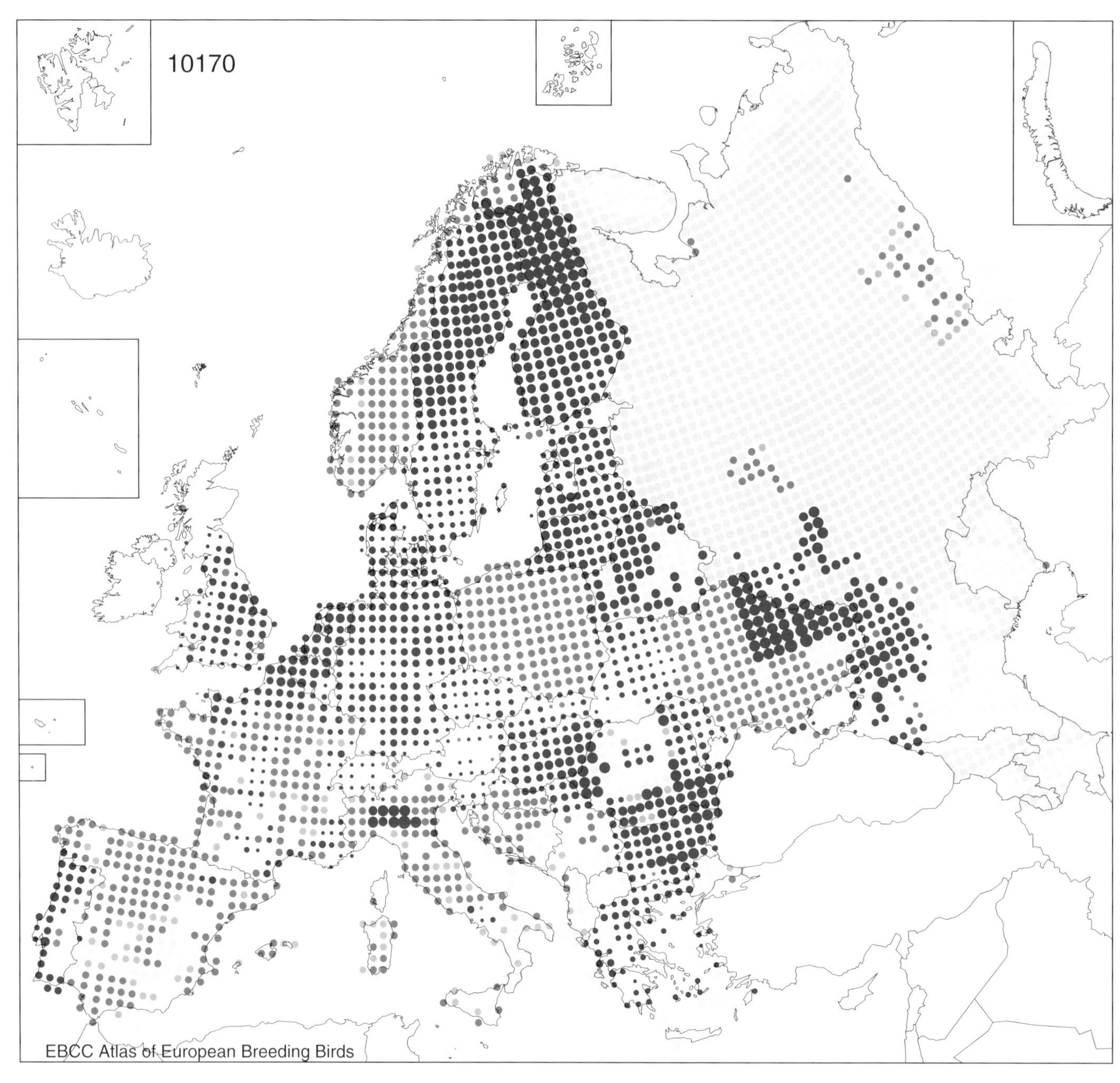

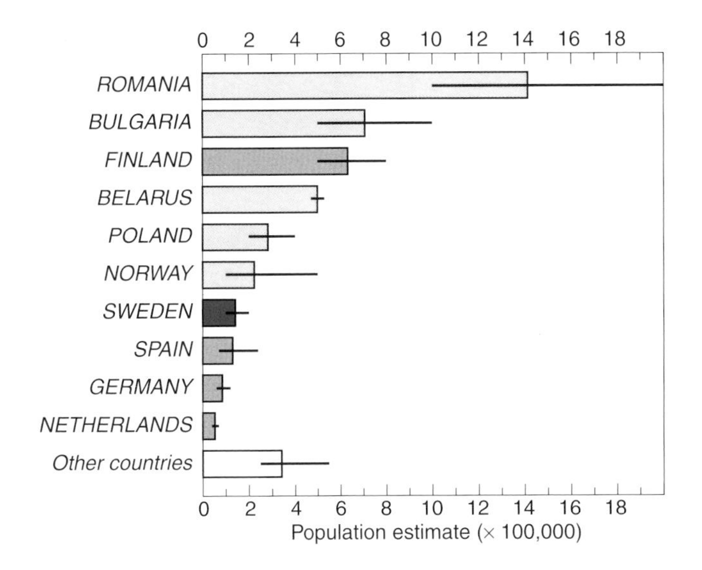

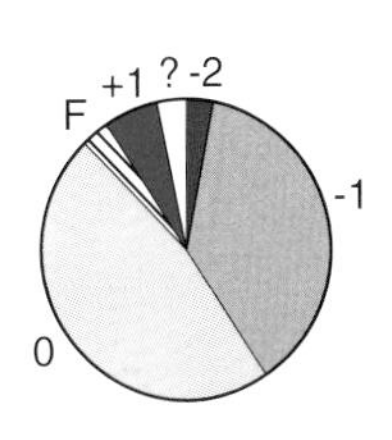

% in top 10 countries: 92.5
Total number of populated European countries: 32
Total European population 3,995,700–5,266,251 (4,507,802)
Russian population 1,000,000–10,000,000 (3,162,278)
Turkish population 100,000–1,000,000 (316,228)

The Yellow Wagtail, a widespread species, breeds up to the 10°C July isotherm in the arctic tundra, subarctic, boreal, temperate, steppe and mediterranean zones. Its distribution covers almost the entire Palearctic, from western Europe to Kamchatka, and across the Bering Straits into Alaska. Between 14 and 18 subspecies are recognized worldwide in a chain of isolates which stretch from E to W, although wide intergradation zones exist. Eleven subspecies breed in the *Atlas*' coverage area.

In its western range the Yellow Wagtail is a lowland species, inhabiting level or gently sloping land, but in the Caucasus it also occupies damp meadows and wetland edges up to 2000–2500m asl (*BWP*). It prefers moist grassy areas, with a dense (>40%) cover and a vegetation height of 45–60cm, usually close to water. In N Europe and Russia, it also occupies *Sphagnum* bogs and large open peatlands. Large-scale arable land has become increasingly important as breeding habitat in W and C Europe. More than half of the Dutch population nowadays resides in such intensively farmed, dry habitats, at densities of 12–36 bp/km^2; in the provinces of Groningen and Drenthe in the 1980s, 95% of 34 400bp bred on arable land (Beintema *et al* 1995). Only rarely do similar or higher densities occur in semi-natural habitats and grasslands, as on floodmeadows along the Oder and Volga (Dittberner & Dittberner 1984).

The total European population is estimated at 4.3M–16.4Mbp. The largest populations are in the E where Russia holds 1M–10Mbp, Romania 1M–2Mbp and Bulgaria 0.5M–1Mbp, equivalent to a large-scale overall density of >10 000 bp/50km square. High values of 1000–3600 bp/50km square apply to Fennoscandia, Belarus, Poland, Denmark and The Netherlands. Densities were lowest in the C European montane regions (the Czech Republic, Slovakia, Austria, Switzerland, N Italy). The map shows a clear westward decline for W Norway, France and Spain. The species is virtually absent from Ireland and most of Scotland, SW England and W and C Wales (Tyler 1993). The maritime climate of western Europe may fit this pattern, but it is difficult to understand what mechanism might apply.

During 1970–90, negative trends have been reported from 13 countries (mainly *flavissima* and *flava*), stability from 16 and increases from only Sweden and Slovenia. Between the first (1968–72) and second (1988–91) BTO Breeding Bird Atlases a range contraction of 9.4% occurred in Great Britain (Tyler 1993). A number of factors may have caused these declines but in Britain changes in agricultural practices probably are responsible. Agricultural intensification has drained favoured wetlands and replaced grassland with cereals. However, in some areas such as the Lincolnshire fens the species is still relatively common, nesting frequently in both cereal and root crops (S. Gillings, pers obs). The species has adapted quite successfully to the creation of artificial wetland habitats such as sewage farms and gravel-pits. Circumstantial evidence implies that the decline in continental Europe during 1970–90 may be attributed to drainage, use of herbicides and manure dumping (Zuppke 1984, Büsche 1985), and similar changes can be expected from E Europe in the near future.

Most Yellow Wagtail populations are migratory and winter in the subtropical and tropical zones. The various subspecies winter from the Afrotropics through India and SE Asia. The subspecies *M.f. pygmaeus*, largely resident, occurs in southernmost Spain, and by breeding before other subspecies have returned, may be reproductively isolated (Simms 1992). An increase in the effective width of the Sahara may jeopardize Yellow Wagtail populations by inevitably requiring a longer non-stop flight during migration, thus possibly increasing mortality rates. Environmental degradation of the Sahel will most likely affect males of southern European races, given the partial segregation in Africa of populations from different breeding latitudes (Wood 1992).

Simon Gillings (GB) Rob G Bijlsma (NL)

Motacilla cinerea — Grey Wagtail

CZ	Konipas horský	**I**	Ballerina gialla
D	Gebirgsstelze	**NL**	Grote Gele Kwikstaart
E	Lavandera Cascadeña	**P**	Alvéola-cinzenta
F	Bergeronnette des ruisseaux	**PL**	Pliszka górska
FIN	Virtavästäräkki	**R**	Горная трясогузка
G	Σταχτοσουσουράδα	**S**	Forsärla
H	Hegyi billegető		

Non-SPEC, Threat status S (P)

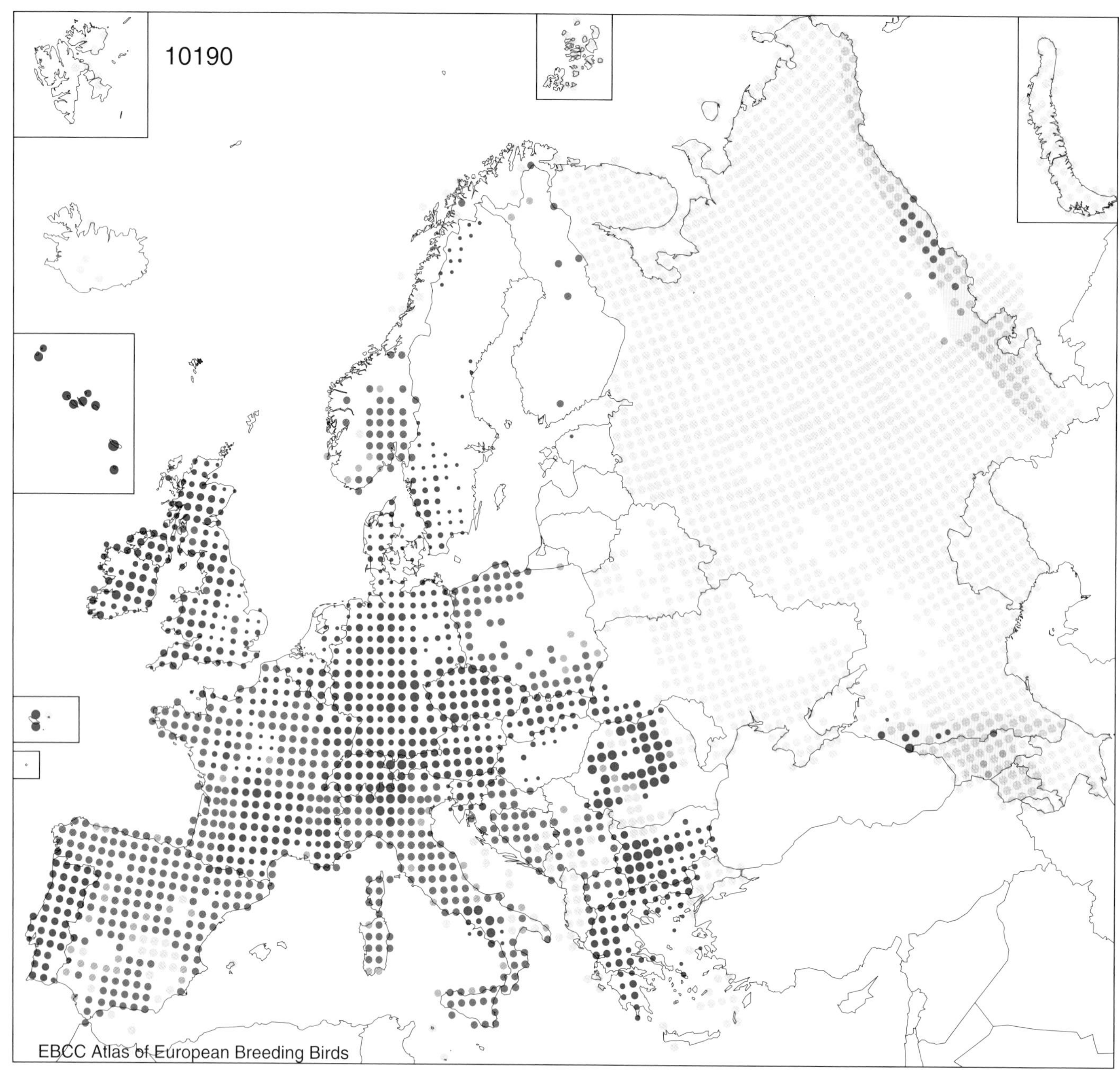

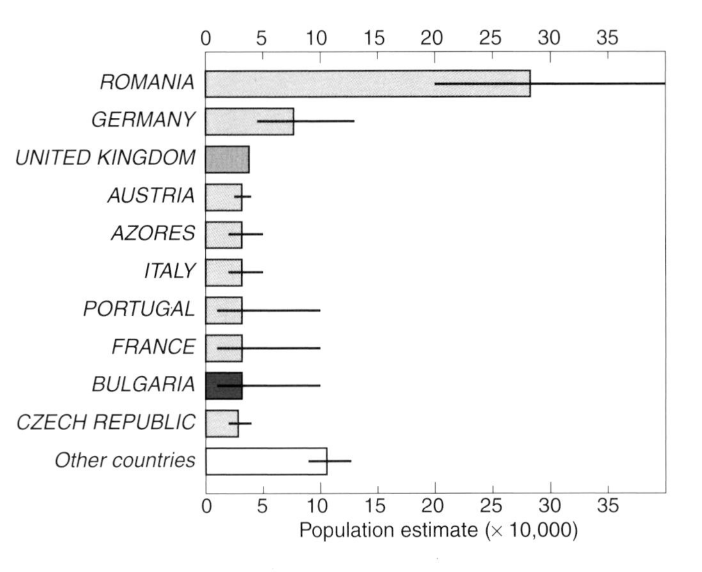

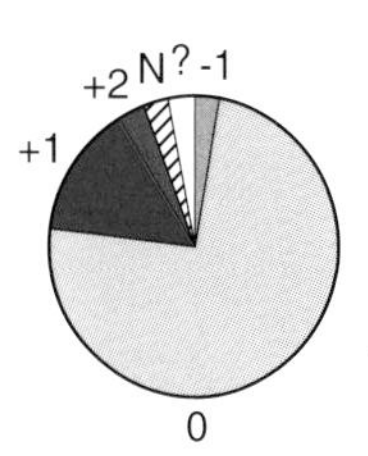

% in top 10 countries: 85.4
Total number of populated European countries: 35
Total European population 622,315–898,346 (720,682)
Russian population 1000–5000 (2236)
Turkish population 10,000–100,000 (31,623)

The Grey Wagtail has two discontinuous distribution areas in the Palearctic: NW Africa and Europe largely SW of a line from Gdansk through the Terek River to Iran (the nominate *M.c. cinerea*) and from the western Urals and Afghanistan to the Amur River (*melanope*); *M.c. robusta* occurs further east in Asia. (These three subspecies are not recognised by all authorities.) The remaining three subspecies are island forms: *patriciae* (Azores, 20 000–50 000bp), *schmitzi* (Madeira, 300–500bp) and *canariensis* (Canary Islands). Small populations occur patchily in the S between Iran and Afghanistan. In the western Palearctic, the species inhabits mainly the temperate and mediterranean middle and lower latitudes, extending slightly into the boreal zone.

Optimal habitats are wild torrents and fast-running rivers, bordered by sheltering woods (a few trees above the timberline). They have a high structural diversity, comprising rocks, boulders, shingle and gravel beds, and sometimes sections of shallow, slow-flowing or stagnant water. The presence of a current is important, whereas water quality (pollution, acidification) apparently has less effect on breeding density (Ormerod & Tyler 1991). Habitat requirements may be met by mills, weirs, dams, bridges, canal locks or reservoir and other outflows in open lowland plains or beside human settlements. The species is rare or absent along very small slow-flowing or treeless brooks and where nest sites are scarce. It is distributed linearly along running waterways, breeding from sea level to 2000m asl, occasionally up to 3000m. The middle reaches of rivers often hold the densest populations. In winter the species occupies a broader range of habitats, including the coast or beside standing water. In Europe, the species is widely distributed in the S and W, more patchily in the N (S Scandinavia) and is restricted locally in, or absent from, the E and NE (Finland, Poland, Russia). It is mostly absent from large lowland plains and coastal areas.

Density varies markedly between and within waterways, but over complete river systems it rarely exceeds 10 bp/10km. Up to 30 bp/10km may hold territories along major rivers or stretches of optimal habitat (NE Bohemia up to 32.9; S Switzerland 30.1) and 10–20 bp/10km is reasonably representative of subalpine and montane regions (Harz Mountains 10.6-11.5 bp/10km, Oelke 1975; N Wales 11.4, Sharrock 1976; Swiss Bernese Oberland 7.9–17.5 [mean 12.6], Breitenmoser-Würsten & Marti 1987). Values usually are less than 10.0 in less hilly areas and *c*5.0 in lowlands and plains (England 3.1–4.9, Sharrock 1976; E Belgium 4.6, de Liedekerke 1980; N Germany 2.5–5.0, rarely 7.5–10.0, Klafs & Stübs 1979). Breeding density may vary with food supply, food availability, current strength, altitude, waterway width and land use (4–5 bp/10km for small brooks, 11–12 for larger, swifter rivers; Oelke 1975).

The species generally has expanded its range since 1850 from the C European mountains to the N German and NE Polish lowland plains, The Netherlands (1915), Denmark (1923), Sweden (1916), Norway (1919), and more recently to Finland (1972), Estonia (1975) and Latvia (1991). In the last three countries, though remaining rare, it is increasing in numbers or range. Mild winters (Ormerod & Tyler 1993), mill- and weir-construction on rivers may have favoured expansion. Substantial mortality in severe winters may produce distinct, but often short-term decreases leading to lower densities or larger-scale absence.

Although some individuals may winter at the northern and eastern distribution limits or at high altitude, the Grey Wagtail essentially is migratory in N and E Europe, partially so in C European and Atlantic regions and mainly resident or locally dispersive in Britain & Ireland, Belgium, France, Iberia and the Mediterranean. High-altitude populations migrate to lower levels. Winter quarters outside the breeding distribution lie in North Africa, East Africa S to Malawi, the Near and Middle East and from Pakistan to China and New Guinea.

Luc Schifferli (CH) Jiri Flousek (CZ)

This species account is sponsored by Natur- und Vogelschutzverein Küsnacht, CH.

Motacilla alba

White Wagtail

CZ	Konipas bílý	I	Ballerina bianca
D	Bachstelze	NL	Witte Kwikstaart
E	Lavandera Blanca	P	Alvéola-branca
F	Bergeronnette grise	PL	Pliszka siwa
FIN	Västäräkki	R	Белая трясогузка
G	Λευκοσουσουράδα	S	Sädesärla
H	Barázdabillegető		

Non-SPEC, Threat status S

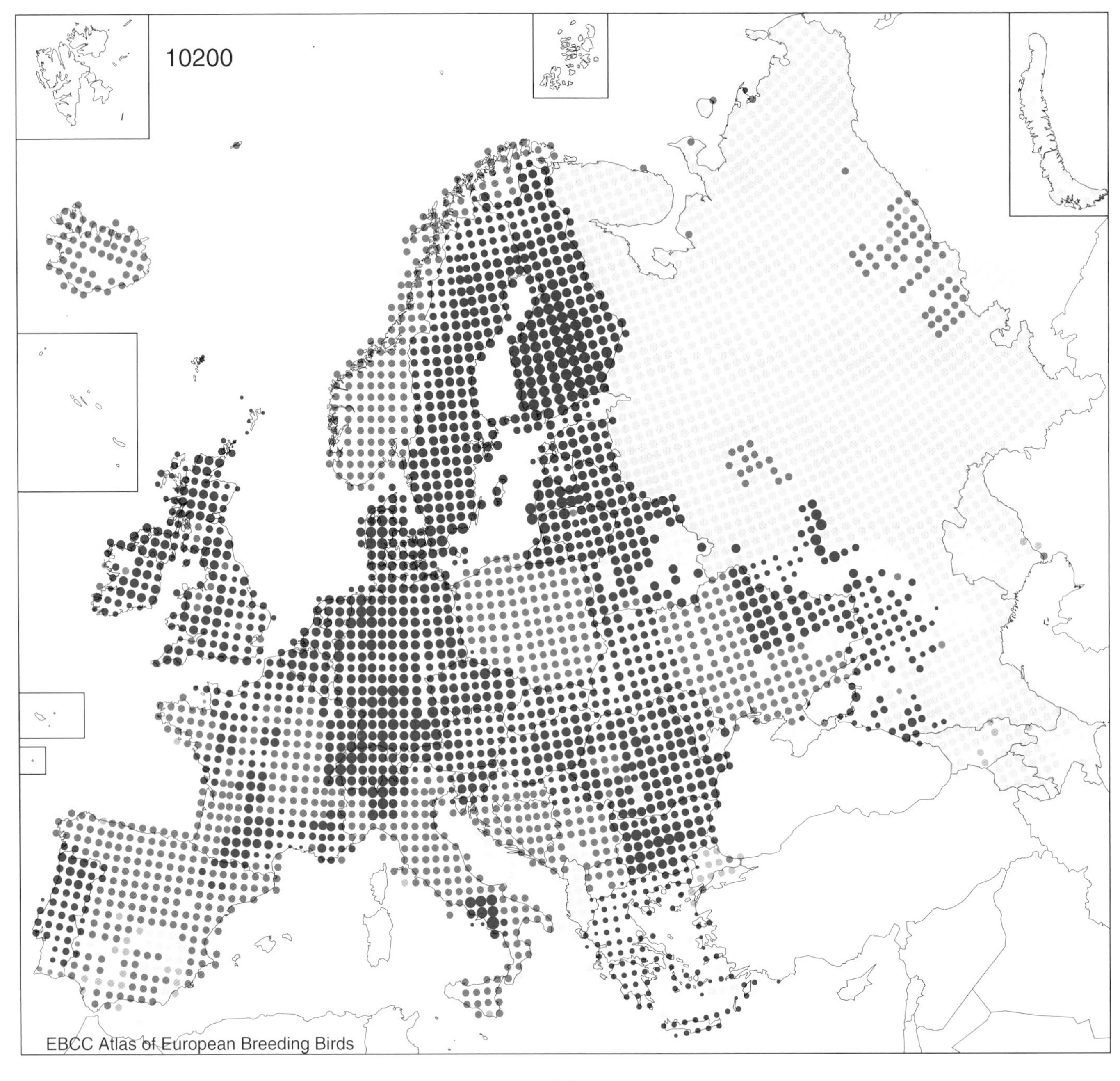

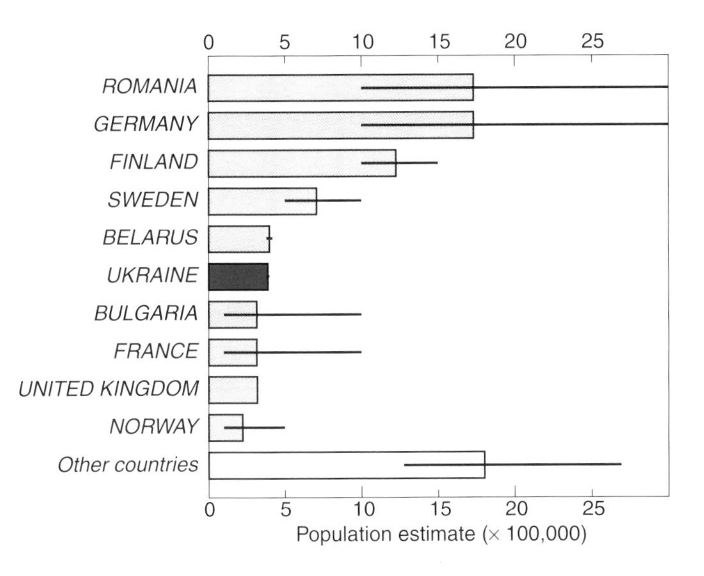

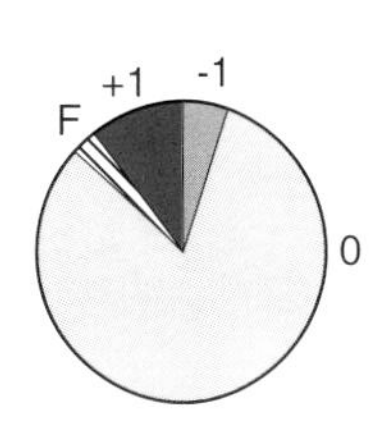

% in top 10 countries: 80.3
Total number of populated European countries: 38
Total European population 8,022,825–11,278,021 (9,162,804)
Russian population 1,000,000–10,000,000 (3,162,278)
Turkish population 50,000–500,000 (158,114)

This common and familiar species of both urban and rural locations in a variety of climate zones is widespread in Europe, Morocco and Asia, N to beyond the Arctic Circle at 75°N, S to Iran, the Himalayas and SW China at 35°S, and E to Japan and the Bering Strait. It also occurs in small numbers in the Levant, E Greenland and W Alaska. Eleven subspecies are recognized, the grey-backed nominate *M.a. alba* being predominant across continental Europe, and the black-backed *yarrellii* (Pied Wagtail) breeding in Britain & Ireland and coastal parts of Denmark, The Netherlands, Belgium and northern France. S of the Sahara the closely related African Pied Wagtail *M. aguimp* replaces the White Wagtail in a widespread but patchy distribution across Africa.

The species is most closely associated with both permanent and temporary waterside habitats of almost any kind, such as rivers, lakeshores and wet meadows. But this belies an adaptability which allows it to exploit an enormous array of wet and dry habitats, with the primary exception of deserts. As a strongly territorial species it is never locally abundant in summer but occupies a multitude of natural and artificial locations, including canals, sewage farms, farmyards, grazing pastures, parks, gardens, beaches and industrial landscapes. It is also encountered frequently in town centres where sometimes it roosts communally in large numbers. The species establishes territories from sea level to well above the timberline (up to *c*3000m asl), especially where there is human habitation (*BWP*). It builds its nest in natural holes and crevices near rivers, but has adapted to use tiled roofs, holes in buildings and externally mounted air-conditioning equipment. It avoids enclosed woodland, tall ground-vegetation and mountain plateaus.

Quantitative data show a fairly even distribution from Ireland to the Ukraine, densities varying between *c*1000 and 10 000 bp/50km square. In the Mediterranean basin from Iberia to Greece, densities reach only 1000 bp/50km square or less. Breeding density has been linked to food supply (Zahavi 1971), and to availability of enclosed nest sites provided by human settlements (Leinonen 1974). In Germany, the species is most numerous in small villages amidst farmland, with densities of 13–43 bp/km^2 (Flade 1994). In Switzerland, maximum average densities range from 5 bp/km^2 in open areas to 10–20 bp/km^2 in and around villages (Ölschlegel 1985), values matched as optimal breeding densities in N Iberia, although not in SE Spain (0.4 birds/km of river near Granada; Pleguezuelos 1992). The species is absent as a regular breeding species only from parts of C and S Iberia, where it is confined to rivers and mountain villages, and from the Balearics, Corsica and Sardinia.

The White Wagtail population apparently has remained stable over most of Europe. The top ten countries exhibit no significant change in population status. However, a recent decrease in aquatic insects because of increasing water pollution may yet prove to be a factor limiting breeding density in some parts of Europe (Simms 1992). The resident and (partially) migratory populations of W and C Europe are susceptible to harsh winter weather, which may cause temporary declines (Marchant *et al* 1990).

Birds breeding in N and E Europe are highly migratory, moving to Mediterranean regions (including the Balearics) and becoming one of the most abundant wintering species, whereas British and Irish populations are rather sedentary S of the Scottish Highlands, but small numbers winter in Brittany and as far S as Portugal. This movement is evident also from the relatively large numbers of spring migrants in the SW Netherlands, where up to 13% of all 'white wagtails' which can be identified at subspecific level belong to *yarrellii* (Meininger & Wolf 1995).

Juan C Alonso (E) Ian Henderson (GB)
Francisco Purroy (E)

Motacilla citreola

Citrine Wagtail

CZ	Konipas citrónový	I	Cutrettola testagialla orientale
D	Zitronenstelze	NL	Citroenkwikstaart
E	Lavandera Cetrina	P	Alvéola-citrina
F	Bergeronnette citrine	PL	Pliszka cytrynowa
FIN	Sitruunavästäräkki	R	Желтоголовая трясогузка
G	Κιτροσουσουράδα	S	Citronärla
H	Citrombillegető		

Non-SPEC, Threat status S (P)

Two of the three subspecies of the Citrine Wagtail breed in the western Palearctic, the nominate *M.c. citreola* in N Russia from the Kanin Peninsula to C Siberia, and *werae* in C Russia E to Manchuria. In Europe the species breeds in the arctic and northern boreal zones, but reaches the subtropics in Asia. The tundra population often nests in osier thickets, principally between 71° and 75°N. The southern boreal populations (Kazhakstan and Iran to the N Himalayas) favour damp areas, or tundra-like terrain in mountains, and sporadically have bred further west, a tendency seemingly turning into a slow range extension.

The Citrine Wagtail first bred in Belarus in 1982 (Yaminnski & Nikiforov 1986) mainly occupying sedge mires and swampy meadows. It now breeds regularly but remains sparsely distributed, usually sharing the habitat of Yellow Wagtail *M. flava*. In Ukraine since 1976, initially in the Kharkov region (Lisetski 1978), it spread to breed in 13 regions, but remains well-dispersed (Klestov & Gavrish 1991). It colonized Lithuania by 1987 (open peat-bog, isolated reed-stands nearby; Pranaitis 1990) and first bred in Estonia in 1991 (mating with a female Yellow Wagtail) and in Latvia in 1993 (sedge-tussock meadow, bulrush *Typha* nearby). An apparent range extension is evident also in Turkey (Roselaar 1995). It breeds in N Poland (P. Chylarecki, pers comm to the Editors) and has recently bred in Finland.

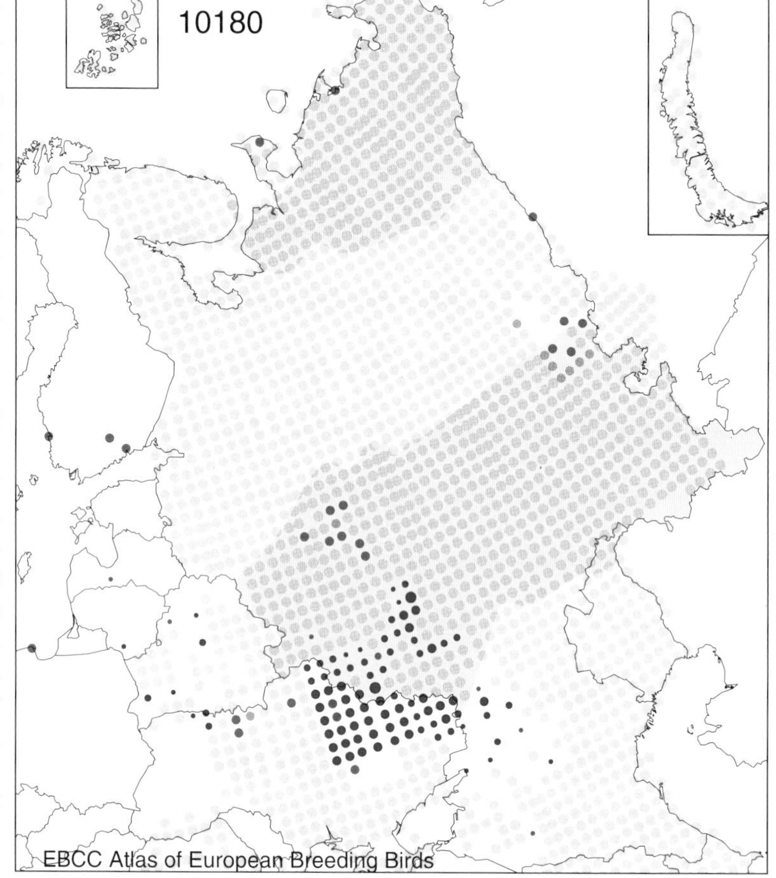

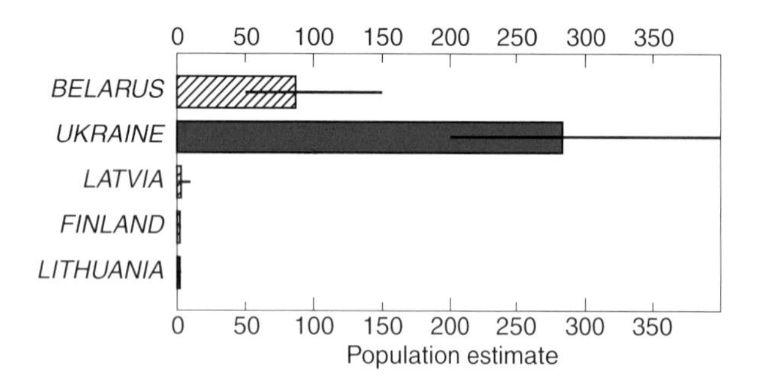

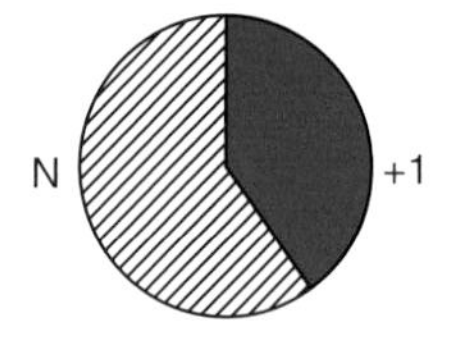

% in top 10 countries: 100.0
Total number of populated European countries: 5
Total European population 285–509 (376)
Russian population 100,000–1,000,000 (316,228)
Turkish population 500–5000 (1581)

The species may nest semi-colonially, but even then pairs are strongly territorial. In several suitable sites in Lugansk, Ukraine, the average breeding density ranged from 0.3 to 0.5 bp/ha (Kochegura 1989). For nesting it usually requires a damp habitat, such as marshy meadows, but otherwise needs water nearby throughout the breeding season so that sufficient insect life (dragonfly larvae, water-beetles) provides food for both adults and young. Even on its wintering grounds it favours aquatic habitats (Simms 1992).

Most birds return to the breeding grounds in April, but northern populations delay breeding until June, although they may manage a second brood. The fledged young remain on the breeding grounds until September. Breeding may take place at any altitude from sea level to 4500m asl.

Janis Baumanis (LAT) Philip Jackson (GB)
Valentin V Serebryakov (UKR)

Bombycilla garrulus

Waxwing

CZ	Brkoslav severní	I	Beccofrusone
D	Seidenschwanz	NL	Pestvogel
E	Ampelis Europeo	P	Tagarela-europeu
F	Jaseur boréal	PL	Jemiołuszka
FIN	Tilhi	R	Свиристель
G	Βομβυκίλλα	S	Sidensvans
H	Csonttollú		

Non-SPEC, Threat status S (P)

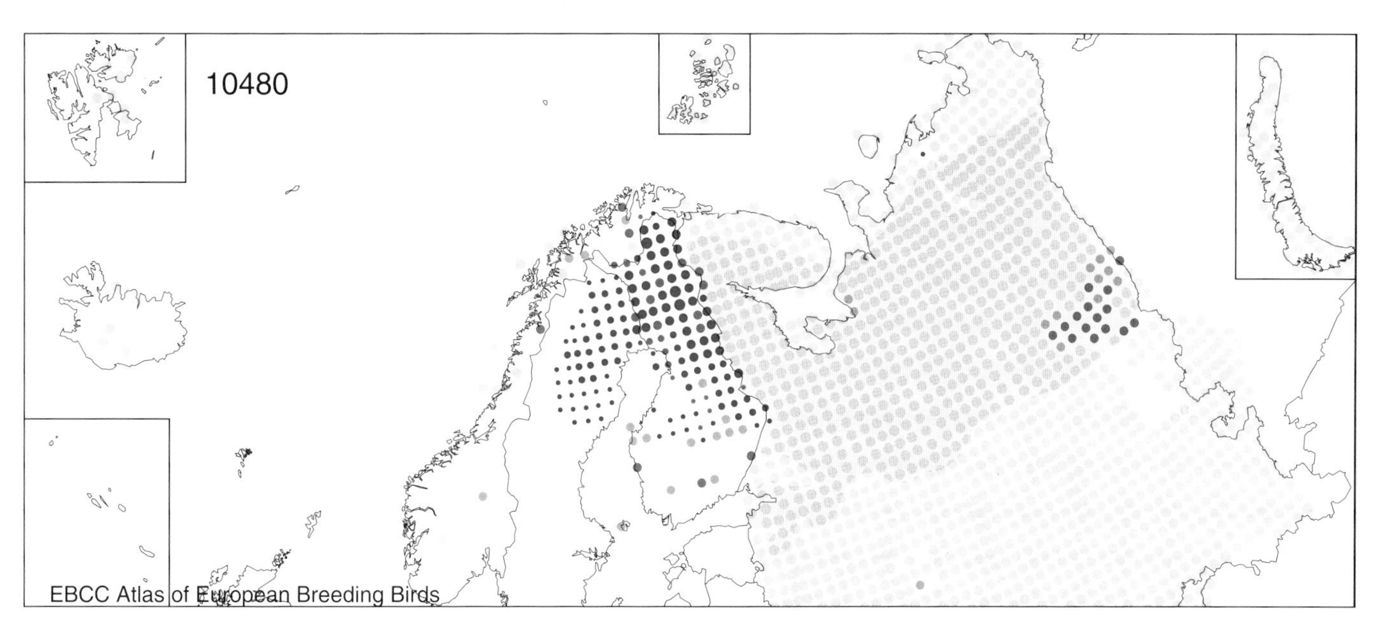

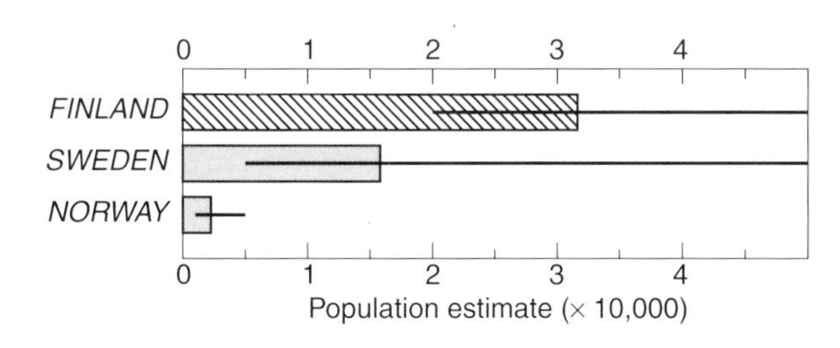

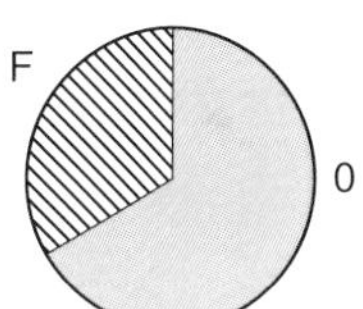

% in top 10 countries: 100.0
Total number of populated European countries: 3
Total European population 33,748–88,583 (49,670)
Russian population 100,000–1,000,000 (316,228)

The Waxwing is one of the most typical birds of the boreal forest of Eurasia. It is a Holarctic species: the distribution area covers northern Eurasia, from the Atlantic to the Pacific, and NW and N–C North America. Of the three subspecies, the nominate *B.g. garrulus* occurs in Europe.

Within the *Atlas*' coverage area, the Waxwing is found as a regular breeder in northern and C Finland and Sweden. In southern Sweden and Norway its distribution is patchy and densities are low. The population density of the species increases from W to E, and the main population of the species inhabits the vast taiga forests of N Russia and Siberia. The most preferred habitats of the Waxwing are mature or old stands dominated by coniferous trees, pine *Pinus* and spruce *Picea* in Fennoscandia. It favours particularly old stands which have a relatively open canopy and a rich field layer.

Outside the breeding season the Waxwing occurs in flocks, which are easily observed and recognized, but during the breeding season it remains inconspicuous. Numbers of breeding pairs fluctuate considerably from one year to another. The species' winter diet comprises berries, and when the rowan-berry *Sorbus aucuparia* crop is good, the Waxwing winters in the N, close to its normal breeding areas. In years of crop failure, large-scale irruptions may occur, and the Waxwing populations move westwards and southwards, often transiting northern Europe rapidly to reach to C and western Europe, even southern Europe.

In prime habitats in northern Fennoscandia, the breeding density of the Waxwing is typically 0.5 bp/km^2 or less, The highest densities observed came from virgin pine *Pinus* forests in Finnish Lapland (1.3 bp/km^2; Virkkala 1987a). Modern forestry management techniques produce even-aged closed-canopy forests whose field layer is scanty, habitat quite unsuited to the Waxwing (Järvinen *et al* 1977). The *Atlas* data do not suggest any major changes in abundance in the species' range.

Pekka Helle (FIN) Timo Pakkala (FIN)

Cinclus cinclus

Dipper

CZ	Skorec vodní	**I**	Merlo acquaiolo
D	Wasseramsel	**NL**	Waterspreeuw
E	Mirlo Acuático	**P**	Melro-d'agua
F	Cincle plongeur	**PL**	Pluszcz
FIN	Koskikara	**R**	Оляпка
G	Νεροκότσυφας	**S**	Strömstare
H	Vízirigó		

Non-SPEC, Threat status S (P)

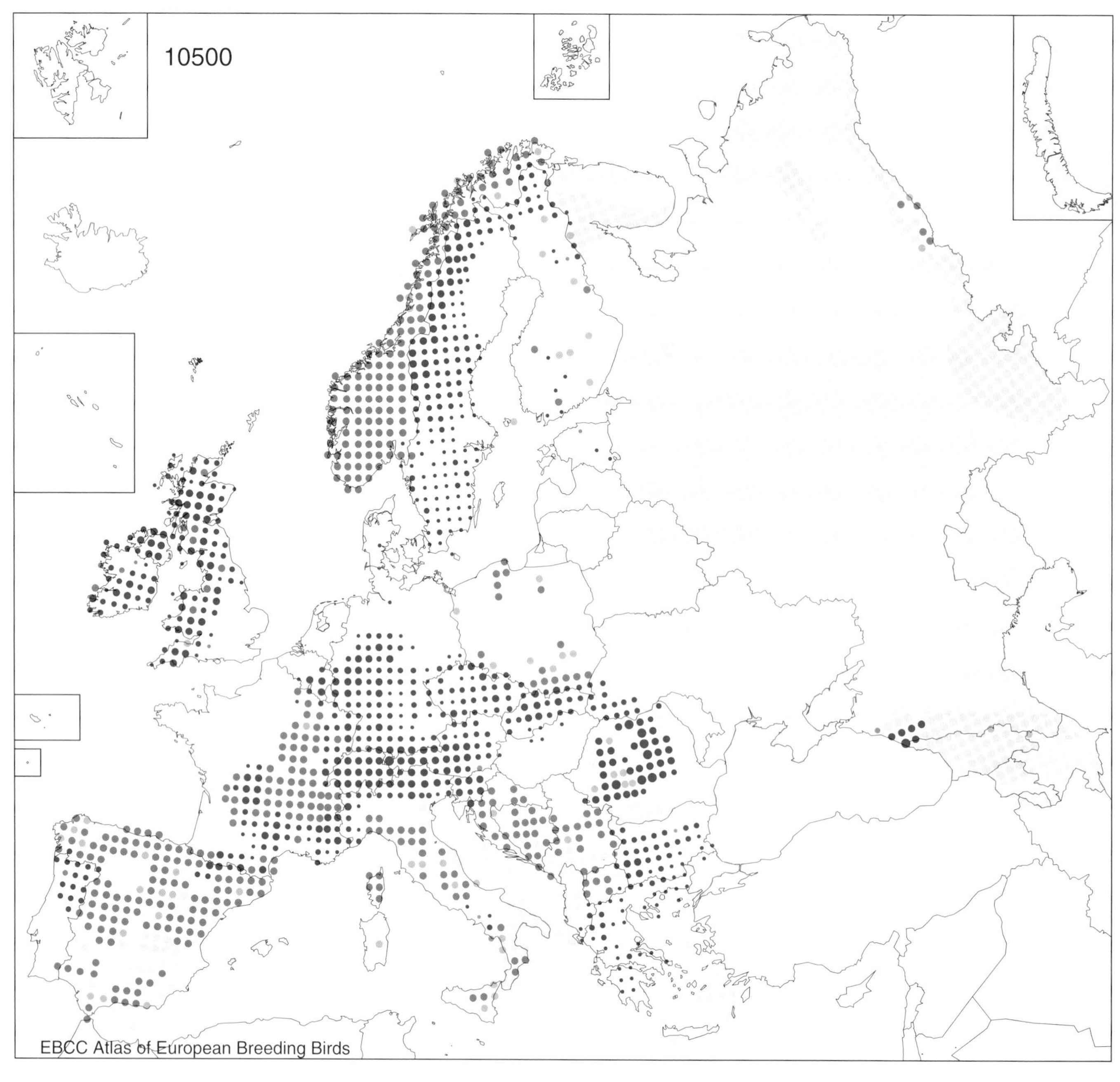

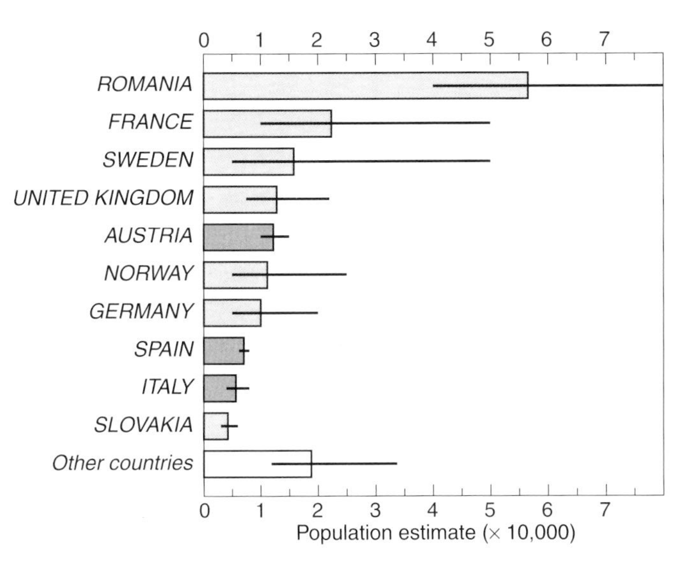

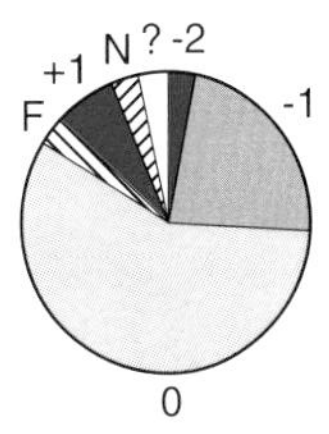

% in top 10 countries: 89.4
Total number of populated European countries: 31
Total European population 151,176–230,908 (176,752)
Russian population 1000–10,000 (3162)
Turkish population 500–5000 (1581)

The Dipper has a Palearctic distribution across Europe, North Africa, Lebanon, Asia Minor, the Urals, Himalayas, Kum Lun, Hindu Kush, Tian Shan, Altai and Sayan. In W China, S Turkestan and the Himalayas it is sympatric with the Brown Dipper *C. pallasi* which ranges eastwards across China and Amurland to Japan. The latter species occupies similar habitats, but in the area of overlap tends to be restricted to lower altitudes and larger rivers (Tyler & Ormerod 1994).

Throughout a breeding range encompassing boreal, temperate, steppe and mediterranean climatic zones, the Dipper breeds alongside, and feed almost exclusively, in well-oxygenated waters of fast-flowing streams and rivers, especially where a stony bed provides preferred invertebrate prey such as mayfly (*Ephemeroptera*) adults and nymphs, caddis (*Trichoptera*) larvae and stonefly (*Plecoptera*) nymphs (Jost 1975). True fly (*Diptera*) larvae may replace mayflies in the diet at high altitudes (C. Breitenmoser-Würsten, pers obs).

The Dipper has a wide altitudinal range, from sea level to over 2100m asl in the Alps, and 5500m asl in the Himalayas, yet it is sedentary except where streams freeze over completely, when some birds move to slower-flowing rivers and lakes at lower altitudes and even to seashores. Some such movements are long-distance (>1000km) and may be regarded as true migrations, birds from Norway and Sweden wintering in Finland, Denmark, the Baltic States and occasionally E England. The European breeding distribution matches closely the hilly or mountainous relief that provides suitable watercourses. The map suggests that breeding densities tend to reduce with decreasing altitude and latitude, and distribution becomes patchy at the southern range limits near the Mediterranean.

The Dipper is strongly territorial during the breeding season. Pairs defend linear territories along streams. On suitable watercourses, densities vary from 1 to 20 bp/10km depending on food and nest-site availability (Breitenmoser-Würsten & Marti 1987, Tyler & Ormerod 1994). Probably there has been little recent change in overall range, although small peripheral populations experience periodic extinction and recolonization (as on islands such as the Isle of Man, Orkneys and Islay); the subspecies *olympicus*, endemic to Cyprus, is now extinct. In parts of Britain & Ireland, population densities have declined and breeding range has contracted recently due to acidification of watercourses, exacerbated by conifer afforestation, which reduces the abundance of invertebrate prey, and may cause calcium shortages for egg-laying females (Ormerod & Tyler 1987, Tyler & Ormerod 1992). In Germany and Poland, reported declines arise more directly from industrial pollution, although water purification schemes are allowing the Dipper to re-occupy some rivers (Mildenberger 1984). Hydroelectric and irrigation schemes may be causing declines in southern Europe by reducing flow rates in otherwise suitable watercourses. On the edge of the breeding range (Denmark, Estonia) there is possible evidence of range extension, perhaps by wintering birds remaining to breed.

Within the *Atlas* coverage, six subspecies, based on marked and complex plumage variation, occur (Tyler & Ormerod 1994). The considerable variation within any single subspecies' range merits caution in interpreting current taxonomy. The nominate *C.c. cinclus* occupies Fennoscandia, Denmark, C France, W Iberia, Corsica and Sardinia. It is the most migratory European subspecies, accounting for most wintering records outside the breeding range in Britain, France, Denmark, Finland and the Baltic States. *C.c. aquaticus* occupies the remainder of continental Europe except for the Caucasus and the Urals where *caucasicus* and *uralensis* occur. Lastly, there are two island endemics, *hibernicus* in Ireland and *gularis* in Britain. Six, perhaps seven, subspecies occur elsewhere in the species' distribution.

Jeremy Wilson (GB)
Christine Breitenmoser-Würsten (CH)

This species account is sponsored by Norsk Ornitologisk Forening, Klaebu, N.

Troglodytes troglodytes **Wren**

CZ	Střízlík obecný	I	Scricciolo
D	Zaunkönig	NL	Winterkoning
E	Chochín	P	Carriça
F	Troglodyte mignon	PL	Strzyżyk
FIN	Peukaloinen	R	Крапивник
G	Τρυποφράχτης	S	Gärdsmyg
H	Ökörszem		

Non-SPEC, Threat status S

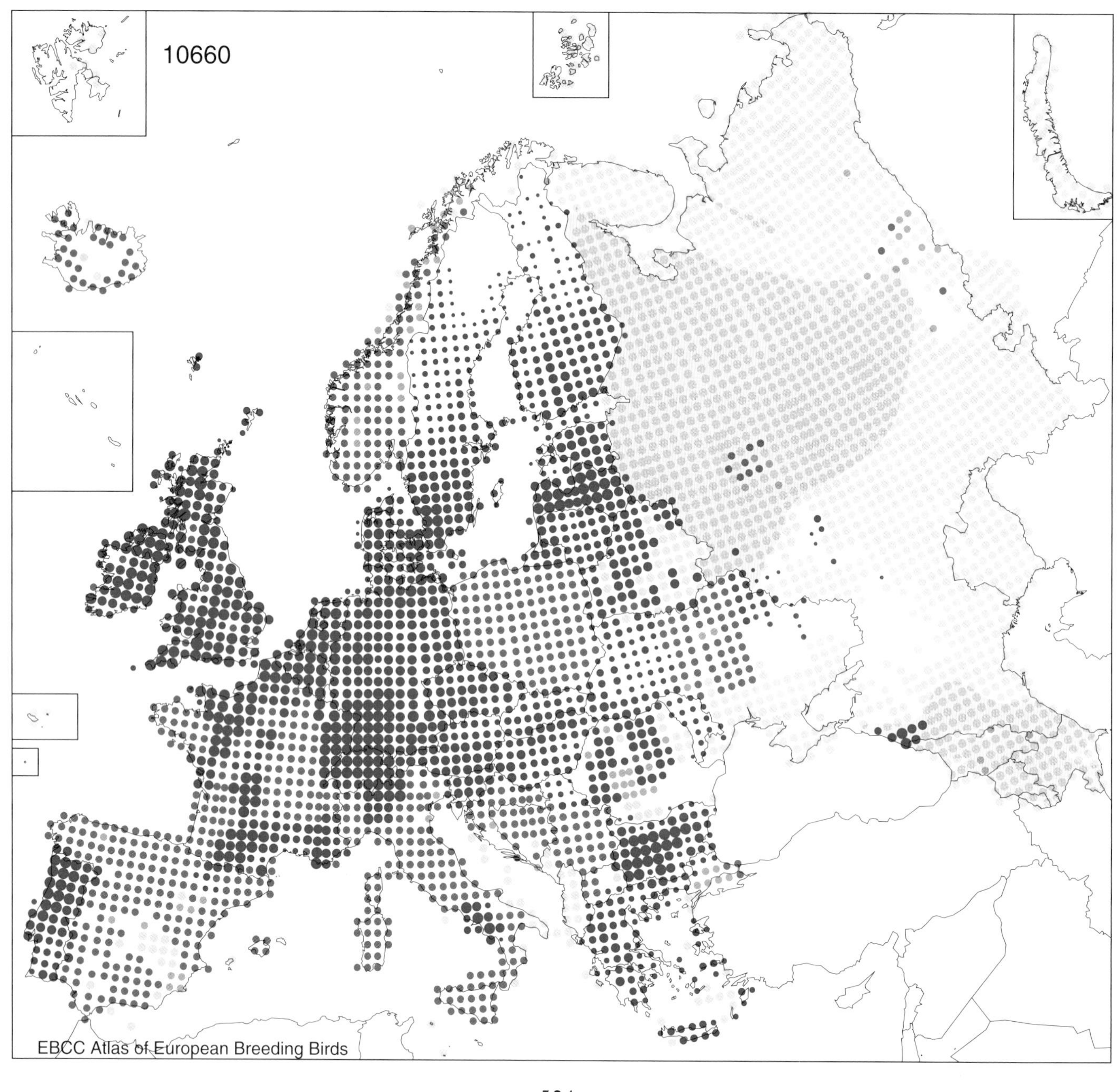

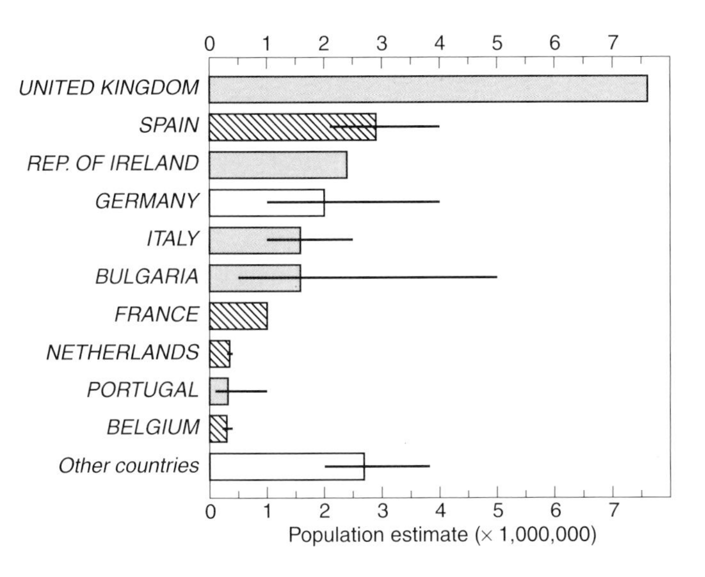

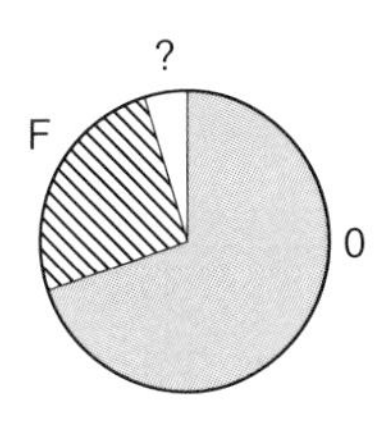

% in top 10 countries: 89.6
Total number of populated European countries: 40
Total European population 20,438,366–26,528,108 (22,238,499)
Russian population 1,000,000–10,000,000 (3,162,278)
Turkish population 50,000–500,000 (158,114)

The Wren is a Holarctic species, breeding in the Palearctic region from Iceland, Ireland and NW Africa, throughout most of Europe, the Caucasus, the mountains of the Middle East and C Asia, Himalayas, N China, Korea up to Taiwan, Japan, Sakhalin and Kamchatka. A chain of insular (Commander and Pribilov Islands) and Alaskan populations joins the Palearctic range with that of continental North America, where the Wren breeds mostly in the boreal forest zone.

The Wren is exceptional and perhaps unique in being an American passerine which has successfully invaded Asia, Europe and North Africa. The existence of a number of Wren subspecies in the vicinity of the Bering Strait supports the hypothesis that the crossing was achieved via the North Pacific, probably fairly recently (Armstrong & Whitehouse 1977).

A very versatile species, it can breed almost anywhere from the seacoast to above the treeline, from extensive forests to completely treeless tundra. It is essential that the habitat is moist and possesses dense ground vegetation and some vertical structures (such as fallen trees, branch tangles, stone walls, cliffs). However, the most favourable habitats are damp deciduous or mixed forests (riverine stands, carrs) usually in overgrown stream valleys possessing a thick ground layer, uprooted trees, fallen logs and tangled branches. Despite this wide versatility, over much of its range (Fennoscandia, C and E Europe) the Wren remains principally a forest bird, like its North American ancestral stock. Only in heavily deforested areas subject to strong oceanic influences (The Netherlands, N France, N Spain, Britain & Ireland) has large-scale colonization of non-wooded areas occurred, marked by a population explosion. Even in such areas woodlands with rich undergrowth still remain the preferred habitat.

The Wren's European breeding range omits only the N and SE. Areas close to the species' northernmost limit are very thinly populated. Breeding density in C and E European woodland in close-to-primeval conditions reaches 5 bp/10ha, whereas values in western European populations occupying secondary habitats can reach 30 bp/10ha (Wesołowski 1983). When the broad spectrum of such habitats which the Wren utilizes in western Europe is taken into account, the very large national populations (>10 000 bp/50km square) found in this region are well-explained.

There have not been any strong recent population changes reported, except for the marked fluctuations observed when severe winters decimate numbers and then milder subsequent winters allow the affected populations to recover (Deppe 1990). Winter severity is an especial danger to this tiny species, because the Wren has a very high surface to volume ratio, and relatively poor capacity to store winter fat. Thus, even a short spell of winter weather severe enough to prevent efficient feeding can result in high mortality (S.G. Nilsson 1986b, Marchant *et al* 1990).

Northeastern and eastern populations are totally migratory, whereas those in western and southern Europe and comprising island populations are partially migratory or sedentary. Northern migrants winter mostly within the species' southern and southwestern breeding distribution, but also occupy Ukraine and S Russia which lie beyond the normal breeding range. The origin of the birds wintering in Iran and Iraq is uncertain.

Within the Wren's extensive range populations are extremely diversified. There are probably some 27–32 subspecies outside Europe, seven insular subspecies within its European range and several others within continental Europe. The nominate *T.t. troglodytes* is most widespread, breeding from Fennoscandia and the Urals S to the Pyrenees, NW Spain, Portugal, Italy and Greece. It grades into *indigenus* in C and S England, into *kabylorum* along the Mediterranean coast of France, C Spain and Sicily and into *hyrcanus* in Romania and SE Ukraine; *hyrcanus* also inhabits the Caucasus.

Tomasz Wesołowski (PL)

This species account is sponsored by Dr Reinhold Oehmen, Rheinberg, D.

Prunella modularis

Dunnock

CZ	Pěvuška modrá	I	Passera scopaiola
D	Heckenbraunelle	NL	Heggemus
E	Acentor Común	P	Ferreirinha-comum
F	Accenteur mouchet	PL	Pokrzywnica
FIN	Rautiainen	R	Лесная завирушка
G	Θαμνοψάλτης	S	Järnsparv
H	Erdei szürkebegy		

SPEC Cat 4, Threat status S

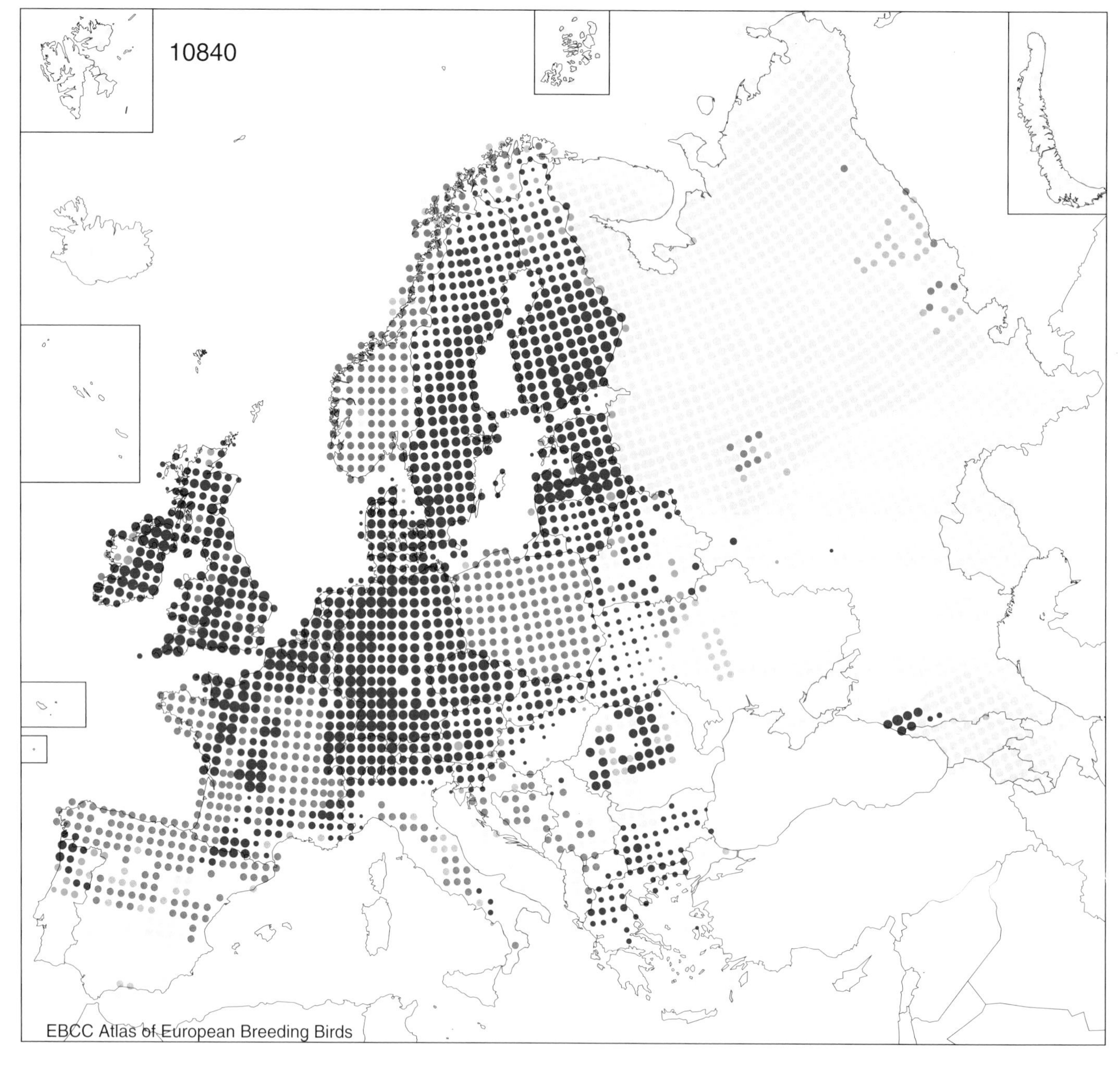

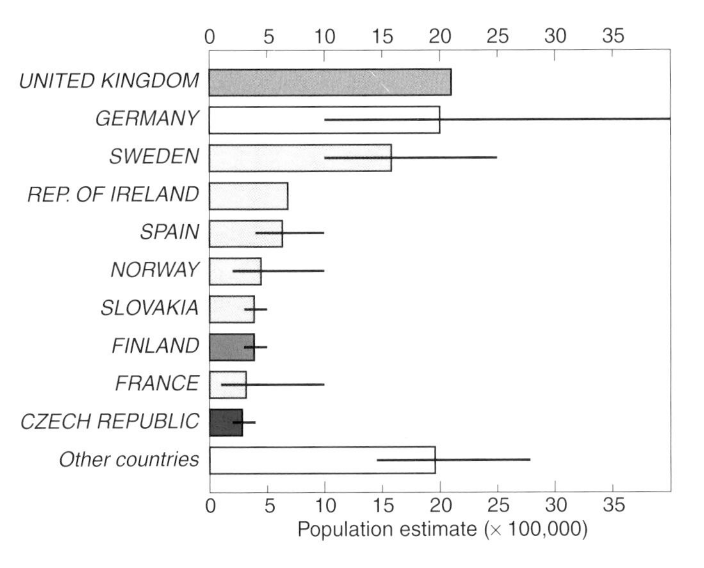

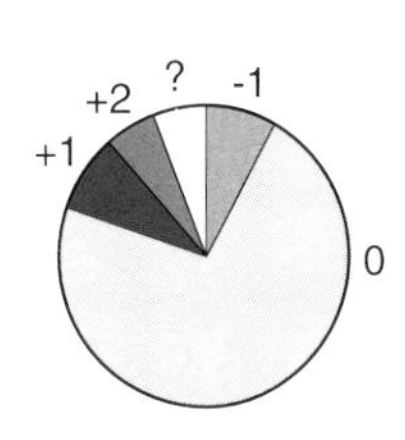

% in top 10 countries: 81.8
Total number of populated European countries: 36
Total European population 9,527,628–13,191,476 (10,770,614)
Russian population 1,000,000–10,000,000 (3,162,278)
Turkish population 10,000–50,000 (22,361)

Essentially a European breeding bird, except for small isolated populations in Turkey (*P.m. euxima*) and Iran, the Dunnock is widely distributed, breeding from high-arctic areas in Fennoscandia and Russia S to the Mediterranean and also in the Caucasus. It is absent from Iceland, Svalbard, the Shetlands, the Faeroes, southern Iberia, most Mediterranean islands, southern Italy, the Hungarian plain and the Danube Valley. The other seven subspecies all occur in the *Atlas*' coverage area.

The Dunnock breeds in the upper and middle latitudes, mainly in the temperate zone, but extending into the subarctic, boreal and mediterranean zones. It breeds in scrubby habitats avoiding high-alpine zones, extensive marshlands and, in the Mediterranean area, lowlands and semi-arid plains. In much of Europe, it is typically a woodland species, densities being highest in young forest plantations, especially of spruce (20–60 bp/km^2; Flade 1994). In the North Sea countries, especially Britain & Ireland, the Dunnock is most numerous in farmland and suburban areas. In agricultural areas it favours hedges, scattered bushes and farmsteads. It is a common breeding bird of cemeteries, parks, orchards and gardens in western Europe whose mosaic of vegetation types provides excellent breeding and feeding conditions and where densities sometimes reach 50 bp/10ha. Under such circumstances, the Dunnock has developed an extraordinarily variable mating system (N.B. Davies 1992).

In woodland it favours areas of secondary growth. High densities occur also in forest margins, clearings and mature coppices, but it usually avoids closed-canopy woodlands and forests lacking a shrubby understorey. Densities are high in humid broad-leaved woods and forests along brooks and rivers. In the Alps it prefers spruce *Picea* and larch *Larix* forests. In Fennoscandia the Dunnock is abundant in several types of forests, in Lapland frequenting the birch *Betula* zone and almost treeless areas where juniper *Juniperus* is present. In S Finland it inhabits the spruce or juniper forest undergrowth, mostly in spruce-dominated coniferous forests, avoiding pure pine *Pinus sylvestris* forest without undergrowth. Densities vary from 4 to >20 bp/100ha depending on forest type (J. Tuomenpuro, pers obs, Vickholm 1983). In Swiss and Austrian woodlands the mean density varies between 4 and 6 bp/10ha, varying little up to 1800m asl; in the Polish broad-leaved Białowieża Forest it is *c*4 bp/10ha, and locally in The Netherlands and Germany, >10 bp/10ha.

Its highest European breeding altitude is *c*2600m in Switzerland. In C European montane woodland, it is numerous where needle-leaved trees are stunted through either lasting winter snow-coverage or intensive grazing by deer. Above the timberline it breeds amongst scattered coniferous scrub and subalpine vegetation such as rhododendron, where nearby boulders provide look-out and song-posts.

Since 1850 the Dunnock has extended its breeding range markedly, colonizing the Outer Hebrides, Orkneys and the suburban areas of NW Europe. A scarce breeder above 64°N in Fennoscandia before the 1950s, its rapid increase is due at least partly to modern forestry practices increasing its favoured spruce-dominated patchy forest (Koskimies 1989a). This trend continues, but at a reduced rate (R. Väisänen, pers comm). Hard evidence of climatic change helping the spread is lacking. Elsewhere in Europe, increases may have been assisted by large-scale reafforestation. The slow population decline in the British population since the mid-1970s is unexplained, although changes in farming practices may have allowed competition from other passerine species, thus forcing the Dunnock into more marginal sites (Marchant *et al* 1990).

Resident in western Europe, it is partially migratory in W–C Europe, many making altitudinal movements in montane areas. Fennoscandian and C European populations E of the Oder are fully migratory, wintering S to the Mediterranean, Israel and the Mesopotamian River basins.

Rob L Vogel (NL) Jari Tuomenpuro (FIN)

This species account is sponsored by Reinhard Vohwinkel, Velbert, D.

Prunella montanella

Siberian Accentor

CZ	Pěvuška horská	I	Passera scopaiola asiatica
D	Bergbraunelle	NL	Bergheggemus
E	Acentor Siberiano	P	Ferreirinha de Pallas
F	Accenteur montanelle	PL	Płochacz syberyjski
FIN	Vuorirautiainen	R	Сибирская завирушка
G	Κιτρινοψάλτης	S	Sibirisk järnsparv
H	Szibériai szürkebegy		

Non-SPEC, Threat status S (P)

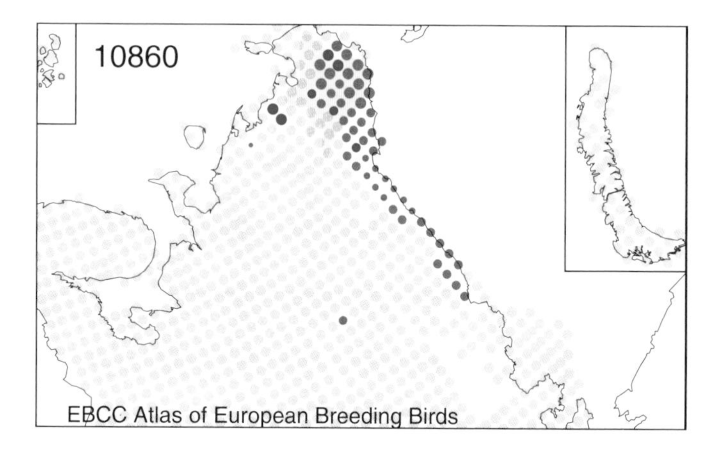

The western distribution of the Siberian Accentor separates into northern and southern belts joining in E Siberia near the Stanovoy Range. Its eastern limits in Asia (*P.m. badia*) are the W-facing main slopes of the Chukotskiy Mountains, the lower reaches of the Anadyr River, the Sea of Okhotsk, N Kamchatka and the Sikhote-Alin ridge.

In Europe the nominate *montanella* inhabits the W-facing main slopes of the Urals, from the northern end S to Tel'posiz Peak, the foot of Pavdinsky Stone Peak and the Bassegy Range (58°50'N, 58°30'E) (Ivanov 1976, Boyarshinov *et al* 1989, V.V. Morozov, unpubl). It also breeds in the Bol'shezemel'skaya tundra, the More-Yu River basin (Uspenski 1965, Estafiev 1979, Morozov 1987) and the Chornaya basin (V.V. Morozov, unpubl). It occurs in the forest-tundra as far W as Inta city (66°04'N, 60°05'E), in the subpolar Urals (the upper Ilyich River reaches) and the Sablya and Western Saledy Ranges (64°45'–65°30'N, 58°55'E) (Estafiev 1977b). Singing males found further W have not been proved to breed.

The species occurs during migration at the Cheloy River (the Pechora basin). It winters in the Tzing-Ling mountains, in NW Hainzhou and in the northern Khalkha.

Single-brooded, on the W slope of the Urals it occupies thinned-out foliaceous and spruce forests containing birch *Betula* and willow *Salix* shrubs, sparse stunted spruce *Picea* forests bordering swamps and willow stands up to 800m asl. In the polar Urals it inhabits not only willow and birch shrub tundras containing dense juniper shrubs *Juniperus sibirica*, but also, on slopes up to 350m asl, alder bushes *Alnus glutinosa* up to 3m high. In the Bol'shezemel'skaya tundra it occupies stunted spruce forests, willow bushes, riverine willow-shrubs up to 1.5m high, scattered shrubs on the slopes of the large ravines of the tundra plateau, and willow–sedge (–*Carex*) bogs at tundra lakes and plain watersheds. The total European breeding population of Siberian Accentor is *c*16 000bp. Breeding densities are given in Table A.

Alexey A Estafiev (R) Sergey K Kotchanov (R)
Vladimir Morozov (R)

Table A Breeding densities of Siberian Accentor, *Prunella montanella* in various habitats

Habitat	bp/km²	Source
Sub-polar Urals, western slope		
Stunted forest	1.4	A.A. Estafiev, pers comm
Foliaceous forest (admixture of spruce & shrubs)	4.8	A.A. Estafiev, pers comm
Willow shrubs	1.7	A.A. Estafiev, pers comm
Shrubby habitat up to 800m asl	1.5	A.A. Estafiev, pers comm
Overall	0.21	A.A. Estafiev, pers comm
Polar Urals		
Willow forest containing dwarf birch	<5.0	V.V. Morozov, pers comm
River valleys containing juniper shrubs	<1.2	V.V. Morozov, pers comm
Bol'shezemel'skaya tundra		
Thinned-out spruce forests (slopes & terraces of river valleys)	0.7–3.1	Estafiev 1979
Shrub-filled spruce forests (floodplain)	1.6	Estafiev 1979
River valley (dwarf birch–willow and juniper)	3.7–5.0	Morozov 1987
Tundra lakes (willow–sedge bogs)	1.02–2.5	Morozov 1987
Overall tundra*	0.18	

* In small concentrations of optimal habitat, densities can be much higher.

Prunella atrogularis

Black-throated Accentor

CZ	Pěvuška černohrdlá	I	Passera scopaiola golanera
D	Schwarzkehlbraunelle	NL	Zwartkeelheggemus
E	Acentor Gorginegro	P	Ferreirinha-de-garganta-preta
F	Accenteur à gorge noire	PL	Płochacz czarnogardły
FIN	Mustakurkkurautiainen	R	Черноголовая завирушка
G	Μαυρόλαιμος Ψάλτης	S	Svartstrupig järnsparv
H	Szakállas szürkebegy		

SPEC Cat 3, Threat status V (P)

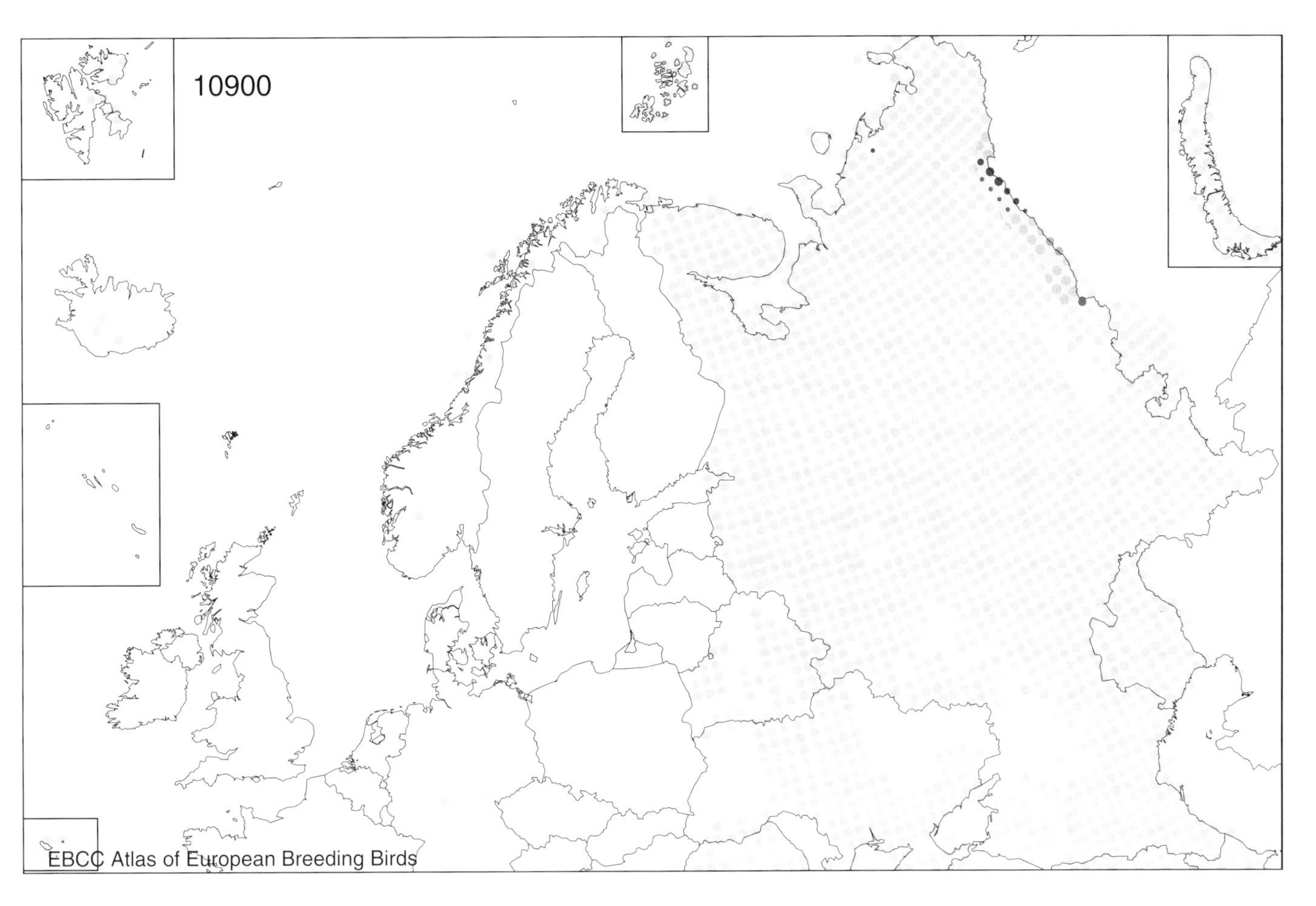

The poorly known Black-throated Accentor breeds in mountain spruce forests in the middle, northern and extreme-northern subzones of the boreal zone and in the coniferous mountain forests of the Urals from 63°N almost to 66°N. Reports of this species from the E coast of the White Sea (Spangenberg & Leonovich 1958) have not been confirmed by recent data. The nominate subspecies *P.a. atrogularis* is isolated in the Ural Mountains from the other subspecies *huttoni* which breeds in the mountains of Russian southwestern Sayan, the Altai (Russia and Mongolia), Saur (China), Dzhungarski Alatau and Ketmen (Kazakhstan), Tian-Shan (Kirghizstan) and northern Alai Khrebet (Kirghizstan and Tajikistan). The Urals population is totally migratory, whereas that of *huttoni* is partially so, the main wintering area lying in SW C Asia (Turkmenistan, Uzbekistan, Iran and Afghanistan).

The Black-throated Accentor breeds in a variety of habitats from spruce *Picea* forests of the foothills to mountain larch *Larix* forests and willow *Salix* bushes. It is more numerous at the treeline limits in the sparsely forested and dwarf-tree zones (Portenko 1937, Estafiev 1977b). It prefers spruce forests in which the ground is grass-covered, a habitat combination rare in the Urals, and where breeding density reaches 10 bp/km². On the much commoner moss-covered ground in spruce-dominated habitats, breeding density is only 0.5 bp/km². Values in larch forests and willow bushes vary from 5 to 12 bp/km², but the highest recorded were in mountain birch forests (24 individuals/km²), reflecting the species' use of this habitat for foraging (Estafiev 1981).

In the Urals the numbers and range of the Black-throated Accentor probably are stable because its European forest habitat is little-exploited and remains well protected. Nevertheless the species is rare and nowhere does it reach high overall densities. The European population is estimated to be *c*3500–4000bp.

Alexey A Estafiev (R) Vladimir N Anufriev (R)

Prunella collaris

Alpine Accentor

CZ	Pěvuška podhorní	I	Sordone
D	Alpenbraunelle	NL	Alpenheggemus
E	Acentor Alpino	P	Ferreirinha-alpina
F	Accenteur alpin	PL	Płochacz halny
FIN	Alppirautiainen	R	Альпийская завирушка
G	Χιονοψάλτης	S	Alpjärnsparv
H	Havasi szürkebegy		

Non-SPEC, Threat status S

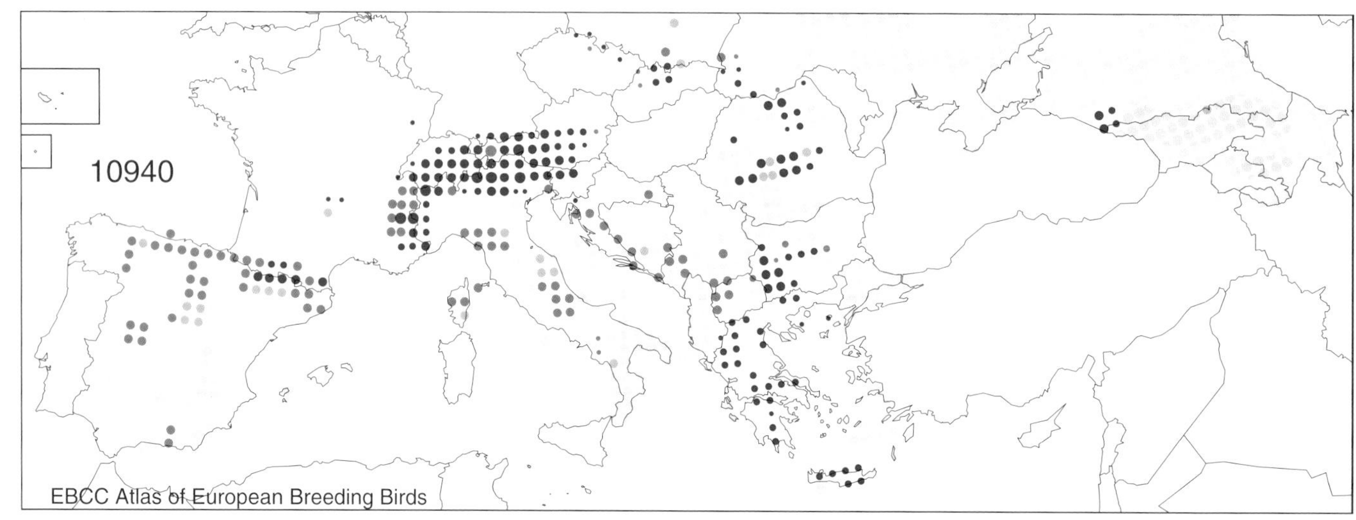

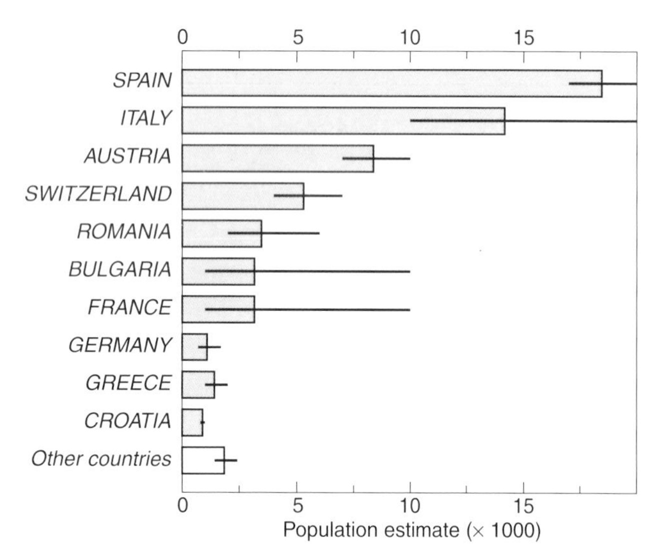

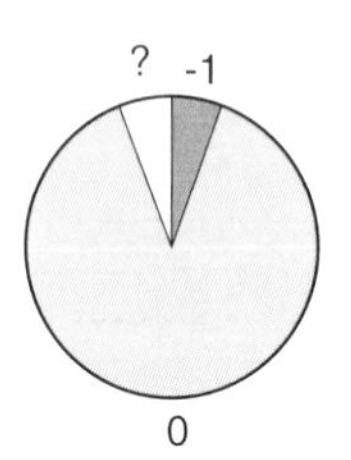

% in top 10 countries: 97.0
Total number of populated European countries: 18
Total European population 55,383–73,232 (61,269)
Turkish population 1000–10,000 (3162)

The Alpine Accentor breeds almost entirely on rocky mountain slopes between the tree-limit and the snowline. Its distribution stretches from NW Africa through W and C Europe, to Romania (*P.c. collaris*), SE Europe and W Turkey (*subalpina*) E to the Caucasus and Turkmeniya (*montana*). The main distribution E of the Hindu Kush to Japan contains six other subspecies.

In prime habitat, the Alpine Accentor breeds in polygynandrous groups whose size is influenced by the temporal availability of fertile females (N.B. Davies, pers comm), and probably also by habitat area. Group sizes were: 24–40 birds in the Krkonoše (Miles 1986), *c*40 on Mount Bliznitsa, Ukraine (Talposh 1977) and 150–300 'pairs' in the Polish Tatra Mountains (Glowacinski & Profus 1992), the number fluctuating annually (P. Profus, pers obs). Breeding populations tend to be stable (from a 1985–95 survey in the Slovakian C Low Tatras), but breeding density varies considerably, probably through annual weather and snow-cover differences (Dyrcz 1976). Prime habitat densities (birds/km^2) were: *c*26 (N Pyrenees, N.B. Davies, pers comm), 12–16 (Swiss Alps), and 10–15 (Tatras; M. Janiga, pers obs, Drgoňová & Janiga 1989). Declines in local densities may arise through natural or feral cat predation in winter. Adverse effects may yet arise from garbage-feeding.

E Carpathian birds winter in the S Carpathians or the Zacarpathian lowlands; High Tatra birds migrate past the Low Tatras; many probably winter in N Hungary. In snow-free winters, some remain in the breeding areas (M. Janiga, pers obs) and others become altitudinal migrants feeding near buildings or roadsides. More young birds and females abandon the breeding sites than do adults and males respectively (Martí *et al* 1989). Males start returning to the alpine zone in March (most in April) and females arrive mainly in early May (M. Janiga, pers obs).

Andrzej Dyrcz (P) Marián Janiga (SLK)

Cercotrichas galactotes

Rufous Bush Robin

CZ	Pěvec ryšavý	I	Usignolo d'Africa
D	Heckensänger	NL	Rosse Waaierstaart
E	Alzacola	P	Rouxinol-do-mato
F	Agrobate roux	PL	Drozdówka rdzawa
FIN	Ruostepyrstö	R	Тугайный соловей
G	Κουφαηδόνι	S	Trädnäktergal
H	Tüskebujkáló		

Non-SPEC, Threat status S

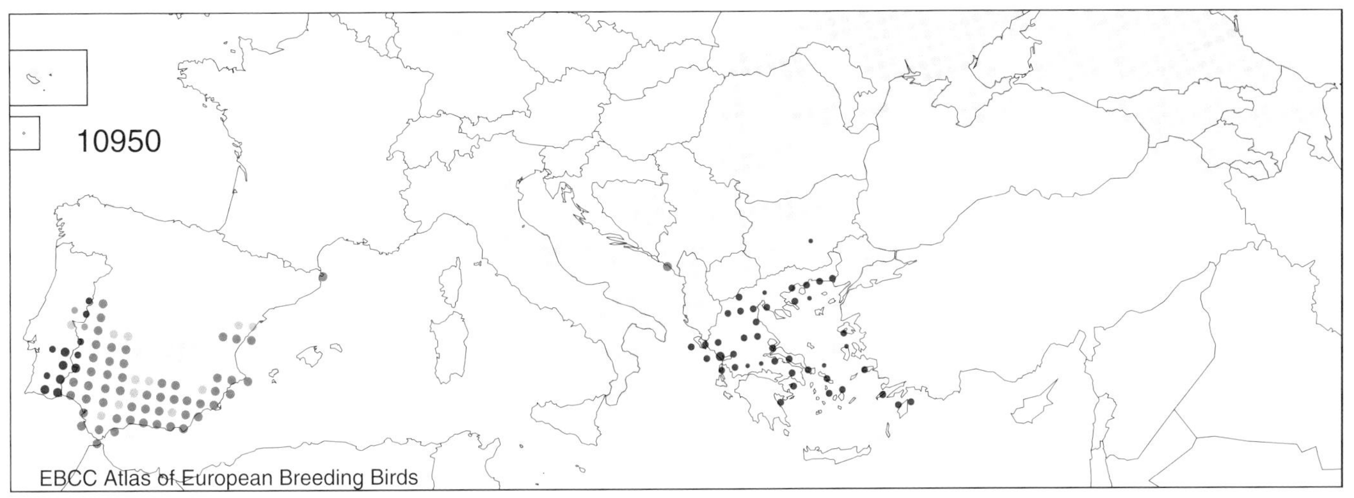

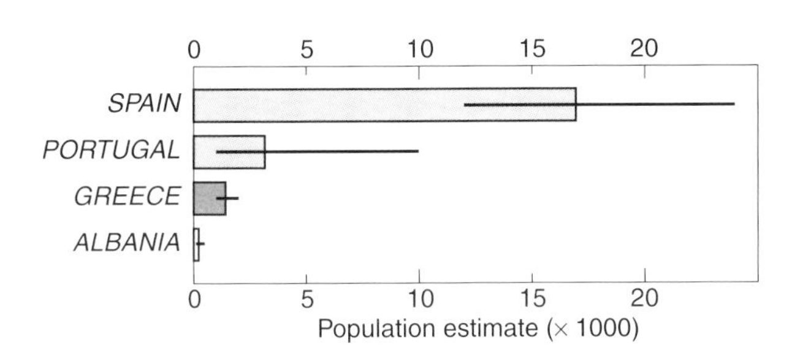

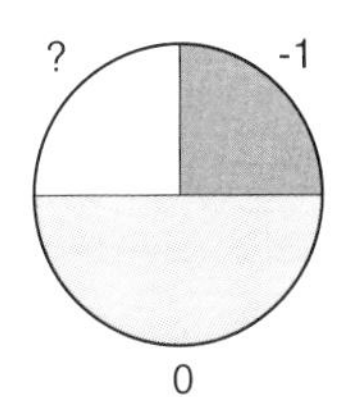

% in top 10 countries: 100,0
Total number of populated European countries: 4
Total European population 16,333–31,599 (21,771)
Turkish population 5000–50,000 (15,811)

The distribution of the Rufous Bush Robin covers the E and W Mediterranean and stretches E through Transcaucasia to C Asia, S of the Aral Sea and Lake Balkhash. Dispersed resident populations occur in Africa above 8°N and in western Arabia. In Europe the two main disjunct populations comprise *C.g. syriacus* of the SW Balkans, Greece and some Aegean islands, and the nominate *galactotes* of southern Iberia. Pleguezuelos (1992) found breeding pairs only below 1000m asl in Sierra Nevaca. Although the map suggests a continuous Iberian distribution, it forms patchy concentrations even when there is ample suitable habitat. Both subspecies remain disjunct, wintering in arid C–E and sub-Saharan Africa. The Transcaucasian subspecies is *familiaris*. The Eurasian and North African populations are migratory, occupying their breeding areas from April to September. There are two other subspecies outside the *Atlas*' coverage area.

In Europe the species breeds mainly in artificial habitats such as olive and almond groves and vineyards, but also in young pine *Pinus* plantations. In the 1960s in Almería (S Spain) part of the population adopted citrus plantations instead of vineyards as preferred breeding habitat (Cano 1960). In an Alicante site (SE Spain) breeding density decreased from 0.36 to 0.07 bp/10ha (1980–84, López & Gil-Delgado 1988) and then later to zero. In Jaén (S Spain) density decreased from 1.54 to 0.16 bp/10ha in olive orchards (1979–83, Muñoz-Cobos 1990). However, a Los Palacios (Sevilla) vineyard has retained stable densities of 8–10 bp/10ha (F. Dominguez, pers comm). Such data suggest a declining trend in E Spain. Earlier records of possible breeding attempts in easternmost Spain indicate a simultaneous range contraction (Ferrer *et al* 1986). Muñoz-Cobos (1990) implied that biocides could be involved with the decrease in Jaén olive groves, but the species also has disappeared from abandoned cultivated land in Alicante although it remains present in pesticide-sprayed vineyards. Alternatively, the effects of Sahelian droughts may have been greater on populations near the edge of the breeding distribution (López & Gil-Delgado 1988).

Jose A Gil-Delgado (E) German López (E)

Erithacus rubecula **Robin**

CZ	Červenka obecná	I	Pettirosso
D	Rotkehlchen	NL	Roodborst
E	Petirrojo	P	Pisco-de-peito-ruivo
F	Rougegorge familier	PL	Rudzik
FIN	Punarinta	R	Зарянка
G	Κοκκινολαίμης	S	Rödhake
H	Vörösbegy		

SPEC Cat 4, Threat status S

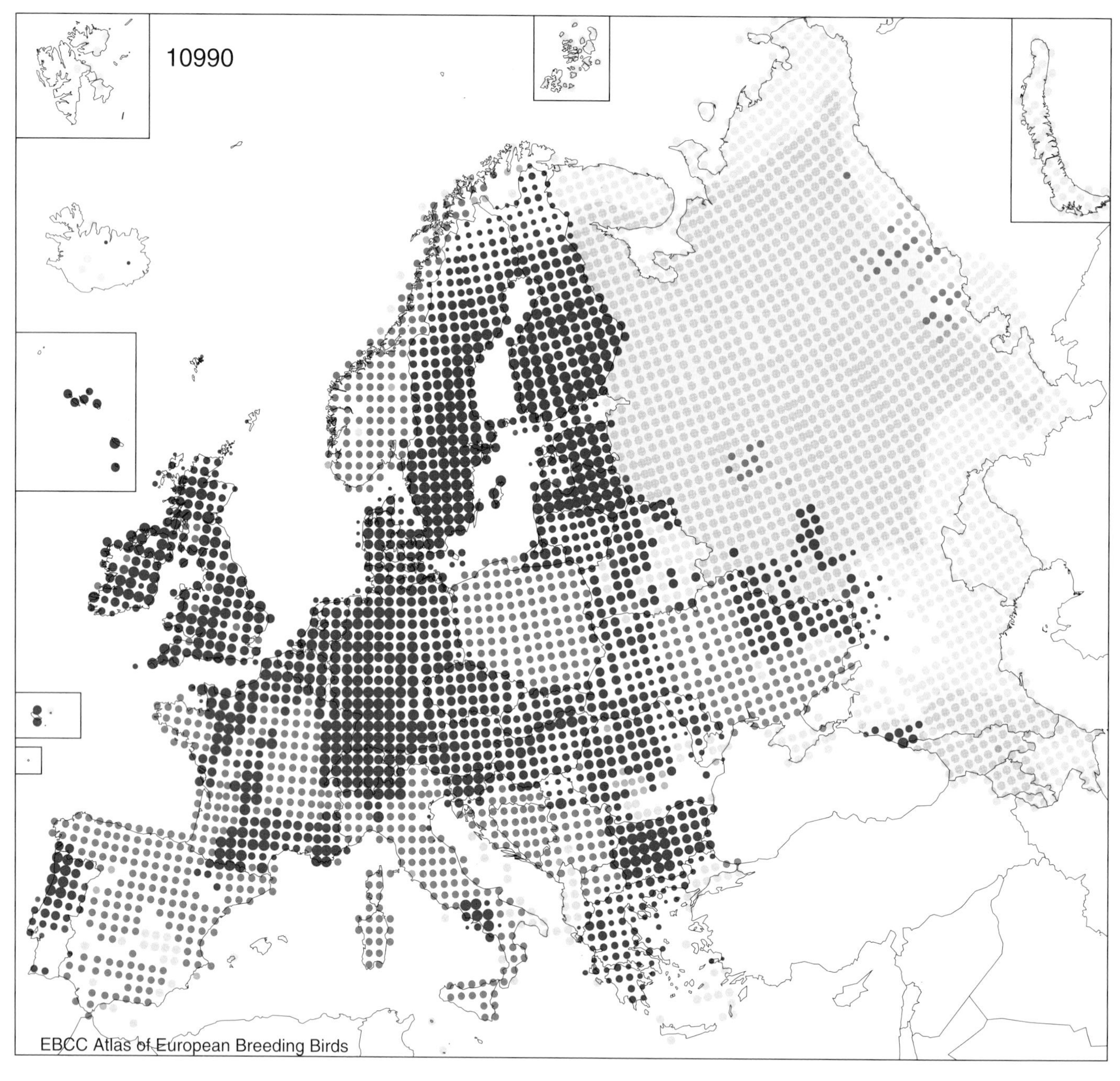

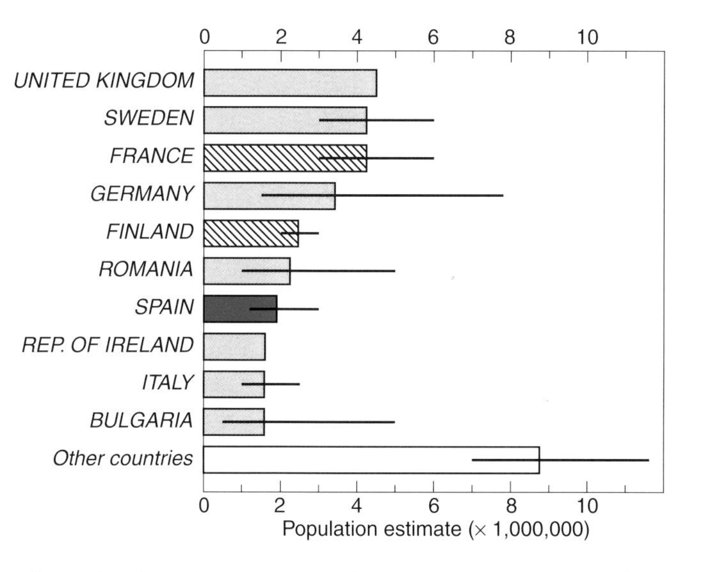

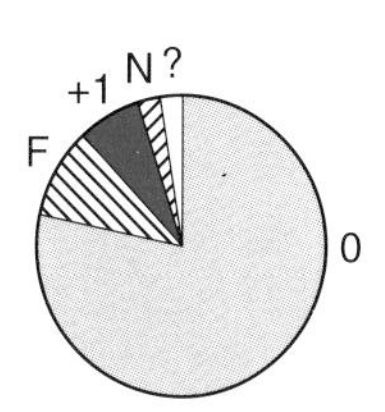

% in top 10 countries: 76.0
Total number of populated European countries: 41
Total European population 32,387,823–42,974,703 (36,500,677)
Russian population 10,000,000–100,000,000 (31,622,777)
Turkish population 10,000–100,000 (31,623)

The Robin breeds over most of Europe, its range extending to NW Africa, Turkey, Iran and E of the Urals to *c*88°E. There are also populations resident in the Azores, Madeira and the Canary Islands. The majority of Scandinavian, C and E European populations migrate to winter in western Europe and around the Mediterranean. In many areas females are more strongly migratory or dispersive than males.

The Robin is a bird of the mediterranean, temperate and boreal habitats which retain moist elements. It requires light or medium cover but avoids the densest woodland. It does not penetrate the tundra nor areas above the treeline. The Robin favours moist habitats and thrives in woodland, scrub, farmland hedges, gardens and parkland. Normally it forages on the ground close to cover but it shuns completely open areas. Often a dominant species of the local avifauna, it is strictly territorial at all times, although summer and winter territories may not necessarily overlap.

Throughout S Europe the Robin is a widely distributed and common bird in the winter but it is absent or scarce as a breeding bird in the drier areas of Iberia; it does not breed in the Balearic Islands, nor in parts of Sardinia and Sicily, the heel of Italy nor areas of coastal Greece. Much of Romania and S Ukraine lack both breeding and wintering populations, but the *Atlas* map may indicate a spread from N Ukraine into the now extensive shelterbelts. To the N, the Robin breeds irregularly on the Faeroes and Shetlands and is absent from Iceland, the N Fennoscandian mountains and northernmost Russia. Such absences relate to the scarcity of trees and bushes.

Overall European densities are remarkably consistent at 20 000–30 000 bp/50km square, but montane and mediterranean regions hold fewer than 10 000 bp/50km square. The very common, widespread and familiar Robin seems to be have occupied all available areas. The local scale has seen expansions to occupy newly forested areas which formerly were open land (Harper 1993) and contractions in areas from which cover has been stripped. In favoured woodland breeding density may reach 100 bp/km^2, a level which may also be attained locally in areas of suburban gardens. Densities of roughly one third of this level are common in farmland comprising relatively small fields and good hedgerows.

Resident Robin populations fluctuate within broad limits, which are driven mainly by cold winter weather (Marchant *et al* 1990). After the worst winters, populations may drop by 50%, but successive milder winters will allow numbers to recover after five or six years. The European population is considered stable, slight expansions in range and numbers during 1970–90 being recorded only in Iberia. The Norwegian population size has increased slightly. Within Great Britain, and in some other areas in western Europe, the Robin tends to associate closely with humans but this is not the case universally (Mead 1984). Recently it has been shown that survival rates of breeding populations are depressed if subjected to heavier hunting pressure in winter (S.R. Baillie, pers comm).

Gran Canaria and Tenerife hold the subspecies *E.r. superbus*, but the nominate *rubecula* occupies the other Atlantic islands and much of continental Europe, but intergrades with *E.r. melophilus* (Ireland, Britain save SE England, and a broad coastal zone from N Portugal to Denmark) and the NW African *witherbyi* (S Spain, Corsica, Sardinia). Crimea holds *valens* and the Caucasus *caucasicus*. The Asian *tataricus* is fully migratory, wintering in SE Kazakhstan and Iran, where *hyrcanus* breeds. The species shows high site fidelity towards its wintering area (Cuadrado 1992). Mediterranean wintering birds are partly frugivorous (Herrera 1981).

Chris Mead (GB)

This species account is sponsored by Ms Elisabeth Thym, Kleve, D.

Luscinia luscinia Thrush Nightingale

CZ	Slavík tmavý	**I**	Usignolo maggiore
D	Sprosser	**NL**	Noordse Nachtegaal
E	Ruiseñor Ruso	**P**	Rouxinol-russo
F	Rossignol progné	**PL**	Słowik szary
FIN	Satakieli	**R**	Обыкновенный соловей
G	Τσιχλαηδόνι	**S**	Näktergal
H	Nagy fülemüle		

SPEC Cat 4, Threat status S

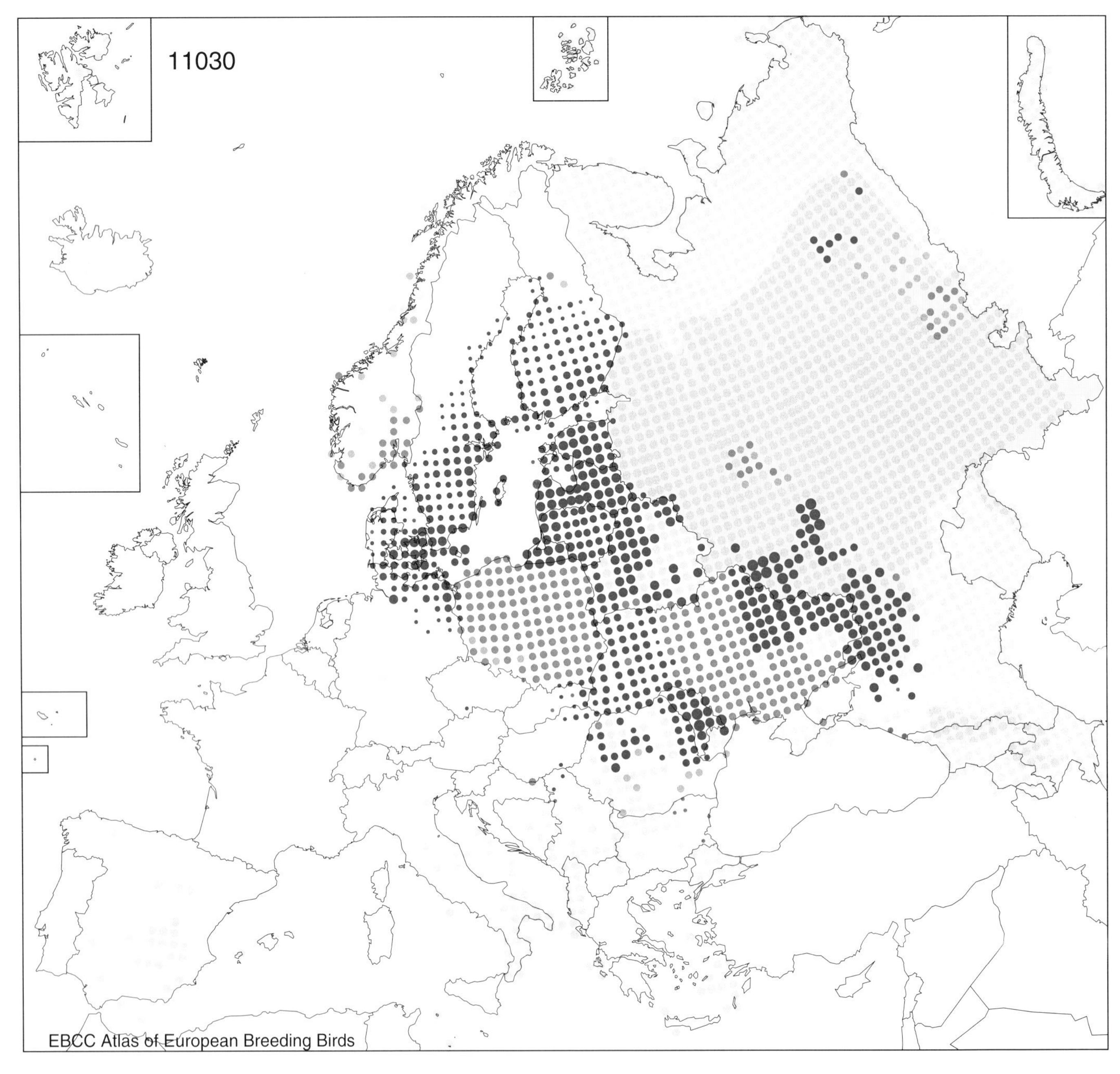

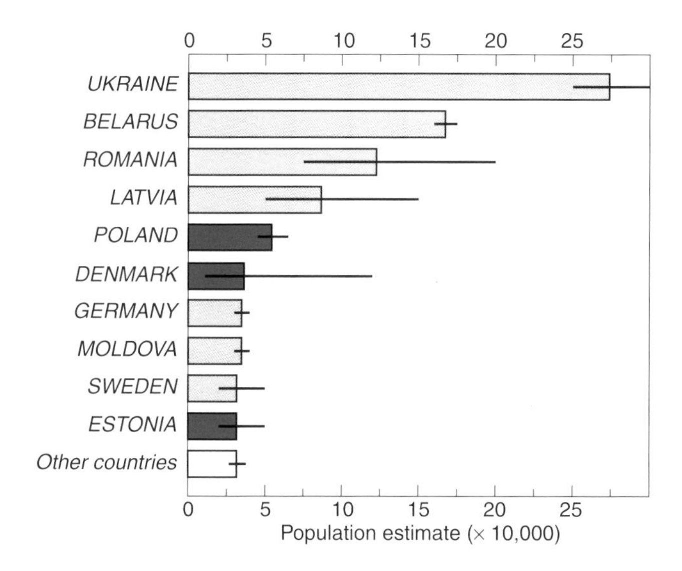

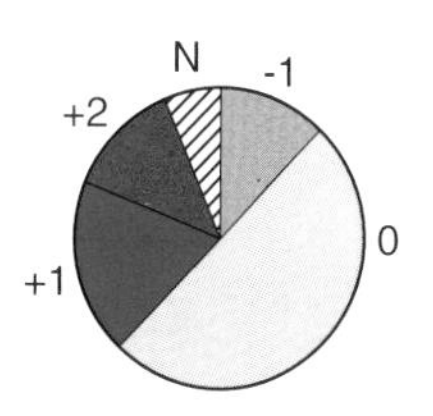

% in top 10 countries: 96.5
Total number of populated European countries: 16
Total European population 832,226–1,041,309 (904,784)
Russian population 100,000–1,000,000 (316,228)

The Thrush Nightingale has an extensive breeding range stretching from eastern Europe through the C Urals to C Asia covering the temperate and continental climate zones and spilling over into the boreal and steppe zones.

It prefers lowland river valleys and patchy woodlands beside lakes, ponds, rivers, meadows or other open country, occupying dense thickets in forest-edge habitats or woods of less than 1ha. Such woodlands comprise young deciduous trees, mostly between 3 and 16m tall and preferably in moist areas.

Its western distribution lies N and E of a line from S Norway via Denmark and Germany to Hungary, reaching 65°N in Sweden and Finland and 62°N in western Russia. It occurs from Krasnoyarsk in the E to Alma-Ata and the Danube Delta in the S. Isolated populations exist on the NE Black Sea coast, Cis-Caucasus and Transcaucasia. In the Carpathians it breeds up to 600m asl (Strautman 1957, Walasz & Mielczarek 1992). It winters mostly in East Africa S of the Equator, being locally common in E Kenya, Zambia, S Malawi and Zimbabwe, but also reaches Namibia and northern South Africa.

In the 1700s, numbers were high from C Sweden to Silesia (environs of Wrocław) and on the Austrian Danube, but by the late 1800s its population and range began to contract, for reasons unknown. In the 1920s these trends began to reverse, at least in the NW, and the 1960s and 1980s saw marked increases over the entire northern and western distribution.

In Finland population fluctuations continued into the 1950s, some areas recording increases, others decreases. However, since the 1960s the southern Finnish population has increased, and there has been a range expansion to the N and W. The Finnish population has grown from *c*200bp (1950s) to 8000bp (1970s) and 15 000–20 000bp (late 1990s), the Swedish from *c*15 000bp (1970s) to 20 000–50 000bp (1980s), and the Norwegian from 200–500bp (1980s) to the present 500–1000bp. The Polish increase apparently began later than in Fennoscandia, reaching Silesia in the late 1970s, the population now being estimated at 45 000–60 000bp. Similarly, breeding incidence increased in eastern Germany in the early 1990s (J. Becker 1995). However, in our opinion, there are indications that the southern populations are decreasing, the lower Romanian estimate probably being nearer the actual numbers. Russia holds the largest European population (0.1M–1Mbp). Densities in the Baltic States, Belarus, Ukraine and Moldova are also high (1300–3300 bp/50km square).

Population fluctuations in Finland seem correlated with changes in habitat composition and climate amelioration. The 19th-century distribution mirrored areas of intensive slash-and-burn cultivation which produced the preferred young deciduous woodlands. When such activities decreased in the early 1900s, numbers diminished. Grazing in forests and shore meadows gradually ceased from 1930 to 1965 and fields were abandoned from the 1960s, increasing suitable Thrush Nightingale habitats greatly (Koskimies 1989a), as did the lowering of lake surface-levels, allowing rapid colonization of the exposed shores by birch *Betula* and alder *Alnus*. Possibly, warmer springs since the 1970s have permitted new breeders to increase density and range. The species seems tolerant of human activity, occupying urban scrub areas, parks, orchards and cemeteries, as in Moscow and other cities, even using thickets beside noisy and busy roads and railways.

In a narrow zone from Denmark to the Balkans the Thrush Nightingale is sympatric with the Nightingale *L. megarhynchos*. Hybridization, proven by ringing, apparently produces unisexual hybrid sterility, hybrid males being fertile and females sterile. The low hybridization rate (*c*6% in eastern Germany) may indicate a restricted gene flow through assortative mating and female sterility. Hybridization may be triggered by the high percentage of non-breeding males in the overlap zone (J. Becker 1995).

Zdzisław Bogucki (PL) Jorma Sorjonen (FIN)

Luscinia megarhynchos **Nightingale**

CZ	Slavík obecný	I	Usignolo
D	Nachtigall	NL	Nachtegaal
E	Ruiseñor Común	P	Rouxinol-comum
F	Rossignol philomèle	PL	Słowik rdzawy
FIN	Etelänsatakieli	R	Южный соловей
G	Αηδόνι	S	Sydnäktergal
H	Fülemüle		

SPEC Cat 4, Threat status S (P)

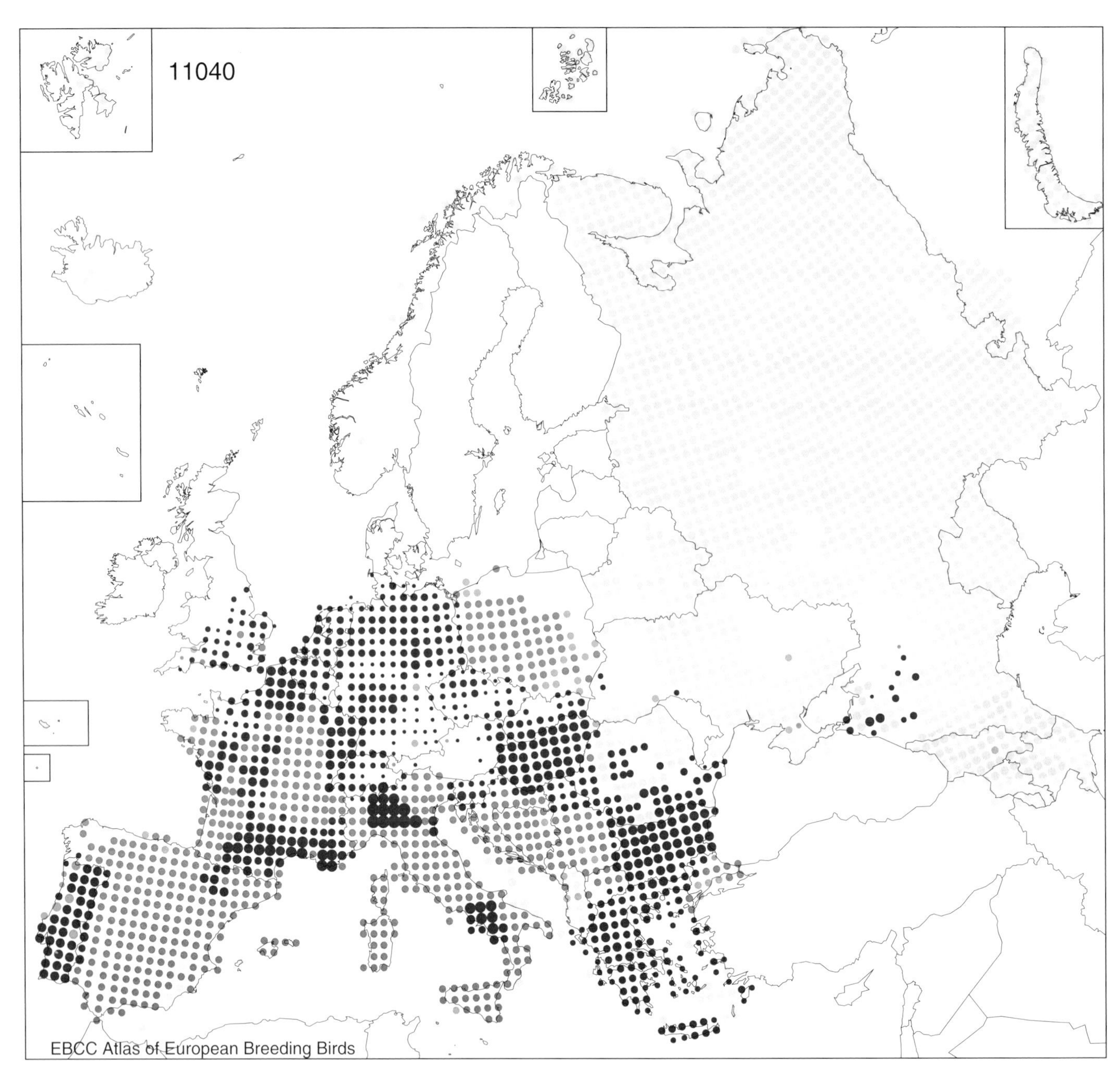

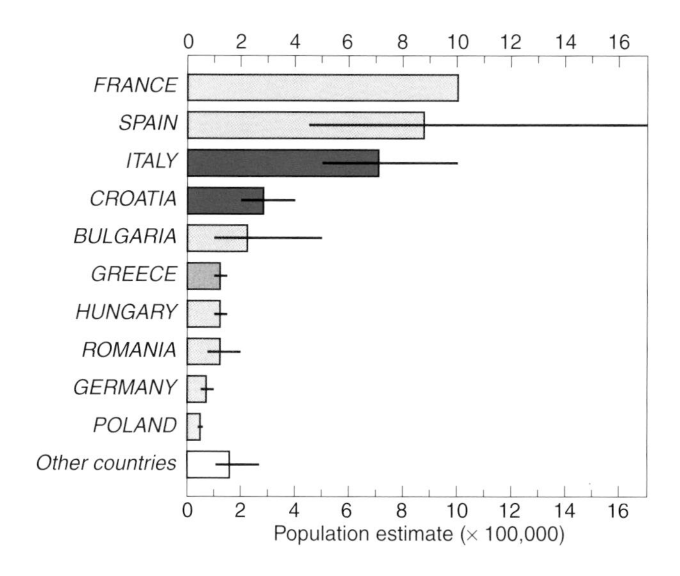

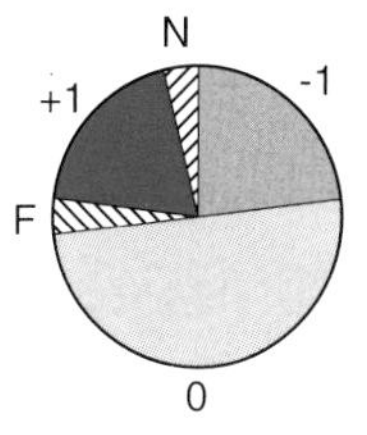

% in top 10 countries: 97.0
Total number of populated European countries: 25
Total European population 3,184,886–4,617,751 (3,684,644)
Russian population 10–100 (32)
Turkish population 50,000–500,000 (158,114)

The inconspicuous Nightingale, famous for its song, is distributed widely through the mediterranean, warm and temperate zones of the SW Palearctic, the nominate *L.m. megarhynchos* occupying most of Europe and the N African Atlas Mountains. Further E, *africana* occurs in the Caucasus and in the Near and Middle East and *hafizi* from Turkmenistan to Mongolia. In C Europe the more continental (Pannonian) southeasterly range holds the densest populations. In the maritime areas of W Europe this climatically sensitive chat-like thrush usually breeds S of the 19°C June isotherm.

In Europe it inhabits three different main habitat types: (1) lowland riverine woodland or thickets bordering running or stagnant water, especially where it overlaps with the Thrush Nightingale *L. luscinia*; (2) broad-leaved woodland (especially oak) margins, pinewoods possessing rich undergrowth, bushland, dry or very dry maquis or garrigue on sandy soils or chalk hillsides in mild or warm climates (near the Mediterranean these habitats occur also at high altitudes); (3) cultivated land with old, tall hedgerows, or suburban habitats such as large gardens and cemeteries with untended bushes and a layer of leaf litter. However, modern agricultural development and the fashionable obsession for neat, tidy gardens have contributed to a serious decline of the species through habitat loss, especially since the 1950s.

In Europe, the Nightingale's range along the Atlantic coast excludes Galicia, the Cantabrian Mountains, Brittany, and most of Great Britain except the lowland SE. The range border runs through the Schleswig-Holstein marshes in the N, and SE through Mecklenburg and Poland to NE Ukraine, where its occurrence towards the Caucasus becomes patchier. Greatly dependent on warm and dry summers, in C and NW Europe the Nightingale occurs mostly below 500m asl, but in S Europe it reaches 1400m asl, as in Abruzzi. Hence the map shows large areas of absence in the Alps and Carpathians, whereas its distribution along the more southerly mountain ridges is continuous (save for the Cordilleras). Its patchy distribution in Albania, N Romania and southern Ukraine probably reflects a lack of data.

The considerable changes in distribution and population at its northeasterly range limit have been well documented since the early 1800s. After a strong decline from 1830 to 1920 in C Europe the Nightingale became restricted towards the more continental SE, but numbers increased and the range expanded from 1930 onwards, and so the position prevailing around 1900 largely has been re-established. The isolated English population has experienced similar declines and range contractions since 1910 and these still continue (Marchant *et al* 1990). Climatic variations probably were more responsible for these fluctuations than habitat loss. At present, European mainland populations mostly are stable or (since the late 1980s) even slightly increasing, as in The Netherlands (Hustings 1988).

The Nightingale's climatic sensitivity is demonstrated on the map by the abundance increase from the NW range limit southwards: from 100–1000 bp/50km square in England to 10 000 bp/50km square in C Europe and even higher in N Italy and S France. Maximum densities in C Europe along narrow riverine woodland strips reached 20 bp/10ha, and on small plots of prime oak dry scrubs up to 22 bp/10ha (Dvorak *et al* 1993); in S Europe 7 bp/10ha were found in moist broad-leaved woodland (Dombes, France) and 3.6 bp/10ha in garrigue in S France (Clavier 1994).

European populations winter in sub-Saharan Africa as far E as Uganda. They leave their breeding areas between late July and September and migrate to the SW, peak passage through C Europe occurring in late August. The Mediterranean and Sahara probably are crossed non-stop. Migrants return to S Europe in late March and to C Europe normally from mid-April onwards.

Alfred Grüll (A) Giancarlo Fracasso (I)

This species account is sponsored by Ms Gertrud Sanders, Goch, D.

Luscinia calliope

Siberian Rubythroat

CZ	Slavík kaliopa	I	Calliope
D	Rubinkehlchen	NL	Roodkeelnachtegaal
E	Ruiseñor Calíope	P	Rouxinol-de-garganta-vermelha
F	Calliope sibèrienne	PL	Słowik rubinowy
FIN	Rubiinisatakieli	R	Соловей-красношейка
G	Ρουμπινολαίμης	S	Rubinnäktergal
H	Rubinbegy		

Non-SPEC, Threat status S (P)

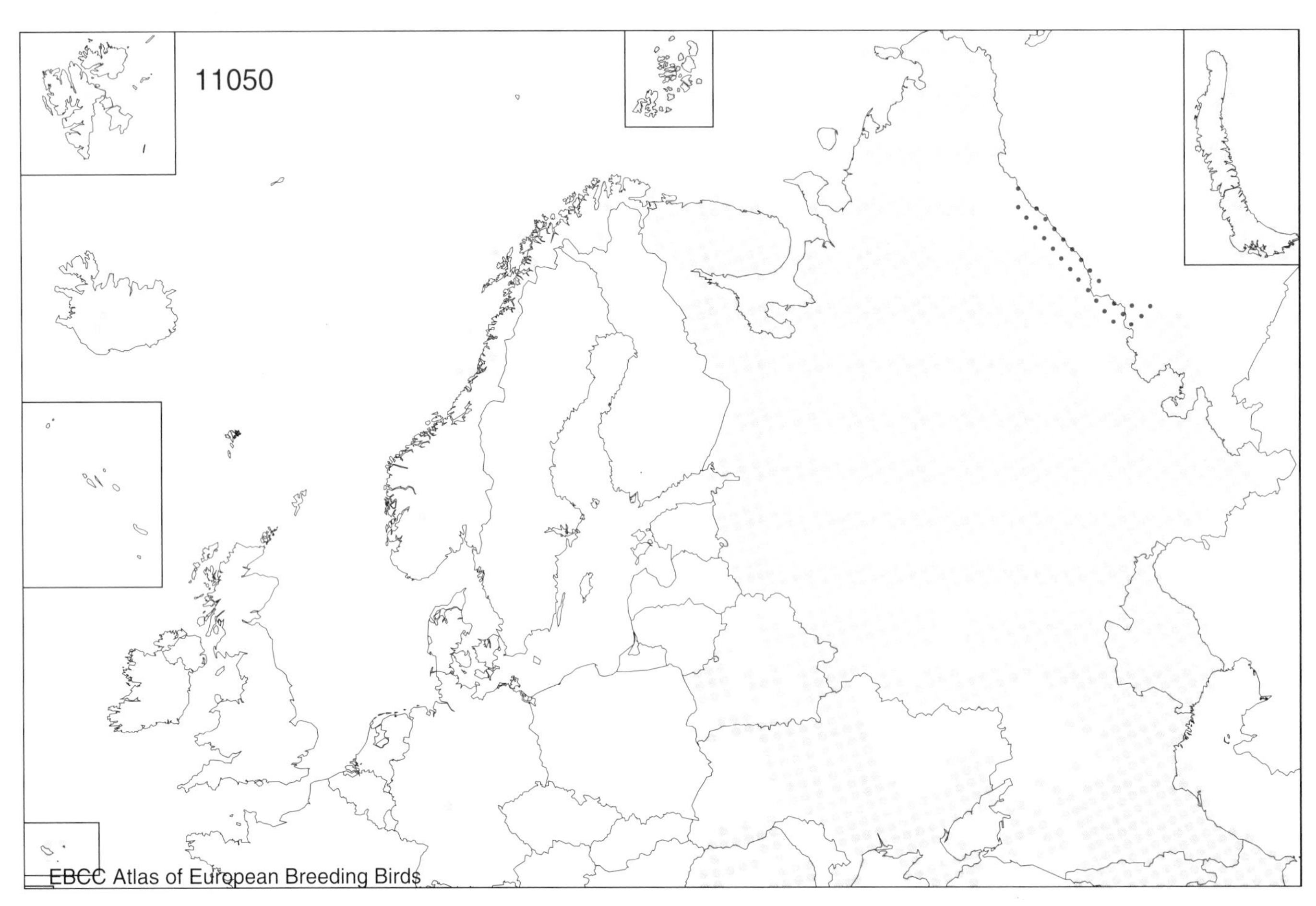

The distribution area of the Siberian Rubythroat has two separate components. The main part includes its European range, which is concentrated mainly on the western slope of the N Urals, between the upper reaches of the Pechora and Kama (E of Perm) Rivers. Into Asia, its main breeding range continues to the Chukotskiy range in the E, Kamchatka, the Commander Isles, Sakhalin and Japan (Hokkaido Island). In the N it penetrates to the upper reaches of the Ilych (Estafiev 1969), to 63°N on the River Ob, and close to the Arctic Circle between the Yenisey and Chukotskiy Mountains. Its southern limit in Europe lies between the Kama Valley and the Urals at *c*55°N (Vorontsov 1949), but in Asia is much further south, to Tobolsk, Tara, the NW Altai, Lake Hövsgöl in Mongolia, the Hangai, the Hentei, the Bolshoi Hingan and the Hungari Basin. The smaller part of its distribution lies isolated in Asia and covers the Qilian Shan mountain range, Lake Kukunor and the upper reaches of the Hwan Ho, N of the Sino-Tibetan mountains (Stepanyan 1978, Sumia & Skriabin 1989).

The Siberian Rubythroat winters in India to the S of Bombay, Raipore and Orissa; in Burma S to Tenasserim; and in Thailand, Taiwan and the Philippines (Gladkov 1954).

In Europe in the upper reaches of the Pechora (River Ilych), it occupies shrubby forest edges near mountain brooks especially where there are fallen trees (A.A. Estafiev, pers obs); in the upper reaches of the Kama (River Us-Va), it frequents dense bushes and stands of bird-cherry *Prunus padus*, dog-rose *Rosa canina*, usually close to fir *Abies* and spruce *Picea* near river meadows (Vorontsov 1949).

It is a rare species in Europe, but there are records during the breeding season over a sizeable area, from the upper reaches of the Ilych (Pechora basin), to the environs of the Ust-Ulsa and the Us-Va Valleys (Kama basin).

Alexey A Estafiev (R)

Tarsiger cyanurus

Red-flanked Bluetail

CZ	Modruška lesní	I	Codazzurro
D	Blauschwanz	NL	Blauwstaart
E	Ruiseñor Coliazul	P	Rouxinol-rabiazul
F	Rossignol à flancs roux	PL	Modraczek
FIN	Sinipyrstö	R	Синехвостка
G	Κυάνουρος	S	Blåstjärt
H	Kékfarkú		

Non-SPEC, Threat status S (P)

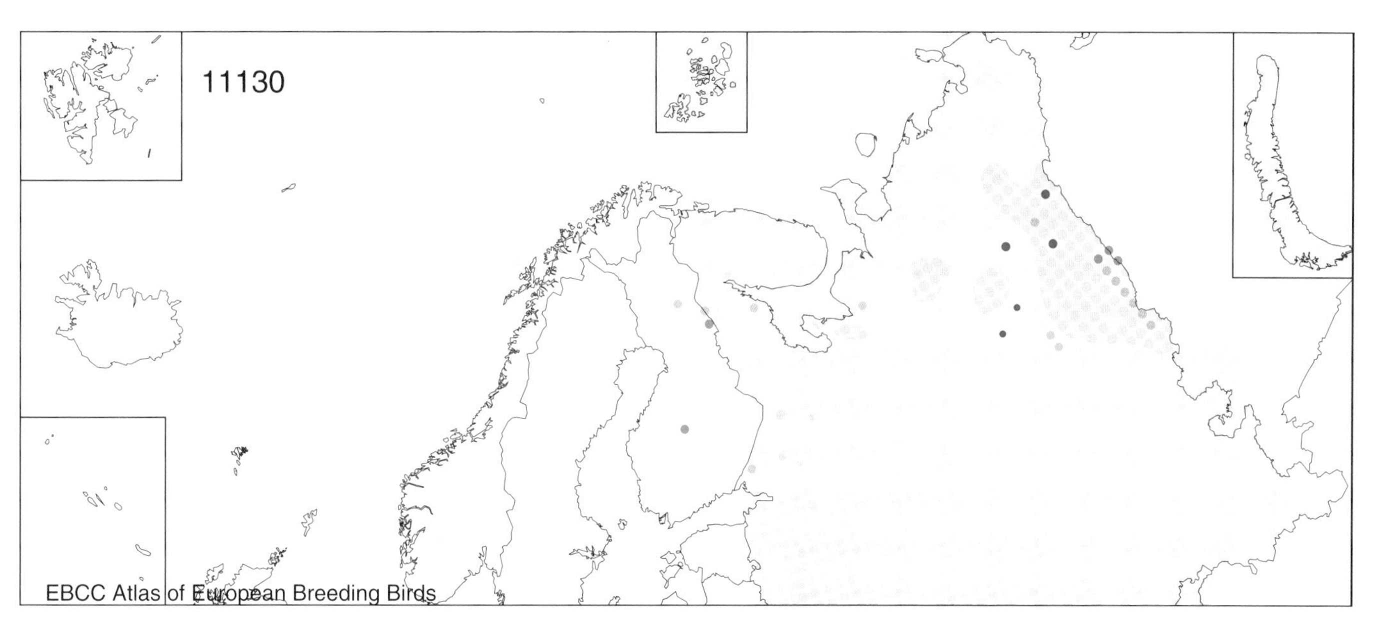

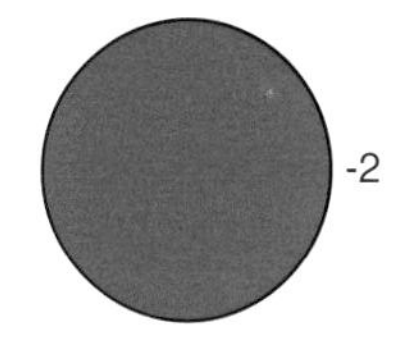

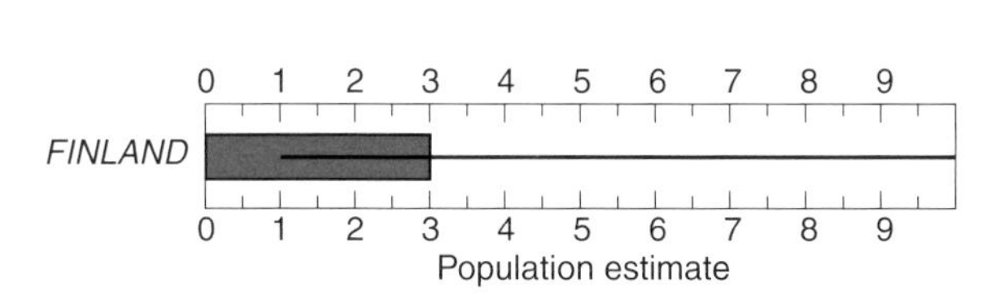

% in top 10 countries: 100.0
Total number of populated European countries: 1
Total European population 1–10 (3)
Russian population 100–1000 (316)

In Europe, the elusive Red-flanked Bluetail breeds only in Russia and Finland. Its distribution in Siberia stretches from W of the Urals to Kamchatka (*T.c. cyanurus*) and S to Japan, and in a separate range along the Himalayas to W China (*rufilatus*). It winters mostly in S China.

The species favours moist spruce *Picea* forests, but also uses pine *Pinus* and mixed forests in its central range. In Finland and western Russia it prefers old virgin spruce forests with fallen trees and sparse undergrowth, usually on hilly slopes (Koskimies 1989a).

Breeding density reaches 0.4–0.7 birds/km² in Ural mountain forests (upper Pechora Valley), up to 120 singing males occurring along 100km of favourable habitat (Estafiev 1981). Densities were 0.2–2.0 birds/km² in the Pechora–Ilych reserve area (S.K. Kotchanov, pers comm).

In European Russia the species is scarce and very patchily distributed. Its overall density is declining sharply W of the Urals. During the 20th century it expanded westwards, reaching Russian Karelia and Finnish Kuusamo in the 1940s. In NW Russia it remains a very rare but regular breeder (Mal'chevski & Pukinski 1983, Zimin *et al* 1993).

In Finland, the species' westernmost outpost, some 40 singing males appeared in the 1950s, mostly in Kuusamo. The species disappeared almost completely in the early 1960s, but 27 birds were found during the breeding seasons in 1969–73 (13 in 1972). From the late 1970s to the 1980s it was absent for many years (even in Kuusamo), only *c*2–3 males being found annually in N Finland. The breeding population in 1990 was 0–10bp (Koskimies 1989a, 1993a). From the early 1990s *c*10 birds were found annually in N Finland (six males in Kuusamo, 1990). At this extreme range limit probably most singing males remain unpaired. In my view Finland may hold 10–50bp and 20–150 unpaired males, subject to large annual fluctuations (P. Koskimies, unpubl).

Pertti Koskimies (FIN)

Luscinia svecica

Bluethroat

CZ	Slavík modráček	**I**	Pettazzurro
D	Blaukehlchen	**NL**	Blauwborst
E	Pechiazul	**P**	Pisco-de-peito-azul
F	Gorgebleue à miroir	**PL**	Podróżniczek
FIN	Sinirinta	**R**	Варакушка
G	Γαλαζολαίμης	**S**	Blåhake
H	Kékbegy		

Non-SPEC, Threat status S

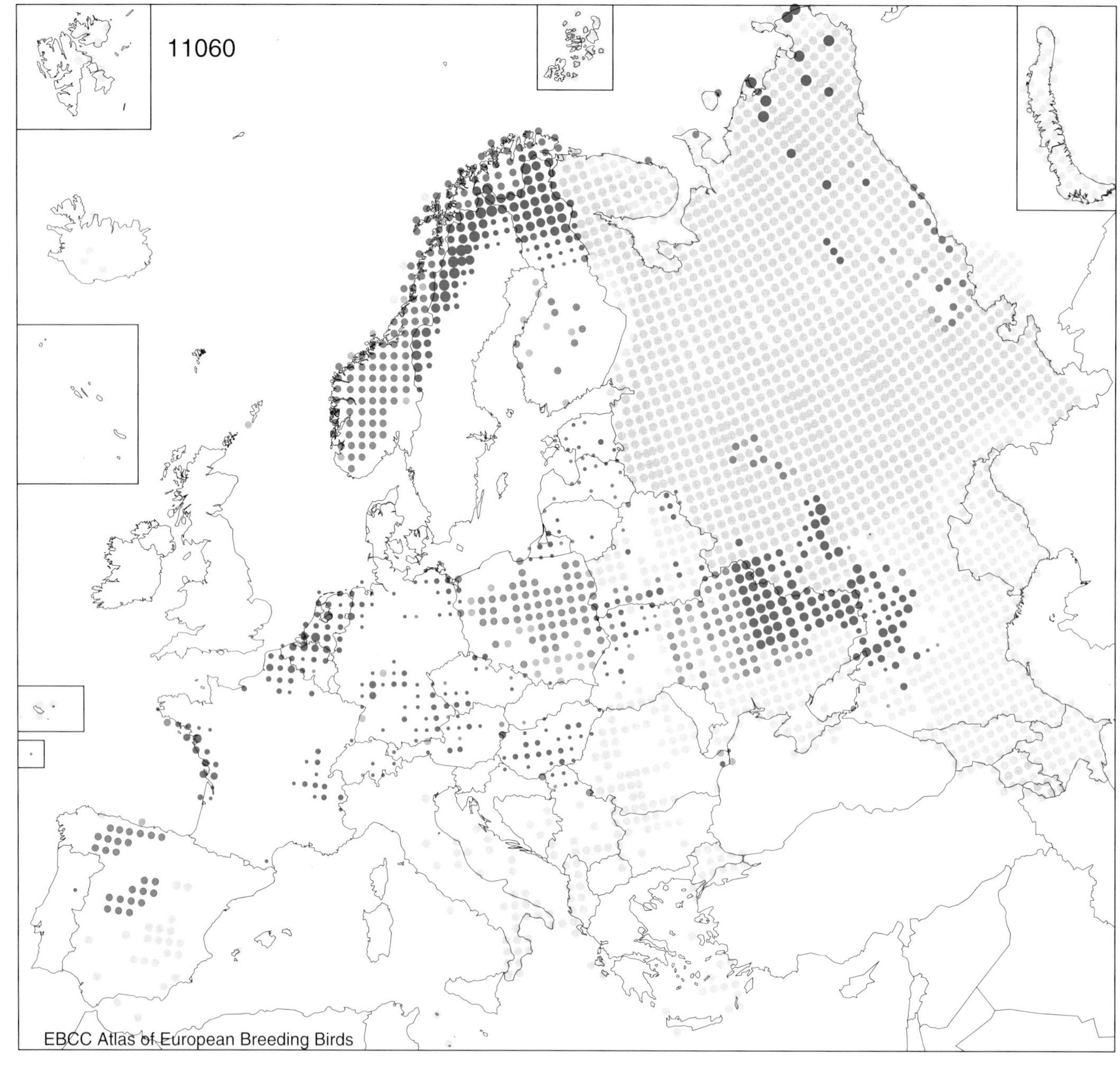

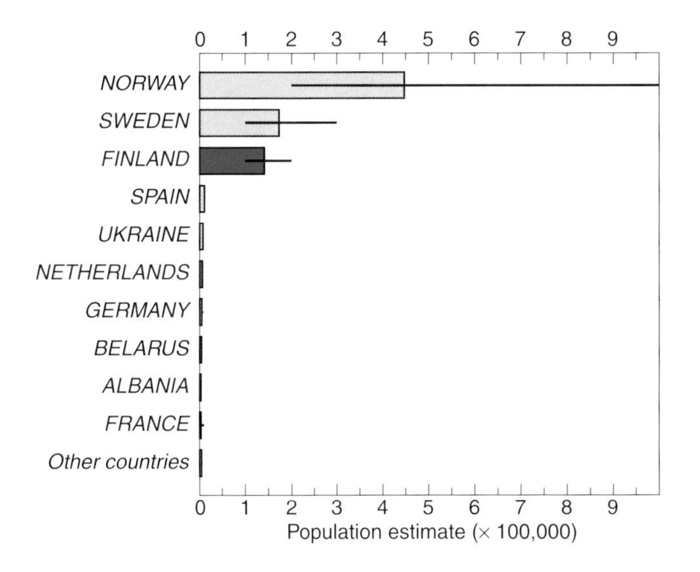

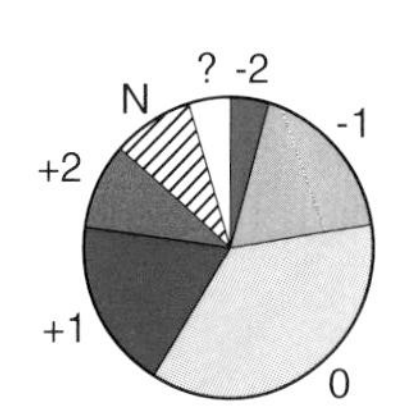

% in top 10 countries: 99.5
Total number of populated European countries: 22
Total European population 545,126–1,376,505 (806,286)
Russian population 100,000–1,000,000 (316,228)
Turkish population 500–1000 (707)

Several Bluethroat subspecies inhabit the Palearctic, the nominate *L.s. svecica* occupying the vast arctic and boreal zones from Fennoscandia eastwards through N Siberia to W Alaska and south to 56°N in Norway. Recently *svecica* began to breed further S in tundra-like habitats in the Austrian Alps (since 1975), the Czech Krkonoše Mountains (1978; Miles & Formánek 1989), the Swiss Alps (1980), the Polish High Tatra (1981), the Italian Alps (1983) (Fraticelli & Gustin 1985) and the Ukrainian Carpathians (1986). The white-throated subspecies *cyanecula* principally is a C European breeding bird, whose range extends into W Europe and eastwards to the Carpathian basin, Ukraine and Belarus. The small subspecies *namnetum* apparently is confined to the French Atlantic coast. The subspecies *volgae* occurs from C European Russia to the Volga, *pallidogularis* in E–SE European Russia and *magna* in the Caucasus; four other subspecies occur elsewhere.

The Bluethroat breeds in any habitats which combine lush vegetation and low trees and shrubs amidst open spaces. Such habitats, comprising open spaces in wooded tundra, wetlands with low woody vegetation, floodplains, riverbanks, reed and shrub-dominated lakeshores and pond edges, often are rather wet or marshy and are intermediate between forests and open plains. The presence of water in itself is not essential, as is evident in Spain, where it nests on dry, stony slopes, and in The Netherlands, where it has taken to oilseed rape and dry ditches in polders.

The European population is *c*800 000–2 500 000bp, 95% of which comprise *svecica* in Fennoscandia and Russia. In Lapp subalpine birch forests densities range from 45 to 50 bp/km^2, but elsewhere in Fennoscandia the average density drops to 5.5 bp/km^2 (Järvinen & Pietiäinen 1981, Thingstad 1994b). The sheer quantity of suitable habitat in northern Europe explains its large population. However, *cyanecula*'s patchy distribution throughout the temperate zone probably reflects the scattered nature of marshland and floodplains. Densities can be high, locally up to 1–2.5 bp/ha in riverine habitats (Schlemmer 1988), 3–4 bp/ha in marshland in the Biesbosch, a major breeding site in The Netherlands (Meijer & van der Nat 1989) and 4–5 bp/10ha in the margins of Neusiedlersee/Austria (Grüll 1988). Most of the temperate breeding localities are characterized by eutrophication and high primary productivity (plant growth). Consequently, many breeding sites tend to suffer encroachment by shrubs and trees, rendering them unsuitable for Bluethroat occupancy. In the harsher environment of Spain, where it breeds up to 2000m, and in the Nordic countries, this process is less significant, creating a more stable environment in which breeding population fluctuations are less marked. Overall, populations in N Europe and Spain were indeed stable during 1970–90, only Finland showing a slight increase in numbers and Norway experiencing a range extension.

In the European temperate regions, the Bluethroat experienced pronounced fluctuations during the 20th century. Some of these trends are explicable by natural succession in marshland, drainage and management practices (reed-cutting, seedling removal, cattle grazing), but others remain a mystery. In The Netherlands, the considerable reduction in Bluethroat numbers since the 1930s has been attributed to uncontrolled flooding, habitat deterioration, and drainage and fragmentation of wetlands, a scenario repeated elsewhere in W Europe. However, when in the 1970s *cyanecula* began to increase in numbers and to expand its range, in The Netherlands the population increased from fewer than 800bp in 1970 to 5500–7500bp in 1990, a trend which still continues (R. Meijer, pers obs). At the same time, considerable increases and range expansions have occurred in Germany, Belgium (>50%), France (not only *cyanecula* but also *namnetum*), Austria, the Czech Republic (>50%) and Slovakia. The *cyanecula* population totals some 60 000bp and continues to increase.

European populations winter chiefly around the Mediterranean and in sub-Saharan savanna regions, the nominate *svecica* probably overshooting *cyanecula*.

Roel Meijer (NL) Karel Šťastný (CZ)

This species account is sponsored by Deutsche Ornithologen-Gesellschaft, D.

Phoenicurus ochruros **Black Redstart**

CZ	Rehek domácí	**I**	Codirosso spazzacamino
D	Hausrotschwanz	**NL**	Zwarte Roodstaart
E	Colirrojo Tizón	**P**	Rabirruivo-preto
F	Rougequeue noir	**PL**	Kopciuszek
FIN	Mustaleppälintu	**R**	Горихвостка-чернушка
G	Καρβουνιάρης	**S**	Svart rödstjärt
H	Házi rozsdafarkú		

Non-SPEC, Threat status S

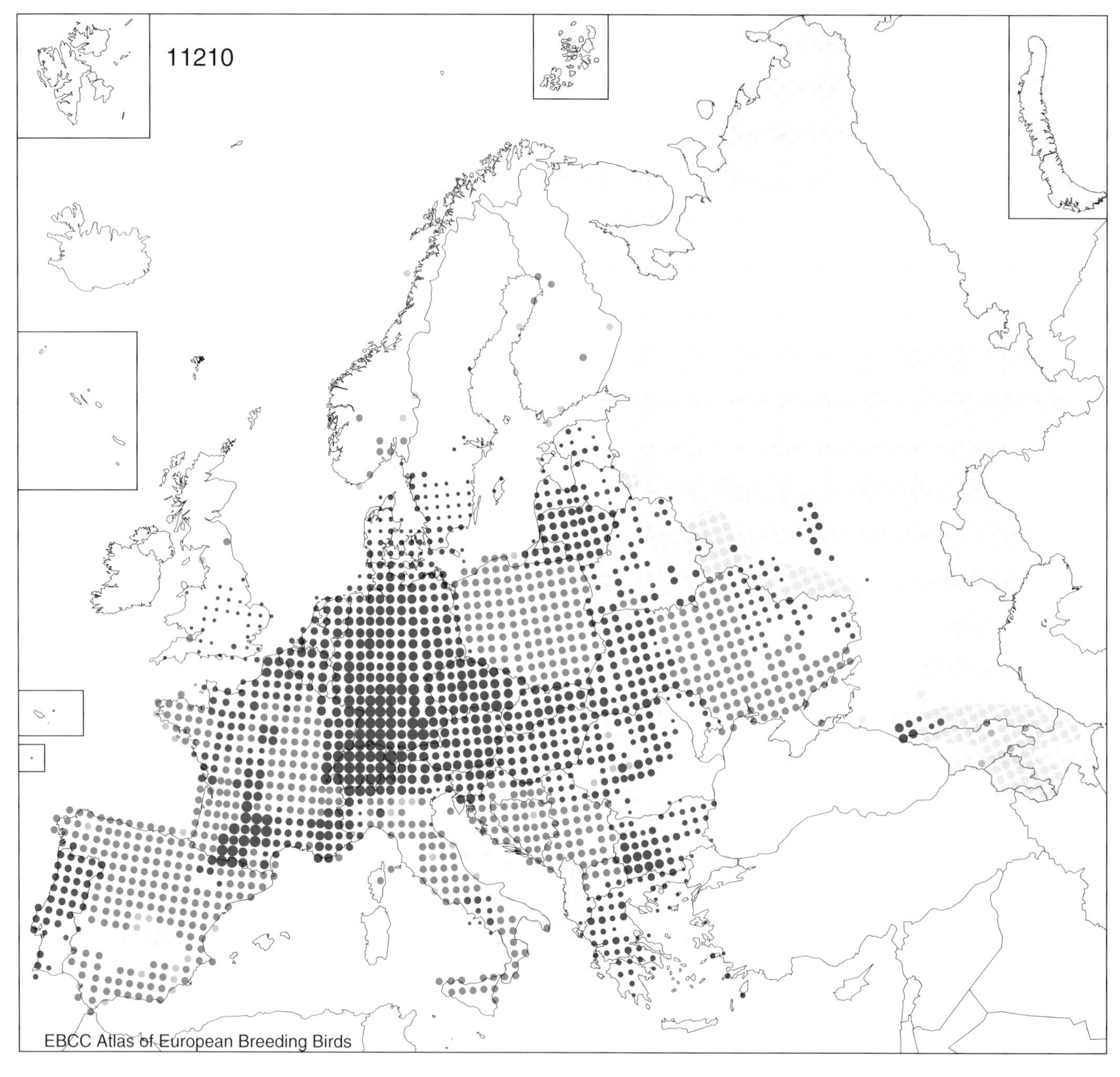

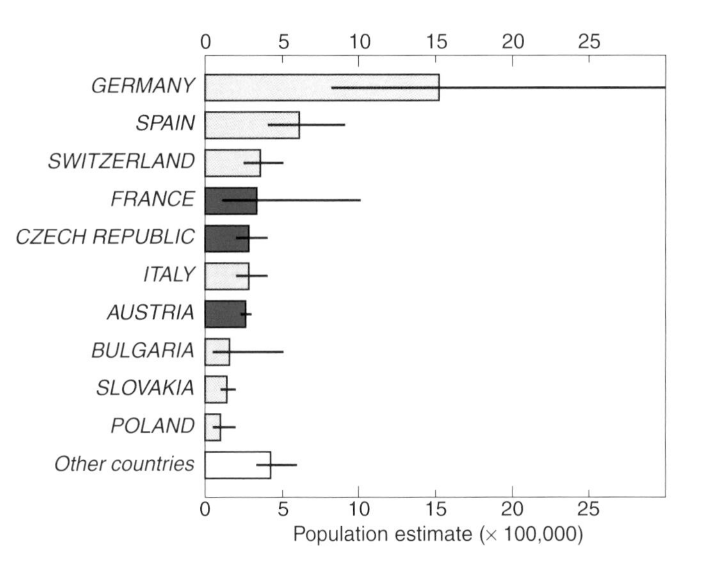

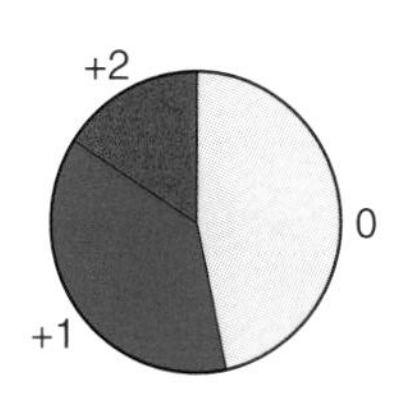

% in top 10 countries: 90.7
Total number of populated European countries: 32
Total European population 3,647,070–6,161,507 (4,479,567)
Russian population 1000–10,000 (3162)
Turkish population 50,000–500,000 (158,114)

The Black Redstart has an extensive Palearctic breeding distribution, generally between 25° and 58°N, which just reaches the Orient. It breeds in NW Africa, and in most European countries eastwards through the Caucasus, Asia Minor, Iran and N Afghanistan to Kashmir, N to montane C Asia and E to the Himalayas and western China.

In Europe the Black Redstart breeds in a fairly broad range of habitats both maritime and continental, but primarily in the drier zones; relatively hot and arid, warm sunny temperate, mediterranean, steppe and montane. It generally avoids cool, wet or humid and densely vegetated habitats, forests or meadows. It favours areas whose plant communities are sparse, typically possessing much exposed rock, pebble-strewn terrain or boulders, and also cliff or crag, glacial outwash watercourses, shaded ravines, and rocky river banks. Thus dry mountain slopes extending to the snowline, and even above 2400m asl, are ideal, as in the Swiss Alps. The Carpathian lower mountain slopes dotted with juniper *Juniperus* and boulder scree provide optimum nesting grounds, sometimes close to human habitation, a trend encountered more often in northern Europe.

Highest densities (>2000 bp/50km square) occur in montane regions in C and southern latitudes, from Luxembourg, Belgium and Spain in the W, through much of C Europe to Bulgaria. Intermediate values of 800–2000 bp/50km square apply to The Netherlands, France, Hungary, Poland, Croatia and Portugal. Still substantial, but somewhat patchily distributed populations breed from Lithuania S to Greece, at densities of 200–400 bp/50km square. Fennoscandia, Denmark, Estonia, Latvia, Russia and Great Britain have peripheral populations, where densities remain below 25 bp/50km square.

Since the 1850s the species' breeding range has expanded progressively across much of NW Europe, colonizing the Danish islands in 1890, Sweden in 1910 and Norway in 1944, perhaps as a consequence of a contemporary period of climatic amelioration (Salomonsen 1948). However, the Black Redstart's consolidation of breeding numbers in southern England from 1940 has been attributed to its exploitation of nesting sites inadvertently created by aerial bombing in urban areas and also to the favourable city environment microclimate (Williamson 1975). Human habitation and associated outbuildings continue to provide a wealth of suitable nest sites, and this element of commensalism (developed only since the 19th century) may have assisted the northwards spread from montane sites across the NW European plains.

The overall European breeding population appears healthy, equal numbers of countries charting stable and increasing populations, and none reporting significant declines. Increases have occurred in the range core where the species is especially abundant, at the eastern margins (Ukraine, Latvia and Estonia), and in relatively recently colonized areas like Denmark, Norway and Finland. Whether the range expansion can be consolidated or maintained is open to question. At the northern range limits breeding birds in countries such as England and Sweden are less prolific than elsewhere. A later, truncated nesting season, fewer second broods and a high predation level with consequent lower fledging success all suggest that these populations may not be self-sustaining (Morgan and Glue 1981, Andersson 1990, Glue 1994). This contrasts sharply with C Europe, where up to 10% of breeding pairs produce third broods (Nicolai 1990).

Populations breeding in the Balkans, Italy and Iberia generally are considered sedentary (Érard & Yeatman 1967). Northern populations are more mobile, ringing recoveries suggesting a migratory divide at *c*18°E (Zink 1981). Most western Palearctic breeders winter in the Mediterranean basin, small numbers preferring the Atlantic coast and some reaching North Africa. Most birds from Asia Minor move to winter in the Middle East, Sudan and Eritrea.

Europe holds three subspecies: *P.o. gibraltariensis* (N Spain to Crimea), *aterrimus* (remainder of Iberia) and the nominate *ochruros* (Transcaucasia, the Caucasus). Elsewhere there are at least four subspecies.

David Glue (GB)

This species account is sponsored by Ms Emilie Pastor, Rheinberg, D.

Phoenicurus phoenicurus Redstart

CZ	Rehek zahradní	**I**	Codirosso
D	Gartenrotschwanz	**NL**	Gekraagde Roodstaart
E	Colirrojo Real	**P**	Rabirruivo-de-testa-branca
F	Rougequeue à front blanc	**PL**	Pleszka
FIN	Leppälintu	**R**	Обыкновенная горихвостка
G	Κοκκινούρης	**S**	Rödstjärt
H	Kerti rozsdafarkú		

SPEC Cat 2, Threat status V

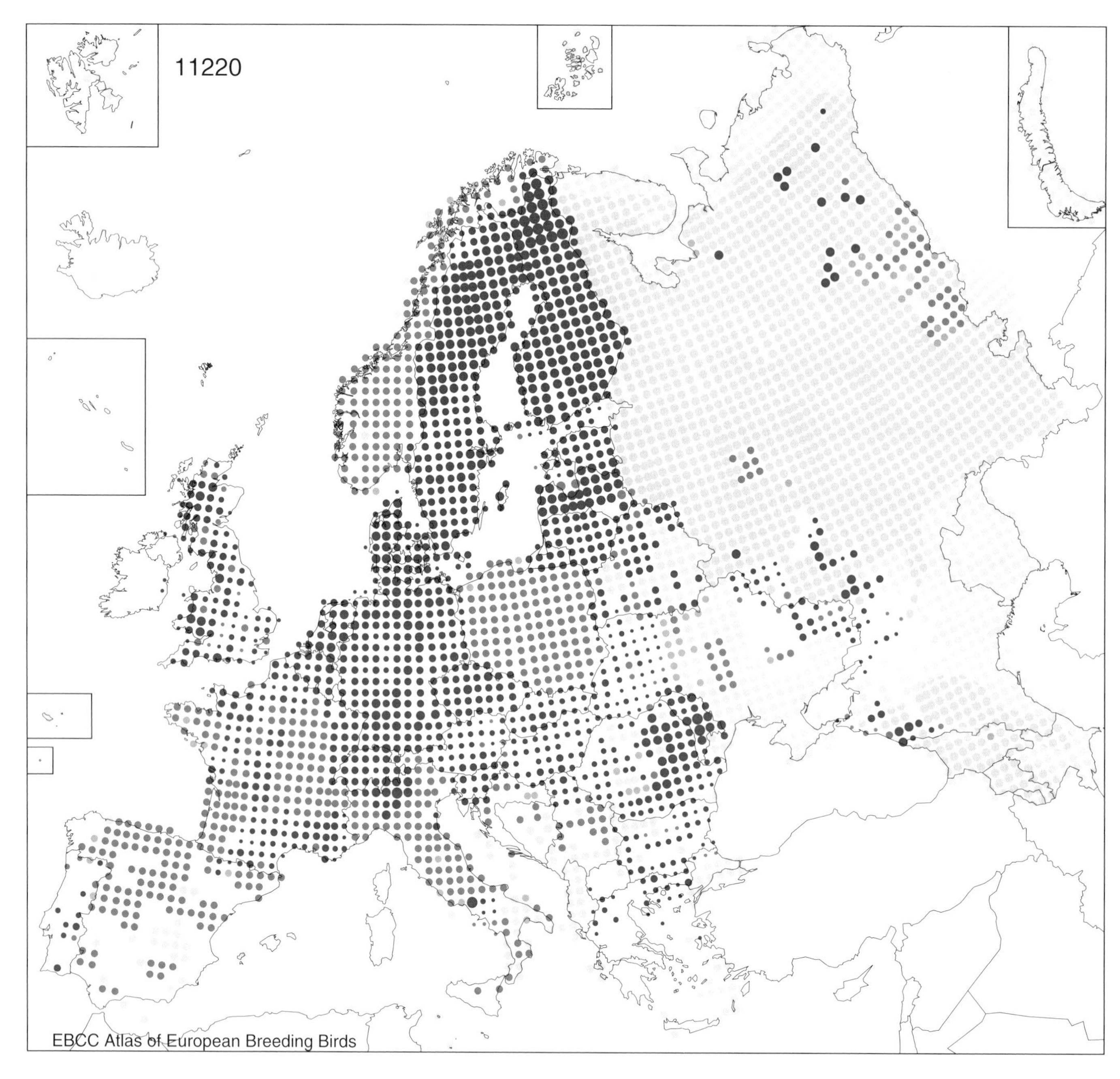

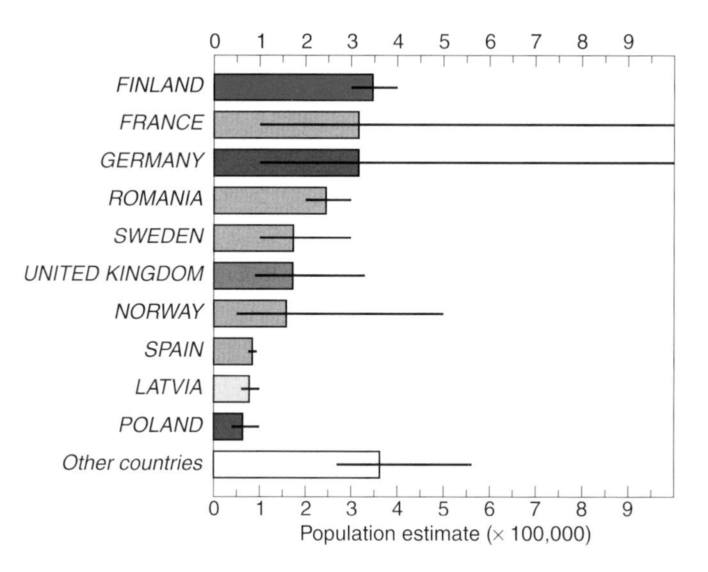

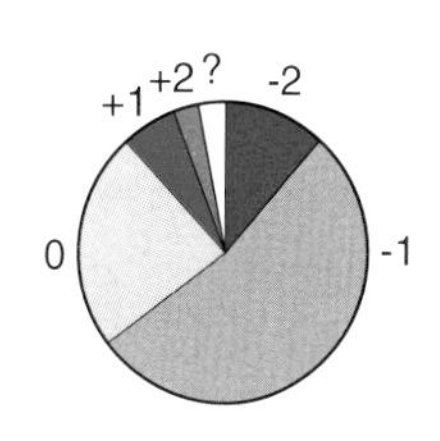

% in top 10 countries: 84.4
Total number of populated European countries: 34
Total European population 1,962,293–3,369,902 (2,314,324)
Russian population 100,000–1,000,000 (316,228)
Turkish population 10,000–100,000 (31,623)

The Redstart occupies the boreal and warm temperate zones, breeding between the July 10°C and 24°C isotherms in Europe and Siberia as far E as Lake Baykal. It is absent from Svalbard, Iceland, Corsica, Sardinia and large areas of Ireland, Greece and S Spain. It winters in sub-Saharan savanna and scrub, and reaches N Europe in late April, leaving in late August.

For breeding habitats the Redstart selects open forests, forest clearings and forest margins, preferably where the undergrowth or herbage is semi-open. In S and C Europe it prefers mainly broad-leaved forests and in N Europe barren pine *Pinus* forests (avoiding closed spruce *Picea* forests). It occurs from subarctic mountain birch forests to southern mountain treelines, reaching *c*700m asl in Fennoscandia, 1300m in the Sudeten Mountains and 2000m in the Alps. It is also common in parks and gardens containing scattered groups of trees. The Redstart nests mainly in tree-holes, nestboxes and buildings, but also in stone-piles and tree-roots and occasionally on the ground.

In the *Atlas*' coverage area the total European population is between 1.5Mbp and 5.8Mbp. In C European parks (study areas >1km²) highest breeding densities exceed 20 bp/km². In N European forests without nestboxes the average is 1–5 bp/km². Both in Swedish (*c*10 bp/km²) and Finnish (*c*4 bp/km²) Lapland, density is relatively high in mountain birch forests where nestboxes are common (Järvinen 1981).

In most of C Europe, Great Britain, S Scandinavia, Finnish and Swedish Lapland and the former USSR the Redstart breeding populations have decreased markedly since the 1960s (Berndt & Winkel 1979, Järvinen 1981, Bruderer & Hirschi 1984, Mason & Hussey 1984). Annual density variations are marked, especially at the northern range limit (Järvinen 1981). It seems that the decreases have been particularly severe since 1968 in C Europe (Berthold *et al* 1993 advised that the decline statistically was the most significant of 35 species studied) and Britain, and in Lapland after 1974. Only the British population has shown signs of partial recovery (Mason & Hussey 1984).

From 1970 to 1990 the trend was decreasing in 23 countries (68%), stable in eight (23%) and increasing in three (9%). In comparison with other information sources, the *Atlas* figures indicate increases in Croatia, Denmark, Finland and Great Britain. Doubtless the Finnish population did increase slightly between 1978 and 1987, but methodological differences may partly explain the *Atlas* increases because the line-transect method used in previous studies tends to underestimate densities. The simultaneous and marked decrease shown for Sweden is otherwise inexplicable.

The long-term decline has been explained by rainfall patterns in the Sahel, especially since the late 1960s, modern forestry (decreasing availability of nest-holes) and increased interspecific competition for natural holes. A combination of several factors is most likely, because C European Redstart populations failed to recover after rainfall conditions in the Sahel improved (Bruderer & Hirschi 1984). Because the site-tenacious Redstart has also declined in areas remote from and unaffected by forestry or other human activities, as in NW Lapland, causes beyond its breeding area may be pre-eminent. Neither in S nor N Europe can the decreasing trends be attributed to reduced productivity (Berndt & Winkel 1979, Järvinen 1981).

Despite a slight recent recovery in N Fennoscandia the Redstart has not returned to pre-crash levels (pers obs). In Britain, the Redstart's recovery since the mid-1970s has been more pronounced than that of many other drought-affected species, suggesting that other factors, possibly relating to interspecific nest-site competition over nestboxes, are at work. Local Redstart increases in pollution-ravaged C European mountain forests are confined to forests that are not yet heavily affected. A decline is apparent in heavily damaged forests (Flousek *et al* 1993).

Antero Järvinen (FIN)

Saxicola rubetra

Whinchat

CZ	Bramborníček hnědý	**I**	Stiaccino
D	Braunkehlchen	**NL**	Paapje
E	Tarabilla Norteña	**P**	Cartaxo-nortenho
F	Tarier des prés	**PL**	Pokląskwa
FIN	Pensastasku	**R**	Луговой чекан
G	Καστανολαίμης	**S**	Buskskvätta
H	Rozsdás csuk		

SPEC Cat 4, Threat status S

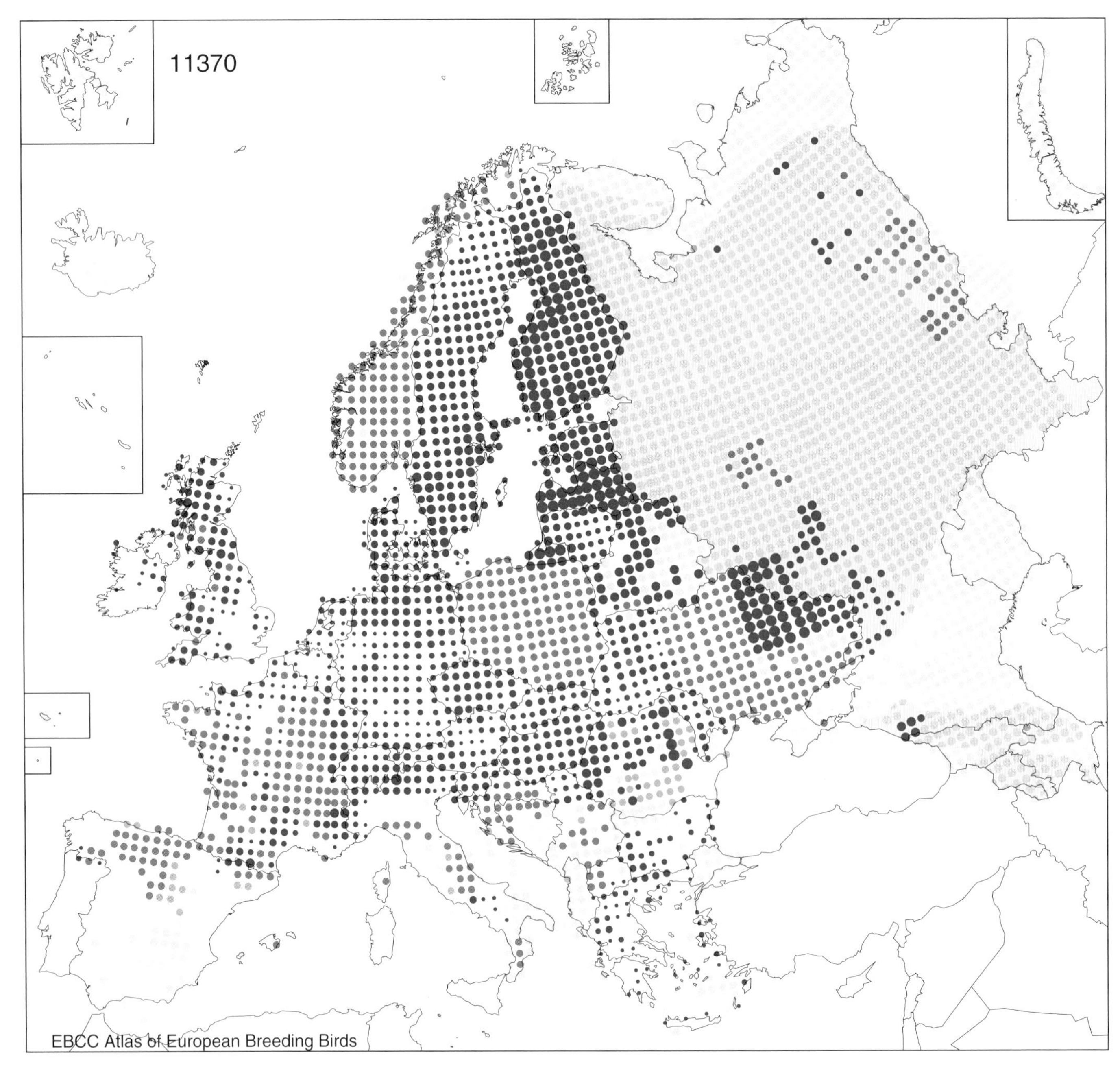

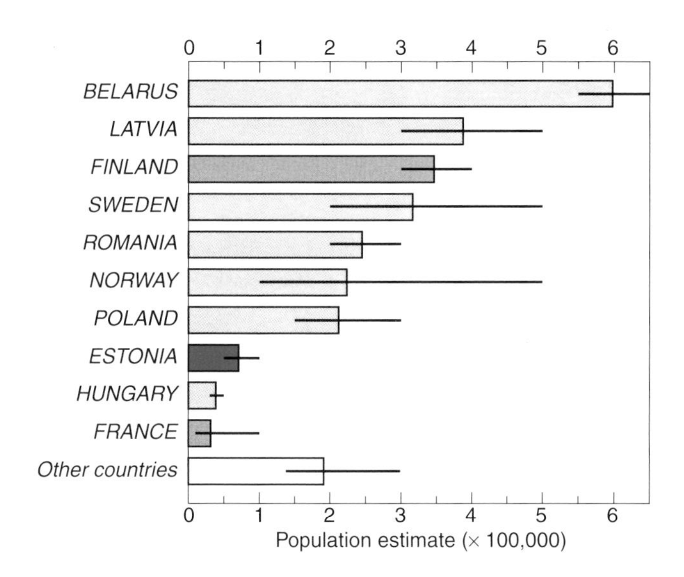

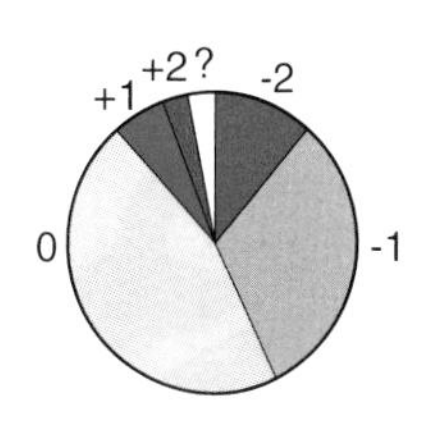

% in top 10 countries: 92.8
Total number of populated European countries: 35
Total European population 2,441,607–3,044,673 (2,660,939)
Russian population 100,000–1,000,000 (316,228)
Turkish population 500–5000 (1581)

The range of the Whinchat, primarily a meadow breeding bird of the W Palearctic, stretches E to the Yenisey and SE to the Altai Mountains. Its range extends N of the Arctic Circle only where the Gulf Stream influences the climate in Europe. Eastwards its northern limit edges S to avoid the prolonged wintry spring frosts of the continental centre. Its southern limits occur at the Mediterranean and Black Seas, the dry meadow-steppe of Kazakhstan and the Himalayan mountain chains.

A trans-Saharan migrant, the Whinchat winters throughout the rainy season on open grassy steppes, savanna and agricultural land of West and East Africa and northern South Africa. Should the rains fail, returning populations reach Europe in poor condition and probably suffer higher mortality rates (Dejaifve 1994b).

Favoured habitats are wet meadows, pastures, bogs, upland grassland, heath, dry or wet open scrubs, but not embankments. The species usually requires: bare ground patches to permit location of and access to food items; solitary shrubs, bushes, trees or fences for use as song-posts, above the surrounding vegetation; and a highly structured soil profile. Uncultivated or partially cultivated wet areas are always preferred to dry or intensively cultivated plots. On some 5–10ha study plots of the best available remaining habitat amid extensively cultivated C European farmland, maximum breeding densities of up to 100 bp/km^2 were recorded (*HVM*). Because the species shows high site fidelity (H-V. Bastian 1992) it remains for many years on locations subject to erosion or to the effects of intensive farming practices. However, when conditions have become too adverse, breeding ceases or the density reduces rapidly to only a few pairs.

Over large areas of prime habitat in NE and E Europe, typical high breeding densities of 20–50 bp/km^2 are achieved (Finland, the Baltic States, Poland, Belarus, Ukraine, Romania). Towards S and W Europe, the overall densities decline and large gaps appear in the distribution pattern (A. Bastian & Bastian 1994). Since 1955, in W and C Europe, most meadows have lost much of their plant and animal structural diversity, because of agricultural intensification and the advancement of first silage harvest to late May. Consequently, the populations in The Netherlands, Great Britain, Luxembourg, Belgium and Germany have dropped by 50% or more. Since 1980 this trend has levelled or slowed due to partial reduction or cessation of cultivation (A. Bastian & Bastian 1994) and an upsurge in numbers in damp nature reserves (The Netherlands; A.J. van Dijk, pers comm). Nevertheless in Germany the population further reduced from *c*66 000bp in 1985 to (in our opinion) 40 000–50 000bp in 1993. In Finland Whinchat numbers have decreased steadily since 1965 (J. Haapala, pers comm), but it remains a stronghold of the species, distribution gaps occurring only in some eastern woodlands and the extreme N (H. Pietiäinen 1983). E European populations are mostly stable, but in Vojvodina the population size has increased since 1985 (T. Gavrilov, pers comm).

In the Mediterranean countries the Whinchat occurs regularly only in the higher mountain ranges, not at all on the coast, and elsewhere occasionally. It is scarce and patchily distributed in the Apennines, Rhodopes and the Balkan Mountains, and absent from the large Mediterranean islands. In Italy it occurs S to Calabria. In the Alps it is widely distributed from high to low altitudes, but in Switzerland low-altitude populations are disappearing, thus increasing the median vertical distribution significantly since 1985 (H. Schmid, pers comm). In Greece the Whinchat breeds regularly only in the N and NE. Its breeding status in Turkey remains unverified, but any NE Anatolian population possibly is contiguous through NW Iran with that in Armenia and Azerbaijan. The highest breeding records are from Armenia (2230m asl), Piedmont and the Swiss Alps (2300m asl).

Hans-Valentin Bastian (D) Anita Bastian (D)
Massimo Bocca (I) Werner Suter (CH)

This species account is sponsored by Klaus-Peter Stirn, München, D.

Saxicola torquata Stonechat

CZ	Bramborníček černohlavý	I	Saltimpalo
D	Schwarzkehlchen	NL	Roodborsttapuit
E	Tarabilla Común	P	Cartaxo-comum
F	Tarier pâtre	PL	Kląskawka
FIN	Mustapäätasku	R	Черноголовый чекан
G	Μαυρολαίμης	S	Svarthakad buskskvätta
H	Cigánycsuk		

SPEC Cat 3, Threat status D (P)

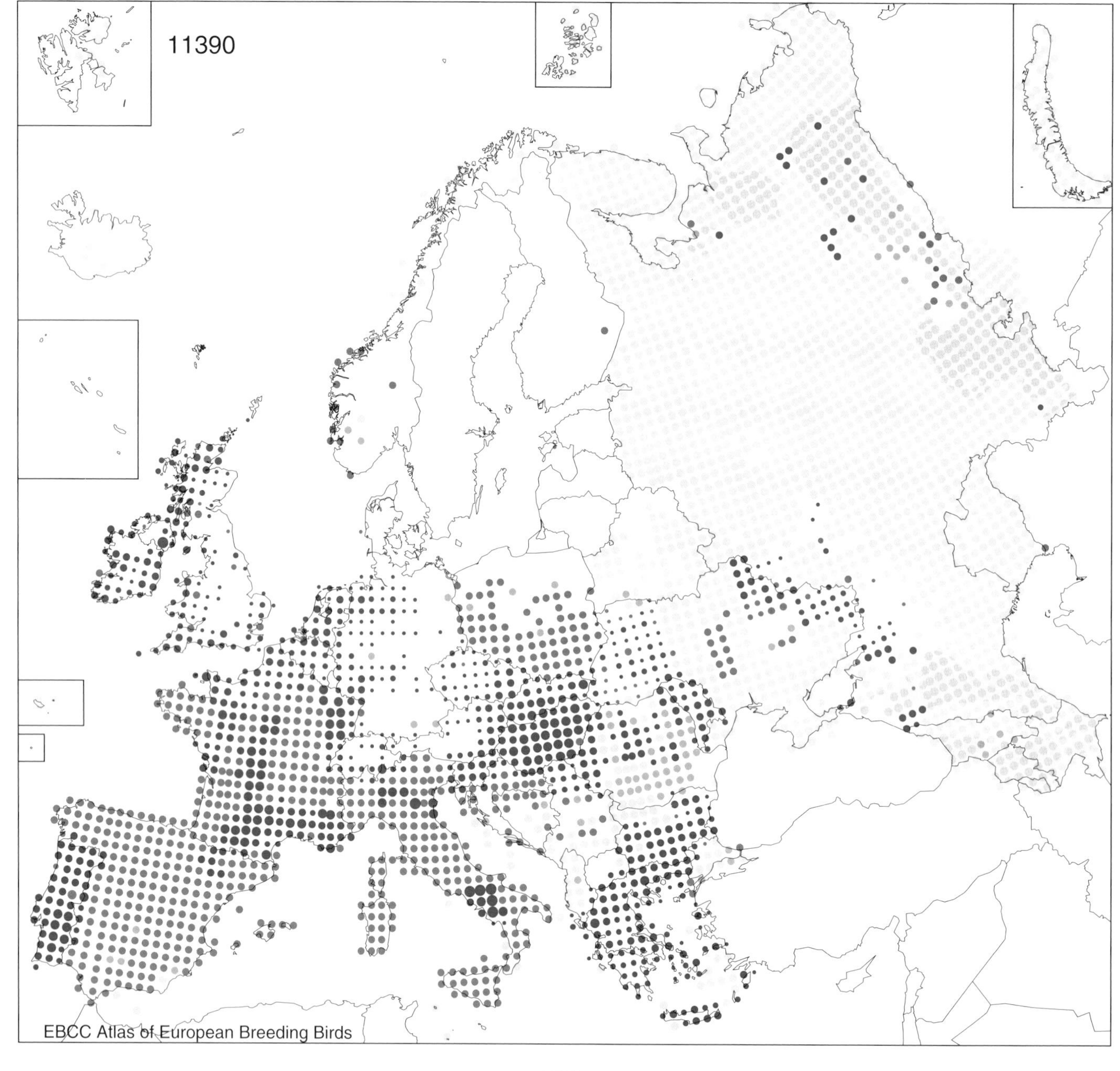

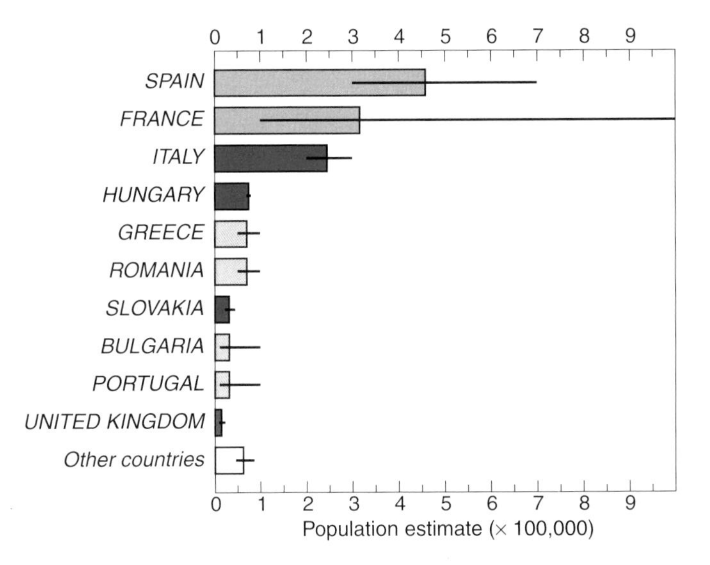

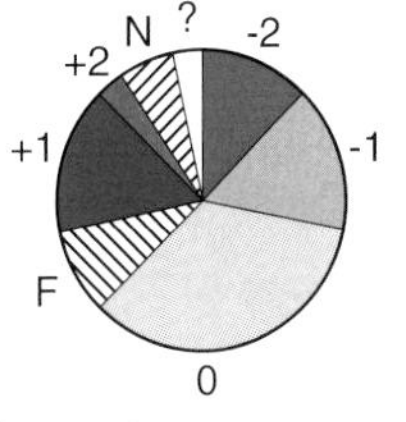

% in top 10 countries: 95.6
Total number of populated European countries: 32
Total European population 1,131,865–2,142,344 (1,407,182)
Russian population 10,000–100,000 (31,623)
Turkish population 10,000–100,000 (31,623)

The Stonechat is distributed widely throughout the Palearctic temperate and boreal zones and discontinuously in the Ethiopian zone. The subspecies *S.t. rubicola* occurs over most of Europe as far as Ukraine and Belarus (V. Serebryakov, pers comm) and North Africa, *hibernans* is found in Britain, Ireland, W France and W Iberia, *variegata* W of the Caspian, *armenica* in E Turkey and SE Transcaucasia, and *maura* in Siberia and over much of N Asia.

In Europe it is generally distributed up to 53°N, but its range extends further N in Great Britain, Denmark and The Netherlands. During the mid-1970s in a northwards range expansion it colonized the coastal zone of Norway, although the population fluctuated in response to severe winters (Størkersen 1994). The subspecies *maura* has bred recently in N Finland in habitat representative of its Siberian range (Jännes & Nikander 1993).

The Stonechat usually breeds in lowlands from sea level up to 400–500m asl. In smaller numbers it occurs in the mountains of C and eastern Europe up to 700–800m, exceptionally, as in the Italian Alps, up to 1850m asl (Brichetti & Canbi 1985). In southern Europe it reaches 2230m (Greece; J. Hölzinger, pers comm).

Its breeding habitat comprises open natural or extensively cultivated areas with varied grass-cover and ample perches as song-posts or vantage points during foraging. Examples are moorland, heathland, wide shrubby river shallows, secondary railways and rural roadsides. In the Atlantic regions it prefers uneven often craggy landscapes containing some gorse *Ulex* spp and coarse heather *Calluna vulgaris* but accepts moist areas with open water, dunes and dune-slacks in the vicinity. In the Mediterranean region the Stonechat breeds primarily amongst traditional agriculture, in the open garrigue with rock-rose *Cistus* spp, and at higher elevations mainly on sunny, grassy slopes possessing thorny shrubs. In S Switzerland and N Italy it breeds also on south-facing traditionally cultivated vineyards on irregular ground rich in pioneer herb vegetation.

The Stonechat's distribution is often uneven, particularly in C Europe, where populations tend to be isolated and at low densities. In prime habitats in the Mediterranean and Atlantic regions and eastern Europe it achieves breeding densities of 15–25 bp/10ha (*HVM*).

Since the 1950s the Stonechat has suffered a progressive reduction of its breeding habitats in farmland, especially in NW and E Europe, due to agricultural intensification and maize replacing traditional cereals (Hustings 1986). It also decreased in the littoral heathland after traditional grazing and burning rotation had ceased (Marchant *et al* 1990). Declines were particularly severe in Britain (from 30 000–60 000bp in 1968–72 to 8500–21 500bp in 1988–91; Callion 1993), Ireland (range contraction of 28% between 1968–72 and 1988–91; Callion 1993), The Netherlands (from 4100-5800bp in 1974–76 to 1600–2300bp in 1982-84, mostly stable thereafter; Hustings 1986) and Germany (>50% decline in numbers in 1970–90; for example, in Nordrhein-Westfalen from 400–500bp in 1970–78 to 150bp in 1982; Flinks & Pfeifer 1984). However, in the Carpathian basin recent large-scale agricultural changes in taking crop-fields out of use or changing them into pasture have produced new habitats and allowed the Stonechat population to increase (Z. Molnár, pers obs). Severe weather conditions in wintering areas also increases Stonechat mortality and causes population fluctuations (Dhondt 1983).

Western and southern European populations are partially or mainly resident, especially in mild winters, but the remainder migrate to the Atlantic seaboard, Iberia (where significant concentrations occur in S and E Spain), the Balearics, North Africa (Bueno 1991), S Italy, Greece, the Middle East, the Nile Valley and E Africa. The Siberian subspecies *maura* is a long-distance migrant, wintering in N India and SW Asia; vagrants occur in Europe.

Roberto Lardelli (CH) Zoltán Molnár (H)

This species account is sponsored by SOVON Birdcensus Work The Netherlands, Beek-Ubbergen, NL.

Oenanthe oenanthe **Wheatear**

CZ	Bělořit šedý	**I**	Culbianco
D	Steinschmätzer	**NL**	Tapuit
E	Collalba Gris	**P**	Chasco-cinzento
F	Traquet motteux	**PL**	Białorzytka
FIN	Kivitasku	**R**	Обыкновенная каменка
G	Σταχτοπετρόκλης	**S**	Stenskvätta
H	Hantmadár		

Non-SPEC, Threat status S

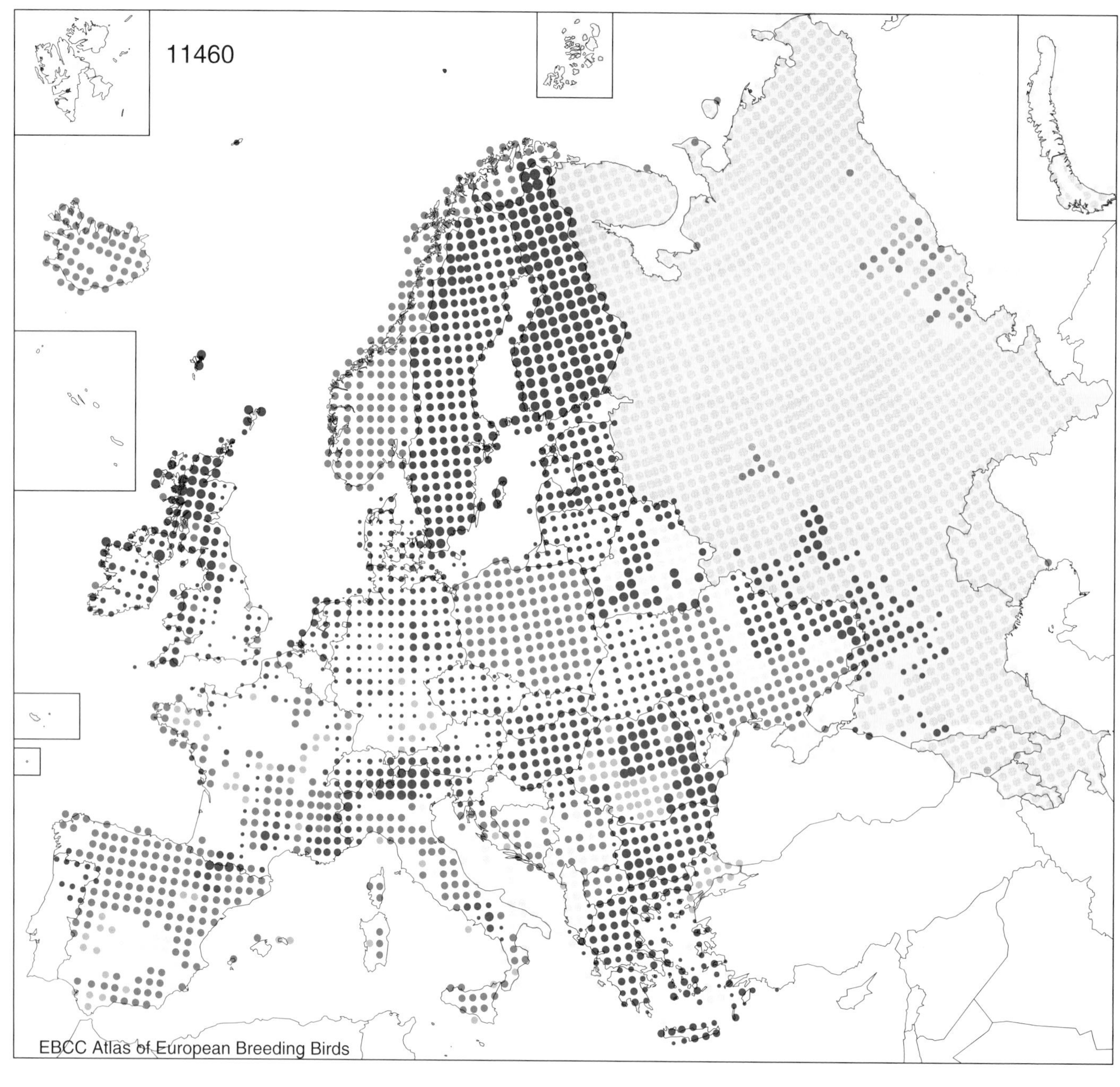

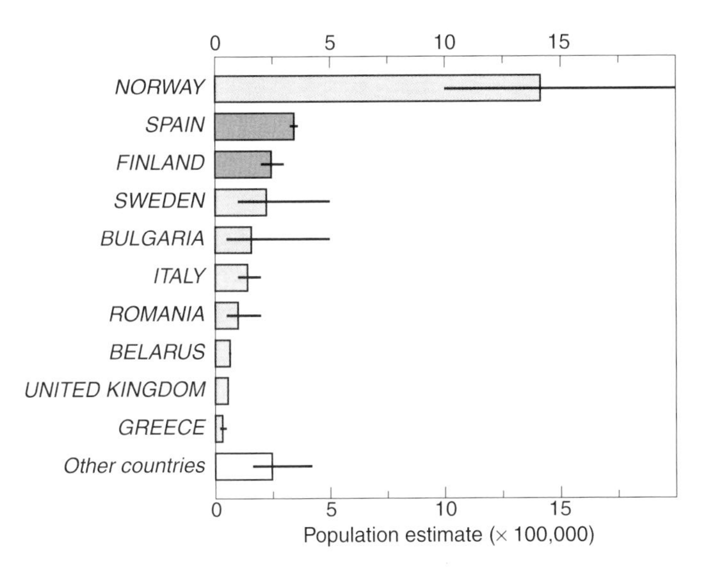

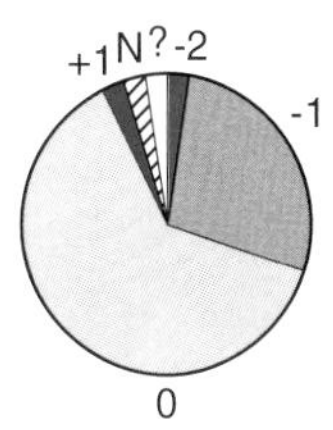

% in top 10 countries: 91.9
Total number of populated European countries: 40
Total European population 2,569,616–3,771,693 (3,023,591)
Russian population 1,000,000–10,000,000 (3,162,278)
Turkish population 50,000–500,000 (158,114)

The Wheatear (also called Northern Wheatear) is the most numerous and widely distributed of its family. Its European breeding range extends from the Mediterranean islands (where generally it is the only breeding wheatear), N to Iceland, the Faeroes, Svalbard and North Cape (72°N). Worldwide, its breeding range extends E across the entire northern and much of the C former USSR, S to the Pamirs and the Tian Shan, extreme NW China and E Siberia, into the Nearctic in western and southern Alaska and the Canadian Yukon region. Westwards its range reaches Greenland and most of NE Canada. Most of the European range is occupied by the nominate subspecies *O.o. oenanthe*, which is replaced in the Faeroes and Iceland (and NE Canada) by *leucorhoa*; *libanotica* occupies SW and SE Europe.

The Wheatear occupies a range of open-ground habitats from sea-level stony heaths to alpine meadows and montane boulder fields above the treeline. It prefers such breeding areas as open plains, meadows and rolling, short-sward grassy areas and tundra. In prime habitat such as in W Wales it reaches densities of 23 bp/km^2 (Lovegrove *et al* 1994) and in small Breckland (E England) plots *c*35 bp/km^2, although elsewhere, particularly in uplands, densities usually are much lower. In Norway, densities range from 5–20 bp/km^2 in the S to 5–10 bp/km^2 in the N (Mehlum 1994); these figures probably are typical for Fennoscandia and N Russia. The lower densities in C and W Europe are the effects of intensive cultivation and lack of suitable habitat.

The Wheatear avoids closed woodlands and, throughout much of Europe, heavily cultivated areas, though it often breeds in small, isolated pockets of low-intensity agriculture and hill pastures shared with grazing sheep. In the Swiss Alps it breeds up to 2500m asl but beyond Europe it reaches 3000m asl in the Altai and the N Iranian mountains. Its presence at high altitude is possible because it nests in sheltered locations excluding the sun and wind, allowing the nestlings to maintain body temperature when the brooding parents are absent (Verbeek 1988).

The vast open tracts within the former USSR hold the largest populations, currently estimated at 1M–10Mbp. It is difficult to assess accurately the total number breeding within Europe because there are substantial populations, amounting to *c*2.05Mbp in Norway, Sweden, Finland and further S in Spain and Italy. The rest of Europe combined (including Iceland) supports a further 1.25Mbp.

Trends in the overall population are difficult to detect because in the summer months the species occupies such a vast area, for much of which data are lacking. However, there have been recent range extensions into NE Canada, probably by way of the Faeroes and Greenland, possibly attributable to the rise in land temperatures in summer. It is equally possible that concomitant increases may have taken place along the tundra of N Scandinavia and arctic Russia. However, Iberia and many W and C European countries reported declines, mostly after the cultivation of natural habitats (Kneis 1982), but also following eutrophication from acidic deposition, which produced exuberant grass growth on formerly sparsely vegetated heaths and sand-dunes (Osieck & Hustings 1994). In Britain a slight decrease occurred between 1968–72 and 1988–91, attributed to afforestation of large upland areas and increasing lowland agricultural intensification (Conder 1993).

Almost all populations, even Nearctic, winter in the Sahel in the broad band of dry tropical savanna from Mauritania and Senegal to Ethiopia, Kenya and northern Tanzania. It is likely that the severe drought years of 1972 and 1983 have reduced the number of birds returning to breed. Small numbers apparently winter in Mesopotamia (*BWP* map).

Peter Clement (GB)

This species account is sponsored by NV PWN Waterleidingbedrijf Noord-Holland, Castricum, NL.

Oenanthe isabellina

Isabelline Wheatear

CZ	Bělořit plavý	I	Culbianco isabellino
D	Isabellsteinschmätzer	NL	Izabeltapuit
E	Collalba Isabel	P	Chasco-isabel
F	Traquet isabelle	PL	Białorzytka płowa
FIN	Arotasku	R	Каменка-плясунья
G	Αμμοπετρόκλης	S	Isabellastenskvätta
H	Pusztai hantmadár		

Non-SPEC, Threat status S (P)

The largest wheatear breeding in the Palearctic, the Isabelline Wheatear is very similar in plumage to a female Wheatear *O. oenanthe*. The Isabelline Wheatear's distribution is centred mainly on the semi-arid, subtropical zone extending from Turkey E to the Caspian, Kazakhstan, W China and N Mongolia. There are also small pockets N and E of the Caspian.

Its European population is at the western end of its range where the subtropical zone merges with the warmer temperate or continental climatic zone of the N Mediterranean. Its breeding habitat is the open country of dry plains, steppes, wadis and desert margins, on sandy, limestone or dry clay soils which have a sparse covering of short grass, shrubs or rocks. Breeding densities in areas of prime habitat depend largely on the availability of rodent holes but according to *BWP* can reach 300–400 bp/km^2 around the Caspian Sea (apparently based on very small study plots).

The Isabelline Wheatear's wintering range consists of a broad band across the dry tropical savanna and desert edge from Senegal to southern Sudan and Somalia, S to the lowlands of Kenya, E into Arabia, the Arabian Gulf environs, most of S Iran to Baluchistan, the lowlands of Pakistan and NW India. Here it occupies habitat similar to that of its breeding range, except it favours more open and sandy areas containing a component of taller vegetation to use as look-out perches.

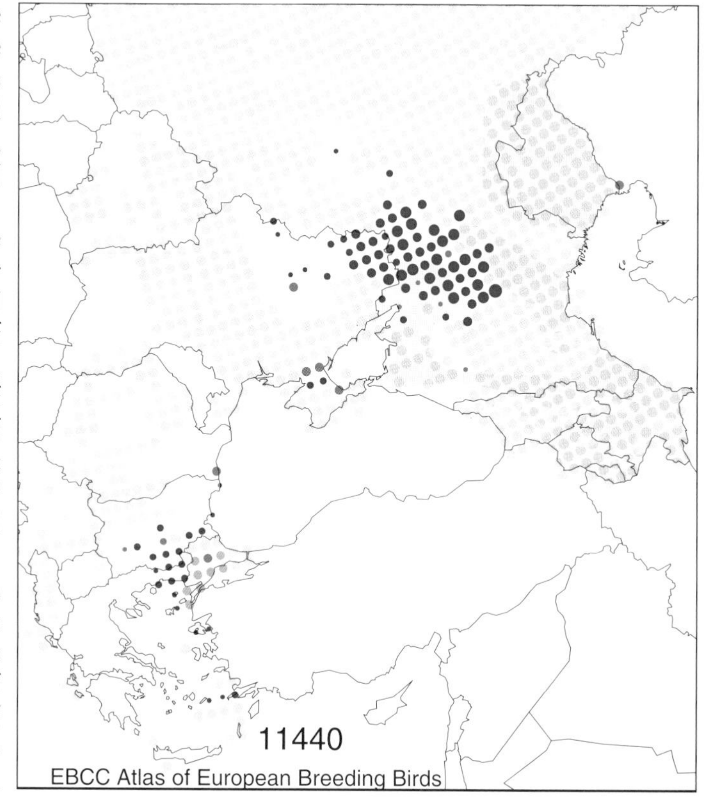

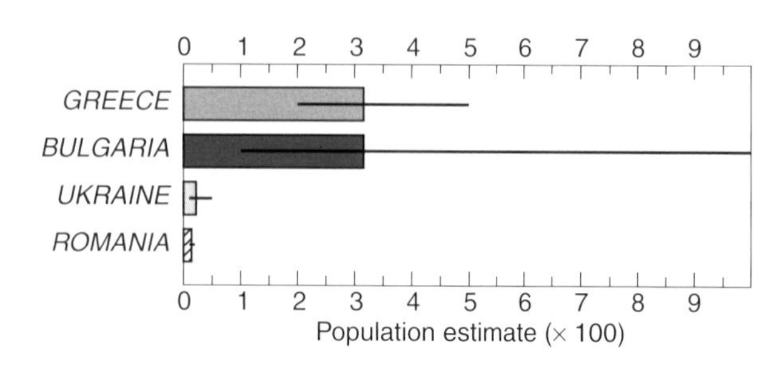

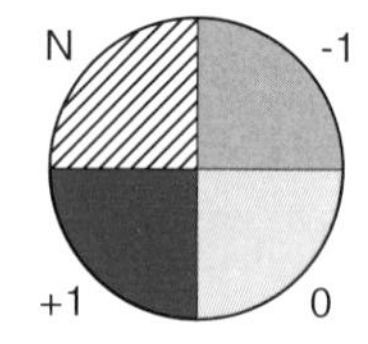

% in top 10 countries: 100.0
Total number of populated European countries: 4
Total European population 423–1378 (669)
Russian population 100,000–1,000,000 (316,228)
Turkish population 100,000–1,000,000 (316,228)

Its breeding range has expanded westwards since 1960, presumably as a direct result of drier summers, first extending into S Ukraine (the Crimea), Thrace, NE Greece and some of the Aegean Islands, and then into Bulgaria and Romania. Trends are difficult to detect, but numbers in Europe appear to be increasing, given that the maximum estimates for Greece and Bulgaria are 500bp and 1000bp respectively.

Peter Clement (GB)

Oenanthe pleschanka

Pied Wheatear

CZ	Bělořit bělohlavý	I	Monachella dorsonero
D	Nonnensteinschmätzer	NL	Bonte Tapuit
E	Collalba Pía	P	Chasco-de-peito-preto
F	Traquet pie	PL	Białorzytka pstra
FIN	Nunnatasku	R	Каменка-плешанка
G	Παρδαλοπετρόκλης	S	Nunnestenskvätta
H	Apácahantmadár		

Non-SPEC, Threat status S (P)

Lightly built, the Pied Wheatear is the eastern counterpart of Black-eared Wheatear *O. hispanica*. Its distribution stretches from W of the Black Sea (encroaching slightly into eastern Bulgaria and coastal eastern Romania (the Dobrujea)), into southern Ukraine (E of the Dnepr delta), E to Siberia, Mongolia, and northern China, and to the S to the Pamirs and the Tian Shan foothills, but it avoids the Himalayas entirely. The Cyprus population is now separated as *O. cypriaca*.

Within this area the Pied Wheatear breeds in areas of stony steppes, rocky hills including cliffs and outcrops of rocks, wooded slopes and edges of cultivated areas. In the E of its range it breeds up to 3500m asl on stony montane slopes, plateau-lands and boulder-fields above the treeline. Its preferred habitat usually comprises stony areas of short grass or other vegetation and scattered with bushes, but it also takes to areas where the vegetation is heavier providing there are adjacent boulders or rocky outcrops. Densities apparently are lower than for other wheatears, averaging *c*15 bp/km^2 in prime habitat in S Ukraine (*BWP*). The species winters in NE Africa mostly E of the Nile from Egypt S to N Tanzania, usually in habitat akin to that of its breeding areas, but also in areas of dry cultivation or even town gardens (*BWP*).

Trends in the population or changes in the distribution are difficult to detect in a bird that breeds over such a vast area, much of which is lacking in quantitative data. However, there are some signs that the range is slowly spreading in SE Europe. The numbers breeding in Bulgaria and Romania appear to be increasing, a view which is supported by a number of recent records from Turkey and eastern Greece. In Bulgaria its range is shared by the Black-eared Wheatear, hybridization occurring widely in the area of overlap.

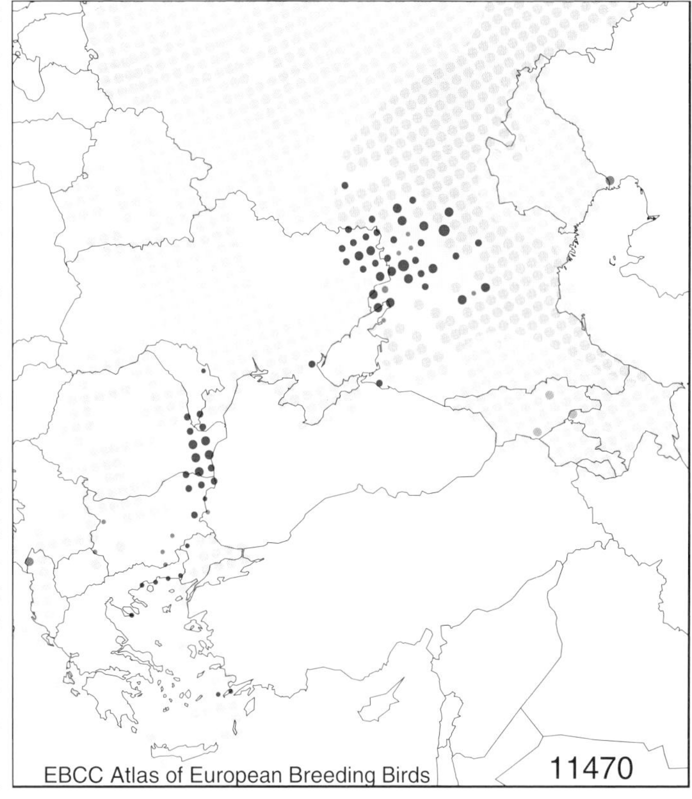

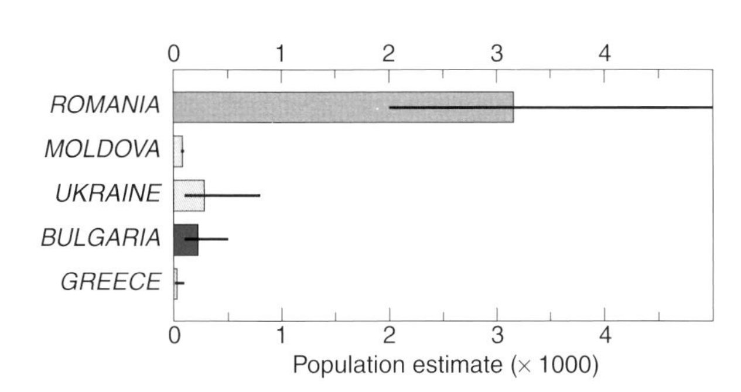

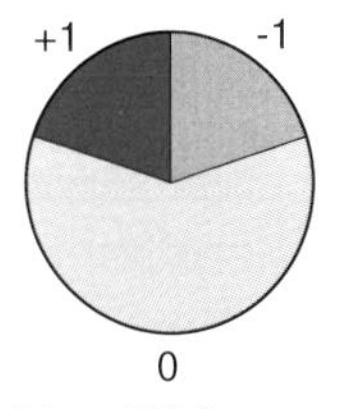

% in top 10 countries: 100.0
Total number of populated European countries: 5
Total European population 2601–5714 (3784)
Russian population 100,000–1,000,000 (316,228)
Turkish population 50–1000 (224)

Peter Clement (GB)

Oenanthe hispanica

Black-eared Wheatear

CZ	Bělořit okrový	I	Monachella
D	Mittelmeer-Steinschmätzer	NL	Blonde Tapuit
E	Collalba Rubia	P	Chasco-ruivo
F	Traquet oreillard	PL	Białorzytka rdzawa
FIN	Rusotasku	R	Чернопегая каменка
G	Ασπροκώλα	S	Medelhavsstenskvätta
H	Déli hantmadár		

SPEC Cat 2, Threat status V

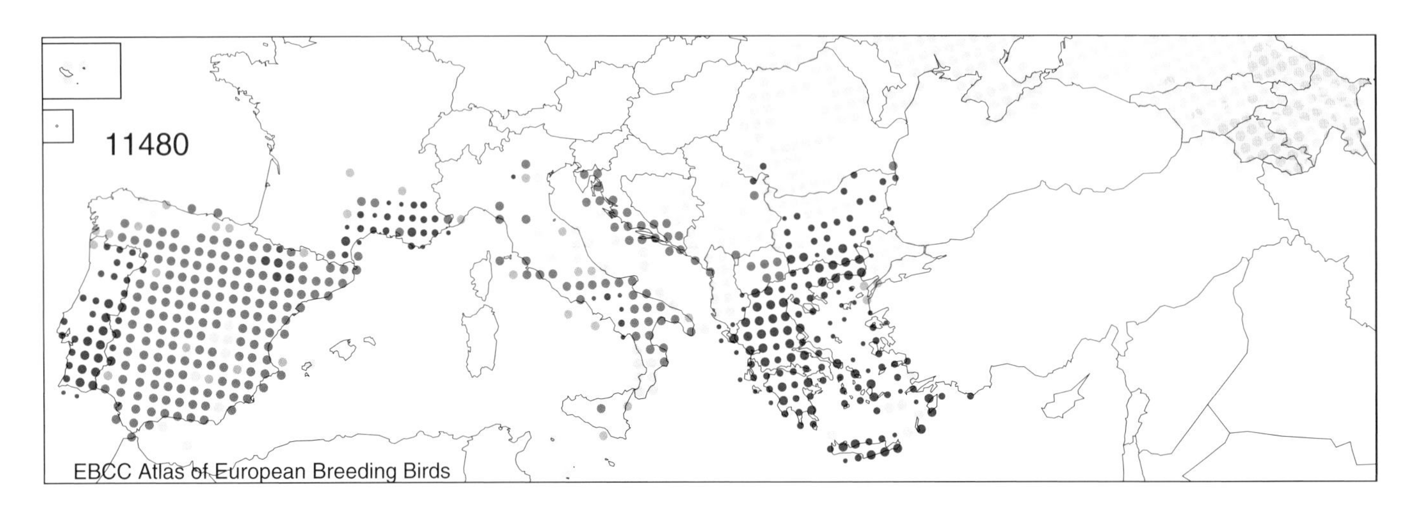

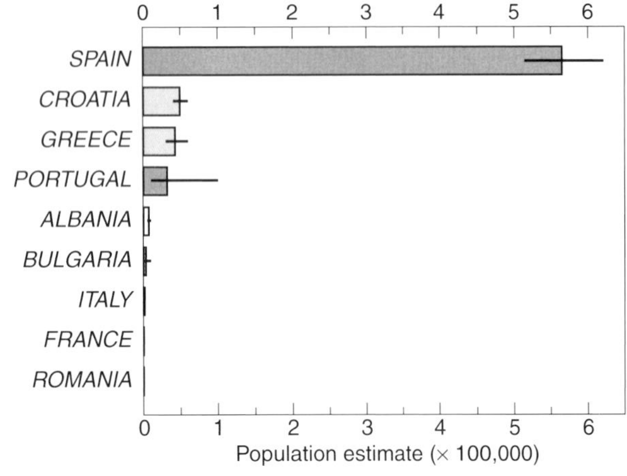

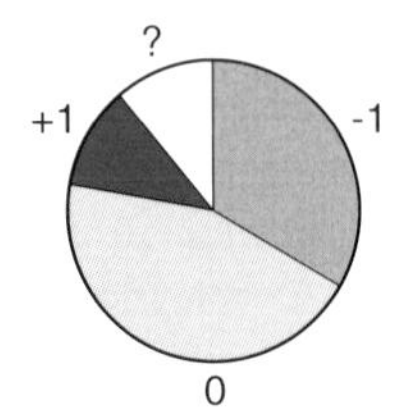

% in top 10 countries: 100.0
Total number of populated European countries: 9
Total European population 641,403–790,042 (698,933)
Turkish population 50,000–500,000 (158,114)

The Black-eared Wheatear is distributed from Portugal eastwards to Turkey, Israel, the southern Caucasus, S to the Arabian Gulf and to NW Africa (Morocco to coastal Libya), but is absent from most Mediterranean islands, Crete being the main exception in the *Atlas*' coverage area. The two relatively distinct subspecies, nominate *hispanica* in the W and *melanoleuca* from southern Italy and Croatia E to Iran, nevertheless intergrade widely in the range centre. The species is closely related to Pied Wheatear *O. pleschanka*, hybridizing where they overlap in Bulgaria.

Europe holds *c*50% of the world breeding population, the largest numbers being in Spain, Portugal and the southern Balkans. Densities in Spain exceptionally reach 26 bp/km², but more typically vary from 5.2 to 19.0 bp/km² in mixed Spanish juniper *Juniperus thurifera* habitats (Peris *et al* 1977). All birds winter in the broad band of the Sahel from Senegal to S Ethiopia in open arid semi-desert containing acacia and thorn-scrub.

Essentially a bird of the warm mediterranean climatic zone, the species prefers habitats such as dry maquis steppe, open sandy or rocky areas, limestone hills scattered with shrubs (including olive-grove edges), open farmland and open areas of juniper and holm oak *Quercus ilex* forests (Vatev & Simeonov 1972). It occurs up to 2300m asl.

Breeding numbers have declined markedly since 1970 in the western range, particularly in Spain (Suárez 1987, Mestre *et al* 1987). Its range has contracted southwards in southern France and C Italy, due to the effects of droughts in its winter quarters and agricultural intensification in Portugal, Spain and southern France reducing the area of breeding habitat (Prodon & Isenmann 1994). In the E the range and population seem stable, with a slight increase in Romania, but the species clearly is vulnerable to any future changes in traditional agricultural practices elsewhere in its range.

Peter Clement (GB) Ilia Vatev (BUL)

Oenanthe deserti

Desert Wheatear

CZ	Bělořit pouštní	I	Monachella del deserto
D	Wüstensteinschmätzer	NL	Woestijntapuit
E	Collalba Desértica	P	Chasco-do-deserto
F	Traquet du désert	PL	Białorzytka pustynna
FIN	Aavikkotasku	R	Пустынная каменка
G	Ερημοπετρόκλης	S	Ökenstenskvätta
H	Sivatagi hantmadár		

Non-SPEC, Threat status S (P)

Small to medium-sized and compact, the Desert Wheatear is a familiar denizen of the deserts of North Africa, Arabia and much of C Asia. It has a wide distribution stretching from S Morocco E across the northern edge of the Sahara to northern Egypt (Sinai), Jordan, S Iran, NE to the Kara and Kyzyl Kum and then E to the plateaulands of Tibet, western China and Mongolia.

The Desert Wheatear essentially is a bird of dry, arid steppes and desert edges possessing little or no vegetation but it frequently occurs in areas of low scrubby vegetation in dry rivercourses, wadis, ruins and flat gravel or stony areas. It generally avoids expanses of open desert and rolling dunes. Its range encompasses habitats from sea level in North Africa to high plateau and mountain passes at over 3000m in C Asia. In Europe it is on the edge of its range and very restricted as a breeding bird, only just qualifying for inclusion in the *Atlas* through its occurrence in Azerbaijan and probably Armenia. The only confirmed breeding record received by the *Atlas*, near the mouth of the Ural River in the N Caspian area of southern Kazakhstan, represents an extension of the known range of the population in C Kazakhstan, but the species has been little studied.

Most of the birds breeding in North Africa are sedentary or move only short distances but the birds breeding in Iran and east of the Caspian Sea move much further to winter in NE Africa from Sudan, Ethiopia and N Somalia, and from Saudi Arabia and the Gulf States to (Makran) coastal Iran, Baluchistan, Pakistan and the Punjab area of NW India.

It is a common bird throughout most of its wide range, especially in North Africa, but territories are more widely separated in the vast expanses of the plateaulands of its eastern distribution. The species comprises four barely distinguishable subspecies which vary only in the tone of the sandy-coloured plumage.

Peter Clement (GB)

Oenanthe finschii

Finsch's Wheatear

CZ	Bělořit skalní	I	Monachella di Finsch
D	Felsensteinschmätzer	NL	Finsch' Tapuit
E	Collalba de Finsch	P	Chasco de Finsch
F	Traquet de Finsch	PL	Białorzytka białogrzbieta
FIN	Valkoselkätasku	R	Черношейная каменка
G	Πετρόκλης του Finsch	S	Finschstenskvätta
H	Török hantmadár		

Non-SPEC, Threat status S (P)

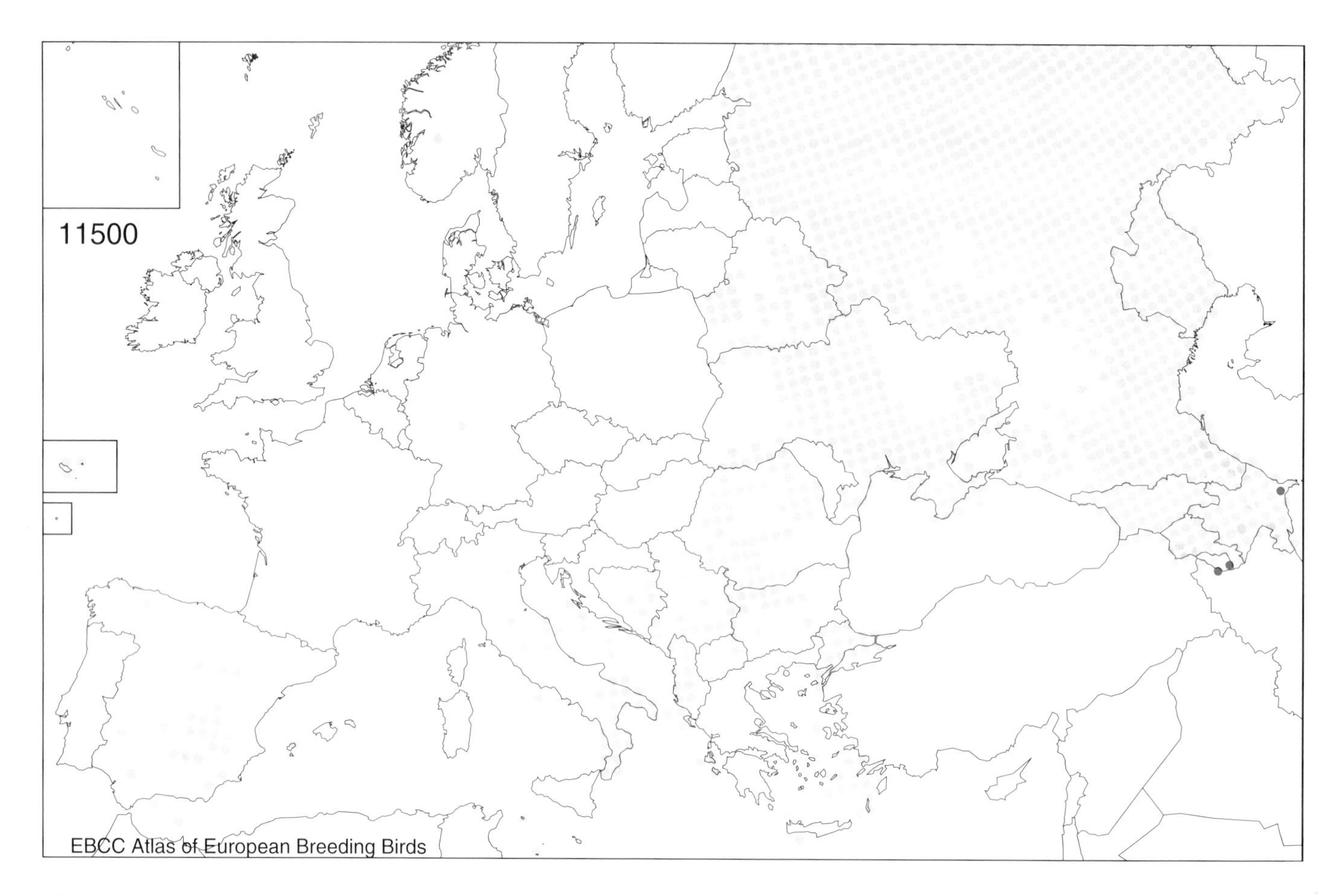

The breeding range of the medium-sized Finsch's Wheatear extends through the warm temperate zone from C–S Turkey E to the foothills of the Pamir and Altai ranges in Turkestan and Hindu Kush. Thus it is found throughout much of the Anatolian, Armenian and Iranian plateaus and the adjoining southern Caucasus, Elburz, Khorasan and Paramisus ranges. There are also isolated outposts in eastern Azerbaijan, the NE Caspian (Mangyshlak Peninsula) and northern Lebanon. In Europe it breeds in the extreme SE of Georgia, in Armenia and southern and eastern Azerbaijan.

Finsch's Wheatear is a typical inhabitant of dry foothills and arid mountains. It nests on stony slopes which have clay outcrops or precipices, in shallow ravines whose steep or gentle slopes are covered sparsely with dry mountain vegetation, and occasionally in the clay banks of dry watercourses and wadis, usually up to 700–800m asl, although it has been recorded at 1620m in Armenia (Dal' 1954) and between 1700 and 2200m in the Elburz range in Iran (Haffer 1977).

In the Nakhichevan territory of Azerbaijan, breeding pairs are distributed unevenly. In preferred habitats (stony bases of foothills studded with talus mounds and shallow dry watercourses) it is common, in separated groups of 5–7bp (E.N. Panov, pers obs), but in the E of the country it has a more scattered distribution, up to 5 bp/km linear density. At the extreme north-west of the breeding range, in SE Georgia, it is a rare species (Jordania 1962).

Southern populations are partly sedentary or make short-distance movements to lower levels. Breeding birds from the C and northern parts of the range winter over a wide area from S Turkey to NW Iran, and also are scattered in discrete populations from Cyprus to Israel, NE Egypt (Sinai), Jordan, Syria, Iraq, N Saudi Arabia and the Gulf area of S Iran. Its wintering habitat is similar to its breeding habitat, often being in flat stony desert at the limits of cultivation.

Peter Clement (GB) Evgeny N Panov (R)

Oenanthe xanthoprymna

Red-tailed Wheatear

CZ	Bělořit červenoocasý	I	Monachella codarossa
D	Rostbürzel-Steinschmätzer	NL	Roodstaarttapuit
E	Collalba Colirroja	P	Chasco-de-dorso-castanho
F	Traquet à queue rousse	PL	Złotorzytka
FIN	Punaperätasku	R	Златогузая каменка
G	Κοκκινόουρος Πετρόκλης	S	Persisk stenskvätta
H	Vörösfarkú hantmadár		

Non-SPEC, Threat status S (P)

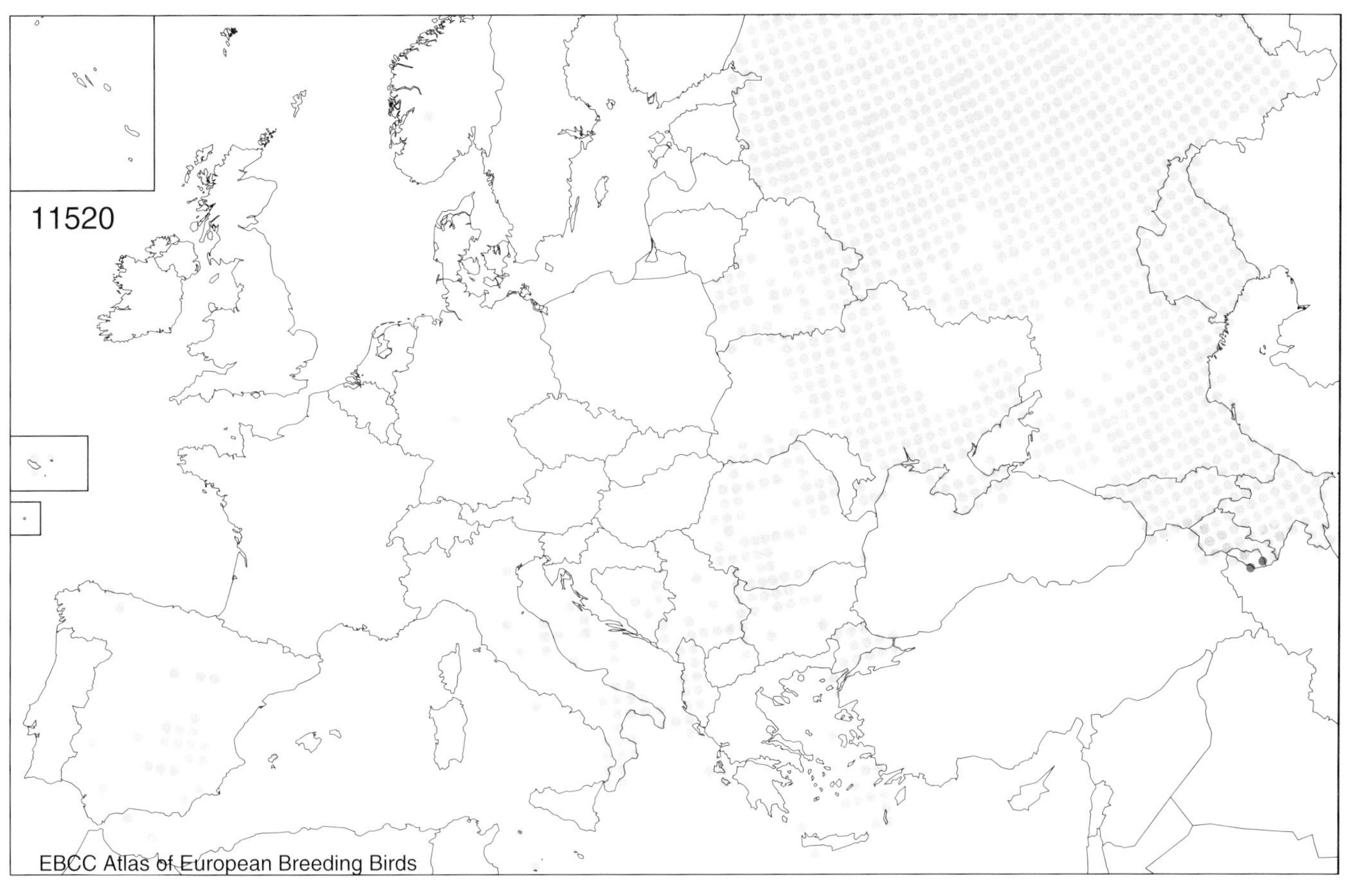

The distribution of the Red-tailed Wheatear is confined to the dry eastern warm temperate zone, mainly the Iranian plateau and the surrounding Zagros, Elburz, Khorasan and Hindu Kush ranges, just reaching the Armenian plateau in the W and the Pamir–Altai in the E. It is divided into several insular breeding ranges (Loskot & Vietinghoff-Scheel 1978). In the *Atlas*' area of coverage the species breeds in the Araks Valley in the extreme south of Armenia and Azerbaijan (Dal' 1954).

The Red-tailed Wheatear prefers dry, barren and steep mountain slopes studded with large boulder screes and talus mounds which are bare or sparsely vegetated, although usually fairly close to a permanent source of water. In Asia it breeds up to 3600–4000m asl (in Badakhshan; E.N. Panov, pers obs), but in Armenia and Azerbaijan only up to 550–860m asl. In the Nakhichevan territory of Azerbaijan its breeding habitats usually are the most desolate stony slopes very sparsely covered by xerophytic bushes (Panov 1974), although elsewhere some pairs breed in comparatively richly vegetated sites adjacent to irrigation ditches.

Its wintering area, mostly lying immediately south of its breeding range, stretches from E Egypt to N Sudan and Ethiopia, across the Arabian Peninsula to C Pakistan (the Indus floodplain), and also includes isolated areas in S Iran and Afghanistan. The habitat is similar to that occupied in summer.

Near Nakhichevan on the slopes of the Araks Valley, it is common or numerous at a linear density of up to 10 bp/km (Panov 1974), a figure which seems to have remained constant over the years.

Of the three subspecies, two are poorly distinguishable, the western *O.x. chrysopygia* occurring in the Transcaucasia and the eastern *kingi*, but the nominate *xanthoprymna* differs markedly, and may even be a separate species. Hybrids between *xanthoprymna* and *chrysopygia* are a recognizable form which has been described as *cummingi*.

Peter Clement (GB) Evgeny N Panov (R)

Oenanthe leucura

Black Wheatear

CZ	Bělořit černý	**I**	Monachella nera
D	Trauersteinschmätzer	**NL**	Zwarte Tapuit
E	Collalba Negra	**P**	Chasco-preto
F	Traquet rieur	**PL**	Białorzytka żałobna
FIN	Mustatasku	**R**	Белохвостая каменка
G	Μαυροπετρόκλης	**S**	Svart stenskvätta
H	Fekete hantmadár		

SPEC Cat 3, Threat status E

The Black Wheatear, a large wheatear, breeds in Europe only in SE France, Portugal and Spain. The European population comprises the nominate subspecies *O.l. leucura*, the male being blacker than in the *syenitica* population (NW Africa). The species prefers arid stony plateaus, mountainous regions and boulder-strewn seacliffs. Its basic requirements are rock faces or walls, denuded soil or low or sparse scrub and scattered rocks (de Juana 1980).

Almost the entire European population lives in Portugal and Spain. Only a few breeding pairs now reside in France (Prodon 1985, *HVM*) in the eastern Pyrenees. In the 18th and 19th centuries it was far more widespread in the S of France (Prodon 1985). Even in the mid-1970s there were 100bp (Yeatman 1976). The Black Wheatear has suffered a widespread decline in range and numbers in Europe, mainly in mountainous regions. The causes of the decline have not been clearly identified but severe winters (especially in January and February 1986 and 1987; Prodon 1991) and degradation of suitable habitats through afforestation probably are the most important.

In Spain the species is present at its highest densities in areas of deep canyons and ravines whose slopes are eroded, and which intersect high plateaus of intense aridity. In one such area, Hoya de Guadix, the highest linear density recorded was 3.8 bp/km of gully (Soler *et al* 1983).

The Black Wheatear is extremely sedentary throughout its breeding range (Prodon 1985), although partial altitudinal migration occurs in some mountainous regions.

An unusual feature of the species is that the male carries many stones to its nest cavity, often building them into piles at the entrance. Not only is stone-carrying a mate-attraction technique, but it is also a post-mating sexual display which allows adjustment of reproductive activities to the phenotypic quality of partners (Soler *et al* 1996).

Manuel Soler (E)

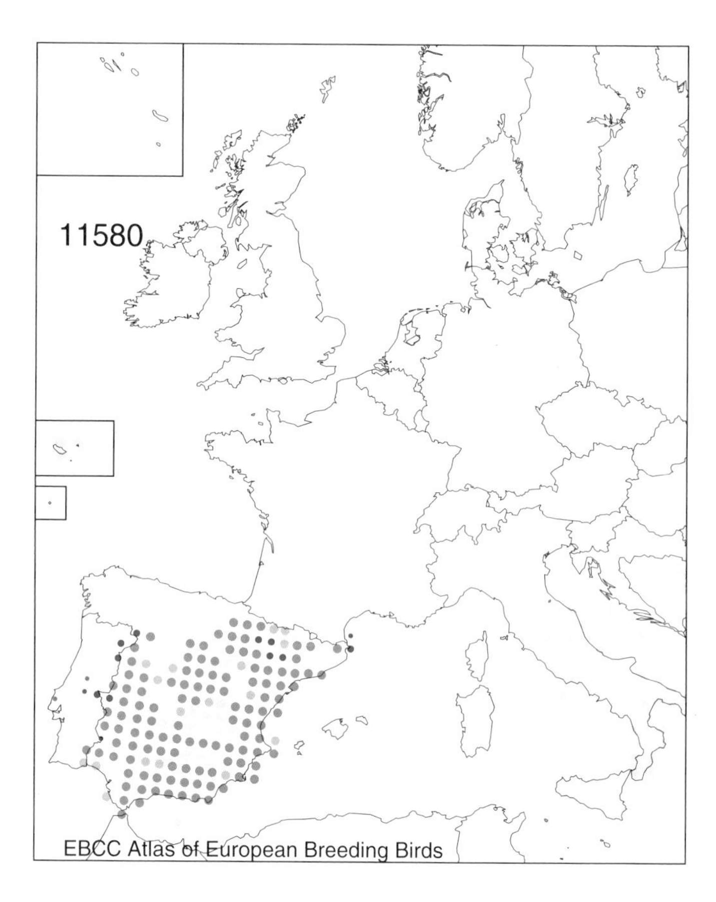

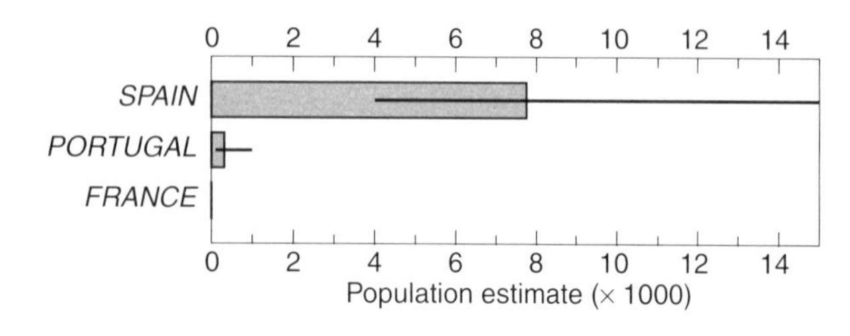

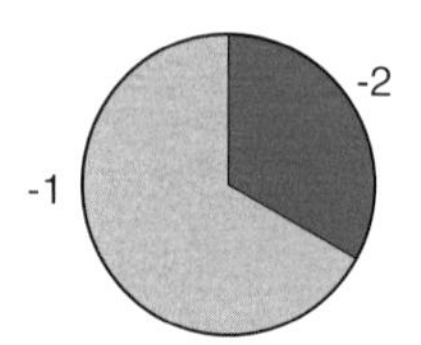

% in top 10 countries: 100.0
Total number of populated European countries: 3
Total European population 4313–15,352 (8065)

Zoothera dauma

White's Thrush

CZ	Drozd pestrý	I	Tordo dorato
D	Erddrossel	NL	Goudlijster
E	Zorzal Dorado	P	Tordo-dourado
F	Grive dorée	PL	Drozd pstry
FIN	Kirjorastas	R	Пестрый дрозд
G	Χρυσότσιχλα	S	Guldtrast
H	Himalájai rigó		

Non-SPEC, Threat status S (P)

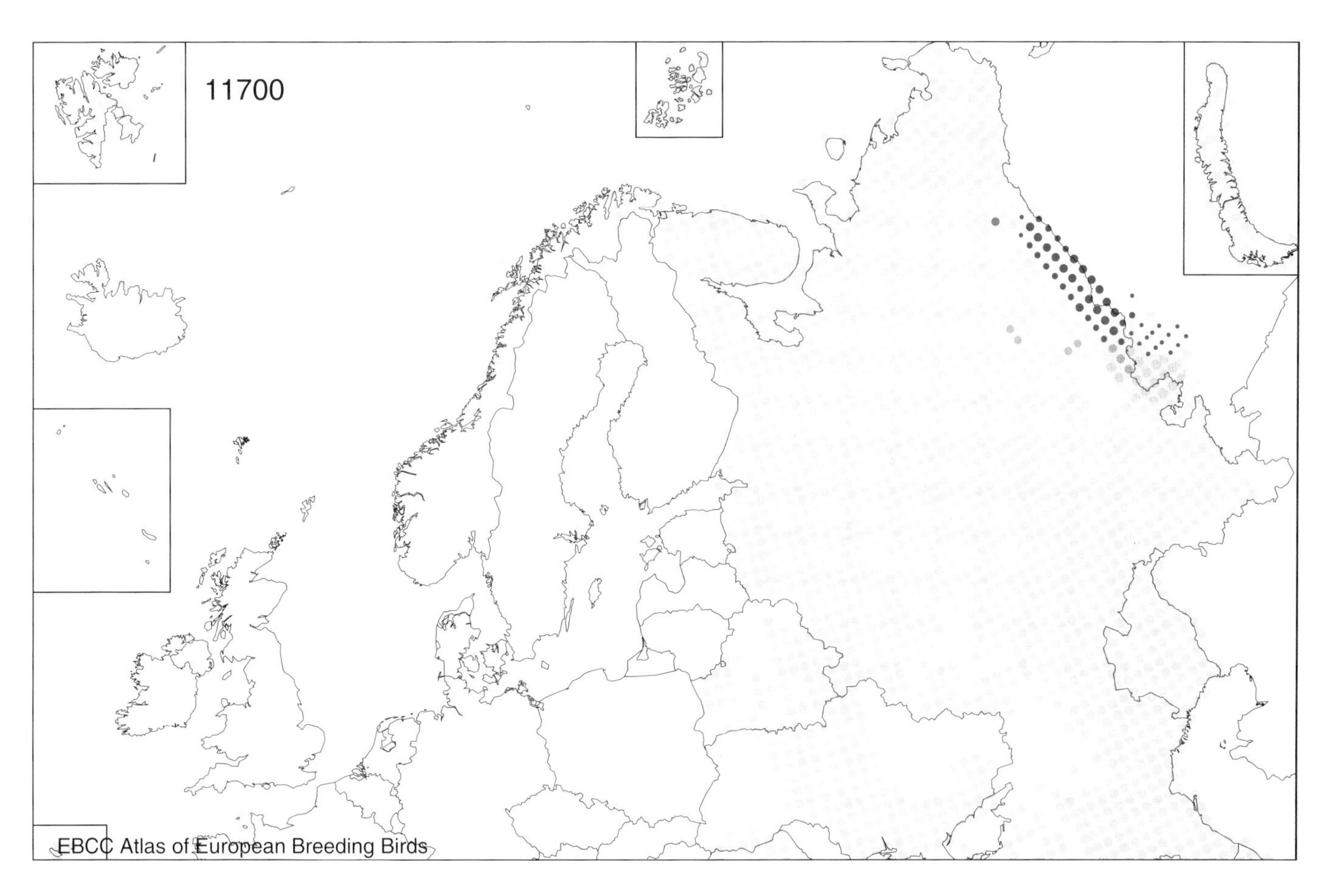

The distribution of White's Thrush only just reaches the *Atlas*' coverage area. This polytypic species has a remarkably disjunct distribution, separate populations existing in the Urals, E Siberia, Japan and Korea, the Himalayas, S India, Malaysia and on several islands from Sumatra to the Solomon Islands. European birds, comprising a small proportion of *Z.d. aurea*, winter probably from the Indian subcontinent eastwards. There are perhaps 14 other subspecies.

The species' preferred breeding habitats are the dark coniferous and mixed forests of the southern and middle subzones of the boreal zone and the dark taiga zone of the Ural foothills. Its European distribution, a narrow longitudinal N–S belt, lies between *c*54° and 63°N (Boyarshinov *et al* 1989). In spring, it may occur far from the breeding areas, as in the subpolar Urals (Shutov 1989) or in the large forest plains near Perm (Shurakov *et al* 1989). Its typical breeding habitat is high spruce *Picea* forests, but more recently it has used atypical habitats, perhaps reflecting an apparent range expansion, which itself may have been induced by intensive forestry management techniques diminishing its preferred habitats.

The well-protected spruce forests in the Ural foothills hold the highest densities, which decrease both eastwards towards the mountains and westwards towards the plains. Usually, White's Thrush is common in its breeding habitats, and its supposed rarity is mainly an artefact of its furtive behaviour. The European population size is *c*20 000–22 000bp, more than half being in the Perm region.

Breeding numbers on the eastern slopes of the Urals are stable (Liakhov 1989), which probably also is the case in Europe. Some decline may have occurred during the 20th century, following intensification of forestry methods, but at present forestry management techniques are more balanced overall, and the decline may have been halted. However, it remains absent from several steppe-zone migratory stop-overs.

Vladimir N Anufriev (R)

Monticola saxatilis

Rock Thrush

CZ	Skalník zpěvný	I	Codirossone
D	Steinrötel	NL	Rode Rotslijster
E	Roquero Rojo	P	Melro-das-rochas
F	Monticole de roche	PL	Nagórnik
FIN	Kivikkorastas	R	Пестрый каменный дрозд
G	Πετροκότσυφας	S	Stentrast
H	Kövirigó		

SPEC Cat 3, Threat status D (P)

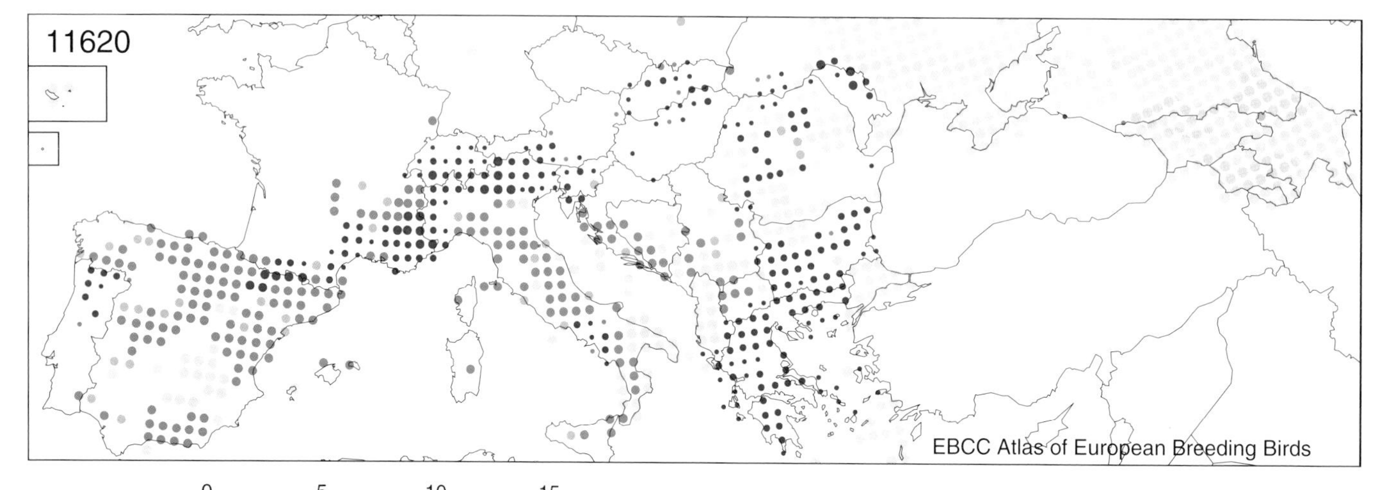

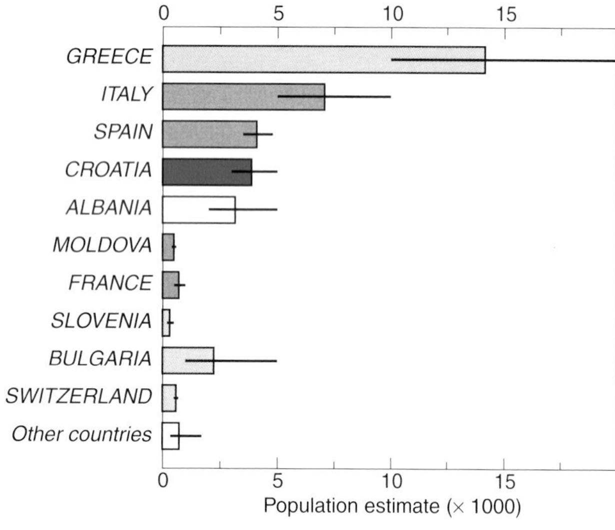

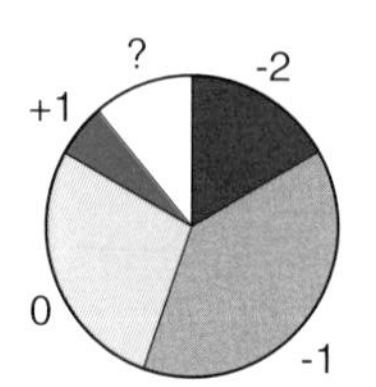

% in top 10 countries: 98.0
Total number of populated European countries: 18
Total European population 32,362–44,924 (37,419)
Turkish population 5000–50,000 (15,811)

The Rock Thrush is a montane monotypic species distributed from the Mediterranean through eastern Europe to C Asia. Its European range is continuous on southern exposures of southern and C mountain chains from N Portugal via the Alps to Sicily, the Carpathians, Moldova, the Balkans and Greece. On large Mediterranean islands it is much more localized. It breeds from 150m asl in Lombardy (Brichetti & Fasola 1990) up to 3000m in Morocco, but normally between 500m and 2000m. In the Sicilian Madonie Mountains the Blue Rock Thrush *M. solitarius* occupies a lower height-band (below 1400m asl) than the Rock Thrush (M. Lo Valvo *et al* 1993).

Its main breeding habitats are sun-exposed mountainside grassy slopes studded with rocky outcrops, others being alpine grassy meadows and lower-altitude deserted quarries or ruins. Site fidelity is common. In Europe, breeding density remains fairly low: 0.7–1.2 bp/km^2 in Canton Ticino and the Brescian pre-Alps (20–30, in the best habitats) and 0.5–1 bp/km^2 in Piedmont (Mingozzi *et al* 1988, Brichetti & Fasola 1990). Such values are unrepresentative over time because large-scale variations occur. Estimating population size is difficult because many sites are inaccessible.

In the 1800s, its distribution included Germany, Moravia, most of Austria and the French Jura. Possibly climatic trends caused the strong decline from the 1900s to the 1960s. During 1970–90, most countries still reported slight declines in range and numbers. There have been local recoveries, as in Switzerland and the Vosges (Dejaifve 1994a). In Slovakia trends remain stable; earlier indications of a slight decrease are now attributed to the irregular occupation of territories by solitary pairs. The present European population is c264 000–543 000bp. The species is a nocturnal trans-Saharan migrant whose movements are little known, considerable ringing effort on small Mediterranean islands trapping few birds (Montemaggiore *et al* 1993). Its extensive winter range extends from N Nigeria and N Cameroon to N Zambia, where C Asian populations also winter.

Pierandrea Brichetti (I) Maurizio Fraissinet (I)
Miroslav Saniga (SLK)

Monticola solitarius

Blue Rock Thrush

CZ	Skalník modrý	I	Passero solitario
D	Blaumerle	NL	Blauwe Rotslijster
E	Roquero Solitario	P	Melro-azul
F	Monticole bleu	PL	Modrak
FIN	Sinirastas	R	Синий каменный дрозд
G	Γαλαζοκότσυφας	S	Blåtrast
H	Kék kövirigó		

SPEC Cat 3, Threat status V (P)

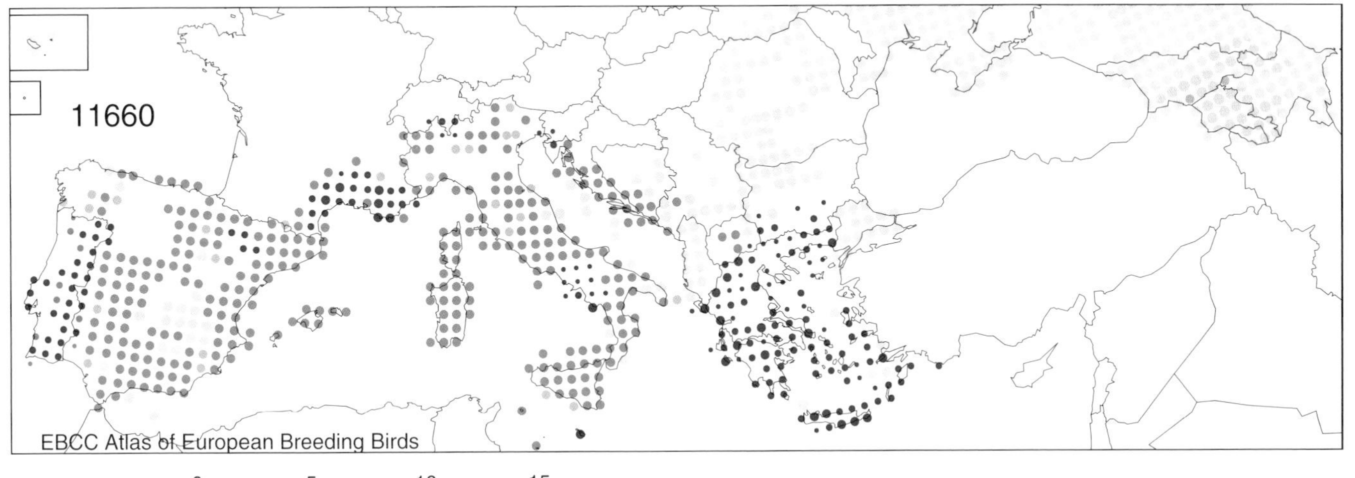

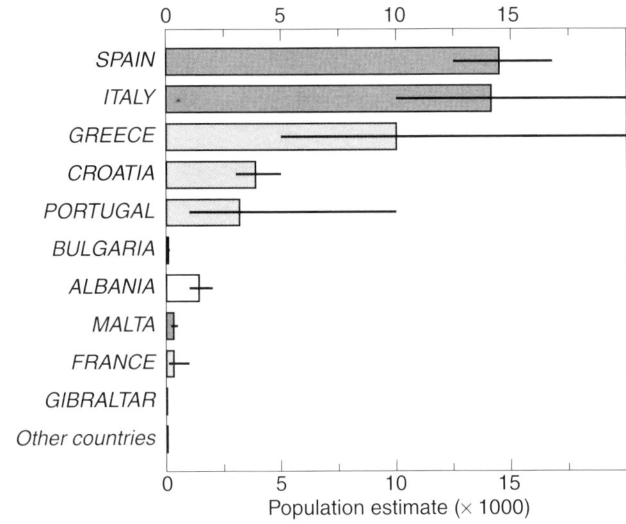

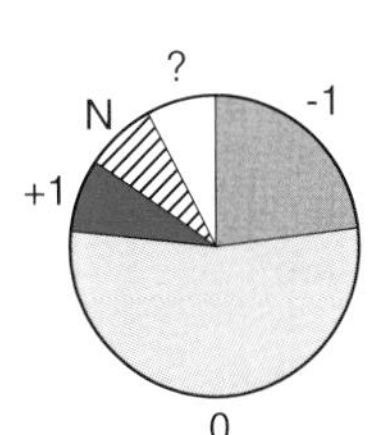

% in top 10 countries: 99.9
Total number of populated European countries: 13
Total European population 40,675–61,602 (47,872)
Turkish population 5000–50,000 (15,811)

The Blue Rock Thrush breeds from the Mediterranean and NE Africa to Asia Minor, the Caucasus, Tibet, China and Japan between 20° and 46°N, and also in Malaysia. The European subspecies *M.s. solitarius* is restricted to the mediterranean climate zone.

It breeds on seacliffs and inland rocky hills and valleys, on fortifications, castles, towers and ruins up to 1000m asl, in Sicily up to 1700m (Iapichino & Massa 1989), in the Sierra Nevada up to 2000m, and in the Peloponnese up to 2070m (J. Hölzinger, pers comm). At its northern distribution limit in N Italy and S Switzerland, it breeds in stone-quarries in alpine valleys up to 1000m, and on lakeside rock faces. Along coastal cliffs there are 2–6 males/km, and 2–3 males/850m in alpine quarries, but frequently pairs are isolated.

In Iberia, it is continuously distributed in a broad northeastern coastal band, but more patchily so on the Atlantic coast. Gaps occur in Castille, Léon and Cantabria. In France it is confined to Corsica, the Midi and the lower Rhône Valley, and in Italy, Croatia and Slovenia largely to the coast and islands. It is widespread in Greece and the Aegean, and occurs also in Bulgaria (Rhodopes) and probably in the Romanian Transylvanian Alps. The European population is estimated at 33 000–75 500bp.

Population and distribution were largely constant during 1970–90, save for a slight increase in Bulgaria and a significant decline in Spain, Malta and Italy brought about by the construction of new coastal buildings and the renovation of old towers and churches. Annual fluctuations are probably related to climate and human activities.

The species is sedentary in warm climate zones (Isenmann 1992), but further N a partial migrant, although it attempts to winter at the northern limits (Fornasari *et al* 1992). European birds winter on most Mediterranean coasts, and in dryish habitats throughout Africa N of 10°N.

Roberto Lardelli (CH) Alfred Schifferli (CH)

This species account is sponsored by Dr Alfred Schifferli, Sempach, CH.

Turdus torquatus

Ring Ouzel

CZ	Kos horský	**I**	Merlo dal collare
D	Ringdrossel	**NL**	Beflijster
E	Mirlo Capiblanco	**P**	Melro-de-peito-branco
F	Merle à plastron	**PL**	Drozd obrożny
FIN	Sepelrastas	**R**	Белозобый дрозд
G	Χιονότσιχλα	**S**	Ringtrast
H	Örvös rigó		

SPEC Cat 4, Threat status S

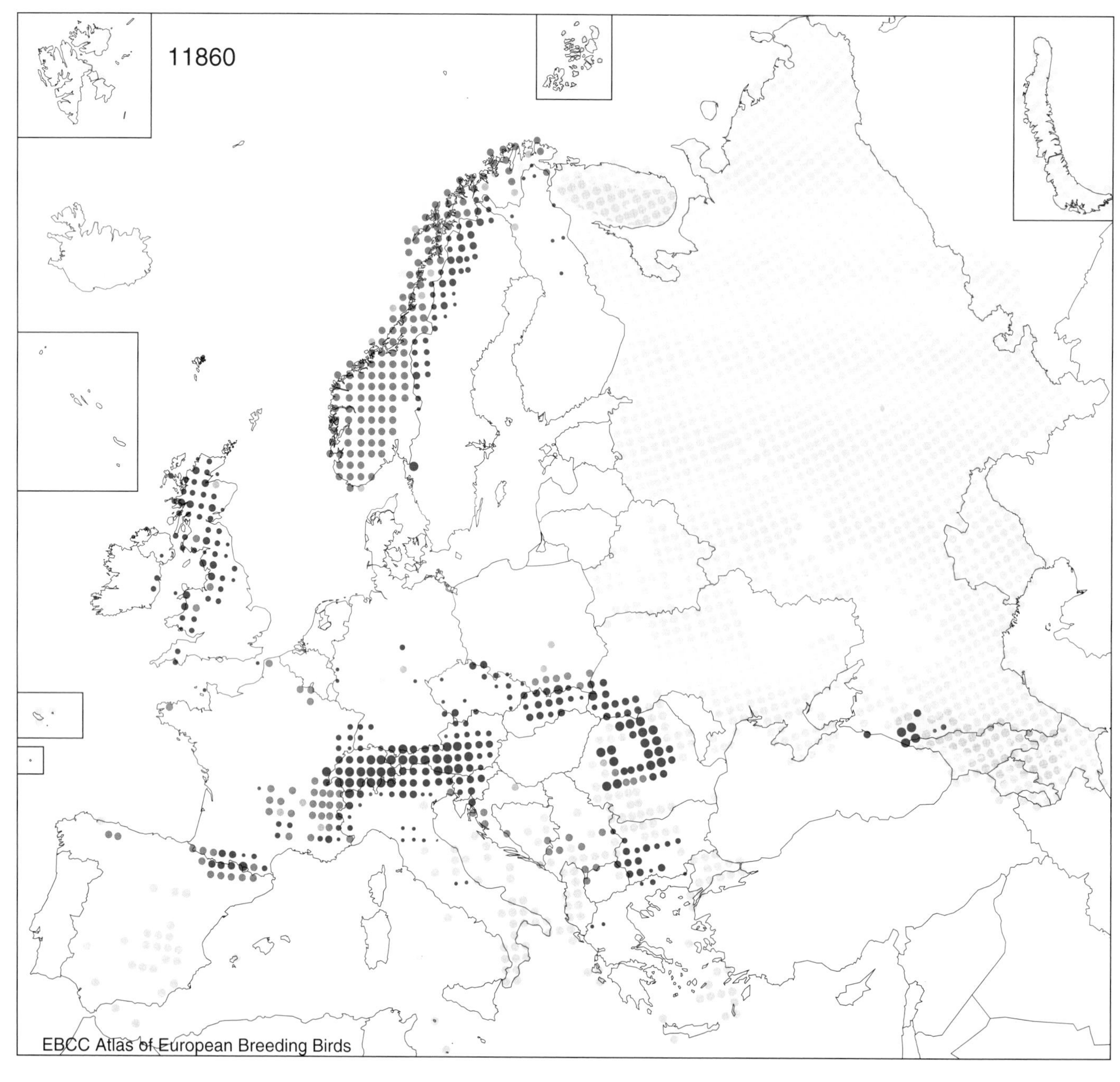

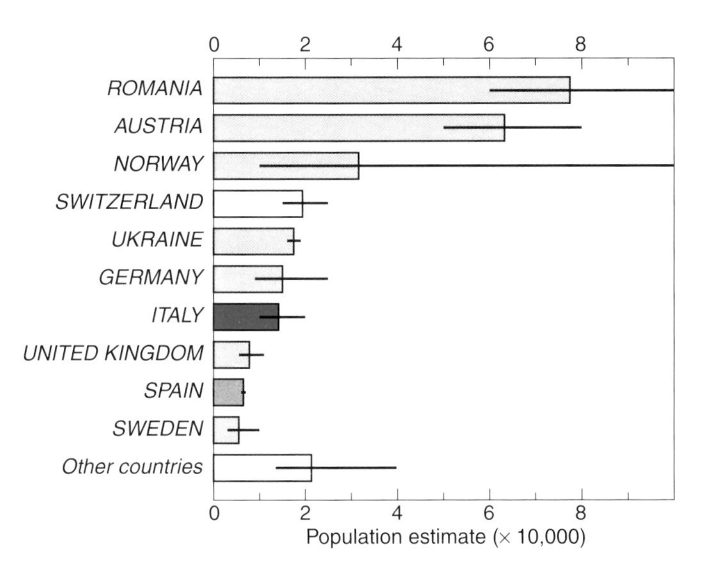

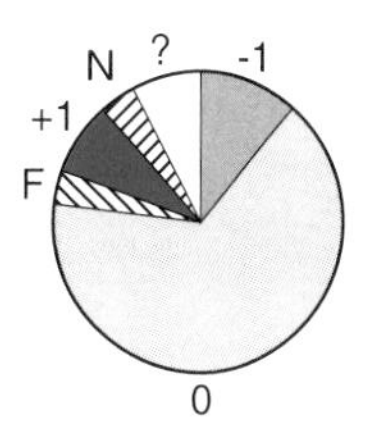

% in top 10 countries: 92.4
Total number of populated European countries: 26
Total European population 247,032–355,281 (279,370)
Russian population 10–100 (32)
Turkish population 1000–10,000 (3162)

The world distribution of the Ring Ouzel is confined to the Palearctic, almost wholly within the western part. Its range stretches from NW Europe to NE Iran in three geographically separated zones, each containing one of three subspecies.

Two subspecies fall within Europe. The British and Scandinavian subspecies, the nominate *T.t. torquatus*, breeds on the ground usually at *c*250m asl on heath and heather moorland containing sheep pasture and scattered stunted trees. Latitude and habitat permitting, it also breeds from sea level to 1200m asl. In Scandinavia the Ring Ouzel breeds in open areas above the pine *Pinus* forests, but also nests in birch *Betula* or spruce *Picea*. In alpine areas of S and C Europe *alpestris* breeds from 600 to 2000m asl, usually between 800 and 1300m in C and E Europe (Janiga 1992), and between 1400 and 1800m in the Alps (Wartmann 1977). The habitats here are conifer or conifer–beech (–*Fagus*) forests, where it favours margins, open areas and avalanche tracks. The remaining subspecies, *amicorum*, occurs in Asia Minor.

In Europe its patchy distribution matches available suitable habitat. In Great Britain it is restricted to upland areas of Scotland, Wales and N and NW England. It is a localized breeding bird in N France and Belgium. In Scandinavia the species is found throughout Norway and NW Sweden, reducing to a scattered distribution in C Sweden and N Finland. In S and C Europe it inhabits the Pyrenees, the Massif Central, the Alps and the Carpathians. It also occurs from S Poland and Ukraine to SE Europe.

In most of its breeding range, populations are stable or decreasing. However, there has been a slight expansion in Belgium and Italy. Records for Brittany are relatively recent, and very recent for the Faeroes. In Britain & Ireland, it declined in many areas between the *Atlas* surveys of 1968–72 and 1988–91, but has increased locally in SW Ireland (Hill 1993). Declines have also occurred in Spain and Andorra, and over the last decade in Slovakia.

From a survey in 1985/86 in SE Scotland (Poxton 1987), considerable variations in breeding densities were observed across apparently identical habitats (steep-sided valleys, with ample heather *Calluna* and bracken *Pteridium aquilinum* for nesting and pasture for feeding). In the Pentland Hills, although some valleys had high densities (less than 500m linear distances between nests; Poxton 1986), others had no birds at all, thus giving rise almost to a colonial distribution. In the Carpathians, some hills grazed by cattle have high densities (less than 100m linear distances between nests; Marisova & Vladyshevsky 1961, M. Janiga, pers obs).

The reasons for the declines are uncertain, but suggestions include increased human disturbance, competition with the Blackbird *T. merula*, and Mistle Thrush *T. viscivorus*, and climatic warming. None seem applicable in SE Scotland (Poxton 1987). In the Tatras, a significant increase in the numbers and dispersion of Fieldfare, *T. pilaris*, has affected Ring Ouzel numbers adversely (M. Janiga, pers obs).

Because breeding territories tend to occur linearly along watercourses, expressing densities in terms of bp/km^2 of prime habitat is seldom possible; nests tend to be *c*500m apart. However, the moorland of the Moorfoot Hills in SE Scotland is bisected by many streams, allowing a density of 34 bp/km^2 to be calculated (Poxton 1987). In the Slovakian or Ukrainian Carpathians, densities may reach 20–30 bp/km^2 (Janiga 1992, Marisova & Vladyshevsky 1961).

The migratory *torquatus* winters mainly in S Spain and in NW Africa in the Atlas Mountains, Scandinavian birds occurring mostly in S France (Büsche 1993). Although *alpestris* moves to higher altitudes immediately after breeding, in winter generally it occupies its southern breeding range, or migrates to Mediterranean islands, some perhaps reaching North Africa.

Marián Janiga (SLK) Ian R Poxton (GB)

Turdus merula | Blackbird

CZ	Kos černý	**I**	Merlo
D	Amsel	**NL**	Merel
E	Mirlo Común	**P**	Melro-preto
F	Merle noir	**PL**	Kos
FIN	Mustarastas	**R**	Черный дрозд
G	Κότσυφας	**S**	Koltrast
H	Fekete rigó		

SPEC Cat 4, Threat status S

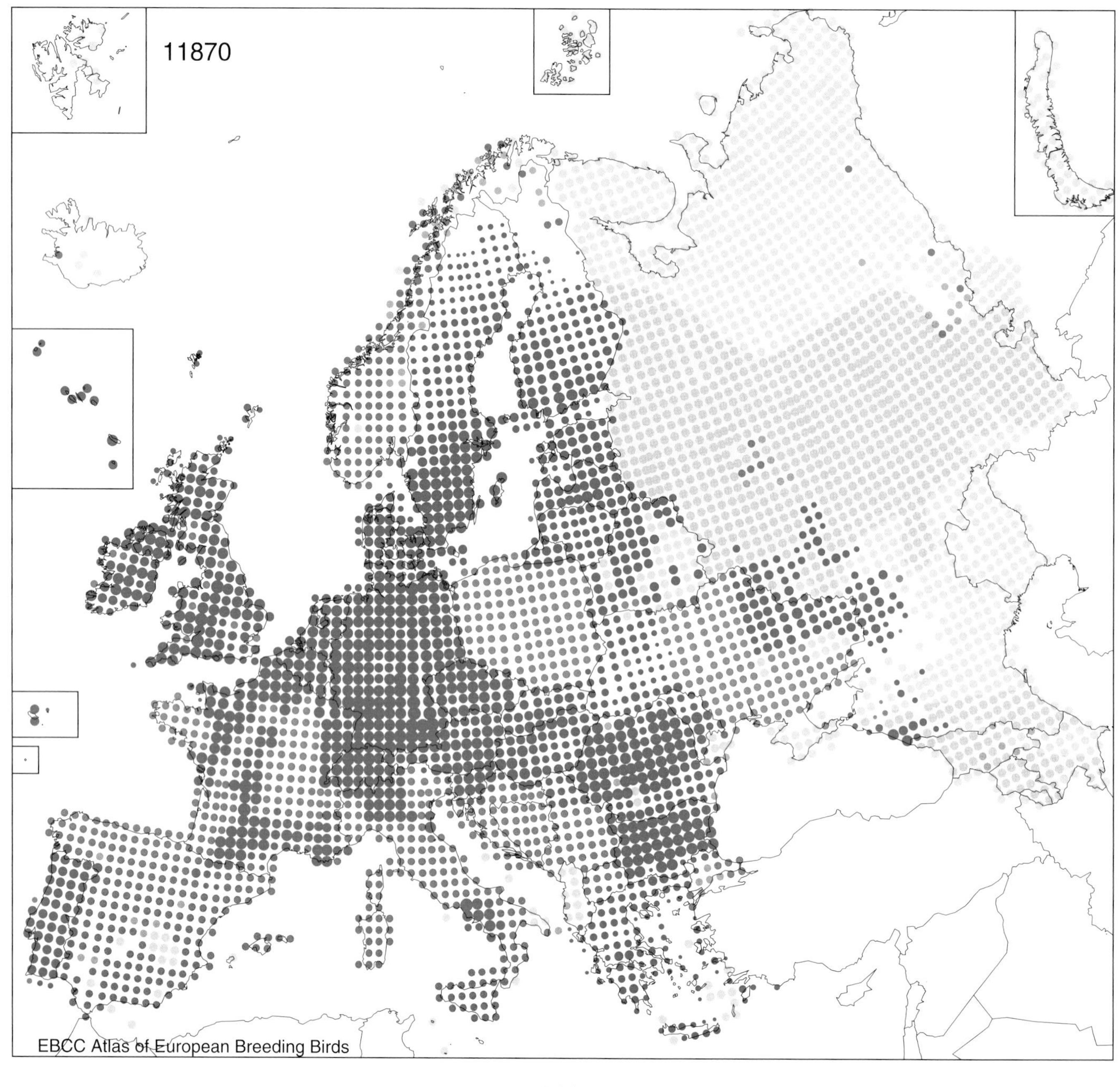

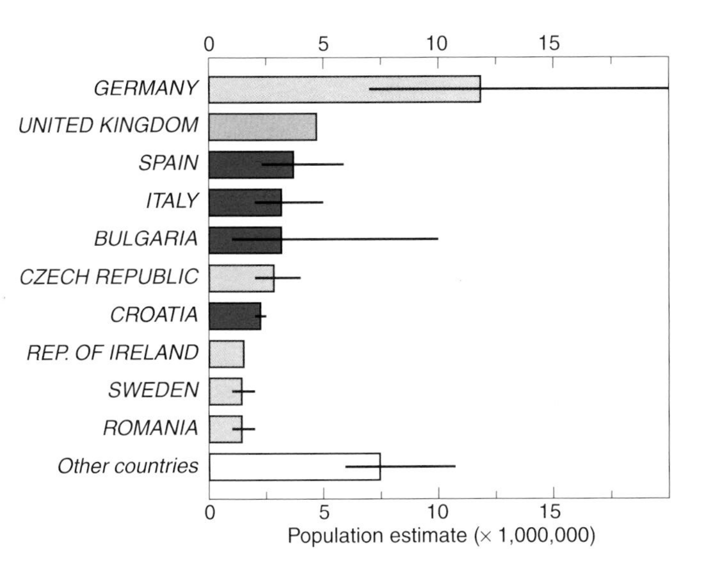

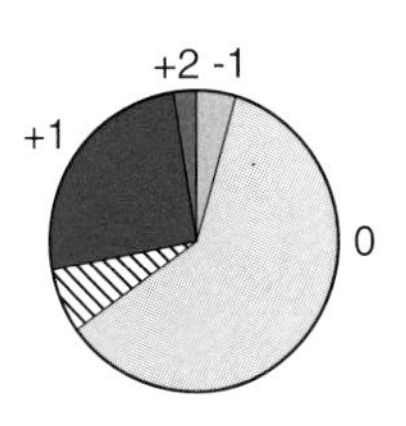

% in top 10 countries: 82.8
Total number of populated European countries: 43
Total European population 37,663,943–54,585,469 (43,373,697)
Russian population 10,000–100,000 (31,623)
Turkish population 100,000–1,000,000 (316,228)

This highly adaptive Palearctic thrush breeds throughout Europe except for northernmost Fennoscandia, the Kola Peninsula and the Russian lowlands NE of Moscow. Its world distribution stretches from North Africa and C Asia through to SE China. Introduced populations exist in Australasia. The Indian and Sri Lankan forms may comprise a distinct species.

The Blackbird breeds in most habitats except open steppes, marshes, fens and tundra. In the coniferous montane and subalpine regions the Ring Ouzel *T. torquatus* replaces it. The dark colour and fluting low-frequency song suggest the Blackbird originated in the lower layer of dense, dark deciduous and mixed forests. Its present populations still occupy all kinds of forest and bushy habitats, but also occur in artificial habitats, chiefly human-inhabited except where it is persecuted, as in some Mediterranean areas. The Blackbird still retains its preference for deciduous habitats. Rural and urban birds often forage in the open, though always close to cover.

The species clearly is more numerous in W and C Europe, where there is a longer history of habitat transformation, than in the E. Locally in places such as the Hamburg residential areas it is commoner than the House Sparrow *Passer domesticus* (*HVM*). The Blackbird is much less abundant in the SE, E and NE of Europe apparently because either the climate is harsher or food is scarcer.

Since the mid-1850s the Blackbird has colonized most European towns. Its urban population continues to expand northeastwards; some cities in N Poland and Russia have yet to be colonized permanently, which generally occurs once there is a regular wintering population. It remains unclear, despite much being published on the subject, whether urban populations recruit from rural populations or vice versa. Urban birds have a more prolonged breeding season, but not inevitably a higher reproductive rate, than birds in rural or forest habitats (*HVM*, Kowschar & Schujko 1984), whereas mortality rates vary widely between and within habitats (*HVM*). Surplus imprinted urban birds may be more likely to colonize unoccupied cities.

The highest densities (normally up to 15–25 territories/10ha, but exceptionally reaching 40) occur in small urban parks and residential areas in W Europe, where fluctuations correlate with the severity of the preceding winter (Karlsson & Källander 1977). In newly colonized eastern Polish and Baltic towns densities are much lower, usually below 5 bp/10ha (Walasz & Mielczarek 1992, Leibak *et al* 1994). Rural birds achieve *c*3–10 territories/10ha, and in the Białowieża primeval forest of eastern Poland, only 1–2.5 (L. Tomiałojć, pers obs).

In S and W Europe the species is resident or largely resident (especially urban individuals), whereas northeastern and montane populations are mostly or wholly migratory. The main autumn migration directions in Europe are to the W and SW; southeastern populations migrate southwards. Wintering occurs mainly within the species' distribution, but some winter slightly further S in North Africa and Mesopotamia. Adult males tend to remain in their breeding areas because early territorial occupation allows a higher reproductive rate subsequently. Why individuals should vary in migratory behaviour is not known. Factors possibly involved are: genetically inherited degree of migratory impulse, phenotypic environmental influences and the population dominance structure, especially in relation to the quality of territory held (Schwabl 1983).

In Europe the Atlantic islands populations (*T.m. cabrerae*, Madeira; *azorensis*, Azores) are distinct; *aterrimus* (SE Europe to Transcaucasia) is generally duller than the nominate *merula* (elsewhere in Europe). There are transitional features (pigmentation and body size gradations) between European and some Asian subspecies. The only known morphological difference between urban and other populations is a higher incidence of albinism in the former. At least nine other subspecies occur beyond Europe.

Ronald Mulsow (D) Ludwik Tomiałojć (PL)

Turdus pilaris **Fieldfare**

CZ	Drozd kvíčala	**I**	Cesena
D	Wacholderdrossel	**NL**	Kramsvogel
E	Zorzal Real	**P**	Tordo-zornal
F	Grive litorne	**PL**	Kwiczoł
FIN	Räkättirastas	**R**	Рябинник
G	Κεδρότσιχλα	**S**	Björktrast
H	Fenyőrigó		

*SPEC Cat 4*W, Threat status S*

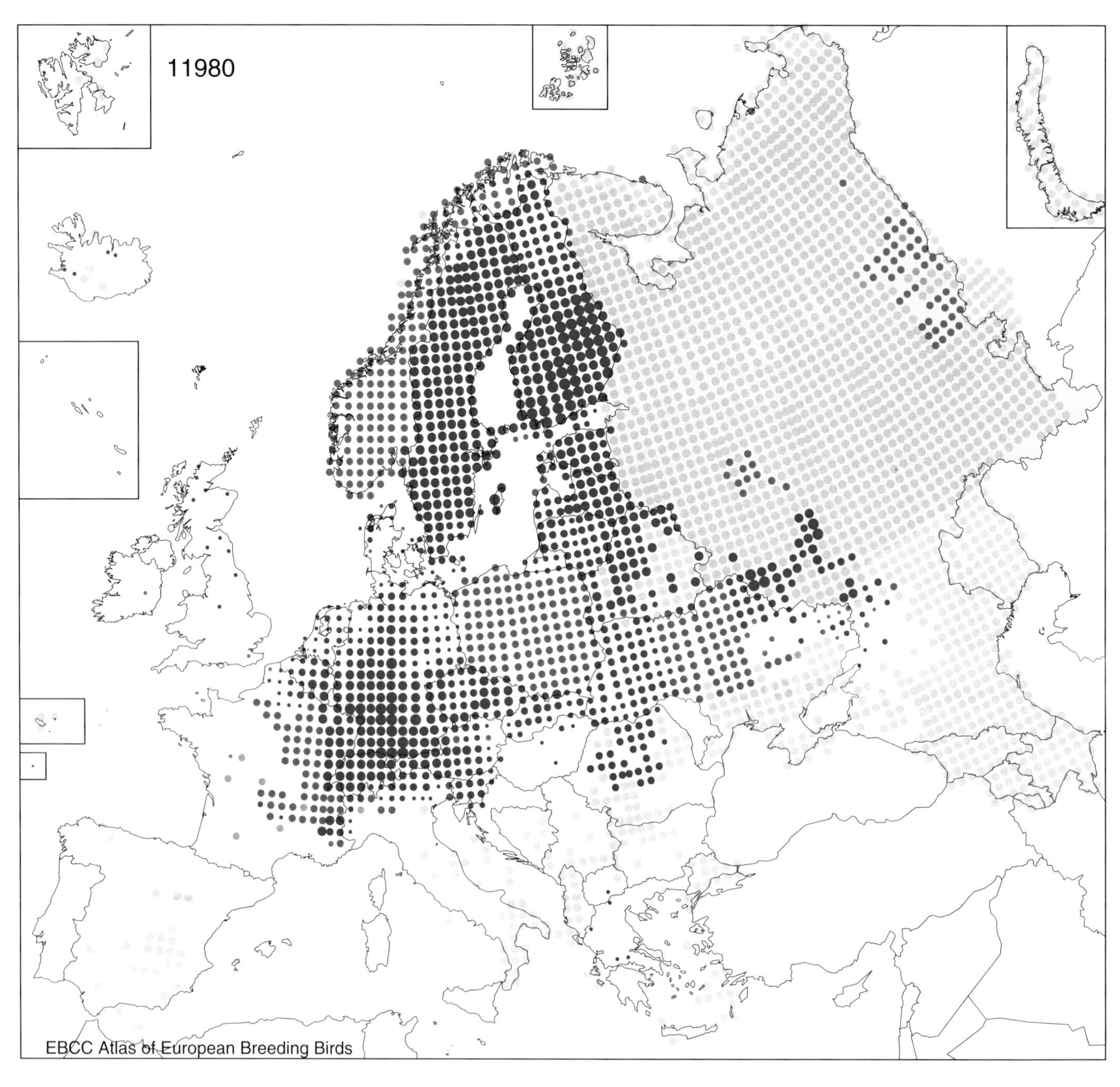

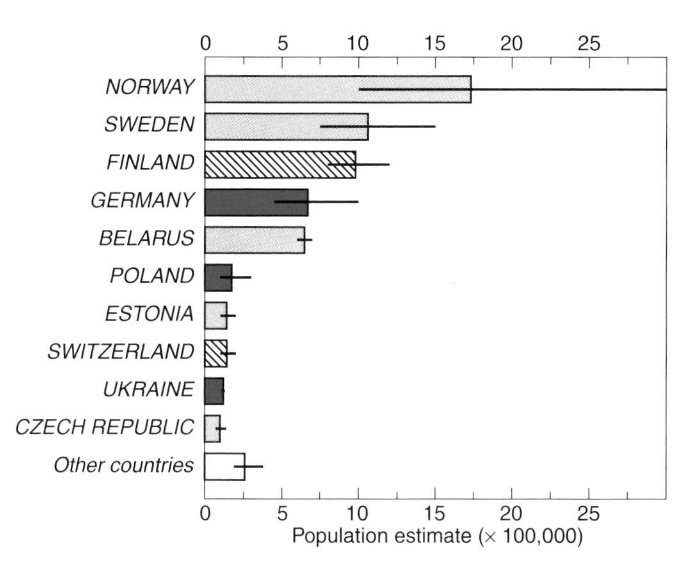

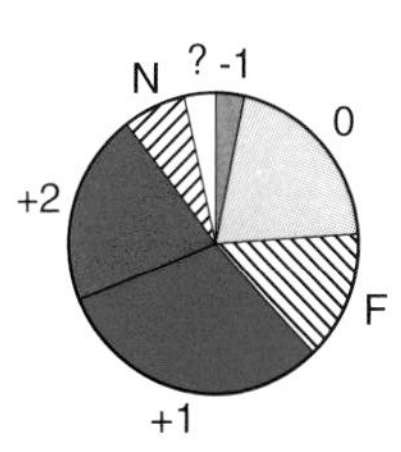

% in top 10 countries: 95.7
Total number of populated European countries: 29
Total European population 5,171,227–7,434,881 (6,023,974)
Russian population 1,000,000–10,000,000 (3,162,278)

The monotypic Fieldfare is distributed from SE France, the Low Countries, Denmark and Norway in the W to the upper Yenisey and Amur Rivers in the E. Its northern range limit reaches the Fennoscandian seacoast, but eastwards is constrained by the timberline. The southern limit runs from the SW Alps through the southern Carpathians and Transylvania eastwards along the forest steppe southern edge.

The Fieldfare is most typical in farmland and other cultivated landscapes where it breeds in orchards, forest edges and hedgerows, feeding in tilled fields and short grass-sward, but also breeds in continuous, park-like light deciduous or mixed forests. Second broods may be raised in a different habitat, such as the forest interior. The species breeds up to the treeline in C European mountains and in Fennoscandia also in bushes beyond it. It commonly nests in human settlements over much of its range, especially the N and E.

The Fieldfare is both a solitary and colonial breeder. Because the inter-nest distance in colonies usually is at least 10m, large colonies can occupy several hectares of woodland. Meaningful density estimates are difficult to make because of coloniality, unless large areas reliably can be covered. In Finland overall densities are highest in the E and centre, 15–20 bp/km^2 of farmland, whereas elsewhere they are 1–10 bp/km^2 (Piiroinen *et al* 1985). Similar or somewhat higher densities prevail in subalpine birch *Betula* forests in Lapland (Enemar *et al* 1984). Density values can be very high in human settlements. In Turku (170 000 inhabitants), densities varied from 15 bp/km^2 in industrial zones to 70 bp/km^2 in suburban zones (Vuorisalo & Tiainen 1993). In Germany and Switzerland, densities of 3–5 bp/km^2 have been reported from large census areas (Lübcke & Furrer 1985).

The Fieldfare is one of the most abundant breeding birds of northern Europe. Excluding Russia, the European breeding population is *c*4.4M–8.7Mbp, of which some 60% inhabit Fennoscandia. Large numbers also breed in C and E Europe, especially in upland and hilly areas, but densities rapidly decrease towards the S and W. Peripheral populations remain small, as in Denmark, The Netherlands, Britain, Hungary, Albania and Greece (1000bp or fewer).

The Fieldfare has expanded its range strongly southwestwards since the 1800s (Lübcke & Furrer 1985). In the early 19th century its distribution reached NE Poland and by the turn of the century, Germany, the Czech Republic and Austria. Expansion slowed, incorporating only Switzerland up to 1950, then accelerated to Slovakia (1950s), Denmark, Belgium, E–C France, N Italy and Romania (1960s), The Netherlands, Great Britain, SE France, Slovenia and Hungary (1970s) and Macedonia and Greece (1980s). The Fieldfare breeds irregularly in the Orkneys, Shetlands and Iceland. It colonized Greenland in 1937, breeding continuing at least until the late 1970s.

Expansion continues westwards, southwards and within the C European range. Population size has increased in most European countries during 1970–90, and in Luxembourg, Italy, Slovenia, Hungary and Romania by more than 50%, numerical increases which accompanied considerable range extensions; the French breeding range increased by 400% between 1970–75 and 1985–89 (Érard 1994). In Fennoscandia the population size is stable but fluctuating.

The species has an elaborate migration system. The Maas–Schelde–Somme and Thames–Humber catchments attract first-year birds migrating from N and W Scandinavia, the Rhône–Languedoc attracts first-year birds from Switzerland and Germany and the Po–Upper Adriatic attracts first-year birds from E Europe, NE Scandinavia, Russia and Siberia. Adults usually migrate further than first-year birds, forming high concentrations in the Gironde–Adour watershed. These catchments provide the birds with good winter food resources (Milwright 1994). The northern winter range is occupied irregularly, but is subject to large irruptions when rowan *Sorbus aucuparia* berries are abundant (Tyrväinen 1975).

Juha Tiainen (FIN) Karel Šťastný (CZ)
Vladimir Bejcek (CZ)

Turdus philomelos

Song Thrush

CZ	Drozd zpěvný	**I**	Tordo bottaccio
D	Singdrossel	**NL**	Zanglijster
E	Zorzal Común	**P**	Tordo-comum
F	Grive musicienne	**PL**	Śpiewak
FIN	Laulurastas	**R**	Певчий дрозд
G	Τσίχλα	**S**	Taltrast
H	Énekes rigó		

SPEC Cat 4, Threat status S

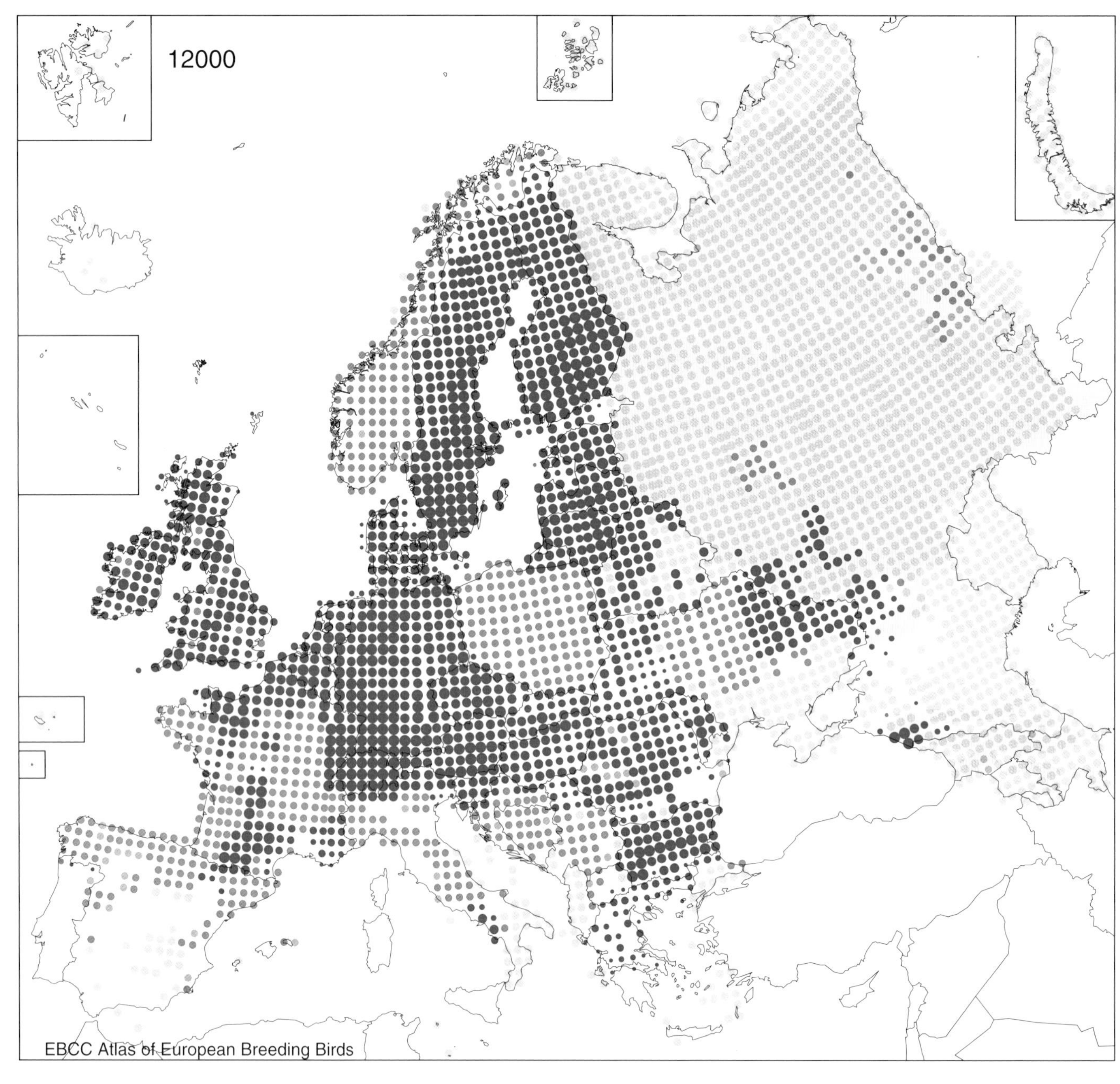

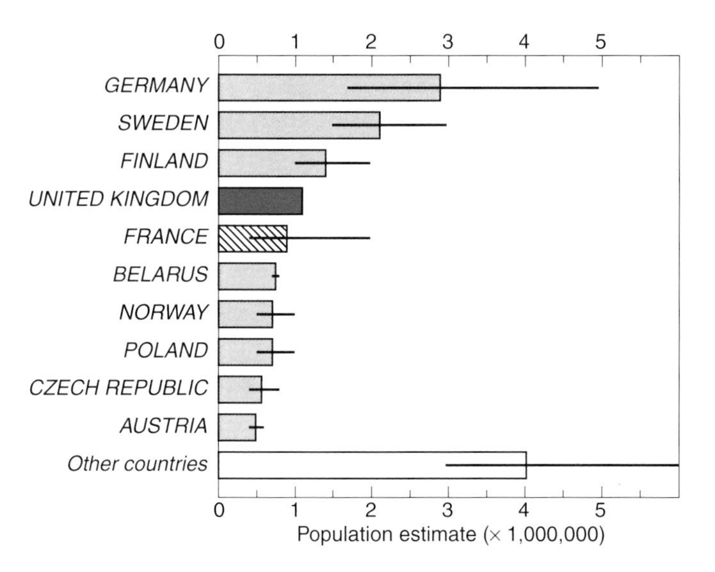

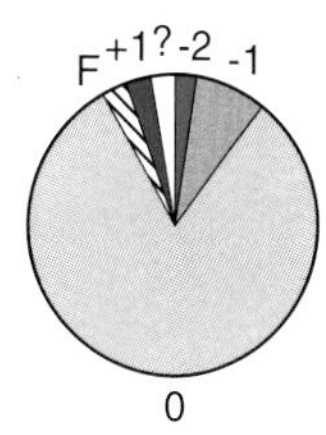

% in top 10 countries: 74.2
Total number of populated European countries: 37
Total European population 14,127,336–18,470,086 (15,715,933)
Russian population 100,000–1,000,000 (316,228)
Turkish population 10,000–100,000 (31,623)

The Song Thrush, a true forest thrush, has a Palearctic distribution stretching (the majority in Europe) from Ireland to Lake Baykal, and from montane S Spain and Iran up to 70°N. Introduced populations exist in New Zealand and in SE Australia.

The Song Thrush breeds in almost all types of forests and woods. The nominate subspecies *T.p. philomelos* prefers spruce *Picea* spp, while those living under oceanic climate conditions, *clarkei* and *hebridensis*, occur in deciduous forests, the latter even in quite open habitats. The species avoids dry (mediterranean, steppe and some urban) regions or habitats (Tomiałojć 1992). It breeds up to 1000m asl in Fennoscandia and 2200m asl in C Europe (Melde & Melde 1991).

The Song Thrush is one of the most numerous of forest birds, and is a rather evenly distributed territorial species. Its numbers may be seriously underestimated unless great care is taken during censusing; the most accurate results are obtained at dusk. At other times breeding males tend to stop singing, while unmated males continue to do so (Tomiałojć & Lontkowski 1989). No clear trends in its overall population size nor in general distribution range have been noted, although since the early 20th century the Song Thrush has expanded to the N in Fennoscandia from *c*60° to 70°N (Melde & Melde 1991). The British population has been decreasing since the mid-1970s at an average rate of 7% per annum from 1975 to 1986. Winter weather conditions and perhaps other factors affecting survival rates are possible causes (Baillie 1990). Declines have occurred also in Ireland and parts of C Europe. From 1900 to the mid-1950s it colonized urban parks and suburban habitats, but since then this trend has tended to reverse (Tomiałojć 1992).

In the N and in mountainous regions the species' distribution may be limited by the presence or character of forest types which may provide unsuitable ecological conditions (Siivonen 1939), whereas the southern limit may be defined where the dry climate affects either the accessibility and suitability of food resources or the characteristic materials it uses to construct its nests (Tomiałojć 1992).

Within its breeding habitat the Song Thrush is distributed fairly evenly, normally at densities of 1–5 bp/10ha, but in the primeval mixed forests of Białowieża, reaches 8.5 bp/10ha (L. Tomiałojć, pers obs). In some altered western habitats densities up to 15–34 bp/10ha have occurred, largely owing to the 'insular/forest-edge effect' (*HVM*) but presumably also because of reduced predator pressure. In eastern and northern Europe breeding densities are lower (usually 0.5–3.0 bp/10ha), which certainly reflects the existing suboptimal climatic and feeding conditions, but also may derive partly from inadequate census methodology producing incomplete results (see above).

Most of the European population breeding E of 8°E and N of 45°N is migratory and winters in SW Europe, chiefly in the Iberian, Italian and Balkan Peninsulas, North Africa, Asia Minor and the Near East, while Siberian birds winter in Mesopotamia, Iran (Melde & Melde 1991) and (perhaps these populations) in western Saudi Arabia. Birds elsewhere in Europe are largely resident, or move comparatively short distances. Although the Song Thrush has been persecuted and exploited for decades, mostly by shooting and trapping in Mediterranean countries, migratory populations nevertheless have not shown signs of decline (Svensson 1990b, L. Tomiałojć, pers obs). However, from 1950 to 1985 the hunting index for the species increased significantly in France, Spain and Italy (McCulloch *et al* 1992), probably indicating an increase in hunting pressure (perhaps compensating for other quarry species, or reflecting more leisure time?).

Most of continental Europe holds the nominate *philomelos*. Skye and the Hebrides contain the resident *hebridensis*. The mostly resident *clarkei* occurs in Britain & Ireland, NW France and the Low Countries.

Ludwik Tomiałojć (PL)

This species account is sponsored by Ernst Alstadt, Neukirchen-Vluyn, D.

Turdus iliacus

Redwing

CZ	Drozd cvrčala	**I**	Tordo sassello
D	Rotdrossel	**NL**	Koperwiek
E	Zorzal Alirrojo	**P**	Tordo-ruivo-comum
F	Grive mauvis	**PL**	Droździk
FIN	Punakylkirastas	**R**	Белобровик
G	Κοκκινότσιχλα	**S**	Rödvingetrast
H	Szőlőrigó		

*SPEC Cat 4*W, Threat status S*

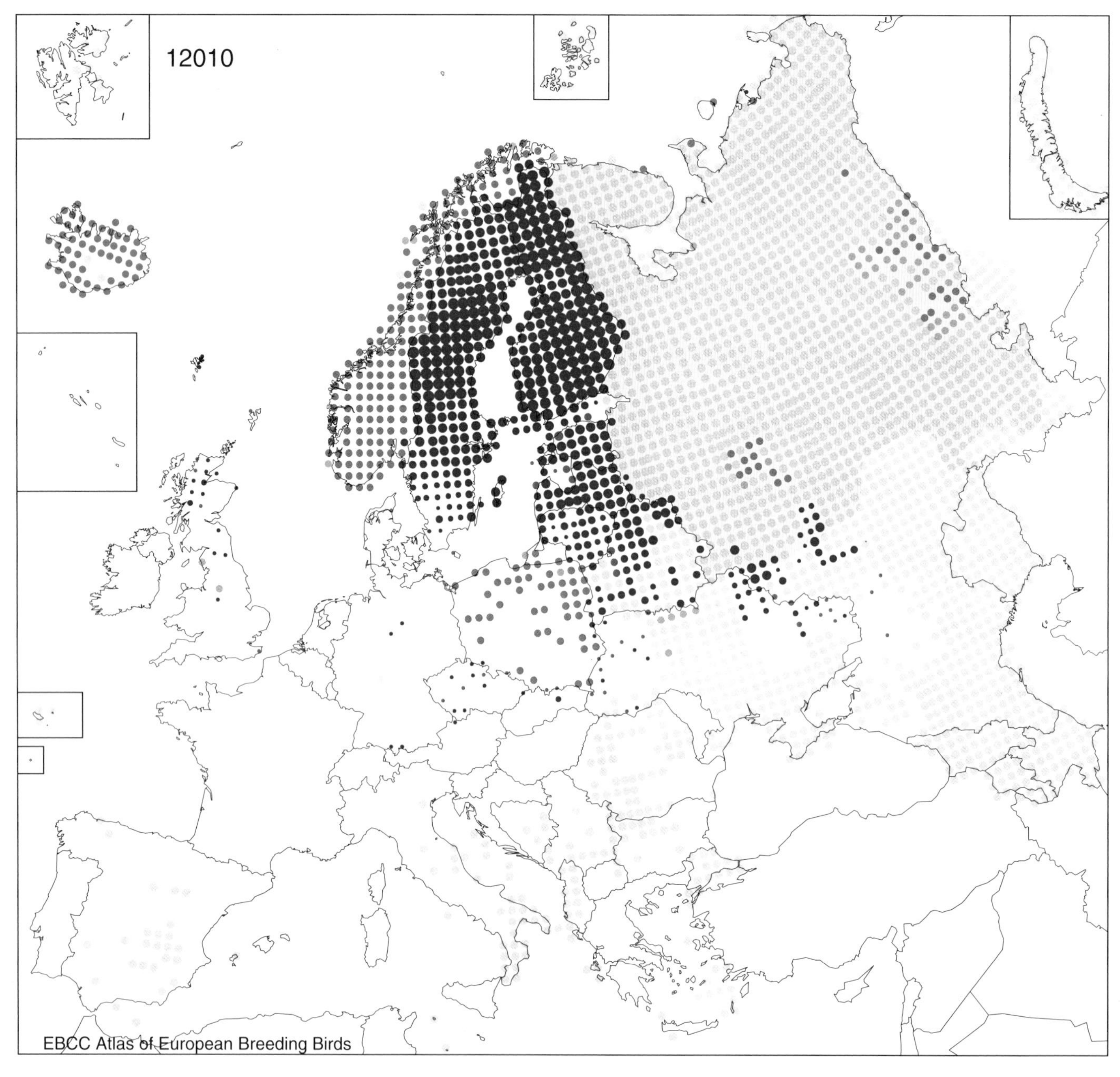

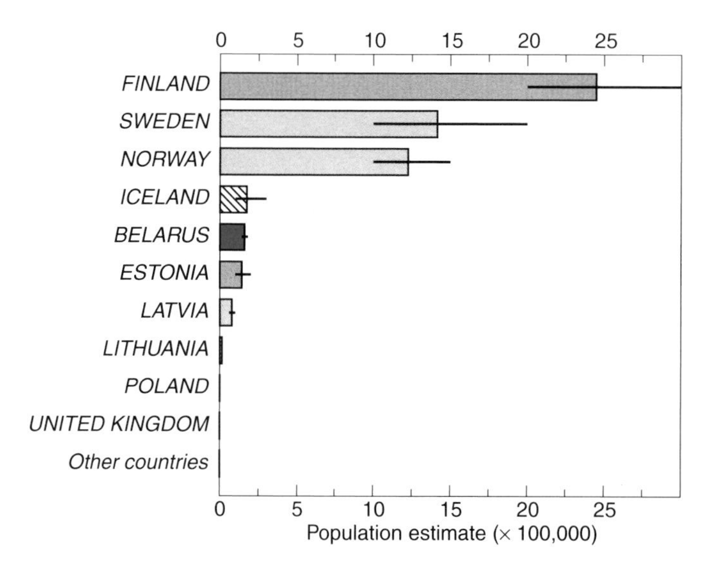

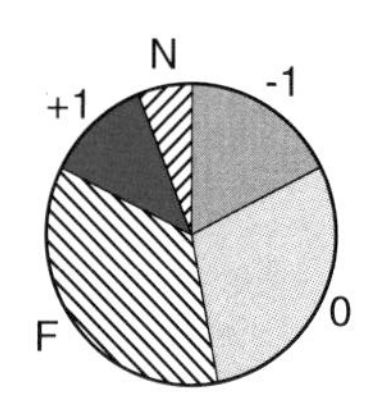

% in top 10 countries: 100.0
Total number of populated European countries: 17
Total European population 4,997,089–6,515,929 (5,654,259)
Russian population 100,000–1,000,000 (316,228)

The Redwing's extensive Palearctic distribution stretches from Iceland to E Siberia, mainly in the boreal taiga, but also in the subarctic and alpine zones, becoming scattered towards its southern breeding range limits in S Sweden, Great Britain, Germany, Czech Republic, Slovakia, Poland and Ukraine. The nominate *iliacus* occurs throughout continental Eurasia, and *coburni* in Iceland and the Faeroes.

A forest generalist, the Redwing favours mosaic environments, especially where the margins of productive deciduous or mixed forests have a well-illuminated undercanopy and a dense broad-leaved bush layer (Tyrväinen 1969). Shore thickets, forest edges by fields and mires and upright sapling stands are typical boreal Redwing breeding habitats, but it often uses various scrubby, semi-open cultivated sites, including parks and gardens. Deeper into forests the Redwing favours clearfelled borders and clearings. The short sparse stands of the northernmost forests allow it to spread away from the edges. It may also occupy tundra willow and birch scrub. In Iceland and in Fennoscandian mountain and oro-arctic areas it may breed in rocky areas almost lacking scrub. Populations form annually constant song dialect areas (*c*40km^2) with clear boundaries (Bjerke & Bjerke 1981).

The population graph is but a snapshot in time. The Redwing may suffer mass mortality in cold winters in its wintering areas (from Britain to NW Africa to the Black and Caspian Seas). Annual monitoring in Finland and Sweden found sharp drops in breeding numbers after the severe winters of 1978/79, 1985/86 and 1986/87, and a rise after subsequent mild winters. Low breeding success in the exceptionally cold summer of 1987 contributed to the temporary population reduction. Extensive line-transect censuses revealed 2.7Mbp in Finland from 1973 to 1977, but only 1.5Mbp from 1986 to 1989 (R.A. Väisänen *et al*, in prep). Such a large decline nevertheless represents the natural variation limits. The mean, 2.1Mbp, is therefore the national estimate. Other nations' estimates should be interpreted accordingly: Sweden, 1M–2Mbp, Norway 1M–1.5Mbp, Russia 100 000–1Mbp, Iceland 100 000–300 000bp and Belarus 140 000–180 000bp.

In the 1940s, the Finnish Redwing population was biased to the N, being *c*8 bp/km^2 in Lapland and 1–3 bp/km^2 in the S, but by the 1970s in areas largely below the Arctic Circle breeding density had increased to *c*10 bp/km^2, producing a fivefold population increase. Doubtless the extremely hard winters of the early 1940s had decreased densities to an exceptional extent, but this factor alone explains neither the geographical pattern nor the magnitude of the increase. The Swedish Redwing population varied similarly, especially in the 1950s and 1960s.

Modern forestry techniques, applied from 1950 onwards in Fennoscandia, are apparently the main reason for the changes, because as shown in Finland, the Redwing benefits from mire drainage and from the change of the forest age-structure towards younger stages (allowing the bush layer to increase) (Järvinen *et al* 1977, Väisänen & Rauhala 1983). Core area breeding density in managed forests in Lapland is double that of virgin tracts (Virkkala 1991a). Additional bushy habitats have also appeared where former fields have been afforested and where forests no longer are grazed by cattle.

Since *c*1930 the Redwing has spread southwards in Lithuania, Belarus and Ukraine. It has bred regularly in N Scotland since the late 1960s. This expansion may be a consequence of population pressure further N. Since 1975 the growth phase has levelled off and most European populations have fluctuated without any regular trend.

Breeding density may reach 70–120 bp/km^2 in rich deciduous forests. In the 1970s when populations were high, breeding density across the 50m-wide main belts of the line transects was 40 bp/km^2 in deciduous forests in S Finland, 30 bp/km^2 in Lapland, and 12 bp/km^2 in subalpine birch forest in N Norway. Coniferous forest values were about half these levels.

Juha Tiainen (FIN) Risto A Väisänen (FIN)

Turdus viscivorus

Mistle Thrush

CZ	Drozd brávník	**I**	Tordela
D	Misteldrossel	**NL**	Grote Lijster
E	Zorzal Charlo	**P**	Tordeia
F	Grive draine	**PL**	Paszkot
FIN	Kulorastas	**R**	Деряба
G	Τσαρτσάρα	**S**	Dubbeltrast
H	Léprigó		

SPEC Cat 4, Threat status S

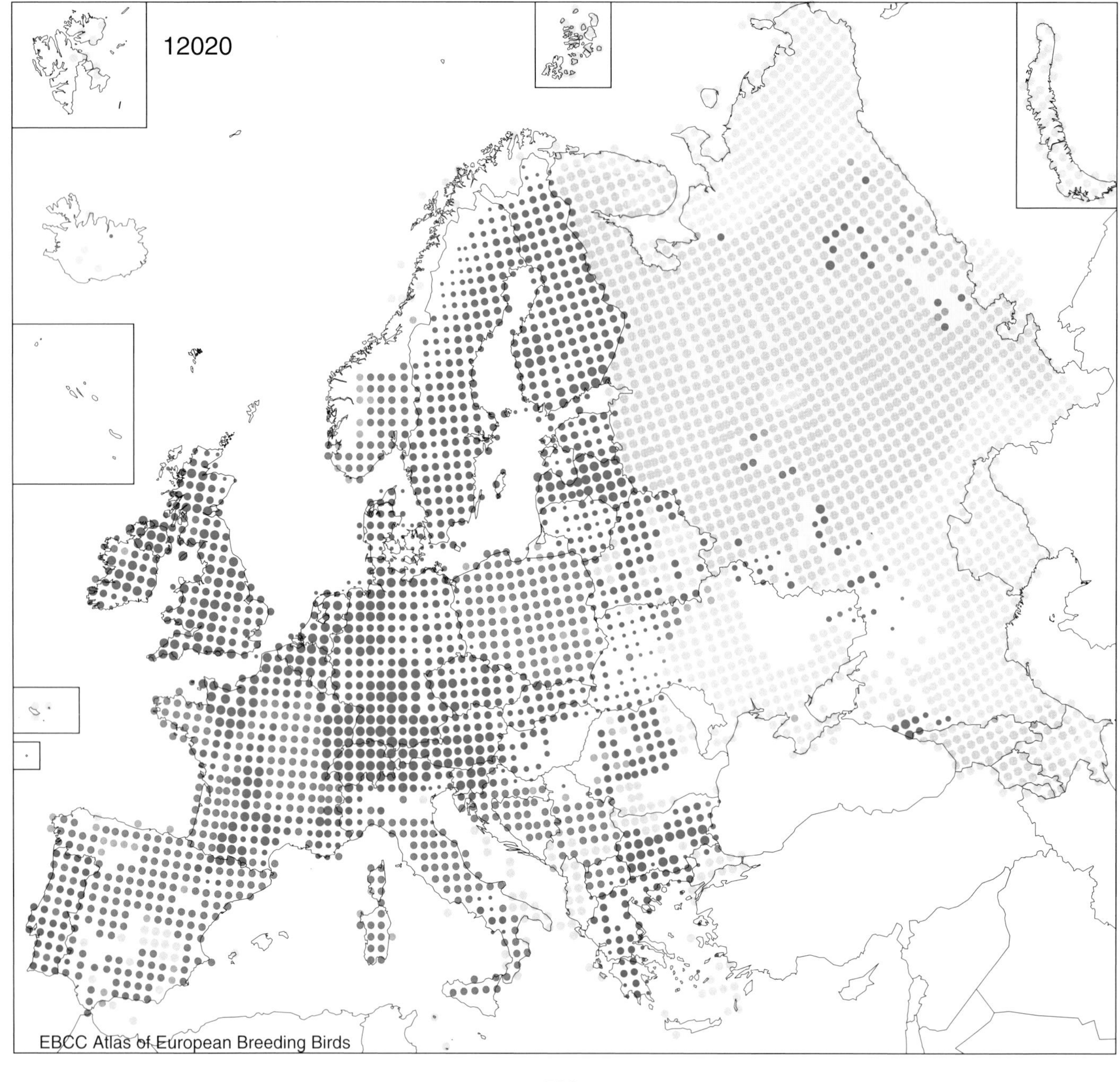

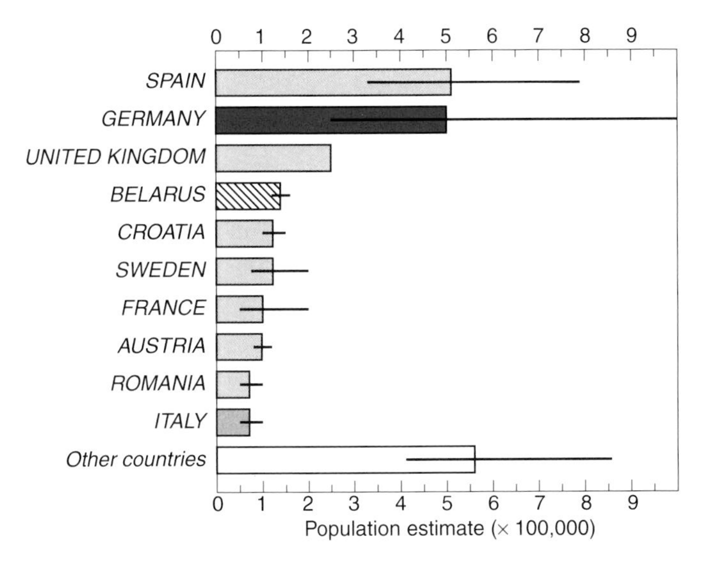

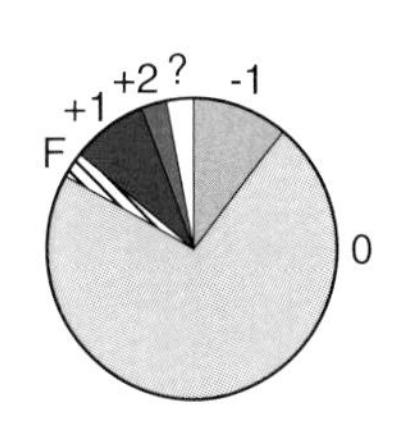

% in top 10 countries: 78.0
Total number of populated European countries: 36
Total European population 2,221,106–3,142,991 (2,543,452)
Russian population 10,000–100,000 (31,623)
Turkish population 5000–50,000 (15,811)

Despite its bold, upright, vociferous and excitable manner, the Mistle Thrush is a rather shy species, flighty and rarely allowing close approach. The nominate *T.v. viscivorus* breeds throughout W and C Europe, from the Mediterranean N to the boreal zone fringe in Fennoscandia and E through W and C Russia. It avoids open tundra, steppe and extensive wetland regions and is absent from much of S Russia, Transcaucasia and Kazakhstan. Further E *bonapartei* breeds in C and E Siberia S to the Himalayas. A third subspecies *deichleri* occurs in Morocco, N Algeria, N Tunisia, Corsica and Sardinia.

The species prefers to nest in large trees but searches for food in grazed or mown grassland, on recently cultivated soil or in woodland glades, being commonest where the two habitats are adjacent. Its occurrence in suburban parks and gardens is a relatively recent phenomenon. In W and C Europe the density in villages now normally exceeds values from various prime habitat types in lowland woodlands (Flade 1994). The Mistle Thrush is more arboreal than the Song Thrush *T. philomelos*, usually being associated with open mature woodland, a dependence reflected in its Palearctic distribution.

In Europe, conspicuous distribution gaps occur only within arid or wetland regions of Spain (much of Castilla-La Mancha) and Italy, the broad plains of E Hungary, Vojvodina and Romania (Danube Delta) and the treeless regions of Fennoscandia. In Poland the species is widespread but generally scarce, becoming locally common in larger forests such as Tuchola, Lubuska and Pisz (Tomiałojć 1990). Historically, the Mistle Thrush was considered primarily a species of wooded mountain slopes and hanging valleys; here densities still exceed those in woodland elsewhere despite its enormous 19th century range expansion into the lowlands. In S Europe, it remains confined mostly to mountainous areas, particularly in the S of France (absent from much of Provence), Italy (absent from the Po Valley and coastal regions along the Apennine Peninsula), Sicily (occupies only the northern mountains), and in Greece and Bulgaria (mostly above 500–600m asl). In Switzerland, densities of 30 bp/km^2 are found at altitudes above 700m asl (breeding occurs up to 1800m asl, and up to 3500m in the Himalayas). In comparison, European wooded lowland densities range from 5 to 10 bp/km^2 (*BWP*). The highest British densities (13 bp/km^2) also relate to the higher wooded valleys (Wales; *BWP*).

In Britain & Ireland, atlas mapping reveals largely stable populations (Gibbons *et al* 1993) as they are for much of Europe. In Russia an apparent northward range expansion to *c*400km N of Perm may reflect improved knowledge or represent fluctuating breeding conditions (A.A. Estafiev, pers comm). Since 1985, Hungary and Denmark have experienced slightly increasing numbers, but declines were recorded in Estonia, Ukraine, Italy and northern Finland. Estonia's marked decline, like some others, has continued from at least the 1960s (Leibak *et al* 1994). The Finnish decrease is attributed to modern forestry practices; felling old forest which allows intensified growth of the tree and shrub layer (Koskimies 1989a). Dutch studies have shown marked short-term fluctuations in response to severe winter weather (van Dijk 1990).

Across most of Europe, northern Mistle Thrush populations tend to be more migratory than southern. In Corsica and Sardinia *deichleri* is largely sedentary. In Britain too, most territorial pairs are resident throughout the year although progeny and non-breeding birds may move SW to Ireland or France during late summer and autumn. Residency is possible because the Mistle Thrush defends fruit-bearing plants against intruders from autumn to early spring, a strategy to provide food throughout winter, unless the severity of the weather brings overwhelming invasion flocks of other thrushes (B.K. Snow & Snow 1984).

Ian Henderson (GB)

Turdus ruficollis

Black-throated Thrush

CZ	Drozd tmavohrdlý	**I**	Tordo golanera
D	Bechsteindrossel	**NL**	Zwart-/Roodkeellijster
E	Zorzal papirrojo y papinegro	**P**	Tordo-de-papo/-ruivo/-preto
F	Grive à gorge rousse	**PL**	Drozd różnogardły
FIN	Mustakaularastas	**R**	Темнозобый дрозд
G	Τσίχλα του Bechstein	**S**	Taigatrast
H	Tajgarigó		

Non-SPEC, Threat status S (P)

The Black-throated Thrush is a typical resident of W and C Siberia, in Europe preferring mixed and coniferous forests in the middle and northern taiga subzones. There are small isolated populations in Armenia and Azerbaijan. Its extensive Asian range reaches *c*116°E and S to *c*37°N. The European and N Siberian populations are attributed to *T.r. atrogularis*. The report of the nominate *ruficollis* nesting in the N Urals requires further substantiation (Boyarshinov *et al* 1989).

In its main European range the Black-throated Thrush nests in the narrow belt of forested Ural foothills in the Perm region (Boyarshinov *et al* 1989) and in the Komi Republic from the middle taiga to the forest-tundra zone. In the northern taiga its distribution is wider, breeding in a variety of mountain habitats, from pure coniferous forests to semi-open habitats (willows *Salix*) and bogs. The major wintering areas lie in Iraq, C Asia and China. The origin of the smaller numbers wintering in Arabia is not known.

The species' European distribution area is well-protected, several nature reserves and national parks being sited along the Urals' western macroslope, including the two largest in Europe; the Yugyd Va Park and the Pechora–Ilych Reserve in the Komi Republic. The Black-throated Thrush nests at high densities in the forested plains up to 66°N, but densities decrease northwards towards the forest-tundra zone. Values decrease similarly southwards from the northern taiga. Typical breeding densities in prime habitats 45 bp/km^2 in mountain larch *Larix* forests, *c*35 bp/km^2 in mountain willow-bushes and only 1 bp/km^2 in bogs (Estafiev 1981).

The species has been observed often in more westerly regions, in the Pechora, Izma and Cilma River valleys, but breeding data are lacking. The European population is probably stable at 50 000–55 000bp, the majority of which breed in the Komi Republic. The population and range trends in the Caucasus are not known.

Alexey A Estafiev (R) Vladimir N Anufriev (R) Sergei K Kotchanov (R)

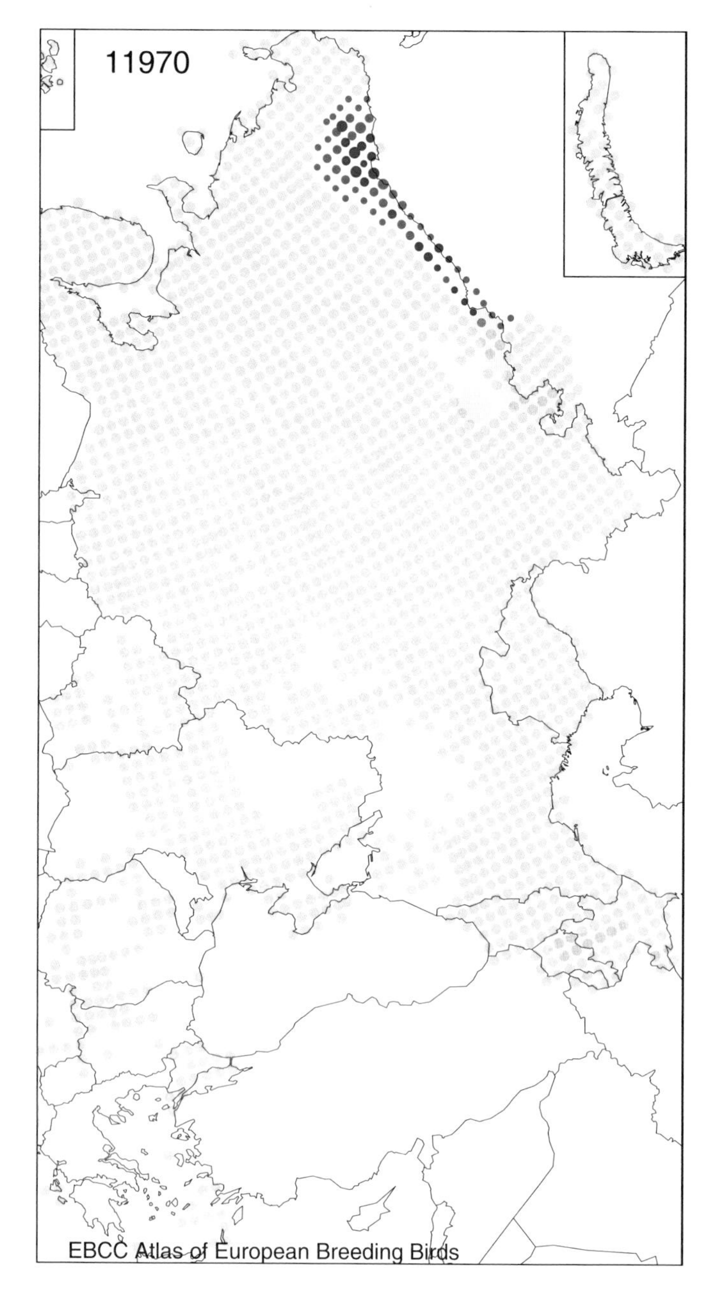

Cettia cetti

Cetti's Warbler

CZ	Cetie jižní	**I**	Usignolo di fiume
D	Seidensänger	**NL**	Cetti's Zanger
E	Ruiseñor Bastardo	**P**	Rouxinol-bravo
F	Bouscarle de Cetti	**PL**	Wierzbówka
FIN	Silkkikerttu	**R**	Широкохвостая камышовка
G	Ψευταηδόνι	**S**	Cettisångare
H	Berki poszáta		

Non-SPEC, Threat status S

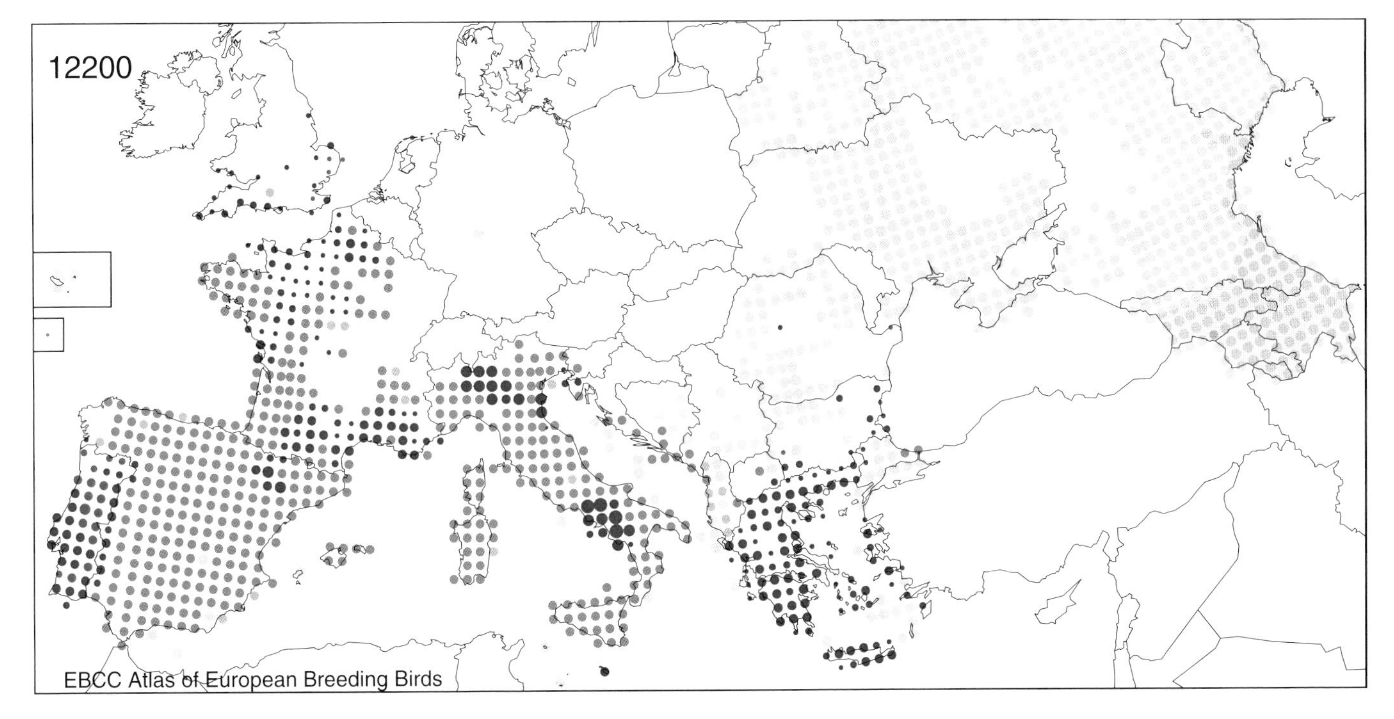

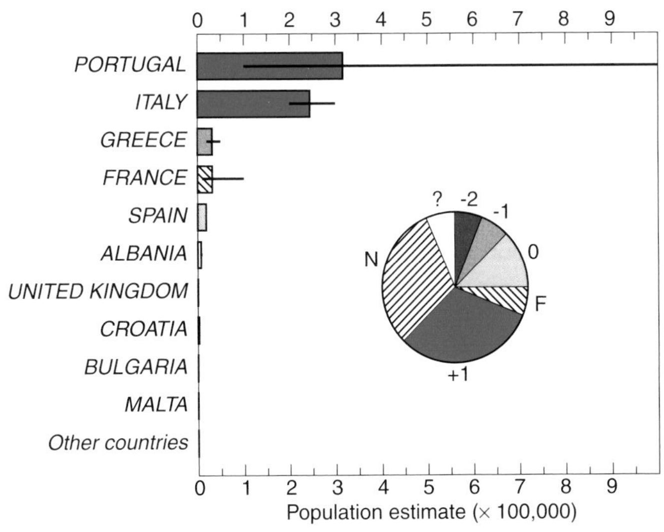

% in top 10 countries: 100.0
Total number of populated European countries: 16
Total European population 431,269–1,343,126 (653,490)
Russian population 7000–15,000 (10,247)
Turkish population 50,000–500,000 (158,114)

Extremely retiring but noisy, the Cetti's Warbler is distributed in S and W Europe, Transcaucasia, NW Africa, and from E Asia Minor to Turkestan and Afghanistan. It occupies the temperate, mediterranean and steppe zones, and even some desert margins, mainly regions where it can survive throughout the year. (It is largely sedentary.) It breeds and forages in impenetrable thickets of young willow *Salix*, poplar *Populus* and tamarisk *Tamarix* intertwined with creepers and interspersed with lush grassy vegetation affording complete ground-cover along rivers, slow-flowing streams or small swamps. Far from water it occupies scrub, dry reedbeds, or isolated dense bushes bordering fields. The nominate *C.c. cetti* occurs in Europe; two other subspecies are recognized.

Local population densities peak in early spring when returning migrants compete with residents (Nankinov *et al* 1977). Territories vary considerably in shape and size. Males are often polygynous (Bibby 1982).

It occurs mostly below 100m asl (in Spanish mountain valleys up to 1400m), but reaches 2400m in Asia. Since *c*1920 Cetti's Warbler has expanded its range to the N and W, colonizing Belgium (1964), S England (1972), Germany (1975), Switzerland (1975) and The Netherlands (1976, but undoubtedly bred earlier), but progress was reversed by three successive severe winters (1984/85–1986/87), except in England where it remains (*c*450bp, 1990). Small population increases occurred in Portugal, Italy, Croatia and Bulgaria in the same period. It is also a new breeder in Slovenia.

Prolonged cold winters extinguish populations, especially in the NW. Its French range contracted southwards after the 1984/85 and 1986/87 winters (Nicolau-Guillaumet 1994). When wintering conditions are unfavourable, birds, especially juveniles and females, may disperse S to the nearest unaffected habitat.

Iztok Geister (SLN) Bojidar Ivanov (BUL)

Cisticola juncidis

Fan-tailed Warbler

CZ	Cistovník rákosníkový	**I**	Beccamoschino
D	Cistensänger	**NL**	Waaierstaartzanger
E	Buitrón	**P**	Fuínha-dos-juncos
F	Cisticole des joncs	**PL**	Chwastówka
FIN	Heinäkerttu	**R**	Веерохвостая камышовка
G	Κιστικόλη	**S**	Grässångare
H	Szuharbújó		

Non-SPEC, Threat status S (P)

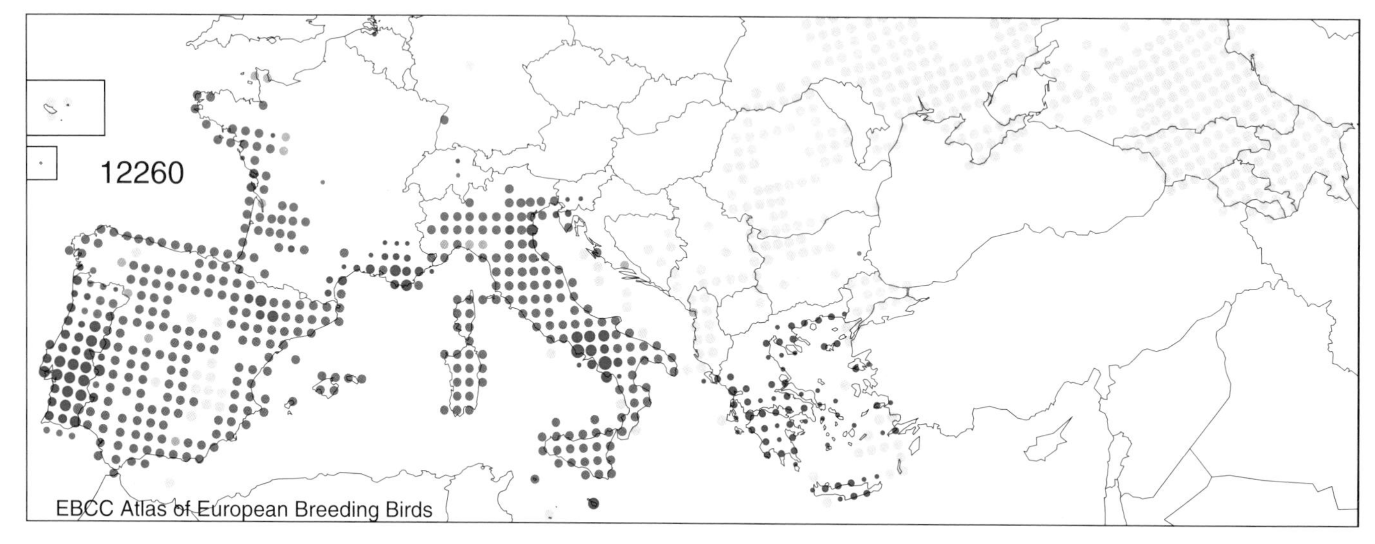

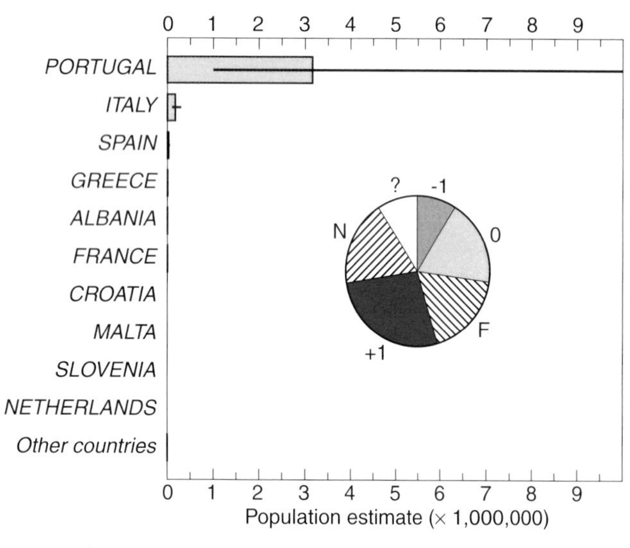

% in top 10 countries: 100.0
Total number of populated European countries: 11
Total European population 1,215,998–10,218,526 (3,379,564)
Turkish population 1000–10,000 (3162)

The Fan-tailed Warbler breeds in the equatorial, tropical and subtropical regions of Africa to Australia, and in Europe up to 1000m asl in the mediterranean zone, from where it spread to predominantly Atlantic climate regions (January isotherms above 3.5°C). Although winter conditions restrict its distribution (three successive days in ten of frost or slight snow-cover may decimate numbers; regions with >15 frost days per winter cannot normally sustain populations), habitat loss (through drainage, irrigation, land reclamation, conversion of meadows into plantations) is the main threat. These two factors underlie most population fluctuations.

The species inhabits open grassy country, floodplains, dry crops and ricefields. Characteristic wet habitats are purple moor-grass *Molinia caerulea* and reed *Phragmites australis* and dry habitat, a sea-couch grass/bramble *Agropyrum pycnanthum/Rubus* spp admixture. It avoids wooded habitats (interference with its wide-ranging song-flights).

In optimal habitat several broods per female and 10–16.5 fledglings per male per year are typical (Taillandier 1993). First-brood young may breed later that summer. Its typically polygynous mating system makes censusing difficult unless directed at territorial males. High male densities occur in the Camargue (16 on 25ha, 1987), at Marais d'Harchies (Belgium) (38 on 80ha, 1974) and at the Slovenian Dragonja River mouth (54 on 350ha, 1979; Geister 1980). Mediterranean countries hold the largest populations, especially Portugal (>1Mbp) and Italy (100 000–300 000bp).

The 1970s saw a strong northward European range expansion. Records of first breeding are: Belgium 1964, The Netherlands, Slovenia and Croatia 1974, Germany and Switzerland 1975. The severe winters of 1978/79, 1982/83 and later in the mid-1980s, resulted in drastic range contractions and population declines in NW and C Europe. Breeding in NW and C France, The Netherlands and Switzerland ceased by the late 1980s. The expansion of the eastern Mediterranean population northwards has been slower (first Bulgarian breeding record 1984). The Dalmatian population (1981) may have originated from either the E or W Mediterranean.

Iztok Geister (SLN)

Locustella lanceolata

Lanceolated Warbler

CZ	Cvrčilka žíhaná	I	Locustella lanceolata
D	Strichelschwirl	NL	Kleine Sprinkhaanzanger
E	Buscarla Lanceolada	P	Felosa-lanceolada
F	Locustelle lancéolée	PL	Świerszczak nakrapiany
FIN	Viirusirkkalintu	R	Пятнистый сверчок
G	Γραμμοτριλιστής	S	Träsksångare
H	Foltos tücsökmadár		

Non-SPEC, Threat status S (P)

The Lanceolated Warbler is widespread in Siberia, N China, Korea and Japan. Up to the 1960s it frequently occurred in the breeding season in much of E European Russia, such as in the River Onega valley. In the 1990s it has occurred in NE European Russia, a female being recorded in the breeding season in Ural Mountain meadows (Beshkarev & Teplov 1993) and a singing male in the post-breeding season near Syktyvkar (S. Kotchanov, pers obs) in the S of the Komi Republic. There are no subspecies.

European nesting data are scanty. Apart from the single old report from the N Kirov region (Efremov 1935), there is only one other from the main western slopes of the Urals in Perm region (the Basegi Nature Reserve) (Boyarshinov *et al* 1989). The species certainly nests on the eastern slopes of the Urals in the southern taiga subzone (Motylev 1989). It is likely that the European breeding range of this little-studied and elusive species consists of a longitudinal belt along the Urals. Its present distribution may be less extensive than it was in the 1890s or even the 1960s. It may undergo long-term fluctuations because its principal habitats are perhaps the least transformed of all, yet it cannot be found in the same locations and habitats in the S Urals where naturalists found it in the 19th century.

The nesting habitats of the Lanceolated Warbler are extremely variable, from open meadows to bushes and thinned-out forests. It prefers semi-open meadows flanked by bushes along rivers and streams. It winters mainly in the Indian subcontinent, the Andaman Islands and in mainland SE Asia.

In our opinion, the present population of the Lanceolated Warbler in Europe, roughly estimated, is no more than 5500–6000bp, which are mostly restricted to the Perm region.

Vladimir N Anufriev (R) Sergey K Kotchanov (R)

Locustella naevia **Grasshopper Warbler**

CZ	Cvrčilka zelená	**I**	Forapaglie macchiettato
D	Feldschwirl	**NL**	Sprinkhaanzanger
E	Buscarla Pintoja	**P**	Felosa-malhada
F	Locustelle tachetée	**PL**	Świerszczak
FIN	Pensassirkkalintu	**R**	Обыкновенный сверчок
G	Θαμνοτριλιστής	**S**	Gräshoppsångare
H	Réti tücsökmadár		

SPEC Cat 4, Threat status S

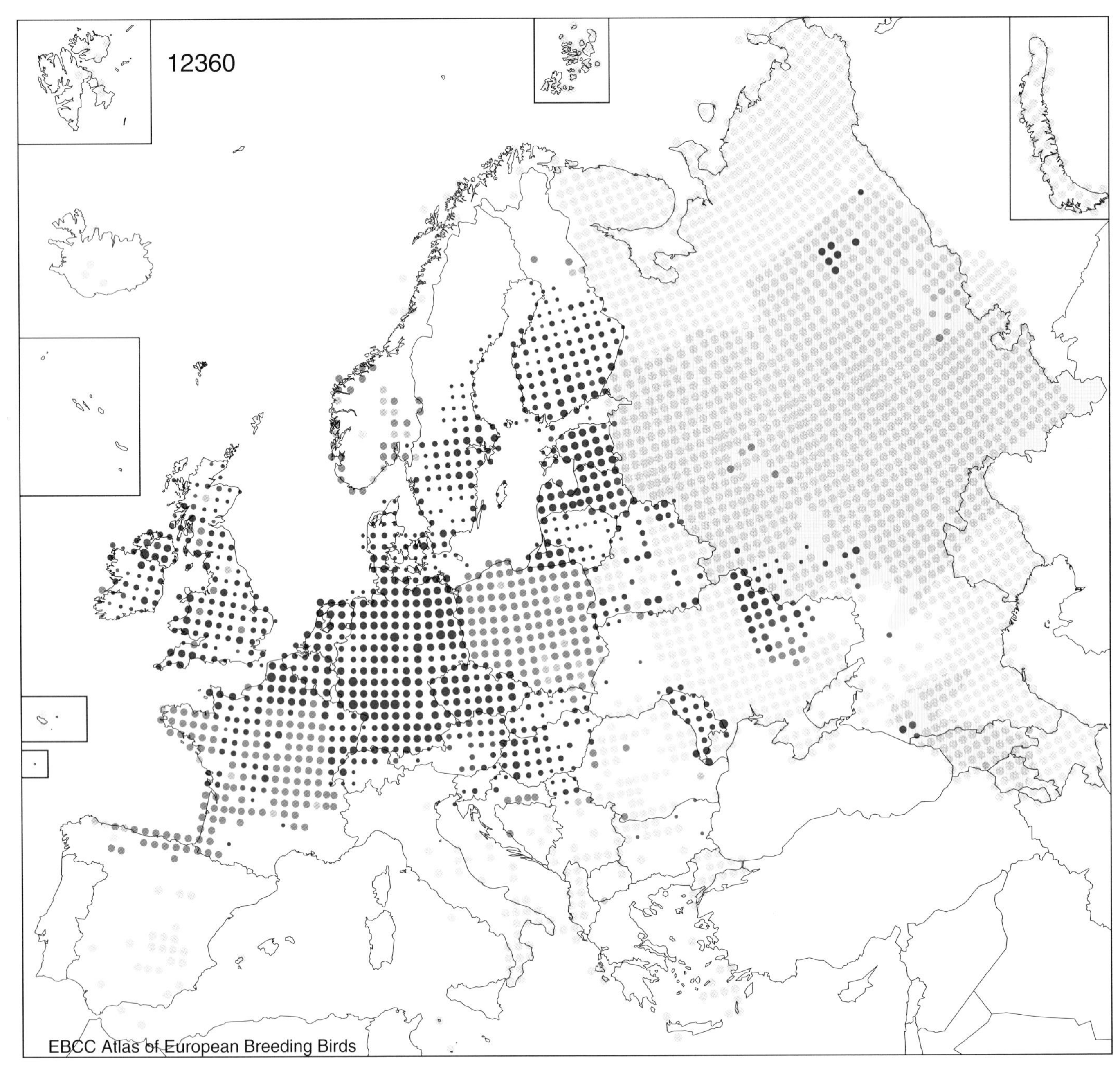

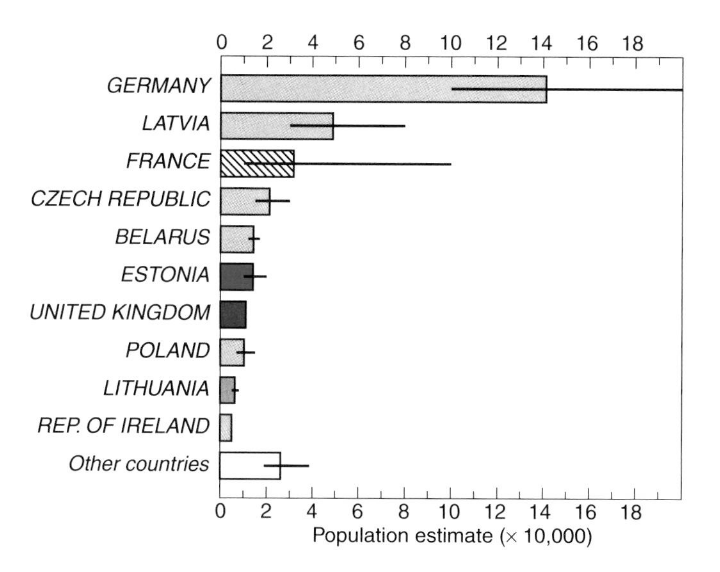

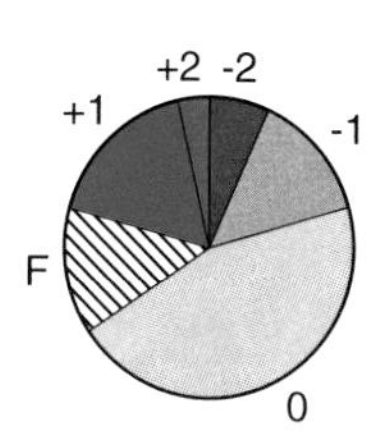

% in top 10 countries: 92.1
Total number of populated European countries: 29
Total European population 279,094–426,546 (330,346)
Russian population 100,000–1,000,000 (316,228)

Still very much an enigmatic species, the Grasshopper Warbler is probably the least understood of all the commoner European warblers, despite its breeding range encompassing all C and northern European countries except Iceland. Occurring between the July 17° and 30°C isotherms, it is generally absent from the Mediterranean region. Its distribution reaches *c*100°E in SE Siberia. Now known to winter in Africa S of the Sahara, it has been recorded in winter in Morocco and Algeria. Only as recently as 1993 were two individuals ringed in Senegal in winter recovered in Great Britain during the breeding season (S.J.R. Rumsey, pers comm).

The male's reeling song is often the only indication of presence, because the species is masterfully adept at skulking in thick tangled cover. It nests in both damp and dry habitats, the necessary criterion seemingly being thick, low-lying vegetation (less than 1m tall) containing several more prominent features, usually bushes, for song perches. Such characteristics are met not only in tussocky grass or sedge, nettle-beds and bramble, all offering a blend of plant types, but also by monotypic young plantations, especially conifer whose profit-based harvesting cycle being rotational, offers a continuous habitat set. Most select agricultural habitats, such as abandoned fields, field edges and roadsides.

Reasonably widespread N of a line from the Pyrenees to S–C Finland, the Grasshopper Warbler has a fairly constant lowland distribution, although it breeds regularly up to 500m asl in Switzerland (Glutz von Blotzheim 1962) and above 1000m (exceptionally up to 1500m in the Caucasus; *BWP*). Generally commonest in its range centre, it has colonized several countries in the mid-20th century, notably Denmark and Norway while increasing further in Sweden, Finland and the former Czechoslovakia (Moritz 1990). Thorough investigation might confirm breeding in both Italy and Greece. So little of substance is known about populations that assessment of true abundance anywhere is very difficult. Being particularly habitat-sensitive and having little avian competition for habitat choice (van der Hut 1986) the Grasshopper Warbler is clearly well-distributed within its range limits. In prime habitats breeding density may rise locally to 20–50 bp/km^2, but more representative figures, as in Finland, are 3–8 bp/km^2 (Koskimies 1989a).

Even countries supporting large populations seem unsure whether the species is in decline or the ascendant. Consequently it is argued that the species may have developed a nomadic tendency, sensitive perhaps to spring temperatures during migration. If this be the case, such behaviour contrasts with that of other warbler species whose adult site fidelity is well-documented, like Reed Warbler *Acrocephalus scirpaceus* and Willow Warbler *Phylloscopus trochilus*. Wind-driven nomadism may account partly for Grasshopper Warbler population fluctuations at the western range limits, as in Spain, Belgium, Britain & Ireland, because the absence of warm easterly winds in spring reduces the numbers of continental drift migrants; a reduction of 40% since 1972 occurred in Britain & Ireland (Glue 1990). Furthermore, in smaller areas, territory numbers fluctuate from year to year, peaks being more than ten times greater than troughs (Koskimies 1989a). The slight increases in the species' northern range and declines in the southeastern range may fall well within natural fluctuations.

Declines in numbers ringed and censused following Sahel droughts suggest also that poor conditions in Africa adversely affect populations (Mead & Hudson 1985, Marchant *et al* 1990). The Grasshopper Warbler remains successful in breeding habitats which are rotational or remain unchanged. However, changing land-use probably is the main cause of range contraction. Eastern Europe may soon see intensive farming supplanting the low-intensity methods which provide so much suitable habitat. Destruction of wetland, grassland and scrub habitats have also proved detrimental in much of western (Glue 1993c) and C Europe.

John Callion (GB) Pertti Koskimies (FIN)

Locustella fluviatilis River Warbler

CZ	Cvrčilka říční	**I**	Locustella fluviatile
D	Schlagschwirl	**NL**	Krekelzanger
E	Buscarla Fluvial	**P**	Felosa-fluvial
F	Locustelle fluviatile	**PL**	Strumieniówka
FIN	Viitasirkkalintu	**R**	Речной сверчок
G	Ποταμοτριλιστής	**S**	Flodsångare
H	Berki tücsökmadár		

SPEC Cat 4, Threat status S

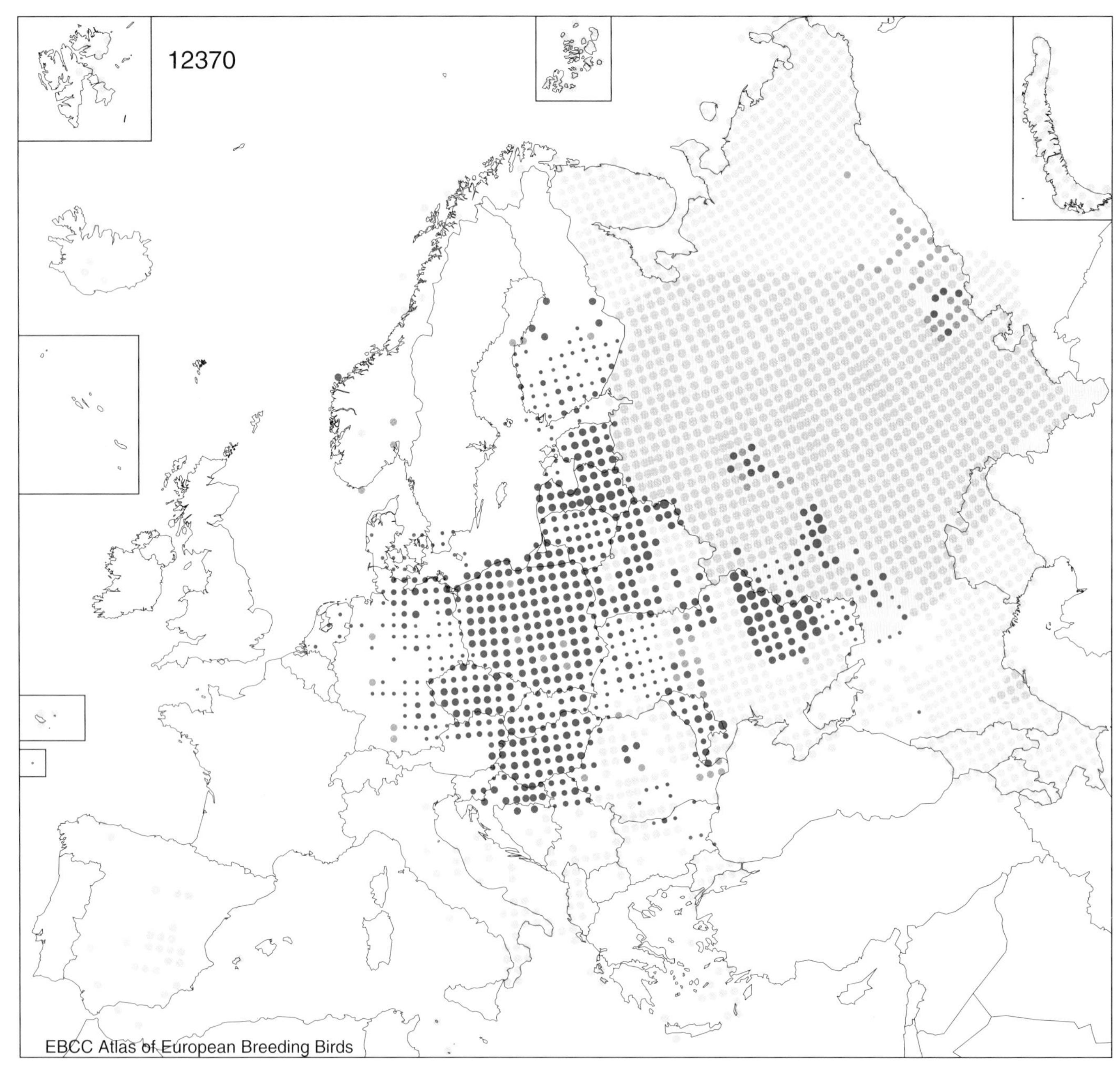

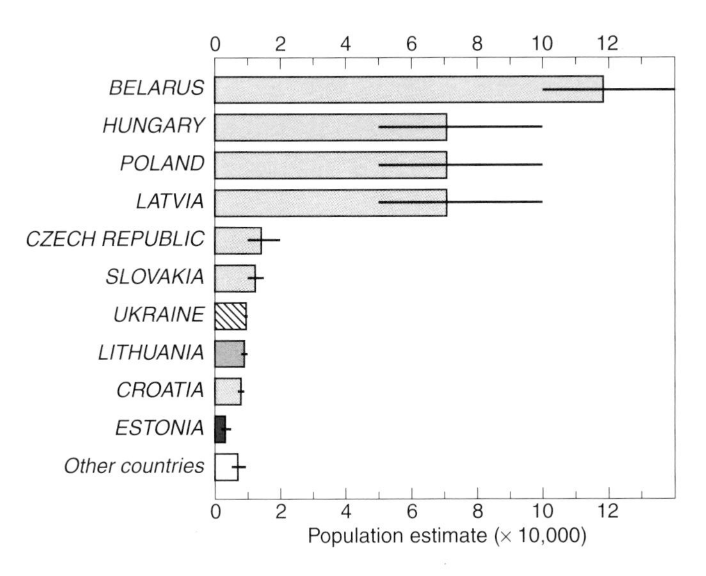

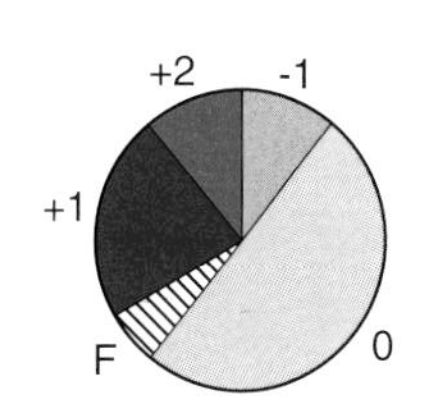

% in top 10 countries: 98.2
Total number of populated European countries: 18
Total European population 352,735–448,947 (393,337)
Russian population 100,000–1,000,000 (316,228)

The River Warbler's western Palearctic breeding range is somewhat smaller and more easterly than those of the Grasshopper *L. naevia* and Savi's *L. luscinioides* Warblers. Over 75% of its range lies in C and E Europe, from Germany and the former Yugoslavia to W Russia, and from the Black Sea to southern Finland. The River Warbler winters in bushy and reedy habitats in a restricted area in eastern Africa from northern South Africa to southern Malawi.

The River Warbler prefers moist, dense vegetation in streams, ditches, river floodlands, lowland eutrophic bogs and near ponds or lakes (particularly eutrophic waters), but it also may breed some distance from water, and in drier habitats (especially northern Europe) such as agricultural margins. It is absent from mountainous areas and barren, coniferous-dominated forests. It is fairly common in its typical habitats, which include wooded swamps, alder carr, sedge marshes, bogs and willow scrub. These usually contain dense undergrowth comprising grasses or thick and luxuriant herbage (nettle *Urtica* spp, meadowsweet *Filipendula ulmaria*, or raspberry *Rubus idaeus*) and a bush layer at 0.5–1.5m above ground level, the layer often comprised of immature hazel *Corylus avellana*, alder *Alnus*, birch *Betula* and willow *Salix*. Its habitats occur as secondary growth in overgrown waters, deciduous forest clearings, orchards and abandoned agricultural land.

The River Warbler is an extremely difficult species to monitor due to its skulking habits. Males use dead branches or twigs in solitary bushes and small trees as singing posts. Although singing males can be counted, paired males cease singing whereas unpaired males do not, which makes accurate pair estimation impossible. In southern Finland, the species' northernmost limit, most males (up to *c*85%) seem to remain unpaired most years (Koskimies 1989a).

Despite the above difficulties the River Warbler has been mapped in most 50km squares in C Europe, but the map resolution cannot show its patchy local distribution reflecting that of suitable habitat. Although concentrations of singing males may occur, such concentrations are often widely separated.

Breeding densities depend on habitat type and area. Values (in bp/km^2) obtained were: in a variety of Polish habitats, from 1 to 160 (Mackowicz 1989); in northwesternmost Russia (highest achieved) *c*40 (Mal'chevski & Pukinski 1983), and in Estonia 26 (the highest locally in 10–20-year-old birch thickets; Leibak *et al* 1994). More representative (mean) values from dozens of study plots in C and N Germany (Flade 1994) were (by plot type): 10 in small riverine willow forests (gallery forests); 2.9 in wet fallow land (with reeds, high herbs, sedges, willow shrubs, etc.); 1.4 in alder carr; 0.6 in semi-open floodplains and lowland eutrophic bogs, and 0.2 in ash–elm–cherry (*Fraxinus–Ulmus–Prunus*).

Russia holds perhaps 50% of the European population (estimated roughly at 100 000–1Mbp) and Belarus 100 000–140 000bp, the remainder breeding mostly in Latvia, Poland and Hungary (50 000–100 000bp each). This core population apparently has been stable at least since the 1970s, and probably for longer. Early records indicate a gradual range expansion in C Europe in the early 20th century, followed by retreat. Probably since the 1950s the northern and western marginal populations have extended their range and increased in numbers, particularly the tiny Finnish (doubled abruptly in the late 1980s; Koskimies 1990) and Swedish populations. Estonia, Germany, Austria and Bulgaria have also experienced increasing trends from 1970 to 1990. Modest declines have occurred in Lithuania and Moldova.

Annual fluctuations, partly correlated with weather conditions during spring migration, are wide. Warm southeasterlies often lead to prolongation of the spring migration, as in Finland. The species has benefited from large-scale abandonment of agricultural land and this may continue in some areas. In C Europe the River Warbler has locally increased probably due to habitat eutrophication.

Pertti Koskimies (FIN) Martin Flade (D)

This species account is sponsored by Dr Arie Cleeren, Stevoort, B.

Locustella luscinioides

Savi's Warbler

CZ	Cvrčilka slavíková	**I**	Salciaiola
D	Rohrschwirl	**NL**	Snor
E	Buscarla Unicolor	**P**	Felosa-unicolor
F	Locustelle luscinioïde	**PL**	Brzęczka
FIN	Ruokosirkkalintu	**R**	Соловьиный сверчок
G	Καλαμοτριλιστής	**S**	Vassångare
H	Nádi tücsökmadár		

SPEC Cat 4, Threat status S (P)

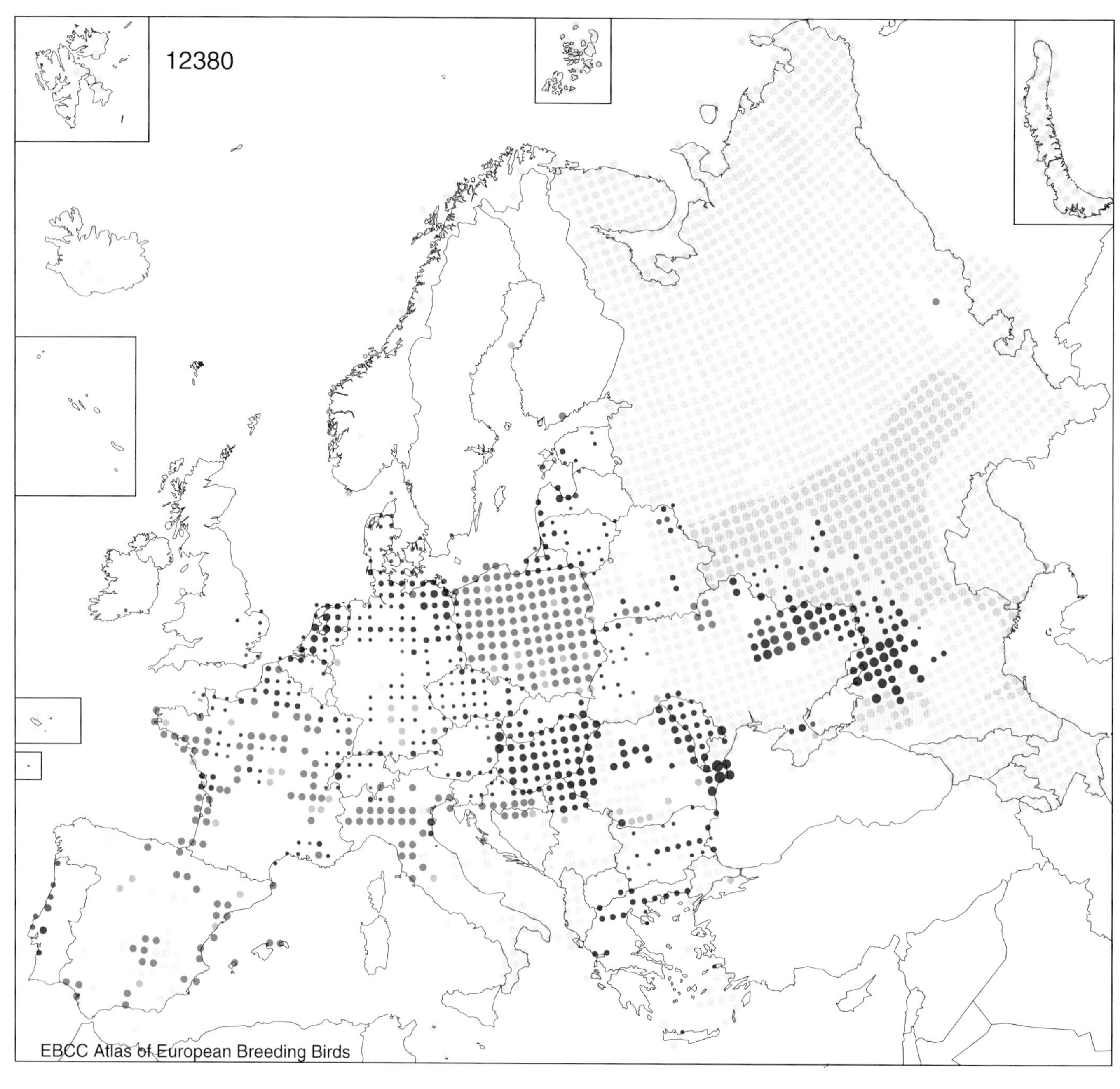

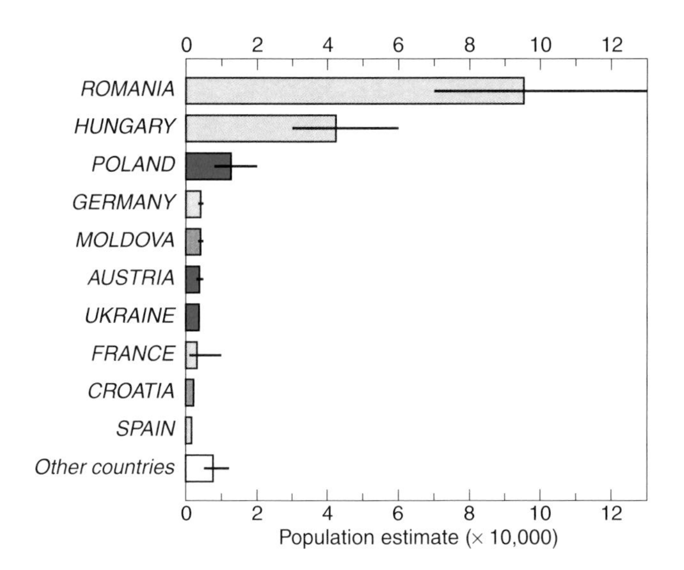

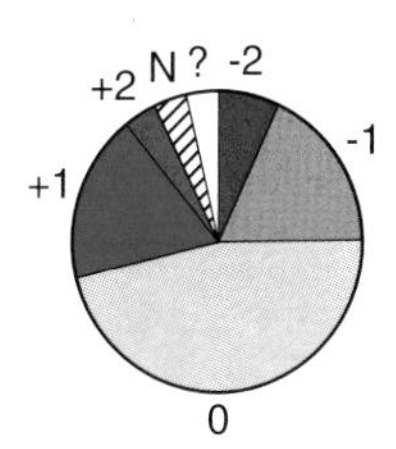

% in top 10 countries: 95.8
Total number of populated European countries: 28
Total European population 152,363–221,293 (181,139)
Russian population 10,000–100,000 (31,623)
Turkish population 1000–10,000 (3162)

Savi's Warbler, being virtually confined to reed and sedge habitats, has a scattered and patchy distribution in a broad band between 36° and 60°N in W, C and E Europe from SE England, NW France and Portugal eastwards to the Volga and the Urals, and from Estonia in the N to the Mediterranean. A separate range exists from the W Caspian to SW Siberia (Ob Valley). A long-distance migrant, the species winters in sub-Saharan Africa N of the tropical rainforest zone, especially in S Sudan. Of the three subspecies the nominate *luscinioides* occurs in Europe E to the Balkans and *sarmatica* elsewhere.

In W and C Europe the species is largely restricted to extensive stands of reed *Phragmites australis* and bulrush *Typha* spp, usually in wet or moist marshland which has medium-height vegetation and a dense ground layer (van der Hut 1986). In E Poland and Belarus it occurs also in sedge *Carex* marshes containing willow *Salix* shrubs, in sparse alder *Alnus* carrs possessing reed-clumps and even within sparse forests along reed-bordered canals. Savi's Warbler has bred up to 500–630m asl in Austria and the Czech Republic.

Its distribution is patchier than the map suggests. Remarkable concentrations occur in a few huge reed marshes, such as Neusiedlersee (Austria) (3000–5000bp; Dvorak *et al* 1993), Brière and Seine-et-Marne (France) (more than 1000bp; *HVM* 1991), the Biebrza and Narew marshes in NE Poland (5000–20 000bp) and the Romanian Danube Delta (Weber 1994). Obtaining reliable estimates of populations and trends is beset by difficulties, such as its abundance in optimal habitats, the inaccessibility of huge reedbeds and the tendency of the species to change territories during the breeding season. However, the highest overall density occurs clearly in Romania (70 000–130 000bp) and in Hungary (30 000–60 000bp).

The highest densities occur in large reedbeds and *Typha* stands which are richly structured vertically, several years old, and possess a dense sedge layer adjacent to waterlogged ground. In representative areas larger than 10ha, average densities of 2.1–8.8 bp/10ha have been recorded in Germany and The Netherlands (van der Hut 1986, Flade 1994) and in the Milicz fishponds in SW Poland even up to 15.8 bp/10ha (Dyrcz *et al* 1991). In tall pure reedbeds (*Scirpo–Phragmitetum*) between open water and larger reedbelts, densities of up to 5.0 bp/10ha have been noted. Yet another optimal habitat comprising early succession stages of alder carr and a mixture of reeds, sedges, tall herbage, bushes and young trees contained up to 11.5 bp/6ha in the Biebrza marshes (Dyrcz *et al* 1985) and 8.8–14.4 bp/10ha in N Germany (Flade 1994).

Short-term population fluctuations are well-known for the Savi's Warbler, probably resulting from habitat changes (drainage, natural changes in water level, natural succession) and weather conditions in the African winter quarters. European trends during 1970–90 were very uneven. Increases were confined mostly to countries in C and E Europe, in the Baltic States and probably also in Belarus. In the Czech Republic, the breeding range expanded by >50%, but numbers remained stable, whereas in Latvia both numbers and range increased by >50%. In contrast, distinct declines have occurred at the western and southern range limits: Portugal, Britain, The Netherlands, Belgium, Italy, Croatia and Moldova. In the early 1970s in The Netherlands, a decrease became apparent. The population declined by 50–75% from 1965–75 to 1993, thinly occupied areas losing all their breeding birds. Although commercial exploitation of reedbeds may play a role, it is more likely that wintering conditions in the Sahelian belt are responsible for this decline, as for the Sedge Warbler *Acrocephalus schoenobaenus* (Osieck & Hustings 1994). Nevertheless, the overall population trend in Europe may be stable at the moment.

Martin Flade (D)

Acrocephalus paludicola

Aquatic Warbler

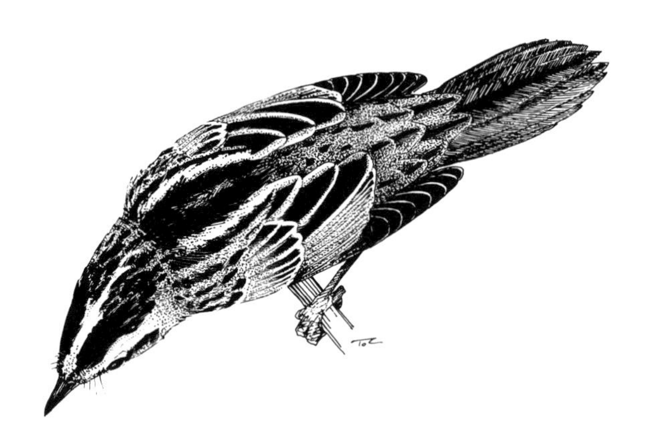

CZ	Rákosník ostřicový	**I**	Pagliarolo
D	Seggenrohrsänger	**NL**	Waterrietzanger
E	Carricerín Cejudo	**P**	Felosa-aquática
F	Phragmite aquatique	**PL**	Wodniczka
FIN	Sarakerttunen	**R**	Вертлявая камышовка
G	Νεροποταμίδα	**S**	Vattensångare
H	Csíkosfejű nádiposzáta		

SPEC Cat 1, Threat status E

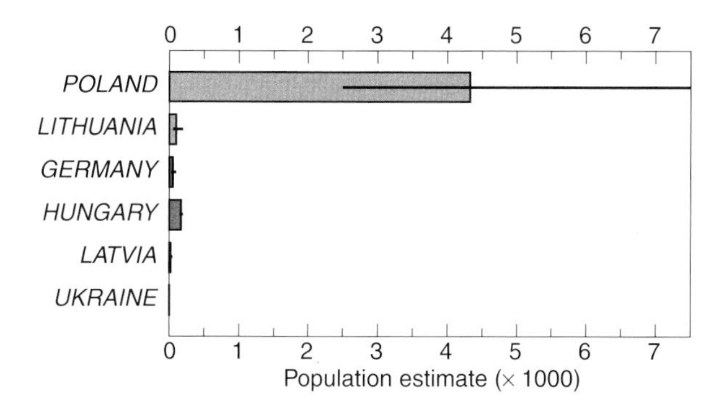

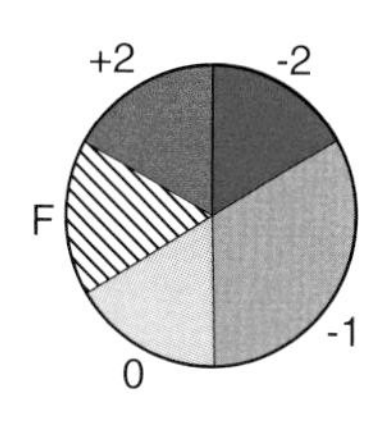

% in top 10 countries: 100.0
Total number of populated European countries: 6
Total European population 2852–7856 (4684)
Russian population 1000–10,000 (3162)

The breeding range of the monotypic Aquatic Warbler is restricted to the western Palearctic between 50° and 60°N, stretching from E Germany to the River Ob in W Siberia (Ravkin 1993). However, its eastern and southern distribution limits are not known precisely.

Its preferred habitat is open, eutrophic marshes, where sedge *Carex* spp up to 80cm tall and mosses are predominant, the water between tufts being a few centimetres deep. The presence of scattered willow bushes (<5% of the total vegetation) or short reeds is favoured. These habitats are characteristic of tributary riverine marshes and of the upper reaches of slow-flowing lowland rivers. The open habitat structure is essential and can be maintained only by very low-intensity farming methods which rotate through several years and which involve cutting or fire. Locally the Aquatic Warbler occurs in partially drained hay meadows, and in calcareous marshes dominated by great fen-sedge *Cladium mariscus*. In some estuaries and coastal sites it nests in the sedge-like, halophilous saltmarsh grass/sea spurrey *Puccinellia/ Spergularia* plant community. Breeding density in *Carex* marshes ranges from 0.5 to 10.9 singing males/10ha, the number of breeding females being slightly lower (Dyrcz and Zdunek 1993).

The species has an unusual reproductive system close to promiscuity (Schulze-Hagen *et al* 1995), the female raising its young without male help (Dyrcz 1993). Abundance of relatively large arthropods in the breeding habitat may explain why such a system would succeed (Schulze-Hagen *et al* 1989).

Its present patchy distribution is a relict of a former more continuous range. Since 1875 the Aquatic Warbler rapidly became extinct in at least eight European countries. The remaining C and probably eastern European distribution contracted drastically due to habitat loss from land improvement and drainage schemes, as in Poland where but three key areas remain. Knowledge of the species' occurrence in Russia, Ukraine and Belarus until 1995 was very poor, but in Belarus that year preliminary surveys of former firing ranges and some extensive boggy areas produced an estimated total of 5000–20 000 singing males (Kozulin *et al* 1996). It is likely that more sites in Belarus will add to this figure. This makes the information in the Atlas database and the charts out-of-date and underlines the need for similar work in Russia and Ukraine, whose currently estimated average number of singing males is only *c*4500 each. The total population in the remaining European countries is between 4680 and 8050 singing males. The westernmost important breeding area is the Biebrza Valley in NE Poland, which is contiguous with the recently discovered Belarussian breeding areas, forming a single geographic unit.

Although several eastern German and Polish breeding sites have been destroyed by drainage projects, even since 1970, populations unafflicted by such schemes have remained stable since the first censuses in the early 1970s of the Biebrza Valley, but annual numbers may fluctuate to some extent (Dyrcz & Zdunek 1993). On the Hortobágy puszta in Hungary, where habitats are being improved through active flooding of grasslands, the population size has steadily grown from *c*20 singing males in 1977 to over 400 in 1994 (Kovács 1994a).

Despite the new discoveries, the Aquatic Warbler is still the rarest migratory passerine in Europe; it remains globally threatened because its main habitats are threatened. In Belarus, land-contamination from the Chernobyl disaster has forced much of the human population to relocate; the newly discovered Aquatic Warbler breeding areas lie close to new large-scale land reclamation projects which are making land available to the displaced people. The Aquatic Warbler's strict habitat requirements make immediate protection measures essential to minimize the likely damage from the inevitable human influx.

C European populations migrate SW in autumn to winter in W Sahelian wetlands, from Senegal and Mali to Ghana, but the extent of the wintering area is poorly known.

Andrzej Dyrcz (PL) Karl Schulze-Hagen (D)

This species account is sponsored by Dr Till Macke, Bonn, D.

Acrocephalus schoenobaenus

Sedge Warbler

CZ	Rákosník proužkovaný	**I**	Forapaglie
D	Schilfrohrsänger	**NL**	Rietzanger
E	Carricerín Común	**P**	Felosa-dos-juncos
F	Phragmite des joncs	**PL**	Rokitniczka
FIN	Ruokokerttunen	**R**	Камышовка-барсучок
G	Βουρλοποταμίδα	**S**	Sävsångare
H	Foltos nádiposzáta		

SPEC Cat 4, Threat status S (P)

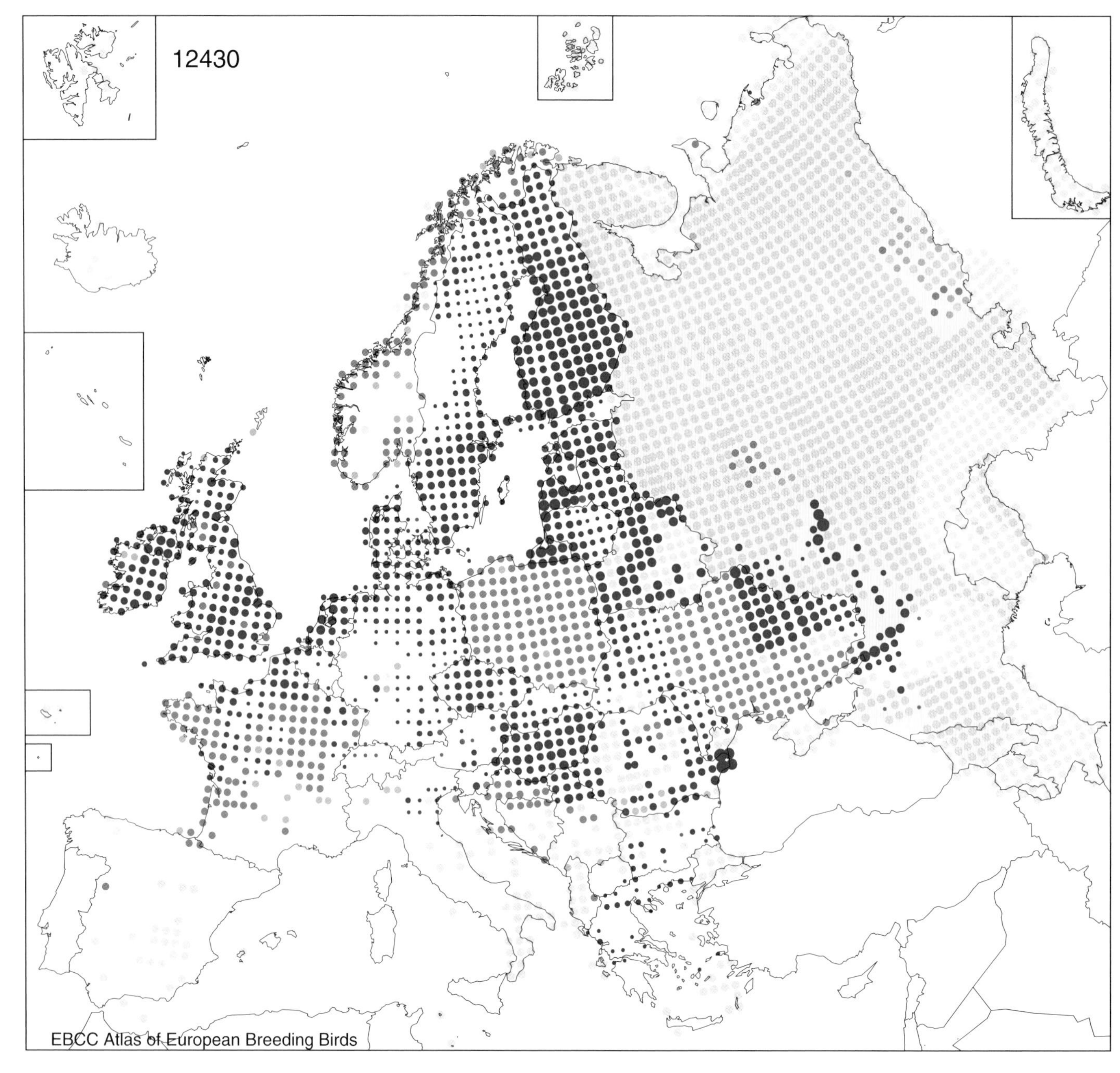

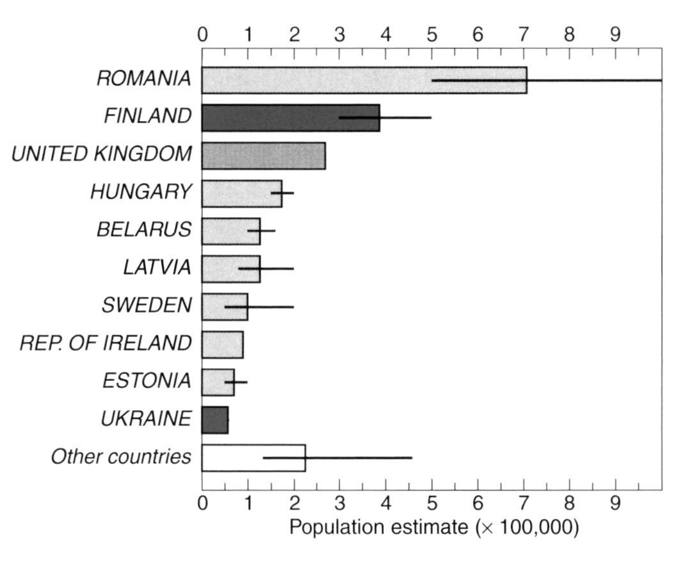

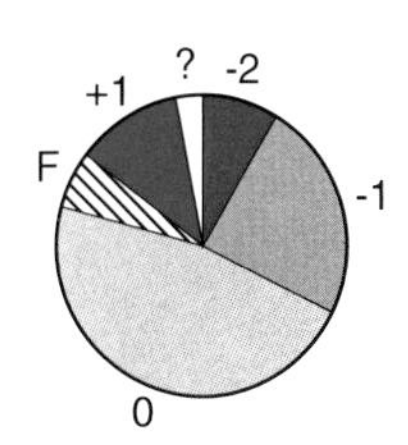

% in top 10 countries: 90.4
Total number of populated European countries: 34
Total European population 2,092,454–2,691,012 (2,333,770)
Russian population 1,000,000–10,000,000 (3,162,278)
Turkish population 1000–10,000 (3162)

The Sedge Warbler is a common breeding species throughout much of Europe. Its breeding range extends from the high arctic of N Fennoscandia to Greece and Turkey in the S, and from Ireland across the Urals to C Siberia (90°E). It is adapted to cool, moist climates, occupying the boreal to temperate climate zones, reaching the mediterranean zone but marginally.

It seemingly prefers lowland marsh and waterside habitats for breeding, although frequently it utilizes drier habitats including hedges, scrub, young conifers and arable crops. It nests in dense vegetation or bushes, usually within 50cm of the ground, using extensive reedbeds only for feeding. The species has attained breeding densities of 300–600 bp/km^2 in patches of prime (damp) habitat. It occurs at very much lower densities in drier and cultivated habitats.

The Sedge Warbler is widespread across northern, western, C and eastern Europe but relatively scarce throughout Mediterranean southern Europe. It is absent from most of Iberia, southern France, Italy and much of the Balkans, where conditions may be too hot and dry to support breeding birds. Within its main breeding range it clearly avoids the highlands of the Alps and the Carpathians, as well as the Norwegian and German mountains. The colonization of the Orkney Islands, the Outer Hebrides, southern Norway and much of Finland (Koskimies 1989a) is probably part of a range expansion, which, starting in the 1850s, may be the consequence of the increase in flooded mineral workings (gravel-pits). Their existence fortuitously created much additional breeding habitat. Increased eutrophication of existing wetlands and waterways may also have supported the expansion. Wetland drainage may have caused breeding range reductions, notably in the Low Countries and eastern Europe.

The species' stronghold comprises NE and E Europe, with large populations exceeding 2000 bp/50km square in Russia, Belarus, Finland, the Baltic States and Romania. In the W, only Britain & Ireland and The Netherlands have densities exceeding 1000 bp/50km square. The vast Russian breeding grounds probably support greater numbers than the rest of Europe combined. Although long-term monitoring data are lacking for most European regions, the species' population has probably increased from 1970 to 1990 in Finland, Norway, Ukraine and Austria, but declined in Britain, The Netherlands, France, Germany and Belgium. The decrease across W Europe has probably been caused by a series of severe droughts in the West African winter quarters (Peach *et al* 1991), where the normal late summer yearly rainfall creates an abundance of wetland habitats for migrants arriving in the extensive floodplains of the Niger and Senegal Rivers. In drought years less habitat is flooded, and by the end of the African dry season (March) wetland habitat is likely to be in short supply. Following the severest African droughts of the mid-1980s, breeding populations reached their lowest recorded levels in Britain, Estonia, Finland, Sweden, The Netherlands and the former Czechoslovakia (Hustings 1988, Väisänen *et al* 1989). After several wetter years in West Africa (the late 1980s), several European breeding populations increased.

The Sedge Warbler winters in Africa from Senegal in the W to Ethiopia in the E and Cape Province (South Africa) in the S. Scandinavian and western European populations appear to migrate southwards to winter in West Africa, whereas Finnish and eastern European birds appear to winter in C and eastern Africa (Dowsett *et al* 1988). Autumn migration begins in July when large fat reserves permit the heaviest birds to fly directly from southern Britain to sub-Saharan Africa (Bibby & Green 1981). Spring passage starts in Africa in February and the first birds reach their breeding grounds as early as late March in western France and early May in southern Finland.

Marta Borowiec (PL) Will Peach (GB)

Acrocephalus melanopogon

Moustached Warbler

CZ	Rákosník tamaryškový	I	Forapaglie castagnolo
D	Mariskensänger	NL	Zwartkoprietzanger
E	Carricerín Real	P	Felosa-real
F	Lusciniole à moustaches	PL	Tamaryszka
FIN	Osmankäämikerttunen	R	Тонкоклювая камышовка
G	Μουστακοποταμίδα	S	Kaveldunsångare
H	Fülemülesitke		

Non-SPEC, Threat status S (P)

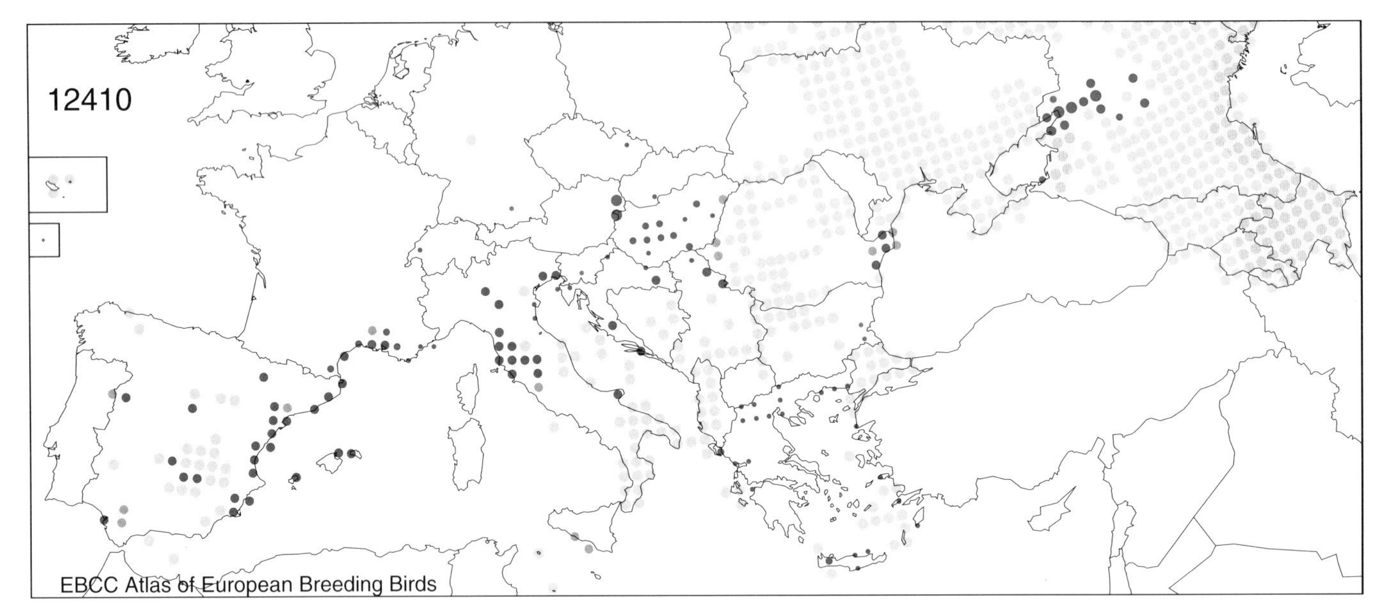

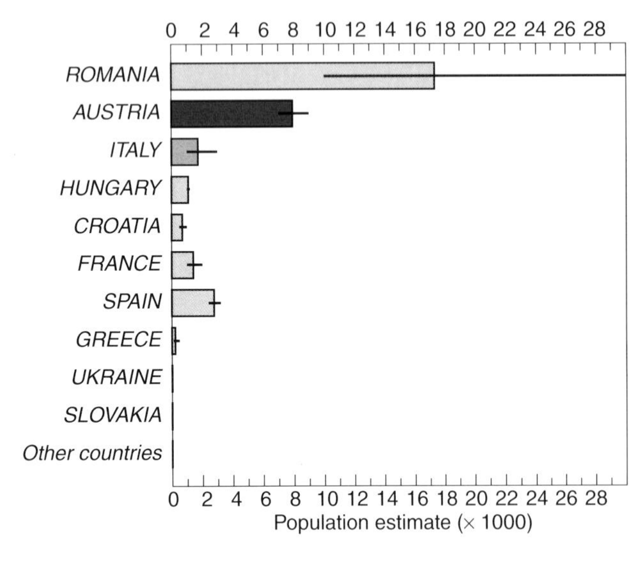

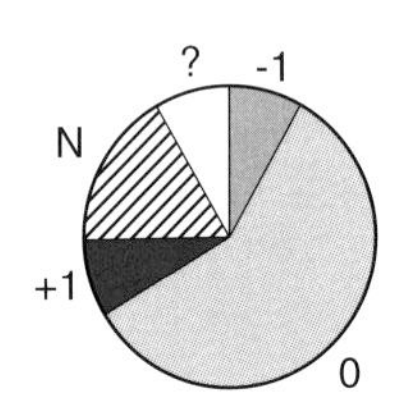

% in top 10 countries: 100.0
Total number of populated European countries: 12
Total European population 25,805–46,062 (33,247)
Russian population 50,000–500,000 (158,114)
Turkish population 5000–15,000 (8660)

The Moustached Warbler is patchily distributed in the S and C Palearctic, its southern outposts being NW Africa, the Arabian peninsula and Pakistan. In Europe, *A.m. melanopogon* occurs E to Kharkiv, *albiventris* E of the Sea of Azov to Krasnodar, and *mimica* in Transcaucasia and E of the lower Volga. It breeds exclusively in flooded reedbeds comprising (mostly mixed) stands of reed *Phragmites*, reedmace *Typha* and fen-sedge *Cladium*. A thick layer of broken stems (for nest-building) is essential, confining breeding to older, dense reedbeds.

Only 14 European countries reported regular breeding, strongholds being extensive delta reedbeds of larger rivers (Don, Volga and Danube) or shallow steppe lakes (Neusiedlersee). Most countries' population sizes are poorly known, especially the larger populations but undoubtedly very large numbers are present in Russia. The two best sites with reliable estimates are the Danube Delta (10 000–30 000bp) and Neusiedlersee/Austria (*c*9000bp; Dvorak *et al* 1994; extensive habitat also exists around the Hungarian part of the lake).

Representative densities are 1–2 bp/ha in average habitats and up to 2.0–3.2 bp/ha in optimal habitats at Neusiedlersee, mainly reedbeds with a high proportion of *Typha* (M. Dvorak, A. Ranner & B. Feßl, unpubl, Grüll & Zwicker 1993).

Most populations appear stable. Only Romania and Italy have reported small declines in range or numbers. Data from Neusiedlersee indicate a marked increase between 1974 and 1983 (Berthold 1987).

Michael Dvorak (A)

Acrocephalus agricola

Paddyfield Warbler

CZ	Rákosník plavý	I	Cannaiola di Jerdon
D	Feldrohrsänger	NL	Veldrietzanger
E	Carricero Agrícola	P	Felosa-agrícola
F	Rousserolle isabelle	PL	Trcinniczek kaspijski
FIN	Kenttäkerttunen	R	Индийская камышовка
G	Κασπικοποταμίδα	S	Fältsångare
H	Rozsdás nádiposzáta		

Non-SPEC, Threat status S

The Paddyfield Warbler is polytypic, the European subspecies being *A.a. septima* (some support *agricola*) whose European distribution stretches from Bulgaria (Dobrudja) and the Danube Delta to Poltava in N Ukraine, as far as Volgograd and E to the lower Ural and Ilek Rivers and S to the River Kuban and the northern edge of the Kavkaz Peninsula. E of the Caspian it replaces Reed Warbler *A. scirpaceus* in reedbeds. There are three other subspecies, distributed in W–C Asia, S Turkestan, Pakistan, N India, N and C China, Manchuria (Tuvins Valley and Lake Uva-Nuur) and Ussuriland. The species winters in the Indian subcontinent, S Nepal, Burma and mainland SE Asia. The Asian subspecies are *agricola*, *capistrata* and *tangorum*.

The Paddyfield Warbler occurs in the forest-steppe and semi-desert zones, inhabiting not only lowlands and plains but also mountain valleys, wherever its rather narrow breeding habitat requirements are met: shallow waterbodies (particularly forest-steppe marshlands) with expanses of sparse reeds usually adjacent to bushes. Such suitable habitats are usually small, discontinuous and patchily distributed across its range. Typically isolated breeding areas exist along the W and N Black Sea coast to Crimea, in the Sivash lagoons and to N of the Sea of Azov. In Crimea, on spits in the Sea of Azov, its breeding density reaches 10–12 bp/ha (Bronskov *et al* 1989). It is distributed sporadically even in its core areas, but nevertheless the species is numerous in some locations. How its Aral Sea

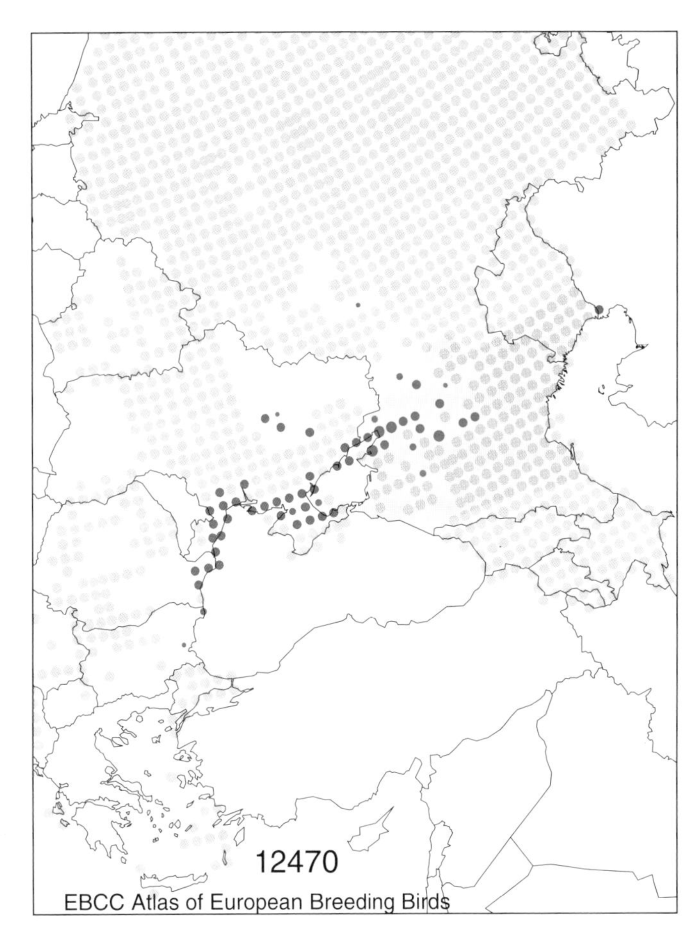

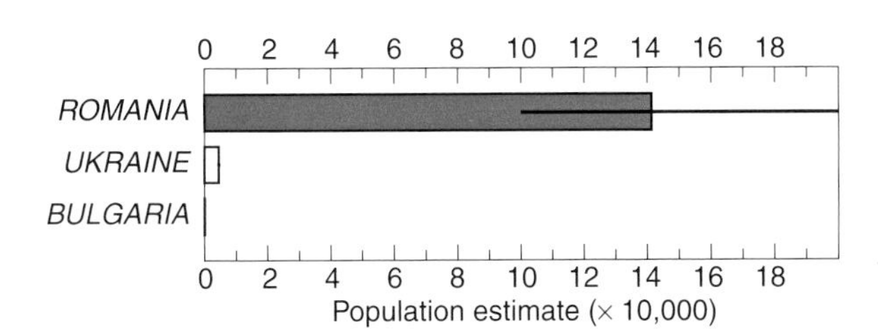

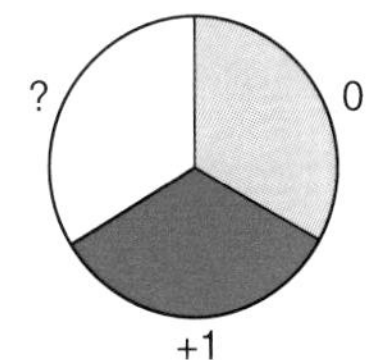

% in top 10 countries: 100.0
Total number of populated European countries: 3
Total European population 104,571–204,577 (145,995)
Russian population 10,000–100,000 (31,623)
Turkish population 10–100 (32)

strongholds have fared is not known, given the virtual disappearance of the water and salination and contamination of the surroundings.

Since the 1960s the Paddyfield Warbler has become common in Ukrainian ricefields. In Bulgaria the first 5–10bp were found at Lake Shabla in S Dobrudja in 1968 (Dontchev 1970a), and subsequently at Lake Durankulak and then Lake Atanassovsko near Burgas, these sites representing the European SW breeding limit. Since 1985 Durankulak has held 80–130bp (Nadler & Ihle 1988). Large-scale reed-cutting and burning adversely affect the Bulgarian populations. The European population is slowly increasing and probably exceeds 500 000bp.

Stephan Dontchev (BUL) Valentin V Serebryakov (UKR)

Acrocephalus palustris | Marsh Warbler

CZ	Rákosní zpěvný	**I**	Cannaiola verdognola
D	Sumpfrohrsänger	**NL**	Bosrietzanger
E	Carricero Políglota	**P**	Felosa-palustre
F	Rousserolle verderolle	**PL**	Łozówka
FIN	Luhtakerttunen	**R**	Болотная камышовка
G	Βαλτοποταμίδα	**S**	Kärrsångare
H	Énekes nádiposzáta		

SPEC Cat 4, Threat status S

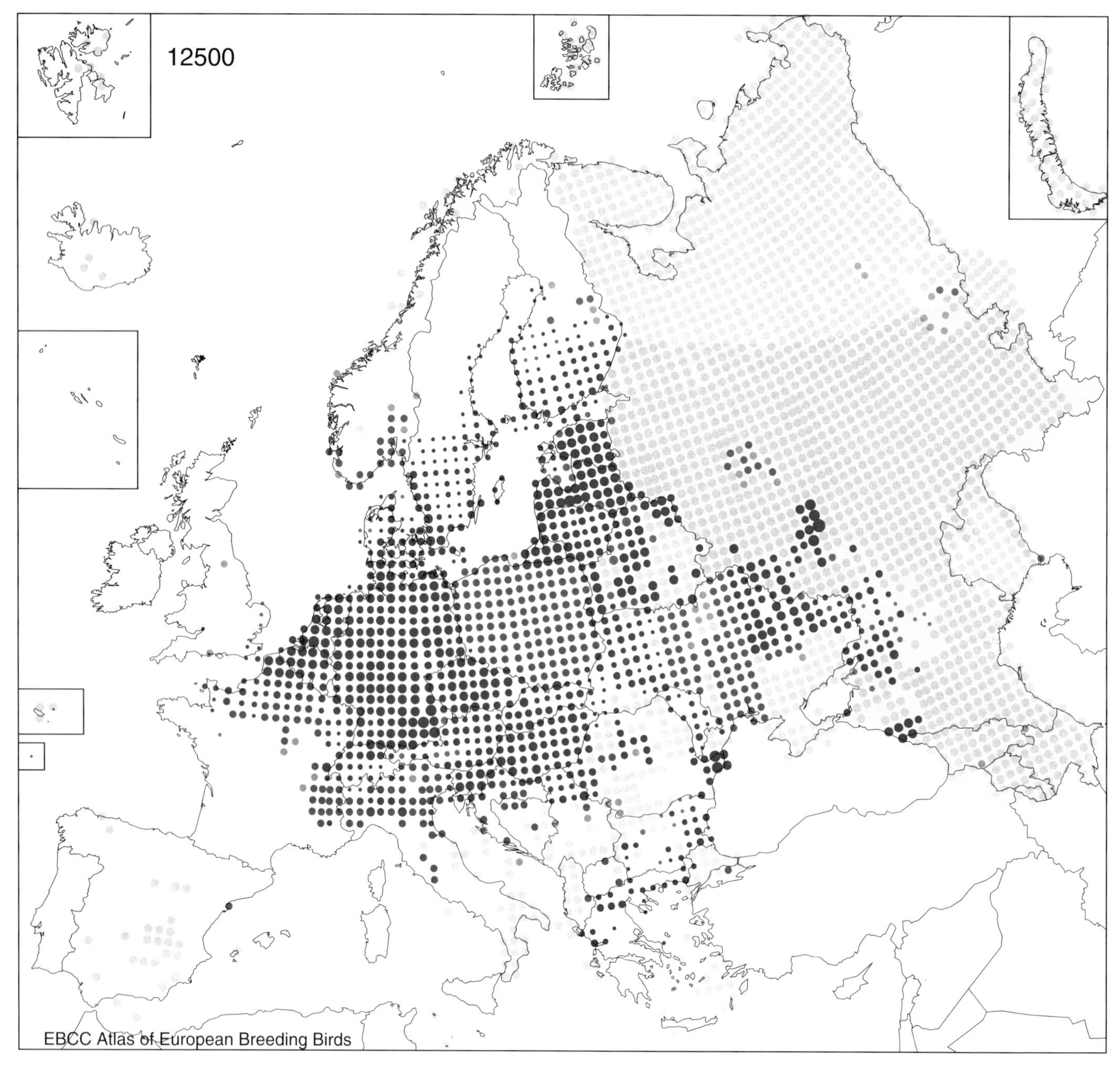

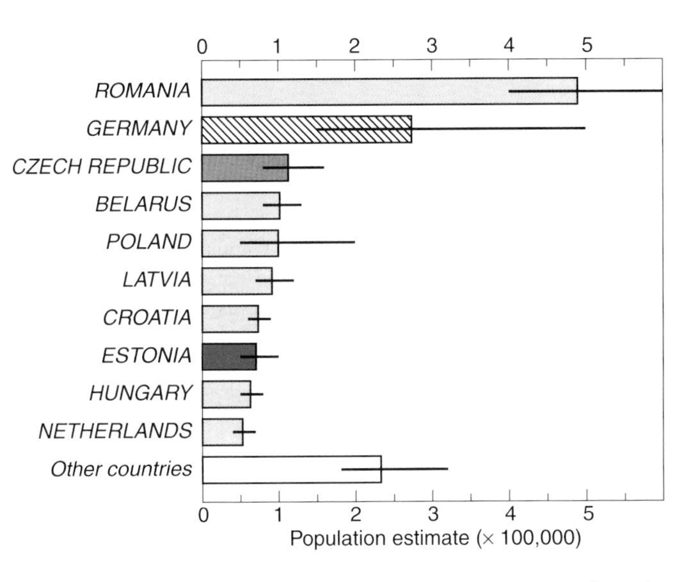

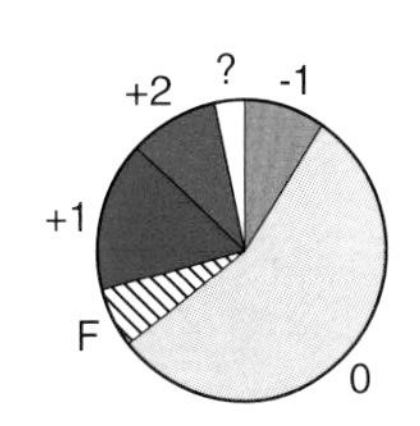

% in top 10 countries: 86.0
Total number of populated European countries: 31
Total European population 1,492,966–1,945,886 (1,663,852)
Russian population 100,000–1,000,000 (316,228)
Turkish population 1000–10,000 (3162)

The monotypic Marsh Warbler's breeding range is largely restricted to the cool temperate latitudes of the western Palearctic, where it inhabits mainly lowlands. Its distribution just reaches beyond the Urals to 69°E.

Typical breeding habitats are stands of tufty, fairly tall herbage, most commonly nettle *Urtica*, meadowsweet *Filipendula*, and willowherb *Epilobium*, sometimes interspersed with reeds *Phragmites* and bushes. This vegetation is characteristic of moist or seasonally flooded soils, which are ecologically somewhat unstable and often transient. In mountain regions the species can occur along river valleys up to 3000m asl as in Georgia (*BWP*).

Like all plain *Acrocephalus* warblers, the Marsh Warbler exhibits a tendency for semi-colonial aggregations. In small areas (1–2ha) of suitable habitat in W and C Europe, densities may even reach 8–13 bp/ha, but over larger areas in Germany, densities of 1–2 bp/10ha are representative (Flade 1994).

The Marsh Warbler reaches its highest breeding densities (1000–5000 bp/50km square) and most even distribution in a small band from the Low Countries in W Europe through C and E Europe to the Baltic States, Russia, Belarus and Ukraine, between the Alps and the Balkans in the S and the Baltic Sea in the N. In this area it breeds in any suitable herbaceous vegetation. Density values reduce rapidly towards the N, starting in Denmark and particularly so in Fennoscandia (to 65°N in Finland). The French distribution is confined to the NE. The patchy distribution and low densities S of the Alps, in much of the Balkans and in SE Europe is typical. The small British population, at the extreme distribution limits, has dwindled since the mid-1950s, only a few breeding pairs remaining in Worcestershire (Kelsey *et al* 1989). An isolated breeding site in the Ebro Delta has persisted since the mid-1960s (F.J. Purroy & E. de Juana, pers comm).

Overall, the Marsh Warbler has extended its range markedly since 1900, mainly at the northern limits (Denmark, S Sweden, S Finland, S Norway, the Baltic States), and somewhat less so in N and E France, W Switzerland, N Italy and Greece. This trend continued unabated during 1970–90, numbers increasing by more than 50% in Estonia, Finland and Sweden. The Swedish population (*c*300bp until the 1940s, confined mainly to Skåne; Holmbring 1982) had increased by the late 1970s to *c*15 000bp, covering the southern third of the country (Risberg 1990). The stronghold populations in the Low Countries, C and E Europe, where often it is the commonest *Acrocephalus* warbler, have been stable from 1970–90. Only the Czech Republic and Moldova reported slight declines.

The causes of the range extensions and concomitant population increases, which originated in eastern Europe and had been noted in C Europe in the 19th century, lie in the clearance of vast areas of woodland areas for farming, which in turn led to eutrophication. Furthermore, in Scandinavia spring temperatures have increased. However, the adoption of intensive agricultural practices has led to regional population decreases. The British population is thought to have declined through isolation and uncompensated emigration losses (Kelsey *et al* 1989).

The Marsh Warbler has the longest migration route of all its congeners. European populations migrate along the eastern Mediterranean coasts and down the Arabian Peninsula to make prolonged stop-overs in Sudan and Ethiopia, from where they continue to their wintering areas in SE Africa from Zambia and Malawi to Natal and Cape Province, South Africa, some even reaching Namibia. In Sudan and eastern Kenya it is one of the commonest migrants, very dependent on the food which appears with the rapid greening of semi-arid bushland, hence its absence from the more equable, permanently green habitats of Uganda (Pearson *et al* 1988).

Karl Schulze-Hagen (D)

Acrocephalus scirpaceus **Reed Warbler**

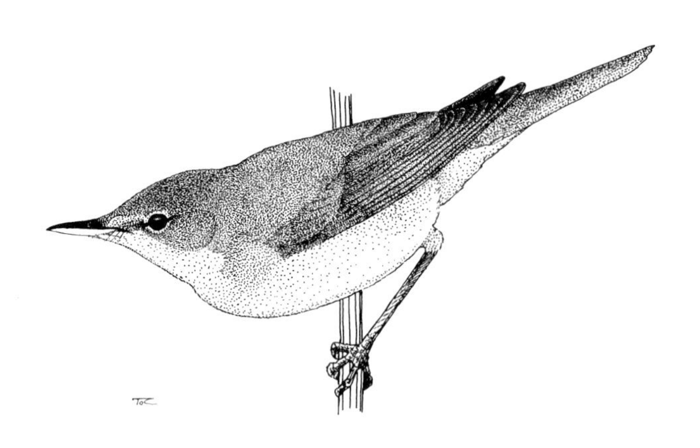

CZ	Rákosník obecný	I	Cannaiola
D	Teichrohrsänger	NL	Kleine Karekiet
E	Carricero Común	P	Rouxinol-pequeno-dos-caniços
F	Rousserolle effarvatte	PL	Trzcinniczek
FIN	Rytikerttunen	R	Тростниковая камышовка
G	Καλαμοποταμίδα	S	Rörsångare
H	Cserregő nádiposzáta		

SPEC Cat 4, Threat status S

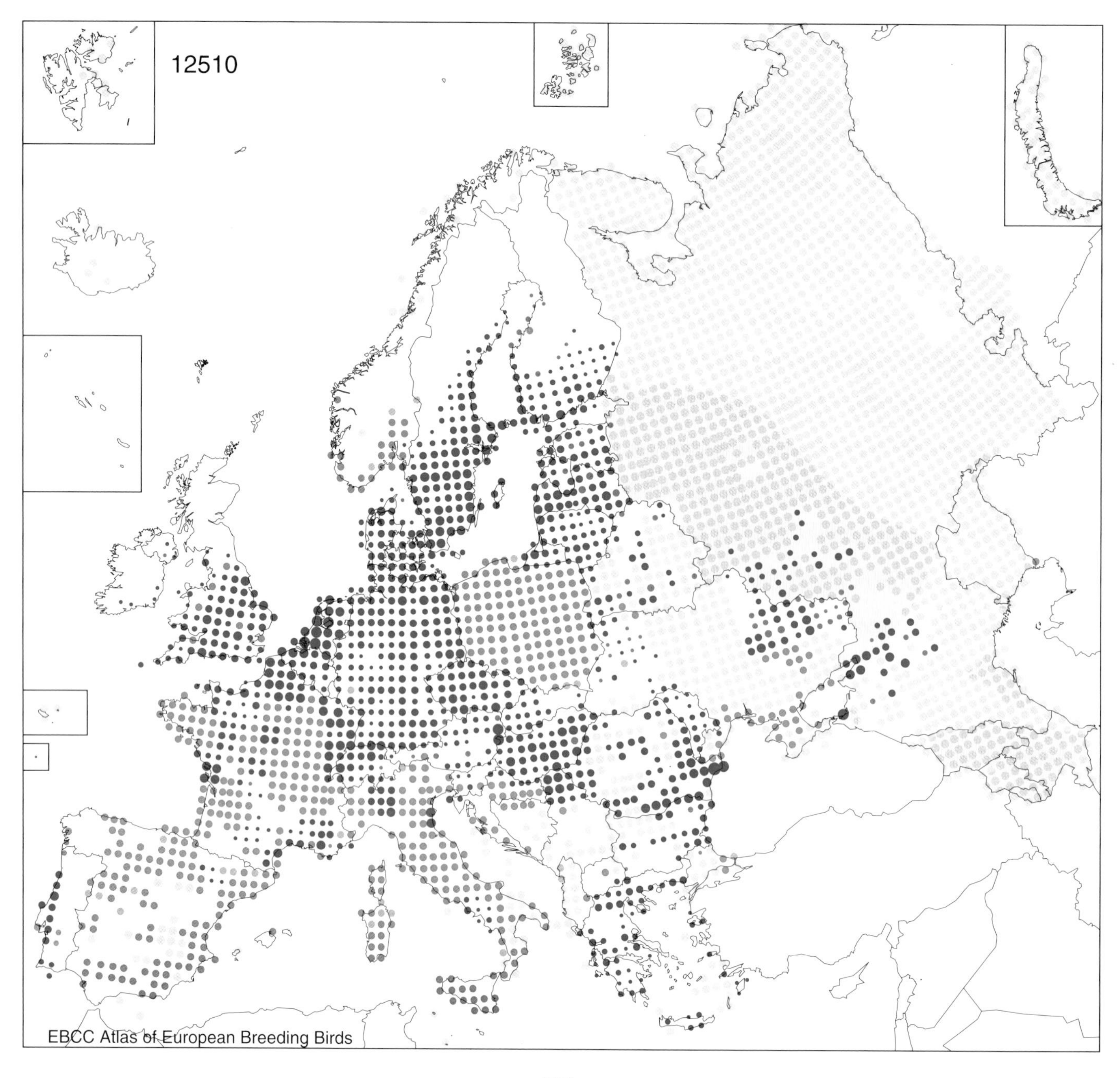

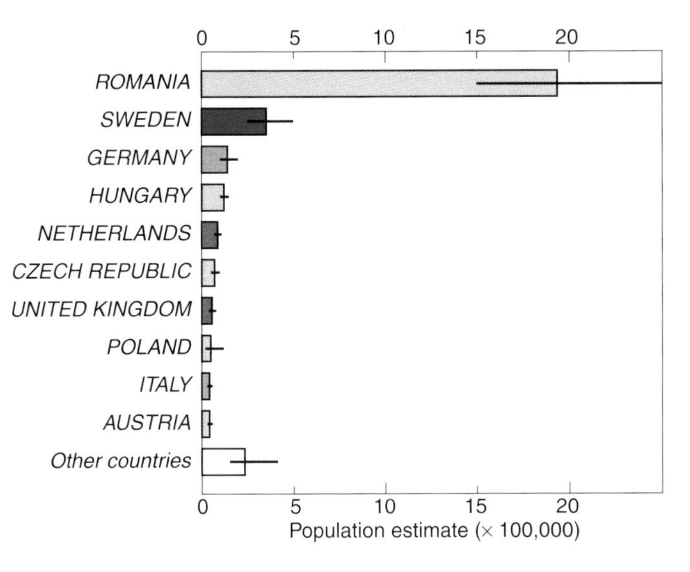

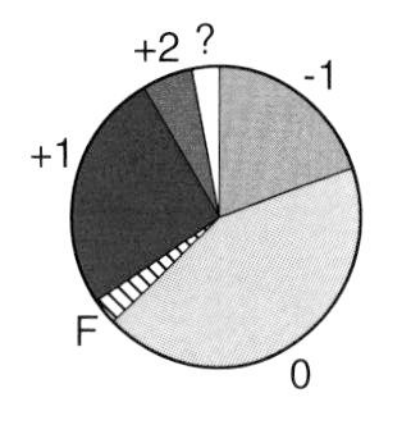

% in top 10 countries: 92.5
Total number of populated European countries: 35
Total European population 2,683,670–3,735,367 (3,138,033)
Russian population 10,000–100,000 (31,623)
Turkish population 5000–50,000 (15,811)

The Reed Warbler breeds in the mid-latitude lowlands of the W and C Palearctic and is a habitat specialist strongly associated with reedbeds. The nominate *A.s. scirpaceus* breeds throughout Europe from the Volga W through Ukraine to the Iberian Atlantic coast, its northern range limit extending up to 65°N in Fennoscandia and the southern to coastal NW Africa wherever reedbeds occur. The eastern subspecies *fuscus*, which occurs in the mapped area in the Caucasus and N Caspian, breeds from Asia Minor through Iran to Kazakhstan.

The Reed Warbler strongly prefers vertical habitat structures in reedbeds, particularly of *Phragmites australis*, of a characteristic reed density of at least 40 stems/m^2 and a minimum height of 120cm. It prefers both aquatic and very wet terrestrial stands of *Phragmites* or *Phragmites–Typha* (–bullrush) communities adjacent to edge-vegetation along rivers, ponds, lakes, or in narrow ditch-margins. Nesting reed-stands may be very small (perhaps only 1m^2). It also frequents brackish reedbeds in coastal regions. The Reed Warbler often breeds at semi-colonial densities, 45 simultaneously active nests being found in 1.17ha (Bibby & Thomas 1985). In the centres of large reedbeds breeding density is much lower.

Reed Warbler distribution in Europe is patchy, largely matching that of reedbeds. Consequently, the species occurs almost entirely below 200m asl, except in alpine regions where it reaches *c*1000m. In much of its range it is by far the commonest reedbed bird. Only in E and S Europe is its density superseded by that of Great Reed Warbler *A. arundinaceus*. The main population centres are the vast reedbeds of river deltas like the Rhine, Rhône, Po, Danube and Volga and shallow lakes like Neusiedlersee/Féherto. In my opinion, the graph seriously underestimates several population sizes, particularly for Poland, Russia and Austria. For example, the 100km^2 reedbeds of the Austrian Neusiedlersee hold an estimated 130 000bp (Grüll & Zwicker 1993), while the graph cites only 30 000–60 000bp for the whole country.

The Reed Warbler has expanded northwards even faster than Marsh *A. palustris* and Great Reed Warblers from the 19th century onwards and particularly since the mid-1940s. SE Norway (first nesting in 1947), S Sweden, S Finland (1920s), NE Germany, N Poland, the Baltic States (Estonia, 1870s; Leibak *et al* 1994) and adjacent Russian areas still showed slight numerical increases (sometimes also of range) during the *Atlas*' period and now hold substantial populations. Elsewhere, a >50% increase in numbers was reported for Great Britain, although Kelsey (1993) thought it probable that the 1990s' population did not differ significantly from the estimate in 1968–72. The increasing Irish population remains insignificant; no more than 40–50 singing males (Kelsey 1993). The increase in The Netherlands was due partly to the creation of huge reedbeds in the recently reclaimed (late 1960s) polders of Zuidelijk Flevoland and Lauwersmeer. Elsewhere in Europe, populations apparently were stable or slightly declining.

Eutrophication of rivers and lakes originally poor in nutrients led to an enormous increase in reed growth, coinciding with increasing average spring temperatures across northern Europe, both phenomena probably having assisted Reed Warbler range expansion and population increases. However, habitat destruction and the recent phenomenon of reedbed die-back (partly due to over-eutrophication, especially since the 1970s; Ostendorp 1993) have caused populations to decline, particularly in regions of high human density and intense industrial development.

The species is a trans-Saharan migrant wintering mainly in the Sudan–Zambezi region, but being a generalist, is able to adapt to local conditions and may therefore stray regularly as far S as Botswana and Namibia (van den Brink & Loske 1990). W, C and N European populations migrate southwestwards; those from the Czech Republic, Hungary and further E migrate southeastwards.

Karl Schulze-Hagen (D)

Acrocephalus arundinaceus **Great Reed Warbler**

CZ	Rákosník velký	**I**	Cannareccione
D	Drosselrohrsänger	**NL**	Grote Karekiet
E	Carricero Tordal	**P**	Rouxinol-grande-dos-caniços
F	Rousserolle turdoïde	**PL**	Trzciniak
FIN	Rastaskerttunen	**R**	Дроздовидная камышовка
G	Τσιχλοποταμίδα	**S**	Trastsångare
H	Nádirigó		

Non-SPEC, Threat status S (P)

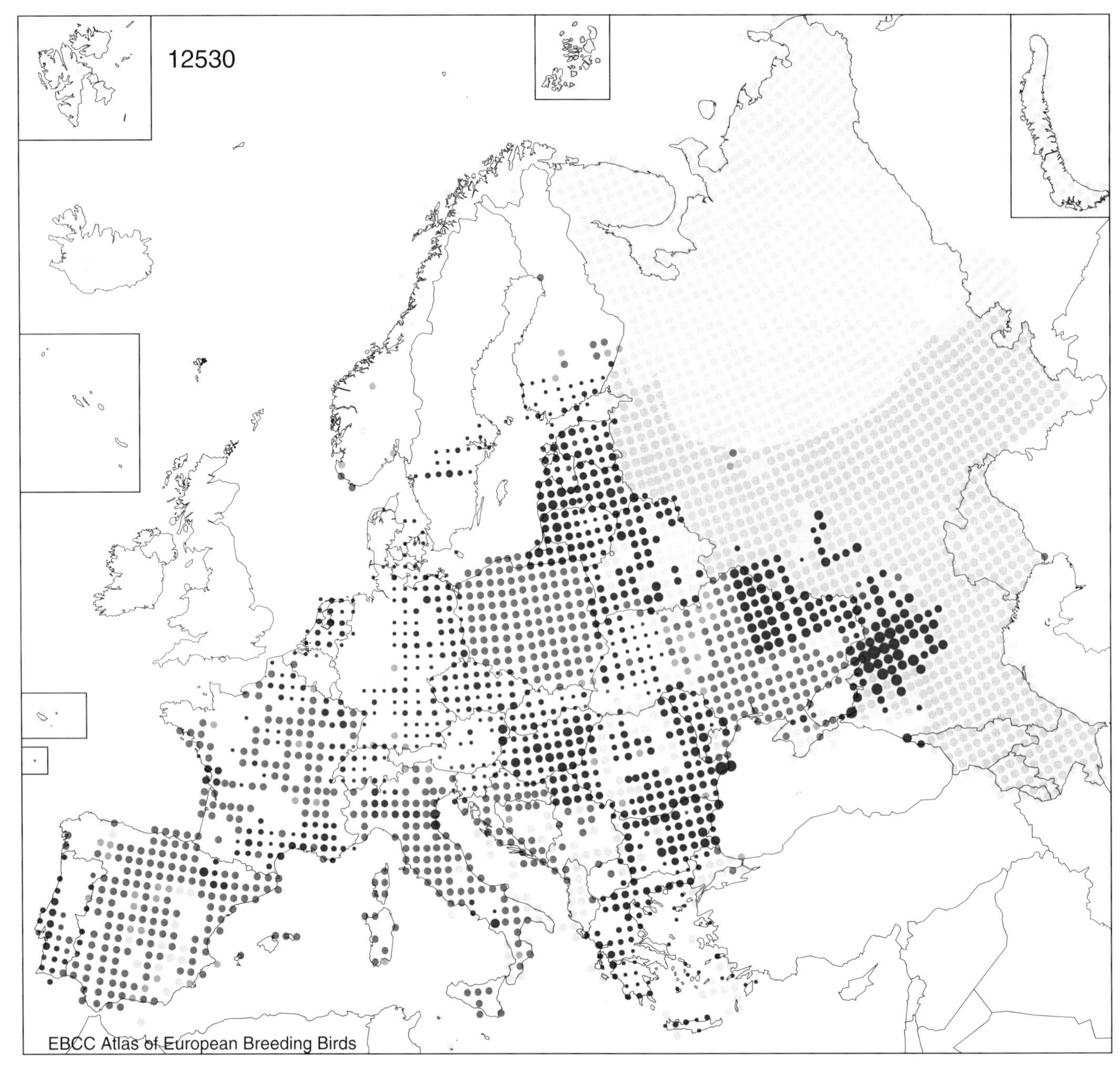

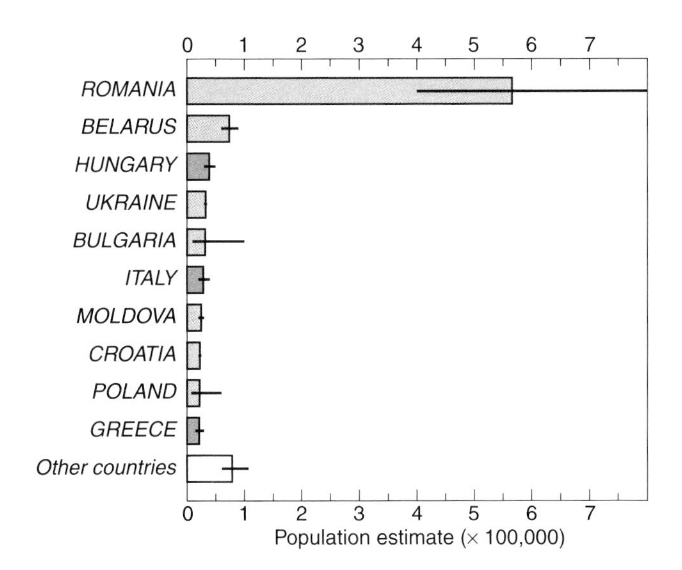

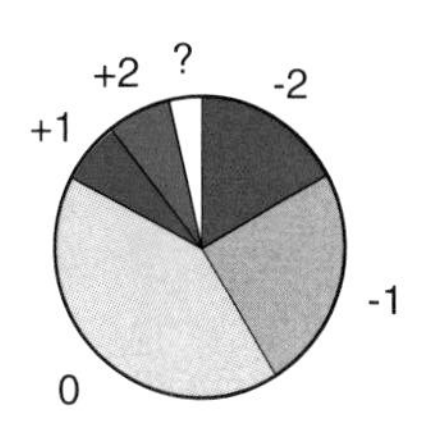

% in top 10 countries: 91.6
Total number of populated European countries: 29
Total European population 769,618–1,187,194 (938,586)
Russian population 500,000–5,000,000 (1,581,139)
Turkish population 10,000–100,000 (31,623)

The Great Reed Warbler inhabits the middle latitudes of the W and C Palearctic between the 17° and 32°C July isotherms. The nominate subspecies *A.a. arundinaceus* breeds from coastal Iberia and NW Morocco to the Urals, Asia Minor and the Caspian, the paler *zarudnyi* occurring from the NE Caspian and the Urals to N–C Asia. The species is restricted to lowland areas up to 650m asl in Europe, but is absent from Britain and Ireland.

Unlike its congeners this, the largest *Acrocephalus* warbler, prefers to breed very near water in the tallest, strongest vertical reedbed structures. It inhabits inundated stands of common reed *Phragmites australis* and lesser bullrush *Typha angustifolia*, at least two years old, whose characteristic stem diameter is >6.5mm, and where reed density is low (34–62 stems/m^2). Highest breeding densities occur at reedbed waterside margins (up to 18 simultaneously active nests/ha counted). Representative nesting densities vary from 1.2 to 11 nests/ha of suitable habitat (*HVM*). Censuses may be biased because of yearly and geographically varying proportions of males acting polygynously (Dyrcz 1986).

The more widespread eastern European reedbeds support a more even distribution, but elsewhere the species' uneven distribution reflects that of reedbeds bordering ponds and lakesides. In Russia, Belarus, Ukraine, Bulgaria, Greece and Iberia it is the commonest *Acrocephalus* warbler, being much commoner over wide areas than the Reed Warbler *A. scirpaceus*, whose distribution bias is more westerly. The vast reedbeds of the Danube and Volga Deltas and large lakes hold the largest populations. The E European population (*c*2.4Mbp) comprises 96% of the European total. Three-quarters of the remaining 3.5% occur in Hungary and Poland.

Since 1900 there have been range expansions, but slower than for other *Acrocephalus* warblers. The first began in the Baltic States and Denmark (1850–70), accelerating in 1938–42 and 1955–56 (Leibak *et al* 1994). The 1972 total of 49bp in S Sweden increased rapidly, the 196 singing males at Tåkern (Östergötland) representing 44% of the Swedish population in the late 1980s (Bensch *et al* 1990). The species now breeds in some S Norwegian coastal locations. Although E European populations remained stable, decreases and range contractions occurred in W, C and S Europe. From 1970 to 1990 declines of >50% were reported in France, Belgium, The Netherlands, Denmark, the Czech Republic and Slovakia, and of 20–50% in Hungary, Italy, Greece, Slovenia, Switzerland and Luxembourg. At Neusiedlersee, still a C European stronghold, the population decreased by *c*85% from 1955 to 1986 (*HVM*). Some of the drastic decreases of 1970 and 1985 apparently have stabilized at much reduced levels, as in Germany (*HVM*) and The Netherlands (van Dijk *et al* 1994c).

Land reclamation, drainage and irrigation schemes, over-eutrophication of lakes and ponds, reedbed die-back (with concomitant reedbed-area shrinkage), the reduction of plant density, poorer plant growth (thinner stems and an increased susceptibility to mechanical damage) and lower arthropod densities are the main causes of C European population reductions. Furthermore, the wetter Atlantic climate during 1960–80 and the impaired habitat conditions at migration stop-over sites and in the wintering quarters of populations migrating SW have probably contributed to the losses (*HVM*), although the situation in West Africa is complicated and not yet fully understood (Hedenström *et al* 1993).

The Great Reed Warbler winters in many African habitats from the southern Sahara to South Africa, but avoids the rainforest belt. W European populations migrate to tropical W Africa, E European and Siberian birds to SE Africa.

Mitochondrial DNA analysis strongly suggests that the Eastern Great Reed Warbler *A. orientalis* and Basra Reed Warbler *A. griseldis* are separate species, the latter being less closely related to *A. arundinaceus* than the former (B. Leisler *et al*, in prep; see also Pearson & Backhurst 1988).

Karl Schulze-Hagen (D)

Acrocephalus dumetorum

Blyth's Reed Warbler

CZ	Rákosník pokřovní	I	Cannaiola di Blyth
D	Buschrohrsänger	NL	Struikrietzanger
E	Carricero de Blyth	P	Felosa-das-moitas
F	Rousserolle des buissons	PL	Zaroślówka
FIN	Viitakerttunen	R	Садовая камышовка
G	Θαμνοποταμίδα	S	Busksångare
H	Berki nádiposzáta		

Non-SPEC, Threat status S (P)

Blyth's Reed Warbler, an exotic species to many, has a C Palearctic range covering the warmer boreal to cool temperate zones, eastwards to Lake Baykal. It winters from Pakistan through India and Nepal to Burma, favouring bushy habitats, bamboo and grain fields.

It breeds in a wide range of shrubby growth with tall herbage, young forests, overgrown clearings, birch *Betula* and willow *Salix* scrub in floodland groves, forest steppes, bush-encroached farmland and swamp and other waterside margins (up to 1200m asl). The prime prerequisite for nesting is a combination of dry, dense bushy and herbaceous vegetation with nearby more open areas. In Finland Blyth's Reed Warbler prefers semi-open bushy meadows possessing luxuriant undergrowth near shores or field edges, roadsides and abandoned arable land (Koskimies 1980, 1989a). In the Baltic States it frequents the widespread overgrown clearfells and abandoned farms.

Blyth's Reed Warbler has expanded its range westwards considerably since the 19th century, not being recorded S and W of Lake Ladoga until the 1960s. Published maximum density estimates from Russia (2–9 bp/km^2) must be serious underestimates; in W and C Siberia up to 101 bp/km^2 have been recorded (*HVM*).

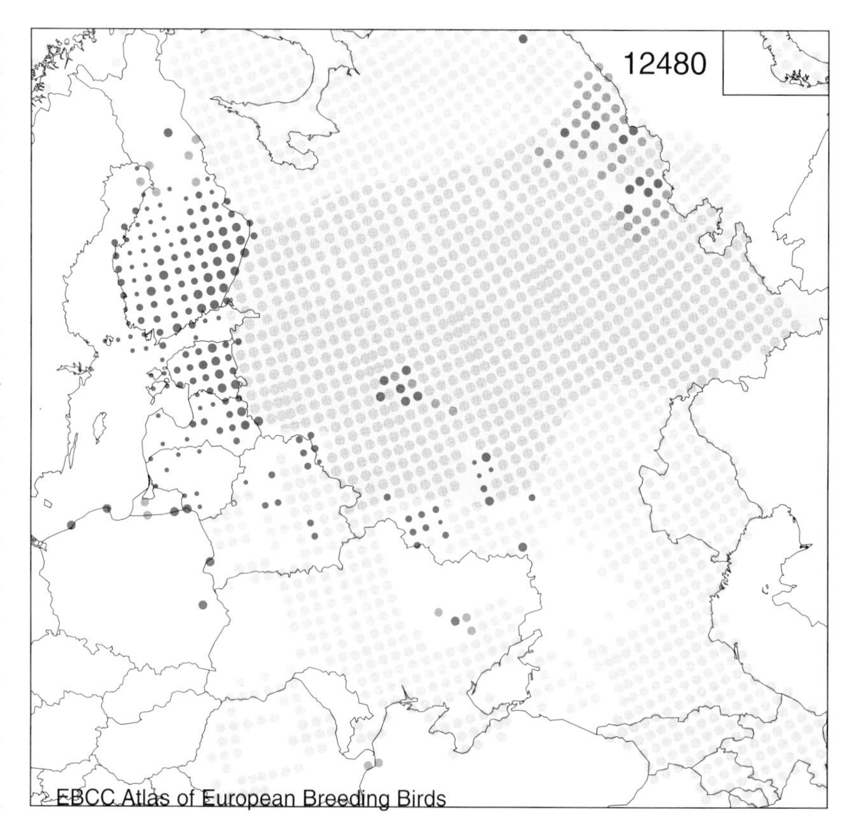

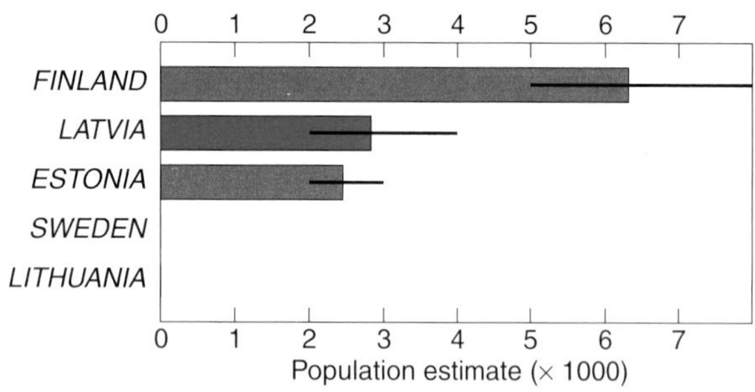

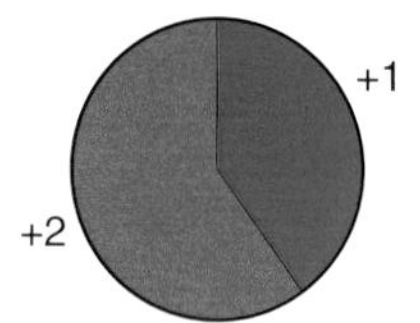

% in top 10 countries: 100.0
Total number of populated European countries: 5
Total European population 9784–13,557 (11,609)
Russian population 100,000–1,000,000 (316,228)

The species colonized Finland from the 1930s to the 1960s (Koskimies 1989a). The present population is estimated at 5000–8000bp, highest densities reaching 25 bp/km^2 in suitable habitat in the SE, whose area is but a fraction of that in the W. Pairs may breed in close proximity, up to 18 nesting in a 5ha meadow (Koskimies 1984). The expansion probably occurred mainly because reduced cattle-grazing and the abandonment of arable land allowed bush encroachment.

From Finland Blyth's Reed Warbler expanded into Sweden in the late 1950s (recorded annually since 1969, 0–10bp yearly at present) and in the 1960s colonized Estonia (2000–3000 singing males) and Latvia (3000–6000 singing males), but annual fluctuations are great and the percentage of unpaired males is high. In Lithuania and NE Poland (P. Chylarecki, pers comm to the Editors) it remains scarce. Eastern Estonia and Latvia have an overall density *c*5–10 times higher than western Estonia, rising locally to 4–10 bp/km^2 (Leibak *et al* 1994). In SE Finland up to 30–40% of males remain unpaired (*HVM*).

Pertti Koskimies (FIN) Janis Priednieks (LAT)

Hippolais pallida

Olivaceous Warbler

CZ	Sedmihlásek šedý	I	Canapino pallido
D	Blaßspötter	NL	Vale Spotvogel
E	Zarcero Pálido	P	Felosa-pálida
F	Hypolaïs pâle	PL	Zaganiacz blady
FIN	Vaaleakultarinta	R	Бледная пересмешка
G	Ωχροστριτσίδα	S	Eksångare
H	Halvány geze		

SPEC Cat 3, Threat status V (P)

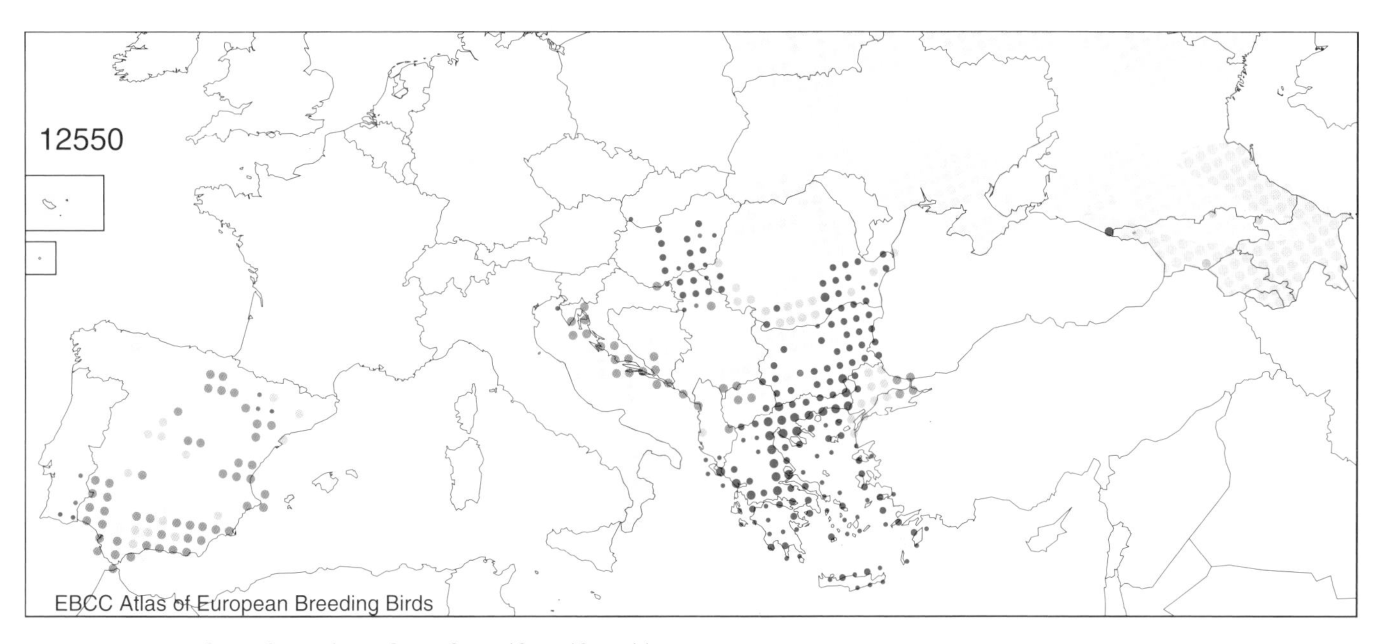

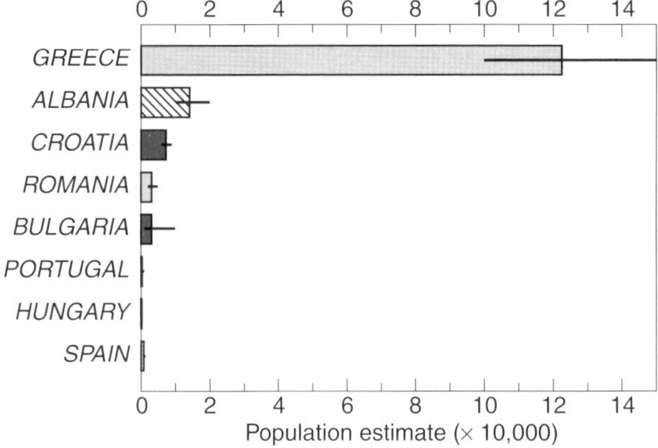

+2
-1
+1
0
F

% in top 10 countries: 100.0
Total number of populated European countries: 8
Total European population 128,609–180,714 (151,636)
Turkish population 500,000–5,000,000 (1,581,139)

The Olivaceous Warbler is a small to medium-sized, polytypic warbler with a western and C Palearctic distribution. In Europe, two well-isolated populations are sufficiently different genetically to be considered separate species (*BWP*, A. Helbig, pers comm); *H.p. opaca* of Spain and NW Africa, and *elaeica* whose range extends E from the Balkans through the Levant and Black Sea regions across S–C Asia to *c*70°E. The wintering areas of the two populations lie in the western and eastern Sahel regions respectively. Here some overlap occurs with various Saharan African subspecies whose populations may also prove to be specifically distinct.

The subspecies *opaca* favours dry habitats containing medium-height and tall trees as in orchards and gardens, but *elaeica* also occurs in bushy and wetter, well-vegetated areas, displaying a wider habitat preference altogether. Wintering birds in West Africa are seen in a wide variety of woodland habitats where they feed predominantly in the canopy. Passage birds in desert and steppe areas of the Middle East use acacia *Acacia* and tamarisk *Tamarix* trees.

In winter it is found singly, but as with other species of this genus neighbourhood groups are commonly encountered in the breeding areas. Occasionally these have been described as (loose) colonies (Meinertzhagen 1920, Beaman *et al* 1975). Nesting densities can be very high, as 6bp in 0.1ha in Cyprus (Flint & Stewart 1983). In Israel at two high-density sites (100bp in 5km^2; 47bp feeding fledglings in 25ha) many allotropic breeding Reed Warbler *Acrocephalus scirpaceus* were also found (Shirihai 1996).

Breeding in Europe is late in May, with many birds not starting until June. However, some passage *elaeica* appear much earlier in Israel (mid-March) where the main passage is in the second week in May (pers obs) and so breeding may occur earlier in places. Second broods are known.

John Morgan (GB) Hadoram Shirihai (ISR)

Hippolais caligata

Booted Warbler

CZ	Sedmihlásek malý	**I**	Canapino asiatico
D	Buschspötter	**NL**	Kleine Spotvogel
E	Zarcero Escita	**P**	Felosa-cítica
F	Hypolaïs botté	**PL**	Zaganiacz mały
FIN	Pikkukultarinta	**R**	Бормотушка
G	Θαμνοστριτσίδα	**S**	Gråsångare
H	Kis geze		

Non-SPEC, Threat status S (P)

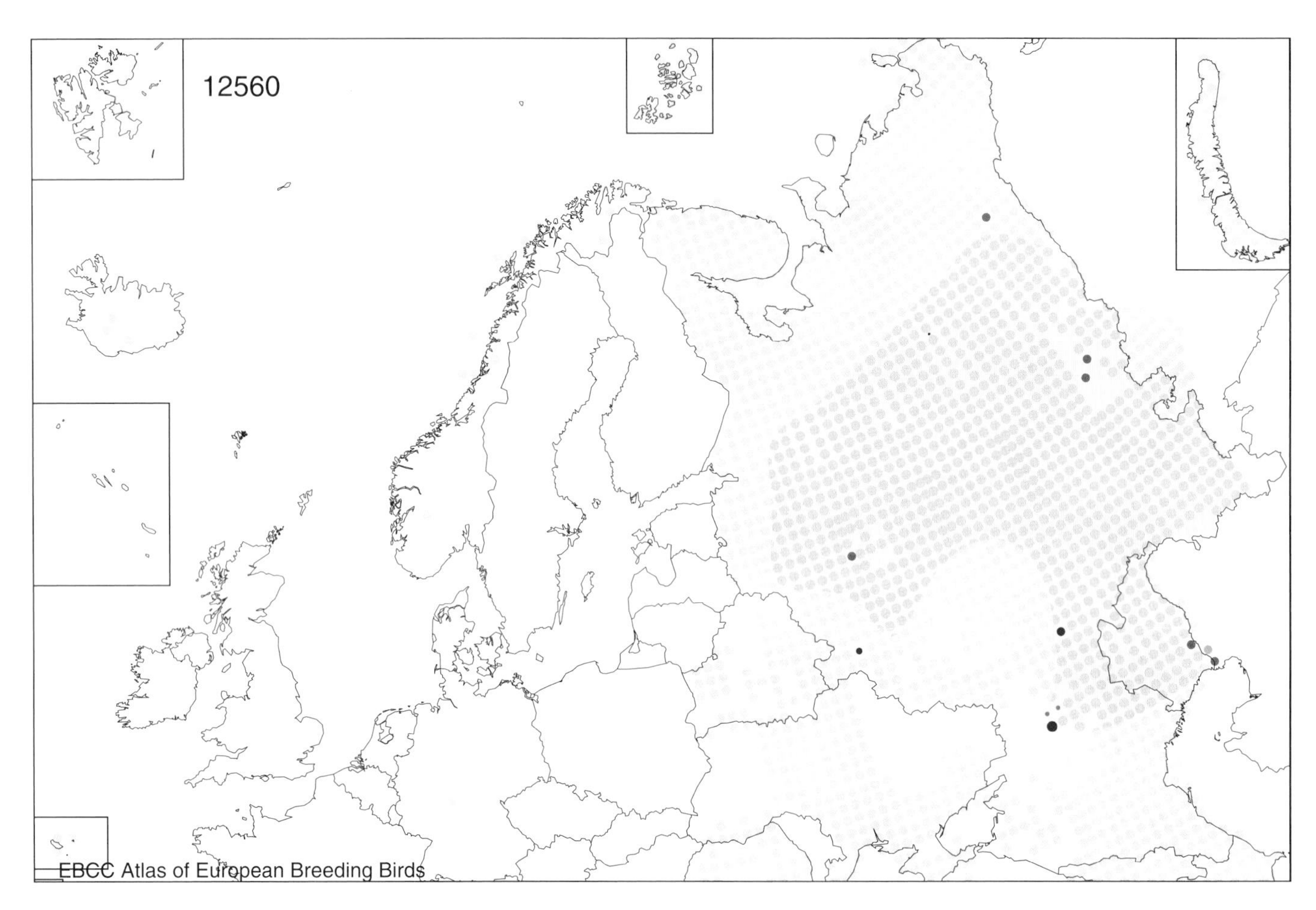

The migrant Booted Warbler has a widespread, mostly Asian distribution. The two subspecies, although usually noticeably different, have an extensive zone of secondary hybridization. In SW and W–C Asia the species breeds to *c*100°E, above 60°N in places, and S to 30°N (*H.c. rama*). The European population is mostly the nominate subspecies *caligata*, breeding from E Russia eastwards, but *rama* occurs from the lower Volga and Ural Rivers (*c*50°N, 45°E to 52°N, 51°E) to the ESE; three mapped records are shown. Much of this species' European distribution coincides with the unmapped areas of Russia.

In the W of its range, the species prefers low-lying river valleys. Elsewhere its choice of habitat is more catholic and *rama* occupies habitats ranging from bushy hill country at 1800m asl or above to arid scrub and even semi-desert. It is solitary and territorial and where it is scarce (in taiga) it reaches linear densities of 1–2 individuals along 1km transects (Rogacheva *et al* 1978). Elsewhere, as for other *Hippolais* and some *Acrocephalus* warblers, nesting pairs form neighbourhood groups which breed at high densities, nests often being only 5m apart. In the C Siberian Iyus forest steppe, where the habitat consists of forest belts of *Caragana* interspersed with solitary elm *Ulmus* spp and poplar *Populus* spp amongst tall grass-cover, densities of 5.5 bp/ha were recorded (Rogacheva 1992). It can be abundant also in tall herbaceous thickets, but in fields interspersed with birch *Betula* spp groves the figure was 0.6 birds/km^2 (Ravkin *et al* 1988).

In the W of its range, it breeds from mid-May to early July. Whether its apparently exclusively insectivorous diet separates it by habitat use from the closely related Olivaceous Warbler *H. pallida* (which also takes fruit) in their relatively small areas of overlap is not known. The Booted Warbler winters in the Indian subcontinent and SE Asia, a few reaching Arabia.

John Morgan (GB) Hadoram Shirihai (ISR)

Hippolais olivetorum

Olive-tree Warbler

CZ	Sedmihlásek olivní	I	Canapino levantino
D	Olivenspötter	NL	Griekse Spotvogel
E	Zarcero Grande	P	Felosa-das-oliveiras
F	Hypolaïs des oliviers	PL	Zaganiacz oliwny
FIN	Oliivikultarinta	R	Средиземноморская пересмешка
G	Λιοστριτσίδα		
H	Olívgeze	S	Olivsångare

SPEC Cat 2, Threat status R (P)

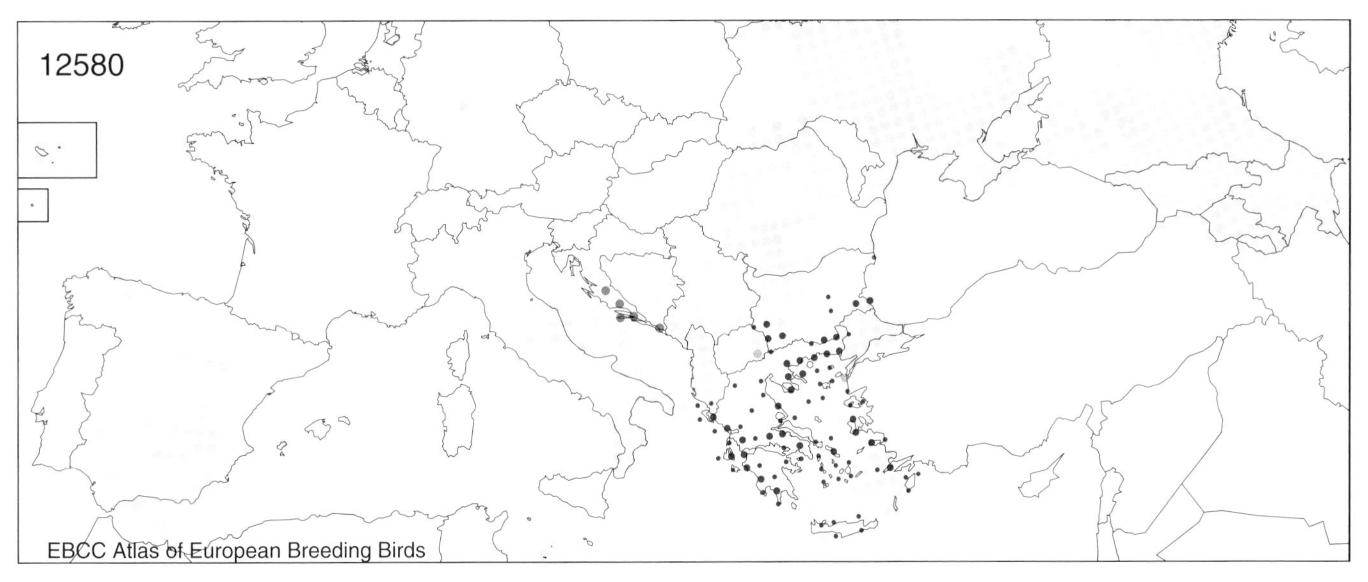

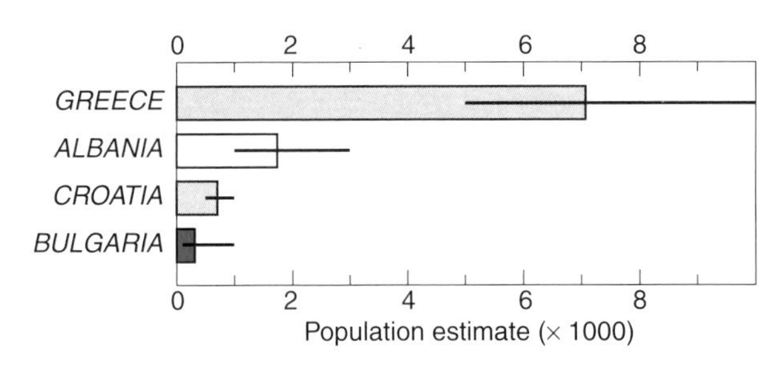

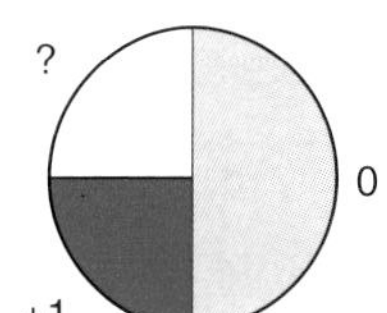

% in top 10 countries: 100.0
Total number of populated European countries: 4
Total European population 7610–13,104 (9826)
Turkish population 1000–10,000 (3162)

The breeding distribution of the Olive-tree Warbler, the largest and most distinctive *Hippolais*, lies entirely within the western Palearctic, extending through the northern E Mediterranean and the southern Balkan Peninsula (mainly S of the mountains), to reach Greece (including the Greek islands), Albania, Croatia, Bulgaria, Romania and beyond the *Atlas*' area of coverage, W and S Turkey. The species winters mainly in East Africa from southern Tanzania to northern South Africa in savanna and other arid habitats. In its European range the Olive-tree Warbler prefers lower or medium altitudes where generally it is commonest in coastal regions, although its occurrence is patchy and often clustered.

Its favoured breeding habitats are dry areas and stone-covered hillsides scattered with bushes, scrubby vegetation and open-canopy trees (Vatev & Simeonov 1972, Nankinov 1993). The Olive-tree Warbler also breeds in areas of traditional agriculture.

Significant numbers breed in Turkey, but in Europe the Olive-tree Warbler is most abundant in Greece and Albania. In Greece and Croatia, the populations seem stable, but although there are no quantitative data for Bulgaria, numbers there are thought to have increased. Some data suggest a range extension northward spreading from Bulgaria to Romanian Dobrogea (Nankinov 1993), and possibly also a westward extension to the former Yugoslavian region of Macedonia through the western tributaries of the Struma River (pers obs). The northern populations are much smaller and more widely dispersed, and in Bulgaria, Romania and probably in some regions of the former Yugoslavia, this is probably a reflection of being at the northern limit of the species' distribution in Europe. Curiously, population fluctuations appear to occur in different years in Bulgaria and northern Greece (pers obs). In good years in typical natural prime habitat it is possible to find 3–4 bp in 2–2.5km^2 in the southern Kresna gorge in SE Bulgaria.

Ilia Vatev (BUL)

Hippolais icterina Icterine Warbler

CZ	Sedmihlásek hajní	**I**	Canapino maggiore
D	Gelbspötter	**NL**	Spotvogel
E	Zarcero Icterino	**P**	Felosa-icterina
F	Hyppolaïs ictérine	**PL**	Zaganiacz
FIN	Kultarinta	**R**	Зеленая пересмешка
G	Κιτρινοστριτσίδα	**S**	Härmsångare
H	Kerti geze		

SPEC Cat 4, Threat status S

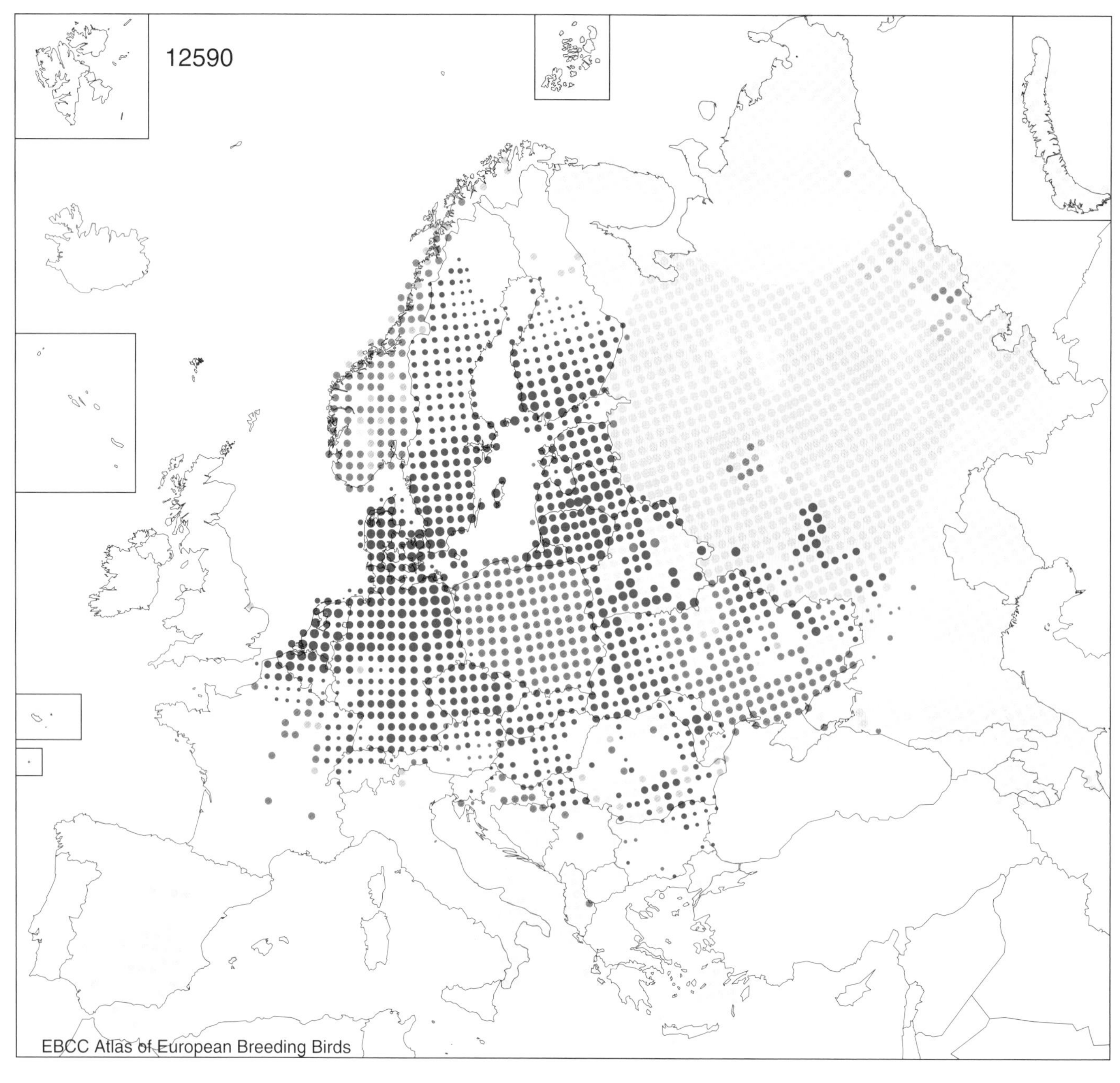

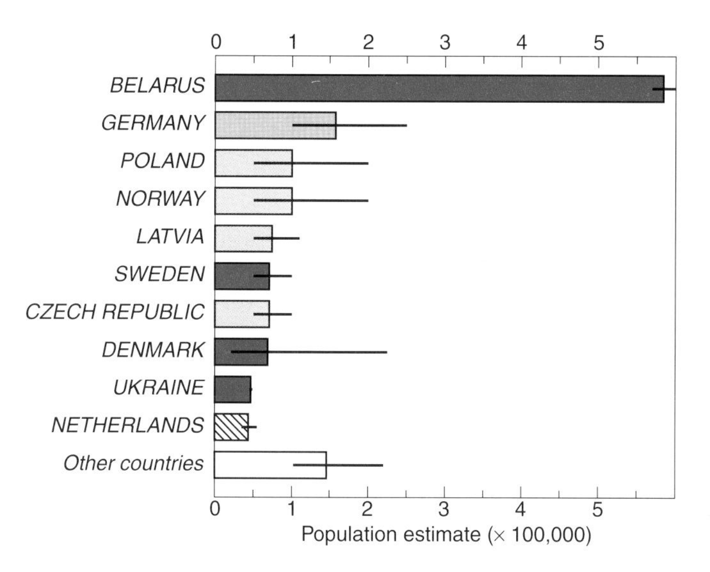

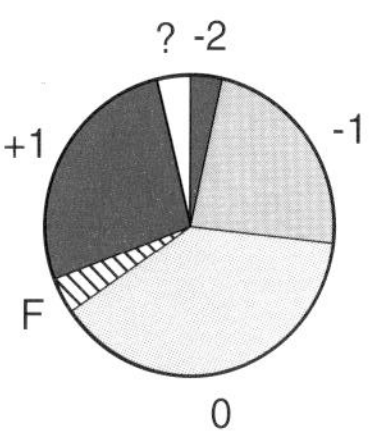

% in top 10 countries: 90.0
Total number of populated European countries: 26
Total European population 1,351,851–1,703,891 (1,464,726)
Russian population 1,000,000–10,000,000 (3,162,278)
Turkish population 1–100 (10)

The distribution of the Icterine Warbler lies mainly in the western Palearctic, except for a narrowing branch extending between 50° and 60°N beyond the Urals into C Siberia, and possibly several small disjunct populations in Iran. In Europe its breeding range largely covers the middle and northern latitudes between the July 15°C and 25°C isotherms. In the W, it is absent from Britain & Ireland, its range boundary cutting through NE France, Switzerland and the northern former Yugoslavia. This boundary follows roughly the northern limit of the breeding range of the closely related Melodious Warbler *H. polyglotta*, so that the two species may be said to be 'parapatric'. Further to the E, the southern limit of the Icterine Warbler's range reaches the Black Sea without touching the mediterranean zone. A small disjunct population, probably one of several around the southern Caspian Sea, is found in Azerbaijan.

The Icterine Warbler's breeding habitat comprises typically bushes and clumps of small trees providing discontinuous cover, usually below 1500m asl, but nesting territories often contain a number of taller trees. This habitat composition occurs in some lightly forested areas, at forest margins and in a variety of wet habitats such as peat bogs or riparian woodlands. The species has adapted to artificial habitats of similar composition such as poplar *Populus* plantations, parks and gardens. In the northern part of its distribution, it may occupy birch *Betula* woods, and in its southern range oak *Quercus* forests. Undergrowth of various kinds seems an important habitat element (*BWP*).

Its pattern of distribution in Europe is patchy, not only because suitable habitat is patchily distributed but also because its occupation of such habitats is incomplete. Where present, it sometimes may be very abundant. Figures for breeding densities in a number of European countries have been derived from a variety of censusing methods and so usually are not directly comparable. However, in prime broad-leaved habitats, average population density may reach *c*1 bp/ha, a figure found in Germany (Gnielka 1975), Poland (Dyrcz *et al* 1991) and France.

The Icterine Warbler has declined along its western border in Belgium (Jacob *et al* 1983), France, Switzerland (Sermet 1980b) to the point of disappearance from previously regular haunts. In the Swiss canton of Fribourg, the species' population decline is estimated to be 80% (Cercle Ornithologique de Fribourg 1993). Similarly, in Burgundy in the 1960s the westernmost breeding sites were *c*25km W of the River Saône, but in 1995 the river itself marked the western border (Ferry & Faivre 1989). Where the Icterine Warbler is sympatric with Melodious Warbler in Burgundy it has shown reduced reproductive success especially where individuals of both species occur in the same place (Faivre 1993), to the extent that the population decreased to local extinction. However, the species apparently has increased in some northern parts of its distribution (Denmark, Sweden, Finland, Belarus).

Apart from habitat availability, the only factor evidently limiting the distribution of Icterine Warbler in Europe is the complementary breeding area of its sibling species the Melodious Warbler. To the E the southern limit seems to follow the edge of the steppe zone, and to the N the limit of the boreal forest or taiga.

The Icterine Warbler is a trans-Saharan migrant to SE and S–C Africa (southern Congo to South Africa), in autumn following an easterly route and in spring returning more to the W. It displays a degree of vagrancy during the migration seasons, being regularly recorded beyond its normal range or migration routes, as in Great Britain.

The present view of modern taxonomists is that the Icterine Warbler is monotypic, and that subspecies proposed earlier are no longer recognized.

Bruno Faivre (F) Camille Ferry (F)

This species account is sponsored by Hans Christoph Stamm, Düsseldorf, D.

Hippolais polyglotta

Melodious Warbler

CZ	Sedmihlásek švitořivý	**I**	Canapino
D	Orpheusspötter	**NL**	Orpheusspotvogel
E	Zarcero Común	**P**	Felosa-poliglota
F	Hypolaïs polyglotte	**PL**	Zaganiacz szczebiotliwy
FIN	Taiturikultarinta	**R**	Многоголосая пересмешка
G	Ορφεοστριτσίδα	**S**	Polyglottsångare
H	Déli geze		

SPEC Cat 4, Threat status S (P)

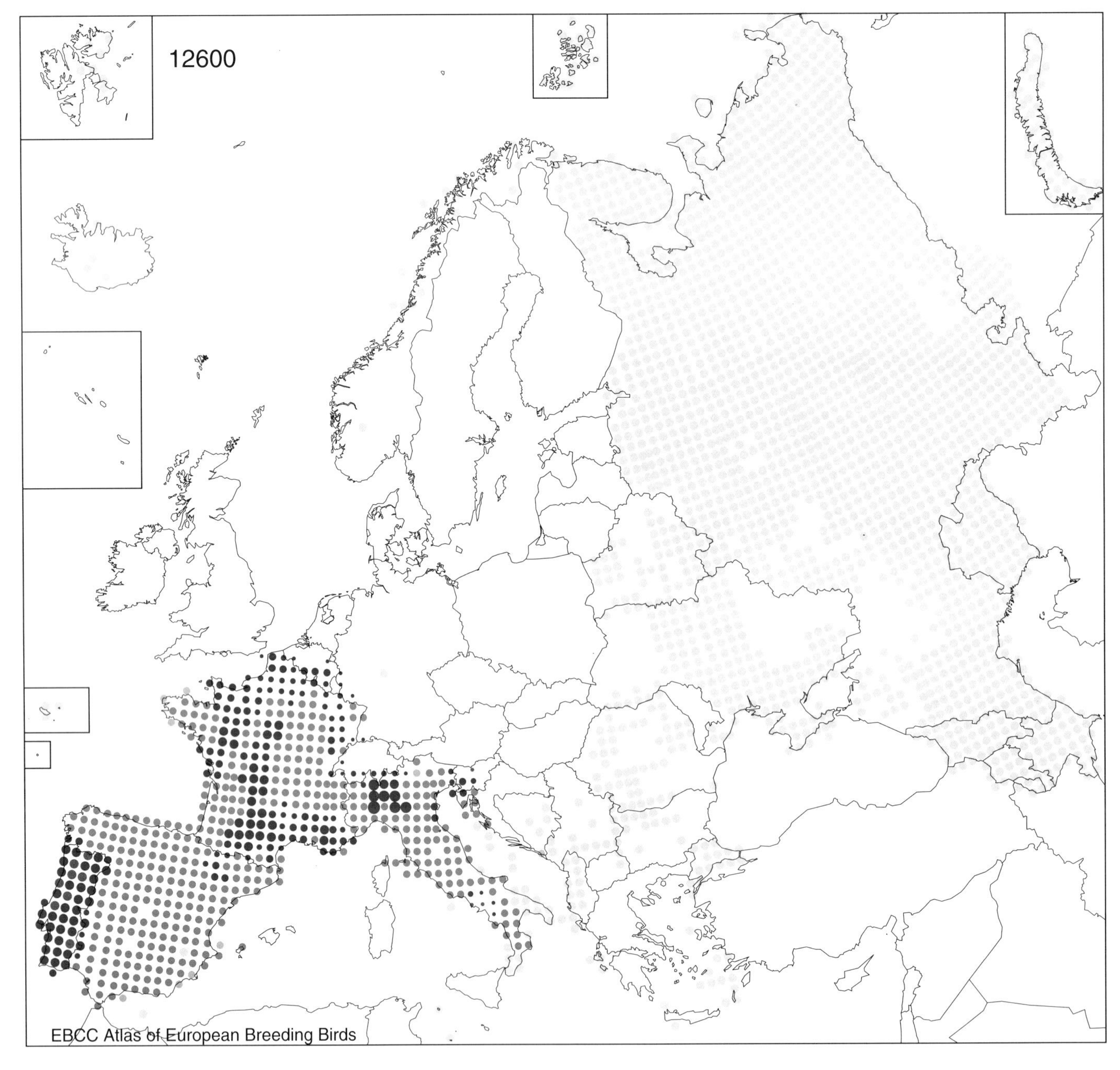

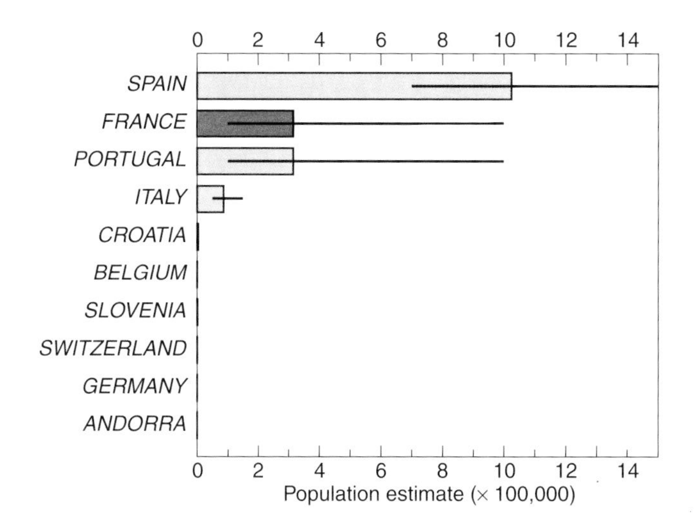

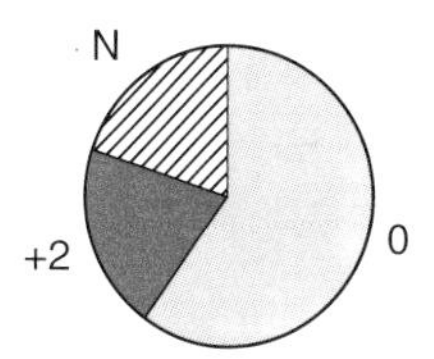

% in top 10 countries: 100.0
Total number of populated European countries: 10
Total European population 1,302,347–2,829,232 (1,749,869)

The Melodious Warbler has a distribution which extends from western and southern Europe to the Mediterranean edge of NW Africa. It breeds between the July 19°C and 30°C isotherms. In the W it is absent from Britain & Ireland, occurring only as a vagrant. The eastern limit of its breeding area passes through southern Belgium, SW Germany, western Switzerland and NW Croatia. There are no subspecies.

Predominantly a lowland species, the Melodious Warbler characteristically occupies incomplete bush-cover in scrub and woodland margins and in larger gardens and orchards in suburban and rural areas. The Melodious Warbler may be locally abundant in such habitats. In Europe (Switzerland) it breeds no higher than 800m to 1000m asl. In prime habitat, breeding density may average 1 bp/ha over 10ha (*BWP*). In France it favours once-open areas under encroachment from tamarisk *Tamarix*, elm *Ulmus* and poplar *Populus*, but will also use acacia *Acacia*, willow *Salix*, and stands of alder *Alnus* and oak *Quercus* where these are small or form low, dense coppices (*BWP*). In S Spain it breeds in bramble *Rubus* and heath *Erica*, especially when scattered with cork oak *Q. suber* (*BWP*). The presence of some trees or tall growth seems almost essential.

Since the 1950s, the breeding range of the Melodious Warbler has expanded northwards, NW to Brittany, N and E to northern France, Belgium and Luxembourg and NE to Germany and Switzerland, and in 1995 the expansion was still continuing. In S Belgium the first breeding record was in 1981, but by 1985 the breeding population already had reached an estimated 100bp (Melchior *et al* 1987). In Saarland from the first breeding record in 1984, only a year had elapsed before 28bp were recorded (Hayo & Weyers 1986). In the Geneva district 3bp in 1977 had increased to 25bp by 1981 (Géroudet *et al* 1983). First breeding in The Netherlands was recorded in 1990, when a pair successfully raised two young (de By *et al* 1992).

With reference to the map and the graph, recent updates of the population database more accurately reflect the balance of numbers between France and Spain, in the opinion of the authors. The Melodious Warbler's stronghold is the Iberian Peninsula, where an average density per 50km square of >5600bp was registered. High numbers were recorded also in Italy (a mean of 719 bp/50km square). Compared to the Italian and Iberian figures, the original database estimates (1990) for the French population (10 000–30 000bp revised 1995 to 100 000–1Mbp) were considerable underestimates. Sizeable populations exist in SW Croatia (173 bp/50km square) and Slovenia (175). Viable populations meanwhile have become established in Belgium (350–560bp), Switzerland (300–350bp) and S Germany (25–100bp). Apart from habitat availability, the only factor apparently limiting the distribution of the Melodious Warbler in Europe is the complementary breeding range of its sibling species Icterine Warbler *Hippolais icterina*. The presence of the Melodious Warbler in the same general area as the Icterine Warbler reduces the latter's reproductive success (Faivre 1993).

The NE boundary of the Melodious Warbler's breeding range overlaps with that of the Icterine Warbler. Here the two species breed close to one another, but territorial overlap has never been observed, and so they remain sexually isolated (Ferry 1977). In extremely rare cases, interbreeding has been recorded between males and females of late-arriving individuals of either species. The hybrids produced by these mixed pairs appear less viable than pure-bred offspring.

The Melodious Warbler is a trans-Saharan migrant to West Africa, where it frequents mainly the savanna belt N of the rainforest. Spring passage is probably more direct and less leisurely than the autumn migration, judging by the numbers caught and ringed en route.

Bruno Faivre (F) Camille Ferry (F)

Sylvia sarda

Marmora's Warbler

CZ	Pěnice sardinská	**I**	Magnanina sarda
D	Sardengrasmücke	**NL**	Sardijnse Grasmus
E	Curruca Sarda	**P**	Toutinegra-sarda
F	Fauvette sarde	**PL**	Pokrzewka czarniawa
FIN	Sardiniankerttu	**R**	Сардинская славка
G	Σαρδοτσιροβάκος	**S**	Sardinsk sångare
H	Szardíniai poszáta		

SPEC Cat 4, Threat status S (P)

Marmora's Warbler is a small warbler endemic to many islands and islets of the W Mediterranean (Érard *et al* 1972) with the exception of Menorca, where it is replaced by the Dartford Warbler *S. undata* (Muntaner *et al* 1984b) and Sicily. It also breeds on Capri, Elba and Pantellaria in Italy and on Zembra off Tunisia (Cantoni 1963). The recent breeding record on Naxos, Aegean Sea, Greece (Magioris 1992) requires substantiation. There are two subspecies, the nominate *S.s. sarda*, and *balearica* which is endemic to the Balearic Islands.

It occupies various Mediterranean scrublands, utilizing low-lying clumps and stands of tall bushes, but it has a marked preference for shrubs <1–2m high (such as cistus *Cistus* and heath *Erica*). It avoids afforested and agricultural areas. The frequent summer fires secure the continuance of suitable habitats or create new areas. The species occurs from sea level usually up to 1300m asl but locally up to 1800m asl in Corsica and Sardinia.

In the Balearic Islands the breeding population averages *c*18 000bp. In Corsica, Lovaty (1993) calculated that there were more than 10 000bp, whereas the maximum estimate of 10 000bp for Sardinia appears very low in relation to the widespread areas of available suitable habitats there.

Where favoured scrub areas exist, similar values of breeding density have been obtained, with a mean of 1.5 bp/10ha on Formentera (Berthold & Berthold 1973), 3.0–4.5 bp/10ha in 1991–93 on Corsica (Lovaty 1995) and between 2.0 and 7.7 bp/10ha on Sardinia (Walter 1988).

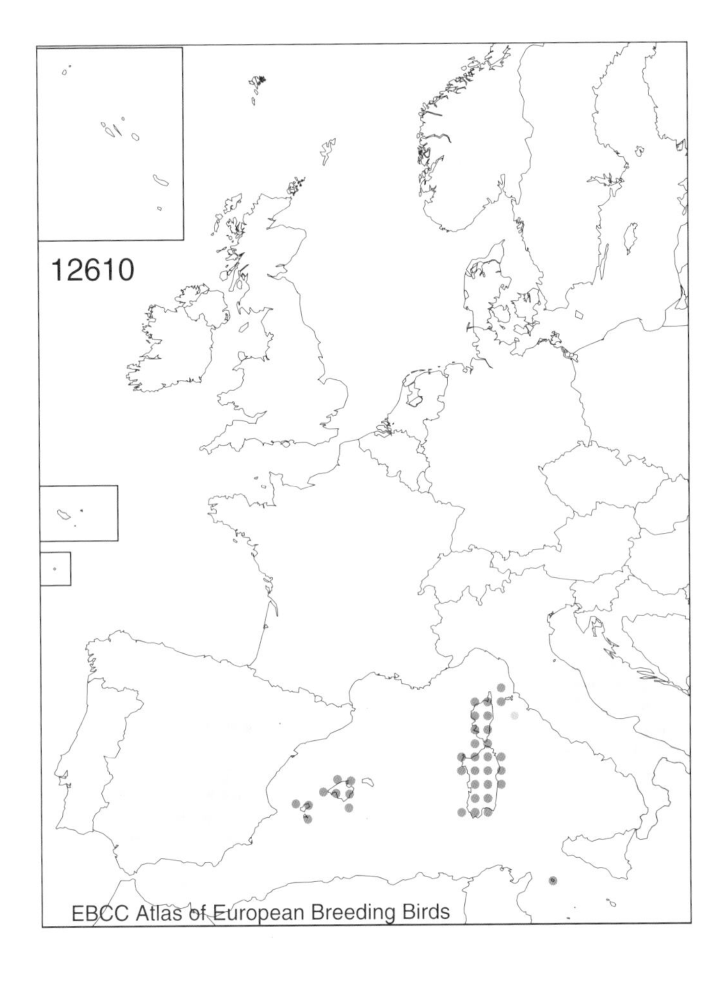

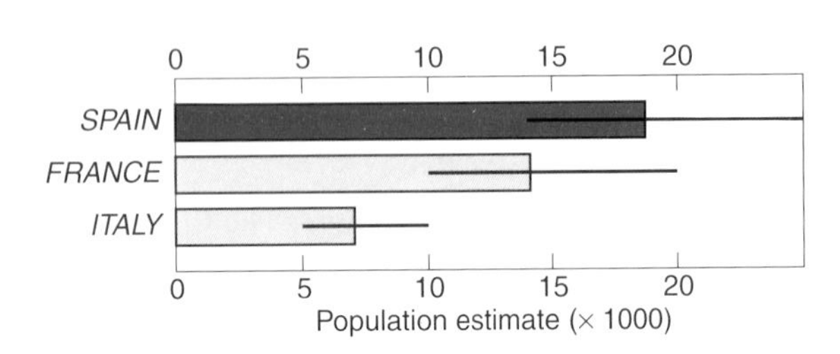

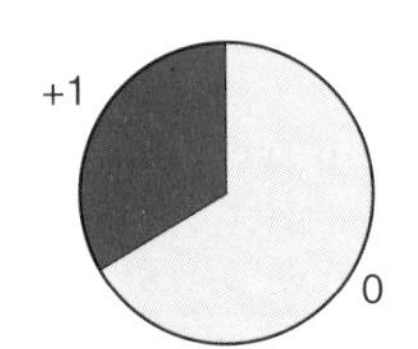

% in top 10 countries: 100.0
Total number of populated European countries: 3
Total European population 33,317–49,003 (39,921)

Marmora's Warbler is generally very sedentary. In Corsica it moves to lower altitudes when snows persist in the mountains. There are regular autumn movements from the Balearic Islands to the E coasts of continental Spain and from Corsica and Sardinia to Sicily, Malta and North Africa.

Jorge Muntaner (E)

Sylvia undata

Dartford Warbler

CZ	Pěnice kaštanová	I	Magnanina
D	Provencegrasmücke	NL	Provençaalse Grasmus
E	Curruca Rabilarga	P	Felosa-do-mato
F	Fauvette pitchou	PL	Pokrzewka kasztanowata
FIN	Ruskokerttu	R	Дартфордская камышевка
G	Προβηγκοτσιροβάκος	S	Provencesångare
H	Bujkáló poszáta		

SPEC Cat 2, Threat status V

The breeding range of the Dartford Warbler stretches N from NW Africa to southern England, and W from Portugal to southern Italy. Its breeding range in England is largely confined to Hampshire, Dorset and Surrey, and in France lies W and S of the January 3°C isotherm (Bost 1994). The species was first discovered breeding on Menorca in 1975 (Muntaner 1980). On Corsica, Sardinia and Sicily it remains scarce, on the former two islands usually more so than Marmora's Warbler *S. sarda* whose habitats it shares. There are at least three subspecies: *undata* (western Mediterranean), *toni* (mostly NW Africa) and *dartfordiensis* (England and W France).

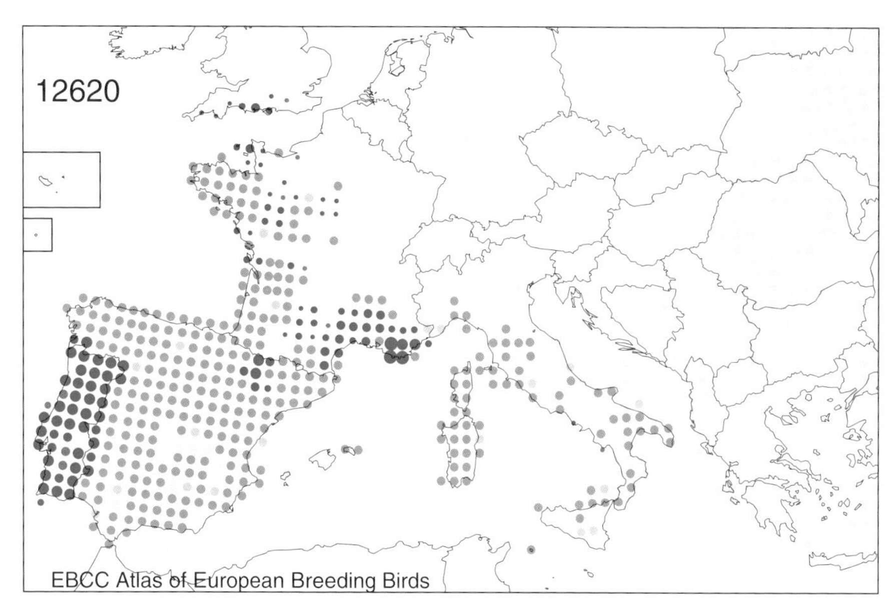

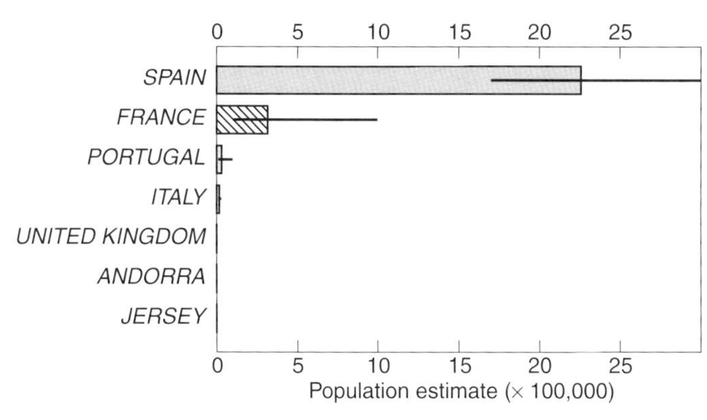

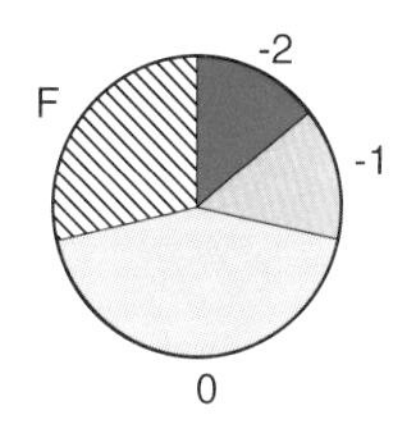

% in top 10 countries: 100.0
Total number of populated European countries: 7
Total European population 2,025,456–3,635,791 (2,624,617)

The Dartford Warbler occupies a wide variety of low (up to 1–2m tall) mediterranean scrublands containing cistus *Cistus*, heaths *Erica* spp, rosemary *Rosmarinus*, and kermes oak *Quercus coccifera*. In Atlantic climate areas it frequents heathlands comprised of heathers *Calluna*, gorse *Ulex*, whin *Genista* and *Erica* (Bibby & Tubbs 1975). It also uses open woodlands of cork oak *Quercus suber* and pines *Pinus* spp) containing dense bushy undergrowth, but avoids agricultural areas. After scrub fires, the Dartford Warbler re-appears 2–6 years later.

The Dartford Warbler is distributed rather evenly, normally reaching 1000m asl in France (locally 1300–1500m) and 1700–1950m in Spain. Population trends are generally stable except in parts of Spain where there is a slow, progressive decline (Cantos 1994). Populations crash following hard winters, but mild winters aid recovery and expansion.

In large heathlands the species always reaches higher breeding densities than in fragmented or isolated components. Values usually vary from 2 to 6 bp/10ha, but can reach 15 bp/10ha in optimum habitat. Habitat destruction or alteration can effect local extinctions (Bibby 1993).

Largely sedentary even in its northernmost range, the Dartford Warbler nevertheless makes seasonal altitudinal movements and short-distance migration (mainly through juvenile dispersal) to winter elsewhere within its breeding range, although some reach the northern Sahara.

Francisco J Cantos (E) Paul Isenmann (F)

Sylvia conspicillata

Spectacled Warbler

CZ	Pěnice brýlatá	I	Sterpazzola di Sardegna
D	Brillengrasmücke	NL	Brilgrasmus
E	Curruca Tomillera	P	Toutinegra-tomilheira
F	Fauvette à lunettes	PL	Pokrzewka okularowa
FIN	Pikkupensaskerttu	R	Очковая славка
G	Ισπανοτσιροβάκος	S	Glasögonsångare
H	Törpeposzáta		

Non-SPEC, Threat status S (P)

The distribution of the Spectacled Warbler comprises two parts. The western and larger component covers the Atlantic islands (except the Azores), the western Mediterranean from Morocco to NW Libya and from Iberia and S France to Italy and the Balearics, Elba, Corsica, Sardinia, Sicily and Malta; there are isolated breeding records in S Switzerland (1989) (Maumary *et al* 1990) and on the Causse de Sauveterre/Lozère in southern France (1982, perhaps 1989) (Lovaty 1990a). The eastern component includes Cyprus, SW Syria, Lebanon, Israel and Jordan. The species may also breed in S and W Turkey (Kasparek 1992).

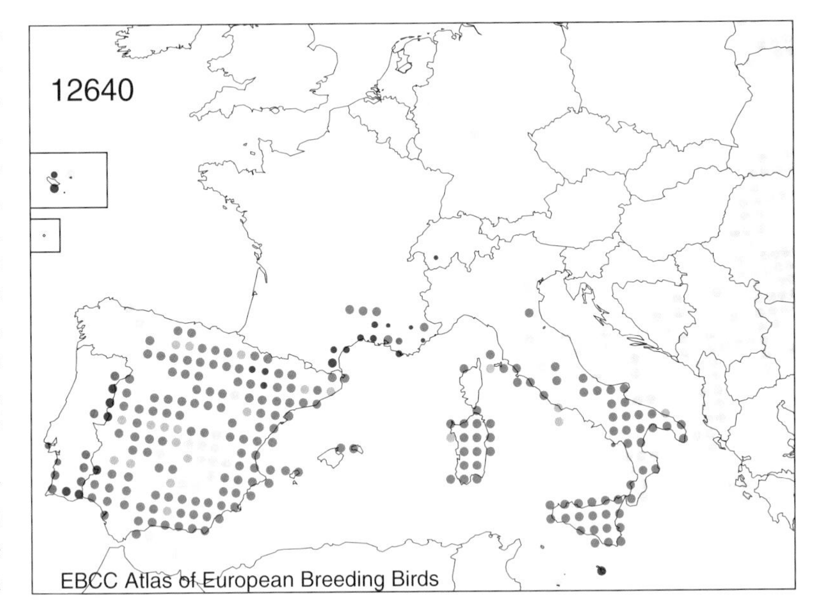

The Spectacled Warbler prefers a habitat of low bushy vegetation (generally taller than 1m) interspersed with open grass, including the characteristic types of short, dry and open mediterranean scrubland (often produced a year or two after fire or intense grazing), *Salicornia* growing in dry coastal saltmarshes, open gorse *Ulex* and broom *Cytisus* heathland, bushy former fields or cultivation margins, and tamarisk *Tamarix* bushes along dry riverbeds. It breeds up to 1000–1050m asl in France, 2000–2500m in S Spain, 2200m in Sicily and 2300–2950m in Morocco.

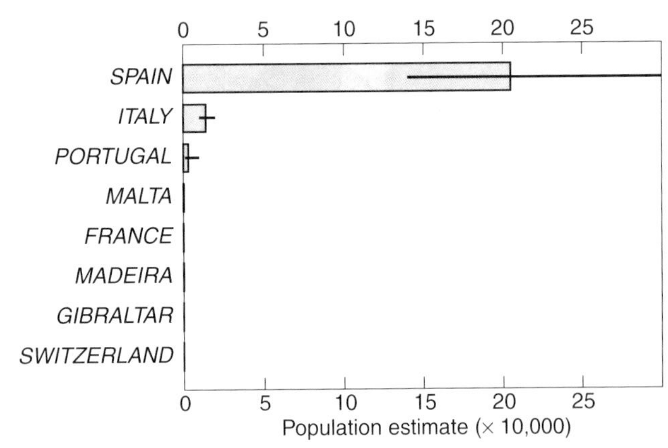

% in top 10 countries: 100.0
Total number of populated European countries: 8
Total European population 157,699–318,292 (222,806)

The species has an uneven breeding distribution which fluctuates strongly from year to year, for reasons unknown. The few available data indicate a breeding density of 2.5–7.5 bp/10ha. No significant population trends are known except for Malta where the species has dramatically declined (Sultana & Gauci 1981-83). Slight recent northward range expansions have occurred in Spain, France and Italy (a small population was discovered in 1986 in the Bologna Apennines; Gellini & Montevecchi 1986).

The species is resident in the Atlantic islands, Malta and Cyprus. Elsewhere, only a few birds overwinter in the northern half of the breeding range, the rest migrating to the Sahara, (mainly S Sahara, N Sahel and SW Mauretania). Autumn migrants leave in September and October, returning in March and April. Two subspecies have been recognized: *orbitalis* on the Atlantic Islands and the nominate *conspicillata* elsewhere.

Paul Isenmann (F) Joe Sultana (MAL)

Sylvia cantillans

Subalpine Warbler

CZ	Pěnice vousatá	I	Sterpazzolina
D	Weissbart-Grasmücke	NL	Baardgrasmus
E	Curruca Carrasqueña	P	Toutinegra-carrasqueira
F	Fauvette passerinette	PL	Pokrzewka wąsata
FIN	Rusorintakerttu	R	Рыжегрудая славка
G	Κοκκινοτσιροβάκος	S	Rödstrupig sångare
H	Vörhenyes poszáta		

SPEC Cat 4, Threat status S

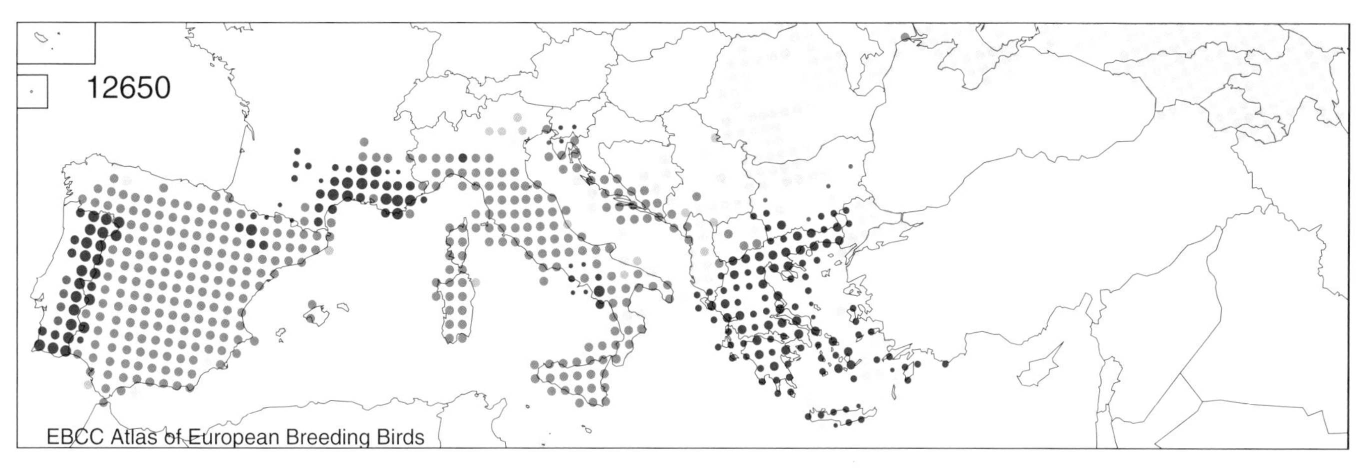

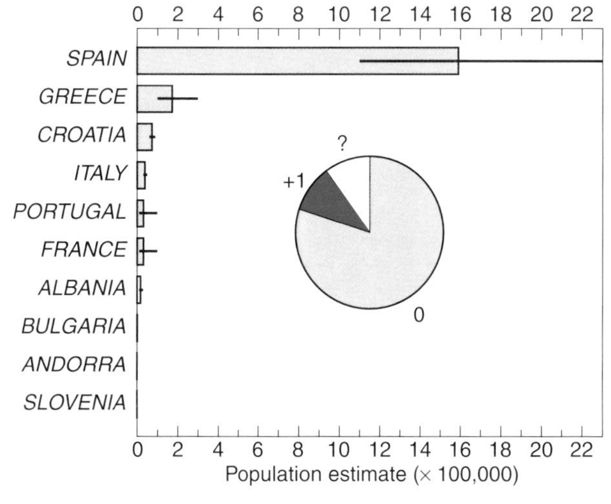

% in top 10 countries: 100.0
Total number of populated European countries: 10
Total European population 1,460,949–2,685,732 (1,958,234)
Turkish population 1000–10,000 (3162)

The breeding range of the Subalpine Warbler includes the Mediterranean area (most islands except Malta and Cyprus) from Morocco and the Iberian Peninsula in the W to westernmost Turkey and NW Libya in the E. It also extends slightly northward from the mediterranean zone, especially in France, Italy and Bulgaria. The species expanded its range recently to Andorra (Clamens 1993), Slovenia and possibly to SW Romania (Weber 1994). It first bred in 1983 and later in 1992 on Mallorca and also in 1992 on nearby Cabrera (Gargallo 1992, 1994, pers comm).

The Subalpine Warbler is a typical inhabitant of dry, warm and mostly evergreen mediterranean shrubland (garrigue, maquis and matorral) normally comprised of low dense bushes and 8–10m high open-canopy woodland possessing dense undergrowth. Breeding density is highest where the vegetation is 1–4m tall. There is considerable habitat overlap with the Sardinian Warbler *S. melanocephala*, but virtually none with the Dartford *S. undata* and Spectacled *S. conspicillata* Warblers (Blondel 1970, *HVM*). Of the eight Mediterranean *Sylvia* species, only the Orphean Warbler *S. hortensis* is more strongly linked with trees and the taller bushes.

Between 200 and 1000m asl, distribution is rather even, but the species breeds up to 1500m asl in France and Spain, 1800m in Sicily and 2200–2350m in Morocco. Average breeding density is *c*4–5 bp/10ha but can reach 12 bp/10ha in optimum habitats. Population trends appear largely stable, except for a slightly increasing trend in Bulgaria.

The Subalpine Warbler winters mostly in the Sahelian belt of tropical Africa from Senegal and Guinea-Bissau eastwards to the Nile Valley, but a few favour the southern Sahara. The spring migration takes place from mid-March to early May; in autumn departures last from mid-July to mid-September.

Three subspecies breed in the *Atlas*' coverage area: *moltonii* on W Mediterranean islands (Gargallo 1994), *cantillans* in the W Mediterranean mainland and *albistriata* in the E Mediterranean. The fourth, *inornata*, breeds in NW Africa.

Paul Isenmann (F)

This species account is sponsored by Dr Walter Gehlhoff, Königswinter, D.

Sylvia mystacea

Ménétries' Warbler

CZ	Pěnice uzdičková	I	Occhiocotto del Caucaso
D	Tamariskengrasmücke	NL	Levantzwartkop
E	Curruca de Menetries	P	Toutinegra de Menetries
F	Fauvette de Ménétries	PL	Pokrzewka kaspijska
FIN	Kaspiankerttu	R	Белоусая славка
G	Τσιροβάκος του Menetries	S	Östlig sammetshätta
H	Kaukázusi poszáta		

Non-SPEC, Threat status S (P)

The migrant Ménétries' Warbler, primarily an Asian species, breeds in Europe only in the Transcaucasus (S Russia), and in E Georgia, Azerbaijan and Armenia. Elsewhere Ménétries' Warbler occurs from Kazakhstan E to *c*70°E, and S through Mesopotamia, particularly the Tigris–Euphrates basin, to the head of the Arabian Gulf (*c*30°N). It winters in SW Arabia south to *c*12°N, and from Sudan to Somalia south to 30°N. It wanders to W Levant, Israel and Egypt.

Within the very arid zone it inhabits, Ménétries' Warbler chooses bushy habitats possessing a short or sparse herb layer, mostly along riverbanks, but will utilize orchards, shelterbelts, palm groves and plant nurseries. It has also been found in wooded areas on lower mountain slopes. In Arabia and Africa it winters commonly in similar habitats, but also in acacia scrub. It eats mainly invertebrates but takes some fruit.

It is usually solitary outside the breeding season, although often within vocal contact range, and uttering its contact note. Usually it forages restlessly in deep cover. Generally, it breeds from March to July, monogamously. In suitable habitat in Tajikistan, estimated breeding densities were 100–200 bp/km² (Abdulsamyamov 1973, Sagitov & Bakaev 1980).

Geographical variation is slight, comprising the nominate *mystacea* (N–NE of the range), *rubescens* (SW) and *turcmenica* (E of *rubescens*). Ménétries' Warbler is often considered conspecific with Sardinian Warbler *S. melanocephala momus/norrissae* (Marchant 1963). The species are best separated on morphological and etho-ecological grounds because of full habitat segregation, as for example in E Turkey where Ménétries' Warbler inhabited tamarisk scrubs along rivers and the Sardinian Warbler drier habitats away from rivers (Konrad 1985).

In the field and in the hand, Ménétries' Warbler is easily confused with other warbler species outside the breeding season, placing uncertainty over some records outside the major passage and wintering areas.

John Morgan (GB) Hadoram Shirihai (ISR)

Sylvia melanocephala

Sardinian Warbler

CZ	Pěnice bělohrdlá	I	Occhiocotto
D	Samtkopfgrasmücke	NL	Kleine Zwartkop
E	Curruca Cabecinegra	P	Toutinegra-de-cabeça-preta
F	Fauvette mélanocéphale	PL	Pokrzewka aksamitna
FIN	Samettipääkerttu	R	Масличная славка
G	Μαυροτσιροβάκος	S	Sammetshätta
H	Kucsmás poszáta		

SPEC Cat 4, Threat status S

The Sardinian Warbler has a chiefly Mediterranean distribution, occurring continuously along European coasts and also along those of the Maghreb, Libya, Syria, Israel, Lebanon and Jordan. It extends from the Levant and the SW coastal regions of the Black Sea to the Canary Islands, the Moroccan Atlantic coast and Atlas Mountains (up to 2400m asl). It is evenly and continuously distributed on all Mediterranean

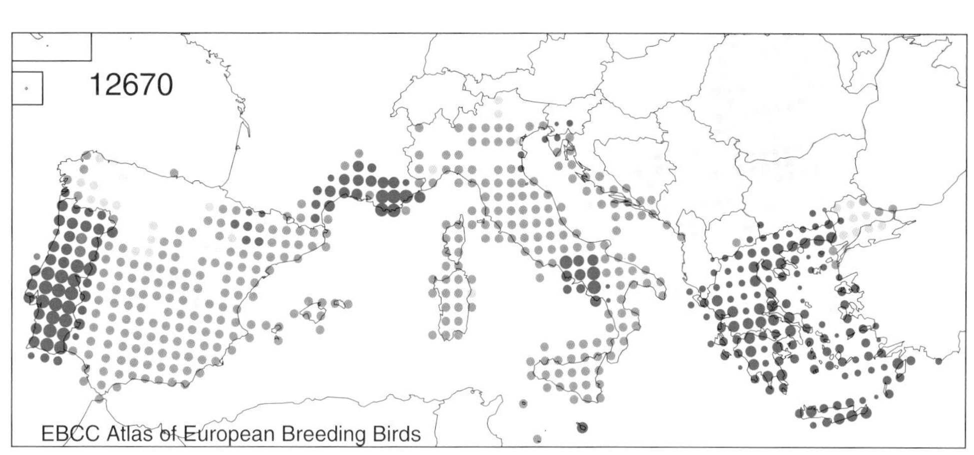

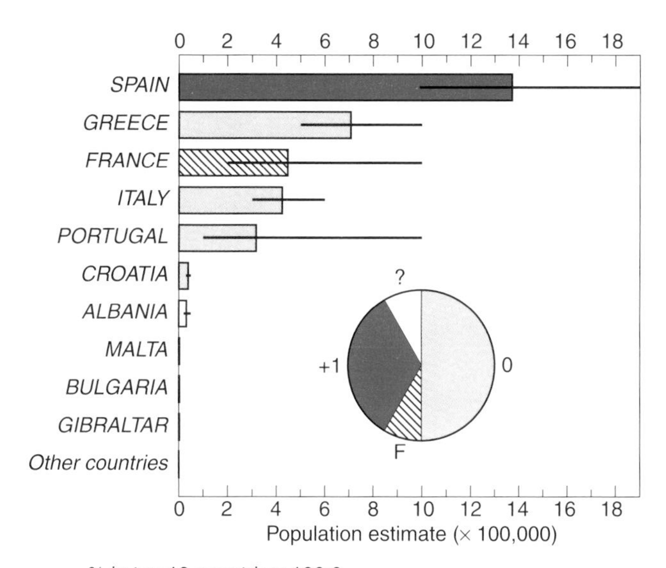

% in top 10 countries: 100.0
Total number of populated European countries: 12
Total European population 2,781,914–4,421,911 (3,340,444)
Turkish population 10,000–100,000 (31,623)

islands except Cyprus where generally it is replaced by the Cyprus Warbler *Sylvia melanothorax*. In Sardinia, Sicily and Malta it is probably the commonest warbler. Probably insufficient coverage is responsible for gaps in mapping the species in Albania and at some Bulgarian and Romanian locations. Only the nominate *S.m. melanocephala* occurs in Europe. There are two other subspecies: *leucogastra* resident in the Canary Isles and *momus* in the Levant.

It breeds in maquis, olive and citrus groves, vineyards, orchards, on oak *Quercus* and pine *Pinus* margins, in uncultivated green areas in urban and suburban environments, and in gardens. In pre-Alpine areas in northern Italy, it also breeds on abandoned farmland where spontaneous shrub vegetation has regrown (Brichetti & Cambi 1979).

At the end of the 19th century the Sardinian Warbler's range began to expand. It has bred in Malta since 1884 (Sultana & Gauci 1990–91). From 1970 onwards, it colonized several warm and dry pre-Alpine areas in Italy, inland in southern France, Bulgaria and probably Romania. In northern Italy new breeding areas are occupied each year and in Cyprus past sporadic breeding may now have become regular with *c*50bp on the Akamas Peninsula in 1995 (R. Frost, pers comm to the Editors). The species is also increasing in Spain, Malta, and Slovenia.

Densities are as high as 20–60 bp/km^2 in coastal maquis (greater than 500 in Coto Doñana) but lower inland (0.6–8.0 in woodland and up to 6.0 at the range and altitude limit in Bulgaria).

Except for the NE, most of the breeding range is also occupied in winter, although many birds move south (mostly short distances: Fraissinet *et al* 1988). The winter range includes large but discontinuous areas of N Africa, the Levant, Turkey and Cyprus (where it shares habitat with the resident Cyprus Warbler).

Maurizio Fraissinet (I) Joe Sultana (MAL)

Sylvia rueppelli

Rüppell's Warbler

CZ	Pěnice Rüpellova	**I**	Silvia del Rüppell
D	Maskengrasmücke	**NL**	Rüppells Grasmus
E	Curruca de Rüppell	**P**	Toutinegra de Rüppell
F	Fauvette de Rüppell	**PL**	Pokrzewka czarnogardła
FIN	Mustakurkkukerttu	**R**	Славка Рюппеля
G	Μουστακοτσιροβάκος	**S**	Svarthakad sångare
H	Feketetorkú poszáta		

SPEC Cat 4, Threat status S (P)

Rüppell's Warbler occurs between the July 25°C and 30°C isotherms in a limited, largely E Mediterranean distribution covering southern Greece, the Aegean islands, Crete, W and S Turkey and a few small areas near the southern coast of the Sea of Marmara. It may also breed in Lebanon and western Syria. It nests in thorn scrub on hill and mountain slopes up to 1600m asl (*BWP*) and in ravines, narrow valleys and rocky clefts, or in the underbrush of mature open woods of oak *Quercus* or cypress *Cupressus*. Although its range and habitat overlap with those of Sardinian Warbler *S. melanocephala*, it prefers the drier low scrub to more substantial vegetation. Rüppell's Warbler breeds at higher altitudes than any other European *Sylvia* species (Simms 1985) and its preference for arid, very warm habitats and avoidance of moist areas allows it a niche where it has relatively little competition. There are no subspecies.

Little is known of the status of Rüppell's Warbler, but possibly neither its distribution nor range have changed much since the 1930s (Meiklejohn 1934, 1935, 1936), although Meiklejohn (1934) was advised of its scarcity on the Greek mainland. It is one of the least-studied European species despite being relatively accessible. The Greek population is estimated as 3000–10 000bp (Tucker & Heath 1994). The estimate for Turkey (5000–50 000bp) is very approximate, but actual numbers probably are near the upper limit, given that the species is widely distributed and locally abundant in the Marmara region and in W and S Turkey, and possibly also in adjacent areas on the C Anatolian plateau and in SE Turkey (Kasparek 1992).

Rüppell's Warbler is entirely migratory, generally wintering in very dry scrub, steppe and savanna on the edge of desert and semi-desert between Chad and Sudan in Africa. There is an isolated wintering area in the southwestern Sahara around Timbuktu.

Haralambos Alivizatos (G) Philip Jackson (GB)

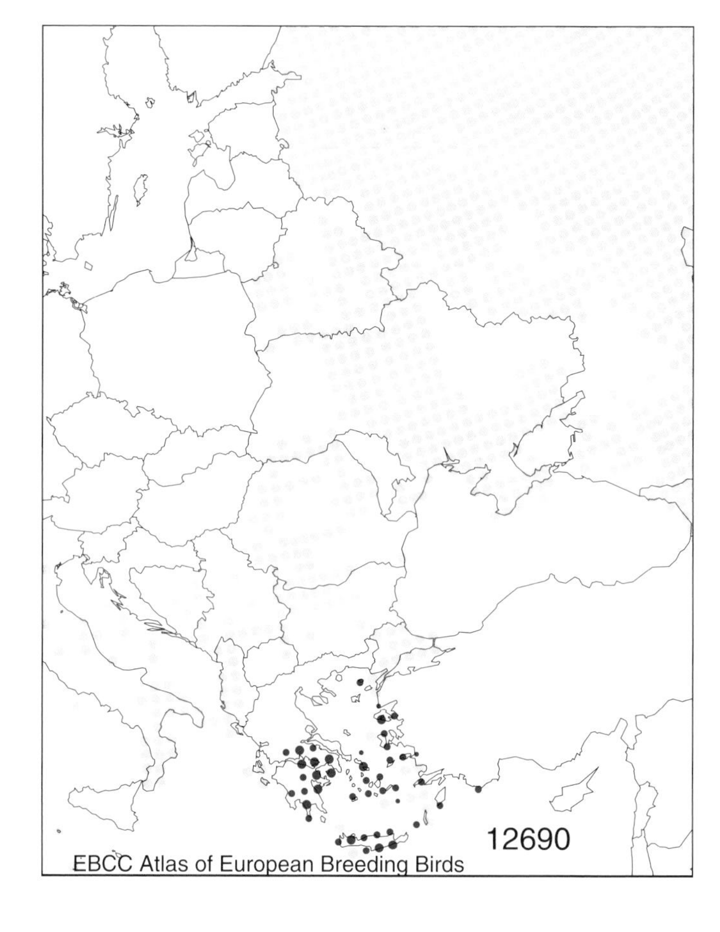

0

% in top 10 countries: 100.0
Total number of populated European countries: 1
Total European population 3000–10,000 (5477)
Turkish population 5000–50,000 (15,811)

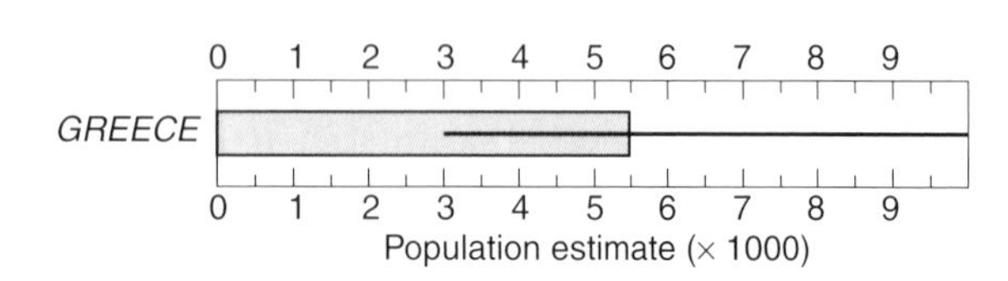

Sylvia hortensis

Orphean Warbler

CZ	Pěnice mistrovská	I	Bigia grossa
D	Orpheusgrasmücke	NL	Orpheusgrasmus
E	Curruca Mirlona	P	Toutinegra-real
F	Fauvette orphée	PL	Pokrzewka lutniczka
FIN	Orfeuskerttu	R	Певчая славка
G	Δενδροτσιροβάκος	S	Mästersångare
H	Dalos poszáta		

SPEC Cat 3, Threat status V

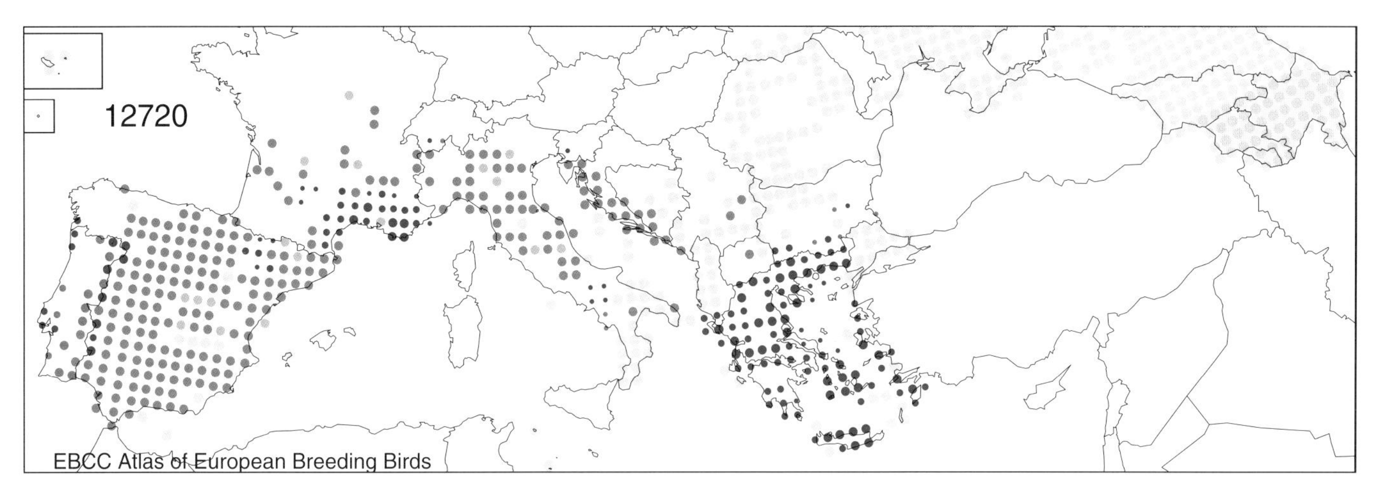

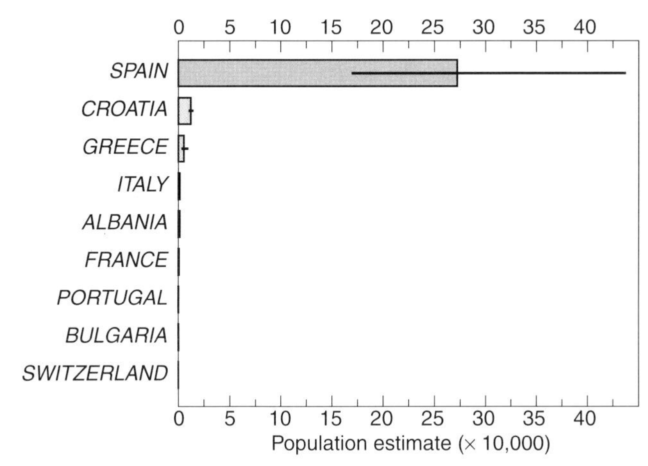

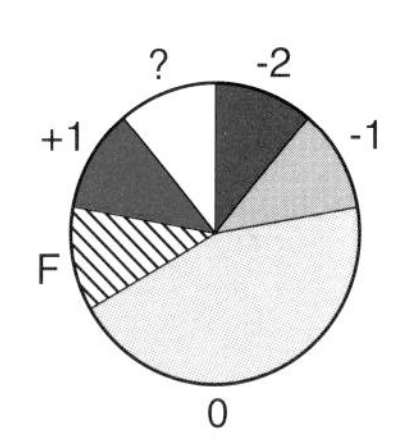

% in top 10 countries: 100.0
Total number of populated European countries: 9
Total European population 191,849–461,994 (295,401)
Turkish population 5000–50,000 (15,811)

The Orphean Warbler, a relatively large warbler, is distributed in mediterranean habitat through S Europe, NW Africa, Asia Minor, Transcaucasia and S–C Asia. The nominate *S. h. hortensis* occurs in SW Europe (Iberian Peninsula, S France, SW Switzerland and mainland Italy) and in NW Africa from Morocco to NW Libya. It is absent from the large W Mediterranean islands. It winters in sub-Saharan Africa, mainly between 14° and 17°N, from S Mauritania and N Senegal to Chad. The other subspecies, *crassirostris*, breeds in Cyrenaica (NE Libya) and from Slovenia and the coastland through Croatia, Albania, Greece and S Bulgaria to W and S Turkey and the Levant. It winters in NE Africa (Sudan and Eritrea). The third subspecies *jerdoni* inhabits SC Asia and winters in the Indian subcontinent and in eastern Arabia. Spring migration occurs from mid-April to mid-May, autumn migration between mid-August and mid-September.

The Orphean Warbler nests in dry shrubland (garrigue, maquis and matorral), mostly where there is a rich mosaic of bushes and trees amid open grassy areas on sunny slopes. It also occupies orchards, olive groves, overgrown fields and open cork oak *Quercus suber* and pine *Pinus* forests. Its distribution is often patchy and breeding locations outside the mediterranean area vary in size and with time. The species regularly reaches 1200–1500m asl in Europe, and up to 2580m in Armenia. Breeding territories generally are large and densities usually do not exceed 2–3 bp/10ha.

Recently, population declines have been reported in *hortensis* populations in France (Tyssandier 1991, Isenmann & Tyssandier 1994) and Spain and Italy (Hallmann 1994a) where agricultural intensification may be the cause, but since the late 1960s *crassirostris* has extended its range in Bulgaria first in the E Rhodopes Mountains (Dontchev 1970b, Simeonov 1970), then on the Black Sea coast (Prostov & Smilova 1983). It has also reached SW Switzerland (Bottani & Praz 1977).

Stephan Dontchev (BUL) Paul Isenmann (F)

Sylvia nisoria

Barred Warbler

CZ	Pěnice vlašská	I	Bigia padovana
D	Sperbergrasmücke	NL	Sperwergrasmus
E	Curruca Gavilana	P	Toutinegra-gavião
F	Fauvette épervière	PL	Jarzębatka
FIN	Kirjokerttu	R	Ястребиная славка
G	Ψαλτοτσιροβάκος	S	Höksångare
H	Karvalyposzáta		

SPEC Cat 4, Threat status S (P)

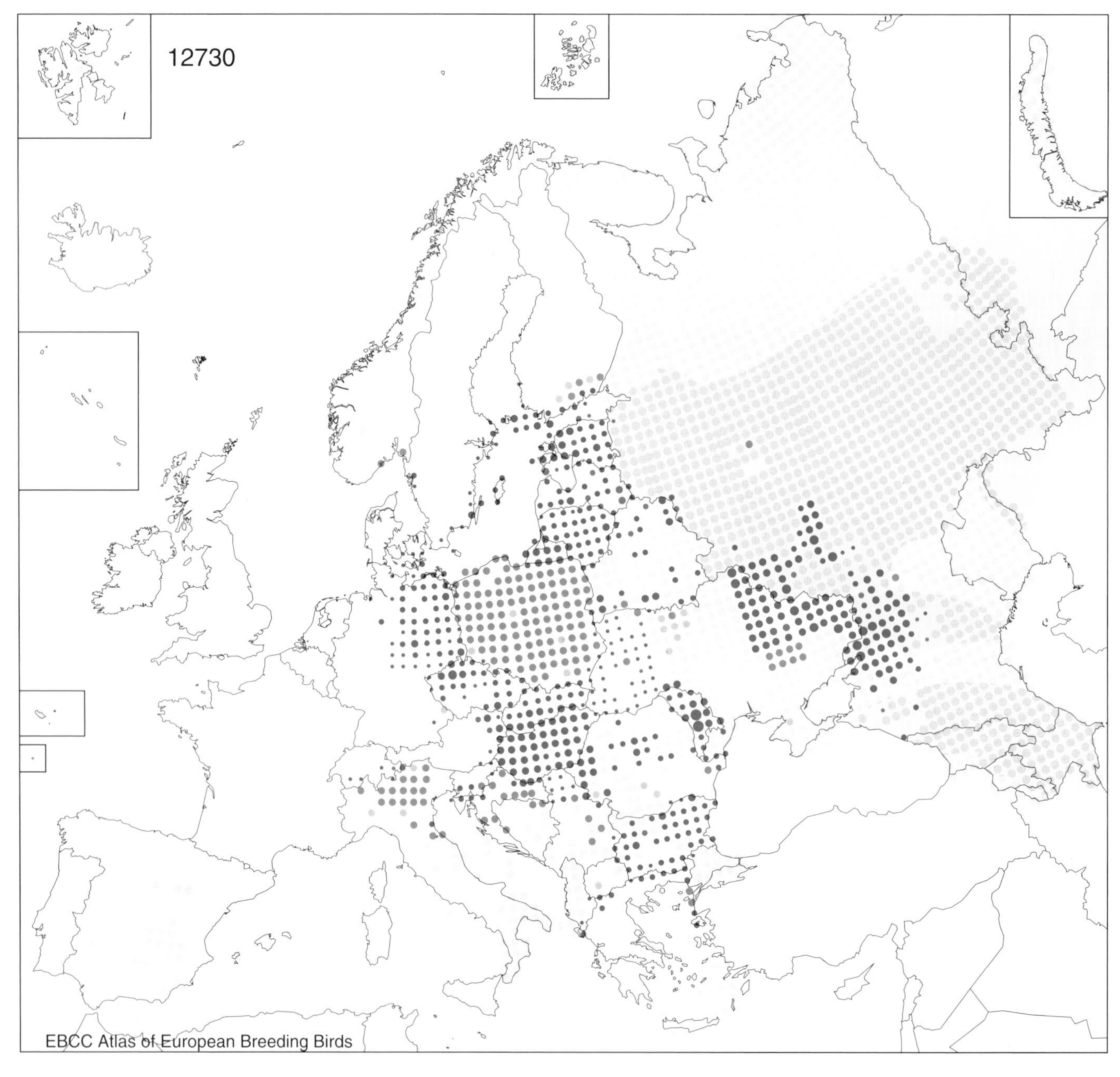

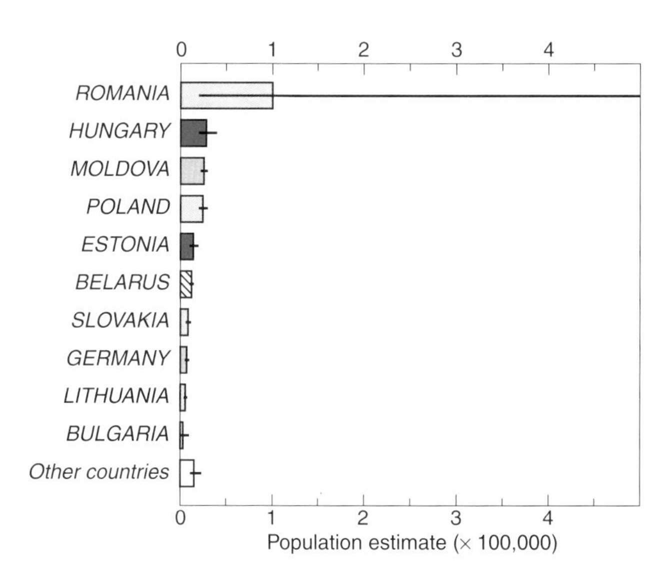

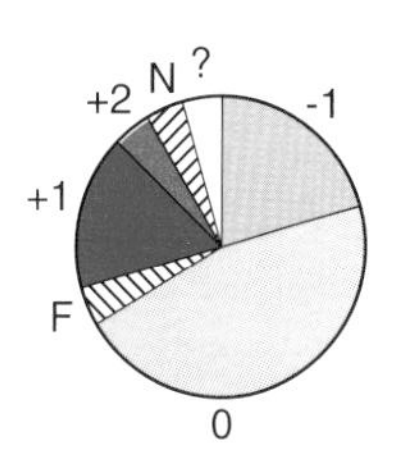

% in top 10 countries: 93.7
Total number of populated European countries: 24
Total European population 163,624–644,926 (244,530)
Russian population 100,000–1,000,000 (316,228)
Turkish population 500–5000 (1581)

The Barred Warbler, of the European-Turkestan faunatype, has a largely C Palearctic distribution stretching from NW Italy to C Asia (Altai, Tian Shan). Its northern limit runs from S Finland along 60°N through Russia E beyond the Urals, then heads SSE reaching 101°E. Its southern limit runs from Italy through Greece and Turkey (Roselaar 1995) to Turkmenistan. It inhabits Europe E of a line from E Denmark through Germany to climatically favourable regions in Switzerland and the Po Valley. It is absent from the Kazakhstan steppes. The nominate subspecies *S.n. nisoria* inhabits Europe and *merzbacheri* occurs beyond it.

The species is widely distributed through regions whose warm, dry summers (normal summer precipitation, <300mm within the 17°C July isotherm) support richly structured, multi-layered copse woodland over fairly extensive areas. Such woodland typically comprises very dense thorny bushes beneath stunted taller bushes and isolated remnant tree stands (important feeding sites and song-posts). However, it also breeds in thinned woodland, bogs with sparse stands of trees and bushes, riverbank willow *Salix* thickets (Poland), sewage farm embankments overgrown with elder *Sambucus* and briar bushes (eastern Germany) or on rocky moorland and sun-exposed loess slopes (Switzerland). In C and E European cultivation, its habitats contain grazing pastures, meadows, unproductive grassland and hedge complexes in depressions. It tends to breed in valley-bottom sites, but in the climatically favourable inner Alpine areas it reaches 1600m asl.

Over its entire European breeding range, the species' occurrence is strongly and typically associated with that of the Red-backed Shrike *Lanius collurio*, a relationship actively sought by the Barred Warbler. This association has the presumed advantage of mutual and more reliable warning against threats (*BWP*). There is some evidence that it also increases the Barred Warbler's productivity (Neuschulz 1988).

The European breeding distribution core lies in C and E Europe, from Poland, Slovakia and Hungary to the Baltic States, Russia, Romania, Moldova and countries immediately to the W, where average densities exceed 200 bp/50km square. Fringe populations in Germany, Denmark, S Fennoscandia and SE Europe are much smaller. The southern Alps (mostly N Italy) population of 1000–2000bp once was contiguous with the Slovenian distribution through S Steiermark in Austria (Dvorak *et al* 1993).

In the early 1900s, the species' range expanded considerably northwards to Finland in the 1920s (Koskimies 1989a). Estonian numbers increased from a handful to 10 000–20 000bp by the 1980s (Leibak *et al* 1994). During 1970–90 population growth continued in both countries (by >50% in Finland). Recently, Slovenia and N Italy experienced slight increases, and the western and southern distribution margins, most notably Germany, Switzerland, Czech Republic and Ukraine, suffered slight number and range declines. However, because countries with large breeding populations lack systematic monitoring programmes, overall trends are hard to assess.

Population and range fluctuations may have climatic causes, especially at the distribution limits, because the species does not tolerate damp, cool, early-summer weather. In eastern Germany, habitat loss through intensified agriculture, the ploughing of grassland and the disappearance of large areas of low-intensity pastures and unproductive grassland, has been the most important factor in the species' decline. The disappearance of the Red-backed Shrike following land-use change or development can also cause the loss of the Barred Warbler, through the interdependence of both species (Neuschulz 1988).

The wintering area of the Barred Warbler, a long-distance migrant, is much smaller than its breeding distribution. The species winters between 15°N and 7°S in East Africa (mainly in N and E Kenya, NE Tanzania, probably S Ethiopia; Lindström *et al* 1993). During migration, European populations cross the eastern Mediterranean.

Frank Neuschulz (D)

Sylvia curruca Lesser Whitethroat

CZ	Pěnice pokřovní	**I**	Bigiarella
D	Klappergrasmücke	**NL**	Braamsluiper
E	Curruca Zarcerilla	**P**	Papa-amoras-cinzento
F	Fauvette babillarde	**PL**	Piegża
FIN	Hernekerttu	**R**	Славка-завирушка
G	Λαλοτσιροβάκος	**S**	Ärtsångare
H	Kis poszáta		

Non-SPEC, Threat status S

12740

EBCC Atlas of European Breeding Birds

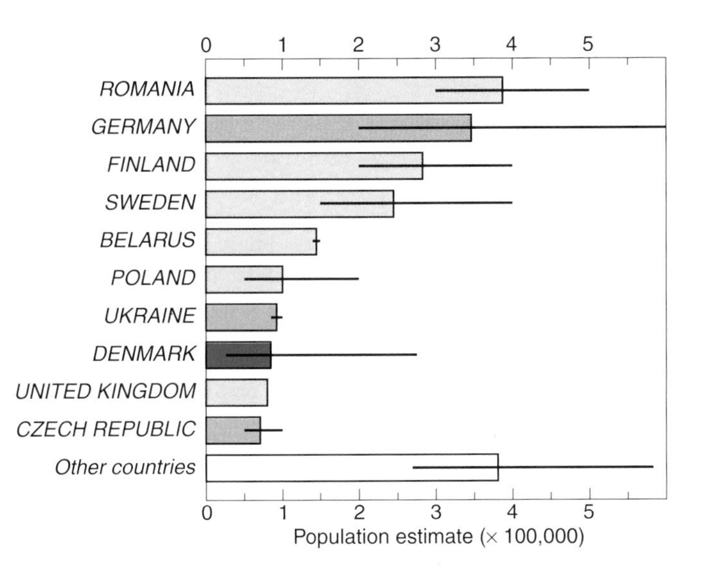

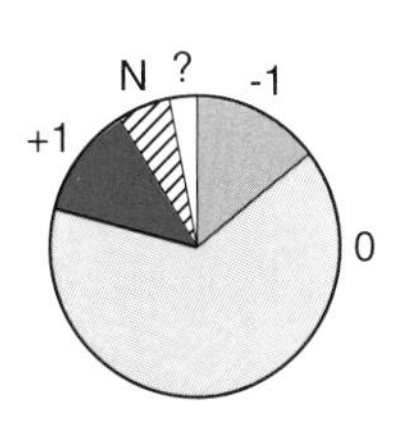

% in top 10 countries: 82.8
Total number of populated European countries: 34
Total European population 1,984,831–2,625,450 (2,214,593)
Russian population 100,000–1,000,000 (316,228)
Turkish population 1000–10,000 (3162)

The Lesser Whitethroat has a vast and virtually continuous distribution stretching from Great Britain in the W to the Yakutsk region of E Siberia (130°E), E Mongolia, and the Tian Shan in China. Its southern range boundary in Europe generally lies between 37° and 43°N, although the distribution has several branches and separate populations further S towards 30°N. In the *Atlas'* area of coverage, the nominate subspecies *S.c. curruca* is predominant, *halimodendri* occurring from the lower Volga eastwards and *caucasica* in the Caucasus. There are at least six subspecies elsewhere, geographical variation being considerable and complex.

Although considered a lowland species, the Lesser Whitethroat breeds in Austria only in the zone between 300 and 2100m asl (Dvorak *et al* 1993) in a wide range of habitats. It favours habitats intermediate between mature forest and open areas, especially in margins, shrubland, young conifer plantations, gardens and hedgerows. In Russia it prefers clearings or glades containing young forests of spruce *Picea* and pine *Pinus* or thickets of juniper *Juniperus*. Sites may be wet, such as bogs and marshes, or dry, as on slopes or steppes. Breeding densities normally are rather low, in Fennoscandia and the Baltic States being 2–10 bp/km^2 in suitable habitats (Koskimies 1989a) but varying from 8 to 49 bp/km^2 in gardens and parks and 18–37 bp/km^2 in cemeteries in Germany (Flade 1994) and Poland (Dyrcz *et al* 1991). The Common Bird Census scheme run by the BTO has shown that densities in English farmland now average *c*1 bp/km^2 (Mead 1993a).

The distribution core lies in European middle and upper-middle latitudes, especially in C Europe, the Low Countries, Denmark, southern Sweden and Finland and the Baltic States. At its range limits the species is noticeably scarce and its distribution pattern becomes patchier, as in N Fennoscandia, N England, Scotland, France (where it is absent S and W of a line from Brittany to the Rhône Delta), N Italy, the Balkans and Greece. The first Irish breeding records come from 1988–91, possibly part of the substantial range extension which incorporated Wales, Anglesey, N England and Scotland (Mead 1993a). A similar northward expansion noted in Finland was attributed to forest fragmentation which allowed the bush layer to increase (Koskimies 1989a). Slight range extensions occurred also along the species' southern distribution border, as in France and Slovenia. The average annual range increase in the 1980s was calculated at 0.4% in Sweden, 1.3% in both Britain and the former Czechoslovakia and 3.6% in Finland (Marchant 1992). However, overall the species has been remarkably stable in numbers throughout 1970–90, slight decreases in five C and E European countries being counterbalanced by slight increases elsewhere.

The European population is estimated at 2.5Mbp, with a range of 1.6M–4.5Mbp (excluding Russia). Large fluctuations in successive years have been recorded in Britain, Germany and The Netherlands, probably due partly to natural variations not only in the scale of spring arrivals towards the breeding range limits (J.H. Marchant *et al* 1990) but also of the adult survival rate (Boddy 1994). It is likely that habitat changes and prevailing climatic conditions in its winter quarters and along migration routes are significant determinants of survival rates (J.H. Marchant 1992). Contrary to most European passerine species, the Lesser Whitethroat migrates in a south-easterly direction, to winter mainly in Sudan and Ethiopia. It is therefore probably almost unaffected by the Sahel drought, which may explain the overall stability of the European population.

Modern intensive agricultural techniques in western Europe have decreased the area of suitable breeding habitat for the Lesser Whitethroat, especially through the removal of hedges. On the other hand, urbanization has created new habitats (gardens, parks), a trend which will continue in the near future.

Rob G Bijlsma (NL) Frank Saris (NL)

Sylvia communis — Whitethroat

CZ	Pěnice hnědokřídlá	**I**	Sterpazzola
D	Dorngrasmücke	**NL**	Grasmus
E	Curruca Zarcera	**P**	Papa-amoras-comum
F	Fauvette grisette	**PL**	Cierniówka
FIN	Pensaskerttu	**R**	Серая славка
G	Θαμνοτσιροβάκος	**S**	Törnsångare
H	Mezei poszáta		

SPEC Cat 4, Threat status S

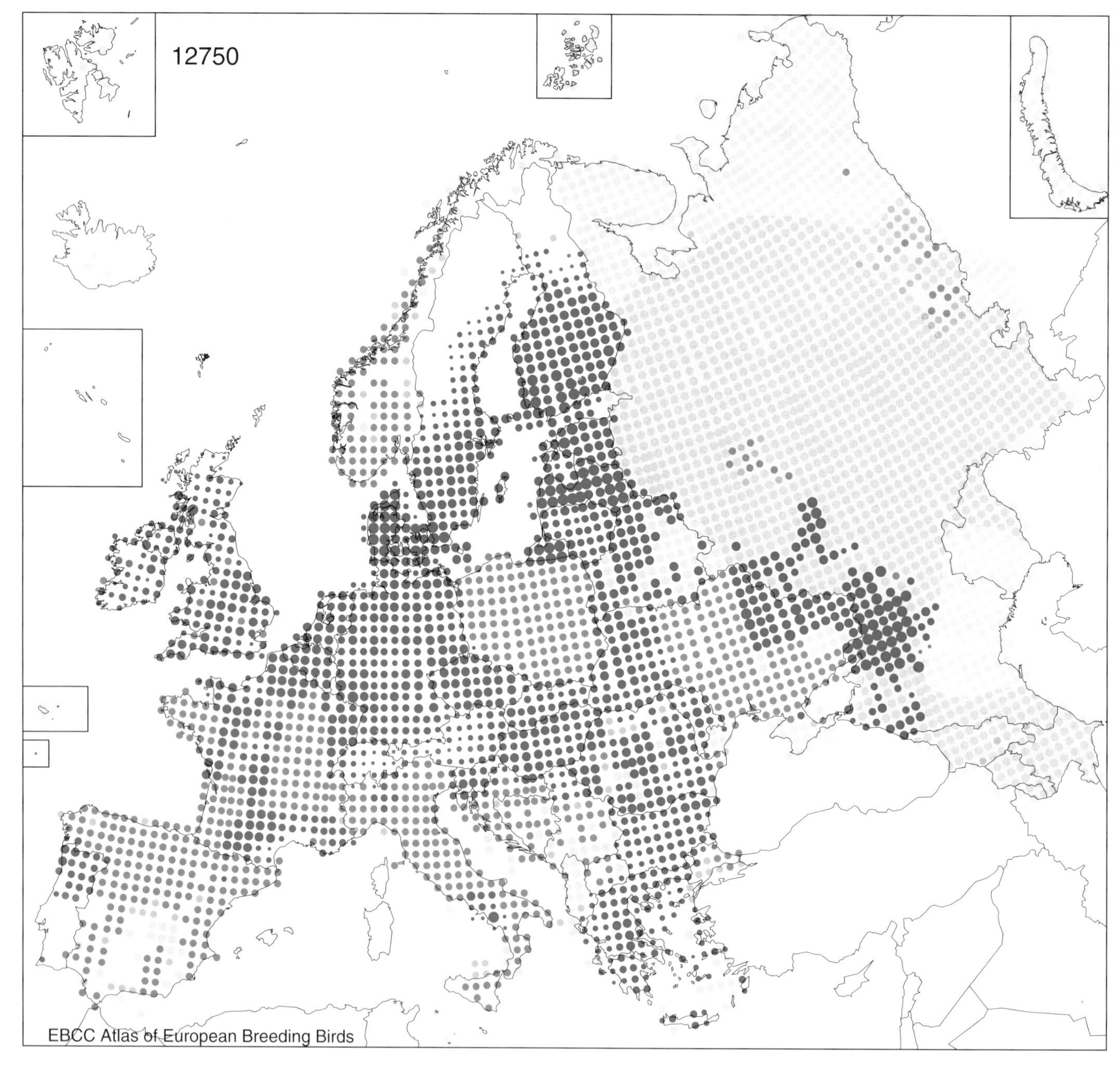

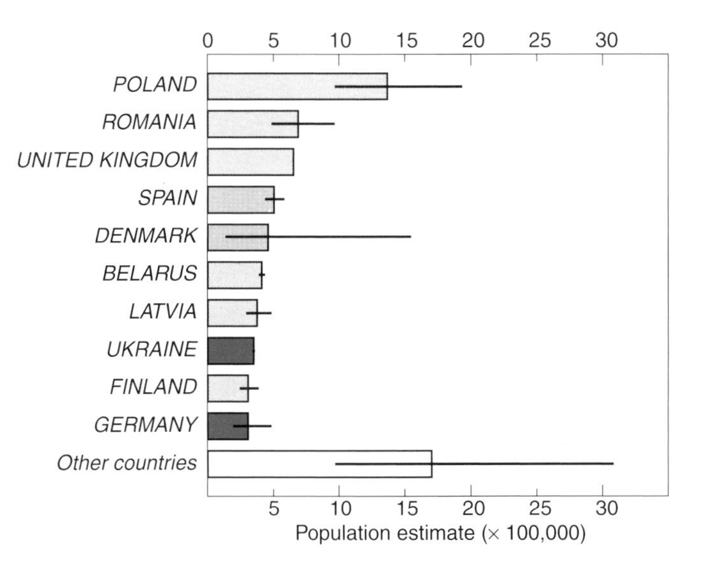

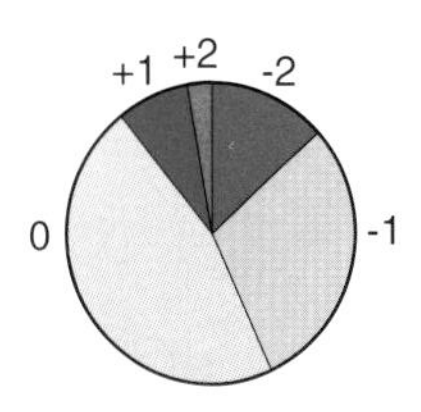

% in top 10 countries: 76.1
Total number of populated European countries: 37
Total European population 6,692,665–8,862,536 (7,347,027)
Russian population 1,000,000–10,000,000 (3,162,278)
Turkish population 50,000–500,000 (158,114)

The Whitethroat's extensive breeding range stretches from the Arctic Circle in Norway to Morocco, and from Ireland to C Siberia (103°E), three of the four subspecies breeding in Europe. The distribution map suggests a lower breeding density along the northern and southern range limits, and shows the species' absence from most of southern Iberia and northern Scandinavia. Predominantly a lowland species, it nevertheless breeds in subalpine scrub up to 1500m asl in the Swiss Alps and 2000m in the Caucasus. However, its breeding distribution probably is patchier in the cooler and more exposed NW European highlands (A. Henderson 1993).

In much of Europe, the Whitethroat is the commonest breeding warbler in open scrub and farmland, building its rather flimsy nest close to the ground amongst tall herbs, grasses or in low bushes. It generally avoids dense scrub, mature woodland and urban habitats but young coniferous plantations and coppiced woodland can support high breeding densities before canopy closure. Males use taller trees and bushes as song-posts. Breeding densities above 100 bp/km^2 can occur in a variety of scrub and young coniferous plantations, but less than 5 bp/km^2 is more typical of cultivated farmland, where hedges and windbreaks provide nesting and foraging sites (Sell & Odderskær 1990, Persson 1971).

The densest breeding populations occur in Russia, Belarus, Poland, the Baltic States, Romania, Great Britain, the Low Countries and Denmark (>5000 bp/50km square), the remainder of Europe mostly having from 1000 to 3000 bp/50km square, dropping below 1000 bp/50km square only towards the distribution limits (Norway, Portugal). The Whitethroat does not breed in Iceland, the Balearics, Corsica and Sardinia.

W and C European breeding populations declined dramatically in the winter of 1968/69 (Winstanley *et al* 1974, Berthold 1974). This crash was best recorded in Britain where the farmland and woodland population fell by *c*67% (Marchant *et al* 1990). Severe drought in the sub-Saharan winter quarters probably caused the sudden decline, through its catastrophic effect on the food supply of wintering birds. Although numbers in W Europe have fluctuated since the 1969 crash, population levels remain depressed. The severe droughts of the mid-1980s heralded yet further declines, especially in Germany (>50% decrease in 1970–90) but also elsewhere, as in Denmark, Spain and Greece. These trends require cautious interpretation because in 1970 numbers were already seriously depleted in much of Europe.

More recently, slightly increasing numbers have been reported from Sweden (in young plantations), Estonia and Ukraine, but this may not represent a recovery from losses since the late 1960s. Loss of habitat through agricultural intensification has caused local decreases. Despite the massive decline in Whitethroat abundance, there is little evidence anywhere in Europe of major changes to its breeding range. There is some evidence from Britain that following the 1969 population crash, losses of birds breeding at higher altitudes were greatest (Marchant *et al* 1990, A. Henderson 1993).

All Whitethroat populations are migratory and winter S of the Sahara in Africa. In West Africa the winter distribution is rather more northerly than for many other sub-Saharan migrants, semi-arid bush savanna and woodland edge being its preferred habitats. Eastern breeding populations occupy similar wintering habitats across a vast area of eastern and southern Africa. There is evidence of a migratory divide within Europe with some Scandinavian birds migrating SW towards Iberia and others moving SE towards the eastern Mediterranean. Autumn migration commences in July and peaks in Europe during August and September. Spring migration begins in March and very few birds remain S of the Sahara by early May. North Africa is likely to be an important spring staging and feeding area for Whitethroats returning to breed in western Europe.

Will Peach (GB) Henrik Sell (DK)

Sylvia borin

Garden Warbler

CZ	Pěnice slavíková	**I**	Beccafico
D	Gartengrasmücke	**NL**	Tuinfluiter
E	Curruca Mosquitera	**P**	Felosa-das-figueiras
F	Fauvette des jardins	**PL**	Gajówka
FIN	Lehtokerttu	**R**	Садовая славка
G	Κηποτσιροβάκος	**S**	Trädgårdssångare
H	Kerti poszáta		

SPEC Cat 4, Threat status S

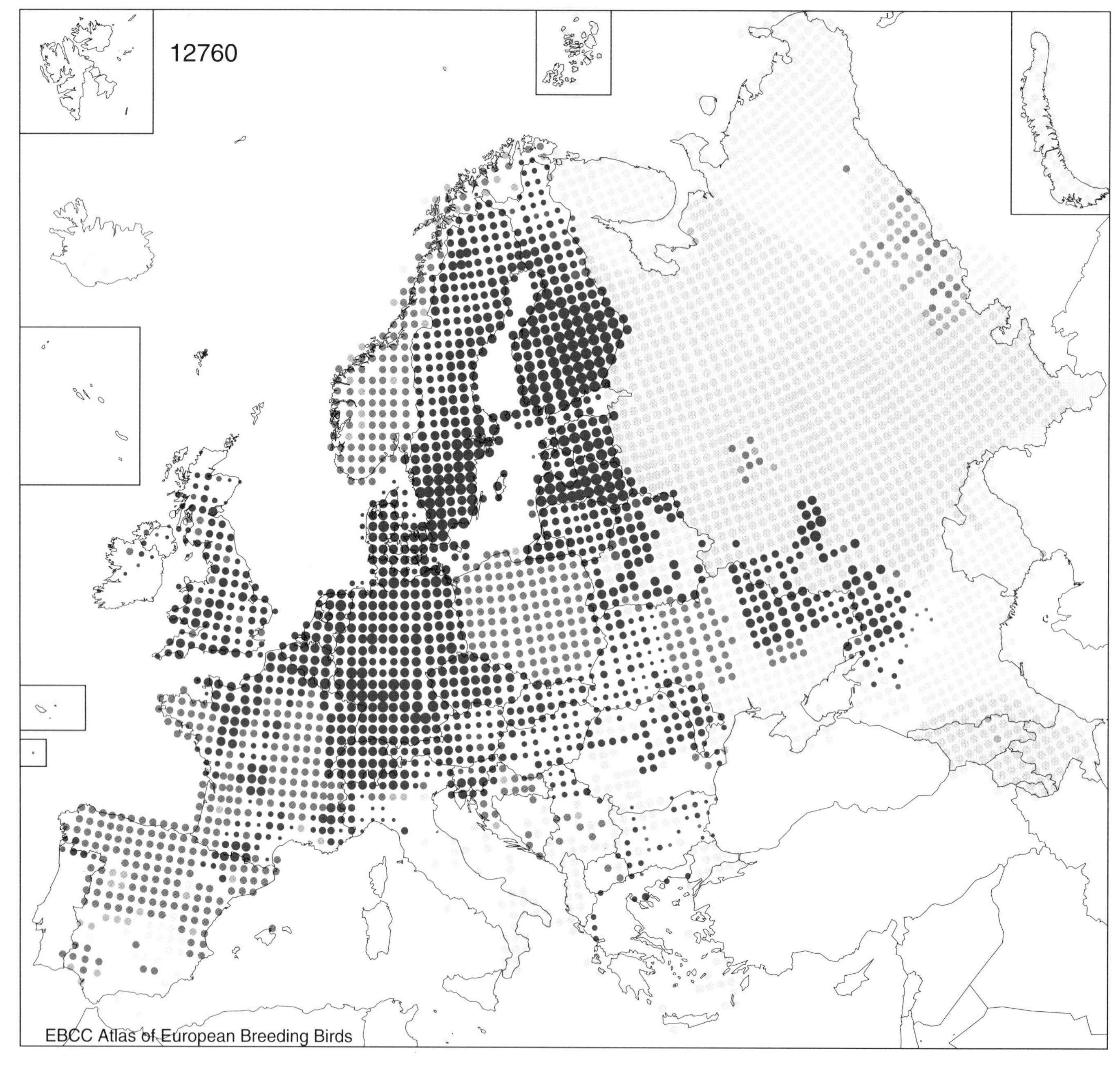

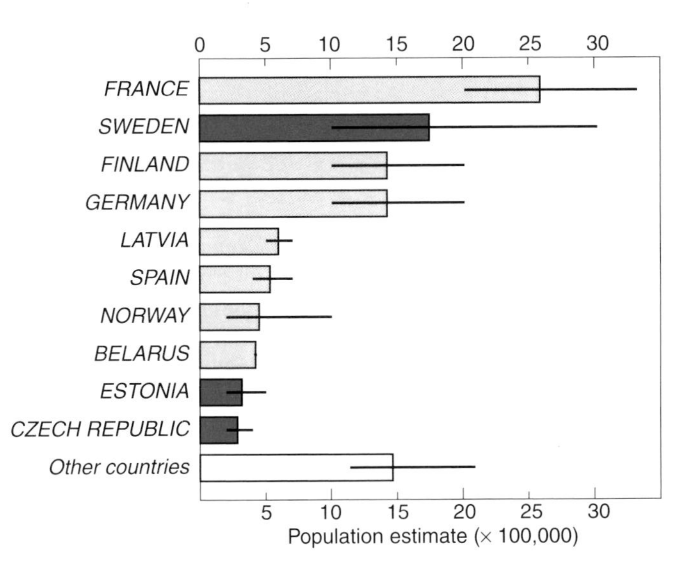

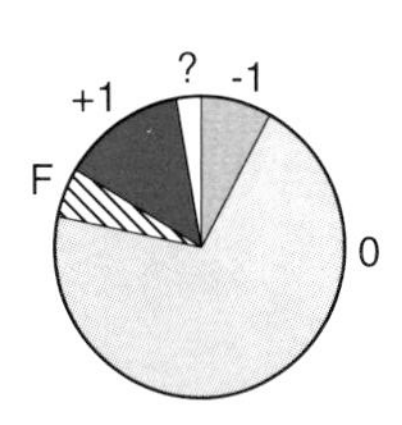

% in top 10 countries: 87.0
Total number of populated European countries: 37
Total European population 10,018,452–12,992,797 (11,170,151)
Russian population 500,000–5,000,000 (1,581,139)
Turkish population 5000–50,000 (15,811)

The Garden Warbler has a Palearctic distribution between 37° and 70°N in the W and *c*52° and *c*64°N in the E, spanning continental and marginally oceanic, mainly temperate climates; it reaches *c*93°E in C Siberia. It breeds throughout most of Europe, tolerating cool conditions well enough to occur close to the North Cape, unlike any other *Sylvia* warbler.

The species inhabits deciduous woodland and scrub, preferring a relatively open canopy and fairly dense ground cover for nesting. It occurs mainly in woodland fringes, glades, regrowth in clearings and scrub. In C Europe, it is particularly associated with small copses and hawthorn *Crataegus monogyna* and blackthorn *Prunus spinosa* clumps, and in Finland with dense raspberry *Rubus idaeus* thickets, but avoids pure coniferous stands, unless these are young and have a dense herb and scrub growth.

Although widespread across Europe, its numbers vary relative to habitat availability, most suitable habitats seemingly being occupied. It is absent from most of Ireland, S Iberia and Italy, and is thinly spread across much of SE Europe. Highest British densities occur in widespread areas of sessile oak *Quercus petraea* (Wales, southern England), but the oakwoods of NW Scotland and W and S Ireland remain largely unoccupied. In the Alps, the species occurs up to 2300m asl. Considerable numbers may breed in the subalpine zone where there is suitable scrub for nesting, mainly various willows (*Salix*) and shrubby clusters of green alder *Alnus viridis* (Widmer 1993).

The species' British range has extended northwards recently, sporadic breeding occurring in most northern Scottish counties. It has not suffered the recent massive population declines of some other long-distance migrants. Instead, numbers are rather stable or even increasing in areas like Fennoscandia, Estonia, Britain, Belgium and the Czech Republic. The map indicates that the species probably has colonized the steppe shelterbelts in SE Russia, possibly meeting the Caucasus population. In the mid-1970s, however, marked declines were reported coinciding with drought conditions in the Sahel, though unlike the Whitethroat *S. communis*, the Garden Warbler does not winter there. Recovery has been rapid and apparently still continues; it seems largely complete in British woodland, but less so in farmland. The recent Finnish increase is due to forest fragmentation and other land-use changes (Koskimies 1989a).

Recent averaged estimates reveal *c*12.5Mbp in Europe. In Great Britain, average densities across regions are from 0.7 bp/km² (farmland) to 5.8 bp/km² (woodland). Similarly, across much of C Europe, average densities seemingly vary from 1 to 5 bp/km² (Flade 1994). Habitat quality determines abundance and territory size, which may be <0.2ha in optimal habitats, but usually is larger; near Oxford it varied from 0.26ha (scrub) to 0.77ha (mixed scrub and deciduous woodland). Hence abundance varies considerably, being locally up to 200 bp/km² in favoured scrub habitat. Average density in prime habitats in S Finland is *c*70 bp/km² (T. Solonen, in prep.), but locally can reach >100 bp/km² (Solonen 1979). Similar values obtain in Estonia in thickets and deciduous wooded strips amidst open floodplain meadows (Leibak *et al* 1994).

The Garden Warbler winters in Africa S of 10°N in the W and of 3°N in the E, where it favours thickets and undergrowth, occupying outlying woods, fringing forests, scrubby savanna, dense thickets at permanent swamps, riverine forests and secondary forest. It appears to avoid closed moist forests but may enter them in the dry season when suitable food plants are fruiting. The western subspecies, nominate *borin*, winters more to the W, occurring progressively more sparsely eastwards where the eastern *woodwardi* predominates. The breeding ground intergradation zone is wide, from Poland to Bulgaria eastwards.

Franz Bairlein (D)

Sylvia atricapilla Blackcap

CZ	Pěnice černohlavá	I	Capinera
D	Mönchsgrasmücke	NL	Zwartkop
E	Curruca Capirotada	P	Toutinegra-de-barrete-preto
F	Fauvette à tête noire	PL	Kapturka
FIN	Mustapääkerttu	R	Славка-черноголовка
G	Μαυροσκούφης	S	Svarthätta
H	Barátposzáta		

SPEC Cat 4, Threat status S

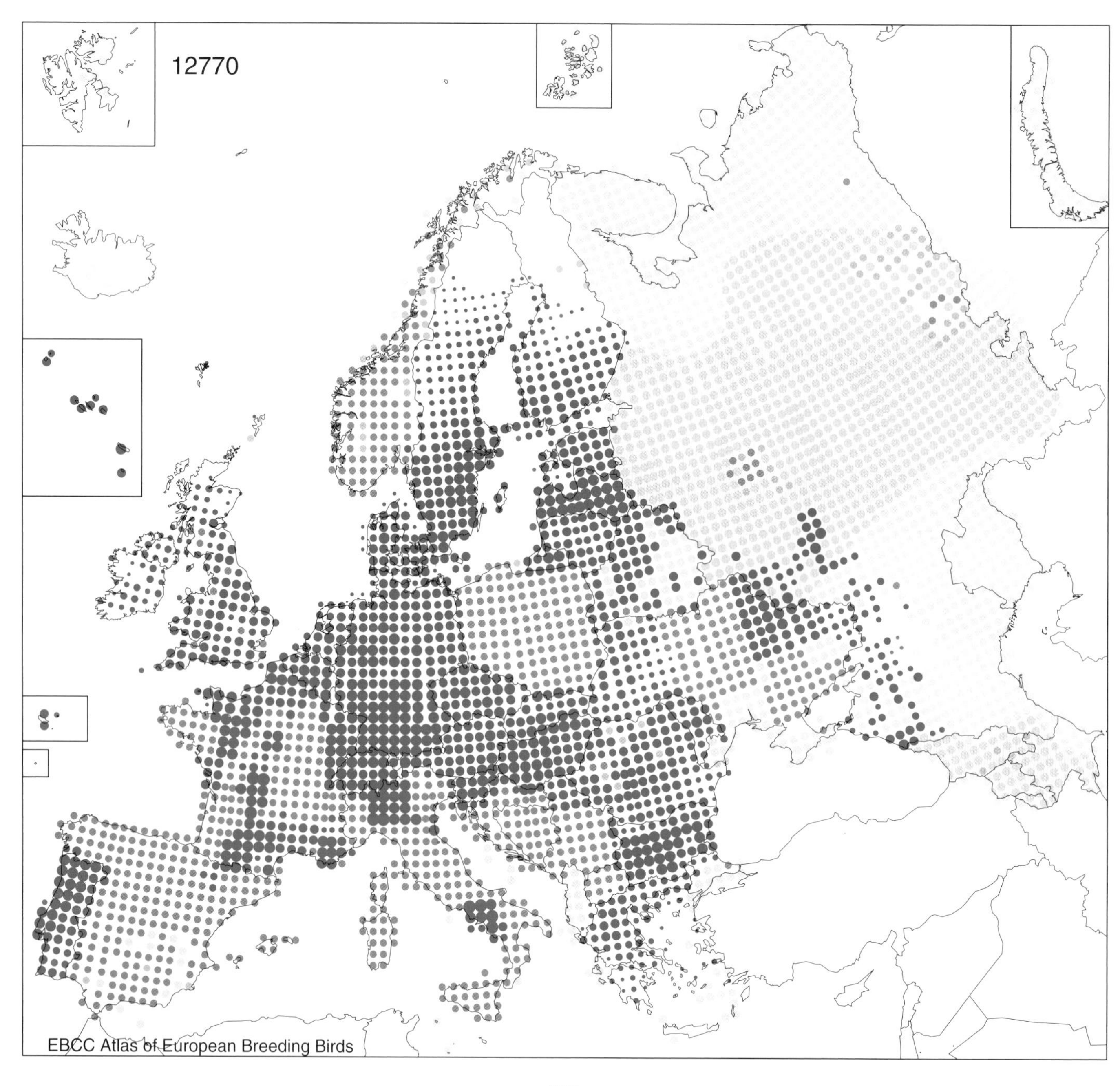

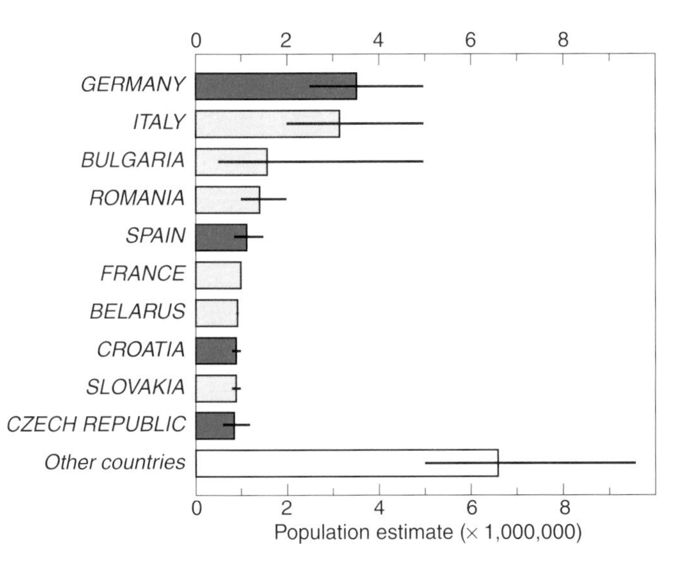

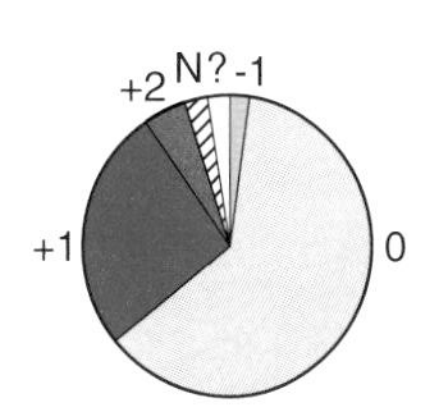

% in top 10 countries: 72.7
Total number of populated European countries: 41
Total European population 19,126,436–25,504,756 (21,161,336)
Russian population 1,000,000–10,000,000 (3,162,278)
Turkish population 50,000–100,000 (70,711)

The Blackcap exhibits a mainly European distribution, with embranchments through NW Africa to the Atlantic islands (Azores to Cape Verde Islands) and in Asia (W Siberia). It breeds in the temperate zone in the continental, oceanic, mediterranean and to some extent, subtropical climates.

Highly arboreal, it prefers mostly mature but especially humid deciduous mixed lowland and riparian forests, although it nests in tall, reasonably dense shrubby undergrowth. It generally avoids dry coniferous woodland. It is relatively evenly distributed throughout its range except for a decreasing gradient to the range limits (particularly N and E), where it becomes scarcer. Locally, uneven occurrence is due to the distribution pattern of suitable habitats. Normally the species breeds below 2000m asl, whereas wintering individuals in Africa may reach 3500m.

The Blackcap is the 8th to 15th most abundant species in typical C European bird communities of cultivated mosaic landscape (Bezzel 1982, Flade 1994, Rheinwald 1994). Maximum densities reaching 8 bp/ha can occur in small areas of optimum lowland forests in S Germany, and 6 bp/ha in deciduous forests in S France, but in larger areas of such habitats, *c*400 bp/km^2 is normally the maximum. Densities of *c*1–5 bp/ha occur in the Atlantic islands, the Mediterranean and C Europe as far as Moscow region, but such values apply in larger areas only for those extensive, lowland optimum-quality forests remaining in the C European belt (France–Russia). In more typical C European fairly open cultivated landscape, average breeding density is only *c*3–7 bp/km^2 (Berthold *et al* 1990). To the N and E maximum densities decline sharply, typically reaching only *c*30 bp/km^2 in S Finland's richest deciduous forests (T. Solonen, in prep). Under 1 bp/km^2 is probably representative of N Greece (Hölzinger 1990).

The Blackcap's distribution has changed little, but its range has extended slightly in Spain, Ireland and Finland. Generally populations have been relatively stable or have increased slightly, but those in Britain & Ireland, Denmark, Scandinavia and the former Czechoslovakia have doubled since *c*1945 (average annual rates of increase 2.7–8.8%; Marchant 1992), partly because of an increase in underbrush through human activity (more gardens, orchards, fewer continuous woodlands); similar circumstances apply in the Atlantic islands (Berthold *et al* 1990).

In contrast to other *Sylvia* species (Garden Warbler *S. borin*, Lesser Whitethroat *S. curruca*) the Blackcap's clutch size does not increase between C and N Europe (whereas that in Africa and S Europe is larger than in C Europe), nor is its breeding season significantly longer than the Garden Warbler's in N Europe (unlike C Europe). Thus there is a possible physiological constraint in N Europe limiting the northern breeding distribution. However, the Blackcap in the Moscow region does lay a significantly larger clutch than conspecifics in C Europe (Berthold *et al* 1990, in prep).

The Blackcap is almost exclusively resident on the Atlantic islands, partially migratory in the Mediterranean, and almost totally migratory in its northernmost range. A migration divide (eastern Alps–Scandinavia) separates western populations (wintering in the W Mediterranean; some in sub-Saharan West Africa) from eastern populations (wintering in SE Africa). Since 1965, a C European subpopulation has developed a new migratory direction to the WNW, to novel wintering areas in Britain & Ireland (Berthold *et al* 1992).

Experimental studies have shown that the Blackcap is characterized by distinct genetic control of annual processes like migration, breeding and moult and by considerable genetic variation of these processes. Some features, like migratory events, have high microevolutionary potentials so that, should further environmental changes occur, additional quite rapid adaptations can be expected (Berthold 1994).

There are five generally accepted subspecies besides the nominate *atricapilla* (*S.a. atlantis* Azores; *dammholzi* Caucasus southeastwards; *gularis* Cape Verdes; *heineken* Madeira, Canaries; *koenigi* Mediterranean islands). This subdivision certainly needs critical revision. None of the subspecies currently shows exceptional population trends (Berthold *et al* 1990).

Peter Berthold (D) Tapio Solenen (FIN)

This species account is sponsored by the Czech Society for Ornithology, CZ.

Phylloscopus trochiloides viridanus Greenish Warbler

CZ	Budníček zelený	I	Luí verdastro
D	Grünlaubsänger	NL	Grauwe Fitis
E	Mosquitero Troquiloide	P	Felosa-troquilóide
F	Pouillot verdâtre	PL	Wójcik
FIN	Idänuunilintu	R	Зеленая пеночка
G	Πρασινοφυλλοσκόπος	S	Lundsångare
H	Zöld füzike		

Non-SPEC, Threat status S (P)

Phylloscopus trochiloides nitidus Green Warbler

The taxonomic position of *nitidus* is uncertain. Some authorities have split it from *P. trochiloides* and assigned it separate species status. Recent genetic evidence (mitochondrial *cyt b* gene) suggests that the two represent a level of differentiation intermediate between subspecies and species (Helbig *et al* 1995), a circumstance met with in other genera. In the *Atlas* the treatment of *nitidus* as conspecific with *P. trochiloides* does not imply that a final taxonomic consensus has been reached.

CZ	Budníček žlutavý	I	Luí giallo
D	Wacholderlaubsänger	NL	Groene Fitis
E	Mosquitero Verde	P	Felosa-verde
F	Pouillot de Caucase	PL	Świstunka kaukaska
FIN	Kaukasianuunilintu	R	Желтобрюхая пеночка
G	Κεδροφυλλοσκόπος	S	Kaukasisk lundsångare
H	Kaukázusi füzike		

Non-SPEC, Threat status S (P)

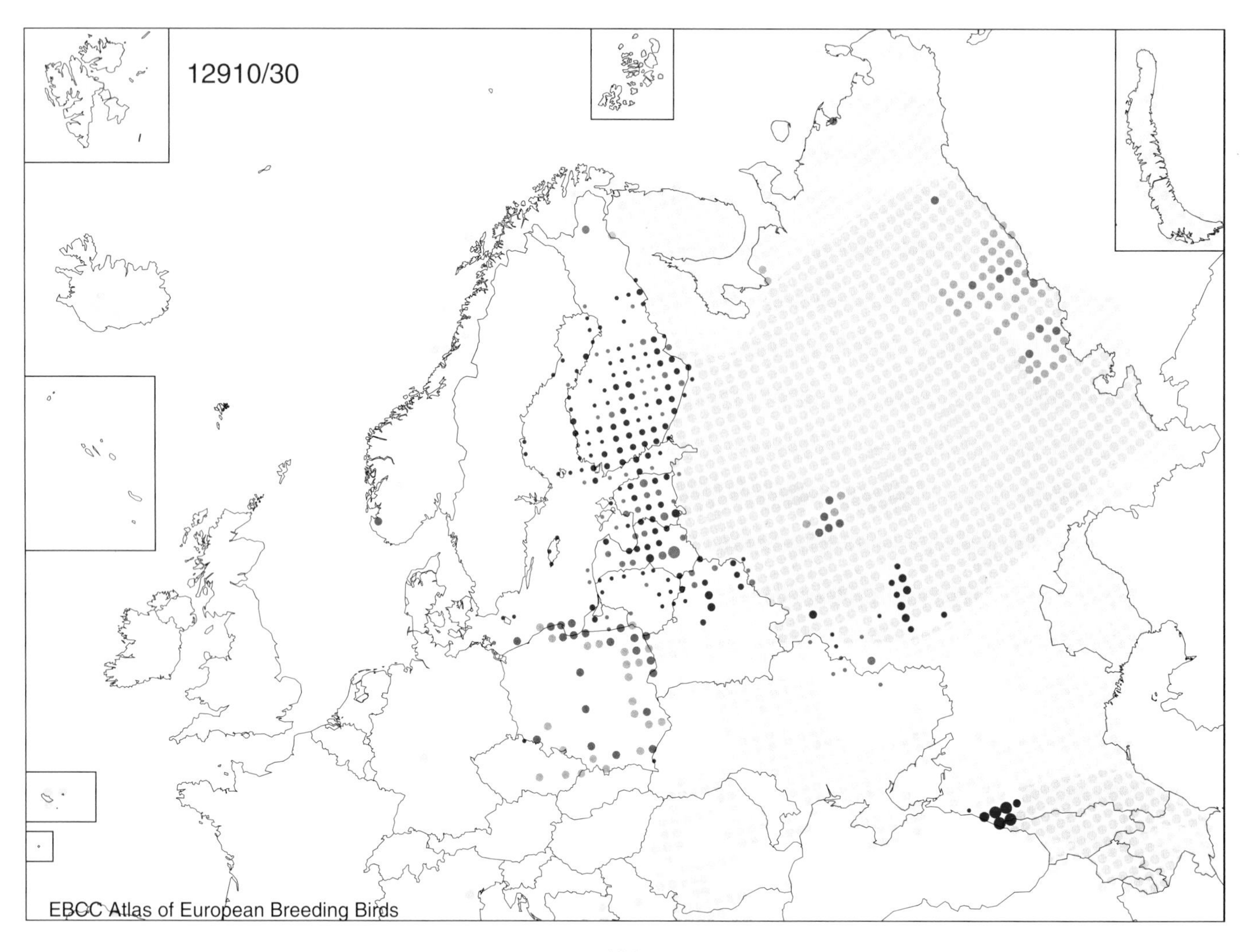

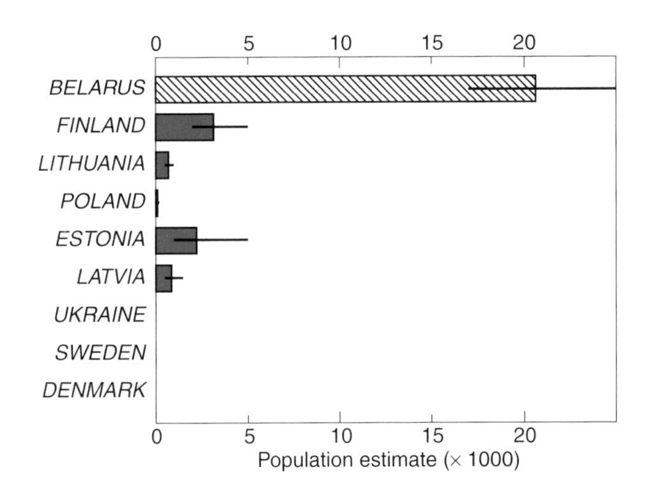

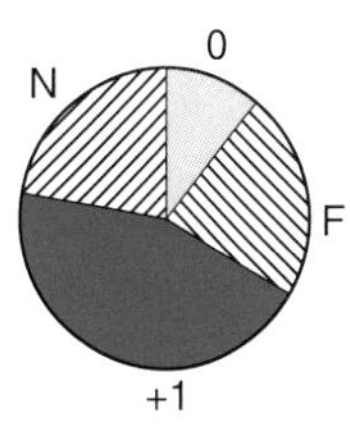

% in top 10 countries: 100.0
Total number of populated European countries: 9
Total European population 23,679–33,239 (27,695)
Russian population 100,000–1,000,000 (316,228)

Greenish Warbler

The Greenish Warbler, the westernmost subspecies of the *P. trochiloides* complex, breeds in NE Europe, its range extending E to the Yenisey and SE to Kashmir. In E Asia it is replaced by *P.(t.) plumbeitarsus*. Allied subspecies, including the nominate, breed in C Asia. It winters in SE India and Sri Lanka, overlapping partially with Green Warbler *P.t. nitidus* (*qv*).

The Greenish Warbler inhabits many forest types but locally prefers the most productive stands. In NE Europe, it prefers old, spruce-dominated (*Picea*) forests with an admixture of broad-leaved trees. Further S however, it occupies mainly broad-leaved stands, mostly of multi-storey structure and artificially rich in tree species, usually dominated by mature beech *Fagus*, maple *Acer* or lime *Tilia*, and interspersed with pine *Pinus* or spruce. Typical haunts are parks and old deciduous avenues. Where resident, typically it occupies clearings, margins, roadsides, streams, slopes and ravines (Ptushenko & Inozemtsev 1968). Furthest S, in the C European mountains it reverts mostly to spruce-dominated areas along gullies, up to 1200m asl (Flousek & Pavelka 1993).

The range expansion from W Asia reached the E Baltic in the early 1900s. Colonization of the SW Baltic basin took *c*50 years, but only since the 1970s has the Greenish Warbler begun to appear in the Bavarian, Czech and S Polish mountains. In the SW Baltic basin, numbers fluctuate from invasion to scarcity between years, this population consisting mostly of single males which may disappear after occupying territories briefly. Genuine breeding records are therefore scarce, comprising *c*5% of all records since the 1960s. Although there is an underlying increasing trend, the peripheral population of the SW Baltic probably depends on invasion recruitment. A significant excess of single males is characteristic also of regions where Greenish Warbler is an abundant breeder, as in the E Baltic basin, Russia (Ptushenko & Inozemtsev 1968, Mal'chevski & Pukinski 1983) and Finland.

Peak years apparently are synchronous over the entire European range (recently 1978, 1988 and 1992) and during mid- to late May are linked with high temperatures and persistent southeasterly movement of warm air masses which would aid extended migration beyond the traditional range for returning birds, allowing occupation of suitable habitat further W. This would account for *viridanus*' southwesterly European breeding range limit being unstable and suggests that westward expansion may be driven by climatic trends.

Densities in Europe remain relatively low, especially toward the SW limit, typically being *c*1–5 males/km^2 (Ptushenko & Inozemtsev 1968, Babenko & Konstantinov 1983, Veromann 1994b), but locally higher. The combination of patchy distribution and erratic population fluctuations prevents greater precision.

Przemek Chylarecki (PL) Jānis Priednieks (LAT)

Green Warbler

The Green Warbler is distributed from Turkey to Turkmenistan, Iran and Afghanistan, its European range covering southeasternmost Russia, the Caucasus, Transcaucasia, Armenia and Azerbaijan. It winters in India, overlapping with *viridanus* (*qv*) and other subspecies.

It is a typical and abundant bird of mountain forests, breeding in broad-leaved and coniferous forests at medium altitudes (800–2000m; Albrecht 1984), riverine forests, and on the timberline, in krummholz and scrub. Censuses in the late 1970s and early 1980s in the W Caucasus found the highest densities in birch forests and stands of grey alder *Alnus incana* (Til'ba & Kazakov 1985, Tkachenko 1966). In the C Caucasus the highest densities were found in pine forest (Afonin 1985, Komarov 1991), about 2–4 times higher than in beech forests and krummholz birch (Afonin 1985), but in river valleys were very low (Komarov 1991). In the Azerbaijan mountain forests density increases with altitude, being 0.3–2.1 birds/km of transect route in lower-level forests and 6–14 at medium altitude (Drozdov 1965).

Peter Til'ba (R)

Phylloscopus borealis

Arctic Warbler

CZ	Budníček severní	I	Luí boreale
D	Wanderlaubsänger	NL	Noordse Boszanger
E	Mosquitero Boreal	P	Felosa-boreal
F	Pouillot boréal	PL	Świstunka północna
FIN	Lapinuunilintu	R	Бурая пеночка
G	Χιονοφυλλοσκόπος	S	Nordsångare
H	Északi füzike		

Non-SPEC, Threat status S (P)

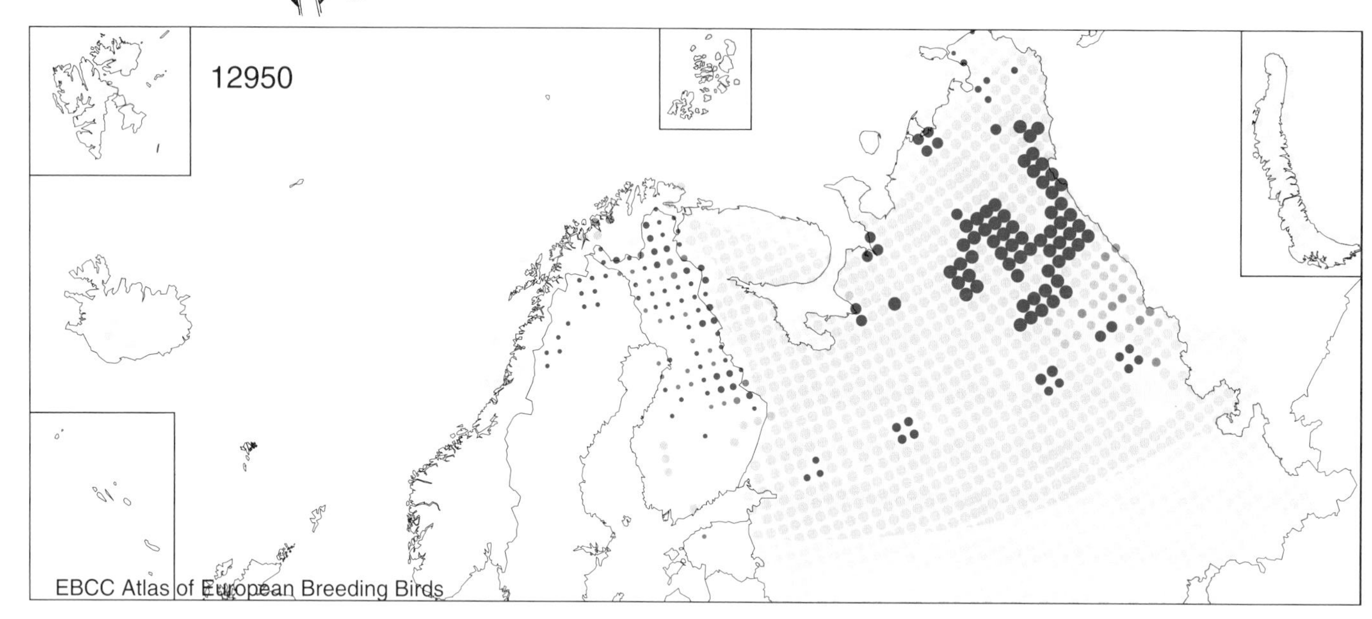

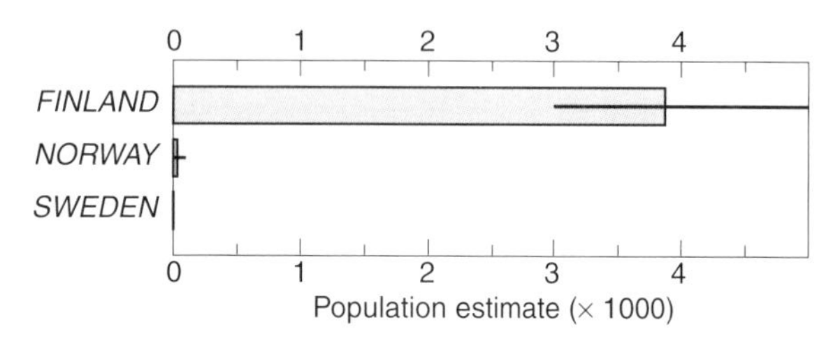

-1
0

% in top 10 countries: 100.0
Total number of populated European countries: 3
Total European population 3035–5037 (3908)
Russian population 1,000,000–10,000,000 (3,162,278)

The vast world distribution of the Arctic Warbler encompasses the boreal and subarctic zones from N Fennoscandia through Russia and Siberia to Japan and W Alaska. The species winters in SE Asia and the East Indies.

In its distribution centre it breeds in various types of coniferous, deciduous and mixed forests, but especially towards the northern range margins it increasingly is confined to lush deciduous woods and shrubs. It is abundant in NE Europe, its breeding densities decreasing towards Fennoscandia and the boreal zone's southern margin. On the Ural slopes densities vary annually from 14 to 88 bp/km^2; in the upper Pechora area from 3 to 56 (Estafiev 1981); in the floodplain forests of the Pechora and Vychegda Rivers from 1.5 to 30 (6–25 in birch *Betula*, 0.2–7.0 in pine *Pinus*); near the northern tree limit, in forests 2–14 and in tundra shrubs and riverside forests 0.5–12 (S.K. Kotchanov, pers obs); and in the Pinega Reserve E of the White Sea 3–21 (Rykova 1986). However, at the range margins in Karelia and the Leningrad region as well as in Finland and N Scandinavia the Arctic Warbler is very scarce. Although not mapped, possible breeding was reported from a square near Bryansk, Russia, 600 km S of St Petersburg.

In the long-term the population is fairly stable, although numbers and range have increased slightly in Finland since the 1970s (Pulliainen *et al* 1990). Numbers have increased also in the Leningrad, Karelian and Vologda regions (Mal'chevski & Pukinski 1983). Scattered data from Norway and Sweden suggest some decrease. The European breeding population amounts to at least 1Mbp, of which 3000–5000bp are in Finland, 10–100bp in Norway and perhaps 10bp in Sweden.

Its migratory journey is one of the longest made by Fennoscandian passerines. Breeding birds arrive in Finland in mid-June and depart as soon as early August. Hence, time available for breeding is short, possibly limiting its breeding range in the NW. Here, migration seems to be prolonged in warm springs, resulting in higher numbers (J. Tiainen, pers obs).

Juha Tiainen (FIN) Sergey K Kotchanov (R)
Alexey A Estafiev (R)

Phylloscopus inornatus

Yellow-browed Warbler

CZ	Budníček pruhohlavý	I	Luí forestiero
D	Gelbbrauen-Laubsänger	NL	Bladkoning
E	Mosquitero Bilistado	P	Felosa-bilistada
F	Pouillot à grands sourcils	PL	Świstunka żółtawa
FIN	Kirjosiipiuunilintu	R	Пеночка-зарничка
G	Γραμμοφυλλοσκόπος	S	Taigasångare
H	Vándorfüzike		

Non-SPEC, Threat status S

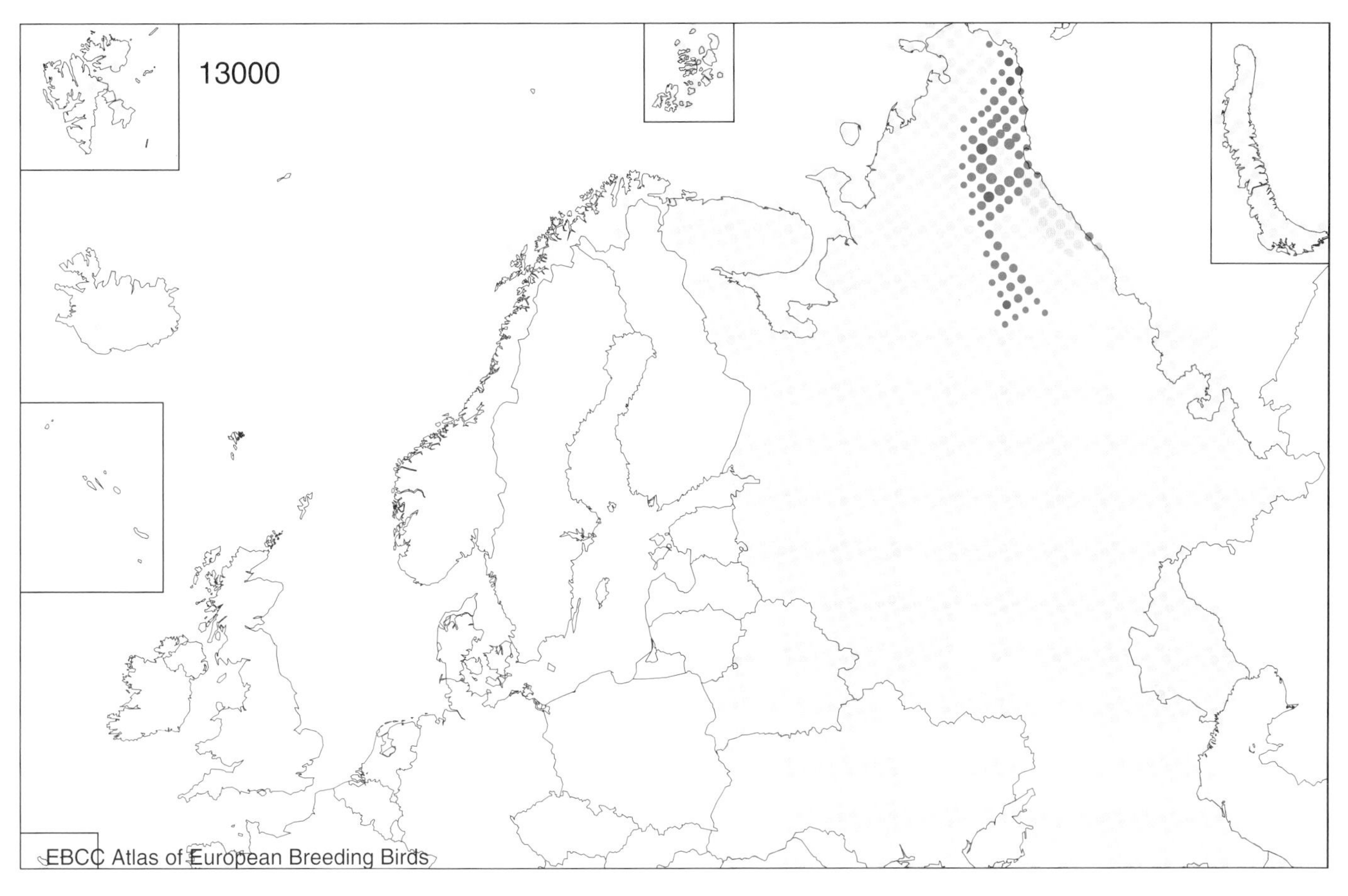

A mainly Asian species, the Yellow-browed Warbler occupies the northern boreal forests. Its European range has the typical Siberian wedge shape, the widest part being in the northern and mid-taiga subzones, where the species occurs from the middle and upper reaches of the Pechora River to the Izma River valley and Syktyvkar. Here its range narrows sharply to the N converging towards the western macroslope of the Urals at the edge of the forest-tundra zone. The distribution also narrows to the S (Morozov 1989). The northern subspecies *P.i. inornatus* winters far to the S in India, SE Asia and S China. It occurs as a vagrant and aberrant migrant over much of Europe, often during the breeding season.

The Yellow-browed Warbler nests in a variety of habitats from forests to semi-open shrubs. It breeds in Europe in birch–spruce (*Betula–Picea*) and other small-leaved forests in the mid-taiga subzone and in most kinds of mixed forests in the northern taiga subzone. In the N it uses sparse, slow-growing spruce forests but avoids the commoner larch *Larix* and birch thin forests (Morozov 1989). Its distribution expands after the breeding season, and it is recorded annually in the Ural Mountain meadows (Beshkarev & Teplov 1993).

Breeding density is low towards the northern and southern limits of its European range, being only 0.2 bp/km^2 in small-leaved forest near Syktyvkar. Conversely, it is much higher in the more central northern taiga subzone, up to 8 bp/km^2 in mixed forest (V.M. Anufriev, in prep).

The population of the Yellow-browed Warbler probably is stable, despite the new observations in the Izma Valley and in the environs of Syktyvkar, because these are more the consequence of the poor previous knowledge of the region and the sporadic character of the species' distribution. In our opinion, the species' European population, which is confined to the Komi Republic, totals *c*45 000–46 000bp.

Vladimir N Anufriev (R) Alexey A Estafiev (R)

Phylloscopus bonelli — Bonelli's Warbler

CZ	Budníček horský	**I**	Luí bianco
D	Berglaubsänger	**NL**	Bergfluiter
E	Mosquitero Papialbo	**P**	Felosa de Bonelli
F	Pouillot de Bonelli	**PL**	Świstunka górska
FIN	Vuoriuunilintu	**R**	Светлобрюхая пеночка
G	Βουνοφυλλοσκόπος	**S**	Bergsångare
H	Bonelli-füzike		

SPEC Cat 4, Threat status S

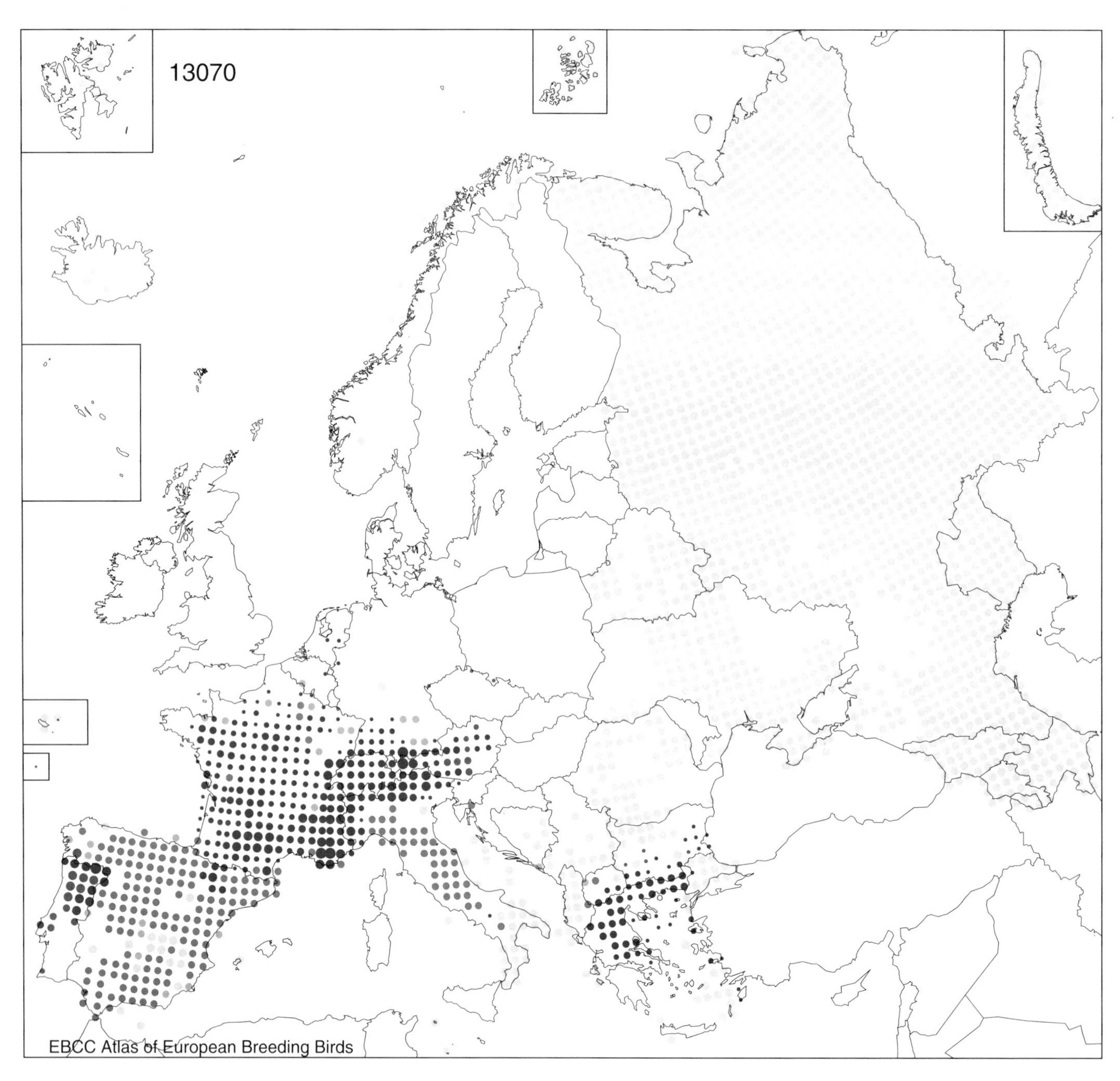

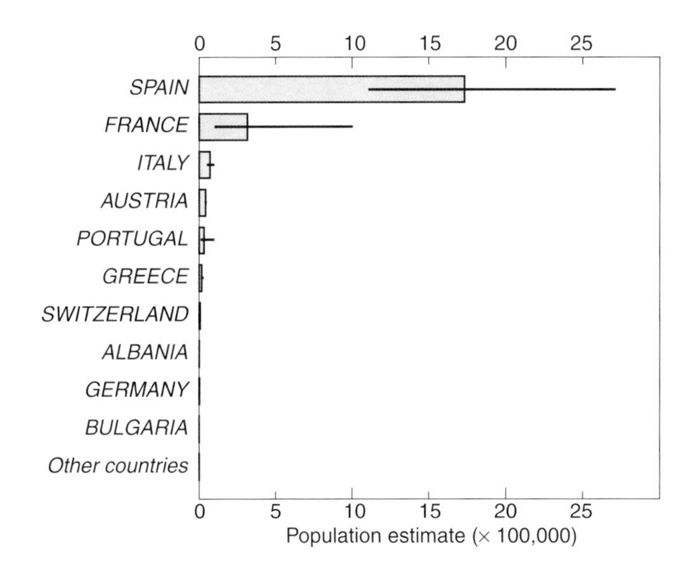

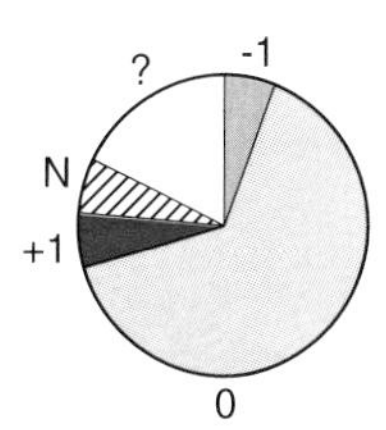

% in top 10 countries: 100.0
Total number of populated European countries: 17
Total European population 1,551,429–3,406,616 (2,211,993)
Turkish population 1000–10,000 (3162)

Bonelli's Warbler, a European leaf-warbler of the warm temperate, mediterranean continental and oceanic zones between the 19° and 31°C July isotherms, breeds outside Europe only in western Anatolia (the western Black Sea coastlands to the Taurus Mountains; Roselaar 1995), in scattered populations in E Iran, Lebanon, N Israel (Shirihai 1996) and southeasternmost Turkey, and in NW Africa (Atlas Mountains). The species' absence from southern Portugal, Italy, Greece and the Mediterranean islands is probably due in part to lack of suitable habitat.

The breeding distribution is disjunct: western and eastern populations are separated by a gap in former Yugoslavia. Conventionally, the two populations have been assigned subspecific status. However, recent behavioural and genetic evidence suggest that they comprise true species. The vocalizations of eastern *Phylloscopus (b.) orientalis* and the western *Ph. bonelli bonelli* seem sufficiently different to prevent interbreeding (Helb *et al* 1982). The mitochondrial genetic difference between the two populations is far greater than is typical for subspecies in the leaf-warbler genus, and is at least as large as between several pairs of recognized sister species (Helbig *et al* 1995).

Bonelli's Warbler prefers warm woodland habitats. It breeds in many kinds of light dry forests containing glades and clearings, but the presence of undergrowth whose composition varies across the range, is essential. In lowlands it favours thin-canopied deciduous woods of such as oak *Quercus*, birch *Betula*, beech *Fagus* and sweet chestnut *Castanea sativa*. In mountainous and hilly country territories are situated on slopes with coniferous or mixed stands, especially containing Scots *Pinus sylvestris* or other pines. N of the Alps in Allgäu and Bavaria, Bonelli's Warbler breeds also on raised bogs where pine and birch grow.

In France, breeding densities of 3.5–4.7 bp/10ha and 1.0–1.6 bp/10ha have been recorded in deciduous and pine habitats respectively (Grafeuille 1994). In the Swiss Alps values were 0.6–3.0 bp/10ha in mountain pine–larch (*–Larix*) and mixed pine–deciduous forests (locally up to 8–10 bp/10ha). Even higher densities are known for Italy. In Bavaria, a large Bavarian raised bog (42km^2) held *c*13 territories (*HVM*).

Western populations total *c*1.5M–4Mbp, but eastern populations in Europe are estimated to reach *c*1% of these levels. Spain holds >65% of the western populations, Bonelli's Warbler often being the predominant forest species (de Garnica 1978), and France 15–20%. The remaining countries hold less than 10% altogether. Greece, Albania and Turkish Thrace have *c*15 000–40 000bp (*orientalis*) and some dozens or hundreds occur in Bulgaria and probably Macedonia. The range margin populations can be dense in suitable habitats, but in a very scattered fashion.

The available information suggests the species has not undergone marked population changes in recent times, but the western population apparently has slowly increased in numbers and range in the 20th century, reaching NE France (leaving gaps only in Brittany and along the northern coastal region) and then Belgium (late 1960s) and The Netherlands (mid-1970s, although its present breeding status is obscure; R.G. Bijlsma, pers comm). A decline in population size has been occurring in Baden-Württemberg since the 1960s and possibly even since the 1940s (Hölzinger & Riedinger 1987). The species' scattered occurrence in the Krkonose Mountains of the Czech Republic and Poland originated in the mid-1970s. The Bulgarian population has noticeably increased in range and numbers recently.

Bonelli's Warbler overwinters in steppe or bushy savannas S of the Sahara, from the Atlantic to Sudan. Eastern populations migrate southwards or southeastwards to northern East Africa, while western populations head SSW to the southern Sahel zone from Sénégal and southern Mauritania to the Lake Chad basin. In Africa the two populations remain separated by a gap from eastern Chad to western Sudan (*HVM*).

Juha Tiainen (FIN)

Phylloscopus sibilatrix **Wood Warbler**

CZ	Budníček lesní	I	Luí verde
D	Waldlaubsänger	NL	Fluiter
E	Mosquitero Silbador	P	Felosa-assobiadeira
F	Pouillot siffleur	PL	Świstunka
FIN	Sirittäjä	R	Пеночка-трещотка
G	Δασοφυλλοσκόπος	S	Grönsångare
H	Sisegő füzike		

SPEC Cat 4, Threat status S (P)

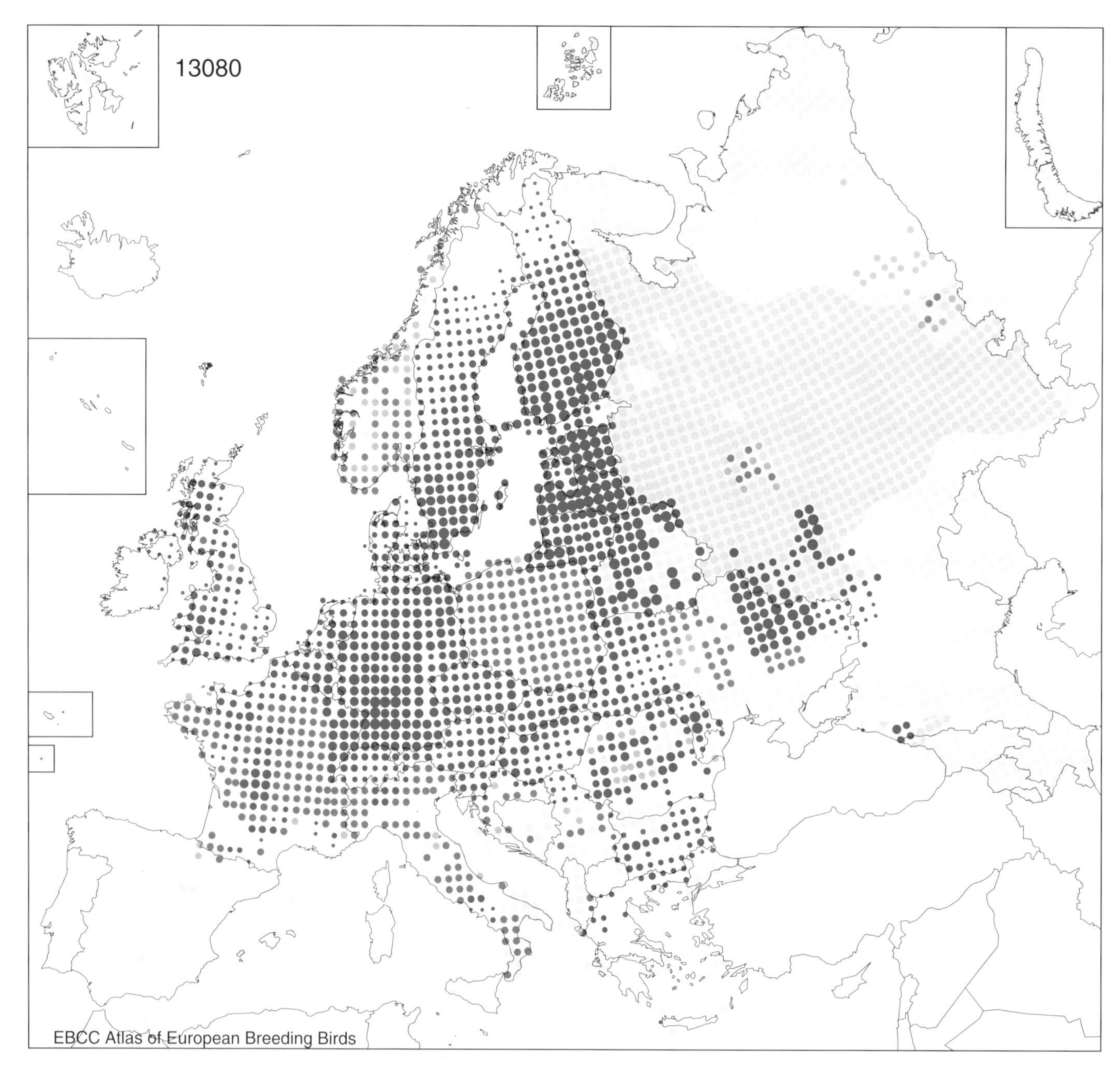

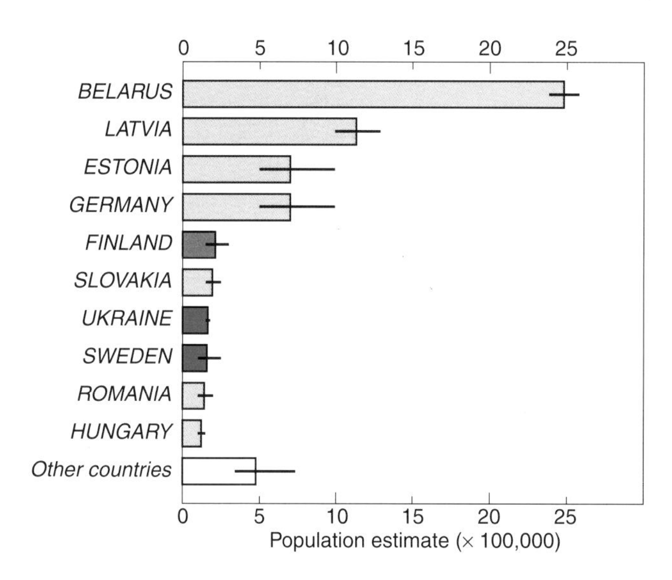

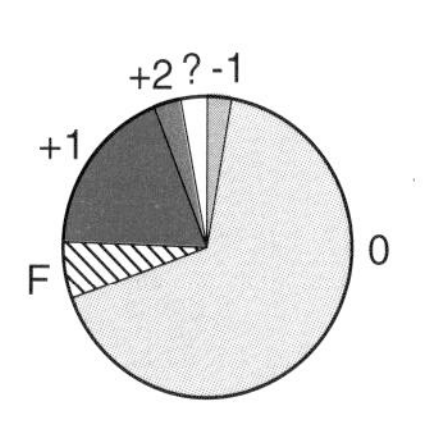

% in top 10 countries: 92.7
Total number of populated European countries: 33
Total European population 6,163,843–7,013,843 (6,523,037)
Russian population 10,000,000–100,000,000 (31,622,777)
Turkish population 1–100 (10)

The monotypic Wood Warbler's western Palearctic breeding distribution stretches from the Pyrenees to the Urals, N as far as southern Lapland, the White Sea coast and the foothills of the C Urals. Southwards its distribution extends along mountain ridges to southern Italy and the Balkan Peninsula, the SE boundary approximating to the southern edge of the forest-steppe zone E to the southern Urals. Southern outposts are in Crimea and the western Great Caucasus. It also occupies C Siberia E to *c*90°N.

A species of the forest interior, it inhabits mature deciduous or mixed stands, although it also accepts coniferous stands containing a proportion of deciduous trees or undergrowth. Its habitat requirements are shady, closed-canopy forest for foraging, a sparse low ground-layer for nesting and thin bush and lower canopy-layers for singing and display. This structural combination allows the Wood Warbler to occupy many different forest types, such as beech–oak (*Fagus sylvatica–Quercus* spp) in its western range, oak–hornbeam–linden (*Quercus* spp–*Carpinus betulus–Tilia cordata*), often mixed with conifers, in its C and E range, and birch or mixed stands in the N. It normally avoids swampy forests, probably because they lack adequate dry nest sites (Piotrowska & Wesołowski 1989), and places with an open park-like canopy or dense undergrowth.

In N and C Europe the Wood Warbler regionally is a widespread lowland species, whereas in more southerly regions its distribution is patchy and mostly limited to low-altitude mountain forest belts (up to 1400m asl). Distribution gaps in Britain & Ireland and Norway are concordant with the absence of forests.

The Wood Warbler has a low site tenacity, changing its breeding areas from year to year, a characteristic which results in wide population fluctuations at a local scale, as exemplified in the Białowieża National Park in Poland, where its numbers varied 18-fold during 19 years of observation, from being the second most numerous forest bird to almost local extinction (Wesołowski 1985, pers obs). It is therefore extremely difficult to assess population sizes, generalizations requiring cautious assessment. However, the species clearly is commonest in its C and NE range from Germany through S Sweden, Poland and the Baltic States to Belarus, Russia and S Finland.

Overall, population size remains stable despite strong local fluctuations. The range expansion in the boreal zone still continues in Fennoscandia, and includes a northward spread and increasing numbers (Hogstad & Moksnes 1990). During 1970–90, numbers increased slightly in Belgium, The Netherlands, Ireland, and perhaps also in Ukraine and Croatia. The species' range is probably limited in the S and W by the distribution of suitable forests, whereas the northern limit seems constrained by low early summer temperatures, which hinder incubation in the relatively poorly insulated nests. The northward range expansion fits well with climatic improvement since the 1960s (Tiainen *et al* 1983b).

Breeding density can be very high. In primeval stands in the Białowieża forest, there may be 10 territories/10ha. This, combined with 30–40% polygyny rates in years of high breeding numbers (Wesołowski 1987) can result in up to 15 nests/10ha. Very similar densities may occur in the Baltic States and S Finland (E. Pēterhofs & J. Priednieks, pers comm; T. Pakkala & J. Tiainen, pers obs). Elsewhere in the N and also in W and C Europe, spatial distribution of territories is normally very clustered, females preferring those males with other males as close neighbours. Areas of good habitat may be left uncolonized. Such clusters show distinct annual variations in location and numbers of breeding pairs (Herremans 1993a).

The Wood Warbler is fully migratory, wintering in forests, woodlands and woodland savanna from Sierra Leone to Sudan and Uganda.

Tomasz Wesołowski (PL) Juha Tiainen (FIN)

Phylloscopus collybita Chiffchaff

CZ	Budníček menší	**I**	Luí piccolo
D	Zilpzalp	**NL**	Tjiftjaf
E	Mosquitero Común	**P**	Felosa-comum
F	Pouillot véloce	**PL**	Pierwiosnek
FIN	Tiltaltti	**R**	Пеночка-теньковка
G	Δενδροφυλλοσκόπος	**S**	Gransångare
H	Csilpcsalpfüzike		

Non-SPEC, Threat status S (P)

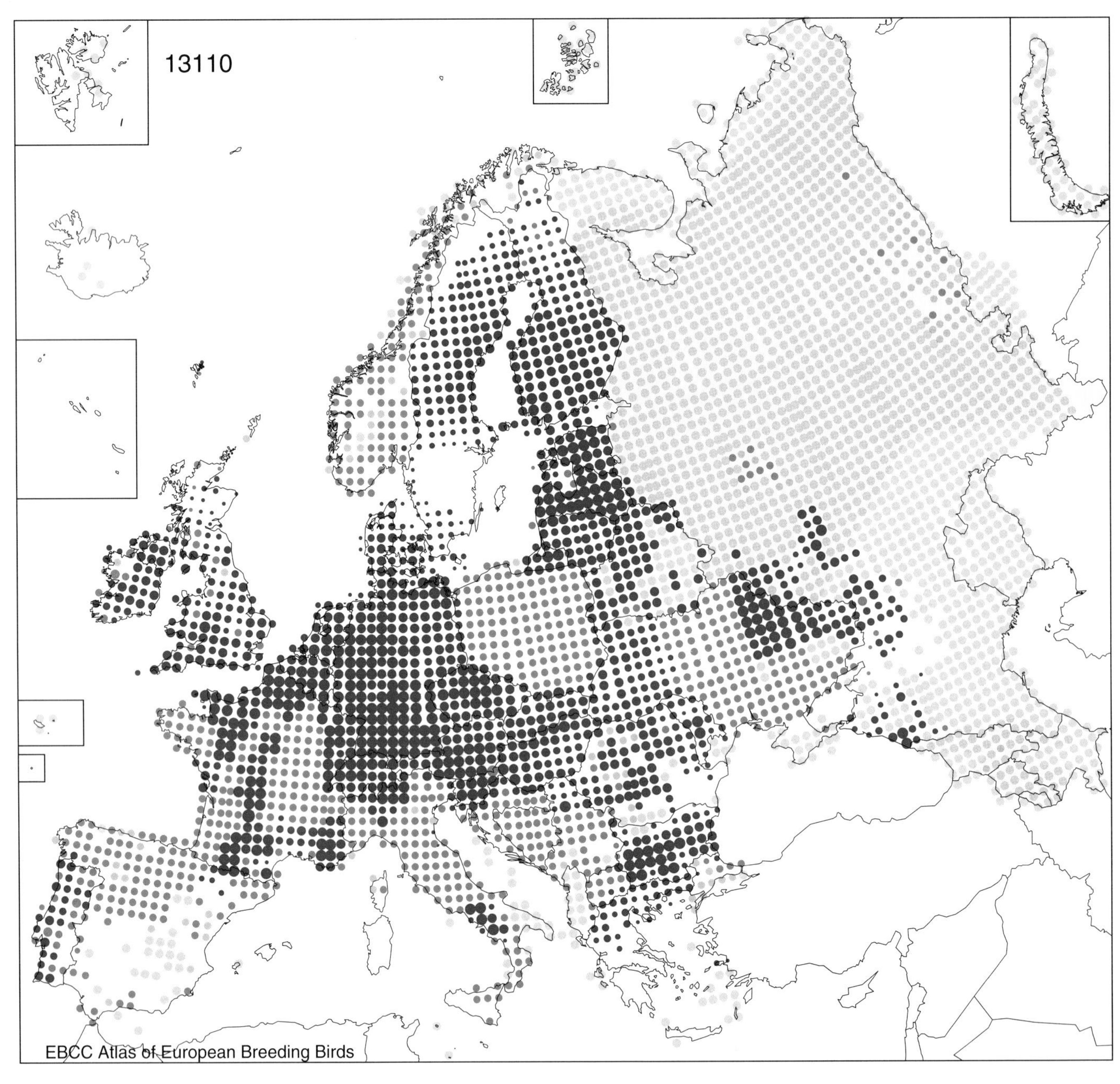

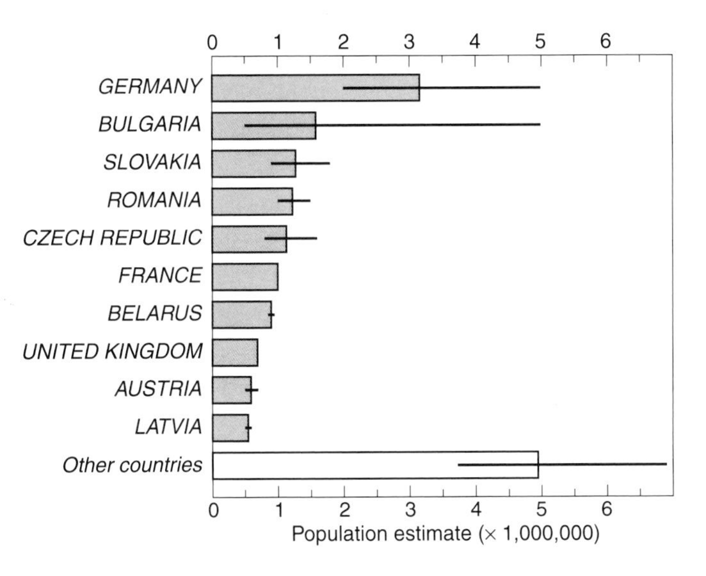

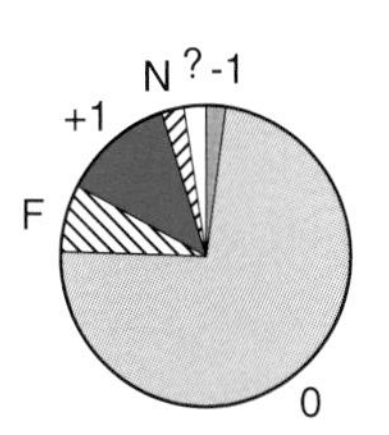

% in top 10 countries: 73.3
Total number of populated European countries: 38
Total European population 14,786,279–20,508,674 (16,506,965)
Russian population 10,000,000–100,000,000 (31,622,777)
Turkish population 10,000–100,000 (31,623)

The breeding distribution of the Chiffchaff stretches from the Canary Islands, NW Africa and Portugal throughout Europe and most of northern Asia to the Kolyma River (155°E), practically the entire boreal and temperate forest area. To the S, its distribution reaches the Black and parts of the Mediterranean Sea coasts, and to the SE, the northern limit of the steppe/semi-desert belt E to C Siberia and the C Asian mountains. The Chiffchaff breeds also in N and W Turkey and in an isolated range from the Caucasus to N Iran. The nominate subspecies *P.c. collybita* covers most of W and C Europe up to S Sweden, in Poland and Ukraine grading into *abietinus* which breeds in much of Fennoscandia, E as far as the Urals and S to N Turkey, the Caucasus and N Iran. It is replaced by *tristis* from the Pechora catchment eastwards. Some authors divide *tristis* into *fulvescens* (W Siberia) and *tristis*, (*sensu stricto*) further E, and recognize *brevirostris* in NW Turkey. Birds in Iberia, SW France and N Africa belong to *brehmii*. The Canary Islands contain *exsul* and *canariensis*. Mountain Chiffchaff *P. lorenzii* (*qv*) was only recently separated from Chiffchaff.

The Chiffchaff, a forest and woodland species, has marked geographical variations in habitat requirements. C and W European birds breed in deciduous and coniferous forests, provided these possess an open canopy, some tall trees and a luxuriant, lofty herb or bush layer. Such a combination usually occurs most often in lush riverine forests, old alder *Alnus* mires and established parks and cemeteries containing abundant growth.

The highest densities in the Polish Białowieża National Park occurred in primeval riverine ash–alder (*Fraxinus–Alnus*) stands, exceeding 5 bp/10ha (Piotrowska & Wesołowski 1989); values in German riverine forest and established cemeteries reached 15 bp/10ha (Schönfeld 1978). In southern Europe the species breeds both in lush riverside woods, and (at lower densities) in drier oak *Quercus* and other deciduous woods of hills and mountains. In Fennoscandia breeding habitats and densities differ again. The species breeds here in continuous mixed coniferous–deciduous forests, and even in almost pure spruce *Picea* forests, avoiding small woodlots (Tiainen *et al* 1983a). It occurs both in the forest interior and close to margins, but avoids the latter when Willow Warbler *P. trochilus* breeding density is high. In areas of southern Finland containing more luxuriant forest types, Chiffchaff breeding density can reach 5–15 bp/km^2.

At *c*12M–25Mbp (excluding *c*10M–100Mbp in Russia), the Chiffchaff is numerous throughout most of Europe. Densities decrease towards the distribution limits, particularly in Scotland, northern Fennoscandia, the Balkan Peninsula and Ukraine. The highest densities of >10 000 bp/50km square obtain in the temperate zone of W, C and E Europe, declining below 5000 bp/50km square in S Europe and below 2000 bp/50km square in Fennoscandia. The species is absent from Iceland, the Balearics, Sardinia and Crete.

No major changes in range or numbers were detected in Europe during 1970–90. Colonization of S Sweden, quite recent and still continuing, probably originated from Denmark. Northern Fennoscandian populations apparently are decreasing slowly because of changes in the forest structure (Svensson *et al* 1992, Väisänen 1994). Numerical fluctuations in the British Chiffchaff population were probably influenced by rainfall variations on the African wintering grounds (Lack 1989).

Most European populations are migratory or partially so. Northwestern birds overwinter in low numbers in western Britain & Ireland. Most birds from western populations winter S of their breeding areas in the Mediterranean region and in sub-Saharan Africa N of the rainforests. Northern and eastern populations are completely migratory and winter from eastern Africa to northern India.

Juha Tiainen (FIN) Tomasz Wesolowski (PL)

This species account is sponsored by W. de Boer, Hengelo, NL.

Phylloscopus trochilus Willow Warbler

CZ	Budníček větší	**I**	Luí grosso
D	Fitis	**NL**	Fitis
E	Mosquitero Musical	**P**	Felosa-musical
F	Pouillot fitis	**PL**	Piecuszek
FIN	Pajulintu	**R**	Пеночка-весничка
G	Θαμνοφυλλοσκόπος	**S**	Lövsångare
H	Fitiszfüzike		

Non-SPEC, Threat status S

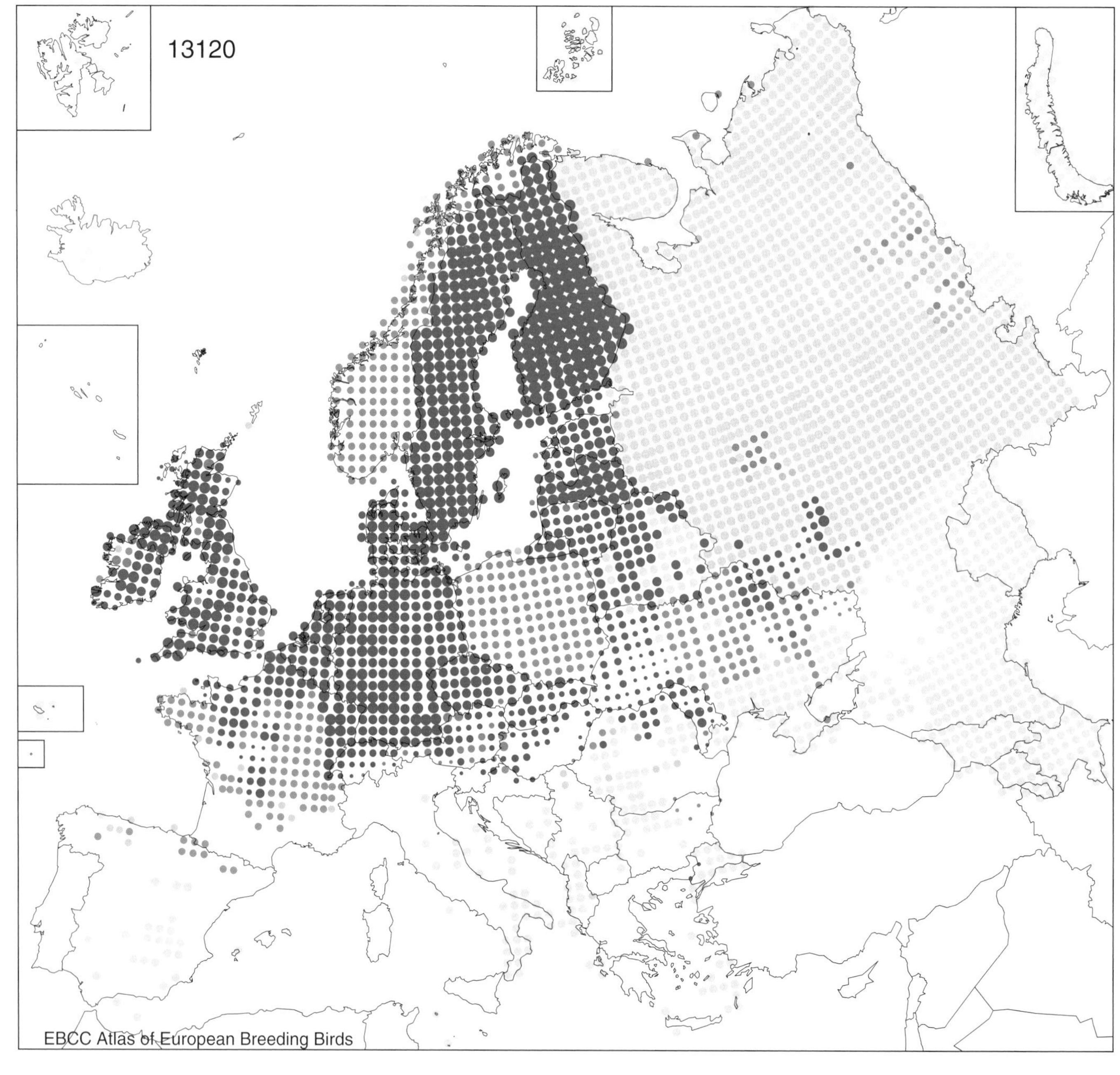

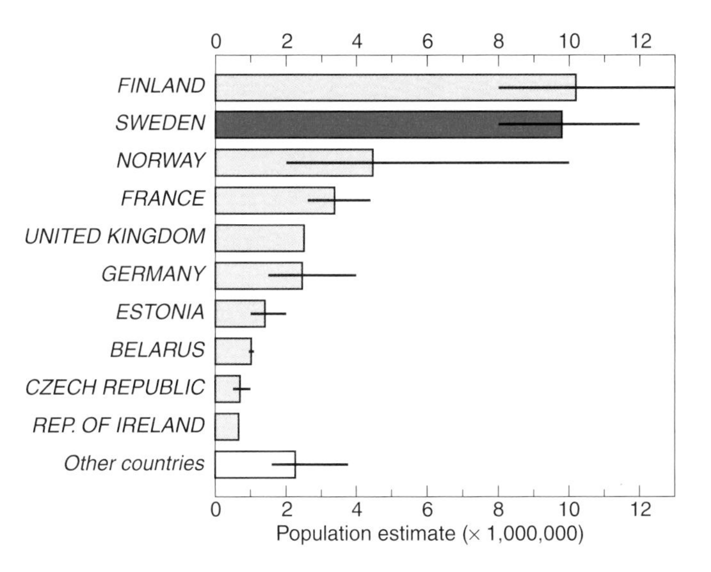

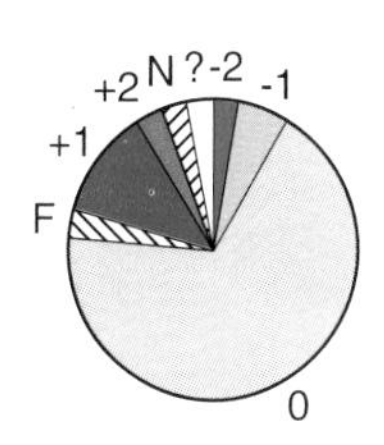

% in top 10 countries: 94.2
Total number of populated European countries: 33
Total European population 34,865,391–45,821,685 (38,870,519)
Russian population 10,000,000–100,000,000 (31,622,777)
Turkish population 1–100 (10)

The Willow Warbler is one of the commonest breeding birds in much of its breeding range which stretches from W Europe E through Siberia to the Chukotskiy Peninsula, between the July 10° and 22°C isotherms. In Europe it does not breed in Iceland and is rare or even absent as a breeding bird S of 45°N. It is completely migratory and spends the winter in Africa S of the Sahara, easternmost breeding birds travelling at least 12 000km.

The mellow song of the Willow Warbler can be heard in all kinds of habitats, provided these have shrubs. Overgrown heaths, young stages of woodland, forest clearings, subalpine birch forests or willow tundra all may hold high densities of up to 100–200 bp/100ha or even more. In most areas the species avoids dense forest, open country and high mountains but Fennoscandian birds are less discriminating and may even inhabit grassy slopes on islands.

In Europe the Willow Warbler is quite evenly distributed N of a line from Bordeaux to Budapest and Odessa. Densities per 50km square tend to increase northwards, reaching their highest values in Fennoscandia and Russia. Here, the species is the most numerous breeding bird, occurring even in the northernmost parts in bewildering numbers. The Fennoscandian breeding population is estimated at 24Mbp (range 18M–35Mbp), equivalent to an average of 55 000bp/50×50km square. The Russian population amounts to 10M–100Mbp. In other northern European countries, the Willow Warbler often is the most numerous summer migrant. Along the species' southernmost breeding range, densities generally are low, as is the case in Switzerland (442 bp/50×50km square), Austria (1687), Hungary (465), Romania (82) and Ukraine (416). In Spain and Greece the Willow Warbler is a rare breeding bird, each country having fewer than 100bp.

Although there is ample evidence that local breeding populations may fluctuate strongly (Tiainen 1983), noticeable country-wide population changes have been reported rarely since the mid-1970s. In most countries populations are thought to have been stable over this period. Sweden has experienced an increase recently, and Finland a longer-term growth, due to widespread forest clearfelling allowing the bush layer to thicken, especially along the newly created margins and in the N (Koskimies 1989a). Conflicting trends are reported from the species' southernmost breeding range.

In the British Common Birds Census from 1965 to 1988 the Willow Warbler was one of the few passerines showing only very limited fluctuations and without obvious long-term trends (J.H. Marchant *et al* 1990). These stable population levels were in marked contrast with those of many other passerines, including other long-distance migrants, a characteristic common to other countries which have long-running monitoring schemes. High site tenacity and high saturation of available habitats (in contrast with species such as Wood Warbler *P. sibilatrix*) contribute to this stability (Nilsson 1986a). Furthermore, the Willow Warbler clearly had remained unaffected by the severe drought in the Sahel region, unlike several other long-distance migrants. The Willow Warbler winters further S of the Sahel than do species like Whitethroat *Sylvia communis*, Sedge Warbler *Acrocephalus schoenobaenus* and Sand Martin *Riparia riparia*, and so its wintering areas are much less affected by desertification.

But even Willow Warbler trends are not completely predictable! In 1986–93 a 50% decline was recorded in southern Britain (Peach *et al* 1995) and in 1989–93 a 25% decline occurred in the dunes in western Netherlands (A.J. van Dijk, SOVON, pers comm). In Britain, and probably in The Netherlands as well, increased mortality amongst adult birds may have caused the decline (Peach *et al* 1995, Foppen & Reijnen in press). However, populations in the N of Britain and in other Dutch habitats have not declined, the reasons for the excess mortality remaining unclear.

Fred Hustings (NL) Ruud Foppen (NL)

This species account is sponsored by Vogelwerkgroep Zuid-Kennemerland, Velsen-Zuid, NL.

Phylloscopus lorenzii

Mountain Chiffchaff

CZ	Budníček kavkazský	**I**	Luí del Caucaso
D	Bergzilpzalp	**NL**	Bergtjiftjaf
E	Mosquitero Montano	**P**	Felosa-serrana
F	Pouillot montagnard	**PL**	Świstunka armenska
FIN	Lännenvuoritiltaltti	**R**	Кавказская пеночка
G	Φυλλοσκόπος του Lorenz	**S**	Berggransångare
H	Hegyi csilpcsalp		

Non-SPEC, Threat status S (P)

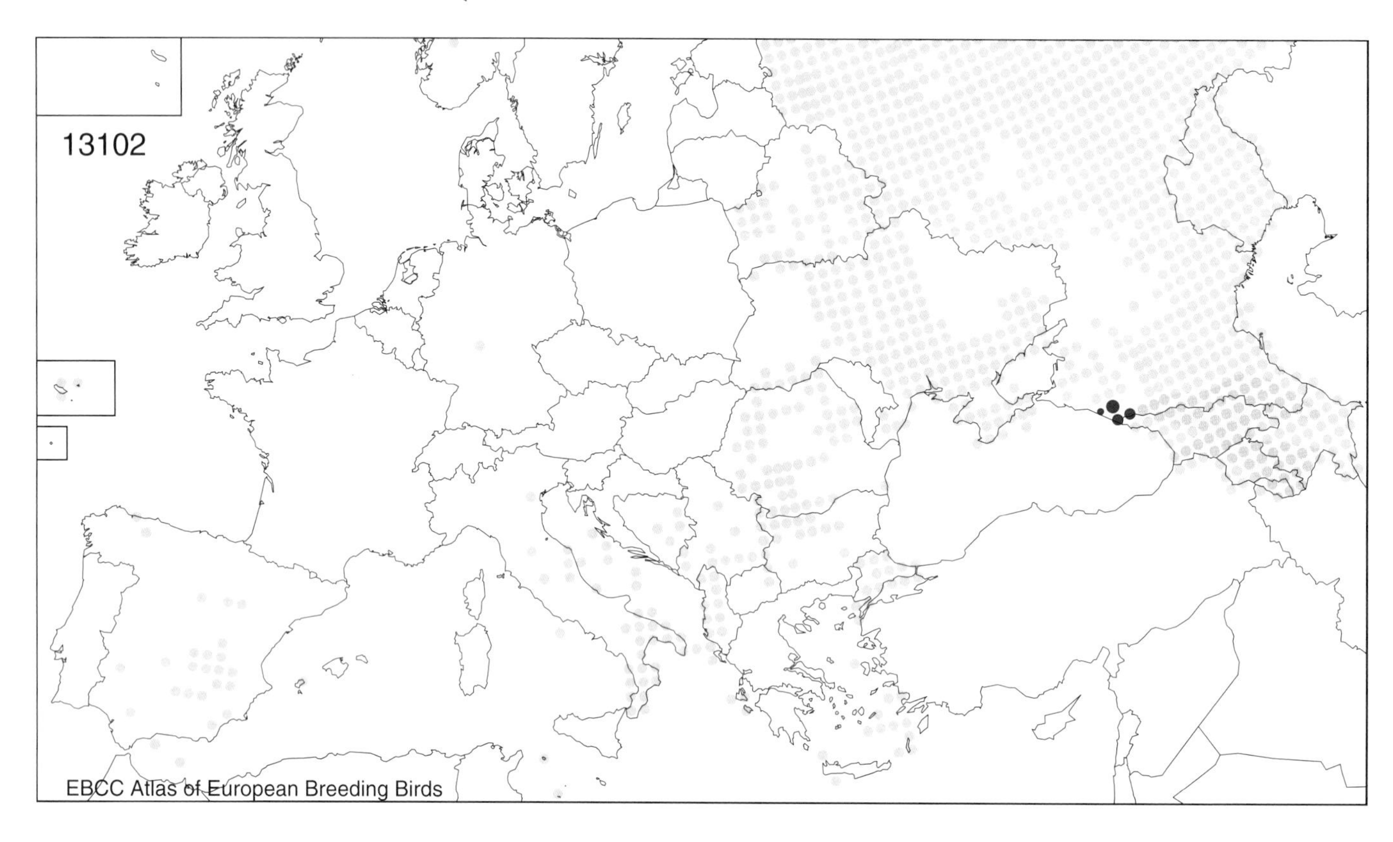

This form has been variously considered conspecific with both *P. collybita* and *P. sindinianus*.

The range of the Mountain Chiffchaff encompasses the mountains of the Great and Little Caucasus, and also E Asia Minor, in Europe being found in SE Russia, Georgia, Armenia and Azerbaijan.

The species is exclusively montane, occupying forest habitats. Characteristically, it prefers to nest in the variety of tree and shrub vegetation associated with the timberline: krummholz, birch *Betula* and beech *Fagus*; scrub-pine forest edges; patches of young birch just above the timberline; thickets of Caucasian rhododendron *Rhododendron caucasicum* situated on the timberline and on much higher slopes and plant communities containing juniper *Juniperus* spp. The Mountain Chiffchaff also can occur in mountain river valleys well below the timberline, such as in the Teberda Valley (W Caucasus) at only 1000–1200m asl (Marova 1993) and at roughly similar altitudes in some locations of the Caucasian Nature Reserve (Til'ba & Kazakov 1985).

The Mountain Chiffchaff is one of the dominant species of high-altitude forests in the Caucasus, but there is scant information on its population size, because only recently has it been accorded full specific status (Stepanyan 1978).

Within the Caucasian Nature Reserve, the maximum population densities at various altitudes are: 40 birds/km^2 at medium altitudes along river valleys in places with inverted relief, 70 birds/km^2 in high-altitude krummholz birch and 85 birds/km^2 in Caucasian rhododendron scrub. Much lower down, density in krummholz is 6 birds/km^2 and in alpine meadows 8 birds/km^2. In subalpine meadows of the C Caucasus, density does not exceed 2–3 birds/km^2 (Komarov 1991).

The winter quarters of the Mountain Chiffchaff largely coincide with its breeding range, the birds descending to or moving locally to south-facing slopes and piedmont plains (Marova 1993), but in some parts of its range, it does not occur in winter, as in the W Caucasus.

Peter Til'ba (R)

Ficedula semitorquata

Semi-collared Flycatcher

CZ	Lejsek černokrký	I	Balia caucasica
D	Halbringschnäpper	NL	Balkanvliegenvanger
E	Papamoscas Semicollarino	P	Papa-moscas-de-meio-colar
F	Gobemouche à demi-collier	PL	Muchołowka półobrożna
FIN	Balkaninsieppo	R	Полуошейниковая мухоловка
G	Δρυομυγοχάφτης	S	Balkanflugsnappare
H	Ál-örvös légykapó		

SPEC Cat 2, Threat status E (P)

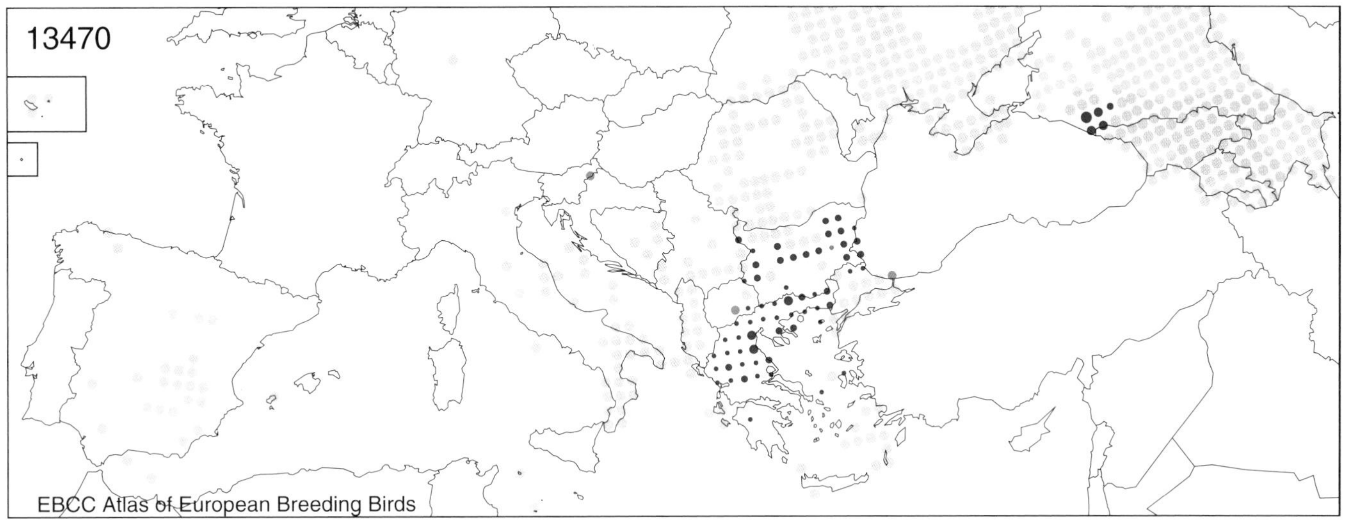

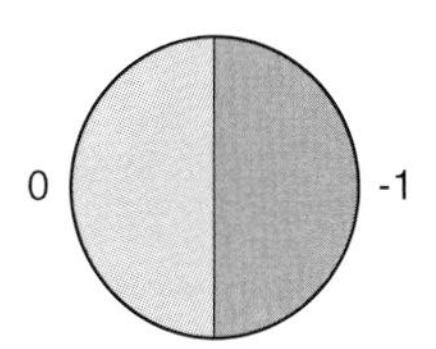

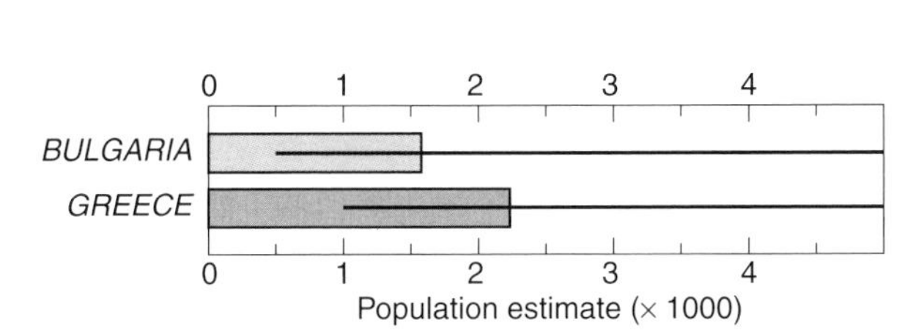

% in top 10 countries: 100.0
Total number of populated European countries: 2
Total European population 2175–8214 (3817)
Russian population 1–1 (1)
Turkish population 1000–10,000 (3162)

The Semi-collared Flycatcher breeds in Greece, Bulgaria, Turkey and also in the eastern Caucasus and NW Iran. Its status as a pure species is under debate. Howard & Moore (1980) treated it first as a Pied Flycatcher *F. hypoleuca* subspecies but subsequently (1991) as a Collared Flycatcher *F. albicollis* subspecies.

In Greece the Semi-collared Flycatcher breeds mostly in beech *Fagus* and oak *Quercus* forests at high altitudes (Curio 1959). However, it probably is not altitude-dependent, but rather occupies suitable breeding habitats wherever available. The Caucasus population apparently inhabits old deciduous forests, beech woods, orchards and also spruce *Picea* forest in Russia, Georgia and Armenia (Curio 1959). Thus its habitat preference is similar to that of Pied and Collared Flycatchers. The breeding density in suitable Balkan habitats is *c*0.6–0.7 bp/ha (calculated from Curio 1959). I know of no nestbox study data in the Semi-collared Flycatcher breeding area.

Its wintering areas probably lie in tropical East Africa, where it has been reported to be fairly common in the Iringa district in southern Tanzania (Lynes 1934). This may be relevant to the ancestry of the black-and-white flycatchers: both *albicollis* and *semitorquata* seem to winter E of *hypoleuca*, possibly suggesting that the two former types have an easterly origin. However, plumage similarity is striking between *hypoleuca* and *semitorquata*, while *semitorquata*'s song is intermediate between *hypoleuca* and *albicollis*.

The Semi-collared Flycatcher is easily confused with Pied; species identification is complicated by hybrids between Pied and Collared Flycatchers resembling the Semi-collared. Furthermore, mixed characters of *albicollis* and *semitorquata* appear in the Pied Flycatcher subspecies *speculigera* and also in the Spanish Pied Flycatcher population, both of which differ markedly from the nominate *hypoleuca* and generally resemble hybrids between the Pied and Collared Flycatcher (Mild 1993). Moreover, *semitorquata*-like flycatchers have been found breeding in Algeria in sympatry with *F.h. speculigera*.

Arne Lundberg (S)

Ficedula parva

Red-breasted Flycatcher

CZ	Lejsek malý	**I**	Pigliamosche pettirosso
D	Zwergschnäpper	**NL**	Kleine Vliegenvanger
E	Papamoscas Papirrojo	**P**	Papa-moscas-pequeno
F	Gobemouche nain	**PL**	Muchołówka mała
FIN	Pikkusieppo	**R**	Малая мухоловка
G	Νανομυγοχάφτης	**S**	Mindre flugsnappare
H	Kis légykapó		

Non-SPEC, Threat status S (P)

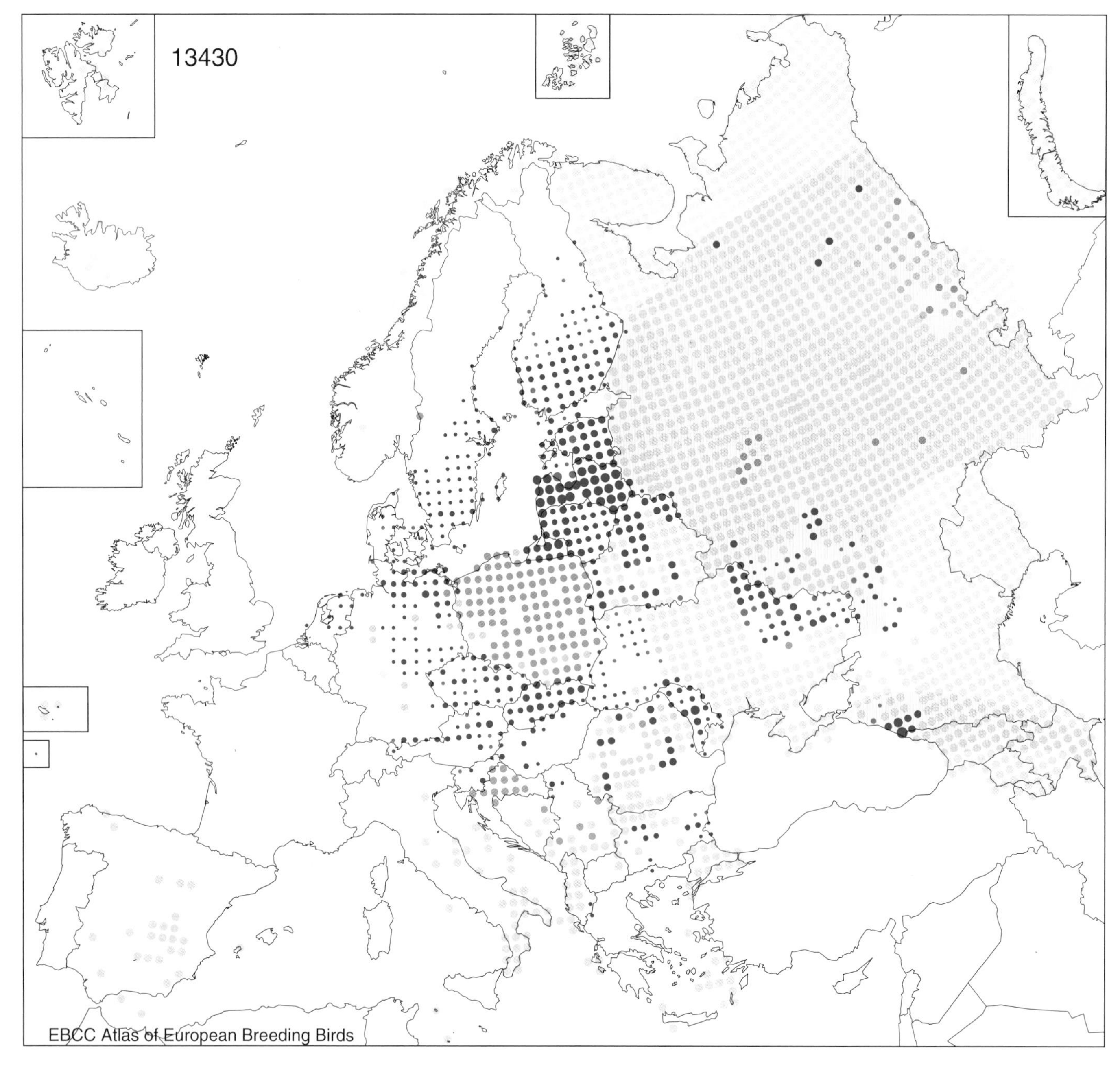

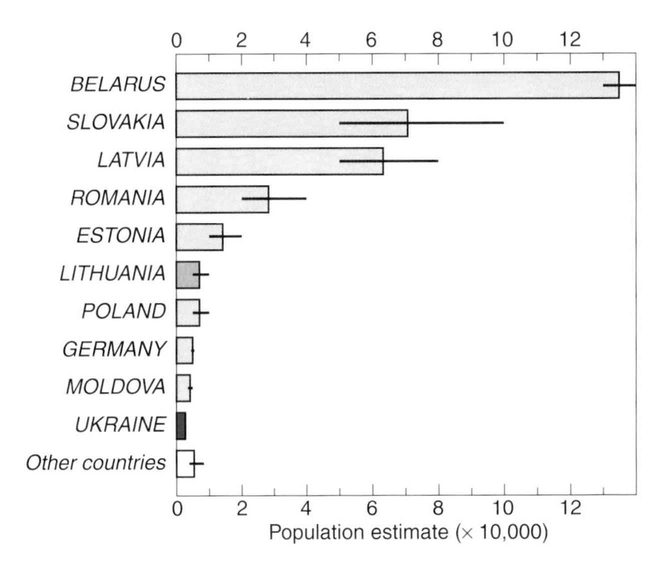

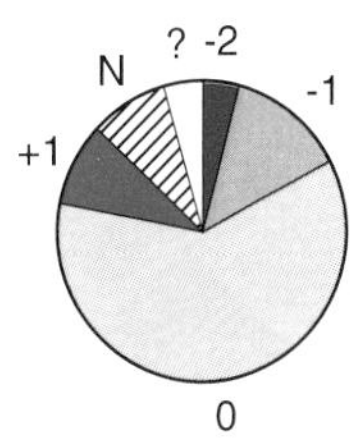

% in top 10 countries: 98.4
Total number of populated European countries: 23
Total European population 315,794–379,521 (342,700)
Russian population 1,000,000–10,000,000 (3,162,278)
Turkish population 1000–10,000 (3162)

The Red-breasted Flycatcher breeds in the boreal taiga and temperate zones of Eurasia from Kamchatka and NW China to C Europe, its western range border just reaching C Sweden, Denmark, N Germany, Austria, Croatia and N Greece. The nominate form *F.p. parva* occurs in Europe W of the Urals and in an isolated high-altitude population whose range in the Caucasus extends into Asia Minor through the mountain forests of N Turkey and the Elburz range of N Iran. *F.p. albicilla* occurs E of 50°E, overlapping with *parva* to 60°E. A long-distance migrant, the species winters mainly in India and Pakistan.

Its preferred habitat in richly structured, mature forest needs a predominantly light canopy, a cool, moist inner climate and an open zone (containing ample perching twigs) between the canopy and a moderately dense shrub layer. Such forest stands seem to be favoured if they include slopes and small valleys.

The Red-breasted Flycatcher displays a remarkable variation in habitat choice within its European range. In Denmark, N Germany and NW Poland it is virtually restricted to old lowland beech *Fagus* forests, whereas in S Germany, the Czech Republic, Slovakia, Austria, Romania and the Balkans, it breeds up to 1100–1300m asl from the Alps and the Bavarian forests to the Carpathians, and up to 2350m asl in the Caucasus, in mixed mountain beech forest containing fairly high proportions of spruce and fir (*Abieti–Fagetum, Aceri–Fagetum*) (Scherzinger 1985). Occasionally it uses old beech and oak *Quercus* stands in parks or villages. In E Poland, where beech is absent, the species prefers subcontinental lime–oak–hornbeam forest (*Tilio–Carpinetum*), but also breeds in alluvial forest, alder carrs (*Alnus*) and moorland birch forest. In Finland, the Baltic States, Belarus and E Europe the species occurs in all types of mixed and broad-leaved forest, but also breeds regularly in coniferous forests containing but few deciduous trees; in Estonia, it even prefers shady spruce *Picea* forest (Leibak *et al* 1994).

It is sparsely distributed in Scandinavia, Denmark, much of Germany, Austria and the Balkan countries, but becomes commoner eastwards, reaching maximum values in Slovakia, E Poland, Belarus, the Baltic States and Romania. Population and range trends seemed to have been stable during 1970–90. In Ukraine a range contraction coincided with decreasing numbers, whereas Finland, Lithuania and Austria experienced only reducing numbers. Conversely, increases occurred in the Czech Republic and Slovenia. In the 1980s, The Netherlands experienced a substantial increase in spring observations (corrected for observer effort) marked by several breeding attempts and prolonged residence by singing males in suitable breeding habitat (Bijlsma & Lensink 1990). In contrast, no such increase occurred in Great Britain between 1958 and 1985 (Dymond *et al* 1989). The evidence for a westward range extension remains weak.

The breeding density of the Red-breasted Flycatcher is no more than 0.6–1.7 bp/10ha in N German lowland beech forest (the mean value over 34 plots being 0.28 bp/10ha; Flade 1994). In E Polish primeval lime–oak–hornbeam forest values varied from 0.6 to 2.0 bp/10ha, with a mean of 1.2 bp/10ha in seven plots totalling 177.6ha (Tomiałojć *et al* 1984). Similar densities apply for Estonian spruce- and birch-dominated forests (Leibak *et al* 1994). Still higher densities are known for primeval mountain beech–fir forest in C Europe, but usually these are extrapolations from very small plots (*HVM*).

Its reliance on old, diversified forests makes the species vulnerable to modern forestry practices, which include shorter rotations and selective felling of old trees, now a common procedure in many N and E European countries. The Red-breasted Flycatcher therefore may face a shortage of suitable nesting sites in the near future.

Martin Flade (D)

Ficedula albicollis

Collared Flycatcher

CZ	Lejsek bělokrký	**I**	Balia dal collare
D	Halsbandschnäpper	**NL**	Withalsvliegenvanger
E	Papamoscas Collarino	**P**	Papa-moscas-de-colar
F	Gobemouche à collier	**PL**	Muchołowka białoszyja
FIN	Sepelsieppo	**R**	Мухоловка-белошейка
G	Κρικομυγοχάφτης	**S**	Halsbandsflugsnappare
H	Örvös légykapó		

SPEC Cat 4, Threat status S

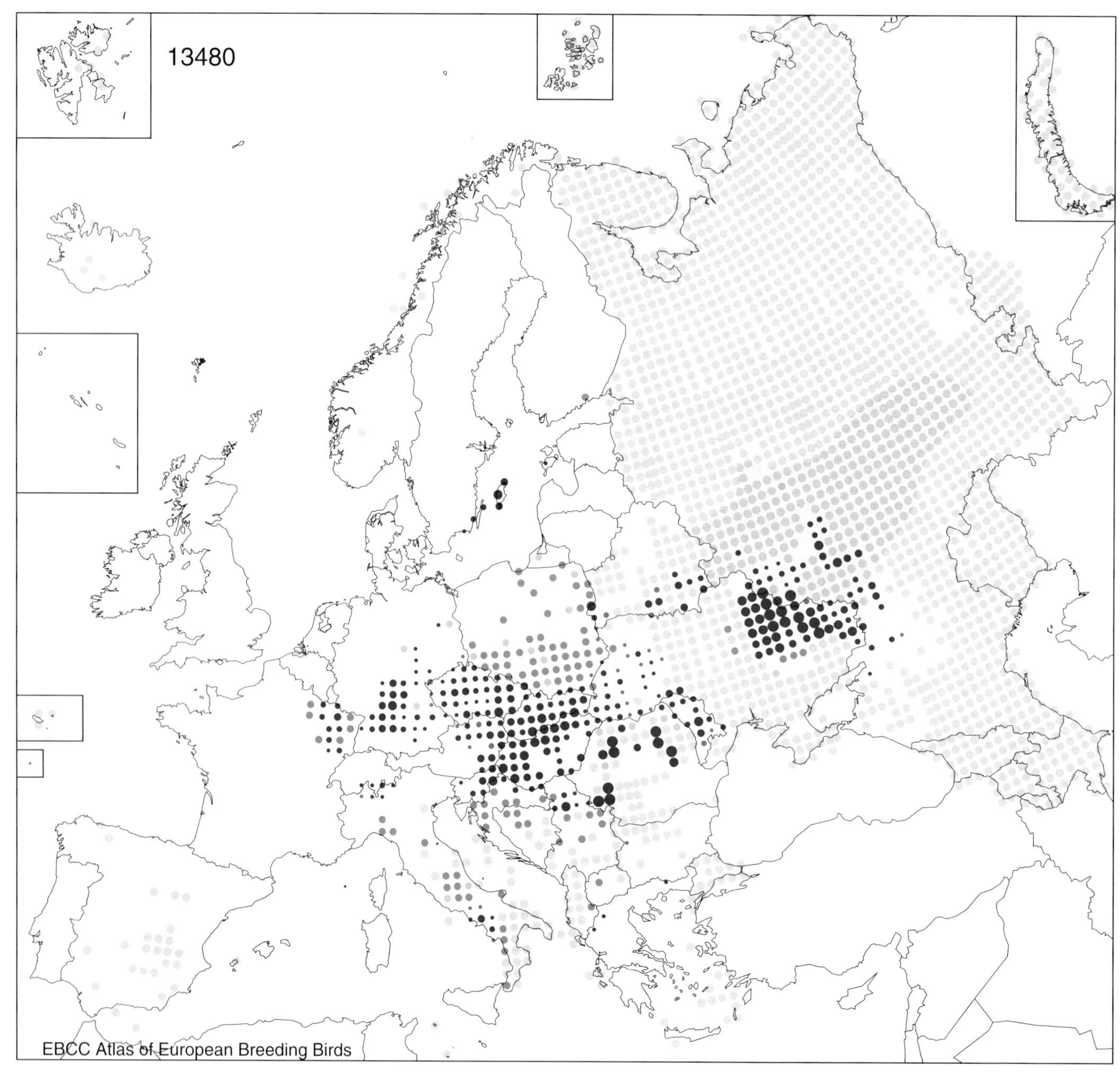

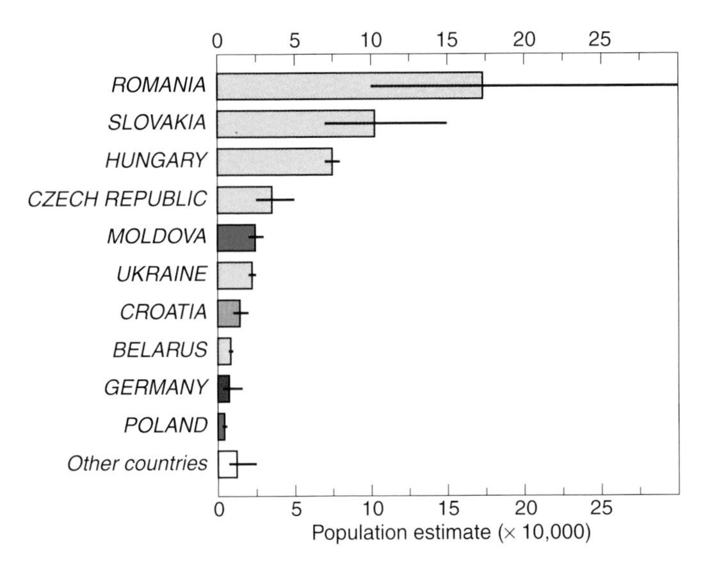

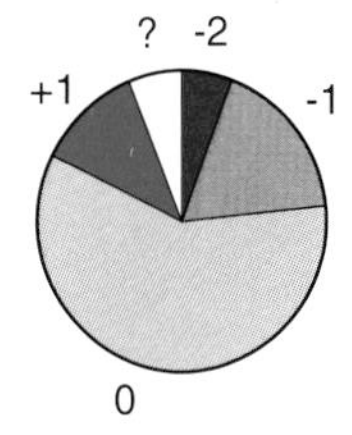

% in top 10 countries: 97.5
Total number of populated European countries: 17
Total European population 397,673–616,058 (478,994)
Russian population 5000–50,000 (15,811)

The Collared Flycatcher breeds in the continental middle latitudes across C Europe from eastern France and southern Germany through the Czech Republic, Slovakia, Austria, Poland, Hungary and Romania to Ukraine and SW Russia. Isolated populations occur in southern Italy and on the Swedish islands of Gotland and Öland in the Baltic.

Like the Pied Flycatcher *F. hypoleuca*, it is a cavity-nesting species breeding in most forest types and preferring deciduous woodland. Its distribution overlaps with that of the Pied Flycatcher in parts of E and C Europe, and in the Balkans probably with that of the Semi-collared Flycatcher *F. semitorquata*. The Collared Flycatcher is dominant in areas of sympatry with the Pied to the extent of almost total exclusion of the latter from prime habitats, such as deciduous forest.

Within its breeding range, the Collared Flycatcher seems most abundant in the former Czechoslovakia, Hungary, Romania, Ukraine and Moldova (>1000 bp/50×50km square), although little is known about altitude-related abundance patterns. Apparently it is almost equally abundant in suitable habitats high in the Carpathian Mountains and on the very flat island of Gotland, suggesting that abundance is limited more by available habitat rather than by altitude or latitude. However, factors limiting the overall distribution are unknown. The world population, estimated at 340 000–762 000bp, is confined to Europe.

In primeval deciduous forest in the Polish Białowieża National Park breeding densities range between 0.3 and 0.6 bp/ha whereas 0.01 bp/ha is representative of coniferous forest (Tomiałojć & Wesołowski 1990). Censuses made in the former Czechoslovakia yielded breeding densities in old oak *Quercus* forests ranging from 0.1 to 2.1 bp/ha (Štástný *et al* 1987) but also revealed that putting up nestboxes can more than double these figures. In a long-term study on the island of Gotland breeding densities as high as 8 bp/ha could be attained in preferred habitats when nestboxes were at saturation levels (Gustafsson 1988), whereas the average density in pine forest rose no higher than 1 bp/ha (L. Gustafsson, pers comm). Adjacent to these areas, in a luxuriant open deciduous forest, breeding density of birds using natural cavities was 1.65 bp/ha (Gustafsson 1987).

The Collared Flycatcher migrates S or SE, reaching its probable main wintering area in S–C tropical Africa, in Zaire, Uganda and Zambia, where it has been found in the 'Miombo' (*Brachystegia*) woodlands. Very little is known about its stop-over areas and their importance to the species.

Collared and Pied Flycatchers have a significant range overlap, and despite clear differences in song and plumage, hybridization does occur. Male hybrids often very much resemble the Semi-collared Flycatcher in possessing an incomplete neck collar. In most aspects 'mixed' pairs perform as well as 'pure' species pairs, the main selective disadvantage of hybridization being that pairs with one hybrid individual hatch fewer eggs and produce fewer offspring (Lundberg & Alatalo 1992). Nothing is known about hybridization between the Collared and the Semi-collared Flycatcher, and the status of the latter (*qv*) as a true species is under debate.

There are several scenarios advanced as explanations of the present distribution of the black-and-white flycatchers. In general terms, one scenario proposes that the distribution range of the ancestral flycatcher split into eastern and western parts during the last glaciation, the western population becoming the present *hypoleuca*, the eastern, *semitorquata*. Following the glaciation *semitorquata* expanded northwestwards, there forming *albicollis* at the secondary contact zone with *hypoleuca* which had spread NE from the SW (von Haartman 1949). Another scenario suggests that *albicollis* is the eastern form while *semitorquata* originated from the W (Lundberg & Alatalo 1992). Other possible scenarios exist. No subspecies of *albicollis* are recognized if *semitorquata* is accepted as a true species.

Arne Lundberg (S)

This species account is sponsored by Ficedula, Società pro avifauna della Svizzera italiana, CH.

Ficedula hypoleuca Pied Flycatcher

CZ	Lejsek černohlavý	**I**	Balia nera
D	Trauerschnäpper	**NL**	Bonte Vliegenvanger
E	Papamoscas Cerrojillo	**P**	Papa-moscas-preto
F	Gobemouche noir	**PL**	Muchołówka żałobna
FIN	Kirjosieppo	**R**	Мухоловка-пеструшка
G	Μαυρομυγοχάφτης	**S**	Svartvit flugsnappare
H	Kormos légykapó		

SPEC Cat 4, Threat status S

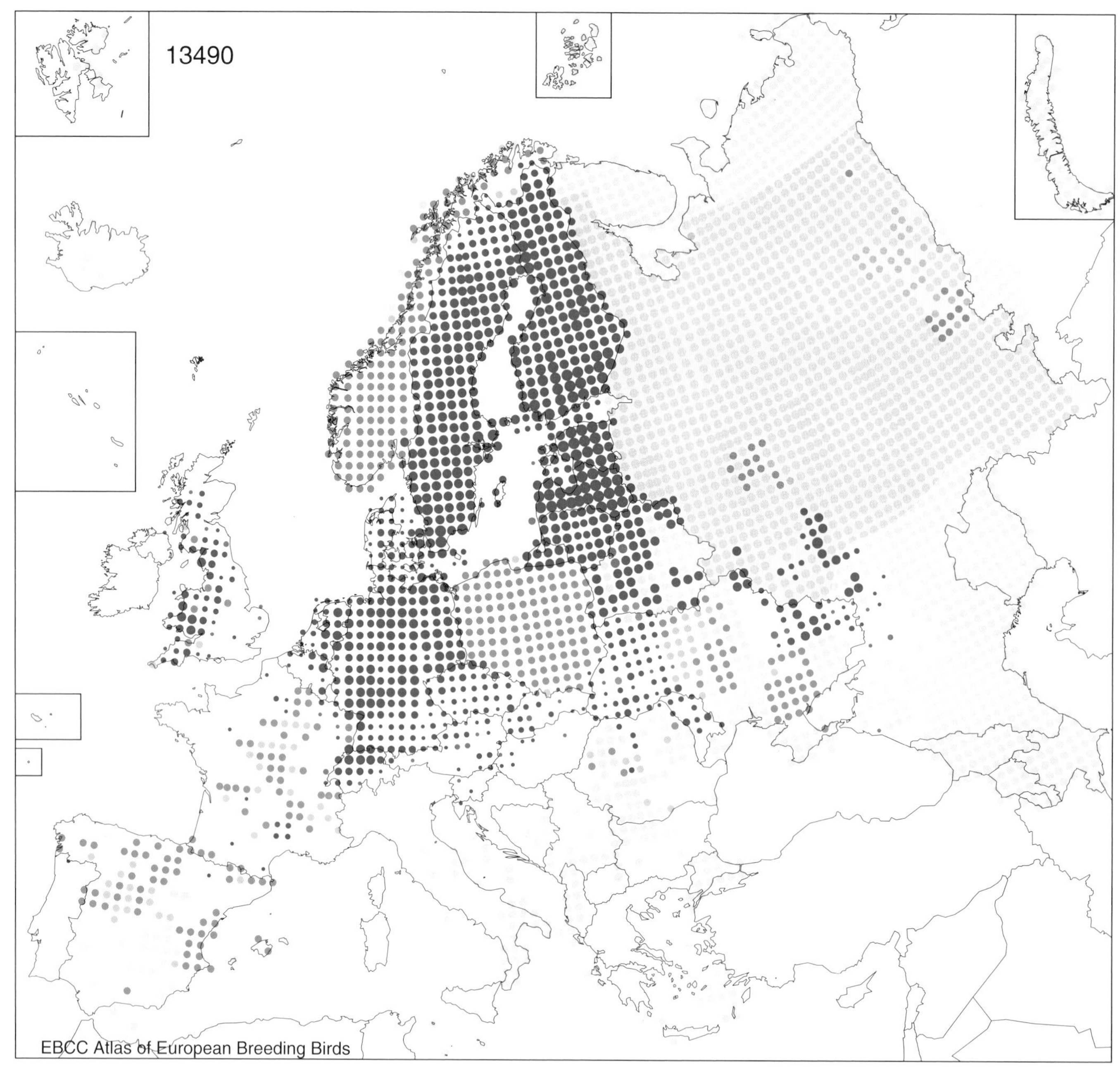

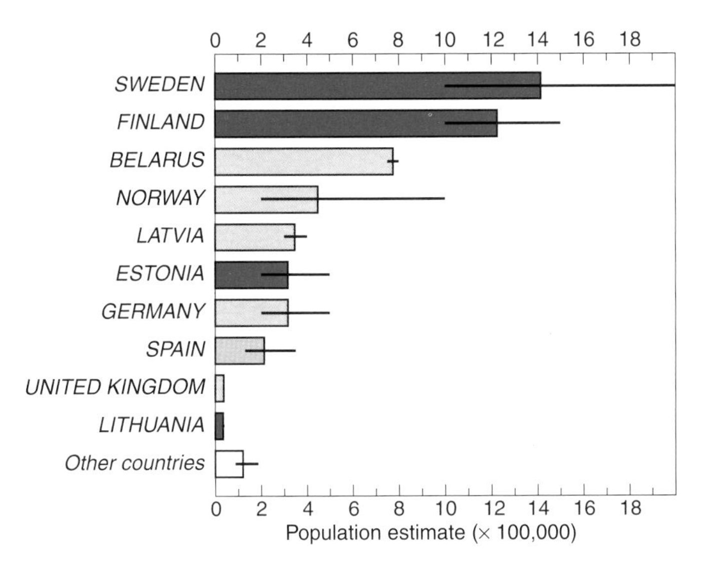

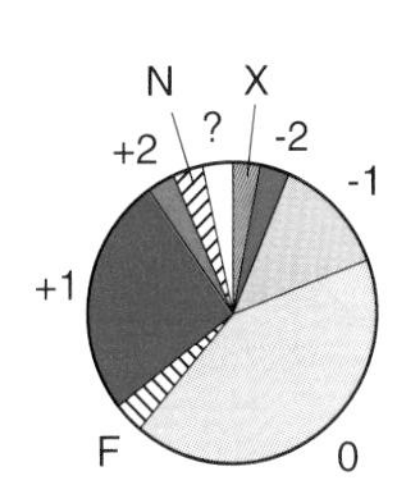

% in top 10 countries: 97.7
Total number of populated European countries: 31
Total European population 4,679,305–6,148,080 (5,245,140)
Russian population 1,000,000–10,000,000 (3,162,278)

The Pied Flycatcher breeds from NW Africa across Europe to C Siberia (*c*90°E). A cavity-nesting species, it breeds in most forest habitats possessing suitable nest-sites. Because deciduous forests contain more natural cavities than coniferous, birds are therefore more abundant in the former. Even if nestboxes are provided at equal densities in both habitats, the increase in abundance is greater in deciduous habitats.

Pied Flycatcher abundance over its latitudinal and altitudinal range is poorly known, showing no clear pattern across Europe. Within its distribution it is commonest in Fennoscandia, the Baltic States, Russia and Belarus (>5000 bp/50×50km square), less so in W Europe (N Spain, France and Great Britain through the Low Countries to Germany and Denmark) (1000–2200 bp/50×50km square) and markedly scarce in C, S and SE Europe (<500 bp/50×50km square), which probably reflects the distribution of breeding habitat. Historical information on the Pied Flycatcher from Sweden suggests that the species has spread across Europe from the SW towards the NE mainly since the early 1800s (Lundberg & Alatalo 1992). Recent changes in distribution and numbers apparently have been small, countries recording more slight increases in range and numbers during 1970–90 than stability or decreases.

In unmanaged deciduous forests natural breeding densities range usually from 0.1 to 1.0 bp/ha, depending on the age-structure of trees and tree species composition, while in coniferous forest natural breeding densities normally vary between 0.05 and 0.15 bp/ha. With ample nestboxes, breeding densities can increase considerably, the maximum recorded (in a very small area) being 21 bp/ha (Tompa 1967). 'Typical' nestbox-enhanced breeding densities in deciduous woodland often range between 1 and 4 bp/ha, and in coniferous forest between 0.5 and 1.5 bp/ha (Lundberg & Alatalo 1992). Analysis of breeding density data in both natural and nestbox-enhanced areas indicates that the preference for deciduous habitats is probably because food availability is better than in coniferous habitats. The Pied Flycatcher male is polygynous and attracts females into distinct and separated territories, complicating breeding density measurement.

Male Pied Flycatcher colouring, especially head and back plumage, varies with population distribution: jet-black and generally darker populations occur mainly in Scandinavia, Britain, Switzerland and Spain, while brown- or greyish-brown populations occur in Germany, Poland and Russia. These latter populations are mostly in areas close to the range of the Collared Flycatcher *F. albicollis*, suggesting that interspecific competition in some way is involved in the development of the brownish males (Røskaft *et al* 1986). The subspecies from NW Africa is also dark-plumaged. However, there is also substantial colour variation within populations remote from any Collared Flycatcher range.

Apart from the nominate *F.h. hypoleuca*, to which the above text mostly applies, two other subspecies are recognized; *speculigera* breeds in the Atlas Mountains in Morocco, Algeria and Tunisia and *tomensis* occurs from the Urals eastwards. Very little is known about their distribution, abundance and population trends. Older work describes the Spanish breeding population as a separate subspecies *iberiae*, a treatment now regarded as obsolete.

The Pied Flycatcher migrates southwestwards, its most important autumn stop-overs being in western Iberia, where numbers remain for several days building up fat stores to fuel the Mediterranean and Sahara crossings (Bibby & Green 1980). The wintering areas probably lie in tropical West Africa from Guinea, the Ivory Coast and Ghana down to the Equator, where it can be found in gallery forest, woodland savanna and citrus groves. In spring birds heading NE apparently take a more easterly migration route, probably because the Iberian stop-over areas are then much less favourable.

Arne Lundberg (S)

This species account is sponsored by David Coker, Bristol, GB.

Muscicapa striata

Spotted Flycatcher

CZ	Lejsek šedý	**I**	Pigliamosche
D	Grauschnäpper	**NL**	Grauwe Vliegenvanger
E	Papamoscas Gris	**P**	Papa-moscas-cinzento
F	Gobemouche gris	**PL**	Muchołowka szara
FIN	Harmaasieppo	**R**	Серая мухоловка
G	Μυγοχάφτης	**S**	Grå flugsnappare
H	Szürke légykapó		

SPEC Cat 3, Threat status D

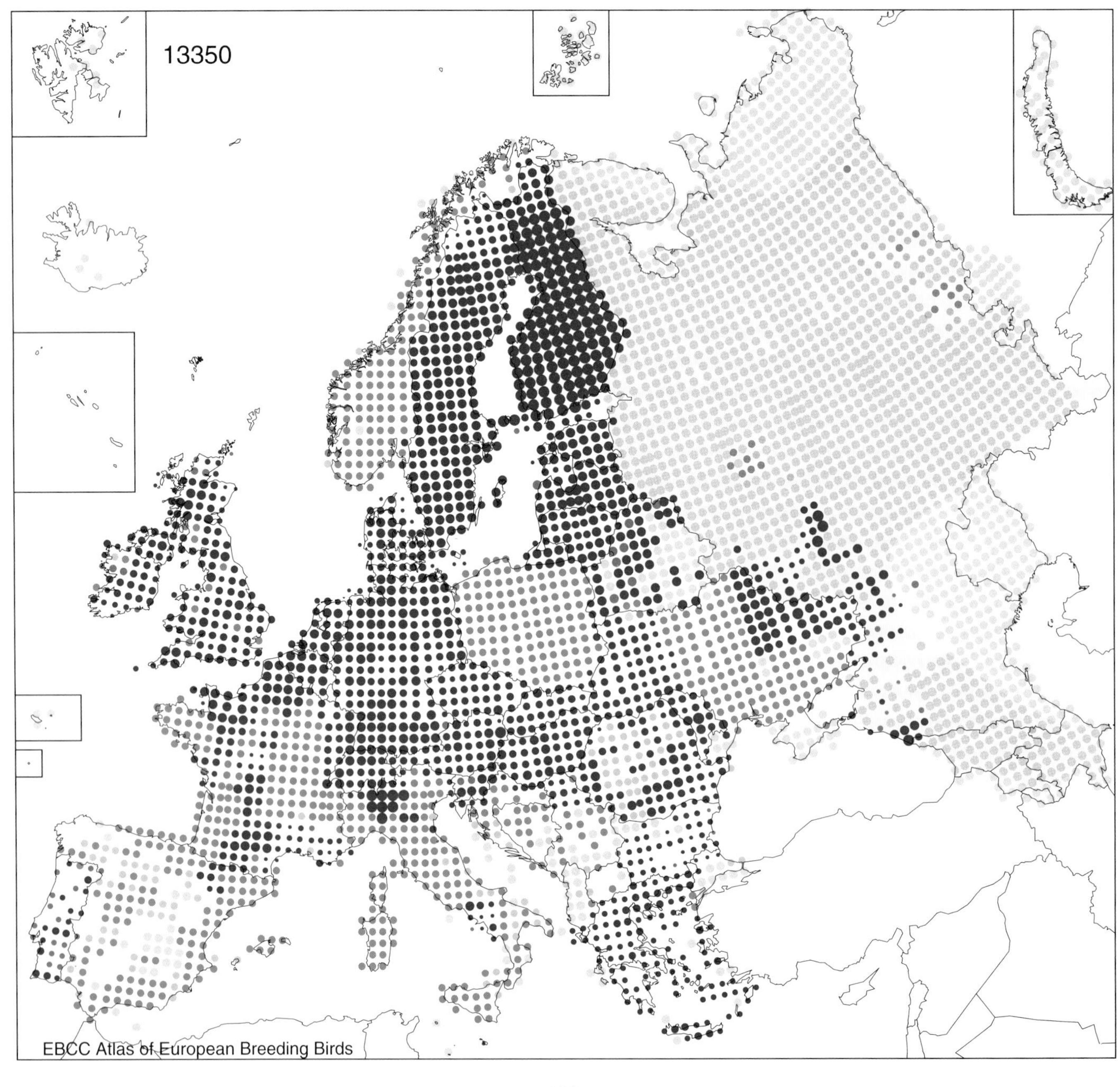

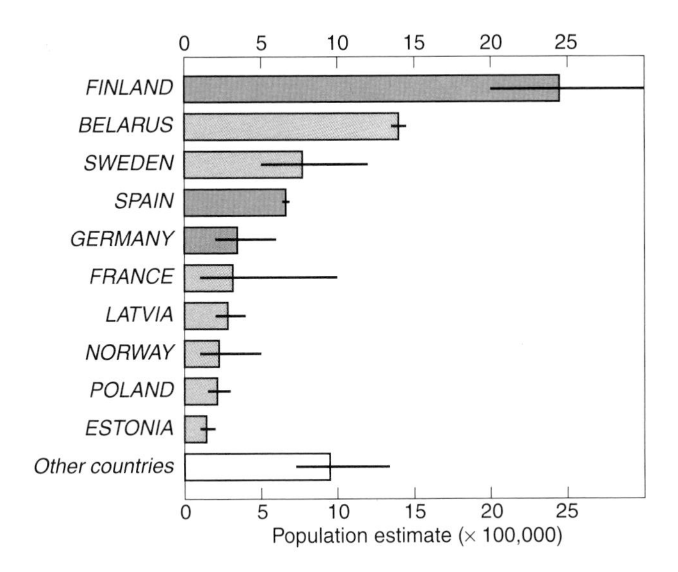

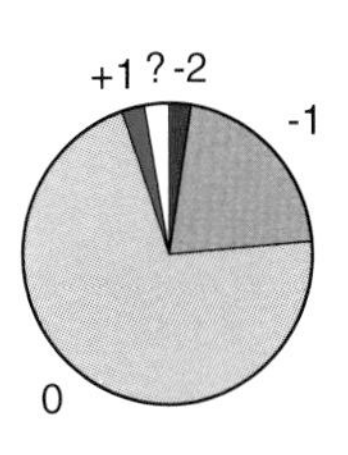

% in top 10 countries: 87.7
Total number of populated European countries: 38
Total European population 7,143,641–8,829,720 (7,761,705)
Russian population 1,000,000–10,000,000 (3,162,278)
Turkish population 5000–50,000 (15,811)

The breeding range of the Spotted Flycatcher comprises almost the whole of Europe and stretches from Morocco and the Atlantic coasts to past Lake Baykal. Over half its range lies in Europe, strongholds occurring in Russia, Finland, Belarus and Sweden. A long-distance migrant, it winters in the southern half of Africa. In Europe, *M.s. neumanni* occurs in the Caucasus, Crete and in the Balkans intergrades with the nominate *striata*, which occurs over much of Europe; *inexpectata* inhabits Crimea, *balearica* the Balearics and *tyrrhenica* Corsica and Sardinia. There are two other subspecies elsewhere.

The Spotted Flycatcher is a widespread and ubiquitous European bird. It may breed almost in any kind of habitat containing trees, from a range of woodland types (open woodland being preferred), parkland, farmland copses and human settlements to mountain forests up to 2000m asl. Near the Caspian it nests in low *Artemisia* bushes on open steppe (Peklo 1987). Nesting locations include shallow tree-holes, recent tree-damage, stem and branch bifurcations, fallen tree root tangles and snags and niches in buildings and rocks. Strongly insectivorous and well-adapted to taking flying insects by sallies from perches, by necessity it occupies primarily fragmented habitats and open woodland.

The highest densities occur in N and C Europe, the species being less common in the extreme W (probably because of the cooler, wetter maritime climate) and in the dry regions of Spain and SE Europe. Originally the species preferred gaps in old forests, particularly in riparian alder *Alnus* woods, birch *Fagus* and pine *Pinus* stands, possibly at margins or clearings. Gradually it came to colonize human settlements where it may occur at much higher densities in parks and cemeteries (1–7 bp/10ha, exceptionally 14.6) than in natural forests in C (0.2–2.5 bp/10ha, sporadically higher; Flade 1994) and N Europe (32–48 bp/km^2 in Estonia; Leibak *et al* 1994).

The species exhibits marked fluctuations in breeding numbers, especially in Great Britain, Finland and Russia (Peklo 1987, *BWP*), making population trend assessment difficult. Since the mid-1960s, at least Ireland, The Netherlands, Germany, the Czech Republic, Spain, Lithuania, Finland and Ukraine have reported numerical declines of *c*25%. In Britain, the decline has been continuous since the Common Birds Census began in 1961–62, the rate apparently having accelerated since the late 1980s (J. H. Marchant & Balmer 1994). These datasets seem to lack a clear geographical pattern, suggesting either regional fluctuations or multiple causes. Furthermore, other datasets are not so conclusive, sometimes being contradictory (Hustings 1988, pers obs). However, long-term migrant ringing programmes suggest a marked decline only in northern and C European populations (*HVM*).

Spotted Flycatcher broods are vulnerable to cool summer spells (Marjakangas 1982). Its claimed high reproductive success (*HVM*) may be confined mostly to human settlements (not replicated in natural forests, pers obs) and also depends on how often second broods can be produced (Epprecht 1985). Its decline in NW Europe may reflect a long sequence of generally cooler summers, which by reducing insect biomass may reduce energy intake rate. Whether cold breeding seasons affect population dynamics more than wintering area droughts is uncertain (Marjakangas 1982, J.H. Marchant *et al* 1990). The latter hypothesis is weakened because the symptoms of decline are not shared by some neighbouring countries. Furthermore, Spotted Flycatcher European populations did not suffer uniformly as did other trans-Saharan insectivorous migrants affected by the post-1968 population crash. Apart from a suggested increasingly unfavourable breeding climate in NW Europe from the 1960s onwards, other possible (so far unproven) adverse factors may include biocide-induced reductions or contamination of insect populations, removal of old trees through modern forestry management and general habitat deterioration (Sachslehner 1992).

Ludwik Tomiałojć (PL)

This species account is sponsored by Edith Rheinwald, St Katharinen, D.

Regulus regulus

Goldcrest

CZ	Králíček obecný	**I**	Regolo
D	Wintergoldhähnchen	**NL**	Goudhaantje
E	Reyezuelo Sencillo	**P**	Estrelinha-de-poupa
F	Roitelet huppé	**PL**	Mysikrólik
FIN	Hippiäinen	**R**	Королек
G	Χρυσοβασιλίσκος	**S**	Kungsfågel
H	Sárgafejű királyka		

SPEC Cat 4, Threat status S (P)

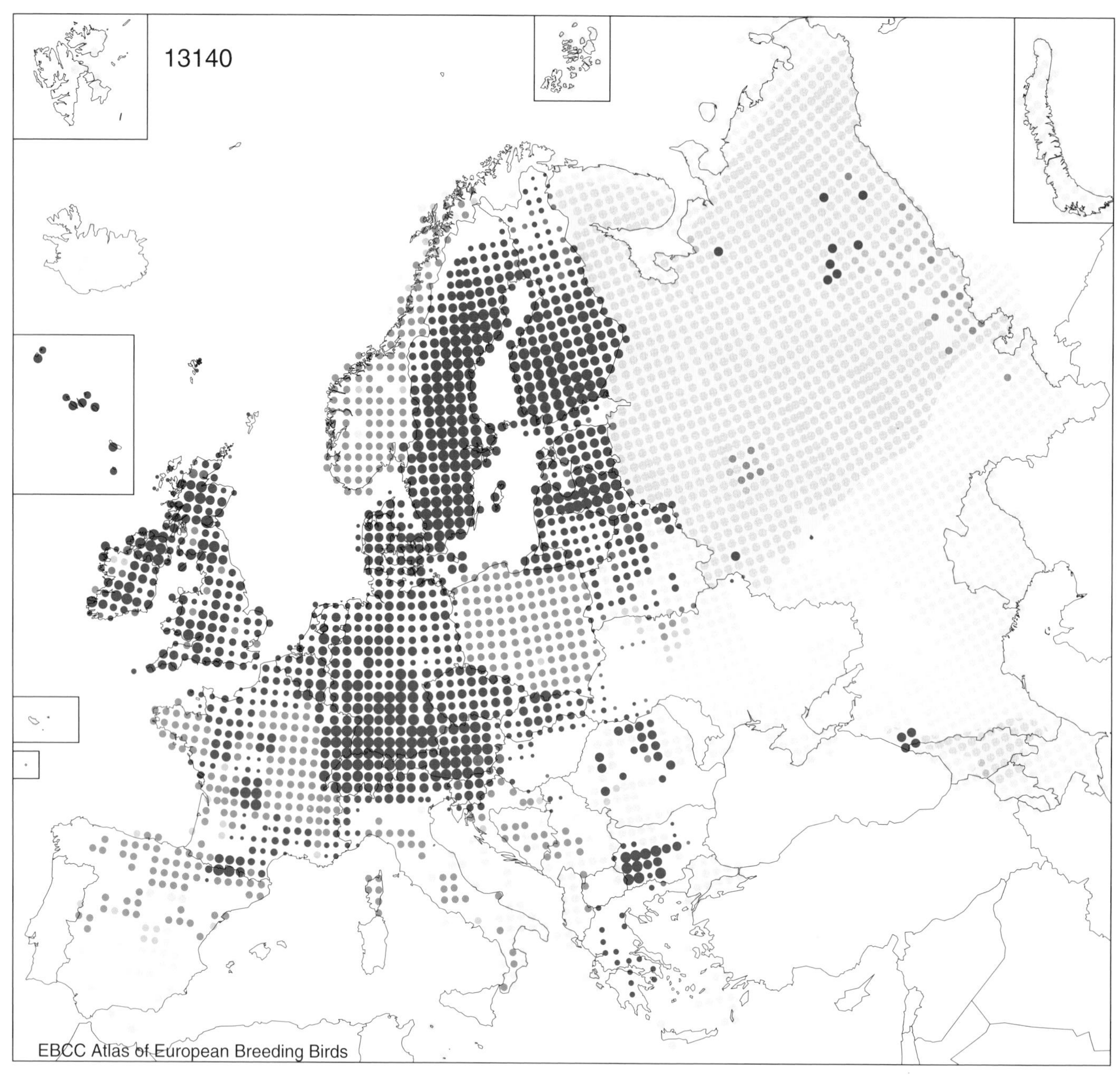

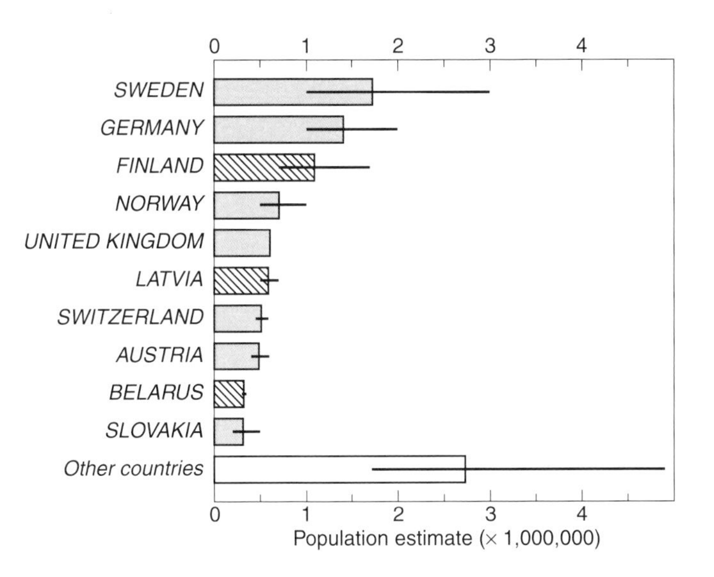

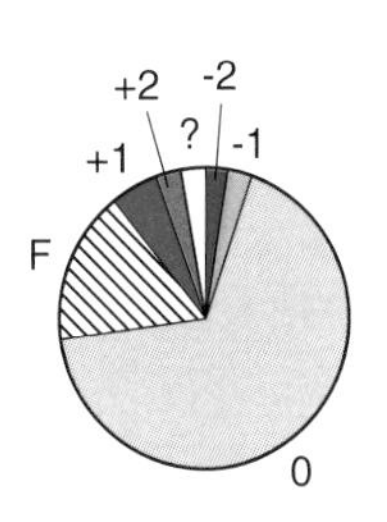

% in top 10 countries: 74.0
Total number of populated European countries: 37
Total European population 9,497,331–12,323,174 (10,526,256)
Russian population 10,000,000–100,000,000 (31,622,777)
Turkish population 10,000–100,000 (31,623)

The Goldcrest, the smallest European passerine, is typically associated with boreal and temperate forest, especially spruce *Picea* and fir *Abies*, breeding across most of N and C Europe and into Asia, with separate populations centred in E and W China. Through clinal variation in size and colour, birds from eastern populations are slightly larger and paler than western individuals. In North America, the Goldcrest is replaced by the closely related Golden-crowned Kinglet *R. satrapa*. The nominate subspecies *R.r. regulus* occurs over most of mainland Europe; only in the Caucasus and (probably) Crimea does *buturlini* replace it. There are three Azorean subspecies, *azoricus* (São Miguel), *sancta-maria* (Santa Maria) and *inermis* (western Azores) and eight outside the *Atlas*' coverage area.

The major populations occur in Russia, Fennoscandia and Germany (*c*80% of 45Mbp), but the species is widespread and evenly distributed across northern Europe, breeding in all countries except Iceland. The northern distribution appears limited by the breeding season mean air temperature, which if lower than 10°C reduces breeding success (Haftorn 1978). Its winter range extends southwards to the drier regions of southern and Mediterranean Europe where as a breeding species it becomes increasingly rare and more localized.

Its occurrence reflects generally the distribution of major spruce and fir forests and stands. Following a series of mild winters, the Goldcrest can become exceptionally numerous in prime habitat. Maximum average densities of 114 bp/km^2 have been recorded locally in Norway in homogeneous stands of old spruce trees, but in pine *Pinus* forests, territory densities normally are less than half this value, average densities below 40 bp/km^2 being more representative of Fennoscandia overall. In SW Ireland, however, maximum estimates of 591 bp/km^2 have been recorded in established spruce plantations (Batten 1976). The Goldcrest remains absent from extremely arid, montane or latitudinal regions beyond the treeline, but in Switzerland it has bred at 2200m asl in suitable habitat (*BWP*). In winter, however, the species may utilize a greater variety of habitats, including mixed woodland, scrub, parks and gardens where typically it associates with flocks of other species such as titmice *Parus* spp (Thaler-Kottek 1990).

The species is prone to large population crashes caused by severe winters, but because it has two broods per year of about nine chicks each, there is great potential to replace such losses when conditions improve. The consequent wide fluctuations in population size can obscure general population trends. In most European countries, however, the status of the Goldcrest is fairly well documented, and only from parts of Russia are quantitative data lacking. The European breeding population is largely stable as evidenced by the absence of major changes in population density or range expansion in any of the top ten countries. There have been local population increases in Hungary and Estonia, but only in Ukraine and on the island of Jersey have significant declines in number probably occurred. However, a slow northward range expansion in Scandinavia may be a consequence of modern forestry's preference for spruce forests (Koskimies 1989a).

Despite its susceptibility to harsh winters, the Goldcrest vacates totally only the most northerly extremes of its range in winter. Cold itself normally cannot disrupt its nocturnal energy balance if adequate food supplies are available (Reinertsen *et al* 1988). Nevertheless, extensive autumnal movements typically result in the more sedentary populations of Britain, Ireland and the Low Countries being augmented by birds of Scandinavian or Baltic origin. Although rare in SW Spain, the Goldcrest occurs regularly on passage in the Balearics, and in the C Mediterranean, in Malta. Its powers of dispersal have also helped establish occasional small populations in the Shetlands and Faeroes.

Svein Haftorn (N) Ian Henderson (GB)

This species account is sponsored by Lëtzebuerger Natur- a Vulleschutzliga, L.

Regulus ignicapillus Firecrest

CZ	Králíček ohnivý	**I**	Fiorrancino
D	Sommergoldhähnchen	**NL**	Vuurgoudhaantje
E	Reyezuelo Listado	**P**	Estrelinha-de-cabeça-listada
F	Roitelet a triple-bandeau	**PL**	Zniczek
FIN	Tulipäähippiäinen	**R**	Красноголовый королек
G	Βασιλίσκος	**S**	Brandkronad kungsfågel
H	Tüzesfejű királyka		

SPEC Cat 4, Threat status S

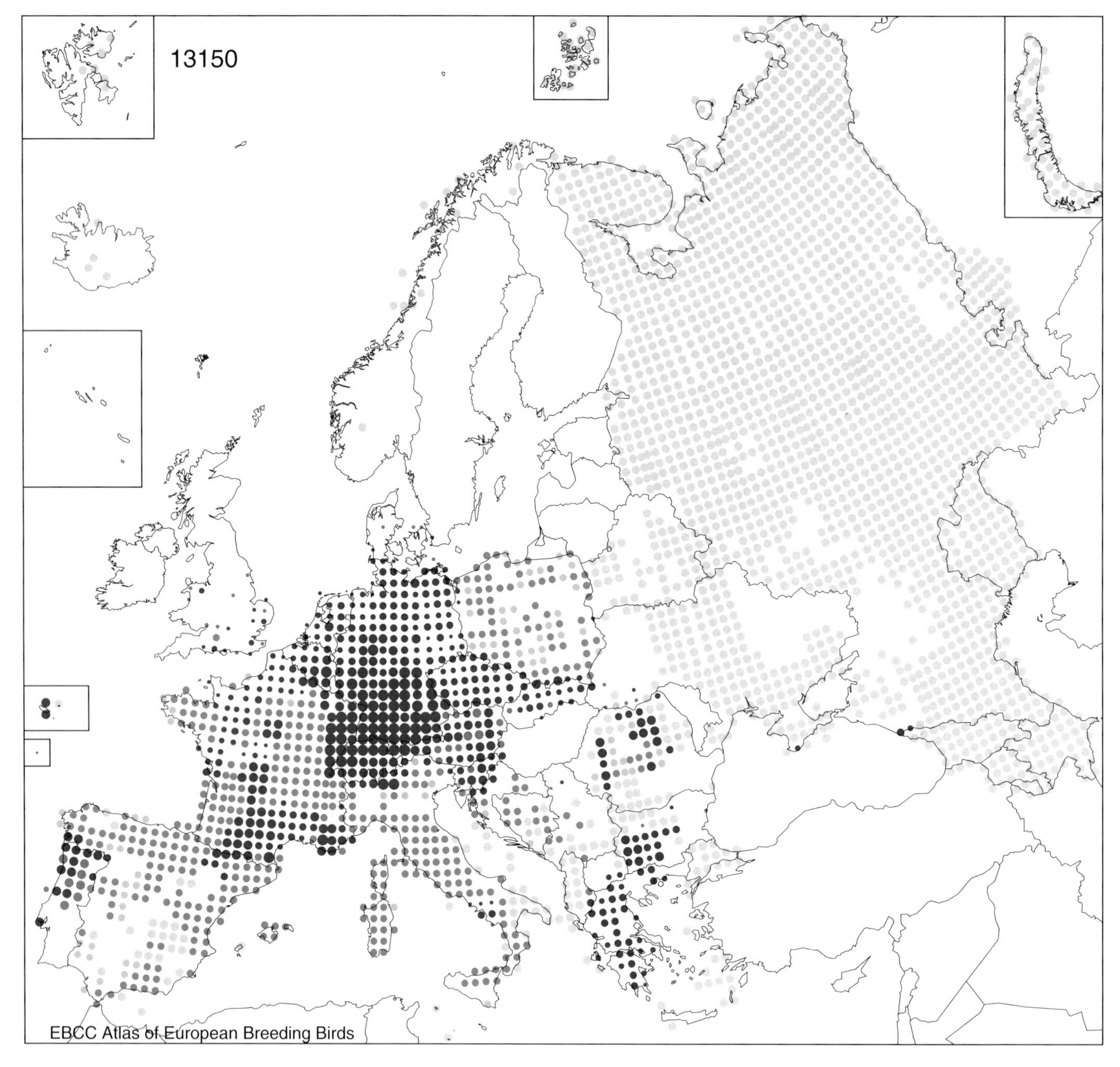

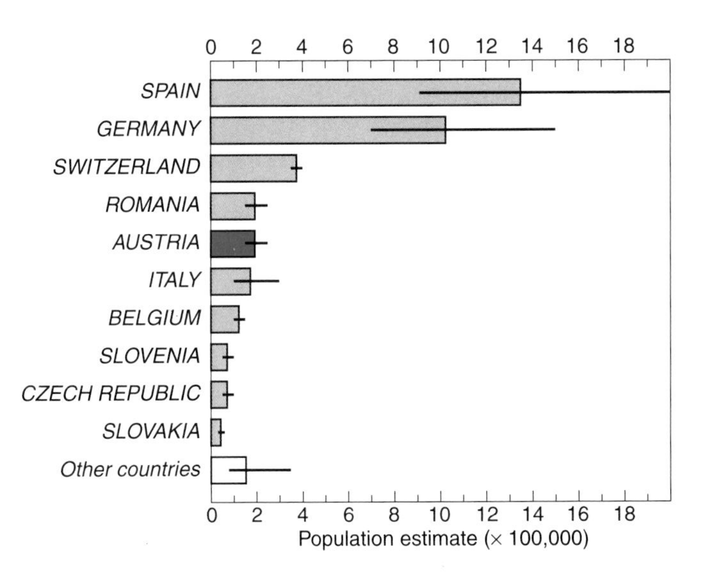

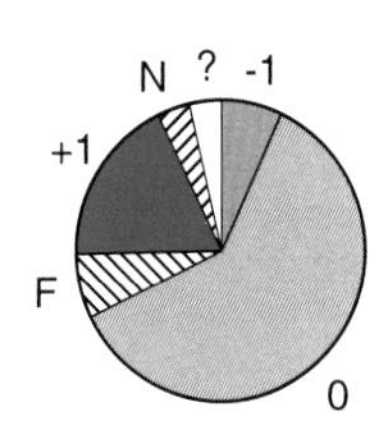

% in top 10 countries: 95.9
Total number of populated European countries: 28
Total European population 3,210,337–4,595,854 (3,767,704)
Turkish population 1000–10,000 (3162)

This tiny avian jewel has a relatively restricted distribution, with its cores in C Europe and Iberia. Three subspecies commonly are recognized, the nominate being the most widespread. The apparently resident population in North Africa and the Balearic Islands is separated as *balearicus*, and that in Madeira as *madeirensis*. A related species, the Taiwan Firecrest *R. goodfellowi*, forms a superspecies with *ignicapillus*, while *R. regulus teneriffae* of the Canary Islands is sometimes treated as a subspecies of Firecrest rather than Goldcrest.

Over most of Europe, habitat choice is broader than that of Goldcrest, its close relative. Even a small admixture of spruce *Picea*, fir *Abies* or pine *Pinus* among deciduous trees forms suitable nesting habitat. In some places apparently it avoids pure conifer woods. In England, however, the Firecrest nests in a subset of Goldcrest habitats and is attracted especially to mature plantations of Norway spruce *Picea abies* and to ornamental grounds with exotic conifers. Cork oak *Quercus suber* and alder *Alnus* woods are prime breeding habitat in S Spain, while on Madeira the species occupies tree heath *Erica arborea* and laurel *Laurus* forests. Towards its southern range, the Firecrest becomes more typical of montane forests.

The Alps and S Germany appear to have the highest breeding densities. The mapped distribution is almost continuous between this core area and the North Sea coast, N Spain, and the Polish and Slovak borders. The high population estimate for Spain (average of >6000 bp/50×50km square) suggests an exceptional breeding density in the N, but this requires confirmation (Portugal's average, 860 bp/50×50km square); the species can be both elusive and highly unevenly distributed, making population estimation everywhere especially uncertain.

BWP shows the breeding range extending from Poland into S Latvia, W Belarus and NW Ukraine, where *Atlas* records are sparse. It also indicates breeding in Crete and the northern and western fringes of Hungary. However, the *Atlas* shows the eastern European outposts in Crimea and Abkhazia, thus representing almost completely the Firecrest's global distribution. Beyond this coverage area, the species nests only in northerly and mountainous regions of NW Africa and Turkey. As yet, there are no records from beyond the western Palearctic.

There has been evidence throughout the 20th century of a slow or sporadic northwestward breeding range extension (Thaler-Kottek 1990). The first Belgian nesting record dates from 1916 (now *c*10 000 bp/50×50km square) and the first Dutch from 1928 (present population 5000–8000bp). Colonization was confirmed in Denmark in 1961 (remains rare) and in England in 1962. The English population has subsequently reached treble figures in some years, but although the range has continued to expand, numbers apparently have changed little since the mid-1970s (J.H. Marchant 1993). Wales was colonized by 1975 and Sweden in 1990. In the E, evidence for range expansion is less clear. Hungary is newly colonized. The species has bred in NE Poland only since 1968, yet its status in Latvia has not consolidated despite breeding records since 1893.

The NE third of the breeding range, from N Germany, the Czech Republic and Slovakia northwards, is evacuated completely in winter (*BWP*) (some may remain through mild winters; Heyer 1984), while the species becomes more widespread and abundant in Great Britain, France, Spain, Portugal, Morocco and Turkey. Regular passage occurs near short sea-crossings in SE England, the Straits of Gibraltar, Malta, Cap Bon in Tunisia, and the Bosphorus. A ringing recovery links Belgium in June with Morocco in February, indicating long southward movements by northerly breeding birds. In Britain, the winter range is more westerly than the breeding distribution, and more associated with coastal scrub and with river valleys. It is not known whether any British breeders remain to overwinter.

John Marchant (GB)

This species account is sponsored by Natur- und Vogelschutzverein Urdorf, CH.

Panurus biarmicus

Bearded Tit

CZ	Sýkořice vousatá	**I**	Basettino
D	Bartmeise	**NL**	Baardmannetje
E	Bigotudo	**P**	Chapim-de-bigode
F	Panure à moustaches	**PL**	Wąsatka
FIN	Viiksitimali	**R**	Усатая синица
G	Μουστακαλής	**S**	Skäggmes
H	Barkóscinege		

Non-SPEC, Threat status S (P)

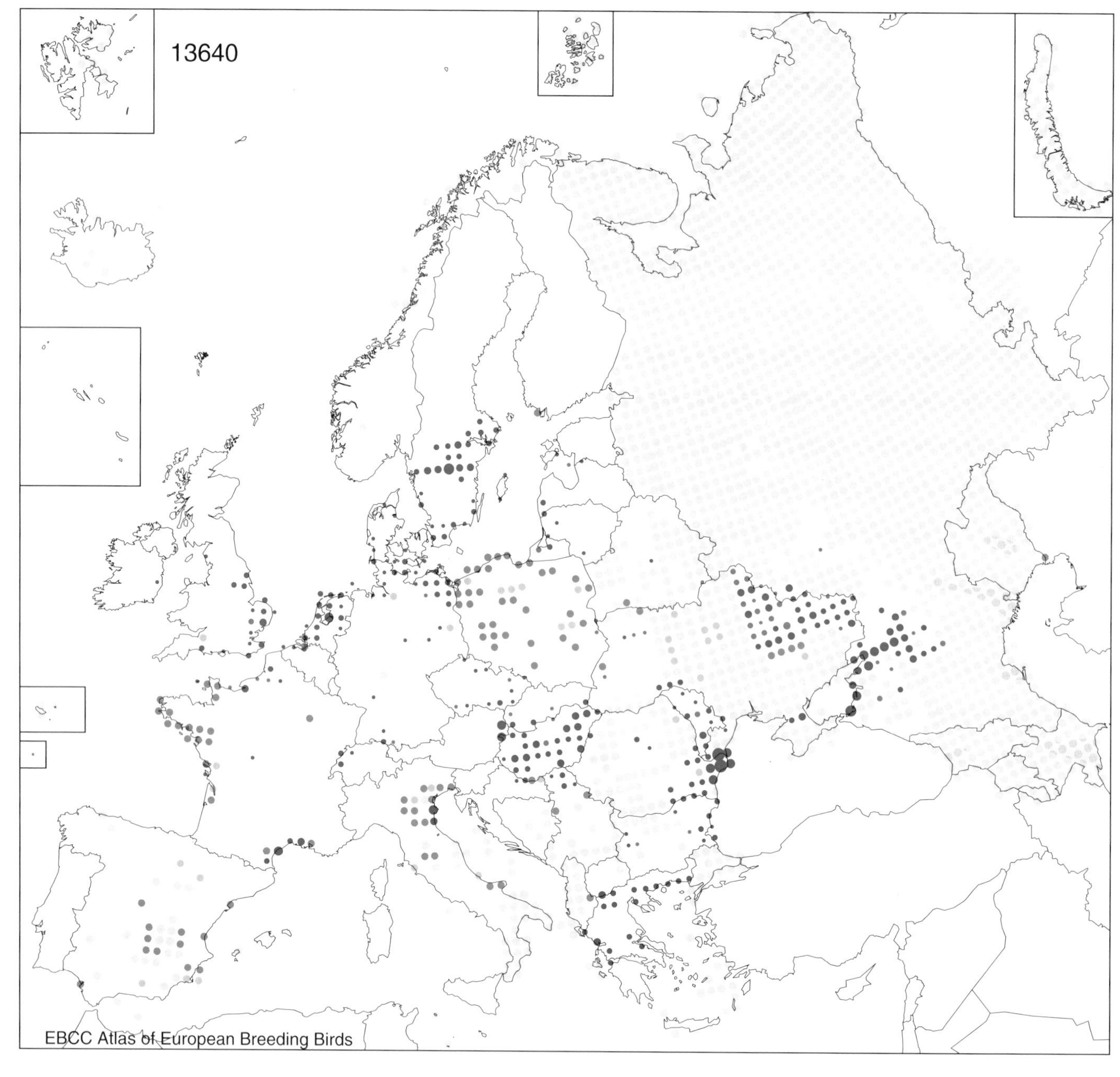

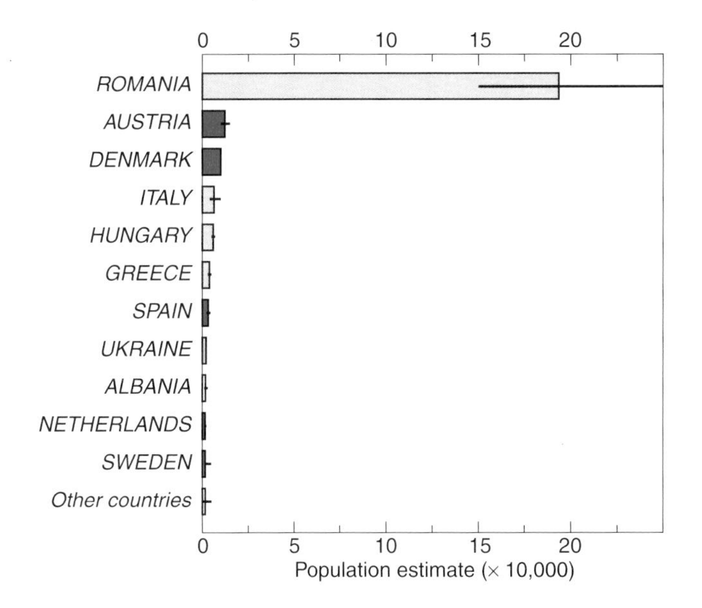

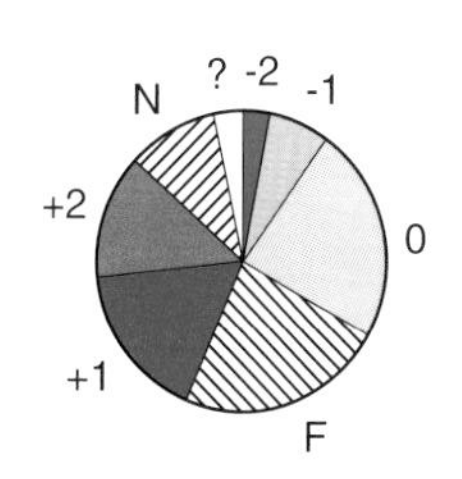

% in top 10 countries: 96.4
Total number of populated European countries: 29
Total European population 195,866–306,386 (244,971)
Russian population 50,000–500,000 (158,114)
Turkish population 1000–50,000 (7071)

The patchy distribution of the Bearded Tit in Europe represents the western arm of an otherwise extensive range through C and E Palearctic, lying between the 17°C and 32°C July isotherms. In detail, its distribution reflects that of the *Phragmites* reedbeds upon which it largely depends, and in particular that of large reed marshes which may support densities equivalent (if based on multiplication from local density) to 2000 bp/km² in prime habitat. In Europe, particularly important concentrations are found in the Danube Delta in Romania (*c*200 000bp), Russia (*c*160 000bp) and the 103km² of reedbeds along the Austrian Neusiedlersee (>10 000bp, but probably substantially more; Dvorak *et al* 1993). Many European countries hold estimated populations in excess of 1000bp (Zink 1987), including Spain, France (mainly Camargue), Hungary, Italy (Po Delta), Ukraine, Turkey, S Sweden and The Netherlands (in 1989–91, 1300–2000bp; *c*80% were in the Oostvaardersplassen alone; Osieck & Hustings 1994). These figures parallel the relative scarcity of suitable habitat across countries. Any significant reduction in its distribution may influence the status of Bearded Tit. However, the European population is presently expanding its range and abundance and this cannot be related to the change in distribution of wetlands which, overall, have declined.

The pattern of population change varies considerably across its European range. Within the core populations containing more than 3500bp, numbers are reported to be stable. However, outside these areas, as might be expected, densities either fluctuate considerably between years but with no clear trend, such as in France, Germany, Latvia, Slovakia, Lithuania and Belgium, or are showing a clear trend. In the latter case, most populations are expanding, as in Spain, Great Britain and Denmark, some even by more than 50% between 1970 and 1990 (Sweden, Poland, Estonia, Czech Republic). In line with this general trend, the species bred for the first time in Finland, Lithuania, Switzerland, Belarus and Norway during this period. However, at the same time, declines of more than 20% (but less than 50%) were reported for Ukraine and Moldova, while in The Netherlands, the population dropped by more than 50%, mainly through habitat destruction. The recent general expansion in range and abundance of the Bearded Tit, following a period of decline, is probably due to the milder climatic conditions since 1987, because the species is noted for its intolerance of severe winters.

Although the Bearded Tit is largely sedentary within its European range, in relation to population expansion and in response to severe winter weather, it is irruptive. Colonization of new sites may follow such movements. Hence a major irruption from The Netherlands in 1965 resulted in movements into Great Britain and the first breeding of the species in W France, S Sweden and parts of N Germany (Zink 1987). After another huge irruption in 1975, Bearded Tit bred for the first time in Ireland in 1976. In some populations, the species may be a partial migrant, with annual emigration of first autumn individuals. Such movements also may lead to colonization of new sites because the Bearded Tit uses the same habitat in winter and for breeding. In other cases, ringing recoveries have shown a return to the source site after migration or irruption.

Considering the fluidity of movement between populations, it is not surprising that little racial variation has been described from within Europe. Three subspecies are recognized although one, *P.b. kosswigi* from southern Turkey, is thought extinct. The nominate *biarmicus* occurs throughout W Europe and the Balkans and *russicus* from C Europe (especially Austria) E into Turkey, differing largely in ground colour, but not in its ability to modify the gizzard seasonally in order to exploit seed in winter and insects in summer (Sluys 1982).

Andrew G Gosler (GB) Sándor Mogyorósi (H)

Aegithalos caudatus

Long-tailed Tit

CZ	Mlynařík dlouhoocasý	**I**	Codibugnolo
D	Schwanzmeise	**NL**	Staartmees
E	Mito	**P**	Chapim-rabilongo
F	Mésange à longue queue	**PL**	Raniuszek
FIN	Pyrstötiainen	**R**	Длиннохвостая синица
G	Αιγίθαλος	**S**	Stjärtmes
H	Őszapó		

Non-SPEC, Threat status S

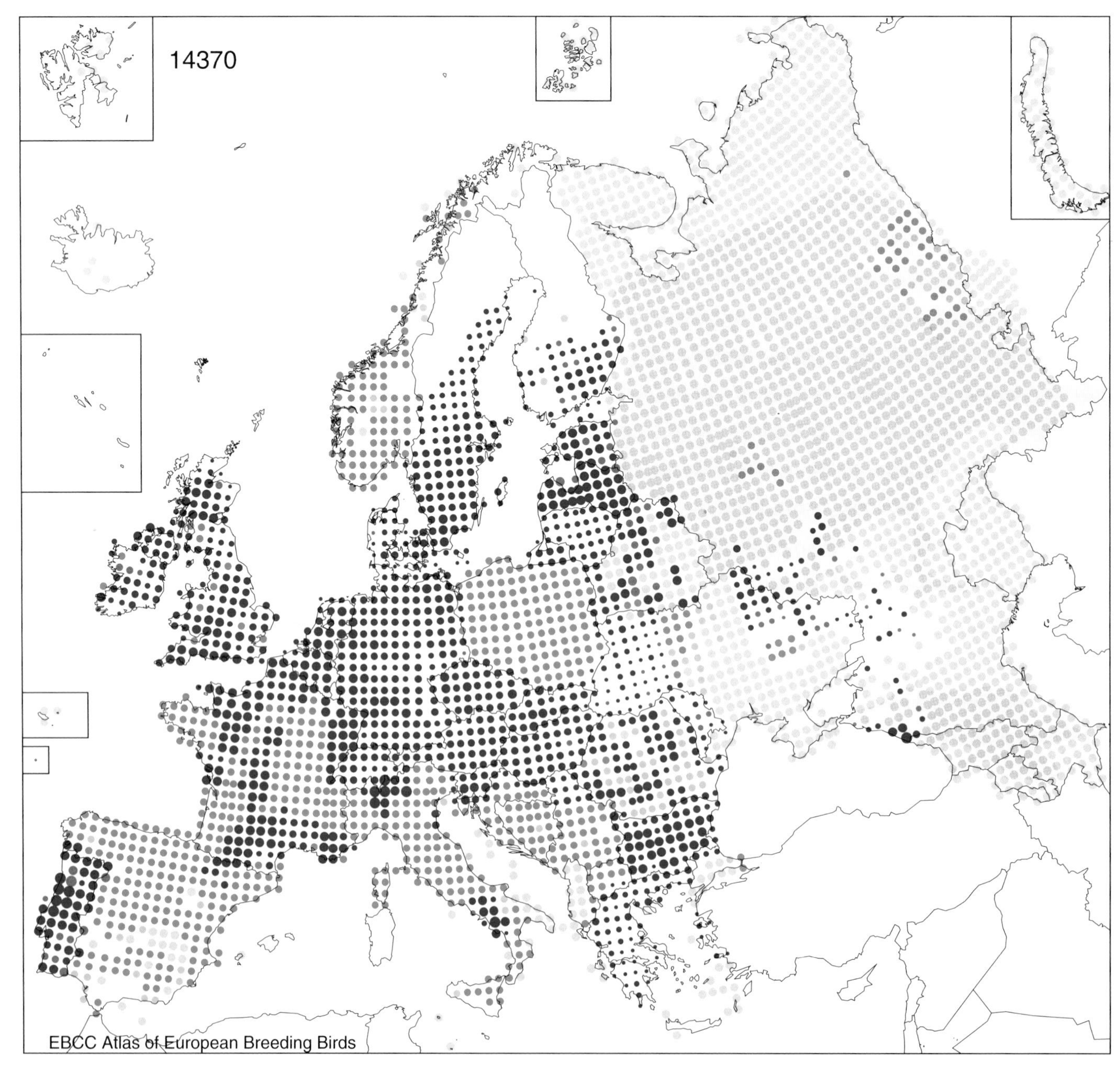

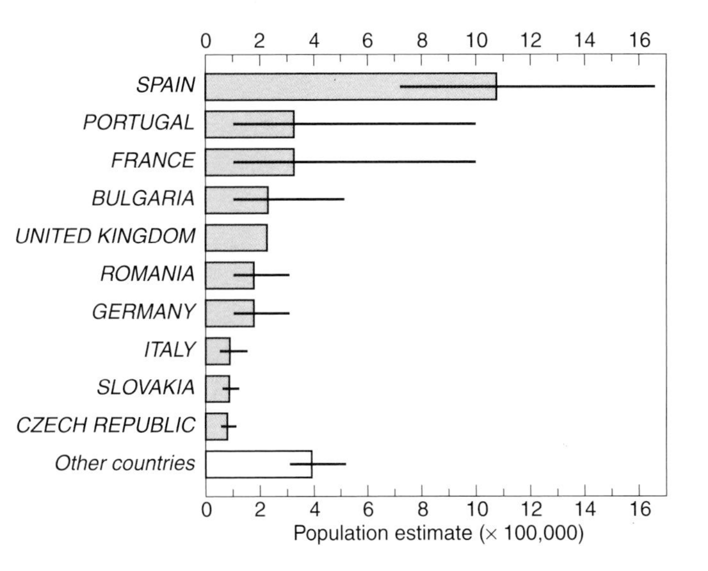

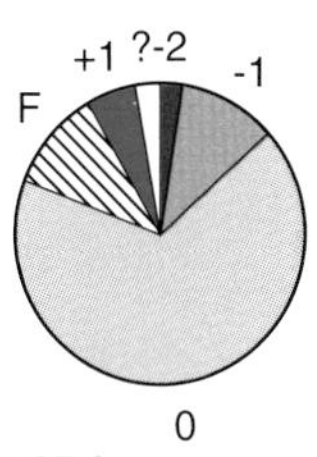

% in top 10 countries: 87.9
Total number of populated European countries: 37
Total European population 2,613,413–4,301,890 (3,126,144)
Russian population 100,000–1,000,000 (316,228)
Turkish population 10,000–100,000 (31,623)

The Long-tailed Tit breeds from Portugal to Ussuriland and S to Iran and C China. It breeds throughout Europe, being absent only from Iceland, N Fennoscandia (mostly N of 66°N), the Balearics, Sardinia and Crete. It breeds mainly in the maritime, temperate and continental latitudes, and to some extent in the boreal and mediterranean zones. At least 12 subspecies occur in Europe, and many elsewhere.

The Long-tailed Tit generally prefers structurally diverse habitats containing numerous margins between wooded and open areas, usually below 1000m asl (1800m in the Alps). Slight differences in habitat preference are seen across Europe. The species favours bogs, fens and moist deciduous and mixed woods possessing well-developed bush layers (often willow *Salix*) in N and C Europe, but in W Europe it is partial to non-woodland sites such as areas of thorny shrubs, hedgerows and even juniper *Juniperus* heaths. In Mediterranean areas the Long-tailed Tit inhabits dense maquis. Recently the species has become commoner in populated areas, inhabiting shrubbery in parks, cemeteries and large gardens.

Modern forestry management techniques often require bogs and fens to be drained. The Finnish (to a lesser extent Swedish) declines in numbers and range have probably been caused by intensive forestry creating vast continuous coniferous stands, normally anathema to the Long-tailed Tit (Koskimies 1989a). Breeding in Sweden and Norway above 62°N is mostly restricted to coastal areas where there are more deciduous stands than inland.

Another feature of Long-tailed Tit ecology which affects the species' distribution is that flocks require large winter territories. In S Sweden, individuals from such flocks roamed an area of 20–25ha of prime habitat. Comparable sizes for winter territories have been reported from Great Britain, Switzerland and Germany (Glen & Perrins 1988). This means that the species may become endangered locally by the increasing fragmentation of its habitat in heavily managed areas.

The Long-tailed Tit, being small (6–8g) and dependent on a year-round insectivorous diet, is very susceptible to severe winter weather, which, especially in its northern range, may eliminate the species from large areas which may remain uncolonized for several years. Even in more southerly parts of its range, population sizes can fluctuate considerably through winter mortality. In Britain, the harsh winter of 1978/79 caused a decline of 49% on farmland and 32% in woodland (J.H. Marchant *et al* 1990). However, during 1970–90, numbers and range remained very stable overall throughout Europe, except for >50% declines in Finland.

The Long-tailed Tit is mainly sedentary, but irruptive movements (sometimes massive) occur in its northern and, to a lesser extent, C range. Seemingly, such irruptions are triggered by high population levels. A massive irruption during 1973 saw more than 10 000 birds moving through Finland, the Baltic States and Sweden. Many probably originated from NW Russia but were later joined by birds from Fennoscandia and the Baltic States. The movement apparently ebbed away in Scandinavia, only small numbers reaching S Sweden and Denmark.

Breeding density estimates are very approximate because of lack of territoriality during breeding, very high nest predation, pairs' second nests being built anywhere within the large winter flock range, and a high frequency of co-operative breeding (Glen & Perrins 1988). Densities per 50km square are lowest in Fennoscandia, Greece, Italy and Ukraine (<100bp), intermediate in E Europe and the Baltic states (<1000bp), rather high in W and C Europe and the Balkans (<5000bp) and very high in Iberia (>5000bp). Small-scale values of 1–10 bp/km² obtain in Polish oak–hornbeam *Quercus–Carpinus betulus* woods (probably secondary habitat) and up to 30 bp/km² in Britain in open areas containing bushes, hedges and small trees.

Jan-Åke Nilsson (S)

Parus palustris

Marsh Tit

CZ	Sýkora babka	**I**	Cincia bigia
D	Sumpfmeise	**NL**	Glanskop
E	Carbonero Palustre	**P**	Chapim-palustre
F	Mésange nonnette	**PL**	Sikora uboga
FIN	Viitatiainen	**R**	Черноголовая гаичка
G	Καστανοπαπαδίτσα	**S**	Entita
H	Barátcinege		

Non-SPEC, Threat status S

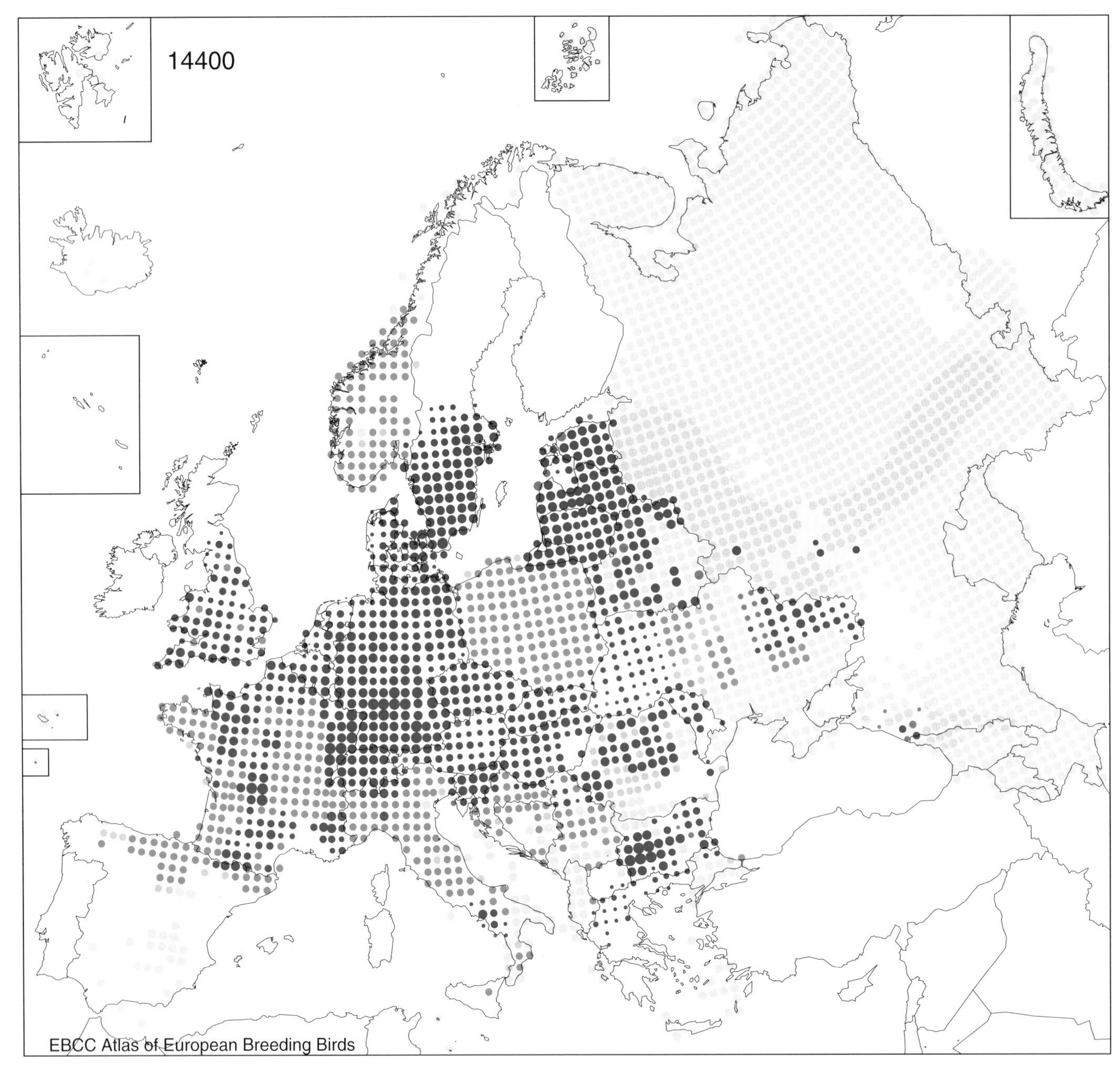

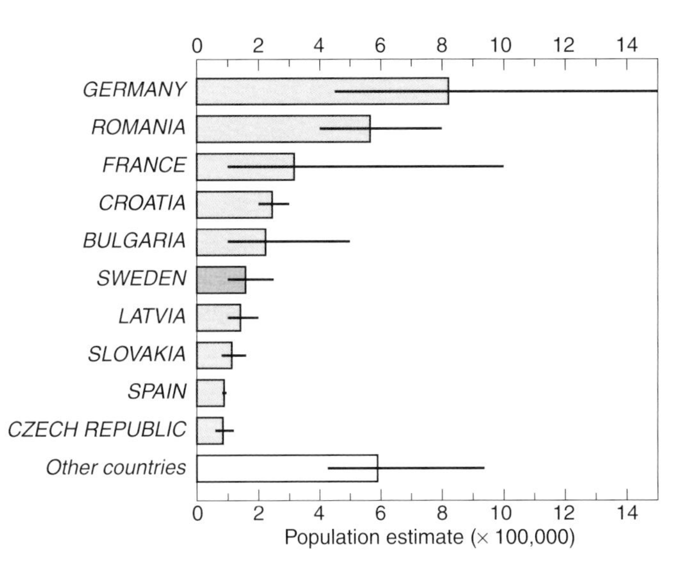

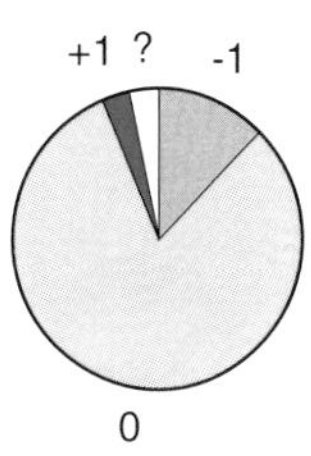

% in top 10 countries: 82.4
Total number of populated European countries: 32
Total European population 2,858,104–4,398,545 (3,348,016)
Russian population 10,000–100,000 (31,623)
Turkish population 1000–10,000 (3162)

The Marsh Tit has a disjunct world distribution. Some 2000km separates the eastern Palearctic range from the western, the eastern comprising Sakhalin, SE Siberia, Korea and N China. In the W, the species inhabits most of Europe, except for Finland, N Scandinavia, Ireland, much of Scotland, most coastal Mediterranean areas, and Iberia S of the Pyrenees and Cantabrians. The Oriental region holds a small population in Burma. There are five subspecies in Europe, *P.p. italicus* occurring in the French Alps and Italy, *kabardensis* in the eastern Great Caucasus, *stagnatilis* from E Bulgaria, E Hungary and E Poland eastwards, *dresseri* from C England through W France to the Massif Central, and the nominate *palustris* in the remainder, including N England and S Scotland; perhaps ten subspecies occur elsewhere.

The Marsh Tit strongly prefers deciduous woods, particularly those dominated by beech *Fagus* (for beechmast, an important winter-food source), and oak *Quercus* (for caterpillars, essential nestling food during the breeding season). Its European distribution apparently is determined by the occurrence of these two tree species. It breeds predominantly in lowlands, occurring locally up to 1300m asl in mountains.

On a smaller scale, the species seemingly prefers mixed deciduous woods possessing a well-developed bush layer. It avoids dry areas and coniferous woods, especially spruce *Picea* plantations. Interestingly, it seems also to avoid pure beech stands in the breeding season, probably because their caterpillar abundance is relatively low and their structure is insufficiently varied, although they comprise good winter habitat.

Three features of Marsh Tit ecology have important distributional implications: firstly, the species is an obligate hole-breeder, restricting it to woods containing a sufficiency of natural holes (crucial, because the Marsh Tit occupies the lowest dominance rank and can use only the holes left unoccupied by more dominant species; J-Å. Nilsson 1984); secondly, the Marsh Tit needs a large territory for a bird of its size (woods must be of at least 4–5ha to support a pair), and thirdly, the species is very sedentary (juveniles take up residence for life on average only 800–1000m from their natal territory (J-A. Nilsson 1989). At Falsterbo, a major migration site in S Sweden, only four individuals have been caught during 34 years of intense observation and netting (Roos 1984).

The increasing fragmentation of suitable woods and forests since the 1950s not only through urbanization and agricultural intensification but also through the supersession of deciduous woods by coniferous plantations, inevitably has had a significant impact on the Marsh Tit which requires comparatively large woods and whose colonization rate is low. Such fragmentation probably has contributed to the negative population size trends experienced in Sweden, Estonia, Denmark and Great Britain. Severe winter weather, one cause of high mortality rates, may eliminate small, isolated populations whose territories may remain unoccupied for many years because the species' colonization rate is low. The low colonization rate probably also accounts for the species' absence from some otherwise suitable islands, such as Ireland and Gotland. The possible decline in Britain, in comparison with thriving populations of other titmice, has been linked with interspecific competition (Mead 1993b). Range extensions are taking place in S Scotland, N Netherlands and Spain. However, the species' extreme sedentariness will constrain the expansion rate sharply.

Marsh Tit breeding density depends more on habitat quality than on the geographical location of breeding sites. In oak-dominated, mixed deciduous woods in S Sweden, up to 25 bp/km^2 occur. Similar values are known from oak woods in England and from France and Germany to Poland and Latvia. The highest densities of 30–40 bp/km^2 were found in 150–200-year-old oak–hornbeam *Quercus–Carpinus* woods in Switzerland.

Jan-Åke Nilsson (S)

Parus montanus **Willow Tit**

CZ	Sýkora lužní	**I**	Cincia bigia alpestre
D	Weidenmeise	**NL**	Matkop
E	Carbonero Sibilino	**P**	Chapim-sibilino
F	Mésange boréale	**PL**	Czarnogłówka
FIN	Hömötiainen	**R**	Буроголовая гаичка
G	Βουνοπαπαδίτσα	**S**	Talltita
H	Kormosfejű cinege		

Non-SPEC, Threat status S (P)

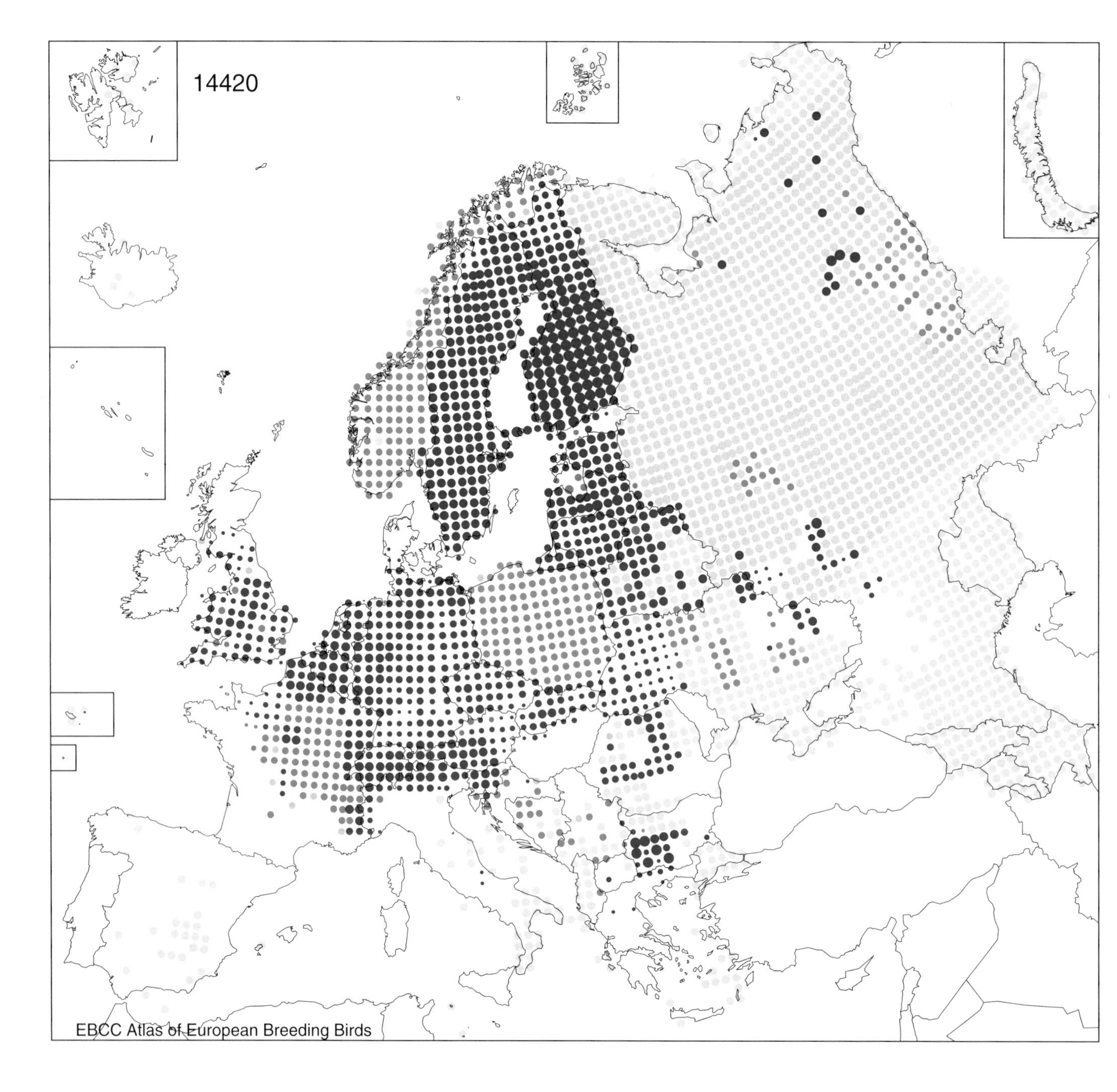

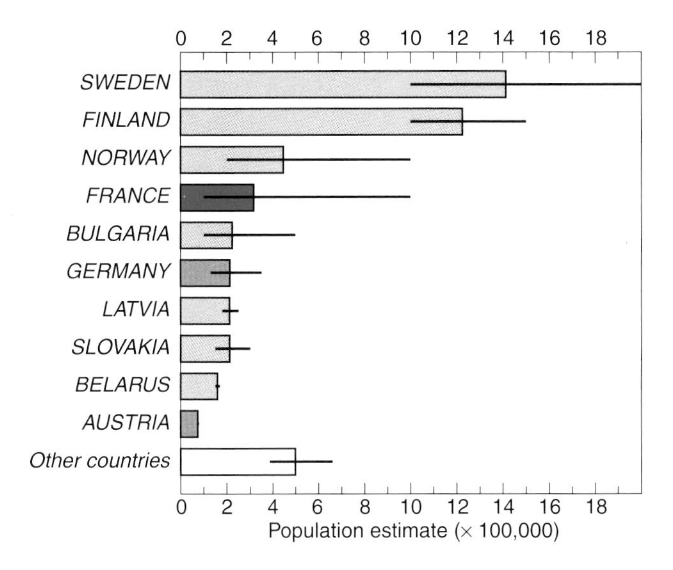

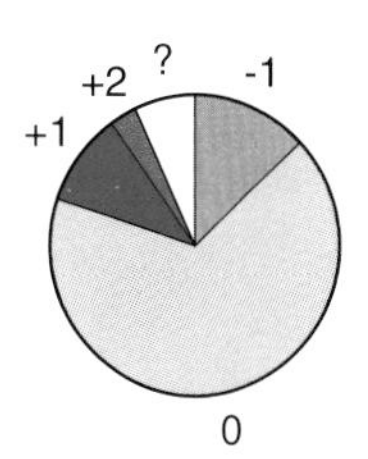

% in top 10 countries: 90.0
Total number of populated European countries: 30
Total European population 4,398,703–6,137,730 (4,997,684)
Russian population 10,000,000–100,000,000 (31,622,777)

The Willow Tit has an extensive distribution across the Palearctic and into the Oriental zoogeographical region, from Great Britain in the W to Anadyr on the Pacific in the E in a belt generally between 50° and 63°N. Its southernmost limits are at 38°N in Europe (Greece) and *c*31°N in Japan. In Europe it also has a wide distribution, lying generally between the 12°C and 21–23°C July isotherms and typically within the temperate middle and upper middle latitudes.

Its range extends through the boreal conifer forest and damp woods of willow *Salix*, birch *Betula* and alder *Alnus*, and in southern Europe into open montane conifer forest up to the treeline. The main habitat component necessary for its occurrence is the presence of decaying tree stumps which are soft enough to allow the bird to excavate its nest cavity, but in some regions, competition with other *Parus* species may be important.

Following these habitat requirements, the greatest population densities are found in Russia, Scandinavia, the Baltic States, the Alps and Bulgaria. Most of these regions hold estimated populations of more than 100 000bp, while Russia, Sweden and Finland may each hold more than 1Mbp. Most European populations are thought to be more or less stable although increases of more than 20% between 1970 and 1990 are believed to have occurred in France, Ukraine, Hungary and Denmark (Denmark's present maximum estimate of 20bp represents a surprising gap in European distribution). The Polish population, for which figures were not available at the time of writing, is undoubtedly important. Equivalent declines were reported from Germany, Austria, Lithuania and Britain.

Population breeding densities typically are low in this species. In the Scandinavian populations, which have been most intensively studied (reviewed by Matthysen 1990), density may reach 3–4 bp/km^2, although each territory is occupied during winter by a social group usually consisting of an adult pair with 2–4 juveniles.

The complex and highly ordered social structure of the Willow Tit is related to high site fidelity and therefore to a highly sedentary pattern with respect to movements, although some far northern populations (especially in Finland) make regular short movements to the south and in some years are irruptive (Zink 1981). It is interesting that the species did not join the mass movements of tits that occurred in Europe in 1957 (Cramp *et al* 1960) and 1959 (Cramp 1963). The food-storing behaviour of this species may be another adaptation, in addition to the social organization and its ability to drop its body temperature by *c*10°C at night (Reinertsen & Haftorn 1983), by which it can survive the harshest European climates and, therefore, resist the need to migrate. Thus, most movements of this species (of which few are exceeding 50km and in Britain most are less than 5km) have been interpreted as post-fledging dispersal.

Given the highly sedentary nature of this species and, in parts of the range, its concentration in isolated or montane regions, it is perhaps not surprising that its subspecific taxonomy in Europe is complex. Through most of its European range it varies clinally, particularly in the colour of the upperparts (the *P.m. salicarius–borealis* group). There are, however, a number of isolated subgroups (the *P.m. montanus* group), particularly in C and S Europe whose relationship to the main clinal complex is not fully understood. These differ generally from the clinal group in their larger size, and also in colour, being more rufous, and in their song, which is markedly different. Up to 12 subspecies generally are recognized. The Willow Tit occasionally hybridizes with the Marsh Tit *P. palustris*, which it resembles closely.

Andrew G Gosler (GB) and Svein Haftorn (N)

Parus lugubris

Sombre Tit

CZ	Sýkora temná	**I**	Cincia dalmatina
D	Trauermeise	**NL**	Rouwmees
E	Carbonero Lúgubre	**P**	Chapim-lúgubre
F	Mésange lugubre	**PL**	Sikora żałobna
FIN	Balkanintiainen	**R**	Средиземноморская гаичка
G	Κλειδωνάς		
H	Gyászos cinege	**S**	Balkanmes

SPEC Cat 4, Threat status S (P)

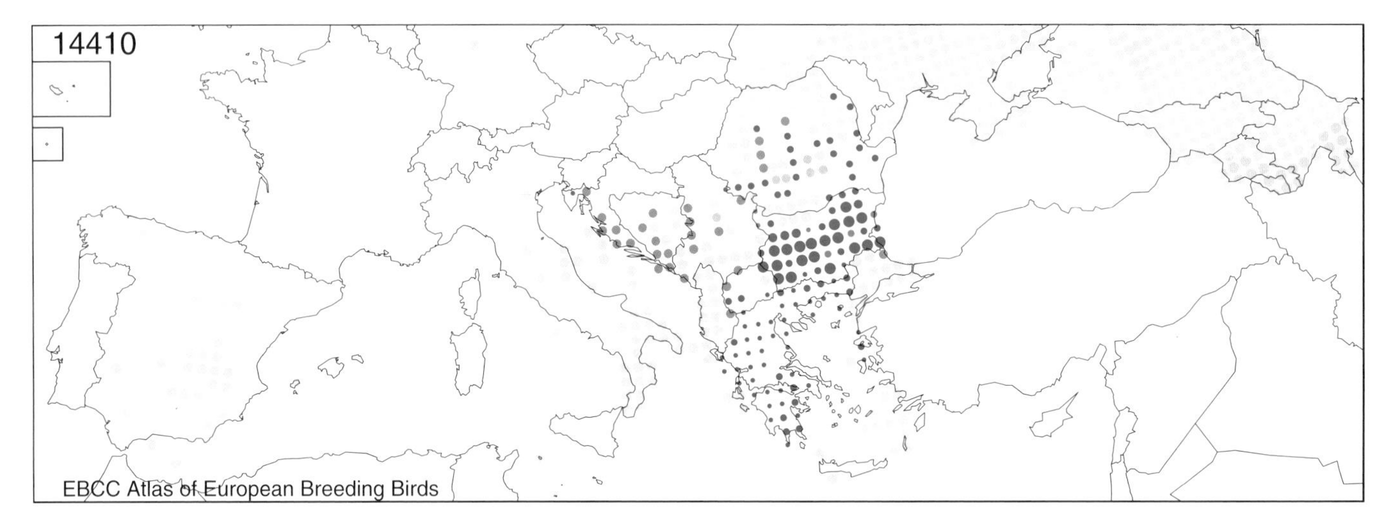

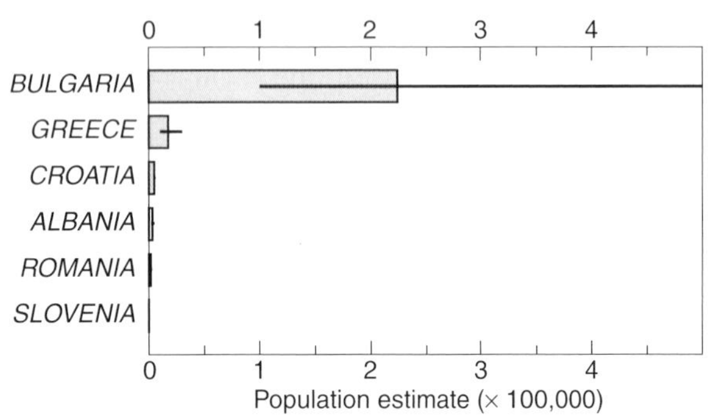

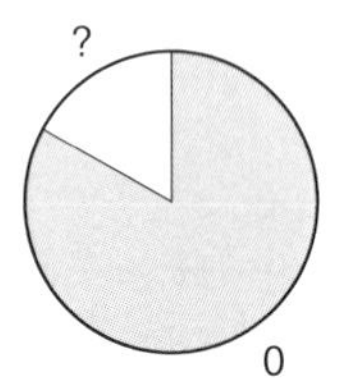

% in top 10 countries: 100.0
Total number of populated European countries: 6
Total European population 126,900–527,430 (250,735)
Turkish population 10,000–100,000 (31,623)

The European range of the Sombre Tit forms a major part of its world distribution, presenting Europe with a special responsibility for the species. In Europe it is typically a bird of the eastern Mediterranean basin and the Balkans. Beyond the distribution illustrated, it extends E into Turkey and N Iran and S into the Lebanon and northern Israel. Its distribution is bounded by the 23° and 30°C July isotherms. Geographical variation is complex and somewhat variable, but in the *Atlas*' coverage area, the nominate *P.l. lugubris* occurs in Greece and the Balkans, *anatoliae* on Lesbos and southern Transcaucasia, and *hyrcanus* (increasingly separated as *P. hyrcanus*, Caspian Tit; Harrap & Quinn 1995) in Azerbaijan. Two other subspecies occur in Iran.

Within its European range, the Sombre Tit may occur in a wide range of generally dry, more or less open habitats in which it breeds typically at very low densities: generally less than 1 bp/km². Breeding habitats include sparsely vegetated sites, scrub, maquis, olive groves and also open woodland habitats, especially of oak *Quercus* spp or pine *Pinus* spp. Although scarce at sea level on the Mediterranean coast, as in Greece, it is normally commoner in such habitats at higher altitudes even over 2000m asl. In C Dalmatia, 4bp were recorded along a 1.5km montane transect of open white oak *Quercus pubescens* woods (Löhrl 1966). The Sombre Tit generally is resident and sedentary, although it (especially first-year birds) joins mobile wintering mixed-species flocks. It has probably extended its range slightly in Romania, but elsewhere no change has been reported. It has been reported as an accidental only from Italy.

Remarkably little is known about the ecology of this species. The nucleus of the European population is clearly Bulgaria, whose population is estimated at 100 000–500 000bp. Turkey and Greece also are important centres with estimated populations of 30 000 and 17 000bp respectively. Croatia, Albania and Romania hold populations in excess of 1000bp. Slovenia holds 10–20bp (Geister 1995). Its density and range are generally assumed to be stable.

Andrew G Gosler (GB)

Parus cinctus — Siberian Tit

CZ	Sýkora laponská	I	Cincia siberiana
D	Lapplandmeise	NL	Bruinkopmees
E	Carbonero Lapón	P	Chapim da Lapónia
F	Mésange lapone	PL	Sikora północna
FIN	Lapintiainen	R	Сероголовая гаичка
G	Σιβηροπαπαδίτσα	S	Lappmes
H	Lappföldi cinege		

Non-SPEC, Threat status S (P)

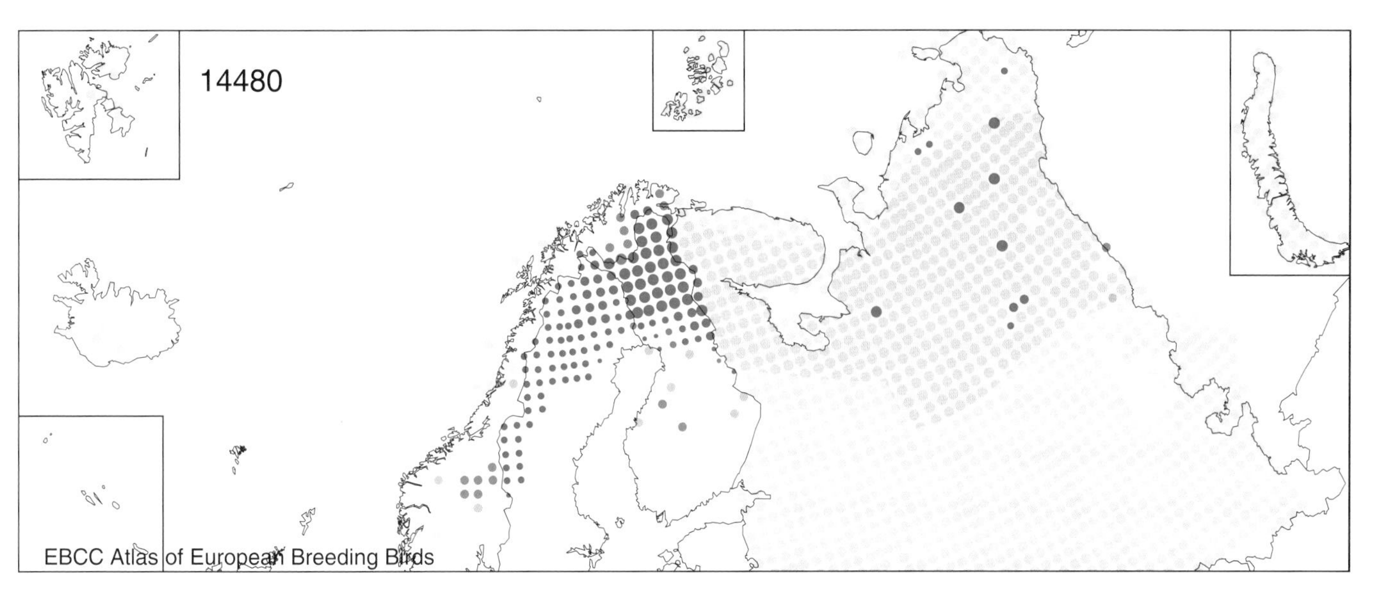

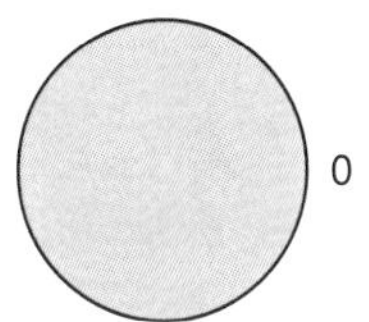

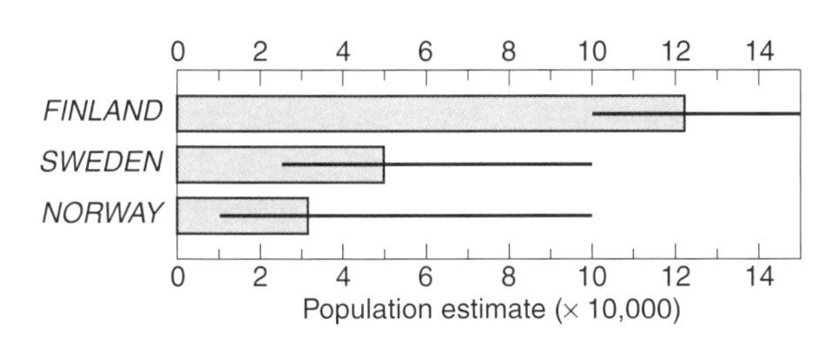

% in top 10 countries: 100.0
Total number of populated European countries: 3
Total European population 164,127–293,165 (204,097)
Russian population 100,000–1,000,000 (316,228)

The Siberian Tit is distributed throughout the Eurasian boreal coniferous forests, and also in those of Alaska and the Canadian Yukon. Its European range is restricted to the northern boreal areas, where it occurs as far N as the northern forest limit. In Fennoscandia, the Siberian Tit prefers old-growth coniferous forests, dominated by both pine *Pinus sylvestris* and spruce *Picea abies* (Virkkala 1987b). It breeds also in the mountain birch *Betula pubescens* forests of the Scandinavian mountains (Järvinen 1982). The subspecies *P.c. lapponicus* occurs from Norway E to the Pechora, where it intergrades with the nominate *cinctus* whose range reaches the Pacific. Two other subspecies occur beyond the *Atlas*' coverage.

The Siberian Tit is sedentary, adult birds being site-tenacious (Virkkala 1990). However, some juveniles migrate S of the breeding range in autumn to areas such as southern Finland. The species is a hole-nester. It has a relatively large home range of at least 15ha, but it may require 50–100ha in marginal areas (Järvinen 1982, Virkkala & Liehu 1990).

Contrary to the data in the graph, the Siberian Tit has declined in Finland (and probably also in Sweden) due to the large-scale clearfelling characteristic of forest management policies implemented after World War II (Järvinen & Väisänen 1979). It therefore has suffered from the fragmentation of formerly uniform old-growth forests, its preferred habitat. It has also suffered in managed forests because of the management policy of removing the dead and dying trees which it uses both for nesting and foraging (Virkkala & Liehu 1990). Furthermore, nesting success of the Siberian Tit is poor in heavily managed forest areas (Virkkala 1990). According to studies carried out in northern Finland, the species' breeding density in virgin, old-growth pine and spruce forests was 3–4 bp/km^2, and in managed, thinned forests about 0.5 bp/km^2 (Virkkala 1987b).

Sustained intensive forestry management since the 1950s has seen the range of the Siberian Tit in Finland recede, the southern boundary of its continuous range retreating 100–200km northwards.

Raimo Virkkala (FIN)

Parus cristatus

Crested Tit

CZ	Sýkora parukářka	**I**	Cincia dal ciuffo
D	Haubenmeise	**NL**	Kuifmees
E	Herrerillo Capuchino	**P**	Chapim-de-poupa
F	Mésange huppée	**PL**	Czubatka
FIN	Töyhtötiainen	**R**	Гренадерка
G	Σκουφοπαπαδίτσα	**S**	Tofsmes
H	Búbos cinege		

SPEC Cat 4, Threat status S

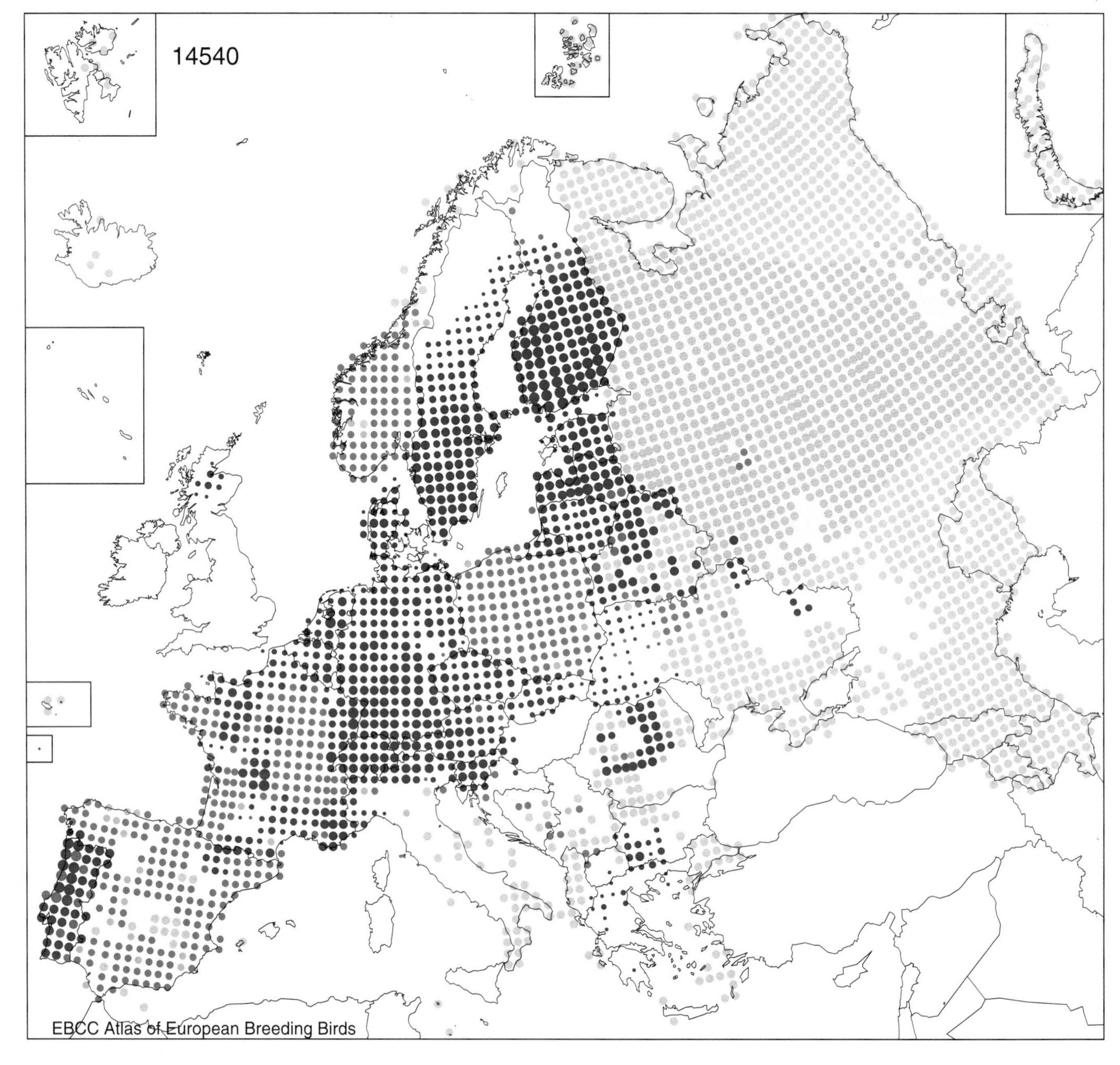

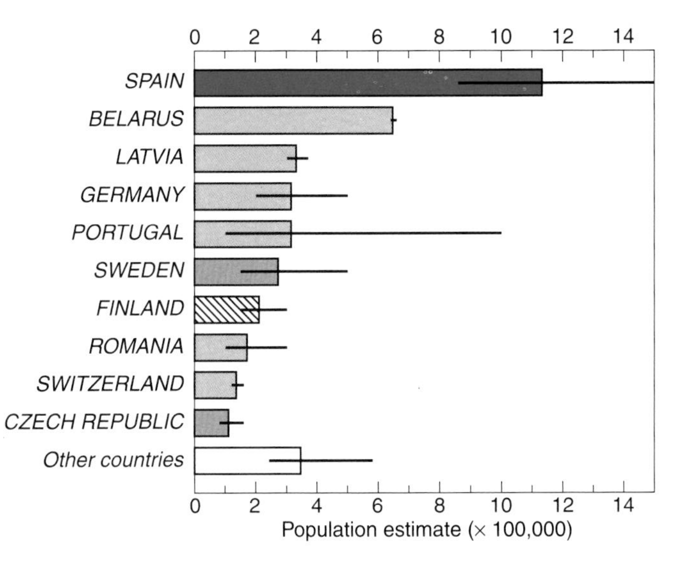

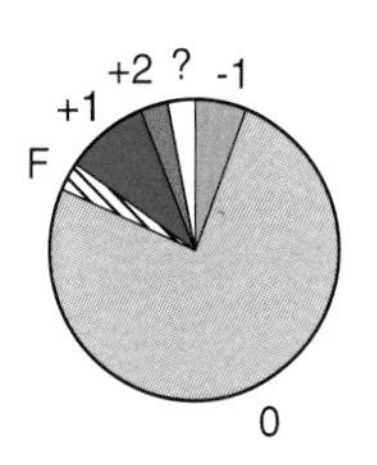

% in top 10 countries: 91.3
Total number of populated European countries: 33
Total European population 3,603,892–4,860,456 (4,009,950)
Russian population 1,000,000–10,000,000 (3,162,278)

The Crested Tit, an engaging little bird, is almost endemic to western Palearctic woodlands, occurring further E only in the Urals. Its range mostly lies in temperate continental latitudes between 45° and 65°N but it also extends S through much of Iberia. Within this area seven subspecies are recognized, only two of which are widespread and abundant: *P.c. mitratus* (most of W and C Europe) and the nominate *cristatus* (Scandinavia E across Russia to the C Urals and S to Romania and N Ukraine). The five other peripheral subspecies are *weigoldi* (SW Iberia), *abadiei* (Brittany), *scoticus* (Scotland), *bashkiricus* (southern Urals) and *bureschi* (southern former Yugoslavia, Albania, Greece, perhaps Bulgaria).

The predominant breeding habitat of the Crested Tit is coniferous woodland. In Fennoscandia and much of W and C Europe, it uses forests of pure Scots pine *Pinus sylvestris* or Norway spruce *Picea abies*, particularly favouring mixed forests. These woodlands often contain a proportion of deciduous species, and in areas of S Sweden at least, deciduous nest sites are common. Further S the species occupies Mediterranean mixed-conifer montane forests in N Italy and Spain. Over much of Iberia a wider habitat choice is apparent including pine *Pinus* spp, cork oak *Quercus suber* and beech *Fagus* woods (Löhrl 1991). The small Scottish population is associated closely with Scots pine woodland, although lodgepole pine *P. contorta* var. *latifolia* and larch *Larix* (but not spruce) are used for foraging.

In Scottish pinewoods, the presence of suitably rotted nest trees may be of great importance during habitat selection. Gradual death and decay permits the development of rot-causing fungi which soften the wood to permit excavation by the Crested Tit. Stumps of live-felled trees appear to dry out more rapidly and prevent the necessary fungi becoming established. Mature pinewoods with a diverse field layer and ample nesting trees at least 22cm in diameter meet the species' preferences much better then younger plantations (Baker 1991).

Despite few reliable quantitative data being available, population sizes in most countries are considered as fluctuating about an approximately stable level. Finland has experienced severe fluctuations of 20% or more. Declines of at least 20% occurred during 1970–90 in Sweden and the Czech Republic whereas similar-magnitude increases affected Spain, Italy, Hungary and Denmark due to range expansions. Before the 1970s, range extensions attributable to the spread of conifer plantations were noted in France, Belgium, The Netherlands, Denmark and Scotland, while N Finland experienced local declines of 90% or more. Locally in C Europe, as exemplified by a study in the Erzgebirge, the negative impact of atmospheric pollution on coniferous forests led to a substantial decline in Crested Tit populations (to 30% of mid-1970s levels, 1974–87), a rise in annual adult mortality (from 38% to 52%) and a reduced lifetime reproduction (from 5.2 to 4.1 young per individual, a rate partly buffered by an increase in the frequency of second broods). Forest degradation also forced juveniles to disperse more widely than usual (Möckel 1992).

Breeding densities (bp/km^2) range from a very high 48 in pine in NE France (Y. Muller 1987), to 20–40 in Portuguese cork oak woods, up to 40 in pine woods in NW Spain (Löhrl 1991), 17.0 in mature Scottish pines (S. Taylor, pers comm), 1.2–4.3 in pine–larch and 5–20 in pine–spruce forests in Germany (Löhrl 1991), 12–13 in pine–bilberry *Pinus–Vaccinium myrtilis* forests in E Poland (Tomiałojć *et al* 1984), 2.3–3.2 in pine-spruce forests in N Finland (Ojanen & Orell 1985) and 1.0 in mixed-age Scottish pine plantations (M. Cook, pers obs).

The Crested Tit has a small home range (6–11ha), shows strong site fidelity and normally takes up residence close to the natal site (Möckel 1992), all reasons why it is recorded only occasionally at migration observatories.

Martin Cook (GB)

Parus ater

Coal Tit

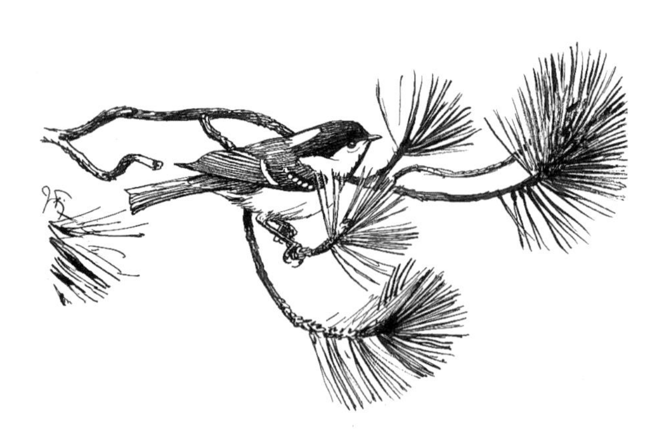

CZ	Sýkora uhelníček	**I**	Cincia mora
D	Tannenmeise	**NL**	Zwarte Mees
E	Carbonero Garrapinos	**P**	Chapim-preto
F	Mésange noire	**PL**	Sosnówka
FIN	Kuusitiainen	**R**	Московка
G	Ελατοπαπαδίτσα	**S**	Svartmes
H	Fenyvescinege		

Non-SPEC, Threat status S

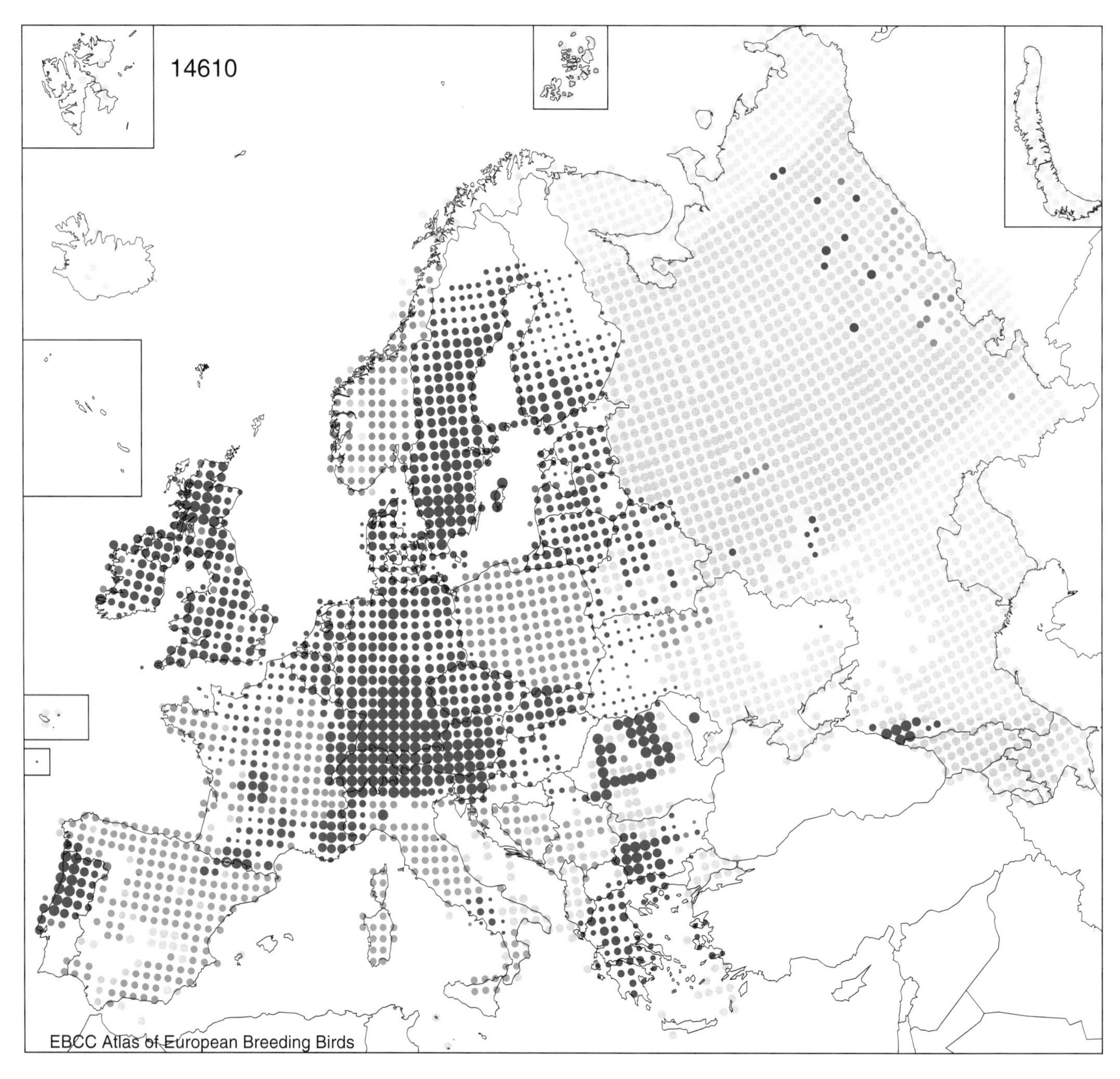

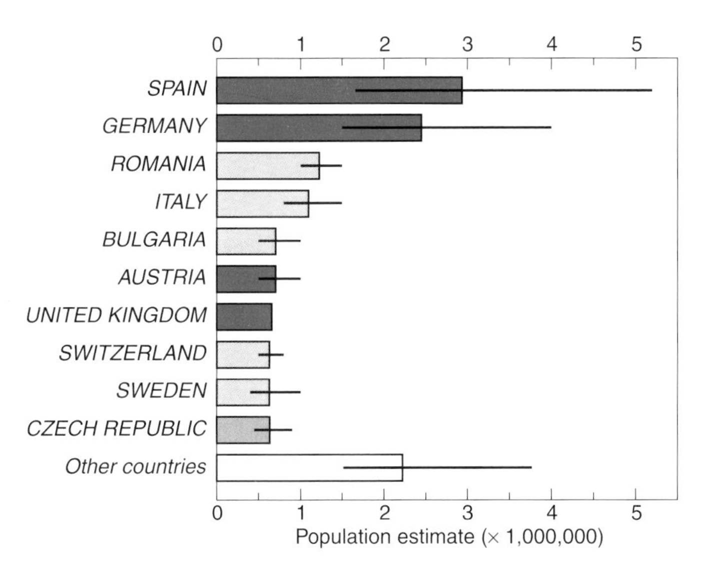

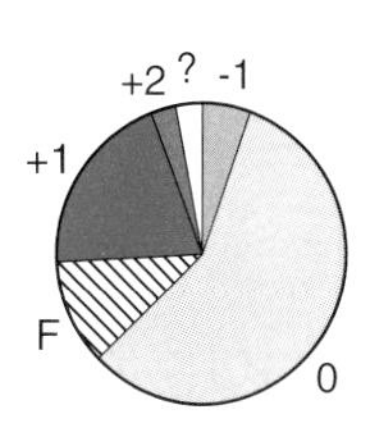

% in top 10 countries: 84.0
Total number of populated European countries: 34
Total European population 12,189,256–16,865,916 (13,906,659)
Russian population 1,000,000–10,000,000 (3,162,278)
Turkish population 100,000–1,000,000 (316,228)

The distribution of the Coal Tit covers the greater part of Europe, the mountains of NW Africa and much of N-C Asia as far as the Pacific, and includes Asia Minor, Iran, the Himalayas, China and Taiwan. In the Palearctic it is widely distributed in the boreal, temperate, mediterranean and montane zones up to *c*65°N. Its distribution is patchier at lower latitudes in western France, southern Europe, N Ukraine and SE Russia, but the species becomes common in these areas in winter after migration, irruption or vagrancy; numbers vary from year to year. In its southern range the Coal Tit often is common in mountainous areas, occurring up to the treeline; it becomes scarce at lower altitudes and mostly is rare in, or absent from, the lowlands. Some nine subspecies, including the nominate, occur in the *Atlas*' coverage.

Over much of its distribution the Coal Tit is closely associated with coniferous forest of varied composition and structure, being one of the commonest (up to 100 bp/km^2 in optimum habitat) and most characteristic species, occupying both pure conifer forest and mixed stands. The species prefers mature forest, especially Norway spruce *Picea abies*. In the Alps it reaches high densities (from 10–30 to 50–70 bp/km^2) in stands of pine *Pinus* and fir *Abies* and reaches lower values in other types of coniferous forest such as larch *Larix* and monospecific stone pine *Pinus cembra* blocks. In Britain & Ireland it will breed in pure broad-leaved woodlands. Similarly, in southern Europe it is less associated with coniferous trees and will occupy beech *Fagus sylvatica* and oak *Quercus* spp woodland. Such adaptability has permitted the species to spread in southern European forests and through widespread planting of conifers in parks and gardens, deep into built-up areas; only a few such trees provide a suitable breeding habitat (Löhrl 1974). The species is extremely catholic in its choice of nest site, taking readily to nestboxes. The marked year-to-year fluctuations in breeding population size (Löhrl 1974) sometimes lead to large-scale irruptions when an imbalance arises between numbers and food supply (van Gasteren *et al* 1992).

In winter it is less closely associated with coniferous woodland even if its greater adaptation to this habitat reduces its need to make the altitudinal movements necessary for other tits. In the Alps it is mostly sedentary. Even though trans-Alpine migrants become prominent in winter in the lowlands and valley bottoms, local populations show high site fidelity to suitable breeding areas even during harsh weather (Müller & Weber 1980, Winkel & Winkel 1988).

The European population, some 11M–32Mbp, is biased largely to the extensive coniferous forests of C and N Europe, the Alps, Carpathians, Transylvanian Alps, Rhodopes and Stara Planina, Transcaucasia and northern Iberia, where average densities exceed 10 000 bp/50km square. Similar densities occur only locally in conifer plantations in Denmark, The Netherlands, Flanders, Britain, Ireland and NW France, whose woodland cover is below 15%. Further range extension into N Fennoscandia is probably limited by the low availability of suitable nest-holes (Koskimies 1989a).

Despite the characteristic large annual fluctuations, population size and distribution trends indicate that numbers largely have been stable or slightly increasing over much of the range, only Hungary experiencing significant increases, and Latvia and the Czech Republic some declines. Large-scale damage to C European spruce forests through industrial emissions, by causing substantial needle-loss, reduced arthropod numbers, especially in winter, leading to serious declines in site-faithful wintering adult Coal Tit populations, particularly those above 500m asl (Zang 1990). The mean lifetime productivity fell from 5.5 to 4.6 young per individual (Möckel 1992). Such declines are masked partly by spring immigration of first-year birds.

Fulvio Genero (I) Roberto Parodi (I)

Parus caeruleus Blue Tit

CZ	Sýkora modřinka	**I**	Cinciarella
D	Blaumeise	**NL**	Pimpelmees
E	Herrerillo Común	**P**	Chapim-azul
F	Mésange bleue	**PL**	Modraszka
FIN	Sinitiainen	**R**	Лазоревка
G	Γαλαζοπαπαδίτσα	**S**	Blåmes
H	Kék cinege		

SPEC Cat 4, Threat status S

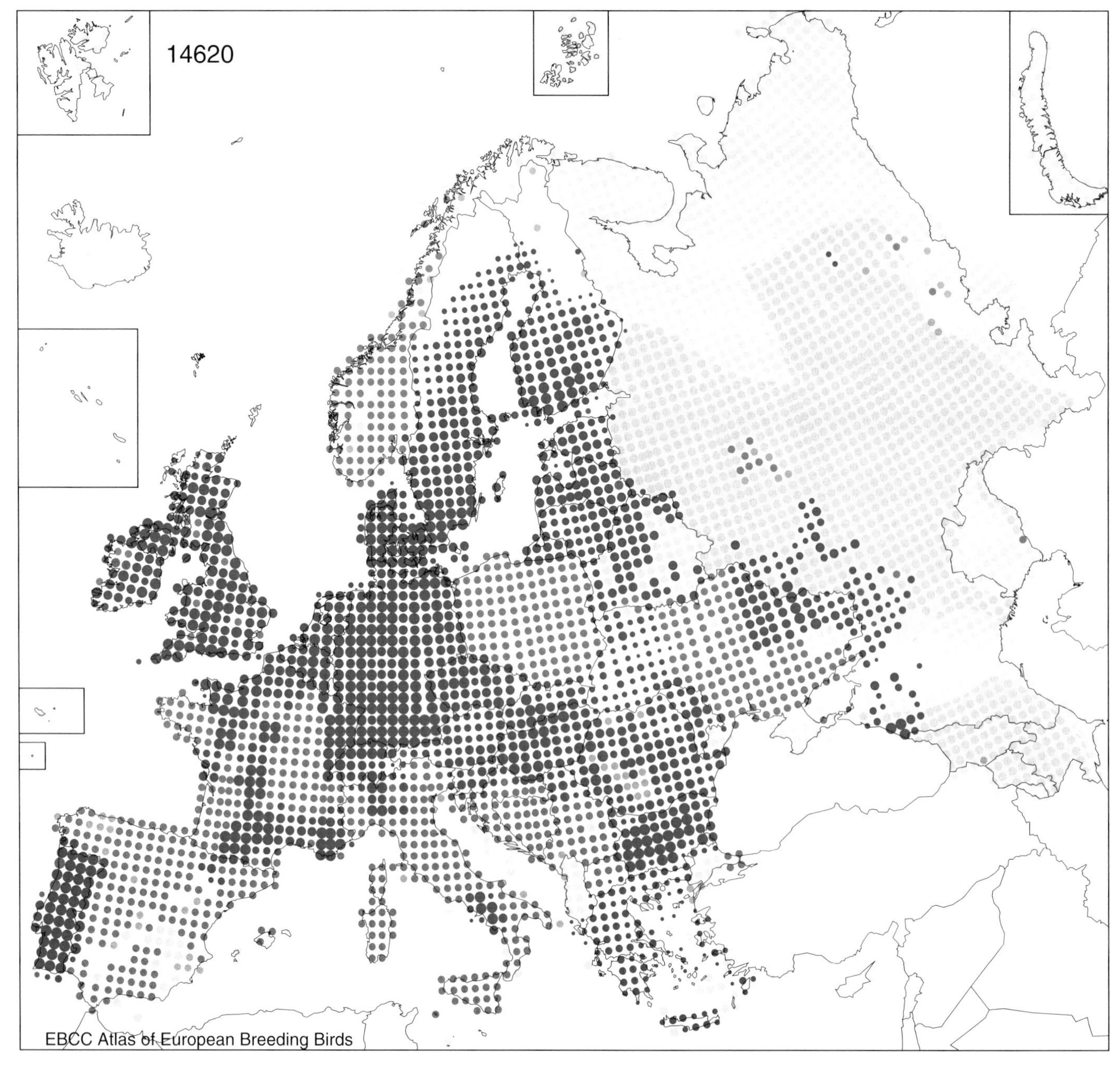

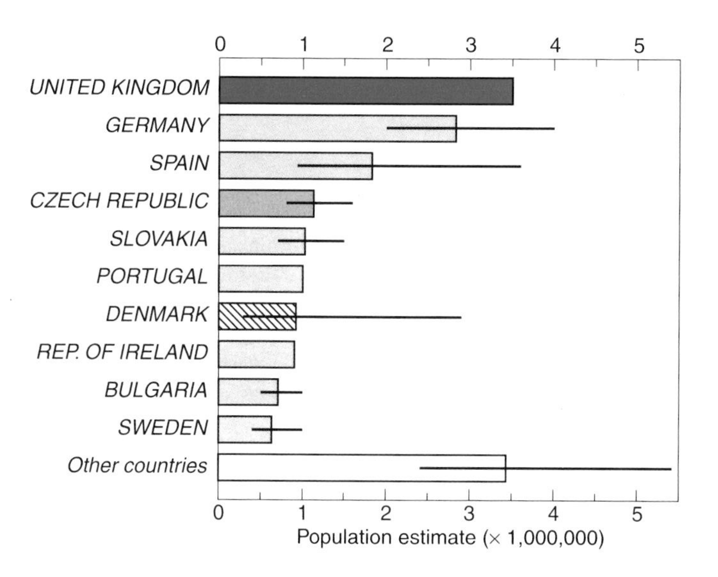

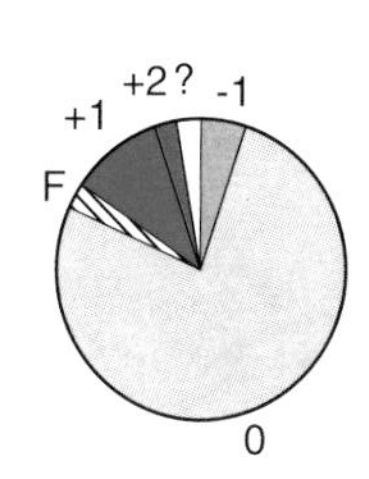

% in top 10 countries: 80.8
Total number of populated European countries: 39
Total European population 16,381,398–21,028,296 (17,902,886)
Russian population 100,000–1,000,000 (316,228)
Turkish population 100,000–1,000,000 (316,228)

The breeding range of the Blue Tit covers almost the entire western Palearctic between 35° and 65°N, from the Canary Islands and N Africa to C Fennoscandia, and southeastwards to the Caucasus and N Iraq. Cyprus is the only large Mediterranean island on which it does not breed regularly.

Primarily adapted to mature oak *Quercus* forests possessing a dense bushy underlayer, the Blue Tit inhabits a great variety of deciduous, evergreen and mixed woodlands including parks, orchards and gardens, but it avoids pure coniferous habitats except those of larch *Larix* in the southern Alps, cedar *Cedrus* in North Africa and pine *Pinus* in the Canary Islands. It prefers lowlands but follows deciduous trees normally only up to 1500m, but it has bred at 1700m in the southern French Alps and at 1800m in the Pyrenees. A broad tolerance to various woodland habitats allows the species to show an even pattern of distribution throughout its range and a particularly high abundance in those woodlands provided with nestboxes or winter feeding tables.

Dramatic changes in distribution have occurred during the 20th century in Fennoscandia where the species' northern breeding limit spread northwards, reaching the northern Bay of Bothnia and N Karelia in the 1930s and eventually the Arctic Circle and occasionally beyond; it has bred in Vardö (70°20'N) in N Norway. The population grew rapidly, especially during periods with exceptionally mild winters and warm summers, as in the early 1970s. Large fluctuations are characteristic, harsh winter weather or cold rainy summers being followed by steep declines, and long-term favourable conditions by rapid increases. Overall, the Finnish population has shown a significant increase since the 1960s (Hildén 1990).

In temperate Europe no significant trend has developed during 1970–90. Numbers are subject to high annual and local fluctuations in relation to habitat carrying capacity, breeding success and winter mortality. If the availability of natural nesting sites is limited, breeding density can be increased significantly by installing nestboxes. Densities (bp/10ha) in oakwoods in The Netherlands averaged 12–17, showing only small annual fluctuations without trend from 1965 to 1986. Contrastingly, densities in mixed woods (with a high proportion of coniferous trees) varied between 0.5 and 2.3, showing fourfold variations between years and a consistent increase during 1965–85. This increase was attributed to habitat changes and possibly an increased winter survival through being fed by people (van Balen & Potting 1990). In Mediterranean evergreen oak habitats breeding density ranges mostly between 5 and 10 bp/10ha.

Environmental constraints on Mediterranean island populations are greater than on the continent, resulting in delayed breeding, a smaller clutch size, absence of second broods and fewer repeat layings following destruction of the first clutch (Blondel *et al* 1987). These differences are most pronounced in Mediterranean geographical isolates which undergo little or no gene flow from non-Mediterranean populations (Martin & Bellot 1990).

The Blue Tit is sedentary or partially migratory, density-dependent eruptive movements varying within populations and within years in the temperate parts of its breeding range (Berndt & Henss 1963, Frelin 1979). Birds from Scandinavia have been recovered in N Germany and those from C Europe from as far south as Spain. Since the 1970s a significant trend towards a more sedentary behaviour has been observed in Germany (Winkel & Frantzen 1991). The British and Mediterranean populations are sedentary all year round.

The birds of the *caeruleus* group (Europe and Middle East) show greater size, stouter bills and shorter tarsae along a NE-oriented cline (Martin 1991). Those of the *teneriffae* group (Canary Islands, North Africa, Pantelleria and NE Libya) are as different from the *caeruleus* group as is the Azure Tit *P. cyanus*, and thus merit consideration as a separate species.

Hans Hudde (D) Paul Isenmann (F)

This species account is sponsored by Natur- und Vogelschutzverein MEISE, Arbon, CH.

Parus major

Great Tit

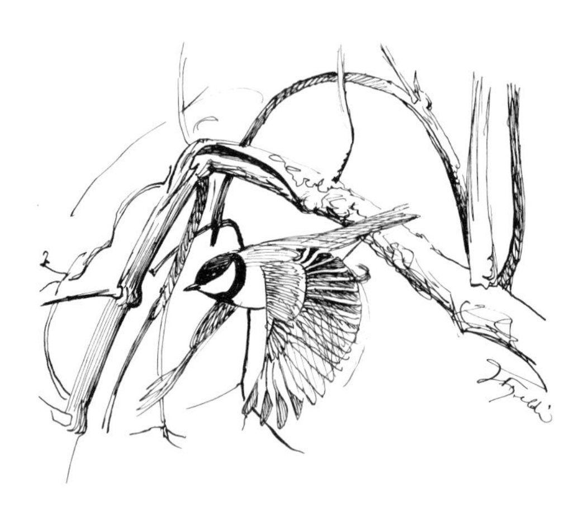

CZ	Sýkora koňadra	**I**	Cinciallegra
D	Kohlmeise	**NL**	Koolmees
E	Carbonero Común	**P**	Chapim-real
F	Mésange charbonnière	**PL**	Bogatka
FIN	Talitiainen	**R**	Большая синица
G	Καλόγερος	**S**	Talgoxe
H	Széncinege		

Non-SPEC, Threat status S

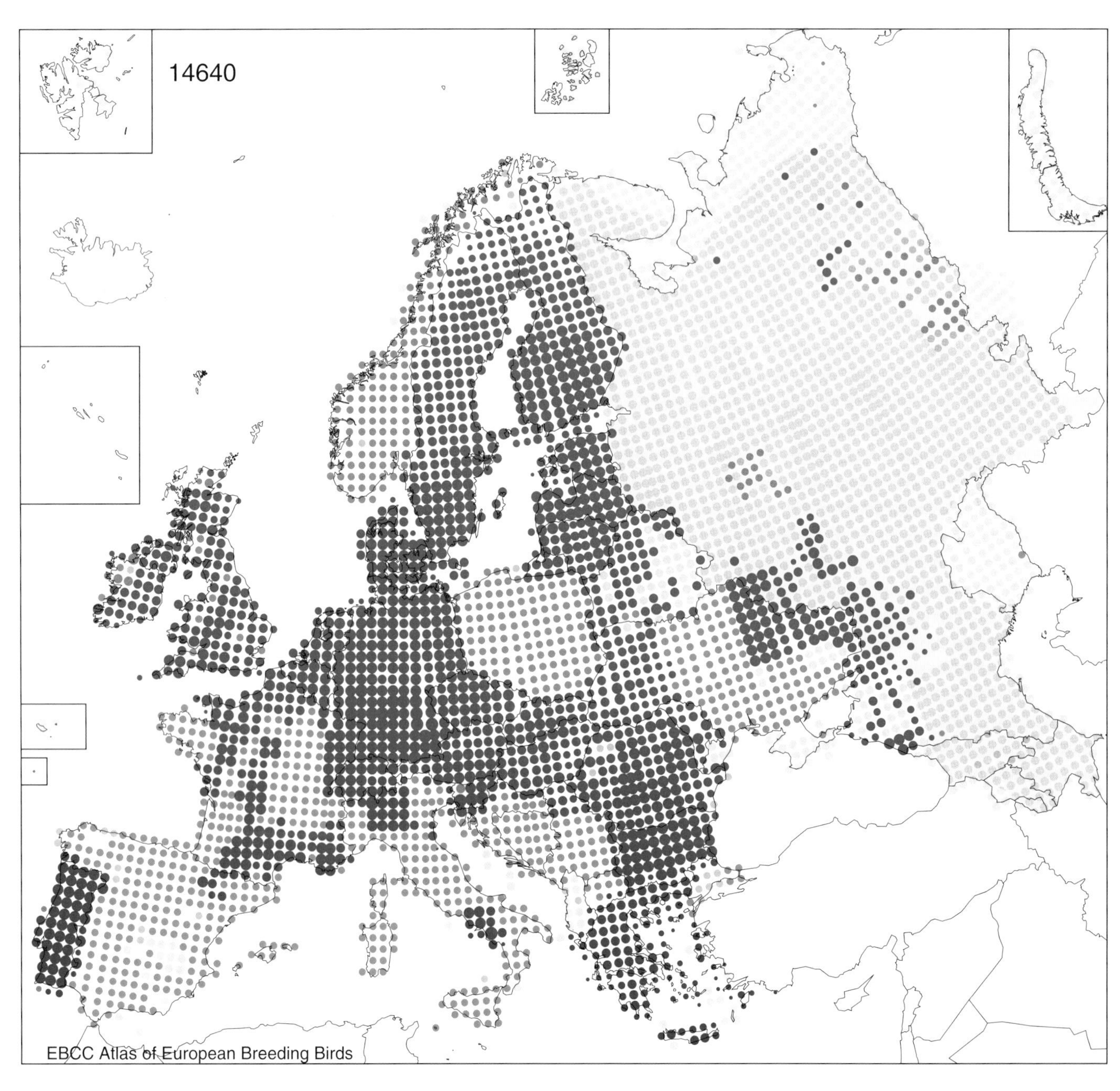

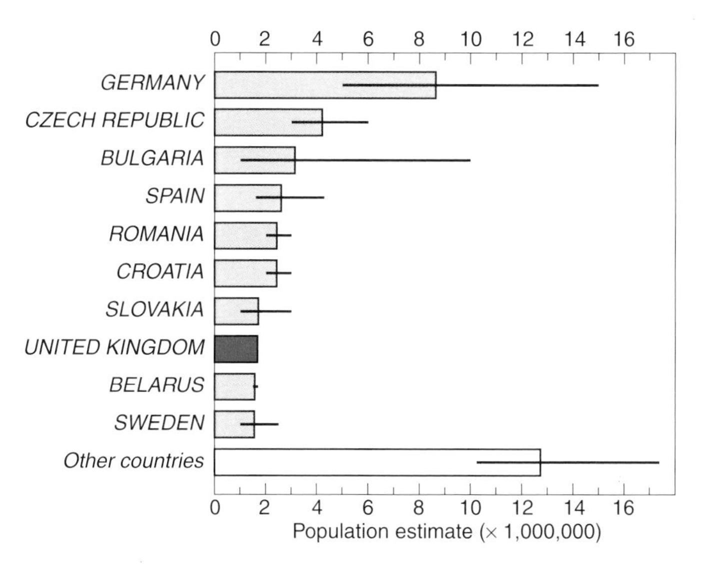

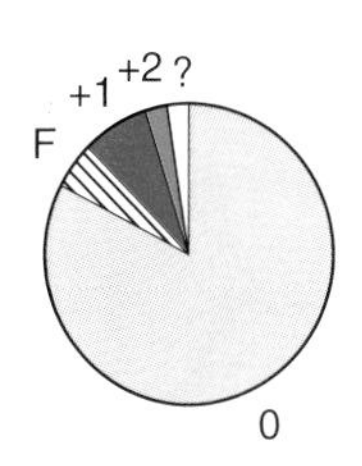

% in top 10 countries: 72.0
Total number of populated European countries: 38
Total European population 37,190,157–52,022,806 (41,962,654)
Russian population 10,000,000–100,000,000 (31,622,777)
Turkish population 1,000,000–10,000,000 (3,162,278)

The Great Tit has the largest geographical range of any European *Parus* species, extending more or less throughout the Palearctic from Portugal and Ireland to Kamchatka and the western Kurile Isles and into the Oriental zoogeographical regions of the Indian subcontinent, SE Asia, Japan, Malaysia and Indonesia. Its evolutionary history, and hence its taxonomy, throughout this vast range is complex (see Gosler 1993 for review).

In Europe, where it occurs in every country, its taxonomy is more readily explained. While in its whole range four more-or-less clearly defined groups of Great Tit are recognized, European birds are all of the *P. major* group, within which, however, at least four subspecies are recognized.

The Great Tit is one of the most abundant species in Europe. No fewer than 17 countries reported estimated populations of at least 1Mbp (eight countries may hold more than 2M) and a further 13 estimated the population at between 500 000 and 1Mbp (figures were unavailable for Poland, whose population probably is substantial). Throughout most of Europe, populations are more-or-less stable. While no countries reported marked decreases, increases of 20–50% were reported from Great Britain, The Netherlands and Estonia, and the population of Ukraine may have increased by more than 50% since 1970.

The secret of this species' great success lies in its behavioural adaptability and, perhaps, intelligence. It occurs in a wide range of habitats including all forms of woodland and scrub, in gardens, and agricultural habitats, indeed virtually anywhere with trees (up to the treeline at 1900m asl in Switzerland; *HVM*), a suitably sized hole in which to nest, and during the breeding season sufficient insect food on which to raise a brood. Another feature of this adaptability is the species' ready acceptance of nestboxes in which to breed, and of 'artificial' food provided in winter by people. These points have made it an important species for population research in Europe (Perrins 1979, Gosler 1993). Nevertheless, not all habitats are equally favoured.

The greatest breeding success and breeding densities are found in deciduous, and particularly oak *Quercus* spp woodland, although a good shrub layer may also be important. In optimal habitat, breeding densities of greater than 5 bp/ha (equivalent to 500 bp/km^2) have been recorded. In coniferous forest and other suboptimal habitats, densities are typically lower and may not exceed 10 bp/km^2. Part explanation of these differences between habitats undoubtedly reflects the availability, both numerically and temporally, of caterpillars, which form the major food for nestlings (reviewed by Gosler 1993).

Outside the breeding season, tree seeds such as beechmast form the principal diet so that Great Tit movements in Europe largely reflect variation between years in the availability of these crops. Most northern and some eastern populations are migratory, moving W or SW in autumn to escape the harshest conditions. Elsewhere in Europe populations are sedentary, irrupting westwards only when seed crops fail and alternative foods are not available.

The *P. major* group to which European birds belong varies on the theme of green upperparts and yellow underparts (which colours differ elsewhere in the world). Furthermore, the Great Tit throughout the continent of Europe is of the subspecies *P.m. major*. Variation through this huge population is largely clinal in size, birds being larger in colder climates. The other three recognized group subspecies are found on European islands; *P.m. newtonii* in Britain & Ireland differs from continental birds in body size and bill shape, *P.m. corsus* occupies Corsica and Sardinia and *P.m. aphrodite* inhabits the islands of the eastern Mediterranean. The latter two subspecies differ in colour from *P.m. major*.

Andrew G Gosler (GB) Jeremy Wilson (GB)

Parus cyanus

Azure Tit

CZ	Sýkora azurová	I	Cinciarella azzurra
D	Lasurmeise	NL	Azuurmees
E	Herrerillo Ciáneo	P	Chapim-de-cabeça-branca
F	Mésange azurée	PL	Sikora lazurowa
FIN	Valkopäätiainen	R	Князек
G	Λαζουροπαπαδίτσα	S	Azurmes
H	Lazúrcinege		

Non-SPEC, Threat status S (P)

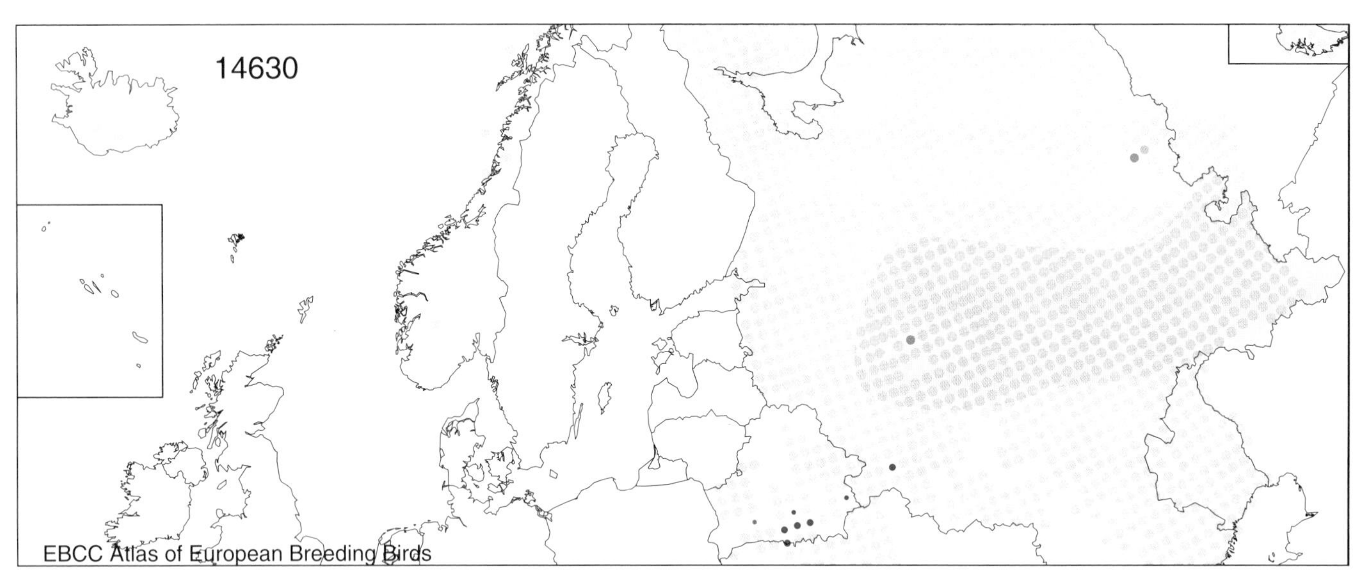

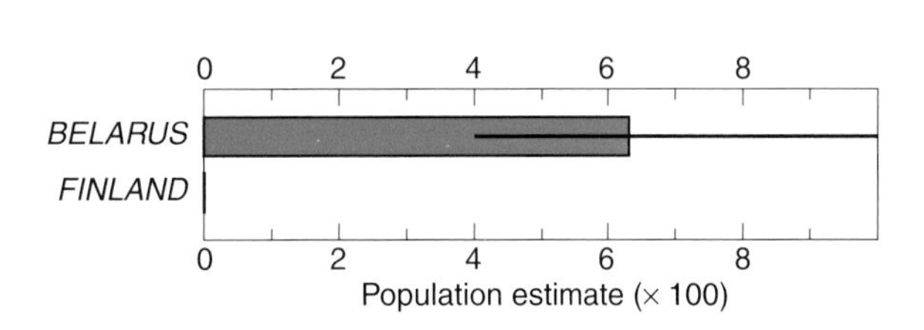

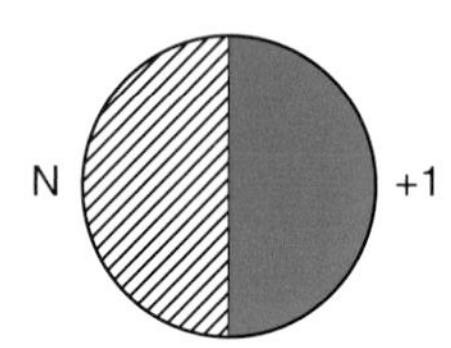

% in top 10 countries: 100.0
Total number of populated European countries: 2
Total European population 401–1001 (634)
Russian population 10,000–100,000 (31,623)

The E European range of the Azure Tit species forms the westernmost limit of an otherwise wide geographical distribution through the eastern Palearctic, to eastern Siberia and the Far East from the C Urals to the mountains of Tian Shan, the Pamirs and Altai to the Amur River and Ussuriland.

In Europe it is represented only in Russia, Belarus and Finland. Of these, Russia holds by far the most significant population, with an estimated 30 000bp. Here, largely through a shortage of information, the population is assumed to be stable. The *c*600bp in the Pripyat Valley, Belarus, may comprise an expanding population (Harrap & Quinn 1985). In Finland perhaps two pairs bred recently. It has, however, been recorded as an accidental in at least 13 other European countries, as far W as France and S as far as Romania, but most often into Scandinavia. These occurrences illustrate that, while generally resident and sedentary, the Azure Tit may make extensive nomadic irruptions under certain conditions and especially in winter. Extralimitally, altitudinal migration is well described, the extent of such movements depending on the severity of the winter.

In eastern Europe, the Azure Tit breeds in mixed and deciduous woodland habitats, especially around lakes and in riverine woodland with abundant shrub vegetation, near reedbeds, peat bogs and other wetland habitats (Nikiforov *et al* 1989). Here they breed at low densities, typically fewer than 10 bp/km^2. The further extension of its range into Europe may be limited by competition with the Blue Tit *P. caeruleus*, with which it is closely related. Irruptions into Europe have resulted in widespread appearance of hybrids between these two species, especially across C European Russia (Portenko *et al* 1982) and in Finland in 1975 when a mixed pair nested successfully in Turku (Koskimies 1989a). Across its range, at least eight subspecies have been described, largely on differences in colour. European birds mostly are of the nominate *P.c. cyanus*, but intergrade into *hyperriphaeus* from 51°E eastwards.

Andrew G Gosler (GB) Valentin Serebryakov (UKR)

Sitta neumayer

Rock Nuthatch

CZ	Brhlík skalní	I	Picchio muratore di roccia
D	Felsenkleiber	NL	Rotsklever
E	Trepador Rupestre	P	Trepadeira-rupestre
F	Sittelle de Neumayer	PL	Kowalik skalny
FIN	Kallionakkeli	R	Малый скалистый поползень
G	Βραχοτσοπανάκος	S	Klippnötväcka
H	Kövi csuszka		

SPEC Cat 4, Threat status S (P)

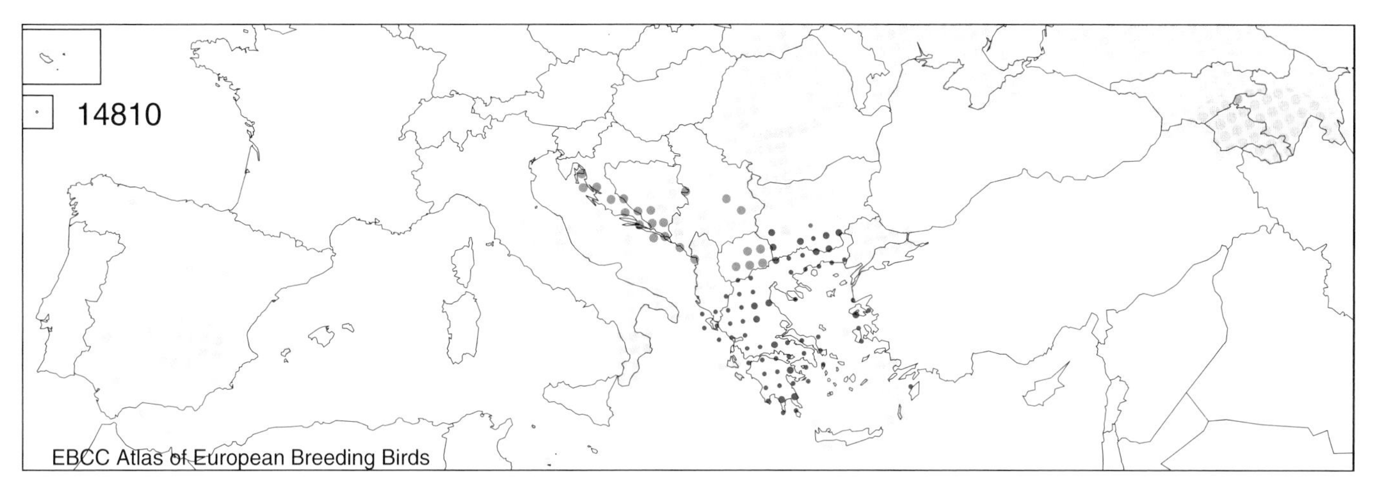

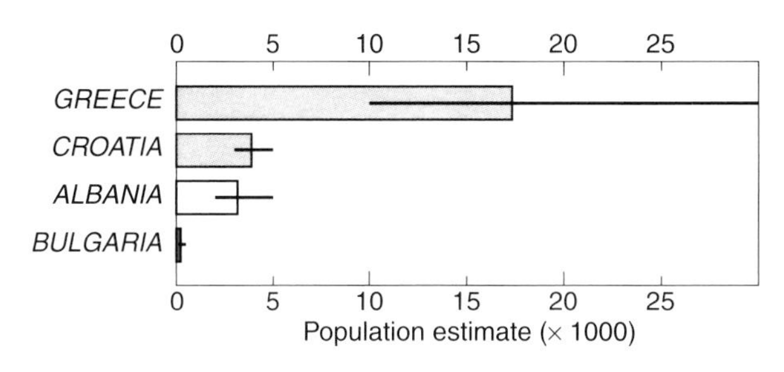

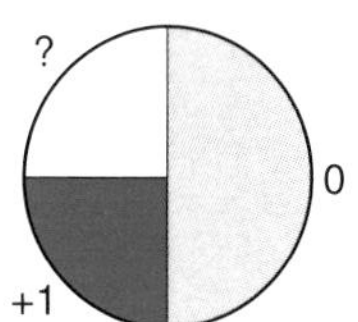

% in top 10 countries: 100.0
Total number of populated European countries: 4
Total European population 17,115–37,444 (24,579)
Turkish population 50,000–500,000 (158,114)

The distribution of the Rock Nuthatch, which inhabits the higher mediterranean habitats, extends from the Balkan Peninsula, Asia Minor and C and eastern Transcaucasia to Iran, Iraq and northern Israel. The nominate subspecies *S.n. neumayer* occupies the Balkan Peninsula and Greece, *rupicola* inhabiting Transcaucasia. Four other subspecies occur outside the *Atlas'* coverage area.

Mainly a sedentary species, it exhibits limited post-breeding dispersal and seasonal altitudinal movements. Outside the breeding season it can be found both above (up to 2200m asl; Paspaleva-Antonova 1965) and below its breeding grounds. Part of the distribution overlap with Eastern Rock Nuthatch *S. tephronota* occurs in Transcaucasia, where the relative subspecies are clearly distinguishable, a circumstance which does not apply to some geographically separated subspecies of the two species. In Transcaucasia, the two species are not altitudinally separated (Harrap & Quinn 1995).

Its preferred breeding habitats lie in mountainous rocky regions, comprising steep cliffs (chiefly calcareous) in valleys; it seldom occurs on hill and mountain slopes or at the coast. Sometimes it breeds on buildings, ruins and old stone bridges (*BWP*, P. Iankov, pers obs). Most nests are found at relatively low altitudes (up to *c*800m asl) where it breeds on solitary rocks or heavily fissured rock massifs usually fringed with dry, mediterranean grasses or shrubs. At higher altitudes (up to *c*1000m) it nests on sunny rocky slopes or faces often edged with conifers (Matvejev 1976, P. Iankov, pers obs).

The species has patchy distribution and abundance. It is rather common in the sub-mediterranean vegetation regions of C Greece, S Croatia, Albania and Bulgaria (highest density 13 bp/100km^2; P. Iankov, pers obs), but it is quite rare in rocky areas in coniferous or deciduous forests (Matvejev 1976, P. Iankov, pers obs). It is more numerous in the W of the Balkan Peninsula than in the E.

The population size and range seem to be stable in Greece and Croatia but slightly increasing in Bulgaria. In 1993 nests were found 25km E and 55km N (P. Iankov, pers obs) of the known Bulgarian limit of nesting in 1963 and 1973 (Dontchev 1964, 1980) although similar evidence of northward expansion is lacking in some other regions (Iankov & Niagolov 1987).

Petar Iankov (BUL)

Sitta europaea

Nuthatch

CZ	Brhlík lesní	**I**	Picchio muratore
D	Kleiber	**NL**	Boomklever
E	Trepador Azul	**P**	Trepadeira-azul
F	Sittelle torchepot	**PL**	Kowalik
FIN	Pähkinänakkeli	**R**	Поползень
G	Δενδροτσοπανάκος	**S**	Nötväcka
H	Csuszka		

Non-SPEC, Threat status S

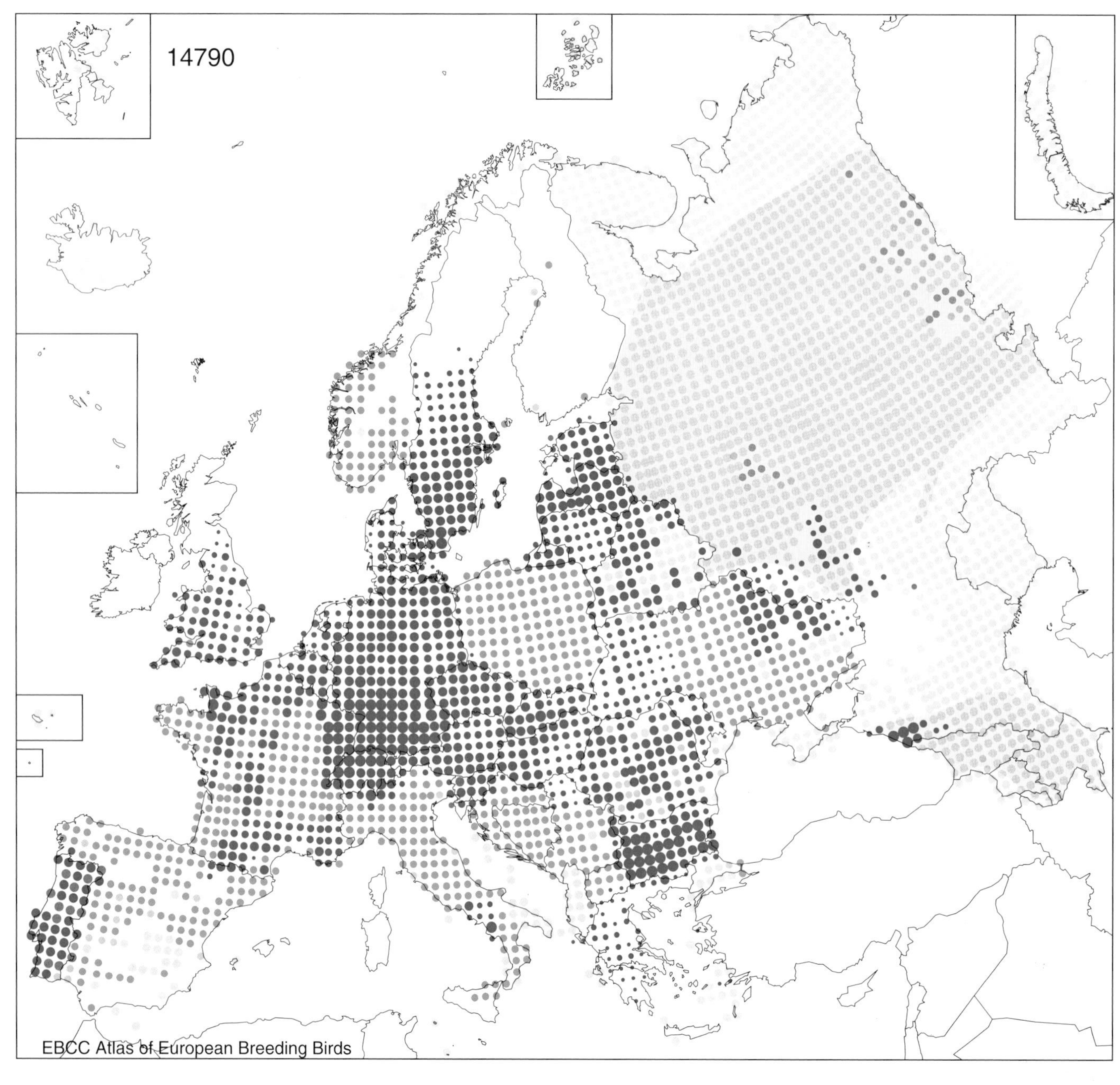

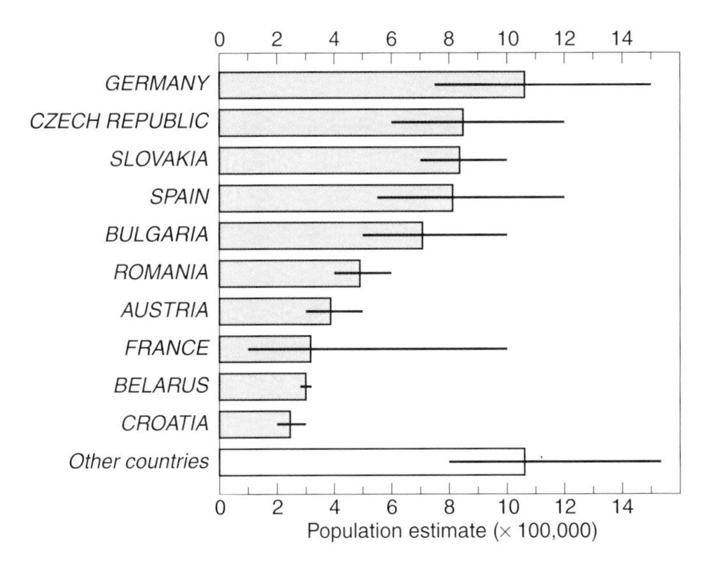

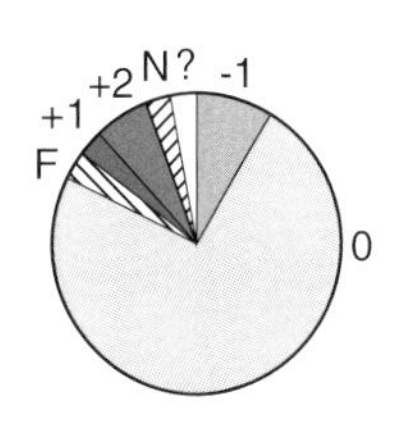

% in top 10 countries: 85.0
Total number of populated European countries: 34
Total European population 6,461,650–8,113,841 (7,063,309)
Russian population 500,000–5,000,000 (1,581,139)
Turkish population 10,000–100,000 (31,623)

The Nuthatch occurs in the continental middle latitudes of the Palearctic, from the warm temperate to the cooler boreal climate zones within the July 16°–27°C isotherms. It occurs eastwards from Morocco and Portugal through Russia to Japan and Kamchatka and then S and W to China, SE Asia into India and the Himalayas.

The species is very much a woodland bird, its prime habitat comprising large old oak *Quercus* and mature beech *Fagus* trees and hazel *Corylus avellana* bushes. However, wherever there are large, mature trees, the Nuthatch occurs in most forest types, although only exceptionally in pure coniferous forest. It also frequents urban parks and gardens, and generally is confiding. Quite commonly it nests only a few metres above a busy street. Furthermore, it visits bird-tables frequently and also takes spilt cereal around farms.

The qualities that allow the Nuthatch to be both tolerant of, and benefit from, human activities may also have contributed to its overall breeding success in Europe, where most suitable habitat is occupied except for most of Scotland and northern Scandinavia. The mapped records for Finland and northernmost Sweden refer to the irruptive subspecies *S.e. asiatica* remaining to breed in subsequent years (Eriksson 1970, Risberg 1990). It is absent from many islands like Ireland, Corsica, Sardinia and Crete. The population stronghold lies in the deciduous and mixed forest belt from E France eastwards through C Europe and the N Balkans to Romania and Bulgaria (average large-scale densities surpassing 5000 bp/50×50km square).

The Nuthatch is expanding its range slowly northwards in Scandinavia and Great Britain (first bred in Scotland 1989). In The Netherlands its range expansion takes the form of colonizing both maturing woods planted in the early 20th century and recently planted (1947–68) poplar *Populus* plantations in polders reclaimed from Lake IJsselmeer (R.G. Bijlsma, pers comm). In rich deciduous forest its breeding density may approach 1 bp/ha but is generally lower. An important determinant of Nuthatch population density is autumn food supply, such as beechmast or hazel nuts (Enoksson 1990, Jacobsen 1992). Because such food sources fluctuate greatly, so may Nuthatch populations.

The map cannot indicate the small-scale distribution pattern. Although overall the species' future apparently appears bright, a threat looms. Forest fragmentation may be a serious threat (Opdam & Schotman 1987). Even when there are surplus adults, populations do not increase simply because apparently suitable habitat is available. The Nuthatch is territorial throughout the year and is very sedentary, juveniles often residing fairly close to their natal territory. The species remains more productive in larger, more continuous woods, but very often seemingly ideal fragments, although large enough to contain a few territories, are thinly inhabited by, or devoid of, Nuthatch breeding pairs (A. Schotman, pers comm to the Editors). The overall area of woodland containing potential Nuthatch territories is significant. Obviously forest clearance leads to local reductions in number and range; it remains to be seen whether the scale of forest clearance over wide areas will have a significant effect on the Nuthatch. Decreases have occurred through forest clearance in Italy in the Po Valley, but these may be offset by increases elsewhere as in Lombardy. Large-scale habitat destruction is the most serious threat. Where mature trees disappear, Nuthatches have to vacate the area.

Of the seven subspecies in the *Atlas*' coverage area, *asiatica* (from E European Russia eastwards) is prone to large-scale irruptions; the nominate *europaea* (N Europe) is sedentary with a slight irruptive tendency; and the others (*caesia*, Britain and much of continental Europe; *hispaniensis*, Iberia save for N Spain; *caucasica*, Transcaucasia except for Lenkoran (*rubiginosa*); *cisalpina*, Sicily, Italy, southern Alps to the former Yugoslavia) are resident.

Bodil Enoksson (S)

This species account is sponsored by Dr Klaus Witt, Berlin, D.

Sitta whiteheadi

Corsican Nuthatch

CZ	Brhlík korsický	I	Picchio muratore corso
D	Korsenkleiber	NL	Corsicaanse Boomklever
E	Trepador Corso	P	Trepadeira-corsa
F	Sittelle corse	PL	Kowalik korsykański
FIN	Korsikannakkeli	R	Корсиканский поползень
G	Κορσικοτσοπανάκος	S	Korsikansk nötväcka
H	Korzikai csuszka		

SPEC Cat 2, Threat status V

This endemic species is sedentary, except for local altitudinal winter movements (down to 600m asl and below; *BWP*); adults may remain territorial year-round. Its main range coincides with *c*15 forests of Corsican pine, *Pinus nigra laricio*, along the inland mountain ridges, from Tartagine in the N, to Ospedale in the S.

The optimal habitat is specialized and fragmented, comprising old pure stands of Corsican pine at 1000–1500m asl (density 0.9–1.5 bp/10ha) with abundant dead and rotting trunks for nest sites. Suboptimal habitats include: Corsican pine forests containing other species, younger stands and exploited forest of Corsican pine (density 0.0–0.6 bp/10ha) (Brichetti & Di Capi 1985), and cluster pine *P. pinaster* above 800m asl (Beck in press, G. Rocamora, in prep). The species excavates its own holes, although these often have been initiated by Great Spotted Woodpecker *Dendrocopos major* (*BWP*, Harrap & Quinn 1995).

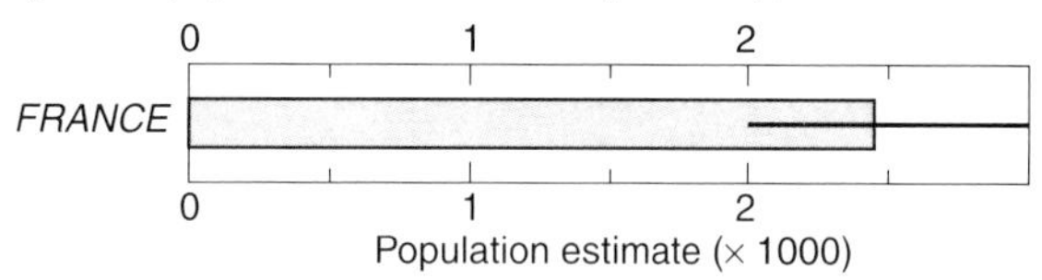

% in top 10 countries: 100.0
Total number of populated European countries: 1
Total European population 2000–3000 (2449)

Brichetti & DiCapi (1985) estimated 2000bp in 24 000ha of suitable habitat, Löhrl (1960) *c*3000 in 43 750ha comprising all conifer forests.

Some local populations have decreased since the mid-1960s through forest exploitation or fires, but total numbers and range are probably stable. Avalanches, fires and clearance of older, dead or rotten trees in managed forests are detrimental (Brichetti & Di Capi 1987).

Pierandrea Brichetti (I) Gérard Rocamora (F)

Sitta krueperi

Krüper's Nuthatch

CZ	Brhlík turecký	I	Picchio muratore di Krüper
D	Turkenkleiber	NL	Turkse Boomklever
E	Trepador de Krüper	P	Trepadeira de Krüper
F	Sittelle de Krüper	PL	Kowalik czarnomorski
FIN	Punarintanakkeli	R	Черноголовый поползень
G	Τουρκοτσοπανάκος	S	Krüpers nötväcka
H	Török csuszka		

SPEC Cat 4, Threat status S (P)

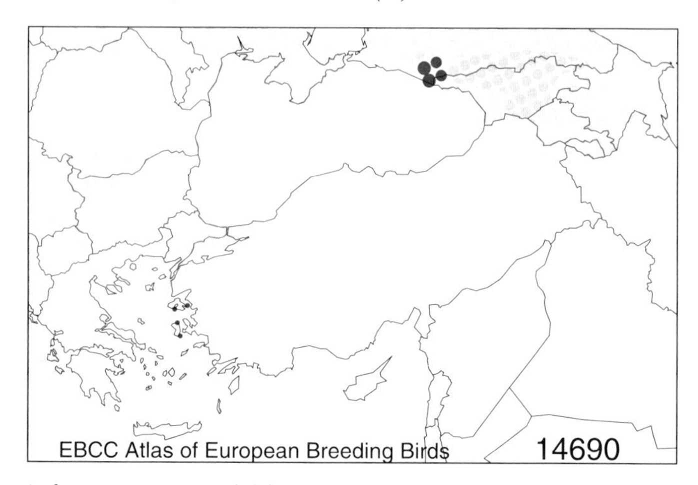

Krüper's Nuthatch is found in the Greek island of Mytilene, parts of Turkey and the Caucasus, in warm dry mediterranean and montane zones, usually at 1200–2200m asl. It inhabits coniferous, mixed fir–beech *Abies–Fagus*, fir–spruce *Abies–Picea* and pine *Pinus* forests, particularly of Calabrian Pine *P. brutia* (Harrap & Quinn 1995). It occurs at only 150m asl on the Black Sea coast near Sutchumi in a woodland park containing introduced conifers (Malandziya 1990). In Turkey it breeds in cedar *Cedrus* and juniper *Juniperus*.

This nuthatch is one of the more abundant species in prime habitat in mountain forests. In Kavkazskiy Zapovednik (W Caucasus), densities (birds/km^2) are 32 in beech–fir, 48 in fir, 34 in pine forest, and 4 in maple *Acer* parklands (Til'ba & Kazakov 1985); at medium altitudes in fir forests of Abkhazia, 32 (Malandziya 1990); in the Teberdinskiy Zapovednik, 50–90 in mixed forests and up to 28 in pine forests (Polivanov & Polivanova 1990). Little information is available on population numbers and trends. The population on Mytilene is *c*600bp. Calabrian pine forests in Azerbaijan and other locations near the Black Sea

Continued opposite

Tichodroma muraria

Wallcreeper

CZ	Zedníček skalní	I	Picchio muraiolo
D	Mauerläufer	NL	Rotskruiper
E	Treparriscos	P	Trepadeira-dos-muros
F	Tichodrome échelette	PL	Pomurnik
FIN	Kalliokiipijä	R	Стенолаз
G	Σβαρνίστρα	S	Murkrypare
H	Hajnalmadár		

Non-SPEC, Threat status S (P)

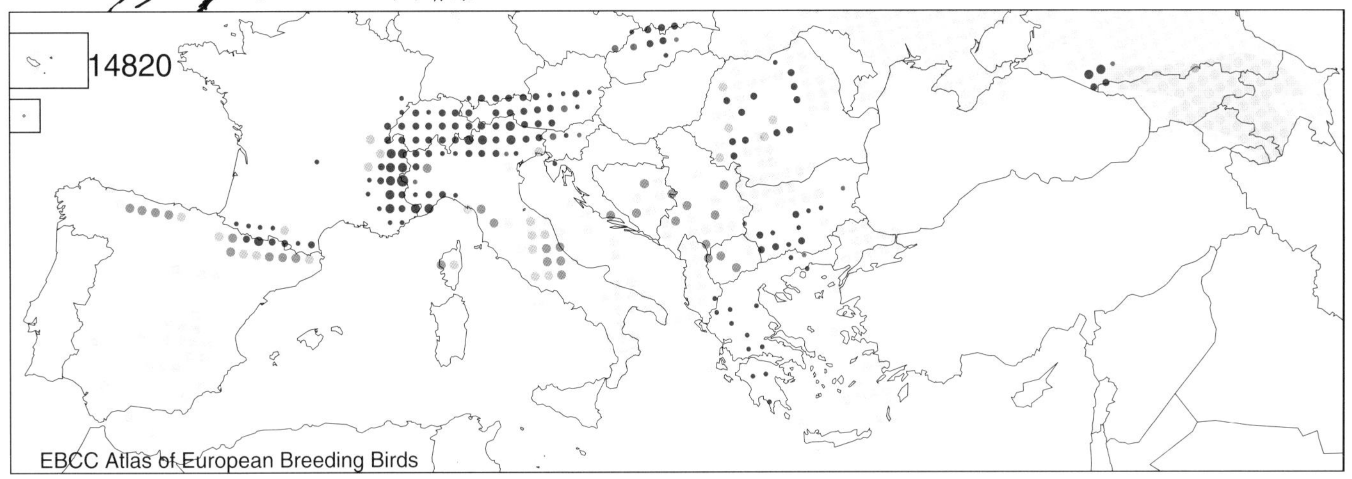

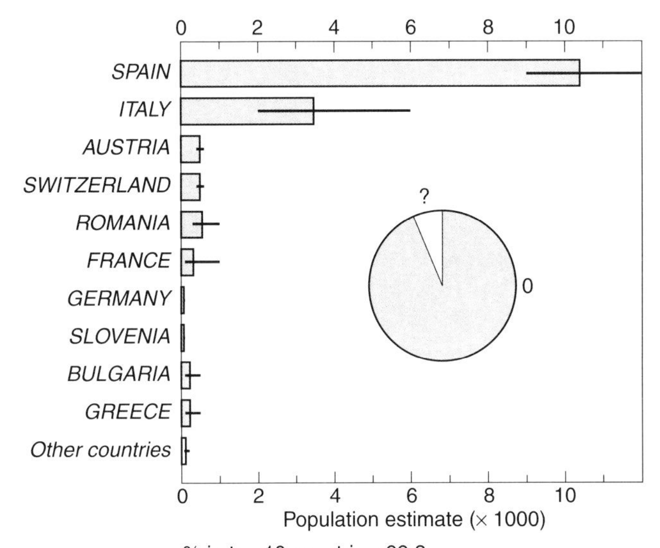

% in top 10 countries: 99.3
Total number of populated European countries: 16
Total European population 14,341–19,542 (16,400)
Turkish population 500–5000 (1581)

The Wallcreeper occupies the highest European and Asian mountain ranges from Iberia to the Caucasus, Iran, the Himalayas and Tian Shan. *T.m. muraria* occurs from Europe to W Iran, *nepalensis* further east. It is a short-distance partial migrant; resident birds move to lower altitudes in winter, appearing on coastal cliffs, quarries and buildings. It breeds in rocky, broken or precipitous terrain, limestone being preferred to granite, often near flowing water. Its breeding range and numbers have remained largely unchanged although some contractions have occurred in Poland and Romania. It breeds in the Cantabrians and the Pyrenees at 1680m and 1930m asl respectively (mean altitudes), elsewhere usually at 1000–2000m (Alps 350–2700m, Slovakia 550–2000m).

The Cantabrian concentration lies in the three Picos de Europa massifs, primarily the C; the Spanish Pyrenees core is skewed to the C and E regions (Hernández *et al* 1992). In 1986 breeding was proved in the Massif Central (Gauthier-Clerc 1994), but the slight apparent increase in the Jura (81 sites with 64–99bp in 1990s; Géroudet & Gauthier-Clerc 1994) probably derives from better coverage. In the Bernese Alps 200–250bp occupy 2895km² (R. Hauri, pers obs), nest-separation usually being >1km (Hauri 1978). The *c*35–40bp breeding in 635km² of the Bavarian Alps extrapolate into *c*100bp for Germany (Bezzel 1993). In 1991 the Slovak Carpathians held 50–60bp (M. Saniga, pers obs).

The increase in climbing and dam-building may threaten breeding and feeding sites through disturbance.

Angel Hernández (E) Rolf Hauri (CH)
Miroslav Saniga (SLK)

S. krueperi – continued

may hold other populations (Harrap & Quinn 1995).

A small proportion of birds descend to lower altitudes in winter, when small numbers are found in the Kolkhida forests in evergreen vegetation or in parkland conifers on the Black Sea coast in Sochi district, Russia.

Peter Til'ba (R) Haralambos Alivizatos (G)

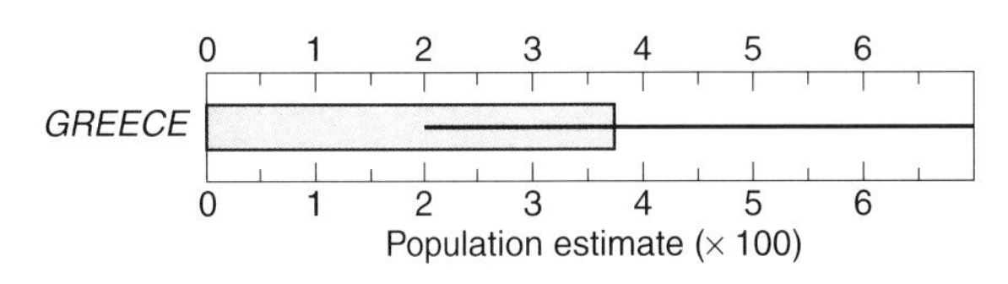

% in top 10 countries: 100.0
Total number of populated European countries: 1
Total European population 200–700 (374)
Turkish population 10,000–100,000 (31,623)

Certhia familiaris

Treecreeper

CZ	Šoupálek dlouhoprstý	I	Rampichino alpestre
D	Waldbaumläufer	NL	Taigaboomkruiper
E	Agateador Norteño	P	Trepadeira-do-bosque
F	Grimpereau des bois	PL	Pełzacz leśny
FIN	Puukiipijä	R	Пищуха
G	Βουνοδενδροβάτης	S	Trädkrypare
H	Hegyi fakusz		

Non-SPEC, Threat status S

The tiny, arboreal and largely sedentary Treecreeper is distributed across the Palearctic from Ireland to the Caucasus, the Himalayas, Siberia and Tian Shan, reaching Korea and Japan. It also occurs in N and C America. It breeds in most European countries, its range lying generally within the July 14°–24°C isotherms, although discrete breeding populations occupy S France, Corsica, the Pyrenees, Apennines and Balkans. Recently, a small

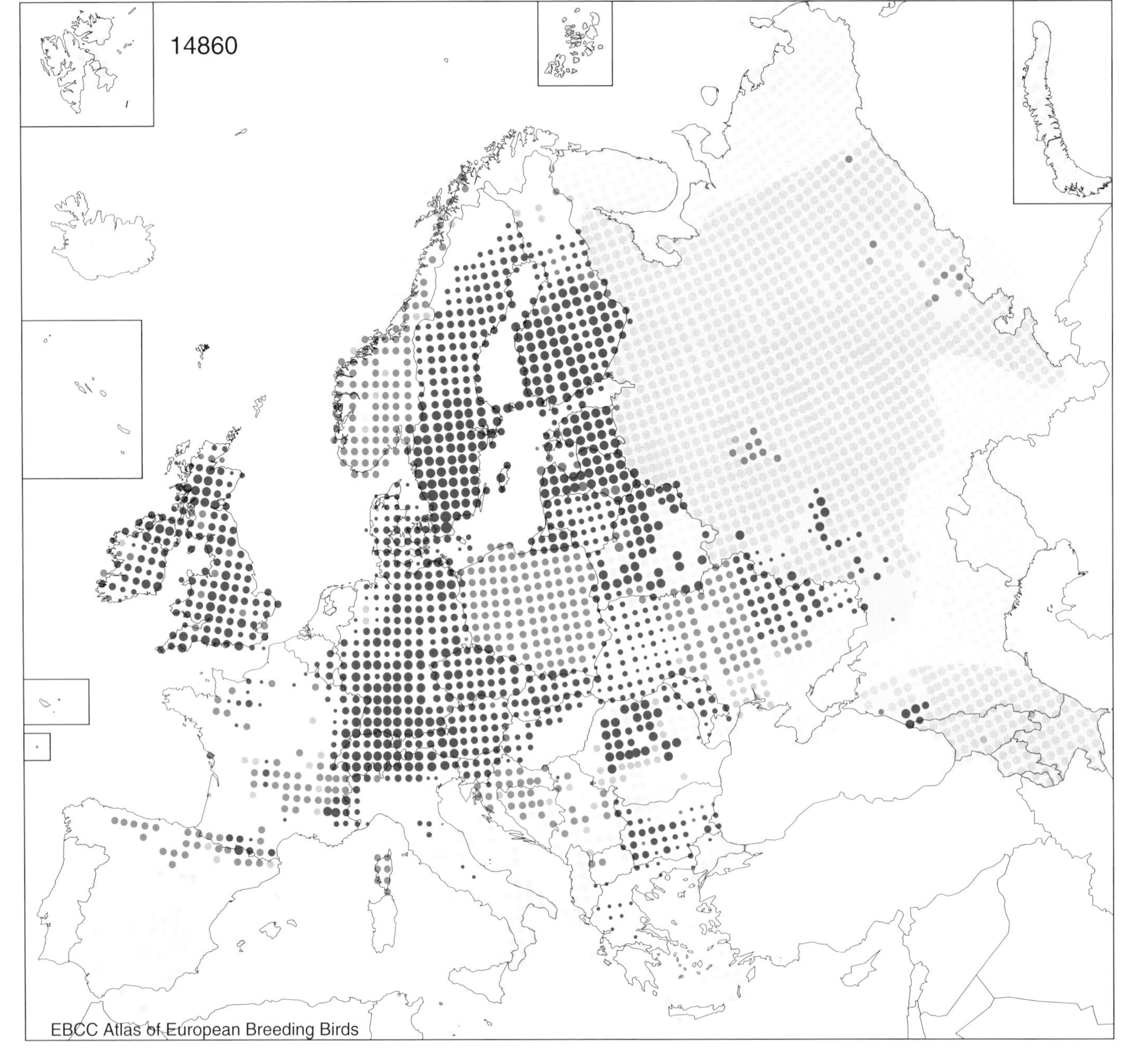

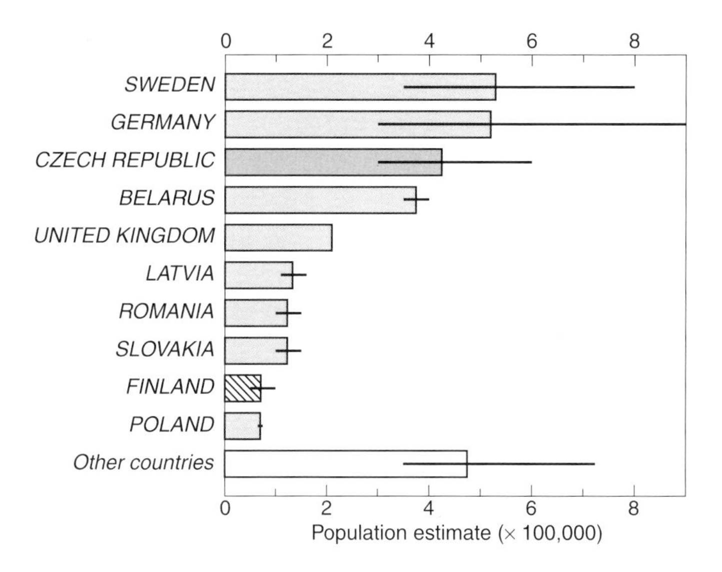

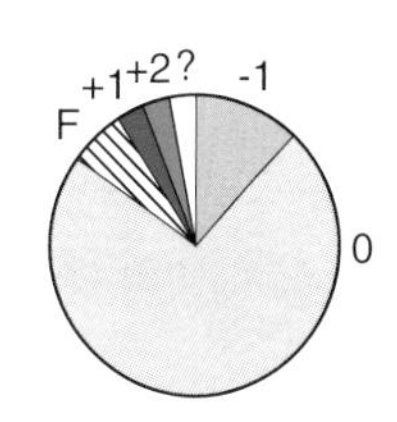

% in top 10 countries: 84.4
Total number of populated European countries: 33
Total European population 2,732,683–3,562,922 (3,049,631)
Russian population 100,000–1,000,000 (316,228)
Turkish population 1000–10,000 (3162)

breeding population was found in the S Netherlands, 13bp occupying 295ha of deciduous and mixed woodland in 1993 (Schepers 1994).

In N Europe, where coniferous habitats predominate, it prefers continuous spruce *Picea* forests over 60 years old, but also uses mixed alder–birch (*Alnus–Betula*) forests. Elsewhere, it prefers spruce-dominated forests (Flade 1994), but also occupies a variety of closed broad-leaved forests, open-land woodlots, parks and even city gardens. Considerable range overlap occurs southwards with its congener, Short-toed Treecreeper *C. brachydactyla* whose preference in sympatric areas like Germany, Hungary and Switzerland tends towards lowlands, the Treecreeper being commoner in more montane regions. However, the Treecreeper is now known to breed frequently in lower-altitude broad-leaved forests at 120–450m asl (Orbån *et al* 1988). In Hungary it is confined largely to beech *Fagus* and poor, or mixed oak *Quercus* woods in continuous and open habitats. Although the Treecreeper has a generalist diet, and thus is not excluded from a wide range of habitats, its preference for spruce is marked.

The Treecreeper is territorial and a solitary breeder. Its foraging technique of searching tree-bark for insects demands a large territory. Because southern habitats are more productive, breeding density is generally higher than in the N. The minimum forest area a breeding pair require shows a clear geographical trend; from <1ha in Britain to >20ha in N Finland. Similarly the minimum forest-island size suitable as a breeding site increases from *c*3ha in Britain to 11ha in SW Finland (Kuitunen & Helle 1988). Breeding densities in sufficiently large plots across Europe ranged from <0.1 to 3.4 bp/10ha, depending on geographical location, forest type and year, highest values occurring in oak *Quercus* forest (Germany) and spruce forest (Czech Republic).

Table A Breeding density in prime habitats

Country/habitat	*bp/10 ha*	*Source*
S Finland/conifer	0.04-0.50	Kuitunen & Helle 1986
Norway/spruce	0.13	Hogstad 1993
S Sweden/?	1.00-1.43	Nilsson 1977
Russia(Valdai)/pine	0.13-0.54	Morozov 1992
Russia(Valdai)/spruce	1.05-1.60	Morozov 1992
Great Britain/?	0.50-1.00	Sharrock 1976
Netherlands/broad-leaved	*c*0.44	Schepers 1994
Germany/conifer	*c*0.4	Steinfatt 1939
Germany/conifer	0.80-1.10	Schnebel 1972
Germany/oak	0.25-3.43	Schönfeld 1983
Czechoslovakia/spruce	1.45-2.86	Repa 1984
Hungary/oak	0.5	Moskát 1987
France (Corsica)/oak	1.6	Blondel 1979

Population size has remained rather stable over much of Europe, but Lithuania, the Czech Republic, Ukraine and Moldova have slight negative trends. Only Hungary and Belgium have experienced range and number increases since 1985. Long-term stability, with fluctuations, probably is typical in Scandinavia (in S Sweden fluctuations from 1970 to 1979 were closely correlated to December–March temperatures in the preceding winters, as expected of a bird whose metabolic rate is high; Svensson 1981). The stability of the Fennoscandian population, as evident in Finnish winter indices since 1965 (Hildén 1986), may also depend on Nordic populations being partly migratory. The European population of 2.3M–3.0Mbp occurs mostly in forest-rich countries. Table A gives representative breeding densities.

Northern populations are partially migratory, heading mainly south-west in autumn and north-east in spring, but normally remaining on the Scandinavian landmass. W European countries may occasionally experience autumn and winter irruptions. British and C European populations are sedentary, although liable to small-scale dispersion outside the breeding season. The Corsican population is predominantly resident.

The Treecreeper is not under threat, but forest fragmentation and modern management practices can influence markedly local abundance and distribution (Koskimies 1989a), primarily because the species is dependent on mature trees in larger, older blocks (Kuitunen & Mäkinen 1993).

Frans Schepers (NL) Janos Török (H)

Certhia brachydactyla

Short-toed Treecreeper

CZ	Šoupálek krátkoprstý	**I**	Rampichino
D	Gartenbaumläufer	**NL**	Boomkruiper
E	Agateador Común	**P**	Trepadeira-comum
F	Grimpereau des jardins	**PL**	Pełzacz ogrodowy
FIN	Etelänpuukiipijä	**R**	Короткопалая пищуха
G	Καμποδενδροβάτης	**S**	Trädgårdsträdkrypare
H	Rövidkarmú fakusz		

SPEC Cat 4, Threat status S

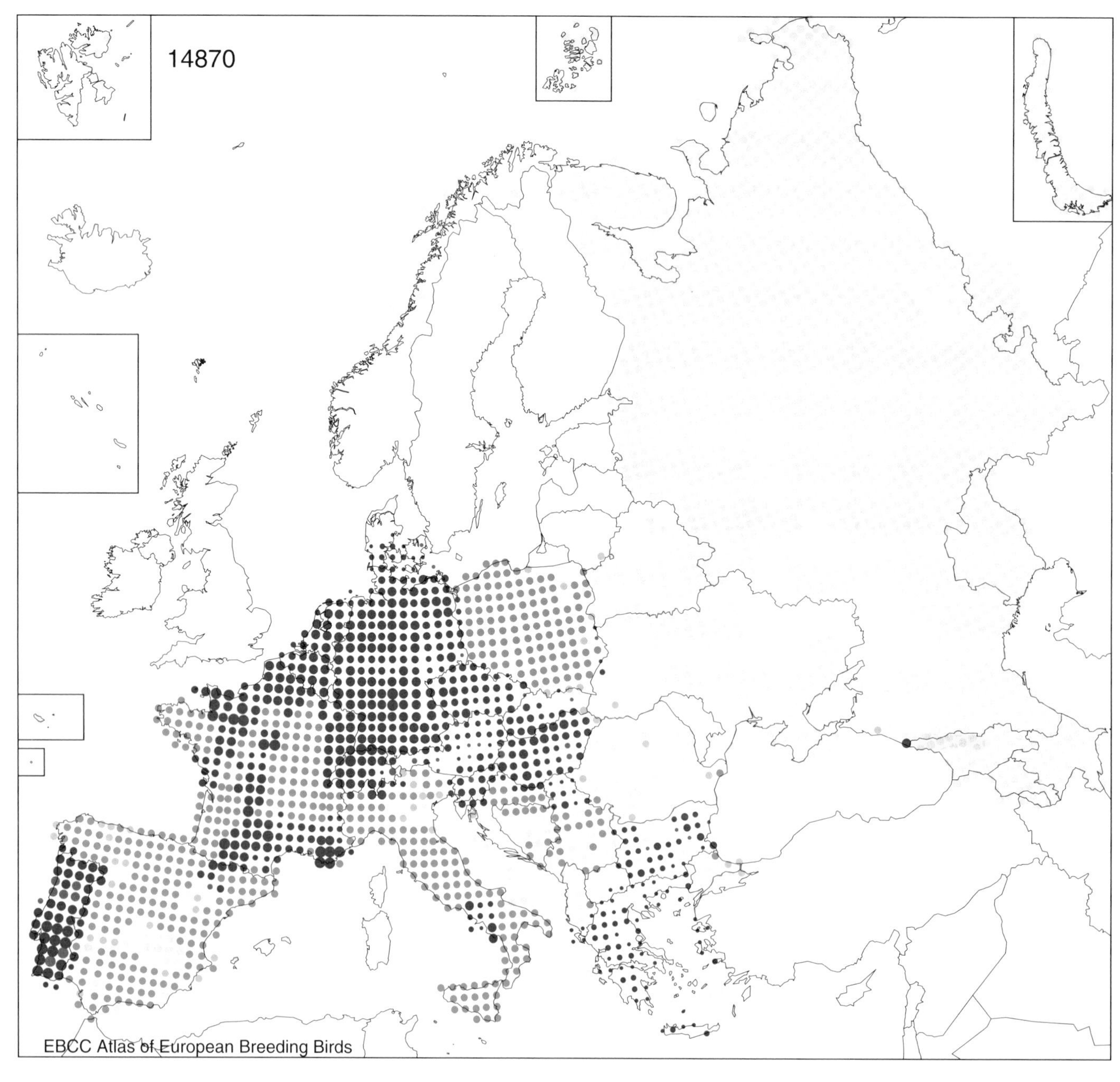

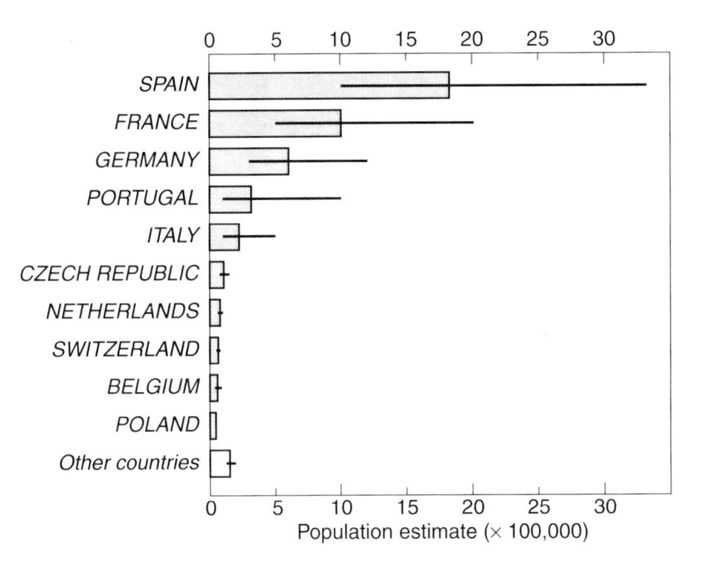

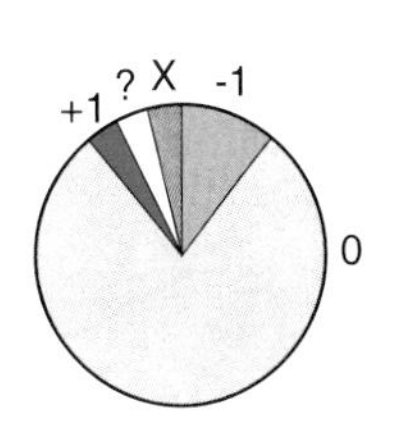

% in top 10 countries: 96.6
Total number of populated European countries: 27
Total European population 3,420,284–6,482,137 (4,455,147)
Turkish population 10,000–50,000 (22,361)

The European breeding distribution of the highly sedentary Short-toed Treecreeper is confined to C and SW Europe, Italy and the Balkan countries. The eastern distribution limit touches the southern border of Lithuania and the western borders of Belarus, Ukraine, Romania and the Black Sea. The easternmost populations occur on the Greek islands off the W Turkish coast and in the Caucasus. Outside the area of *Atlas* coverage the species also breeds in W Turkey, Morocco and Algeria.

In W and N Europe, the species is absent from Britain & Ireland, N Denmark, Fennoscandia, Corsica, Sardinia and the Balearic Islands, where it is often replaced by the sympatric Treecreeper *C. familiaris*. The distribution of both treecreepers overlaps in C Europe (E France, Germany, Poland, Switzerland, Austria, the former Yugoslavia and Romania) and parts of SW Europe (N Spain) and SE Europe (N Greece). Where both species occur, identification is a problem, not only because of the great physical similarity between them, but also because males in areas of sympatry may produce mixed songs and imitations (Clausen & Toft 1988).

Within its breeding range, the highly arboreal Short-toed Treecreeper occupies a broad variety of habitats at lower and medium altitudes, normally below *c*1000m asl. It inhabits broad-leaved, mixed and coniferous forests and woodlands. The species also is common away from forests, in places such as parks, gardens, avenues, hedgerows and orchards. However, it favours richly structured habitats like older oak *Quercus* forests, where trunk density is high and bark surface (as a feeding substrate) is extensive, and where the insect fauna is rich and diverse. Here, the Short-toed Treecreeper can reach high breeding densities; mean values range from 0.5 to 2.0 bp/10ha, although densities peak at 5–6 bp/10ha in suitable habitats (Flade 1994, Orsini 1994).

The European population is estimated at 2.4M–8.7Mbp. The most abundant population occurs in the Iberian Peninsula, where the average density exceeds 8000 bp/50km square. Much of W and C Europe, including France, the Low Countries, Germany, Switzerland and the Czech Republic, have average densities of 3000–4000 bp/50km square. Further E and N, the Short-toed Treecreeper becomes much scarcer. Very little information is available on the isolated Caucasus population (*HVM*).

There are no recent indications of distribution changes, except for Denmark, where the species is expanding slowly N (first bred 1946, and reached 250–300bp in the 1980s; Clausen & Madsen 1986). A similar range expansion has occurred in Poland, where in the early 1900s it bred only in the western half of the country. Nowadays it breeds across the whole of Poland, except for the mountains and eastern Mazury and the Podlasie region (Tomiałojć 1990). In most European countries populations of the Short-toed Treecreeper seem rather stable. However, it is not unlikely that the continuing disappearance of old forests, caused by intensive forestry activities, and the replacement of deciduous woodlands by conifer plantations, will affect breeding numbers and densities in future.

The Short-toed Treecreeper is strictly resident, only a very few birds straying more than 10km from the ringing site. It has been postulated – on the basis of ringing recoveries in Baden-Württemberg – that the species may be an obligate partial migrant in recently occupied breeding areas along the edge of its breeding range, such as the western Netherlands, Denmark and Poland (Bauer & Kaiser 1991). This hypothesis seems to be corroborated by the desertion of polder districts in the northern Netherlands in winter, the birds concentrating in nearby forested areas (van den Brink *et al* 1992).

Frans Schepers (NL)

This species account is sponsored by Vogelwerkgroep Arnhem e.o., Arnhem, NL.

Remiz pendulinus

Penduline Tit

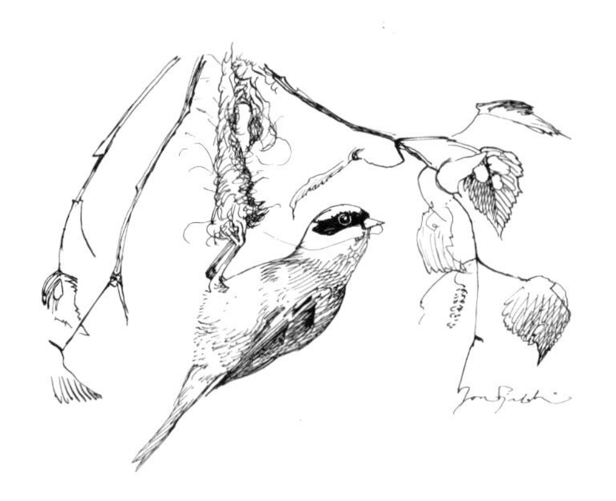

CZ	Moudivláček lužní	**I**	Pendolino
D	Beutelmeise	**NL**	Buidelmees
E	Pájaro Moscón	**P**	Chapim-de-faces-pretas
F	Rémiz penduline	**PL**	Remiz
FIN	Pussitiainen	**R**	Ремез
G	Σακουλοπαπαδίτσα	**S**	Pungmes
H	Függőcinege		

Non-SPEC, Threat status S (P)

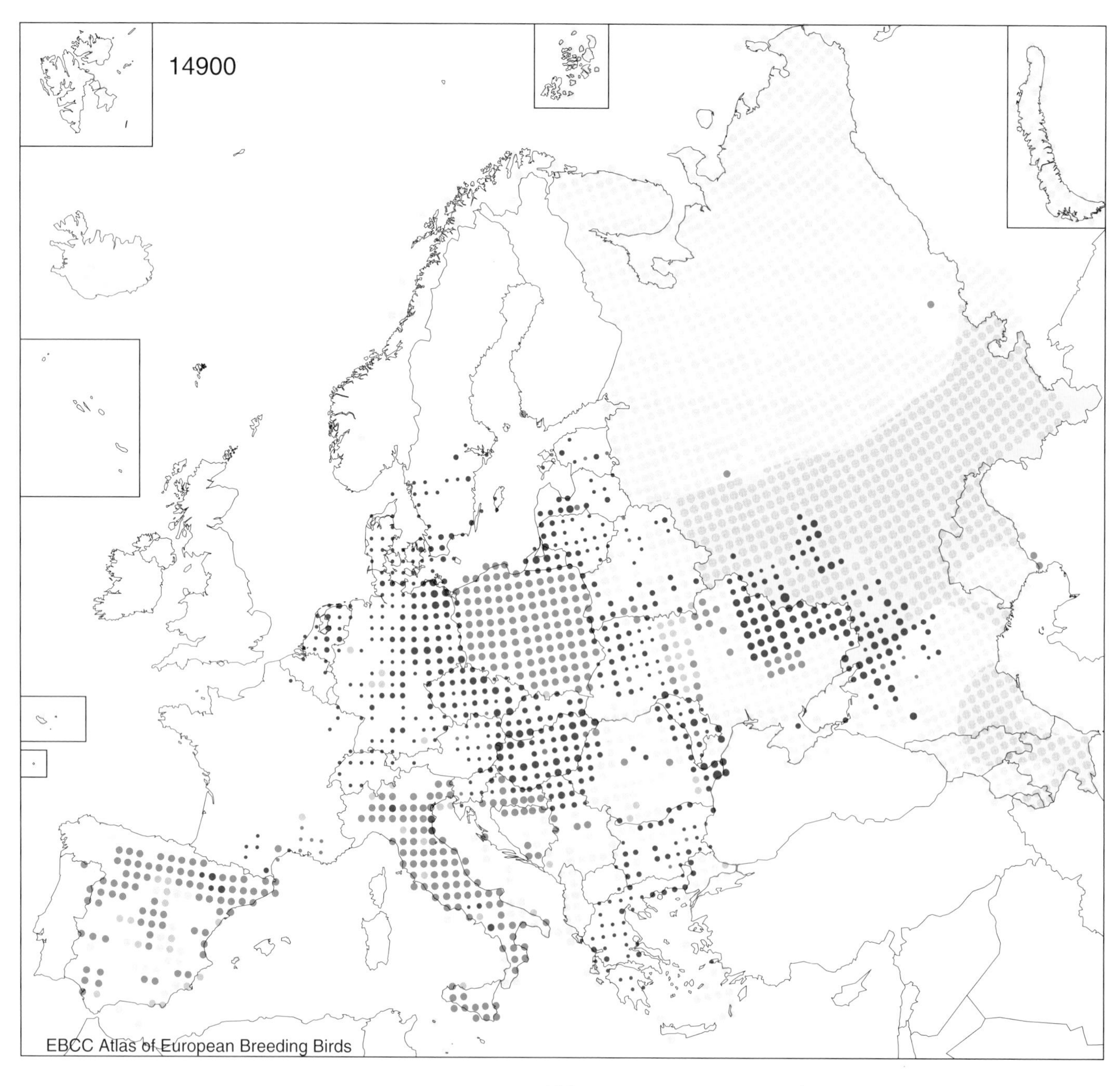

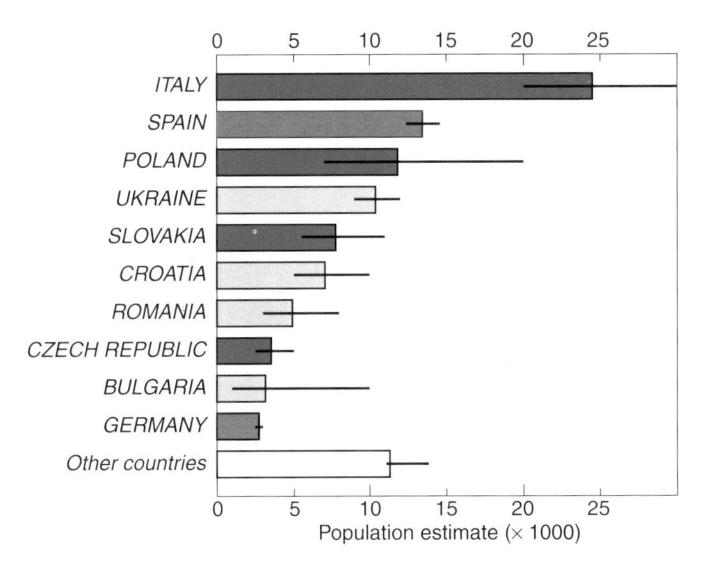

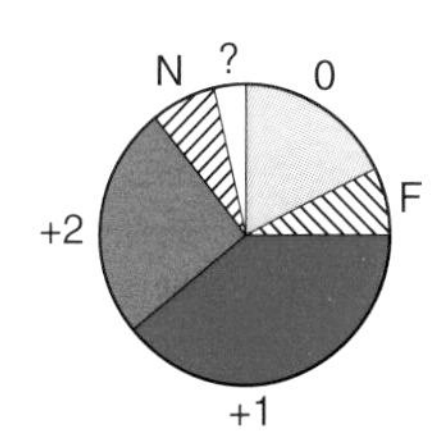

% in top 10 countries: 89.0
Total number of populated European countries: 28
Total European population 91,823–113,971 (100,439)
Russian population 10,000–100,000 (31,623)
Turkish population 50,000–500,000 (158,114)

The world distribution of the Penduline Tit comprises the southern Palearctic between S Finland, C Sweden, Portugal, S Spain, Iran and NE China, but the range of the nominate *R.p. pendulinus* is restricted to Turkey and Europe W of the Don/Volga watershed. The populations W of the Oder Valley winter in SW Europe (SW France to Portugal), the eastern populations migrating south to Hungary, Italy, Greece and the Black Sea. A Latvian wintering population of 100–500 birds has now become established, mostly in coastal lagoon reedbeds (J. Lipsbergs, pers obs). S European populations are mostly resident.

The extensive western range expansion of this small, but conspicuous and attractive species has been very well documented (*HVM*). The Penduline Tit extended its range westwards from the 1950s onwards, in several waves from E and C Poland, Slovakia and eastern Austria to eastern Germany by 1965, S Sweden and C Germany (1975), S Finland, C Sweden, Denmark, N Netherlands and NE France (1985) and Belgium (1987–89) (Flade *et al* 1986, Bekhuis *et al* 1993). This expansion was accompanied by a gradual southwesterly displacement of wintering sites, examples being the Camargue, the French Atlantic coast and C and SW Spain. In SW Europe the expansion started from a very restricted breeding range in disparate areas of the French and Spanish Mediterranean coasts in the early 1960s, since when it has encompassed large areas of Spain, moving up the Ebro, Duero, Tajo, Guadiana and Guadalquivir Rivers (Valera *et al* 1990).

It is likely that habitat changes have greatly assisted the expansion (Valera *et al* 1990, Schönfeld 1994, M. Flade, unpubl, *HVM*). Wetland eutrophication is widespread, allowing nest-material plants such as nettle *Urtica dioica* and wild hop *Humulus lupulus* to increase. It has also led to an increase of the mealy plum aphid *Hyalopterus pruni* (a main late-summer food) in reedbeds. Suitable habitats have also developed artificially where gravel extraction and opencast coalmining have occurred.

Although sometimes distinct declines follow new colonization before numbers stabilized, as in E Germany, the strong population increase continues, especially in Estonia, Latvia, Sweden, NW and W Germany, The Netherlands, France and Spain. Only the populations in E and SE Europe (Russia, Ukraine, Romania, Bulgaria, Croatia and Greece) seem stable. Nowhere is the Penduline Tit very common, but within its scattered distribution it forms concentrations along the larger river valleys and other suitable wetlands. Even within its core range it remains mostly a scarce species.

Colonies form in semi-open wetlands such as river- and lake-sides, marshes, fishponds and abandoned opencast mines, up to 600–750m asl. The species, characteristic of the early succession stages of riverine and other wetland forests, prefers as nesting habitats riparian gallery forests, willow thickets, small woods, hedges and even solitary trees within wetlands, especially larger reedbeds. Habitat selection is governed by the occurrence of suitable nesting trees or tall bushes with drooping, resilient twigs (preferably willow *Salix* and birch *Betula*, but also poplar *Populus*, alder *Alnus* and false acacia *Robinia pseudacacia*), a good supply of plants for nest material (nettle, hop, reedmace *Typha latifolia*, reed *Phragmites* spp; in late spring also fruiting poplar and willow) and a rich spatial structure of potential breeding locations.

Because the Penduline Tit has a polygamous mating system and because there is no pair-bonding, it is very difficult to determine breeding density. Abundance, as measured in breeding nests (bn) or simultaneously reproductive females (srf) per unit area, in areas larger than $10km^2$, can attain from 9.4 to 13.8 bn/$10km^2$ per season, or 4.8–7.8 srf/$10km^2$, and within smaller plots of homogeneous habitat exceptionally attains 6.0 bn/10ha per season, or (on average) 0.7–1.5 srf/10ha.

Jules Diederich (L) Martin Flade (D)
Juris Lipsbergs (LAT)

Oriolus oriolus

Golden Oriole

CZ	Žluva hajní	**I**	Rigogolo
D	Pirol	**NL**	Wielewaal
E	Oropéndola	**P**	Papa-figos
F	Loriot d'Europe	**PL**	Wilga
FIN	Kuhankeittäjä	**R**	Иволга
G	Συκοφάγος	**S**	Sommargylling
H	Sárgarigó		

Non-SPEC, Threat status S

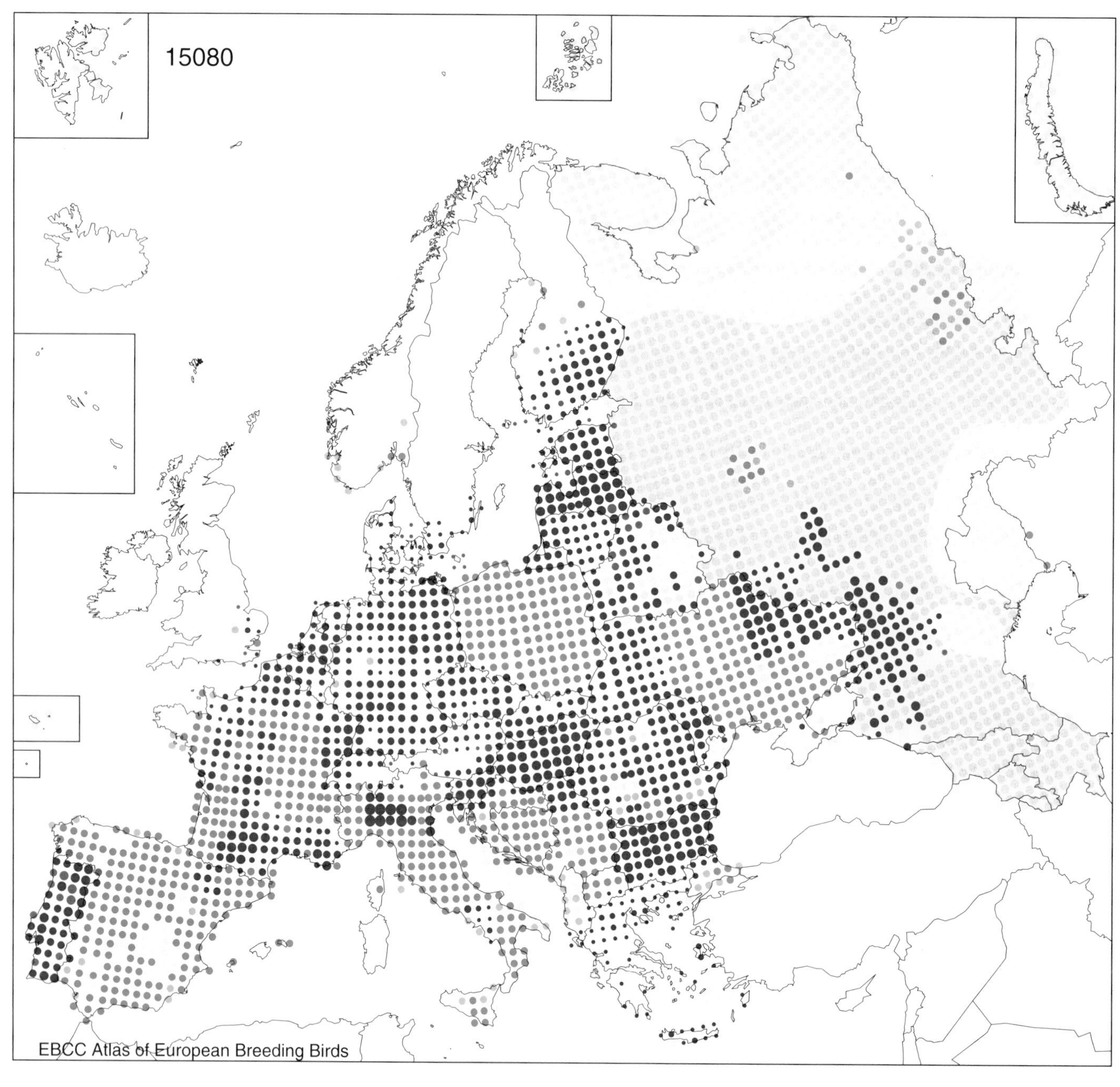

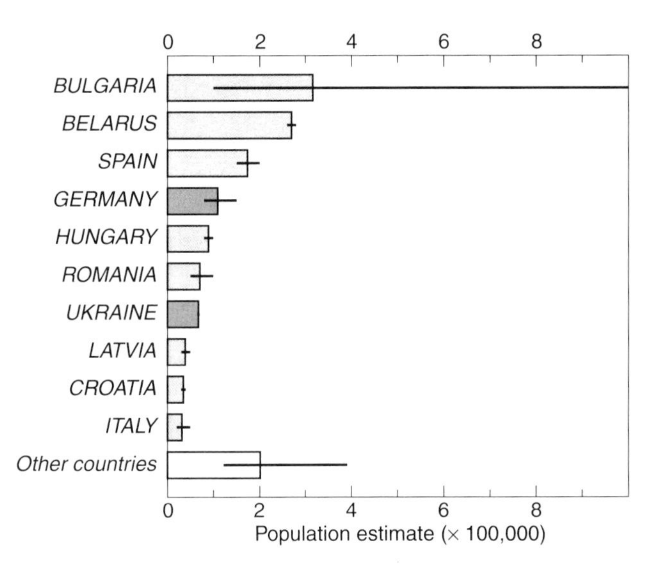

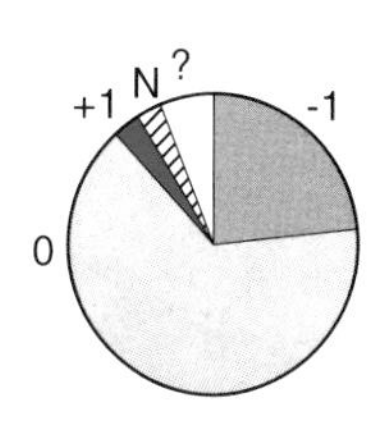

% in top 10 countries: 85.7
Total number of populated European countries: 34
Total European population 1,178,499–2,096,348 (1,402,520)
Russian population 100,000–1,000,000 (316,228)
Turkish population 50,000–500,000 (158,114)

The Golden Oriole (including the eastern *O.o. kundoo*) inhabits the Palearctic eastwards as far as the Altai Mountains and India. Its geographical representative in tropical Africa is African Golden Oriole *O. auratus*, the two forming a superspecies. Numerous physiological and behavioural characteristics indicate the Golden Oriole to be an exotic, a bird of tropical woodland origin (Wassmann in *HVM*). Its European northern breeding range limit runs from Denmark via S Sweden, SE Finland, S Karelia and then at *c*60–61°N through Russia to Siberia. To the S it reaches the Mediterranean, including Corsica (rare since 1976) and Sicily. Overall, its distribution matches essentially that of oak *Quercus* spp, particularly below 200–400m asl, but normally not above *c*600–650m. It breeds locally and sporadically up to 1000m (Apennines and S Pyrenees) and as high as 1500m in Sicily (Etna).

The species resides in open woodland which has a light understorey and is adjacent to small waterbodies. Its preferred habitats, generally south-facing, are lightly-wooded hillsides, riverine copses, oakwoods, poplar *Populus* stands, marshy and moist meadow woodland, sheltered mixed deciduous woods, large gardens, traditional orchards and tree avenues, but choice may show considerable geographical variation (Feige 1986).

European population density varies with habitat, altitude and geographical location, but rises with increasing continental climatic influence from the W and NW (Britain, Denmark, Sweden) to the S and SE, as the graph and map show. The largest populations (some >100 000bp) occur in Bulgaria, Russia, Belarus and Spain. However, my own detailed research (Wassmann in *HVM*) suggests that the population estimates at least for Germany and Hungary should be lower than the graph indicates, mostly because general census methodology is less effective for this species and results in overestimation. Consequently, these estimates should be: Germany 38 000–60 000bp, Hungary 40 000–70 000bp. The graph may overestimate for several countries. My data suggest 15 000–30 000bp for Poland.

The species is patchily distributed at low densities at the range limits, particularly in Britain (East Anglian poplar plantations only; *c*30bp in 1987–93; Dagley 1994), Denmark (100bp), S Norway and S Sweden, including Öland (>50bp). Densities in core breeding habitats can be high, especially in poplar and riverine woodland. In recently reclaimed Dutch polders (Flevoland), 173bp occupied 1466ha (1.2 bp/10ha) of poplar plantations (biased towards Black Poplar *P. nigra* cultivars) and 23bp occupied 123ha (1.9 bp/10ha) of willow *Salix* stands (Bijlsma 1995), similar to values in N Germany for poplar (1.9 bp/10ha; 5 plots, 83.6ha) (Flade 1994). In Danubian swamp forests, even higher values occur; 1.9–3.6 bp/10ha on Austrian plots of 10–40ha (Dvorak *et al* 1993).

Brood size is strongly dependent on weather conditions, which may cause large, albeit short-term, population fluctuations at regional or supra-regional level (Hovorka 1991), but especially at the breeding range limits. In the 19th century the Finnish population was numerous, but around 1900 it crashed; it has recovered since the 1940s to *c*5000bp. Many European countries have suffered large fluctuations, but without clear trends. Seven sizeable national populations have experienced declining population trends, notably in Germany, France, Ukraine, Estonia and Greece. The causes are not known, but in N Germany habitat loss corresponds with population reductions. The effect of persecution in Greece cannot yet be quantified. Overall, the European population is *c*1M–5Mbp and is not endangered, despite these declines.

The Golden Oriole winters primarily in the climatically temperate, equatorial African high woodlands and moist montane forests of East Africa (Uganda, Kenya, N Mozambique) but also occupies arid thornbush country S as far as South Africa, Natal and Madagascar. Although trans-Mediterranean migration is on a broad front, C European populations probably perform a loop migration, easterly in autumn, further W in spring, other populations adhering to fixed routes.

Ralf Wassmann (D)

This species account is sponsored by De Wielewaal, B.

Lanius collurio

Red-backed Shrike

CZ	Ťuhýk obecný	**I**	Averla piccola
D	Neuntöter	**NL**	Grauwe Klauwier
E	Alcaudón Dorsirrojo	**P**	Picanço-de-dorso-ruivo
F	Pie-grièche écorcheur	**PL**	Gąsiorek
FIN	Pikkulepinkäinen	**R**	Сорокопут-жулан
G	Αετομάχος	**S**	Törnskata
H	Tövisszúró gébics		

SPEC Cat 3, Threat status D (P)

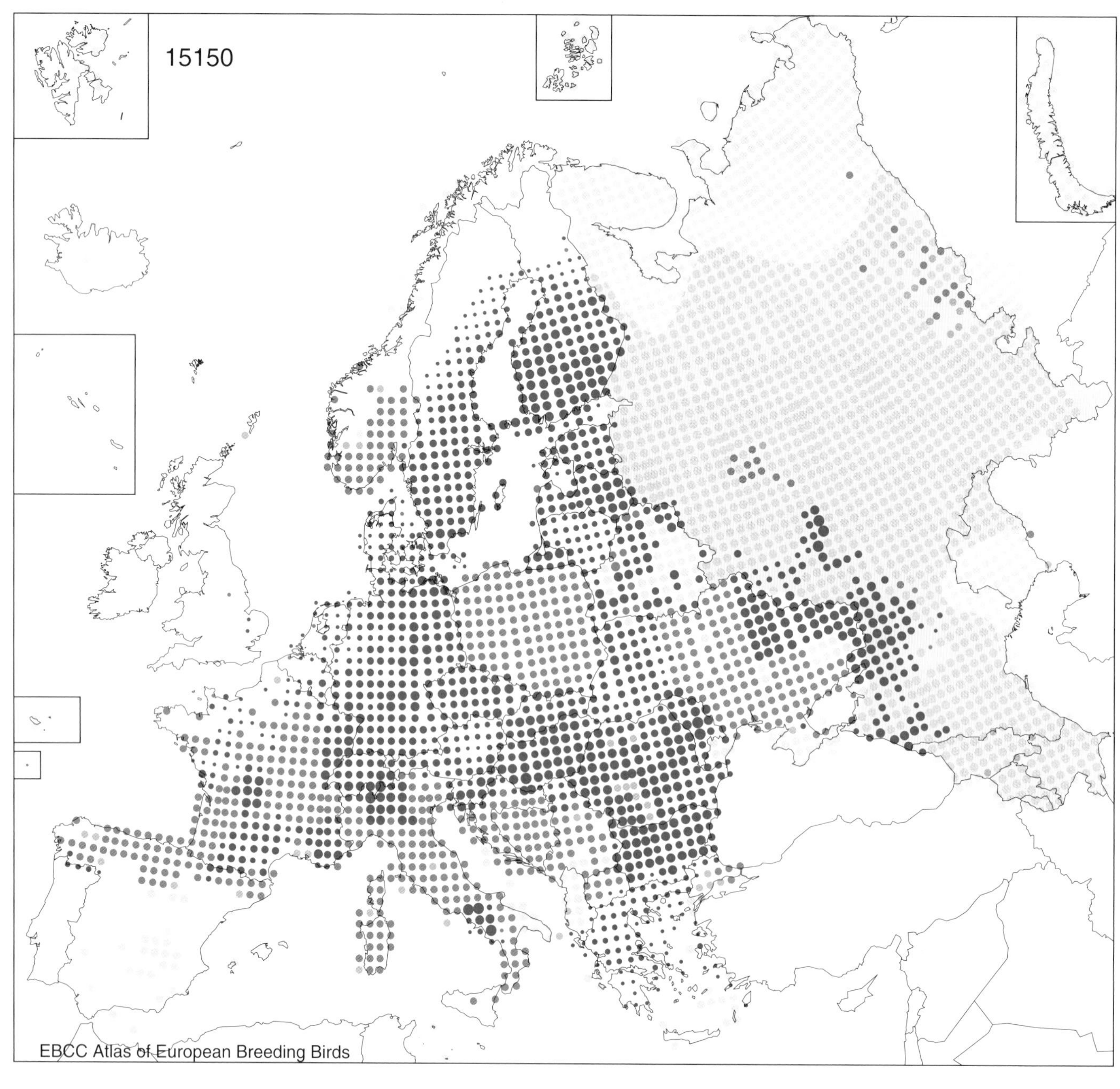

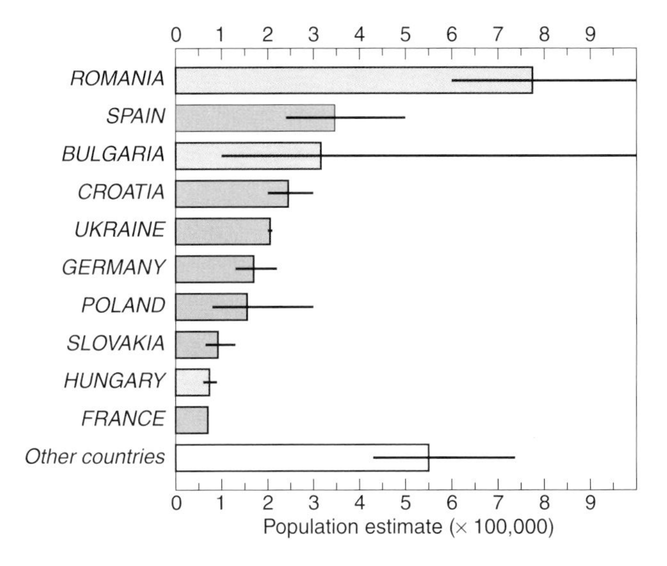

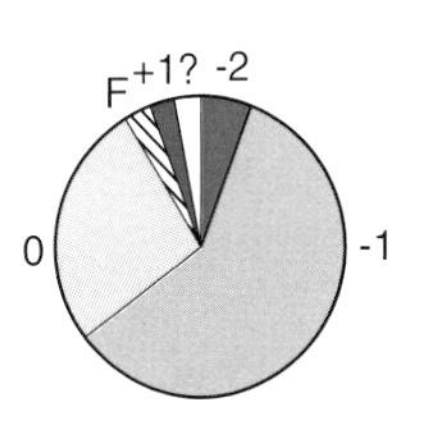

% in top 10 countries: 83.6
Total number of populated European countries: 33
Total European population 2,610,076–3,684,956 (2,926,571)
Russian population 100,000–1,000,000 (316,228)
Turkish population 50,000–500,000 (158,114)

The Red-backed Shrike breeds across most of Europe. The subspecies *kobylini* occurs in Crimea, the Caucasus and the southern Balkans and the nominate *collurio* inhabits the rest of its European distribution. Its world range reaches *c*90°E in a swathe E of the Volga between *c*48° and *c*64°N. The species' distribution in its climatic range appears limited by: heavy summer rainfall (NW), very low minimum temperatures (N) and very dry warm summer weather (16°C July isotherm) (S). Its eastern range limit overlaps with those of the Isabelline *L. isabellinus* and Brown Shrikes *L. cristatus*.

The species occupies a wide variety of half-open habitats possessing thick bushes and scrub (nesting), prominent perches (hunting) and abundance of insect prey; low-intensity farmland interspersed with heaths, hedgerows, orchards, vineyards, young forest plantations, shrubby meadows, river valleys, traditional pastures and overgrown clearings. In the E Baltic region it also nests in bogs.

It breeds from sea level up to *c*1700–1800m asl in the Alps (maximum recorded, 2050m, but mostly between 200 and 400m in the southern Alps), 1400m in the Pyrenees and 1000m in the Vosges (Lefranc 1993). Its distribution reflects the patchiness of its habitat, especially in lowland farmland. Typical breeding densities in optimal habitats are 0.6 bp/ha, each male defending an area of 0.4–1.0ha. Lithuanian local densities reach 1 bp/ha in small areas of coniferous plantations. High densities still occur locally in remnants of prime habitat at the NW range limit, as in SE Belgium (1986–87: 57bp on 2000ha; van Nieuwenhuyse & Vandekerkhove 1989) and in E Netherlands (1992: 105bp on 2000ha, H. van Berkel, pers comm). In Lithuanian low-intensity farmland overall density is 1 bp/150ha (1975–80; P. Kurlavičius, in prep), in various W Polish habitats 0.8–6.2 bp/10ha (Kuźniak 1991) and in Germany 3–6 bp/150ha (Jakober & Stauber 1987).

The European population is estimated at *c*2.2Mbp. The species still remains numerous in much of Europe, increasingly so from W to E. Densities in France, Germany and Poland average 1200–1500 bp/50km square, but may reach >5000 bp/50km square in N Italy, northern Balkans, Romania, Moldova, Bulgaria and probably Ukraine and S Russia. Application of improved census methods across wider areas may indicate higher populations than previously recorded. For example, a census in Lombardy (N Italy) in 1992 suggested 30 000bp, equivalent to the minimum estimate for Italy in the European Bird Database (EBD). Similarly, recent research by the Lithuanian shrikes working group suggested 20 000–30 000bp, rather than the EBD's 5000–10 000bp. Such results signify improved knowledge, not that declines have been reversed.

The species has been in decline for decades, a trend seen in much of Europe during 1970–90. Declines were most noticeable at the northern and western range limits, the species now being extinct in Great Britain and having declined in The Netherlands from 5000–15 000bp in 1900 to 150–220bp in 1989–90 (Hustings & Bekhuis 1993). However, the presented data show that the entire European population is declining, 21 countries reporting a decrease of at least 20%. Stable populations were mostly reported from the range core in E Europe, where monitoring data are few, making valid assessment of trends extremely difficult.

It has been proposed that the decline has been climatically induced, with cooler and wetter summers reducing insect prey numbers, hence the retreat from the Atlantic climate belt. However, deterioration and destruction of prime farmland habitats is likely to have played an important, if not decisive role (Hustings & Bekhuis 1993). The last 20 years' chronic drought in the Kalahari, the species' main wintering area, may also exert a negative influence on numbers (Bruderer & Bruderer 1993, Herremans 1993b). Most birds seemingly perform a loop migration around the eastern Mediterranean (shifted E in spring). A steady decline in numbers migrating through Ethiopia was also recorded: >1000 in 1971, *c*500 in 1973 and 100 in 1974 (Ash 1993).

Lorenzo Fornasari (I) Petras Kurlavičius (LITH)
Renato Massa (I)

This species account is sponsored by Klaus ter Veer, Düsseldorf, D.

Lanius minor Lesser Grey Shrike

CZ Ťuhýk menší
D Schwarzstirnwürger
E Alcaudón Chico
F Pie-grièche à poitrine rose
FIN Mustaotsalepinkäinen
G Γαϊδουροκεφαλάς
H Kis őrgébics
I Averla cenerina
NL Kleine Klapekster
P Picanço-pequeno
PL Dzierzba czarnoczelna
R Чернолобый сорокопут
S Svartpannad törnskata

SPEC Cat 2, Threat status D (P)

15190

EBCC Atlas of European Breeding Birds

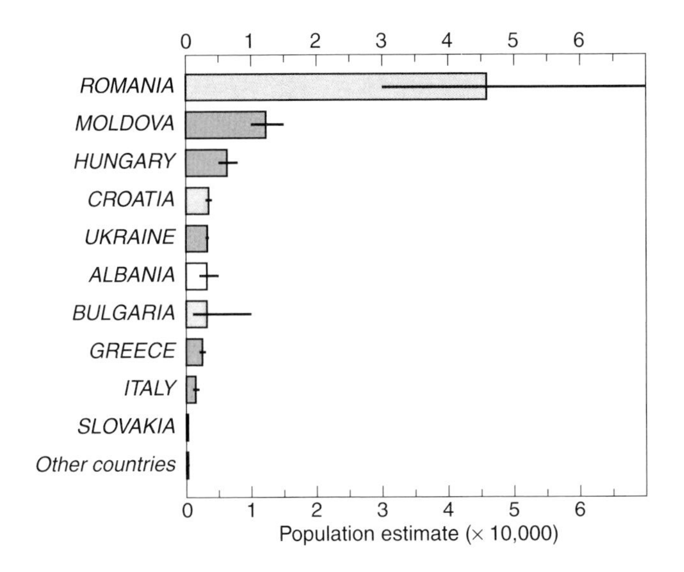

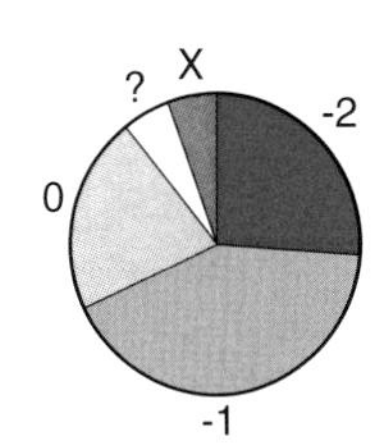

% in top 10 countries: 99.7
Total number of populated European countries: 19
Total European population 65,580–107,242 (81,827)
Russian population 10,000–100,000 (31,623)
Turkish population 10,000–100,000 (31,623)

The Lesser Grey Shrike has a rather restricted breeding range which extends only slightly beyond Europe to C Asia, from NE Spain in the W to the headwaters of the Rivers Ob and Irtysh in the Altai in the E. In European Russia it reaches 55°N; its southern limits are northern Iran and the northern coasts of the Mediterranean Sea.

A typical steppe species, its presence is governed by the continental climate of hot summers with little rain. Primarily a bird of low-lying land or hilly country up to 900m asl in E Europe, it has adapted well to cultivated areas provided that it can find trees tall enough to conceal its nest, and hunting grounds with low vegetation or even large patches of bare soil which contain sufficient large insects. In Europe it will nest in territories which include extensively managed orchards, potato, beetroot, melon and tobacco fields, as well as in vineyards and meadows (Kristín 1991a, Lefranc 1993).

In the 19th and early 20th centuries the Lesser Grey Shrike was reasonably common in S and C Europe reaching well into Germany and France. After 1850 its populations decreased in these countries and in several other regions, but a recovery occurred in the 1880s when locally it could be the commonest shrike. It also then bred in Luxembourg and S Belgium. Numbers diminished sharply after World War I, as its range contracted severely. In the early 1930s, it reappeared in areas vacated two decades earlier. It gradually decreased in the early 1960s, eventually disappearing from C and NE France (1979), Switzerland (1972), Germany (1978), the Czech Republic (1980) and W Poland (Silesia: 1968). Austria's few breeding pairs are concentrated near Neusiedlersee (Niehuis 1968, Dvorak 1993 *et al*). Its numbers are declining in Slovakia (400–600bp; A. Krištín, pers obs), Hungary (5000–8000bp), E Poland (10–50bp), W Ukraine (3000–3500bp), Belarus (50–200bp) and the Baltic States (<25bp in Lithuania and Latvia combined). Inadequate and conflicting data mask its status in Russia, Romania and Moldova (Tomiałojć 1994). Numbers have also slumped since 1975 in southern areas like Italy (probably fewer than 2000bp) and the French mediterranean region (only *c*30bp known in 1994). Remarkably, despite a southeastwards migration in autumn, it still breeds in NE Spain in two relict populations, each of *c*35bp (Lefranc 1993).

The historic population fluctuations in W Europe have been linked largely to climatic fluctuations, long series of wet summers leading to 'atlantization' of some areas, but the more recent sharp decline is very probably more closely connected to changes in agricultural practices which reduce the numbers and variety of large insects. Furthermore, recent research showed that the Kalahari (mainly in Botswana) is the major wintering area in Africa (M. Herremans, pers comm). Because the species selects drier and more open acacia habitats, an understanding of the relationship between its decline and the Kalahari's chronic drought since the mid-1970s is required urgently (Herremans 1993b).

The Lesser Grey Shrike tends to nest in loose colonies. In 1994, near Béziers (France) 22–25bp nested in an area of *c*24 km² 'lost' in the middle of Europe's largest intensive vineyard (N. Lefranc, pers obs). In C Slovakia density can reach 23–26 bp/10km², peaking at 4 nests/ha (Krištín 1991a).

The species is a long-distance migrant, spending less than four months on its breeding grounds. In autumn, migration from W and C Europe flows through Greece and its islands. After two months the wintering grounds in Botswana, Namibia, Zimbabwe and South Africa are reached. The spring migration begins in late February or early March. Like the Red-backed Shrike *L. collurio*, the Lesser Grey performs a loop-migration within Africa, and usually arrives at its European breeding grounds from late April to mid-May.

Anton Krištín (SLK) Norbert Lefranc (F)

Lanius excubitor

Great Grey Shrike

CZ	Ťuhýk šedý	**I**	Averla maggiore
D	Raubwürger	**NL**	Klapekster
E	Alcaudón Real	**P**	Picanço-real
F	Pie-grièche grise	**PL**	Srokosz
FIN	Isolepinkäinen (Lapinharakka)	**R**	Серый сорокопут
G	Διπλοκεφαλάς	**S**	Varfågel
H	Nagy őrgébics		

SPEC Cat 3, Threat status D

The Great and Southern Grey Shrikes are now commonly treated as separate species (Isenmann & Bouchet 1993, Isenmann & LeFranc 1994), but were considered conspecific during the *Atlas* surveys. *L. meridionalis* of S France and Iberia differs from *excubitor* in colour, size, voice and behaviour; it prefers to nest in low bushes, in habitats with closer spacing of scrub and small trees than that of *excubitor*; it breeds at higher densities. The populations N (and E) of the Caspian (*pallidirostris*) are treated by some author as *meridionalis*, by others as a distinct species.

Primarily a perch-hunting bird, whose diet consists mainly of voles, the Great Grey Shrike prefers open country interspersed with trees, bushes, fence-posts and power lines. Typical perch densities in C and N Europe are 5–15/ha. It is important that much of its territory is covered by sparse or low vegetation, as occurs in such habitats as peat-bogs, heathland, clearfells and much low-intensity cultivation, whose shrinkage has affected the species severely. Territory size, dependent on local food supply and

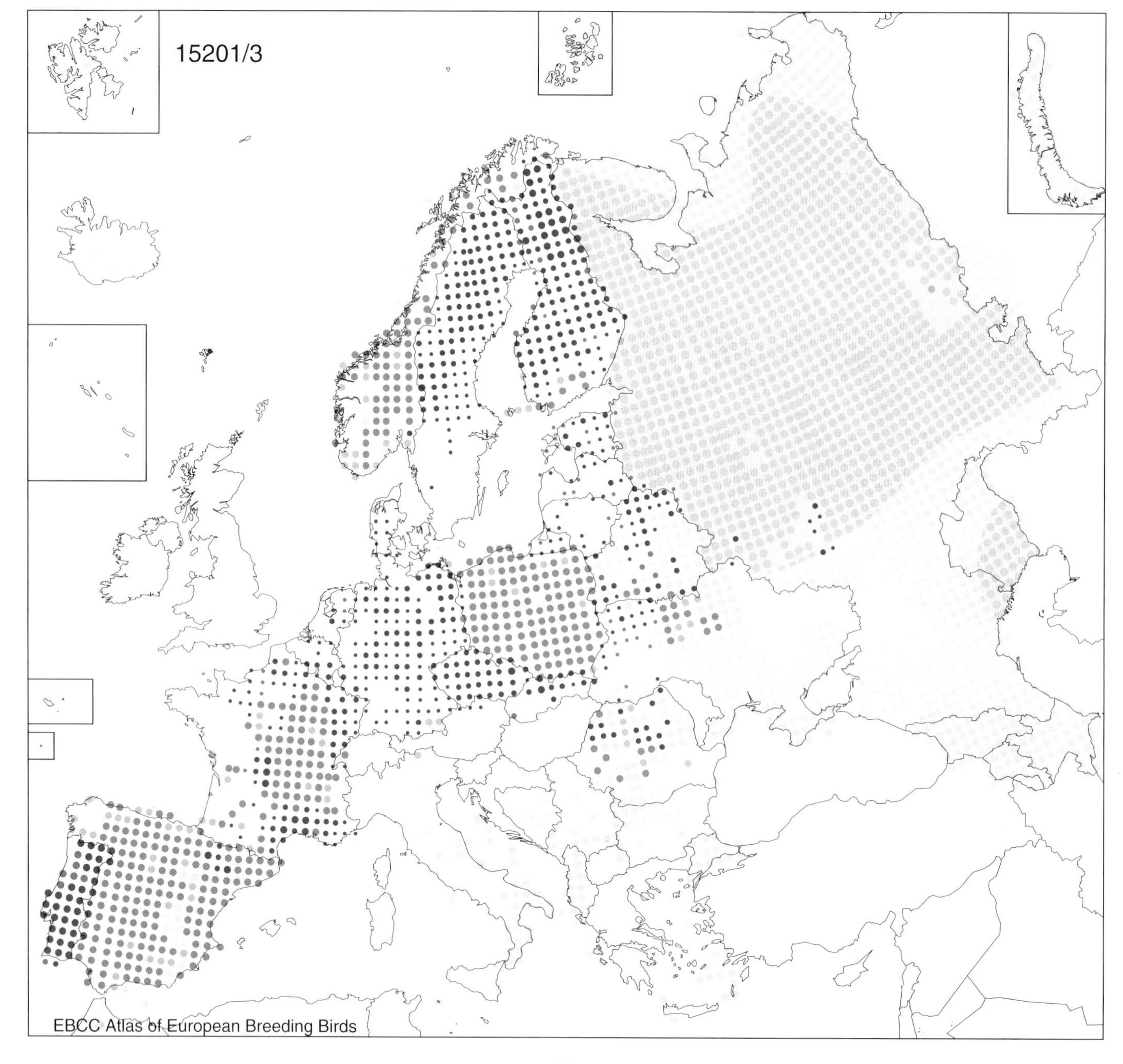

Lanius meridionalis

Southern Grey Shrike

CZ	Ťuhýk stepní	I	Averla maggiore meridionale
D	Mittelmeer-Raubwürger	NL	Steppeklapekster
E	Alcaudon Meridional	P	Picanço-real-meridonal
F	Pie-grièche méridionale	PL	Srokosz południowy
FIN	Etelänisolepinkäinen	R	Иберийский серый сорокопут
G	Διπλοκεφαλάς του Νότου	S	Varfågel
H	Déli őrgébics		

Criteria not applied

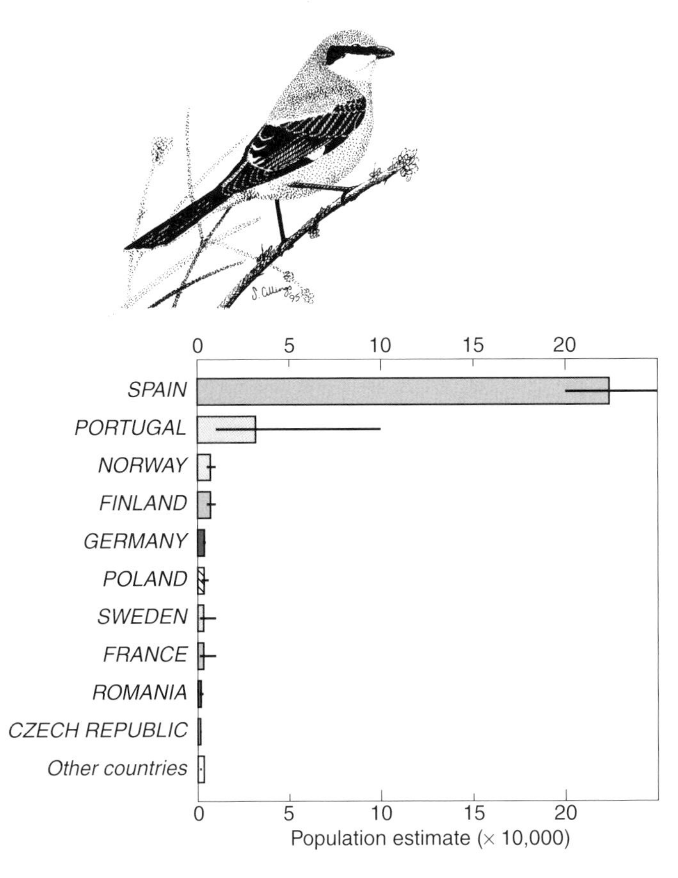

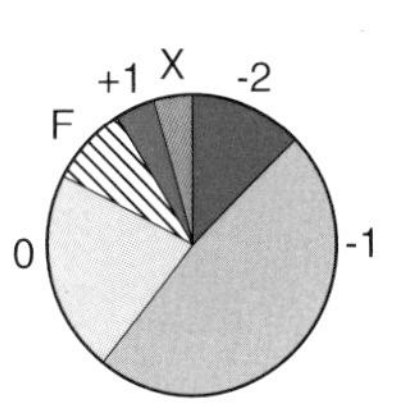

% in top 10 countries: 98.9
Total number of populated European countries: 23
Total European population 256,938–363,391 (289,282)
Russian population 100,000–1,000,000 (316,228)

habitat structure, is at least 18ha, densities seldom exceeding 0.3 bp/km² (Schönn 1994b).

The Fennoscandian and Russian stronghold contains at least 330 000bp (future Russian censuses may reveal greater numbers) and Iberia 210 000–260 000bp. Remaining populations, in C and E Europe (13 000bp) and W Europe (3400bp) are relatively insignificant. In N Europe (including Russia) the trend probably has been stable since the 1980s, although systematic forest clearfelling in Sweden and Finland initially created more breeding and hunting habitats, producing range and numbers increases (Olsson 1980). Numbers in Spain apparently are decreasing.

Its widespread population decline over much of W, C and E Europe, due largely to habitat destruction and deterioration, created considerable distribution gaps (Rothaupt 1992) at regional level, where severe winters help create losses often large enough to overcome the compensatory effect of immigration from elsewhere (Reinsch 1995). The present low recruitment rate in C European populations is a further impediment (Schönn 1994a). The species has become extinct in Switzerland (1986), and in Austria, SW Germany and several other regions only a few breeding pairs remain. There is no evidence that the species has ever bred in Britain, Ireland, Hungary, Italy, Yugoslavia, Bulgaria, Albania or Greece.

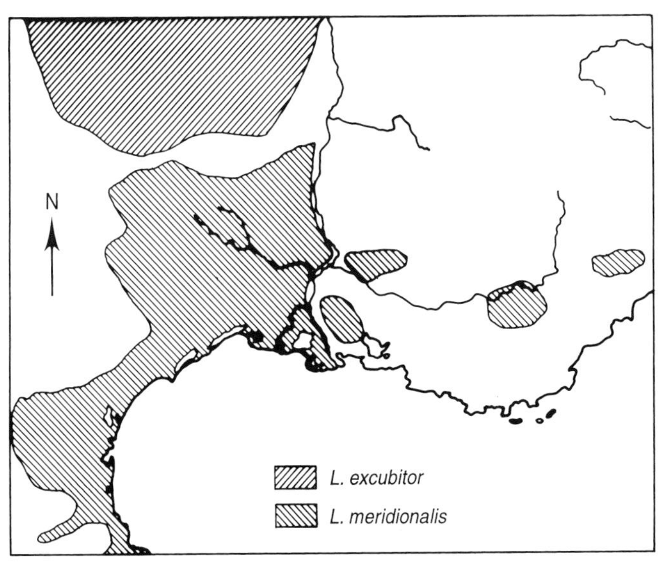

The distribution of *L. excubitor* (in the north) and *L. meridionalis* in S France (after Isenmann & Bouchet *Alauda* 61, 1993) (Courtesy *Alauda* and Paul Isenmann).

The Great Grey Shrike is resident in southern and much of C Europe. Even in S Sweden and S Finland a significant proportion does not migrate. Only the area N of 60°N is deserted completely in winter (some exceptions up to 68°N). The main migration directions are SW and S predominantly to C Europe, where wintering numbers have been decreasing since the mid-1970s, probably because of a combination of reducing C European populations and changing migratory strategy of northern birds (increasingly remaining in S Fennoscandia). Wintering birds often occupy areas and habitats not used for breeding.

Gerhard Rothaupt (D) Dries van Nieuwenhuyse (B)

This species account is sponsored by Gesellschaft für Naturschutz und Ornithologie Rheinland-Pfalz, D.

Lanius senator

Woodchat Shrike

CZ	Ťuhýk rudohlavý	**I**	Averla capirossa
D	Rotkopfwürger	**NL**	Roodkopklauwier
E	Alcaudón Común	**P**	Picanço-barreteiro
F	Pie-grièche à tête rousse	**PL**	Dzierzba rudogłowa
FIN	Punapäälepinkäinen	**R**	Красноголовый сорокопут
G	Κοκκινοκεφαλάς	**S**	Rödhuvad törnskata
H	Vörösfejű gébics		

SPEC Cat 2, Threat status V

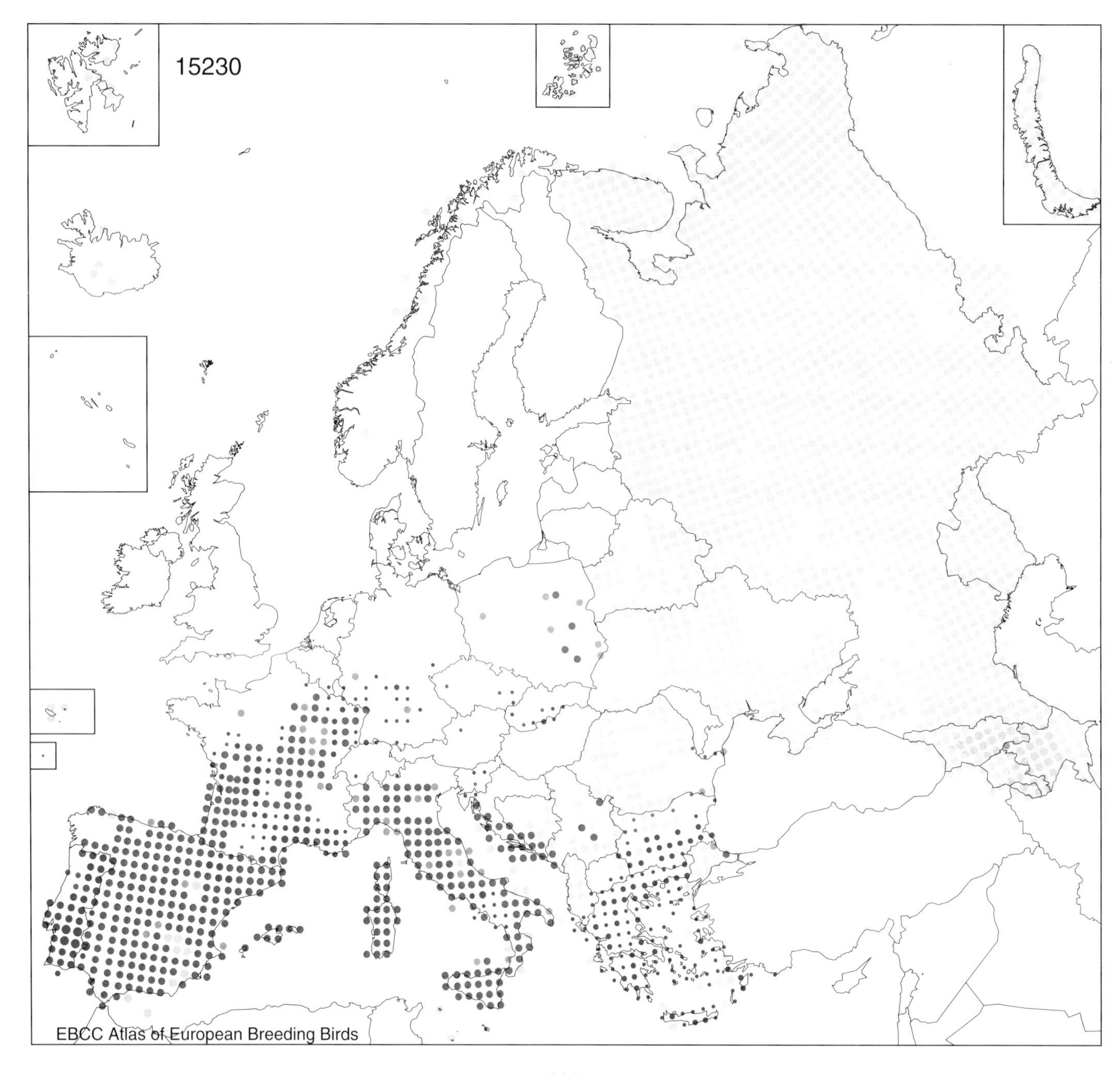

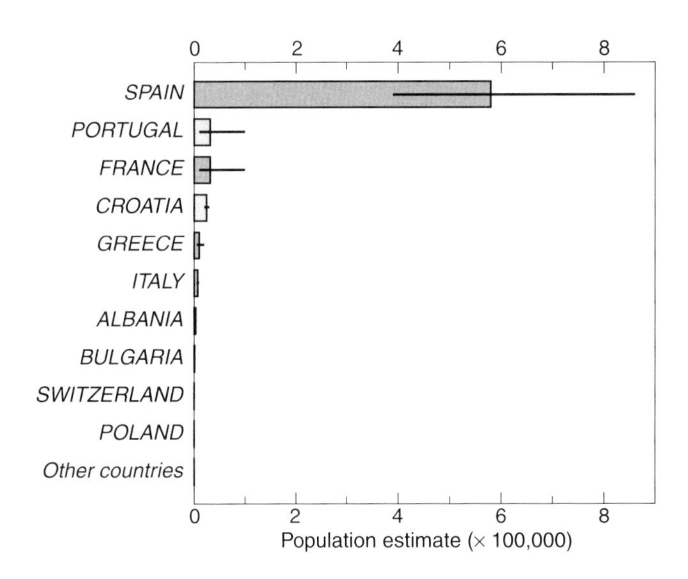

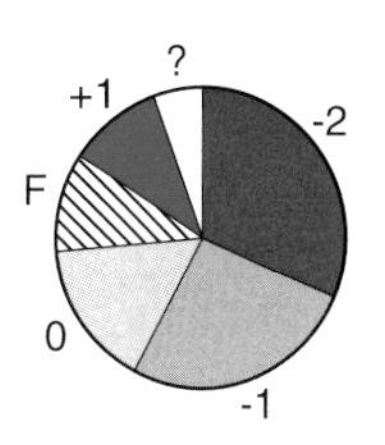

% in top 10 countries: 100.0
Total number of populated European countries: 19
Total European population 496,436–985,453 (688,163)
Turkish population 5000–50,000 (15,811)

The Woodchat Shrike breeds mostly in the western Palearctic from Portugal to the Caucasus and from Poland to North Africa; it also breeds in the Levant and from Turkey to Iran. The species inhabits the mediterranean and (in the W) the temperate zones within the July 19°C isotherm; to the SE its distribution reaches the steppe-desert margin. In the *Atlas*' coverage area all four subspecies occur: the nominate *L.s. senator* in Europe S to the Pyrenees, in mainland Italy, Greece and on Sicily; *rutilans* in Iberia; *badius* on the Balearic Islands, Corsica, Sardinia and Capri; and *niloticus* in the Caucasus.

In Europe the Woodchat Shrike occurs in maquis scrub on dry hillsides, in open ground or heathland scattered with shrubs or trees, and in olive *Olea* groves, orchards, gardens, forest edges and clearings, hedges, riversides and cultivation interspersed with trees. The species normally breeds below 1000m asl, a major exception being the mountains of S France and S Spain. Three habitat elements are necessary: shrublike or arboreal cover, open ground offering a rich supply of invertebrates (especially large insects) and perches with a commanding view of the area. Generally, the species seems to share habitat with the Red-backed Shrike *L. collurio* without competition (*BWP*). The Woodchat Shrike nests in trees or tall shrubs, frequently 3m or more above the ground.

The majority of the European population inhabits the Mediterranean region. The Iberian Peninsula may hold over 600 000bp, representing over 85% of the total European population. In Spain, the highest densities are reached in open forests of holm *Quercus rotundifolia* and Pyrenean *Q. pyrenaica* oak (1.5–3.0 birds/10ha; Hernández 1994). In NW Spain the density reduces from 15 bp/km^2 in Pyrenean oak to 0.8 bp/km^2 in cultivation scattered with shrubs and trees (Hernández 1994). The species becomes more abundant in Portugal towards the S (Rufino 1989). The French population estimate of 10 000–100 000bp dates from the mid-1970s, but local evidence supports the suggested decrease of 20–50%, coincident with a southeastwards range contraction (Bersuder 1994).

During the 20th century and particularly since the mid-1960s marked contractions have occurred in the N and W of its breeding range, superimposed upon marked annual fluctuations (Lefranc 1980). In The Netherlands, Belgium, Luxembourg and Austria, it is extinct or nearly so, having bred only sporadically from 1960 to 1990. In other peripheral populations, such as Poland, Germany, the Czech Republic, Slovakia, Switzerland and Ukraine, numbers (often also range) have decreased by more than 50% since 1970. Typical examples are the area NW of Lake Constance, where the species disappeared as a breeding bird between 1948 and 1977 (Sonnabend & Poltz 1978), and Switzerland, where numbers decreased from >100bp in 1977–79 to <50bp in 1989 (Zbinden & Biber 1989). Smaller declines were reported from Spain, France, Italy and Greece, indicating that even in its strongholds the species is retreating. Only in Bulgaria and Romania has some northward range expansion occurred since 1950, but this apparently contrary trend partly may reflect improved coverage.

Long-term climatic changes bringing wetter springs probably have caused the northern breeding range limit to contract southwards. The disappearance of low-intensity agriculture whose farmland mosaics of shrub and tree growth were ideal for the Woodchat Shrike, and the rise of modern intensive agricultural techniques have also contributed to the population decrease through habitat loss; in Switzerland traditional orchards largely have been replaced either by intensive agriculture or buildings (Zbinden & Biber 1989).

The Woodchat Shrike winters in Africa S of the Sahara but N of the Equator, mainly in open bush country, dry acacia savanna, and cultivated patches where vegetation provides perches. Many birds effect a loop migration, returning by a more easterly route. The effects of Sahel droughts on this species are unclear.

Angel Hernández (E)

This species account is sponsored by Dietrich Pfeilsticker, Moers, D.

Lanius nubicus

Masked Shrike

CZ Ťuhýk černohřbetý
D Maskenwürger
E Alcaudón Enmascarado
F Pie-grièche masquée
FIN Valko-otsalepinkäinen
G Παρδαλοκεφαλάς
H Álarcos gébics
I Averla mascherata
NL Maskerklauwier
P Picanço-núbio
PL Dzierzba białoczelna
R Маскированный сорокопут
S Masktörnskata

SPEC Cat 2, Threat status V (P)

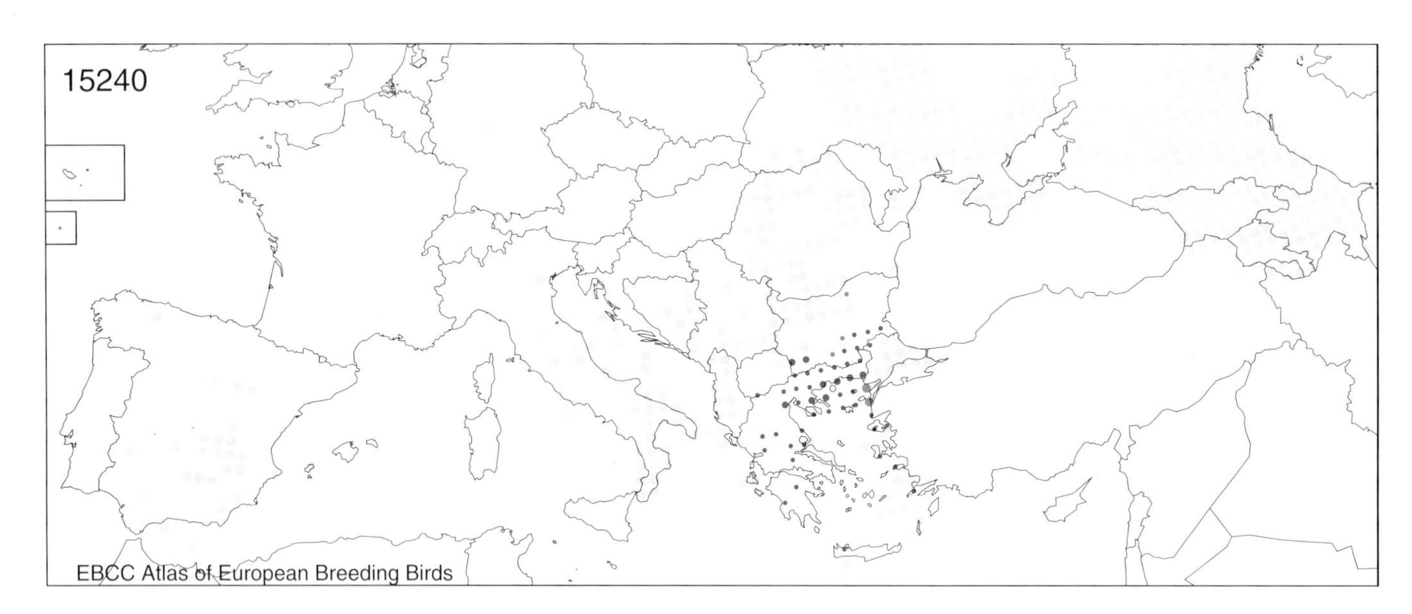

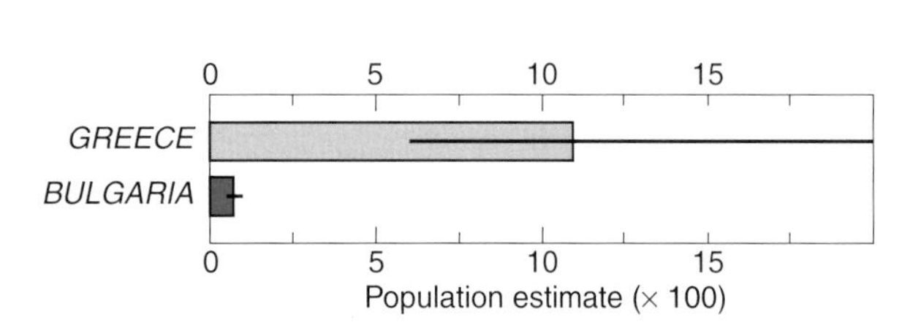

+1 -1

% in top 10 countries: 100.0
Total number of populated European countries: 2
Total European population 670–2071 (1166)
Turkish population 5000–50,000 (15,811)

The medium-sized Masked Shrike breeds in the mediterranean warm temperate zone. Its world distribution is restricted to the Balkan countries, S and W Turkey, Cyprus and parts of W Iran and N Iraq. Like most shrikes it breeds in open park-like terrain, but unlike them has a strong preference for more arboreal habitats, often occupying areas with high tree cover, particularly light forest with thorny undergrowth, often inhabiting olive groves, orchards and poplar *Populus* plantations. Usually found near wood margins, it prefers deciduous trees for nesting, although it also uses coniferous and mixed woods.

Beyond the *Atlas*' coverage, Asian Turkey, possibly holding up to 50 000bp, has the majority of the world population. The total European population of 650–2100bp occurs mostly in Greek and Turkish Thrace, Bulgaria (and possibly S Macedonia) holding the remainder. Locally it may be fairly common, for instance 6bp on 1km^2 in Thrace and 5bp on 4km^2 on the island of Lesbos (Lefranc 1993). The Bulgarian population is somewhat increasing in number and range for reasons which are unclear. Despite local increases, the Greek population is declining in number and in range and is defined as *RARE* in the *Red Data book of Greece* (Choremi *et al* 1993). Likely causes of the declining trends include the degradation of favoured diverse habitats through drainage, burning, mature woodland clearance, afforestation and pesticide use (Hallmann 1994b). Its occupation of plantations which have replaced natural woodlands is a recent adaptation and may be of long-term conservation benefit.

Like many Mediterranean passage migrants, it suffers from indiscriminate shooting in Turkey, the Middle East and Africa. Locally in Greece, it is a bird of ill-omen and is subject to persecution (Hallmann 1994b).

The Masked Shrike is migratory, leaving from mid-August onwards to winter in subtropical Africa and Arabia S to 10°N. There are no subspecies.

Simon Gillings (GB) Ben Hallmann (G)

Perisoreus infaustus

Siberian Jay

CZ	Sojka zlověstná	I	Ghiandaia siberiana
D	Unglückshäher	NL	Taigagaai
E	Arrendajo Funesto	P	Gaio da Sibéria
F	Mésangeai imitateur	PL	Sójka złowroga
FIN	Kuukkeli	R	Кукша
G	Ταϊγκόκισσα	S	Lavskrika
H	Északi szajkó		

SPEC Cat 3, Threat status D (P)

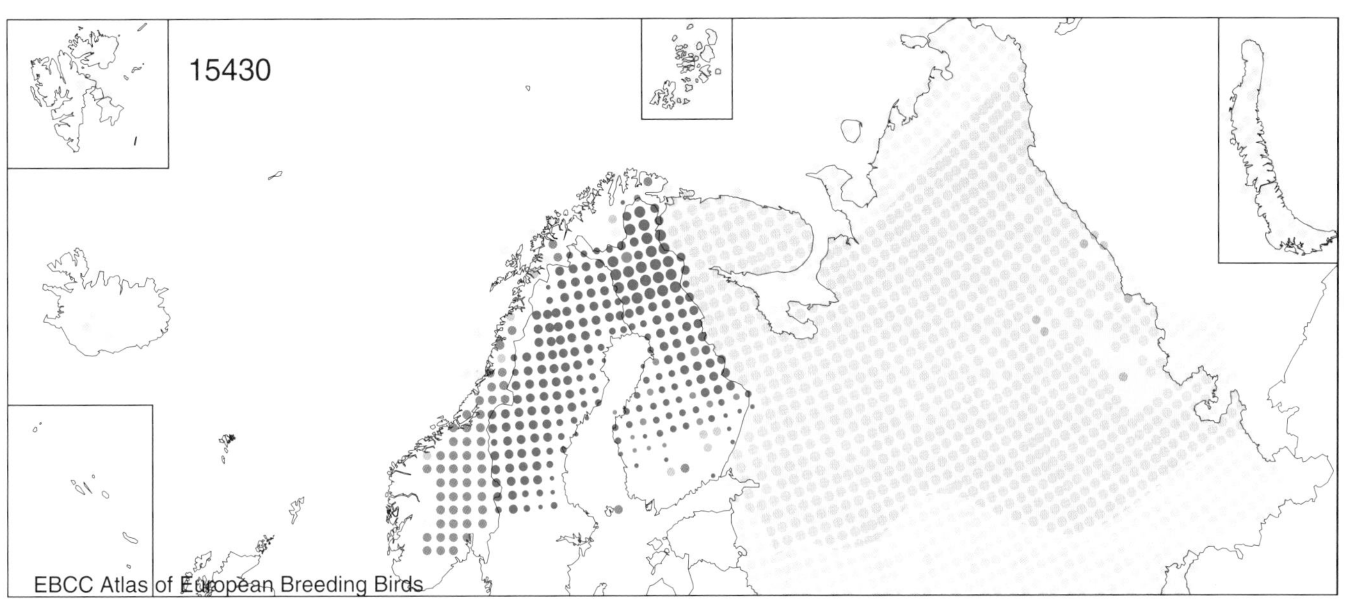

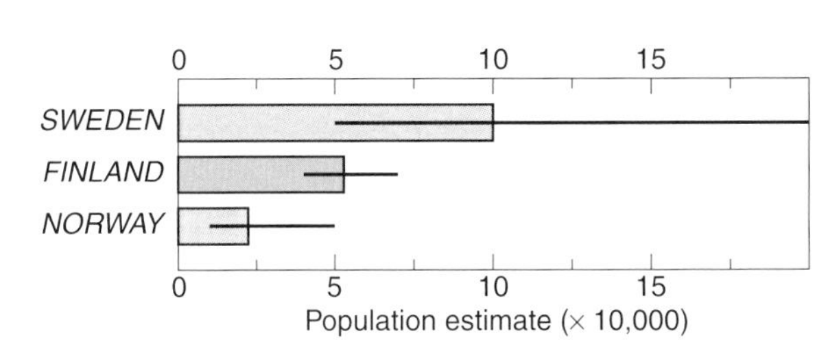

% in top 10 countries: 100.0
Total number of populated European countries: 3
Total European population 122,176–280,422 (175,276)
Russian population 10,000–100,000 (31,623)

The Siberian Jay is a highly sedentary inhabitant of the Eurasian taiga, its continuous range being closely restricted to the boreal coniferous forest mainly between 50° and 70°N from Norway in the W to the Pacific and upper Omolon River (*c*163°E) in the E. In Europe the species occurs mostly inland in Norway, in N and C Sweden and Finland, and in N Russia. Three subspecies occur in the *Atlas*' coverage area, the nominate *P.i. infaustus* in Fennoscandia and the Kola Peninsula, grading into *ostjakorum* eastwards and *ruthenus* southwards and eastwards of Lake Onezhskoye. Up to 13 subspecies exist elsewhere.

The species prefers mature closed-canopy coniferous forest (Rogacheva 1992), concentrating in large uninhabited areas which have a good proportion of old forest. Increased human exploitation of virgin forests through felling, road-building, settlements and agriculture has diminished severely the area of suitable habitat. To some extent, the Siberian Jay has been able to adapt to changing forestry practices and it therefore remains in areas with soundly managed forests.

However, the scale and speed of land-use changes has both reduced the species' distribution area and decreased dramatically its population density. Furthermore, forest fragmentation has been suggested as another reason for the decline (Helle & Järvinen 1986). Repeated censuses in N Finland reveal that its population density in the 1970s was only 30% of the 1940s figure (Väisänen 1983). The *Atlas* data suggest a further decline in the 1980s.

Väisänen (1989) calculates the population density in prime N Finnish habitat to be *c*1 bp/km². In virgin forest in Russia and Sweden the value is higher (up to 2 bp/km² in parts of N Sweden). However, even in its southern range, surprisingly high densities have been reported in places in Finland and Sweden (B-G. Lillandt, in prep, Ekholm 1989). In the southern taiga of C Siberia, densities of 12–16 birds/km² occurred in fir–birch *Abies–Betula* and larch *Larix*–deciduous forests (Rogacheva 1992).

The Siberian Jay is believed to be sedentary in Europe, although in C Siberia, northern taiga populations disperse S in winter to the mid-taiga (Rogacheva 1992).

Pekka Helle (FIN) Bo-Göran Lillandt (S)

Garrulus glandarius **Jay**

CZ	Sojka obecná	I	Ghiandaia
D	Eichelhäher	NL	Vlaamse Gaai
E	Arrendajo	P	Gaio-comum
F	Geai des chênes	PL	Sójka
FIN	Närhi	R	Сойка
G	Κίσσα	S	Nötskrika
H	Szajkó		

Non-SPEC, Threat status S (P)

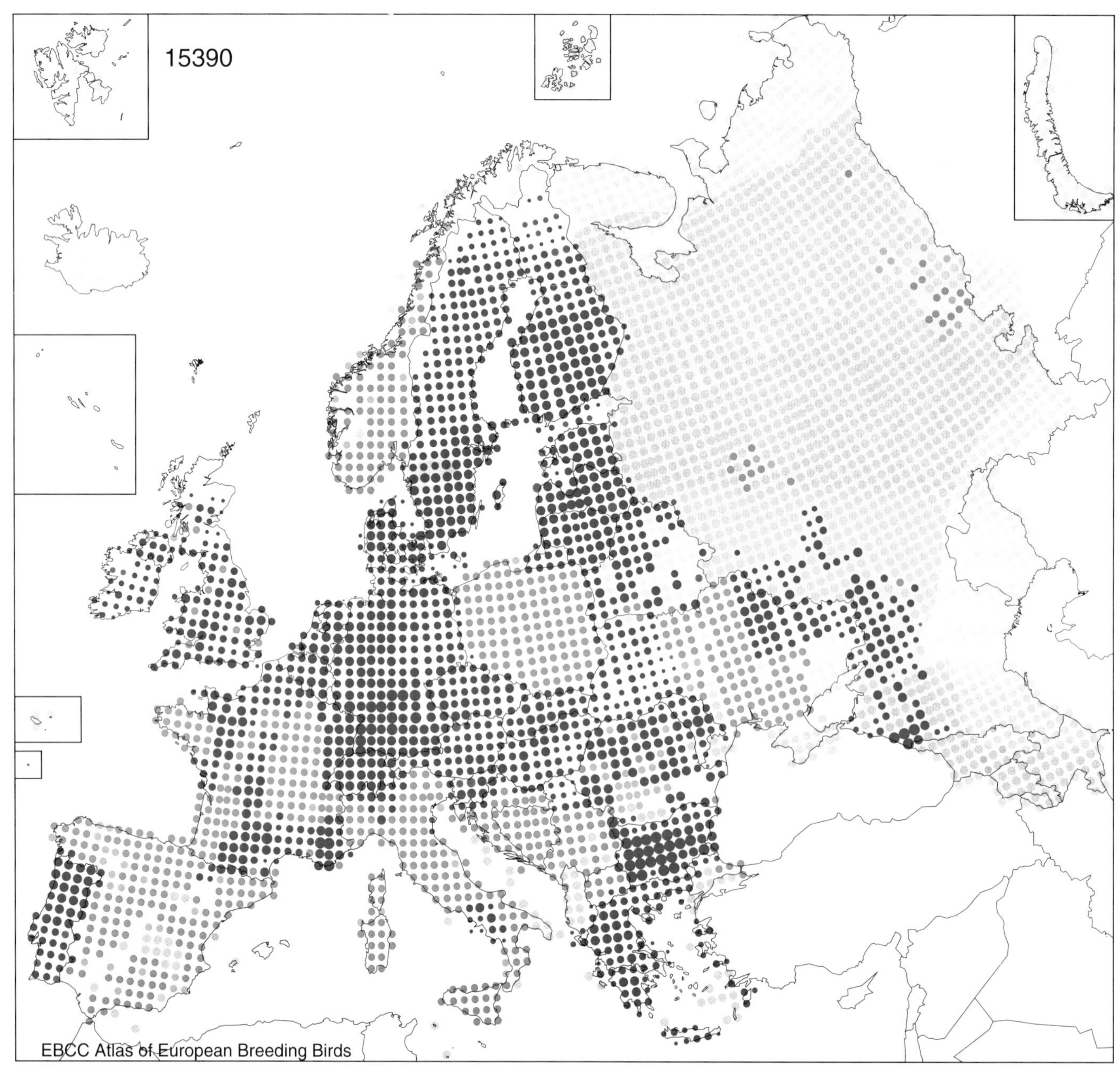

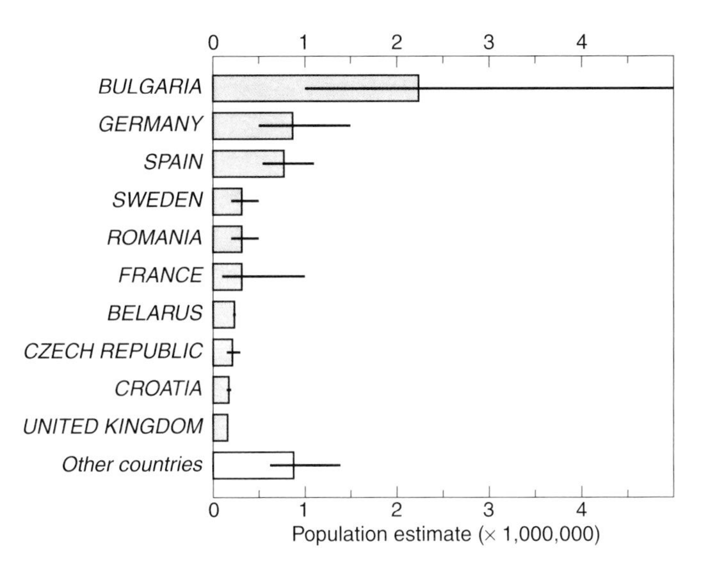

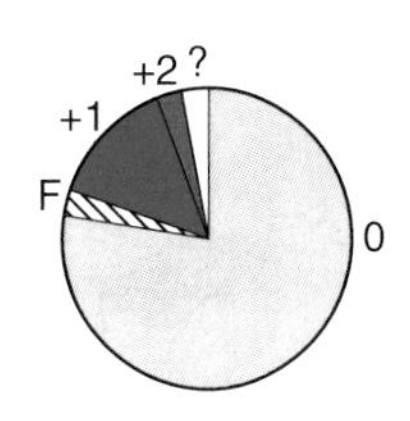

% in top 10 countries: 86.5
Total number of populated European countries: 36
Total European population 5,133,654–9,429,388 (6,475,122)
Russian population 1,000,000–10,000,000 (3,162,278)
Turkish population 100,000–1,000,000 (316,228)

The Jay, a medium-sized corvid, is ubiquitous throughout the Palearctic and much of the Oriental region. Its breeding range extends from Ireland and Portugal in the W to Japan in the E, and in a separate band from the S Himalayas to China. It is also found in NW Africa from the western Atlas range to Tunisia. It is absent from Iceland, N Scotland, the Balearics, above 68°N in Scandinavia and Russia, and from C Asia.

The Jay prefers mixed and broad-leaved woodland, especially those containing oak trees *Quercus* spp, acorns being its preferred food in winter. However, in Fennoscandia and W and C Europe, it commonly breeds in all types of coniferous forests, especially where spruce *Picea* or fir *Abies* occur in thickets (probably an adaptation to Goshawk *Accipiter gentilis* and Sparrowhawk *A. nisus* predation). It is catholic in its habitat choice, as seen from its colonization of parks and gardens from the 1930s onwards in W and C Europe, and more recently in E Europe; Riga, Latvia in the 1960s (Janaus 1983), and Ukraine in the 1970s. It now also breeds in Russian city parks. As a generalist feeder, it can adapt to many different habitats. However, its preference for acorns may lead to short-scale displacements after the breeding season, from coniferous to mixed or deciduous forests.

The European population is estimated at 5M–23Mbp, the wide range being an indication of the lack of reliable census data over large areas. Breeding numbers in Europe are considered more or less stable, only Belgium, Hungary, Lithuania, Estonia and Moldova experiencing slight increases during 1970–90. In Britain numbers have increased considerably in the 20th century, probably because widespread destruction of potential predators of gamebirds and their eggs no longer occurs. The Jay had suffered local extinctions before 1914, but began to recover quickly especially during and after the World Wars. Since 1975 it has increased in Great Britain from 100 000bp to 160 000bp. Contrastingly, a striking range contraction occurred in Ireland between 1968–72 and 1988–91 (Fuller 1994).

The Jay breeds up to the subalpine zone where there are suitable nesting trees: up to 1400–1500m asl in the Polish Carpathians and the Slovakian High Tatra and up to 2000m in the Swiss Alps. Habitat quality determines breeding densities, but generally nesting density is highest near woodland edges, in clearings with successive growth and in copses. Home range area is 25–40ha in S Sweden (Andrén 1990). Breeding densities in C Europe were 0.3–5.5 bp/10ha in SE Poland (Walasz & Mielczarek 1992), and in Hungary, 3–6 bp/10ha in continuous woodland and 5 bp/10ha in woodland whose mosaic of clearings had successive growth (Haraszthy 1984). Optimal mixed forest habitat at Cassonay, Switzerland, produced 12 bp/10ha (Schifferli *et al* 1980). N Europe usually has 1–5 bp/km^2 (Koskimies 1989a).

The Jay is largely sedentary but some subspecies have migratory populations, especially those breeding in northern coniferous forests. Such autumn migration is mainly to the SW, and may even resemble irruptions in some years. In NW Russia, large numbers occur in such years, 15 000–35 000 being counted at a single census point near St Petersburg (Mal'chevski & Pukinski 1983). From 19 September to 17 October 1964, 35 000 birds overflew Gdańsk (Tomiałojć 1990).

In the Palearctic region alone 28 subspecies, some with very differing plumages, have been recognized, nine occurring in Europe: the nominate *G.g. glandarius* inhabits Scandinavia, C Europe, France, N Italy, N Hungary, N Romania, N Bulgaria, Slovenia, Croatia and C and SE of Russia; *rufitergum* inhabits The Netherlands, Belgium and Great Britain; *hibernicus* Ireland; *fasciatus* Spain; *albipectus* Italy, Albania, Serbia and Macedonia; *cretorum* Greece and Crete; *krynicki* S Bulgaria and S Romania; *iphigenia* Crimea, and *severtzovii* E of a line from Ukraine to Finland.

Vladimír Bejček (CZ) Igor Gorban (UKR)

Pica pica **Magpie**

CZ	Straka obecná	**I**	Gazza
D	Elster	**NL**	Ekster
E	Urraca	**P**	Pega-rabuda
F	Pie bavarde	**PL**	Sroka
FIN	Harakka	**R**	Сорока
G	Καρακάξα	**S**	Skata
H	Szarka		

Non-SPEC, Threat status S

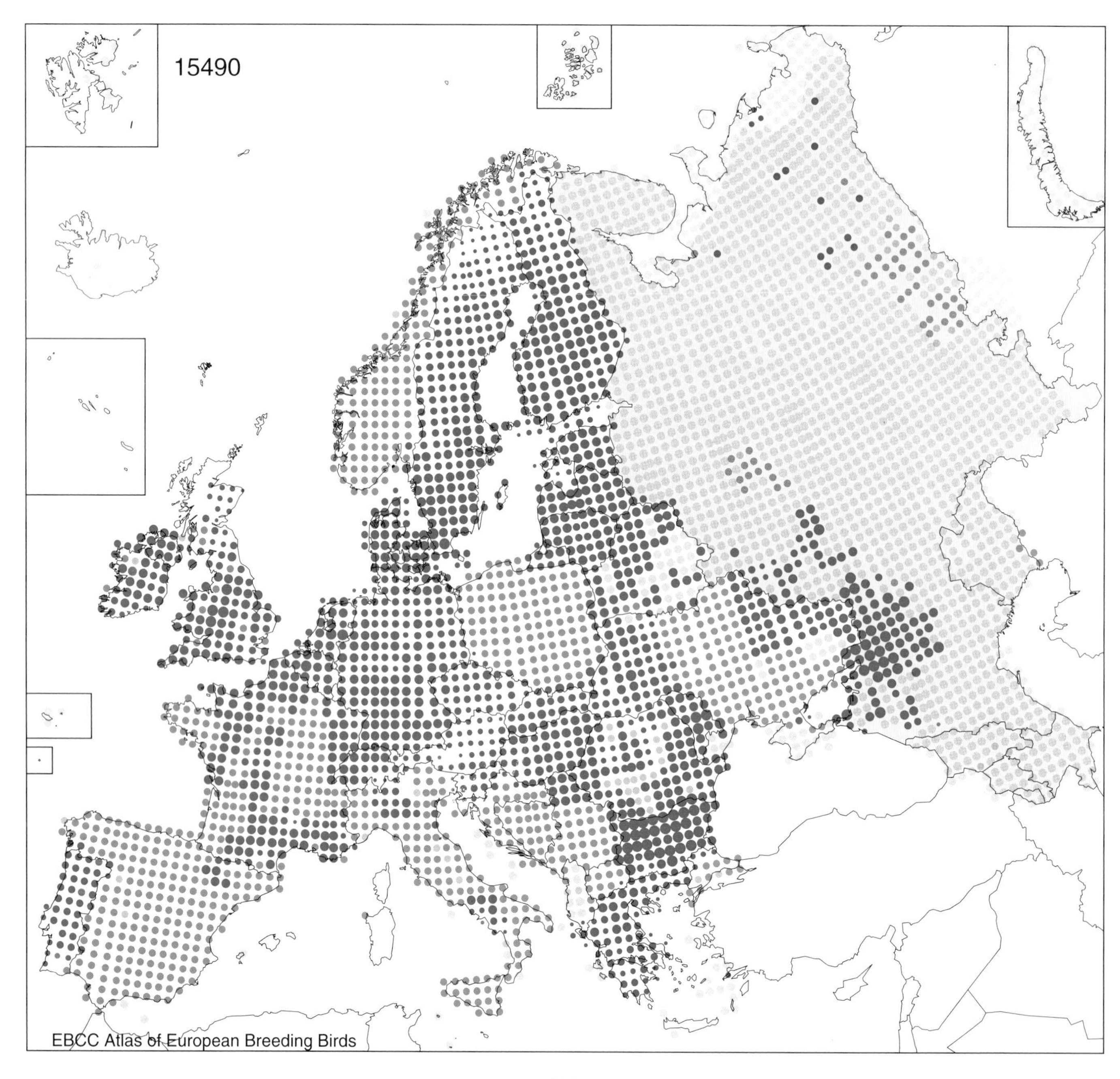

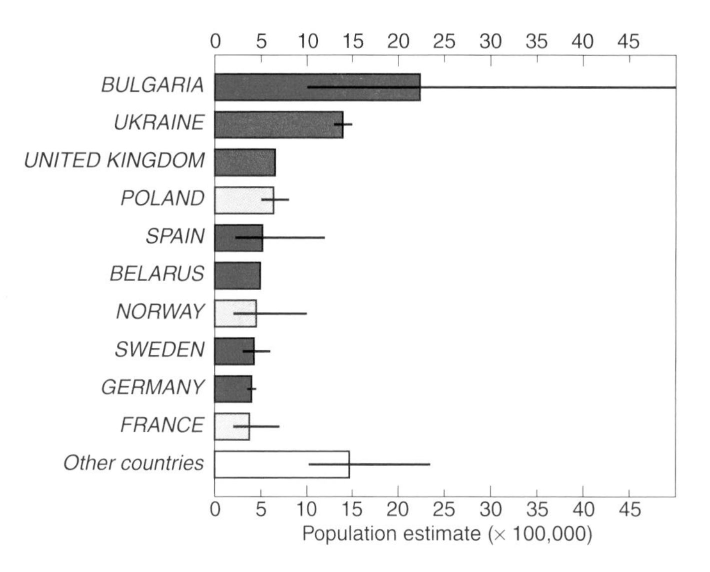

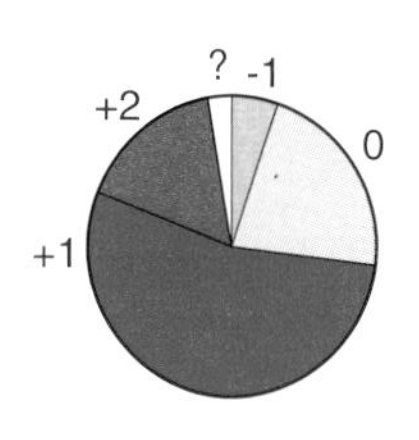

% in top 10 countries: 83.7
Total number of populated European countries: 37
Total European population 7,696,302–11,984,013 (9,028,781)
Russian population 1,000,000–10,000,000 (3,162,278)
Turkish population 1,000,000–10,000,000 (3,162,278)

The Magpie is confined to the Northern Hemisphere between 15° and 70°N. Its range is continuous throughout Europe and Asia. In the W of North America it occurs from NW Alaska to N Arizona, New Mexico and W Texas. Thirteen subspecies have been distinguished (Goodwin 1976), including isolated populations in Anadyr and Kamchatka, in NW Africa (Morocco and Algeria) and in Saudi Arabia. Europe has five subspecies, the nominate *P.p. pica* from Ireland and N France W to N Poland and most of Norway and Sweden, *fennorum* in NW Russia and the rest of Fennoscandia, *melanotos* in Iberia, *galliae* from E France (including Italy and Greece) to W-C and SW European Russia, and *hemileucoptera* and *bactriana* in E-C and SE Russia respectively.

The Magpie breeds from sea level up to 900m asl, or to 2500m provided that nesting trees and human activities such as tourism occur up to this altitude. It is evenly distributed in urban, rural and natural landscapes where tall hedges, bushes, scrub or clumps of trees are scattered in open ground comprising low vegetation or bare soil. It frequents parks, gardens, most farmland, heaths, freshwater wetland, dunes, woodland and forest fringes. Where persecution is low, it prefers to nest near towns, villages and farms.

Breeding pairs are sedentary throughout the season in their territories which are regularly spaced (Birkhead 1991), although aggregated nesting has been reported from Spain (Redondo & Castro 1992). From 1978 to 1993 urban breeding densities in Europe varied from 1.1 to 33.3 bp/km^2 and rural densities from 0.04 to 42 bp/km^2. Non-breeders tend to roam in small flocks (10–25 birds) over a radius of *c*1–10km. In winter the Magpie may wander in search of food, but otherwise it does not migrate. Juveniles establish territories generally within 10km of where they hatched.

Since 1965, Magpie densities have increased in most European countries. Census data show the highest numbers occurring in Bulgaria, Belarus, Ukraine, Poland, Great Britain and Spain. Urban densities have increased spectacularly in Britain & Ireland, Germany, Denmark, Poland, Hungary and Russia (L. Jerzak, in prep) and since 1980 a Magpie population has developed in the Russian tundra in association with human colonization. In this treeless landscape it nests on the ground or on buildings.

Locally, Magpie densities are lower where medium-sized raptors or Carrion Crow *Corvus corone* are present. The Magpie avoids raptor nests to reduce predation risks and the Carrion Crow disrupts the Magpie's breeding activities or drives it from its territory (Baeyens 1981).

Adaptable and omnivorous, the Magpie has few limits to its distribution. In most countries human actions, such as tree planting in urban environments, have influenced breeding possibilities significantly (Jerzak 1988, 1992). The Magpie can exploit the food resources in any type of habitat possessing low vegetation and bare soil. Expansion and density increase may also be related to reduced persecution. Association with humans may guarantee a supply of food and reduce the threat from raptors, although the Magpie has become the main prey of the Goshawk *Accipiter gentilis* where the latter has begun to colonize cities (Würfels 1994).

The Magpie is relatively easy to census and map because of the longevity of its conspicuous domed nest, but each breeding pair usually builds more than one, and abandoned nests may survive for 6–12 years.

The Magpie generally is disliked throughout Europe because it plunders eggs of domestic, game- and songbirds in overt and noisy fashion, but it has never been proven to have a directly detrimental effect on the overall breeding success of other bird species. However, the persistence of hostility towards the Magpie may be due to its depiction in the songs and tales of folklore as a harbinger of death.

Gert Baeyens (B) Leszek Jerzak (PL)

This species account is sponsored by Berliner Ornithologische Arbeitsgemeinschaft, D.

Cyanopica cyanus

Azure-winged Magpie

CZ	Straka modrá	I	Gazza azzurra
D	Blauelster	NL	Blauwe Ekster
E	Rabilargo	P	Pega-azul
F	Pie bleue	PL	Sroka błękitna
FIN	Siniharakka	R	Голубая сорока
G	Γαλαζοκαρακάξα	S	Blåskata
H	Kékszarka		

Non-SPEC, Threat status S

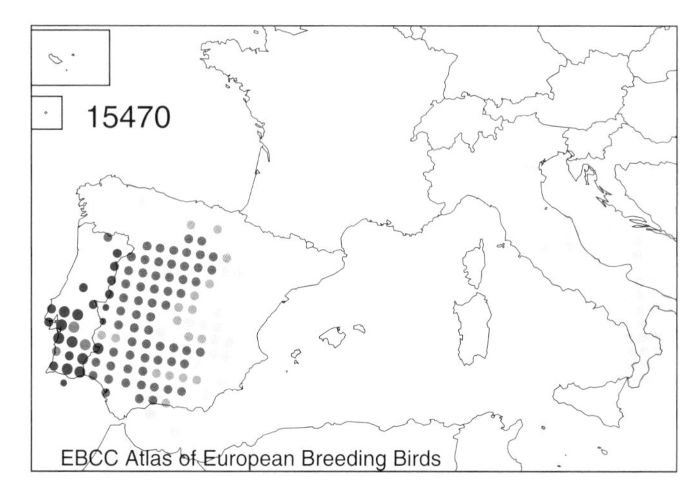

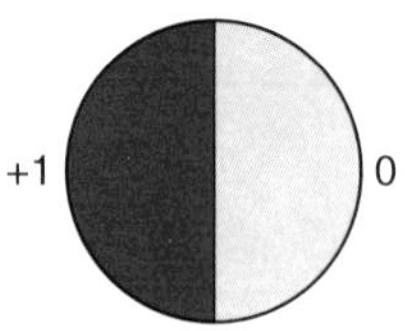

% in top 10 countries: 100.0
Total number of populated European countries: 2
Total European population 257,683–350,557 (281,423)

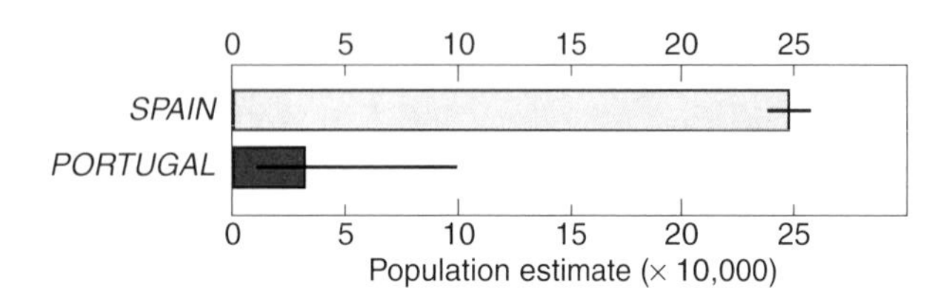

The world distribution of the Azure-winged Magpie, a graceful blue, buff and black corvid, is split into two well-separated areas of Eurasia: SW Europe and eastern Asia. Within its European range only the subspecies *C.c. cooki* occurs. In Asia nine other subspecies are described, showing a N–S trend both in size and colour.

This disjunct distribution could have resulted either through isolation during glaciations from an originally continuous distribution between the Mediterranean basin and eastern Asia (Goodwin 1975), or from releases of birds brought from Asia by Portuguese navigators during the 16th century (Santos 1968). Sacarrão (1974), noting that the Zoological Society obtained the *C.c. cooki* type specimen in 1830, suggests that it is unprecedented and unlikely that subspeciation would occur in only 200 years.

In its European range the species is predominantly an open woodland dweller and occurs in evergreen oak stands, of both cork oak *Quercus suber* and holm oak *Q. rotundifolia*, as well as in stone pine *Pinus pinea* woods, and in mixed pine–oak stands which sometimes comprise a mosaic with pasture and orchards. At the edge of its distribution the Azure-winged Magpie also breeds in deciduous open woods of Pyrenean oak *Q. pyrenaica* and in mediterranean almond *Prunus dulcis* and olive *Olea europaea* groves. Habitat availability may be the major factor limiting its distribution, as may competition with Magpie *Pica pica* (Sacarrão 1974). Indeed, only occasionally do the two species occur together. Their largely exclusive ranges are not clearly evident from the 50km resolution of the map.

The Azure-winged Magpie's distribution and numbers seem to have remained stable since at least 1975, except for a small expansion to the NW in Portugal. Non-breeders are present sporadically in NE Spain (Ferrer 1987). Its preferred habitat of open evergreen oak stands ('montados' in Portugal and 'dehesas' in Spain) has not only decreased since 1965, but has also suffered variable and inappropriate management which has tended to remove the understorey completely. However, data are lacking about the effects of these changes on the species' distribution and numbers.

Being a social species which breeds in small groups (5–15 individuals) and forms loose colonies, its abundance is difficult to assess. It is locally abundant only in Extremadura and W Andalucía in Spain, and in S Portugal. Nest density averages *c*2–5 nests/ha, ranging from 1 to 15 (Cruz 1988, Alonso *et al* 1991).

The Azure-winged Magpie is not known to undertake any migration but it shows complex post-breeding dispersal movements.

Juan C Alonso (E) Renato Neves (P) Rui Rufino (P)

This species account is sponsored by

Instituto da Conservação da Natureza, Lisboa, P.

Pyrrhocorax graculus

Alpine Chough

CZ	Kavče žlutozobé	I	Gracchio alpino
D	Alpendohle	NL	Alpenkauw
E	Chova Piquigualda	P	Gralha-de-bico-amarelo
F	Chocard à bec jaune	PL	Wieszczek
FIN	Alppinaakka	R	Альпийская галка
G	Κιτρινοκαλιακούδα	S	Alpkaja
H	Havasi csóka		

Non-SPEC, Threat status S (P)

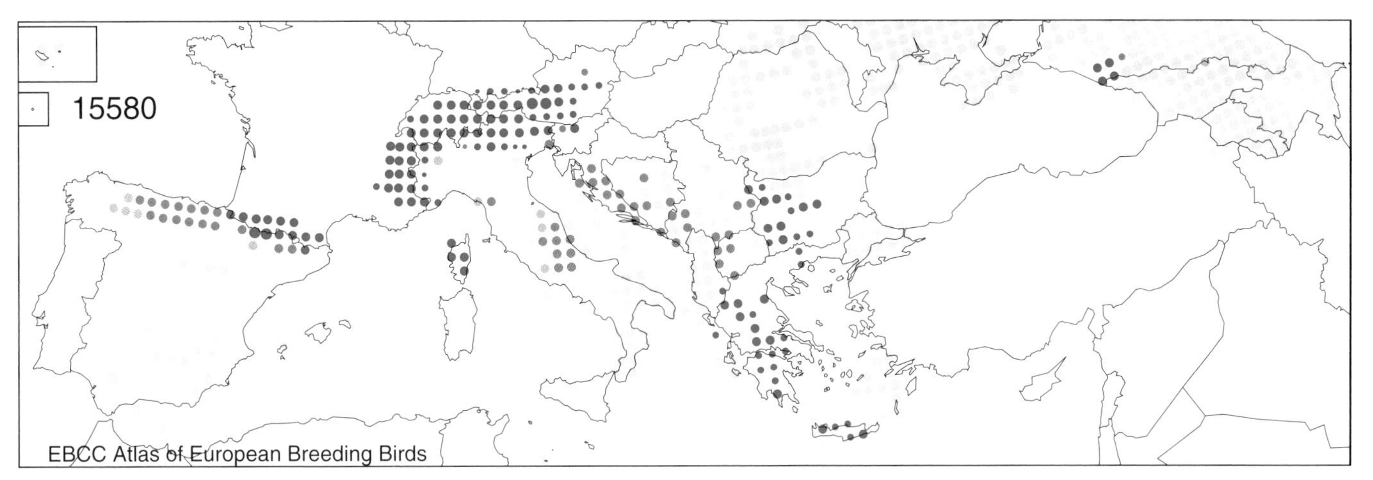

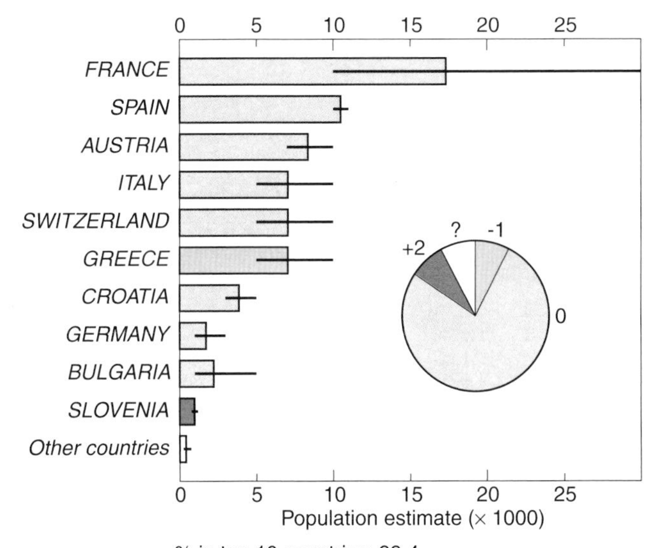

% in top 10 countries: 99.4
Total number of populated European countries: 13
Total European population 58,167–80,764 (66,619)
Turkish population 10,000–100,000 (31,623)

The highly gregarious Alpine Chough occurs throughout the mountain ridges of the warm temperate climate zone of the S Palearctic (Morocco to China). The nominate *P.g. graculus* covers probably Europe, North Africa and N Iran. Two other subspecies occur outside Europe.

The species usually forms stable family groups associating in transient flocks of 3–90 birds during summer. Generally, local flocks are highly resident, regularly each day splitting into smaller parties and family groups to feed in a 7–17km² area around communal roosting sites (Raboud 1988, Rolando & Patterson 1993, Delestrade 1994). It inhabits steep and rugged mountainous terrain, foraging in adjacent subalpine and alpine zone pastures, stony hillsides and grasslands above the treeline. In the Swiss Alps it breeds solitarily at 1600–3400m asl (up to 6250m in the Himalayas), nest-separation distance being 50–4800m (Büchel 1974, Raboud 1988), whereas throughout Mediterranean stony highlands it nests and roosts frequently in low-altitude crevices, caves and grottos at ground level (Dendaletche & Saint-Lebe 1987).

During winter local parties aggregate in large flocks (30–500 birds) on suitable feeding grounds at lower altitudes, arriving in a fixed daily routine, descending 500–1900m, some 5–20km from their roosts. Individual parties now winter throughout the Alps at higher elevations around active ski-resorts and hotels.

In S and C Europe the species occupies the Cantabrians, Pyrenees, Alps, Abruzzi Apennines, Balkan ridges and the Caucasus. Crete and Corsica hold isolated populations. Of the European total of *c*48 000–96 000bp, 24 300–51 900bp inhabit the Alpine stronghold (Alpes Maritime to Slovenia and E Austria). Across Europe, numbers and range mostly are stable, except for Greece's slight decline and Slovenia's >50% increase in both categories (1970–90). Alpine tourism and sport, having improved inadvertently year-round food supply, may have created a long-term increase; thawing conditions and nest-site and food availability have more impact on early-summer nesting success and juvenile mortality than do winter feeding conditions and mortality (Büchel 1974, 1994).

Peter Sackl (A)

Pyrrhocorax pyrrhocorax **Chough**

CZ	Kavče červenozobé	I	Gracchio corallino
D	Alpenkrähe	NL	Alpenkraai
E	Chova Piquirroja	P	Gralha-de-bico-vermelho
F	Crave à bec rouge	PL	Wrończyk
FIN	Alppivaris	R	Клушица
G	Κοκκινοκαλιακούδα	S	Alpkråka
H	Havasi varjú		

SPEC Cat 3, Threat status V

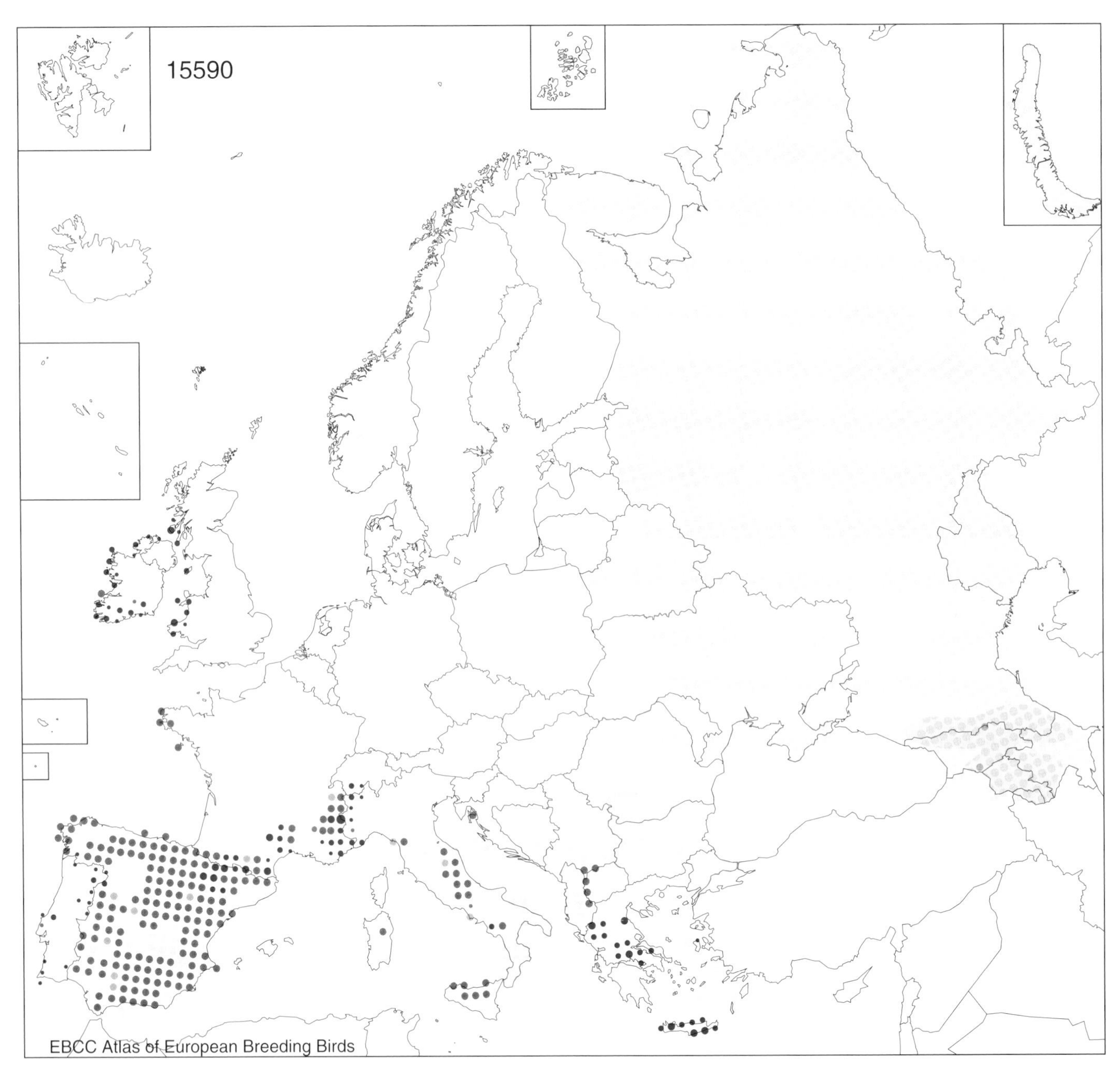

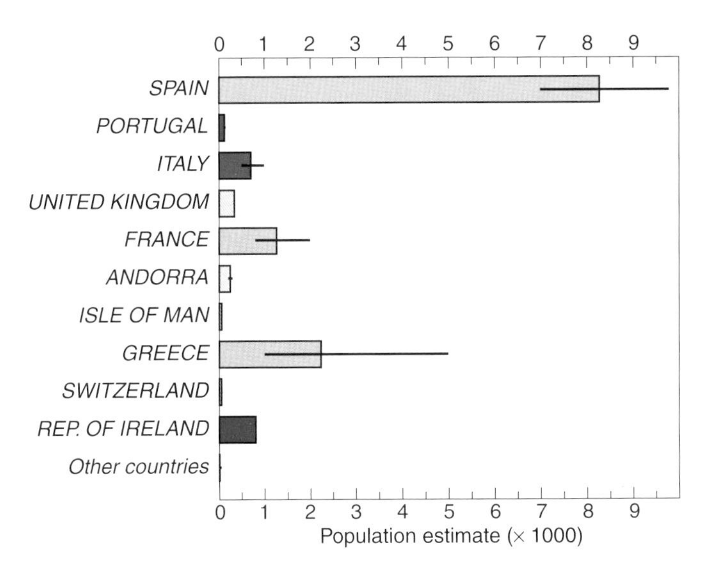

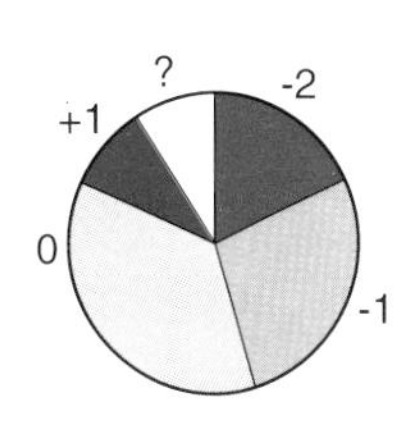

% in top 10 countries: 99.9
Total number of populated European countries: 11
Total European population 12,265–17,370 (14,118)
Turkish population 5000–50,000 (15,811)

Though a comparatively rare corvid, the Chough does have a fairly extensive world distribution, occurring across much of southern Europe and C Asia to 122°E. A few isolated populations also occur in Morocco, the Canary Islands and Ethiopia (Ethiopian populations lie over 2000km from any other). The European distribution is very patchy, scattered populations occurring from Greece along the northern Mediterranean into the Pyrenees and Iberia. Further small groups occur in Switzerland, Brittany and on the W coasts of Scotland, Wales and Ireland. The nominate *P.p. pyrrhocorax* inhabits Britain & Ireland, *docilis* occurs from southern former Yugoslavia through Greece E to the Caucasus to Afghanistan, and *erythrorhamphus* elsewhere in Europe, beyond which there are five other subspecies.

The Chough is highly social, often feeding and roosting in large flocks especially outside the breeding season, and in general is fairly sedentary. It is associated mainly with low-lying, rugged cliffs and pastoral, low-intensity agricultural systems. It breeds on coastal and inland cliffs and in gullies, caves, mine-shafts and on both derelict and inhabited buildings. In its northern range in Britain & Ireland, it is confined to the western seaboards, thus gaining it the descriptions 'sea crow' or 'bird of the Celtic fringe'. However, elsewhere in its range it occurs well inland, and so this northern coastal distribution is probably partly determined by those climatic factors that influence the availability of the soil invertebrates on which the bird relies. The western coasts of Britain & Ireland are characterized by a relatively mild maritime climate and there is a close association between the present distribution of the Chough in Britain & Ireland and climatic factors (Monaghan *et al* 1989).

Information on the status of most populations is scant, only a few areas have been thoroughly censused. Numbers in Turkey are relatively unknown, estimates ranging from 5000 to 50 000bp, but nevertheless this comprises an important population, as does that of Spain, estimated at 7000–9800bp. However, as more information becomes available, it is evident that what were thought to be areas of continuous, relatively widespread distribution in Iberia, are in fact much patchier (*vide* papers in Bignal & Curtis 1989). Numbers elsewhere in Europe are relatively small and only in Greece and Spain are the minimum breeding populations estimated to be over 1000bp. In France, the population in 1990 was estimated at 800–2000bp, showing marked fluctuations but an overall stability since the mid-1960s. Earlier, a strong decline had been noted, especially in Brittany where the species eventually disappeared (Cerail 1994). In Britain & Ireland, very marked declines during the 18th and 19th centuries forced the species' northernmost limit to retreat (Bullock *et al* 1983, Monaghan *et al* 1989). European populations overall are declining to a variable extent in most areas, perhaps with the exception of Ireland, whose population may have increased by 20% since 1982 (Bignal 1993).

Changing agricultural practices, together with persecution, seem to be the main factors involved (Bignal & Curtis 1989). Areas of the kind of low-intensity, traditional farming on which the Chough depends are declining in Europe, often being considered unacceptably underdeveloped and impoverished. Their cultural and ecological richness, and importance in wildlife conservation, has been recognized only recently (see Curtis *et al* 1991). In Scotland, the availability to the only surviving population on the island of Islay of invertebrates associated with dung of out-wintered stock appears to be very important, and thus changes in husbandry practices which come about through misplaced modernization could have serious detrimental effects. Attempts are now being made to conserve these systems, for which the Chough, like birds such as the Corncrake *Crex crex* and the Golden Eagle *Aquila chrysaetos*, is a flagship species.

Patricia Monaghan (GB)

Nucifraga caryocatactes

Nutcracker

CZ	Ořešník kropenatý	**I**	Nocciolaia
D	Tannenhäher	**NL**	Notekraker
E	Cascanueces	**P**	Quebra-nozes
F	Cassenoix moucheté	**PL**	Orzechówka
FIN	Pähkinähakki	**R**	Кедровка
G	Καρυδοσπάστης	**S**	Nötkråka
H	Fenyőszajkó		

Non-SPEC, Threat status S (P)

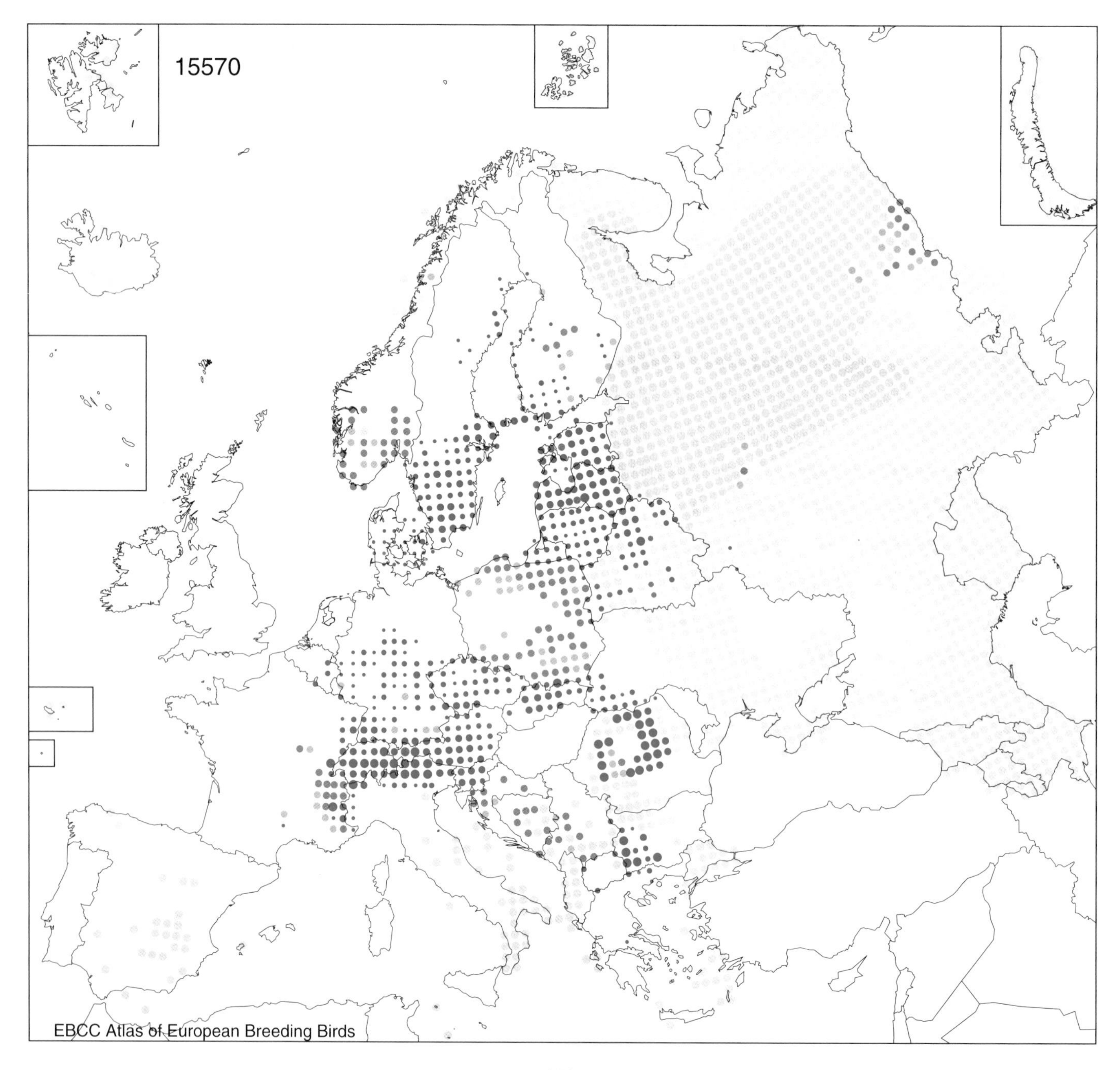

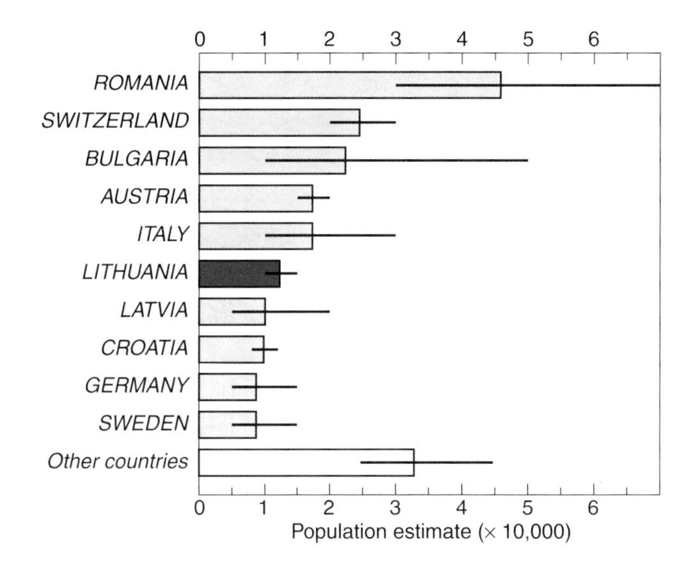

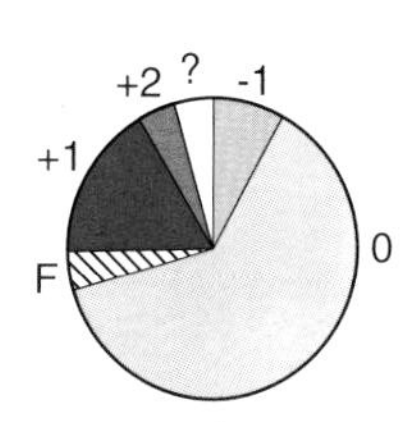

% in top 10 countries: 84.3
Total number of populated European countries: 24
Total European population 185,977–251,403 (209,473)
Russian population 10,000–100,000 (31,623)

The Nutcracker is distributed throughout the boreal and altitudinal boreal zones of the Palearctic. Separate distribution arms reach down from C and E Siberia respectively to E Kazakhstan and the Himalayas (via NE China). The nominate *N.c. caryocatactes* breeds throughout the boreal coniferous forest belt of N Europe from Scandinavia to the Urals, and in the mountains of C and SE Europe. The Siberian taiga E of the Urals to the Pacific coast, including Kamchatka and Sakhalin, contains *macrorhynchos*. Other subspecies exist in C Asia, Japan and Taiwan.

The species' prime nesting habitats comprise boreal and subalpine coniferous forests dominated by spruce *Picea abies* and Swiss stone pine *Pinus cembra*. Woodlands of fir *Abies alba*, Scots *Pinus sylvestris*, black *P. nigra* and Macedonian pine *P. peuce* and mixed coniferous forests are less densely populated. Resident populations throughout Europe depend on regular, on-site availability of Swiss stone pine, Macedonian pine and hazel *Corylus avellana* for seeds to store winter supplies (Mattes 1978).

The distribution of spruce and hazel corresponds almost exactly with that of the continuous distribution of northern populations of *caryocatactes* from Scandinavia to the Urals, where it breeds from sea level up to the alpine treeline. The Nutcracker's core breeding areas in N Europe lie in lowland S Sweden, Lithuania, Latvia and Estonia (25 000–60 000bp). Following strong irruptions since the 1970s, small populations of *macrorhynchos* have become established in Siberian pine *P. sibiricus* plantations in W and S Finland (Lanner & Nikkanen 1990) and so it may be assumed that the natural Siberian pine forests in the Pechora basin and the northern Urals hold high resident densities of *macrorhynchos*.

The C European population's main breeding areas are concentrated particularly in the Alps, the Beskidian range, the Carpathians and Rhodopes, at altitudes from 250m asl in the secondary mountains of S Germany up to the treeline at 1900–2300m asl throughout the Alps. The map shows the species absent from Albania and N Greece, probably due to lack of observers, but its absence from Iberia, Asia Minor and the Caucasus reflects that apparently it never colonized these mountains during postglacial dispersal. However, since the 1930s the Nutcracker has expanded its range, coincident with the modern practice of conifer cultivation, throughout C Europe from the Alps and Bohemian highlands to the furthest limit of the mountain chains in Belgium (mainly E Ardennes; Bulteel 1992) and Germany. The mountain basins of Germany, the Czech Republic and Slovakia were colonized relatively recently. Furthermore, there is now evidence from SE Poland that the C and N European populations are beginning to meet. Only Ukraine has suffered a negative range size trend recently.

Nutcracker population numbers and breeding densities are difficult to estimate, hence reliable data for breeding densities are few. In the Swiss Alps maximum densities of 2.3 bp/10ha were found in Swiss stone pine forests, whereas in forests dominated by spruce, breeding density clearly depends on the hazelnut supply, locally reaching only up to 1.1 bp/10ha (Swanberg 1956, Mattes 1978, Crocq 1990).

Through its habit of storing nuts and seeds for later consumption during winter, the Nutcracker is highly resident in the breeding areas, although some populations may descend more regularly than others into broad-leaved forests outside the breeding season. When large-scale failures occur of seed production amongst the conifers on which *macrorhynchos* is dependent, strong irruptions are triggered. During large invasions, as in 1968, the Siberian Nutcracker regularly reaches C and W Europe as far as France and Britain (Hollyer 1970). In 1995 their numbers in Finland swamped the small resident population of *macrorhynchos*. Following massive irruptions, breeding outside *macrorhynchos*' normal range has occurred, particularly in N Germany, Denmark and France.

Hermann Mattes (D) Peter Sackl (A)

Corvus monedula

Jackdaw

CZ	Kavka obecná	**I**	Taccola
D	Dohle	**NL**	Kauw
E	Grajilla	**P**	Gralha-de-nuca-cinzenta
F	Choucas des tours	**PL**	Kawka
FIN	Naakka	**R**	Галка
G	Κάργια	**S**	Kaja
H	Csóka		

SPEC Cat 4, Threat status S (P)

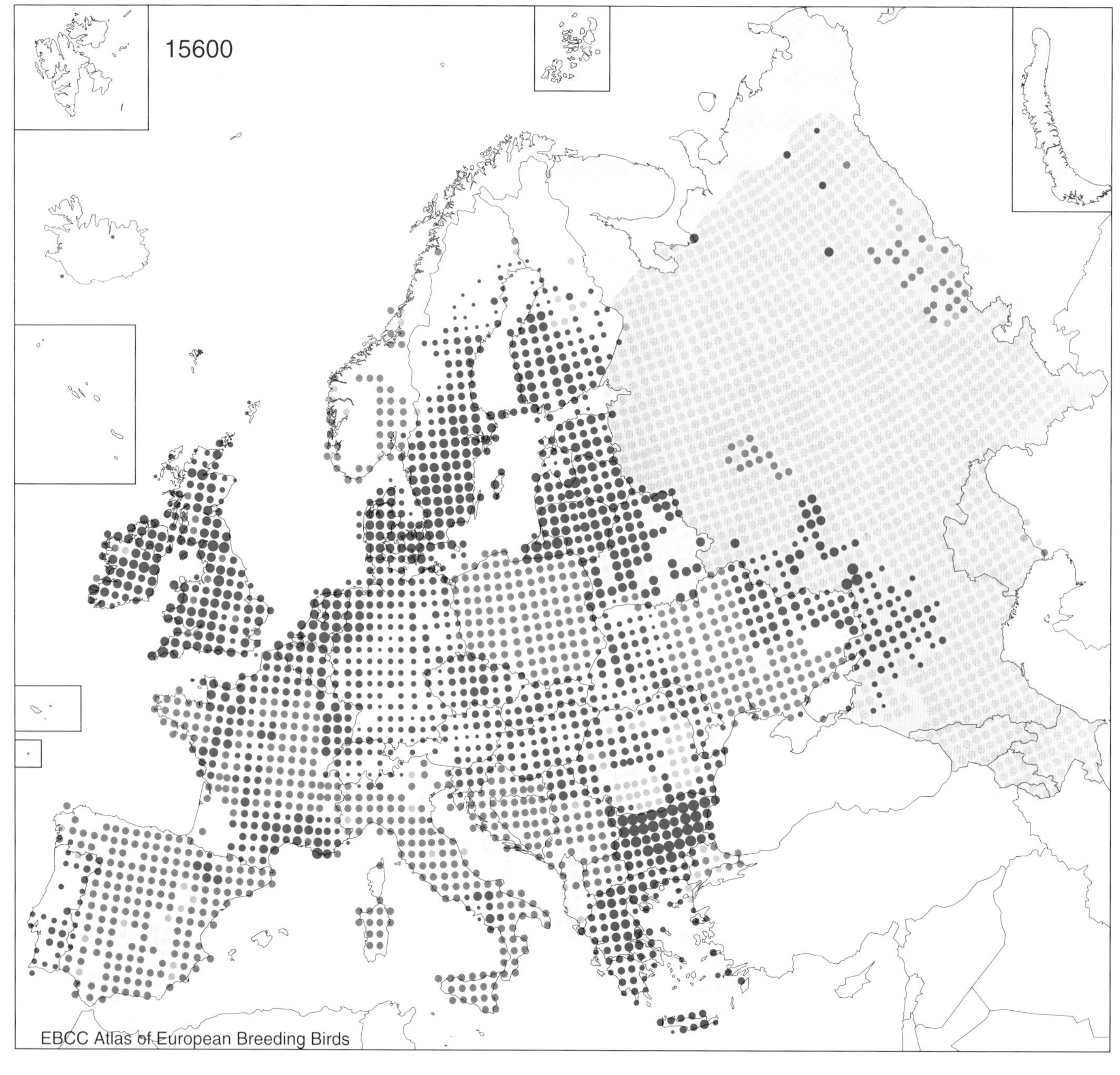

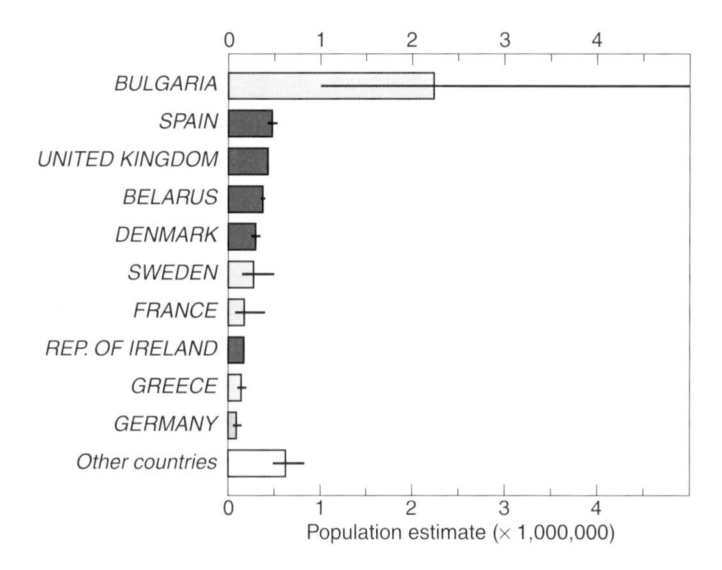

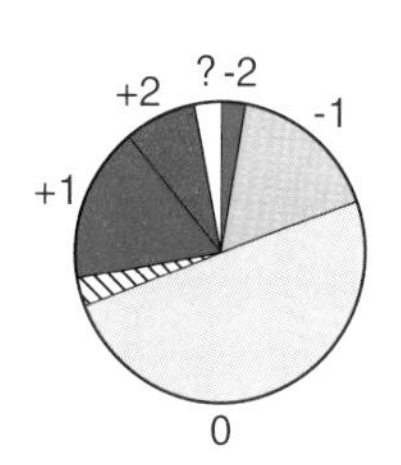

% in top 10 countries: 88.2
Total number of populated European countries: 36
Total European population 4,033,405–8,069,284 (5,283,621)
Russian population 1,000,000–10,000,000 (3,162,278)
Turkish population 1,000,000–10,000,000 (3,162,278)

The Jackdaw, a lively, adaptable and gregarious member of the crow family, breeds throughout Europe and the western Palearctic from subarctic Finland to the Mediterranean, S to Morocco and Algeria and E to the Himalayas and W Siberia. Sporadic natural vagrancy to North America is suspected, although the largest group of 52 (Quebec 1984) is known to have been ship-assisted and subsequently eradicated (K.J. McGowan, pers comm). At least four subspecies are recognized, three of which (including the nominate *C. m. monedula*) occur over sizeable areas of Europe, the fourth being confined to NW Africa.

The size of breeding Jackdaw colonies tends to reflect the availability of nest sites, typically chimney pots, cliffs and holes in trees or old buildings. Nests may number in the hundreds in larger cliff colonies, or be very dispersed in sparsely wooded country. The highest breeding density occurs in localities where many nest sites lie adjacent to mixed agricultural land, especially unimproved, stock-grazed grassland which possesses ample invertebrate fauna. In Great Britain it may average 5 bp/km^2 in areas where rural towns and villages offer a profusion of chimney nest sites (Sitters 1988), but in parks and urban areas in Silesia, SW Poland densities ranged between 0.8 and 41.7 bp/10ha (Dyrcz *et al* 1991).

The Jackdaw's distribution across Europe is fairly even. It is absent only from high mountain plateau, tundra, extensive wetland or afforested areas and a few small islands. Despite lower atlas coverage in parts of France, Spain, Italy, Poland and the former Yugoslavia, the species probably breeds regularly in most 50km squares in these regions. Spain, for example, is one of the top four most important countries for this species. Where semi-quantitative population estimates have been made in suitable habitat, lowest rural breeding densities occurred in N Fennoscandia and most of C and E Europe, and highest in lowland areas of Britain and continental Europe.

Since 1975, the Jackdaw population in many regions of Europe has either remained stable or shown a slight increase, particularly in each of the top ten countries. Its range extension in northern Fennoscandia may be part of a general northward expansion (J.H. Marchant *et al* 1990). In Britain and Slovenia, the population has risen by over 50% and only in the Czech Republic has there been a decline of this magnitude. However, in C Europe (Germany, Switzerland, Austria and Liechtenstein) smaller decreases of *c*25% are reported. In Italy during the 1970s and 1980s the Jackdaw expanded into urban areas (Fraissinet 1989), and the species has become abundant in many E European cities.

Clearly, the Jackdaw is associated most closely with mixed agriculture, yet the large population increase in Britain remains something of a puzzle because it coincides with progressive agricultural intensification over the same period. The availability of nest sites has not improved greatly since 1975. It is therefore probable that an increase in food quality or supply has encouraged population growth. Jackdaw breeding productivity depends heavily on the nestlings receiving a regular and ample supply of invertebrates, amongst other factors (Henderson & Hart 1993), and the post-fledging survival prospects of juveniles may have been improved by the profusion of early-ripening grain crops. Certainly the link between food availability, climate and agricultural practice merits further study.

In Britain adult birds are remarkably sedentary throughout the year but in continental Europe the species undergoes extensive south-westerly movements in autumn, particularly in northern regions. Fennoscandian birds, for example, may retreat in considerable numbers to the Low Countries, France, Britain and Ireland in winter. In general, however, adults show great fidelity to their home range (philopatry) and will return to their original breeding site if left undisturbed.

Maurizio Fraissinet (I) Ian Henderson (GB)
Danila Mastronardi (I)

This species account is sponsored by Ms Ilse Finken, Issum, D.

Corvus frugilegus **Rook**

CZ	Havran polní	**I**	Corvo
D	Saatkrähe	**NL**	Roek
E	Graja	**P**	Gralha-calva
F	Corbeau freux	**PL**	Gawron
FIN	Mustavaris	**R**	Грач
G	Χαβαρόνι	**S**	Råka
H	Vetési varjú		

Non-SPEC, Threat status S

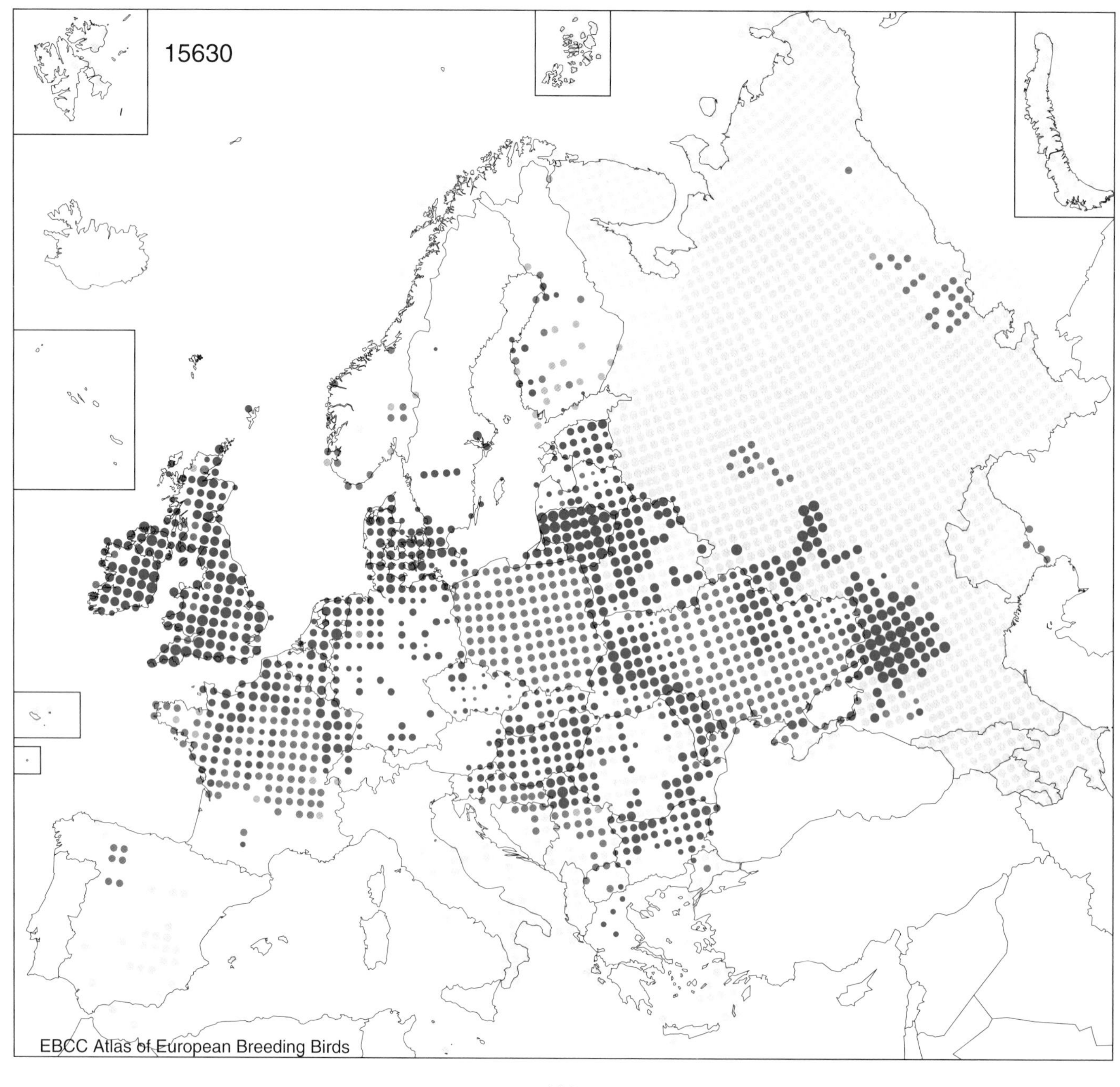

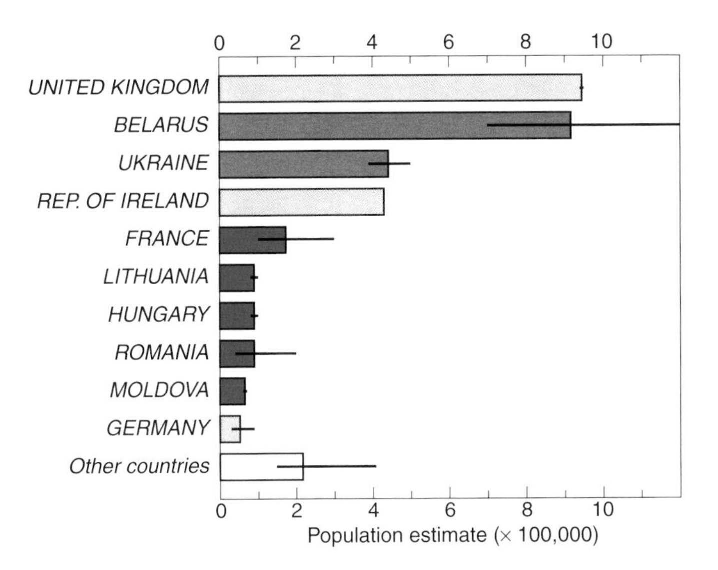

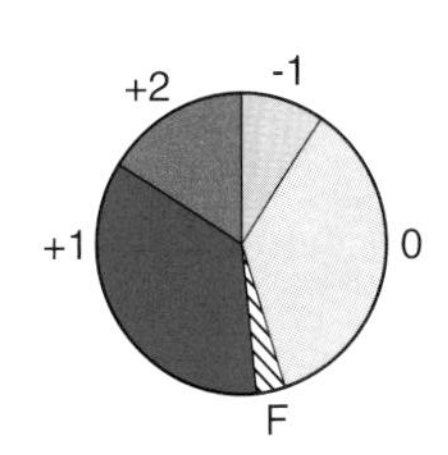

% in top 10 countries: 93.8
Total number of populated European countries: 31
Total European population 3,264,038–3,866,246 (3,507,869)
Russian population 1,000,000–10,000,000 (3,162,278)
Turkish population 10,000–50,000 (22,361)

The Rook, a highly gregarious Palearctic corvid, is widely distributed across the temperate and boreal middle latitudes of Europe and in the boreal, steppe and desert zones of Asia Minor to the Yenisey River, NW Altai and NW Sinkiang. The subspecies *C.f. pastinator* breeds in continental E Asia from the Yenisey and C Altai to E Siberia, Japan, Korea and E China, the nominate *frugilegus* occurring elsewhere.

In the breeding season, the Rook occupies low-altitude agricultural land (usually below 600m asl), building very conspicuous nests in the crowns of tall coniferous or broad-leaved trees (Goodwin 1986). It associates closely with mixed farming regimes, and benefits from easy access to the variety of invertebrate and vegetative food provided by both pasture and arable land. Proximity to grassland is important, because the high density and diversity of invertebrate food provide a vital source of protein for young nestlings, more so than from regularly cultivated land. Since the late 1940s the shift towards intensified and specialized agriculture in W Europe changed farming methods and reduced pasture, factors thought responsible for the breeding population reductions from the 1950s to the 1970s. However, in Great Britain this trend appears to have stabilized (Sage & Whittington 1985). Population trends throughout W Europe indicate that numbers are increasing once again.

Although a common European species, its numbers are known exceptionally accurately (excluding Russia and Poland which only have broad estimates), because colonies (rookeries) are easy to locate and census. There are two strongholds, one comprising the regions bordering the North and Baltic Seas (particularly Britain & Ireland, NW France and the Baltic States), the other the plains of E-C Europe (mainly Russia and Poland). Elsewhere, the Rook is poorly represented in the C European and Mediterranean mountains and is absent above *c*66°N.

Since 1900, European Rook populations have fluctuated due mainly to changing agricultural land-use, application of pesticides and seed dressings (mercury) and persecution. Nowadays numbers probably are quite stable in western Europe, where persecution never was a long-term controlling factor. Furthermore, the rate of change of land-use has decreased, the Rook populations being able to adjust accordingly. Elsewhere, as in Latvia, persecution may still have an effect, the population there being halved from *c*16 000 to 8 000bp between the mid-1970s and the mid-1980s.

Rook densities can exceed 20 bp/km^2 in preferred habitat in parts of agricultural Britain (Brenchley 1986) and Ireland (Reid 1993). In Britain and Belarus, its highest overall density reaches 4.4 bp/km^2, comparing favourably with the overall European mean density (excluding Russia and Poland) of only 0.7 bp/km^2. However, in S Russia and Ukraine since the 1950s, the planting of extensive shelterbelt forest strips on virgin steppe allowed a range extension and very high linear breeding densities to the detriment of ground-nesting birds like Black-winged Pratincole *Glareola nordmanni* (*qv*). In Ukraine, a partial survey in 1984 counted 398 690 nests, which extrapolates to a national 2.5Mbp, an overall density of 4.1 bp/km^2 (Serebryakov & Grishchenko 1990).

Breeding distribution is limited by food availability and the absence of nesting sites (tall trees). In boreal and mountain zones, where food is difficult to find in winter, the Rook migrates to more temperate zones, often further S or at lower altitudes. Many of the W European populations are largely resident or sedentary but may be augmented in winter by birds from N, E and C Europe (Busse 1969). This phenomenon is apparently decreasing in Belgium (J. Tahon, pers obs). Occasionally, when winter conditions are particularly harsh, Rook flocks move to warmer areas such as the Mediterranean basin. Many migratory eastern populations move southwards into Iran, NW India and China.

Anne Brenchley (GB) Jacques Tahon (B)

Corvus corone

Carrion Crow

CZ	Vrána obecná	I	Cornacchia
D	Aaskrähe	NL	Kraai
E	Corneja	P	Gralha-preta
F	Corneille noire	PL	Wrona
FIN	Varis	R	Черная ворона
G	Κουρούνα	S	Kråka
H	Kormos varjú		

Non-SPEC, Threat status S

This versatile corvid occupies an enormous range across Eurasia. The species' two distinct colour forms, the grey-and-black Hooded Crow (*cornix* species group) and the all-black Carrion Crow (*corone* species group), are treated as subspecies of *Corvus corone*, because they can readily interbreed, producing fertile hybrids. Unfortunately the *Atlas* dataset did not distinguish between them, because the original instructions were open to misinterpretation. The two forms probably evolved during the last ice-age, when Crow populations in Europe may have become restricted in southern Europe to two isolated groups which developed into distinct colour forms, but were not separated for sufficient time to become reproductively isolated. When the two populations later expanded N they eventually met, but

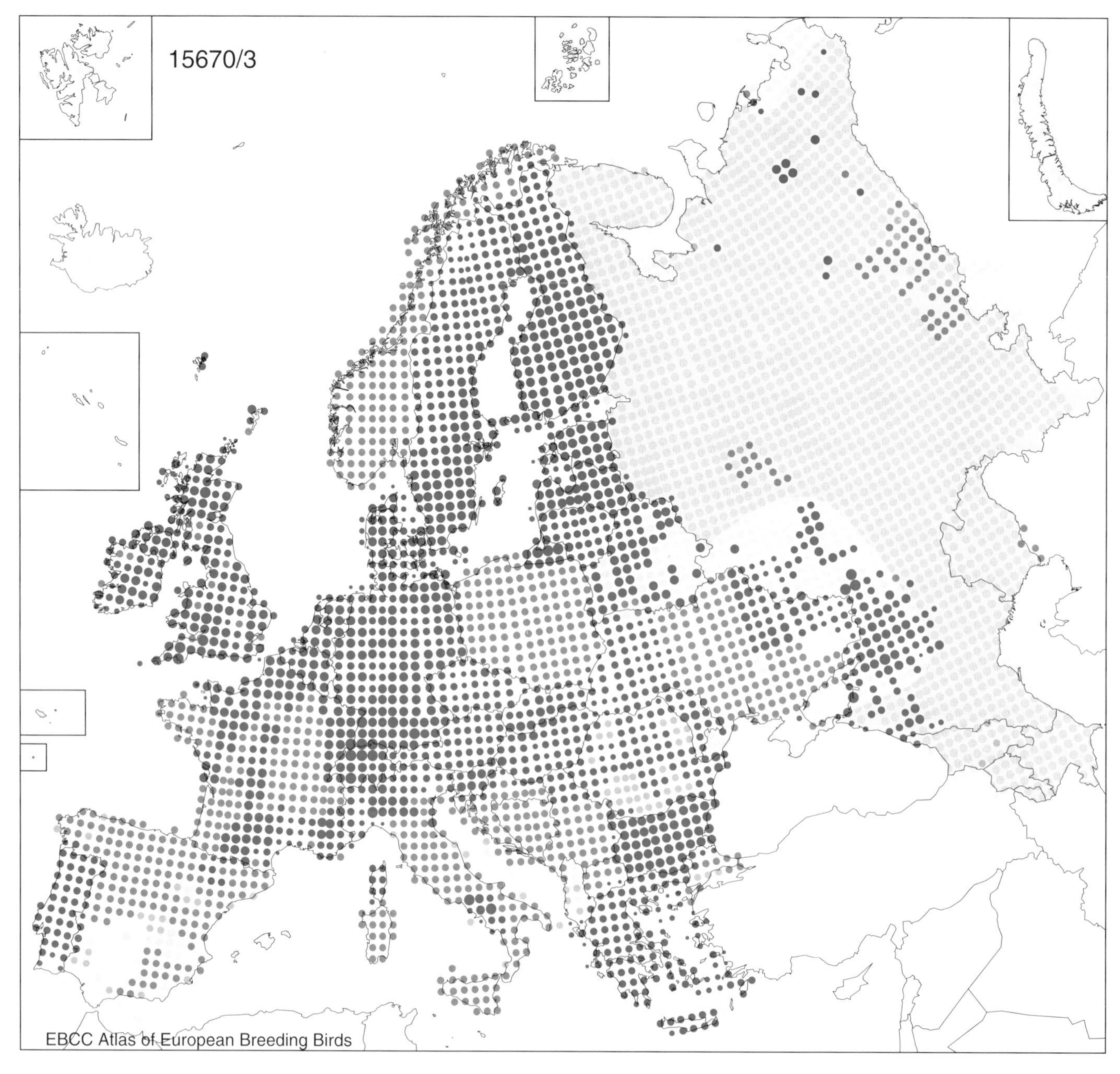

corone group (Carrion Crow)

CZ Vrána obecná černá
D Rabenkrähe
E Corneja
F Corneille noire
FIN
G Μαυροκουρούνα
H Kormos varjú
I Cornacchia nero
NL Zwarte kraai
P Gralha-preta
PL Czarnowron
R Черная ворона
S Svartkråka

cornix group (Hooded Crow)

CZ Vrána obecná šedá
D Nebelkrähe
E Corneja Cenicienta
F Corneille mantelée
FIN
G Σταχτοκουρούνα
H Dolmányos varjú
I Cornacchia grigia
NL Bonte kraai
P Gralha-cinzenta
PL Wrona siwa
R Серая ворона
S Kråka

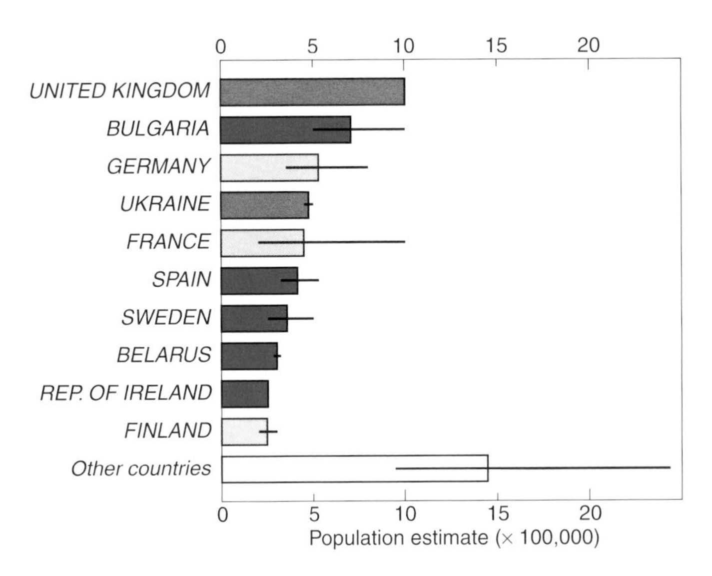

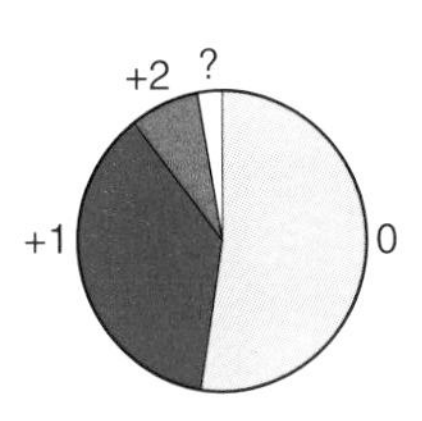

% in top 10 countries: 76.6
Total number of populated European countries: 38
Total European population 5,715,474–6,985,806 (6,156,620)
Russian population 1,000,000–10,000,000 (3,162,278)
Turkish population 100,000–1,000,000 (316,228)

remained distinct, divided by only a narrow hybrid zone. The border between Hooded and Carrion Crow distribution wanders erratically across Europe (Cook 1975).

Abundant throughout its entire distribution, *Corvus corone* is among the most widespread of all Palearctic bird species, obviously thriving as well in northern Norway as on the Mediterranean coast. Probably no other bird scores consistently such high density ranks on 50km squares throughout such an extensive European range. Its distribution continues eastwards to the Palearctic's Pacific limit and encompasses Japan, the Nile Valley, southern Iran, the Pamirs and NW China.

The species occupies most habitats and is absent really only from dense forests. It is most abundant in lowland open landscapes scattered with trees and woodland. Although usually a tree-nester, it will use tall bushes or scrub in treeless areas. It nests solitarily but often forms foraging groups in winter. Probably its success depends on two factors; firstly, its natural cunning and intelligence allows it to seek out a great variety of foods, and secondly, it has developed a close association with human activity (Houston 1977). It thrives in most farming communities, and in some parts of its range it is also a common urban scavenger (Coombs 1978). Almost half the European countries experienced range increases since the mid-1970s, thus reflecting the Crow's ability to adapt to artificial changes in the environment, particularly habitat fragmentation (Andrén 1992). Five countries probably each hold 1Mbp or more.

Over most of its range it is resident, making only short-distance movements, but in its northern range it migrates S and W in winter. Since the 1960s, wintering numbers of *cornix* have declined markedly in the Low Countries and N France (Dubois 1994), apparently reflecting a shift in wintering areas (increased residency in E Europe and Fennoscandia; Siefke 1994), because breeding area numbers have remained stable or increased.

The Carrion Crow occurs in two separated populations, in SW Europe and in the eastern Palearctic; sandwiched between is the Hooded Crow, in northern and C Europe. In the western Palearctic the hybrid zone runs from Ireland, through Scotland, Denmark, C Germany and Austria and down the southern limit of the Alps to reach the Mediterranean coast. It has moved only slightly in historical times. Hooded and Carrion Crows appear to select mates at random, and if a pair is composed of mixed parents it will produce offspring intermediate in coloration between the parents (Goodwin 1976). However, the hybrid offspring obviously are less viable than the pure strains, because otherwise the hybrid zone, which follows no obvious climatic or habitat contours, would not have remained so distinct.

The subspecies *sardonius*, a smaller, paler form of the Hooded Crow occurs on Mediterranean islands and some Mediterranean coasts. Some authors support a subspecies *sharpii* which incorporates *sardonius* and those *cornix* populations from Corsica and S Italy E to Romania and Transcaucasia.

David Houston (GB)

Corvus corax Raven

CZ	Krkavec velký	**I**	Corvo imperiale
D	Kolkrabe	**NL**	Raaf
E	Cuervo	**P**	Corvo
F	Grand Corbeau	**PL**	Kruk
FIN	Korppi	**R**	Ворон
G	Κόρακας	**S**	Korp
H	Holló		

Non-SPEC, Threat status S (P)

15720

EBCC Atlas of European Breeding Birds

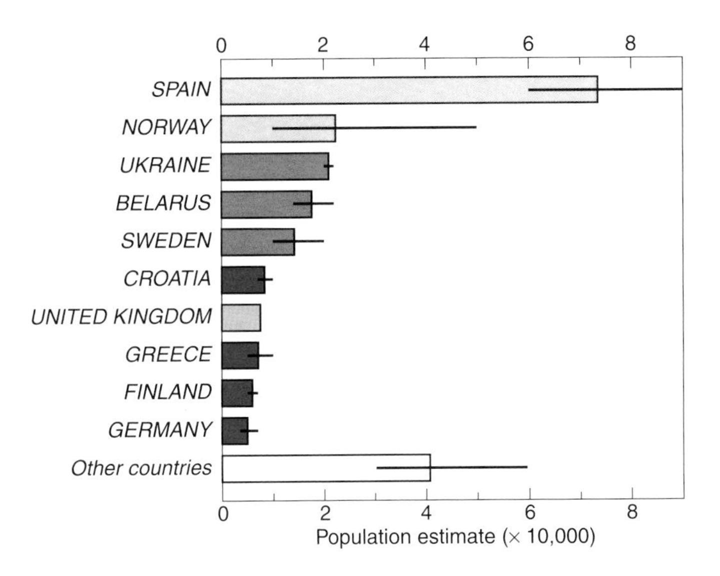

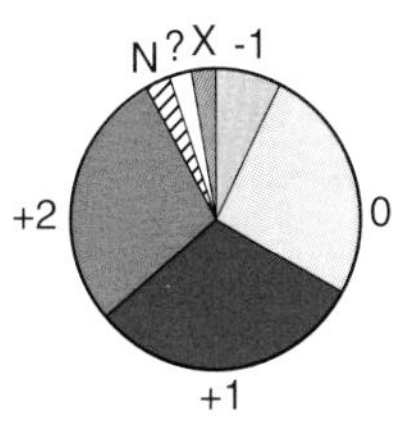

% in top 10 countries: 81.7
Total number of populated European countries: 39
Total European population 203,417–257,184 (223,026)
Russian population 100,000–1,000,000 (316,228)
Turkish population 5000–50,000 (15,811)

The Raven is a polytypic, widely distributed Holarctic species. In Europe, the nominate *C.c. corax* occurs in the boreal zone from the Shetlands in the N and most Mediterranean islands in the S to the Urals and C Siberia, *varius* inhabits the Faeroes and Iceland, *hispanus* occupies Iberia and the Balearics and *laurenci* E Greece to the lower Volga basin. At least six other subspecies occur elsewhere.

This wide distribution derives from a catholic choice of breeding locations. The Raven nests in a variety of forest types and cultivated land and even in the open, sometimes using tall electricity pylons. It also breeds on crags on seacliffs and in mountains, but rarely above the treeline and usually near forested areas. It does not avoid human presence, especially in southern and C Europe, where increasingly it penetrates into cities.

The Raven is distributed very unevenly, according to the quality of available habitat. As a 'food searcher', it usually occupies large territories, resulting in low overall breeding densities. On the continent it rarely exceeds 3–4 bp/100km^2, but in optimal habitats it may reach 7.7–10.3 bp/100km^2 (*HVM*). Higher cited values often have resulted from methodological errors. The highest overall Raven breeding density occurs in Great Britain, values of 13.6 bp/100km^2 being obtained from Shetland cliffs (Ewins *et al* 1986) and of 10.5–16.6 bp/100km^2 from the Welsh mountains (Dare 1986).

After almost 100 years of steady decline in European numbers and range the early 1950s marked the start in many areas of a largely natural recolonization process which still continues, at least 24 countries experiencing (sometimes considerable) increases during 1970–90. Only five countries reported declines; in Britain afforestation, improved sheep husbandry and conversion of pasture to arable farming all contributed to this trend (Wilson 1993). Reintroduction programmes have assisted recolonization (Germany, the Czech Republic) or generated new populations (The Netherlands, whose natural population became extinct in the 1920s, Belgium; Glandt 1991). In The Netherlands, 178 Raven immatures released between 1966 and 1992 produced by 1976–86 some 3–9bp which increased rapidly to 400–475 birds (including 50bp) by 1992 (Renssen & Vogel 1993).

The Raven breeds throughout Europe (except Luxembourg and Malta). In the 20th century Raven populations expanded from several core centres; these comprise four main ecotypes. Out of the European total (*c*0.5Mbp), the most numerous population (*c*408 000bp), whose prime habitat is coniferous forest, originated in the NE, the distribution extending W to eastern Norway, eastern Germany and the Czech Republic. The southern mountain population (*c*117 000bp), which nests almost exclusively on rocks, occupies southern Europe below the Danube, the northern pre-Alps, the Massif Central and the Pyrenees. The cliff coasts and some of the mountain ranges in Norway, Britain & Ireland, Normandy and Brittany hold the separate northern mountain and cliff population (*c*30 600bp). The northern plains of Europe in Denmark and NW Germany hold the smallest population (*c*3150bp) whose principal habitat is deciduous woods, mainly beech *Fagus*.

Currently (and probably in the foreseeable future), the Raven is a scarce breeder over much of the NW European lowlands (suitable cliff-nesting sites lacking). Furthermore, the deciduous forest population is too small to have an immediate impact, and the coniferous forest population, despite a westward expansion, has for the time being ceased to do so in eastern Germany. Moreover, the NW European lowlands are intensively farmed, woodland is scarce and most areas are exposed to human disturbance on a large scale. Similar considerations may explain the species' absence from Hungary and N Italy.

Raven immatures are social and dispersive. Within flocks of non-breeding birds, pairs are formed which after some years settle to become strictly resident. Northern populations are more liable to move S in winter.

Jan Bednorz (PL)

Sturnus vulgaris

Starling

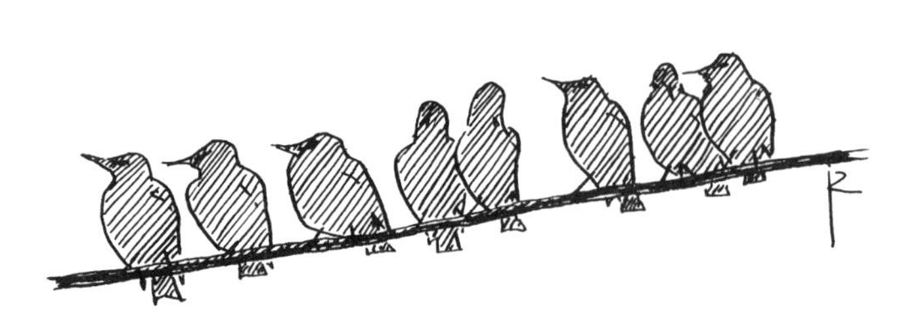

CZ	Špaček obecný	**I**	Storno
D	Star	**NL**	Spreeuw
E	Estornino Pinto	**P**	Estorninho-malhado
F	Étourneau sansonnet	**PL**	Szpak
FIN	Kottarainen	**R**	Обыкновенный скворец
G	Ψαρόνι	**S**	Stare
H	Seregély		

Non-SPEC, Threat status S

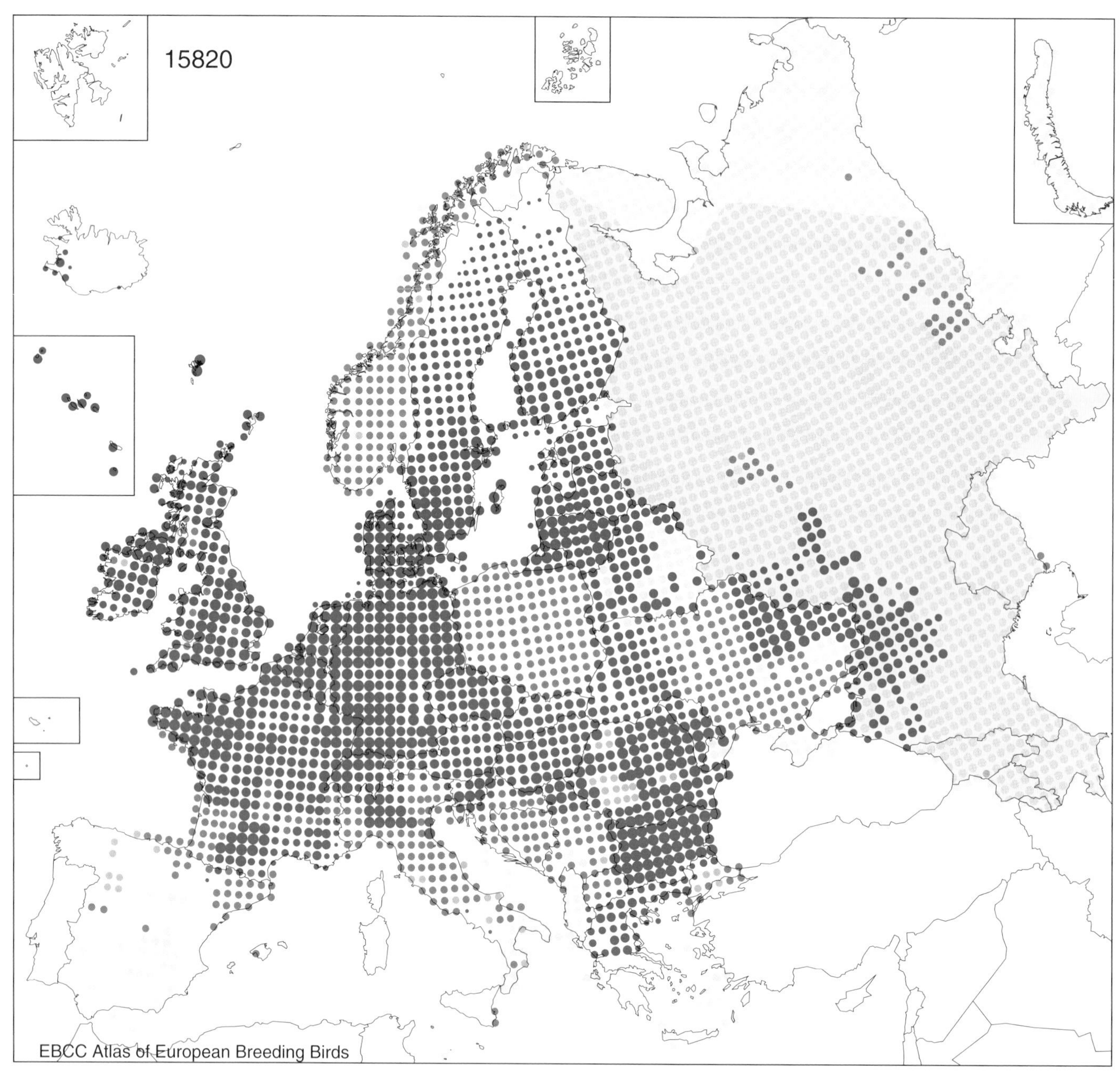

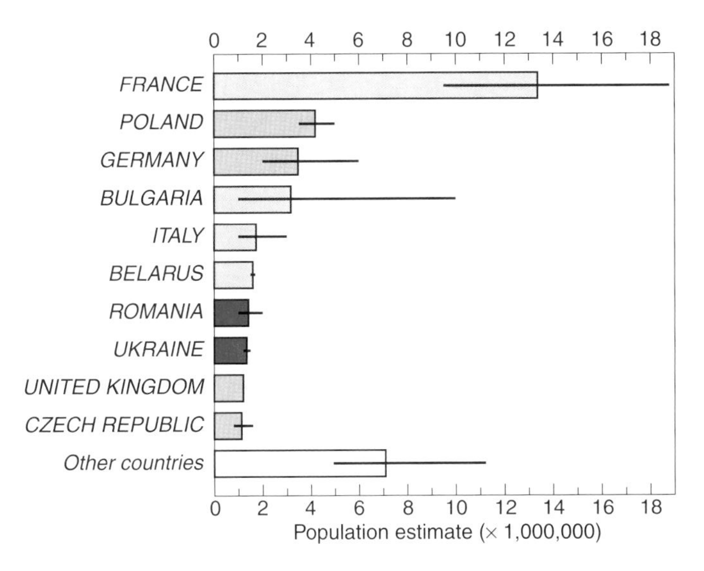

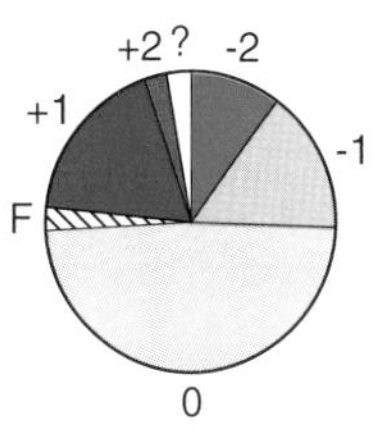

% in top 10 countries: 82.1
Total number of populated European countries: 39
Total European population 34,830,415–49,111,373 (39,687,021)
Russian population 5,000,000–50,000,000 (15,811,388)
Turkish population 500,000–5,000,000 (1,581,139)

The Starling is widespread in the Palearctic between 40° and 70°N. Introduced birds colonized successfully North America, southernmost Africa, southern Australia, Tasmania and New Zealand. In Europe, the species occupies the temperate and boreal climate zones, extending into the mediterranean and steppe zones. Although typically a lowland species, it breeds regularly up to 800m asl in the Swiss Alps and locally even higher. Perhaps ten subspecies occur in Europe, and at least four elsewhere.

The Starling breeds in holes and cavities in trees and rocks, in nestboxes, buildings and other human constructions, feeds in short-sward habitats and within these wide constraints readily adapts to many habitats. Its main breeding environment nowadays is pasture and meadow farmland, but roadside verges, gardens and lawns are attractive alternative feeding locations, enabling the species to breed in densely-populated human settlements, sometimes in near-colonial aggregates. Journeys of less than 0.5km from the nest are sufficiently energy-efficient to maintain breeding success.

The breeding range covers most of Europe quite uniformly. In N Norway, it reaches Varangerfjord. Iceland was colonized in the 1930s. Breeding densities decrease from the core towards C Fennoscandia and the Mediterranean. The Starling is absent from Corsica, Sardinia, S Italy, S Greece and most of Iberia (where the closely related Spotless Starling *S. unicolor* replaces it). Densities (bp/50km square) are lowest in Iceland, Fennoscandia, the Baltic States, N Spain and Greece (<5000). Intermediate densities (5000–20 000) apply to Belarus, Ukraine, Romania, Hungary, Italy, Austria, Switzerland and Britain & Ireland. The generally low-lying, intensively cultivated and densely populated region of Denmark, the Low Countries, France, Germany, the Czech Republic, Slovakia, Poland and Bulgaria form the European core of high densities (20 000–70 000).

After a continuous increasing trend from the 19th century until the 1950s, overall a population decline has become apparent, especially since the 1970s. This decline was first noted, and probably started, in the Finnish range periphery, then affected Karelia, Russia, Sweden, Poland and western Europe. Clear decreases followed of wintering populations in Britain, France and Spain (Feare *et al* 1992). In Finland, the decline relates clearly to major habitat changes which have decreased reproductive output severely, and is unconnected with persecution or pesticide usage on the wintering grounds (Tiainen *et al* 1989, Solonen *et al* 1991). Because dairy farms have almost disappeared in various southern regions (by 70–90%), so have pastures, the species' main foraging habitat. Finnish rural breeding densities were 10 bp/km^2 in the 1930s. Now they are halved.

Major changes in land-use, notably decreases in the acreage of fallow and grassland, and increases in autumn-sown arable crops, probably have reduced the winter invertebrate supply, thus contributing to the decline in British Starling numbers (Feare 1994). Habitat changes may also be involved elsewhere in W and C Europe.

The numerical decline has led to a range contraction in Fennoscandia. In N Finland fledging success is insufficient to balance adult mortality (J. Tiainen, *et al*, in prep) and further S reproduction success has been insufficient to support northwards immigration of surplus offspring. Conversely, populations in Italy, S France and N Spain have spread slowly southwards recently, but in Spain has been checked by the simultaneous northwards spread of the Spotless Starling.

Northern, C, and eastern Starling populations migrate in a broad front to western and southern Europe, northern birds tending to move westwards and eastern birds southwards (Fliege 1984). Fennoscandian Starlings overwinter in Britain & Ireland, the Low Countries and northern France, while C and eastern European birds head towards southern France, Iberia, North Africa and Italy. Southern and western (even up to the Arctic Circle on Norwegian coasts) populations are partially migratory or sedentary.

Juha Tiainen (FIN) Timo Pakkala (FIN)

This species account is sponsored by Bird Watching Magazine, EMAP Pursuit Publishing, Peterborough, GB.

Sturnus unicolor

Spotless Starling

CZ	Špaček jednobarvý	I	Storno nero
D	Einfarbstar	NL	Zwarte Spreeuw
E	Estornino Negro	P	Estorninho-preto
F	Étourneau unicolore	PL	Szpak jednobarwny
FIN	Mustakottarainen	R	Черный скворец
G	Μαυροψάρονο	S	Svartstare
H	Egyszínű seregély		

SPEC Cat 4, Threat status S

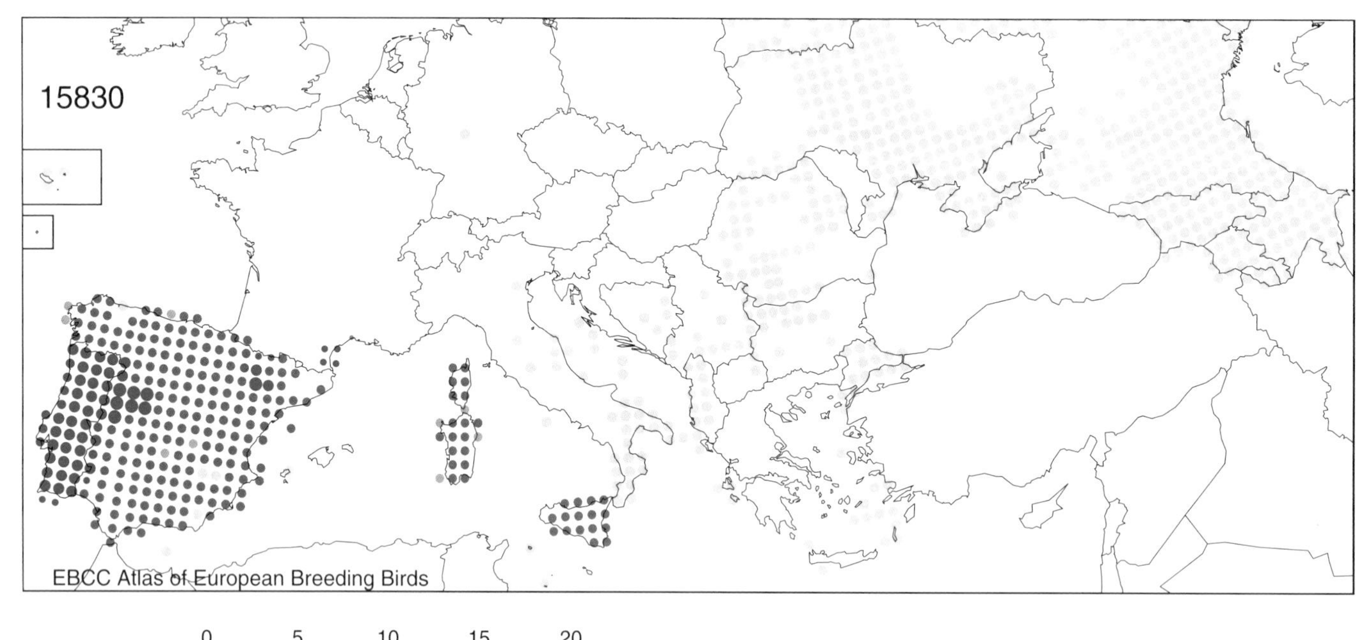

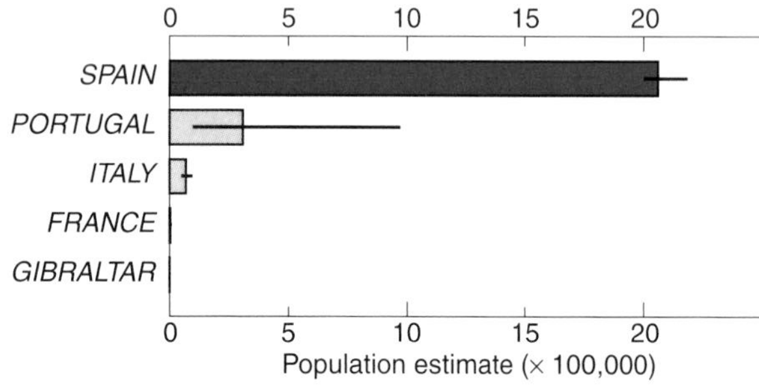

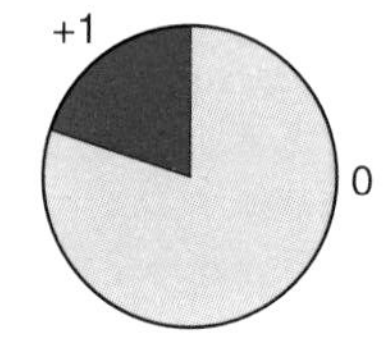

% in top 10 countries: 100.0
Total number of populated European countries: 5
Total European population 2,262,649–3,207,885 (2,511,460)

The Spotless Starling has a restricted W Mediterranean range, occurring throughout the Iberian Peninsula and being locally common in Corsica, Sardinia, Sicily and North Africa (S to 31°14'N). It is basically resident, though subject to nomadic (*c*40km) or partial short-distance (*c*500km) dispersal.

The Spotless Starling occupies diverse habitats including mediterranean woodland, farmland, parks, seacoasts and olive and citrus groves. Its prime habitat comprises open woodland from which it has access to grazed land. As a suburban–rural bird, it breeds under roof-tiles over its entire range. It may forage on grasslands up to 2500m asl, but breeding above 1500m asl is exceptional. The species does not normally breed, or is otherwise scarce, in steppe or desert areas in SE Spain. It also avoids coniferous forests, mediterranean maquis and scrub-heath landscape. However, where nestboxes are provided, it will readily breed in otherwise unsuitable areas.

Breeding densities in Spain vary from 0.2 birds/10ha in chestnut *Castanea* forests to 0.8–8.0 birds/10ha in holm oak *Quercus ilex* forests in W-C regions (Peris & Carnero 1988). In a plot of 10.5ha in the Sardinian town of Oristano, a maximum density of 90 bp/10ha was measured (Walter & Demartis 1972).

In the years from 1950 to 1990, the Spotless Starling underwent a marked range expansion in Spain at an average rate of 4.7km per year (Ferrer *et al* 1991), mainly to the N and NE. At the same time, numbers increased wherever land came under irrigation (Peris *et al* 1987). This new agricultural practice appears to be the key factor in its expansion. SE France was colonized in 1989–90, breeding first being proved in 1983. This population was estimated at 300bp in 1992 (Kayser & Rousseau 1994, Renard 1994).

Hybrids between Spotless Starling and Starling *S. vulgaris* have been observed in areas where their respective ranges overlap in NE Spain (Motis 1992).

Salvador J Peris (E)

Sturnus roseus

Rose-coloured Starling

CZ	Špaček růžový	I	Storno roseo
D	Rosenstar	NL	Roze Spreeuw
E	Estornino Rosado	P	Estorninho-rosado
F	Martin roselin	PL	Pasterz
FIN	Punakottarainen	R	Розовый скворец
G	Αγιοπούλι	S	Rosenstare
H	Pásztormadár		

Non-SPEC, Threat status S (P)

The Rose-coloured Starling's breeding range extends from C Asia to W and S Russia N to a yet ill-defined limit. It inhabits mainly the lower middle latitudes, preferring the steppe, semi-desert and mediterranean zones. Irruptive range extensions of up to 1200km towards SE and E Europe occur occasionally in spring, often in successive years at an 8–10 year periodicity. Most irruptive birds do not breed.

In its typical habitat of steppe and dry grassland, it breeds in colonies of tens or hundreds of pairs. It is gregarious year-long, sometimes forming huge swarming flocks. In the breeding season, it is mainly insectivorous, locusts and grasshoppers being particularly important. Locust outbreaks may govern the irruptions.

The distribution core lies in S Russia, with smaller nuclei in the Pannonian Plain (Hungary, rarely Vojvodina) and S of the Danube in Bulgaria, Macedonia and Montenegro (rarely NW Greece). SE Europe may have held *c*15 000bp in the early 1990s, but normally numbers are appreciably smaller. Hungary experienced a small influx in 1989, a huge invasion in 1994 (Kovács 1994b, Gorman 1994) which was repeated in 1995 (G. Kovacs, pers comm to the Editors). The 1994 pattern saw thousands arriving in SE Bulgaria from the N (P. Iankov, pers comm) and thousands crossing Romania to occupy the Hungarian Tisza Plain, several hundred pairs breeding (Kovács 1994, Gorman 1994). The coincident massive locust invasion of the Mediterranean region may not have triggered this irruption. Population growth may contribute to the irruption genesis, especially after successive years of high breeding success.

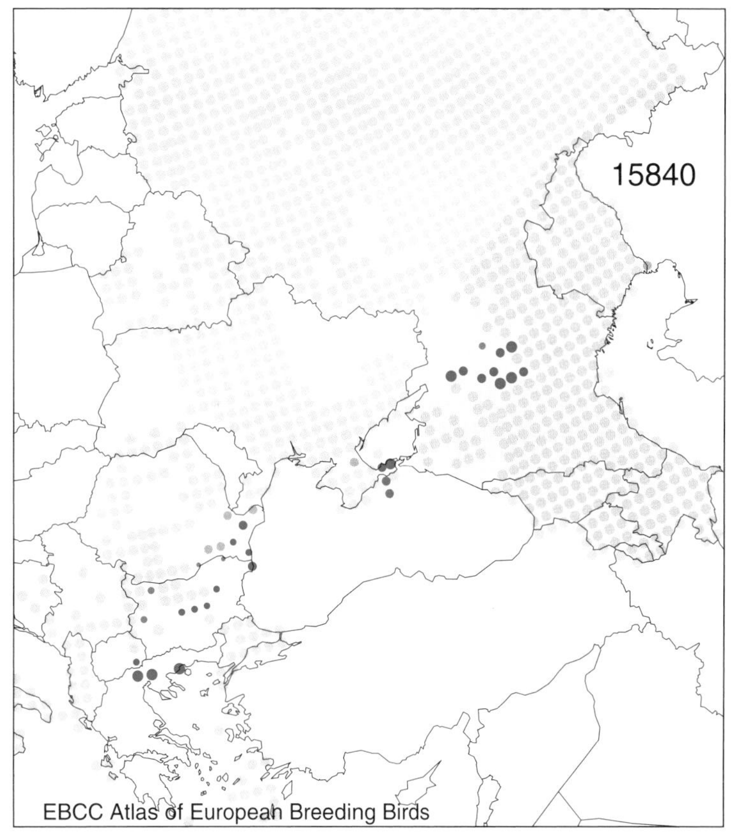

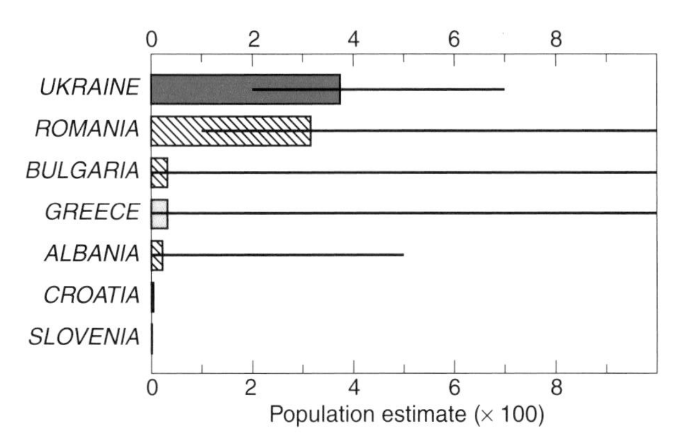

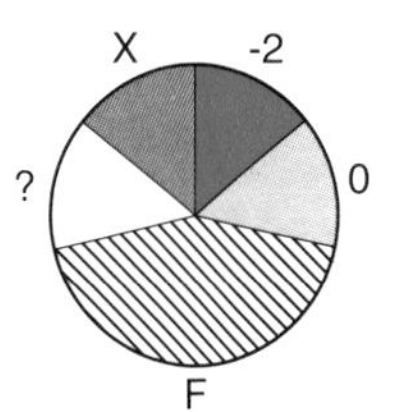

% in top 10 countries: 100.0
Total number of populated European countries: 7
Total European population 499–2418 (781)
Russian population 10,000–100,000 (31,623)
Turkish population 5000–100,000 (22,361)

Little is known of the species' long-term trends. Widespread spraying campaigns from the 1920s onwards directed against breeding centres of *Locusta migratoria* in the Kuma and Kuban catchments exterminated *Locustidae* in the Cis-Caucasus steppes, and consequently Rose-coloured Starling numbers and distribution declined sharply. It now occurs only periodically in this region after mass breeding of the locust *Calliptamus italicus*. In 1985–86 the hypertoxic heptachlorane was directed against this pest, causing further mass mortality of the Rose-coloured Starling (Belik & Mihalevich 1994).

Dan Munteanu (ROM)

Passer montanus — Tree Sparrow

CZ	Vrabec polní	**I**	Passera mattugia
D	Feldsperling	**NL**	Ringmus
E	Gorríon Molinero	**P**	Pardal-montez
F	Moineau friquet	**PL**	Mazurek
FIN	Pikkuvarpunen	**R**	Полевой воробей
G	Δενδροσπουργίτης	**S**	Pilfink
H	Mezei veréb		

Non-SPEC, Threat status S

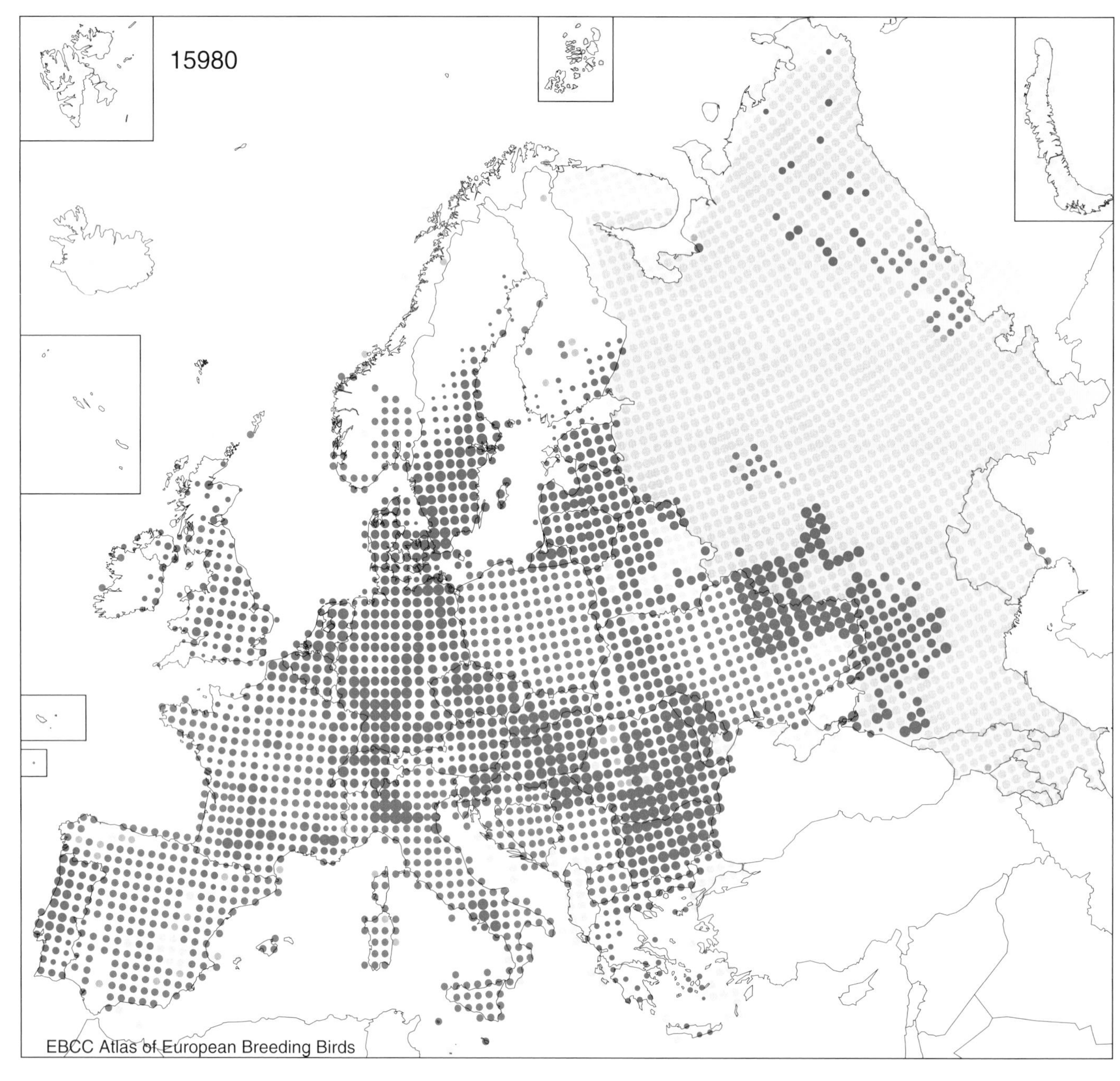

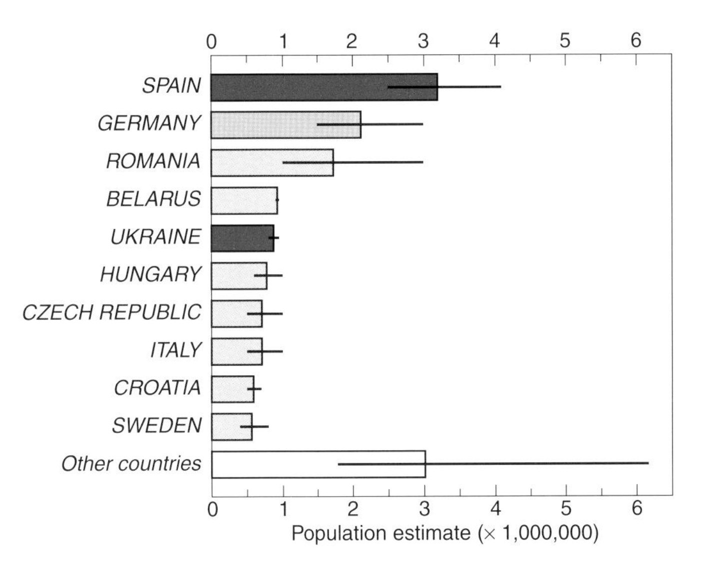

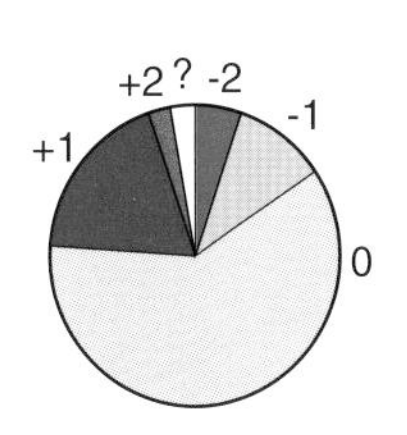

% in top 10 countries: 80.2
Total number of populated European countries: 38
Total European population 13,889,917–17,471,933 (15,215,759)
Russian population 1,000,000–10,000,000 (3,162,278)
Turkish population 5000–50,000 (15,811)

The Tree Sparrow is widely distributed over Eurasia, being absent only in the extreme N (above *c*62–64°N, though occurring sporadically up to 70°N in river valleys) and southern Asia from S Turkey through S Iran to India S of the mountain ranges (Noskov 1981, Summers-Smith 1988). The subspecies *transcaucasicus* occurs in the *Atlas* area from the Caucasus W to Bulgaria where it intergrades with the nominate *montanus* which occupies the rest of Europe. Perhaps nine subspecies exist elsewhere.

In the extreme N the Tree Sparrow is present only in small villages. In Great Britain, it is predominantly a bird of open cultivation and light woodland, but in continental Europe it occupies woodland and parkland as well as open areas in the breeding season, though in the winter it occupies mainly agricultural areas and human settlements. To the E it is increasingly found in urban areas, particularly where the House Sparrow *P. domesticus* is absent or a summer visitor.

In Europe it seldom occurs above 1500m asl, but reaches 4400m in Asia. In open country it breeds in holes in trees, rocks, earth banks, the foundations of large nests or builds open nests in trees (especially in S Europe and in the steppes) and towards the E of its range it nests increasingly in holes in houses.

Populations have been established successfully in Australia (introduced 1863, now widespread in Victoria and New South Wales) and the USA (released 1870, in St Louis, Missouri, and has a limited foothold in adjoining Illinois). Numbers are highest in mid-continental Europe from Belgium and The Netherlands to Romania, where there are typically 10–40 birds/km^2; in suitable habitat breeding densities range from 15 to 90 bp/km^2 (Dyer *et al* 1977).

In the extreme W it undergoes large population fluctuations. For example, in Britain & Ireland, numbers increased fivefold from *c*1955 to 1960, remained there for *c*20 years before falling rapidly to the pre-1955 level (Summers-Smith 1989), a net reduction of 85% (Fuller *et al* 1995). Similar changes occurred in The Netherlands, Germany and Switzerland about the same time (Wesołoswki 1991, Winkel 1994). A major factor in the recent decrease is probably reduction in food availability (both the invertebrate food required for the nestlings and the seeds comprising the major part of its diet) following such changes in agricultural practice in western Europe as autumn sowing of cereal crops and the increased use of pesticides and herbicides. In Switzerland, the reproductive rate in 1962–79 was 21% lower than in 1940–61, probably because of massive application of organochlorines in farming (Wesołowski 1991).

In contrast to its decline in W Europe, the Tree Sparrow has been expanding in numbers and range at the boundaries, especially in Fennoscandia since the 1960s and 1970s. In the S it colonized Corsica, Sardinia and Malta in the 20th century and even appeared in the Canary Islands in 1989. A slight increase in range and numbers was also apparent in Iberia during 1970–90.

The species has been spreading similarly in SE Asia into Indonesia and the Philippines since the late 19th century. How much these most recent expansions relate to introductions or involuntary ship-assisted passage is not known.

Tree Sparrow adults are largely sedentary. Young birds make random movements in late summer, autumn and winter, usually no further than 500–600km, though one from St Petersburg, Russia, travelled 3500km to Portugal. In the extreme N some move southwards, others withdraw into towns. In the steppes and desert regions, birds wander during the winter. Some winter S of the breeding range in Europe, reaching NW Africa, the Middle East, Iraq and Egypt. Movement also occurs from C Asia through the Tian Shan passes (Noskov 1981, Gavrilov & Gistsov 1985), some birds reaching the Makran coast of Pakistan.

Bojidar Ivanov (BUL) J Denis Summers-Smith (GB)

Passer domesticus

House Sparrow

CZ	Vrabec domácí	**I**	Passera europea
D	Haussperling	**NL**	Huismus
E	Gorrión Común	**P**	Pardal-comum
F	Moineau domestique	**PL**	Wróbel
FIN	Varpunen	**R**	Домовый воробей
G	Σπουργίτης	**S**	Gråsparv
H	Házi veréb		

Non-SPEC, Threat status S

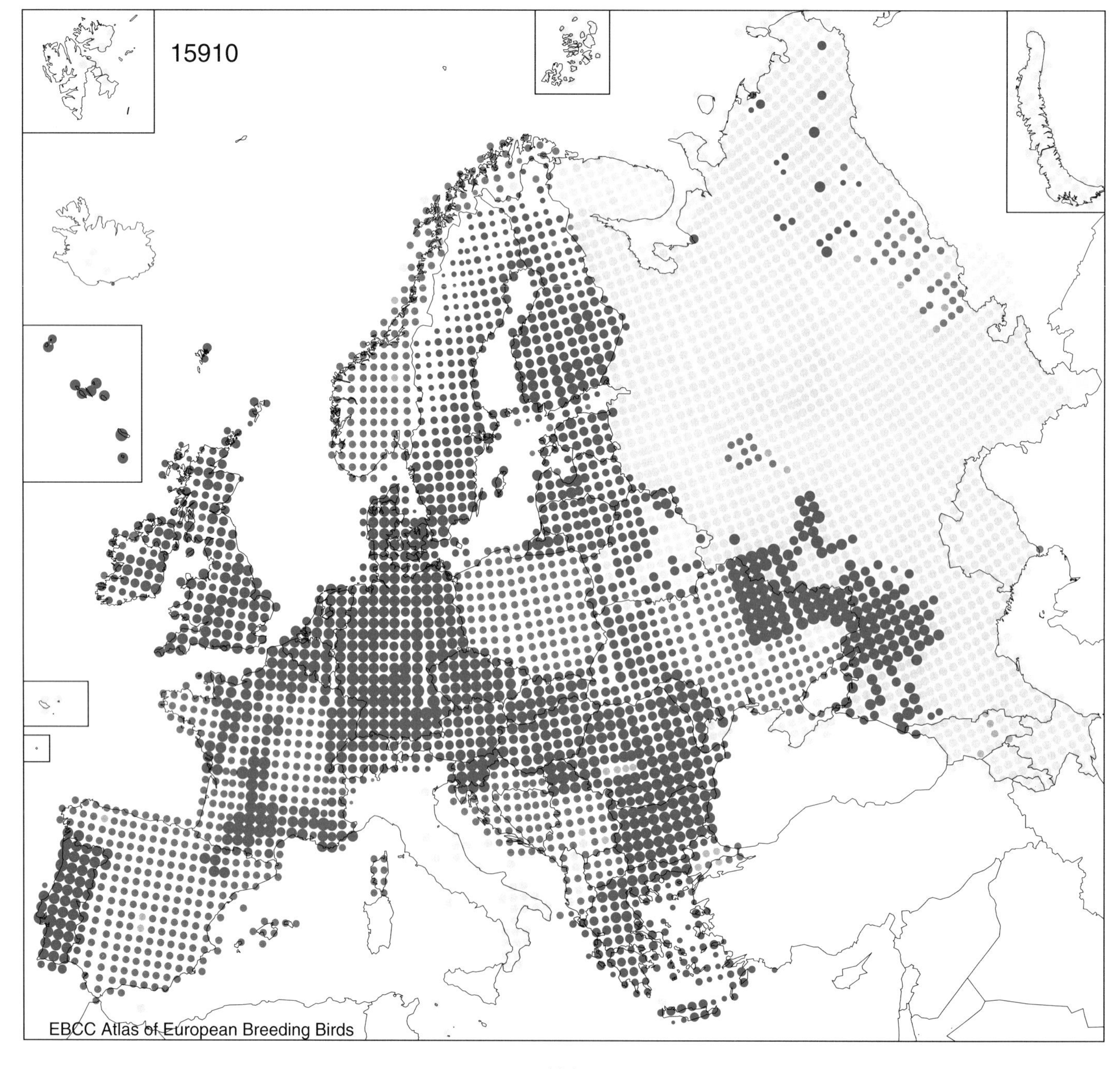

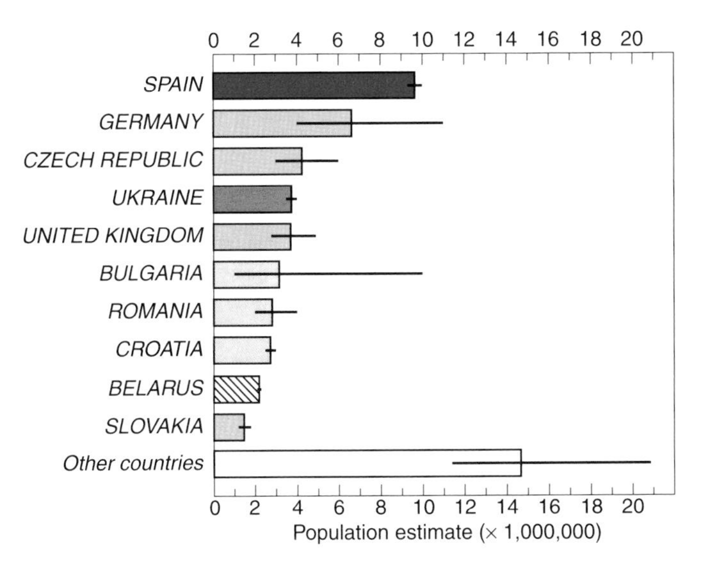

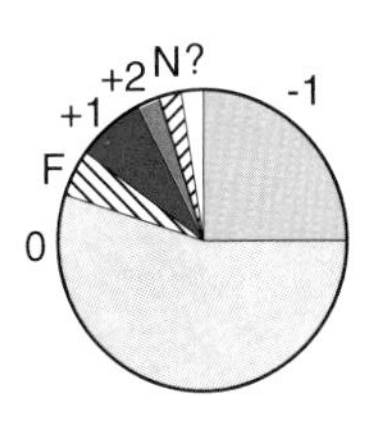

% in top 10 countries: 74.7
Total number of populated European countries: 40
Total European population 50,031,037–62,953,086 (54,034,549)
Russian population 10,000,000–100,000,000 (31,622,777)
Turkish population 1,000,000–10,000,000 (3,162,278)

There is probably no more familiar bird in Europe, or for that matter much of the rest of the world, than the House Sparrow, living as it does in close association with human beings. Its extensive natural range covers Eurasia, NW Africa and the Nile Valley, extending above the Arctic Circle in the W and up to 62°N in Siberia. It is absent from Siberia only E of *c*130°E, and from China, Japan and Indochina.

It is characteristically a bird of built-up areas and the surrounding agricultural land, although in Afghanistan and from Turkmenistan to Kazakhstan (where it is but a summer visitor) the resident Tree Sparrow *P. montanus* has taken over the urban role and forced the House Sparrow out into open country away from habitation and cultivation. The House Sparrow breeds up to 2300m asl in the Swiss Alps and up to 4600m in the Himalayas.

The species breeds primarily in holes in inhabited houses or other artificial structures, though towards the S of its range free-standing nests in trees are increasingly common as the bird spreads more into open country (Indykiewicz 1991). The migratory populations breed mostly in holes in cliffs and earth banks.

Outside its natural range, the species has been introduced to many other parts of the world and probably is now the most widely distributed passerine species, being absent only from much of tropical Africa and South America and western and northern Australia. Its expansion continues with recent colonizations of the Azores (1960), Iceland (1962), Senegal (*c*1970), Kenya (1979) and Ascension Island (1985). Summers-Smith (1988) gives details of its present distribution. The European population comprises *c*60M–200Mbp.

In its optimum habitat, built-up areas (particularly suburbs and town edges with a high proportion of open land), it reaches breeding densities of 100–400 bp/km^2 (Dyer *et al* 1977, Heij 1985). However, this impression of abundance must be tempered by a recent decline in numbers, most particularly in western Europe. Much of the evidence for this is anecdotal, but observations are so widespread in Great Britain, The Netherlands and western Germany that there is little doubt that a significant decrease (probably highly significant in SE England; A. Prowse, pers comm) has occurred since the 1970s. Most probably this decline is related to changes in agricultural practices, such as autumn sowing of cereals and increased use of pesticides and herbicides; all these alterations have reduced the availability not only of the invertebrate food essential for rearing the nestlings but also the cereal and weed seeds that form the major proportion of the bird's diet. Not only have the built-up edge and rural populations been affected, but so also have those in some urban areas, possibly through the use of garden insecticides. However, despite previous opinions to the contrary, there is no discernible difference between densities in poorer eastern and affluent western Berlin (K. Witt 1996).

The House Sparrow throughout most of its range is almost completely sedentary with most individuals leading their lives within a compass of only a few kilometres. In contrast, the populations of the former Soviet C Asian Republics and Afghanistan are completely migratory, withdrawing S in winter to the plains of northern Pakistan and India.

House Sparrow populations have been separated into two subgroups: the *domesticus* subgroup which occurs in Europe, Siberia, North Africa, Egypt and much of the Middle East and comprises generally larger individuals; and the *indicus* subgroup, which includes the migratory subspecies *bactrianus* (from the former Soviet C Asian Republics and Afghanistan) and *parkini* (from the Himalayas) and comprises generally smaller and more brightly plumaged individuals. These subgroups comprise 5 and 6 subspecies respectively.

Piotr Indykiewicz (PL) J Denis Summers-Smith (GB)

This species account is sponsored by London Natural History Society, Frinton-on-Sea, Essex, GB.

Passer hispaniolensis

Spanish Sparrow

CZ	Vrabec pokřovní	I	Passera sarda
D	Weidensperling	NL	Spaanse Mus
E	Gorrión Moruno	P	Pardal-espanhol
F	Moineau espagnol	PL	Wróbel południowy
FIN	Pajuvarpunen	R	Испанский воробей
G	Χωραφοσπουργίτης	S	Spansk sparv
H	Berki veréb		

Non-SPEC, Threat status S (P)

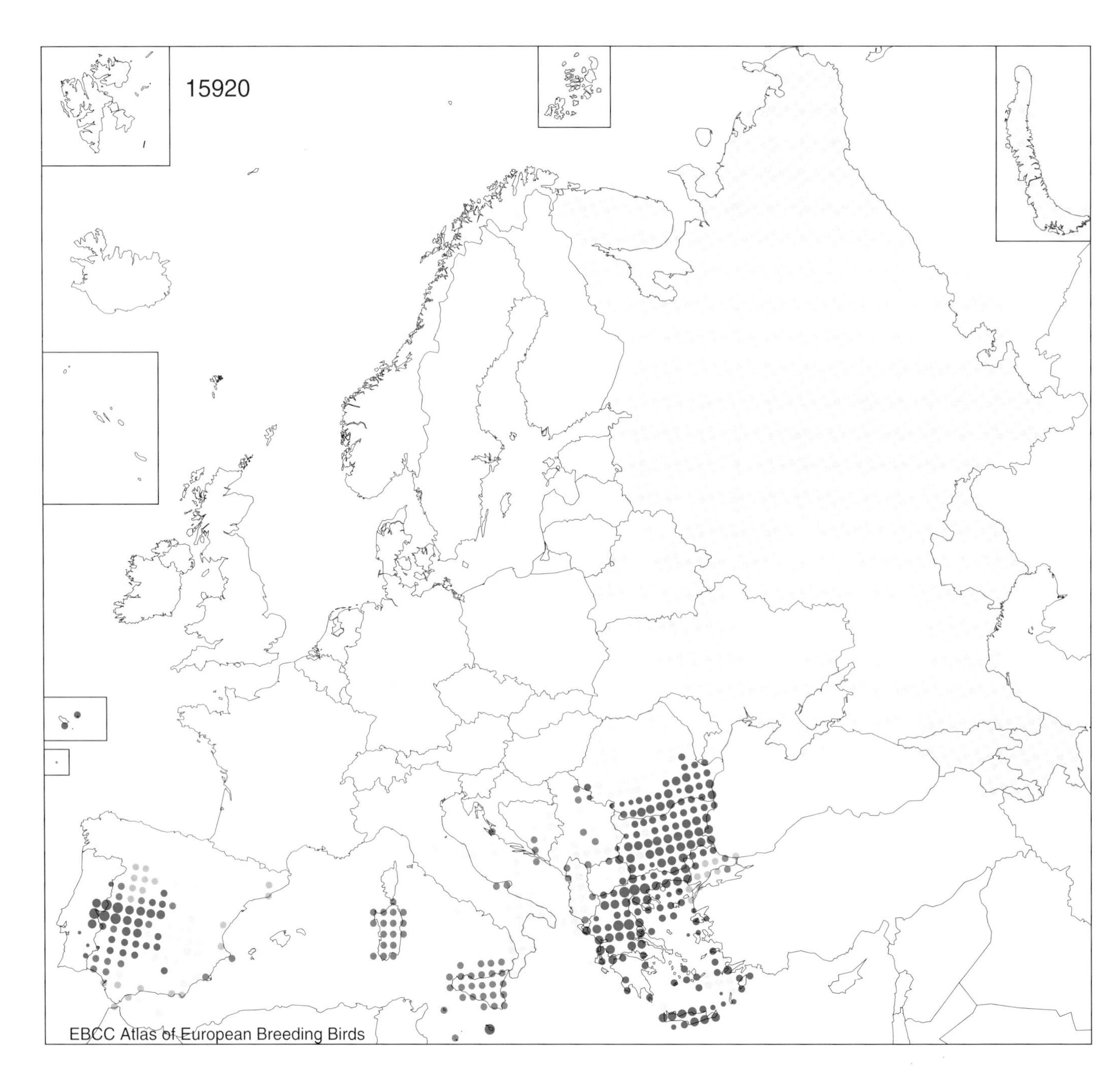

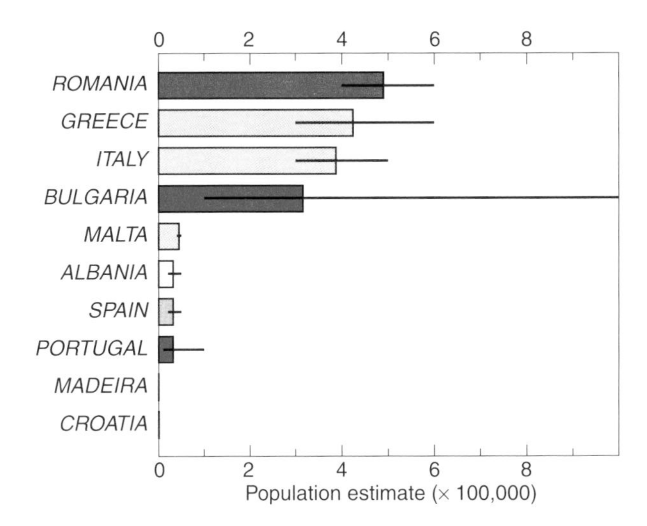

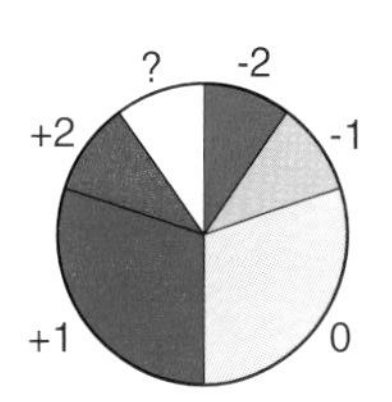

% in top 10 countries: 100.0
Total number of populated European countries: 10
Total European population 1,477,571–2,485,103 (1,758,033)
Turkish population 100,000–1,000,000 (316,228)

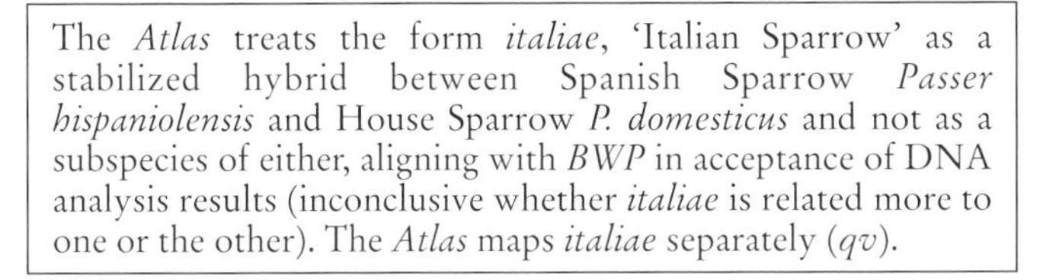
The *Atlas* treats the form *italiae*, 'Italian Sparrow' as a stabilized hybrid between Spanish Sparrow *Passer hispaniolensis* and House Sparrow *P. domesticus* and not as a subspecies of either, aligning with *BWP* in acceptance of DNA analysis results (inconclusive whether *italiae* is related more to one or the other). The *Atlas* maps *italiae* separately (*qv*).

The highly gregarious Spanish Sparrow breeds in the countries around the Mediterranean as far E as Kazakhstan and Afghanistan. Apart from the form *italiae*, there are two subspecies. In Europe the nominate *hispaniolensis* occurs in Iberia, Madeira, Sardinia, Sicily, the former Yugoslavia, Romania, Albania, Macedonia, Bulgaria and Greece (absent from Corfu and the Peloponnese and Aegean Islands). It occurs also in Cyprus and NW Africa, an extensive hybridization zone between House and Spanish Sparrows existing from NE Algeria to NW Libya. *P.h. transcaspicus* occurs from E Turkey eastwards. Occasional hybrids between *domesticus* and *hispaniolensis* or *italiae* appear in several Mediterranean locations (Alonso 1985, Summers-Smith 1988).

The nominate *hispaniolensis* prefers open woodland or farmland, usually far from human habitation. Typical colony locations are on riverbanks in holm *Quercus ilex* or cork *Q. suber* oak, pine *Pinus*, poplar *Populus*, eucalyptus *Eucalyptus* or shrubs, at 0–500m asl. Its use of non-urban nesting sites enables it to live in sympatry with the House Sparrow (Alonso 1984, 1986a). Where the latter is absent (Italy, Sicily, Malta, Crete and Madeira), the Spanish Sparrow assumes the urban niche.

In Iberia it is locally abundant only along the Tajo Valley in W Spain and E Portugal, and much more scarce and local in the Guadiana and Guadalquivir Valleys, apparently being absent from most of S and E Iberia and the Balearic islands. Although the species is strictly a colonial breeder, nest densities vary considerable geographically and between years through its local and irregular distribution, extremes being 180 nests in one tree and >1000 nests/km^2. Larger scale examples are a total of 7740 nests (groups of 14–2500) in 19 colonies in 972km^2 of prime habitat in Extremadura, and 910 nests (groups of 10–347) in 8 colonies in 430km^2 in Toledo province (Alonso 1984, 1986b). It is relatively abundant, albeit rather local in the former Yugoslavia, Albania and Greece, from where it spread NE during the 1950s to Bulgaria, S Romania and Moldova. The Madeiran islands were colonized following persistent easterly winds in 1935. It is unclear if colonization of the Canary and Cape Verde Islands was natural.

The Spanish Sparrow forms large post-breeding communal roosts on irrigated farmland, frequently jointly with the House Sparrow, although both species remain ecologically segregated (Alonso 1986a). By October these roosts disperse in nomadic flocks for winter, when few remain near the breeding sites, many then being seen in S Portugal (F.J. Walker, pers comm to the Editors) and S Spain in autumn, particularly near Gibraltar. The Iberian populations probably tend to migrate S and may even cross to Africa (Alonso 1984, 1986b). Such movements would align with the nomadic behaviour of North African populations and with the migratory behaviour of *transcaspicus*, all of which tend to winter S of their respective breeding areas (Summers-Smith 1988).

Although W. Meise suggested in 1936 a likely hypothesis on the origin and evolution of sparrow forms around the Mediterranean (see Summers-Smith 1988), there is little detailed information on recent trends and numbers. In my opinion the species originally may have occupied a larger area of the Mediterranean basin than at present, only to decrease in range and abundance when increasing urban expansion favoured the House Sparrow, which is ecologically less selective and is more adaptable to habitats created by people. Where the House Sparrow is absent the Spanish Sparrow is often displaced from urban or suburban nesting sites by the Tree Sparrow *P. montanus* which, also being more adapted to human activities, has recently expanded its range.

Juan C Alonso (E)

Passer × italiae

Italian Sparrow

CZ	Vrabec italský	I	Passera d'Italia
D	Italiensperling	NL	Italiaanse Mus
E	Gorrion italiano	P	Pardal-italiano
F	Moineau cisalpin	PL	Wróbel włoski
FIN	Italianvarpunen	R	Итальянский воробей
G	Ιταλοσπουργίτης	S	Italiensk sparv
H	Olasz veréb		

Criteria not applied

The *Atlas* treats the form *italiae*, 'Italian Sparrow' as a stabilized hybrid between Spanish Sparrow *Passer hispaniolensis* and House Sparrow *P. domesticus*, aligning with *BWP* in acceptance of DNA analysis results (inconclusive whether *italiae* is related more to one than the other; D. Parkin, pers comm, M. Milone, pers comm). Formerly *italiae* was considered a separate species; Stephan (1986) retained that view, based on his interpretation of individual phenotypic variability. Most authors assume it to be a subspecies of *P. domesticus* (eg C. Vaurie and R.E. Moreau), but Summers-Smith (1988) considered it a subspecies of *P. hispaniolensis*. Although *italiae* is found in mainland Italy, Sicily, Malta, Corsica and Crete, in N Italy there is a narrow but varying hybridization zone with *P. domesticus* (Lockley 1992) and in S Italy an extensive intergradation zone with *hispaniolensis*. The typical Italian Sparrow population in central hybridization form occurs from the Italian Alps S to roughly C Italy. Johnston (1969) then regarded it as a stabilized hybrid, whose phenotypic variability follows a N–S cline; Lo Valvo & Lo Verde (1987) have proposed it as an emergent interspecies; they and Massa (1989) believe the 'Sicilian Sparrow' populations belong to *hispaniolensis*.

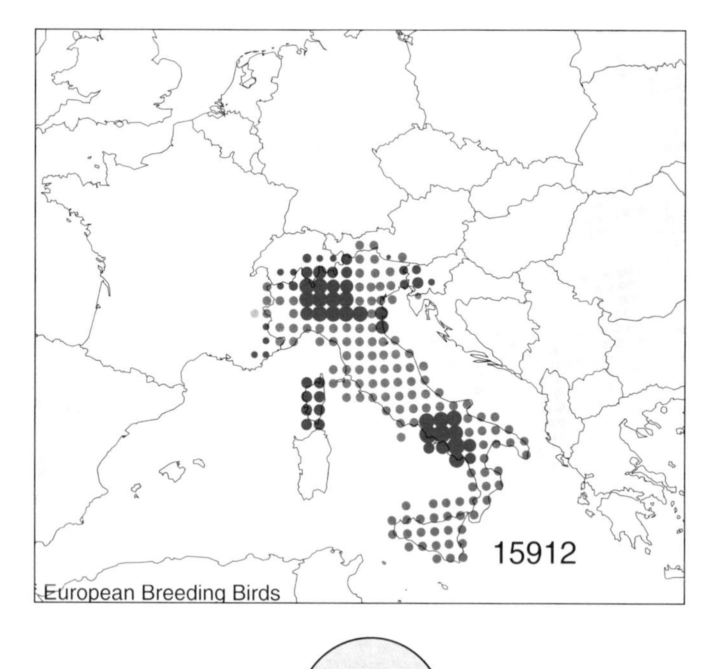

0

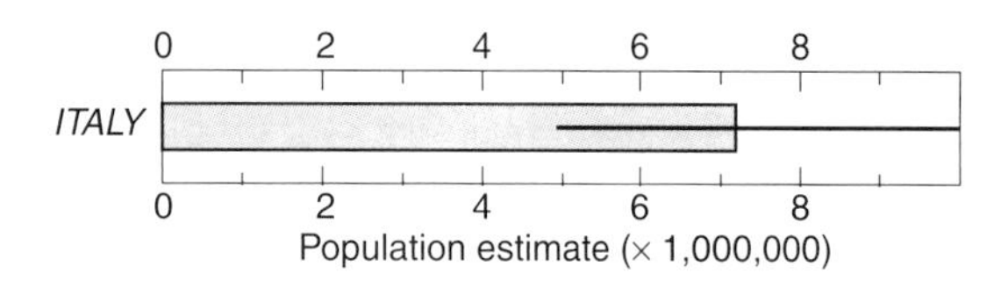

% in top 10 countries: 100.0
Total number of populated European countries: 1
Total European population 5,000,000–10,000,000 (7,071,068)

The northern boundary between the Italian Sparrow and the House Sparrow follows the Alpine arc. The southern boundary with the Spanish Sparrow is more indeterminate: it intersects the C-E Mediterranean islands from Corsica and the Aeolian Isles to the NE coast of Sicily E to Crete and the Dodecanese (Lo Valvo & Lo Verde 1987, Summers-Smith 1988, Massa 1989, J.D. Summers-Smith, pers comm, S. Coghlan, pers comm, M. Milone, pers obs). Because the Italian Sparrow's plumage varies with the seasons, unsupported sight records of *italiae*-like sparrows are of doubtful value as taxonomic evidence (Lo Valvo & Lo Verde 1987, Massa 1989).

The Italian Sparrow breeds practically everywhere, but prefers rocky habitats both natural (where it is often colonial) and artificial. Its strong commensal links with human beings have increased its use of artificial structures. It breeds from the coast to the mountains (up to 2213m asl, Sella Pass 1992; M. Milone, pers obs).

Its population density varies from *c*10 to 200 bp/km^2 throughout. Generally it is increasing steadily, probably through unrestrained urbanization and road-building (Lockley 1992). In Campania (S Italy) its annual rate of increase since 1986 has been 2–3%, some 20–30% inhabiting city centres and 15–45% rural habitats, always maintaining its community dominance (M. Milone, pers obs). In suburban areas with patches of dense vegetation it is subordinate to the Tree Sparrow *P. montanus*.

Wintering populations are nomadic, often associating with finches and buntings. Small groups may wander at least 50–300km beyond their breeding range, creating the potential for further hybridization. Whether such groups are absorbed by House or Spanish Sparrow or retain a form of identity is unknown.

Bruno Massa (I) Mario Milone (I) Peter Groselj (SLN)

Petronia petronia

Rock Sparrow

CZ	Vrabec skalní	I	Passera lagia
D	Steinsperling	NL	Rotsmus
E	Gorrión Chillón	P	Pardal-francês
F	Moineau Soulcie	PL	Wróbel skalny
FIN	Kalliovarpunen	R	Каменный воробей
G	Πετροσπουργίτης	S	Stensparv
H	Kövi veréb		

Non-SPEC, Threat status S

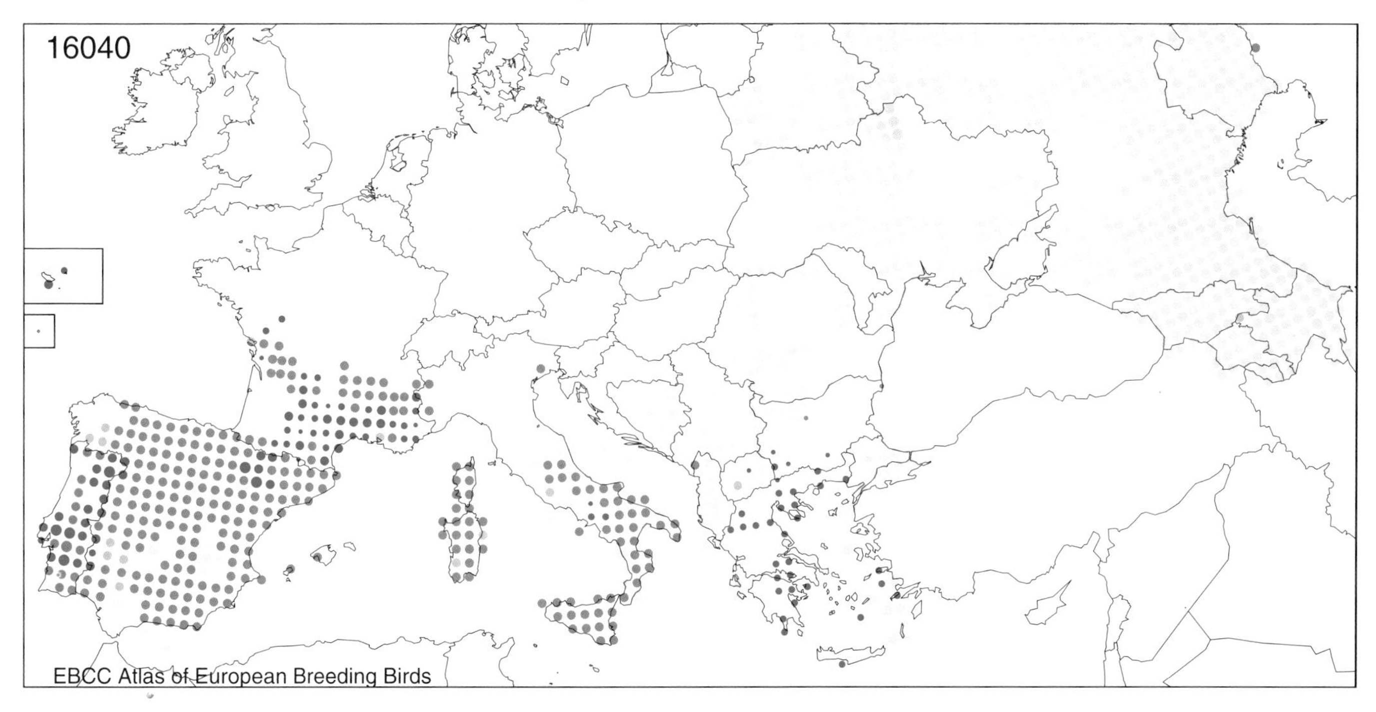

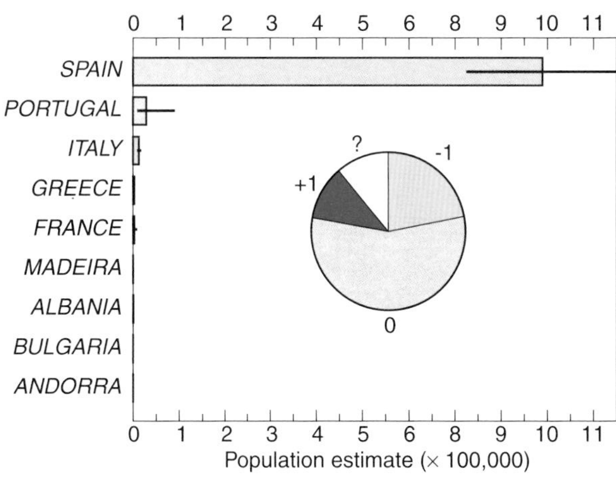

% in top 10 countries: 100.0
Total number of populated European countries: 9
Total European population 876,613–1,216,296 (1,027,289)
Russian population 100–1000 (316)
Turkish population 10,000–100,000 (31,623)

The distribution of the unobtrusive Rock Sparrow extends throughout S Europe, North Africa, the Middle East and C Asia E to Manchuria. The nominate *P.p. petronia* occupies most of the European range, except for *exigua* in the Transcaucasia and *kirhizica* E of the lower Volga; there are four other subspecies. It occurs mostly in open barren areas exposed to the sun, on rocky slopes or dry stony grasslands, sometimes scattered with shrubs and trees, but is also found in pastures and croplands. It breeds in deep holes or cracks in rocks, ruins and in buildings, but accepts hollow trees, mainly oak *Quercus*, and old Bee-eater *Merops apiaster* burrows (Catalunya, Sardinia and S France).

The Rock Sparrow breeds from the coast to the mountains, usually below 1600m asl, exceptionally up to 1840m in Piedmont (Mingozzi *et al* in press) and 2040m asl in Queyras (Lebreton 1977) in the western Alps. In France, a correlation has been established between its distribution pattern and an annual minimum of 2000 hours of sunlight (Lebreton 1975).

Although the map shows a widespread range throughout SW Europe the species is unevenly distributed over much of that region, being absent in apparently favourable areas. It breeds in lone pairs or more often in small groups (2–10 nests) and has a very complex mating strategy (Biddau *et al* 1995). Spanish data reveal (spring census): 1.64 birds/10ha in uncultivated land and 0.02 birds/10ha in cropland (Bernis 1988).

The species disappeared from SW Germany and NE France at the end of the 19th century. Slight decreases in numbers are occurring in Greece and perhaps in S Italy, although elsewhere populations seem stable. Mainly resident, the Rock Sparrow is highly gregarious after breeding: in Spain flocks of 500–2000 birds may gather in winter (A. Onrubia, pers obs).

Toni Mingozzi (I) Alejandro Onrubia (E)

Montifringilla nivalis Snowfinch

CZ	Pěnkavák sněžní	**I**	Fringuello alpino
D	Schneefink	**NL**	Sneeuwvink
E	Gorrión Alpino	**P**	Pardal-alpino
F	Niverolle alpine	**PL**	Śnieżka
FIN	Lumivarpunen	**R**	Снежный вьюрок
G	Χιονόστρουθος	**S**	Snöfink
H	Havasi pinty		

Non-SPEC, Threat status S (P)

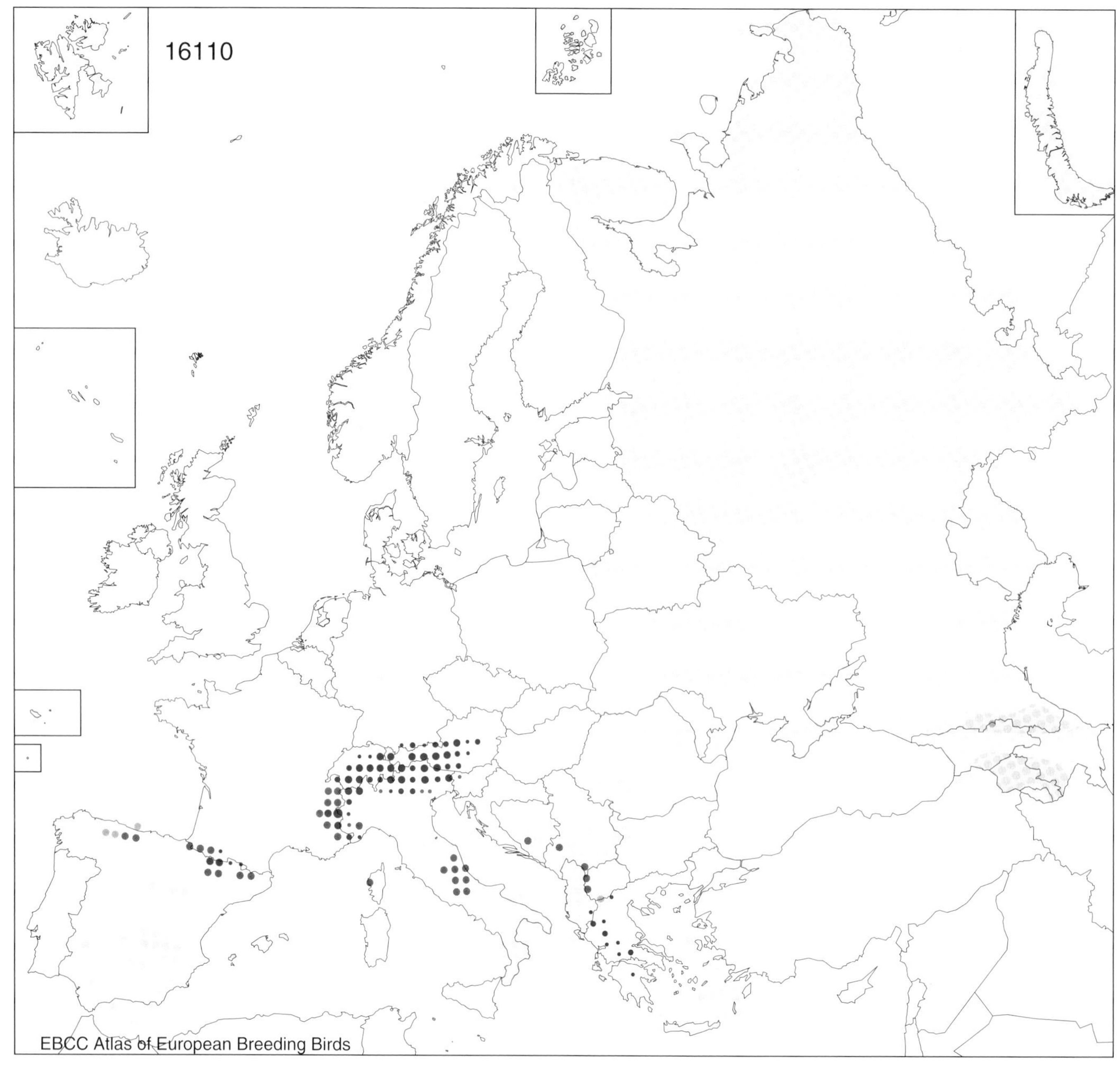

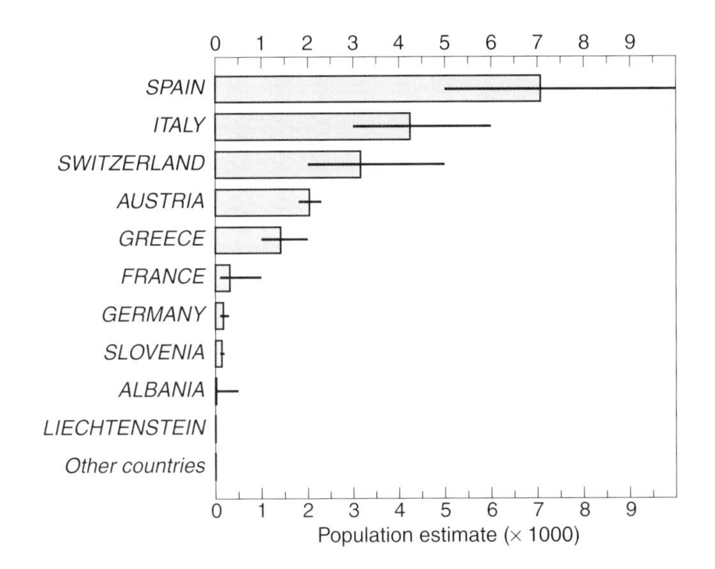

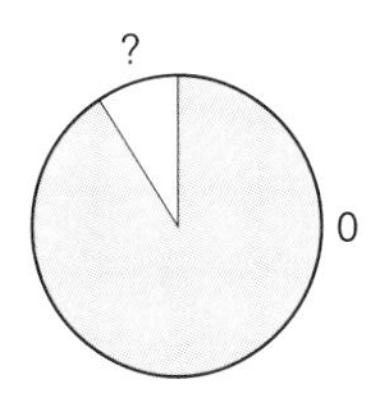

% in top 10 countries: 100.0
Total number of populated European countries: 11
Total European population 15,858–22,611 (18,590)
Turkish population 10,000–100,000 (31,623)

The distribution of the Snowfinch, a high-altitude sparrow, extends throughout the mountain chains of S Europe, Asia Minor, the Caucasus, SW Iran E to the Pamirs, the Altai and NE China. The Snowfinch forms a species-group with Tibetan Snowfinch *M. henrici*.

The Snowfinch occurs in the alpine zone and below the permanent snowline on grassy areas between cliffs, rock outcrops, boulder-strewn slopes, screes and moraines and often near glaciers. However, even in the apparently most favourable areas it is often distributed irregularly, being patchily dispersed in small 'colonies' of 2–6bp, sometimes more. Lone pairs occur less often than 'colonies' (Mingozzi *et al* 1988). The Snowfinch breeds in sheltered rock cracks and niches or on buildings (refuges, fortifications, alpine huts). In the Swiss Jungfrau region the species prefers to nest on buildings and ski-lift pylons in alpine meadows rather than in the more distant rocks (Heiniger 1991). Those breeding pairs nesting on buildings may, like the House Sparrow *Passer domesticus*, develop a close association with human beings, such as occurs along the Grossglockner scenic road or in the upper Ötz Valley, in Austria (Dvorak *et al* 1993).

Because of its ecological preferences, the Snowfinch breeds at high altitudes. The main altitudinal belts lie between 1900m and 2500m asl (eastern Alps), 2100–2200m (western Alps), 2800–3000m asl (Pyrenees) and 2750–3160m (Caucasus). Normally it breeds down to *c*1800–1900m, but exceptionally single sites are known as low as 1680m asl in the Italian Alps (Maestri & Voltolini 1985) and the Navarre Pyrenees (Elosegui 1985) and 1440m in Switzerland (Schifferli *et al* 1980). Breeding occurs frequently above 3000m asl, the highest European records being at 3450m on the Swiss Jungfrau (Schifferli *et al* 1980) and at 3650m on Monte Rosa in Italy (Mingozzi *et al* 1988). The Snowfinch has bred at 5300m in Tibet (*BWP*).

The map shows the Alps as the European range core, but the species is unevenly distributed, indeed as over most of the Swiss and Austrian Alps where generally limestone areas hold more birds than crystalline massifs. The suggestion that these lower densities are related to a paucity of the flora on which the Snowfinch feeds is not borne out in the western Alps. The Snowfinch also breeds in the Cantabrian Mountains, the C Apennines and in the Balkan mountain ridges S to the Kilini Mountains in the northern Peloponnese (Hölzinger 1993). An isolated population occurs in the Corsican Cinto Massif. All the above populations are comprised of the nominate subspecies *M.n. nivalis*; *alpicola* occurs in the Caucasus. There are six other subspecies elsewhere.

Few data on population density are available. In the Austrian Alps (Hohe Tauern, Grossglockner area), a census (two study plots, each 300ha, at 2000–2700m asl) revealed densities of 4.8 bp/km^2 and 2.2–2.9 bp/km^2 respectively, but the plot with fewer pairs suffered severer snow conditions (Winding 1985). On a third (69ha, 1960–2360m asl) study in the Fusch Valley (Hohe Tauern), 4.3–5.8 bp/km^2 were recorded (N. Winding, pers comm). Censuses in the Cantabrian Mountains revealed densities of 1 bp/10ha and linear densities of 0.7–4.57 bp/km (A. Onrubia, pers comm).

To date, no special dynamic trend seems to affect populations, except for normal fluctuations due to weather hazards. The effects of growing ski tourism on this species are unknown.

Post-breeding, the Snowfinch is highly gregarious, forming flocks from a few tens up to 200–300 in the western Alps. The species is mainly resident, making short winter altitudinal movements, although it may wander widely outside its breeding range (Lebrun 1994).

Toni Mingozzi (I) Andreas Ranner (A)

Fringilla coelebs

Chaffinch

CZ	Pěnkava obecná	**I**	Fringuello
D	Buchfink	**NL**	Vink
E	Pinzón Vulgar	**P**	Tentilháo-comum
F	Pinson des arbres	**PL**	Zięba
FIN	Peippo	**R**	Зяблик
G	Σπίνος	**S**	Bofink
H	Erdei pinty		

SPEC Cat 4, Threat status S

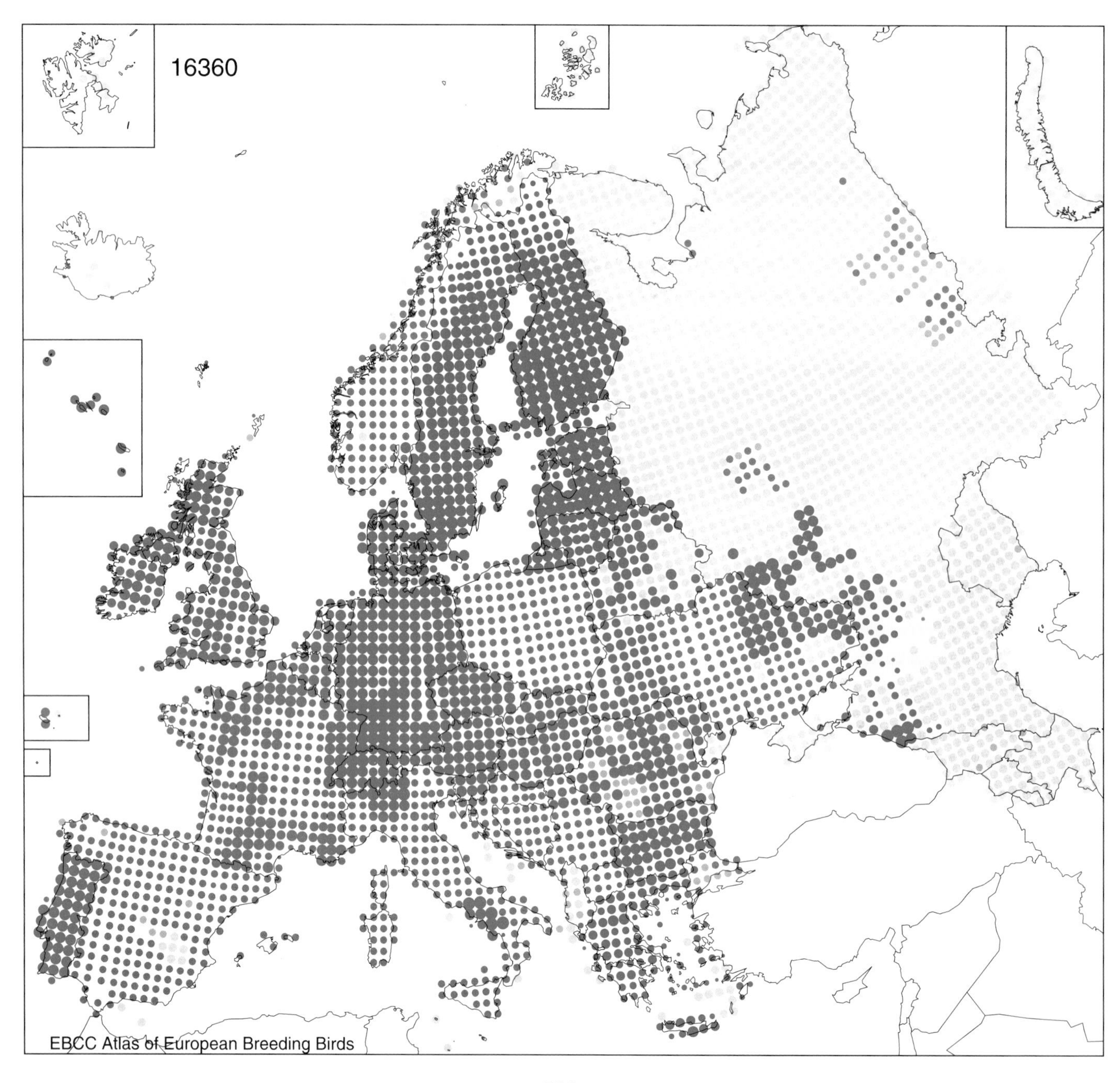

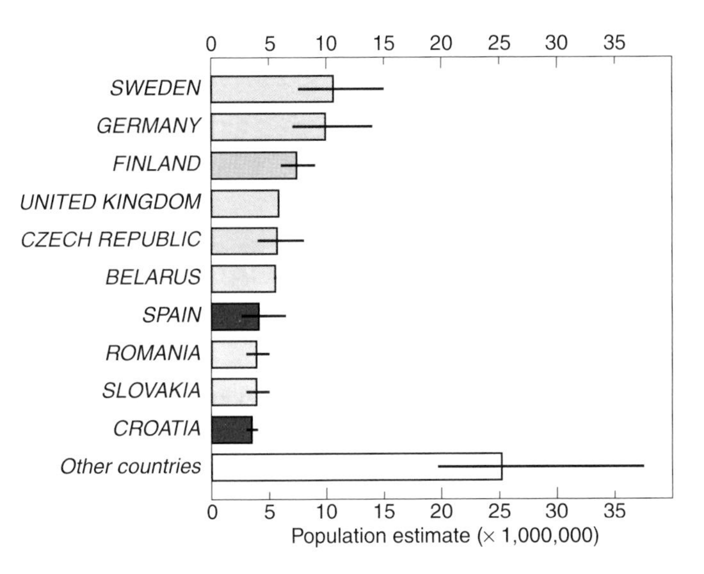

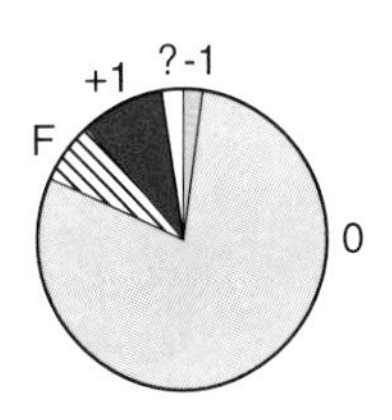

% in top 10 countries: 70.5
Total number of populated European countries: 44
Total European population 79,567,350–95,523,553 (85,261,240)
Russian population 10,000,000–100,000,000 (31,622,777)
Turkish population 1,000,000–10,000,000 (3,162,278)

A bird of the western Palaearctic, in boreal, temperate and mediterranean zones, the Chaffinch is distributed in Europe northwards almost to the limit of the trees, southwards to North Africa and Iran, eastwards into Siberia, and as far W as the Azores and Madeira. It is one of the most familiar and widespread of European birds, breeding in all types of woody habitats, from lowland to montane and subalpine zones, and from extensive forests and woods to tall hedgerows, orchards, parks and gardens, including those in the centres of some towns and cities.

During the 20th century, it is perhaps in northern boreal regions where Chaffinch numbers have changed most markedly, as the species has gradually increased and spread northwards. In Finland, numbers increased substantially from the 1920s to the 1940s (Järvinen & Väisänen 1979). Although this coincided with a period of climatic warming, the main reason for the increase may be that this generalist species was favoured by a change in forest management which increased the area of dense high forest and the amount of edge, where the Chaffinch occurs at densities up to 2.5 times higher than in the forest interior. It may also have benefited locally from the felling of patches of forest to create farmland.

Short-term fluctuations, especially in northern areas, are often associated with weather patterns. For example, the Finnish population decrease of 20% during 1984–88 is associated with two hard winters in the C European wintering areas (1984/85 and 1986/87) and one very cold summer (1987) in the breeding areas, but in the following milder years numbers rapidly reached their previous level. National monitoring programmes showed increases of 10–20% in Finland, Estonia, Sweden, Denmark, The Netherlands and Great Britain in the 1970s and 1980s, and further increases were noted in Ukraine, Croatia and Spain.

In summer, its territorial behaviour and conspicuous song make the Chaffinch easy to count reliably, although territory boundaries may fluctuate widely within a single breeding season (Bergmann 1993). In woodland habitats, it is one of the most numerous species, often forming between one fifth and two fifths of the total bird population. The total European population, including the huge numbers in Russia, amounts to some 230 000 000bp. In Fennoscandia, where most studies have been made, Chaffinch breeding densities in various deciduous woods reach 50–150 bp/km^2, in spruce *Picea* woods *c*100 bp/km^2 and in pine *Pinus* woods *c*10–30 bp/km^2, depending on latitude, soil type, vegetation structure and other factors. Numbers may remain more stable from year to year in favoured broad-leaved woods than in poorer pine woods (Glas 1960). Outside the breeding season, the Chaffinch is also found on open farmland, wherever suitable seeds are available.

The species winters entirely within the western Palearctic region, but nearly all the birds from the NE of the range migrate for the winter, augmenting those in the SW, where they are resident (Newton 1972). At this season the birds feed mainly on seeds on the ground, including those of trees and herbaceous plants. As shown by ringing recoveries, to some extent the sexes differ in migratory habits, with hens moving further than cocks from the same breeding areas. Linnaeus named the Chaffinch *coelebs* (bachelor) because the few individuals that remained to winter in his homeland (Sweden) were mostly cocks.

Geographical variation among Chaffinches is marked, with three distinct groups of races, differing mainly in the pattern of the head and the colour of the underparts. The *coelebs* group (7 subspecies) occurs in western Eurasia and the Middle East, the *spoliogenys* group (2 subspecies) in North Africa and the *canariensis* group (5 subspecies) on the Atlantic islands.

Ian Newton (GB) Risto A Väisänen (FIN)

Fringilla montifringilla Brambling

CZ	Pěnkava jikavec	**I**	Peppola
D	Bergfink	**NL**	Keep
E	Pinzón Real	**P**	Tentilhão-montez
F	Pinson du nord	**PL**	Jer
FIN	Järripeippo	**R**	Юрок
G	Χειμωνόσπινος	**S**	Bergfink
H	Fenyőpinty		

Non-SPEC, Threat status S

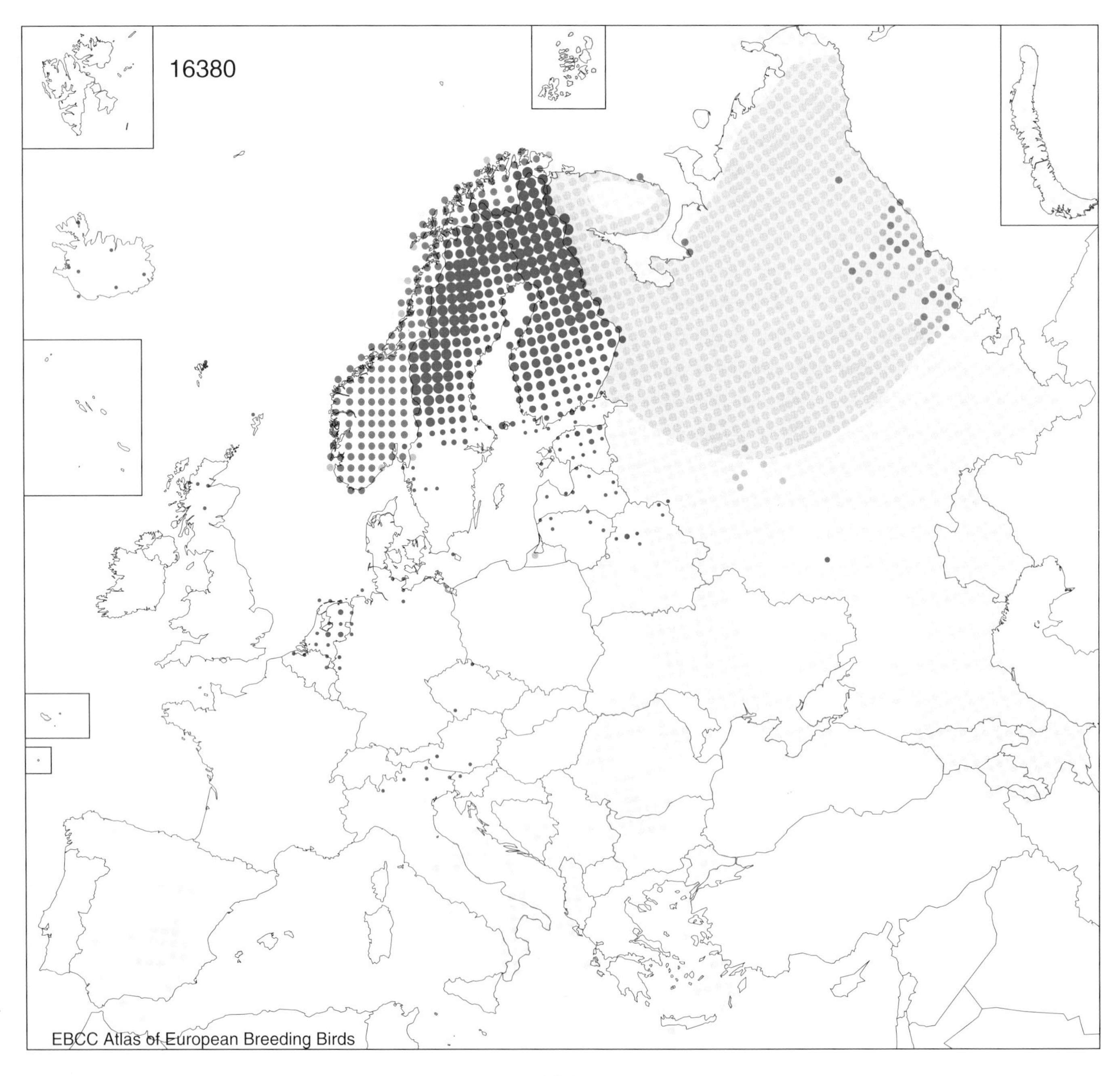

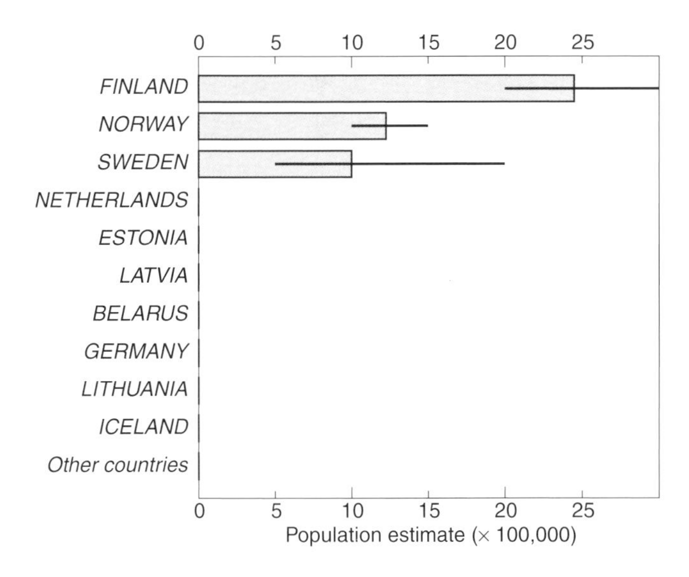

% in top 10 countries: 100.0
Total number of populated European countries: 15
Total European population 3,965,685–5,848,829 (4,674,594)
Russian population 1,000,000–10,000,000 (3,162,278)

The Brambling, the northern boreal ecological counterpart of the Chaffinch *F. coelebs*, belongs to the Siberian fauna and is distributed extensively from Scandinavia to eastern Siberia. It displays low site tenacity (Mikkonen 1983) which causes wide annual variations to the southern margin of its breeding range. In spring, birds make nomadic reconnaissances to choose suitable nesting sites, but low temperatures add a southerly bias, so that breeding in southern Finland and in Norwegian lowland forests becomes quite common. Breeding numbers vary from year to year, and in subalpine birch forests density is dependent on the abundance of defoliating caterpillars of the geometrid moth *Epirrita autumnata* (Hogstad 1985, Lindström 1987).

The Brambling inhabits many types of northern forests, favouring mountain birch *Betula* forests in Fennoscandia, but the main population breeds in open, mixed or conifer forests in the taiga of the subarctic and mid-boreal zones. In Norway it is also common in riverine alder *Alnus* forests and it may occur in the Russian tundra in the riverine willow *Salix* zone. Occasionally it breeds in birch scrub or mixed woodland in C Europe, far S of its normal range.

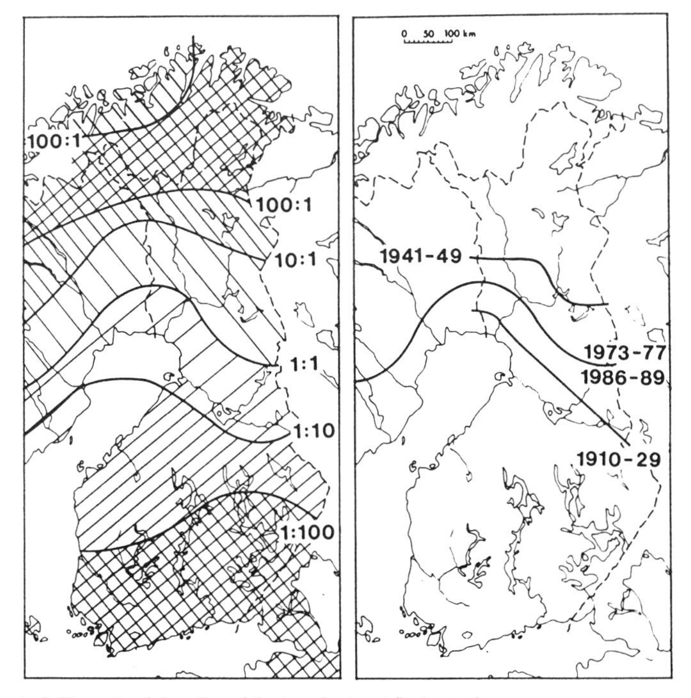

Left: The ratio of densities of the two dominant finch species, the Brambling and the Chaffinch, in N Fennoscandia in 1973–77. Right: The 1:1 zones of the two dominant finch species in four study periods (Järvinen & Väisänen, completed 1979). Note that the position of the 1:1 zone did not change during the last two periods.

In Fennoscandia breeding density is highest in mountain birch forests, Brambling being among the most numerous species, commonly 20–30 bp/km² in barren (heath) and 50–70 (occasionally 100–150) bp/km² in eutrophic (meadow) forest (Hogstad 1975). In northern-boreal Finnish Lapland typical densities (in bp/km²) are: pine forest 12, spruce 34 and mixed 16 (R.A. Väisänen *et al*, in prep). The average Fennoscandian breeding density in favoured habitat reaches 15–20 bp/km², whereas the adjacent arctic and mid-boreal areas host only 5–10 bp/km² (R.A. Väisänen *et al*, in prep). In C and S Fennoscandia breeding density decreases sharply away from mountainous areas, being very low in the S of the region where breeding occurs in moderate numbers only 2–3 times per decade. The more southerly marginal populations in Europe are unstable.

The Brambling's breeding range and population size has remained stable overall. In Finland the average population size has been relatively stable since 1925, except for a temporary reduction of *c*50% in the 1940s, due possibly to increased mortality in its wintering areas in C and W Europe during the extremely cold winters of 1939–42 (Järvinen & Väisänen 1979).

The abundance gradient between the two *Fringilla* species is steep. The diagram shows that a 100:1 ratio becomes inverted within 600km, a 10 000-fold change! In the overlap zone, the position of their 1:1 occurrence has varied over a 200km distance in a N-S direction, mainly because the Brambling's numbers and range have fluctuated, although the position of the 1:1 line remained static during 1973–77 and 1986–89. However, Chaffinch populations have not fluctuated in a complementary manner, indicating that there exists, at most, diffuse competition between the two finches.

Russia holds the largest Brambling population, estimated at 1M–10Mbp, followed by Finland (average 1.7Mbp, annual range 1M–2.5Mbp), Norway (1M–2Mbp) and Sweden (0.5M–2Mbp); in comparison other European populations are tiny. A crude estimate of the total European population, based on suitable boreal habitat, is 15Mbp.

Olav Hogstad (N) and Risto A Väisänen (FIN)

Estrilda astrild

Common Waxbill

CZ Astrild vlnkovaný
D Wellenastrild
E Pico de Coral
F Astrild ondulé
FIN Vahanokka
G Λαμπρόσπιζα
H Helena-pinty
I Astrilde comune
NL Sint-Helenafazantje
P Bico-de-lacre
PL Astryld falisty
R Волнистый астрильд
S Helenaastrild

Criteria not applied

A small passerine from tropical Africa, very popular as a cagebird, the Common Waxbill was introduced into C-W Portugal during the late 1960s (Xavier 1968). The discontinuity of its distribution through to the 1980s suggests that further introductions took place in parts of the southern coast and within the Tejo (Tagus) and Sado catchments.

Its European range is still expanding and by 1995 was almost continuous not only along the W and SW coasts of Iberia, but also inland, following the main river valleys. The species reached Spain in 1977 and by 1995 was distributed mainly along the Guadiana River (Guerrero *et al* 1989). Furthermore, there are a number of breeding records from elsewhere in Spain, in Malaga, Andalucía (de Juana 1991) and in Galicia (R. Costas & Reino, pers comm).

When first introduced, the Common Waxbill initially was dependent on wetland margins such as reedbeds and overgrown embankments, particularly adjacent to ricefields. Nowadays, although it shows preference for such habitats when they are plentiful, it can be found in a wide variety of open habitats, like mosaic farmland comprising small fields and hedges, but usually near water. It remains absent from areas (such as mountains) which experience wide temperature fluctuations.

Its long breeding season, from April to December, and a benign year-round climate, are probably the main reasons why the Common Waxbill has successfully adapted to SW Europe (Ferreira 1982).

It is highly gregarious, forming flocks several hundred strong in prime habitat patches, and although it is resident, it must make significant dispersal movements to account for its fast range expansion. It is likely that several subspecies, possibly from Guinea-Bissau and Cape Verde (former Portuguese colonies), were involved in its introduction, but little is known of the natural origins of the European population. Some 16 subspecies are recognized in Africa. The Common Waxbill has naturalized populations on many tropical and subtropical islands (Lever 1987), but that of Brazil, originating in the 19th century, is also a candidate source for the European population, because of the links between Brazil and Portugal.

Florentino de Lope (E) Renato Neves (P) Rui Rufino (P)

Estrilda melpoda

Orange-cheeked Waxbill

CZ Astrild oranžovolící
D Orangebäckchen
E Estrilda Carita de Naranja
F Astrild à joues oranges
FIN Savannivahanokka
G Πορτοκαλομάγουλη Λαμπρόσπιζα
H Narancsfejű asztrild
I Astrilde guancearancio
NL Oranjekaakje
P Bico-de-lacre-de-face-laranja
PL Astryld rudouchy
R Оранжевощекий астрильд
S Orangekindad astrild

Criteria not applied

The Orange-cheeked Waxbill is an African species whose natural distribution starts in sub-Saharan Africa from Senegal to northern Zaire, S to N Zambia and W to the Atlantic. Its natural habitats range from open savanna to cleared areas in dense tropical forest, anywhere which has a reliable source of millet-like grass seeds. The Orange-cheeked Waxbill is a popular cagebird, and has established populations from escapes and releases on numerous subtropical and tropical islands throughout the world (Clement *et al* 1993).

It breeds in several localities in Castellón Province in eastern Spain. The first regular observations took place in 1990 at the mouth of the River Mijares. Its numbers have since increased, as has its local range (citrus orchards at Onda, and marshes at Almenara, both in Castellón) up to 250m asl. It inhabits dense vegetation growing beside rivers or small streams.

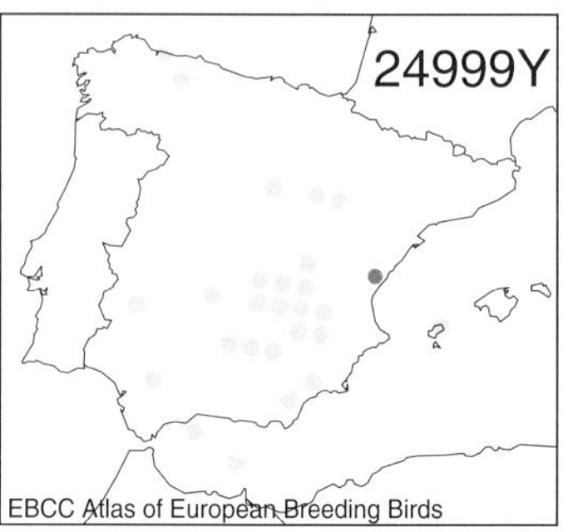

During regular ringing in two localities, young were trapped from August onwards, despite the species being present year-round, which suggests a late breeding season. Trapped birds have normal fat levels and good body condition, and so seem well-adapted to this area. The presence of grasses closely related to millet, such as *Echinocloa curs-galli*, *E. colonum* and *Setaria pumila*, on which it feeds frequently, probably has contributed to its survival. Although probably originating from escapes, the population may grow without significant reinforcement from captive stock.

In its extensive natural range, the Orange-cheeked Waxbill displays considerable plumage variation even in local populations (Clement *et al* 1993). Only two subspecies are recognized, and it is unlikely that birds breeding in Europe cam be assigned safely to either.

Joan Castany (E) German López (E)

Amandava amandava

Red Avadavat

CZ	Astrild tygří	I	Bengalino
D	Tigerfink	NL	Tijgervink
E	Bengalí Rojo	P	Bengalim-mosqueado
F	Bengali rouge	PL	Bengalik
FIN	Punatiikeripeippo	R	Тигровый астрильд
G	Αμαντάβα	S	Tigerfink
H	Tigrispinty		

Criteria not applied

The natural distribution of the Red Avadavat stretches from Pakistan across the Indian subcontinent to SW China, Thailand, Cambodia and Vietnam, a separate population occupying the Lesser Sundas.

Its bright colouring has made it a very popular cagebird, and so it is not surprising that there are numerous records of escapes and introductions, some of which have resulted in permanent populations (Lever 1987). Sedentary naturalized populations have existed in Spain and Italy since 1974 and 1983 respectively. Since 1978 the principal Spanish population has been that of Extremadura, along 130km of river margins along the Tajo, Guadiana and Guadalquivir. A secondary population inhabits the Mediterranean coastal marshes. None of the European populations seem to compete with indigenous species, which would reduce constraints against expansion. Habitats occupied include wetlands where reed *Phragmites* and reedmace *Typha* predominate, meadows and irrigated crops (Spain) and rush *Juncus* and sedge *Carex* (*BWP*).

The total Spanish population is estimated at 6000 birds. In Italy 80–90bp (300 birds) can be found along the River Sile

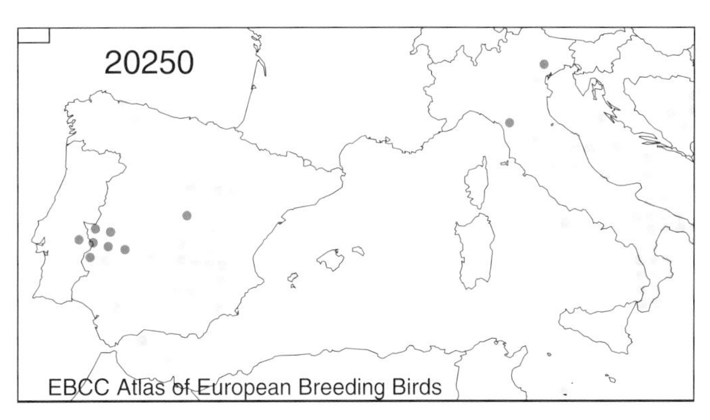

(*BWP*). Both Spanish populations are showing an increasing trend but are vulnerable to drastic reductions in severe winters. The species is trapped by local bird traders, an action which may affect numbers. It is a late breeder, usually between July and December. It is found usually in pairs or small flocks and roosts communally in reedbeds (Clement *et al* 1993).

Florentino de Lope (E)

Serinus pusillus

Red-fronted Serin

CZ	Zvonohlík zlatočelý	I	Verzellino frouterossa
D	Rotstirngirlitz	NL	Roodvoorhoofdkanarie
E	Verdecillo Frontigualdo	P	Chamariz-de-testa-vermelha
F	Serin à front d'or	PL	Kulczyk królewski
FIN	Kultahemppo	R	Королевский вьюрок
G	Σκαρθάκι του Καυκάσου	S	Rödpannad gulhämpling
H	Piroshomlokú csicsörke		

Non-SPEC, Threat status S (P)

The range of the Red-fronted Serin stretches from the Caucasus through Asia Minor and C Asia to Iraq, SW Tibet, China and the Indian subcontinent. In the *Atlas*' area of coverage, it occurs in SE Russia and the Caucasus republics.

It breeds from low to high altitude in montane steppe scattered with shrubs, in sparse forest on rocky cliffs and scree slopes and in the timberline subalpine zone. In winter it descends to lower levels to frequent river valleys in montane steppe or woodland glades, sometimes visiting human settlements. In some parts of its range, in the Caucasus and Kazakhstan for example, the species is unevenly distributed in a mosaic of presence and absence.

Continued on p.709

Serinus serinus **Serin**

CZ	Zvonohlík zahradní	**I**	Verzellino
D	Girlitz	**NL**	Europese Kanarie
E	Verdecillo	**P**	Chamariz-comum
F	Serin cini	**PL**	Kulczyk
FIN	Kanarianhemppo	**R**	Европейский вьюрок
G	Σκαρθάκι	**S**	Gulhämpling
H	Csicsörke		

SPEC Cat 4, Threat status S

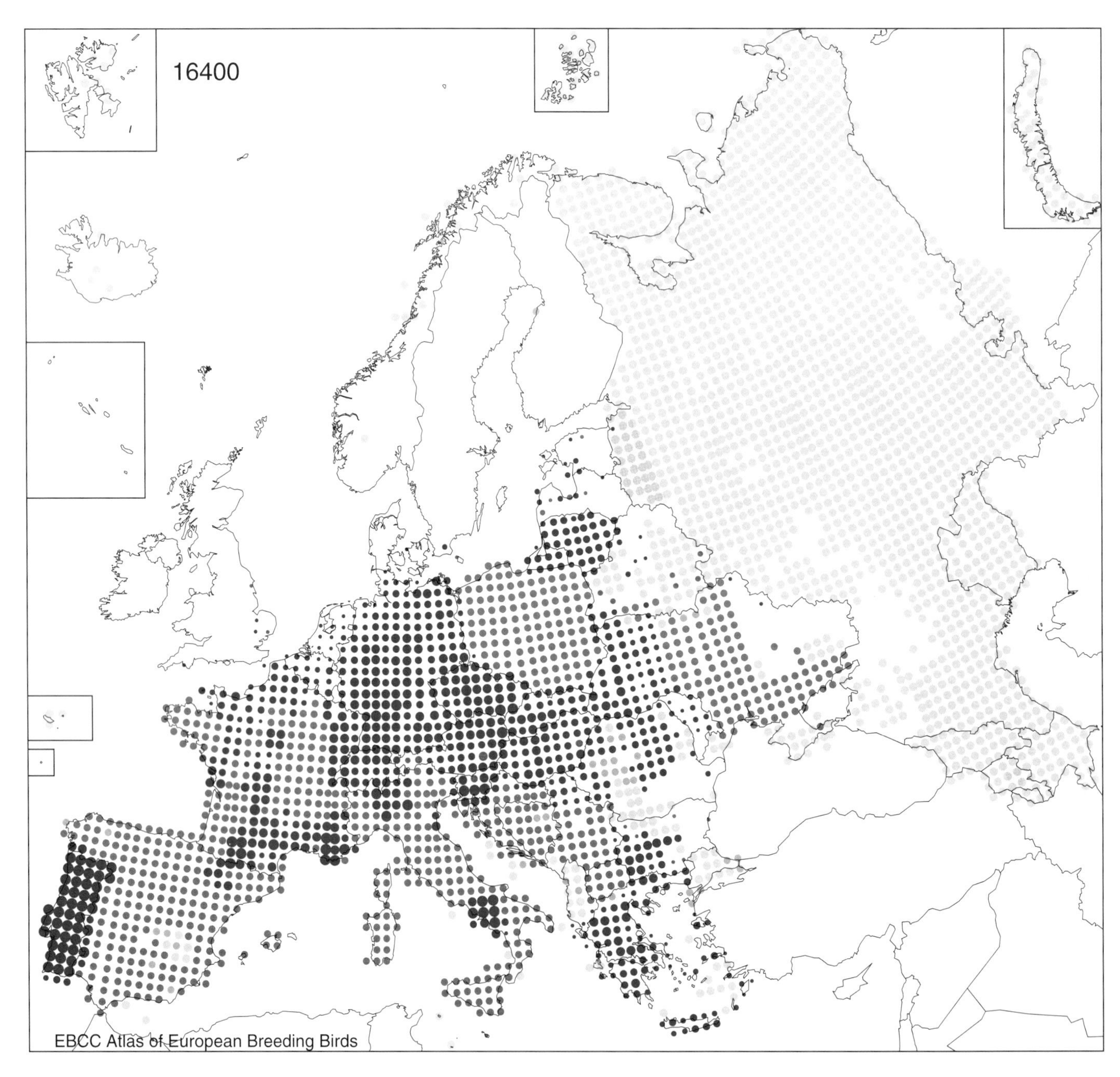

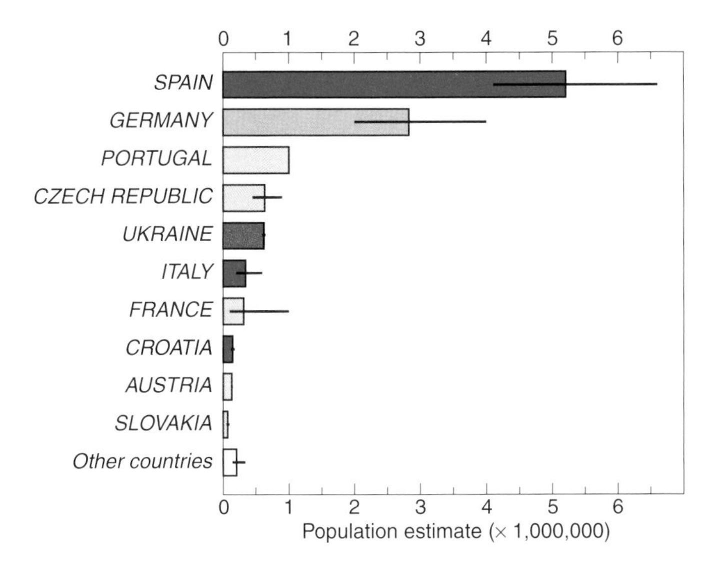

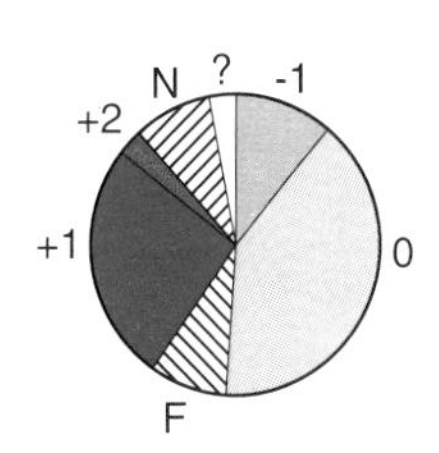

% in top 10 countries: 98.2
Total number of populated European countries: 35
Total European population 10,095,566–13,496,108 (11,511,967)
Russian population 100–1000 (316)
Turkish population 10,000–100,000 (31,623)

The Serin is found only in the western Palearctic. Its original distribution was confined to the southern European countries bordering the Mediterranean, the western Mediterranean islands, and North Africa from Morocco to Tunisia. However, from the 19th century onwards the Serin increased in numbers and expanded its distribution northwards and by 1875 already had reached C Europe. In the 20th century it has become established in The Netherlands, N Germany and England. Breeding in Finland and Sweden is sporadic and is largely so in Denmark. The species underwent a further range expansion eastwards where the present distribution reaches eastern Ukraine, Belarus and western Russia near St Petersburg, and also to Turkey and Cyprus. It has also extended its altitudinal limits, as in the Carpathians where the limit rose from 850m asl in 1963 to 1200m in 1982 (Newton 1985, Gorban *et al* 1987).

The adaptation to associate with artificial habitats can explain the range expansions which possibly arose from the population increases. Its original habitat comprised the clearings and margins of Mediterranean woodlands, but now the highest densities occur in cultivated land, town parks and gardens and around villages. This can be illustrated by comparing breeding densities in Iberia; in fruit plantations density averages 29 bp/10ha (Gil-Delgado 1981) but in natural habitats varies between 1.4 and 3.1 bp/10ha (Peris *et al* 1975). In C Europe breeding densities fluctuate between 3.6–18.7 bp/10ha (Czech parks), 0.9–2.0 (German small parks) and 0.2–16.4 (Poland; Dyrcz *et al* 1991). Spain, with between 4M and 6.6Mbp, holds the largest population, followed by Germany with up to 4Mbp. Most European countries' populations are stable or increasing.

C European populations are migratory, arriving from late March until early May. They winter in southern Europe, mainly in Spain; a few remain in the breeding grounds. Other populations mostly are resident, but some winter in North Africa (Asensio 1985) from late September onwards.

José A Gil-Delgado (E) Igor Gorban (UKR)

Serinus pusillus – continued from p.707

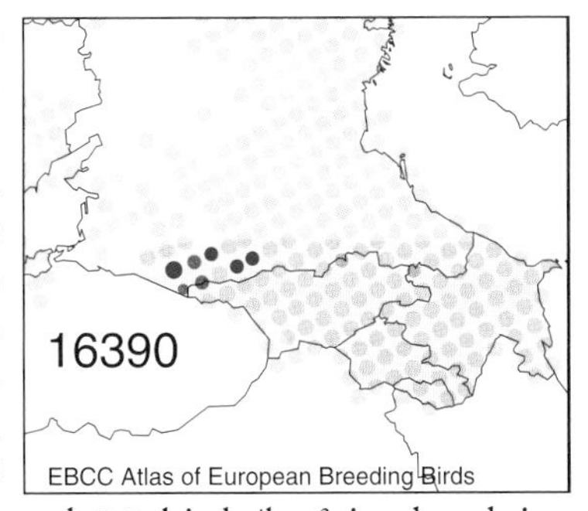

In typical habitats, the Red-fronted Serin is common, but there is little information on population size. In the Teberda Nature Reserve (W Caucasus), censuses undertaken in the 1960s found population densities of 37 birds/km² in the upper forest zone and 3.5 birds/km² in the alpine zone (Tkachenko 1966). The species is more abundant in the C Caucasus. In the North Ossetian Nature Reserve censuses undertaken in 1977 registered the highest density in cultivated landscape (up to 116 birds/km²) and in pine forests (67 birds/km²), whereas densities were lower in river valleys (up to 39 birds/km²) and in subalpine meadows (2–5 birds/km²) (Komarov 1991). The Red-fronted Serin is numerous also in the high mountains of Azerbaijan, where in 1961 the density in subalpine meadows in summer was 65 birds/km², in maple parklands on the timberline 110 and in alpine meadows 31 (Drozdov 1965). It is also common in the E of its range (Korelov 1974, Kovshar' 1979), but there are reports of a decline in numbers in some regions. For example, near Alma-Ata (Almaty) in Kazakhstan, a significant decrease has been recorded since the late 1960s, attributed to trapping for the cagebird trade (Korelov 1974).

Peter Til'ba (R)

Serinus canaria

Canary

CZ	Kanár divoký	I	Canarino
D	Kanarengirlitz	NL	Kanarie
E	Canario	P	Canário
F	Serin des Canaries	PL	Kanarek
FIN	Kanarialintu	R	Канарейка
G	Αγριο Καναρίνι	S	Kanariefågel
H	Kanári		

SPEC Cat 4, Threat status S

Large populations of the Canary are found only on Madeira, the Azores and the Canary Islands where it is common throughout. Two thirds of the total population inhabit the Canary Islands archipelago. The species may have reached the Azores through colonization or introduction (Bannerman & Bannerman 1966). The introduced population on Hawaii may still exist (Lever 1987). The Canary is sedentary in habit although local movements (sometimes inter-island) influenced by food availability, do occur in the Madeiran and Azores archipelagos (Bannerman 1963, Bannerman & Bannerman 1965). The species has long been a popular cagebird around the world, breeding readily in captivity.

The Canary has a wide habitat preference and a catholic choice of plant diet. Within the Madeiran archipelago it occurs on Madeira, Porto Santo and the Desertas at all altitudes where there is suitable habitat, which can be very varied. On Madeira, with the exception of Ponta de Sao Lourenço, its favoured habitat is the vegetation around vineyards, fields and orchards in open countryside. On Porto Santo it occupies much drier terrain, similar to that found at Ponta de Sao Lourenço. On the Desertas it breeds on semi-arid ground almost free of vegetation. In the Azores, it breeds in myrtle *Myrica* and tamarisk *Tamarix* (Bannerman & Bannerman 1966) up to *c*1100m asl. In the Canary Islands it nests in tree-heath *Erica*, pine *Pinus* and almond *Prunus* (Martín 1987).

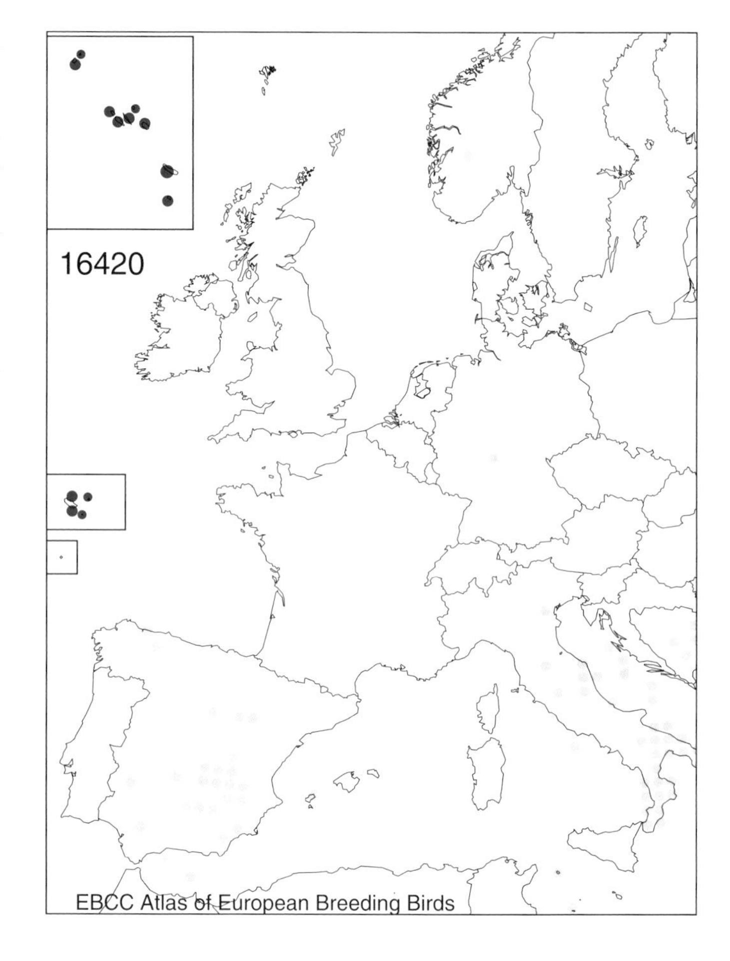

On the island of Madeira there have been regular censuses of the population since 1989 and the population is known to be stable. The populations of Porto Santo and the Desertas are also thought to be stable. The species faces no known threats at present, but the advent of widespread application of agro-chemicals may well have an effect on Canary distribution and numbers in the future.

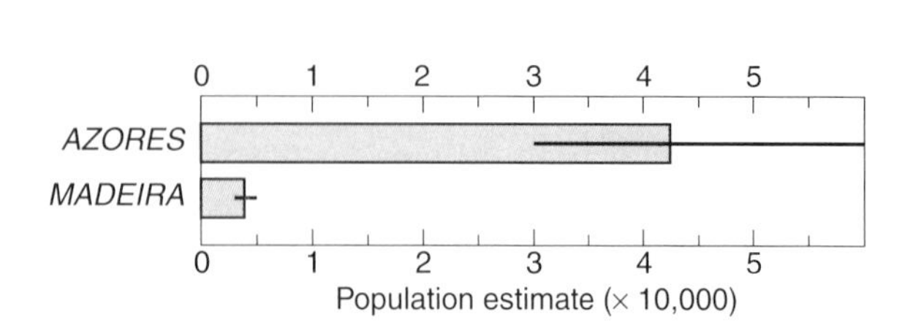

0

% in top 10 countries: 100.0
Total number of populated European countries: 2
Total European population 33,842–63,909 (46,229)

Paulo Oliveira (P) Francis Zino (P)

Serinus citrinella

Citril Finch

CZ	Zvonohlík citrónový	I	Venturone
D	Zitronengirlitz	NL	Citroenkanarie
E	Verderón Serrano	P	Verdilhão-serrano
F	Venturon montagnard	PL	Osetnik
FIN	Sitruunapeippo	R	Лимонный вьюрок
G	Σταχτοσκαρθάκι	S	Citronsiska
H	Citromcsíz		

SPEC Cat 4, Threat status S

The Citril Finch breeds only in certain mountain systems of C and SW Europe. A very distinct form *S.(c.)? corsicana* occurs over most of Corsica, Sardinia (except cultivated lowlands), Elba, Capri and Gorgona. Over its entire continental range the nominate *citrinella* favours the subalpine zone containing open coniferous forests, but it often occurs at the treeline and on montane pastures scattered with trees. Likewise *corsicana* appears to reach its highest densities in such habitats, although frequently it uses maquis or patchy cultivation at sea level. During years of pine *Pinus* seed abundance *citrinella* may extend temporarily its breeding range in Catalonia into sub-mediterranean habitats (500–1600m asl) bordering the subalpine zone (Borras & Senar 1991).

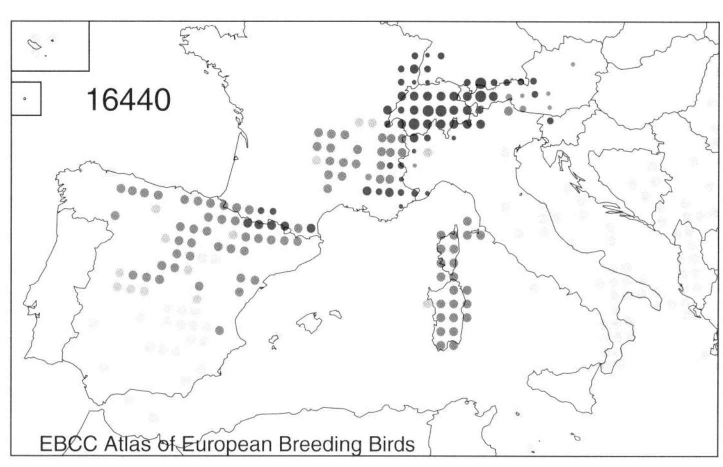

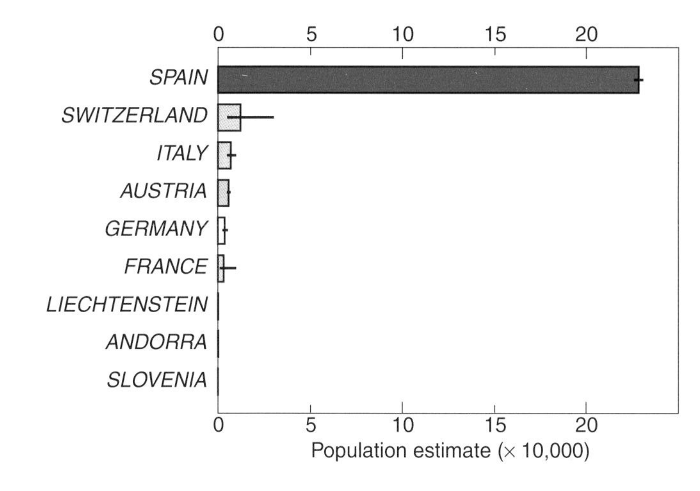

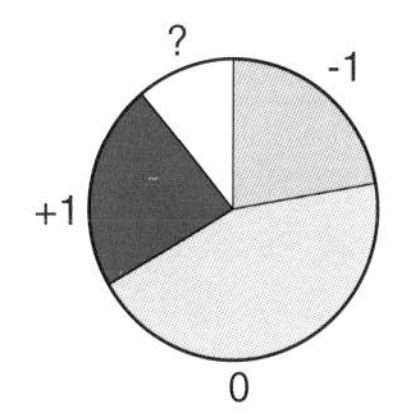

% in top 10 countries: 100.0
Total number of populated European countries: 9
Total European population 251,722–279,620 (260,091)

Along the northern Alpine slopes the species is continuously distributed only between Haut-Vercors (France) and Mangfallgebirge (Germany). Elsewhere in the alpine range it occurs less regularly, density decreasing toward the S and E. Its distribution in the Pyrenees, Cantabrians and Sierras of C Spain is relatively continuous.

Most populations are stable, despite being fairly small and well separated on the heights of the Black Forest (Germany), Vosges, Massif Central, Mt Ventoux (France), Jura (France/Switzerland) and Mt Triglav (Slovenia). The species commonly has occurred beyond its normal limits (Märki 1976), although it has not sustained range expansions permanently. Its eastern Austrian (Dvorak *et al* 1993) and Swiss northern limits (Lake Geneva to Lake Thun) (H. Märki, pers obs) are unchanged since the mid-1960s.

The species is mainly migratory in the northern Alps, usually abandoning its breeding grounds when snow-cover prevents feeding at *c*1220m asl (October). The more southerly populations tend to winter locally. Depending on snowfall depth, in southern France it shifts its winter range downslope temporarily. S of the Po Valley it apparently is irregular (di Carlo 1976). It was first recorded in Morocco in spring 1992. The extent of *corsicana*'s movements are poorly known, although large flocks occur on Corsican coasts (Thibault 1983).

Nicola Baccetti (I) Hans Märki (CH)

Carduelis chloris — Greenfinch

CZ	Zvonek zelený	I	Verdone
D	Grünling	NL	Groenling
E	Verderón Común	P	Verdilhão-comum
F	Verdier d'Europe	PL	Dzwoniec
FIN	Viherpeippo	R	Зеленушка
G	Φλώρος	S	Grönfink
H	Zöldike		

SPEC Cat 4, Threat status S

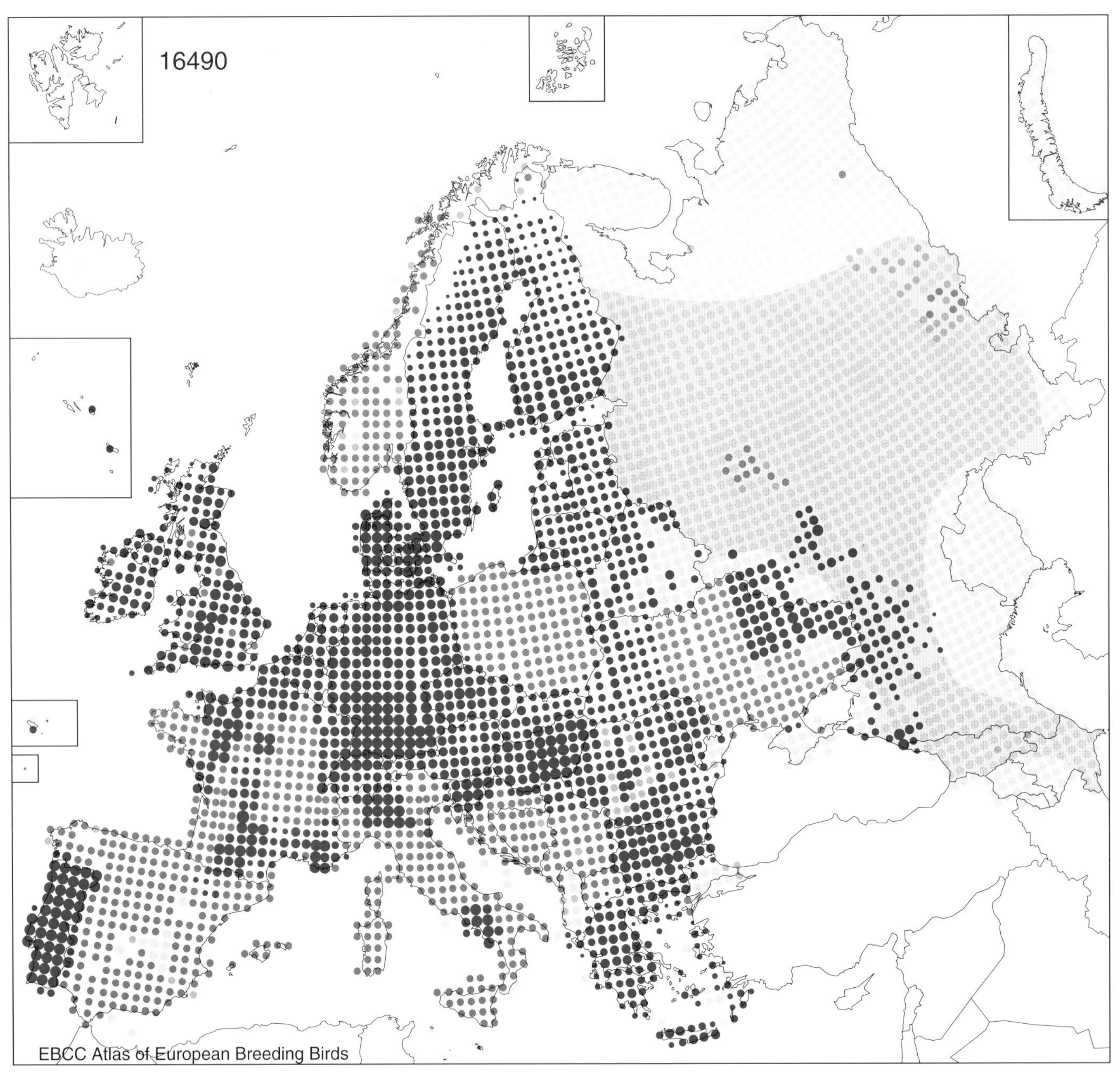

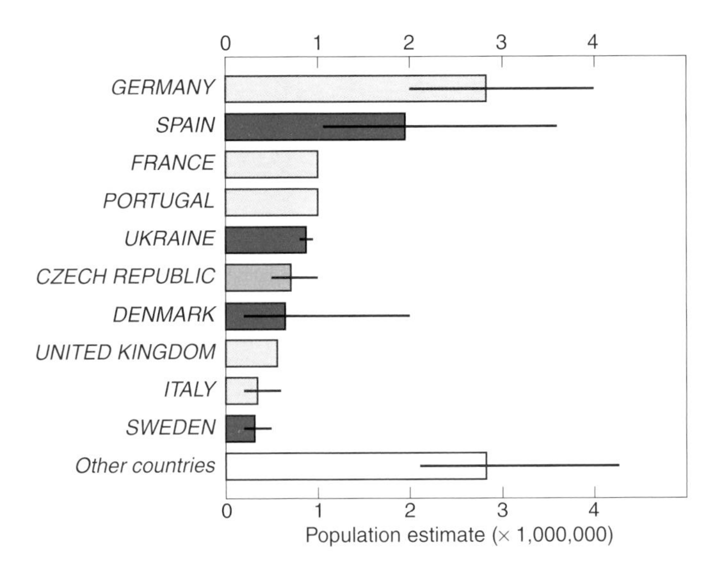

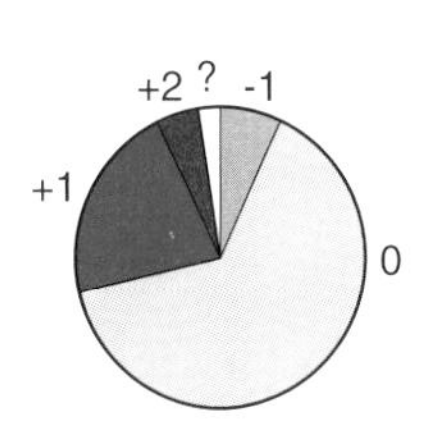

% in top 10 countries: 78.3
Total number of populated European countries: 41
Total European population 12,205,838–14,533,963 (13,039,097)
Russian population 100,000–1,000,000 (316,228)
Turkish population 50,000–500,000 (158,114)

The Greenfinch breeds over much of the western Palearctic in the boreal, temperate, steppe and mediterranean zones, its range extending from *c*70°N in Scandinavia and *c*62°N in Russia S to NW Africa and to N Sinai, and from Ireland E to the western Urals and through the Caucasus to N Iran. A population isolated by a belt of steppe and desert inhabits the highlands of Russian Turkestan. The Greenfinch has been introduced to the Azores, SE Australia, New Zealand and locally in SE South America.

Originally a bird of forest edge and open bushy areas, the Greenfinch now breeds throughout cultivated landscapes, wherever there are thick tall bushes for nesting. It is most numerous in lowlands, but occasionally breeds up to 1400m asl in C European mountains. Since the 1950s it has become increasingly common in towns and villages, especially in its western range, nesting in parks and gardens. It has spread northwards in Europe (associated with winter feeding) and southwards in Israel and Egypt (with the establishment of human settlements). Otherwise, over most of its range the species has apparently remained fairly stable since the mid-1970s, in both numbers and distribution, but with increases recorded in some areas and declines in others.

Across its range, the species has an almost continuous distribution within suitable bushy habitat, being absent only from extensive stretches of closed forest, treeless open land and desert. In winter, however, it becomes more widely distributed, and may be found in woodland, or on seacoasts and open land at least 1km from cover, wherever suitable food plants occur. The Greenfinch takes the seeds of a wide range of woody and herbaceous plants, either directly or from the ground below (Eber 1956, Newton 1967, 1972). It is a frequent visitor to gardens, wherever peanuts, sunflower and other seeds are provided, in Britain being present in the average garden for 75% of spring weeks and 60% of summer weeks (D. Toomer, pers comm).

The species is most numerous in lowland areas of its southern and western ranges, where longer growing seasons and less snow ensure a greater food supply. Its recent spread in Fennoscandia is attributed to householders providing winter food, without which the species would probably be less numerous in the summer in boreal regions, and would not winter so far N.

Because the Greenfinch can breed in loose colonies, with pairs sometimes nesting less than 10m apart, it can achieve locally high nesting densities, but individual birds may range over much wider areas (up to 3km from their nests) to obtain food (Blümel 1983). Over large areas of suitable nesting habitat, it can achieve densities exceeding 20 bp/km^2, reaching more than 80 bp/km^2 in some parks and cemeteries (Flade 1994). It feeds in small parties or flocks, wherever food is temporarily available. Flocks tend to be largest in the autumn, sometimes containing several hundred individuals. Communal roosts occur in thick bushy areas, often being used year after year.

Most birds from the colder northern and eastern breeding ranges leave for the winter, concentrating in milder southern and western regions. There is some movement beyond the southern breeding range into Iran, Iraq, the Levant and NW Egypt. The general direction of migration is therefore southwestwards. Ringing has shown that some birds move more than 2000km, but most cover much shorter distances. In areas where the species occurs year-round, however, birds make frequent dispersal movements, moving varying distances and directions in search of food.

Geographical variation in size and colour is mostly clinal and there is much gradation between subspecies, of which seven occur in the coverage area, distributed mostly in rather complex fashion, and three beyond Europe.

José A Gil-Delgado (E) Ian Newton (GB)

Carduelis carduelis Goldfinch

CZ	Stehlík obecný	**I**	Cardellino
D	Stieglitz	**NL**	Putter
E	Jilguero	**P**	Pintassilgo
F	Chardonneret élégant	**PL**	Szczygieł
FIN	Tikli	**R**	Щегол
G	Καρδερίνα	**S**	Steglits
H	Tengelic		

Non-SPEC, Threat status S (P)

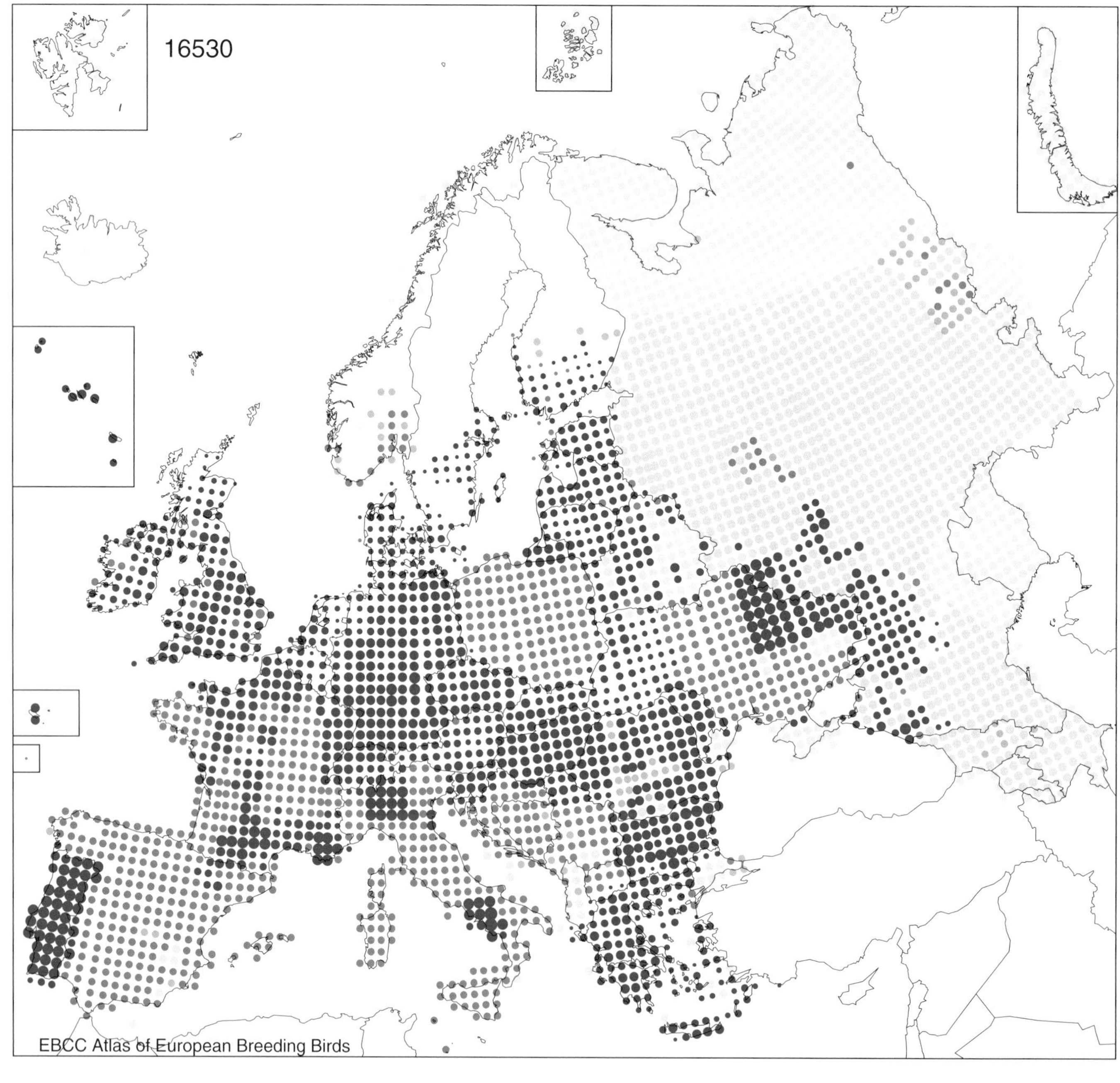

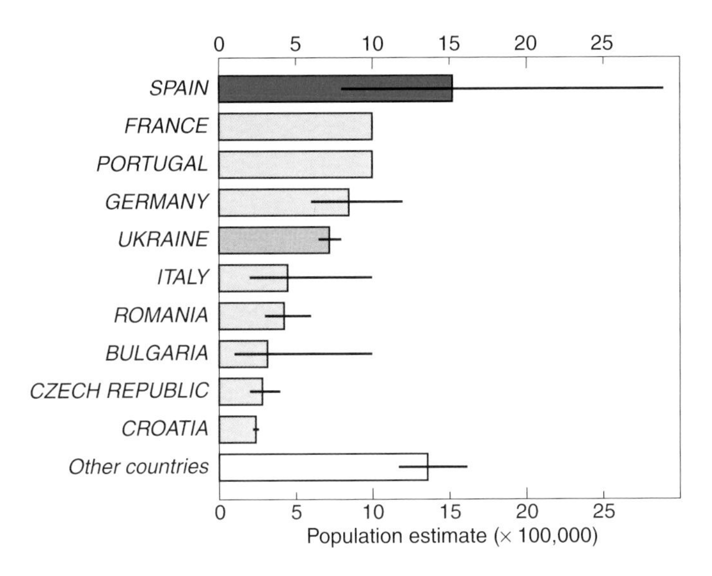

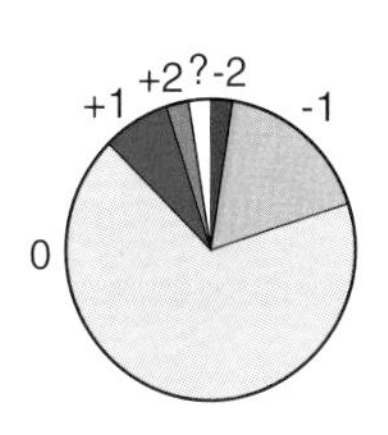

% in top 10 countries: 83.3
Total number of populated European countries: 39
Total European population 7,177,191–9,775,870 (8,161,433)
Russian population 100,000–1,000,000 (316,228)
Turkish population 1,000,000–10,000,000 (3,162,278)

The Goldfinch has a Palearctic distribution, from Portugal E to *c*96°E, from the boreal zone margins (above 60°N), southward through the temperate and mediterranean zones into steppe and desert fringes, from the level of southern Fennoscandia S into North Africa, the Canary Islands, Nile Valley and Himalayas. The distribution comprises two groups: a western (*carduelis*) form (black-crowned), which occupies the entire *Atlas* coverage area, and a more eastern (*caniceps*) form (grey-crowned, the grey merging into the back colour). The species also occurs through introductions in the Azores and Cape Verde Islands, SE and SW Australia, Tasmania, New Zealand, Bermuda and very locally in SE South America.

Originally a bird of sunny forest edge and open woodland, the Goldfinch now breeds throughout the cultivated landscapes of Europe, often nesting in trees in orchards, towns and villages. It is thus predominantly a lowland species, but extends into mountains around alpine meadows and other open areas. It is most often seen singing from a tree or other high perch, or feeding from the seed-heads of thistles and other food plants on waste ground. More than any other finch, it specializes on daisy family (*Compositae*) seeds, on which its numbers and distribution largely depend (Newton 1967, 1972, Glück 1980, 1985). In winter it becomes more widely distributed, foraging in open land far from trees, or to areas of seed birch *Betula* and alder *Alnus* trees.

Since the 1960s, it has spread northwards in Scotland and Fennoscandia, and southwards, especially up the Nile Valley in Egypt (following irrigation and human settlement), where it reaches its most southerly natural distribution (23°N). Otherwise, the overall population seems to have remained fairly stable since 1975, in both numbers and distribution, but with some increases in parts of the range and declines in others.

In its southern range, where food plants are commonest and seed occurs over much of the year, the species reaches its greatest abundance. In many Mediterranean countries it is one of the commonest birds. Over much of its range, it has long been a popular cagebird, to the extent that population size increases since 1950 in Britain & Ireland and Belgium have been attributed to the decline of commercial bird-catching, an activity which still thrives in some Mediterranean countries.

The species sometimes breeds in loose (usually 2–5bp) colonies, in which pairs may nest within 10m of each other, achieving high nesting densities locally, but individuals forage often up to 500m from their nests (Glück 1980). The species feeds gregariously throughout the year, concentrating wherever suitable seeding food plants occur. The largest flocks, sometimes hundreds or thousands strong, form in autumn, when food is plentiful and the year's population is at its highest level.

The northernmost and easternmost breeding ranges are largely vacated in autumn, the birds migrating to winter further S and W but mostly still within the overall breeding distribution. In winter, enormous numbers concentrate in the Mediterranean region, especially Iberia, adding to the already large local population. In general, females migrate in greater proportion and over longer distances than males, producing a sex-ratio gradient in winter, from a predominance of males in the N and E and of females in the S and W. There is some movement beyond the southern breeding range into Sinai and Mesopotamia.

Throughout this range, variation in the species is mainly clinal, the birds becoming slightly larger and paler towards the NE. Ten subspecies occur within the coverage area, the nominate *C.c. carduelis* occurring over most of mainland Europe, the other nine in mostly complex fashion in the remainder. Some six subspecies occur from Iran westwards.

Ian Newton (GB)

Carduelis spinus **Siskin**

CZ	Čížek lesní	I	Lucarino
D	Erlenzeisig	NL	Sijs
E	Lúgano	P	Lugre
F	Tarin des aulnes	PL	Czyż
FIN	Vihervarpunen	R	Чиж
G	Λούγαρο	S	Grönsiska
H	Csíz		

SPEC Cat 4, Threat status S

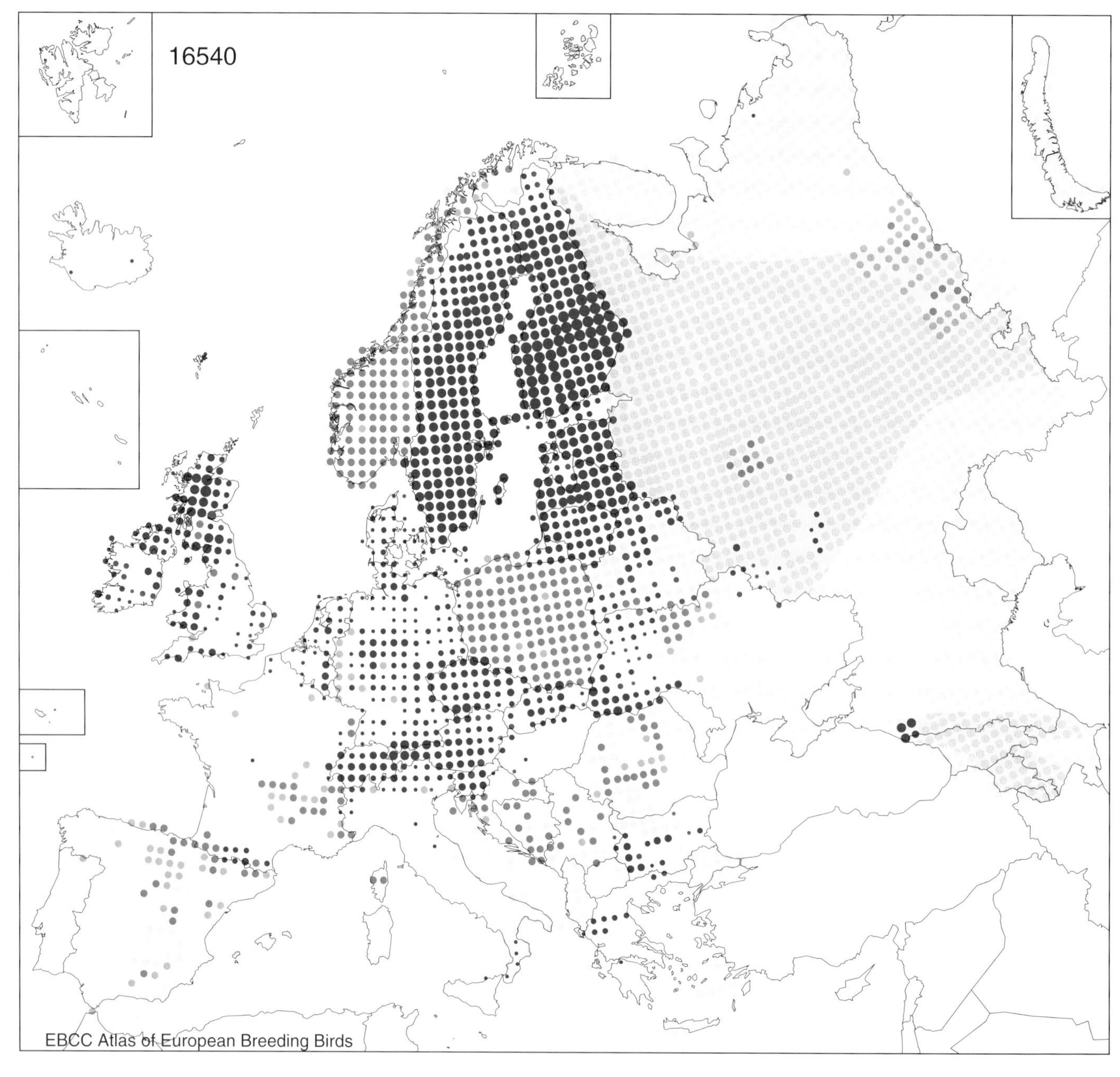

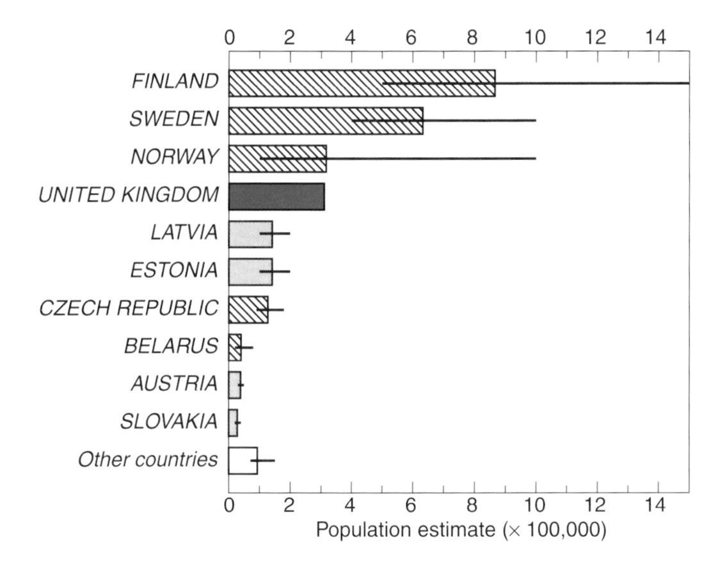

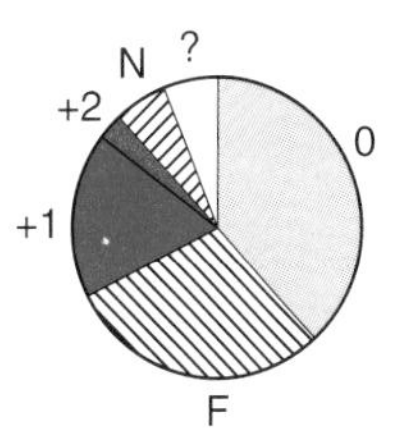

% in top 10 countries: 96.6
Total number of populated European countries: 34
Total European population 2,245,132–3,743,607 (2,735,238)
Russian population 1,000,000–10,000,000 (3,162,278)
Turkish population 500–50,000 (5000)

The Siskin breeds in the coniferous forests of the boreal and temperate zones, from Britain & Ireland to Sakhalin in the Far East. To the N its European range just reaches 70°N and to the S the C European mountains, the Pyrenees (a scattering through Iberia), the Balkan mountains and the Lesser Caucasus. The two parts of its world population are separated by a gap at *c*100°E which apparently does not lack suitable habitat. Nevertheless, the species is monotypic.

Although it breeds in any coniferous forest type, it prefers spruce-dominated (*Picea*) forests. During good seed years, mass breeding may also occur in larch *Larix*, fir *Abies* and pine *Pinus*, especially in western Europe where it has experienced an increase since the late 1960s. Outside the breeding season, the Siskin also frequents deciduous trees, especially birch *Betula* and alder *Alnus* along watercourses.

The Siskin may perform irruptive movements, during which it spreads into otherwise unoccupied areas and even into less favoured habitats. Such peaks probably result from an abundance of food in the preceding years promoting successful breeding and high survival rates (Newton 1972). Breeding begins earlier in good cone years (Shaw 1990) and may trigger the production of second broods (as deduced from the prolonged breeding season and bimodal fledgling production; R.G. Bijlsma, pers obs).

The population core lies in the spruce-dominated forests of Fennoscandia, the Baltic States and Russia, which hold probably some 90% of the European population of 3M–15Mbp. Densities fluctuate markedly in response to seed production, reaching 10–80 bp/km^2 in Finland (Koskimies 1989a). In Estonia, numbers ranged from 11–40 bp/km^2 of forest in mature spruce-dominated, up to 24 in mature birch–spruce, 21 in pine boreal, and 0–16 in various broad-leaved (Leibak *et al* 1994). Rather high large-scale densities also exist in Scotland, the Alps and the Carpathians (between 1000 and 3000 bp/50km square, probably in years with good cone crops). In its remaining distribution, the Siskin is patchily distributed in relatively trivial numbers. In S and SE Europe it is largely restricted to montane coniferous forests, as in the Pyrenees, the Massif Central, Corsica, Calabria, the former Yugoslavia, Macedonia, Carpathians, Stara Planina and Rhodopi Planina. Numbers here are usually low.

Despite large fluctuations in numbers, populations in the main breeding area in N Europe and Russia appeared largely stable throughout 1970–90. At the same time, marked increases in range and numbers were recorded in Britain & Ireland, Denmark, The Netherlands, Romania and Hungary. Since 1970, the British population size has increased tenfold, accompanied by a substantial range expansion in Wales, in the Peak and Lake Districts and in the Pennines (Jardine 1993a). This development was thought to reflect changes in the age-class structure of coniferous forests, the maturing of post-war plantations providing the Siskin with new breeding habitat and ample food. This circumstance possibly also applies to The Netherlands, where coniferous forests were planted mostly in 1920–45, for until the early 1970s, the Siskin was a scarce breeder, but since then has increased markedly, particularly in 1989 and 1992 when mass seed production of larch, spruce and fir coincided with large irruptions. Consequently, the Dutch population increased from several dozen in the early 1970s to 300–700bp in 1979–83, 700–900bp in 1985–88 and 1800–2400bp in 1989 and 1992 (van Dijk *et al* 1994b). However, in poor seed years, numbers may drop to only 10% or less of peaks.

Most northerly populations are migratory, wintering from S Scandinavia southwards to S Europe (Payevski 1994). The birds show low site fidelity, moving around nomadically in response to seed crops of coniferous trees and birch and alder. In some years the Siskin may be totally absent over much of W and S Europe.

Rob G Bijlsma (NL)

Carduelis cannabina Linnet

CZ	Konopka obecná	**I**	Fanello
D	Bluthänfling	**NL**	Kneu
E	Pardillo Común	**P**	Pintarrôxo-comum
F	Linotte mélodieuse	**PL**	Makolągwa
FIN	Hemppo	**R**	Коноплянка
G	Φανέτο	**S**	Hämpling
H	Kenderike		

SPEC Cat 4, Threat status S

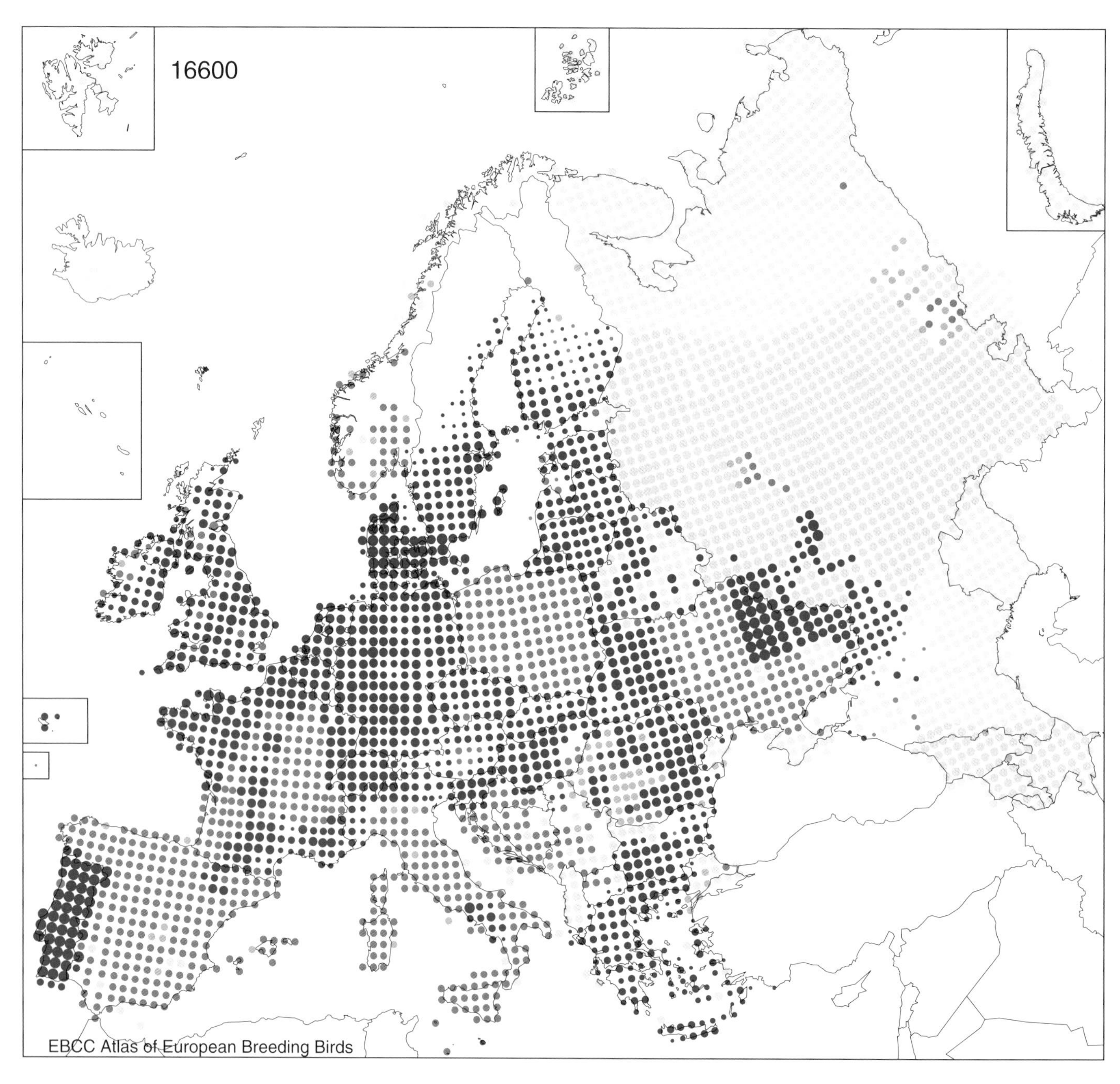

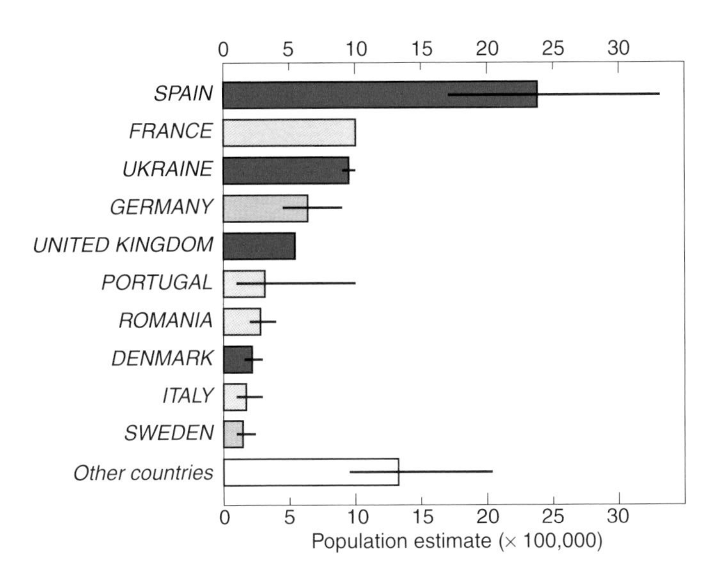

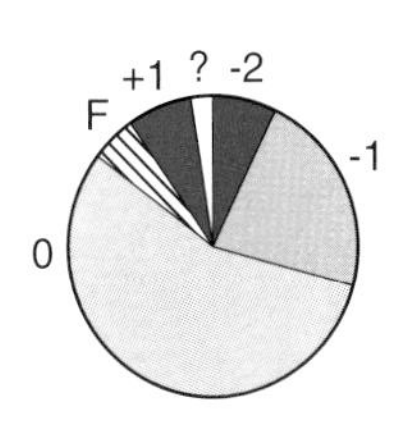

% in top 10 countries: 85.1
Total number of populated European countries: 39
Total European population 7,050,782–9,058,147 (7,802,675)
Russian population 10,000–100,000 (31,623)
Turkish population 1,000,000–10,000,000 (3,162,278)

The Linnet is distributed widely throughout the western Palearctic (except Iceland, N Fennoscandia and N Russia), much of C Siberia (to *c*93°E) and C Asia and patchily in the Near East and NW Africa. In the *Atlas*' coverage, *C.c. bella* occurs in Crimea and Transcaucasia, *mediterranea* from Spain to southern former Yugoslavia, Bulgaria and Greece (including Mediterranean islands, S Italy), *guentheri* on Madeira, *autochthona* in Scotland, and the nominate *cannabina* elsewhere in Europe. Perhaps three other subspecies are recognized.

The species often nests semi-colonially, usually involving fewer than 10bp, occasionally several dozen. It occupies a variety of open habitats containing shrubs or young plantations, including overgrown heathland, woodland edges, forest clearings and fragmented farmland. It avoids densely forested areas. Breeding in urban habitats, such as gardens, parks and cemeteries, has increased since the 1960s. In Europe, it has bred up to 2300m asl in Switzerland (*BWP*), although normally it is a lowland species. Populations in northern, eastern and C Europe are migratory whereas those in western Europe are partially so. Southern European populations are sedentary.

The European population is very roughly estimated at 7M–12Mbp. A uniformly high large-scale density of >4000 bp/50×50km square obtains in western Europe, from Denmark through Germany, the Low Countries, France and Iberia, and including Britain & Ireland. In the E, similar densities were reported only from Ukraine, perhaps indicating that Poland (no estimate available) also has a dense population. Throughout the Baltic States and C and S Europe, values normally average 1000–3000 bp/50km square, declining further in Fennoscandia and the large C European mountain ranges. Balkan distributional gaps probably reflect lack of coverage.

A common species in the early 20th century in low-intensity farmland, Linnet numbers declined dramatically, by >50% from 1970 to 1990 in Finland, Great Britain and The Netherlands and by 20–50% in much of C and NW Europe. In southern Europe populations seem stable or even increasing (Spain) whereas eastern European trends are contradictory; decreases occurred in Estonia, the Czech Republic and Slovakia, but Ukraine experienced an increase.

Despite these declines, the distribution generally has remained unchanged since the mid-1960s, at least at the 50km map resolution. A major exception is Finland, where the species' breeding range has contracted markedly to the S. Comparable contractions were noted there in the 1920s and 1930s, but a northward extension occurred in the 1960s (Koskimies 1989a).

In Britain the steep decline since the mid-1970s is attributed to changes in farming practices (J.H. Marchant *et al* 1990). Chemical weed-control of agricultural crops has resulted in reduced Linnet breeding success. Probably even more importantly, it has caused food (seeds) to be in short supply in winter as well as in summer. Conversion of Spanish cereal fields into grasslands for livestock-rearing also will reduce the carrying capacity of the Iberian plateaus for wintering seed-eating birds (Tellería *et al* 1995). Because farmland-use has changed considerably over much of N, W and C Europe, it is likely that Linnet declines in these regions mostly have similar causes (Robertson & Berg 1992). Another important factor has been the destruction or deterioration of suitable nesting habitat, like hedges or small forest patches in farmland (Büsche 1991, Kurlavičius 1987). In some areas, like Schleswig-Holstein, densities in built-up areas nowadays are much higher than in surrounding farmland (Büsche 1991). It is not known whether climatic factors are involved in the southward range contraction in Finland.

In some countries in southern and eastern Europe, where traditional farming remains, Linnet populations have better maintained their population levels. However, intensive agriculture is spreading rapidly here too, and so further declines are likely in the near future.

Fred Hustings (NL) Petras Kurlavičius (LITH)

This species account is sponsored by Vogelwerkgroep Rijk van Nijmegen e.o., Nijmegen, NL.

Carduelis flavirostris — Twite

CZ	Konopka žlutozobá	**I**	Fanello nordico
D	Berghänfling	**NL**	Frater
E	Pardillo Piquigualdo	**P**	Pintarrôxo-de-bico-amarelo
F	Linotte à bec jaune	**PL**	Rzepołuch
FIN	Vuorihemppo	**R**	Горная чечетка
G	Κιτρινοραμφόσπιζα	**S**	Vinterhämpling
H	Sárgacsőrû kenderike		

Non-SPEC, Threat status S

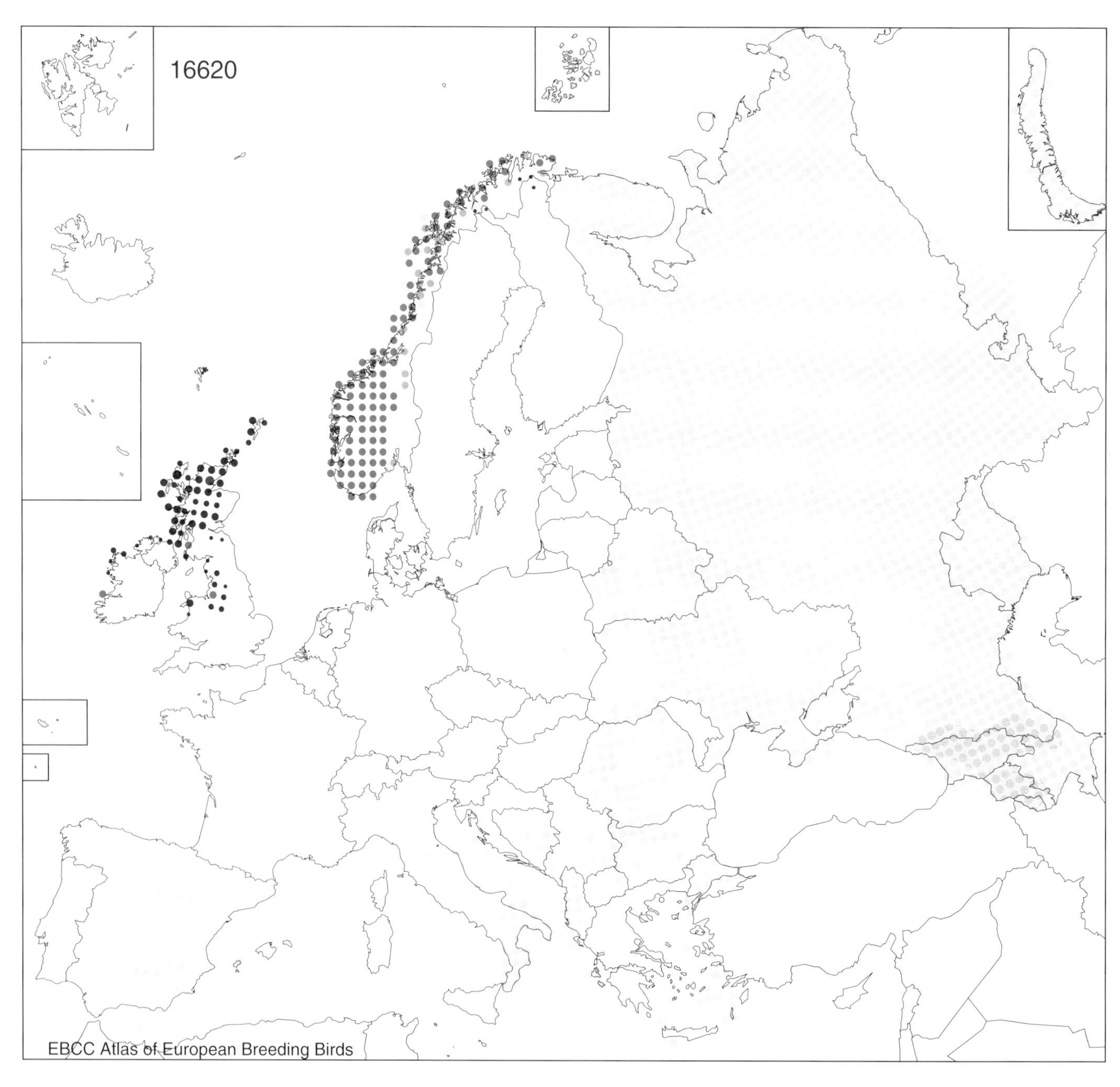

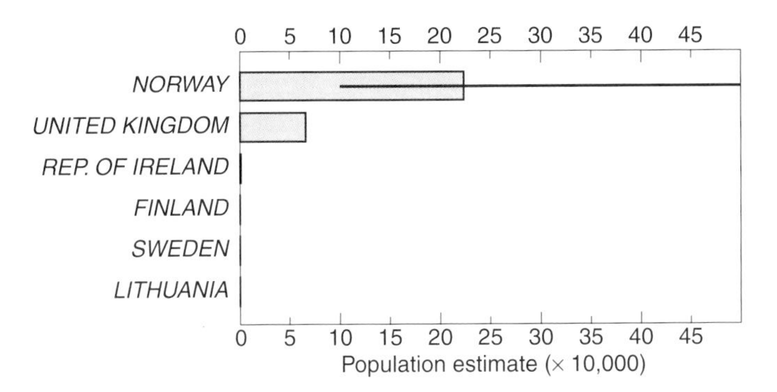

F -2
0

% in top 10 countries: 100.0
Total number of populated European countries: 6
Total European population 166,880–566,880 (290,487)
Russian population 100–1000 (316)
Turkish population 1000–10,000 (3162)

Few species, except possibly the Azure-winged Magpie *Cyanopica cyanus*, can rival the unusually disjunct world distribution of the Twite. The world population of Twite is split into two centres, one in NW Europe, the other some 2500km distant embracing the Caucasus to C and E Asia. The NW European breeding range reaches the July 10°C isotherm in the tundra, boreal and marginal temperate zones. Of the 11 subspecies, the nominate *C.f. flavirostris* (Scandinavia, NW Russia), *bensonorum* (Outer Hebrides), *pipilans* (Britain & Ireland) and *brevirostris* (SE Russia and Transcaucasia) occur in Europe.

The Twite prefers to breed in open terrain possessing few bushes, scrub or trees (*BWP*). NW European populations breed in moorland and rocky short-sward grassland. Others occupy subalpine to dry alpine rocky meadows, mountain steppe, tundra and scrub. Birds typically nest between 2500m and 3500m asl (C. Harrison 1982) in the Caucasus (even up to 4800m in Tibet) but British and Irish populations essentially are lowland breeders on heather moors, hill farms and upland (750m asl) pastures. Scandinavian breeders tend to nest at somewhat higher altitudes than British and Irish birds, often on barren slopes and precipices (*BWP*).

The disjunct distribution arose probably as a result of range expansion during the last glaciation 18 000–20 000 years ago. The population radiated NW from the ancestral Asian population into the steppe-like tundra which then existed in C Europe. As the climate warmed, C Europe lost this habitat. Most of the Twite population retreated S, but a small proportion tracked the cold zone surrounding the Scandinavian ice shield as it retreated N, and became separated permanently from the main population (Stresemann 1920). The Twite is therefore the only European representative of the Tibetan fauna.

The Norwegian breeding population numbers roughly 100 000–500 000bp and despite the crudity of the limits, represents the majority of the total NW European population. Britain & Ireland hold a significant population (*c*67 000bp) but only a few breed in Finland and Sweden. Russia's total of 100–1000bp refers only to the NW European population. The numbers breeding in Georgia, Armenia, Azerbaijan and Cis-Caucasus are not known, but given that the species is fairly common in eastern Turkey (Roselaar 1995), they are probably significant. Breeding populations on the whole are believed stable. Declines are known only for British and Irish populations, numbers throughout Scotland having decreased probably as a result of moorland habitat degradation through overgrazing and fragmentation by agricultural reclamation. Over the period 1970–90 the British range contracted overall by 1.1%, most severely in NW Scotland and less so in Lancashire, Cheshire and Derbyshire (Gibbons *et al* 1993; Brown *et al* 1995). This contraction has been partly offset by a southeasterly range expansion in SE Scotland (Brown *et al* 1995) and the appearance of a new population in Wales (Jardine & Reid 1993). Range contraction has been severest in Ireland where a 53% decline occurred over the same period (Gibbons *et al* 1993).

Highest British densities occur on low-intensity coastal agriculture and on the S Pennines (N England) grouse moors (200–400bp; Brown *et al* 1995). Density estimates vary from 2 bp/100ha (Staffordshire moors; Waterhouse 1985 in Davies 1988) to 9 bp/100ha (B. Campbell from BTO Nest Record Cards).

Migratory behaviour varies both between and within subspecies. Scottish and Irish populations are more or less sedentary whereas birds from breeding areas in N England disperse SE in late August and winter in coastal habitats between Lincolnshire and N Kent (*BWP*). Scandinavian populations migrate to N and E Europe, many birds wintering around German cities (*BWP*, Bub 1985). *C.f. brevirostris* undertakes altitudinal migration but is also nomadic and unpredictable (*BWP*).

The late Hans Bub (D) Hans Oelke (D)
Simon Gillings (GB)

Contributions acknowledged from:
Siegfried Eck (D) Svein Haftorn (N) Klaus Liedel (D)
Burkhard Stephan (D)

This species account is sponsored by Prof. Dr Hans Oelke, Peine, D.

Carduelis flammea **Redpoll**

CZ	Čečetka zimní	**I**	Organetto
D	Birkenzeisig	**NL**	Barmsijs
E	Pardillo Sizerín	**P**	Pintarrôxo-de-queixo-preto
F	Sizerin flammé	**PL**	Czeczotka
FIN	Urpiainen	**R**	Обыкновенная чечетка
G	Σημυδόσπιζα	**S**	Gråsiska
H	Zsezse		

Non-SPEC, Threat status S (P)

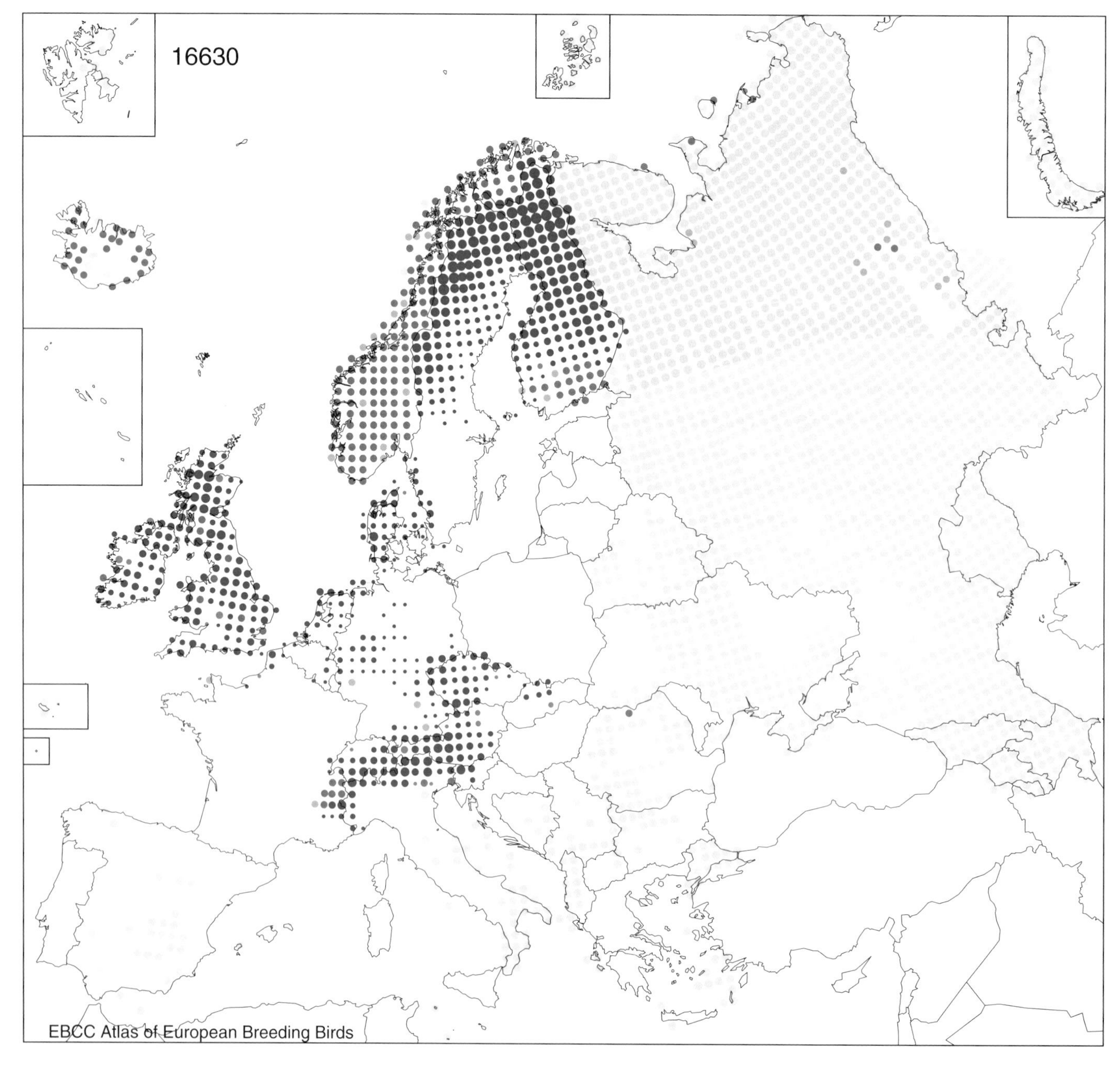

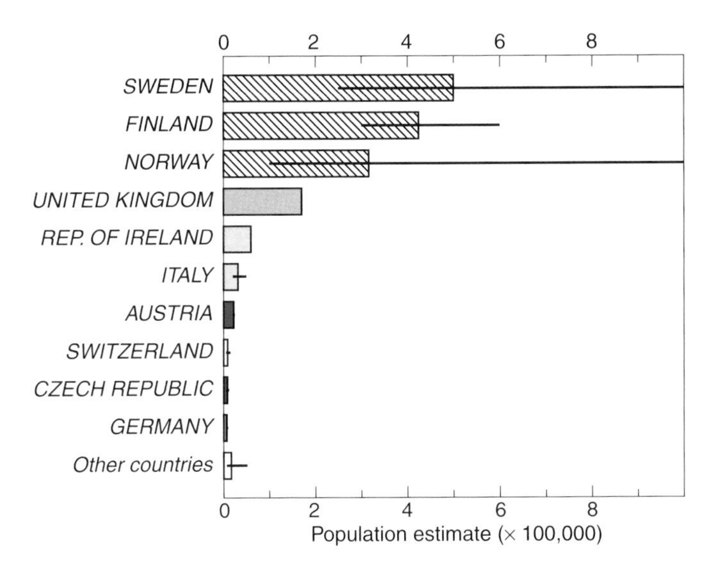

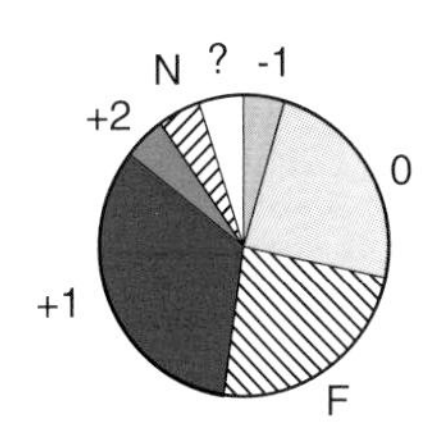

% in top 10 countries: 98.9
Total number of populated European countries: 21
Total European population 1,211,898–2,430,898 (1,565,302)
Russian population 10,000,000–100,000,000 (31,622,777)

The Redpoll has a continuous circumpolar distribution broadly coincident with the subarctic and coniferous boreal zones to the tundra edge. There are several subspecies, three of which breed in Europe.

The nominate subspecies *C.f. flammea* occurs in Norway, N and C Sweden, Finland and N Russia. It breeds in lowland coniferous forests, but the largest populations inhabit alpine birch *Betula* forests, where the Redpoll is one of the most characteristic bird species. It also breeds in alpine willow *Salix* scrub above the treeline. About 95% of the breeding population of *c*10M–100Mbp breeds in Russia. Long-term, there are no known changes in its numbers and distribution. However, the population size varies greatly from year to year, mainly reflecting the abundance of birch seed. During a good seed-crop year birds winter in alpine valleys to breed there in large numbers the following spring, but if the seed-crop is poor they move away. In Swedish Lapland, populations can increase tenfold in a peak year and then fall to a low level. Young birds particularly have little natal philopatry, and act opportunistically to find areas suitable that year for breeding (Enemar & Nyström 1981).

The Redpoll makes irregular migratory movements. Seed-crop failures in breeding areas may force it to wander in winter to most of Europe, even to the Black Sea and some Mediterranean countries, and if the wintering grounds have a rich spruce *Picea* seed-crop the species may remain to breed well to the S of its normal area.

In the mid-1800s, the small, dark subspecies *cabaret* was confined largely to N Britain, Ireland and the Alps, breeding in fairly open woodlands, mostly at higher altitudes, but by 1910 had increased in lowland Britain. Its range then contracted rapidly, only to expand again quite dramatically from the 1950s onward, spilling over the Channel to reach The Netherlands, Germany and Denmark, and in the 1970s, S Sweden and two locations in Belgium (the Ardennes, and the coast). It first nested in the French Ardennes in 1983, but numbers remain very low (Duquet 1994). The western and C European population numbers *c*300 000bp, almost 80% being in Britain & Ireland.

The C European expansion also started in the 1950s. In the former Czechoslovakia, *cabaret* first bred in 1952. Colonization of the High Tatra, the Sudeten Mountains, the Bohemian forests, the Erzgebirge and finally C Germany followed, allowing this population to meet that spreading from the Ardennes (Ernst 1988, 1989).

The *cabaret* expansion probably relates to 20th-century land-use changes. Many former heaths and bogs are now suitable breeding habitat through natural afforestation or planting. Where mountain *Pinus mugo* and black *P. nigra* pine plantations lie along the North Sea coast, *cabaret* numbers are very high. In much of Europe *cabaret* occurs in town parks and gardens, now breeding from Britain to Romania. In most areas it is still increasing although significant reductions have affected Britain since the 1970s (Jardine 1993b), The Netherlands (decimation during 1984–93, inland breeding ceasing; van Dijk & Hustings 1994) and Belgium (Schmitz 1987).

In Britain, the Redpoll leaves higher ground and most northern areas in winter. Many birds winter within Britain or just across the English Channel but, if food is scarce, may continue to Iberia. Birds from Denmark have been found wintering in The Netherlands. C European *cabaret* populations are mainly short-distance or altitudinal migrants.

Iceland contains an endemic and apparently mainly sedentary subspecies, *islandica*, of uncertain taxonomic status and affinities (2000–20 000bp). It nests in the SW, along the N coast and in the E, in native birch woods and birch scrub, in parks and gardens, and in small plantations of introduced conifers.

Alan Knox (GB) Bodil Nyström (S) Hans Nyström (S)

Carduelis hornemanni

Arctic Redpoll

CZ	Čečetka bělavá	I	Organetto artico
D	Polarbirkenzeisig	NL	Witstuitbarmsijs
E	Pardillo Ártico	P	Pintarrôxo de Hornemann
F	Sizerin blanchâtre	PL	Czeczotka tundrowa
FIN	Tundraurpiainen	R	Тундряная чечетка
G	Αρκτικόσπιζα	S	Snösiska
H	Szürke zsezse		

Non-SPEC, Threat status S (P)

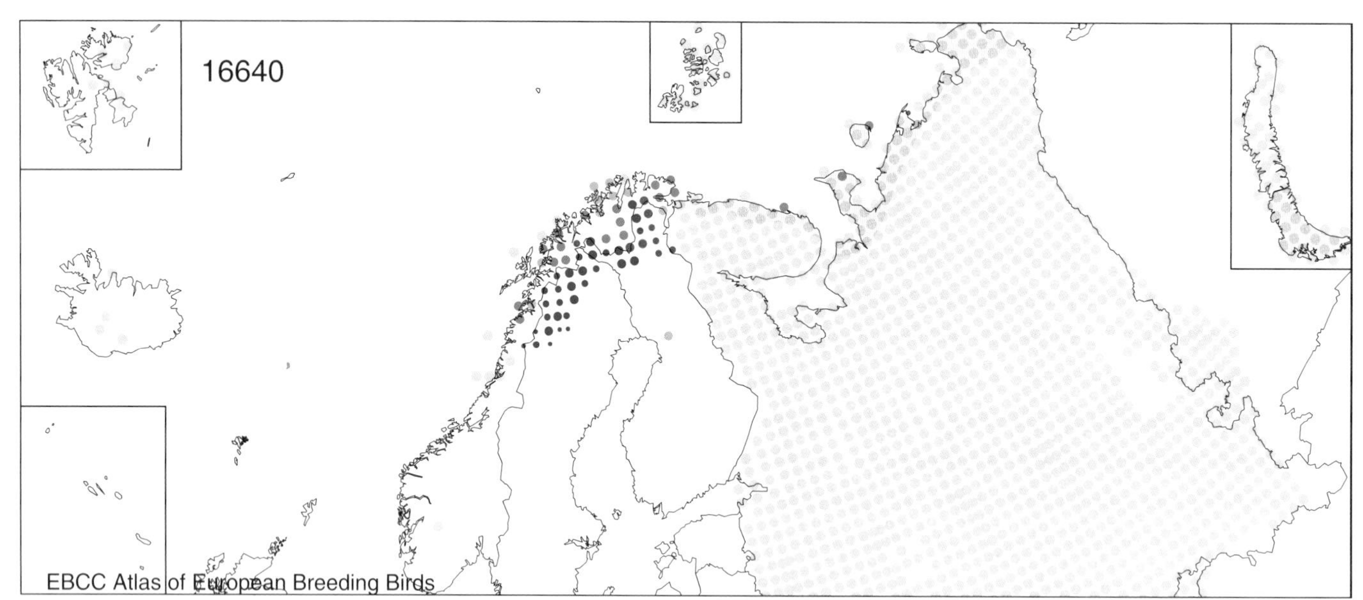

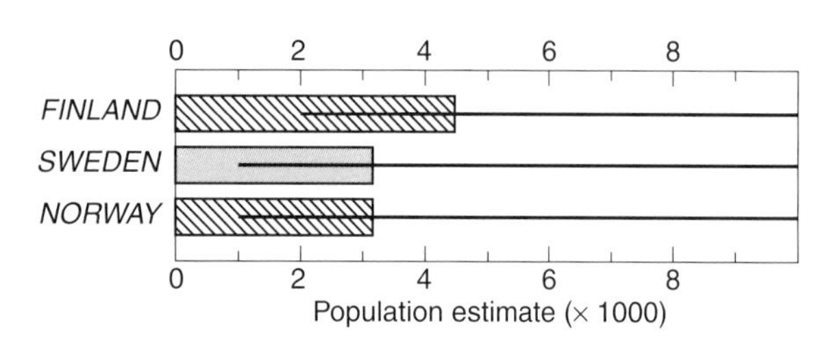

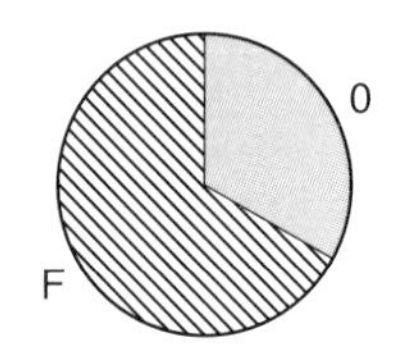

% in top 10 countries: 100.0
Total number of populated European countries: 3
Total European population 6864–21,935 (10,797)
Russian population 100,000–1,000,000 (316,228)

The Arctic Redpoll has a circumpolar subarctic and high-arctic distribution. The nominate subspecies *C.h. hornemanni* breeds in N Greenland and the adjacent islands of the Canadian arctic, and the subspecies *exilipes* across N Eurasia, Alaska and the remainder of northern Canada. There may be a separate Icelandic population (*BWP*). The species' breeding range broadly overlaps with the northernmost range of Redpoll *C. flammea*.

In Europe the Arctic Redpoll breeds in northernmost Russia (including southern Novaya Zemlya), Finland, Sweden and Norway. On the Arctic coast nests have been found down to sea level. In the Swedish fjeld chain it breeds S to at least 66°N. However, the Arctic Redpoll's distribution is not known in detail mainly because of the difficulties in separating it from the Redpoll (Lansdown *et al* 1991). The relationships between the various populations of *C. hornemanni* and *C. flammea* remain to be finalized (*BWP*), but here Arctic Redpoll and Redpoll are treated separately.

It has been claimed that the Arctic Redpoll favours alpine willow *Salix* scrub above the treeline, whilst the Common Redpoll prefers birch *Betula* woods, but this is an oversimplification. There is apparently a broad overlap of nesting habitats, in relation to which further research is desirable. In S Lapland the two species breed side by side both in the alpine birch forests and above the treeline (Nyström & Nyström 1987, pers obs).

Although it is probably often overlooked, the Arctic Redpoll is scarcer than the Redpoll throughout Scandinavia, but it probably experiences similarly large population fluctuations. Russia may hold an estimated 100 000–1Mbp, Greenland, Finland, Sweden and Norway each harbouring 1000–10 000bp. The species winters mainly within or near the breeding range, much further N than the Redpoll. However, some migrate with the latter species and have been found as far S as Britain and C Europe.

Alan Knox (GB) Bodil Nyström (S) Hans Nyström (S)

Loxia leucoptera

Two-barred Crossbill

CZ	Křivka bělokřídlá	I	Crociere fasciato
D	Bindenkreuzschnabel	NL	Witbandkruisbek
E	Piquituerto Franjeado	P	Cruza-bico-franjado
F	Beccroisé bifascié	PL	Krzyżodziób modrzewiowy
FIN	Kirjosiipikäpylintu	R	Белокрылый клест
G	Λωριδοσταυρομύτης	S	Bändelkorsnäbb
H	Szalagos keresztcsőrű		

Non-SPEC, Threat status S (P)

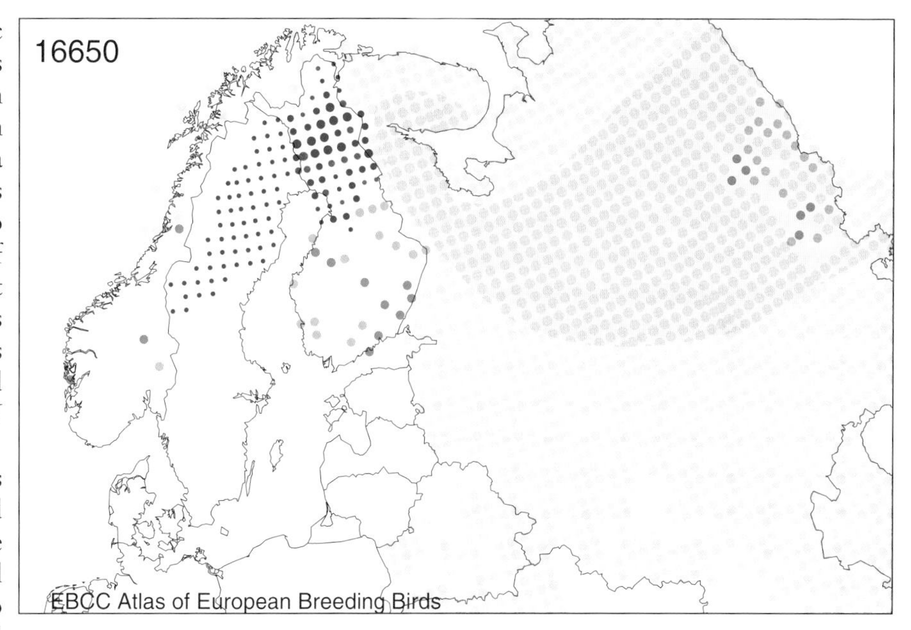

The Two-barred Crossbill is a Holarctic species occurring in boreal coniferous forests of the Northern Hemisphere. In the Old World it breeds regularly in coniferous forests in N European Russia and Siberia where larch *Larix* seeds are its main food. In NW Europe the *Larix* spp are scarce, but the bird also eats seeds of Norway spruce *Picea abies*, a dominant tree species in Fennoscandia. In years when the Norway spruce seed-crop is extremely good, the Two-barred Crossbill may also breed in N Fennoscandia.

As with many other coniferous species, the larch does not produce good seed-crops every year, and when the cone-crops fail, the Two-barred Crossbill migrates in search of food and so thousands may irrupt in late summer and autumn into western Europe. The largest irruptions probably occur when a poor cone-crop follows a year of abundance when the birds have bred well.

If large irruptions should bring birds into areas where suitable trees such as larch or Norway spruce bear a good cone-crop, many birds are liable to remain to breed the following spring. The 1987 good Norway spruce seed-crop in N Finland resulted in the Two-barred Crossbill becoming the third most numerous breeding species in spruce forests in part of N Finland (see Table; Virkkala 1989, 1991b). In other study years (1982–86, 1988–89) the species was either not observed or extremely rare. Such invasions occur in Finland and elsewhere in Fennoscandia, approximately every 7 years (Pulliainen 1983, Larsen & Tombre 1989). The most recent irruption in 1990/91 (Ebels 1993) led to a successful breeding attempt in Berlin in 1991, *c*1700km SW of the normal breeding range (Fischer *et al* 1992), an extreme example of the species' nomadism which is typical throughout its range.

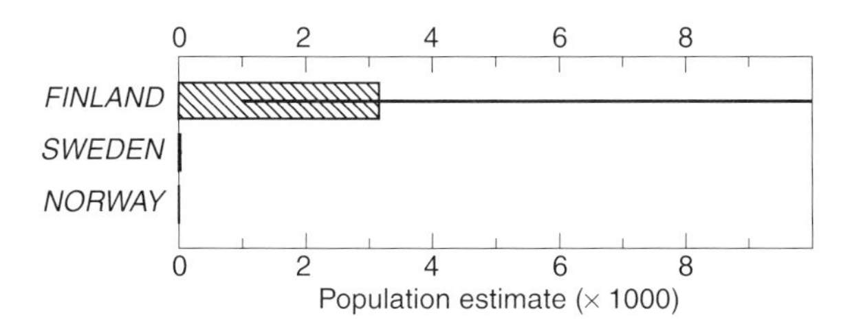

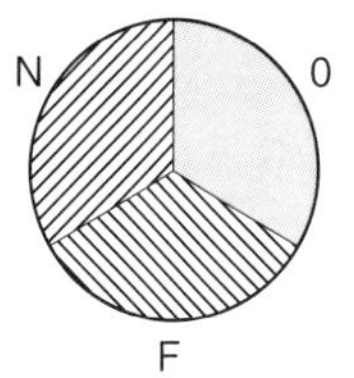

% in top 10 countries: 100.0
Total number of populated European countries: 3
Total European population 1032–10,032 (3194)
Russian population 10,000–100,000 (31,623)

The occurrence of the Two-barred Crossbill *Loxia leucoptera* in virgin coniferous forests of Sompio Nature Reserve (68°10'N, 27°20'E) in northern Finland in 1982–89. The data are based on yearly repeated line-transect censuses (20km) carried out in June (see Virkkala 1989, 1991b).

	1982	1983	1984	1985	1986	1987	1988	1989
No. of observations	1	-	-	-	-	31	1	-
Density (bp/km^2)	0.1	-	-	-	-	4.2	0.1	-

Alan Knox (GB) Raimo Virkkala (FIN)

Loxia curvirostra Crossbill

CZ	Křivka obecná	**I**	Crociere
D	Fichtenkreuzschnabel	**NL**	Kruisbek
E	Piquituerto Común	**P**	Cruza-bico-comum
F	Bec-croisé des sapins	**PL**	Krzyżodziób świerkowy
FIN	Pikkukäpylintu	**R**	Клест-еловик
G	Σταυρομύτης	**S**	Mindre korsnäbb
H	Keresztcsőrű		

Non-SPEC, Threat status S

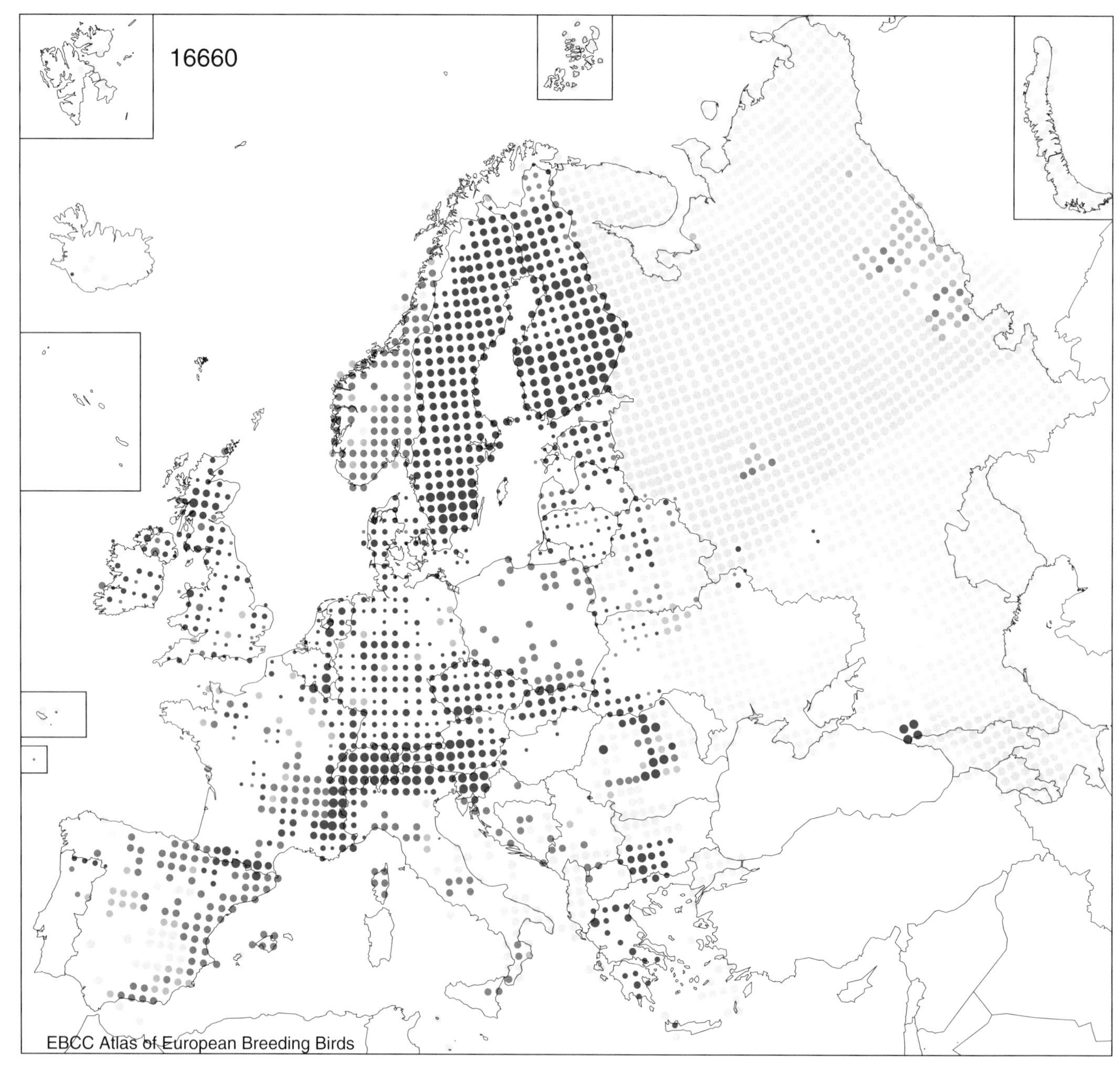

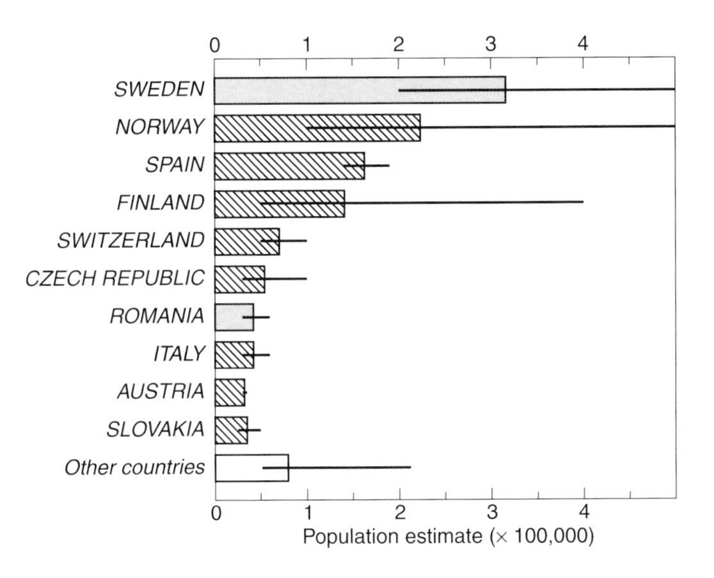

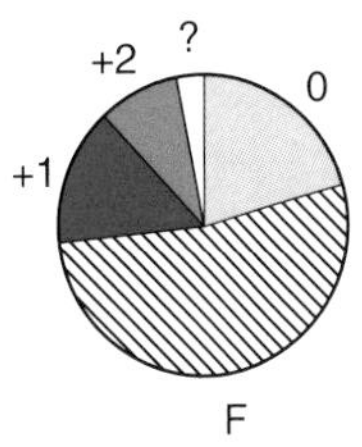

% in top 10 countries: 93.4
Total number of populated European countries: 34
Total European population 1,004,141–1,632,437 (1,202,176)
Russian population 100,000–1,000,000 (316,228)
Turkish population 1000–10,000 (3162)

The Crossbill occurs throughout the coniferous forests of the Northern Hemisphere, being known in the New World as the Red Crossbill. Several subspecies occur from Alaska S to Central America and E to Newfoundland. In the Old World, the nominate *L.c. curvirostra* breeds throughout European and Siberian forests to Japan. There are four distinctive Mediterranean subspecies and others in S Asia (S to the Himalayas, Vietnam and the Philippines).

In mainland Europe and Great Britain the Crossbill breeds mostly in forests of native or planted spruce *Picea* (mainly Norway spruce *P. abies*), larch *Larix* spp and Scots pine *Pinus sylvestris*, but also in plantations of exotic conifers like Sitka spruce *Picea sitchensis* and Douglas fir *Pseudotsuga menziesii*. The birds inhabit open woodland or close-planted forestry at any altitude, favouring mature trees with good numbers of cones.

Populations of breeding crossbills are difficult to census accurately: breeding males do not usually defend discrete territories, they feed singly or in flocks together with other breeding birds and they can travel far from the nest.

Spruce and larch cone-crops in particular may vary from abundant to nil. The number of crossbills in any area, being dependent on seed weight, cone toughness and seedfall phenology of the predominant conifers present (Marquiss & Rae 1994), therefore changes greatly from year to year. If cones are scarce, some or all of the birds move out in search of food, perhaps flying only short distances, but when the crop fails widely, hundreds of thousands of birds may irrupt across the whole of Europe. When the birds find an area with a good cone-crop, they may settle to breed for one or more years before moving on again or returning whence they came. Because individual woods and whole forests vary in their cone-crops from year to year, and because forests are maturing or being felled, crossbills travel from place to place in a manner not fully understood (Gatter 1993).

The map is somewhat misleading because it is composed of data from a number of seasons and includes nesting records following several massive irruptions. In any one year, the birds would be less widely distributed, but the overall pattern would be much the same. The Crossbill's main breeding areas are the large forests of Fennoscandia and Russia, although Spain and several C European countries hold significant populations. With the increase in the area of conifer plantation throughout much of Europe since the 1920s, Crossbill numbers have grown significantly and the species now breeds regularly in several countries and in many areas where previously it was rare or absent. For example, the species has nested regularly in The Netherlands only since the mid-1970s, with the greatest numbers (>5000bp) in years following irruptions (1984, 1991), when the reproductive rate was poor (in 1991, 0.14 young/pair) through predation and the late onset of egg-laying in relation to seed availability (Bijlsma 1994b). Similar circumstances applied in NE Scotland that year (Marquiss & Rae 1994).

An endemic subspecies in the Balearics *L.c. balearica* feeds on the seeds of Aleppo pine *Pinus halapensis*, as does the subspecies *poliogyna* in North Africa. The Cyprus subspecies *guillemardi* lives in forests of Austrian, or black, pine *Pinus nigra* and the Corsican subspecies *corsicana* lives a widely cultivated subspecies, *P.n. larico*, of that tree (Massa 1987). Pines produce cones more reliably than spruce or larch. With a stable food supply, birds of these subspecies are fairly sedentary. Some populations of nominate *curvirostra* (particularly in S Europe) also occupy habitats dominated by pines and these, too, are more sedentary and less liable to irrupt (Senar *et al* 1993).

Alan Knox (GB)

Loxia pytyopsittacus

Parrot Crossbill

CZ Křivka velká
D Kiefernkreuzschnabel
E Piquituerto Lorito
F Bec-croisé perroquet
FIN Isokäpylintu
G Πευκοσταυρομύτης
H Nagy keresztcsőrű
I Crociere delle pinete
NL Grote Kruisbek
P Cruza-bico-pagagaio
PL Krzyżodziób sosnowy
R Клест-сосновик
S Större korsnäbb

SPEC Cat 4, Threat status S

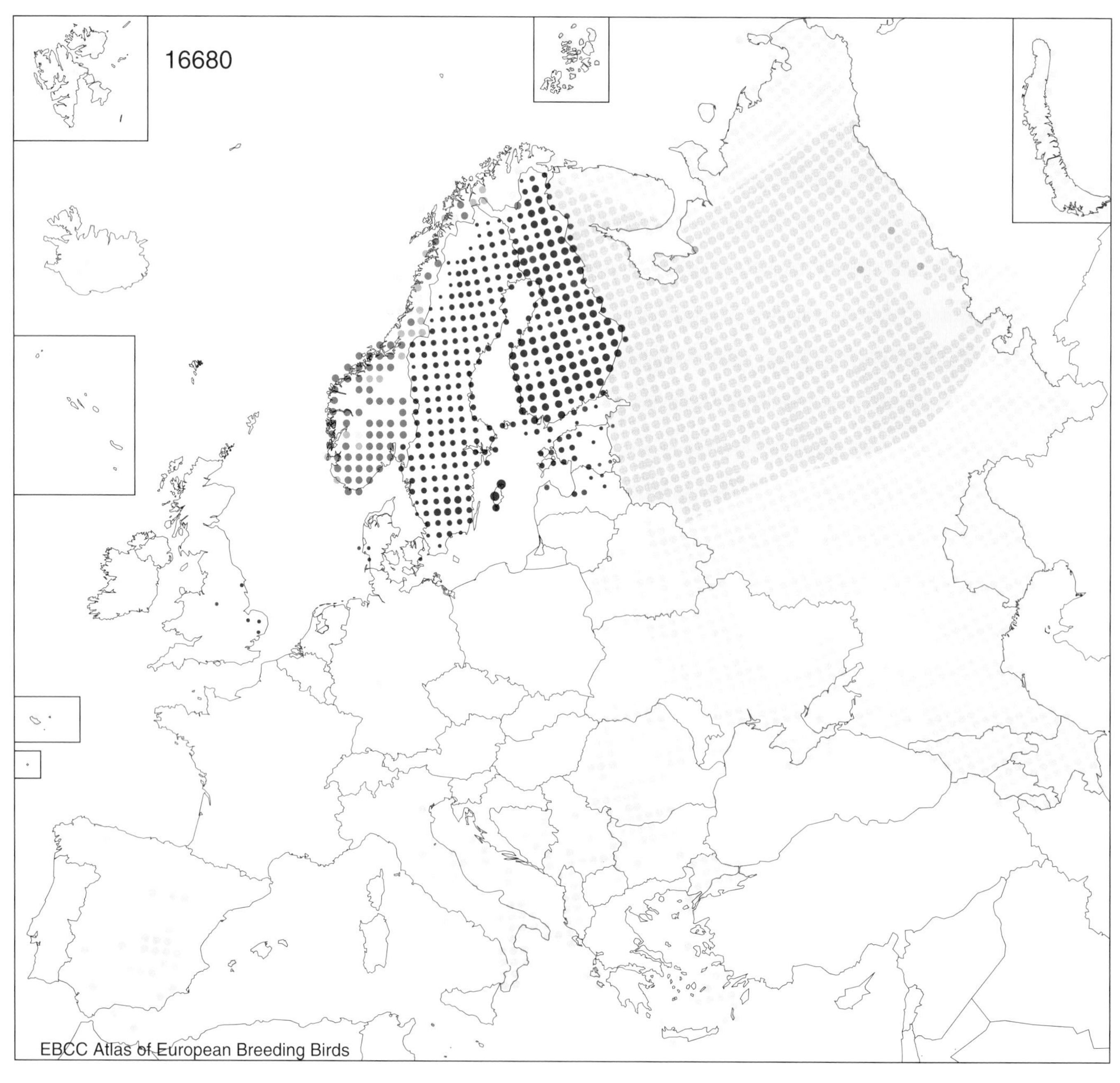

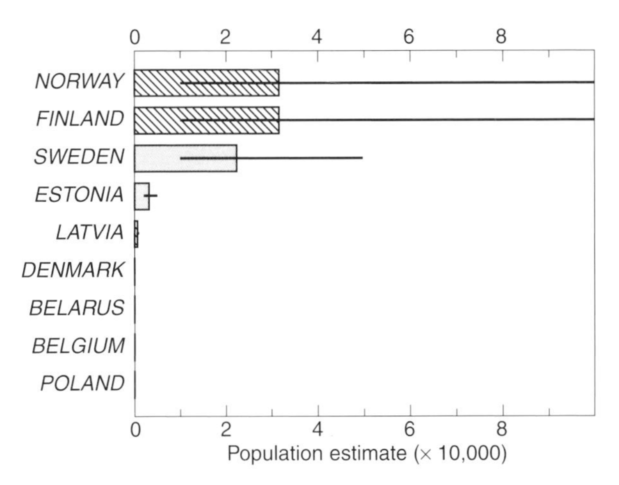

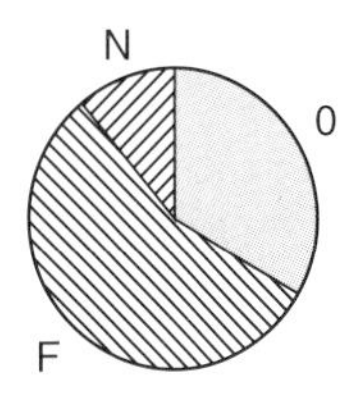

% in top 10 countries: 100.0
Total number of populated European countries: 9
Total European population 56,415–190,009 (89,419)
Russian population 10,000–100,000 (31,623)

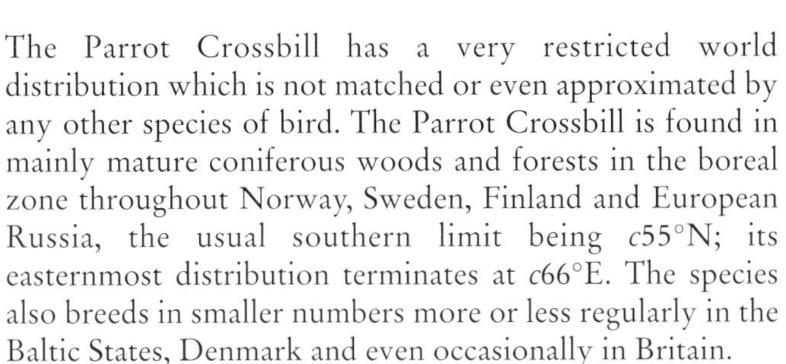

The Parrot Crossbill has a very restricted world distribution which is not matched or even approximated by any other species of bird. The Parrot Crossbill is found in mainly mature coniferous woods and forests in the boreal zone throughout Norway, Sweden, Finland and European Russia, the usual southern limit being *c*55°N; its easternmost distribution terminates at *c*66°E. The species also breeds in smaller numbers more or less regularly in the Baltic States, Denmark and even occasionally in Britain.

Throughout its range, the preferred conifer is the Scots pine *Pinus sylvestris*, although the Parrot Crossbill is also found regularly in forests of Norway spruce *Picea abies*, and less frequently, in Larch *Larix* spp. These latter tree species are more often thought of as the main habitat of the Crossbill *L. curvirostra* and Two-barred Crossbill *L. leucoptera*, respectively. However, all three species can be found, at least sometimes, in each of these three conifers. In recent decades, the Parrot Crossbill has been found nesting also in plantations and coastal shelterbelts of introduced conifers, usually large-coned species.

As with other crossbill species, Parrot Crossbill numbers vary considerably in any one place from year to year in line with cone abundance. In years with good cone-crops, birds can be very abundant, only to disappear completely in later seasons if the crop fails. As the main food, Scots pine, is less unpredictable and variable in its annual cone-crop than Norway spruce, the Parrot Crossbill is less irruptive than the Crossbill and it undertakes mass-migrations across western Europe more rarely, as in 1981/82 and 1990/91 when significant numbers reached NW Europe (Catley & Hursthouse 1985).

In prime habitats, the highest breeding densities of crossbills (Parrot Crossbill and Crossbill combined) reach several pairs/km^2. Where both species occur together, the abundance ratio between the Crossbill and the Parrot Crossbill often varies between 3:1 and 10:1 (Merikallio 1958), although sometimes the Parrot Crossbill outnumbers its smaller relative.

Detailed long-term census data suggest that Crossbill and Parrot Crossbill numbers have both decreased in northern Europe (for Finland, see Järvinen & Väisänen 1978a). This decrease probably was a consequence of intensive forestry management procedures which have changed the age-class distribution of trees significantly. A recent expansion at the Parrot Crossbill's western range limit has not compensated numerically for losses in its main range.

The Parrot Crossbill is a difficult bird to map and census. Firstly, it is very hard to distinguish it from the Crossbill, and for this reason many studies provide a combined density for the two species. Furthermore, their separate or relative abundances are not usually reported. Secondly, crossbills breed very early in spring, often in February and March, much earlier than most atlas fieldwork. Thirdly, numbers of breeding pairs fluctuate greatly from one year to another, and it is likely that within a five-year period, for example, the average population density would be a very misleading statistic. The birds' mobility and the annual variation in numbers also mean that a distribution map based on several years' data would make the birds appear to be commoner and more widespread than they would be in any single year.

The Parrot Crossbill moves unpredictably from year to year within its main range. During times usually thought to be associated with high population densities and widespread crop failures, or a combination of both, varying numbers may irrupt, apparently mainly to the W. Following such irruptions, birds may nest in areas peripheral to the main range for a year or two before disappearing again, as in Britain, Denmark (Catley & Hursthouse 1985) and The Netherlands (Bijlsma 1994b).

Pekka Helle (FIN) Alan Knox (GB)

Loxia scotica

Scottish Crossbill

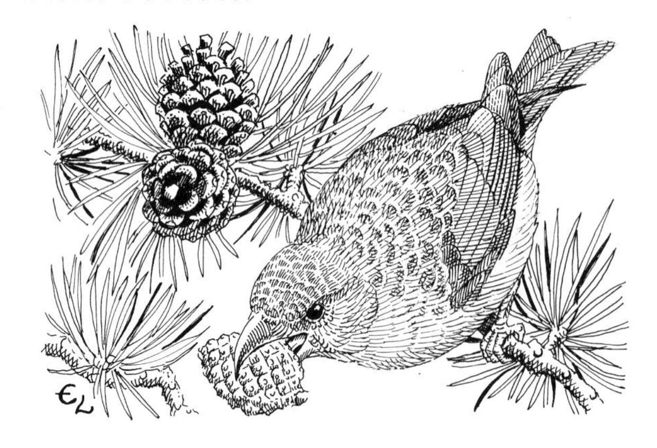

CZ	Křivka skotská	**I**	Crociere di Scozia
D	Schottischer Kreuzschnabel	**NL**	Schotse Kruisbek
E	Piquituerto Escocés	**P**	Cruza-bico-escocês
F	Beccroisé d'Écosse	**PL**	Krzyżodziób szkocki
FIN	Skotlanninkäpylintu	**R**	Шотландский сосновик
G	Σκωτσέζικος Σταυρομύτης	**S**	Skotsk korsnäbb
H	Skót keresztcsőrű		

SPEC Cat 1, Threat status INS

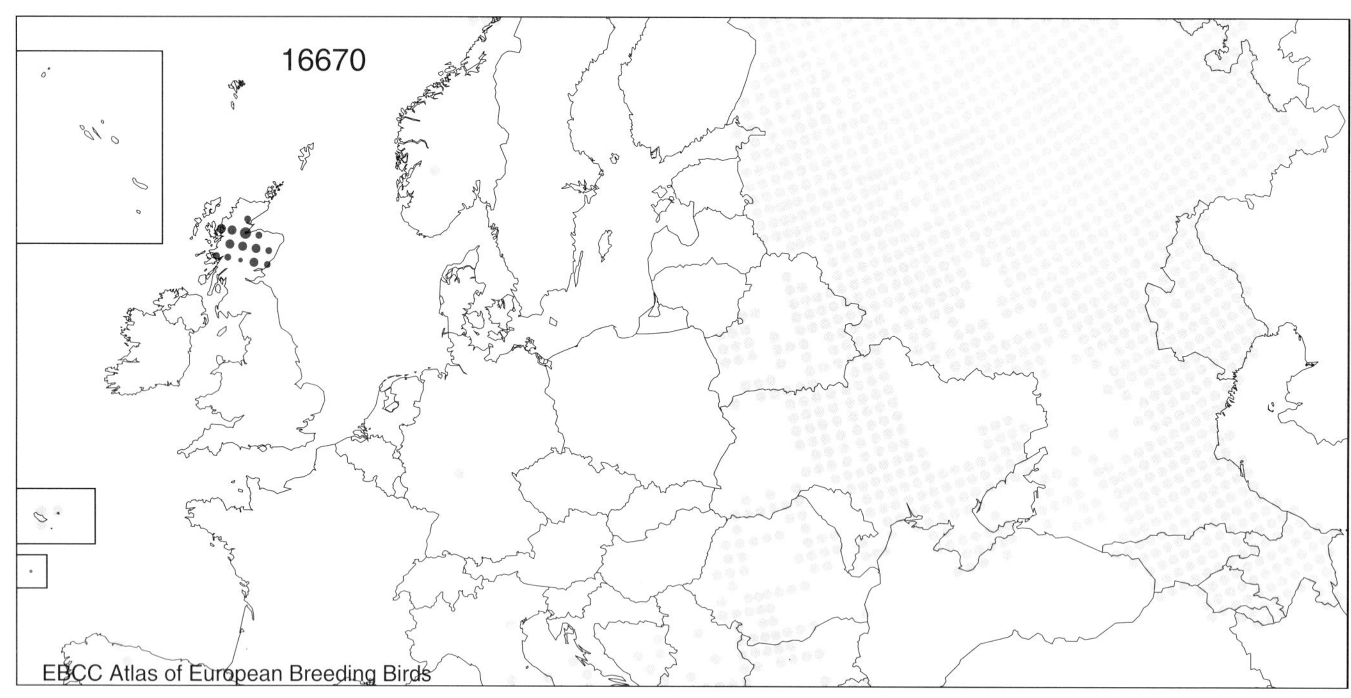

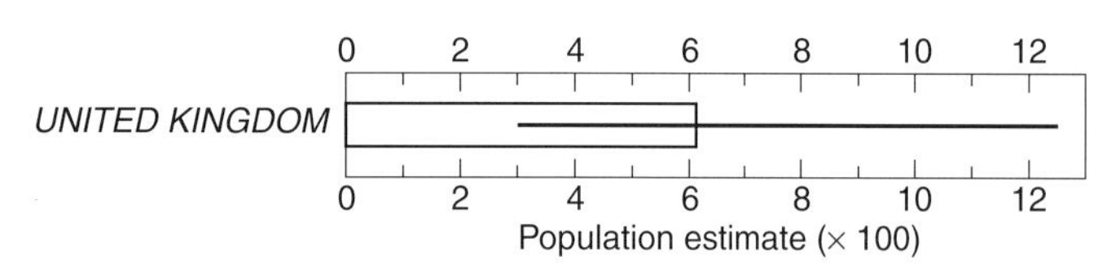

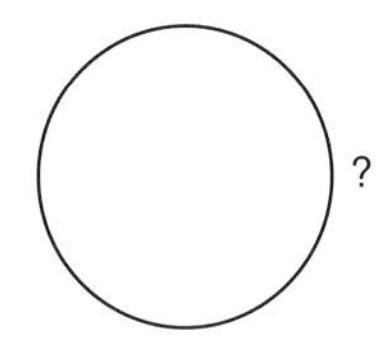

% in top 10 countries: 100.0
Total number of populated European countries: 1
Total European population 300–1250 (612)

The Scottish Crossbill is one of the very few species of birds that are endemic to Europe. It is confined to the Highlands of northern Scotland where it occurs mainly in old woods of Scots pine *Pinus sylvestris*. In earlier times, the species would probably have been widespread throughout the ancient Caledonian pine forests which once covered much of the Scottish highlands. These forests have now been reduced to small fragments, most of which are under threat from modern forestry and from the browsing of young trees by sheep and red deer *Cervus elaphus*. The Scottish Crossbill is found in many of the remaining patches of native pine as well as in plantations, most frequently of Scots pine. It avoids young plantations, favouring especially trees more than 70 years of age. It also prefers open woodland to closed-canopy stands for both feeding and nesting.

The Scottish Crossbill is resident but not sedentary. As with other crossbill species, it is highly dependent on the size of the local seed-crop. The birds move from wood to wood and from one forest or glen to another as the seed-crop varies. Unlike spruce *Picea*, the seed crop of pine rarely fails simultaneously over a wide area and the Scottish Crossbill has not been known to leave the Highlands.

The Crossbill *L. curvirostra*, whose bill is more adapted to spruce cones (*BWP*), also nests in the Highlands of Scotland, sometimes in the same woods as the Scottish Crossbill (Knox 1990). Problems with their identification have made estimating the abundance of both species difficult in the Scottish Highlands. Hybridization may not occur (*BWP*). The only recent estimate of the population size of the Scottish Crossbill suggests that there are about 1500 adults at the start of the breeding season (Nethersole-Thompson 1975).

Alan Knox (GB)

Carpodacus rubicilla

Great Rosefinch

CZ	Hýl velký	I	Ciuffolotto scarlatto maggiore
D	Berggimpel	NL	Grote Roodmus
E	Camachuelo Grande	P	Pintarrôxo-grande
F	Roselin tacheté	PL	Dziwonia kaukaska
FIN	Rakkapunavarpunen	R	Большая чечевица
G	Μεγάλη Ροδόσπιζα	S	Större rosenfink
H	Kaukázusi pirók		

SPEC Cat 3, Threat status E (P)

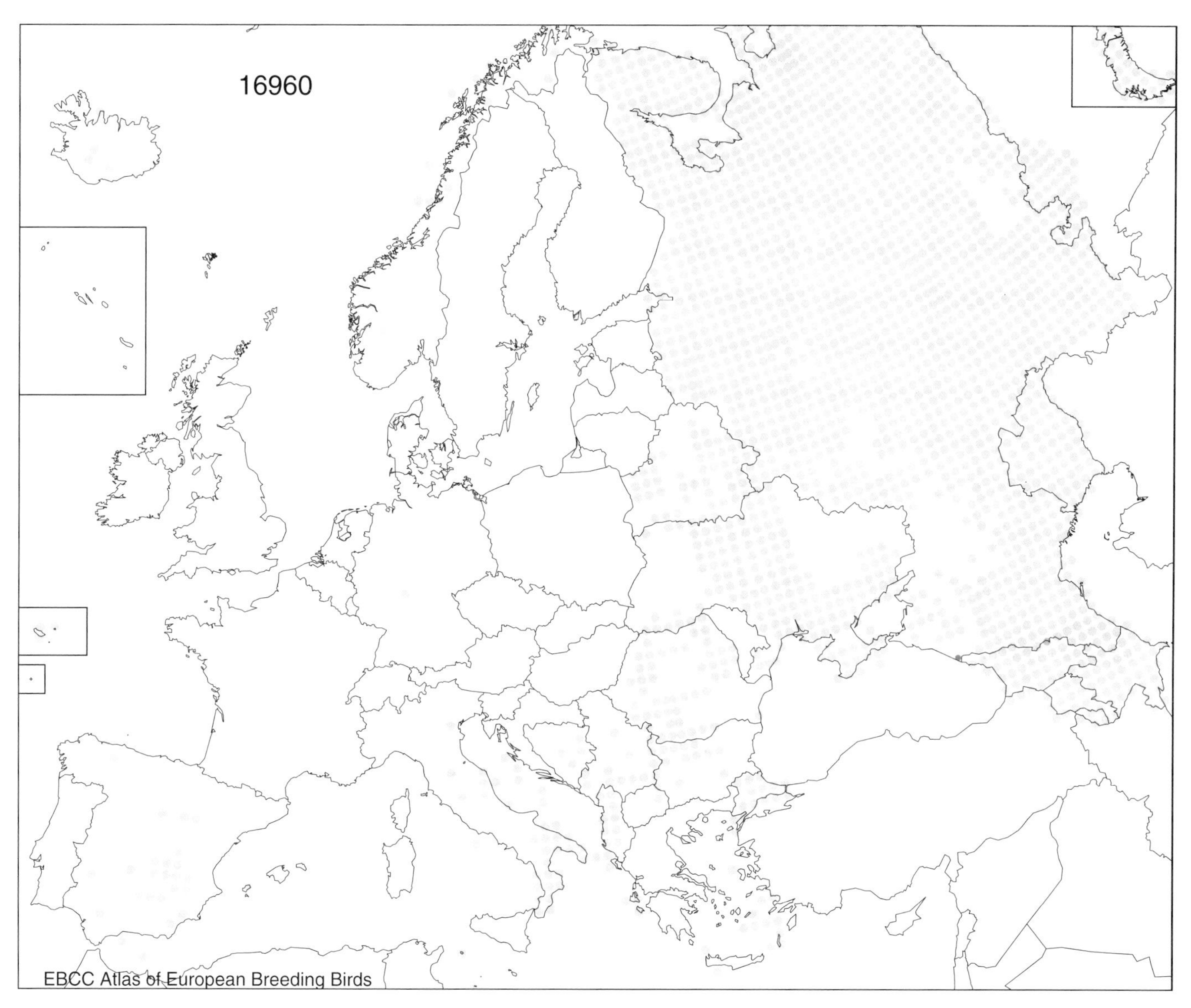

The main range of the Great Rosefinch lies between Afghanistan and N–C China, but outlying populations are found in Mongolia and in the northern Caucasus. The nominate subspecies *C.r. rubicilla* occurs in SE Russia and northern Georgia and Azerbaijan, inhabiting alpine meadows and treeless foothills above 2500m asl, breeding up to 3500m. Elsewhere the other three subspecies occupy plains and semi-deserts up to 5000m asl, moving to lower ground in winter (Clement *et al* 1993). Primarily a ground-feeding species, it will visit bushes for seeds and insects. In summer the Great Rosefinch may be seen on glaciers, and may remain above 2000m even in winter, travelling perhaps 10–15km to seek shelter at *c*500m asl only in the severest weather.

Its preference for high-altitude habitats may delay its breeding until July, and the fledging of young until August. The European population may be as low as 500–1500bp, the decline mainly being attributed to the destruction of habitats rich in its winter food, sea buckthorn *Hippophae rhamnoides* scrub (Loskot 1994c) and to predation by Alpine Chough *Pyrrhocorax graculus*.

Philip Jackson (GB)

Carpodacus erythrinus | Scarlet Rosefinch

CZ	Hýl rudý	I	Ciuffolotto scarlatto
D	Karmingimpel	NL	Roodmus
E	Camachuelo Carminoso	P	Pintarrôxo-carmíneo
F	Roselin cramoisi	PL	Dziwonia
FIN	Punavarpunen	R	Обыкновенная чечевица
G	Ροδόσπιζα	S	Rosenfink
H	Karmazsinpirók		

Non-SPEC, Threat status S (P)

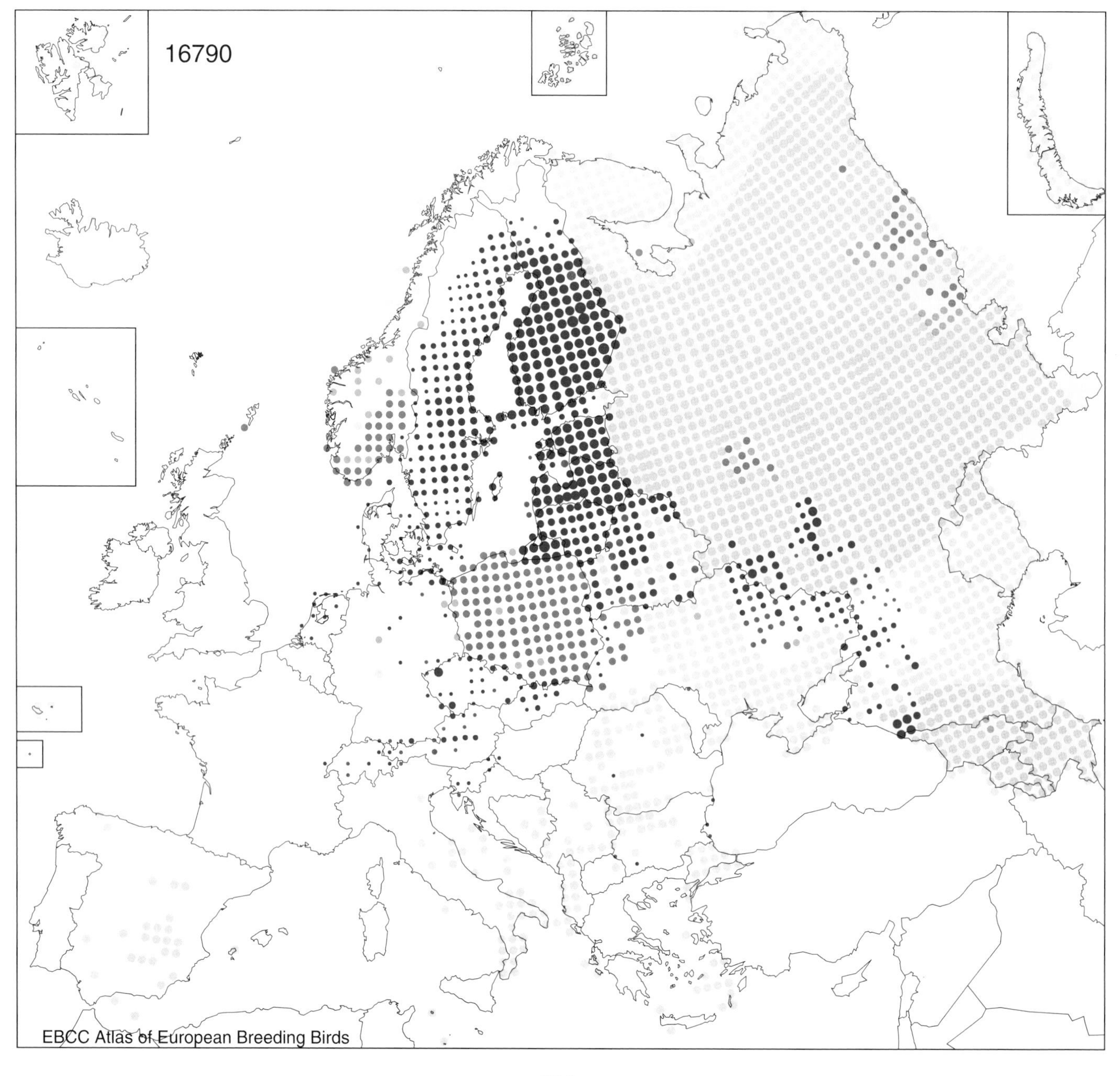

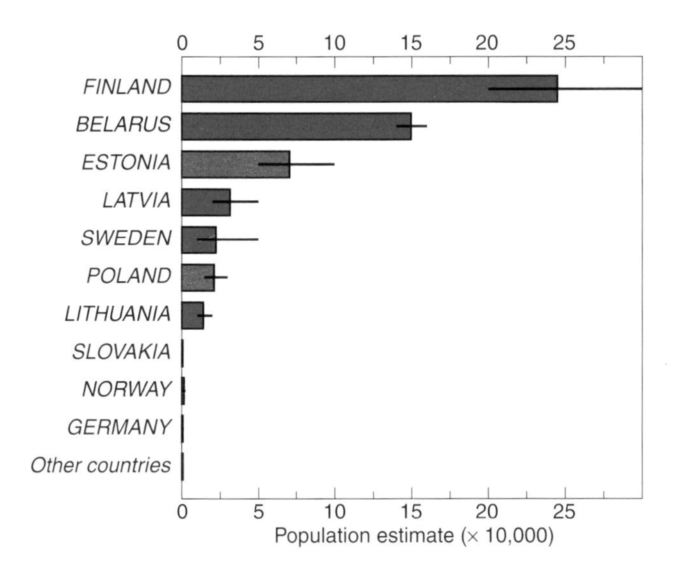

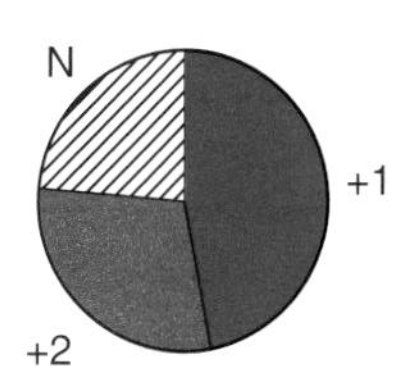

% in top 10 countries: 99.8
Total number of populated European countries: 17
Total European population 505,004–630,914 (558,735)
Russian population 1,000,000–10,000,000 (3,162,278)
Turkish population 5000–50,000 (15,811)

Few European breeding birds spend as little time in Europe as this beautiful scarlet finch. A late migrant, it normally occupies its breeding grounds for only two months, arriving usually in late May, and beginning to depart in late July. It spends the rest of the year in its Asian wintering areas or on migration. In Europe the nominate subspecies *C.e. erythrinus* breeds primarily at lower latitudes, mostly below 200m asl, occasionally up to 1850m asl. The other lowland subspecies, *grebnitskii* of E Siberia and C Asia, normally inhabits mountain slopes. In the Caucasus area *kubanensis* occurs.

The species' very large breeding range extends from Fennoscandia and C Europe eastwards through Russia to the Pacific. The European breeding range of *erythrinus* stretches roughly from the Arctic Circle in the N southwards to *c*47°N. It is fairly common from Sweden and C Poland eastwards, but further W and SW its distribution becomes gradually patchier. It breeds regularly but in small numbers in Norway (1000–2500bp), Denmark (1990, 75bp; Sørensen 1995), Germany (500–1500bp), The Netherlands (1992, 50–60bp; SOVON), Switzerland (1992, >10bp; Maumary *et al* 1993), Austria (50–100bp) and N and W France (1993, >10bp, including first breeding; Anonymous 1994).

The Scarlet Rosefinch breeds in a variety of bushy and deciduous wooded biotopes mostly created or affected by human beings. It prefers groves and luxurious forest-edges facing farmland, rivers, lakes or swamps but also occurs in parks and gardens, often breeding in loose concentrations. From 1965 to 1972, the Fennoscandian overall average breeding density was 3.4 bp/km^2, the highest, in lakeshore woodlands, being 8.8 bp/km^2 (Stjernberg 1979).

Following a period of regression in Europe in the late 19th century, few birds bred outside Russia by 1900, since when there has been a marked increase and a westward spread (Bozhko 1980). Finland experienced a significant breeding range extension in the 1940s. The species started breeding regularly in Sweden in the 1950s, and in Norway and Denmark in the 1970s. Since 1985 this trend apparently has stabilized, although most E and C European countries report increasing numbers (Hill 1986). From line transects, the Finnish population was estimated at 10 000bp in the 1940s, 50 000bp in the 1950s, 450 000bp in the 1970s and 560 000bp in the late 1980s. Sweden has experienced a similar but smaller-scale increase (Risberg & Risberg 1975). Since 1900 such expansion and increases have been equalled by few other European species.

Typically, range expansion starts some distance from the continuous breeding range through small isolated populations which grow sufficiently to merge later with the main population. Many reasons have been suggested for these trends: warmer spring and early summer weather since the 1930s has promoted the development of nest-concealing vegetation and has enhanced nesting success; the species has shifted into more open habitats, where nesting success is twice as high as in more closed habitats, as in Finland (Stjernberg 1985); the drastic change in landscape utilization in W, N and C Europe has created many open habitats suited to the species, and in areas where cattle-grazing has ceased, bushes and trees have encroached on farmland, notably beside waterbodies. Furthermore, forestry methods have changed from cautious timber felling to extensive clearfells amid tree plantations, at least in Fennoscandia (Stjernberg 1985). Moreover, warm autumn weather since the 1960s may have favoured dispersal of first-year birds, which apparently act as pioneers (the first colonizers are often grey-plumaged males; 78% of 178 males in Germany; Jung 1983, Hill 1986).

The wintering areas of European populations are poorly known, but the species winters in S Asia, from Iran to SE China. Presumably European birds mostly winter in Iran, N and C India, in hillside scrub and cultivated areas containing bushes and scattered trees.

Lennart Risberg (S) Torsten Stjernberg (FIN)

Bucanetes mongolicus

Mongolian Trumpeter Finch

CZ	Hýl mongolský	**I**	Trombettiera mongolo
D	Mongolengimpel	**NL**	Mongoolse Woestijnvink
E	Camachuelo Mongol	**P**	Pintarrôxo da Mongólia
F	Roselin de Mongolie	**PL**	Gilak mongolski
FIN	Rotkotulkku	**R**	Понгольский пустынный
G	Ερημοπύρρουλας της Μογγολίας	**S**	Mongol fink
H	Mongol süvöltő		

Non-SPEC, Threat status S (P)

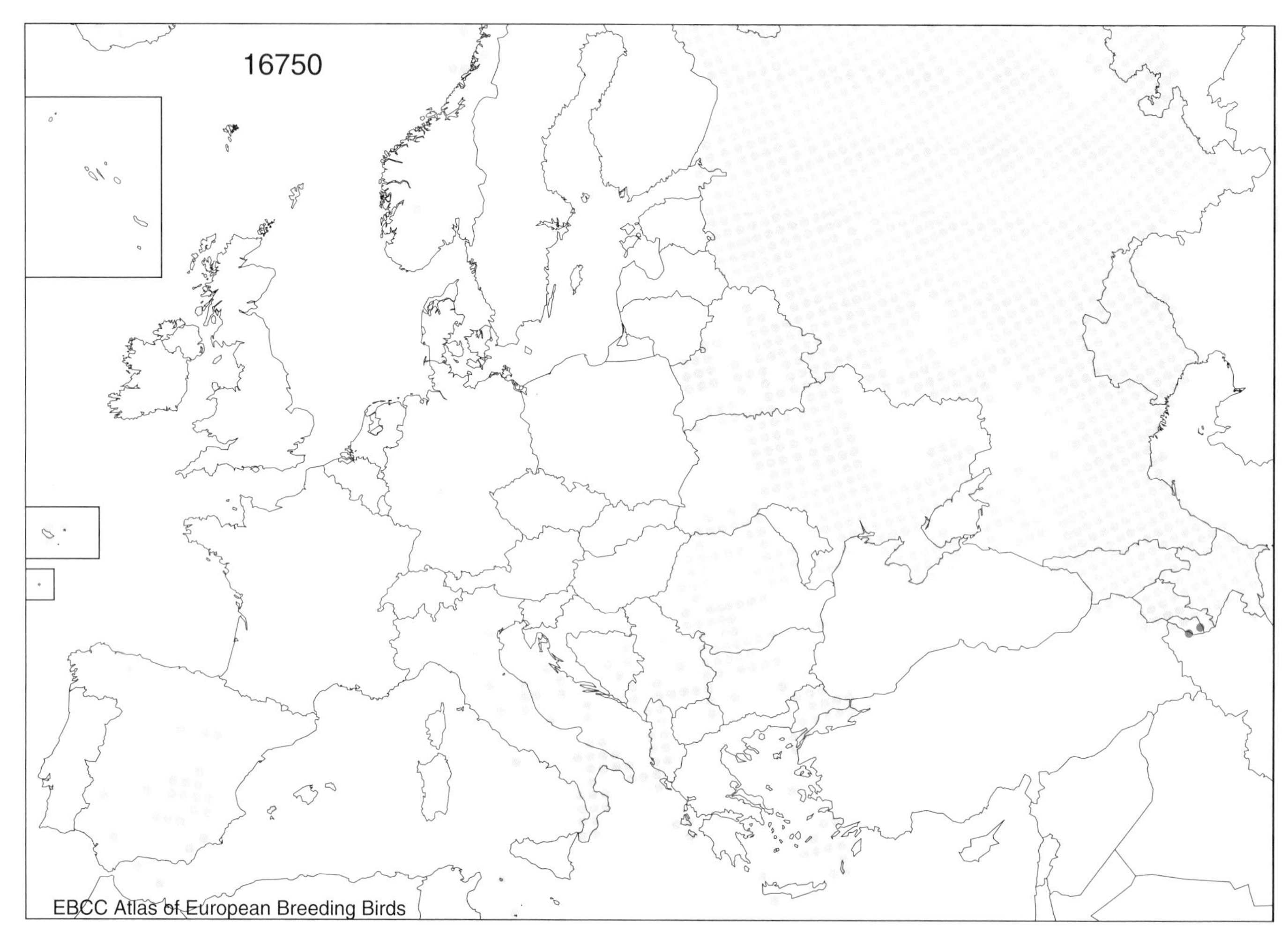

The Mongolian Trumpeter Finch, the size of a Chaffinch *Fringilla coelebs*, is a typical representative of the C Asian avifauna. It breeds from SE Transcaucasia and the Elburz Mountains in the W to the Huang He basin in the E, in a belt lying between 40–50°N and 30–35°N, thus covering most of Kazakhstan and the former Soviet C Asia, and including N and E Iran, Afghanistan, the extreme N of India and Pakistan, S Siberia, Mongolia and NW China.

It inhabits various landscape types, from sand desert (as in Kyzylkum) and hilly plains to mountain alpine zones, at altitudes from 400 to 4600m asl (Kozlova 1975). It nests in stony outcrops, on scattered rocks in the dry steppe, the sides of dry valleys and ravines, and in clay and stony slopes of foothills. Where such natural structures are absent, as in the high upland stony semi-desert of the S Altai, the species nests in artificial structures. The Mongolian Trumpeter Finch is sedentary, wintering mainly where it breeds in the same habitat, especially in its southern range.

In Transcaucasia the Mongolian Trumpeter Finch was once regarded as a rare vagrant (Lyaister & Sosnin 1944), but in fact it is a common and possibly abundant inhabitant of clay and shingle slopes and semi-desert plateaus in the Nakhichevan territory of Azerbaijan (Panov & Bulatova 1972). It is very frequently encountered here along almost vertical precipices and the tops of the low mountain ranges to the N of the Araks River valley. A tentative estimate of linear density is *c*5 bp/km. At present, the Mongolian Trumpeter Finch is not a threatened species because its habitats are not useful to human beings. Although formerly considered conspecific with Trumpeter Finch *B. githagineus*, it breeds sympatrically with the latter without hybridization in Nakhichevan territory of Azerbaijan (Panov & Bulatova 1972).

Eugene N Panov (R)

Bucanetes githagineus

Trumpeter Finch

CZ	Hýl pouštní	I	Trombettiere
D	Wüstengimpel	NL	Woestijnvink
E	Camachuelo Trompetero	P	Pintarrôxo-trombeteiro
F	Roselin githagine	PL	Gilak pustynny
FIN	Aavikkotulkku	R	Пустынный снегирь
G	Ερημοπύρρουλας	S	Ökentrumpetare
H	Sivatagi süvöltő		

SPEC Cat 3, Threat status R

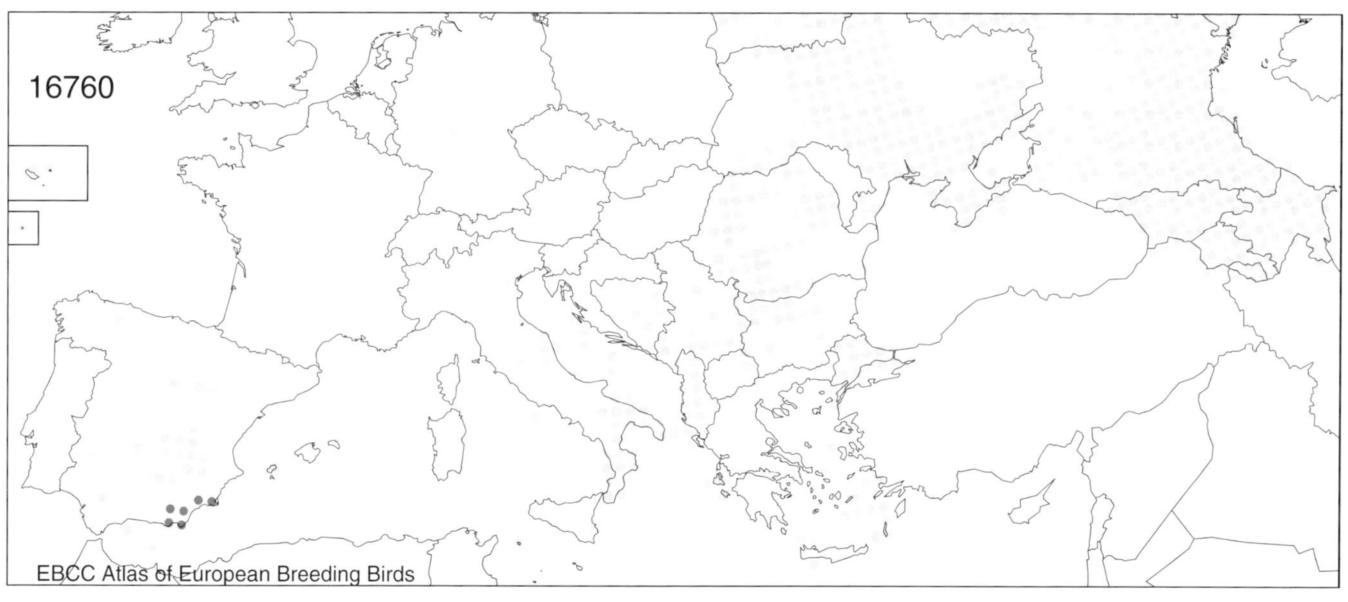

+1

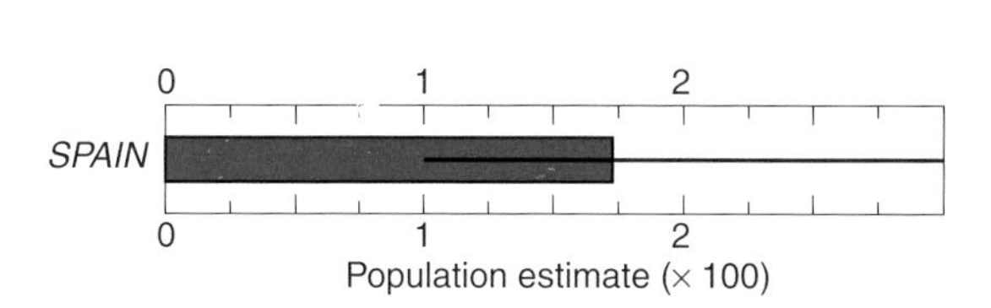

% in top 10 countries: 100.0
Total number of populated European countries: 1
Total European population 100–300 (173)
Turkish population 1–50 (7)

The Trumpeter Finch breeds and winters from the Canary Islands eastwards across North Africa, the Middle East, Iran, Afghanistan, W Pakistan and NE India. Its distribution reaches as far S as the Hoggar. In continental Europe it is restricted to the extreme SE of the Iberian Peninsula, and to Azerbaijan (certainly Nakhichevan territory) and probably Armenia.

SE Iberia is characterized as completely deforested and one of Europe's most arid zones, which aligns well with the species' preference for sparsely vegetated steppe terrain. It avoids not only forested areas or dense shrub formations but also sandy expanses. In Iberia and the Canary Islands, it occupies areas characterized by sparse scrub less than 100cm tall covering 15–50% of the land, generally close to sea level (Cuyás 1971, Manrique & Miralles 1988).

The Spanish population has increased in size and range since the mid-1970s (Manrique & Miralles 1988). This expansion has developed from the main nucleus in the arid zones of Almería, moving eastwards along the coastal mountain chains to the province of Murcia. As a breeding bird, however, it occupies much of its range intermittently, being dependent on the presence of nearby water sources. During the reproduction period, it seems to display an almost semi-colonial behaviour in its favourite enclaves (J. Manrique & M. Yanes, pers obs). In the post-nuptial period, this tendency is accentuated and the species forms flocks frequenting flat, sandy coastal zones possessing sparse and very low vegetation cover. Apparently periodic irruptive movements occur on Tenerife (Canary Islands) (Martín 1987). Generally, the species is erratically nomadic and dispersive.

The continental European population belongs to the subspecies *B.g. zedlitzi*, *crassirostris* inhabits Transcaucasia and *amantum* the Canary Islands. The nominate *githagineus* occurs SE and E of the *Atlas*' coverage.

Juan Manrique (E) Miguel Yanes (E)

Pinicola enucleator

Pine Grosbeak

CZ	Hýl křivčí	I	Ciuffolotto delle pinete
D	Hakengimpel	NL	Haakbek
E	Camachuelo Picogrueso	P	Pintarrôxo-de-bico-grosso
F	Durbec des sapins	PL	Łuskowiec
FIN	Taviokuurna	R	Щур
G	Πευκοπύρρουλας	S	Tallbit
H	Nagy pirók		

Non-SPEC, Threat status S

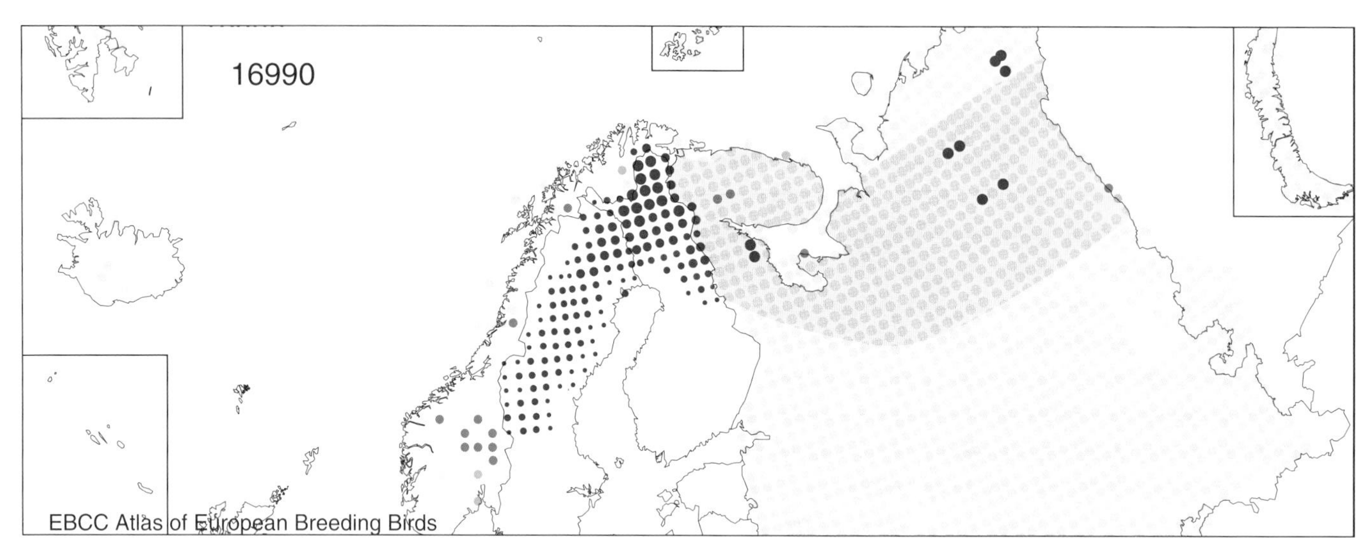

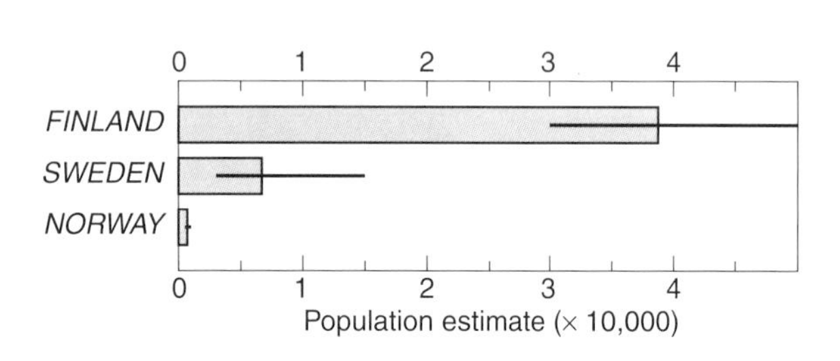

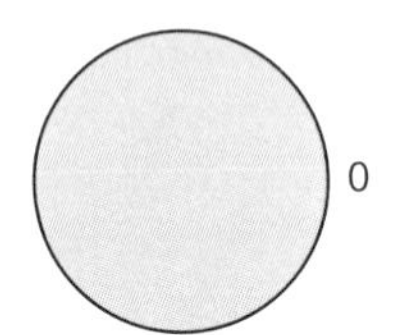

% in top 10 countries: 100.0
Total number of populated European countries: 3
Total European population 36,658–60,140 (46,145)
Russian population 10,000–100,000 (31,623)

The Pine Grosbeak has a Holarctic distribution and prefers forests in the northern taiga and mountain birch *Betula* forest zones throughout the Northern Hemisphere. Its European breeding range covers northern Norway, Sweden, Finland and Russia. Usually it nests in spruce *Picea*, pine *Pinus* and mixed coniferous forests and even in juniper *Juniperus* occurring near the upper limit of the mountain birch forest. Once regarded as a wilderness dweller (Montell 1917) it is now known to breed near northern taiga villages. The nominate subspecies *P.e. enucleator* breeds in Europe; there are at least 10 other subspecies worldwide.

Its range in Fennoscandia has remained fairly stable, Finland having the highest breeding population (30 000–50 000bp) and Sweden and Norway only 3000–15 000bp and 500–1000bp respectively; the latter figures reflect the relative availability of suitable breeding habitat areas on the Scandinavian mountain slopes (Haftorn 1971). Unlike most Pine Grosbeak populations, which tend to be stable, that of southern Finland (in Kainuu) has declined since the mid-1960s.

Despite its narrow breeding zone and migratory nature, the species remains in Europe throughout, moving but a short distance southwards. Breeding birds from Finnish Forest Lapland migrate in September–October and return early in February–March (Pulliainen 1974). During winter they roam around C and S Finland or further S. Irregularly, exceptionally large flocks may appear in these areas, indicating massive winter invasions from the E.

The annual migration-flight strategy of the Pine Grosbeak differs from those of other passerines, in that it has a predator-avoidance component. Because it has developed special anatomical adaptations, such as an exceptionally long small intestine, it can specialize by being able to metabolize such food as spruce and willow *Salix* buds and rowanberry *Sorbus aucuparia* seeds, which in winter are available in quantity in areas where raptor numbers are smaller than in most passerines' wintering grounds (Pulliainen 1974).

Erkki Pulliainen (FIN)

Pyrrhula murina

Azores Bullfinch

CZ	Hýl Azorský	I	Ciuffolotto delle Azzorre
D	Azorengimpel	NL	Azorengoudvink
E	Camachuelo de las Azores	P	Priôlo
F	Bouvreuil des Açores	PL	Gil azorski
FIN	Azorienpunatulkku	R	Азорский снегирь
G	Πύρρουλας των Αζορών	S	Azordomherre
H	Azori süvöltő		

Criteria not applied

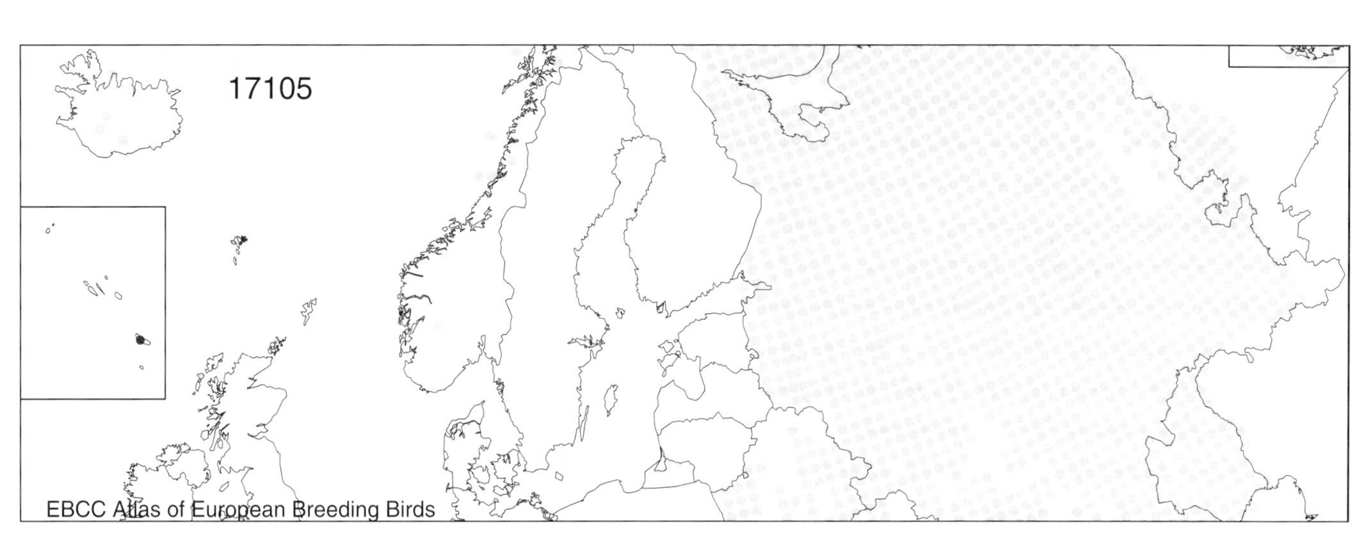

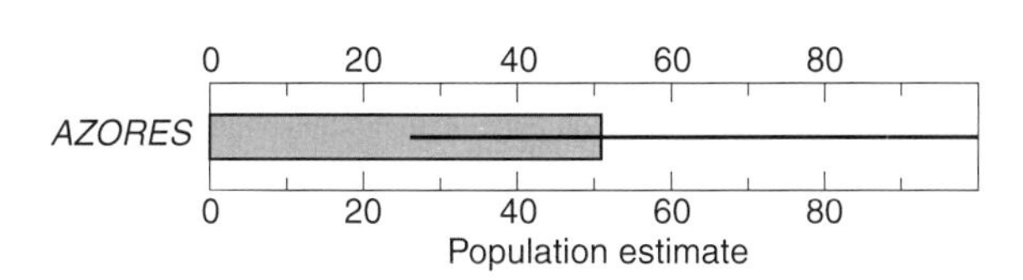

% in top 10 countries: 100.0
Total number of populated European countries: 1
Total European population 26–100 (51)

The large and monomorphic Azores Bullfinch is known only from the eastern part of Sao Miguel island in the Azores. The population of *c*120bp (J. Ramos, pers obs) is now restricted to *c*580ha of high-altitude native forest, although from 1840 to *c*1920 it had a wider range and was regarded as a pest in orange orchards, being easily collected for museums (Bannerman & Bannerman 1966, Ramos 1993). Its range contains two main patches of native vegetation, the larger being centred on Pico da Vara summit, where birds breed and occur all year round and the smaller being at Salto do Cavalo, in the W of its range, where birds occur only from September to December (Ramos in press). The vegetation around Salto do Cavalo is less diverse and has significantly lower densities of native food plants, especially the Azorean holly *Ilex perado*, whose berries are consumed during the winter food scarcity period (Ramos 1995).

To complete its annual cycle the Azores Bullfinch needs a habitat mosaic of several vegetation types. It uses native vegetation intensively year-round but in summer it also selects open areas containing herbaceous vegetation and forest margins, both of native and exotic trees such as Japanese cedar *Cryptomeria japonica* and cheese-wood *Pittosporum undulatum* (Ramos in press). Birds move from area to area following the fruiting of food plants. They are more mobile in summer than in winter, making movements of *c*3km along streams, from higher to lower altitudes in late spring (Ramos in press).

Random population fluctuations probably affect numbers, but may not be a major factor because the population trend appears to be stable (Ramos 1994), some recently introduced exotic plant species providing food over winter and early summer (Ramos 1995). However, the plant community equilibrium on which the Azores Bullfinch depends is being upset by the loss of native vegetation and by the large-scale invasion of native forest by *P. undulatum*, ginger lily *Hedychium gardnerianum* and lily-of-the-valley tree *Clethra arborea*, leading to the gradual contraction of its range and small population.

Jaime A Ramos (P)

Pyrrhula pyrrhula **Bullfinch**

CZ	Hýl obecný	I	Ciuffolotto
D	Gimpel	NL	Goudvink
E	Camachuelo Común	P	Dom-fafe
F	Bouvreuil pivoine	PL	Gil
FIN	Punatulkku	R	Снегирь
G	Πύρρουλας	S	Domherre
H	Süvöltő		

Non-SPEC, Threat status S

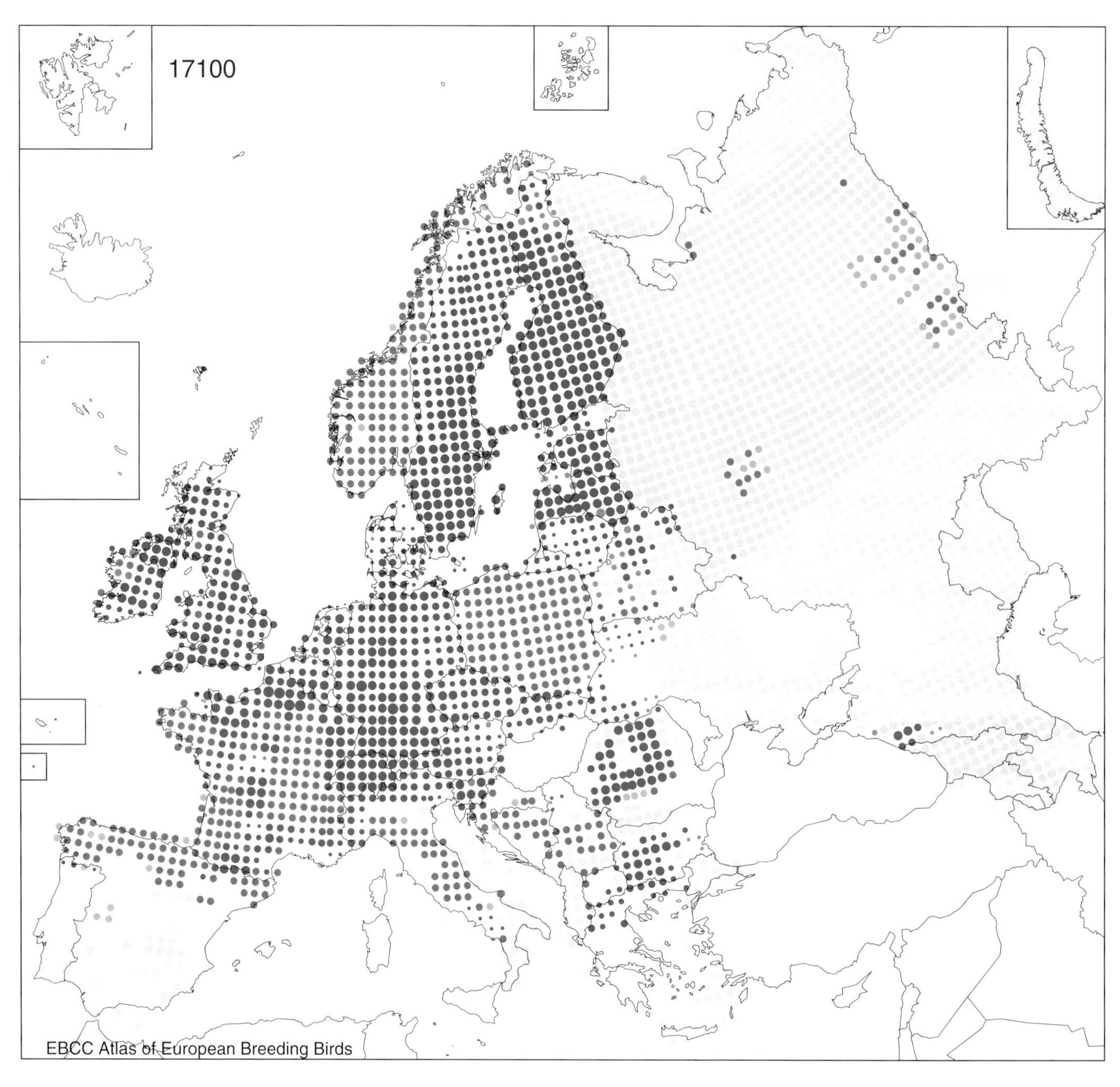

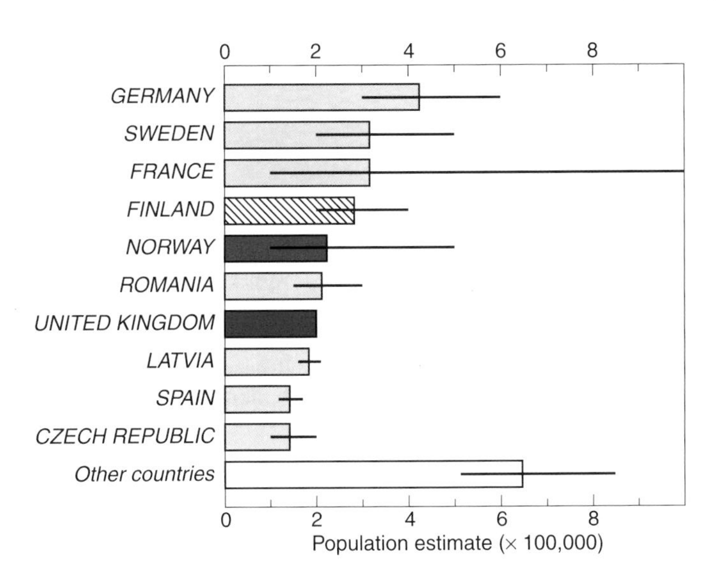

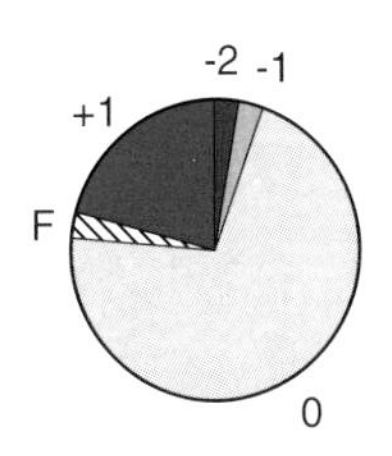

% in top 10 countries: 79.1
Total number of populated European countries: 34
Total European population 2,760,888–3,887,259 (3,087,354)
Russian population 1,000,000–10,000,000 (3,162,278)
Turkish population 1000–10,000 (3162)

The Bullfinch breeds in forest and other woody habitats across the Palearctic region, occurring in boreal, temperate and montane areas. Its distribution thus extends from Ireland across Eurasia to Japan and Kamchatka, and from near the northern treeline southwards to high mountains from the Cantabrians to the Caucasus.

Over much of its range, the species occurs primarily in forests dominated by conifers, but in western Europe it also occurs commonly in broad-leaved woodland and scrub, and in the bushy town parks and gardens. Everywhere it prefers areas with dense undergrowth. In boreal regions, it often visits garden feeding trays for sunflower and other seeds. In fruit-growing areas, it frequents orchards during late winter and spring to feed on flowerbuds, sometimes to the fruit-grower's detriment (Newton 1964).

Despite striking coloration, the Bullfinch is relatively inconspicuous and secretive. It betrays its presence mainly by its soft, piping call-notes, and by its white rump flashing as it darts into cover after being disturbed while feeding. Large-scale densities are quite consistent throughout its range, from 1500–4000 bp/50km square average in Fennoscandia and the Baltic States to 1000–5000 bp/50km square in W, C and E Europe. Lower values of <100 bp/50km square obtain in S Europe.

In much of its European range, the species seemingly has not changed greatly in numbers or distribution since the mid-1960s, but small increases occurred in some regions and declines in others. In Great Britain, a marked decline in the 1980s followed a 30-year period of unusual abundance, coincident with the scarcity of its main predator, the Sparrowhawk *Accipiter nisus* (Newton 1993b).

In the breeding season pairs nest solitarily but show no obvious territorial or other conspicuous behaviour, so can be difficult to find (Newton 1972). The greatest densities are reached in thick bushy areas, including young conifer plantations, where numbers exceeding 20 bp/km^2 have been recorded, often in semi-colonial clusters (Bijlsma 1982, Newton 1993b). However, in most woody areas much lower densities are usual, for the Bullfinch seldom is among the commonest of woodland breeding birds. Pairs forage up to 500m from the nest, wherever suitable food plants occur. For most of the year they eat the seeds and fruits of various woody and herbaceous plants, including berries and other fleshy fruits, turning to buds in late winter and spring (Newton 1972, Gatter 1989). In the breeding season, the species is seen mostly as singletons or pairs, but in autumn and winter forms parties of up to a dozen or more. While feeding the birds seldom venture more than *c*10m from cover.

In the northern and eastern European breeding ranges the Bullfinch is a partial migrant, leaving in greatest numbers in years when favoured seeds are scarce. As for some other finches, females and juveniles tend to migrate in greater proportions than the adult males (Savolainen 1987). Elsewhere the species is resident or dispersive, but the numbers seen in particular localities depend largely on the local food supply and may vary greatly from year to year, and from month to month within a winter. The species winters mainly within the breeding distribution, but also appears sporadically in some lowland Mediterranean areas beyond it. Recent studies with radio-tagged birds have revealed that individuals may remain for weeks or months within a short distance of a good food source, before suddenly moving up to several kilometres to a new site (Greig-Smith & Wilson 1984).

Geographical variation is mainly clinal, the birds becoming larger and brighter towards the N and E. Azores Bullfinch *P. murina* (*qv*) has recently been separated. In all, nine subspecies currently are recognized, including five in the coverage area.

Ian Newton (GB)

This species account is sponsored by W. de Boer, Hengelo, NL.

Coccothraustes coccothraustes **Hawfinch**

CZ	Dlask tlustozobý	**I**	Frosone
D	Kernbeißer	**NL**	Appelvink
E	Picogordo	**P**	Bico-grossudo
F	Grosbec casse-noyaux	**PL**	Grubodziób
FIN	Nokkavarpunen	**R**	Дубонос
G	Χοντρομύτης	**S**	Stenknäck
H	Meggyvágó		

Non-SPEC, Threat status S

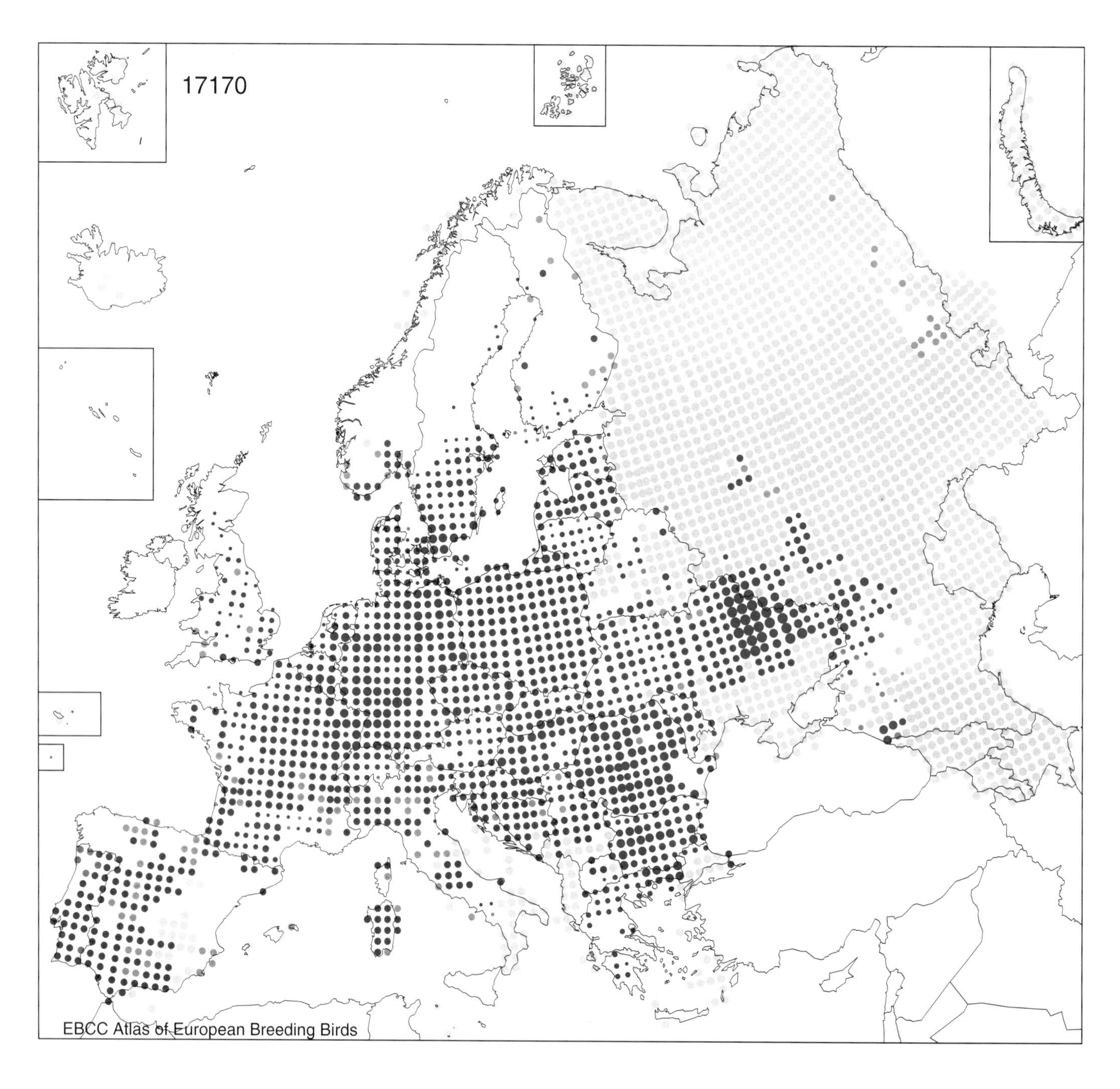

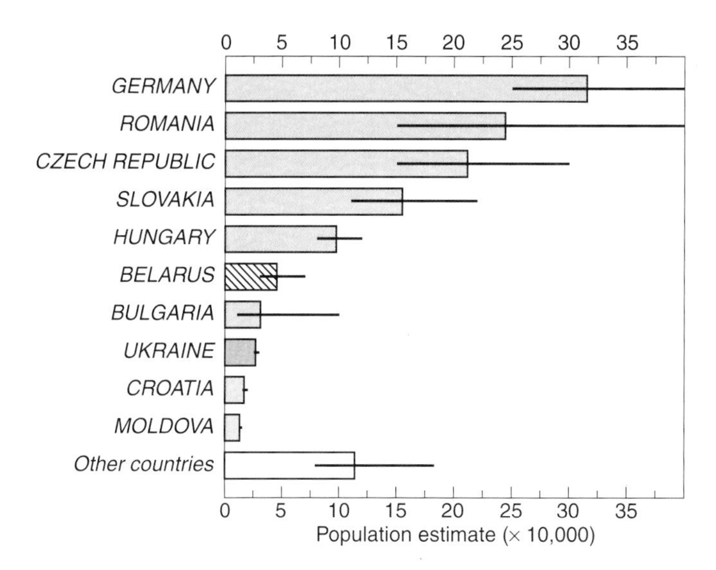

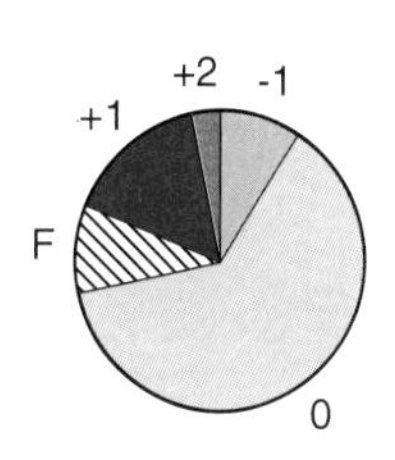

% in top 10 countries: 91.0
Total number of populated European countries: 32
Total European population 1,133,732–1,498,490 (1,276,869)
Russian population 10,000–100,000 (31,623)
Turkish population 1000–10,000 (3162)

At 18cm long and 50–60g in weight, the Hawfinch is the second largest western Palearctic finch. Its huge conical bill enables it to break open the hard fruits of certain deciduous trees, which ultimately determine its distribution. The species breeds patchily across the Palearctic from the southern boreal, through temperate and mediterranean zones, into the fringes of steppe or desert, provided suitable large seeds are available. It thus occurs from Great Britain eastwards to Japan, but in the *Atlas*' coverage area it is absent as a breeder from Ireland, much of N and E Spain, S Italy and Sicily, and is extremely localized in Great Britain and in Fennoscandia beyond *c*60°N. Breeding plumage differentiation indicates three subspecies, the nominate *C.c. coccothraustes* inhabiting Europe.

The Hawfinch occupies primarily broad-leaved woodland, reaching its greatest densities in the oak–hornbeam *Quercus–Carpinus betulus* forest of temperate regions. In its northern range it occurs chiefly in the deciduous component of the mainly coniferous landscape, and to the S it inhabits the steppe-woodlands and thorn thickets of desert-fringes. Where common, the species also uses orchards (especially cherry), large well-timbered gardens and parks, sometimes in towns and cities (Mountfort 1957, Bijlsma 1979). It feeds mainly in the canopy in summer, but descends to the ground for fallen seeds in winter (Newton 1972), when it becomes more generally distributed, moving into areas where it does not breed, usually forming small flocks, but occasionally in parties more than 100 strong.

The Hawfinch breeds solitarily or in small groups, nests of different pairs sometimes being less than 20m apart, but the species forages over wider areas, often more than 100m from the nest (Mountfort 1957, Krüger 1979). Breeding success of birds breeding semi-colonially is significantly higher than for solitary pairs (Bijlsma 1979). In the best broad-leaved woodland habitats, such as oak–hornbeam stands in the Białowieża National Park, the species achieves densities of up to 68 bp/km^2 (Tomiałojć 1995), and in favoured Dutch town parks and gardens, up to 40 bp/km^2 (R.G. Bijlsma, pers comm).

Since the 1960s the species appears to have increased over much of its range. In Fennoscandia, Karelia and the Baltic States, a slight expansion followed the planting of broad-leaved trees around towns. Since the 1980s, much anecdotal evidence has been published about increases in W and C Europe, and particularly since 1985/86. The Dutch population has at least quadrupled since the 1970s. In well-studied areas increases have been even greater; SW-Veluwe (110km^2), from 100–200bp (1974–84) to 550–745bp (1985–87; Bijlsma 1987b), and Drenthe province (2680km^2) from *c*75bp (1975–80) to 2100bp (1985–91; A.J. van Dijk, pers comm). A progressive trend also developed in Spain, where migrant numbers from W Germany, Belgium, the Czech Republic, Slovakia and Switzerland increased during the 1980s (Asensio & Antón 1990). In contrast, Britain suffered a range contraction, and Lithuania, Denmark and Ukraine declining numbers, probably related to destruction and fragmentation of deciduous woodland, and the removal of old orchards.

The northernmost Hawfinch populations are migratory, the southernmost being resident. The general direction of migration in Europe is NE to SW, movements exceeding 1000km having been recorded by ringing. In winter the species occurs in Europe outside its breeding range, such as in parts of Spain and Italy. Females and juveniles tend to migrate in greater proportion and over greater distances than adult males. The species' occurrence in winter is dependent on the presence of suitable tree seeds, and because seed-crops often fluctuate from year to year, winter distribution is to some extent sporadic. Localities holding large flocks in one year may not hold flocks every year (Axelsson *et al* 1977). Local dispersive movements therefore also are common.

Ian Newton (GB)

This species account is sponsored by KNNV-Vogelwerkgroep Wageningen, Wageningen, NL.

Plectrophenax nivalis **Snow Bunting**

CZ	Sněhule severní	**I**	Zigolo delle nevi
D	Schneeammer	**NL**	Sneeuwgors
E	Escribano Nival	**P**	Escrevedeira-das-neves
F	Bruant des neiges	**PL**	Śnieguła
FIN	Pulmunen	**R**	Пуночка
G	Χιονοτσίχλονο	**S**	Snösparv
H	Hósármány		

Non-SPEC, Threat status S (P)

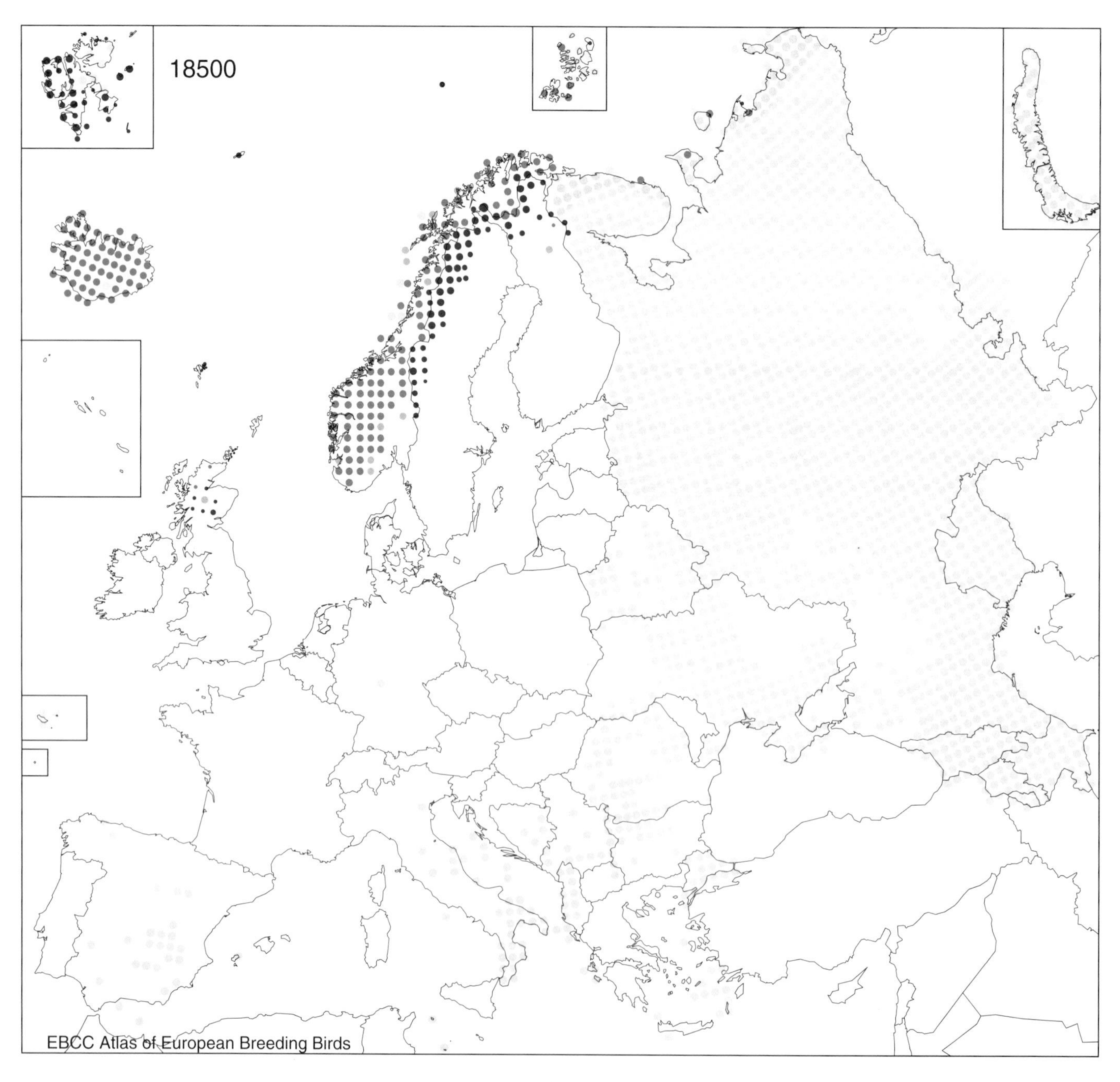

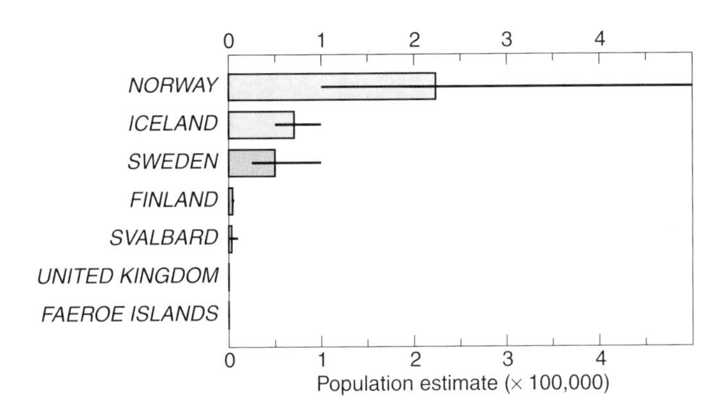

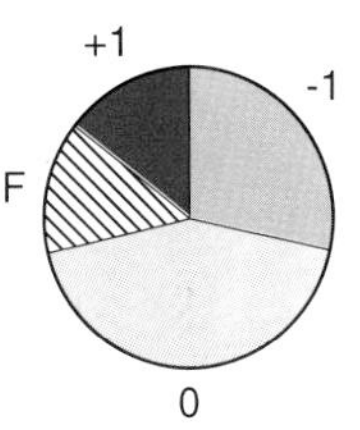

% in top 10 countries: 100.0
Total number of populated European countries: 7
Total European population 223,986–634,300 (351,809)
Russian population 10,000–100,000 (31,623)

No other land bird has such a northerly breeding distribution as the Snow Bunting. It inhabits sparsely vegetated tundra on the fringes of the Arctic Ocean, Alaska, N Canada, Greenland, Iceland, and the mountains of Scotland and Scandinavia (with a few on particularly barren parts of the Norwegian coast), areas where midsummer mean temperatures rarely exceed 10°C. In the high arctic it ranges from sea level to mountain tops, even onto Greenland icecap nunataks.

The Snow Bunting nests in rock crevices, in scree, and under boulders; it often breeds on seabird cliffs. It is rare where ground is unbroken and covered with continuous vegetation, which provides few nest sites, but common in many arctic settlements, where it nests in buildings. The young consume invertebrates but the adults are opportunistic, taking seeds, bulbils or invertebrates depending on availability. Nests commonly are near water (where insects are abundant) or snow patches (from which insects are readily collected).

Nests may be close together in settlements and in rocky places surrounded by flat tundra that provides feeding areas but no nest sites. Overall densities are typically 5–30 bp/km^2 (Koskimies 1989a, Boertmann *et al* 1991). In many parts of its range the Snow Bunting is by far the commonest land bird; it specializes in barren landscapes where there is little competition from other species. Densities are low on Jan Mayen (too barren), in marshy regions of Iceland (few nest sites), and on the southern margins of the range in S Norway and Scotland (Moksnes 1973, Nethersole-Thompson 1993). Numbers in Scotland have increased in recent decades (Nethersole-Thompson 1993) but there is no general evidence of long-term population changes.

Most birds (especially females) leave the breeding grounds in winter, though often late in autumn after other migrants have departed. They winter in open country with low and sparse vegetation, where winds are strong enough to clear snow from patches of ground. The main winter range is in the steppe country extending from E Europe across Asia at 45–55°N (and the corresponding zone in North America); some occur in similar habitats in C and W Europe and on barren shingle beaches, saltmarshes and sand-dunes (and adjoining stubble fields) around the North Sea. Many Icelandic birds are resident but Icelandic birds make up two thirds of the W European winter population (Scandinavia is probably the source of the others). Most E Greenland birds fly via N Russia to C and S Russia (W Greenland birds go to America). At least some of the winter populations appear to move about as weather and food availability change; the southern extremes of the winter range may be used only in mid-winter (Erdmann 1985). Winter flocks may comprise just a few birds or thousands. They rarely mix with other species.

The return to the breeding grounds (especially for males) may occur many weeks before breeding starts. The birds establish territories on mild days but return to flocks during harsh weather. Snow-free patches, cleared by wind or around settlements, are favoured feeding sites. Some southern populations are double-brooded but the breeding cycle can be fitted into a short period; post-nuptial moult may begin with chicks still in the nest and is so rapid that the birds may become flightless. Although second broods produce only 10% of future recruits to the breeding population, the costs to adults of attempting second broods are low enough to make it apparently cost-effective (Smith & Marquiss 1995).

Snow Bunting subspecies are: the nominate *nivalis*, extending from W Alaska through Canada, Greenland and Europe (not Iceland); *vlasowae* from Pechora to E Siberia; *townsendi* on most Bering Sea islands and the southern part of the E Siberian coastal range; *insulae* on Iceland (and, mixed with *nivalis*, Scotland); *hyperboreus* on Hall and St Matthew Islands (Bering Sea). The first three intergrade.

Jeremy J D Greenwood (GB)

Calcarius lapponicus

Lapland Bunting

CZ	Strnad severní	I	Zigolo di Lapponia
D	Spornammer	NL	IJsgors
E	Escribano Lapón	P	Escrevedeira da Lapónia
F	Bruant lapon	PL	Poświerka
FIN	Lapinsirkku	R	Лапландский подорожник
G	Λαπωνοτσίχλονο	S	Lappsparv
H	Sarkantyús sármány		

Non-SPEC, Threat status S (P)

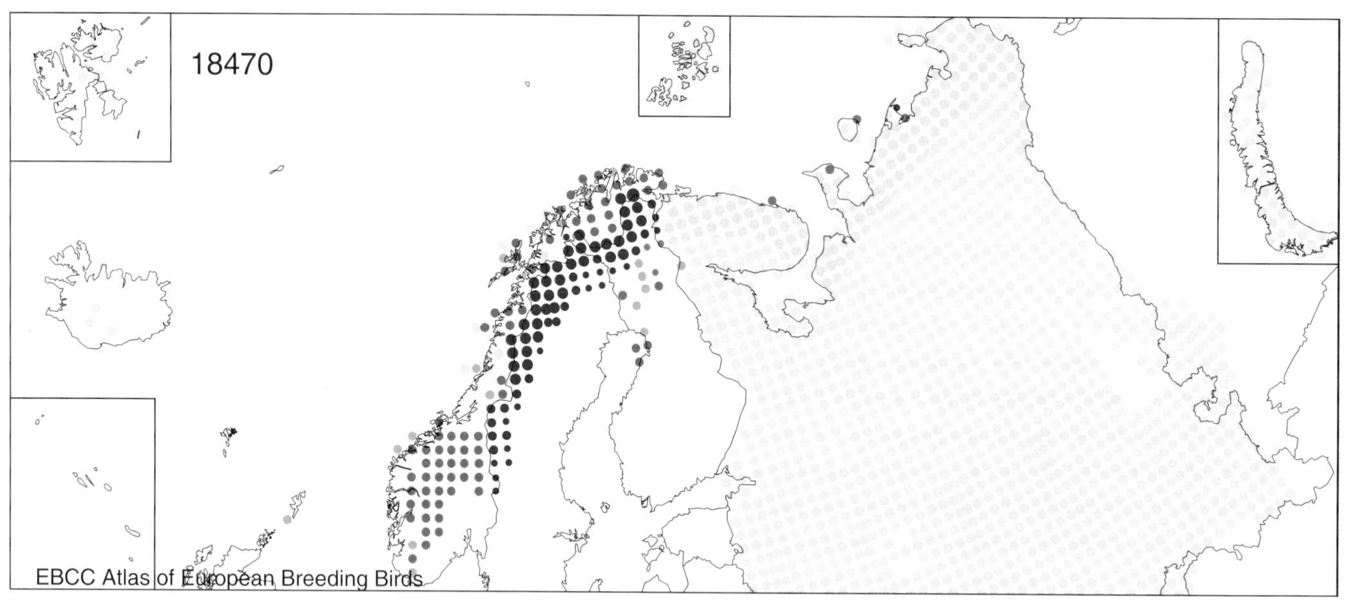

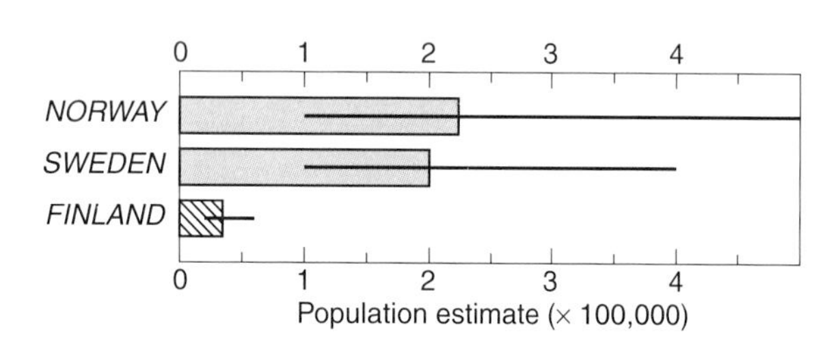

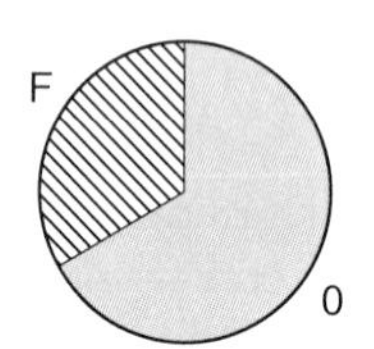

% in top 10 countries: 100.0
Total number of populated European countries: 3
Total European population 298,583–800,353 (458,248)
Russian population 1,000,000–10,000,000 (3,162,278)

The Lapland Bunting has a circumpolar distribution largely above 60°N and is one of the most abundant of all arctic nesting passerines. The European subspecies, one of five, is the nominate *C.l. lapponicus*. Throughout its range, the species nests in low-arctic tundra, and is especially abundant in low-arctic biotopes which have well-developed willow *Salix* scrub up to 1m tall. Even in the C Canadian arctic, where the Lapland Bunting is extremely abundant and widespread, the greatest densities are associated with hummock vegetation supporting dwarf willow growth. In Europe, it breeds extensively from southern Norway northwards through Sweden and Finland into arctic Russia, coincident with the distribution of such habitat. Extralimital breeding has occurred very irregularly (1977, 1980) in northern Great Britain (Gibbons *et al* 1993).

Its wintering areas comprise coastal fields and saltmarshes around North Sea coasts, particularly the soft coasts of the Wadden Sea. However, the majority of the enormous Russian population winters some 5° further S in more arid zones from the northern Black Sea coasts eastwards to the Sea of Japan.

Breeding densities in one study area in Swedish Lapland apparently increased from a mean of 23.4 bp/km^2 for 1963–83 to 29.2 bp/km^2 for 1984–89 (Gierow & Gierow 1991), very similar to values of 26 and 24 bp/km^2 at Hardangervidda in 1986–87 (Bjørnsen 1988). During a 16-year survey in Alaska, densities ranged between 50 and 95 bp/km^2 (Custer & Pitelka 1977).

Very little is known about the changes in distribution and abundance of a species breeding over such a vast and remote area, but generally the lack of land-use change in both the arctic breeding areas and intertidal areas of the coastal fringe support the general impression of little change in overall abundance in recent years. Late springs may affect breeding success, resulting in natural fluctuations in population size, as in W Greenland (Fox *et al* 1987). Several consecutive years of high predation, probably related to a disrupted lemming cycle, depress nesting success and may temporarily lead to a marked population decline (in Alaska; Custer & Pitelka 1977).

Tony Fox (GB) Jesper Madsen (DK)

Emberiza leucocephalos

Pine Bunting

CZ	Strnad bělohlavý	I	Zigolo golarossa
D	Fichtenammer	NL	Witkopgors
E	Escribano de Gmelin	P	Escrevedeira de Gmelin
F	Bruant à calotte blanche	PL	Trznadel białogłowy
FIN	Mäntysirkku	R	Седоголовая овсянка
G	Ελατοτσίχλονο	S	Tallsparv
H	Fenyősármány		

Criteria not applied

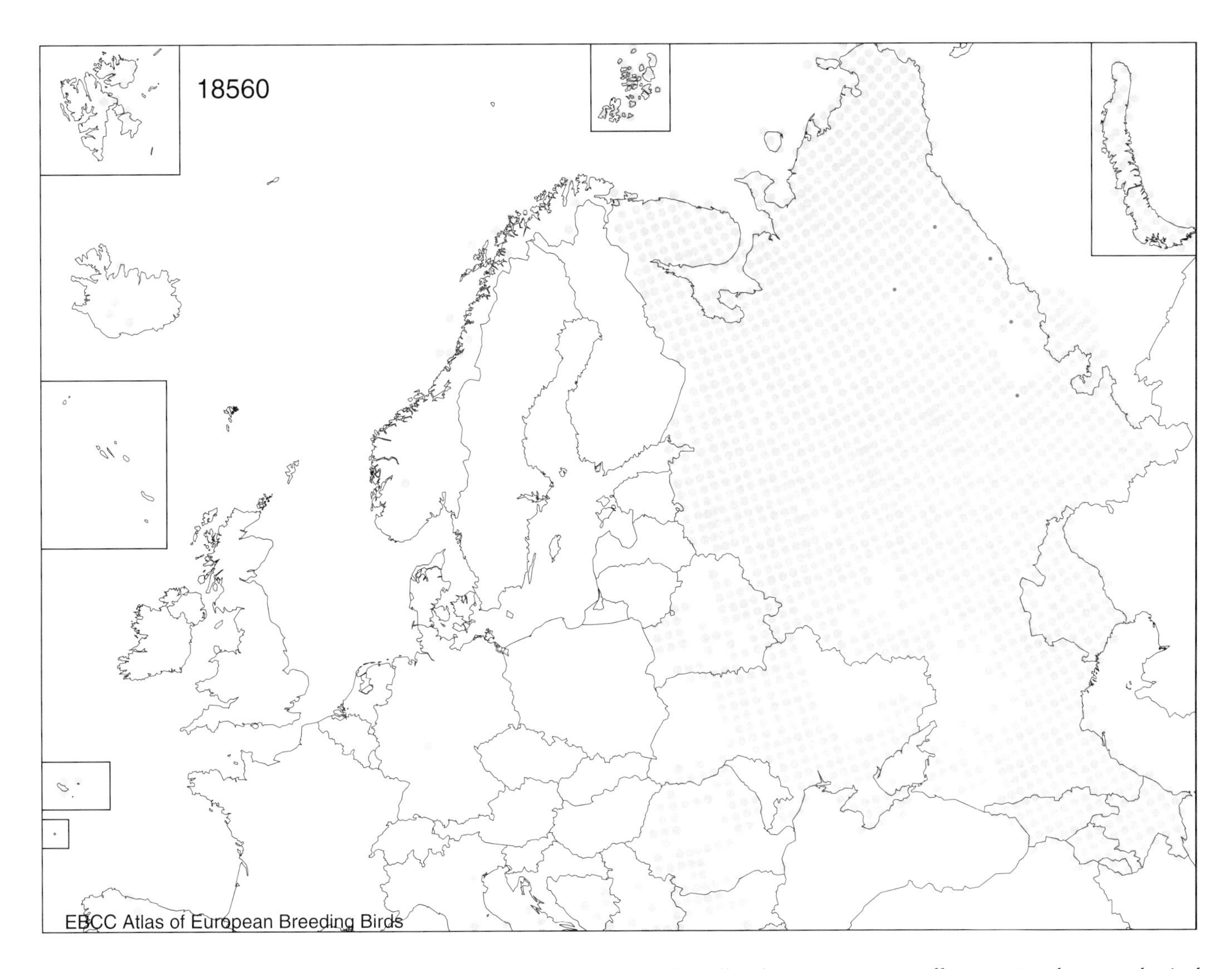

The Pine Bunting is a typical representative of the eastern Palearctic avifauna, the distribution of the nominate subspecies *E.l. leucocephalos* lying generally between 45° and 66°N from the Urals to Ussuriland and Kamchatka. An isolated population, comprising the only other subspecies *fronto*, occurs in NW China.

In Europe it is a rare but occasionally numerous species in some localities. The Pine Bunting occurs in the western foothills of the mid-Urals, near Denezhkin Kamen Peak (Spangenberg & Sudilovskaya 1954), breeding occasionally up to 2000m. Twice it has been observed in the Pechora–Ilych Reserve (Beshkarev & Teplov 1993). In its westernmost range the species has been encountered in the environs of the cities of Syktyvkar (Estafiev 1977a) and Perm (Prieszhev 1978) and in this region it hybridizes freely with Yellowhammer *E. citrinella* (*BWP*), whose ecological niche it largely shares except for subarctic and warm continental aspects, thus making the Pine Bunting more migratory (C. Harrison 1982).

The Pine Bunting's preferred habitats are thinned-out and islet-like light coniferous and foliaceous forests and also forest margins. The European population is estimated at present (1994) at 250–300bp but the numbers probably fluctuate greatly annually. The Pine Bunting is migratory, its westernmost population probably wintering in N Iran or Kazakhstan. The main wintering areas lie in C Asia and in a belt running from the Sea of Japan SW to the Chinese breeding area of *fronto*.

Alexey A Estafiev (R) Sergey K Kotchanov (R)

Emberiza citrinella Yellowhammer

CZ	Strnad obecný	**I**	Zigolo giallo
D	Goldammer	**NL**	Geelgors
E	Escribano Cerillo	**P**	Escrevedeira-amarela
F	Bruant jaune	**PL**	Trznadel
FIN	Keltasirkku	**R**	Обыкновенная овсянка
G	Χρυσοτσίχλονο	**S**	Gulsparv
H	Citromsármány		

SPEC Cat 4, Threat status S (P)

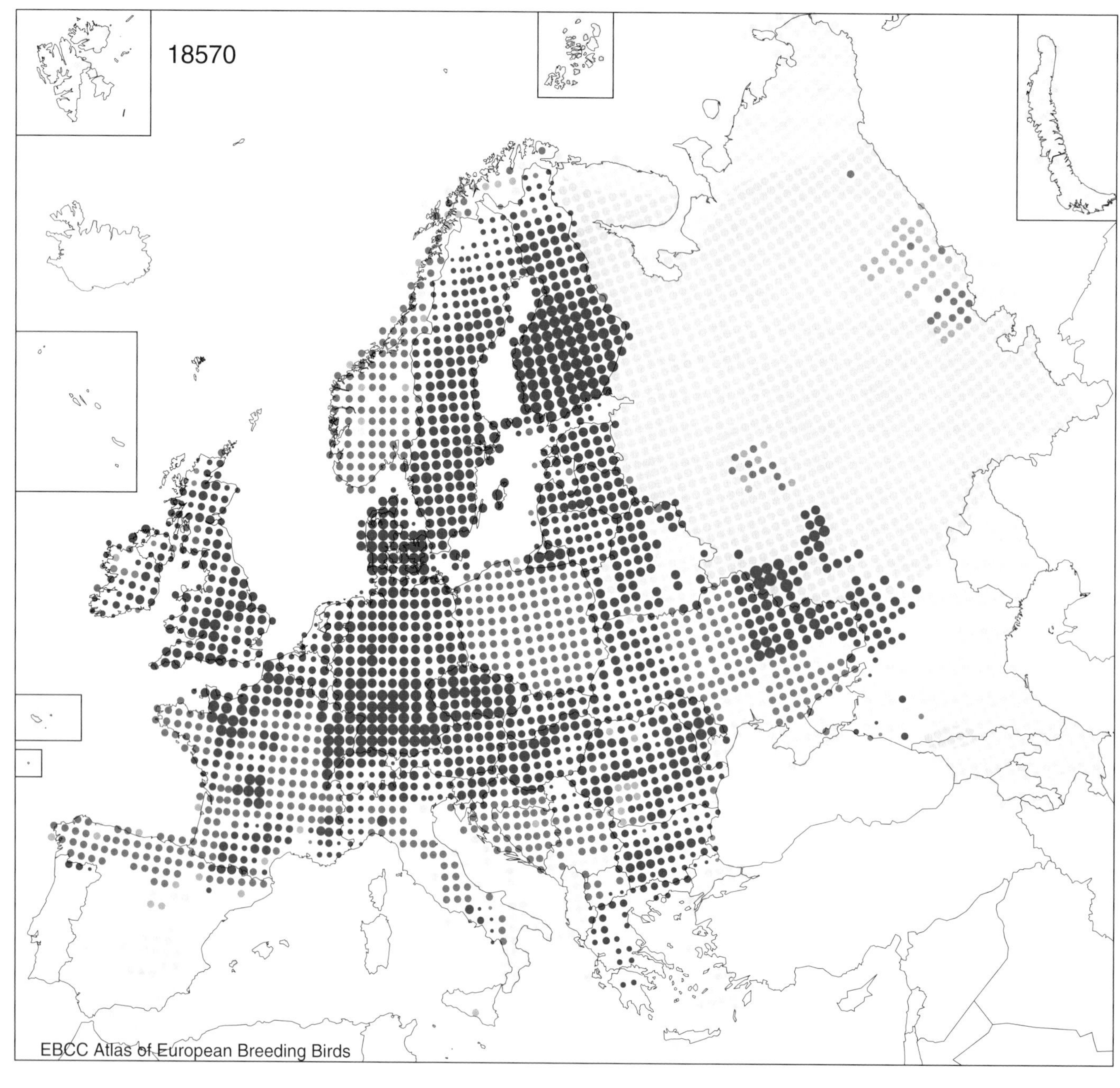

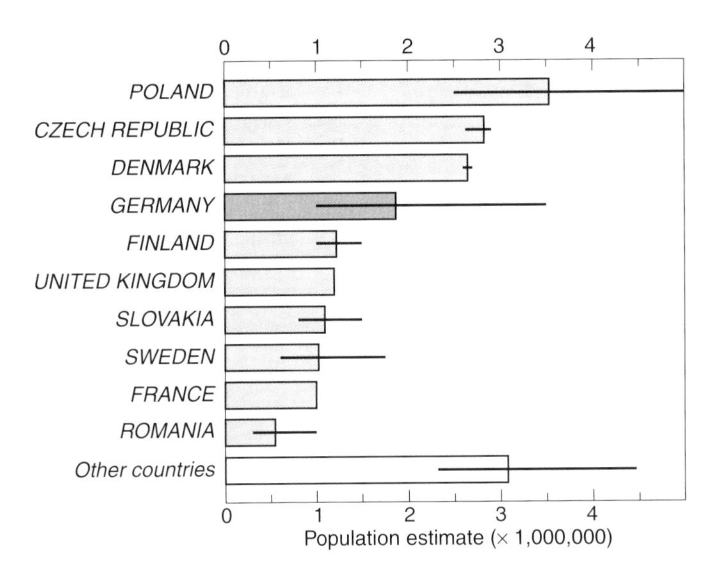

? -2
-1
0

% in top 10 countries: 87.0
Total number of populated European countries: 36
Total European population 18,902,342–19,710,652 (19,302,266)
Russian population 10,000,000–100,000,000 (31,622,777)
Turkish population 1–500 (22)

The Yellowhammer has a trans-Palearctic distribution in temperate and boreal climatic zones and mountain regions. The breeding area of the nominate *E.c. citrinella* covers most of Europe, from 40° to 65°N (*c*71°N near North Cape) W of a line from *c*40°E in the N to *c*25°E in the S, and reaching the Mediterranean mountain ranges. Scotland, Wales and Ireland hold *erythrogenys* and *caliginosa* occurs E of the nominate, hybridizing with Pine Bunting *E. leucocephalos* in the western mid-Urals. The Yellowhammer was introduced to New Zealand between 1862 and 1871 and is now very common throughout on farmland.

The species is common at all altitudes. It penetrates the subalpine zone and breeds up to the treeline, locally at 1800m asl in the Swiss Alps and up to 2100m in the Italian Alps. Its typical habitat is the transition zone between woodland and open country, especially forest margins and cultivated areas containing hedges, forest clearings, plantations, scrub, heathland, rough grassland and parkland.

The Yellowhammer nests low in bushes or on the ground in tall herbaceous vegetation (such as nettle *Urtica*) and crops. During the breeding season, it requires an abundant and predictable supply of arthropods for rearing the young successfully, but at other times it eats weed and herb seeds (Petersen 1995). Its breeding density is dependent on the extent of scrub vegetation. In Swiss farmland with hedgerows 0.4–0.7 bp/10ha in a 22 km^2 study area was typical, the maximum breeding density being 3.7 bp/10ha on a 1km square (O. Biber 1993). Optimal Swiss traditional farmland habitats possessing a multiplicity of hedgerows (up to 10 km/km^2) held up to 4.7 bp/10ha (Schifferli 1989). Mean breeding density of 1460 mapping studies in N Germany in the period 1950–85 was 0.2 bp/10ha (Flade & Steiof 1990). Important and rapid variations in densities may be due to habitat changes, such as a drop from 14 to 3.5 bp/10ha in a forest clearing plot over 7 years through tree growth (Christen 1989).

The breeding range apparently has remained unchanged since the early 1900s. Highest large-scale densities (>10 000 bp/50km square) occur in a broad band from Great Britain through Denmark and Germany to the Czech Republic, Slovakia, Hungary, Poland, S Finland and Russia, an area holding *c*90% of the European population of 52Mbp (*c*32Mbp in Russia alone). In the remainder of N, W and C Europe, densities range between 1000 and 8000 bp/50km square. The Yellowhammer is much scarcer in S and SE Europe, where values (bp/50km square) vary from 750 in Spain and Bulgaria to <100 in Portugal and Greece.

Between 1970 and 1990, populations seemingly were stable in many countries, but in some parts, notably C and NW Europe, numbers have declined during the 20th century. This trend was particularly evident in Ireland, Belgium, The Netherlands (rapid decline), Germany, Austria and also Italy and Latvia. These declining populations represent only an insignificant proportion of the European population. In Sweden, a decline in the 1950s, thought to be linked to the use of mercury seed-dressings in agriculture, was followed in the mid-1960s by a recovery when these chemicals had been banned, at least until 1977 (Otterlind & Lennerstedt 1964, Hjort & Lindholm 1978). Following analyses of 1460 studies in N Germany from 1950 to 1985 the Yellowhammer was categorized as a clearly declining species (Flade & Steiof 1990). Populations in Britain declined slightly (by 12%) during 1968–91, during which period the causes of nest failure remained essentially unchanged (Crick *et al* 1994).

The Yellowhammer is sedentary in Britain & Ireland and a partial short-distance migrant in large parts of its range elsewhere. Most northerly breeding sites are vacated in winter. It winters chiefly within the limits of its breeding range and in the Mediterranean and occasionally S to NW Africa.

Olivier Biber (CH)

This species account is sponsored by Ornis consult, Copenhavn, DK.

Emberiza cirlus

Cirl Bunting

CZ	Strnad cvrčivý	**I**	Zigolo nero
D	Zaunammer	**NL**	Cirlgors
E	Escribano Soteño	**P**	Escrevedeira-de-garganta-preta
F	Bruant zizi	**PL**	Cierlik
FIN	Pensassirkku	**R**	Огородная овсянка
G	Σιρλοτσίχλονο	**S**	Häcksparv
H	Sövénysármány		

SPEC Cat 4, Threat status S (P)

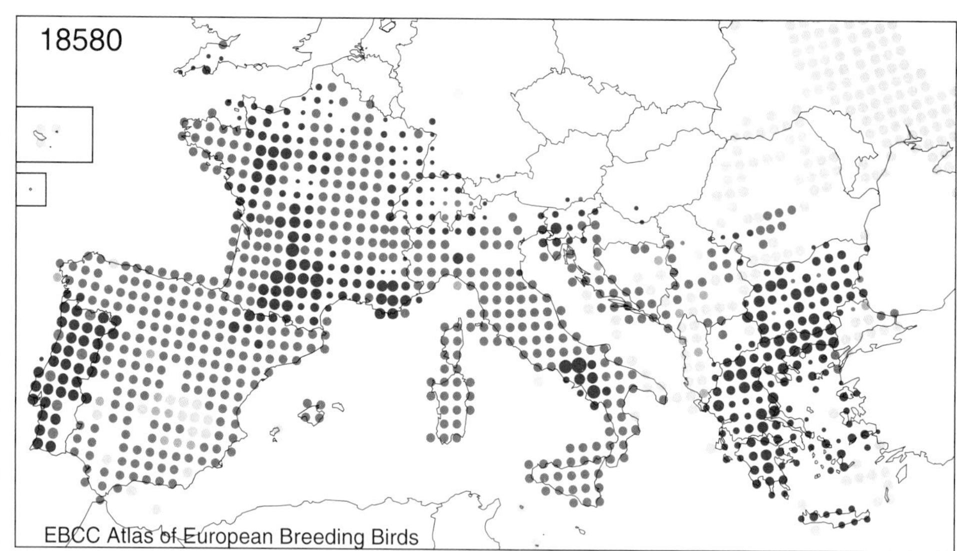

The breeding range of this monotypic, delicately coloured bunting covers the SW Palearctic. An introduced population exists in New Zealand. It is mainly resident S of a line running SSE from S Wales through Strasbourg, SW Hungary and NE Bulgaria to Trebizond in NW Turkey including NW Africa and the large Mediterranean islands. It may vacate colder parts of its range in winter.

The Cirl Bunting breeds mainly in the mediterranean zone in open areas on plains, foothills, valleys and warm gorges rich in a variety of bush and tree species. It requires weed-rich stubble fields in winter, and during the breeding season, plentiful sources of invertebrates for feeding the nestlings (Sitters & Evans 1993), thick bushes as nesting places and for concealment, and tall trees as song-posts.

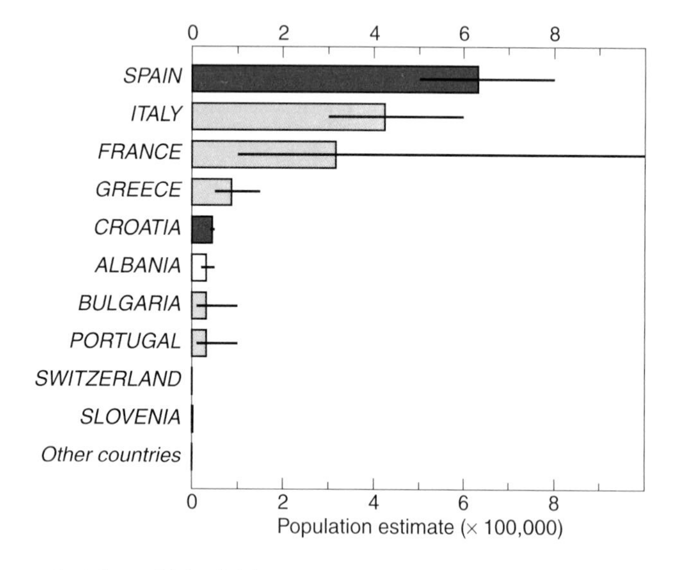

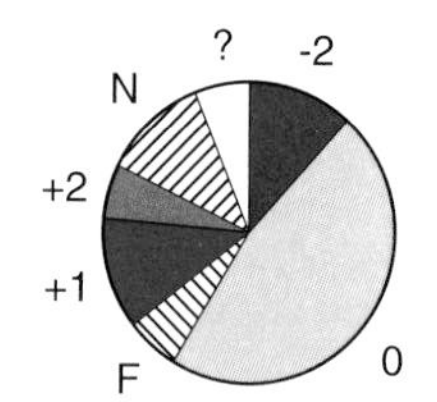

% in top 10 countries: 100.0
Total number of populated European countries: 17
Total European population 1,316,013–2,337,678 (1,602,671)
Turkish population 100,000–1,000,000 (316,228)

The European population is estimated at 1.1M–3.9Mbp, of which almost 90% breeds in Spain, Italy, France and Turkey. Other sizeable populations occur in Greece, the Balkan countries and Portugal. Breeding density in Normandy ranged from 0.25 to 1.0 bp/10ha (Chartier 1989) and in Switzerland from 2 to 3 bp/10ha (Glutz von Blotzheim 1964).

The western population suffered from a major decline in numbers, to the extent of extinction in Belgium and coupled with range contractions in France and Britain (Evans 1992). A recent increase in the British population is considered the result of the application of results from greater research effort, discovery of previously unknown subpopulations and good breeding success during fine summers in 1989 and 1990 (Sitters & Evans 1993). The populations in France, Switzerland and Germany are fluctuating, with a tendency to long-term decline, large annual changes being recorded in response to weather conditions and habitat changes (Gröh 1975, Ritter & Hölzinger 1987, Spitz 1994). In the 1980s, its breeding range expanded in Spain and also in the E, reaching Hungary, W and S Austria (Dvorak *et al* 1993) and new parts of Vojvodina.

Stephan Dontchev (BUL) Gabór Magyar (H)

Emberiza cia

Rock Bunting

CZ	Strnad viničný	I	Zigolo muciatto
D	Zippammer	NL	Grijze Gors
E	Escribano Montesino	P	Cia
F	Bruant fou	PL	Głuszek
FIN	Vuorisirkku	R	Горная овсянка
G	Βουνοτσίχλονο	S	Klippsparv
H	Bajszos sármány		

SPEC Cat 3, Threat status V

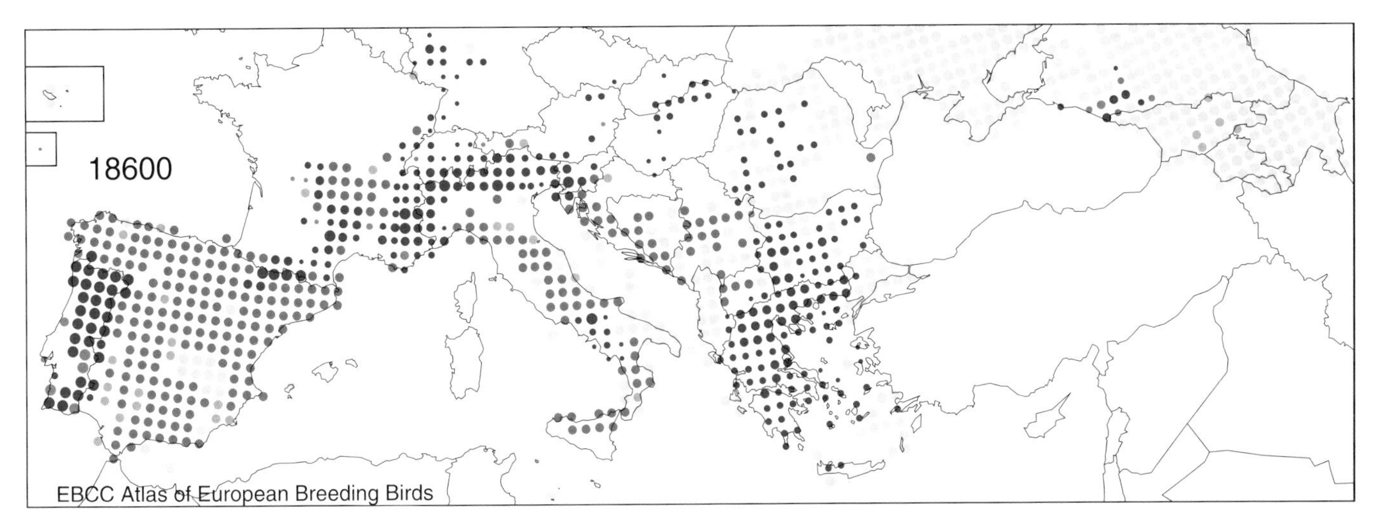

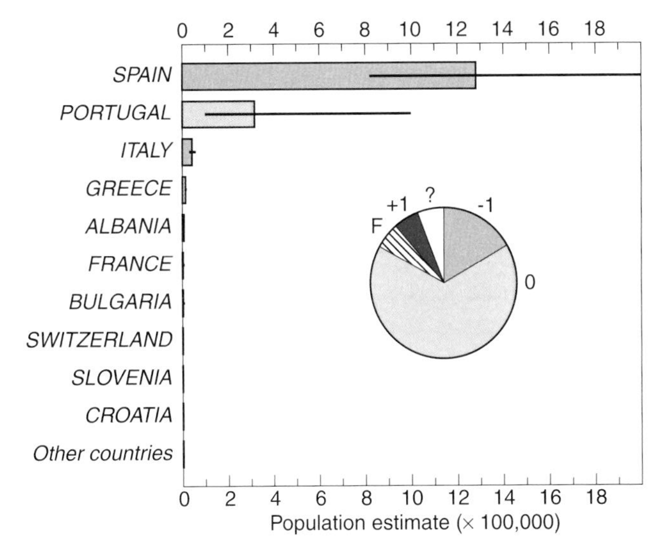

% in top 10 countries: 99.9
Total number of populated European countries: 18
Total European population 1,163,966–2,665,720 (1,673,000)
Turkish population 100,000–1,000,000 (316,228)

18600

The Rock Bunting occupies the large mountain ranges of the S Palearctic from Morocco, S Europe, Asia Minor, and Transcaucasia to E Iran. Another separate range exists N of the western Himalayas. *E.c. cia* occupies Europe except for Transcaucasia, which holds *prageri*. Three other subspecies occur elsewhere.

The Rock Bunting favours semi-arid, sparsely vegetated areas at lower and middle altitudes, preferring south-facing, often steep hillsides containing rocky outcrops and a scattering of bushes or trees (for cover, perches). It also uses quarries and vineyards. It avoids flat areas, densely vegetated grassland, arable land and forests. In Switzerland the Rock Bunting is uncommon above 1500m asl and exceptional above 2000m asl (Schifferli *et al* 1980).

Iberia holds *c*80% of the European population (1M–4Mbp), distribution being quite even at Mediterranean lower montane levels, but patchier to the N. The northernmost populations occur along the Rivers Mosel and Main.

The few studied populations seem rather stable without major fluctuations, as in Slovakia. The species has decreased recently at its NW limit through habitat loss (construction, disturbance, viniculture intensification; Mann *et al* 1990). Breeding densities vary greatly, being very low N of the Alps through lack of suitable habitat. In Switzerland, Slovakia and Bulgaria densities may reach 4.0–4.4 bp/10ha in rock-steppe habitat (P. Mosimann, pers obs, Krištín 1991b, Petrov 1982).

Winter distribution and movements are poorly understood but may include cultivated lowland areas away from typical breeding habitats. Resident over much of its range, the species is a short-distance migrant at least in C Europe; altitudinal movements also occur. It is a rare but regular passage migrant (October–November) at Swiss alpine passes (Winkler 1984). In Slovakia, snow-cover forces most individuals down to lowland cultivation (Krištín 1991b).

Anton Krištín (SLK) Paul Mosimann (CH)

This species account is sponsored by Dr Till Macke, Bonn, D.

Emberiza cineracea

Cinereous Bunting

CZ	Strnad šedý	I	Zigolo cinereo
D	Türkenammer	NL	Smyrnagors
E	Escribano Cinéreo	P	Escrevedeira-de-cabeça-amarela
F	Bruant cendré	PL	Trznadel popielaty
FIN	Keltapääsirkku	R	Серая овсянка
G	Σμυρνοτσίχλονο	S	Gulgrå sparv
H	Török sármány		

SPEC Cat 2, Threat status V (P)

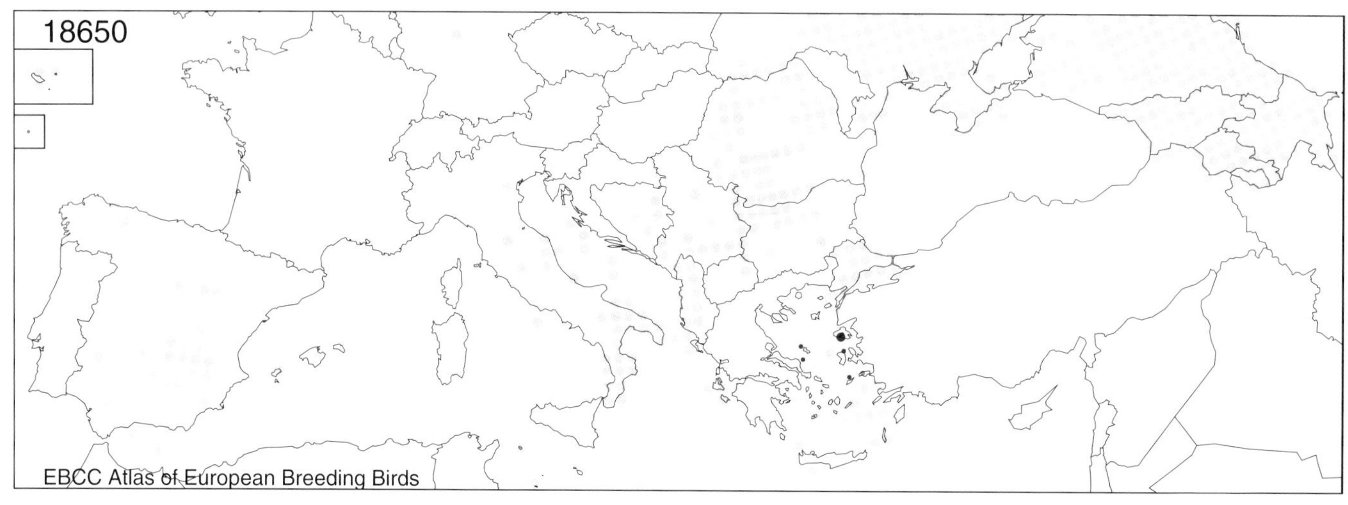

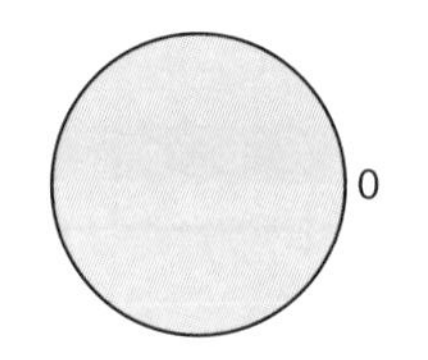

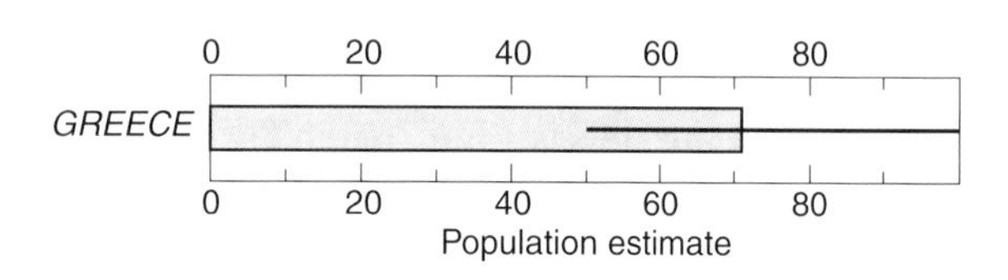

% in top 10 countries: 100.0
Total number of populated European countries: 1
Total European population 50–100 (71)
Turkish population 500–5000 (1581)

The Cinereous Bunting has a globally restricted breeding range largely confined to Asiatic Turkey. Within the *Atlas*' area of coverage, the western subspecies *E.c. cineracea* was confirmed as breeding on Mytilene (Lesbos), Chios, Ikaria and Skyros and suspected on Samos, all Greek isles in the Aegean Sea. On these isles it breeds exclusively on undisturbed rocky slopes or plateaus possessing short vegetation. Reliable estimates for both past and present population sizes are virtually non-existent. Recent surveys on Mytilene recorded a breeding density of *c*0.18 bp/ha in prime habitat, which is found only in the west of the isle (P. de Knijff, in prep), whereas the other isles contained only a few isolated pairs (Hölzinger 1995). Based on these censuses it is likely that the species is more numerous than the current Greek estimate of 100bp.

The Cinereous Bunting is a short-distance migrant, the nominate subspecies *E.c. cineracea* regularly being recorded on Cyprus and in Israel not only in spring but also in autumn when it is less numerous (de Knijff 1991). Recently it was also recorded in low numbers on autumn migration in eastern Sudan (G. Nikolaus, pers comm). Wintering quarters probably lie in southern Sudan, Eritrea and Yemen.

The species' preference on Mytilene for rocky slopes containing low-lying vegetation may make this population very vulnerable because part of this habitat is used as a military firing range even during the breeding season. This preference is in marked contrast with information from Turkey, where the eastern subspecies *semenowi* was found breeding not only at lower altitudes amongst lush vegetation which often is grazed by sheep and goats, but also in partly cultivated sheltered valleys containing orchards and small fields. Perhaps this explains the markedly higher density (0.4 bp/ha) reported for *semenowi* in eastern Turkey (Chappuis *et al* 1973). It is tempting to speculate that these different breeding ecologies could be subspecies-specific. The scarce quantitative data available at present indicate no immediate threat to the European population (de Knijff 1991). However, until detailed long-term studies of its breeding ecology and wintering grounds have been completed, the future of this species will remain far from secure.

Peter de Knijff (NL) Haralambos Alivizatos (G)

Emberiza caesia

Cretzschmar's Bunting

CZ	Strnad šedokrký	I	Ortolano grigio
D	Grauortolan	NL	Bruinkeelortolaan
E	Escribano Ceniciento	P	Escrevedeira-cinzenta
F	Bruant cendrillard	PL	Trznadel modrogłowy
FIN	Ruostekurkkusirkku	R	Красноклювая овсянка
G	Σκουρόβλαχος	S	Rostsparv
H	Rozsdás sármány		

SPEC Cat 4, Threat status S (P)

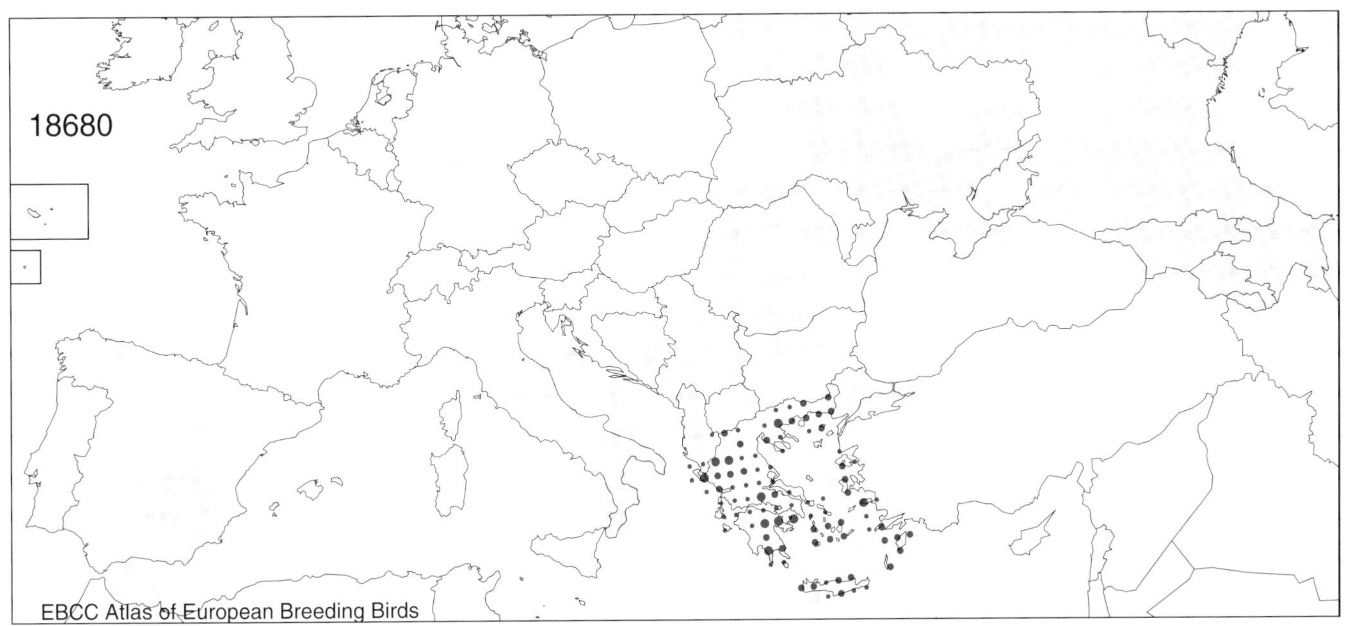

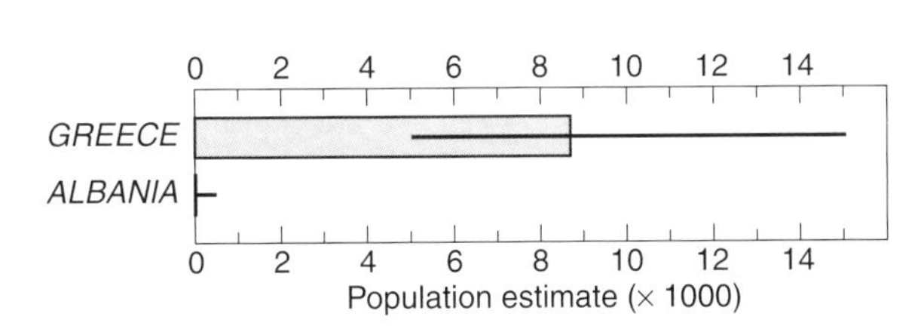

? 0

% in top 10 countries: 100.0
Total number of populated European countries: 2
Total European population 5022–15,040 (8683)
Turkish population 10,000–100,000 (31,623)

Brightly coloured, Cretzschmar's Bunting has a very restricted distribution, breeding only in the eastern Mediterranean warm temperate zone of the W Palearctic. It forms a species group (the 'ortolan bunting group') with Grey-necked *E. buchanani*, Cinereous *E. cineracea* and Ortolan *E. hortulana* Buntings as a result of their shared preference for dry, open habitats (*BWP*). Both Ortolan and Cretzschmar's Bunting breed in dry regions but the latter prefers more barren habitats, usually including some low-lying vegetation on hillsides, rocky islands and cultivated land. Cretzschmar's Bunting usually breeds at high altitude (up to *c*1300m asl the Pindos Mountains), often by the sea.

Competitive exclusion occurs where both Ortolan and Cretzschmar's Buntings overlap. On the mainland this leads to altitudinal or habitat segregation (*hortulana* usually higher altitude) whereas on the islands complete exclusion has been suggested. *BWP* states that Cretzschmar's is usually dominant and that overlap only occurs on two Greek islands. The *Atlas* maps suggest that matters are more complex because at least 10 islands show overlap.

In Europe it is found in Greece and to a lesser extent Albania, and elsewhere breeds only in Turkey, Cyprus and the Levant. Populations appear to be stable but those in Greece are threatened by bird liming. There are no density estimates but its abundance in Greece appears lower than for other buntings. It is thinly distributed in N Greece, but common on Chios (Choremi *et al* 1993).

Migratory, it winters in dry savanna, steppe, cultivated areas and gardens of the subtropical zone in NW Africa S to 11°N and in S Arabia. Migration is nocturnal on a broad front across and around the E Mediterranean (*BWP*). Birds depart in July–August and return late February–March, males *c*10 days earlier than females (Paz 1987).

Simon Gillings (GB) Ben Hallmann (G)

Emberiza hortulana

Ortolan Bunting

CZ	Strnad zahradní	**I**	Ortolano
D	Ortolan	**NL**	Ortolaan
E	Escribano Hortelano	**P**	Sombria
F	Bruant ortolan	**PL**	Ortolan
FIN	Peltosirkku	**R**	Садовая овсянка
G	Βλάχος	**S**	Ortolansparv
H	Kerti sármány		

SPEC Cat 2, Threat status V (P)

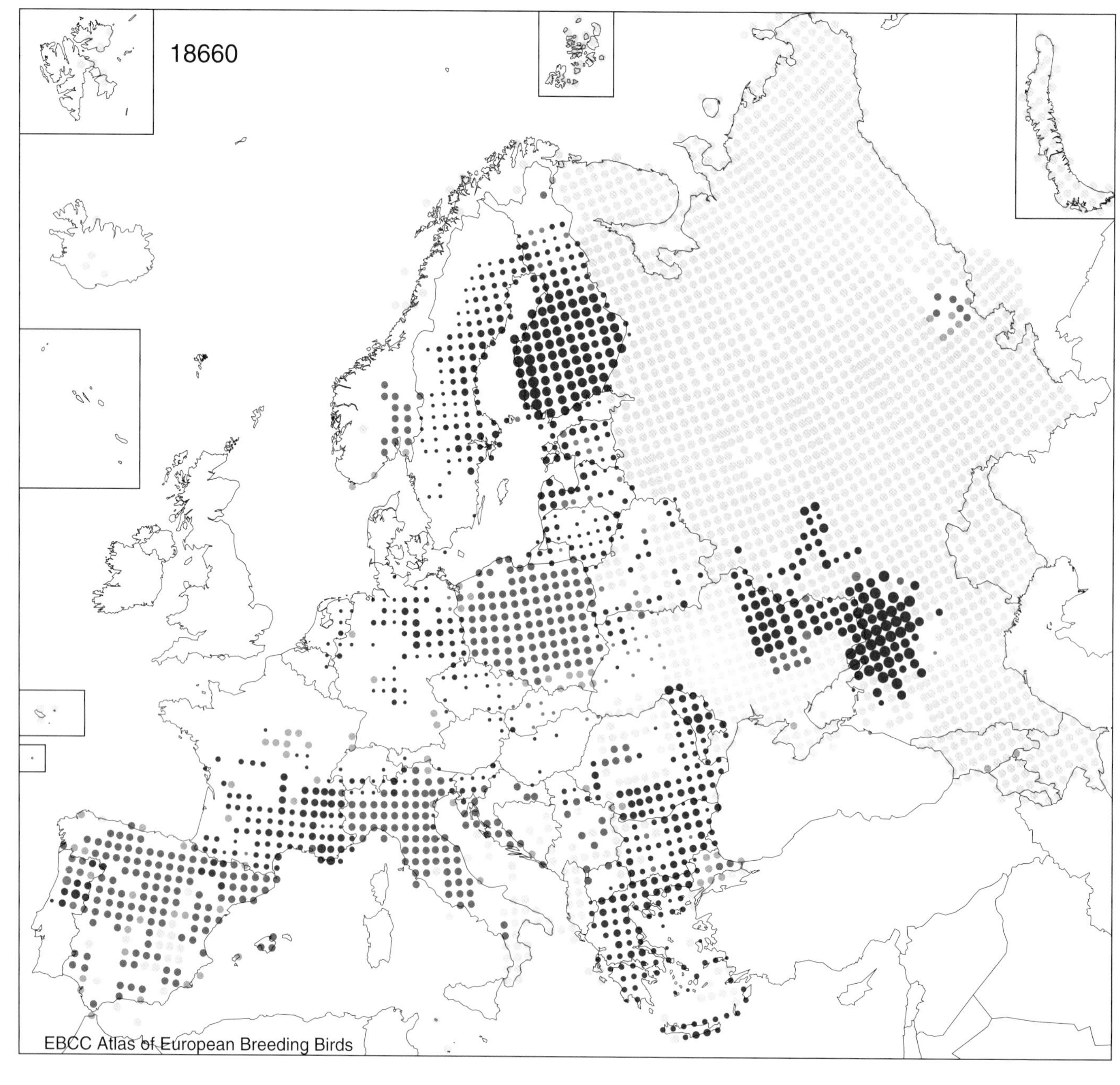

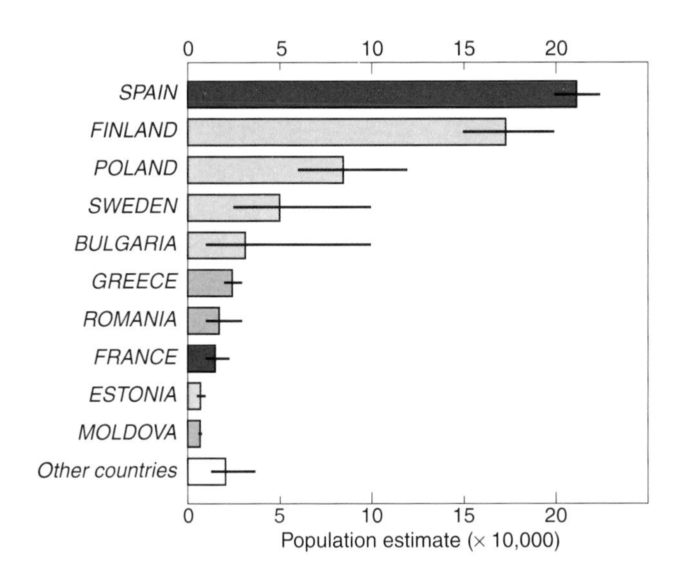

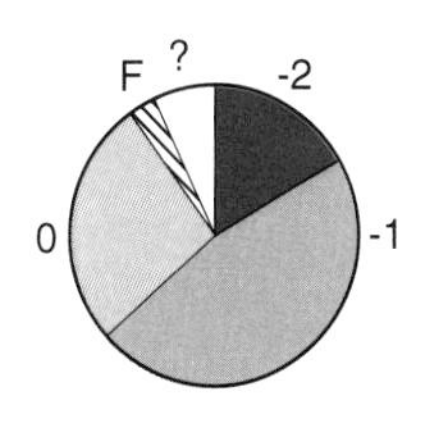

% in top 10 countries: 96.8
Total number of populated European countries: 30
Total European population 593,409–741,582 (643,522)
Russian population 10,000–100,000 (31,623)
Turkish population 1,000,000–10,000,000 (3,162,278)

The Ortolan Bunting has a generally western Palearctic and European distribution; a broad swathe extends to Mongolia and a narrow belt S of the Caspian reaches Afghanistan. A long-distance migrant, it winters in sub-Saharan Africa, from Mount Nimba in West Africa to Ethiopia.

Generally, the species prefers areas whose continental climate has many hours of sunshine and low rainfall. It is absent from much of coastal W Europe and from the larger Mediterranean islands, except for Crete. Its indicated presence on Gotland in the Baltic is probably an accidental occurrence. Its western limits may be conditioned by maritime climate influence (Wallgren 1954)

There has been a declining trend in Ortolan Bunting populations over the whole of western Europe since the 1980s. In parts of C, N and E Europe a longer-term decline has left large gaps in its distribution. In France, Switzerland, Austria, Hungary, Germany and Sweden its present distribution is sparse and discontinuous and its occurrence is patchy. Apparently stable high-density populations occur in Finland and Poland, and probably also in areas further E and SE. In S Europe, Portugal, Spain, France and Italy are experiencing a declining trend.

The Ortolan Bunting uses a variety of breeding habitat sets whose selection differs between geographical regions. From Benelux in the W, through the plains of Germany, Poland and Belarus to the Baltic States, Finland and Russia (also Bulgaria) it is associated mainly with cultivated land, preferring low-intensity, mixed farmland on light (sandy and loamy) soils possessing sparsely vegetated spots (for feeding) and a plethora of prominent perches (song-posts) both natural and artificial. Roadside tree plantations are an important element in C Europe. In treeless regions of Ukraine it also inhabits steppe ravine slopes covered sparsely with shrubs. In forested areas of Fennoscandia and Russia, it occupies forest margins, clearings and clearfells. Further S, it is a mountain dweller in C Spain, Greece and the Caucasus at high altitude (above 2000m asl in Armenia) often in rugged gully-strewn countryside.

Localized patches of prime breeding habitat can attract good numbers, such as 15 singing males on 15ha near Willanzheim, Germany (Lang *et al* 1990), nest-separation distances of 100–200m near Kamyshin, Russia (Dement'iev & Gladkov 1970), and pairs 100–200m apart (S Sweden, 1940) in an area from which the species had disappeared by 1960 (Swanberg 1976). Densities over large stretches of suitable habitat are on average in the range of 5–20 bp/km^2, as in Finland (Koskimies 1989a) and France (Claessens 1992).

In NW, W and C European breeding populations, there has been a continuous long-term decline since the 1950s, the main reason probably being the replacement of small-scale, mixed farming by large-scale agricultural intensification which introduced widespread application of insecticides and herbicides. Habitat losses through urbanization (W and C Europe) and extensive reafforestation (C Spain) have also contributed. Although breeding success in Sweden since 1950 is unchanged from earlier decades (Stolt 1993), the situation in W and C Europe therefore may be different. The British analogy of Corn Bunting *Miliaria calandra* decline perhaps is valid: the relative importance of losses through farming processes was much greater after 1970 (21%) than before (7%) (Crick *et al* 1994). Both species are declining almost in parallel in Europe. Claessens (1992) further suggested that large-scale traditional autumn hunting in SW France, when added to the other adverse factors, now may be a threat to the W European populations which stop-over. However, declines in eastern and Iberian populations remain poorly understood. Winter survival rates are important for most small passerines, but little is known of the Ortolan Bunting on its wintering grounds.

Bengt-Olov Stolt (S)

Emberiza rustica

Rustic Bunting

CZ	Strnad rolní	**I**	Zigolo boschereccio
D	Waldammer	**NL**	Bosgors
E	Escribano Rústico	**P**	Escrevedeira-rústica
F	Bruant rustique	**PL**	Trznadel czubaty
FIN	Pohjansirkku	**R**	Овсянка-ремез
G	Δασοτσίχλονο	**S**	Videsparv
H	Erdei sármány		

Non-SPEC, Threat status S (P)

The Rustic Bunting breeds across the entire European and Asian boreal zone. Uniquely among western Palearctic birds, its habitat preference is for low spruce-dominated (*Picea*) mires containing a mixture of birch *Betula* and undergrowth of low dwarf shrubs and grasses (Ukkonen 1983), but territories may be located in patches possessing a hectare or so of prime wet boreal forest habitat. In the distribution centre the species may also use damp conifer forest, especially at water margins. In Lapland it nests in drier birch-dominated heaths interspersed with juniper *Juniperus* (Pulliainen & Saari 1989).

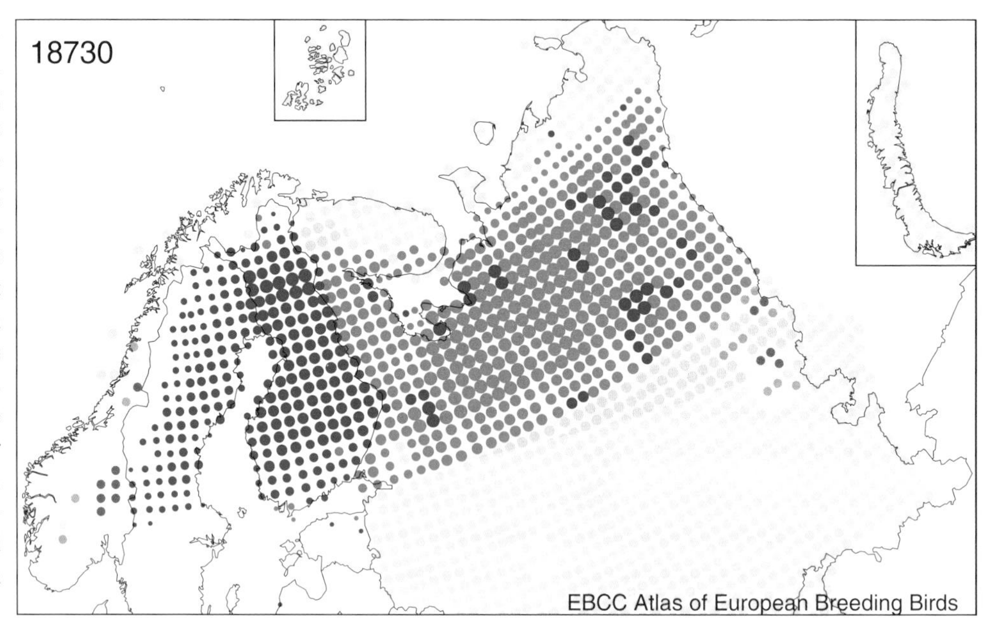

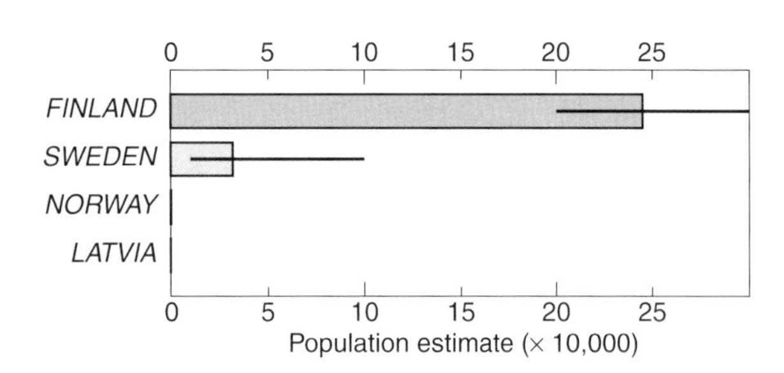

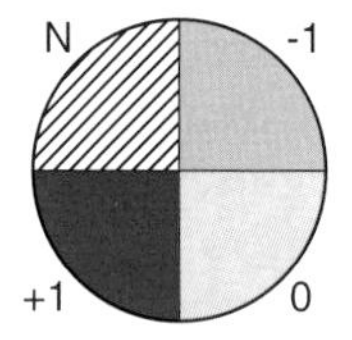

% in top 10 countries: 100.0
Total number of populated European countries: 4
Total European population 226,919–364,583 (276,799)
Russian population 4,100,000–6,900,000 (5,318,834)

In Finland and N Sweden the average overall breeding density is 4 and 2 bp/km^2 in the mid-boreal and northern boreal zones respectively (R.A. Väisänen, pers obs). Normal densities in mid-boreal spruce mires are 5–10 bp/km^2 and in pine *Pinus* mires 2–4 bp/km^2, but near St Petersburg reached 27 bp/km^2 in damp mixed forest (Rymkevich 1979). Outside the boreal areas the species is very scarce.

Its breeding range has expanded westwards since 1895, most rapidly in Finland in the 1910s and 1920s, in Sweden up to 1960 and in Norway in the 1960s to 1970s; first breeding occurred in Estonia in 1979 and in Latvia in 1985.

Line-transect censuses indicate that the Finnish population peaked in the 1940s, decreased by *c*50% by the 1950s, increased moderately by the 1970s and decreased strongly in the 1980s to about a third of the 1940s level. Drainage of peatlands for forestry does not affect the Rustic Bunting, and hence does not explain its decline (Ukkonen 1983, Väisänen & Rauhala 1983). Instead, environmental or climatic conditions in its remote wintering areas (Iran to China) may be responsible.

The censuses of 1986–89 revealed 230 000bp (annual range 150 000–300 000) in Finland and 130 000 in Sweden (R.A. Väisänen, pers obs). Russia holds the largest European population, roughly estimated at 4M–7Mbp. Norway has 100–500bp, Estonia 0–50 and Latvia 0–10.

Markku Ukkonen (FIN) Risto A Väisänen (FIN)

Emberiza pusilla

Little Bunting

CZ	Strnad malinký	I	Zigolo minore
D	Zwergammer	NL	Dwerggors
E	Escribano Pigmeo	P	Escrevedeira-pigmeia
F	Bruant nain	PL	Trznadelek
FIN	Pikkusirkku	R	Овсянка-крошка
G	Νανοτσίχλονο	S	Dvärgsparv
H	Törpesármány		

Non-SPEC, Threat status S (P)

The Little Bunting's range, covering the subarctic and cooler boreal zones from E Fennoscandia to E Siberia (*c*167°E), is more northerly than for any other *Emberizidae* except the Lapland Bunting *Calcarius lapponicus* and Snow Bunting *Plectrophenax nivalis*, and rapidly expanded westwards in the late 1900s (Koskimies 1989a). In winter the Little Bunting inhabits grassy plains and foothills in China and SE Asia.

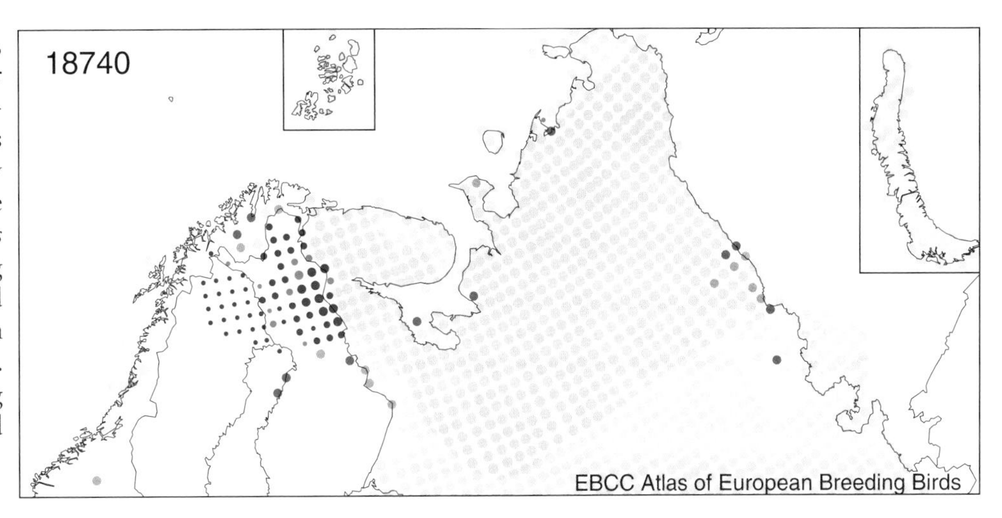

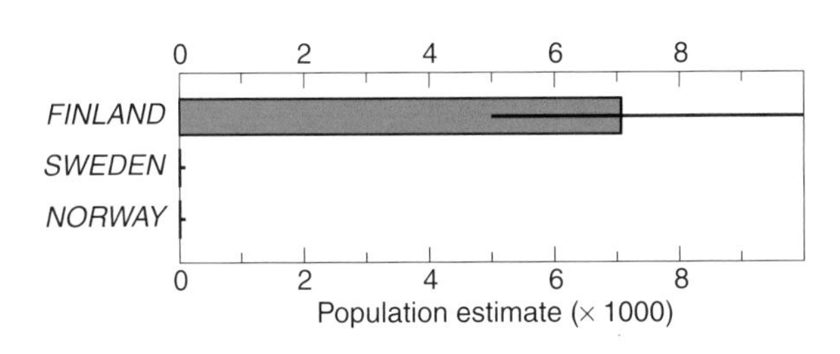

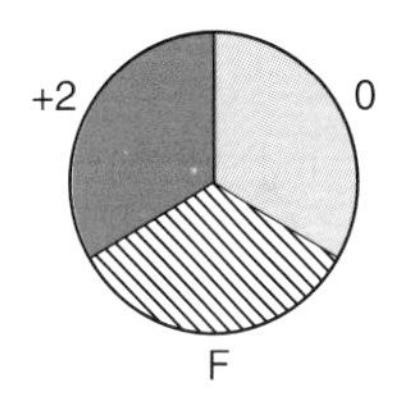

% in top 10 countries: 100.0
Total number of populated European countries: 3
Total European population 5020–10,023 (7091)
Russian population 100,000–1,000,000 (316,228)

The Little Bunting breeds in the moist and shrubby tundra and in the northern taiga, its preferred habitats being dwarf birch *Betula* and willow *Salix* bushes below taller birch, alder *Alnus*, spruce *Picea* or pine *Pinus* on mossy or swampy ground. In Finland it breeds in damp thickets and scattered shrubs bordering rivers and lakes, usually in peat-bogs forested with pine and birch, dwarf birch providing the undergrowth. Typically several pairs may reside close together (Koskimies 1989a), such aggregations in the Russian tundra locally reaching 8–10 bp/ha; in Finland up to 16 bp/km^2 occurs (Jokimäki 1989).

In Russian Karelia between Lake Ladoga and the White Sea the species supposedly is a scarce breeder (maximum density recorded, 4.3 bp/km^2; Zimin *et al* 1993), but this may reflect its unobtrusive nature. It has colonized the western Kola Peninsula since the mid-1970s, probably having spread along the coast to the Ponoy estuary. The lower limit estimated for European Russia (100 000bp) may be too conservative.

In Finland breeding remained unconfirmed until 1935, probably having occurred long before. Long regarded as a patchily distributed and rare breeder in easternmost Forest Lapland (Koskimies 1989a), it advanced very rapidly northwards and westwards, especially since the mid-1980s, scattered observations being made further S (Jokimäki 1989, Koskimies 1989c). Nowadays it occupies the whole of N Finland, although in highly fluctuating numbers correlated at least partly with spring temperatures. The Finnish population, only 1000bp in the late 1980s (Koskimies 1989a), reached 5000–10 000bp in the early 1990s. In poorly known N Sweden and in eastern Finnmark (N Norway), breeding remains scarce (Frantzen 1994c), but probably annual, perhaps 100bp in the best years in each country. The Swedish distribution as depicted may not reflect an average year.

Pertti Koskimies (FIN)

Emberiza aureola

Yellow-breasted Bunting

CZ	Strnad obojkový	I	Zigolo dal collare
D	Weidenammer	NL	Wilgegors
E	Escribano Aureolado	P	Escrevedeira-aureolada
F	Bruant auréole	PL	Trznadel złotawy
FIN	Kultasirkku	R	Дубровник
G	Σημυδοτσίχλονο	S	Gyllensparv
H	Réti sármány		

Non-SPEC, Threat status S (P)

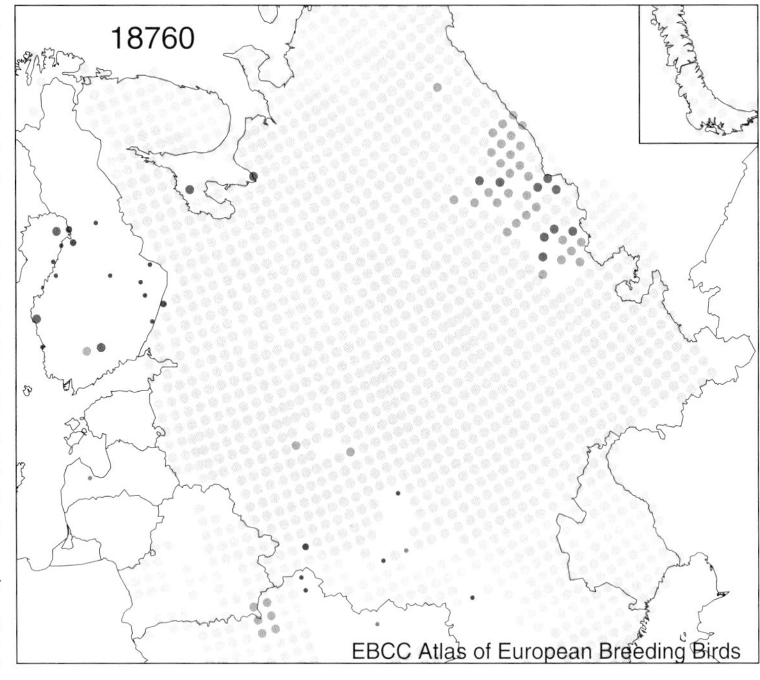

The Yellow-breasted Bunting is an Asiatic species, breeding in the boreal zone from Kamchatka Sakhalin, and Japan through Russia into Finland and Latvia and wintering in S China and SE Asia. The nominate subspecies *E.a. aureola* breeds from Europe to Anadyrland, the other subspecies *ornata* occupying the southern Asian range.

In Europe, it occupies a wide range of moist or wet fragmented habitats, such as river valleys, wet scrub-meadows and bogs with a scattering of bushes. It also accepts cultivated areas, light conifer plantations and dry meadows comprising dense tall grasses and small bushes. It prefers open, wet meadows where patches of willow *Salix*, alder *Alnus* or birch *Betula* (2–4m high) are intermixed with sedge *Carex*, grass, marsh cinquefoil *Potentilla palustris* or similar vegetation. In winter it frequents cultivated and poor-quality arable land and grassland (Byers *et al* 1995).

Everywhere in Russia, it is numerous in areas of suitable habitat. In W Russia, the species forms colonies of a few to 20bp in preferred sites in optimal years. However, numbers are low overall in Russian Karelia and in Finland (*c*170bp). It has also bred in Latvia whose population is perhaps 5bp.

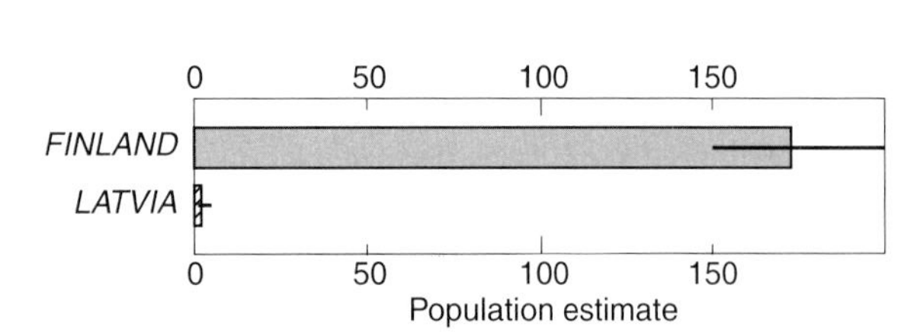

N
-1

% in top 10 countries: 100.0
Total number of populated European countries: 2
Total European population 152–202 (175)
Russian population 10,000–100,000 (31,623)

The wet, luxuriant meadows of Liminganlahti and Kempeleenlahti in Finland are traditional breeding sites, where adults show high site tenacity, especially males (N Fritzén, pers comm). Other sites are few in number. It colonized its westernmost breeding areas in the 20th century. The first wave reached Russian Karelia and Finland from 1910 to the 1920s. During the second, more sustained wave of the 1940s to the 1960s, the species achieved a more stable population and began to occupy many other suitable sites.

The Yellow-breasted Bunting increased slowly in Finland up to the early 1980s but has declined since. The reason for the decrease possibly was a low reproductive rate, but more probably is related to the large-scale clearance of much of its wintering habitat for agricultural use. The outlying breeding areas may contain sink-populations, which are sustainable only if surplus individuals are recruited from Russian sources. The 6000–9000km long migration route restricts the breeding period and its onset in W Russia and Finland, especially during prolonged adverse weather.

Mikko Ojanen (FIN)

Emberiza pallasi

Pallas's Reed Bunting

CZ Strnad šedoramenný
D Grauschulter-Rohrammer
E Escribano de Pallas
F Bruant de Pallas
FIN Pikkupajusirkku
G Καλαμοτσίχλονο του Pallas
H Pallas nádisármány
I Migliarino di Pallas
NL Pallas' Rietgors
P Escrevedeira de Pallas
PL Trznadel czarnogardły
R Полярная овсянка
S Dvärgsävsparv

Criteria not applied

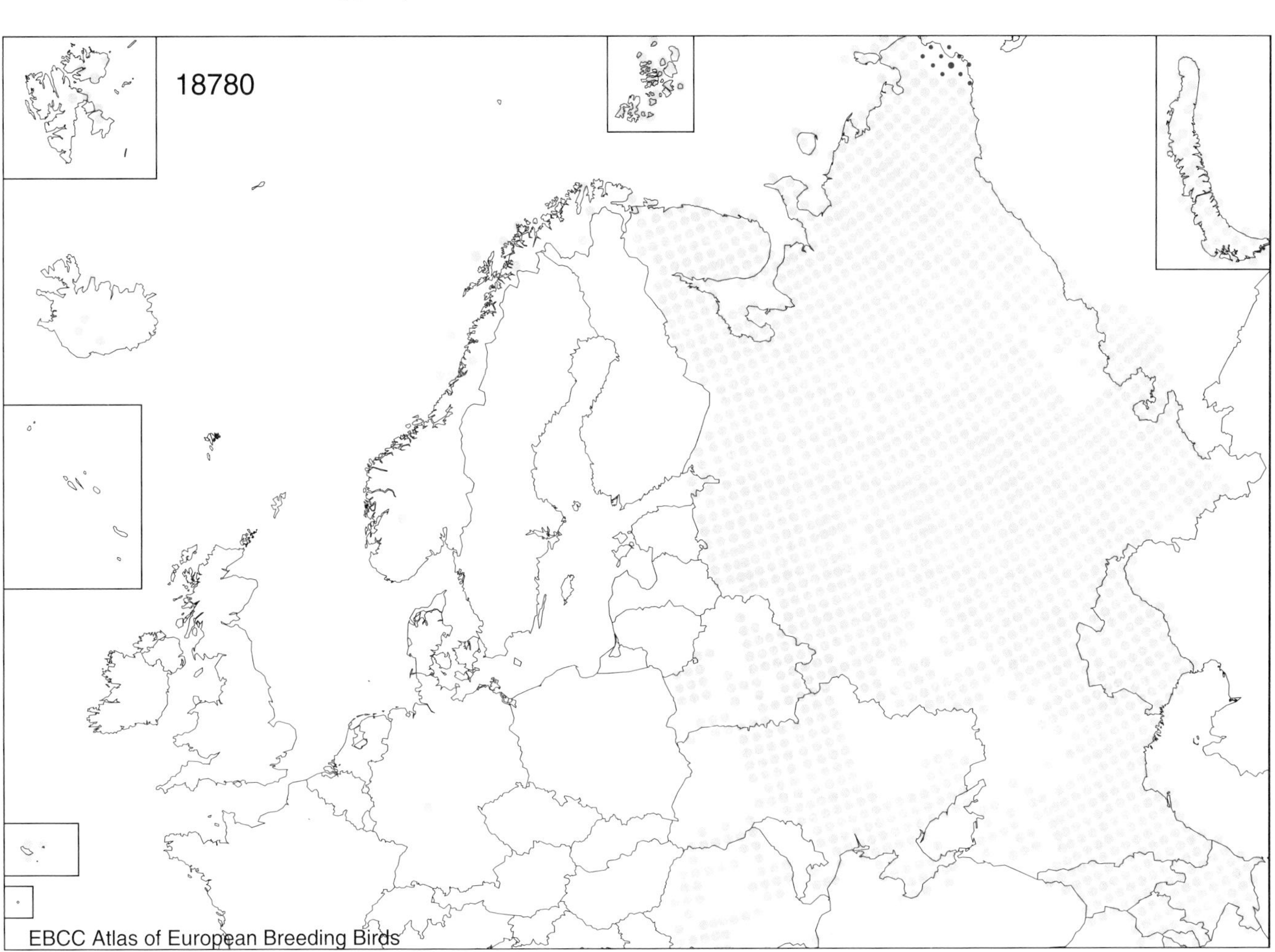

Pallas's Reed Bunting, rather smaller than the similar Reed Bunting *E. schoeniclus*, breeds mainly in Siberia E as far as the Anadyr River basin, the Koryakian Plateau, the coast of the Sea of Okhotsk, the Altai and Sayan ranges, Mongolia and N China. A separate population exists in the eastern Tian Shan (Loskot 1986).

The species is distributed in Europe on the western macroslope of the polar Ural Mountains and at the eastern end of the Bol'shezemel'skaya tundra between 66°45'–68°50'N, as far west as 63°00'E. It winters in E Asia, in S Primorye, Korea, Mongolia and China.

In the N of its breeding range Pallas's Reed Bunting breeds in forest-tundra and the southern edge of the true tundra, preferring dense dwarf birch *Betula nana* and willow *Salix* shrubs along river valleys and at watersheds around lakes. In the Siberian taiga zone, the Far East, and the Altai and Sayan ranges it occupies the subalpine zone mainly from 1800 to 2500m asl, but it also has an affinity for dry shrub tundras in the mountains. At the southern limits of its breeding range in Tuva, Transbaikalia and Mongolia, it is found in dry steppe characterized by occasional shrubs or bushes. The steppe populations are of the subspecies *E.p. lydiae*.

In Europe Pallas's Reed Bunting is a typical bird of zonal dwarf birch tundra on watersheds and on mountain slopes of the polar Urals up to 300m asl. Its breeding density in the Bol'shezemel'skaya tundra in dwarf birch shrub tundras is 0.1–9.0 bp/km^2 (Morozov 1987). In optimal habitats small aggregations of nesting birds can occur, at densities which reach 25–35 bp/km^2 in some years (V.V. Morozov, unpubl). The total European population is estimated at 10 000–15 000bp.

Vladimir V Morozov (R)

Emberiza schoeniclus

Reed Bunting

CZ	Strnad rákosní	**I**	Migliarino di palude
D	Rohrammer	**NL**	Rietgors
E	Escribano Palustre	**P**	Escrevedeira-dos-caniços
F	Bruant des roseaux	**PL**	Potrzos
FIN	Pajusirkku	**R**	Камышовая овсянка
G	Καλαμοτσίχλονο	**S**	Sävsparv
H	Nádi sármány		

Non-SPEC, Threat status S

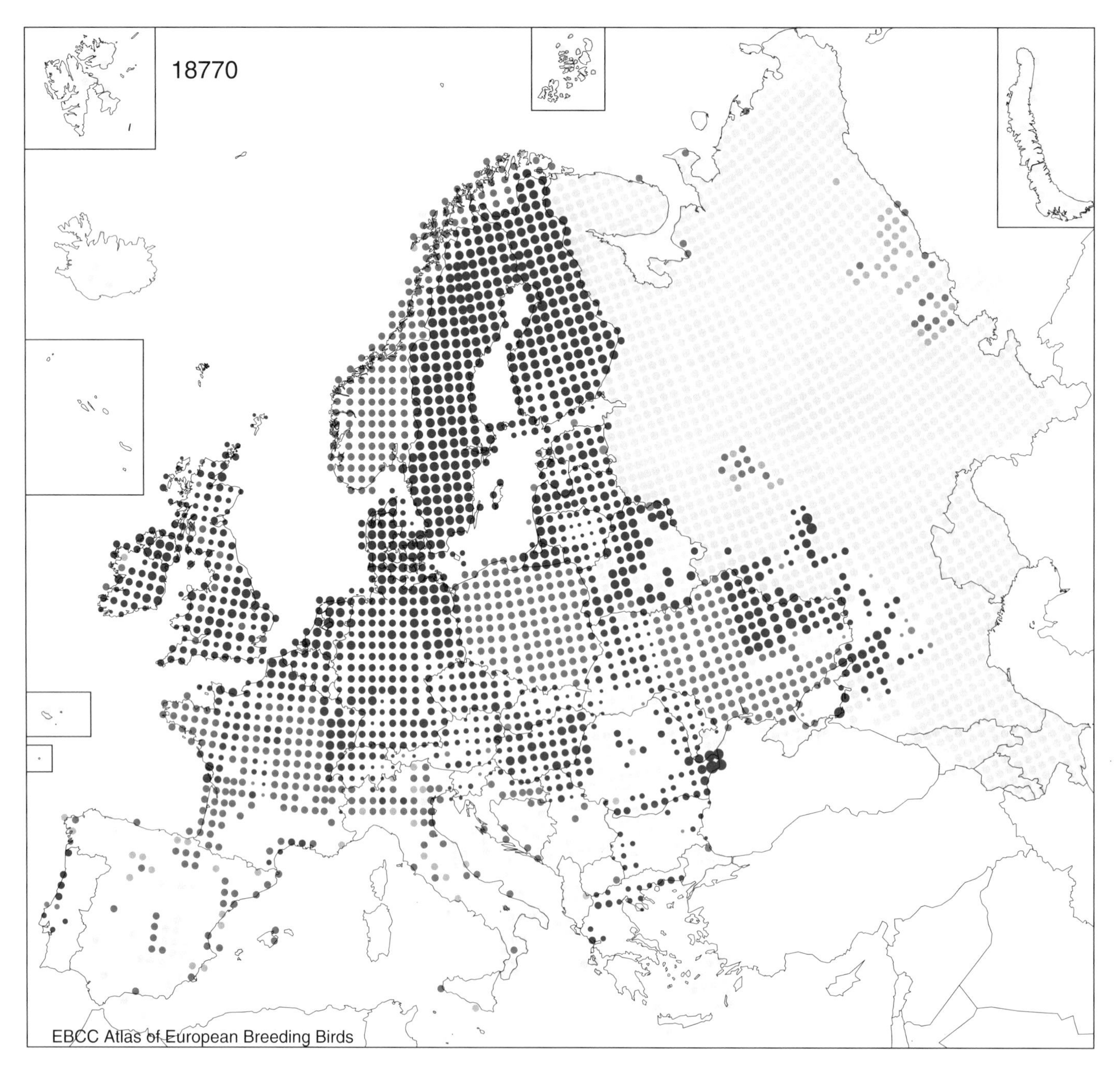

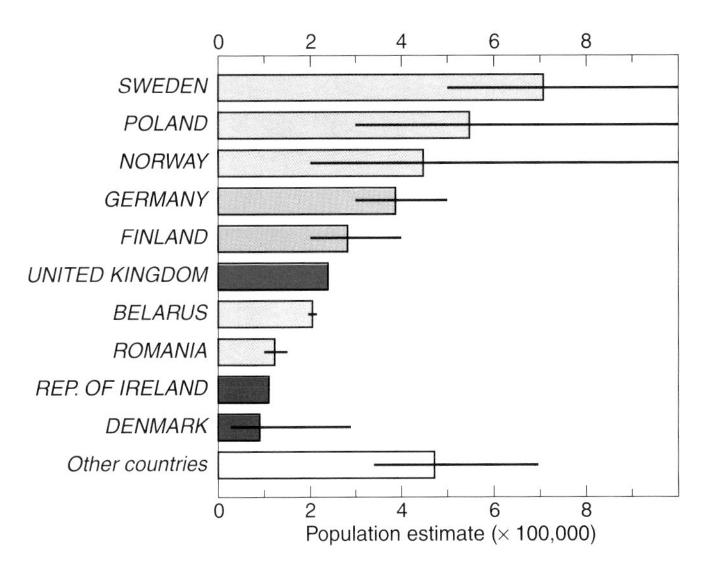

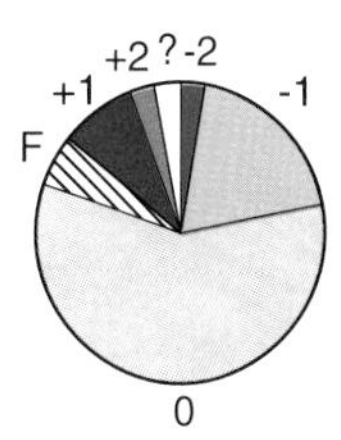

% in top 10 countries: 86.9
Total number of populated European countries: 36
Total European population 3,179,727–4,429,879 (3,611,117)
Russian population 100,000–1,000,000 (316,228)
Turkish population 5000–15,000 (8660)

The Reed Bunting has a Palearctic breeding distribution, occurring in several distinctive subspecies (9 of at least 20 breed in Europe) from western Europe to Japan and Sakhalin, from the subarctic (just reaching 70°N) to the warm continental zone of C Asia. It is one of the most widely distributed of European buntings. Although abundant and widespread in northern and N–C Europe, it becomes much more scattered further S. It is absent from Iceland and from much of the mediterranean zone.

The species inhabits a range of dense, low vegetation types usually near still or running water, bogs, marshes and tundra partially colonized by alder *Alnus*, birch *Betula* or willow *Salix* (Okulewicz 1989). It generally avoids homogeneous habitats, but is adaptable, and will readily occupy a wide variety of artificially created wetlands such as fishponds and former sand- and gravel-pits.

From the 1960s onwards it spread, although at very low densities, into drier habitats such as young woodland (spruce *Picea*, poplar *Populus*) and farmland (maize). In Belgium, France and especially Great Britain this spread is best explained by the overflow of surplus birds from the traditional wetter habitats. In cereal and oil-seed rape fields the Reed Bunting overlaps with the Yellowhammer *E. citrinella* and Corn Bunting *Miliaria calandra*. Breeding density in prime habitat may reach 3–6 bp/ha (Zwin and Limbourg, Belgium; Zeeland, The Netherlands; Guérande, Jura; P. Gailly, pers obs).

NW Europe suffered severe declines during the 1970s. Populations in 15 countries now appear relatively stable, but another eight are declining (by 20–50% in Germany, Finland, Belgium, Italy, Lithuania, Moldova, Greece; by >50% in Britain) and only four increasing (Ukraine, Ireland, Denmark, Slovenia). Following a slight increase after 1986 (J.H. Marchant & Gregory 1994), the British population has steadily declined since. Reasons for the previous declines are not known, but increased field drainage, loss of wetlands, removal of cover and the disappearance of low-intensity farming under agricultural intensification probably all have contributed since 1988. Farmland populations are worst affected, although in Britain in 1975–83 the species also decreased in wetter habitats (J.H. Marchant *et al* 1990), suggesting that a series of severe winters was also involved. Some other farmland seed-eaters declined simultaneously, indicating agricultural intensification (linked with Reed Bunting declines in Denmark; Møller 1980) as the principal cause. The Reed Bunting is likely to benefit year-round from set-aside and similar schemes. Habitat destruction, particularly through drainage, remains a long-term threat to much of the wetland-breeding population. Locally, field drainage, saltmarsh reclamation, and clearance of bankside vegetation are likely to have adverse effects.

In Finland, the species increased throughout much of the 20th century, possibly because eutrophication promoted waterside vegetation growth (Koskimies 1989a), but now a slight decline is apparent. The only recent significant range change was the spread into the Kola Peninsula. The small Slovenian population (200–400bp) is increasing steadily (Geister 1995). Russia, Norway, Poland and Sweden, as may France (for which the figures in the *Atlas* database may be serious underestimates). The British population probably halved during 1974–95 (BTO figures).

Northern populations are mainly migratory, birds from Scandinavia and Finland wintering in France and northern Italy, whereas C and southern European breeding populations are mainly sedentary except where there are prolonged periods of snow-cover (Prŷs-Jones 1984). In winter, birds tend to move towards drier habitats such as scrub and farmland. The species' winter habitat requirements are poorly known, but a shortage of winter habitat has been implicated in the declines of two other buntings (Evans & Smith 1994; Donald & Evans 1994). The steady increase of the Reed Bunting's appearance in gardens in winter to feed may reflect a shortage of winter habitat.

Paul Donald (GB) Paul Gailly (B)

This species account is sponsored by AVES, Société d'études ornithologiques, B.

Emberiza bruniceps

Red-headed Bunting

CZ	Strnad hnědehlavý	I	Zigolo testa aranciata
D	Braunkopfammer	NL	Bruinkopgors
E	Escribano Carirrojo	P	Escrevedeira-de-face-ruiva
F	Bruant à tête rousse	PL	Trznadel rudogłowy
FIN	Ruskopääsirkku	R	Желчная овсянка
G	Καστανοκρασοπούλι	S	Stäppsparv
H	Barnafejû sármány		

Non-SPEC, Threat status S

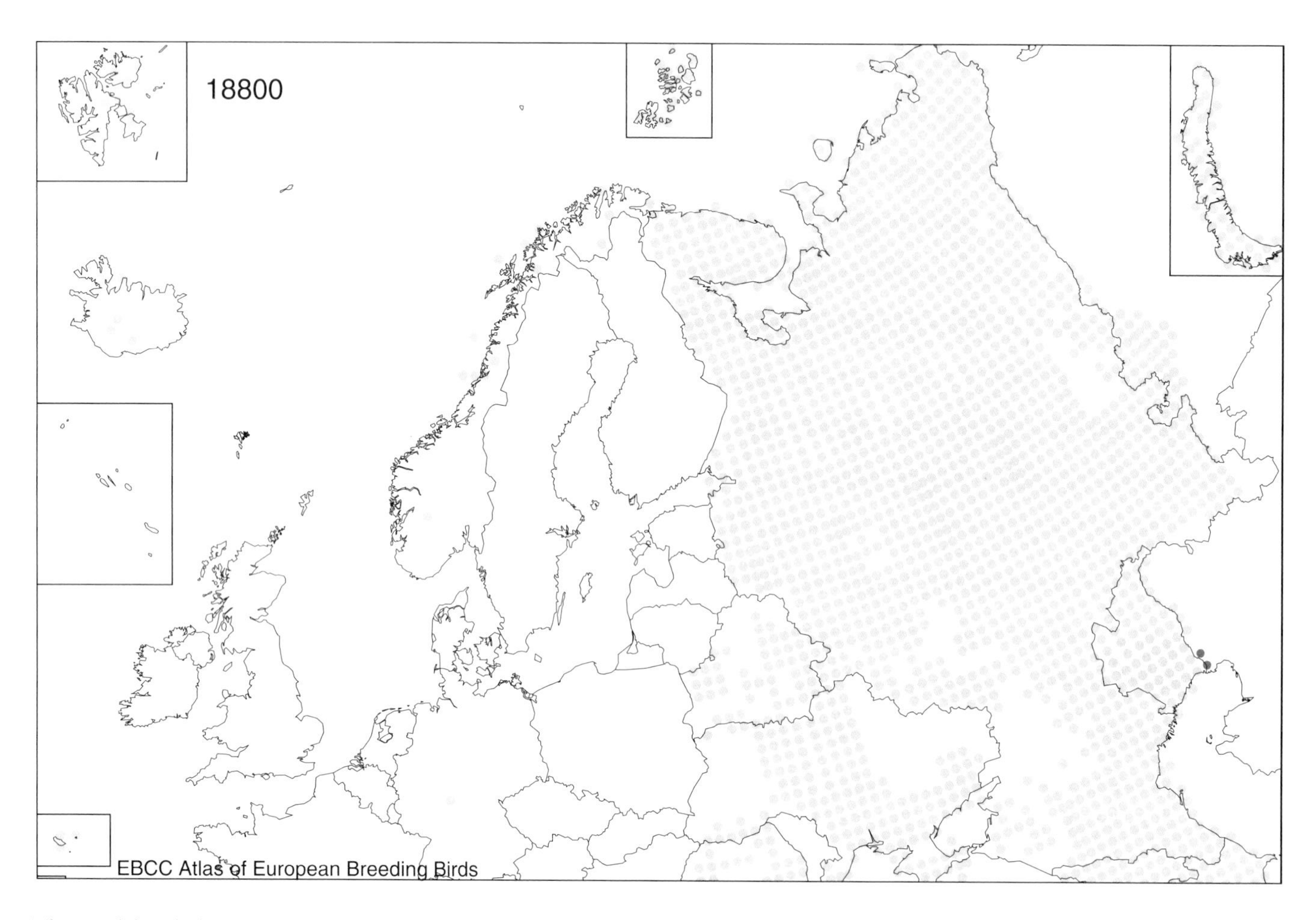

The Red-headed Bunting is a distinctive C Asian species that winters in India, but breeds in sparsely vegetated deserts and arid mountain regions from Iran and Pakistan in the S to Kazakhstan in the N. It expanded its range into Europe only in the 20th century, becoming widespread in the area between the Volga and Ural Rivers. By the 1950s the Red-headed Bunting had extended its range 800–900km to the W, reaching the W bank of the Volga at Volgograd by 1953 (Formozov 1959). However, in subsequent decades, numbers fell sharply in the western Kazakhstan population, and the western limit of its range retreated SE to the shores of the Caspian and to the Ural River valley. Climatic fluctuations are probably the underlying causes of the initial expansion and subsequent retreat (Varshavski 1965).

The Red-headed Bunting is a very characteristic bird of irrigated farmland, where it occurs in areas of scrub and tall herbage along field-borders, canal banks and edges of groves. In Europe, its main nesting habitat is tree shelter-belts or similar plantations, and also sparse bushes and scrub along river valleys in the deserts (Formozov 1959, Kovshar' 1974). The Red-headed Bunting is absent from open, waterless deserts.

There are no quantitative data from which to estimate the European population, but it is widespread in suitable habitat. The European population migrates in August, travelling fairly quickly to the Indian wintering grounds, and its return to the breeding territories occurs usually before mid-May (Kovshar' 1974, Roberts 1992). The Red-headed Bunting does not appear to be under immediate threat, but any conservation strategy devised for the species should examine one aspect of its biology which may be of benefit to farmers. In spring the Red-headed Bunting switches from a granivorous to an insectivorous diet (Roberts 1992), and is reported as helping suppress crop pests (especially during caterpillar infestations).

Victor Belik (R)

Emberiza melanocephala

Black-headed Bunting

CZ	Strnad černohlavý	I	Zigolo capinero
D	Kappenammer	NL	Zwartkopgors
E	Escribano Cabecinegro	P	Escrevedeira-de-cabeça-preta
F	Bruant mélanocéphale	PL	Trznadel czarnogłowy
FIN	Mustapääsirkku	R	Черноголовая овсянка
G	Αμπελουργός	S	Svarthuvad sparv
H	Kucsmás sármány		

SPEC Cat 2, Threat status V (P)

The Black-headed Bunting is distributed from C Italy to Greece continuously along the eastern Adriatic coast. To the N it reaches Bulgaria, Romania and Ukraine and to the E, SE Russia, the Caucasus, Turkey, the Near East and W and S Iran. It winters in W and C India.

The Black-headed Bunting lives in open areas sparsely interspersed with trees and low shrubs, often in low-intensity farming areas, occurring in cornfields, vineyards and groves (Byers *et al* 1995). On the Adriatic coast it mostly inhabits warm karst valleys. Although generally a lowland species, in C Turkey it occurs up to 2100m asl provided some cultivation is present (Roselaar 1995).

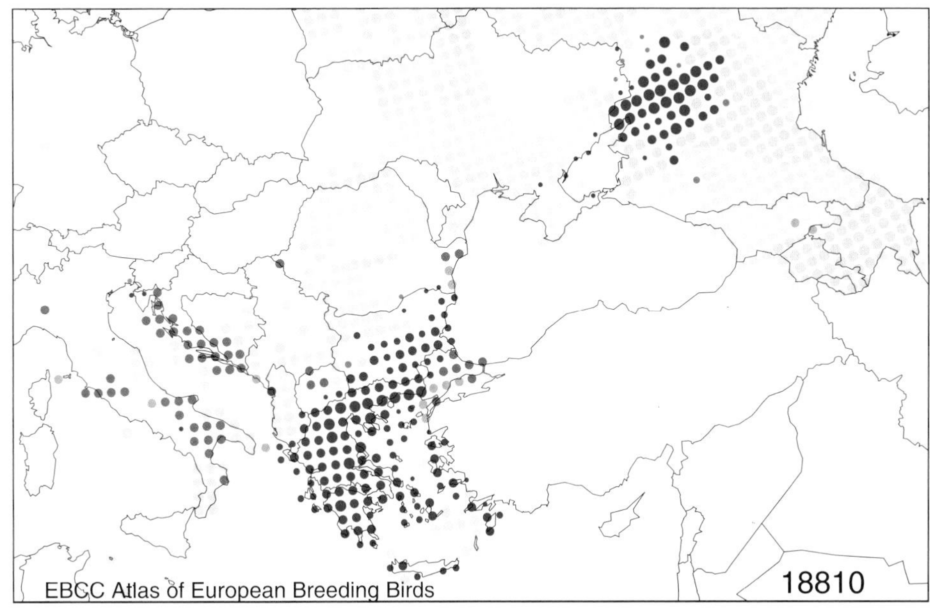

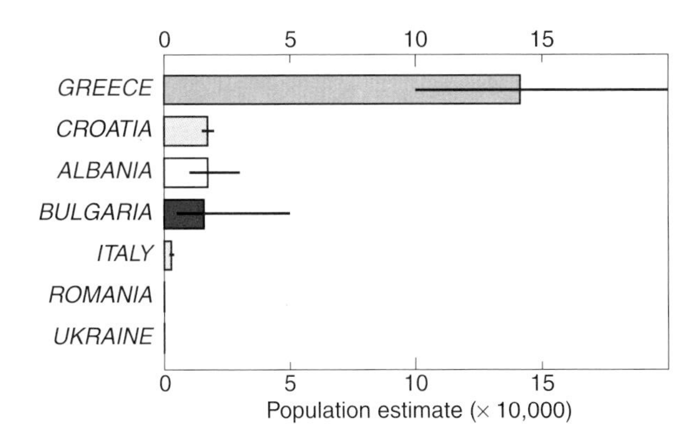

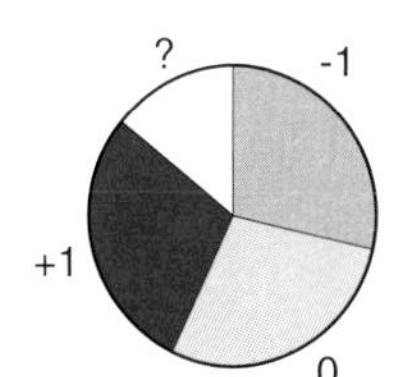

% in top 10 countries: 100.0
Total number of populated European countries: 7
Total European population 151,226–263,789 (194,726)
Russian population 1000–10,000 (3162)
Turkish population 1,000,000–10,000,000 (3,162,278)

Being a late spring (mainly May) and early autumn migrant (late July–early August), it is single-brooded. The female alone probably builds the nest and rears the young; that the males sing continuously may indicate a polygamous breeding strategy. The species breeds usually in low vegetation (in Istria, vetch *Vicia* spp), in wild vines or wheat.

The species forms small post-breeding groups which in winter coalesce into large flocks. Although the range-limit population density is less than 10 bp/km^2, it reaches 30–50 bp/km^2 in SE Europe and in the Near East can exceed 100 bp/km^2, some 1M–10Mbp in Turkey being indicative of its abundance. SE European densities decline from E to W, although Croatia holds substantial numbers (15 000–20 000bp). Trends are inconclusive, declining slightly in Greece, increasing slightly in Bulgaria, but overall appearing rather stable.

The ever-increasing application of intensive agricultural practices (destruction of hedgerows and shrubs to create larger fields, heavy pesticide use) which have superseded the small, richly structured fields and have created the 'cultural steppe', poses a severe threat to the species (Hallmann 1994c). These changes are particularly evident in Greece (olive groves replaced by maize fields) and Slovenia (cornfields replaced by commercial fruit-growing).

Iztok Geister (SLN)

Miliaria calandra

Corn Bunting

CZ	Strnad luční	**I**	Strillozzo
D	Grauammer	**NL**	Grauwe Gors
E	Triguero	**P**	Trigueirão
F	Bruant proyer	**PL**	Potrzeszcz
FIN	Harmaasirkku	**R**	Просянка
G	Τσιφτάς	**S**	Kornsparv
H	Sordély		

SPEC Cat 4, Threat status S (P)

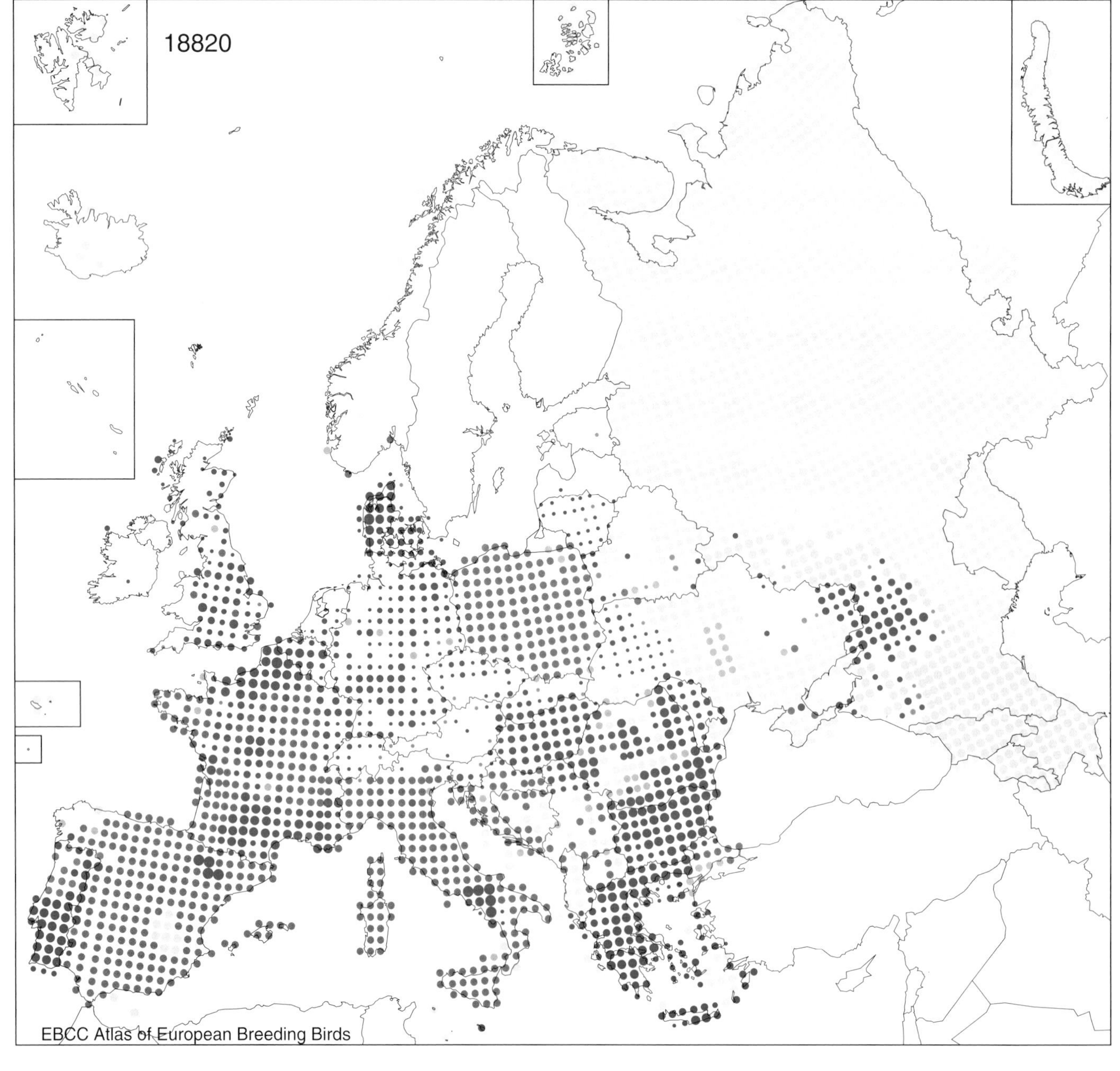

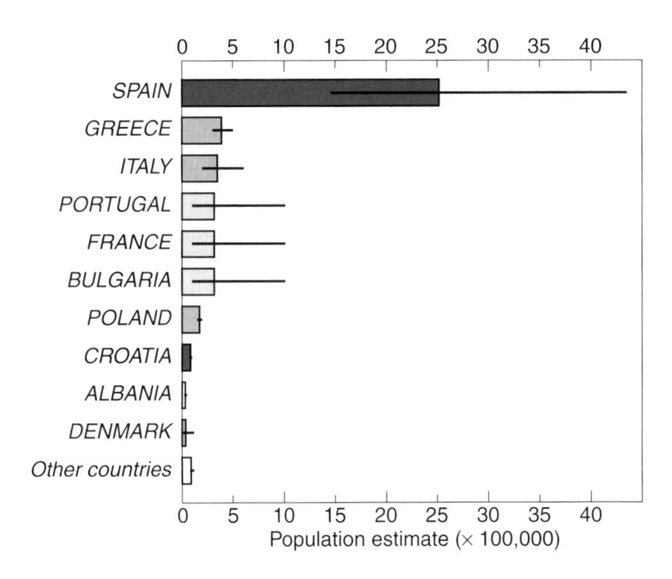

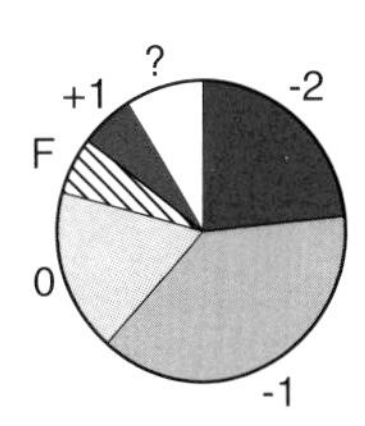

% in top 10 countries: 98.1
Total number of populated European countries: 34
Total European population 3,456,957–6,768,134 (4,583,988)
Russian population 1000–10,000 (3162)
Turkish population 1,000,000–10,000,000 (3,162,278)

The Corn Bunting, the largest European bunting, is distributed from the Canary Islands in the W to 83°E in C Asia, and from N-C Europe S to North Africa and SE to Iran and Iraq. It is widespread throughout C and S Europe but rarely occurs further N than northern Scotland, Denmark and Lithuania. The nominate subspecies *M.c. calandra* occurs E to Transcaucasia and most of Asia Minor, *clanceyi* inhabits western Ireland and western Scotland, and *buturlini* the Levant, SE Turkey and elsewhere.

In its northern range the species is confined mainly to farmland, preferring cereals and hay meadows in many areas. The European population occurs mostly in southern Europe, occupying most types of open country, including dry grassland and steppes. The species is mainly sedentary although some migratory populations dwell in eastern Europe. Populations in C Europe are partially migratory. The western Palearctic holds most of the world population, Spain having in excess of 1Mbp and Greece, Italy, Bulgaria, France and Portugal more than 250 000bp each.

Since the 1950s the Corn Bunting has declined alarmingly throughout much of its range (Donald *et al* 1994). In Great Britain the population fell by over 60% between 1970 and 1990 and the range contracted by 35%. In The Netherlands, the decline probably began during the 1950s, the population crashing from a maximum of 1250bp (1975) to 100–200bp (1990) (Hustings *et al* 1990). During the 19th century the Corn Bunting bred in southern Sweden in 'uncountable numbers' but thorough surveys in 1991 located just 10 singing males, making it one of Sweden's most endangered birds (Jönsson 1992). In Schleswig-Holstein (NW Germany) the population fell from 3000–4000bp (1955) to just 40bp (1987) (Busche 1989b). Similar declines have been quantified elsewhere in Germany, in Belgium, Switzerland and Denmark (Donald *et al* 1994). Very few countries reported stable (or even slightly increasing: Spain) populations. Indeed, the decline is widespread enough to put in question reported stable trends in regions with high-density populations and few observers. The graph indicates stability in France (1970–90) yet (considerable) declines now exist in Vaucluse, Amiens, Picardie and Sarthe (Bernard & Broyer 1994).

The declines are likely to be due at least in part to recent agriculture changes, which have been linked to population declines of many farmland bird species. Such changes include a reduction in the cropped area of spring-sown cereals (particularly barley *Hordeum*), earlier harvesting dates of temporary grassland (reflecting the switch from traditional hay meadows to intensively cultivated silage), the increased use of pesticides and the removal of hedgerows (Donald *et al* 1994). Recent research indicates that the British decline is probably not caused by decreased crop diversity, changes in the relative areas of tillage and grassland nor hedgerow-loss, but rather by reduced winter food supplies resulting from the loss of spring tillage, increased pesticide usage and improved harvesting and storage techniques (Donald & Evans 1995, Donald & Forrest 1995). Winter-sown cereals affect the species adversely in two ways: nest-losses rise because such crops are harvested earlier than spring-sown cereals (the species nests late), and winter-sown cereal stubbles are ploughed in for the next crop, depriving the species of the majority of its most important wintering habitat. In parts of The Netherlands and Belgium a general reduction in the cropped area of cereals (replaced mostly by green maize) was followed by a decline in Corn Bunting numbers (Schepers *et al* 1992). In Russia, Romania and Bulgaria, where farming is not yet so industrial as in western Europe, the species apparently continues to flourish. That the most severe declines have taken place along the species' northern range limits might also suggest that land-use changes make the species more vulnerable to climatic extremes in those regions.

Paul Donald (GB) Fred Hustings (NL)

Oceanodroma monorhis

Swinhoe's Petrel

CZ	Buřňáček vlaštovčí	I	Uccello delle tempeste di Swinhoe
D	Swinhoewellenläufer	NL	Chinees Stormvogeltje
E	Paíño de Swinhoe	P	Paínho de Swinhoe
F	Océanite de Swinhoe	PL	Nawałnik brunatny
FIN	Pikkukeiju	R	Вилохвостая качурка
G	Κυματοβάτης του Swinhoe	S	Swinhoes stormsvala
H	Japán viharfecske		

Criteria not applied

First observed on Selvagem Grande in 1983 (James & Robertson 1985) Swinhoe's Petrel was identified from its call. Further birds were caught on Selvagem Grande in 1988 (Bretagnolle *et al* 1991) and 1991 (Cubitt *et al* 1992). Other birds have since been caught much further N at Tynemouth in England and at Banneg in NW France (Cubitt *et al* 1992). The species identity was confirmed by DNA testing (Dawson 1992). Its known world distribution is confined to a few islands scattered across the Pacific, the S Atlantic, and the Cape Verde Islands.

Although it has been suspected of breeding in the Azores or Madeira archipelagos for some time, it was not until 1993 that the first evidence was obtained, when a one-legged Swinhoe's Petrel, found at the base of a wall on Selvagem Grande, was discovered to have a very vascular brood patch. In 1994 it was netted within 5m of the same spot and in 1995 it was again found at the base of the wall, and both times its brood patch was very vascular. The bird caught on Selvagem Grande in 1991 was found inside a wall in a nest usually used by a Madeiran Storm-petrel *Oceanodroma castro* and also had a very vascular brood patch. On this evidence Swinhoe's Petrel is categorized as a possible breeder on Selvagem Grande. Given the difficulties of observing and counting other very rare nocturnal seabirds in these archipelagos, it may breed in small numbers.

Francis Zino (P)

Pluvialis fulva

Pacific Golden Plover

CZ	Kulik žlutý	I	Piviere dorato orientale
D	Wanderregenpfeifer	NL	Kleine Goudplevier
E	Chorlito Dorado	P	Tarambola-dourada-siberiana
F	Asiático		
FIN	Pluvier fauve Siperiankurmitsa	PL	Siewka złotawa
		R	Бурокрылая ржанка
G	Βροχοπούλι του Ειρηνικού	S	Sibirisk tundrapipare
H	Szibériai lile		

Criteria not applied

The Pacific Golden Plover breeds from W Alaska and the Chukotskiy Peninsula S to the Gulf of Anadyr and along the Arctic coasts of Siberia W to the Yamal Peninsula, extending inland as far as the treeline. On several occasions, birds have been seen in summer in suitable breeding habitat on both sides of Karskaya Inlet, just inside the *Atlas*' area of coverage and only some 80km from the Yamal Peninsula (Estafiev 1991); although these birds were considered at the time passage migrants, under the *Atlas*' definitions, occurrences in suitable habitat during the breeding season form the lowest degree of acceptability, and hence this species is provisionally assessed as possibly breeding.

Until recently the Pacific Golden Plover was considered conspecific with American Golden Plover *P. dominica*, but studies in Alaska so far indicate that interbreeding does not occur where the two forms overlap (McCaffery & Maron 1993). However, the Russian view generally remains that Pacific Golden Plover should be described as *P.d. fulva*. Given that many migrant species to W Europe come E of the Yamal Peninsula, it seems worth considering whether some European records of vagrant Pacific Golden Plover should be attributable to birds from the Yamal region, rather than to North American (or E Siberian) birds, though they are generally assumed to come from the E.

The Pacific Golden Plover nests in short vegetation or on bare ground in well-drained tundra, mostly N of areas occupied by Golden Plover *P. apricaria*. In the overlap zone, Pacific Golden Plover prefers more open areas (Hayman *et al* 1986). Its wintering areas stretch from East Africa, particularly Ethiopia and Somalia, to the Indian and Pacific Ocean coasts.

Philip Jackson (GB)

Numenius tenuirostris

Slender-billed Curlew

CZ	Koliha velká	**I**	Chiurlottello
D	Dünnschnabel-Brachvogel	**NL**	Dunbekwulp
E	Zarapito Fino	**P**	Maçarico-de-bico-fino
F	Courlis à bec grêle	**PL**	Kulik cienkodzioby
FIN	Kaitanokkakuovi	**R**	Тонкоклювый кроншнеп
G	Λεπτομύτα	**S**	Smalnäbbad spov
H	Vekonyscörü póling		

SPEC Cat 1 (known only on passage)

There is no firm evidence that the Slender-billed Curlew has ever nested in Europe, though extensive searches for the species are planned within the *Atlas*' coverage area, between the Volga and Ural Rivers. The only fully confirmed nesting records of the species were those in 1914 and 1924 (Ushakov 1916, 1925) near Tara in S-C Siberia, some 1000km E of the Urals. Other possible records come from elsewhere in S-C Siberia, but several other records are considered highly doubtful.

Gretton (1991) discusses the unconfirmed reports from the 19th century onwards of the species breeding in the Volga–Ural steppes N of the Caspian, from NE Iran, and from several Mediterranean countries, including southern France, northern Greece, Malta and Algeria (all in Dresser 1871), and Romania. The only claimed observations of eggs occurred in Egypt (Captain Loche in Dresser 1871) and Spain (a clutch in the IRSNB museum, Brussels); both are mystifying and not fully documented.

The current world population of the species is estimated as 50–270 individuals (Gretton 1994). With no breeding observations since Ushakov's in 1924, there is no way of estimating how many pairs may still nest. The recent observations in early 1995 of at least 18 birds in southern Italy give some hope that there may still be a surviving nucleus of breeding birds. Searches of the supposed breeding grounds have continued since 1989, led by A.K. Yurlov from Novosibirsk. Further W, the Volga–Ural steppes and parts of Kazakhstan will also be surveyed (Belik 1994b, van Impe 1995). The species is the most threatened bird of mainland Europe. A BirdLife International action plan has recently been agreed and sets out the necessary actions.

Adam Gretton (GB)

Sterna elegans

Elegant Tern

CZ	Rybák kouřový	**I**	Sterna elegante
D	Schmuckseeschwalbe	**NL**	Californische Kuifstern
E	Charrán Elegante	**P**	Garajau-elegante
F	Sterne élégante	**PL**	Rybitwa kalifornijska
FIN	Kaunotiira	**R**	Змегантная крачка
G	Ταξιδογλάρονο του Ειρηνικού	**S**	Aztektärna
H	Kontyos csér		

Criteria not applied

The Elegant Tern is a monotypic Nearctic species whose restricted breeding range lies on the western seaboard of North America from southern California to Mexico. Breeding birds migrate S in September to Ecuador, Peru and Chile. There are occasional records from Texas (P. Harrison 1983). The species' Pacific breeding distribution and its coastal habits all year had made it an unlikely candidate for vagrancy to Europe. However, from 1974 to at least 1985, in the large Sandwich Tern *S. sandvicensis* colony at Banc d'Arguin, near Arcachon in SW France, an Elegant Tern formed a mixed pair with a Sandwich Tern. In 1984, there were two mixed pairs. Eggs hatched in various years and young fledged at least in 1984 (possibly in some other years too, particularly in 1979 when a possible hybrid was seen). Possibly a different individual was at the same colony, again paired with a Sandwich Tern, from 1987 to at least 1993 (Dubois & Comité d'Homologation National 1994). The unexpected occurrence of this species on the E Atlantic coast led to its original identification as a Lesser Crested Tern *S. bengalensis* (Petit 1976).

Northward movements in late summer, as occur in the Pacific, might help explain a sight record of a bird, presumably the Banc d'Arguin breeder, 300km N of its breeding location. There is also a record, possibly of one of the French birds, from a Sandwich Tern colony at Greencastle, Northern Ireland in June/July 1982 and later off the Irish S coast (Lewington *et al* 1991).

Pierre Yésou (F) Simon Gillings (GB)

Melanocorypha bimaculata

Bimaculated Lark

CZ	Kalandra horská	I	Calandra asiatica
D	Bergkalanderlerche	NL	Bergkalanderleeuwerik
E	Calandria Bimaculada	P	Calhandra-bimaculada
F	Alouette monticole	PL	Kalandra dwuplamista
FIN	Ylänkökiuru	R	Двупятнистый жаворонок
G	Κηλιδωτή Γαλιάντρα	S	Asiatisk kalanderlärka
H	Hegyi kalandra		

Non-SPEC, Threat status S (P)

This large, distinctive and strong-billed lark of the eastern warm temperate dry zones (C. Harrison 1982) has a breeding range extending from NE Turkey and southern Transcaucasia to N and E Iran and the southern Urals, but is most numerous in Kazakhstan. In the breeding season the Bimaculated Lark occupies montane areas, usually between 1200 and 2000m asl and exceptionally up to 2700m asl at the limit of arable land. Breeding habitats typically are sparsely vegetated, such as arid heath bordering cultivated land (C. Harrison 1982), shrubland, stony soil and thorn desert. Adamyan (1963) found the species avoided standing crops but foraged regularly on harvested fields. It largely replaces Calandra Lark *M. calandra* in rougher steppes and on higher ground, the Calandra Lark preferring grassier low-lying areas, though the two overlap to some extent (*BWP*).

In the breeding season the Bimaculated Lark is solitary, but during the rest of the year it is more gregarious and forms flocks. Demographic and trend data are lacking, but it can be common, and in some areas numerous (V.E. Flint *et al* 1984). Its preference for poorer quality steppe may make it less vulnerable to agricultural intensification than other larks.

Some European birds are short-distance migrants, wintering on the range limit on the Muganskaya steppe in Azerbaijan and around Dushanbe in Tajikistan (Dementiev & Gladkov 1954). The majority of the population migrates further S during October and November to Iran, Pakistan, India (Ali & Ripley 1972), the Middle East and NE Africa. Large migratory flocks have been reported from the Levant, and some over 3000-strong from Turkey. Wintering birds occupy bare semi-desert, sparse cultivation, harvested and fallow fields, margins of jheel and dry tidal mudflats (*BWP*).

Simon Gillings (GB) Philip Jackson (GB)

Melanocorypha yeltoniensis

Black Lark

CZ	Kalandra černá	I	Calandra nera
D	Mohrenlerche	NL	Zwarte Leeuwerik
E	Calandria Negra	P	Calhandra-negra
F	Alouette nègre	PL	Kalandra czarna
FIN	Mustakiuru	R	Черный жаворонок
G	Μαυρογαλιάντρα	S	Svartlärka
H	Szerecsenpacsirta		

SPEC Cat 3, Threat status V (P)

The monotypic Black Lark is distributed through the temperate steppe zone from the Volga River through Kazakhstan to C Asia. In the breeding season it occupies the wormwood *Artemisia* and feather-grass *Stipa* steppes and solonchak (pale salty soil), usually in less arid areas than the closely related White-winged Lark *M. leucoptera*, and often near water (C. Harrison 1982).

Like so many species of this region, its population data are minimal, but its population of European Russia is very roughly estimated at between 6000 and 10 000bp. In prime breeding habitats its density may exceed 10 bp/km^2. The overall population size trend is thought to be downwards, as in Kazakhstan (Shishkin 1976) as a result of ploughing and development of the steppes for cultivation, which has destroyed much habitat. Degradation of grassland through overgrazing and trampling is now threatening remaining populations (Galushin *et al* 1994).

The Black Lark is a partial migrant, some individuals remaining in nomadic flocks throughout the winter and moving in response to cold weather (Dementiev & Gladkov 1954). Others migrate a short distance to the W or WSW in September and October. Western birds winter in the Ukraine and SE European Russia. Females and immatures typically disperse further than males. No real habitat preferences exist in winter but the species is faithful to areas with the least snow-cover. Hence, birds can be found foraging on roads, behind herds of horses and even in human settlements. Migrants return to the breeding grounds early in March (*BWP*).

Simon Gillings (GB) Philip Jackson (GB)

Prunella ocularis

Radde's Accentor

CZ	Pěvuška skalní	I	Passera scopaiola di Radde
D	Felsenbraunelle	NL	Steenheggemus
E	Acentor de Radde	P	Ferreirinha de Radde
F	Accenteur de Radde	PL	Płochacz pstry
FIN	Kaukasianrautiainen	R	Пестрая завирушка
G	Θαμνοψάλτης του Radde	S	Svartkronad järnsparv
H	Török szürkebegy		

SPEC Cat 3, Threat status V (P)

Radde's Accentor, one of five accentors breeding in Europe, occupies the alpine altitudinal regions of the warm temperate zone (C. Harrison 1982). The species has two main distribution areas, one through C and E Turkey, the other in the eastern Elburz range in N Iran. Smaller isolated populations occur, such as those in the *Atlas*' coverage area in Armenia and Nakhichevan territory of Azerbaijan (Flint *et al* 1984) where its status is uncertain (Beaman *et al* 1975), and where perhaps 100bp live (Loskot 1994a). Radde's Accentor is found also in isolated areas of SW and S Iran. No subspecies have been described. Its relationships to other accentors are unclear.

During the breeding season the species is found exclusively in the band of xerophytic vegetation growing on dry stony terrain between 2500m and 3250m asl. This vegetation includes patches of thorny overgrown shrubs with dense crowns such as juniper *Juniperus* and barberry *Berberis*. Additional habitat requirements include a water source, bare ground, scattered grass (<30% by area) and overhanging rocks for shade (Loskot 1994a). An altitudinal migrant, it winters below 1000m asl (Jonsson 1992) in shrubby growth alongside mountain streams (C. Harrison 1982). Population data are minimal. Outside Europe it is apparently a local but not uncommon resident in summer at high altitudes in E Turkey and mountains adjacent to the Black Sea coast, but its extensive range causes local breeding groups to be widely dispersed. Present rough estimates suggest 500–5000bp occur in Turkey, but these probably are underestimates.

Low-intensity grazing may benefit this species by providing good foraging conditions but threats from habitat degradation through intensification of pastoral agriculture in its wintering areas could be detrimental to population levels (Loskot 1994a).

Simon Gillings (GB) Philip Jackson (GB)

Irania gutturalis

White-throated Robin

CZ	Slavík bělohrdlý	I	Irania golabianca
D	Weißkehlsänger	NL	Perzische Roodborst
E	Ruiseñor Pintado	P	Rouxinol-de-garganta-branca
F	Iranie à gorge blanche	PL	Iranka
FIN	Kivikkosatakieli	R	Соловей-белошейка
G	Ασπρολαίμης	S	Vitstrupig näktergal
H	Fehértorkú fülemüle		

Non-SPEC, Threat status S (P)

The White-throated Robin, a large monotypic chat, breeds in the dry warm temperate zone. Its world distribution stretches from Turkey to E Kazakhstan and includes isolated populations in Iran and Israel. In the *Atlas*' area of coverage it breeds in the mountains of Armenia and the Nakhichevan territory of Azerbaijan, usually being found at altitudes of 1100–2000m asl and occasionally up to 2350m asl (C. Harrison 1982). It prefers dry slopes which have thickets of shrubs such as juniper *Juniperus*, almond *Prunus* and climbers like honeysuckle *Lonicera* growing among crags, ravines and screes. This species often occurs alongside the Shore Lark *Eremophila alpestris* in such areas (*BWP*). In its European range pairs are fairly widespread and the species is not uncommon, though populations may fluctuate from year to year (Beaman *et al* 1975). Males are strongly territorial.

The White-throated Robin winters in NE Africa (mainly in Kenya) and Arabia in dense scrub and undergrowth of ravines and rivers. Breeding grounds are deserted by the end of August, birds returning, apparently synchronously, in April and May. It has recently been recorded as breeding on the fringes of the Turkish Black Sea coastlands but there are few other data on population or range changes. This species may be relatively unaffected by clearance of subalpine vegetation in the Caucasus, but evidence is lacking.

Simon Gillings (GB) Philip Jackson (GB)

Phoenicurus erythrogaster

Güldenstädt's Redstart

CZ	Rehek bělotemenný	I	Codirosso di Güldenstädt
D	Rieseur Rotschwanz	NL	Witkruinroodstaart
E	Collirrojo Coronado	P	Rabirruivo-de-coroa-branca
F	Rougequeue de Güldenstädt	PL	Pleszka kaukaska
FIN	Siperianleppälintu	R	Краснобрюхая горихвостка
G	Ερυθρόγαστρος Κοκκινούρης	S	Bergrödstjärt
H	Hegyi rozsdafarkú		

SPEC Cat 3, Threat status INS

Güldenstädt's Redstart occupies the alpine altitudinal band of the temperate to warm temperate zones (C. Harrison 1982). The majority of the world population (subspecies *P.e. grandis*) lies in a broad area from the Altai to C China, a branch reaching northeastwards into C Siberia and another southwards from China along the Himalayas. The only other subspecies, nominate *erythrogaster*, is restricted to the N Caucasus and Armenia. This form is rare and little is known of its ecology and status.

Güldenstädt's Redstart is a montane species whose preferences are more similar to an accentor *Prunella* than to those of other redstarts (*BWP*). In its main range it breeds between 4000 and 5500m asl just below the perennial snow and glacier line. In the Caucasus this zone lies between 2800m and 3700m asl. It nests in rocky areas, near rapid mountain streams and areas of glacial moraine sediment (Loskot 1994b).

There are no data on population sizes, but numbers are probably low in the former USSR (Dementiev & Gladkov 1954), the total in the Caucasus probably not exceeding 2500–3000 birds (Loskot 1994b), where breeding density is probably less than 1 bp/km^2. This restricted subspecies has an unusually low reproductive rate, all nests found containing either a maximum of 4 eggs or an average 3.2 nestlings (Loskot 1994b).

The species is a short-distance altitudinal migrant, wintering below 500m asl in river valleys containing its main food, Siberian buckthorn *Hippophae rhamnoides* (Dementiev & Gladkov 1954). Its reliance on this shrub renders it vulnerable in the Caucasus because much has been cleared for development, and elsewhere the berries are harvested locally (Loskot 1994b). The females move further from the breeding grounds than the males, some of which remain on territory throughout the year. Migrants return to breed in March (*BWP*).

Simon Gillings (GB) Philip Jackson (GB)

Hippolais languida

Upcher's Warbler

CZ	Sedmihlásek ostnitý	I	Canapino di Upcher
D	Dornspötter	NL	Grote Vale Spotvogel
E	Zarcero de Upcher	P	Felosa de Upcher
F	Hyppolaïs d'Upcher	PL	Zaganiacz pustynny
FIN	Harmaakultarinta	R	Пустынная пересмешка
G	Στριτσίδα του Upcher	S	Orientsångare
H	Keleti geze		

Non-SPEC, Threat status S (P)

A medium-sized migrant warbler whose S–C Asian distribution extends W as far as the Levant, Upcher's Warbler breeds in the *Atlas*' coverage only in S Azerbaijan and Armenia. Eastwards its range reaches *c*75°E, and southwards *c*30°N. Its western breeding limit lies in S Turkey, Lebanon and N Israel. It winters in East Africa between 15°N and 5°S, the end of a passage route which the birds take across C and southern Arabia (Fry 1990). Stop-over sites have not been located and so continuous migration cannot be ruled out. Off-passage migrants mainly have been reported in April–May and July–August (Shirihai 1995).

In Eritrea, Ethiopia and Somalia, wintering birds are seen much earlier than in Kenya, where it is abundant, and onward movement seems timed to coincide with the end of the East African monsoon in December (*BWP*). There are no extra-limital records from Europe, and very few outside the Levantine breeding areas or in NE Africa.

Upcher's Warbler inhabits a characteristically structured habitat, from low elevations up to 2400m asl in places, most frequently on hillsides and long mountain slopes. It breeds on the open, arid steppe and in lightly wooded areas of the Irano-Turanian region in habitat akin to garrigue. It inhabits medium-height, somewhat tangled but open thickets of buckthorn *Rhamnus*, tamarisk *Tamarix*, *Pistacia*, almond *Amygdalus*, rose *Rosa* and similar shrubs, wherever this degree of vegetation density can be supported, such as near cultivation, in ravines and dry river beds, along the edges of depressions. Although *BWP* records its use of open woodland, birds in Israel and Turkey are more selective (Shirihai 1996). Wintering birds in E Africa frequent acacia woodland but tend to avoid the taller trees.

The species usually is solitary outside the breeding season, but breeding pairs seem to form neighbourhood groups, most likely because of the restricted habitat requirements. Breeding density can be high, such as 3–4bp in 100 × 30m (Kumerloeve 1967) and *c*6 singing males in 800–900m² (Schubert 1979) in SE and C Turkey respectively. The average estimated pair-separation distance in Israel is 200m (Shirihai 1996).

John Morgan (GB) Hadoram Shirihai (ISR)

Sylvia nana — Desert Warbler

CZ	Pěnice malá	I	Sterpazzola nana
D	Wüstengrasmücke	NL	Woestijngrasmus
E	Curruca Sahariana	P	Toutinegra do Sara
F	Fauvette naine	PL	Pokrzewka pustynna
FIN	Kääpiökerttu	R	Пустынная славка
G	Ερημοτσιροβάκος	S	Ökensångare
H	Sivatagi poszáta		

Non-SPEC, Threat status S (P)

The Desert Warbler, the smallest of its genus, has but a breeding toehold in Europe, in SE Russia, where the migratory *S.n. nana* breeds in steppe-desert areas to the northwest of the Caspian Sea, its range extending through Kazakhstan into C Asia. Otherwise its occurrence in Europe is as a vagrant to the southern North Sea countries and to the Baltic region. Occurrences in Malta and Spain have involved the mainly sedentary North African subspecies *deserti*.

The patchy breeding distribution of *deserti* in NW Africa is from *c*25° to 35°N, reaching *c*10°E, but *nana* only winters at these latitudes, or further S as far as 10°N just E of the Nile Valley, and eastwards throughout Arabia to 75°E (NW India). *S.n. nana* breeds between 33° and 48°N in W–C Asia. The two forms have different breeding seasons, January–May for *deserti* and March–June for *nana*.

Both subspecies inhabit open, flat, arid steppe and semi-desert habitat containing sparse low vegetation, typically on sandy or occasionally pebble-strewn substrate. Outside the breeding season, wintering birds and vagrants also prefer such habitats, avoided by congeners but the preserve of larks, coursers, stone curlews and wheatears. Indeed in S Israel, wintering Desert Warblers (Oct–Mar) often follow Desert Wheatears *Oenanthe deserti*. The Desert Warbler usually forages on the ground at the base of dwarf shrubs, but sometimes is seen higher in broom *Haloxylon* bushes, its main diet being insects.

Individuals are normally solitary outside the breeding season, although occasional post-breeding dispersal in small groups occurs (*BWP*). High breeding densities have been noted in Kazakhstan, singing males being some 50–60m apart (*BWP*).

In the 1920s, it was supposedly extending its range westwards, across the deserts near the Caspian Sea (Worobiew 1929). Nowadays the species appears to have been affected by habitat loss through overgrazing and changing agricultural practices, leading to changes in the patterns of dispersal and location of wintering areas (Shirihai 1996).

John Morgan (GB) Hadoram Shirihai (ISR)

Sitta tephronota

Eastern Rock Nuthatch

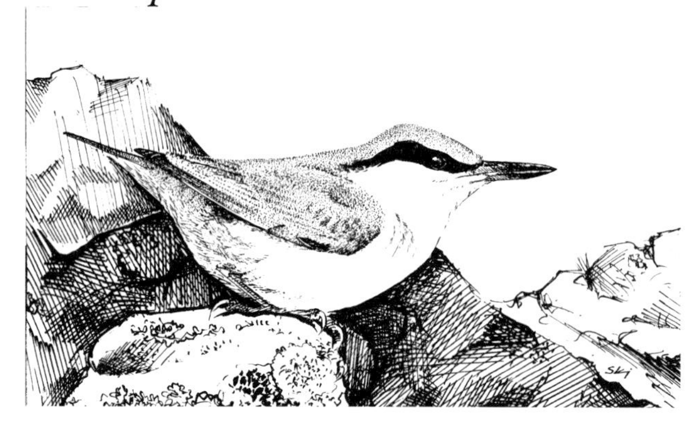

CZ	Brhlúk východní	I	Picchio muratore di roccia orientale
D	Klippenkleiber	NL	Grote Rotsklever
E	Trepador Armenio	P	Trepadeira-oriental
F	Sittelle des rochers	PL	Kowalik duży
FIN	Vuorinakkeli	R	Большой скалистый поползень
G	Ανατολικός Βραχοτσοπανάκος	S	Östlig klippnötväcka
H	Szirti csuszka		

Non-SPEC, Threat status S (P)

A resident of the warm temperate zone (C. Harrison 1982), this species is found from E Turkey through most of Iran to Afghanistan and C Asia, entering the *Atlas*' area in Armenia and Azerbaijan. In the former USSR, it breeds up to 2600m asl amongst rocks, on cliffs, and in boulder screes (Dementiev & Gladkov 1954); in Afghanistan, at *c*1070m–3000m asl (Paludan 1959). In parts of the Caucasus it may overlap with its western counterpart, the (Lesser) Rock Nuthatch *S. neumayer* but the latter is more restricted to rocky habitats, *S. tephronota* occurring regularly in arboreal habitats (Löhrl 1988), particularly in winter.

It forages on cliffs, rocks, on the ground and in trees, preferring snails but also takes insects and seeds, the latter from autumn to spring. It nests in tree- or rock-holes, natural or artificial, and reduces the entrance hole with mud. The same site may be used for several years. Streams seem important, birds visiting dry streambeds to seek food. No demographic data are currently available but the species does not appear to be under immediate threat, although much of the Caucasus subalpine habitat is changing through spreading agriculture and wood-collection.

Of the four subspecies, *obscura* is resident in Armenia and Azerbaijan, although some post-breeding and seasonal altitudinal movements do occur (*BWP*).

Simon Gillings (GB) Philip Jackson (GB)

Acridotheres tristis

Common Myna

CZ	Majna obecná	I	Maina comune
D	Hirtenmaina	NL	Treurbeo
E	Miná Común	P	Estorninho-de-mascarilha-amarela
F	Martin triste	PL	Majna brunatna
FIN	Pihamaina	R	Обыкновенная майна
G	Κοινή Μάινα	S	Brun majna
H	Pásztormejnó		

Criteria not applied

The Common Myna occurs in Europe probably only as a naturalized species, where escapes or releases occur (Goodwin 1956). A small population existed in France between 1986 and 1989 (Hars 1991) but the only self-sustaining European population is in southern Russia around Sochi and Gagra (*BWP*). The natural distribution is from Afghanistan and Kazakhstan to SW China and Indochina, in forest-edges and open country near human habitation, particularly agricultural land and settlements (Long 1981). Naturalized populations also occur in Africa, Australia and on many oceanic islands, including Ascension. Most are *A.t. tristis*, *tristoides* or *tristis/tristoides* intermediates. This identifies their origin as being Turkmenistan, S Kazakhstan, Iran, Pakistan and India (*tristis*), and Nepal and Burma (*tristoides*). The natural range has expanded eastward recently as a result of natural colonization assisted by escapes (Lever 1987). The closest population to S Russia comprises *tristis*, and so westward expansion could account for these birds (D.R. Wells, pers comm) although Mauersberger & Möckel (1987) believe that captive origin is more plausible.

The Common Myna's broad habitat requirements and its preference for human-inhabited areas make it an adaptable species. Some populations have been introduced to control agricultural pests, but mynas may themselves harm crops or local fauna: e.g. they may out-compete the endangered Seychelles Magpie Robin *Copsychus sechellarum* for nest sites.

Because birds from both native and natural populations are sedentary (Long 1981, Mauersberger & Möckel 1987), the activities of the cagebird trade will probably determine the species' future European distribution.

Simon Gillings (GB)

Acridotheres cristatellus

Chinese Jungle Myna

CZ	Majna chocholatá	I	Maina crestata
D	Haubenmaina	NL	Kuifmaina
E	Miná Chino	P	Mainato-de-crista
F	Martin huppé	PL	Majna czubata
FIN	Riisimaina	R	Китайская майна
G	Κινέζικη Μάινα	S	Större tofsmajna
H	Kínai dszungelmejnó		

Criteria not applied

The natural range of this species (also known as the Crested Myna) is C and SE China, NE Myanmar (Burma, but possibly only a vagrant here), Cambodia, Vietnam and C Laos. On the mainland of S China and Vietnam the species is a characteristic and very common resident, breeding near human settlements in open lowland and urban habitats interspersed with pastureland, scattered trees, woodlands and parks. It is a popular cagebird. Breeding populations originating from accidental or deliberate releases exist around Tokyo, in the Philippines (Manila), Malaysia (Penang) (Long 1981, Lever 1987) and probably also in the United Arab Emirates. Since the 1890s, released cagebirds established a population of 2000–3000 birds (Mackay & Hughes 1963) in suburban areas of Vancouver, British Columbia, remaining numerous in the mid-1980s (Scott 1986).

During the *Atlas* survey a population of unknown origin existed in the outer suburbs of Graz, Austria. Numbers increased from 4 in July 1983, when the species was first seen, to 14 in November 1986 (Kresse & Kepka 1988). The resident flock frequented suburban gardens, parks, orchards and pastureland within a small area of the Graz-Liebenau housing estate, associating occasionally with grazing cattle and Starling *Sturnus vulgaris* flocks. In winter it visited bird-feeders. From 1984 to 1986 1–3bp nested successfully in a hollow tree and garden nestboxes (Kresse & Kepka 1988). The remaining 3 individuals were seen for the last time in the area in June and July 1991 (E. Kresse, pers comm).

Peter Sackl (A)

Carpospiza brachydactyla

Pale Rock Sparrow

CZ	Vrabec plavý	I	Passera lagia chiara
D	Fahlsperling	NL	Bleke Rotsmus
E	Gorrión Pálido	P	Pardal-pálido
F	Moineau pâle	PL	Wróbel krótkopalcowy
FIN	Arovarpunen	R	Короткопалый воробей
G	Πετροσπουργίτης της Ερήμου	S	Blek stensparv
H	Halvány köviveréb		

Non-SPEC, Threat status S (P)

This species inhabits low to middle latitudes in warm mediterranean and subtropical zones (*BWP*). Within the *Atlas*' area the species is a regular breeder only in the Lesser Caucasus. Elsewhere it breeds from SE Turkey through Syria, Lebanon, Israel, Saudi Arabia and Iran E to Baluchistan. It has bred in the United Arab Emirates (1988; Clement *et al* 1993). It is a nomadic breeder, preferred habitats being arid, rocky and very sparsely vegetated with grass and scattered trees, shrubs and thickets of such species as pistachio *Pistacia*. It frequents hillsides, barren ravines and mountain habitats up to *c*2300m asl (*BWP*) where it nests in cliff crevices, precipices and holes in buildings (Flint *et al* 1984).

The Pale Rock Sparrow breeds in lone pairs or occasionally semi-colonially. It is numerous in the Nakhichevan territory of Azerbaijan but rare in the Gobushan region of eastern Azerbaijan (E.N. Panov, pers comm to Editors). There are no published trend data but the species is probably stable.

The Pale Rock Sparrow is a short-distance migrant, moving S to SW from August to October and wintering in southern Iraq, western Saudi Arabia, Ethiopia and Sudan S to 12°N. Outside the breeding season, when it may form flocks numbering several hundred (Clements *et al* 1993), it occupies more open habitats, including cultivated areas below 300m asl. In the S of its wintering range it favours cereal fields.

Simon Gillings (GB)

Rhodopechys sanguinea

Crimson-winged Finch

CZ	Hýl červenekřídlý	I	Trombettiere alirosse
D	Rotflügelgimpel	NL	Rode Steenvink
E	Camachuelo Ensangrentado	P	Pintarrôxo-d'asa-rosada
F	Roselin à ailes roses	PL	Gilak ciemnogłowy
FIN	Ruususiipitulkku	R	Чернокрылый чечевичник
G	Κοκκινόφτερη Σπίζα	S	Bergökenfink
H	Pirosszárnyú sivatagipinty		

Non-SPEC, Threat status S (P)

This resident of the warm temperate zone is distributed discontinuously in isolated patches (small to very large) from Morocco (*R.s. aliena*) through Turkey, the southern Caucasus, Iran and Afghanistan to the Tian Shan (nominate *sanguinea*; Clement *et al* 1993). It breeds generally at 1700–3200m asl in sparsely vegetated dry areas such as bare mountain-tops, slopes and boulder-fields (Roselaar 1995). Occasionally it nests in the scrub and juniper *Juniperus* zone above the treeline.

There are no population data for Armenia or Azerbaijan. Almost certainly it occurs in southern Georgia and may have extended its range N to the Great Caucasus (*BWP*). At least 100 000bp occur in Turkey. Despite its wide distribution, it is generally scarce or only locally common. It usually remains on the ground and difficult to census. It rarely uses trees and bushes, normally only as song-posts.

A ground-nester, its breeding season begins in June and July but varies with altitude. Northern populations in C Asia are short-distance migrants and fly E to winter in NC China (Clement *et al* 1993). Most populations are sedentary, though altitudinal migration may occur in response to severe weather, particularly heavy snowfalls; the affected birds then winter in low-lying bare areas, including arable cultivation (*BWP*). Agricultural intensification would reduce the species' preferred wintering habitat. Formerly considered rare in C Turkey, its present widespread status there (though only locally common; Roselaar 1995) may suggest an increase.

Simon Gillings (GB) Philip Jackson (GB)

Emberiza buchanani

Grey-necked Bunting

CZ	Strnad Buchananův	I	Ortolano collogrigio
D	Steinortolan	NL	Steenortolaan
E	Escribano Cabecigrís	P	Escrevedeira-serrana
F	Bruant à cou gris	PL	Trznadel skalny
FIN	Kivikkosirkku	R	Скалистая овсянка
G	Σταχτοτράχηλο Τσιχλόνι	S	Bergortolansparv
H	Hegyi sármány		

Non-SPEC, Threat status S (P)

The south-eastern counterpart of the Cinereous Bunting *E. cineracea*, this species breeds in the montane temperate and warm temperate zones of the Caucasus (its only occurrence in the *Atlas*' area), C Asia, Kazakhstan and the southern Altai (Flint *et al* 1984).

In most of its range the species occurs at 900m –1400m asl. In these areas birds inhabit dry, rocky, sparsely vegetated slopes. However, in Afghanistan the species is numerous amongst tussock grass on slopes at 3000m asl (*BWP*). In all regions patches of grass and other xerophytic plants such as spurge *Euphorbia* form essential habitat (Ali & Ripley 1974) but wooded slopes are avoided. In these respects the Ortolan Bunting *E. hortulana* can be considered a low-altitude ecological counterpart, though the two may overlap at medium altitudes (*BWP*).

The Grey-necked Bunting is migratory, southern populations leaving in September and northern populations as early as the first week of August (*BWP*). Caucasian birds migrate south-eastward to winter in the subtropical and tropical zones of Pakistan and W India. There it typically occupies more barren and arid areas than the Ortolan Bunting, occasionally on agricultural stubbles (C. Harrison 1982). Birds return to their breeding areas in late April (Jonsson 1992) and nest from May onwards (Flint *et al* 1984). Nests are on the ground, often protected by a bush or overhanging vegetation.

Few demographic data exist but *BWP* found no reports of range or population changes. Flint *et al* (1984) state that the species occurs in pairs or flocks.

Simon Gillings (GB) Philip Jackson (GB)

The Conservation Status of Europe's Birds

(Adapted from Tucker and Heath 1994)

INTRODUCTION

Information on the conservation status of the species described in this *Atlas* is given at the top of each species account. This is based on an assessment carried out by BirdLife International and published in *Birds in Europe: their conservation status* (Tucker and Heath 1994). That publication reviewed the conservation status of all birds in Europe through the documentation and analysis of current knowledge on species populations and trends and, for the first time, provided a full picture of what is happening to Europe's avifauna. The following account (adapted from *Birds in Europe*) provides some background information on this assessment and its implications for the conservation of Europe's avifauna.

DATA COLLECTION

To assess the conservation status of Europe's birds reliably and comprehensively, it was necessary to obtain detailed population information on all species, in each European country, for both breeding and midwinter populations. To do this, BirdLife collaborated widely with Europe's ornithologists through the BirdLife International network of Partners, Sections and Representatives in conjunction with the European Ornithological Atlas project, resulting in contributions from several hundred professional and amateur ornithologists.

As detailed in the **History** section, BirdLife collaboration with the European Ornithological Atlas project dates back to 1990. When the European Ornithological Atlas Committee (EOAC) questionnaire was already in use, BirdLife International started its Dispersed Species Project, the first phase of which aimed to assess the conservation status of all birds in Europe with a view to identifying those in urgent need of conservation action. This required data on national population sizes and trends. To avoid duplication of effort and to ensure consistency between the data-sets, BirdLife International and EOAC decided to combine their questionnaires into a single cooperative project. Having computerized the data so far obtained by EOAC, BirdLife used its European network, in collaboration with the European Atlas contributors, to update existing data, to obtain data from the countries that had not so far contributed, and to obtain the midwinter population data and other additional information required for the Dispersed Species Project.

Data on the following were collected for breeding and wintering populations from each country:

- Population size
- Population trend (over the period 1970–1990)
- Range trend (over the period 1970–1990)

Some of these breeding population size and trend data are presented in the bar-charts in the species accounts in this *Atlas*. **Table 2** (following the **Introduction**) lists and defines the Population Codes, and Population and Range Trend Codes.

ASSESSMENT OF CONSERVATION STATUS

The aim of the assessment was to identify species that are of conservation concern on a European scale. The definition of Europe covered by *Birds in Europe* also included the Canary Islands, Turkey and Cyprus. These birds are termed Species of European Conservation Concern (SPECs) and are divided into four categories (**Table 4**) depending on their global conservation status, the proportion of their world population in Europe and their European Threat Status (see **Diagram 1**). Species are considered to have an Unfavourable Conservation Status if their European Threat Status is Localized, Declining, Rare, Vulnerable, Endangered or Insufficiently Known in Europe according to the criteria summarized in **Table 5** and

Table 4

Species of European Conservation Concern (SPECs).

Category 1 Species of global conservation concern because they are classified as Globally Threatened, Conservation Dependent or Data Deficient in *Birds to Watch 2: the World List of Threatened Birds* (Collar *et al.* 1994).

Category 2 Species whose global populations are concentrated in Europe (i.e. more than 50% of their global population or range in Europe) and which have an Unfavourable Conservation Status in Europe (see Table 7).

Category 3 Species whose global populations are not concentrated in Europe, but which have an Unfavourable Conservation Status in Europe.

Category 4 Species whose global populations are concentrated in Europe (i.e. species with more than 50% of their global population or range in Europe) but which have a Favourable Conservation Status in Europe (see Table 7).

described in full in **Table 6** (see **Table 7** for definition and explanation of terms).

The criteria for identifying SPECs and the European Threat Status of each species take into consideration the quality and availability of information on European bird populations. Thus, calculations are based on categories of population trend, rather than on precise figures. Also, to take account of the broad ranges involved in most estimates of population size, analyses were performed using both population minima and maxima, and, as a precautionary measure, the higher of the two resulting population decline levels was used in the assessment of a species' European Threat Status.

The assessment of European Threat Status was based on the percentage of the total European population which occurs in countries where populations have declined. Due to data limitations it was not possible to use an exact measure of population decline in each country to calculate the rate of a species' decline in Europe as a whole. Consequently, a species that has, for example, 45% of its population in

Table 5

Summary of European Threat Status criteria and categories.

Criteria: European population size/trend	<250 pairs	<2,500 pairs	<10,000 pairs	>10,000 pairs
Large decline	ENDANGERED	ENDANGERED	ENDANGERED	VULNERABLE
Moderate decline	ENDANGERED	ENDANGERED	VULNERABLE	DECLINING
No decline	ENDANGERED	VULNERABLE	RARE	SECURE

In addition, species that have more than 10,000 pairs in Europe are categorized as LOCALIZED if more than 90% of the population occurs at 10 sites or fewer. See Tables 6 and 7 for full details of criteria.

Notes

- Winter population criteria use flyway population levels of less than 1,000, 10,000 and 40,000 individuals as respective equivalents to the figures of 250, 2,500 and 10,000 pairs used above for breeding populations.
- Due to inadequate data for most species, declines in winter populations are only considered for Anatidae, Haematopodidae, Charadriidae and Scolopacidae.

Table 6

Classification of European Threat Status.

All population size thresholds refer to minimum population estimates.

Insufficiently Known Suspected to be Localized, Declining, Rare, Vulnerable or Endangered (as below), but insufficient information is available to attribute a European Threat Status, even provisionally.

Remaining categories are ranked here in ascending order of threat.

Secure Population more than 10,000 breeding pairs or 40,000 wintering birds, and neither in moderate or large decline nor Localized. Secure species have a Favourable Conservation Status.

Localized Population more than 10,000 breeding pairs or 40,000 wintering birds, and neither in moderate nor in large decline, but with more than 90% of the population occurring at 10 or fewer sites (Important Bird Areas), as listed in Grimmett and Jones (1989).

Declining Population in moderate decline (see Table 7) and population more than 10,000 breeding pairs or 40,000 wintering individuals.

Rare Population neither in moderate nor in large decline but fewer than 10,000 breeding pairs and not marginal to a larger non-European population; or European wintering population and entire flyway population less than 40,000 birds and therefore at risk due to the susceptibility of small populations to:
- break-up of social structure;
- loss of genetic diversity;
- large-scale population fluctuations and chance events;
- existing or potential exploitation, persecution, disturbance and interference by man.

Vulnerable Any of the following.
- Population in large decline (see Table 7) and of more than 10,000 breeding pairs or 40,000 wintering individuals.
- Population in moderate decline *and* population fewer than 10,000 breeding pairs and not marginal to a larger non-European population or European wintering and entire flyway population fewer than 40,000 birds.
- Population neither in moderate nor in large decline but fewer than 2,500 breeding pairs and not marginal to a larger non-European population; or European wintering and entire flyway population fewer than 10,000 birds and therefore at risk due to the susceptibility of small populations to the factors described under 'Rare' above.

Endangered Any of the following.
- Population in large decline *and* population fewer than 10,000 breeding pairs and not marginal to a larger non-European population or European wintering and entire flyway population fewer than 40,000 birds.
- Population in moderate decline *and* population fewer than 2,500 breeding pairs and not marginal to a larger non-European population or European wintering and entire flyway population fewer than 10,000 birds.
- Population neither in moderate nor in large decline but fewer than 250 breeding pairs and not marginal to a larger non-European population; or European wintering and entire flyway population fewer than 1,000 birds and therefore at risk due to the susceptibility of small populations to factors described above.

Diagram 1

The classification of Species of European Conservation Concern (SPECs).

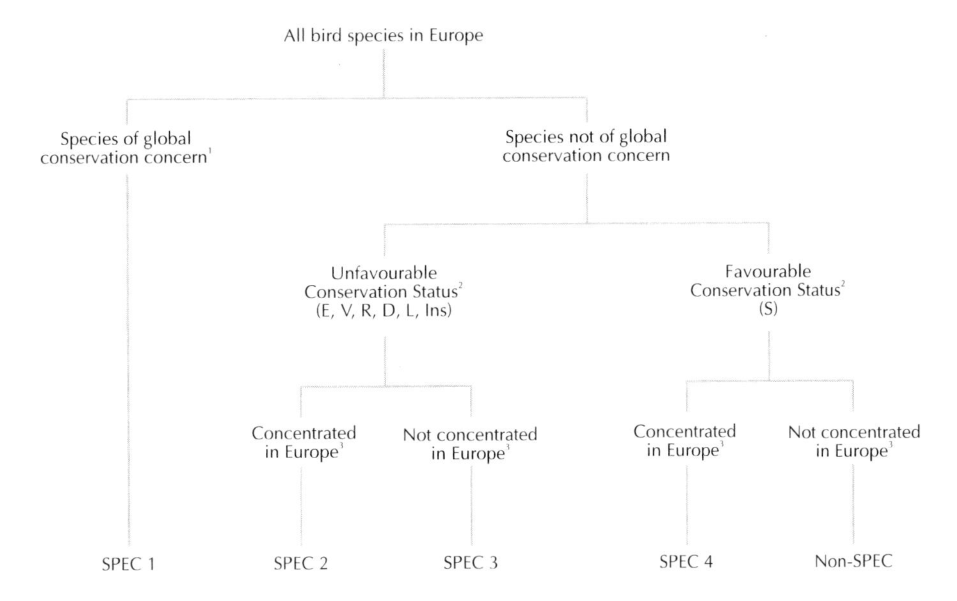

[1] Species listed as Globally Threatened, Conservation Dependent or Data Deficient by Collar *et al.* (1994).
[2] Determined by European Threat Status:
E Endangered V Vulnerable R Rare D Declining L Localized Ins Insufficiently Known S Secure
A European Threat Status category is also assigned to SPEC 1 species but these species are not dependent on this for their SPEC classification.
[3] Concentrated in Europe: species with more than 50% of their global population or range lying within Europe.

countries where it has declined by 20–49% could have a higher overall rate of decline than a species that has 70% of its population in countries where it has declined by 20–49%. Also, assessments of the decline in range were based on the percentage of the European population (rather than range) occurring in countries where range has declined. Inevitably therefore, range declines in large populations were given greater weight than those in marginal parts of the range.

Despite the use of flexible and easily applied criteria, data limitations sometimes meant that it was prudent to allocate European Threat Status categories only provisionally. This was the case when: more than 50% of the population size data were of poor or unknown quality; or more than 50% of the population or range trend data were poor, unknown or missing. Provisional categories are indicated in parenthesis. The assessments of European Threat Status

Table 7

Definitions of terms used in the criteria.

Concentrated in Europe More than 50% of the species' breeding or wintering population or range occurs in Europe, according to range maps in Cramp *et al.* (1977–1993) or Harrison (1982) or to global population estimates where available.

Conservation Dependent A species which does not qualify as Globally Threatened but is the focus of a continuing conservation programme, the cessation of which would result in the species qualifying as Globally Threatened (Collar *et al.* 1994).

Data Deficient A species for which there is inadequate information to make a direct or indirect assessment of its risk of global extinction (Collar *et al.* 1994).

Favourable Conservation Status The European Threat Status is classed as Secure (see Table 6).

Large decline Applied to a breeding or wintering population which has declined in size or range by at least 20% in at least 66% of the population or by at least 50% in at least 25% of the population between 1970 and 1990, and where the total size of populations that declined is greater than the total size of populations that increased. Only wintering populations of waterbirds of the families Anatidae, Haematopodidae, Charadriidae and Scolopacidae are considered because these are typically the only species which have well monitored winter populations.

Marginal population European populations that are considered to have adequate potential for repopulation from large non-European populations (the combined total of which is 10,000 pairs or more) and which are therefore not at risk from small population size.

Moderate decline Applied to a breeding or wintering population which has declined in size or range by at least 20% in 33–65% of the population or by at least 50% in 12–24% of the population between 1970 and 1990, and where the total size of populations that declined is greater than the total size of populations that increased. See also 'Large decline' (above) for restriction on species covered.

Unfavourable Conservation Status The European Threat Status is classed as Endangered, Vulnerable, Rare, Declining, Localized or Insufficiently Known (see Table 6).

were made on the basis of breeding season data unless a species qualified on winter data. Assessment of overall population trends solely on the basis of the available quantitative data would introduce regional biases and would therefore be invalid. Bird populations in E and SE Europe, for example, are particularly poorly known, largely due to the lower number of ornithologists in these regions. Clearly, the population trends in these areas may often be different from those in other parts of Europe.

For selected well-monitored waterbirds the identification of SPECs and the assessment of European Threat Status was carried out separately on breeding and on wintering populations. SPEC and European Threat Status categories were allocated according to breeding population data if these categories indicate an equal or higher degree of threat than those based on winter populations. This is because winter populations may well be inadequately monitored and declines may be obscured by variable immigration from Europe and by influxes of migrants from outside the region. Consequently, conservation measures should cover the whole year for such species when they winter in significant numbers in Europe. However, it would often be inappropriate to apply a higher SPEC category to breeding populations where this is based on winter populations, as breeding and wintering populations may differ considerably in both size and origin. Conservation measures for breeding populations could be misplaced for such birds, especially where breeding populations are apparently secure. In such circumstances, therefore, SPEC and European Threat Status categories are given for both breeding and winter populations. If a species only qualifies as a SPEC according to winter data then this is indicated.

The importance of this assessment is that it allows national priorities to be put into an international framework. Although many countries have already produced lists of nationally threatened species, their national conservation aims and therefore their species selection criteria may often differ from those appropriate to a European scale. Now, the overall European population trends of species should be taken into account in assessing national conservation priorities.

In general, conservation importance should be allocated according to SPEC category (ie highest importance given to the conservation of species of global concern, category 1) and the urgency for action should take into account the species' European Threat Status. However, the SPEC category and European Threat Status alone do not necessarily indicate the importance of, or urgency for, conservation actions at the national level. Assessment of these should also take into account the proportion of the global and European populations in the country, the species' national population status, the potential for successful action, its costs, the species' potential as a 'flagship' to promote conservation, the effects of action on other species, and other logistical, political and strategic considerations.

Therefore absence of a species from the SPEC list or its allocation to a low European Threat Status does not justify its exclusion from national conservation actions or from regional European programmes (eg within the European Union), as the maintenance of regional European and national bird diversities and population levels is highly desirable. Rather, recognition as a Species of European Conservation Concern should be regarded as an additional justification for conservation measures.

OVERVIEW OF RESULTS

Birds in Europe revealed that of the 514 species regularly occurring in Europe, 278 qualify as being Species of European Conservation Concern (**Diagram 2**). Twenty-four of these are of global conservation concern (SPEC category 1) and are clearly of highest conservation importance, requiring stringent conservation measures wherever they occur regularly. This is particularly important in cases where Europe holds large proportions, or all, of their world populations, and especially when they are also highly threatened, as is the case of the Spanish Imperial Eagle *Aquila adalberti*.

In total, 195 of the 278 species have an Unfavourable Conservation Status (SPEC categories 1–3) because their populations are either declining, or are small and non-marginal, or are highly localized in Europe. These species comprise approximately 38% of the European avifauna. A further 83 species fall into SPEC category 4 because, although they have a Favourable Conservation Status, the majority of their breeding or midwinter populations are in Europe. Although their European populations are not currently at risk, Europe has a special responsibility for these species and should take measures to safeguard and monitor their numbers. Such species would immediately qualify for SPEC category 2 if their conservation status were to become unfavourable, and in some cases they could quickly become Globally Threatened, especially where their populations or ranges are small. Furthermore, 23 of the SPEC category 4 species (28%) are only provisionally regarded as secure, such as Little Crake *Porzana parva*,

Diagram 2

The proportion of European species within each category of Species of European Conservation Concern (SPEC).

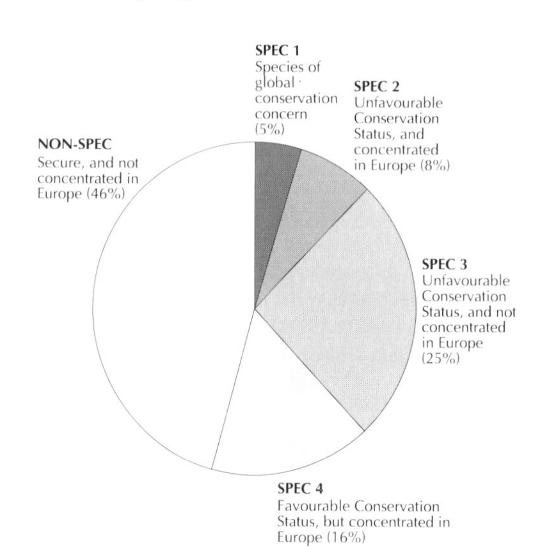

The BirdLife listing of species occurring regularly in Europe (inclusive of the Canary Islands, Turkey in Asia Minor and Cyprus) comprises Appendix 1 of *Birds in Europe: their conservation status*, Tucker & Heath 1994, p470 *et seq, qv*.

Ruff *Philomachus pugnax* and Nightingale *Luscinia megarhynchos*, and should therefore be subject to particular scrutiny.

Of those species with an Unfavourable Conservation Status, 33 are considered to be Endangered in Europe and are thus particularly in need of urgent conservation actions, or the continuation of conservation programmes where these are already in place. Also of particular concern is the high proportion of European species that are subject to a substantial decline, and indeed, 101 species qualify as having an Unfavourable Conservation Status on this criterion alone (39 have shown moderate declines and therefore qualify as Declining, while 62 have shown large declines and are classed as Vulnerable). More alarming still, however, is the fact that the total number of declining species, including those that qualify on other threat criteria, amounts to 129 (25% of all European species), and 86 of these have shown large declines.

Nineteen species are classed as Rare and, although these species may not be declining, they are at some risk due to their susceptibility to the effects of population fluctuations, natural catastrophes, existing or potential exploitation, persecution, disturbance or other forms of human interference. Isolated and particularly small or fragmented populations may also be subject to the detrimental effects of loss of genetic diversity and disruptions to social behaviour or may simply be prone to extinction through the cumulative effects of chance demographic events.

Sixteen species are classed as Localized and are therefore susceptible because of their dependence on a small number of sites. Consequently, although these species may not currently be affected by detrimental environmental changes, they are dependent on the protection and appropriate management of their key sites, important for species whose global populations are concentrated in Europe, such as Storm Petrel *Hydrobates pelagicus* and Gannet *Morus bassanus*.

Scottish Crossbill *Loxia scotica* and three Caucasus species are classed as Insufficiently Known and require studies to assess their population sizes and trends and, in the case of the crossbill, its taxonomic status. However, in the meantime, conservation measures should be taken as appropriate according to the precautionary principle that the benefit of doubt over a species' status should rest with the species until proven otherwise.

Some 29 species covered in *Birds in Europe* either breed outside the *Atlas*' coverage area, or winter but do not breed in the *Atlas*' coverage area. Conversely, the *Atlas* includes a number of species not covered in *Birds in Europe* – species recorded as possibly breeding in Europe (as defined by the *Atlas*), species that breed irregularly in tiny numbers in Europe, or species that have become naturalized.

CONSERVATION STRATEGY

The results presented in *Birds in Europe* are very clear: the numbers, range and overall diversity of European birds are under considerable threat from widespread environmental change, largely as a result of the growing intensity of land use over the continent. Furthermore, since birds act as good environmental indicators, these conclusions have serious implications regarding the health of the European environment in general.

In the short term, targeted conservation action is needed for bird species classified as SPECs. Measures which to date have mainly focused on site conservation and species protection, must be reinforced. However, from now on, much greater emphasis must be given to incorporating environmental considerations into the management of the wider countryside. Therefore a European bird conservation strategy with the following three components should be developed and implemented by all relevant agencies:

a. Protection of species from persecution and over-exploitation through the strengthening and effective enforcement of species-protection laws, and the development of hunting management plans and regulations that ensure sustainable use of species.

b. Conservation of sites through the full protection of all those classified as Important Bird Areas (Grimmett and Jones 1989, Heath in prep), and the development and implementation of management plans for them.

c. Conservation in the wider environment through tighter regulation of pollution and the integration of environmental objectives into all land-use policies, especially those relating to agriculture, fisheries, forestry and water management.

Also of fundamental importance is the development of a European bird monitoring strategy. Indeed for some species in some countries available data are insufficient to assess population size and trends reliably. This fact was taken into account in the review but in the long term the adequate censusing and monitoring of all species in all countries is essential to improve the reliability and accuracy of assessments of conservation status. Indeed it should be the responsibility of all governments to ensure that the effects of land-use activities on the environment, including its biodiversity, are adequately monitored (as, for example, stipulated in Article 7 of the Convention on Biological Diversity). *Birds in Europe* demonstrates the value of monitoring studies and at the same time the urgent need for better information. In the longer term it is hoped that this study will stimulate and further the growth of bird monitoring throughout Europe and contribute to the development of a European bird monitoring strategy.

Melanie Heath & Graham Tucker

Species Included in the *Atlas*: EURING code, SPEC Category and Threat Status

The Categories and assessment of Threat Status are explained in the preceding chapter (notes to Diagram 1 list the abbreviations used for Threat Status). (P) represents Provisional Threat Status.

EURING code	*Scientific name*	*SPEC Category*	*Threat Status*
00020	Gavia stellata	3	V
00030	Gavia arctica	3	V
00040	Gavia immer	Non-SPEC	S (P)
00050	Gavia adamsii	Non-SPEC	S (P)
00070	Tachybaptus ruficollis	Non-SPEC	S
00090	Podiceps cristatus	Non-SPEC	S
00100	Podiceps grisegena	Non-SPEC	S
00110	Podiceps auritus	Non-SPEC	S (P)
00120	Podiceps nigricollis	Non-SPEC	S
00220	Fulmarus glacialis	Non-SPEC	S
00262	Pterodroma feae	1	E
00263	Pterodroma madeira	1	E
00340	Bulweria bulwerii	3	V
00360	Calonectris diomedea	2	V (P)
00461	Puffinus puffinus	2	L (P)
00462	Puffinus yelkouan	4	S
00463	Puffinus mauretanicus	Criteria not applied	
00480	Puffinus assimilis	3	V
00510	Pelagodroma marina	3	L
00520	Hydrobates pelagicus	2	L (P)
00550	Oceanodroma leucorhoa	3	L (P)
00560	Oceanodroma monorhis	Criteria not applied	
00580	Oceanodroma castro	3	V
00640	Phaethon aethereus	Criteria not applied	
00710	Morus bassanus	2	L
00720	Phalacrocorax carbo	Non-SPEC	S
00800	Phalacrocorax aristotelis	4	S
00820	Phalacrocorax pygmeus	2	V
00880	Pelecanus onocrotalus	3	R
00890	Pelecanus crispus	1	V
00950	Botaurus stellaris	3	V (P)
00980	Ixobrychus minutus	3	V (P)
01040	Nycticorax nycticorax	3	D
01080	Ardeola ralloides	3	V
01110	Bubulcus ibis	Non-SPEC	S
01190	Egretta garzetta	Non-SPEC	S
01210	Egretta alba	Non-SPEC	S
01220	Ardea cinerea	Non-SPEC	S
01240	Ardea purpurea	3	V
01310	Ciconia nigra	3	R
01340	Ciconia ciconia	2	V
01360	Plegadis falcinellus	3	D
01440	Platalea leucorodia	2	E
01470	Phoenicopterus ruber	3	L
01520	Cygnus olor	Non-SPEC	S
01530	Cygnus columbianus	3*W	L*W
01540	Cygnus cygnus	4*W	S
01570	Anser fabalis	Non-SPEC	S
01580	Anser brachyrhynchus	4	S
01590	Anser albifrons	Non-SPEC	S
01600	Anser erythropus	1	V
01610	Anser anser	Non-SPEC	S
01660	Branta canadensis	Criteria not applied	
01670	Branta leucopsis	4/2	L*W
01680	Branta bernicla	3	V
01700	Alopochen aegyptiacus	Criteria not applied	
01710	Tadorna ferruginea	3	V
01730	Tadorna tadorna	Non-SPEC	S
01770	Aix sponsa	Criteria not applied	
01780	Aix galericulata	Criteria not applied	
01790	Anas penelope	Non-SPEC	S
01820	Anas strepera	3	V
01840	Anas crecca	Non-SPEC	S
01860	Anas platyrhynchos	Non-SPEC	S
01890	Anas acuta	3	V
01910	Anas querquedula	3	V
01940	Anas clypeata	Non-SPEC	S
01950	Marmaronetta angustirostris	1	E
01960	Netta rufina	3	D
01980	Aythya ferina	4	S
02020	Aythya nyroca	1	V
02030	Aythya fuligula	Non-SPEC	S
02040	Aythya marila	3*W	L*W
02060	Somateria mollissima	Non-SPEC	S
02070	Somateria spectabilis	Non-SPEC	S
02090	Polysticta stelleri	1	L*W
02110	Histrionicus histrionicus	3	V
02120	Clangula hyemalis	Non-SPEC	S
02130	Melanitta nigra	Non-SPEC	S
02150	Melanitta fusca	3*W	L*W
02170	Bucephala islandica	3	E
02180	Bucephala clangula	Non-SPEC	S

EURING code	Scientific name	SPEC Category	Threat Status
02200	Mergus albellus	3	V
02210	Mergus serrator	Non-SPEC	S
02230	Mergus merganser	Non-SPEC	S
02250	Oxyura jamaicensis	Criteria not applied	
02260	Oxyura leucocephala	1	E
02310	Pernis apivorus	4	S
02350	Elanus caeruleus	3	V
02380	Milvus migrans	3	V
02390	Milvus milvus	4	S
02430	Haliaeetus albicilla	3	R
02460	Gypaetus barbatus	3	E
02470	Neophron percnopterus	3	E
02510	Gyps fulvus	3	R
02550	Aegypius monachus	3	V
02560	Circaetus gallicus	3	R
02600	Circus aeruginosus	Non-SPEC	S
02610	Circus cyaneus	3	V
02620	Circus macrourus	3	E
02630	Circus pygargus	4	S
02670	Accipiter gentilis	Non-SPEC	S
02690	Accipiter nisus	Non-SPEC	S
02730	Accipiter brevipes	2	R
02870	Buteo buteo	Non-SPEC	S
02880	Buteo rufinus	3	E (P)
02900	Buteo lagopus	Non-SPEC	S
02920	Aquila pomarina	3	R
02930	Aquila clanga	1	E
02942	Aquila nipalensis	3	V
02951	Aquila heliaca	1	E
02952	Aquila adalberti	1	E
02960	Aquila chrysaetos	3	R
02980	Hieraaetus pennatus	3	R
02990	Hieraaetus fasciatus	3	E
03010	Pandion haliaetus	3	R
03030	Falco naumanni	1	V (P)
03040	Falco tinnunculus	3	D
03070	Falco vespertinus	3	V
03090	Falco columbarius	Non-SPEC	S
03100	Falco subbuteo	Non-SPEC	S
03110	Falco eleonorae	2	R
03140	Falco biarmicus	3	E (P)
03160	Falco cherrug	3	E
03180	Falco rusticolus	3	V
03200	Falco peregrinus	3	R
03260	Bonasa bonasia	Non-SPEC	S
03290	Lagopus lagopus	Non-SPEC	S
03300	Lagopus mutus	Non-SPEC	S
03320	Tetrao tetrix	3	V
03330	Tetrao mlokosiewiczi	2	INS
03350	Tetrao urogallus	Non-SPEC	S (P)
03410	Callipepla californica	Criteria not applied	
03450	Colinus virginianus	Criteria not applied	
03500	Tetraogallus caucasicus	4	S
03510	Tetraogallus caspius	3	INS
03550	Alectoris chukar	3	V
03570	Alectoris graeca	2	V (P)
03580	Alectoris rufa	2	V
03590	Alectoris barbara	3	E (P)
03640	Francolinus francolinus	3	V
03670	Perdix perdix	3	V
03700	Coturnix coturnix	3	V
03930	Syrmaticus reevesii	Criteria not applied	
03940	Phasianus colchicus	Non-SPEC	S
03960	Chrysolophus pictus	Criteria not applied	
03970	Chrysolophus amherstiae	Criteria not applied	
03990	Meleagris gallopavo	Criteria not applied	
04000	Turnix sylvatica	3	E
04070	Rallus aquaticus	Non-SPEC	S (P)
04080	Porzana porzana	4	S
04100	Porzana parva	4	S (P)
04110	Porzana pusilla	3	R
04210	Crex crex	1	V
04240	Gallinula chloropus	Non-SPEC	S
04270	Porphyrio porphyrio	3	R
04290	Fulica atra	Non-SPEC	S
04310	Fulica cristata	3	E
04330	Grus grus	3	V
04410	Anthropoides virgo	Non-SPEC	S
04420	Tetrax tetrax	2	V
04460	Otis tarda	1	D
04500	Haematopus ostralegus	Non-SPEC	S
04550	Himantopus himantopus	Non-SPEC	S
04560	Recurvirostra avosetta	4/3*W	L*W
04590	Burhinus oedicnemus	3	V
04650	Glareola pratincola	3	E
04670	Glareola nordmanni	3	R
04690	Charadrius dubius	Non-SPEC	S (P)
04700	Charadrius hiaticula	Non-SPEC	S
04770	Charadrius alexandrinus	3	D
04790	Charadrius leschenaultii	3	E (P)
04800	Charadrius asiaticus	3	V (P)
04820	Charadrius morinellus	Non-SPEC	S (P)
04842	Pluvialis fulva	Criteria not applied	
04850	Pluvialis apricaria	4	S
04860	Pluvialis squatarola	Non-SPEC	S (P)
04870	Hoplopterus spinosus	3	E (P)
04910	Chettusia gregaria	1	E
04920	Chettusia leucura	Non-SPEC	S (P)
04930	Vanellus vanellus	Non-SPEC	S (P)
04960	Calidris canutus	3*W	L*W
04970	Calidris alba	Non-SPEC	S
05010	Calidris minuta	Non-SPEC	S (P)
05020	Calidris temminckii	Non-SPEC	S (P)
05070	Calidris melanotos	Criteria not applied	
05100	Calidris maritima	4	S (P)
05120	Calidris alpina	3*W	V*W
05140	Limicola falcinellus	3	V (P)
05170	Philomachus pugnax	4	S (P)
05180	Lymnocryptes minimus	3*W	V*W (P)
05190	Gallinago gallinago	Non-SPEC	S (P)
05200	Gallinago media	2	V (P)
05210	Gallinago stenura	Non-SPEC	S
05290	Scolopax rusticola	3*W	V*W
05320	Limosa limosa	2	V
05340	Limosa lapponica	3*W	L*W
05380	Numenius phaeopus	4	S (P)
05400	Numenius tenuirostris	1	(known only on passage)
05410	Numenius arquata	3*W	D*W
05450	Tringa erythropus	Non-SPEC	S

EURING code	*Scientific name*	*SPEC Category*	*Threat Status*
05460	Tringa totanus	2	D
05470	Tringa stagnatilis	Non-SPEC	S (P)
05480	Tringa nebularia	Non-SPEC	S
05530	Tringa ochropus	Non-SPEC	S (P)
05540	Tringa glareola	3	D
05550	Xenus cinereus	Non-SPEC	S (P)
05560	Actitis hypoleucos	Non-SPEC	S
05610	Arenaria interpres	Non-SPEC	S
05640	Phalaropus lobatus	Non-SPEC	S (P)
05650	Phalaropus fulicarius	Non-SPEC	S (P)
05660	Stercorarius pomarinus	Non-SPEC	S (P)
05670	Stercorarius parasiticus	Non-SPEC	S (P)
05680	Stercorarius longicaudus	Non-SPEC	S (P)
05690	Stercorarius skua	4	S
05730	Larus ichthyaetus	Non-SPEC	S
05750	Larus melanocephalus	4	S
05780	Larus minutus	3	D
05790	Larus sabini	Non-SPEC	S
05820	Larus ridibundus	Non-SPEC	S
05850	Larus genei	Non-SPEC	S (P)
05880	Larus audouinii	1	L
05900	Larus canus	2	D
05910	Larus fuscus	4	S
05920	Larus argentatus	Non-SPEC	S
05927	Larus cachinnans	Non-SPEC	S (P)
05929	Larus armenicus	Non-SPEC	S (P)
05980	Larus glaucoides	Non-SPEC	S (P)
05990	Larus hyperboreus	Non-SPEC	S
06000	Larus marinus	4	S
06020	Rissa tridactyla	Non-SPEC	S
06040	Pagophila eburnea	3	E (P)
06050	Gelochelidon nilotica	3	E (P)
06060	Sterna caspia	3	E (P)
06090	Sterna bengalensis	Criteria not applied	
06110	Sterna sandvicensis	2	D
06120	Sterna elegans	Criteria not applied	
06140	Sterna dougallii	3	E
06150	Sterna hirundo	Non-SPEC	S
06160	Sterna paradisaea	Non-SPEC	S
06230	Sterna fuscata	Criteria not applied	
06240	Sterna albifrons	3	D
06260	Chlidonias hybridus	3	D
06270	Chlidonias niger	3	D
06280	Chlidonias leucopterus	Non-SPEC	S
06340	Uria aalge	Non-SPEC	S
06350	Uria lomvia	Non-SPEC	S
06360	Alca torda	4	S
06380	Cepphus grylle	2	D
06470	Alle alle	Non-SPEC	S (P)
06540	Fratercula arctica	2	V
06610	Pterocles orientalis	3	V
06620	Pterocles alchata	3	E
06650/1	Columba livia	Non-SPEC	S
06680	Columba oenas	4	S
06700	Columba palumbus	4	S
06710	Columba trocaz	1	V
06840	Streptopelia decaocto	Non-SPEC	S (P)
06870	Streptopelia turtur	3	D
06900	Streptopelia senegalensis	Non-SPEC	S (P)
24999X	Myiopsitta monachus	Criteria not applied	
07120	Psittacula krameri	Criteria not applied	
07160	Clamator glandarius	Non-SPEC	S
07240	Cuculus canorus	Non-SPEC	S
07250	Cuculus saturatus	Non-SPEC	S (P)
07350	Tyto alba	3	D
07390	Otus scops	2	D (P)
07440	Bubo bubo	3	V
07490	Nyctea scandiaca	3	V
07500	Surnia ulula	Non-SPEC	S (P)
07510	Glaucidium passerinum	Non-SPEC	S (P)
07570	Athene noctua	3	D
07610	Strix aluco	4	S
07650	Strix uralensis	Non-SPEC	S (P)
07660	Strix nebulosa	Non-SPEC	S
07670	Asio otus	Non-SPEC	S
07680	Asio flammeus	3	V (P)
07700	Aegolius funereus	Non-SPEC	S (P)
07780	Caprimulgus europaeus	2	D (P)
07790	Caprimulgus ruficollis	Non-SPEC	S
07940	Apus unicolor	4	S
07950	Apus apus	Non-SPEC	S
07960	Apus pallidus	Non-SPEC	S (P)
07980	Apus melba	Non-SPEC	S (P)
07990	Apus caffer	Non-SPEC	S
08310	Alcedo atthis	3	D
08390	Merops superciliosus	Non-SPEC	S (P)
08400	Merops apiaster	3	D
08410	Coracias garrulus	2	D (P)
08460	Upupa epops	Non-SPEC	S
08480	Jynx torquilla	3	D
08550	Picus canus	3	D
08560	Picus viridis	2	D
08630	Dryocopus martius	Non-SPEC	S
08760	Dendrocopos major	Non-SPEC	S
08780	Dendrocopos syriacus	4	S (P)
08830	Dendrocopos medius	4	S
08840	Dendrocopos leucotos	Non-SPEC	S
08870	Dendrocopos minor	Non-SPEC	S
08980	Picoides tridactylus	3	D
09590	Chersophilus duponti	3	V
09610	Melanocorypha calandra	3	D (P)
09620	Melanocorypha bimaculata	Non-SPEC	S (P)
09650	Melanocorypha leucoptera	4*W	S (P)
09660	Melanocorypha yeltoniensis	3	V (P)
09680	Calandrella brachydactyla	3	V
09700	Calandrella rufescens	3	V
09720	Galerida cristata	3	D (P)
09730	Galerida theklae	3	V
09740	Lullula arborea	2	V
09760	Alauda arvensis	3	V
09780	Eremophila alpestris	Non-SPEC	S (P)
09810	Riparia riparia	3	D
09910	Ptyonoprogne rupestris	Non-SPEC	S
09920	Hirundo rustica	3	D
09950	Hirundo daurica	Non-SPEC	S
10010	Delichon urbica	Non-SPEC	S
10050	Anthus campestris	3	V
10060	Anthus berthelotii	4	S
10080	Anthus hodgsoni	Non-SPEC	S (P)
10090	Anthus trivialis	Non-SPEC	S

EURING code	*Scientific name*	*SPEC Category*	*Threat Status*
10110	Anthus pratensis	4	S
10120	Anthus cervinus	Non-SPEC	S (P)
10141	Anthus spinoletta	Non-SPEC	S
10142	Anthus petrosus	4	S
10170	Motacilla flava	Non-SPEC	S
10180	Motacilla citreola	Non-SPEC	S (P)
10190	Motacilla cinerea	Non-SPEC	S (P)
10200	Motacilla alba	Non-SPEC	S
10480	Bombycilla garrulus	Non-SPEC	S (P)
10500	Cinclus cinclus	Non-SPEC	S (P)
10660	Troglodytes troglodytes	Non-SPEC	S
10840	Prunella modularis	4	S
10860	Prunella montanella	Non-SPEC	S (P)
10880	Prunella ocularis	3	V (P)
10900	Prunella atrogularis	3	V (P)
10940	Prunella collaris	Non-SPEC	S
10950	Cercotrichas galactotes	Non-SPEC	S
10990	Erithacus rubecula	4	S
11030	Luscinia luscinia	4	S
11040	Luscinia megarhynchos	4	S (P)
11050	Luscinia calliope	Non-SPEC	S (P)
11060	Luscinia svecica	Non-SPEC	S
11130	Tarsiger cyanurus	Non-SPEC	S (P)
11170	Irania gutturalis	Non-SPEC	S (P)
11210	Phoenicurus ochruros	Non-SPEC	S
11220	Phoenicurus phoenicurus	2	V
11280	Phoenicurus erythrogaster	3	INS
11370	Saxicola rubetra	4	S
11390	Saxicola torquata	3	D (P)
11440	Oenanthe isabellina	Non-SPEC	S (P)
11460	Oenanthe oenanthe	Non-SPEC	S
11470	Oenanthe pleschanka	Non-SPEC	S (P)
11480	Oenanthe hispanica	2	V
11490	Oenanthe deserti	Non-SPEC	S (P)
11500	Oenanthe finschii	Non-SPEC	S (P)
11520	Oenanthe xanthoprymna	Non-SPEC	S (P)
11580	Oenanthe leucura	3	E
11620	Monticola saxatilis	3	D (P)
11660	Monticola solitarius	3	V (P)
11700	Zoothera dauma	Non-SPEC	S (P)
11860	Turdus torquatus	4	S
11870	Turdus merula	4	S
11970	Turdus ruficollis	Non-SPEC	S (P)
11980	Turdus pilaris	4*W	S
12000	Turdus philomelos	4	S
12010	Turdus iliacus	4*W	S
12020	Turdus viscivorus	4	S
12200	Cettia cetti	Non-SPEC	S
12260	Cisticola juncidis	Non-SPEC	S (P)
12350	Locustella lanceolata	Non-SPEC	S (P)
12360	Locustella naevia	4	S
12370	Locustella fluviatilis	4	S
12380	Locustella luscinioides	4	S (P)
12410	Acrocephalus melanopogon	Non-SPEC	S (P)
12420	Acrocephalus paludicola	1	E
12430	Acrocephalus schoenobaenus	4	S (P)
12470	Acrocephalus agricola	Non-SPEC	S
12480	Acrocephalus dumetorum	Non-SPEC	S (P)
12500	Acrocephalus palustris	4	S
12510	Acrocephalus scirpaceus	4	S
12530	Acrocephalus arundinaceus	Non-SPEC	S (P)
12550	Hippolais pallida	3	V (P)
12560	Hippolais caligata	Non-SPEC	S (P)
12570	Hippolais languida	Non-SPEC	S (P)
12580	Hippolais olivetorum	2	R (P)
12590	Hippolais icterina	4	S
12600	Hippolais polyglotta	4	S (P)
12610	Sylvia sarda	4	S (P)
12620	Sylvia undata	2	V
12640	Sylvia conspicillata	Non-SPEC	S (P)
12650	Sylvia cantillans	4	S
12660	Sylvia mystacea	Non-SPEC	S (P)
12670	Sylvia melanocephala	4	S
12690	Sylvia rueppelli	4	S (P)
12700	Sylvia nana	Non-SPEC	S (P)
12720	Sylvia hortensis	3	V
12730	Sylvia nisoria	4	S (P)
12740	Sylvia curruca	Non-SPEC	S
12750	Sylvia communis	4	S
12760	Sylvia borin	4	S
12770	Sylvia atricapilla	4	S
12910/30	Phylloscopus trochiloides	Non-SPEC	S (P)
12950	Phylloscopus borealis	Non-SPEC	S (P)
13000	Phylloscopus inornatus	Non-SPEC	S
13070	Phylloscopus bonelli	4	S
13080	Phylloscopus sibilatrix	4	S (P)
13102	Phylloscopus lorenzii	Non-SPEC	S (P)
13110	Phylloscopus collybita	Non-SPEC	S (P)
13120	Phylloscopus trochilus	Non-SPEC	S
13140	Regulus regulus	4	S (P)
13150	Regulus ignicapillus	4	S
13350	Muscicapa striata	3	D
13430	Ficedula parva	Non-SPEC	S (P)
13470	Ficedula semitorquata	2	E (P)
13480	Ficedula albicollis	4	S
13490	Ficedula hypoleuca	4	S
13640	Panurus biarmicus	Non-SPEC	S (P)
14370	Aegithalos caudatus	Non-SPEC	S
14400	Parus palustris	Non-SPEC	S
14410	Parus lugubris	4	S (P)
14420	Parus montanus	Non-SPEC	S (P)
14480	Parus cinctus	Non-SPEC	S (P)
14540	Parus cristatus	4	S
14610	Parus ater	Non-SPEC	S
14620	Parus caeruleus	4	S
14630	Parus cyanus	Non-SPEC	S (P)
14640	Parus major	Non-SPEC	S
14690	Sitta krueperi	4	S (P)
14700	Sitta whiteheadi	2	V
14790	Sitta europaea	Non-SPEC	S
14800	Sitta tephronota	Non-SPEC	S (P)
14810	Sitta neumayer	4	S (P)
14820	Tichodroma muraria	Non-SPEC	S (P)
14860	Certhia familiaris	Non-SPEC	S
14870	Certhia brachydactyla	4	S
14900	Remiz pendulinus	Non-SPEC	S (P)
15080	Oriolus oriolus	Non-SPEC	S
15150	Lanius collurio	3	D (P)
15190	Lanius minor	2	D (P)
15201	Lanius excubitor	3	D

EURING code	Scientific name	SPEC Category	Threat Status
15203	Lanius meridionalis	Criteria not applied	
15230	Lanius senator	2	V
15240	Lanius nubicus	2	V (P)
15390	Garrulus glandarius	Non-SPEC	S (P)
15430	Perisoreus infaustus	3	D (P)
15470	Cyanopica cyanus	Non-SPEC	S
15490	Pica pica	Non-SPEC	S
15570	Nucifraga caryocatactes	Non-SPEC	S (P)
15580	Pyrrhocorax graculus	Non-SPEC	S (P)
15590	Pyrrhocorax pyrrhocorax	3	V
15600	Corvus monedula	4	S (P)
15630	Corvus frugilegus	Non-SPEC	S
15670/3	Corvus corone	Non-SPEC	S
15720	Corvus corax	Non-SPEC	S (P)
15820	Sturnus vulgaris	Non-SPEC	S
15830	Sturnus unicolor	4	S
15840	Sturnus roseus	Non-SPEC	S (P)
15870	Acridotheres tristis	Criteria not applied	
15890	Acridotheres cristatellus	Criteria not applied	
15910	Passer domesticus	Non-SPEC	S
15912	Passer × italiae	Criteria not applied	
15920	Passer hispaniolensis	Non-SPEC	S (P)
15980	Passer montanus	Non-SPEC	S
16010	Carpospiza brachydactyla	Non-SPEC	S (P)
16040	Petronia petronia	Non-SPEC	S
16110	Montifringilla nivalis	Non-SPEC	S (P)
16150	Estrilda astrild	Criteria not applied	
24999Y	Estrilda melpoda	Criteria not applied	
20250	Amandava amandava	Criteria not applied	
16360	Fringilla coelebs	4	S
16380	Fringilla montifringilla	Non-SPEC	S
16390	Serinus pusillus	Non-SPEC	S (P)
16400	Serinus serinus	4	S
16420	Serinus canaria	4	S
16440	Serinus citrinella	4	S
16490	Carduelis chloris	4	S
16530	Carduelis carduelis	Non-SPEC	S (P)
16540	Carduelis spinus	4	S
16600	Carduelis cannabina	4	S
16620	Carduelis flavirostris	Non-SPEC	S
16630	Carduelis flammea	Non-SPEC	S (P)
16640	Carduelis hornemanni	Non-SPEC	S (P)
16650	Loxia leucoptera	Non-SPEC	S (P)
16660	Loxia curvirostra	Non-SPEC	S
16670	Loxia scotica	1	INS
16680	Loxia pytyopsittacus	4	S
16730	Rhodopechys sanguinea	Non-SPEC	S (P)
16750	Bucanetes mongolicus	Non-SPEC	S (P)
16760	Bucanetes githagineus	3	R
16790	Carpodacus erythrinus	Non-SPEC	S (P)
16960	Carpodacus rubicilla	3	E (P)
16990	Pinicola enucleator	Non-SPEC	S
17100	Pyrrhula pyrrhula	Non-SPEC	S
17105	Pyrrhula murina	Criteria not applied	
17170	Coccothraustes coccothraustes	Non-SPEC	S
18470	Calcarius lapponicus	Non-SPEC	S (P)
18500	Plectrophenax nivalis	Non-SPEC	S (P)
18560	Emberiza leucocephalos	Criteria not applied	
18570	Emberiza citrinella	4	S (P)
18580	Emberiza cirlus	4	S (P)
18600	Emberiza cia	3	V
18650	Emberiza cineracea	2	V (P)
18660	Emberiza hortulana	2	V (P)
18670	Emberiza buchanani	Non-SPEC	S (P)
18680	Emberiza caesia	4	S (P)
18730	Emberiza rustica	Non-SPEC	S (P)
18740	Emberiza pusilla	Non-SPEC	S (P)
18760	Emberiza aureola	Non-SPEC	S (P)
18770	Emberiza schoeniclus	Non-SPEC	S
18780	Emberiza pallasi	Criteria not applied	
18800	Emberiza bruniceps	Non-SPEC	S
18810	Emberiza melanocephala	2	V (P)
18820	Miliaria calandra	4	S (P)

Derived Maps

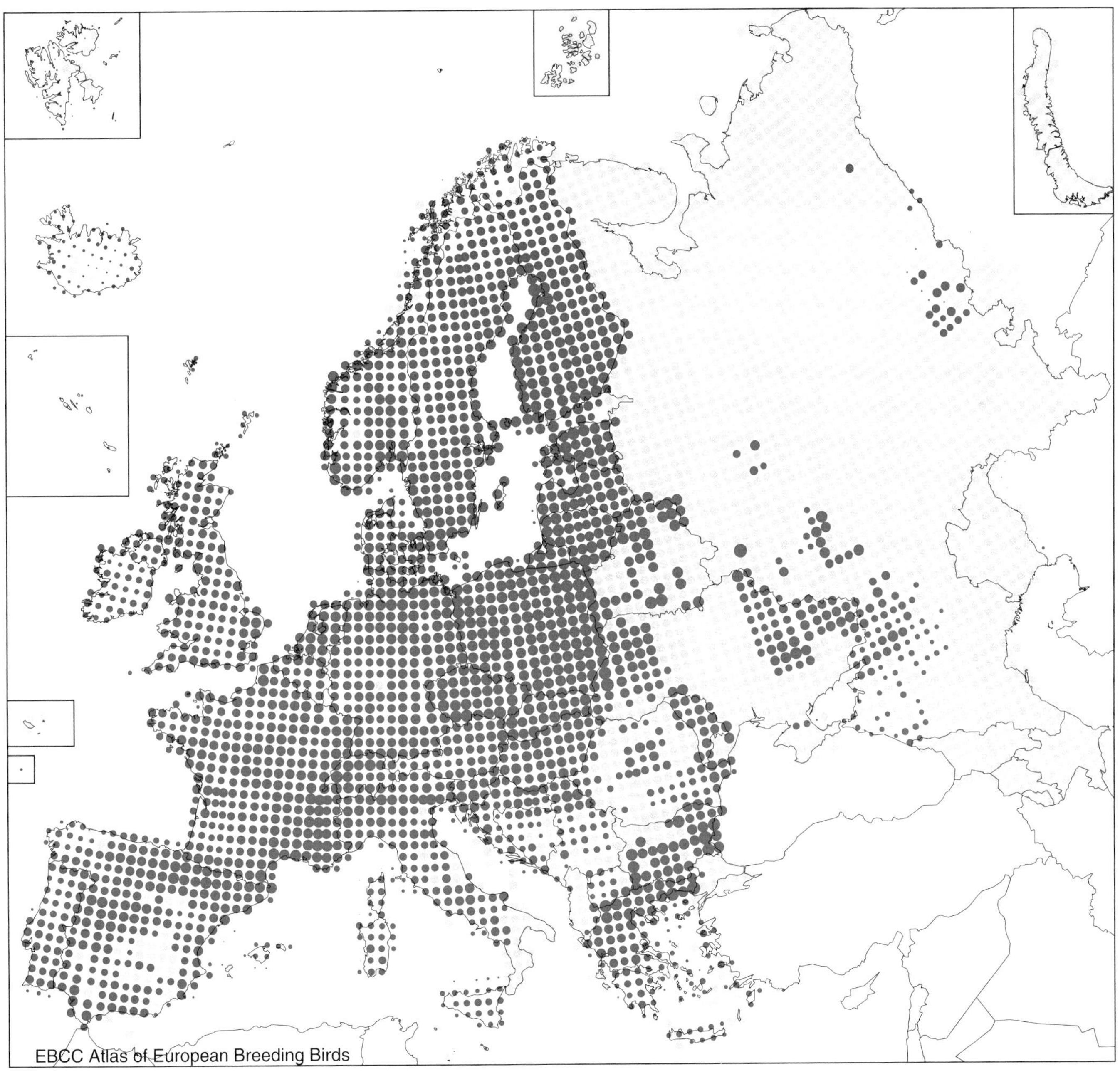

Figure 5 Map showing the species richness expressed as the number of breeding bird species per square, indicated by varying the dot size accordingly, representing between 1 and 201 (the maximum recorded) species, where:

- 1 species
- 20 species
- 50 species
- 100 species
- 125 species
- 150 species
- 200 species

Squares with an incomplete or non-existent dataset are indicated by grey dots.

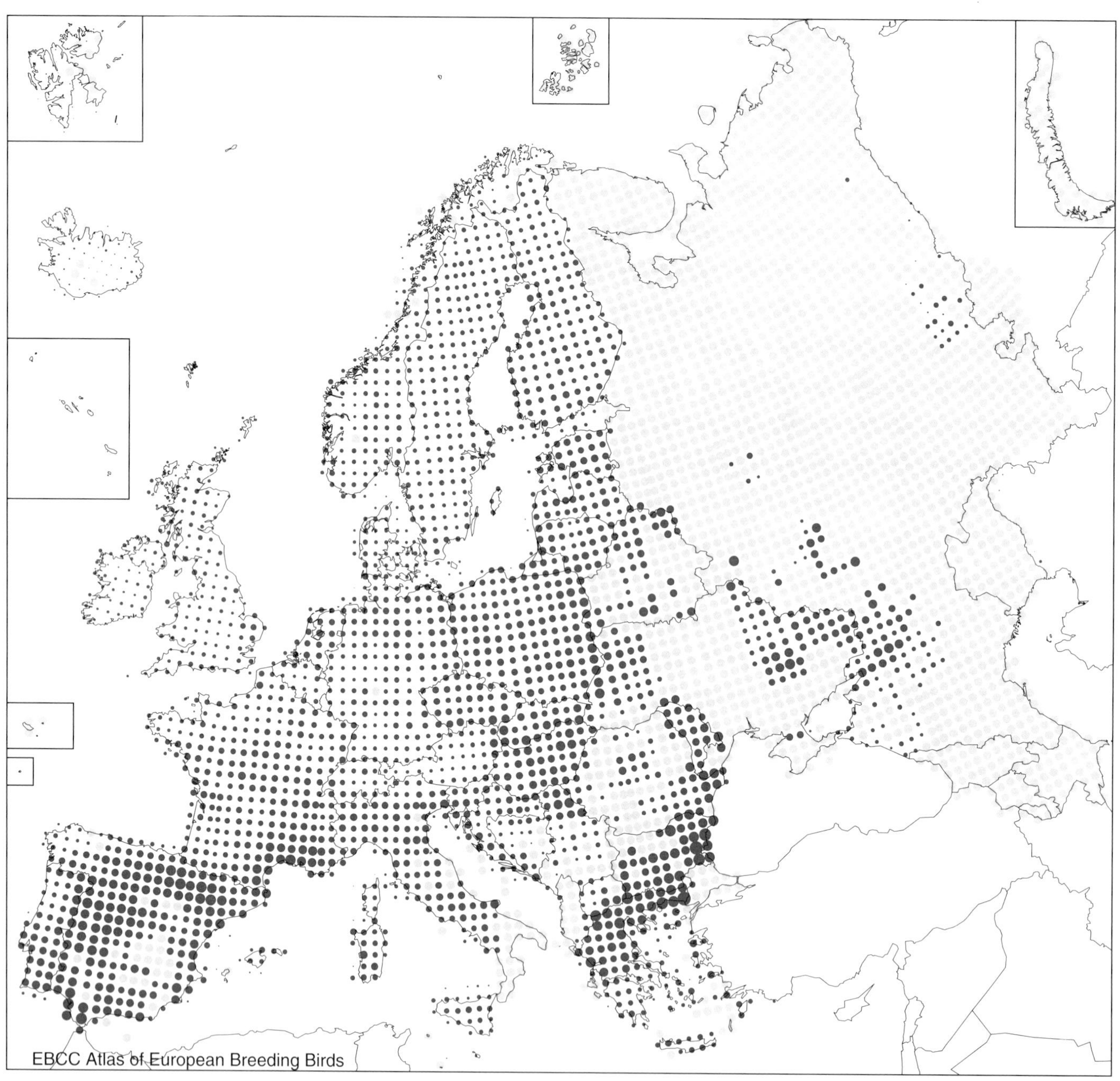

Figure 6 Map showing the number of SPEC Category 1 species per square. Because no square holds more than 6 SPEC Category species, the map contains only 6 dot sizes. Refer to Diagram 1 and Table 4 for a detailed explanation of the SPEC categories.

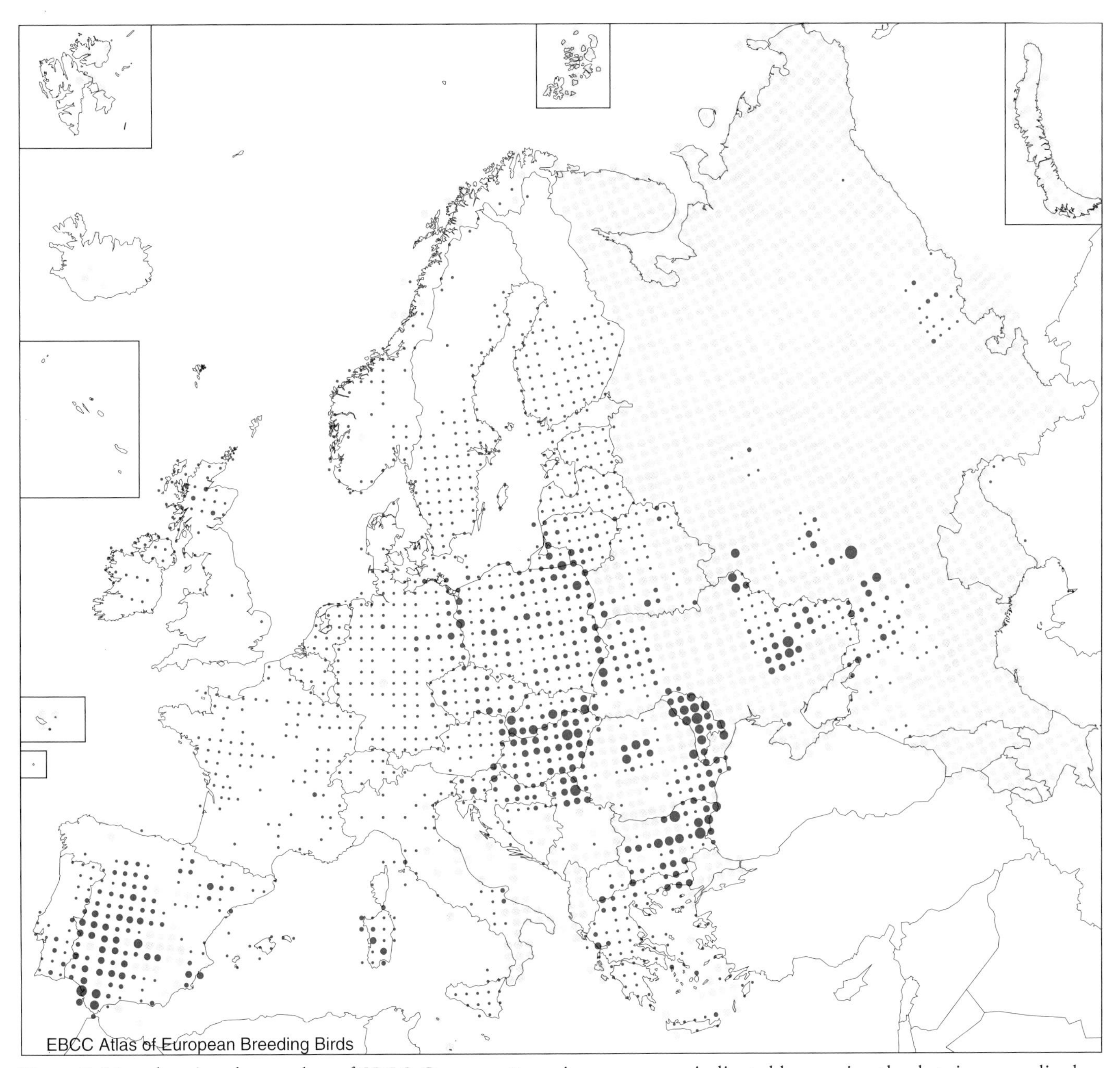

Figure 7 Map showing the number of SPEC Category 2 species per square, indicated by varying the dot size accordingly, representing between 1 and 20 species, where:

- 1 SPEC 2 species
- 3
- 5
- 10
- 15
- 20 (maximum number of SPEC 2 species in a square)

Squares with an incomplete or non-existent dataset are indicated by grey dots. Refer to Diagram 1 and Table 4 for a detailed explanation of the SPEC categories.

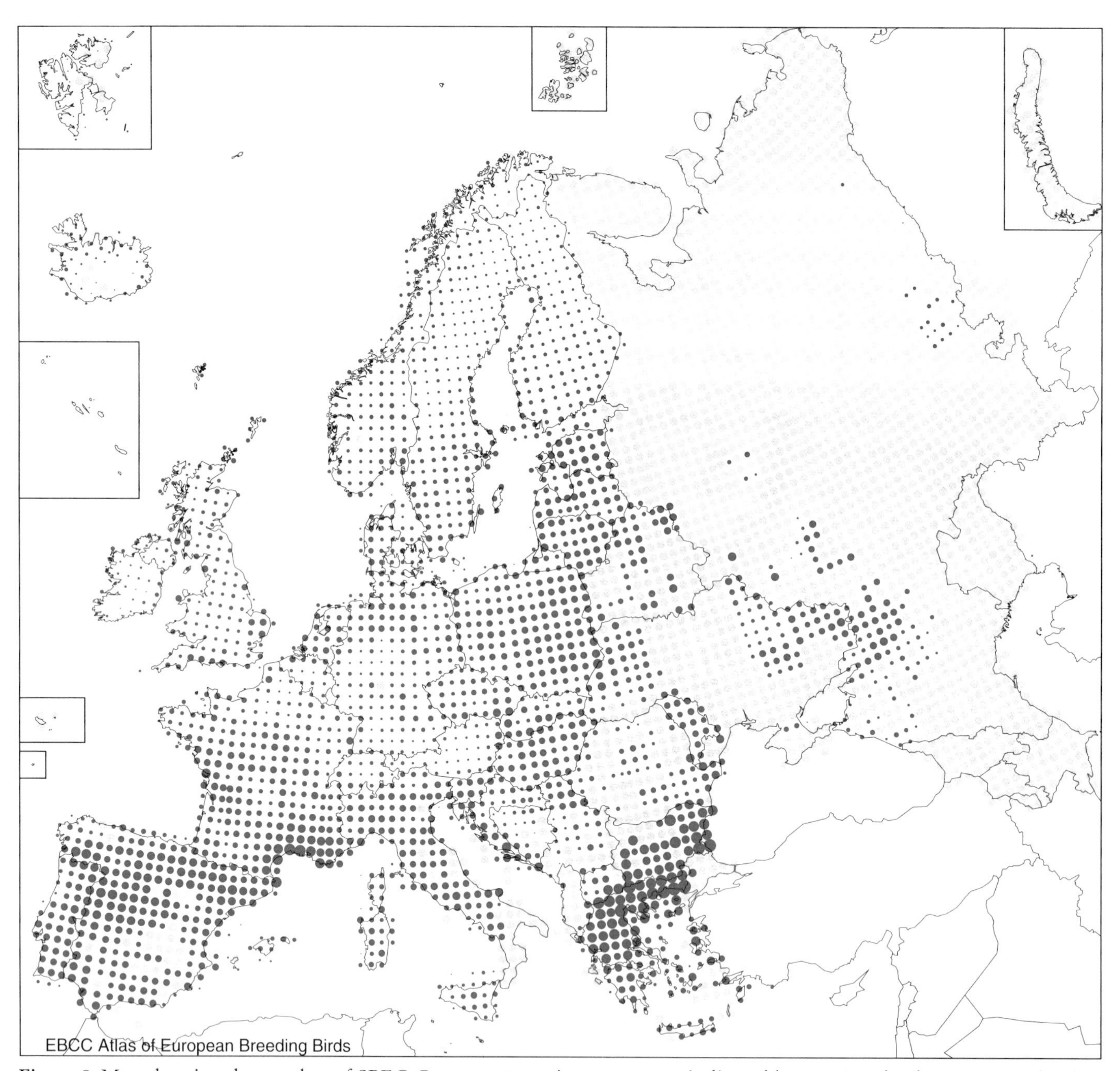

Figure 8 Map showing the number of SPEC Category 3 species per square, indicated by varying the dot size accordingly, representing between 1 and 57 species, where:

- 1 SPEC 3 species
- 15
- 25
- 35
- 45
- 56 (maximum number of SPEC 3 species in a square)

Squares with an incomplete or non-existent dataset are indicated by grey dots. Refer to Diagram 1 and Table 4 for a detailed explanation of the SPEC categories.

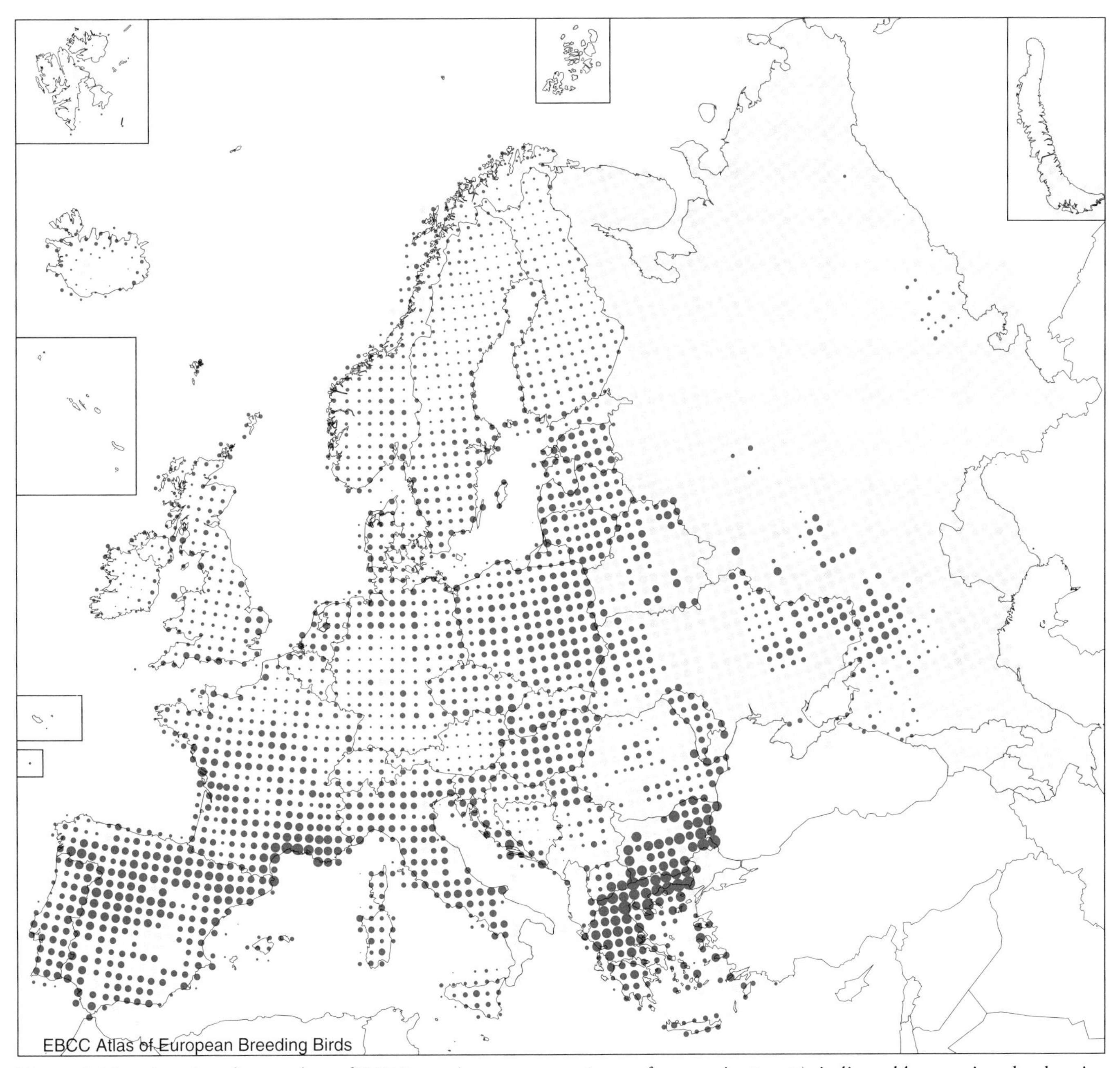

Figure 9 Map showing the number of SPEC species per square (sum of categories 1 to 3), indicated by varying the dot size accordingly, representing between 1 and 80 species, where:

. 1 SPEC category 1, 2 or 3 species
• 15
• 30
• 45
● 60
● 70 (maximum number of SPEC 1, 2 or 3 species in a square)

Squares with an incomplete or non-existent dataset are indicated by grey dots. Refer to Diagram 1 and Table 4 for a detailed explanation of the SPEC categories.

Technical Appendix

6° MERIDIAN SQUARES

The Universal Transverse Meridian (UTM) grid is a popular choice for many map-makers. Its structure is simple on the north–south axis, the latitudinal components being at 100km intervals from the equator. The *Atlas*, covering Europe, was restricted to the northern hemisphere, and used as a basis the grid devised for *Atlas Florae Europaeae*, which used the basic interval of the 50km unit.

Meridians of longitude converge towards the poles. At the equator, the UTM longitudinal components are at 100km intervals and are grouped in sectors every 6° of longitude. The *Atlas* grid uses cells which are 50km × 50km at the equator. The *Atlas* 6° sectors take the forms of long thin wedges on the map. Clearly, fewer cells can be accommodated within a 6° sector nearer the poles than at the equator. This means either that all grid cells should reduce progressively in width towards the poles, or that some method must be adopted to reduce gradually in a northwards direction the number of cells within each 6° sector. (The same reasoning applies for maps using variants of the UTM grid in the southern hemisphere.)

On a European scale, the *Atlas'* dot maps would require the minimum cell size to be sufficiently large to accommodate the largest dot. On the ground, cell-size had to remain large enough for the survey results to suffer minimum skew. Consequently, the method selected of reducing the number of cells in a northwards direction across the width of a 6° sector was that which reduced, then eliminated cells at the edges of the 6° sectors. Sector edge cells which had diminished to approximately 30–40km in width were 'topped off'. The reason for a variable width lies in the mathematics of fitting the maximum number of near-identically sized cells into 6° sectors of spheres.

At various latitudes on the basic *Atlas* UTM map (47°N, 49°N, 57°N, 59°N, 67°N, 69°N, 79°N and 81°N), the edge cells of adjacent 6° sectors disappear, and are replaced by a single cell, the boundary between sectors being displaced slightly to the east as 47°N then to the west at 49°N, and so on.

The diagrams indicate how cell reduction and elimination occurred across Europe.

Cell-configuration on the transition boundaries differs:

- At 47°, 57° and 67°N, two cells reduce to one thus:

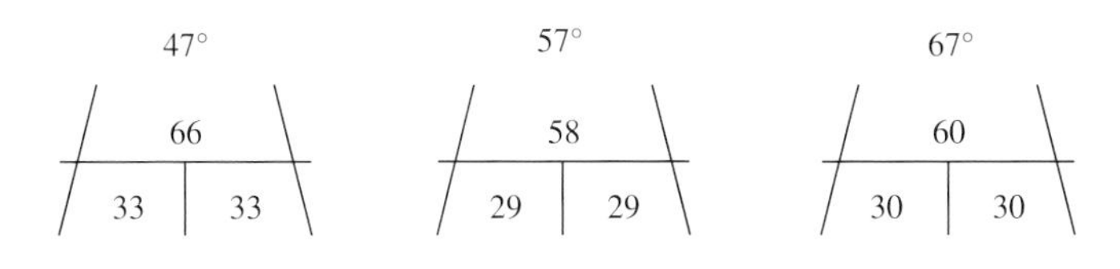

(Note that the transition boundary length differs in each case, being 66, 58 and 60km respectively.)

- At 49°, 59° and 69°, a single reduced cell 40km wide at the apex and two standard 50km cells become two cells each 70km wide at the base.

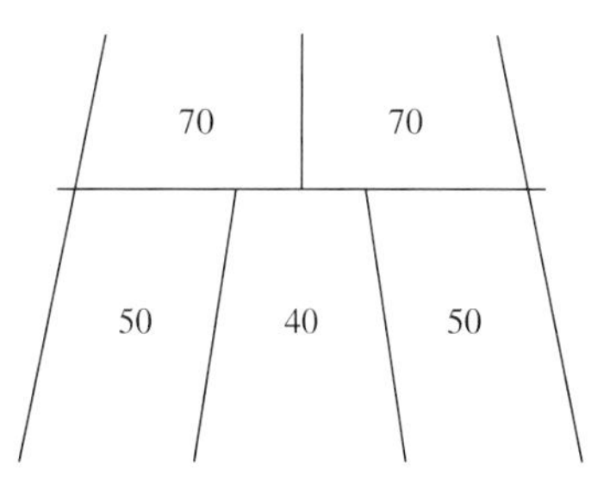

(Note that the transition boundary length is the same (140km) in all three cases.)

- At 79° and 81° (Svalbard) cells are reducing in width so rapidly that both the above methods occur in rapid succession.

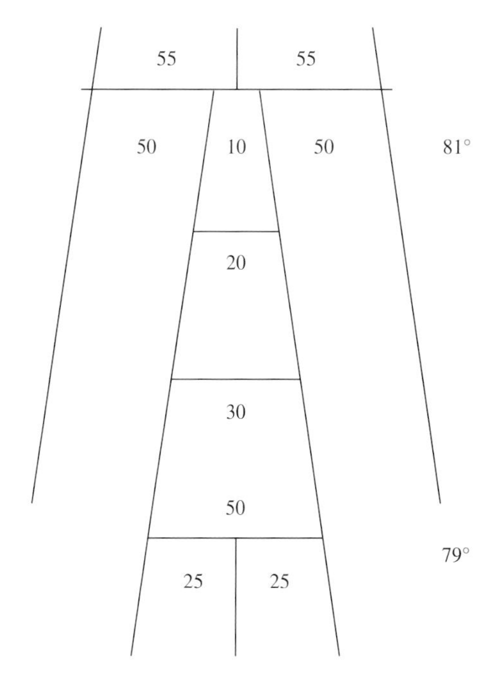

Therefore, except for Svalbard, the minimum width of edge cells at the transition boundaries is 29km and the maximum 70km. For Svalbard the values are 10km and 55km respectively. At all other points on the map the cells are 50km × 50km.

TRANSPOSITION OF ISLAND AND COASTAL SQUARES

A 50km × 50km subdivision of the Universal Transverse Mercator (UTM) 100km × 100km was used in this *Atlas* but in places the positions of some squares differ from the layout of both the basic UTM map and the *Atlas Florae Europaeae* map.

In addition to the amendments at the 6° meridians (explained above), some island and coastal squares have been transposed, but not all transpositions made in *Atlas Florae Europaeae* were adopted. There were several reasons for making the transpositions:

- Often, where a tiny piece of coastline occurred in a 50km square, observer and recording effort could be reduced by transposing the data to a neighbouring square which covered a significant area of land. This action reduced the number of dots which appear to be largely in the sea on the printed map outline. For example, the physical location of the 50km square which just covered Land's End in SW England was moved southwards to better reflect the physical geography of the map. One square therefore replaced two.
- Often, where there were isolated small islands, or where there were island groups whose extent did not lie conveniently within the boundaries of 50km squares, either the data were transposed to neighbouring squares or the boundaries were redrawn better to partition the land area enclosed. For example, the data from the square covering the St Kilda island group are included in the northernmost 50km square covering the Hebrides.
- Conversely, some of the *Atlas Florae Europaeae* 50km squares, particularly in the Aegean Sea, had undergone transposition to an extent that would have concealed distribution peculiarities of some bird species, and so there had to be a re-transposition exercise to reposition islands on the map nearer to an accurate representation of their position.

All the above activities comprised a rationalization of the numbers of 50km squares, the overall effect being to reduce the total number handled in data-collection and data-processing. In general, the 50km squares represented in this *Atlas* coincide with those in *Atlas Florae Europaeae*, but in a number of cases revert to the UTM base map. Such an example is the location of the coastal squares of SW Norway; in the *Atlas*, they revert to their UTM identities, whereas *Atlas Florae Europaeae* had assigned them to neighbouring UTM regions. The total number of transpositions made across Europe are too complex and numerous to describe in detail.

The basic template of the 50km squares used in this *Atlas*, as derived from *Atlas Florae Europaeae*, was further modified by the addition of 50km squares to cover Franz Josef Land and Novaya Zemlya in the north and Madeiran archipelago and the Salvage Islands (Selvagens) in the southwest. The UTM square identities and locations required for these modifications were derived by extrapolation.

THE *ATLAS'* USE OF EURING CODES

The European Union for Bird Ringing (EURING) devised a numerical method of identifying species and subspecies to simplify recording during both ringing (banding) and subsequent analysis. It comprises five-figure reference numbers or, more correctly, codes for species and subspecies, and forms a list several thousand long. The system is intended for use in the western Palearctic, but contains codes for many vagrant species from other avifaunal regions, including the Nearctic. Although the list generally follows the Voous order, where applicable, it does not possess any taxonomic authority, nor is it comprehensive enough to cover all subspecies. It is simply a highly convenient and effective administrative method of dealing with large numbers of species. The *EBCC Atlas*, with the permission of EURING, has used the EURING codes during data-collection, computerization and at all times when lists were required. EURING codes also provided an invaluable additional method of data validation.

The EURING list has been amended a number of times with improving knowledge of bird distributions. Also, many introduced or established feral species have been added. The basic principle of the EURING five-figure code is that the species code ends in 0, and subspecies end in 1 (the nominate) to 9. Apart from the nominate subspecies, the remainder numbered follow no particular sequence. The list generally excludes extralimital subspecies, but may not cover all subspecies occurring in the western Palearctic.

Taxonomy is being revised constantly, and so what has been regarded previously as a subspecies may become a full species (splitting), and a former species may lose that distinction (lumping). In cases of splitting, the *EBCC Atlas* retains the subspecies' EURING code for the new species, as for 05927 Yellow-legged Gull *Larus cachinnans* and 05929 Armenian Gull *L. armenicus*, which now are separated from 05920 Herring Gull *L. argentatus*. The code 05920 is retained for Herring Gull and not changed to 05921 *L.a. argentatus* because the other subspecies of Herring Gull are not mapped separately. (For some other species, it was possible to use 1 for the nominate.) Undoubtedly further taxonomic developments in the Herring Gull/Lesser Black-backed Gull complex will bring further changes; indeed, the transfer of the subspecies *heuglini* from *argentatus* to *fuscus* now has strong acceptance, but the *EBCC Atlas* recorded data do not allow clearly-mapped separation. Conversely, 12910 Green Warbler *Phylloscopus trochiloides nitidus* (Transcaucasia) is now lumped with 12930 Greenish Warbler *P. trochiloides viridanus*. The *EBCC Atlas* uses the hybrid EURING code 12910/30. In some cases, because subspecies codes did not exist, the *EBCC Atlas* uses the first unused last digit in the list supplied by EURING to form a new subspecies code. All such cases are interim, and should not be taken as final; EURING may later assign a different subspecies code.

EURING already has faced the problem of having to provide a code for a species new to the list, but for which a numerical vacancy in sequence does not exist. EURING assigns an out-of-Voous-order code, such as 20250 Red Avadavat *Amandava amandava*; in the *EBCC Atlas*, it appears approximately in Voous order. The *EBCC Atlas* records two species for which no EURING codes exist. These two species possess established, self-sustaining, and expanding populations. For such cases, EURING advises the use of code 24999 for species not defined by them. The *EBCC Atlas* uses suffixes to distinguish the two species,

24999X Monk Parakeet *Myiopsitta monachus* and 24999Y Orange-cheeked Waxbill *Estrilda melpoda*.

The EBCC is grateful for the agreement of EURING for the *EBCC Atlas* to use the EURING code system.

COMMON NAMES OF SPECIES IN VARIOUS LANGUAGES

The use of the common name of a bird in any language can be important in helping to popularize a species and in seeking support for its conservation. From a scientific point of view, a species' common name is relatively trivial, yet because a species may have more than one common name, selecting one may offend. For English names, the *EBCC Atlas* follows *Birds of the Western Palearctic* (Concise Edition) as the preferred way of maintaining a broad, if conservative, consensus. Because English common names continue to evolve, there may be some differences between the two sources after publication. There are now several other sources of English common names, all with their own advocates, but in our view none is yet demonstrably pre-eminent.

There simply is not enough space in the *Atlas* to include the name of every species in every language. Indeed, many species do not yet have a name in every language. The EOA Working Group (EOA WG) decided to include as many languages as space permitted, but to select those which could be understood across Europe by the vast majority of the readership. Only 14 languages, including English could be accommodated. No matter which languages were chosen, the EOA WG could be criticized; the WG therefore apologizes for any offence caused, but not for making the decision.

A species list was drawn up and sent to EBCC delegates in the countries whose languages were to be featured. The results may differ widely from earlier publications because many countries have adopted new standard lists of common names. Most national lists thus obtained have at least the tacit approval of the appropriate national committee. Any transcription errors from their corrections are the responsibility of the editors. To ensure that the names used were as up-to-date as possible, lists were circulated for correction at a late stage; unfortunately, some changes were notified too late for inclusion.

The following particular sources were used. Swedish: Kjellén and Olsson (1995); Polish: Anon (1994); Hungarian: Magyar and Hadarics (1996); Spanish: Bernis *et al* (1994a, 1994b, 1996); Italian: Massa *et al* (1993), Brichetti and Gariboldi (1997). Sandberg (1992) provides names in Danish, Icelandic and Norwegian.

AVAILABLE TRANSLATIONS

At the time of going to press, translations of the summary species accounts are available (or potentially available) from the following.

Karel Šťastný & Vladimir Bejček
Institute of Applied Ecology & Ecotechnology
Agricultural University of Prague
Suchdol
28163 Kostelec na Cernymi
CZECH REPUBLIC

Goetz Rheinwald (for ordering German translations in Germany)
Zoolog. Forchingsinstitut &
Museum Alexander Koenig
Adenauerallee 160
D-53113 Bonn
GERMANY

Ward Hagemeijer
SOVON Bird Census Work The Netherlands
Rijksstraatweg 178
6573 DG Beek-Ubbergen
THE NETHERLANDS
tel: +31 24 6848111
fax: +31 24 6848188
email: SOVON@inter.nl.net

Paul Weber
Muzeul Municipal Medias
str. Viitorului nr. 46
3125 Medias
ROMANIA

Helena Rogacheva
Academy of Sciences
Institute of Ecology & Evolution
Leninsky Prospect 33
117071 Moscow
RUSSIA

Ramón Martí (for Spanish queries – no actual Spanish booklet)
SEO BirdLife
Ctra de Humeda 63-1
28224 Pozuela Alarcon
SPAIN

Luc Schifferli (for ordering German translations in Switzerland)
Schweiz. Vogelwarte
CH-6204 Sempach
SWITZERLAND

References

ABDULSALYAMOV, I.A. 1973. *Fauna Tadzhikskoy SSR. 19 Ptitsy* 2. Dushanbe. (*Fauna of the Tadzhik SSR*) (in Russian).

ADAMYAN, M.S. 1963. Bimaculated Lark in Armenia. *Ornitologiya* 6: 238–245.

ADRIAENSEN, F., P. ULENAERS and A.A. DHONDT. 1993. Ringing recoveries and the increase in numbers of European Great Crested Grebes. *Ardea* 81: 59–70.

AEBISCHER, N.J., J.C. COULSON and J.M. COLEBROOK. 1990. Parallel long-term trends across four marine trophic levels and weather. *Nature* 347: 753–755.

AFONIN, P.V. 1985. [Structure of the bird population of high altitude zones in Kalbardino-Balkariya.] *Ornitologiya* 20: 104–112 (in Russian).

AGAFONOV, A.V., D.S. RESINKO, A.A. ROCHKOV and N.M. SEMENOV. 1957. [On the ecology of the Steppe Eagle.] *Byull. Mosk. Obch. Isp. Prir. Biol.* 62: 33–41 (in Russian).

AGENCIA DE MEDIO AMBIENTE, CORDOBA. 1991. Evolución de la población ibérica de Malvasía (*Oxyura leucocephala*). In: Jesús Martos, M. and J. Fernández Palacios (Eds) *Plan Rector de Uso y Gestión de las Reservas Naturales de las Lagunas de Cádiz*. Junta de Andalucía, Consejeria de cultura y medio ambiente, Agencia de Medio Ambiente: 145–151.

AHLÉN, I. and M. TJERNBERG. 1992. *Artfakta, Sveriges hotade och sällsynta ryggradsdjur*. Databanken for hotade arter, Uppsala (in Swedish).

AIRUMIAN, K.A. and N.A. MARGARIAN 1974. [Game bird resources in Armenia.] *Proceedings of the 6th All-Union Ornithological Conference, Moscow* (in Russian).

ALAPULLI, J. 1964. Über die Verbreitung der Haustaube (*Columba livia*) in Nordfinnland 1900–64. *Ornis Fennica* 41: 43–48 (in Finnish, with German summary).

ALBRECHT, J.S.M. 1984. Some notes on the identification, song and habitat of the Green Warbler in the western Black Sea coastlands of Turkey. *Sandgrouse* 6: 69–75.

ALENDAL, E., K.E. ERIKSTAD and J.A. KÅLÅS. 1982. [The bird fauna in the NE of Northwest-Spitsbergen national park – a census of breeding birds in the high arctic tundra.] *Fauna* 35: 106–113 (in Norwegian).

ALI, S. and S.D. RIPLEY. 1972. *Handbook of the Birds of India and Pakistan*, Vol. 5. Oxford University Press, London.

ALI, S. and S.D. RIPLEY. 1974. *Handbook of the Birds of India and Pakistan*, Vol. 10. Oxford University Press, London.

ALLAN, J.R., J.S. KIRBY and C.J. FEARE. 1995. The biology of Canada Geese (*Branta canadensis*) in relation to the management of feral populations. *Wildlife Biol.* 1: 129–143.

ALONSO, J.A., R. MUÑOZ PULIDO, L.M. BAUTISTA and J.C. ALONSO. 1991. Nest-site selection and nesting success in the Azure-winged Magpie in Central Spain. *Bird Study* 38: 45–51.

ALONSO, J.C. 1984. *Contribución a la biología del Gorrión Moruno,* Passer hispaniolensis *(Temm.) en la Península Ibérica, y sus relaciones ecológicas con el Gorrión Común,* Passer domesticus *(L.).* Doctoral Thesis 12/84, Universidad Complutense, Madrid.

ALONSO, J.C. 1985. Description of intermediate phenotypes *Passer hispaniolensis x domesticus. Ardeola* 32: 31–38.

ALONSO, J.C. 1986a. Ecological segregation between sympatric Spanish Sparrows (*Passer hispaniolensis* Temm.) and House Sparrows (*Passer domesticus* (L.)) during winter. *Ekologia Polska* 34: 63–73.

ALONSO, J.C. 1986b. On the status and distribution of the Spanish Sparrow *Passer hispaniolensis* in Iberia. *Int. Studies Sparrows* 13: 35–43.

ALONSO, J.C. and J.A. ALONSO (Eds). 1990. *Distribucion y demografia de la grulla comun (*Grus grus*) en España.* Collección Técnica, ICONA-CSIC, Madrid.

ALONSO, J.C. and J.A. ALONSO. (1996). The Great Bustard *Otis tarda* in Spain: present status, recent trends and an evaluation of earlier censuses. *Biol. Conservation* 77: 79–86.

ALONSO, J.C., J.A. ALONSO, E. MARTIN and M. MORALES. 1995. Range and patterns of Great Bustard movements at Villafáfila, NW Spain. *Ardeola* 42: 73–81.

AMAT, J.A. 1993. Status of Kentish Plover in Spain. *Wader Study Group Kentish Plover Project Newsletter* 2: 2–4.

AMCOFF, M., TJERNBERG and Å. BERG. 1994. Bivråkens *Pernis apivorus* boplatsval. *Ornis Svecica* 4: 145–158. (Nest site choice of Honey Buzzard *Pernis apivorus*) (in Swedish with English summary).

AMORES, F. and A. FRANCO. 1981. Alimentation et écologie du Circaète Jean-le-Blanc dans le sud de l'Espagne. *Alauda* 49: 59–64.

ANDERSSON, M. 1981. Reproductive tactics of the Long-tailed Skua *Stercorarius longicaudus*. *Oikos* 37: 287–294.

ANDERSSON, R. 1990. Svarta rödstjärtens *Phoenicurus*

ochruros häckningsbiologi i Västsverige. *Vår Fågelvärld* 49: 201–210.

ANDRÉN, H. 1990. Despotic distribution, unequal reproductive success, and population regulation in the Jay. *Ecology* 71: 1796–1803.

ANDRÉN, H. 1992. Corvid density and nest predation in relation to forest fragmentation: a landscape perspective. *Ecology* 73: 794–804.

ANGELSTAM, P.K. 1988. Population dynamics in Tetraonids: the role of extrinsic factors. *Acta XIX Congr. Int. Ornithol.*: 2458–2477.

ANKER-NILSSEN, T. 1987. The breeding performance of Puffins *Fratercula arctica* on Røst, northern Norway in 1979–1985. *Fauna norv. Ser. C, Cinclus* 10: 21–38.

ANKER-NILSSEN, T. and R.T. BARRETT. 1991. Status of seabirds in northern Norway. *Brit. Birds* 84: 329–341.

ANON. 1994. Ptaki Palearktyki Zachodniej-nazewnictwo i status krajowy. *Not. Orn.* 35, special issue: 1–37.

ANONYMOUS. 1994. Le Roselin cramoisi *Carpodacus erythrinus* nicheur en France. *Ornithos* 1: 44–45.

ANSELIN, A. and V. GEERS. 1994. Broedgevallen van de Canadese Gans, *Branta canadensis*, in Vlaanderen. *VLAVICO-Nieuws* 7(1): 3–8. (Breeding cases of the Canada Goose, *Branta canadensis*, in Flanders) (in Dutch).

ANSTEY, S. 1989. *The Status and Conservation of the White-headed Duck Oxyura leucocephala*. Special Publication No. 10. International Waterfowl and Wetlands Research Bureau, Slimbridge, UK.

ARDAMACKAJA (= ARDAMATSKAYA), T.B. 1990. Über einen isolierten Brutbestand der Eiderente, *Somateria mollissima*, im Schwarzmeer-Naturschutzgebiet (Südwest-Ukraine). *Mitt. Zool. Mus., Suppl. Ann. Orn.* 14, Berlin 66: 35–48.

ARDAMATSKAYA, T.B., V.D. SIOKHIN, N.A. TARINA, A.B. GRINCHENKO, M.E. ZHMUD, A.I. KORZYUKOV, I.I. CHERNICHKO and G.N. MOLODAN. 1989. [The number of colonial breeding gulls on the South of Ukraine, 1987 census.] *All-Union Wildlife Inventory and Census Workshop*. Abstracts, Part III, Ufa: 9–11 (in Russian).

ARLETTAZ, R. 1984. Écologie d'une population de Huppes, *Upupa e. epops*, en Valais: répartition spatiale, biotopes et sites de nidification. *Nos Oiseaux* 37: 197–222.

ARLETTAZ, R., J. FOURNIER, M. JUILLARD, A. LUGON, D. ROSSEL and A. SIERRO. 1991. Origines du déclin de la population relictuelle du Hibou petit-duc, *Otus scops*, dans les Alpes valaisannes (sud-ouest de la Suisse): une approche empirique. In: Juillard, M. (Ed) *Rapaces nocturnes*. Société romande pour l'étude et la protection des oiseaux, Prangins: 15–30.

ARMSTRONG, E.A. and H.L.K. WHITEHOUSE. 1977. Behavioural adaptations of the Wren (*Troglodytes troglodytes*). *Biol. Rev.* 52: 235–294.

ARROYO, B., E. FERREIRO and V. GARZA. 1990a. *Segundo censo nacional de buitre leonado (*Gyps fulvus*): Población, distributión, demografia y conservación*. Colección Técnica, ICONA, Madrid.

ARROYO, B., E. FERREIRO and V. GARZA, 1990b. *El Aguila real en España. Censo, distribución, reprodución, y conservación*. Serie Técnica, ICONA, Madrid.

ARVIDSSON, B.L., U. BOSTRÖM, B. DAHLÉN, A. de JONG, U. KOLMODIN and S.G. NILSSON. 1992. The importance of mires as breeding habitat for wetland birds in Sweden. *Ornis Svecica* 2: 67–76.

ASBIRK, S. 1978. Tejsten *Cepphus grylle* som ynglefugl i Danmark. *Dansk. orn. Foren. Tidsskr.* 72: 161–178.

ASENSIO, B. 1985. Migración en Espana del Verdecillo (*Serinus serinus*) según los resultados del anillamiento. *Ardeola* 32: 173–178.

ASENSIO, B. and C. ANTÓN. 1990. Situación del Picogordo (*Coccothraustes coccothraustes*) en España. *Ardeola* 37: 29–35. (The status of the Hawfinch *Coccothraustes coccothraustes* in Spain) (in Spanish, with English summary).

ASH, J.S. 1993. Migration of Palaearctic birds in inland Ethiopia. *Scopus* 17: 19–25.

AUBRECHT, G., H. LEUZINGER, L. SCHIFFERLI and S. SCHUSTER. 1990. Starker Einflug von Samtenten *Melanitta fusca* ins mitteleuropäische Binnenland in den Wintern 1985/86 und 1988/89. *Orn. Beob.* 87: 89–97.

AULÉN, G. 1988. *Ecology and distribution history of the white-backed woodpecker* Dendrocopos leucotos *in Sweden*. Report No. 14, Department of Wildlife Ecology, Swedish University of Agricultural Sciences, Uppsala.

AVERIN, U.V. 1938. [The birds of the mountains of the NW Caucasus.] *Proceedings of the Caucasian Reserves, No. 1*, Moscow: 5–56 (in Russian).

AVERY, M.I. and A. del NEVO. 1991. Action for Roseate Terns. *RSPB Conservation Rev.* 5: 54–59.

AXELROD, D.I. 1975. Evolution and biogeography of Madrean-Tethyan sclerophyll vegetation. *Ann. Missouri Botan. Garden* 62: 280–334.

AXELROD, D.I. 1976. *History of the Coniferous Forests, California and Nevada*. University of California Press, Berkeley.

AXELSSON, P., H. KÄLLANDER and S. NILSSON. 1977. Stenknäcken och avenboken. *Anser* 16: 241–246. (The Hawfinch *Coccothraustes coccothraustes* and the hornbeam) (in Swedish, with English summary).

BABAYEV, I.P. 1991. [Black Francolin in Azerbaijan.] *X Vsesojuznaja Ornitologiches*. Konfer, Vitebsk (in Russian).

BABENKO, V.G. and V.M. KONSTANTINOV. 1983. [The bird fauna and the bird populations of anthropogenic landscapes in Central European USSR.] In: Flint, V.E. and P.S. Tomkovich (Eds) [*Distribution and Systematics of Birds: Research on Fauna of the Soviet Union*.] University of Moscow, Moscow: 160–185 (in Russian).

BACON, P.J. and P. ANDERSEN-HARILD. 1987. Colonial breeding in Mute Swans (*Cygnus olor*) associated with an allozyme of lactate dehydrogenase. *Biol. J. Linnean Soc.* 30: 193–228.

BAEYENS, G. 1981. Magpie breeding success and carrion crow interference. *Ardea* 69: 125–139.

BAGYURA, J., L. HARASZTHY and T. SZITTA. 1994. Methods and results of Saker Falcon *Falco cherrug* management and conservation in Hungary. In: Meyburg, B-U. and R.D. Chancellor (Eds) *Raptor Conservation Today*. WWGBP, Berlin: 391–395.

BAILLIE, S.R. 1990. Integrated population monitoring of breeding birds in Britain and Ireland. *Ibis* 132: 151–166.

BAINES, D. and P.J. HUDSON. 1995. The decline of Black Grouse in Scotland and northern England. *Bird Study* 42: 122–131.

BAIRLEIN, F. 1991. Population studies of White Storks (*Ciconia ciconia*) in Europe. In: Perrins, C.M., J-D. Lebreton and G.J.M. Hirons (Eds) *Bird Population Studies*. Oxford University Press, Oxford: 207–229.

BAKER, H. 1991. *Habitat use by the Crested Tit* Parus cristatus *in Scottish pinewoods*. DPhil Thesis, University of Dundee.

BALEN, J.H. van and R.P.J. POTTING. 1990. Comparative reproductive biology of four Blue Tit populations in The Netherlands. In: Blondel, J., A. Gosler, J-D. Lebreton and R. McCleery (Eds) *Population Biology of Passerine Birds*. Springer-Verlag, Berlin: 19–38.

BALLUET, P. 1993. La progression du Martinet à ventre blanc, *Apus melba*, sur la bordure nord-orientale du Massif Central. *Nos Oiseaux* 42: 171–180.

BALMER, D.E., S.J. BROWNE and M.M. REHFISCH. 1996. A year in the life of golden pheasants *Chrysolophus pictus* L. In: Holmes, J.S. and J.R. Simons (Eds) *The Introduction and Naturalisation of Birds*. HMSO, London: 87–93.

BANKOVICS, A. 1978. [Migrations of Purple Herons of the Carpathian Basin.] In: Kistchinski, S. (Ed) [*Migrations of Birds of Eastern Europe and Northern Asia*.] Moscow: 212–220 (in Russian).

BANNERMAN, D.A. 1962. *The Birds of the British Isles*, Vol II. Oliver and Boyd, Edinburgh.

BANNERMAN, D.A. 1963. *Birds of the Atlantic Islands*, Vol 1. Oliver and Boyd, Edinburgh.

BANNERMAN, D.A. and W.M. BANNERMAN. 1964. On the status of *Puffinus assimilis baroli* in the Azores archipelago. *Bull. Brit. Orn. Club* 84: 111–112.

BANNERMAN, D.A. and W.M. BANNERMAN. 1965. *Birds of the Atlantic Islands*, Vol. 2. Oliver and Boyd, Edinburgh.

BANNERMAN, D.A. and W.M. BANNERMAN. 1966. *Birds of the Atlantic Islands*, Vol. 3. Oliver and Boyd, Edinburgh.

BANNERMAN, D.A. and W.M. BANNERMAN. 1968. *History of the Birds of the Cape Verde Islands*. Oliver and Boyd, Edinburgh.

BARBIERI, F. and P. BRICHETTI. 1992. Airone rosso *Ardea purpurea*. In: Brichetti, P., P. de Franceschi and N. Baccetti (Eds) *Fauna d'Italia, Aves I*. Edizioni Calderini, Bologna: 202–210.

BARBRAUD, C. and J-C. BARBRAUD. 1994. Circaète Jean-le-Blanc *Circaetus gallicus*. In: Yeatman-Berthelot, D. and G. Jarry (Eds) *Nouvel Atlas des Oiseaux Nicheurs de France 1985–1989*. Société Ornithologique de France, Paris: 178–179.

BÁRCENA, F., A.M. TEIXEIRA and A. BERMEJO. 1984. Breeding seabird populations in the Atlantic sector of the Iberian Peninsula. In: Croxall, J.P., P.G.H.Evans and R.W.Schreiber (Eds) *Status and Conservation of the World's Seabirds*. Technical Publication No. 2, International Council For Bird Preservation, Cambridge: 335–345.

BASTIAN, A. and H-V. BASTIAN. 1994. Bestände und Bestandstrends des Braunkehlchens (*Saxicola rubetra*). *Limicola* 8: 242–270.

BASTIAN, H-V. 1992. Breeding and natal dispersal of Whinchats *Saxicola rubetra*. *Ringing and Migration* 13: 13–19.

BATTEN, L.A. 1976. Bird communities of some Killarney woodlands. *Proc. Roy. Irish Acad.* 76: 285–313.

BAUDVIN, H. 1986. La reproduction de la Chouette effraie (*Tyto alba*). *Le Jean-le-Blanc* 25: 1–125.

BAUER, H-G. 1994. Ruddy Duck (*Oxyura jamaicensis*) and White-headed Duck (*O. leucocephala*) in Germany: occurrence and legal status. *Oxyura* 7: 49–60.

BAUER, H-G. and A. KAISER. 1991. Herbstfangdaten, Verweildauer, Mauser und Biometrie teilziehender Gartenbaumläufer (*Certhia brachydactyla*) in einem südwestdeutschen Rastgebiet. *Vogelwarte* 36: 85–98.

BAUER, K.M. 1952. Der Blutspecht (*Dryobates syriacus*) Brutvogel in Österreich. *J. Ornithol.* 93: 104–111.

BAUMGART, W. 1991. *Der Sakerfalke*. Neue Brehm-Bücherei 514, Ziemsen, Wittenberg.

BAUMGART, W. 1994. Saker *Falco cherrug*. In: Tucker, G.M. and M.F. Heath (Eds) *Birds in Europe – their conservation status*. BirdLife International, Cambridge: 198–199.

BAUMGART, W., A. GAMAUF, J. BAGYURA, L. HARASZTHY, J. CHAVKO and A. PEKLO. 1992. Biologie und Status des Sakerfalken in Osteuropa. *Greifvögel und Falknerei* 1992: 102–106.

BAVOUX, Ch., G. BURNELEAU, A. LEROUX and P. NICOLAU-GUILLAUMET. 1989. Le busard des roseaux *Circus a. aeruginosus* en Charente-Maritime (France). II – Chronologie et paramètres de la reproduction. *Alauda* 57: 247–262.

BAVOUX, Ch., G. BURNELEAU and P. NICOLAU-GUILLAUMET. 1991. Aspects de la biologie du Hibou petit-duc *Otus scops*. *Alauda* 59: 65–71.

BAZIEV, D. Kh. 1978. [*The Snowcocks of the Caucasus: ecology, morphology, evolution*.] Nauka, Leningrad (in Russian).

BEAMAN, M., R. PORTER and A. VITTERY (Eds). 1975. *Ornithological Society of Turkey Bird Report 1970–1973*. OST, Sandy.

BECK, N. In press. 1992. Conservation de la Sitelle corse, *Sitta whiteheadi* Sharpe, 1884: sa place dans les aménagements forestiers. *Travaux du Parc Naturel Régional et des Réserves Naturelles de Corse* 40: 1–32.

BECKER, J. 1995. Sympatrisches Vorkommen und Hybridisierung von Sprosser *Luscinia luscinia* und Nachtigall *L. megarhynchos* bei Frankfurt (Oder), Brandenburg. *Vogelwelt* 116: 109–118.

BECKER, P. 1983. Zum Brutvorkommen des Zwergsumpfhuhns (*Porzana pusilla*) in Niedersachsen. *Beitr. Naturkd. Niedersachsens* 36: 193–203.

BECKER, P.H. and M.E. ERDELEN. 1987. Die Bestandsentwicklung von Brutvögeln der deutschen Nordseeküste 1950–1979. *J. Ornithol.* 128: 1–32.

BECKER, P. and C. SCHMIDT. 1990. Kennzeichen und Kleider der europäischen kleinen Rallen und Sumpfhühner *Rallus* und *Porzana*. *Limicola* 4: 93–144.

BECKER, P.H., W.A. HEIDEMANN, A. BÜTHE, D. FRANK and C. KOEPFF. 1992. Umweltchemikalien in Eieren von Brutvögeln der deutschen Nordseeküste: Trends 1981–1990. *J. Ornithol.* 133: 109–124.

BEEBE, W. 1936. *Pheasants: their lives and homes*. Doubleday, Doran and Co., Garden City, New York.

BEEKMAN, J.H. and M. PLATTEEUW. 1994. *Het Nonnetje Mergus albellus in het IJsselmeergebied*. International Report No. 37 Lio, Rijkswaterstaat directorate Flevoland, Lelystad (in Dutch).

BEEKMAN, J.H., B. LAUBEK and L. LEHO. 1994. *Report on Bewick's Swan stop-over ecological studies, Estonia, Spring 1993*. Report to the University of Groningen.

BEINTEMA, A.J. and N. DROST. 1986. Migration of the Black-tailed Godwit. *Le Gerfaut* 76: 37–62.

BEINTEMA, A.J. and J.D.M. MÜSKENS. 1983. Changes in the migration pattern of the Common Snipe. *Proceedings of the 2nd European Woodcock and Snipe Workshop 1982*. International Wetlands Research Bureau, Slimbridge: 146–160.

BEINTEMA, A.J. and A. TIMMERMAN. 1976. De Tureluur als 'zoutliefhebber'. *Vogeljaar* 24: 17–21. (The Redshank as 'salt lover') (in Dutch).

BEINTEMA, A.J., R.J. BEINTEMA-HIETBRINK and G.J.D.M. MÜSKENS. 1985. A shift in the timing of breeding in meadow birds. *Ardea* 73: 83–89.

BEINTEMA, A., O. MOEDT and D. ELLINGER. 1995. *Ecologische Atlas van de Nederlandse Weidevogels*. Schuyt and Co., Haarlem. (*Ecological Atlas of Meadow Birds in the Netherlands*) (in Dutch, with English summary).

BEKHUIS, J.F. 1990. Hoe lang nog broedende Woudaapjes *Ixobrychus minutus* in Nederland? *Limosa* 63: 47–50. (How long will Little Bitterns breed in the Netherlands?) (in Dutch, with English summary).

BEKHUIS J. and M. ZIJLSTRA. 1991. Opkomst van de Blauwe Kiekendief *Circus cyaneus* als broedvogel in Nederland. *Limosa* 64: 143–153. (Increase of the Dutch breeding population of the Hen Harrier *Circus cyaneus*) (in Dutch).

BEKHUIS, J., J. NIENHUIS, E. WYMENGA, N. BEEMSTER and R. VAN BEUSEKOM. 1993. Opmars van de Buidelmees *Remiz pendulinus* in Nederland in de periode 1988–92. *Limosa* 66: 97–106. (Increase of the Dutch Penduline Tit *Remiz pendulinus* population in 1988–92) (in Dutch, with English summary).

BELIK, V.P. 1989. [Further range expansion of the White-tailed Lapwing.] In: Davygora, A.V. and E.V. Gavlyuk (Eds) *Rasprostranenie i fauna ptits Urala* [*Birds of the Ural Mountains and their Distribution*]. Orenburg: 29–31 (in Russian).

BELIK, V.P. 1990. [Distribution and numbers of rare birds of Rostov Region: Materials for the Red Data Book of the North Caucasus.] *Caucasian Ornithol. News* 4: 21–68 (in Russian).

BELIK, V.P. 1994a. Sociable Plover. In: Tucker, G.M. and M.F. Heath (Eds) *Birds in Europe – their conservation status*. Conservation Series No 3, BirdLife International, Cambridge, UK.

BELIK, V.P. 1994b. Where on earth does the Slender-billed Curlew nest? *Wader Study Group Bull.* 75: 37–38.

BELIK, V.P. (in prep). *History and Current Status of the East European Population of the Little Bustard* Tetrax tetrax *(Gruiformes, Otidae)*. BirdLife International, Cambridge, UK.

BELIK, V.P. In press. The current state of populations of rare and protected wader species in South Russia. *Wader Study Group Bull.*

BELIK, V.P. and I. MIHALEVICH. 1994. Pesticide use in the European steppes and its effects on birds. *J. Ornithol.* 135, Suppl.: 233.

BELIK, V.P. and V.V. SIDELNIKOV. 1989. The Little Bustard in the Rostov region. In: Ilyashenko, V.Ju. and L.N. Mazin (Eds) [*Rare and Important Animals in Conservation: Materials for the Red Data Book*.] Moscow: 82–88 (in Russian).

BELIK, V.P., A.N. KHOKHLOV, A.I. KUKISH, P.A.TIL'BA and Ju.E. KOMAROV. 1994. [Rare and scarce birds of the north Caucasus which are in need of particular protection]. In: Ilyashenko, V.Ju. and L.N. Mazin (Eds) *Izuchenie redikh zhivotnikh v RSFSR*. Moscow: 94–106 (in Russian).

BELL, M.V. 1989. Wintering wildfowl and waders at Aberdeen, 1975–1986. *Scottish Birds* 15: 106–113.

BENGTSON, S-A. 1972. Breeding ecology of the Harlequin Duck *Histrionicus histrionicus* (L.) in Iceland. *Ornis Scand.* 3: 1–19.

BENGTSON, S-A. and S. ULFSTRAND. 1971. Food resources and breeding frequency of the Harlequin Duck *Histrionicus histrionicus* in Iceland. *Oikos* 22: 235–239.

BENSCH, S., L. GEZELINS and D. HASSELQUIST. 1990. Hur många trastsångare finns det i Tåkern? *Vingspegeln* 9: 51–59 (in Swedish).

BERG, H-M. 1992. Status und Verbreitung der Eulen (Strigiformes) in Österreich. *Egretta* 35: 4–8.

BERGERUD, A.T. and M.W. GRATSON (Eds). 1988. *Adaptive Strategies and Population Ecology of Northern Grouse*. University of Minnesota Press, Minneapolis.

BERGH, L.M.J. van den. 1984. Verplaatsingen van Rietganzen *Anser fabalis* tussen West– en Middeneuropese overwinteringsgebieden. *Limosa* 57: 116–118. (Movements of Bean Geese *Anser fabalis* between west and central European wintering areas) (in Dutch, with English summary).

BERGIER, P. and O. BADAN. 1991. Evaluation of some breeding parameters in a population of Eagle Owls *Bubo bubo* in Provence (South Eastern France). *Birds of Prey Bull.* 4: 57–61.

BERGMAN, G. and K.O. DONNER. 1964. An analysis of the spring migration of the Common Scoter and the Long-tailed Duck in southern Finland. *Acta Zool. Fenn.* 105: 1–59.

BERGMANIS, U., A. PETRINŚ and M. STRAZDS. 1990. Lesser Spotted Eagle in Latvia: numbers, distribution and ecology. *Baltic Birds* 5(1): 35–38.

BERGMANN, H-H. 1993. *Der Buchfink*. Aula-Verlag, Wiesbaden.

BERNARD, A. 1994. Outarde canepetière *Tetrax tetrax*. In: Yeatman-Berthelot, D. and G. Jarry (Eds) *Nouvel Atlas des Oiseaux Nicheurs de France 1985–1989*. Société Ornithologique de France, Paris: 262–265.

BERNARD, A. and J. BROYER. 1994. Bruant proyer *Miliaria calandra*. In: Yeatman-Berthelot, D. and G. Jarry (Eds) *Nouvel Atlas des Oiseaux Nicheurs de France 1985–1989*. Société Ornithologique de France, Paris: 722–723.

BERNARD-LAURENT, A. 1984. Hybridation naturelle entre Perdrix bartavelle (*Alectoris graeca saxatilis*) et Perdrix rouge (*Alectoris rufa rufa*) dans les Alpes-Maritimes. *Gibier Faune Sauvage* 2: 79–96.

BERNARD-LAURENT, A. and P.F. de FRANCESCHI. 1994. Statut, évolution et facteurs limitant les populations de Perdrix bartavelle (*Alectoris graeca*): synthèse bibliographique. In: *Plans de restauration pour quelques galliformes européens: gelinotte, grand tétras, tétras-lyre et perdrix bartavelle*, Vol. 1. Gibier Faune Sauvage – Game and Wildlife 11, hors série: 206–307.

BERNDT, R.K. and G. BUSCHE. 1991. *Vogelwelt Schleswig-Holsteins*, Vol. 3. Wachholtz, Neumünster.

BERNDT, R. and M. HENSS. 1963. Die Blaumeise als Invasionsvogel. *Vogelwarte* 22: 93–100.

BERNDT, R. and W. WINKEL. 1979. Zur Populationsentwicklung von Blaumeise (*Parus caeruleus*), Kleiber (*Sitta europaea*), Gartenrotschwanz (*Phoenicurus phoenicurus*) und Wendehals (*Jynx torquilla*) in mitteleuropäischen Untersuchungsgebieten von 1927 bis 1978. *Vogelwelt* 100: 55–69.

BERNIS, F. 1970. *Aves Migradoras Ibéricas*, Vol. 6. Sociedad Española de Ornitología, Madrid.

BERNIS, F. 1972. Status of the wetlands of international importance in Spain and the new Spanish Hunting Law. In: Carp, E. (Ed) *Proceedings of the International Conference on the Conservation of Wetlands and Waterfowl, Ramsar, Iran, 30 January–3 February 1971*. International Waterfowl Research Bureau, Slimbridge.

BERNIS, F. 1983. Migration of the common griffon vulture in the western Palearctic. In: Wilbur, S.R. and J.A. Jackson (Eds) *Vulture Biology and Management*. University of California Press, Berkeley: 185–196.

BERNIS, F. (Ed). 1988. *Aves de los medios urbano y agrícola en las mesetas españolas*. Monograph No. 2, Soc. Española de Ornitología, Madrid.

BERNIS, F., E. de JUANA, J. del HOYO, X. FERRER, M. FERNÁNDEZ-CRUZ, R. SÁEZ-ROYUELA, and J. SARGATAL. 1994a. Nombres en castellano de las aves del mundo recomendados por la Sociedad Española de Ornitología – Primera parte: Struthioniformes – Anseriformes. *Ardeola* 41: 79–89.

BERNIS, F., E. de JUANA, J. del HOYO, X. FERRER, M. FERNÁNDEZ-CRUZ, R. SÁEZ-ROYUELA, and J. SARGATAL. 1994b. Nombres en castellano de las aves del mundo recomendados por la Sociedad Española de Ornitología – Segunda parte: Falconiformes – Galliformes. *Ardeola* 41: 183–191.

BERNIS, F., E. de JUANA, J. del HOYO, M. FERNÁNDEZ-CRUZ, X. FERRER, R. SÁEZ-ROYUELA and J. SARGATAL. 1996. Nombres en castellano de las aves del mundo recomendados por la Sociedad Española de Ornitogía-Tercera parke: Opisthocomiformes, Gruiformes y Charadrüformes. *Ardeola* 43: 231–238.

BERNONI, M. 1994. [The White-backed Woodpecker in the Abruzzo National Park.] *Contributi Scientifici Alla Conoscenza del parco Nazionale d'Abruzzo* 46: 1–68 (in Italian, with English summary).

BERSUDER, D. 1994. Pie-grièche à tête rousse *Lanius senator*. In: Yeatman-Berthelot, D. and G. Jarry (Eds) *Nouvel Atlas des Oiseaux Nicheurs de France 1985–1989*. Société Ornithologique de France, Paris: 642–645.

BERTELSEN, J. and N.H. SIMONSEN. 1986. [*Documentation on bird hunting and the conservation status of the species involved: Situation in 1986*.] Game and Wildlife Administration, Copenhagen (in Danish).

BERTHOLD, P. 1974. Die gegenwärtige Bestandsentwicklung der Dorngrasmücke (*Sylvia communis*) und anderer Singvogelarten im westlichen Europa bis 1973. *Vogelwelt* 95: 170–183.

BERTHOLD, P. 1987. Das 'Mettnau-Reit-Illmitz-Programm': Übersicht, Bestandsentwicklung, Ausblick unter besonderer Berücksichtigung der Daten vom Neusiedlersee. *Biol. Forschungsinst, Burgenland – Bericht* 63: 93–101.

BERTHOLD, P. 1994. Microevolution of migratory behaviour in a bird species, the Blackcap *Sylvia atricapilla*: 1993 Witherby Lecture. *Bird Study* 42: 89–100.

BERTHOLD, P. and H. BERTHOLD. 1973. Zur Biologie von *Sylvia sarda balearica* und *Sylvia melanocephala*. *J. Ornithol.* 114: 79–95.

BERTHOLD, P., U. QUERNER and R. SCHLENKER. 1990. *Die Mönchsgrasmücke* Sylvia atricapilla. Neue Brehm-Bücherei 603, Ziemsen, Wittenberg.

BERTHOLD, P., A.J. HELBIG, G. MOHR and U. QUERNER. 1992. Rapid microevolution of migratory behaviour in a wild bird species. *Nature* 360: 668–669.

BERTHOLD, P., A. KAISER, U. QUERNER and R. SCHLENKER. 1993. Analyse von Fangzahlen im Hinblick auf die Bestandsentwicklung von Kleinvögeln nach 20jährigem Betrieb der Station Mettnau, Süddeutschland. *J. Ornithol.* 134: 283–299.

BESHKAREV, A.B. and V.V. TEPLOV. 1993. [New bird species in the Pechoro-Ilich Reserve (North-western Urals).] *Russ. J. Ornithol.* 2(1): 90–92 (in Russian).

BEUKEMA, J.J. 1991. Changes in composition of bottom fauna of a tidal-flat area during a period of eutrophication. *Marine Biol.* 111: 293–301.

BEZZEL, E. 1969. *Die Tafelente*. Neue Brehm-Bücherei, Ziemsen, Wittenberg.

BEZZEL, E. 1982. *Vögel in der Kulturlandschaft*. Ulmer, Stuttgart.

BEZZEL, E. 1993. Der Mauerläufer *Tichodroma muraria* im Werdenfelser Land, Oberbayern. *Limicola* 7: 35–48.

BEZZEL, E. 1995. Steinadler *Aquila chrysaetos*. In: Kostrzewa, A. and G. Speer (Eds) *Greifvögel in Deutschland: Bestand, Situation, Schutz*. Aula-Verlag, Wiesbaden: 53–57.

BEZZEL, E. and I. GEIERSBERGER. 1993. Bestandsentwicklung des Graureihers (*Ardea cinerea*) in Mitteleuropa. Erfolge und Probleme aus der Sicht des Artenschutzes. *Z. Ökologie u. Naturschutz* 2: 145–155.

BEZZEL, E. and D. HASHMI. 1989. Nimmt der Zwergtaucher (*Tachybaptus ruficollis*) ab? Indextrends von Rastbeständen aus Südbayern. *Vogelwelt* 110: 42–51.

BIANKI, V.V. 1977. Gulls, shorebirds and alcids of Kandalaksha Bay. *Proc. Kandalaksha State Reservation*, No. 6. Israel Program for Scientific Translations, Jerusalem.

BIANKI, V.V. 1992. Seaducks of the White Sea. *IWRB Seaduck Bull.* 2: 23–29.

BIANKI, V.V. and A.S. KORYAKIN. 1990. *Somateria mollissima in Kandalaksha Bay in the White Sea*. Special Publication No. 12, International Wetlands Research Bureau, Slimbridge: 49.

BIANKI, V.V., V.D. KOKHANOV, A.S. KORYAKIN, Ju.V. KRASNOV, T.D. PANEVA, I.P. TATARINKOVA, R.G. CHEMIAKIN, F.N. SHKLAREIVCH and E.V. SHUTOVA. 1993. [The birds of the Kola peninsula and the White Sea.] *Russian J. Ornithol.* 2(4): 491–586 (in Russian).

BIBBY, C. 1981. Wintering Bitterns in Britain. *Brit. Birds* 74: 1–10.

BIBBY, C.J. 1982. Polygyny and breeding ecology of the Cetti's Warbler *Cettia cetti*. *Ibis* 124: 288–301.

BIBBY, C.J. 1993. Dartford Warbler *Sylvia undata*. In: Gibbons, D.W., J.B. Reid and R.A. Chapman (Eds) *The New Atlas of Breeding Birds in Britain and Ireland: 1988–1991*. Poyser, London: 336–337.

BIBBY C.J. and B. ETHERIDGE. 1993. Status of the Hen Harrier *Circus cyaneus* in Scotland in 1988–89. *Bird Study* 40: 1–11.

BIBBY, C.J. and R.E. GREEN. 1980. Foraging behaviour of migrant pied flycatchers, *Ficedula hypoleuca*, on temporary territories. *J. Anim. Ecol.* 49: 507–521.

BIBBY, C.J. and R.E. GREEN. 1981. Autumn migration strategies of Reed and Sedge Warblers. *Ornis Scand.* 12: 1–12.

BIBBY, C.J. and A.J. del NEVO. 1991. A first record of *Pterodroma feae* from the Azores. *Bull. Brit. Orn. Club.* 111: 183–184.

BIBBY, C.J. and D.K. THOMAS. 1985. Breeding and diets of the Reed Warbler at a rich and a poor site. *Bird Study* 32: 19–31.

BIBBY, C.J. and C.R. TUBBS. 1975. Status, habitats and conservation of the Dartford Warbler in England. *Brit. Birds* 68: 177–195.

BIBER, J-P. 1982. *Brutbiologische Untersuchungen an einer Population des Wasserpiepers* (Anthus spinoletta *L.*). PhD Thesis, Basle University.

BIBER, J-P. 1986. Rock Pipit and Water Pipit *Anthus (s.) petrosus* and *A. (s.) spinoletta*. In: Lack, P. (Ed) *The Atlas of Wintering Birds in Britain and Ireland*. Poyser, Calton: 296–299.

BIBER, J-P. 1993. Status and distribution of the Gull-billed Tern (*Sterna nilotica*) in the Western Palearctic (Preliminary results of an inquiry). In: Aguilar, J.S., X. Monbailliu and A.M. Paterson (Eds) *Status and Conservation of Seabirds. Proceedings of the 2nd Mediterranean Seabird Symposium, Calviá, 21–26 March 1989*. SEO, BirdLife and MEDMARAVIS, Madrid: 87–95.

BIBER, J-P. 1994a. Gull-billed Tern *Gelochelidon nilotica*. In: Tucker, G.M. and M.F. Heath (Eds) *Birds in Europe: their conservation status*. Conservation Series No. 3, BirdLife International, Cambridge: 292–293.

BIBER, J-P. 1994b. Pipit spioncelle *Anthus spinoletta*. In: Yeatman-Berthelot, D. and G. Jarry (Eds) *Nouvel Atlas des Oiseaux Nicheurs de France 1985–1989*. Société Ornithologique de France, Paris: 476–477.

BIBER, J-P. 1995. *International Action Plan for the Lesser Kestrel (Falco naumanni).* In: Heredia, B., L. Rose and M. Painter (Eds) Globally Threatened Birds in Europe. Action Plans. Council for Europe Publishing, Strasbourg: 191–203.

BIBER, O. 1993. Bestand und Bruterfolg der Goldammer *Emberiza citrinella* in einer intensiv genutzten Agrarlandschaft (Schweizer Mittelland). *Orn. Beob.* 90: 53–65.

BIDDAU, L., T. MINGOZZI and N. FEDREGHINI. 1995. Trophic resource availability and mating systems: a progressive study concerning an alpine population of *Petronia petronia* (L.). In: Pandolfi, M. and U.F. Foschi (Eds) *Atti del VI Convegno Italiano di Ornitologia. Suppl. Ric. Biol. Selavaggina* 22: 225–230.

BIGNAL, E. 1993. Chough. In: Gibbons, D.W., J.B. Reid and R.A. Chapman (Eds) *The New Atlas of Breeding Birds in Britain and Ireland: 1988–1991*. Poyser, London: 388–389.

BIGNAL, E. and D.J. CURTIS (Eds). 1989. Choughs and land-use in Europe. *Proceedings of International Workshop on Conservation of the Chough* Pyrrhocorax pyrrhocorax *in the EC, 11–14 November 1988, Pembroke*. JNCC, Peterborough.

BIJLSMA, R.G. 1979. De ecologie van de Appelvink *Coccothraustes coccothraustes* op de Zuidwest-Veluwe, speciaal met betrekking tot de broedbiologie. *Limosa* 52: 53–71. (The ecology of the Hawfinch *Coccothraustes coccothraustes* on the Zuidwest-Veluwe, with special reference to the breeding biology) (in Dutch, with English summary).

BIJLSMA, R.G. 1980. De invloed van predatie op de broedresultaten van de Houtduif *Columba palumbus* op de Zuidwest-Veluwe. *Limosa* 53: 11–19. (The influence of predation on the breeding results of the Woodpigeon *Columba palumbus* on the South-west Veluwe) (in Dutch, with English summary).

BIJLSMA, R.G. 1982. Breeding season, clutch size and breeding success in the Bullfinch *Pyrrhula pyrrhula*. *Ardea* 70: 25–30.

BIJLSMA, R.G. 1987a. Explosieve toename van de Appelvink. *Limosa* 60: 155. (Explosive increase of the Hawfinch) (in Dutch).

BIJLSMA, R.G. 1987b. *Bottleneck Areas for Migratory Birds in the Mediterranean*. Study report No. 18, International Council For Bird Preservation, Cambridge.

BIJLSMA, R.G. 1990a. Population trends in Black Grouse, Grey Partridge, Pheasant and Quail in The Netherlands. In: Lumeij, J.T. and Y.R. Hoogeveen (Eds) *De toekomst van de wilde hoenderachtigen in Nederland*. Organisatiecommissie Nederlandse Wilde Hoenders, Amersfoort: 16–43. (*The Future of Wild Galliformes in The Netherlands*).

BIJLSMA, R.G. 1990b. Habitat, territoriumgrootte en broedsucces van Duinpiepers *Anthus campestris*. *Limosa* 63: 80–81. (Habitat, territory size and breeding success of Tawny Pipits *Anthus campestris*) (in Dutch, with English summary).

BIJLSMA, R.G. 1991. Trends in European Goshawks *Accipiter gentilis*: an overview. *Bird Census News* 4(2): 3–47.

BIJLSMA, R.G. 1993. *Ecologische Atlas van de Nederlandse Roofvogels*. Schuyt and Co., Haarlem. (*Ecological Atlas of Raptors in The Netherlands*) (in Dutch, with English summary).

BIJLSMA, R.G. 1994a. Ontstaan en groei van een populatie Mandarijneenden *Aix galericulata*. *Limosa* 67: 173–174. (Establishment and growth of a population of Mandarin Ducks *Aix galericulata*) (in Dutch, with English summary).

BIJLSMA, R.G. 1994b. Habitatgebruik, broeddichtheid en broedsucces van Kruisbek *Loxia curvirostra* en Grote Kruisbek *L. pytyopsittacus* in West-Drenthe in 1991. *Drentse Vogels* 7: 59–70. (Habitat use, breeding density and breeding success of Common Crossbills *Loxia curvirostra* and Parrot Crossbills *L. pytyopsittacus* in West-Drenthe in 1991) (in Dutch, with English summary).

BIJLSMA, R.G. 1995. Wielewalen *Oriolus oriolus* en

populieren *Populus* spec. beneden zeeniveau. *Limosa* 68: 21–28. (Golden Orioles *Oriolus oriolus* and poplars *Populus* spec. below sea level) (in Dutch, with English summary).

BIJLSMA, R.G. and R. LENSINK. 1990. Opmars van de Kleine Vliegenvanger *Ficedula parva*? *Limosa* 63: 114–116. (Increase of Red-breasted Flycatcher *Ficedula parva*?) (in Dutch, with English summary).

BIJLSMA, R.G., A.J. van DIJK, F. HUSTINGS, R. LENSINK and F. POST. 1988. Strenge winters en schommelingen in de stand van de Boomleeuwerik *Lullula arborea* in Nederland: een verband? *Limosa* 61: 91–95. (Severe winters and fluctuations in the Woodlark *Lullula arborea* population in the Netherlands: a connection?) (in Dutch, with English summary).

BIRKHEAD, T.R. 1991. *The Magpies*. Poyser, London.

BJERKE, T.K. and T.H. BJERKE. 1981. Song dialects in the Redwing *Turdus iliacus*. *Ornis Scand*. 12: 40–50.

BJØRNSEN, B. 1988. The truth in advertising of the Lapland Bunting male, *Calcarius lapponicus*: Strophe length, song display, plumage coloration and biometry, in relation to territoriality and reproductive success of Lapland Bunting males. *Cand. scient. oppgave, Zool. Mus., Univ. i Bergen*.

BLAKERS, M., S.J.J.F. DAVIES and P.N. REILLY. 1984. *The Atlas of Australian Birds*. Melbourne University Press, Melbourne.

BLANCO, J.C. and J.L. GONZALEZ (Eds). 1992. *Libro Rojo de los Vertebrados de España*. Colección Técnica, ICONA, Madrid.

BLOMERT, A-M., M. ENGELMOER and Y. NTIMAO-BAIDU. 1991. The Banc d'Arguin, Mauritania, as a meeting point for Avocets during spring migration. *Ardea* 78: 185–192.

BLONDEL, J. 1970. Biogéographie des oiseaux nicheurs en Provence occidentale, du Mont Ventoux à la mer Méditerranée. *L'Oiseau et R.F.O.* 40: 1–47.

BLONDEL, J. 1988. Biogéographie évolutive à différentes échelles: l'histoire des avifaunes méditerranéennes. In: Ouellet, H. (Ed) *Acta XIX Congr. Int. Ornithol., Ottawa 1986*: 155–188.

BLONDEL, J. 1990. Biogeography and history of forest bird faunas in the Mediterranean zone. In: Keast, A. (Ed) *Biogeography and Ecology of Forest Bird Communities*. SPB Academic Publishing, The Hague: 95–107.

BLONDEL, J. and J. ARONSON. 1994. Biodiversity and ecosystem function in the Mediterranean basin. In: Davis, G. and D. Richardson (Eds) *Biodiversity and Ecosystem Function in Mediterranean-type Ecosystems*. Springer-Verlag, Berlin: 43–119.

BLONDEL, J., A. CLAMENS, P. CRAMM, H. GAUBERT and P. ISENMANN. 1987. Population studies on tits in the Mediterranean region. *Ardea* 75: 21–34.

BLUME, D. 1981. *Schwarzspecht, Grünspecht, Grauspecht*. Neue Brehm-Bücherei 300, Ziemsen, Wittenberg.

BLÜMEL, H. 1983. *Der Grünling*. Neue Brehm-Bücherei 490, Ziemsen Wittenberg.

BLUMS, P. and H. LITZBARSKI. 1982. [*Migration of the birds of Eastern Europe and Northern Asia* – Fulica atra.] Nauka, Moscow: 209–273 (in Russian).

BOANO, G. and M. CUCCO. 1989. Breeding biology of the Pallid Swift (*Apus pallidus*) in north-western Italy. *Gerfaut* 79: 133–148.

BOCHENSKI, Z. 1985. The development of western Palearctic avifaunas from the fossil evidence. *Acta XVIII Congr. Intern. Ornithol., Moscow* 1: 338–347.

BOCK, F. and W. WALTER. 1976. Zur Vogelfauna der Insel Krk und benachbarter Inseln der Kvarner Bucht. *Egretta* 19: 11–22.

BODDY, M. 1994. Survival/return rates and juvenile dispersal in an increasing population of Lesser Whitethroats *Sylvia curruca*. *Ringing and Migration* 15: 65–78.

BOERE, G., K. ROSELAAR and M. ENGELMOER. 1984. The breeding origins of Purple Sandpipers *Calidris maritima* present in the Netherlands. *Ardea* 72: 101–110.

BOERTMANN, D., H. MELTOFTE and M. FACHHAMMER. 1991. Population densities of birds in central Northeast Greenland. *Dansk Orn. Foren. Tidsskr.* 85: 151–160.

BOGLIANI, G., F. BARBIERI and E. TISO. 1994. Nest-site selection by the Hobby (*Falco subbuteo*) in poplar plantations in northern Italy. *J. Raptor Res.* 28: 13–18.

BOJARSHINOV, V.D., S.A. SHURAKOV and G.V. SEMJANNIKOV. 1989. [The list of the 'Basegi' Reserve birds.] In: Davygora, A.V. (Ed) [*The Distribution of the Birds and Avifauna of the Urals*.] Sverdlovsk: 24–26 (in Russian).

BOLDREGHINI, P., P.L. MEININGER and R. SANTOLINI. 1992. Preliminary results of ringing Mediterranean Gulls (*Larus melanocephalus*) breeding in the Netherlands, Belgium and Italy. *Avocetta* 16: 73–74.

BONCZAR, Z. 1991. *Karpacka populacja jarzabka* (Bonasa bonasia) *i jej mozliwosti uzytkowania*. Rozprava habilitacyjna, Academia Rolnicza, Kraków.

BOOBYER, G. 1992. *Population Trends of the Golden Plover* Pluvialis apricaria *in Britain*. JNCC Report, JNCC, Peterborough.

BORODIN, A.M. 1984. *Red Data Book of the USSR: Rare and endangered species of animals and plants*, Vol. 1: *Animals*, 2nd edn. Promyshlennost, Moscow (in Russian).

BOROVIKOV, G.A. 1907. [Ornithological material from Ekaterinoslavski gubernia (district). *Proceedings of Students Group at Imperial Novorossiyski University*.] Odessa. No. 2: 1–272 (in Russian).

BORRAS, A. and J.C. SENAR. 1991. Opportunistic breeding of the Citril Finch *Serinus citrinella*. *J. Ornithol.* 132: 285–289.

BOSCH, F. van den, R. HENGEVELD and J.A.J. METZ. 1992. Analyzing the velocity of animal range expansion. *J. Biogeogr.* 19: 135–150.

BOSSERT, A. 1995. Bestandsentwicklung und Habitatnutzung des Alpenschneehuhns im Aletschgebiet, Schweizer Alpen. *Orn. Beob.* 92: 307–312.

BOST, C-A. 1994. Fauvette pitchou *Sylvia undata*. In: Yeatman-Berthelot, D. and G. Jarry (Eds) *Nouvel Atlas des Oiseaux Nicheurs de France 1985–1989*. Société Ornithologique de France, Paris: 562–563.

BOSTANZHOGLO, V.N. 1911. [Ornithological fauna of the Aral-Caspian steppes. Materials for investigation of flora and fauna of the Russian empire.] *Russ. Dept. Zool.* No. 11 (in Russian).

BOTTANI, C. and J-C. PRAZ. 1977. La répartition et la biologie de la Fauvette orphée *Sylvia hortensis* en Valais. *Nos Oiseaux* 34: 155–158.

BOURGONJE, A. 1994. Overwinterende Oeverpiepers *Anthus spinoletta littoralis* in het Verdronken Land van Saeftinghe. *Limosa* 67: 117–118. (Wintering Scandinavian Rock Pipits *Anthus spinoletta littoralis* at 'Verdronken Land van Saeftinghe') (in Dutch, with English summary).

BOURNE, W.R.P. 1984. Preface to the Limpback Edition of Fisher, J. (1952) *The Fulmar*. Collins, London.

BOURNE, W.R.P., E.J. MACKRILL, A.M. PATERSON and P. YÉSOU. 1988. The Yelkouan Shearwater *Puffinus (puffinus?) yelkouan*. *Brit. Birds* 81: 306–319.

BOWDEN, C. and R. HOBLYN. 1990. The increasing importance of restocked conifer plantations for Woodlarks in Britain: implications and consequences. *RSPB Conservation Rev.* 4: 26–31.

BOYARSHINOV, V.D., S.A. SHURAKOV and G.V. SEMYANNIKOV. 1989. [The list of the 'Basegi' Reserve birds.] In: Davygora, A.V. (Ed) *The Distribution of the Birds and Avifauna of the Urals*. Sverdlovsk: 24–26 (in Russian).

BOYD, H. 1992. Arctic summer conditions and British Knot numbers: an exploratory analysis. In: Piersma, T. and N. Davidson (Eds) *The Migration of the Knot. Wader Study Group Bull.* 64, Suppl: 144–152.

BOYD, H. and S.K. ELTRINGHAM. 1962. The Whooper Swan in Great Britain. *Bird Study* 9: 217–241.

BOZHKO, S.I. 1980. *Der Karmingimpel*. Neue Brehm-Bücherei 529, Ziemsen, Wittenberg.

BRANSON, N.J.B.A. and C.D.T. MINTON. 1976. Moult, measurements and migration of the Grey Plover. *Bird Study* 23: 257–266.

BRAZIL, M. 1981. Geographical variation in the bill patterns of Whooper swans. *Wildfowl* 32: 129–131.

BREHME, S. 1991. Vogelbeobachtungen in Bulgarien. *Orn. Mitt.* 43: 187–190.

BREIEHAGEN, T. 1989. Nesting biology and mating system in an alpine population of Temminck's Stint *Calidris temminckii*. *Ibis* 131: 389–402.

BREIEHAGEN, T. 1994. Temmincksnipe *Calidris temminckii*. In: Gjershaug, J.O., P.G. Thingstad, S. Eldøy and S. Byrkjeland (Eds) *Norsk Fugleatlas*. Norsk Ornitologisk Forening, Klæbu: 182–183 (in Norwegian).

BREIFE, B., E. HIRSCHFELD, N. KJELLÉN and M. ULLMAN. 1990. Rare birds in Sweden. *Vår Fågelvärld*, suppl. 13: 1–214 (in Swedish).

BREITENMOSER-WÜRSTEN, C. and C. MARTI. 1987. Verbreitung und Siedlungsdichte von Wasseramsel *Cinclus cinclus* und Bergstelze *Motacilla cinerea* im Saanenland (Berner Oberland). *Orn. Beob.* 84: 151–172.

BRENCHLEY, A. 1986. The breeding distribution and abundance of the rook (*Corvus f. frugilegus* L.) in Great Britain since the 1920s. *J. Zool., Lond.* 210: 261–278.

BRETAGNOLLE, V., M. CARRUTHERS, M. CUBITT, F. BIORET and J–P. GUILLANDRE. 1991. Six captures of a dark-rumped, fork-tailed storm-petrel in the northeastern Atlantic. *Ibis* 133: 351–356.

BRICHETTI, P. 1992. Mignattaio *Plegadis falcinellus*. In: Brichetti, P., P. de Franceschi and N. Baccetti (Eds) *Fauna d'Italia, Aves I*. Edizioni Calderini, Bologna: 226–233.

BRICHETTI, P. and D. CAMBI. 1979. L'occhiocotto *Sylvia melanocephala* (Gmelin) nell'Italia settentrionale. *Gli Uccelli d'Italia* 4: 68–78.

BRICHETTI, P. and D. CAMBI. 1985. *Atlante degli uccelli nidificanti in provincia di Brescia (Lombardia) 1980–1984*. Monografie di Natura Bresciana, No. 8.

BRICHETTI, P. and C. di CAPI. 1985. Distribution, population and breeding ecology of the Corsican Nuthatch *Sitta whiteheadi* Sharpe. *Riv. ital. Orn.* 55: 3–26.

BRICHETTI, P. and C. di CAPI. 1987. Conservation of the Corsican nuthatch *Sitta whiteheadi* Sharpe, and proposal for habitat management. *Biol. Conservation* 39: 13–21.

BRICHETTI, P. and M. FASOLA. 1990. *Atlante degli uccelli nidificanti in Lombardia (1983–1987)*. Editoriale Ramperto, Brescia.

BRICHETTI, P. and U.F. FOSCHI. 1987. The Lesser Crested Tern in the Western Mediterranean and Europe. *Brit. Birds* 80: 276–280.

BRICHETTI, P. and A. GARIBOLDI. 1997. *Manuale pratico di ornitologia*. Edagricole, Bologna.

BRICHETTI, P. and B. MASSA. 1984. Check-list degli uccelli italiani. *Riv. ital. Orn.* 54: 3–37.

BRICHETTI, P., U.F. FOSCHI and S. GELLINI. 1988. Distribuzione e consistenza delle colonie di Apodidae del promontorio del Gargano (Puglia). *Riv. ital. Orn.* 58: 53–58.

BRICHETTI, P., P. DE FRANCESCHI, and N. BACCETTI, 1992. *Fauna d'italia. Aves I. Gaviidae-Phasianidae*. Edizioni Calderini, Bologna.

BRIGGS, K. 1983. The distribution and reproduction of Ringed Plovers breeding coastally and inland in north-west England. *Bird Study* 30: 222–228.

BRINK, B. van den and K-H. LOSKE. 1990. Botswana and Namibia as regular wintering quarters for European Reed Warblers? *Ostrich* 61: 146–147.

BRINK, H. van den, J. FURDA, J. van KLINKEN and K. van SCHARENBURG (Eds). 1992. *Vogelatlas van Groningen*. Vereniging Avifauna Groningen, SOVON district Groningen and Provincie Groningen, Groningen. (*Bird Atlas of Groningen*) (in Dutch).

BRODKORB, P. 1971. Origin and Evolution of Birds. In: Farner, D.S. and J.R. King (Eds) *Avian Biology*, Vol. 1. Academic Press, New York: 19–55.

BRONSKOV, A.I., G.N. MOLODAN and A.V. GOVYADOV. 1989. [Breeding Passerines in natural ecosystems of Donetsk district.] *All-Union Wildlife Inventory and Census Workshop*. Abstracts, Part III, Ufa: 26–28 (in Russian).

BROOKE, M. 1990. *The Manx Shearwater*. Poyser, London.

BROWN, A.F., H.Q.P. CRICK, and R.A. STILLMAN. 1995. The distribution, numbers and breeding ecology of Twite *Acanthis flavirostris* in the south Pennines of England. *Bird Study* 42: 107–121.

BROWN, L. 1971. *African Birds of Prey*. Houghton Mifflin, Boston: 193–197.

BROWN, L.H. and B.E. BROWN. 1973. The relative numbers of migrant and resident rollers in eastern Kenya. *Bull. Brit. Orn. Club* 93: 126–130.

BROWN, R.G.B. and D.E. GASKIN. 1988. The pelagic ecology of the Grey and Red-necked Phalaropes *Phalaropus fulicarius* and *P. lobatus* in the Bay of Fundy, eastern Canada. *Ibis* 130: 234–250.

BROWN, R.G.B., N.G. BLURTON JONES and D.J.T. HUSSELL. 1967. The breeding behaviour of Sabine's Gull. *Behaviour* 28: 110–140.

BROYER, J. 1994. La régression du râle de genêts *Crex crex* en France et la gestion du milieux prairiaux. *Alauda* 62: 1–7.

BRUDERER, B. and H. BRUDERER. 1993. Distribution and habitat preferences of Redbacked Shrikes *Lanius collurio* in southern Africa. *Ostrich* 64: 141–147.

BRUDERER, B. and W. HIRSCHI. 1984. Langfristige Bestandsentwicklung von Gartenrötel *Phoenicurus phoenicurus* und Trauerschnäpper *Ficedula hypoleuca*. *Orn. Beob.* 81: 285–302.

BRUIJN, O. de. 1994. Population ecology and conservation of the Barn Owl *Tyto alba* in farmland habitats in Liemers and Achterhoek (The Netherlands). *Ardea* 82: 1–109.

BUB, H. 1985. Die Planberingung des Berghänflings (*Carduelis f. flavirostris*) 1952–1970 in Mitteleuropa. *Beitr. Vogelkd.* 31: 189–213.

BÜCHEL, H.P. 1974. Beobachtungen über die winterliche Kulturfolge, die Brutbiologie sowie einige vermutlich angeborene Verhaltensweisen der Alpendohle. *Mitt. Naturf. Ges. Luzern* 24: 72–94.

BÜCHEL, H.P. 1994. Lebenserwartung, Todesursachen and Flügelmaße der Alpendohle *Pyrrhocorax graculus*. *Orn. Beob.* 91: 43–48.

BUCKLAND, S.T., D.R. ANDERSON, K.S. BURNHAM and J.L. LAAKE. 1993. *Distance Sampling: Estimating Abundance of Biological Populations*. Chapman and Hall, Glasgow and New York.

BUENO, J.M. 1991. Migración e invernada de pequeños turdinos en la Península Ibérica. II. Collalba gris (*Oenanthe oenanthe*), tarabilla norteña (*Saxicola rubetra*) y tarabilla común (*Saxicola torquata*). *Ardeola* 38: 117–129.

BÜHLER, U. 1976. *Untersuchung über die Rolle der waldbaulichen Betriebsart und der Waldstruktur für die Verbreitung des Mittelspechts (*Dendrocopos medius *L.)*. Diplomarbeit. Inst. f. Waldbau, ETH Zürich.

BÜHLER, U. 1991. Populationsökologie des Sperbers *Accipiter nisus* L. in der Schweiz – ein Predator in einer mit chemischen Rückständen belasteten Umwelt. *Orn. Beob.* 88: 341–452.

BÜHLER, U. and P.A. OGGIER. 1987. Bestand und Bestandsentwicklung des Habichts *Accipiter gentilis* in der Schweiz. *Orn. Beob.* 84: 71–94.

BUKACIŃSKI D., J.P. CYGAN, M. KELLER, M. PIOTROWSKA and J. WÓJCIAK. 1995. [Numbers and distribution of the waterfowl nesting in the Vistula middle course – fluctuations in 1973–1993.] *Notatki Ornitologiczne* 35: 5–47 (in Polish).

BULAKHOV, V.L., O.M. MYASOEDOV, An.A. GUBKIN and Al.A. GUBKIN. 1990. [Water reservoirs and brackish lagoons of the Lower Dnieper River as places of concentrations of migrant waders.] *Ornitologiya* 24: 141–142 (in Russian).

BULLOCK, I.D., D.R. DREWETT and S.P. MICKLEBURGH. 1983. The chough in Britain and Ireland. *Brit. Birds* 76: 377–401.

BULTEEL, G. 1992. Le Cassenoix moucheté en Ardenne: Répartition, effectifs, cadre biogéographique. *Aves* 29: 1–36.

BUNZEL, M. and J. DRÜKE. 1989. Kingfisher. In: I. Newton (Ed) *Lifetime Reproduction in Birds*. Academic Press, London: 106–116.

BURGERS, J., J.J. SMIT and H. VAN DER VOET. 1991. Origins and systematics of two types of the Bean Goose *Anser fabalis* (Latham, 1787) wintering in the Netherlands. *Ardea* 79: 307–315.

BÜRKLI, W., M. JUON and K. RUGE. 1975. Zur Biologie des Dreizehenspechts. 5. Beobachtungen zur Fütterungszeit und zur Grösse des Aktionsgebietes. *Orn. Beob.* 72: 23–28.

BURTON, J.F. 1995. *Birds and Climate Change*. Christopher Helm, London.

BUSCHE, G. 1985. Zur Bestandsabnahme der Schafstelze (*Motacilla flava*) in Schleswig-Holstein. *Vogelwarte* 33: 109–114.

BUSCHE, G. 1989a. Drastische Bestandseinbußen der Feldlerche *Alauda arvensis* auf Grünlandflächen in Schleswig-Holstein. *Vogelwelt* 110: 51–59.

BUSCHE, G. 1989b. Niedergang des Bestandes der Grauammer (*Emberiza calandra*) in Schleswig-Holstein. *Vogelwarte* 35: 11–20.

BUSCHE, G. 1991. Bestandseinbußen des Hänflings *Carduelis cannabina* im Westen Schleswig-Holsteins. *Vogelwelt* 112: 162–176.

BUSCHE, G. 1993. Zur Zugphänologie der Ringdrossel (*Turdus t. torquatus*) in Schleswig-Holstein – ein Beitrag zur Schleifenzug-Theorie. *Vogelwarte* 37: 12–18.

BUSSE, P. 1969. Results of ringing of European Corvidae. *Acta Ornithol.* 11: 263–328.

BY, R.A. de, A.B. van den BERG and CDNA. 1992. Zeldzame en schaarse vogels in Nederland in 1990. *Limosa* 65: 137–146. (Rare and scarce birds in the Netherlands in 1990) (in Dutch, with English summary).

BYERS, C., U. OLSSON and J. CURSON. 1995. *Buntings and Sparrows: a guide to the buntings and North American sparrows*. Pica Press, Robertsbridge.

BYSHNEV, I.I. In press. Black Stork in the Berezinsky Biosphere Reserve. In: Brouwer, K., C. King and M. Strazds (Eds). *The Black Stork in the Changing World. Proceedings of the 1st International Black Stork Conservation and Ecology Symposium, Jurmala, Latvia.* Latvian Ornithological Society Riga.

CADE, T.J., J.H. ENDERSON, C.G. THELANDER and C.M. WHITE (Eds). 1988. *Peregrine Falcon Populations. Their management and recovery*. The Peregrine Fund, Boise, Idaho.

CALDERON RODRIGUEZ, J.M. 1964. El colin en España. *Doc. Tecnicos*. Seriel cinegetica No. 2. Madrid.

CALLAGHAN, D.A. and A.J. GREEN. 1993. Wildfowl at risk. *Wildfowl* 44: 149–169.

CALLION, J. 1993. Stonechat *Saxicola torquata*. In: Gibbons, D.W., J.B. Reid and R.A. Chapman (Eds) *The New Atlas of Breeding Birds in Britain and Ireland: 1988–1991*. Poyser, London: 308–309.

CALVO, B., M. MAÑEZ and L.J. ALBERTO. 1993. The Collared Pratincole *Glareola pratincola* in the National Park of Doñana, south-west Spain. *Wader Study Group Bull.* 67: 81–87.

CAMPHUYSEN, C.J. 1994. Ivory Gull *Pagophila eburnea*. In: G.M. Tucker and M.F. Heath (Eds) *Birds in Europe – their conservation status*. Conservation Series No. 3, BirdLife International, Cambridge: 290–291.

CAMPHUYSEN, C.J. and M.F. LEOPOLD. 1994. *Atlas of seabirds in the southern North Sea*. IBN Research

Report 94/6, NIOZ-Report 1994–8, IBN-DLO and NZG, Texel.
CANO, A. 1960. Sobre nidificación de *Erythropygia galactotes* en Pechina, Almeria. *Ardeola* 6: 320–323.
CANTONI, J. 1963. Sur la présence de *Sylvia sarda* à l'Île de Zembra. *Alauda* 31: 61–63.
CANTOS, F.J. 1994. *Sylvia undata*. In: Tucker, G.M. and M.F. Heath (Eds) *Birds in Europe – their conservation status*. Conservation Series No. 3, BirdLife International, Cambridge: 400–401.
CARBAJO MOLINERO, F. and J.J. FERRERO CANTISÁN. 1985. Ecology and status of the Black-shouldered Kite in Extremadura, Western Spain. In: Newton I. and R.D. Chancellor (Eds) *Conservation Studies on Raptors*. ICBP Tech. Publ. No. 5, International Council for Bird Preservation, Cambridge: 137–141.
CARLO, E. A. di. 1976. Il Venturone nell' Italia centrale. *Gli Uccelli d'Italia. Società Ornitologica Italiana* 1: 137–139.
CARLON, J. 1987. Effectifs, répartition et densité de l'aigle botté *Hieraaetus pennatus* (Gmelin 1788) dans les Pyrénées-Atlantiques. *Alauda* 55: 81–92.
CARNERO, J.I. and S.J. PERIS. 1988. *Atlas Ornitológico de la provincia de Salamanca*. Ediciones de la Diputación de Salamanca, Serie Ciencias, 5. Salamanca.
CARTER, S.P. 1993a. Goosander *Mergus merganser*. In: Gibbons, D.W., J.B. Reid and R.A. Chapman (Eds) *The New Atlas of Breeding Birds in Britain and Ireland: 1988–1991*. Poyser, London: 92–93.
CARTER, S.P. 1993b. Red-breasted Merganser *Mergus serrator*. In: Gibbons, D.W., J.B. Reid and R.A. Chapman (Eds) *The New Atlas of Breeding Birds in Britain and Ireland: 1988–1991*. Poyser, London: 90–91.
CATALISANO, A., F. Lo VALVO, G. Lo VERDE and B. MASSA. 1988. Dati biometrici dell'Uccello delle tempeste (*Hydrobates pelagicus*). *Atti IV Conv. ital. Orn., Naturalista sicil.* 12 (suppl.): 261–265.
CATLEY, G.P. and D. HURSTHOUSE. 1985. Parrot Crossbills in Britain. *Brit. Birds* 78: 482–505.
CATZEFLIS, F. 1978. Sur la biologie de reproduction du Pipit spioncelle alpin. *Nos Oiseaux* 34: 287–302.
CAVÉ, A.J. 1983. Purple Heron survival and drought in tropical West-Africa. *Ardea* 71: 217–224.
CAVÉ, A.J. and J. VISSER. 1985. Winter severity and breeding numbers in a Coot population. *Ardea* 73: 129–138.
CELMINS, A., J. BAUMANIS and A. MEDNIS. 1993. Gandrs, *List of Latvian bird species 1993*. Gandrs, Riga.
CEMPULIK, P. 1994. Bestandsentwicklung, Brutbiologie und Ökologie der Zwergdommel *Ixobrychus minutus* an Fisch- und Industrieteichen Oberschlesiens. *Vogelwelt* 115: 19–27.
CENTRE ORNITHOLOGIQUE DU GARD. 1994. Rollier d'Europe *Coracias garrulus*. In: Yeatman-Berthelot, D. and G. Jarry (Eds) *Nouvel Atlas des Oiseaux Nicheurs de France 1985–1989*. Société Ornithologique de France, Paris: 424–425.
CERAIL, M. 1994. Crave à bec rouge *Pyrrhocorax pyrrhocorax*. In: Yeatman-Berthelot, D. and G. Jarry (Eds) *Nouvel Atlas des Oiseaux Nicheurs de France 1985–1989*. Société Ornithologique de France, Paris: 654–655.
CERCLE ORNITHOLOGIQUE de FRIBOURG. 1993. *Atlas des Oiseaux nicheurs du canton de Fribourg*. Fribourg: 257.
CHABLOZ, V. and P. WEGMÜLLER. 1994. Nidification du Pic tridactyle *(Picoides tridactylus)* dans le Jura vaudois (Suisse). *Nos Oiseaux* 42: 261–266.
CHABRZYK, G. and J.C. COULSON. 1976. Survival and recruitment in the Herring Gull. *J. Anim. Ecol.* 44: 187–203.
CHANTLER, P. and G. DRIESSENS. 1995. *Swifts: A guide to the swifts and treeswifts of the world*. Pica Press, Robertsbridge.
CHAPPUIS, C., H. HEIM de BALSAC and J. VIEILLARD. 1973. Distribution, réproduction, manifestions vocales et affinités du Bruant cendré, *Emberiza cineracea*. *Bonn Zool. Beitr.* 24: 302–316.
CHARALAMBIDES, M. 1994. Black Francolin. In: Tucker, G.M. and M.F. Heath (Eds) *Birds in Europe – their conservation status*. Conservation Series No. 3, BirdLife International, Cambridge.
CHARTIER, A. 1989. Bruant zizi *Emberiza cirlus*. In: *GONm: Atlas des oiseaux de Normandie et des îles Anglo-Normandes. Le Cormoran* 7: 190.
CHERNEL, I. 1899. *Magyarország madárvilága különös tekintettel gazdasági jelentóségükre*. Budapest (in Hungarian).
CHERNICHKO, I. 1993. Breeding population and distribution of seabirds (gulls and terns) on the northern coast of the Black Sea and the Sea of Azov. In: Aquilar, J.S., X. Monbailliu and A.M. Paterson (Eds) *Status and Conservation of Seabirds. Proceedings of the 2nd Mediterranean Seabird Symposium, Calvia, 21–26 March 1989*. Sociedad Espanola de Ornitologia, Madrid: 125–131.
CHERNICHKO, I.I., V.B. GRINCHENKO, M.E. ZHMUD and G.N. MOLODAN. 1990. [Numbers of colonial waders in the southern Ukraine, based on censuses in 1984–85.] *Ornitologiya* 24: 165–166 (in Russian).
CHEYLAN, G. 1981. Le statut des Falconiformes de Provence. In: Cheylan, G. and J-C. Thibault (Eds) Rapaces Mediterranéens. *Annales du CROP* 1: 22–27.
CHEYLAN, G. 1985. Le statut de la canepetière *Tetrax tetrax* en Provence. *Alauda* 53: 90–99.
CHEYLAN, G. 1994a. Aigle de Bonelli *Hieraaetus fasciatus*. In: Yeatman-Berthelot, D. and G. Jarry (Eds) *Nouvel Atlas des Oiseaux Nicheurs de France*. Société Ornithologique de France, Paris: 200–201.
CHEYLAN, G. 1994b. Ganga cata *Pterocles alchata*. In: Yeatman-Berthelot, D. and G. Jarry (Eds) *Nouvel Atlas des Oiseaux Nicheurs de France 1985–1989*. Société Ornithologique de France, Paris: 366–367.
CHIAVETTA, M. 1981. *Rapaci d'Italia e d'Europa*. Rizzoli, Milano.
CHIAVETTA, M., and D. MARTELLI. 1991. Dinamica di popolazione del Lanario (*Falco biarmicus*) nell' Appennino Emiliano nell' ultimo ventennio. *Atti II Conv. Naz. Biol. Selvaggina*. INFS, Bologna: 605–608.
CHOREMI, J., D. CHOULIS and V. SPINTHAKIS. 1993. *The Birds of Chios*. Municipality of the City of Homeroupolis.
CHRISTEN, W. 1989. Veränderungen des Brutvogelbestandes einer Jungwaldfläche zwischen 1982 und 1989. *Orn. Beob.* 86: 329–336.

CLAESSENS, O. 1992. La situation du Bruant ortolan *Emberiza hortulana* en France et en Europe. *Alauda* 60: 65–76.

CLAMENS, A. 1993. L'habitat de la Fauvette passerinette *Sylvia cantillans* en Andorre (Pyrénées); influence du changement des activités humaines. *Alauda* 61: 100–104.

CLAUSAGER, I. 1974. Migration of Scandinavian woodcock (*Scolopax rusticola*) with special reference to Denmark. *Dan. Rev. Game Biol.* 8: 1–38.

CLAUSEN, P. and J. MADSEN. 1986. Forekomsten af Korttået Træløber Certhia brachydactyla i Danmark. *Dansk Orn. Foren. Tidsskr.* 80: 9–16 (in Danish, with English summary).

CLAUSEN, P. and S. TOFT. 1988. Mixed singers and imitation singers among Short-toed Treecreepers. *Brit. Birds* 81: 496–503.

CLAVEL, J., E. MARTORELL, D.M. SANTOS and D. SOL. 1991. Distribució de la Cotoretta de Pit Gris *Myiopsitta monachus* a Catalunya. *Bull. GCA* 8: 15–18.

CLAVIER, J-L. 1994. Rossignol philomèle *Luscinia megarhynchos*. In: Yeatman-Berthelot, D. and G. Jarry (Eds) *Nouvel Atlas des Oiseaux Nicheurs de France 1985–1989*. Société Ornithologique de France, Paris: 502–503.

CLEMENT, P., A. HARRIS and J. DAVIS. 1993. *Finches and Sparrows: an identification guide*. A. and C. Black, London.

COLLAR, H.P. 1995. *Draft Action Plan for the Great Bustard*. Unpublished report, Birdlife International, Cambridge.

COLLAR, N.J., M.J. CROSBY and A.J. STATTERSFIELD. 1994. *Birds to Watch 2: the world list of threatened birds*. Conservation Series No. 4, BirdLife International, Cambridge.

COMBREAU, O. 1992. *Études des variations saisonnières du regime, des exigences et de la sélectivité alimentaire chez la caille des blés (*Coturnix c. coturnix*). Approche causale et fonctionnelle*. PhD Thesis, Université de Rennes I, Rennes.

CONDER, P. 1993. Wheatear *Oenanthe oenanthe*. In: Gibbons, D.W., J.B. Reid and R.A. Chapman (Eds) *The New Atlas of Breeding Birds in Britain and Ireland: 1988–1991*. Poyser, London: 310–311.

CONSELLERIA D'AGRICULTURA i PESCA. 1988. *Proyecto de Reintroducción del Calamón en el Parque Natural de L'Albufera*. Generalitat Valenciana.

COOK, A. 1975. Changes in the Carrion/Hooded Crow hybrid zone and the possible importance of climate. *Bird Study* 22: 165–168.

COOMBS, F. 1978. *The Crows – a study of the Corvids of Europe*. Batsford, London.

CORMIER, J-P. 1994. Busard Saint-Martin *Circus cyaneus*. In: Yeatman-Berthelot, D. and G. Jarry (Eds) *Nouvel Atlas des Oiseaux Nicheurs de France 1985–1989*. Société Ornithologique de France, Paris: 184–185.

COSTERS, R. 1992. Hoe vergaat het de Stormmeeuw *Larus canus* bij Petten? *Sula* 6: 93–99. (The fate of Common Gulls *Larus canus* breeding near Petten) (in Dutch, with English summary).

COULSON, J.C. and M.P. JOHNSON. 1993. The attendance and absence of adult Kittiwakes *Rissa tridactyla* from the nest site during the chick stage. *Ibis* 135: 372–378.

COULSON, J.C., J. BUTTERFIELD, N. DUNCAN, S. KEARSEY, P. MONAGHAN and C. THOMAS. 1984. Origin and behaviour of Great Black-backed gulls wintering in northeast England. *Brit. Birds* 77: 1–11.

COWLEY, E. 1979. Sand Martin population trends in Britain, 1965–1978. *Bird Study* 26: 113–116.

CRAMP, S. 1963. Movements of tits in Europe in 1959 and after. *Brit. Birds* 56: 237–263.

CRAMP, S., A. PETTET and J.T.R. SHARROCK. 1960. The irruptions of tits in autumn 1957. Parts 1–3. *Brit. Birds* 53: 49–77, 99–117, 176–192.

CRAMP, S., W.R.P. BOURNE and D. SAUNDERS. 1974. *The Seabirds of Britain and Ireland*. Collins, London.

CRAMP, S., K.E.L. SIMMONS and C.M. PERRINS. 1977–94. *Handbook of the Birds of Europe, the Middle East and North Africa (Birds of the Western Palearctic)*. Vols 1–9. Oxford University Press, Oxford.

CRANSWICK, P.A., R.J. WATERS, J. EVANS and M.S. POLLITT. 1995. *The Wetland Bird Survey 1993–94: Wildfowl and Wader Counts*. BTO/WWT/RSPB/JNCC, Slimbridge.

CREUTZ, G. 1981. *Der Graureiher*. Neue Brehm-Bücherei 530, Ziemsen, Wittenberg.

CRICK, H.Q.P. 1992. *Trends in the Breeding Performance of Golden Plover in Britain*. BTO Research Report No. 76, British Trust for Ornithology, Thetford.

CRICK, H.Q.P. 1993. Trends in breeding success of Merlins (*Falco columbarius*) in Britain from 1937–1989. In: Nicholls, M.K. and R. Clarke (Eds) *Biology and Conservation of Small Falcons*. Hawk and Owl Trust, London: 30–38.

CRICK, H.Q.P. and D.A. RATCLIFFE. 1994. The Peregrine *Falco peregrinus* population of the United Kingdom in 1991. *Bird Study* 42: 1–19.

CRICK, H.Q.P., C. DUDLEY, A.D. EVANS and K.W. SMITH. 1994. Causes of nest failure among buntings in the UK. *Bird Study* 41: 88–94.

CRIVELLI, A.J. 1994. The importance of the former USSR for the conservation of pelican populations nesting in the Palearctic. In: Crivelli, A.J., V.G. Krivenko and V.G. Vinogradov (Eds) *Pelicans in the Former USSR*. Special Publication No. 27, International Waterfowl and Wetlands Research Bureau, Slimbridge: 1–4.

CRIVELLI, A.J. and R.W. SCHREIBER. 1984. Status of the Pelecanidae. *Biol. Conservation* 30: 147–156.

CRIVELLI, A.J., Y. LESHEM, T. MITCHEV and H. JERRENTRUP. 1991a. Where do Palearctic Great White Pelicans (*Pelecanus onocrotalus*) presently overwinter? *Rev. Ecol. (Terre et Vie)* 46: 145–171.

CRIVELLI, A.J., G. CATSADORAKIS, H. JERRENTRUP, D. HATZILACOS, and T. MITCHEV. 1991b. *Conservation and Management of Pelicans Nesting in the Palearctic*. Technical Publication No.12, International Council For Bird Preservation, Cambridge: 137–152.

CROCQ, C. 1990. *Le casse-noix moucheté (*Nucifraga caryocatactes*)*. R. Chabaud - Lechevalier, Vineuil.

CRUZ, C. de la. 1988. [*A contribution to knowledge about the Azure-winged Magpie (*Cyanopica cyana *Pall., 1776)*.] PhD Thesis, University of Badajoz (in Spanish).

CUADRADO, M. 1992. Year to year recurrence and site-fidelity of Blackcaps *Sylvia atricapilla* and Robins

Erithacus rubecula in a Mediterranean wintering area. *Ringing and Migration* 13: 36–42.

CUADRADO, M., S. ÁRJONA and M. RODRIGUEZ. 1985. Hivernage du Martinet pâle *Apus pallidus* dans le Sud d'Espagne. *Alauda* 53: 306–307.

CUBITT, M., M. CARRUTHERS and F. ZINO. 1992. Unravelling the mystery of the Tyne Petrels. *Birding World* 5: 438–442.

CUISIN, M. 1985. Range-expansion of the Black Woodpecker in Western Europe. *Brit. Birds* 78: 184–187.

CURIO, E. 1959. Beobachtungen am Halbringschnäpper, *Ficedula semitorquata*, im mazedonischen Brutgebiet. *J. Ornithol.* 100: 176–209.

CURRY-LINDAHL, K. (Ed). 1960. *Våra Fåglar i Norden*. Vol. 2. Bockforläget Natur och Kultur, Stockholm.

CURTIS, D.J., E.M. BIGNAL and M.A. CURTIS (Eds). 1991. Birds and Pastoral Agriculture in Europe. *Proceedings of the Second European Forum on Birds and Pastoralism, 26–30 October 1990, Isle of Man*. JNCC, Peterborough.

CUSTER, T.W. and F.A. PITELKA. 1977. Demographic features of a Lapland Longspur population near Barrow, Alaska. *Auk* 94: 505–525.

CUYÁS J. 1971. Algunas notas sobre las aves observadas durante tres visitas a las Islas Canarias (1964 and 1967). *Ardeola* vol. esp.: 103–153.

DAGLEY, J.R. 1994. Golden Orioles in East Anglia and their conservation. *Brit. Birds* 87: 205–219.

DAL', S.K. 1954. [*Animal World of Armenian SSR*.] Academy of Sciences of the Armenian SSR, Erevan (in Russian).

DALLINGA, J.H. and S. SCHOENMAKERS. 1985. Regional decreases in the number of White Storks (*Ciconia c. ciconia*) in relation to food resources. *Colonial Waterbirds* 10: 167–177.

DANCHIN, E. and J-Y. MONNAT. 1992. Population dynamics modelling of two neighbouring Kittiwake *Rissa tridactyla* colonies. *Ardea* 80: 171–180.

DANCHIN, E., B. CADIOU, J-Y. MONNAT and R. RODRIGUEZ ESTRELLA. 1991. Recruitment in long-lived birds: conceptual framework and behavioural mechanisms. *Acta XX Congr. Int. Ornithol.*: 1641–1656.

DANELL, K. and K. SJÖBERG. 1979. Abundance and productivity of ducks on boreal lakes in northern Sweden. *Ann. Zool. Fennici* 16: 123–128.

DANILOV, N.N., V.N. RYZHANOVSKY and V.K. RYABITSEV. 1984. [*Birds of the Yamal*.] Nauka, Moscow (in Russian).

DANKO, Š. 1996. Bisherige Ergebnisse der Beringung beim Kaiseradler (*Aquila heliaca*) im Nordwesten seines Brutareals. In: Meyburg, B-U. and R.D. Chancellor (Eds) *Eagle Studies*. WWGBPO. *Birds of Prey Bull.* 5: 389–403.

DANKO, Š. and J. CHAVKO. 1996. Breeding of the Imperial Eagle *Aquila heliaca* in Slovakia. History, present status, breeding success and conservation problems. In: B-U. Meyburg and R.D. Chancellor (Eds) *Eagle Studies*. WWGBPO. *Birds of Prey Bull.* 5: 415–423.

DANKO, Š., T. DIVIŠ, J. DVORSKÁ, M. DVORSKÝ, J. CHAVKO, D. KARASKA, B. KLOUBEC, P. KURKA, H. MATUŠIK, L. PEŠKE, L. SCHRÖPFER and R. VACÍK. 1994. [The state of knowledge of breeding numbers of birds of prey (*Falconiformes*) and owls (*Strigiformes*) in the Czech and Slovak Republics as of 1990 and their population trends in 1970–1990.] *Buteo* 6: 1–89 (in Czech, with English summary).

DARAKCHIEV, A., D. NANKINOV and I. BOYUKLIEV. 1986. Distribution of the Bee-eater (*Merops apiaster* L.) in the district of Plovdiv. *Collection of Research Works of the Plovdiv University 'Paisy Hilendarsky', Biology*, Vol. 24, book 1, 191–196 (in Bulgarian).

DARE, P.J. 1966. The breeding and wintering population of the Oystercatcher (*Haematopus ostralegus* Linnaeus) in the British Isles. *Fishery Investigations*, Series 2, Vol. 25(5).

DARE, P.J. 1986. Raven *Corvus corax* populations in two upland regions of north Wales. *Bird Study* 33: 179–189.

DAU, C.P. 1992. Population size and migration phenology of Soviet breeding Steller's Eiders at the Izambek National Wildlife Refuge. *Alaskan Bird Conference and Workshop – Shared Avian Resources of Beringia*. Anchorage Press, Anchorage.

DAUNICHT, W. 1985. Das Vorkommen der Heidelerche (*Lullula arborea*) in Schleswig-Holstein. *Corax* 11: 1–44.

DAVIES, A.K. 1988. The distribution and status of the Mandarin Duck *Aix galericulata* in Britain. *Bird Study* 35: 203–208.

DAVIES, A.K. and G.K. BAGGOTT. 1989. Clutch size and nesting sites of the Mandarin Duck *Aix galericulata*. *Bird Study* 36: 32–36.

DAVIES, M. 1988. The importance of Britain's Twites. In: Cadbury, C.J. and M. Everett (Eds) *RSPB Conservation Review* 2: 91–94. RSPB, Sandy.

DAVIES, N.B. 1992. *Dunnock Behaviour and Social Evolution*. Oxford University Press, Oxford.

DAVYGORA, A.V. and V.P. BELIK. 1994. The Pallid Harrier *Circus macrourus* as an endangered species in the Palaearctic. In: Meyburg, B-U. and R.D. Chancellor (Eds) *Raptor Conservation Today*. WWGBPO, Berlin: 93–96.

DAWSON, R. 1992. Blood, sweat and petrels. *Birding World* 5: 443–444.

DAY, J.C.U. 1981. Status of Bitterns in Europe since 1976. *Brit. Birds* 74: 10–16.

DEBOUT, G., N. RØV and R.M. SELLERS. 1995. Status and population development of Cormorants *Phalacrocorax carbo carbo* breeding on the Atlantic coast of Europe. *Ardea* 83: 47–59.

DEJAIFVE, P-A. 1994a. Merle de roche ou Monticole merle-de-roche *Monticola saxatilis*. In: Yeatman-Berthelot, D. and G. Jarry (Eds) *Nouvel Atlas des Oiseaux Nicheurs de France 1985–1989*. Société Ornithologique de France, Paris: 522–523.

DEJAIFVE, P-A. 1994b. Écologie et comportement d'un migrateur paléarctique, le Traquet tarier, *Saxicola rubetra* (L) au Zaïre et sa répartition hivernale en Afrique. *Rev. Ecol. (Terre et Vie)* 49: 35–52.

DELACOUR, J. 1951. Taxonomic notes on the Bean Geese, *Anser fabalis* Lath. *Ardea* 39: 135–142.

DELANY, S.N. 1992. Survey of introduced geese in Britain, summer 1991: provisional results. *Report to the Joint Nature Conservation Committee, the Ministry of Agriculture, Fisheries and Food and the National Trust*. The Wildfowl and Wetlands Trust, Slimbridge.

DELANY, S.N. 1993. Introduced and escaped geese in Britain in summer 1991. *Brit. Birds* 86: 591–599.

DELESTRADE, A. 1994. Factors affecting flock size in the Alpine Chough *Pyrrhocorax graculus*. *Ibis* 136: 91–96.

DELIUS, J.D. 1963. Das Verhalten der Feldlerche. *Z. Tierpsychol.* 20: 297–348.

DELMÉE, E., P. DACHY and P. SIMON. 1978. Quinze années d'observations sur la reproduction d'une population forestière de Chouettes hulottes (*Strix aluco*). *Gerfaut* 68: 590–650.

DEMENTIEV, G.P. 1951. Order Lari or Lariformes. In: Dementiev, G.P. and N.A. Gladkov (Eds) *Birds of the Soviet Union*, Vol. 3. Nauka, Moscow: 563–565.

DEMENTIEV, G.P. and N.A. GLADKOV (Eds). 1951. [*Birds of the Soviet Union.* Vol 5]. Nauka, Moscow (in Russian).

DEMENTIEV, G.P. and N.A. GLADKOV (Eds). 1954. [*Birds of the Soviet Union.* Vol 5]. Nauka, Moscow (in Russian).

DEMENTIEV, G.P. and N.A. GLADKOV. 1970. *Birds of the Soviet Union.* Israel Program of Scientific Translations, Jerusalem.

DEMETER, L. 1995. The spatial distribution of Great Bustard (*Otis tarda*) nests in relation to solitary males of eastern Hungary. *Aquila* 102: 53–60.

DEMONGIN, L. 1994. Le Harle huppé *Mergus serrator* nicheur en France en 1993. *Ornithos* 1: 49.

DENDALETCHE, C. and N. SAINT-LEBE. 1987. Données nouvelles sur le Chocard dans les Pyrénées. *Acta biol. mont.* 7: 115–122.

DENNIS, R. 1995. Ospreys *Pandion haliaetus* in Scotland – a study of recolonisation. *Vogelwelt* 116: 193–195.

DENNIS, R.H. and H. DOW. 1984. The establishment of a population of Goldeneyes *Bucephala clangula* breeding in Scotland. *Bird Study* 31: 217–222.

DENNIS, R.H., P.M. ELLIS, R.A. BROAD and D.R. LANGSLOW. 1984. The status of the Golden Eagle in Britain. *Brit. Birds* 77: 592–607.

DEPPE, H–J. 1990. Langfristige Brutbestandskontrollen beim Zaunkönig *Troglodytes troglodytes* im nördlichen Schleswig-Holstein. *Vogelwelt* 111: 238–244.

DEVOS, K., P. MEIRE, P. MAES, L. BENOY, J. GABRIËLS, F. De SCHEEMAEKER, W. De SMET and J. van IMPE. 1991. Broedvogelpopulaties van steltlopers in België, 1989–1990. *Oriolus* 57: 43–56 (in Flemish).

DHONDT, A.A. 1983. Variations in the number of overwintering Stonechats possibly caused by natural selection. *Ringing and Migration* 4: 155–158.

DIJK, A.J. van. 1990. Strenge winters zetten de toon in de eerste vijf jaar BMP. *Limosa* 63: 141–152. (Severe winters have strong impact on first five years of BMP) (in Dutch, with English summary).

DIJK, A.J. van. 1995. Weidevogels in het BMP in 1993–94. *SOVON-Nieuws* 8(2): 14–16. (Meadow birds in breeding monitoring plots in 1993–94) (in Dutch).

DIJK, A.J. van and F. HUSTINGS. 1994. Broedvogel Monitoring Project 1993. *SOVON-Nieuws* 7(4): 11–14. (Breeding Bird Monitoring Project 1993) (in Dutch).

DIJK, A.J. van, F. HUSTINGS and R. OFFEREINS. 1994a. Broedgevallen van de Roodhalsfuut *Podiceps grisegena* in Nederland in 1980–92. *Limosa* 67: 76–78. (Breeding records of Red-necked Grebe *Podiceps grisegena* in The Netherlands in 1980–92) (in Dutch, with English summary).

DIJK, A.J. van, F. HUSTINGS and T. VERSTRAEL. 1994b. *SOVON Broedvogelverslag 1993.* SOVON-monitoringrapport 1994/03, Beek-Ubbergen. (*SOVON Breeding Bird Report 1993*) (in Dutch).

DIJK, A.J. van, F. HUSTINGS and T. VERSTRAEL. 1994c. *SOVON Broedvogelverslag 1992.* SOVON-monitoringrapport 1994/03, Beek-Ubbergen. (SOVON breeding bird report for 1992). (in Dutch).

DIRKSEN, S. and J.H. BEEKMAN. 1991. Population size, breeding success and distribution of Bewick's Swans *Cygnus columbianus bewickii* wintering in Europe in 1986–87. In: Sears, J. and P.J. Bacon (Eds) *Proceedings of the Third IWRB International Swan Symposium, Oxford 1989. Wildfowl.* Special Supplement No.1: 120–124.

DITTBERNER, H. and W. DITTBERNER. 1984. *Die Schafstelze.* Neue Brehm-Bücherei 559, Ziemsen, Wittenberg.

DITTBERNER, H. and W. DITTBERNER. 1987. Zur Brutbiologie der Löffelente (*Anas clypeata*). *Vogelwelt* 108: 81–98.

DITTBERNER, H. and W. DITTBERNER. 1993. Brutökologie der Trauerseeschwalbe (*Chlidonias niger*) in der Uckermark. *Ökol. Vögel* 15: 17–84.

DIVOKY, G.J. and A.M. SPRINGER. 1988. Pelagic and coastal birds. In: Hameedi, G.J. and A.S. Naidu (Eds) *The Environment and Resources of the Southeastern Chukchi Sea.* US Department of the Interior, Minerals Management Service, Alaska OCS Region, OCS Study MMS 87–0113: 69–84.

DOLBIK, M.S. 1959. *Ptitsy belorusskogo Polesja.* Acad. Nauk BSSR, Minsk (in Russian).

DOLGUSHIN, I.A. (Ed). 1962. *Ptitsy Kazakhstana*, Vol. 2. Akademii Nauk Kazakhskoy SSR, Alma-Ata (in Russian).

DOLGUSHIN, I.A. and M.N. KORELOV. (Eds) 1970. *Ptitsy Kazakhstana*, Vol. 3. Alma-Ata (in Russian).

DOLZ, J.C., M.G. RIPOLL and J.H. PEDRERO. 1991. Status of some threatened Anatidae species in the Comunidad Valenciana, East Spain. *IWRB Threatened Waterfowl Research Group Newsletter* 1: 7–8.

DONALD, P.F. and A.D. EVANS. 1994. Habitat selection by Corn Buntings *Miliaria calandra* in winter. *Bird Study* 41: 199–210.

DONALD, P.F. and A.D. EVANS. 1995. Habitat selection and population size of Corn Buntings *Miliaria calandra* breeding in Britain in 1993. *Bird Study* 42: 190–204.

DONALD, P.F. and C. FORREST. 1995. The effects of agricultural change on population size of Corn Buntings *Miliaria calandra* on individual farms. *Bird Study* 42: 205–215.

DONALD, P.F., J.D. WILSON and M. SHEPHERD. 1994. The decline of the Corn Bunting. *Brit. Birds* 87: 106–132.

DONÁZAR, J.A. 1988. Selección del lugar de nidificación por el búho real (*Bubo bubo*) en Navarra. *Ardeola* 35: 233–245.

DONÁZAR, J.A. 1993. *Los buitres ibéricos. Biología y Conservación.* J.M. Reyero Ediciones, Madrid.

DONÁZAR, J.A. and C. FERNANDEZ. 1990. Population trends of the griffon vulture *Gyps fulvus* in northern Spain between 1969 and 1989 in relation to conservation measures. *Biol. Conservation* 53: 83–91.

DONÁZAR, J.A., O. CEBALLOS and C. FERNÁNDEZ. 1989. Factors influencing the distribution and abundance of seven cliff-nesting raptors: a multivariate study. In: Meyburg, B-U. and R.D. Chancellor (Eds) *Raptors in the Modern World*. WWGBPO. Berlin: 545–552.

DONÁZAR, J.A., J. BUSTAMENTE, J.J. NEGRO and F. HIRALDO. 1994. *Estudio del cernícalo primilla en el suroeste de España: factores determinantes de la distribución y densidad de población*. Sociedad Española de Ornitologia, Madrid.

DONK, J. van. 1976. An [18]O record of the Atlantic Ocean for the entire Pleistocene. *Mem. Geol. Soc. America* 145: 147–164.

DONTCHEV, S. 1963. New records on migration, wintering and distribution of some bird species in Bulgaria. *Bull. Inst. Zool.* 14: 111–125.

DONTCHEV, S. 1964. [On the distribution of some new and rare birds in Bulgaria.] *Bull. Inst. Zool. and Museum Sofia* 16: 23–28 (in Bulgarian, with German summary).

DONTCHEV, S. 1970a. [The Paddyfield Warbler *Acrocephalus agricola* (Jerdon, 1845). A new species in Bulgarian ornithofauna.] *Bull. Inst. Zool. and Museum Sofia*. 32: 181–183 (in Bulgarian, with German summary).

DONTCHEV, S. 1970b. Verbreitung für die Mittelmeerfauna charakteristischer Vögel in Bulgarien. *Beitr. Vogelkd.* 15: 391–394.

DONTCHEV, S. 1980. New habitats of some species of southern origin in Bulgaria. *Aquila* 87: 27–29.

DOROPHEEV, M. (Ed). 1993. [*The Republic of Belarus Red Data Book*.] Minsk, Byelaruskaya enciklopedia (in Belarussian).

DOUMERET, A. 1994. Milan noir *Milvus migrans*. In: Yeatman-Berthelot, D. and G. Jarry (Eds) *Nouvel Atlas des Oiseaux Nicheurs de France 1985–1989*. Société Ornithologique de France, Paris: 160–163.

DOVRAT, E. 1991. The Kefar Kassem raptor migration survey, autumns 1977–1987: a brief summary. In: Yekutiel, D. (Ed) *Raptors in Israel: Passage and wintering populations*. International Birdwatching Center Eilat, Eilat: 13–30.

DOWSETT, R.J., G.C. BACKHURST and T.B. OATLEY. 1988. Afrotropical ringing recoveries of Palaearctic migrants 1. Passerines (Turdidae to Oriolidae). *Tauraco* 1: 29–63.

DRENCKHAHN, D. 1974. Graureiher – *Ardea cinerea*. In: Berndt, R.K. and D. Drenckhahn (Eds) *Vogelwelt Schleswig-Holsteins*, Vol. 1. Ornithologische Arbeitsgemeinschaft für Schleswig-Holstein und Hamburg e.V., Kiel: 138–161.

DRESSER, H.E. 1871. *A History of the Birds of Europe*, Vol. 8. London.

DRGOŇOVÁ, N. and M. JANIGA. 1989. Nests structure of Alpine Accentors (*Prunella collaris*) (Scop., 1769) in the Low Tatras. *Biológia Bratislava* 44: 983–993.

DRIMAL, J. 1989. [*The Wild Turkey in Czechoslovakia*]. Unpublished thesis. Agricultural University, Brno (in Czech).

DROBELIS, E. 1993. On the biology and protection of the Black Stork (*Ciconia nigra* L.) in Lithuania. *Acta Ornithol. Lituanica* 7–8: 94–99.

DRONNEAU, C. 1994. Gélinette des bois. In: Yeatman-Berthelot, D. and G. Jarry (Eds) *Nouvel Atlas des Oiseaux Nicheurs de France 1985–1989*. Société Ornithologique de France, Paris: 212–215.

DRONNEAU, C. and B. WASSMER. 1994. Faucon hobereau *Falco subbuteo*. In: Yeatman-Berthelot, D. and G. Jarry (Eds) *Nouvel Atlas des Oiseaux Nicheurs de France 1985–1989*. Société Ornithologique de France, Paris: 208–209.

DRÖSCHER, L. 1988. A study on radio-tracking of the European Cuckoo (*Cuculus canorus canorus*). *Proc. Int. 100. DO-G Meeting, Current Topics Avian Biol.*, Bonn: 187–193.

DROZDOV, N.N. 1965. [Geography of the summer bird population in selected habitats of Azerbaijan.] *Ornitologiya* 20: 104–112, 166–199 (in Russian).

DUBOIS, P.J. 1992. Migration et hivernage de l'Échasse blanche (*Himantopus himantopus*) dans l'Ouest du Paléarctique et de l'Afrique. *Nos Oiseaux* 41: 347–366.

DUBOIS, P.J. 1994. L'hivernage de la Corneille mantelée *Corvus corone cornix* en France occidentale: disparition et persistance. *Ornithos* 1: 25–30.

DUBOIS, P.J. and COMITÉ D'HOMOLOGATION NATIONAL. 1994. La Sterne élégante *Sterna elegans* en France. *Ornithos* 1: 74–79.

DUBOIS, P.J. and R. MAHEO. 1986. *Limicoles nicheurs de France*. Minist. Env./LPO/BIROE, Marennes.

DUNN, E.K. 1994. White-winged Lark. In: Tucker, G.M. and M.F. Heath (Eds) *Birds in Europe – their conservation status*. Conservation Series No. 3. BirdLife International, Cambridge: 448.

DUNNET, G.M. and M. HEUBECK. 1995. The monitoring of breeding seabirds and eiders. *Proc. Roy. Soc. Edinburgh* 103B: 137–164.

DUQUET, M. 1994. Sizerin flammé *Carduelis flammea*. In: Yeatman-Berthelot, D. and G. Jarry (Eds) *Nouvel Atlas des Oiseaux Nicheurs de France 1985–1989*. Société Ornithologique de France, Paris: 702–703.

DUQUET, M. and J-Y. FRÉMONT. 1995. Identification du Martinet pâle *Apus pallidus*. Statut actuel en France. *Ornithos* 2: 68–76.

DUQUET, M. and H. MICHEL. 1994. La nidification de la Cigogne noire *Ciconia nigra* en France: historique et statut actuel. *Ornithos* 1: 67–71.

DURINCK, J., H. SKOV and P. ANDELL. 1993. Seabird distribution and numbers in selected offshore parts of the Baltic Sea, winter 1992. *Ornis Svecica* 3: 11–26.

DURINCK, J., H. SKOV, F.P. JENSEN and S. PIHL. 1994. Important marine areas for wintering birds in the Baltic Sea. EU DG XI research contract no. 224/90-09-01, Ornis Consult, Copenhagen: 1–110.

DVORAK, M., A. RANNER and H-M. BERG (Eds). 1993. *Atlas der Brutvögel Österreichs*. Umweltbundesamt, Wien.

DVORAK, M., I. WINKLER, Ch. GRABMAYER and E. STEINER. 1994. *Stillgewässer Österreichs als Brutgebiete für Wasservögel*. Monographien 44, Umweltbundesamt, Wien.

DYBBRO, T. 1970. Hvidbrystet Præstekrave (*Charadrius alexandrinus*) som ynglefugl i Danmark. *Dansk Orn. Foren. Tidsskr.* 64: 205–222 (in Danish).

DYBBRO, T. 1978. *Oversikt over Danmarks fugle*. Dansk Ornithologisk Förening, Copenhagen (in Danish).

DYER, M.I., J. PINOWSKI and B. PINOWSKA. 1977. Population dynamics. In: Pinowski, J. and S.C. Kendeigh (Eds) *Granivorous Birds in Ecosystems*. Cambridge University Press, London: 53–105.

DYMOND, J.N., P.A. FRASER and S.J.M. GANTLETT. 1989. *Rare Birds in Britain and Ireland*. Poyser, Calton.

DYRCZ, A. 1976. Materialy do biologii plochacza halnego *(Prunella collaris)*. *Notatki Ornitologiczne* 17: 79–92 (in Polish).

DYRCZ, A. 1986. Factors affecting facultative polygyny and breeding results in the Great Reed Warbler (*Acrocephalus arundinaceus*). *J. Ornithol.* 127: 447–461.

DYRCZ, A. 1993. Nesting biology of the Aquatic Warbler *Acrocephalus paludicola* in the Biebrza marshes (NE Poland). *Vogelwelt* 114: 2–15.

DYRCZ, A. and W. ZDUNEK. 1993. Breeding ecology of the Aquatic Warbler *Acrocephalus paludicola* on the Biebrza marshes, northeast Poland. *Ibis* 135: 181–189.

DYRCZ, A., J. OKULEWICZ and J. WITKOWSKI. 1985. Bird communities on natural eutrophic fen mires in the Biebrza river valley, NE Poland. *Vogelwarte* 33: 26–52.

DYRCZ, A., W. GRABIŃSKI, T. STAWARCZYK and J. WITKOWSKI (Eds). 1991. *Ptaki Śląska*. University of Wrocław, Wrocław. (*The Birds of Silesia*) (in Polish, with English summary).

EBBINGE, B.S. 1989. A multifactorial explanation for variation in breeding performance of Brent Geese *Branta bernicla*. *Ibis* 131: 196–204.

EBBINGE, B.S. and B. SPAANS. 1995. The importance of body reserves accumulated in spring staging areas in the temperate zone for breeding in Dark-bellied Brent Geese *Branta b. bernicla* in the high Arctic. *J. Avian Biol.* 26: 105–113.

EBBINGE, B.S., H.T. van der MEULEN and J.J. SMIT. 1984. Changes in winter distribution and population size of Pink-footed Geese breeding in Svalbard. *Nor. Polarinst. Skr.* 181: 11–17.

EBELS, E.B. 1993. Invasie van Witbandkruisbekken in Nederland en Westeuropa in 1990–91. *Dutch Birding* 15: 206–214. (Invasion of Two-barred Crossbills in The Netherlands and western Europe in 1990–91) (in Dutch, with English summary).

EBER, G. 1956. Vergleichende Untersuchungen über die Ernährung einige Finkenvögel. *Biol. Abh.* 13–14: 1–60.

EERDEN, M.R. van and J. GREGERSEN. 1995. Long-term changes in the northwest European population of Cormorants *Phalacrocorax carbo sinensis*. *Ardea* 83: 61–79.

EFREMOV, P.G. 1935. [Some materials on avifauna of Kaisk district (Kirov region).] *The Scientific Transactions of Gorky University* 4: 37–51 (in Russian).

EINARSSON, A. 1988. Distribution and movements of Barrow's Goldeneye *Bucephala islandica* young in relation to food. *Ibis* 130: 153–163.

EINARSSON, A. 1990. Settlement into breeding habitats by Barrow's Goldeneyes *Bucephala islandica*: evidence for temporary oversaturation of preferred habitat. *Ornis Scand.* 21: 7–16.

EINARSSON, O. 1994. *Breeding biology of the Whooper Swan and factors affecting its breeding success, with notes on its social dynamics and life cycle in the wintering range*. PhD Thesis, University of Bristol, England.

EKHOLM, A. 1989. Lavskirikan i Gästrikland. *Fåglar i X-län* 20: 4014.

ELANDER, M. and S. BLOMQVIST. 1986. The avifauna of central Northeast Greenland, 73°15'N – 74°05'N, based on a visit to Myggbukta, May–July 1979. *Meddeleiser om Grønland. Bioscience* 19: 1–44.

ELKINS, N. and B. ETHERIDGE. 1974. The Crag Martin in winter quarters at Gibraltar. *Brit. Birds* 67: 376–387.

ELOSEGI, I. 1989. Vautour fauve (*Gyps fulvus*), Gypaète barbu (*Gypaetus barbatus*), Percnoptère d'Egypte (*Neophron percnopterus*): Synthèse bibliographique et recherches. *Acta Biologica Montana*, Série documents de travail 3. Pau University, Pau.

ELOSEGUI, J. 1985. *Atlas de las aves nidificantes de Navarra*. Caja de Ahorros de Navarra.

ENEMAR, A. and B. NYSTRÖM. 1981. Om gråsiskans *Carduelis flammea*, beståndsväxlingar, föda och häckning i fjällbjörkskog, södra Lappland. *Vår Fågelvärld* 40: 409–426 (in Swedish, with English summary).

ENEMAR, A., L. NILSSON and B. SJÖSTRAND. 1984. The composition and dynamics of the passerine bird community in a subalpine birch forest, Swedish Lapland. A 20-year study. *Ann. Zool. Fennici* 21: 321–338.

ENGELER, A. 1994. Die Kolonien des Alpensegler (*Apus melba*) in der Stadt Bern. Jahresbericht 1993. *Berner Ala*, Bern.

ENOKSSON, B. 1990. Autumn territories and population regulation in the nuthatch *Sitta europaea*: an experimental study. *J. Anim. Ecol.* 59: 1047–1062.

ENS, B.J., M. KERSTEN, A. BRENNINKMEIJER and J.B. HULSCHER. 1992. Territory quality, parental effort and reproductive success of Oystercatchers (*Haematopus ostralegus*). *J. Anim. Ecol.* 61: 703–715.

EPPLE, W. 1987. Uhu – *Bubo bubo* (Linné, 1758). In: Hölzinger, J. (Ed) *Die Vögel Baden-Württembergs, Band 1.2*. Eugen Ulmer, Stuttgart: 1069–1080.

EPPLE, W. 1992. Einführung in das Artenschutz-symposium Wendehals. *Beih. Veröff. Naturschutz Landschaftspflege Bad.-Württ.* 66: 7–18.

EPPRECHT, W. 1985. 21 Jahre Grauschnäpperbruten *(Muscicapa striata)* am gleichen Nestort. *Orn. Beob.* 82: 169–184.

ÉRARD, C. 1994. Grive litorne *Turdus pilaris*. In: Yeatman-Berthelot, D. and G. Jarry (Eds) *Nouvel Atlas des Oiseaux Nicheurs de France 1985–1989*. Société Ornithologique de France, Paris: 530–531.

ÉRARD, C. and L. YEATMAN. 1967. Sur les migrations de *Phoenicurus ochruros gibraltariensis* d'apres les données du baguage. *Oiseaux et R.F.O.* 37: 20–47.

ÉRARD, C., J-J. GUILLOU and J. VIELLIARD. 1972. Réflexions sur la répartition de *Sylvia sarda*. *Alauda* 40: 293–296.

ERDMANN, G. 1985. Zum Auftreten der Schneeammer auf dem Territorium der DDR. *Falke* 32: 84–87.

ERIKSSON, K. 1970. The invasion of *Sitta europaea asiatica* (Gould) into Fennoscandia in the winters of 1962/63 and 1963/64. *Ann. Zool. Fennici* 7: 121–140.

ERIKSSON, M.O.G. and P. SUNDBERG. 1991. The choice of fishing lakes by the Red-throated Diver *Gavia stellata* and Black-throated Diver *G. arctica* during the breeding season in south-west Sweden. *Bird Study* 38: 135–144.

ERIKSSON, P. and T. HENRICSSON. 1990. Bean Goose, *Anser fabalis*, in the south of Swedish Lapland. *Vår Fågelvärld* 49: 7–14.

ERNST, S. 1988. Die Ausbreitung des Alpenbirkenzeisigs, *Carduelis flammea cabaret* P.L.S. Müller, in Europa bis zum Jahre 1986. *Mitt. Zool. Mus. Berl. 64, Suppl: Ann. Ornithol.* 12: 3–50.

ERNST, S. 1989. An amazing little finch and its success in Europe. *Birds International* 1: 53–62.

ESILEVSKAYA, M.A. and E.V. BRYUKHANOV. 1991. [Nesting of the Levant Sparrowhawk (*Accipiter brevipes*) in broad-leaved forest of forest-steppe of the Ukraine.] *Ornitologiya* 25: 158 (in Russian).

ESSELINK, H. and J.H. BEEKMAN. 1991. Between year variation and causes of mortality in the non-breeding population of the Mute Swan *Cygnus olor* in the Netherlands, with special reference to hunting. *Wildfowl*, Suppl. No. 1: 110–119.

ESSEN, L. von. 1991. A note on the Lesser White-fronted Goose in Sweden and the result of a re-introduction scheme. *Ardea* 79: 305–306.

ESSEN, L. von, T. MARKKOLA, T. AARVAK and J.J. OIEN. In press. (1996). The Lesser Whitefronted Goose (*Anser erythropus*) in Fennoscandia — past and present distribution. In: Birkan, M., J. van Vessem, P. Havet, B. Trolliet and M. Moser (Eds) *Proceedings of the Anatidae 2000 Conference, Strasbourg, France, 5–9 December 1994. Gibier Faune Sauvage, Game Wildl.*, 13: 1313–1314.

ESTAFIEV, A.A. 1969. [Ornithogeographical characteristic of the upper Pechora Basin.] *Transactions of the Komi Branch of the USSR Academy of Sciences* 21: 101–108 (in Russian).

ESTAFIEV, A.A. 1977a. [*Birds of the taiga zone of the Pechora river.*]. Abstract, PhD Thesis, Leningrad: 21 (in Russian).

ESTAFIEV, A.A. 1977b. [Birds of the western slope of the pre-Polar Urals.] *Transactions of the Komi Branch of the USSR Academy of Sciences* 34: 44–101 (in Russian).

ESTAFIEV, A.A. 1979. [The nesting of Siberian Accentor in north-east European USSR. *Migration and Ecology of Siberian birds.*] Yakutsk: 142–143 (in Russian).

ESTAFIEV, A.A. 1981. [Present state, distribution and protection of avifauna in the taiga of Pechora basin.] Preprint Series *'Scientific Reports' of the K[illegible] Branch of the USSR Academy of Sciences*, Syktyvkar. 68: 1–54 (in Russian).

ESTAFIEV, A.A. 1991. [*Fauna and ecology of waders in the Bol'shezemel'skaya tundra and Yugorskiy Peninsula.*] Nauka, Leningrad (in Russian).

ESTRADA, A. and T.H. FLEMING. (Eds) 1986. *Frugivores and Seed Dispersal.* Dr. W. Junk, Dordrecht.

ESTRADA, J. and A. CURCO. 1991. La Xurra, *Pterocles orientalis*, i la Ganga, *Pterocles alchata*, a Catalunya: evolució i situació actual. *Bulletí del Grup Catala d'Anillament* 8: 1–8.

ETHERIDGE, B. 1982. Distribution of Dunlin *Calidris alpina* nests on an area of South Uist Machair. *Bird Study* 29: 239–243.

ETHERIDGE, B. and R.W. SUMMERS. In press. Nest survival and productivity of Hen Harriers *Circus cyaneus* breeding in different habitats. *Proceedings Raptor Research Foundation/Hawk and Owl Trust. Biology and Conservation of Harriers. Canterbury 1993.*

EVANS, A.D. 1992. The numbers and distribution of Cirl Buntings *Emberiza cirlus* breeding in Britain in 1989. *Bird Study* 39: 17–22.

EVANS, A.D. and SMITH, K.W. 1994. Conservation of Cirl Buntings in the UK. In: Hagemeijer, E.J.M. and T.J. Verstrael (Eds) Bird Numbers 1992. Distribution, monitoring and ecological aspects. *Proceedings of the 12th International Conference of IBCC and EOAC, Noordwijkerhout, The Netherlands.* Poster Appendix. Statistics Netherlands, Voorburg/Heerlen and SOVON, Beek-Ubbergen: 23–28.

EVANS, I.M. (Ed). 1994. *Important Bird Areas in the Middle East.* BirdLife International, Cambridge.

EVANS, I.M. and M.W. PIENKOWSKI. 1991. World status of the Red Kite: a background to the experimental reintroduction to England and Scotland. *Brit. Birds* 84: 171–187.

EVANS, P.G.H. 1984. Status and conservation of seabirds of northwest Europe (excluding Norway and the U.S.S.R.). In: Croxall, J.P., P.G.H. Evans and R.W. Schreiber (Eds) *Status and Conservation of the World's Seabirds.* Technical Publication No. 2, ICBP, Cambridge: 293–322.

EVANS, P.G.H. and D.N. NETTLESHIP. 1985. Conservation of the Atlantic Alcidae. In: Nettleship, D.N. and T.R. Birkhead (Eds) *The Atlantic Alcidae.* Academic Press, London: 427–488.

EWINS, P.J. 1985. Colony attendance and censusing of Black Guillemots *Cepphus grylle* in Shetland. *Bird Study* 32: 176–185.

EWINS, P.J. and D.A. KIRK. 1988. The distribution of Shetland Black Guillemots *Cepphus grylle* outside the breeding season. *Seabird* 11: 50–61.

EWINS, P.J. and M.L. TASKER. 1985. The breeding distribution of Black Guillemots *Cepphus grylle* in Orkney and Shetland, 1982–84. *Bird Study* 32: 186–193.

EWINS, P.J., J.N. DYMOND and M. MARQUISS. 1986. The distribution, breeding and diet of Ravens *Corvus corax* in Shetland. *Bird Study* 33: 110–116.

EWINS, P.J., P.M. ELLIS, D.B. BIRD and A. PRIOR. 1988. The distribution and status of Arctic and Great Skuas in Shetland 1985–86. *Scott. Birds* 15: 9–20.

FADAT, C. 1991. Bécasse des bois *Scolopax rusticola*. In: Yeatman-Berthelot, D. (Ed) *Atlas des Oiseaux de France en Hiver.* Société Ornithologique de France, Paris: 246–247.

FAIVRE, B. 1993. La prédation joue t-elle un rôle dans la régression de l'Hypolaïs ictérine *Hippolais icterina*? *Rev. Ecol. (Terre et Vie)* 48: 399–420.

FAIVRE, B. and C. FERRY. 1989. La régression du Grand Contrefaisant (*Hippolais icterina*) en Bourgogne. *Aves* 26, No. spécial: 153–166.

FALANDYSZ, J., N. YAMASHITA, S. TANABE, R. TATSUKAWA, T. MIZERA and B. JAKUCZUN. 1994. Highly toxic non-ortho-chlorine substituted coplanar PCBs in White-tailed Sea Eagles *Haliaeetus albicilla* from Poland. In: Meyburg, B-U. and R.D. Chancellor (Eds) *Raptor Conservation Today.* WWGBPO, Berlin: 725–730.

FARTHOUAT, J.P. 1980. La Perdrix rouge en France: sa situation, son évolution, les recherches entreprises. In: Coles, C.L., M. Reydellet, G. van Tuyll, L. van Maltzahn and J. Bugalho (Eds) *Partridges of the Genus Alectoris.* International Council for Game and Wildlife Conservation, Paris: 25–39.

FASCE, P., L. FASCE and J. TORRE. 1989. Census and observations of the biology of the Bearded Vulture (*Gypaetus barbatus*) on the island of Corsica. In:

Meyburg, B-U, and R.D. Chancellor (Eds) *Raptors in the Modern World*. WWGBPO, Berlin: 335–339.

FASOLA, M. 1986. Distribuzione e popolazione dei laridi e sternidi nidificanti in Italia. *Supplemento alle Ricerche di Biologia della Selvaggina*, 11 (1): 121–127, 129–136, 137–141.

FASOLA, M. and R. ALIERI. 1992a. Nest site characteristics in relation to body size in herons in Italy. *Colonial Waterbirds* 15: 185–191.

FASOLA, M. and R. ALIERI. 1992b. Conservation of heronry sites in North Italian agricultural landscapes. *Biol. Conservation* 62: 219–228.

FASOLA, M. and A. GARIBOLDI. 1985. Status del Colino della Virginia *Colinus virginianus* in Italia. *Proc. III Conv. ital. Ornithol., Pavia*: 25–26.

FASOLA, M. and A. GARIBOLDI. 1987. Il Colino della Virginia, *Colinus virginianus*, In Italia. *Riv. ital. Orn.*, 57: 3–13.

FASOLA, M. and X. RUIZ. 1996. The value of rice fields as substitutes of natural wetlands for waterbirds in the Mediterranean Region. *Colonial Waterbirds* 19 (Special Publication 1): 122–128.

FASOLA, M., L. CANOVA and N. SAINO. 1996. Rice fields support a large portion of herons breeding in the Mediterranean region. *Colonial Waterbirds* 19 (Special Publication 1): 129–134.

FEARE, C.J. 1994. Changes in numbers of Common Starlings and farming practice in Lincolnshire. *Brit. Birds* 87: 200–204.

FEARE, C.J., P. DOUVILLE de FRANSSU and S.J. PERIS. 1992. The Starling in Europe: multiple approaches to a problem species. *Proc. Vertebrate Pest Conference* 15: 83–88.

FEIGE, K-D. 1986. *Der Pirol*. Neue Brehm-Bücherei 578, Ziemsen, Wittenberg.

FEN-QI, H. and L. TAI-CHUN. 1991. Changes in status and distribution of China's Pheasants since 1978. *W.P.A. News* 31: 19–24.

FERNANDEZ, C. 1994. *Censo, evolución demográfica de las colonias y productividad del buitro leonado (Gyps fulvus H.) en Navarra*. Gobierro de Navarra, Pamplona.

FERNÁNDEZ PALACIOS, J.M. and C. RAYA. 1991. Biología de la focha cornuda (*Fulica cristata*) en Cádiz y otros humedales del Bajo Guadalquivir. In: Fernández Palacios J.M. and M.J. Martos (Eds) *Plan rector de Uso y Gestión de las Reservas Naturales de las lagunas de Cádiz*. Junta de Andalucía. Agencia de Medio Ambiente, Sevilla: 97–117.

FERNANDEZ-CRUZ, M., G. FERNANDEZ-ALCAZAR, F. CAMPOS and P. DIAS. 1992. Colonies of Ardeids in Spain and Portugal. In: Finlayson, C.M., G.E. Hollis and T.J. Davis (Eds) *Managing Mediterranean Wetlands and their Birds. Proc. Symp. Grado, Italy, 1991*. Special Publication No. 20, International Wetlands Research Bureau, Slimbridge: 76–78.

FERREIRA, L.F. 1982. [*New data on the biology of Estrilda astrild in Portugal*.] Graduating Report, Fac. de Ciências da Universidade Clássica de Lisboa: 25–26 (in Portuguese).

FERRER, M. 1993. *El Aguila Imperial Ibérica*. Eurofauna 1st edn, Quercus, Madrid.

FERRER, X. 1987. [The presence of Azure-winged Magpies (*Cyanopica cyana*) in the north-east Iberian peninsula.] *Ardeola* 34: 110–113 (in Spanish).

FERRER, X., A. MARTINEZ and J. MUNTANER. 1986. *Historia Natural dels Paisos Catalans*, Vol. 12. *Ocells*. Enciclopedia Catalana, Barcelona.

FERRER, X., A. MOTIS and S.J. PERIS. 1991. Changes in the breeding range of Starlings in the Iberian Peninsula during the last 30 years: competition as a limiting factor. *J. Biogeography* 18: 631–636.

FERRERO, J.J. 1993. The Montagu's Harrier in Spain – population trends and conservation efforts. *Proceedings of the International Montagu's Harrier Conference, Kiel-Raisdorf, 1–2 July 1993*: 56–57.

FERRERO, J.J., V.M. PIZARRO, J.A. ROMAN and A. SANCHEZ. In press. The migration and wintering of the Black Stork in Extremadura (Spain). In: Brouwer, K., C. King and M. Strazds (Eds) *The Black Stork in the Changing World. Proceedings of the 1st International Black Stork Conservation and Ecology Symposium, Jurmala, Latvia. Latvian Ornithological Society Riga*.

FERRY, C. 1977. The mapping method applied to problems of species interspecific territoriality of *Hippolais icterina* and *H. polyglotta*. *Pol. ecol. Stud.* 3: 145–146.

FERRY, C. 1984. Coadaptation des oiseaux et des plantes à la dissémination de ces dernières. In Parrot, J.L. and Y. Leroy (Eds) *La Fin et les Moyens; Etudes sur la finalité biologique et ses mécanismes*. Maloine, Paris: 147–165.

FIALA, V. 1988. Populationsgröße und Bruterfolg bei *Aythya ferina* und *Aythya fuligula*. *Folia Zool.* 37: 41–57.

FIALA, V. 1991. Zweiter Beitrag zur Brutbiologie des Schwarzhalstauchers (*Podiceps nigricollis*). *Folia Zool.* 40: 241–260.

FILCHAGOV, A.V. 1993. The Armenian Gull in Armenia. *Brit. Birds* 86: 550–560.

FILCHAGOV, A.V. and V.V. LEONOVICH. 1992. Breeding range expansion of Barnacle and Brent Geese in the Russian European North. *Polar Res.* 11: 41–46.

FILCHAGOV, A.V., V.V. BIANKI and K.T. MIKHAILOV. 1985. [Bean Goose *Anser fabalis* on the Kola Peninsula.] *Ornitologija* 20: 26–32 (in Russian).

FILCHAGOV, A.V., P. YÉSOU and V.I. GRABOWSKI. 1992. Le Goéland du Taïmyr *Larus heuglini taimyrensis*: répartition et biologie estivales. *L'Oiseau et R.F.O.* 62: 128–148.

FINLAYSON, C. 1992. *Birds of the Strait of Gibraltar*. Poyser, London.

FINLAYSON, J.C. and J.E. CORTES. 1987. The birds of the Strait of Gibraltar. *Alectoris* 6 (special edition): 1–74.

FISCHER, F. and A. von PELZELN. 1886. Vögel von Jan Mayen. *Mitt. Orn. Ver. Wien* 10 (17,18) (transl. W. Eagle Clarke, *Zoologist* (3) 14: 1–16, 41–51, 1890).

FISCHER, S., G. MAUERSBERGER, H. SCHIELZETH and K. WITT. 1992. Erster Brutnachweis des Bindenkreuzschnabels (*Loxia leucoptera*) in Mitteleuropa. *J. Ornithol.* 133: 197–202.

FISHER, J. 1952. *The Fulmar*. Collins, London.

FISHER, J. 1966. The fulmar population of Britain and Ireland, 1959. *Bird Study* 13: 5–76.

FIUCZYNSKI, D. 1987. *Der Baumfalke*. Neue Brehm-Bücherei 575, Ziemsen, Wittenberg.

FIUCZYNSKI, D. 1991. Feinddruck und Nistplatzangebot als limitierende Faktoren für Siedlungsdichte und

Bruterfolg beim Baumfalken (*Falco subbuteo*). *Birds of Prey Bull.* 4: 63-71.

FJELDSÅ, J. 1973. Territory and the regulation of population density and recruitment in the Horned Grebe *Podiceps auritus arcticus*, Boje, 1822. *Vid. Medd. Dansk Naturhist. for.* 136: 117–189.

FLADE, M. 1994. *Die Brutvogelgemeinschaften Mittel- und Norddeutschlands: Grundlagen für den Gebrauch vogelkundlicher Daten in der Landschaftsplanung*. IHW-Verlag, Eching.

FLADE, M. and K. STEIOF. 1990. Bestandstrends häufiger norddeutscher Brutvögel 1950–1985: Eine Analyse von über 1400 Siedlungsdichte-Untersuchungen. *Proc. Int. 100. DO-G Meeting, Current Topics Avian Biol., Bonn 1988*: 249–260.

FLADE, M., D. FRANZ and A. HELBIG. 1986. Die Ausbreitung der Beutelmeise (*Remiz pendulinus*) an ihrer nordwestlichen Verbreitungsgrenze bis 1985. *J. Ornithol.* 127: 261–287.

FLADE, M., S. KOZULIN, G. MATIUKAS, A. POLUDA and A. TISHECHKIN. 1997. Actual distribution, population size and trend in the globally threatened Aquatic Warbler *Acrocephalus paludicola*. *Vogelwelt* 118.

FLIEGE, G. 1984. Das Zugverhalten des Stars (*Sturnus vulgaris*) in Europa: Eine Analyse der Ringfunde. *J. Ornithol.* 125: 393–446.

FLINKS, H. and F. PFEIFER. 1984. Zur Verbreitung und Populationsentwicklung des Schwarzkehlchens (*Saxicola torquata*) in Nordrhein-Westfalen. *Vogelwelt* 105: 41–51.

FLINT, P.F. and P.E. STEWART. 1983. *Birds of Cyprus*. BOU Checklist No. 6, BOU, London: 109.

FLINT, P.F. and P.E. STEWART. 1992. *Birds of Cyprus*, 2nd edn. BOU Checklist No 6, BOU, London.

FLINT, V.E. 1985. Ordnung Gaviiformes, Seetaucher. In: Il'ičev, V.D. and V.E. Flint (Eds) *Handbuch der Vögel der Sowjetunion*, Vol. 1. AULA-Verlag, Wiesbaden: 206–237.

FLINT, V.E., R.L. BOEHME, Y.V. KOSTIN and A.A. KUZNETSOV. 1984. *A Field Guide to the Birds of the USSR*. Princeton University Press, New Jersey.

FLOUSEK, J. and J. PAVELKA. 1993. [The Greenish Warbler (*Phylloscopus trochiloides*) in Czechoslovakia.] *Sylvia* 29: 57–68 (in Czech).

FLOUSEK, J., K. HUDEC and U.N. GLUTZ VON BLOTZHEIM. 1993. Immissionsbedingte Waldschäden und ihr Einfluß auf die Vogelwelt Mitteleuropas. In: Glutz von Blotzheim, U.N. and K.M. Bauer (Eds) *Handbuch der Vögel Mitteleuropas*, Vol. 13/I. AULA-Verlag, Wiesbaden: 11–30.

FOPPEN, R. and R. REIJNEN. In press (1996). De Fitis *Phylloscopus trochilus* in de problemen, Afrika in het spel? (The Willow Warbler *Phylloscopus trochilus* in trouble, Africa involved?). *Limosa* 69: 51–56.

FORMOZOV, A.N. (Ed). 1959. *Geographija naselenija nazemnikh zhivotnikh i metody ego izuchenija*. Moscow: 172–194 (in Russian).

FORNASARI, L., L. BOTTONI, R. MASSA, M. FASOLA, P. BRICHETTI and V. VIGORITA (Eds). 1992. *Atlante degli Uccelli svernanti in Lombardia*. Regione Lombardia and Università degli Studi di Milano, Milano.

FORSMAN, D. 1991. Die Bestimmung von Schell – *Aquila clanga*, Schrei – *A. pomarina* und Steppenadler – *A. nipalensis*. *Limicola* 5: 145–185.

FOUARGE, J.P. 1992. Résultats du recensement des nids d'Hirondelle de fenêtre (*Delichon urbica*) à Bruxelles en 1992. *Aves* 29: 191–195.

FOWLER, J.A. 1982. Leach's Petrels present on Ramna Stacks, Shetland. *Seabird Report* 6: 93.

FOX, A.D. 1986. The breeding Teal (*Anas crecca*) of a coastal raised mire in central West Wales. *Bird Study* 33: 18–23.

FOX, A.D. 1988. Breeding status of the Gadwall in Britain and Ireland. *Brit. Birds* 81: 51–66.

FOX, A.D. 1991. History of the Pochard breeding in Britain. *Brit. Birds* 84: 83–98.

FOX, A.D., I.S. FRANCIS, J. MADSEN and J.M. STROUD. 1987. The breeding biology of the Lapland Bunting *Calcarius lapponicus* in West Greenland during two contrasting years. *Ibis* 129: 541–552.

FRAISSINET, M. 1989. Espansione della taccola, *Corvus monedula*, nei capoluoghi di provincia italiani. *Riv. ital. Orn.* 59: 33–42.

FRAISSINET, M., G. DEL MONACO and M. MILONE. 1988. Alcune considerazioni sulla migrazione dell'Occhiocotto, *Sylvia melanocephala*. *Riv. ital. Orn.* 58: 177–185.

FRANTZEN, B. 1984. Laksandas *Mergus merganser*. In: Gibbons, D.W., J.B. Reid and R.A. Chapman (Eds) *The New Atlas of Bredding Birds in Britain and Ireland: 1988–1991*. Poyser, London: 92–93.

FRANTZEN, B. 1994a. Steller's Eider *Polysticta stelleri*. In: Tucker, G.M. and M.F. Heath (Eds) *Birds in Europe – their conservation status*. Conservation Series No. 3, BirdLife International, Cambridge: 134–135.

FRANTZEN, B. 1994b. Siland *Mergus serrator*. In Gjershaug, J.O., P.G. Thingstad, S. Eldøy and S. Byrkjeland (Eds) *Norsk Fugleatlas*. Norsk Ornitologisk Forening, Klæbu: 104–105 (in Norwegian).

FRANTZEN, B. 1994c. Dvergspurv *Emberiza pusilla*. In: Gjershaug, J.O., P.G. Thingstad, S. Eldøy and S. Byrkjeland (Eds) *Norsk Fugleatlas*. Norsk Ornitologisk Forening, Klæbu: 502–503 (in Norwegian).

FRANZTEN, B., H. DRANSFELD and O. HUNSDAL. 1991. *Fugleatlas for Finnmark*. Trykkforum AS, Vadso (in Norwegian).

FRATICELLI, F. and M. GUSTIN. 1985. European News. Bluethroat *Luscinia svecica*. *Brit. Birds* 78: 344.

FREDRIKSSON, S. 1979. Skrattmåsen *Larus ridibundus* i Sverige. *Vår Fågelvärld* 38: 173–200 (in Swedish).

FRELIN, C. 1979. Physiological adaptions of Blue Tits (*Parus caeruleus*) to migration. *Vogelwarte* 30: 33–41.

FRÉMONT, J-Y. 1994. Ibis falcinelle *Plegadis falcinellus*. In: Yeatman-Berthelot, D. and G. Jarry (Eds) *Nouvel Atlas des Oiseaux Nicheurs de France 1985–1989*. Société Ornithologique de France, Paris: 727–728.

FREY, H. and M. BIJLEVELD VAN LEXMOND. 1994. The reintroduction of the Bearded Vulture, *Gypaetus barbatus aureus* into the Alps. In: Meyburg, B-U. and R.D. Chancellor (Eds) *Raptor Conservation Today*. WWGBPO, Berlin: 459–464.

FRUCTUOSO, G. 1981. *Livro segundo das Saudades da Terra*, 2nd edn. Instituto Cultural de Ponta Delgada, Ponta Delgada.

FRY, C.H. 1984. *The Bee-eaters*. Poyser, Calton.

FRY, C.H. 1990. Foraging behaviour and identification of Upcher's Warbler. *Brit. Birds* 83: 217–221.

FRYCKLUND, I. 1984. Boinventering av haussvala i Uppsala. *Fågl. Uppl.* 11: 83–95 (in Swedish).

FUCHS, E. 1978. Bestand und Verbreitung des Haubentauchers *Podiceps cristatus* in der Schweiz. *Orn. Beob.* 75: 19–32.

FUCHS, E. 1979. Der Brutvogelbestand einer naturnahen Kulturlandschaft im Schweizerischen Mittelland. *Orn. Beob.* 65: 235–246.

FULLER, R.J. 1978. Breeding populations of Ringed Plovers and Dunlins in the Uists and Benbecula, Outer Hebrides. *Bird Study* 25: 97–102.

FULLER, R.J. 1994. Jay *Garrulus glandarius*. In: Gibbons, D.W., J.B. Reid and R.A. Chapman (Eds) *The New Atlas of Breeding Birds in Britain and Ireland: 1988–1991*. Poyser, London: 384–385.

FULLER, R.J. and B.D. MORETON. 1987. Breeding bird populations of Kentish Sweet Chestnut *Castanea sativa* coppice in relation to age and structure of coppice. *J. Appl. Ecol.* 39: 73–88.

FULLER, R.J., T.M. REED, N.E. BUXTON, A. WEBB, T.D. WILLIAMS and M.W. PIENKOWSKI. 1986. Populations of breeding waders *Charadrii* and their habitats on the crofting lands of the Outer Hebrides, Scotland. *Biol. Conservation* 37: 333–361.

FULLER, R.J., R.D. GREGORY, D.W. GIBBONS, J.H. MARCHANT, J.D. WILSON, S.R. BAILLIE and N. CARTER. 1995. Population declines and range contractions among lowland farmland birds in Britain. *Conservation Biol.* 9: 1425–1441.

FURNESS, R.W. 1987. *The Skuas*. Poyser, Calton.

FURNESS, R.W. 1990. Evolutionary and ecological constraints on the breeding distributions and behaviour of skuas. *Proc. Int. 100 D.O.G. Meeting, Current Topics Avian Biology*, Bonn, 1988: 153–158.

FURNESS, R.W. and S.R. BAILLIE. 1981. Factors affecting capture rate and biometrics of Storm Petrels on St. Kilda. *Ringing and Migration* 3: 137–148.

FURNESS, R. W. and J.J.D. GREENWOOD. 1993. *Birds as Monitors of Environmental Change*. Chapman and Hall, London.

FURNESS, R.W. and L.R. MONTEIRO. 1995. Red-billed Tropicbird *Phaethon aethereus* in the Azores: first breeding record for Europe. *Bull. Brit. Orn. Club* 115(1): 6–8.

GABRIELSON, G.W., J.E. SKAARE, A. POLDER and V. BAKKEN. 1995. Chlorinated hydrocarbons in Glaucous Gull (*Larus hyperboreus*) at the southern part of Svalbard. *Sci. Total Environ.* 160/161: 337–346.

GALBRAITH, H., S. MURRAY, S. RAE, D.P. WHITFIELD and D.B.A. THOMPSON. 1993. Numbers and distribution of Dotterel (*Charadrius morinellus*) breeding in Great Britain. *Bird Study* 40: 161–169.

GALEOTTI, P. 1990. Territorial behaviour and habitat selection in an urban population of the Tawny Owl *Strix aluco* L. *Boll. Zool.* 57: 59–66.

GALEOTTI, P. and A. GARIBALDI. 1994. Territorial behaviour and habitat selection by the Scops Owl *Otus scops* in a Karstic Valley (NE Italy). In: Meyburg, B-U. and R.D. Chancellor (Eds) *Raptor Conservation Today*. WWGBPO, Berlin: 501–505.

GALUSHIN, V.M. 1962. [The Greater Spotted Eagle in the valley of the Oka river and its influence on the numbers of some birds.] *Uch. zapiski Moskov. pedag. inst. im. Lenina* 186: 115–151 (in Russian).

GALUSHIN, V.M. 1992. The Saker Falcon *Falco cherrug* in European Russia and Ukraine. *Abstract IV. World Conference on Birds of Prey, Berlin 10–17 May 1992*: 56.

GALUSHIN, V.M. 1994. Levant Sparrowhawk *Accipiter brevipes*. In: Tucker, G.M. and M.F. Heath (Eds) *Birds in Europe – their conservation status*. Conservation Series No. 3, BirdLife International, Cambridge: 166–167.

GALUSHIN, V.M. In press. The Black Vulture in the eastern part of its range. *Proceedings of the International Black Vulture Workshop, Dadia (Greece), 1993.*

GALUSHIN, V.M., A.V. DAVYGORA and V.N. MOSEIKIN. 1994. Black Lark. In: Tucker, G.M. and M.F. Heath (Eds) *Birds in Europe: their conservation status*. Conservation Series No. 3, BirdLife International, Cambridge: 354–355.

GALUSHIN, V.M., A.B. KOSTIN, V.N. MOSEIKIN, A.V. GENEROZOV, I.L. MAREEV and V.E. REIF. 1996. The Levant Sparrowhawk and other raptors of the Middle Volga River. *Ibis* 138: 149–150.

GAMAUF, A. 1991. *Greifvögel in Österreich: Bestand – Bedrohung – Gesetz*. Umweltbundesamt, Wien.

GARANIN, V.I. 1977. [Cuculiformes. In: *Birds of the Volga–Kama region*, Vol. 2. *Nonpasserines*.]. Nauka, Moscow: 234–238 (in Russian).

GARCIA, L. and F.J. PURROY. 1973. Evaluación de comunidades de aves por el método de la parcela. Resultados obtenidos en el matorral mediterráneo de la Punta del Sabinar (Almería). *Bol. Est. Central de Ecología* 4: 41–49.

GARCIA, L., J. CALDERON and J. CASTROVIEJO. 1987. *Las Aves de Doñana y su entorno*. Estación Biológica de Doñana.

GARCIA, L., C. RAMO, J. CALDERÓN and J. CHANS. In prep (1994). Crested coot. In: Vessem, J. van (Compiler) *Actions to prevent avoidable mortality for threatened waterbirds in the European Community.* International Waterfowl and Wetlands Research Bureau, Slimbridge: 107–123.

GARDARSSON, A. 1975. Islenskir cotlendisfuglar. *Rit Landverndar* 4: 100–134. (The birds of Icelandic wetlands) (in Icelandic, with a summary in English).

GARDARSSON, A. 1978. Islenski husandarstofninn. *Natturufrasedingurinn* 48: 162–191. (Distribution and numbers of the Barrow's Goldeneye (*Bucephala islandica*) in Iceland) (in Icelandic, with a summary in English).

GARDARSSON, A. 1979. Waterfowl populations of Lake Myvatn and recent changes in numbers and food habits. *Oikos* 32: 250–270.

GARDARSSON, A. 1988. Cyclic population changes and some related events in Rock Ptarmigan in Iceland. In: Bergerud, A.T. and M.W. Gratson (Eds) *Adaptive Strategies and Population Ecology of Northern Grouse*. University of Minnesota Press, Minneapolis: 300–329.

GARDARSSON, A. and A. EINARSSON. 1994. Responses of breeding duck populations to changes in food supply. *Hydrobiologia* 279–280: 15–27.

GARDARSSON, A. and K.H. SKARPHEDINSSON. 1985. Veturseta alftar a Islandi. *Bliki* 4: 45–56. (The wintering of Whooper Swans *Cygnus cygnus* in Iceland.)

GARGALLO, G. 1992. Primeres dades de nidificació del

Busqueret de garriga (*Sylvia cantillans*) a l'Arxipèlag de Cabrera. *Anuari Ornitològic de les Balears* 7: 62–63.

GARGALLO, G. 1994. On the taxonomy of the western Mediterranean islands populations of Subalpine Warbler *Sylvia cantillans*. *Bull. Brit. Orn. Club* 114: 31–36.

GARNICA, P.R. de. 1978. Comunidades de aves en los encinares leoneses. *Naturalia Hispanica* 13: 1–31. Instituto Nacional para la Conservación de la Naturaleza, Madrid.

GARRIGÓS, B. and J. SARGATAL. 1990. *Proyecto Calamón: Memoria julio 1989–julio 1990*. DEPANA.

GARZA, V. and F. SUAREZ. 1989. La invernada de la Alondra de Dupont *Chersophilus duponti*, en la Península Ibérica. *Ardeola* 36: 107–110.

GARZA, V. and F. SUAREZ. 1990. Distribución, población y selección de hábitat de la Alondra de Dupont (*Chersophilus duponti*) en la Península Ibérica. *Ardeola* 37: 3–12.

GARZA, V., F. SUÁREZ, B. PECO and M. CASTEJÓN. 1989. *Estudio para la evaluación y corrección de impactos ambientales por actuaciones localizadas en zonas esteparias de la Península Ibérica*. Informe inédito, M.O.P.U., Madrid.

GASTEREN, H. van, K. MOSTERT, H. GROOT and L. van RUTTEN. 1992. De irruptie van de Zwarte Mees *Parus ater* in het najaar van 1989 in Nederland en NW-Europa. *Limosa* 65: 57–66. (The irruption of the Coal Tit *Parus ater* in the autumn of 1989 in The Netherlands and NW–Europe) (in Dutch, with English summary).

GATTER, W. 1989. Zur vegetabilischen Ernährung des Gimpels *Pyrrhula pyrrhula* auf der Schwäbischen Alb. *Vogelwelt* 110: 100–112.

GATTER, W. 1993. Explorationsverhalten, Zug und Migrationsevolution beim Fichtenkreuzschnabel *Loxia curvirostra*. *Vogelwelt* 114: 38–55.

GATTER, W., R. GARDNER and K. PENSKI. 1990. Abnahme ziehender Ringeltauben *Columba palumbus* in Süddeutschland. *Vogelwelt* 111: 111–116.

GAUTHIER-CLERC, M. 1994. Tichodrome échelette *Tichodroma muraria*. In: Yeatman-Berthelot, D. and G. Jarry (Eds) *Nouvel Atlas des Oiseuax Nicheurs de France 1985–1989*. Société Ornithologique de France, Paris: 620–621.

GAVRILOV, E.I. and A.P. GISTSOV. 1985. *Sezonnye perelety ptits v predgor'yakh zapadnogo Tyan'-Shanya*. Alma-Ata (in Russian).

GAVRILOV, N.N. 1993. [*Distribution, numbers and dynamics of the breeding sites of colonial waterfowl in the Volga Delta in the North Caspian Sea*.] Abstract of candidate thesis, Moscow (in Russian).

GEISTER, I. 1980. [Distribution of the Fan-tailed Warbler (*Cisticola juncidis*) and the question of its population increase and decrease]. *Biološki vestnik* 28: 25–44. Ljubljana (with English summary).

GEISTER, I. 1995. *Ornitološki Atlas Slovenije*. DZS, Ljubljana: 124, 280 (in Slovenian with English introduction).

GELLINI, S. and N. MONTEVECCHI. 1986. Nidificazione di Sterpazzola di Sardegna, *Sylvia conspicillata*, nell' Italia settentrionale (Appennino Bolognese). *Riv. ital. Orn.* 56: 225–230.

GÉNOT, J-C. 1994. Chouette chevêche ou Chevêche d'Athéna *Athene noctua*. In: Yeatman-Berthelot, D. and G. Jarry (Eds) *Nouvel Atlas des Oiseaux Nicheurs de France 1985–1989*. Société Ornithologique de France, Paris: 398–401.

GÉNSBØL, B. 1995. *Rovfuglene i Europa, Nordafrika og Mellemøsten*. G.E.C. Gads Forlag, Copenhagen: 192–194 (in Danish).

GEORGE, K. 1994. Zur Überwinterung von Rotmilanen *Milvus milvus* im nördlichen Harzvorland (Sachsen-Anhalt). *Vogelwelt* 115: 127–132.

GÉROUDET, P. 1985. Essai de synthèse sur l'évolution du Harle bièvre, *Mergus merganser*, dans le bassin du Léman. *Nos Oiseaux* 38: 1–18.

GÉROUDET, P. 1995. Analyse et commentaires sur les colonisations marginales de Goéland cendré *Larus canus* en Europe Occidentale. *Alauda* 63: 1–14.

GÉROUDET, P. and M. GAUTHIER-CLERC. 1994. Le Tichodrome échelette *(Tichodroma muraria)* nicheur: nouvelle mise au point pour le Jura français et synthèse jurassienne franco-suisse. *Nos Oiseaux* 42: 411–418.

GÉROUDET, P., C. GUEX and M. MAIRE. 1983. *Les oiseaux nicheurs du canton de Genève*. Museum d'Histoire Naturelle de Genève, Genève: 173.

GIBB, J. 1956. Food, feeding habits and territory of the Rock Pipit *Anthus petrosus*. *Ibis* 98: 506–530.

GIBBONS, D.W. 1986. Brood parasitism and cooperative nesting in the moorhen, *Gallinula chloropus*. *Behav. Ecol. Sociobiol.* 19: 221–232.

GIBBONS, D.W. 1989. Seasonal reproductive success of the Moorhen *Gallinula chloropus*: the importance of male weight. *Ibis* 131: 57–68.

GIBBONS, D.W. 1993. Moorhen *Gallinula chloropus*. In: Gibbons, D.W., J.B. Reid and R.A. Chapman (Eds) *The New Atlas of Breeding Birds in Britain and Ireland: 1988–1991*. Poyser, London: 152–153.

GIBBONS, D.W., J.B. REID and R.A. CHAPMAN (Eds). 1993. *The New Atlas of Breeding Birds in Britain and Ireland: 1988–1991*. Poyser, London.

GIEROW, P. and M. GIEROW. 1991. Breeding biology of the Lapland Bunting *Calcarius lapponicus* in Lapland, Sweden. *Ornis Svecica* 1: 103–111.

GIL-DELGADO, J.A. 1981. La avifauna del naranjal valenciano. III. El Verdecillo (*Serinus serinus*). *Mediterranea Ser. Biol.* 5: 97–114.

GILLANDT, L. 1974. Beobachtungen an einer Thorshühnchen-Population (*Phalaropus fulicarius*) in Südwest-Island (Aves: Charadriiformes: Phalaropodidae). *Abh. Verh. Naturwiss. Ver. Hamburg* 17: 55–83.

GIRARD, O. 1992. La migration des limicoles en France métropolitaine à partir d'une synthèse bibliographique. *Alauda* 60: 13–33.

GIRARD, O. and P. YÉSOU. 1989. Reproduction de l'Avocette (*Recurvirostra avosetta*) sur le marais d'Olonne: chronologie, devenir des pontes. *Gibier Faune Sauvage* 6: 225–243.

GJERSHAUG, J.O. 1994. Fjellvråk *Buteo lagopus*. In: Gjershaug, J.O., P.G. Thingstad, S. Eldøy and S. Byrkjeland (Eds) *Norsk Fugleatlas*. Norsk Ornitologisk Forening, Klæbu: 122–123.

GJERSHAUG, J.O., P.G. THINGSTAD, S. ELDØY and S. BYRKJELAND (Eds). 1994. *Norsk Fugleatlas*. Norsk Ornitologisk Forening, Klæbu (in Norwegian).

GLADKOV, N.A. 1954. Rubythroat *Luscinia calliope*. In:

Dementiev, G.P. and N.A. Gladkov (Eds) *Birds of the Soviet Union*, Vol. 6. Nauka, Moscow: 585–586.

GLANDT, D. (Ed). 1991. Der Kolkrabe in Mitteleuropa. *Metelener Schriftenreihe Naturschutz* 2: 1–118.

GLAS, P. 1960. Factors governing density in the Chaffinch (*Fringilla coelebs*) in different types of wood. *Arch. néerl. Zool.* 13: 466–472.

GLEN, N.W. and C.M. PERRINS. 1988. Co-operative breeding by Long-tailed Tits. *Brit. Birds* 81: 630–641.

GLOWACINSKI, Z. and P. PROFUS. 1992. Structure and vertical distribution of the breeding bird communities in the Polish Tatra National Park. *Ochrona Przyrody* 50: 65–94.

GLÜCK, E. 1980. Ernährung und Nahrungsstrategie des Stieglitzes *Carduelis carduelis* L. *Ökol. Vögel* 2: 43–91.

GLÜCK, E. 1985. Seed preference and energy intake of Goldfinches *Carduelis carduelis* in the breeding season. *Ibis* 127: 421–429.

GLUE, D.E. 1990. Breeding biology of the Grasshopper Warbler in Britain. *Brit. Birds* 83: 131–145.

GLUE, D.E. 1993a. Little Owl *Athene noctua*. In: Gibbons, D.W., J.B. Reid and R.A. Chapman (Eds) *The New Atlas of Breeding Birds in Britain and Ireland: 1988–1991*. Poyser, London: 248–249.

GLUE, D.E. 1993b. Rock Pipit *Anthus petrosus*. In: Gibbons, D.W., J.B. Reid and R.A. Chapman (Eds) *The New Atlas of Breeding Birds in Britain and Ireland: 1988–1991*. Poyser, London: 284–285.

GLUE, D.E. 1993c. Grasshopper Warbler *Locustella naevia*. In: Gibbons, D.W., J.B. Reid and R.A. Chapman (Eds) *The New Atlas of Breeding Birds in Britain and Ireland: 1988–1991*. Poyser, London: 326–327.

GLUE, D.E. 1994. The Black Redstart: Rise and Fall. *Birdwatch* 29: 4–7.

GLUE, D.E. and T. BOSWELL. 1994. Comparative nesting ecology of the three British breeding woodpeckers. *Brit. Birds* 85: 253–269.

GLUE, D.E. and G.J. HAMMOND. 1974. Feeding ecology of the Long-eared Owl in Britain and Ireland. *Brit. Birds* 67: 361–369.

GLUTZ von BLOTZHEIM, U.N. 1962. *Die Brutvögel der Schweiz*. Aargauer Tagblatt AG, Aarau.

GLUTZ von BLOTZHEIM, U.N. 1964. *Die Brutvögel der Schweiz*. Aargauer Tagblatt AG, Aarau: 531–533.

GLUTZ von BLOTZHEIM, U.N., K.M. BAUER and E. BEZZEL. 1966–97. *Handbuch der Vögel Mitteleuropas*. 14 Vols. Akademische Verlagsgesellschaft AULA-Verlag, Wiesbaden.

GNIELKA, R. 1975. Brutstatistik zweier Populationen des Gelbspötters, *Hippolais icterina*. *Mitt. Interessengem. Avifauna DDR* 8: 91–101.

GNIELKA, R. 1985. Die Verbreitung der Heidelerche im Bezirk Halle. *Apus* 6: 21–23.

GOC, M. 1986. Colonial versus territorial breeding of the great crested grebe *Podiceps cristatus* on Lake Druzno. *Acta Ornithol.* 22: 95–145.

GOETHE, F. 1983. Common Gull (*Larus canus*, L.) In: Wolff, W.J. (Ed) *Ecology of the Wadden Sea*. Balkema, Rotterdam.

GOETHE, F. 1991. Mantelmöwe *Larus marinus* L. 1758. In: Zang, H., G. Großkopf and H. Heckenroth (Eds) *Die Vögel Niedersachsens, Raubmöwen bis Alken*. Naturschutz Landschaftspfl. Niedersachs. B, Heft 2.6: 114–118.

GOLOVKIN, A.N. 1984. Seabirds nesting in the USSR: the status and protection of populations. In: Croxall, J.P., P.G.H. Evans and R.W. Schreiber (Eds) *Status and Conservation of the World's Seabirds*. Technical Publication No. 2, International Council For Bird Preservation, Cambridge: 473–486.

GOMEZ-MANZANEQUE, A. 1991. Situation actuelle de la population de la Cigogne blanche en Espagne. *Actes du Colloque International sur les Cigognes d'Europe*: 183–188.

GONZÁLEZ, J.L. and M. MERINO. 1988. El primer censo de Cigüena negra en España confirma el garve peligro de extinctión de la especie. *Quercus* 30: 12–17.

GONZÁLEZ, J.L. and M. MERINO (Eds). 1990. *El Cernicalo primilla (*Falco naumanni*) en la Peninsula Iberica. Situación, problemática y aspectos biológicos.* ICONA, Madrid.

GONZÁLEZ, L.M. 1990. Situación de las poblaciones de Aguila Imperial y Buitre Negro en España. *Quercus* 58: 16–22.

GONZÁLEZ, L.M. 1991. *Historia Natural del Aguila Imperial Ibérica* (Aquila adalberti *Brehm, 1861)*. Colección Técnica, ICONA, Min. de Agricultura, Madrid.

GONZÁLEZ, L.M. 1995. Tendencias poblacionales y estatus de conservación del Aguila Imperial Ibérica (*Aquila adalberti*) en España, durante los ultimos veintre años. In: Muntaner, J. and J. Mayol (Eds) *Biología y Conservación de las Rapaces Mediterráneas*. Monografías No. 4, Sociedad Espanola de Ornitologia, Madrid.

GONZÁLEZ, L.M., J. BUSTAMANTE and F. HIRALDO. 1992. Nesting habitat selection by the Spanish Imperial Eagle *Aquila adalberti*. *Biol. Conservation* 59: 45–50.

GOODWIN, D. 1956. Editorial: Captive birds at large. *Brit. Birds* 49: 339–349.

GOODWIN, D. 1975. Studies of less familiar birds. 178. Azure-winged Magpie. *Brit. Birds* 68: 484–488.

GOODWIN, D. 1976. *Crows of the World*. British Museum (Natural History), London.

GOODWIN, D. 1986. *Crows of the World*, 2nd edn. British Museum, London.

GORBAN, I.M., L.I. DAVYDOVICH and J.J. HARAMBURA. 1987. [Modern nest ornithofauna of the Cherhory range of Ukrainian Carpathians.] *Herald of Lviv University*. Biological Series, Vol. 17. Vyscha shkola: 72–75 (in Ukrainian).

GORMAN, G. 1994. The Rose-coloured Starling invasion, and breeding in Hungary. *Birding World* 7: 316–318.

GORSKI, W. 1989. *Factors determining growth rate of a Collared Dove (*Streptopelia decaocto*) population in Slupsk in 1973–1985*. Pedagogical Institute, Slupsk (in Polish, with English summary).

GORY, G. 1987. Influence du climat méditerranéen sur la reproduction du Martinet noir (*Apus apus* L.). *L'Oiseau et R.F.O.* 57: 69–84.

GOSLER, A.G. 1993. *The Great Tit*. Hamlyn, London.

GOSSOW, H., F. HAFNER, S. PSEINER-PETRJANOS, G. VONKILCH and G. WATZINGER. 1992. The status of Grey Partridge (*Perdix perdix*) and Rock Partridge (*Alectoris graeca*) populations in relation to human land use in Austria: a review. In: Birkan, M., G.R. Potts , N.J. Aebischer and S.D. Dowell (Eds) *Perdix VI,*

First International Symposium on Partridges, Quails and Francolins. Gibier Faune Sauvage 9: 515–521.

GOUTNER, V. 1985. Breeding ecology of Avocet (*Recurvirostra avosetta* L.) in the Evros delta (Greece). *Bonn. Zool. Beitr.* 36: 37–50.

GOUTNER, V. 1987. Vegetation preferences by colonies of Mediterranean Gulls (*Larus melanocephalus*) and Gull-billed Terns (*Gelochelidon nilotica*) in the Evros delta. *Seevögel* 8: 29–31.

GOUTNER, V. 1988. The Lesser Crested Tern (*Sterna bengalensis*) in the Evros delta (Greece): a case of pairing with the Sandwich Tern (*Sterna sandvicensis*)? *Kartierung mediterr. Brutvögel* 1: 7–11.

GOUTNER, V. and P. ISENMANN. 1993. Breeding status of the Mediterranean Gull (*Larus melanocephalus*) in the Mediterranean basin. In: Aguilar, J.S., X. Monbailliu and A.M. Paterson (Eds) *Status and Conservation of Seabirds. Proceedings of the 2nd Mediterranean Seabird Symposium, Calviá, 21–26 March 1989*. Sociedad Espanola de Ornitologia, BirdLife and MEDMARAVIS, Madrid: 59–63.

GOY, D. 1994. Torcol fourmilier *Jynx torquilla*. In: Yeatman-Berthelot, D. and G. Jarry (Eds) *Nouvel Atlas des Oiseaux Nicheurs de France 1985–1989*. Société Ornithologique de France, Paris: 428–429.

GRAFEUILLE, D. 1994. Pouillot de Bonelli *Phylloscopus bonelli*. In: Yeatman-Berthelot, D. and G. Jarry (Eds) *Nouvel Atlas des Oiseaux Nicheurs de France 1985–1989*. Société Ornithologique de France, Paris: 580–581.

GRANADEIRO, J.P. 1993. Variation in measurement of Cory's Shearwater between populations and sexing by discriminant analysis. *Ringing and Migration* 14: 103–112.

GRAND, G. le. 1980. Avifaune de Corvo Arquipelago. *Ser. Cienc. Nat.* 1: 53–80.

GRAND, G. le, K. EMMERSON and A. MARTIN. 1984. The status and conservation of seabirds in the Macronesian islands. In: Croxall, J.P., P.G.H. Evans and R.W. Schreiber (Eds) *Status and Conservation of the World's Seabirds*. Technical Publication No. 2, International Council For Bird Preservation, Cambridge: 377–391.

GRANT, M.C. 1991. Nesting densities, productivity and survival of breeding Whimbrel *Numenius phaeopus* in Shetland. *Bird Study* 38: 160–169.

GRANT, M.C. 1993. The Curlew. In: Gibbons, D.W., J.B. Reid and R.A. Chapman (Eds) *The New Atlas of Breeding Birds in Britain and Ireland: 1988–1991*. Poyser, London: 184–185.

GRANT, P.J. 1986. *Gulls: an Identification Guide*. Poyser, London.

GRANT, P.J. 1987. Notes on Armenian Herring Gull. In: Grant, P.J. and H. Shirihai (Eds) *Proceedings of the 4th International Identification Meeting in Eilat, 1–8 November 1986*: 43.

GREEN, A.J. 1993. *The status and conservation of the Marbled Teal* Marmaronetta angustirostris. Special Publication No. 23, International Waterfowl and Wetlands Research Bureau, Slimbridge.

GREEN, A.J. and S. ANSTEY. 1992. The status of the White-headed Duck *Oxyura leucocephala*. *Bird Conservation International* 2: 185–200.

GREEN, R.E. and G.H. GRIFFITHS. 1994. Use of preferred nesting habitat by Stone Curlews *Burhinus oedicnemus* in relation to vegetation structure. *J. Zool., London* 233: 457–471.

GREEN, R.E., S.R. BAILLIE and M.I. AVERY. 1990. Can ringing recoveries explain the population dynamics of British terns? *The Ring* 13: 133–138.

GREIG, S.A., J.C. COULSON and P. MONAGHAN. 1986. A comparison of foraging at refuse tips by three species of gull (*Laridae*). *J. Zool. London* 210: 459–472.

GREIG-SMITH, P.W. and G.M. WILSON. 1984. Patterns of activity and habitat use by a population of Bullfinches (*Pyrrhula pyrrhula* L.) in relation to bud-feeding in orchards. *J. Appl. Ecol.* 21: 401–422.

GRENQUIST, P. 1965. Changes in abundance of some duck and sea bird populations off the coast of Finland 1949–1963. *Finnish Game Res.* 27.

GRETTON, A. 1991. *Conservation of the Slender-billed Curlew*. Monograph No. 6, International Council For Bird Preservation, Cambridge.

GRETTON, A. 1994. Slender-billed Curlew. In: Tucker G.M. and M.F. Heath (Eds) *Birds in Europe – their conservation status*. Conservation Series No. 3, BirdLife International, Cambridge.

GRIMMETT, R. F. A. and T.A. JONES. 1989. *Important Bird Areas in Europe*. Technical Publication No. 9, International Council for Bird Preservation, Cambridge.

GRISHCHENKO, V. 1993. Die gegenwärtige Verbreitung des Kaiseradlers (*Aquila heliaca*) in der Ukraine. *Orn. Mitt.* 45: 247–250.

GRISHCHENKO, V. 1994. Expansion of the Black Stork breeding in Ukraine. *J. Ornithol.* 135, Suppl: 218.

GRITCHIK, V.V. 1995. [On the fauna and breeding performance of the birds of Yugorsky Peninsula (extreme north-east of European Russia).] *Fauna and Taxonomy* 1: 271–288. Nauka i tekhnica, Minsk (in Russian).

GROEN, N.M., J.J. FRIESWIJK and J. BOUWMEESTER. 1995. Waarom broeden Visdieven *Sterna hirundo* op daken? *Limosa* 68: 65–72. (Why do Common Terns *Sterna hirundo* breed on roofs?) (in Dutch, with English summary).

GRÖH, H. 1975. Zur Biologie der Zaunammer in Pfalz. *Mitt. Pollichia* 63: 72–139.

GRUBAC, R.B. 1989. The Egyptian Vulture *Neophron percnopterus* in Macedonia. In: Meyburg, B-U. and R.D. Chancellor (Eds) *Raptors in the Modern World*. WWGBPO, Berlin: 331–333.

GRUBAC, R.B. 1991. Status and biology of the Bearded Vulture *Gypaetus barbatus aureus* in Macedonia. *Birds of Prey Bull.* 4: 101–115.

GRÜLL, A. 1988. Zu Verbreitung, Bestand und Habitatwahl des Weißsternigen Blaukehlchens (*Luscinia svecica cyanecula*) im Neusiedlerseegebiet. *Biol. Forschungsinst. Burgenland*, Bericht 66: 57–65.

GRÜLL, A. and E. ZWICKER. 1993. Zur Siedlungsdichte von Schilfsingvögeln (*Acrocephalus* und *Locustella*) am Neusiedlersee in Abhängigkeit vom Alter der Röhrichtbestände. *Beih. Veröff. Naturschutz Landschaftspflege Bad.-Württ.* 68: 159–171.

GRUSSU, H. 1994. Popolazioni di Ardeidae e Treskiornithidae coloniali in Sardegna. *Gli Uccelli d'Italia* 19: 3–24.

GUDMUNDSSON, F. 1960. Some reflections on Ptarmigan cycles in Iceland. *Proc. Int. Ornithol. Congr.* 12: 259–265.

GUDMUNDSSON, F. 1971. Straumendur (*Histrionicus histrionicus*) á Islandi. *Nátturufraedingurinn* 41: 1–28 and 64–98. (The Harlequin Duck (*Histrionicus histrionicus*) in Iceland) (in Icelandic, with a summary in English).

GUDMUNDSSON, G.A. and Å. LINDSTRÖM. 1992. Spring migration of Sanderlings *Calidris alba* through SW Iceland: Wherefrom and whereto? *Ardea* 80: 315–326.

GUERRERO, J., F. de LOPE and C. de la CRUZ. 1989. Un nouvelle *Estrildidae* nicheur dans le sud-ouest de l'Espagne: *Estrilda astrild*. *Alauda* 57: 234.

GURNEY, J.H. 1913. *The Gannet, a Bird with a History*. Witherby, London.

GUSTAFSSON, J. and L. WAHLÉN. 1985. Hur mår trädlärkorna? *Fåglar i Sörmland* 18: 42–46. (What is happening with the Woodlark *Lullula arborea*?) (in Swedish, with English summary).

GUSTAFSSON, L. 1987. Interspecific competition lowers fitness in Collared Flycatchers *Ficedula albicollis*: an experimental demonstration. *Ecology* 68: 291–296.

GUSTAFSSON, L. 1988. Inter- and intraspecific competition for nest holes in a population of the Collared Flycatcher *Ficedula albicollis*. *Ibis* 130: 11–16.

GUTHMANN, E., T. MEBS, G. MÜSKENS and J. THISSEN. (Arbeitsgruppe Greifvögel). 1996. Die Bestandsentwicklung und der Bruterfolg des Baumfalken (*Falco subbuteo*) in Nordrhein-Westfalen von 1972 bis 1994. *Charadrius* 32: 8–23.

GUYOT, A. 1990. Première nidification réussie en France de l'Élanion blanc, *Elanus caeruleus*. *Nos Oiseaux* 40: 465–477.

HAAG, D. 1988. Die dichteabhängige Regulation im Brutschwarm der Strassentaube *Columba livia* forma *domestica*. *Orn. Beob.* 85: 209–224.

HAAPALA, J., J. LEHTONEN and P. SAUROLA. 1992. Breeding and population trends of common raptors and owls in Finland in 1991. *Lintumies* 27: 2–13 (in Finnish, with English summary).

HAAPANEN, A. 1991. Whooper swan *Cygnus c. cygnus* population dynamics in Finland. In: Sears, J. and P.J. Bacon (Eds) *Proceedings of the 3rd IWRB International Swan Symposium, Oxford, 1989. Wildfowl Suppl.* 1: 137–141.

HAAPANEN, A. and L. NILSSON. 1979. Breeding waterfowl populations in northern Fennoscandia. *Ornis Scand.* 10: 145–219.

HAAPANEN, A., M. HELMINEN and H.K. SUOMALAINEN. 1973. Population growth and breeding biology of the Whooper Swan, *Cygnus c. cygnus*, in Finland in 1950–1970. *Finnish Game Res.* 33: 137–141.

HAARTMAN, L. von. 1949. Der Trauerfliegenschnäpper. I. Ortstreue und Rassenbildung. *Acta Zool. Fennici* 56: 1–104.

HAARTMAN, L. von. 1973. Changes in the breeding bird fauna of North Europe. In: *Breeding Biology of Birds*. National Academy of Sciences, Washington D.C.: 448–481.

HAARTMAN, L. von, O. HILDÉN, P. LINKOLA, P. SUOMOLAINEN and R. TENOVUO. 1963–72. *Pohjolan linnut värikuvin*. Otava, Helsinki (in Finnish).

HABLE, E., P. SACKL and O. SAMWALD. 1991. Zur Brutverbreitung und Arealausweitung der Felsenschwalbe (*Ptyonoprogne rupestris*) in der Steiermark (Aves). *Mitt. Abt. Zool. Landesmus. Joanneum* 45: 11–22.

HADASCH, J. 1994. Erster westfälischer Nachweis der Steppenweihe, *Circus macrourus*, seit 40 Jahren – mit einer Auswertung der Steppenweihennachweise aus Deutschland von 1851 bis 1990. *Falke* 41: 90–92.

HADDON, P.C. and R.C. KNIGHT. 1983. *A Guide to Little Tern Conservation*. RSPB, London.

HAFFER, J. 1977. Secondary contact zones of birds in Northern Iran. *Bonn. Zool. Monogr.* 10.

HAFNER, H. 1994. Héron garde-bœufs *Bubulcus ibis*. In: Yeatman-Berthelot, D. and G. Jarry (Eds) *Nouvel Atlas des Oiseaux Nicheurs de France 1985–1989*. Société Ornithologique de France, Paris: 94–95.

HAFNER, H. and M. FASOLA. 1992. *The Relationship between Feeding Habitat and Colonially Nesting Ardeidae*. Special Publication No. 20, International Wetlands Research Bureau, Slimbridge: 194–201.

HAFTORN, S. 1971. *Norges fugler*. Universitetsforlaget, Oslo (in Norwegian).

HAFTORN, S. 1978. Energetics of incubation by the Goldcrest *Regulus regulus* in relation to ambient air temperatures and the geographical distribution of the species. *Ornis Scand.* 9: 22–30.

HAGEMEIJER, E.J.M. 1993. Ecological aspects of the Lesser Kestrel (*Falco naumanni*) in Extremadura, Spain. In: Nicholls, M.K. and R. Clarke (Eds) *Biology and Conservation of Small Falcons*. Hawk and Owl Trust, London: 19–23.

HAGEMEIJER, E.J.M. 1994. Invasie van Roodpootvalk *Falco vespertinus* in het voorjaar van 1992: grootste invasie van deze soort in Nederland. *Limosa* 67: 7–14. (Largest-ever invasion of Red-footed Falcon *Falco vespertinus* in The Netherlands in spring 1992) (in Dutch, with English summary).

HAGEMEIJER, E.J.M. and F. HUSTINGS. 1994. Ruimt de Velduil het veld? *SOVON-Nieuws* 7(3): 6–7. (Is the Short-eared Owl disappearing?) (in Dutch).

HAGEN, T.K. 1994. Topplerke *Galerida cristata*. In: Gjershaug, J.O., P.G. Thingstad, S. Eldøy and S. Byrkjeland (Eds) *Norsk Fugleatlas*. Norsk Ornitologisk Forening, Klaebu: 312–313 (in Norwegian).

HAGEN, Y. 1956. The irruption of Hawk Owls (*Surnia ulula* (L.)) in Fennoscandia 1950–51 with some remarks on recent micro-rodent cycles. *Sterna* 24: 3–22.

HAGEN, Y. 1959. Snowy Owl on Harddangervidda in the summer of 1959. *Papers of the Norwegian State Game Research* 2 (7).

HAILA, Y. and O. JÄRVINEN. 1990. Northern conifer forests and their bird species assemblages. In: Keast, A. (Ed) *Biogeography and Ecology of Forest Bird Communities*. SPB Academic Publishing, The Hague: 61–85.

HAILA, Y., O. JÄRVINEN and S. RAIVIO. 1987. Quantitative versus qualitative distribution patterns of birds in the western Palearctic taiga. *Ann. Zool. Fennici* 24: 179–194.

HALLER, H. 1982. Raumorganisation und Dynamik einer Population des Steinadlers in den Zentralalpen. *Orn. Beob.* 79: 163–211.

HALLET-LIBOIS, C. 1985. Modulations de la stratégie alimentaire chez le martin-pêcheur (*Alcedo atthis*). *Cahiers Ethologie appliquée* 5(4): 1–206.

HALLMANN, B. 1985. *Status and Conservation Problems of Birds of Prey in Greece*. Technical Publication No. 5, International Council for Bird Preservation, Cambridge: 55–59.

HALLMANN, B. 1994a. Orphean Warbler *Sylvia hortensis*. In: Tucker, G.M. and M.F. Heath (Eds) *Birds in Europe – their conservation status*. Conservation Series No. 3, BirdLife International, Cambridge: 402–403.

HALLMANN, B. 1994b. Masked Shrike *Lanius nubicus*. In: Tucker, G.M. and M.F. Heath (Eds) *Birds in Europe – their conservation status*. Conservation Series No. 3, BirdLife International, Cambridge: 418–419.

HALLMANN, B. 1994c. Black-headed Bunting *Emberiza melanocephala*. In: Tucker, G.M. and M.F. Heath (Eds) *Birds in Europe – their conservation status*. Conservation Series No. 3, BirdLife International, Cambridge: 434–435.

HÄLTERLEIN, B. and K. BEHM-BERKELMANN. 1991. Brutvogelbestände an der deutschen Nordseeküste im Jahre 1990 – Vierte Erfassung durch die Arbeitsgemeinschaft 'Seevogelschutz'. *Seevögel* 12: 47–51.

HÄLTERLEIN, B. and B. STEINHARDT. 1993. Brutvogelbestände an der deutschen Nordseeküste im Jahre 1991 – Fünfte Erfassung durch die Arbeitsgemeinschaft 'Seevogelschutz'. *Seevögel* 14: 47–51.

HAM, I. 1975. Fluctuations in numbers of heron couples (Ardeidae) in the inundation area of the Bergey river (Carska Bare) during the period 1950–1976. *Arch. Bioloskli Seanka* 27: 61–68.

HAMER, K.C., R.W. FURNESS and R.W.G. CALDOW. 1991. The effects of changes in food availability on the breeding ecology of Great Skuas, *Catharacta skua* in Shetland. *J. Zool. London* 223: 175–188.

HAN, L-X., Y. LAN and B-i. ZHENG. 1989. [Observations on the breeding ecology of Lady Amherst's Pheasant.] *Zool. Res.* 10: 285–294 (in Chinese, with English summary).

HANDRINOS, G. 1985. *The Status of the Vultures in Greece*. Technical Publication No. 5, International Council for Bird Preservation, Cambridge: 103–116.

HANSEN, S.G. 1976. Some aspects of the migration-biology of the Goosander (*Mergus merganser*) populations in northwestern Europe on basis of the existing ringing data. *Danske Fugle* 28: 164–178.

HARASZTHY, L. 1984. *Magyarorzoy feszkelo madarai*. Budapest.

HARASZTHY, L. and J. BAGYURA. 1993. A comparison of the nesting habits of the Red-footed Falcon (*Falco vespertinus*) in colonies and in solitary pairs. In: Nicholls, M.K. and R. Clarke (Eds) *Biology and Conservation of Small Falcons*. Hawk and Owl Trust, London: 80–85.

HARASZTHY, L., J. BAGYURA, T. SZITTA, Z. PETROVICS and L. VISZLÓ, L. 1996. Biology, status and conservation of the Imperial Eagle in Hungary. In: Meyburg, B-U. and R.D. Chancellor (Eds) *Eagle Studies*. WWGBPO. *Birds of Prey Bull.* 5: 425–428.

HARDMAN, J.A. 1974. Biology of the skylark. *Ann. Appl. Biol.* 76: 337–341.

HARIO, M. and K. SELIN. 1988. Thirty-year trends in an Eider population: timing of breeding, clutch size, and nest site preferences. *Finnish Game Res.* 45: 3–10.

HARIO, M., T. NUMMINEN and R. YRJÖLÄ. 1987. [Report of rare birds in Finland in 1986.] *Lintumies* 22: 195–206 (in Finnish, with English summary).

HARPER, D. 1993. Robin *Erithacus rubecula*. In: Gibbons, D.W., J.B. Reid and R.A. Chapman (Eds) *The New Atlas of Breeding Birds in Britain and Ireland: 1988–1991*. Poyser, London: 298–299.

HARRAP, S. and D. QUINN. 1995. *Tits, Nuthatches and Treecreepers*. A&C Black, London.

HARRIS, M.P. 1984. *The Puffin*. Poyser, Calton.

HARRIS, M.P. 1991. Breeding changes in British Common Murres and Atlantic Puffins, 1969–88. In: Gaston, A.J. and R.D. Elliot (Eds) *Studies of High-latitude Seabirds. 2 Conservation biology of Thick-billed Murres in the Northwest Atlantic Ocean.* Occasional Paper No. 69, Canadian Wildlife Service, Ottawa: 52–58.

HARRISON, C. 1982. *An Atlas of the Birds of the Western Palearctic*. Princeton University Press, Princeton, NJ.

HARRISON, P. 1985. *Seabirds: an identification guide*. 2nd edn. Croom Helm, Beckenham.

HARS, D. 1991. Le Martin triste *Acridotheres tristis*, une espèce exotique installée à Dunkerque (Nord) depuis 1986. *Héron* 24: 289–292.

HARTWIG, E. and J. PRÜTER. 1990. Studies on the decrease of breeding populations of the Common Gull (*Larus canus*) in a Baltic nature reserve. *Proceedings of the Vth Conference on the Study and Conservation of Migratory Birds of the Baltic Basin, Riga 1987. Baltic Birds* 1: 123–127.

HASHMI, D. 1989. Zur Situation des Wachtelkönigs *Crex crex* in Europa. *Ber. Dtsch. Sekt. Int. Rat Vogelschutz* 28: 9–25.

HASPER, H. and W. van MANEN. 1994. Ruigpootuilen *Aegolius funereus* in Drentse boswachterijen na 1980. *Drentse Vogels* 7: 31–34. (Tengmalm' Owls *Aegolius funereus* in forestries of Drenthe after 1980) (in Dutch, with English summary).

HAURI, R. 1978. Beiträge zur Brutbiologie des Mauerläufers *Tichodroma muraria*. *Orn. Beob.* 75: 173–192.

HAVELKA, P. and K. RUGE. 1993. Trends der Populationsentwicklung bei Spechten (*Picidae*) in der Bundesrepublik Deutschland. *Beih. Veröff. Naturschutz Landschaftspflege Bad.-Württ.* 67: 33–38.

HAWKES, B. 1986. Ring-necked Parakeet. In: Lack, P. (Ed) *The Atlas of Wintering Birds in Britain and Ireland.* Poyser, Calton: 268–269.

HAWORTH, P.F. and A. FIELDING. 1988. Conservation and management implications of habitat selection in the Merlin *Falco columbarius* L. in the South Pennines, UK. *Biol. Conservation* 46: 247–260.

HAYMAN, P., J.H. MARCHANT and A. PRATER. 1986. *Shorebirds*. Croom Helm, Beckenham.

HAYO, L. and H. WEYERS. 1986. Zum Brutvorkommen des Orpheusspötters (*Hippolais polyglotta*) im Saarland. *Lanius* 24: 15–43.

HAZEVOET, C.J. 1994. Status and conservation of seabirds in the Cape Verde Islands. In: Nettleship, D.N., J. Burger and M. Gochfeld (Eds) *Seabirds on Islands. Threats, case studies and action plans.* Conservation Series No. 1, BirdLife International, Cambridge: 279–294.

HAZEVOET, C.J. and L.B. HAAFKENS. 1989. *Nature Reserve Development and Ornithological Research in the Republica de Cabo Verde*. Report on phase 1, International Council for Bird Preservation, Amsterdam.

HEDENSTRÖM, A., S. BENSCH, D. HASSELQUIST, M. LOCKWOOD and U. OTTOSSON. 1993. Migration, stopover and moult of the Great Reed Warbler *Acrocephalus arundinaceus* in Ghana, West Africa. *Ibis* 135: 177–180.

HEGGBERGET, T.M. 1991. Establishment of breeding populations and population development in the Canada Goose *Branta canadensis* in Norway. *Ardea* 79: 365–370.

HEIJ, C.J. 1985. *Comparative ecology of the House Sparrow* Passer domesticus *in rural, suburban and urban situations*. Thesis, Vrije Universiteit, Amsterdam.

HEIM de BALSAC, H. and N. MAYAUD. 1962. *Les oiseaux du Nord-Ouest de L'Afrique*. Lechevalier, Paris.

HEINIGER, P.H. 1991. Anpassungsstrategien des Schneefinken *Montifringilla nivalis* an die extremen Umweltbedingungen des Hochgebirges. *Orn. Beob.* 88: 193–207.

HELANDER, B. 1990. The international colour-ringing programme for White-tailed Sea Eagles (*Haliaeetus albicilla* L.). *Baltic Birds* 5(1): 136–140.

HELB, H.W., H-H. BERGMANN and J. MARTENS. 1982. Acoustic differences between populations of western and eastern Bonelli's Warbler (*Phylloscopus bonelli* Sylvidae). *Experientia* 38: 356–357.

HELBIG, A.J. 1987. Feldbestimmung des Waldpiepers *Anthus hodgsoni* und sein Auftreten in Europa. *Limicola* 1: 73–85.

HELBIG, A.J., I. SEIBOLD, J. MARTENS, and M. WINK. 1995. Genetic differentiation and phylogenetic relationships of Bonelli's Warbler *Phylloscopus bonelli* and Green Warbler *P. nitidus*. *J. Avian Biol.* 26: 139–153.

HELD, J.J. den. 1981. Population changes in the Purple Heron in relation to drought in the wintering area. *Ardea* 69: 185–191.

HELLE, P. 1985. Effects of forest regeneration on the structure of bird communities in northern Finland. *Holarctic Ecol.* 8: 120–132.

HELLE, P. and O. JÄRVINEN. 1986. Population trends of North Finnish land birds in relation to their habitat selection and changes in forest structure. *Oikos* 46: 107–115.

HÉMERY, G. and E. D'ELBÉE. 1985. Discrimination morphologique des populations atlantique et méditerranéenne de Pétrels-tempête *Hydrobates pelagicus*. In: Oiseaux marins nicheurs du Midi et de la Corse. *Annales du CROP* 2: 63–67.

HENDERSON, A. 1993. Whitethroat *Sylvia communis*. In: Gibbons, D.W., J.B. Reid and R.A. Chapman (Eds) *The New Atlas of Breeding Birds in Britain and Ireland: 1988–1991*. Poyser, London: 340–341.

HENDERSON, I.G. and P.J.B. HART. 1993. Provisioning, parental investment and reproductive success in Jackdaws *Corvus monedula*. *Ornis Scand.* 24: 142–148.

HENGEVELD, R. 1993. What to do about the North American invasion by the Collared Dove? *Field Ornithol.* 64 (4): 477–489.

HENNY, C.J., S.A. GANUSEWVICH, E. PRESCOTT WARD and T.R. SCHWARTZ. 1994. Organochlorine pesticides, chlorinated dioxins and furans, and PCBs in Peregrine Falcon *Falco peregrinus* eggs from the Kola Peninsula, Russia. In: Meyburg, B-U. and R.D. Chancellor (Eds) *Raptor Conservation Today*. WWGBPO, Berlin: 739–749.

HENRIKSEN, K. 1991. Status och Bestandsutwikling hos Stor Regnspove *Numenius arquata* i Nordeuropa. *Danske Vildtundersögelser* 46. Miljøministeriet, Danmarks Miljøundersøgelser, Copenhagen.

HEREDIA, B. 1995. *Action plan for the Cinereous Vulture*. BirdLife International/Council of Europe, Cambridge/Strasbourg.

HEREDIA, R. and B. HEREDIA (Eds). 1991. *El Quebrantahuesos (*Gypaetus barbatus*) en los Pirineos. Caracteristicas ecológicas y biología de la conservación*. Serie Técnica, ICONA, Madrid.

HERNÁNDEZ, A. 1994. Selección de hábitat en tres especies simpátricas de alcaudones *Lanius* spp.: segregación interespecífica. *Ecología* 8: 395–413.

HERNÁNDEZ, A., J. ALEGRE, T. VELASCO and V.M. CASAS. 1992. El Treparriscos en la Península Ibérica. *Quercus* 71: 16–22.

HERNÁNDEZ, F. and E. PELA. 1987. Sobre comunidades de aves esteparias en planicies del valle medio del Ebro. *Actas I Congreso Internacional de Aves Esteparias*, León: 379–393.

HERREMANS, M. 1993a. Clustering of territories in the Wood Warbler *Phylloscopus sibilatrix*. *Bird Study* 40: 12–23.

HERREMANS, M. 1993b. Seasonal dynamics in sub-Kalahari bird communities with emphasis on migrants. *Proc. VIII Pan-Afr. Orn. Congr.*: 555–564.

HERREMANS, M., C.J. BROWN, W.D. BORELLO and D. HERREMANS-TONNOEYER. 1994. The abundance of European Rollers *Coracias garrulus* in Botswana and Namibia. *Ostrich* 94: 93–94.

HERRERA, C.M. 1981. Fruit food of Robins wintering in southern Spanish Mediterranean scrubland. *Bird Study* 28: 115–122.

HESS, R. 1983. Verbreitung, Siedlungsdichte und Habitat des Dreizehenspechts, *Picoides tridactylus alpinus* im Kanton Schwyz. *Orn. Beob.* 80: 153–182.

HEYER, J. 1984. Zum Wintervorkommen des Sommergoldhähnchens, *Regulus ignicapillus* (Temminck), in Thüringen. *Thür. Orn. Mitt.* 32: 57–58.

HILDÉN, O. 1964. Ecology of duck populations in the island group of Valassaaret, Gulf of Bothnia. *Ann. Zool. Fennici* 1: 153–279.

HILDÉN, O. 1975. Breeding system of Temminck's Stint *Calidris temminckii*. *Ornis Fennica* 52: 117–146.

HILDÉN, O. 1977. Occurrence of irregular migrants in Finland in 1976. *Ornis Fennica* 54: 170–179 (in Finnish, with English summary).

HILDÉN, O. 1978a. [Occurrence and breeding biology of the little stint *Calidris minuta* in Norway.] *Anser*, Suppl 3: 96–100 (in Swedish, with English summary).

HILDÉN, O. 1978b. Population dynamics in Temminck's Stint *Calidris temminckii*. *Oikos* 30: 17–28.

HILDÉN, O. 1986. Muuttuva Suomen Talvilinnusto. *Lintumies* 20: 262–268. (Long-term trends in the Finnish winter birds) (in Finnish, with English summary).

HILDÉN, O. 1987. [The Shorelark vanishing from Finland.] *Lintumies* 22: 51–59 (in Finnish, with English summary).

HILDÉN, O. 1988. Zur Brutbiologie des Zwergstrandläufers, *Calidris minuta*, in Finnmark. *Vogelkundliches Tagebuch Schleswig-Holstein* 16: 245–265.

HILDÉN, O. 1990. Long-term study of a northern population of the Blue Tit *Parus caeruleus*. In: Blondel, J., A. Gosler, J-D. Lebreton and R. McCleery (Eds) *Population Biology of Passerine Birds*. Springer-Verlag, Berlin: 65–75.

HILDÉN, O. and M. HARIO. 1993. *Muuttuva saaristolinnusto*. Forssa, Finland. (*The Status of the Bird Fauna of the Archipelago*) (in Finnish).

HILDÉN, O. and R. HILDÉN. 1995. Berthelot's Pipit *Anthus berthelotí* nesting in early January on Lanzarote. *Ibis* 137: 422–423.

HILDÉN, O. and K. HYYTIÄ. 1981. [The population changes and present status of waders in Finland.] *Proc. Second Nordic Congr. Ornithol.* 1979: 19–37 (in Swedish, with English summary).

HILDÉN, O. and T. PAHTAMAA. 1992. Development of the Razorbill population of the Quark in 1957–1990. *Ornis Fennica* 69: 33–38.

HILL, A. 1986. Die Einwanderung des Karmingimpels (*Carpodacus erythrinus*) in die Bundesrepublik Deutschland. *Orn. Mitt.* 38: 72–84.

HILL, D.A. 1984a. Factors affecting nest success in the mallard and tufted duck. *Ornis Scand.* 15: 115–122.

HILL, D.A. 1984b. Population regulation in the Mallard (*Anas platyrhynchos L.*). *J. Anim. Ecol.* 53: 192–202.

HILL, D.A. 1984c. Clutch predation in relation to nest density in the Mallard and Tufted Duck. *Wildfowl* 35: 151–156.

HILL, D.A. 1985. The feeding ecology and survival of pheasant chicks on arable farmland. *J. appl. Ecol.* 22: 645–654.

HILL, D.A. 1988. Population dynamics of the Avocet (*Recurvirostra avosetta*) breeding in Britain. *J. Anim. Ecol.* 57: 669–683.

HILL, D.A. 1993. Ring Ouzel. In: Gibbons, D.W., J.B Reid and R.A. Chapman (Eds) *The New Atlas of Breeding Birds in Britain and Ireland: 1988–1991*. Poyser, London: 312–313.

HILL, D.A. and P.A. ROBERTSON. 1988a. *The Pheasant: Ecology, management and conservation*. Blackwell Scientific Publications, Oxford.

HILL, D.A. and P.A. ROBERTSON. 1988b. Breeding success of wild and hand-reared pheasants *Phasianus colchicus*. *J. Wildlife Management* 52: 446–450.

HINO, T. 1990. Palaearctic deciduous forests and their bird communities: comparisons between East-Asia and West-Central Europe. In: Keast, A. (Ed) *Biogeography and Ecology of Forest Bird Communities*. SPB Academic Publishing, The Hague: 87–94.

HIRONS, G. 1983. A five-year study of the breeding behaviour and biology of the woodcock in England – a first report. In: Kalchreuter, H. (Ed) *Proceedings of the 2nd European Woodcock and Snipe Workshop*. IWRB, Slimbridge: 51–67.

HIRONS, G. and T.H. JOHNSON. 1987. A quantitative analysis of habitat preferences of woodcock, *Scolopax rusticola*, in the breeding season. *Ibis* 129: 371–381.

HJORT, C. and C-G. LINDHOLM. 1978. Annual bird ringing totals and population fluctuations. *Oikos* 30: 387–392.

HOBLYN, R. 1992. 1992 is a bumper year for Woodlarks. *BTO News* 181: 15.

HOFER, J. and C. MARTI. 1988. Beringungsdaten zur Überwinterung des Gänsesägers *Mergus merganser* am Sempachersee: Herkunft, Zugverhalten und Gewicht. *Orn. Beob.* 85: 97–122.

HÖGLUND, N.H. 1955. Body temperature, activity and reproduction in the Capercaillie. *Viltrevy* 1: 1–87 (in Swedish, with English summary).

HOGSTAD, O. 1975. Structure of small passerine communities in subalpine birch forests in Fennoscandia. In: Wielgolaski, F.E. (Ed) *Fennoscandian tundra ecosystems*, 2: 94–104. *Ecological Studies. Analysis and Synthesis*. Vol. 17. Springer-Verlag, Berlin.

HOGSTAD, O. 1985. Annual variation in mean body size of a Brambling *Fringilla montifringilla* population. *Ornis Fennica* 62: 13–18.

HOGSTAD, O. 1993. Structure and dynamics of a passerine bird community in spruce-dominated boreal forest. A 12-year study. *Annales Zoologici Fennici* 30(1): 43–54.

HOGSTAD, O. and A. MOKSNES. 1990. Expansion and present status of the Wood Warbler *Phylloscopus sibilatrix* in Central Norway. *Fauna norv. Ser. C, Cinclus* 9: 49–54.

HOLLAND, P.K. and D.W. YALDEN. 1991. Population dynamics of Common Sandpipers *Actitis hypoleucos* breeding along an upland river system. *Bird Study* 38: 151–159.

HOLLYER, J.N. 1970. The invasion of Nutcrackers in autumn 1968. *Brit. Birds* 63: 353–373.

HOLMBRING, J-Å. 1982. Kärrsångaren *Acrocephalus palustris* i Sverige. *Vår Fågelvärld* 41: 95–104. (The Marsh Warbler in Sweden) (in Swedish, with English summary).

HOLZ, R. 1987. Populationsentwicklung des Sandregenpfeifers (*Charadrius hiaticula*) im südwestlichen Ostseeraum: Ursachen und Konsequenzen veränderter Habitatnutzung. *Natur und Naturschutz in Mecklenburg* 25: 1–80.

HÖLZINGER, J. (Ed). 1987. *Die Vögel Baden-Württembergs*, Vol. 1.2. Eugen Ulmer, Stuttgart.

HÖLZINGER, J. 1990. Mönchsgrasmücke *Sylvia atricapilla* Brutvogel auf dem Peloponnes. *J. Ornithol.* 131: 167–171.

HÖLZINGER, J. 1991. Wetlands on the Greek islands Limnos: a bird habitat of international significance. *Kartierung mediterraner Brutvögel*. 6.

HÖLZINGER, J. 1993. Schneefink (*Montifringilla nivalis*) Brutvogel in Griechenland. *J. Ornithol.* 134: 405–411.

HÖLZINGER, J. 1995. The Cinereous Bunting *Emberiza cineracea* breeding on Skyros (Greece). *Zool. Middle East* 11: 31–36.

HÖLZINGER, J. and H.J. RIEDINGER. 1987. Berglaubsänger *Phylloscopus bonelli*. In: Hölzinger, J. (Ed) *Die Vögel Baden-Württembergs*, Vol. 1.2. Eugen Ulmer, Stuttgart: 1236–1240.

HÖLZINGER, J., M. MICKLEY and K. SCHILHANSL. 1973. Untersuchungen zur Brut- und Ernährungsbiologie der Sumpfohreule (*Asio flammeus*) in einem süddeutschen Brutgebiet mit Bemerkungen zum Auftreten der Art in Mitteleuropa. *Anz. orn. Ges. Bayern* 12: 176–197.

HOODLESS, A.N. and J.C. COULSON. 1994. Survival rates and movements of British and Continental Woodcock *Scolopax rusticola* in the British Isles. *Bird Study* 41: 48–60.

HOPKINS, D.M. 1967. The cenozoic history of Beringia. In: Hopkins, D.M. (Ed) *The Bering Land Bridge*. Stanford University Press: 451–484.

HORVÁTH, L. 1955. Red-footed Falcons in Ohat-woods, near Hortobágy. *Acta Zool. Acad. Scient. Hung.* 1: 245–287.

HÖTKER, H. 1989. *Der Wiesenpieper*. Neue Brehm-Bücherei 595, Ziemsen, Wittenberg.

HÖTKER, H. and C. SUDFELDT. 1982. Untersuchungen zur Nistplatzwahl einer nordwestdeutschen Population des Wiesenpiepers (*Anthus pratensis*). *Vogelwelt* 103: 178–187.

HOUSTON, D.C. 1977. The effects of Hooded Crows on hill sheep farming in Argyll, Scotland. *J. appl. Ecol.* 14: 1–29.

HOVORKA, W. 1991. *Zur Autökologie des Pirols* Oriolus o. oriolus *(L., 1758) unter Berücksichtigung populationsökologischer Aspekte*. Dissertation, University of Wien.

HOWARD, R. and A. MOORE. 1980. *A Complete Checklist of the Birds of the World*. Oxford University Press, Oxford.

HOWARD, R. and A. MOORE. 1991. *A Complete Checklist of the Birds of the World*, 2nd edn. Academic Press, London.

HUDEC, K. and K. ŠŤASTNÝ. 1979. Zur Ausbreitungstendenz des Wiesenpiepers (*Anthus pratensis* L.) in der Tschechoslovakei. *Egretta* 22: 18–26.

HUDEC, K. and W. ÈERNÝ (Eds). 1977. *Fauna ÈSSR. Ptáci - Aves* 2. Academia, Praha.

HUDSON, A.V. and R.W. FURNESS. 1988. Utilization of discarded fish by scavenging seabirds behind whitefish trawlers in Shetland. *J. Zool. London* 215: 151–166.

HUDSON, A.V. and R.W. FURNESS. 1989. The behaviour of seabirds foraging at fishing boats around Shetland. *Ibis* 131: 225–237.

HUDSON, P.J. and A.P. DOBSON. 1988. The ecology and control of parasites in gamebird populations. In: Hudson, P.J. and M.R.W. Rands (Eds) *Ecology and Management of Gamebirds*. Blackwell Scientific Publications, Oxford: 98–113.

HUDSON, R. 1974. Feral parakeets near London. *Brit. Birds* 67: 33, 174.

HUGHES, B. In prep (1996). The ruddy duck *Oxyura jamaicensis* in the Western Palearctic and the threat to the white-headed duck *Oxyura leucocephala*. In: Holmes, J.S. and J.R. Simons (Eds) *The Introduction and naturalisation of Birds*. HMSO, London: 79–86.

HUGHES, B. and GRUSSU, M. 1994. The Ruddy Duck (*Oxyura jamaicensis*) in the United Kingdom: distribution, monitoring, current research and implications for European colonisation. *Oxyura* 7: 29–47.

HUHTALA, K. and S. SULKAVA. 1981. Environmental influences on Goshawk breeding in Finland. In: Kenward, R. and I. Lindsay (Eds) *Understanding the Goshawk*. International Association for Falconry and Conservation of Birds of Prey, Oxford: 89–104.

HULSCHER, J.B., K-M. EXO and N. CLARK. In press (1996). Why do Oystercatchers migrate? In: Goss-Custard, J.D. (Ed) *The Oystercatcher – from individuals to populations*. Oxford University Press, Oxford: 155–185.

HUME, R. 1993. *The Common Tern*. Hamlyn, London.

HUME, R.A. and D.A. CHRISTIE. 1989. Sabine's Gulls and other seabirds after the October 1987 storm. *Brit. Birds* 82: 191–208.

HUNT, G.L. and R.W. FURNESS. 1996. Seabird/Fish Interactions, with particular reference to seabirds in the North Sea. *ICES Cooperative Research Report 216*. International Council for the Exploration of the Sea, Copenhagen.

HUNTER, E.N. 1970. Great Northern Diver breeding in Scotland. *Scottish Birds* 6: 195.

HUNTLEY, B. and H.J.B. BIRKS. 1983. *An Atlas of Past and Present Pollen Maps for Europe: 0–13000 years ago*. Cambridge University Press, Cambridge.

HUSTINGS, F. 1986. Veranderingen in de stand van de Roodborsttapuit *Saxicola torquata* in 1970–84. *Limosa* 59: 153–162. (Population changes in the Stonechat *Saxicola torquata* during 1970–84) (in Dutch, with English summary).

HUSTINGS, F. 1988. *European Monitoring Studies of Breeding Birds*. SOVON, Beek-Ubbergen.

HUSTINGS, F. 1991. Explosieve toename van broedende Geoorde Futen *Podiceps nigricollis* in 1983–89 in Nederland. *Limosa* 64: 17–24. (Explosive increase of breeding Black-necked Grebes *Podiceps nigricollis* in The Netherlands in 1983–89) (in Dutch, with English summary).

HUSTINGS, F. and J. BEKHUIS. 1993. Grauwe Klauwieren *Lanius collurio* in het Nederland van nu: restanten van een glorieuzer verleden. *Vogeljaar* 41: 2–17. (Red-backed Shrikes in present-day Netherlands: remnants of a glorious past) (in Dutch).

HUSTINGS, F., F. POST and F. SCHEPERS. 1990. Verdwijnt de Grauwe Gors *Miliaria calandra* als broedvogel uit Nederland? *Limosa* 63: 103–111. (Is the Corn Bunting *Miliaria calandra* disappearing as a breeding bird in the Netherlands?) (in Dutch, with English summary).

HUSTINGS, F., J. BEKHUIS, R.G. BIJLSMA and F. POST. 1992. Kuifleeuweriken *Galerida cristata* op hun retour. *Vogeljaar* 40: 145–156. (Crested Larks *Galerida cristata* declining) (in Dutch, with English summary).

HUT, R.M.G. van der. 1986. Habitat choice and temporal differentiation in reed passerines of a Dutch marsh. *Ardea* 74: 159–176.

HUTCHINSON, C.D. and B. NEATH. 1978. Little Gulls in Britain and Ireland. *Brit. Birds* 71: 563–582.

HUYSKENS, G.P.R. 1986. Het Europese Rietganzenprobleem *Anser fabalis*. *Oriolus* 52: 105–256 (in Dutch).

HYYTIÄ, K., E. KELLOMÄKI and J. KOISTINEN (Eds). 1983. *Suomen lintuatlas*. SLY:n Lintutieto Oy, Helsinki (in Finnish).

IANKOV, P. 1991. Pallid Swift *Apus pallidus* in Bulgaria. *Bird Census News* 4(1): 24–27.

IANKOV, P. and K. NIAGOLOV. 1987. [Observations on the birds in the Eastern Rhodopes mountains in 1984.] *Orn. Inf. Bull.* 21–22: 42–54 (in Bulgarian).

IANKOV, P., K. KHRISTOV and S. AVRAMOV. 1995. Changes in the status of the Black Vulture *Aegypius monachus* in Bulgaria for the period 1980–1990. In: Meyburg, B-U. and R.D. Chancellor (Eds) *Raptor Conservation Today*. WWGBPO, Berlin: 139–142.

IAPICHINO, C. and B. MASSA. 1989. *The Birds of Sicily*.

B.O.U. Checklist No. 11. British Ornithologists' Union, Tring.

IBAÑEZ, F. and B. TROLLIET. 1990. Le Canard souchet *Anas clypeata* nicheur dans le Marais breton: effectif, répartition et liaison avec les limicoles. *Gibier Faune Sauvage* 7: 95–106.

ILLNER, H. 1988. Langfristiger Rückgang von Schleiereule *Tyto alba*, Waldohreule *Asio otus*, Steinkauz *Athene noctua* und Waldkauz *Strix aluco* in der Agrarlandschaft Mittelwestfalens 1974–1986. *Vogelwelt* 109: 145–151.

ILYICHEV, V.D. and V.E. FOMIN. 1988. [*Bird fauna and the change of environment.*] Nauka, Moscow: 248 (in Russian).

ILYICHEV, V.D. and V.A. ZUBAKIN (Eds). 1988. [*Birds of the USSR – Gulls and terns.*] Izdat. Nauka, Moscow (in Russian).

IMHOF, Th. 1984. Zur Ökologie von Grün- und Grauspecht im bernisch-solothurnischen Mittelland. *Lizentiatsarbeit 2. Teil., Zool. Inst. Univ. Bern*, Typoskript S. 20–76.

IMPE, J. van. 1987. La migration d'automne, les quartiers d'hivernage et de reprodution de *Anser fabalis fabalis* et de *Anser fabalis rossicus* en relation avec la loi de Bergmann. *Gerfaut* 77: 63–88.

IMPE, J. van. 1995. Considerations sur les causes de la disparition du courlis à bec grêle *Numenius tenuirostris. Alauda* 63: 111 –114.

INDYKIEWICZ, P. 1991. Nest and nest-sites of the House Sparrow *Passer domesticus* (Linnaeus, 1758) in urban, suburban and rural environments. *Acta zool. Cracov* 34: 475–495.

IRBY, H.L. 1895. *The Ornithology of the Straits of Gibraltar.* 2nd ed. Taylor & Francis, London.

IRIBARREN, J.J. 1975. Biologia des Aguila calzada (*Hieraaetus pennatus*) durante el periode de nidificación en Navarra. *Ardeola* 21: 305–320.

ISAKOV, Y.A. 1970. [Wintering of waterfowl in the USSR.] In: *Proceedings of International Regional Meeting on Conservation of Wildfowl Resources, Leningrad 1968*: 239–254 (in Russian).

ISAKSEN, K. and V. BAKKEN (Eds). 1995. *Seabird Populations in the Northern Barents Sea.* Meddelelser No. 135, Norsk Polarinstitutt, Oslo.

ISENMANN, P. 1987. L'évolution récente de la distribution du Pipit farlouse *Anthus pratensis* en France. *L'Oiseaux et R.F.O.* 57: 52–55.

ISENMANN, P. 1992. Merle bleu *Monticola solitarius*. In: Yeatman-Berthelot, D. (Ed) *Atlas des Oiseaux de France en Hiver.* Société Ornithologique de France, Paris: 394–395.

ISENMANN, P. and M-A. BOUCHET. 1993. L'aire de distribution française et le statut taxonomique de la Pie-grièche grise meridionale *Lanius elegans meridionalis. Alauda* 61: 223–227.

ISENMANN, P. and N. LEFRANC. 1994. Le statut taxonomique de la Pie-grièche meridionale *Lanius meridionalis* (Temminck 1820). *Alauda* 62: 138.

ISENMANN, P. and P. TYSSANDIER. 1994. Fauvette orphée *Sylvia hortensis*. In: Yeatman-Berthelot, D. and G. Jarry (Eds) *Nouvel Atlas des Oiseaux Nicheurs de France.* Société Ornithologique de France, Paris: 570–571.

ISENMANN, P., J-D. LEBRETON and R. BRANDL. 1991. The Black-headed Gull in Europe. *Acta XX Congressus Internationalis Ornithologici, Christchurch*: 2384–2389.

IVANOV, A.I. 1976. *Katalog Ptits SSSR.* Nauka, Leningrad. (*The Catalogue of the Bird Species of the USSR*) (in Russian).

IVANOVSKY, V.V. 1992. [Ecology of the Short-toed Eagle nesting in the Byelo-russian Poozerje.]. In: Kurochkin, E.N. (Ed) [*Modern Ornithology 1991.*] Nauka, Moscow: 69–77 (in Russian).

IVANOVSKY, V.V. 1993a. [Materials on comparative ecology of the Greater Spotted Eagle (*Aquila clanga*) and Lesser Spotted Eagle (*Aquila pomarina*).] *ONP NPEC 'Veras-eco'.* Inst. of Zool. of Academy of Sciences of Belarus: 15–25 (in Russian).

IVANOVSKY, V.V. 1993b. [The Greater Spotted Eagle in the Vitebsk Region. In: *Problems of the Conservation of Biological Diversity in Belarus*]. *Abstract of International Scient.-Pract. Conference, Minsk*: 213–215 (in Russian).

IWRB Goose Research Group. 1994. Recent population status of Brent Geese. *IWRB Goose Research Group Bull.* 5: 5–7.

JAAKOLA, E. 1972. *Nittykirvisen ja lapinkirvisen pesimäbiologiasta Utsjoen Karigasniemellä.* MSc Thesis, Department of Zoology, University of Helsinki.

JACOB, J-P. D., van der ELST, J-P. SCHMITZ, M. PAQUAY and F. MARECHAL. 1983. Progression de l'Hypolaïs polyglotte (*Hippolais polyglotta*) en Belgique et au Grand-Duché de Luxembourg. *Aves* 20: 92–102.

JACOBSEN, E.M. 1992. *Danske vinterfugles forekomst 1975–1990.* Dansk Ornitologisk Forening, Copenhagen (in Danish).

JAKOBER, H. and W. STAUBER. 1987. Habitatsansprüche des Neuntöters (*Lanius collurio*) und Maßnahmen für seinen Schutz. *Beih. Veröff. Naturschutz Landschaftspflege Bad.-Württ.* 48: 25–53.

JALAS, J. and J. SUOMINEN (Eds). 1972. *Atlas Florae Europaeae.* Botanical Museum, Finnish Museum of Natural History, Helsinki University, Helsinki, Finland.

JALAS, J. and J. SUOMINEN (Eds). 1988. *Atlas Florae Europaeae* (Revised). Cambridge University Press, Cambridge.

JAMES, P.C. and H.A. ROBERTSON. 1985. First record of Swinhoe's Storm Petrel *Oceanodroma monorhis* in the Atlantic Ocean. *Ardea* 73: 105–106.

JANIGA, M. 1992. Growth allometry in the Ring Ouzel, *Turdus torquatus.* Multivariate study. *Oecologia Montana* 1: 21–30.

JÄNNES, H. and P.J. NIKANDER. 1993. Rariteetkomitean hyväksymät vuoden 1992 harvinaisuushavainnot. *Linnut* 28(6): 9–19 (in Finnish).

JARDINE, D.C. 1993a. Siskin *Carduelis spinus*. In: Gibbons, D.W., J.B. Reid and R.A. Chapman (Eds) *The New Atlas of Breeding Birds in Britain and Ireland: 1988–1991.* Poyser, London: 414–415.

JARDINE, D.C. 1993b. Redpoll *Carduelis flammea*. In: Gibbons, D.W., J.B. Reid and R.A. Chapman (Eds) *The New Atlas of Breeding Birds in Britain and Ireland: 1988–1991.* Poyser, London: 420–421.

JARRY, G. 1992. *Biologie de la Tourterelle des bois (*Streptopelia turtur*) au Sénégal – Région de M'Bour.* CRBPO Report, Paris.

JARRY, G. 1994. Tourterelle des bois *Streptopelia turtur*. In: Yeatman-Berthelot, D. and G. Jarry (Eds) *Nouvel Atlas des Oiseaux Nicheurs de France 1985–1989*. Société Ornithologique de France, Paris: 380–383.

JARRY, G. and F. BAILLON. 1991. *Hivernage de la Tourterelle des bois (*Streptopelia turtur*) au Sénégal. Etude d'une population dans la région de Nianing.* CRBPO/ORSTOM Report, Paris.

JÄRVINEN, A. 1981. Population trends in the Redstart *Phoenicurus phoenicurus* in northern Fennoscandia. *Ornis Fennica* 58: 129–131.

JÄRVINEN, A. 1982. Ecology of the Siberian Tit *Parus cinctus* in NW Finnish Lapland. *Ornis Scand.* 13: 47–55.

JÄRVINEN, A. and J. PIETIÄINEN. 1981. The Bluethroat *Luscinia s. svecica* population at Kilpisjärvi, Finnish Lapland: density, habitat selection, age structure and nesting success in 1981. *Proc. 3rd Nordic Congr. Ornithol.*: 189–194.

JÄRVINEN, O. and S. ULFSTRAND. 1980. Species turnover of a continental fauna: Northern Europe, 1850–1980. *Oecologia* 46: 186–195.

JÄRVINEN, O. and R.A. VÄISÄNEN. 1978a. Recent changes in forest bird populations in northern Finland. *Ann. Zool. Fennici* 15: 279–289.

JÄRVINEN, O. and R.A. VÄISÄNEN. 1978b. Habitat distribution and conservation of land bird populations in northern Norway. *Holarctic Ecol.* 1: 351–361.

JÄRVINEN, O. and R.A. VÄISÄNEN. 1978c. Ecological zoogeography of North European waders, or Why do so many waders breed in the North? *Oikos* 30: 496–507.

JÄRVINEN, O. and R.A. VÄISÄNEN. 1979. Climatic changes, habitat changes and competition: dynamics of geographical overlap in two pairs of congeneric bird species in Finland. *Oikos* 33: 261–271.

JÄRVINEN, O., K. KUUSELA and R.A. VÄISÄNEN. 1977. Metsien rakenteen muutoksen vaikutus pesimälinnustoomme viimeisten 30 vuoden aikana. *Silva Fennica* 11: 284–294. (Effects of modern forestry on the numbers of breeding birds in Finland in 1945–1975) (in Finnish, with English summary).

JÄRVINEN, O., J. KOUKI and U. HÄYRINEN. 1987. Reversed latitudinal gradients in total density and species richness of birds breeding on Finnish mires. *Ornis Fennica* 64: 67–73.

JENKINS, D., A. WATSON and G.R. MILLER. 1963. Population studies on Red Grouse, *Lagopus lagopus scoticus* (Lath.) in north-east Scotland. *J. Anim. Ecol.* 32: 317–376.

JENNY, D. 1992. Bruterfolg und Bestandsregulation einer alpinen Population des Steinadlers. *Orn. Beob.* 89: 1–43.

JENNY, M. 1990a. Nahrungsökologie der Feldlerche *Alauda arvensis* in einer intensiv genutzten Agrarlandschaft des schweizerischen Mittellandes. *Orn. Beob.* 87: 31–53.

JENNY, M. 1990b. Territorialität und Brutbiologie der Feldlerche *Alauda arvensis* in einer intensiv genutzten Agrarlandschaft. *J. Ornithol.* 131: 241–265.

JENSEN, A. 1981. Ornithological winter observations on Selvagem Grande. *Bocagiana* 62: 1–7.

JERRENTRUP, H. 1988. White-tailed Eagle: Population developments and threats in the eastern Mediterranean. Proposal for conservation measures in Greece. In: *Proceedings of the Meeting of the EC Working Group on the White-tailed Eagle*: 23–28.

JERRENTRUP, H. 1994. Spur-winged Plover. In: Tucker, G.M. and M.F. Heath (Eds) *Birds in Europe – their conservation status.* Conservation Series No. 3, BirdLife International, Cambridge: 256–257.

JERZAK, L. 1988. Distribution and nest sites of Magpie in non-urban habitats in Poland. *Notatki Ornithol.* 29: 27–41.

JERZAK, L. 1992. Breeding density and nest site characteristics of the Magpie (*Pica pica* L.) in Lubuska district towns in 1985 and 1987. *Przyroda srodkowego Nadodrza* 2: 65–77.

JOENSEN, A. H. 1976. Moulting and wintering seaducks in Denmark. In: *Bird Migration*. Valgus, Tallinn.

JOHANSEN, B.T. 1989. Sortspættens *Dryocopus martius* bestandsstørrelse, territoriestørrelse og yngleresultater i Tisvilde Hegn, Nordsjælland, 1977–1986. *Dansk Orn. Foren. Tidsskr.* 83: 113–118. (Population, territory size and breeding success of Black Woodpeckers in Tisvilde Hegn, northern Zealand, 1977–1986) (in Danish, with English summary).

JOHNSON, A.R. 1989. Movements of Greater Flamingos *Phoenicopterus ruber roseus* in the western Palearctic. *Rev. Ecol. (Terre et Vie)* 44: 75–94.

JOHNSON, A.R. 1992. The western Mediterranean population of flamingos: is it at risk? In: Finlayson, C.M., G.E. Hollis and T.J. Davis (Eds) *Managing Mediterranean Wetlands and their Birds.* Special Publication No. 20, International Wetlands Research Bureau, Slimbridge: 215–219.

JOHNSON, A.R., R.E. GREEN and G.J.M. HIRONS. 1991. Survival rates of Greater Flamingos in the Western Mediterranean Region. In: Perrins, C.M., J-D. Lebreton and G.J.M. Hirons (Eds) *Bird Population Studies.* Oxford University Press, Oxford: 249–271.

JOHNSSON, K., S.G. NILSSON and M. TJERNBERG. 1993. Characteristics and utilization of old Black Woodpecker *Dryocopus martius* holes by hole-nesting species. *Ibis* 135: 410–416.

JOHNSTON, R.F. 1969. Taxonomy of House Sparrows in the Mediterranean basin. *Condor* 71: 129–139.

JOKIMÄKI, J. 1989. [The occurrence of the Little Bunting in Lapland in the 1980s.] *Kokko* 11: 3–4 (in Finnish).

JONCOURT, G. 1986. *L'Épervier d'Europe: étude d'une population en basse Bretagne.* Fonds d'intervention pour les rapaces, La Garenne-Colombes.

JONES, G. 1986. The distribution and abundance of Sand Martin breeding in Central Scotland. *Scottish Birds* 14: 33–38.

JONES, G. 1993. Sand Martin *Riparia riparia*. In: Gibbons, D.W., J.B. Reid and R.A. Chapman (Eds) *The New Atlas of Breeding Birds in Britain and Ireland: 1988–1991.* Poyser, London: 274–275.

JONES, M.J. 1990. A survey of the distribution, density and habitat preferences of the Long-toed Pigeon, *Columba trocaz*. *Bol. Mus. Mun. Funchal* 42 (219): 71–86.

JONKERS, D.A. and H.N. LEYS. 1994. Monitoring van de Huiszwaluw *Delichon urbica* in 1993 in Nederland. *Vogeljaar* 42: 159–161. (Monitoring of the House Martin in The Netherlands in 1993) (in Dutch, with English summary).

JONSSON, L. 1992. *Birds of Europe with North Africa and the Middle East*. Croom Helm, London.

JÖNSSON, P.E. 1988. *The Ecology of the southern Dunlin* Calidris alpina schinzii. PhD Thesis, University of Lund, Sweden.

JÖNSSON, P.E. 1992. [The Corn Bunting *Miliaria calandra* in Scania, S. Sweden, 1990–1991 – a report from a conservation project.] *Anser* 31: 101–108 (in Swedish).

JÖNSSON, P.E. 1993. Projekt Svartbent strandpipare – årsrapport 1992. *Anser* 32: 29–34 (in Swedish).

JORDANIA, R.G. 1962. [*Ornithofauna of Caucasus Minor*.] Academy of Science, Georgian SSR, Tbilisi (in Russian).

JØRGENSEN, H.E. 1989. *Danmarks Rovfugle – en statusoversigt*. Jørgensen, Frederikshus. (*Danish Birds of Prey – a review*) (in Danish, with English summary).

JOST, O. 1975. Zur Ökologie der Wasseramsel (*Cinclus cinclus*) mit besonderer Berücksichtigung ihrer Ernährung. *Bonn. Zool. Monogr.* 6: 1–183.

JOUANIN, C. and F. ROUX. 1965. Contribution à l'étude de la biologie de *Pelagodroma marina hypoleuca* (Webb, Berthelot and Mouquin-Tandon). *Bol. Mus. Mun. Funchal* 19: 16–42.

JOUANIN, C., F. ROUX and P.A. ZINO. 1969. Visites aux lieux de nidification de *Pterodroma mollis* 'deserta'. *Oiseau* 39: 161–175.

JUANA, E.A. de. 1980. *Atlas Ornitológico de La Rioja*. Instituto de Estudios Riojanos, Logroño.

JUANA, E.A. de. 1984. The status and conservation of seabirds in the Spanish Mediterranean. In: Croxall, J.P., P.G.H. Evans and R.W. Schreiber (Eds) *Status and Conservation of the World's Seabirds*. Technical Publication No. 2, International Council for Bird Preservation, Cambridge: 473–486.

JUANA, E.A. de. 1991. [Ornithological news.] *Ardeola* 38(2): 349 (in Spanish).

JUANA, E.A. de and J.M. VARELA. 1993. La población mundial reproductora de la Gaviota de Audouin (*Larus audouinii*). In: Aguilar, J.S., X. Monbailliu and A.M. Paterson (Eds) *Status and Conservation of Seabirds*. SEO/BirdLife and MEDMARAVIS, Madrid: 71–85.

JUANA, E.A. de, P.M. BRADLEY, J.M. VARELA, and H-H. WITT. 1987. Sobre los movimientos migratorios de la Gaviota de Audouin (*Larus audouinii*). *Ardeola* 34: 15–24.

JUANA, E.A. de, T. SANTOS, F. SUAREZ and J.L. TELLERIA. 1988. Status and conservation of steppe birds and their habitats in Spain. In: Goriup, P.D. (Ed) *Ecology and Conservation of Grassland Birds*. International Council for Bird Preservation, Cambridge: 113–123.

JUDIN, K.A. and L.V. FIRSOVA. 1990. *Larus glaucoides*, Polarmöwe. In: Il'icev, V.D. and V.A. Zubakin (Eds) *Handbuch der Vögel der Sowjetunion*, Vol. 6, Part 1. Ziemsen Verlag, Wittenberg Lutherstadt: 142–145.

JUILLARD, M. 1984. *La Chouette chevêche*. Nos Oiseaux, Prangins.

JUNCO, O. del. 1984. Estudio sobre una población de águilas perdiceras (*Hieraaetus fasciatus*). In: Alamy, O., A. de Juan, X. Parellada, J. Ramón and J. Ticó (Eds) *Rapinyaires mediterranis* II. Centre de Recerca i Protecció de Rapinyaires: 80–85.

JUNCO, O. del and B. GONZALEZ. 1966. Una especie para la avifauna europea: *Apus affinis*. *Ardeola* 12: 7–9.

JUNG, N. 1983. Strukturen und Faktoren der Expansion des Karmingimpels (*Carpodacus erythrinus*) in Europa und Kleinasien. *Beitr. Vogelk.* 29: 249–273.

KALABÉR, L. 1973. Contributions à la connaissance de la biologie de reproduction et du développement postembryonnaire des poussins du Hibou petit-duc. *Studi si comunicàri. Muz. Stiintele Nat. Bacàu* 6: 345–354 (in Romanian).

KALABÉR, L. 1984. Status of diurnal birds of prey in Romania and the problem of their protection. *WWGBPO Bull.* 2: 37–43.

KÅLÅS, J.A. and I. BYRKJEDAL. 1981. Vadefuglenes hekkestatus i Norge med Svalbard . *Proc. 2nd Nordic Congr. Ornithol. 1979*: 57–74. (The status of breeding waders *Charadrii* in Norway including Svalbard) (in Norwegian, with English summary).

KÅLÅS, J.A., P. FISKE and J. HÖGLUND. In prep. Food availability and occurrences of lekking Great Snipes (*Gallinago media*); natural versus sexual selection.

KALELA, O. 1946. Zur Ausbreitungsgeschichte der Vögel vegetationsreicher Seen. *Ann. Acad. Scient. Fennica, Biol.* 12.

KALELA, O. 1949. Changes in geographic ranges in the avifauna of Northern and Central Europe in relation to recent changes in climate. *Bird Banding* 20: 77–103.

KALYAKIN, V.N. 1984. [Breeding waterfowl of the Yugorski Peninsula.] In: *Recent Status of Resources of Waterfowl*. Moscow: 14–17 (in Russian).

KAMPP, K. 1982. Notes on the Long-tailed Skua *Stercorarius longicaudus* in West Greenland. *Dansk Orn. Foren. Tidsskr.* 76: 129–135.

KANYAMIBWA, S., A. SCHIERER, R. PRADEL and J.-D. LEBRETON. 1990. Changes in adult annual survival rates in a western European population of the White Stork *Ciconia ciconia*. *Ibis* 132: 27–35.

KAPOCSY, G. 1979. *Weißflügel- und Weißbartseeschwalbe* Chlidonias leucopterus *und* Chl. hybrida. Neue Brehm-Bücherei 516, Ziemsen, Wittenberg.

KARLSSON, J. and H. KÄLLANDER. 1977. Fluctuations and density of suburban populations of the Blackbird *Turdus merula*. *Ornis Scand.* 8: 139–144.

KARPOVICH, V.N. and V.D. KOKHANOV. 1967. [The bird fauna of Vaygach Island and the northeast of Yugorskiy Peninsula.] *Trudy Kandalakch. Zapovednika* 5: 268–338 (in Russian).

KASPAREK, M. 1985. *Die Sultanssümpfe. Naturgeschichte eines Vogelparadieses in Anatolien*. Max Kasparek Verlag, Heidelberg.

KASPAREK, M. 1991. Zur Verbreitung der Palmtaube *Streptopelia senegalensis* im Vorderen Orient. *Orn. Verh.* 25: 51–64.

KASPAREK, M. 1992. *Die Vögel der Türkei: eine Übersicht*. Max Kasparek Verlag, Heidelberg.

KAUPPINEN, J. 1993. Densities and habitat distribution of breeding waterfowl in boreal lakes in Finland. *Finnish Game Res.* 48: 24–45.

KAUPPINEN, J. 1994. *Composition and dynamics of wetland waterfowl communities in a Finnish inland lake area*. MS.

KAUPPINEN, J. and R.A. VÄISÄNEN. 1993. Ordination

and classification of waterfowl communities in south boreal lakes. *Finnish Game Res.* 48: 3–23.

KAYSER, Y. and E. ROUSSEAU. 1994. Premières données sur l'Étourneau unicolore *(Sturnus unicolor)* dans le sud de la France. *Nos Oiseaux* 42: 369–378.

KAYSER, Y., J. WALMSLEY, O. PINEAU and H. HAFNER. 1994. Évolution récente des effectifs de Hérons cendrés (*Ardea cinerea*) et de Hérons pourprés (*Ardea purpurea*) sur le littoral méditerranéen français. *Nos Oiseaux* 42: 341–355.

KEAR, J. 1990. *Man and Wildfowl.* Poyser, London.

KEAST, A. (Ed). 1990a. *Biogeography and Ecology of Forest Bird Communities.* SPB Academic Publishing bv, The Hague.

KEAST, A. 1990b. Distribution and origins of forest birds. In: Keast, A. (Ed) *Biogeography and Ecology of Forest Bird Communities.* SPB Academic Publishing bv, The Hague: 45–49.

KELLER, M. and P. PROFUS. 1992. Present situation, reproduction and food of the Black Stork in Poland. In: Meriaux, J-L., A. Schierer, C. Tombal and J-C. Tombal (Eds) *Les Cigognes d'Europe.* Institut Européen d'Ecologie, Metz: 227–236.

KELSEY, M.G. 1993. Reed Warbler *Acrocephalus scirpaceus.* In: Gibbons, D.W., J.B. Reid and R.A. Chapman (Eds) *The New Atlas of Breeding Birds in Britain and Ireland: 1988–1991.* Poyser, London: 334–335.

KELSEY, M.G., G.H. GREEN, M.C. GARNETT and P.V. HAYMAN. 1989. Marsh Warblers in Britain. *Brit. Birds* 82: 239–256.

KEMP, M. 1983. The Nightjar in Avon. *Avon Bird Report 1982*: 49–66.

KERLINGER, P. and M. ROSS LEIN. 1986. Differences in winter range among age-sex classes of Snowy Owls *Nyctea scandiaca* in North America. *Ornis Scand.* 17: 1–17.

KERLINGER, P. and M. ROSS LEIN. 1988. Population ecology of Snowy Owls during winter on the Great Plains of North America. *Condor* 90: 866–874.

KERTELL, K. 1991. Disappearance of the Steller's Eider from the Yukon-Kuskokwim delta, Alaska. *Arctic* 44: 177–184.

KERY, M. 1991. Brutbestand und Verbreitung der Felsenschwalbe *Ptyonoprogne rupestris* im Schweizer Jura in den achtziger Jahren. *Orn. Beob.* 88: 209–216.

KESSLER, A. 1986. Zur aktuellen Bestandssituation des Grünspechts (*Picus viridis*) nebst ergänzenden Angaben zur Brutverbreitung im Oldenburgischen. *Jahresber. Orn. Arbeitsgem. Oldenb.* 10: 23–27.

KHANMAMEDOV, A.I. 1971. *Azerbaijanyn tojygkimiljari* [*Galliformes of Azerbaijan*]. Baku (in Azerbaijanian).

KHOKHLOV, A.N. 1989. [Great Black-headed Gull in Stavropol Region.] *Rare and Threatened Animals.* Moscow: 91–95 (in Russian).

KILPI, M. and P. SAUROLA. 1984. Migration and wintering strategies of juvenile and adult *Larus marinus*, *Larus argentatus* and *Larus fuscus* from Finland. *Ornis Fennica* 61: 1–8.

KILPI, M. and P. SAUROLA. 1985. Movements and survival areas of Finnish common gulls *Larus canus. Ann. Zool. Fennici* 22: 157–168.

KIRBY, J.S. 1993. Ruff. In: Gibbons, D.W., J.B. Reid and R.A. Chapman (Eds). *The New Atlas of Breeding Birds in Britain and Ireland: 1988–1991.* Poyser, London.

KIRBY, J.S. and C. MITCHELL. 1993. Distribution and status of wintering Shovelers *Anas clypeata* in Great Britain. *Bird Study* 40: 170–180.

KIRBY, J.S., J.R. FERNS, R.J. WATERS and R.P. PRŶS-JONES. 1991. *Wildfowl and Wader Counts 1990–91.* Wildfowl and Wetlands Trust, Slimbridge.

KIRCHNER, H. 1978. *Bruchwasserläufer und Waldwasserläufer.* Neue Brehm-Bücherei 309, Ziemsen, Wittenberg.

KIRWAN, G.M. and R.P. MARTINS. 1994. Turkey Bird Report 1987–91. *Sandgrouse* 16: 76–117.

KISTCHINSKY, A.A. 1975. Breeding biology and behaviour of the Grey Phalarope *Phalaropus fulicarius* in East Siberia. *Ibis* 117: 285–301.

KISTCHINSKY, A.A., P.S. TOMKOVICH and V.E. FLINT. 1983. [Birds of the Kanchalan basin, Chukotsk Autonomous Area.] *Arch. Zool. Mus., Moscow State University, Moscow, MGU*: 3–76 (in Russian).

KISTYAKIVSKI, A.B. 1957. [*The Fauna of Ukraine*, Vol. 4. *Birds*.] AN USSR Kiev (in Russian).

KJELLÉN, N. 1994. Gladan: en rovfågel på frammarsch i Sverige. *Vår Fågelvärld* 53(6): 6–19 (in Swedish).

KJELLÉN, N. and U. OLSSON (Eds). 1995. *Holarktis Fåglar. SOF: s officiella svenska namulista med retenskapliga och engelska namn.* Swedish Ornithological Society, Stockholm.

KLAFS, G. and J. STÜBS. 1979. *Die Vogelwelt Mecklenburgs. Avifauna der Deutschen Demokratischen Republic 1.* VEB Gustav Fischer Verlag, Jena.

KLAUS, S. and H-H. BERGMANN. 1994. Distribution, status and limiting factors of Capercaillie (*Tetrao urogallus*) in Central Europe, particularly in Germany, including an evaluation of introductions. *Gibier Faune Sauvage, Game and Wildlife* 11 (Special number Part 2): 57–80.

KLAUS, S., A.V. ANDREEV, H-H. BERGMANN, F. MÜLLER, J. PORKERT and J. WIESNER. 1989. *Die Auerhühner.* Neue Brehm-Bücherei 86, Ziemsen, Wittenberg.

KLAUS, S., H.-H. BERGMANN, C. MARTI, F. MÜLLER, O.A. VITOVIC and J. WIESNER. 1990. *Die Birkhühner.* Neue Brehm-Bücherei 397, Ziemsen, Wittenberg.

KLESTOV, N.L. and G.G. GAVRISH. 1991. [On the distribution of the Citrine Wagtail in Ukraine.] *Abstracts from the All-Union Ornithological Conference*, Part 2: 279–280 (in Russian).

KLINKEN, A. van. 1994. De opkomst van de Wulp als akkervogel. *Vogeljaar* 42: 202–204. (Curlews invading arable land) (in Dutch).

KLINNER, B. 1991. Breeding waders on wet grasslands (inland sites) in West Germany: recent data. *Wader Study Group Bull.* 61, Suppl: 22–25.

KLOMP, N.I. and R.W. FURNESS. 1992a. The dispersal and philopatry of Great Skuas from Foula, Shetland. *Ringing and Migration* 13: 73–82.

KLOMP, N.I. and R.W. FURNESS. 1992b. Non-breeders as a buffer against environmental stress: declines in numbers of Great Skuas on Foula, Shetland, and prediction of future recruitment. *J. appl. Ecol.* 29: 341–348.

KNEIS, P. 1982. Zur Verbreitung und Bestandsentwicklung, Habitat- und Nistplatzwahl sowie Reproduktion des Steinschmätzers *Oenanthe oenanthe* in der DDR: Analyse der Beringungsdaten 1964 bis 1976. *Ber. Vogelwarte Hiddensee* 3: 55–81.

KNIJFF, P. de. 1991. Little-known West Palaearctic birds: Cinereous Bunting. *Birding World* 4: 384–391.

KNOX, A.G. 1990. The sympatric breeding of Common and Scottish Crossbills *Loxia curvirostra* and *L. scotica* and the evolution of crossbills. *Ibis* 132: 454–466.

KOCHEGURA, V.L. 1989. [Qualitative and quantitative estimates of the fauna of Streltsova Steppe Reserve and its buffer zone.] *All-Union Kadastr. Conf. Ufa.* III: 121–123.

KOMAROV, Yu.E. 1991. [Seasonal changes in the bird population density of selected habitats of the North Ossetian Nature Reserve.] *Kavkaz. orn. Vestnik (Stavropol')* 1: 48–72 (in Russian).

KONDRATIEV, A.I. 1982. [*Wader Biology in Tundras of North-Eastern Asia*.] Nauka, Moscow (in Russian).

KONING, F.J. and G. BAEYENS. 1990. *Uilen in de duinen*. Stichting Uitgeverij Koninklijke Nederlandse Natuurhistorische Vereniging, Utrecht. (*Owls in the Dunes*) (in Dutch).

KONRAD, V. 1985. Samtkopf-Grasmücke (*Sylvia melanocephala*) und Tamarisken-Grasmücke (*Sylvia mystacea*) doch zwei 'gute' Arten? *Orn. Mitt.* 37: 81.

KOOIKER, G. 1990. Bestandsentwicklung und Bruterfolg einer Kiebitzpopulation *Vanellus vanellus* im Agrarraum bei Osnabrück. *Vogelwelt* 111: 202–216.

KOOY, H. van der. 1994. Het broedseizoen 1993 van de Purperreiger in Nederland. *Vogeljaar* 42: 218–220. (Breeding season 1993 of the Purple Heron in The Netherlands) (in Dutch).

KÖPPEN, U. 1989. Zu Bestandsentwicklung und gegenwärtigem Status des Höckerschwans (*Cygnus olor*) in Mitteleuropa. *Beitr. Vogelkd.* 35: 182–192.

KORELOV, M.N. 1974. [The genus *Serinus*.] In: *Ptitsy Kazakhstana* [*The Birds of Kazakhstan*], Vol. 5. Alma-Ata: 251–258 (in Russian).

KORPIMÄKI, E. 1981. On the ecology and biology of Tengmalm's Owl (*Aegolius funereus*) in Southern Ostrobothnia and Suomenselkä, western Finland. *Acta Universitatis Ouluensis. Series A. Scientiae Rerum Naturalium* 118: 1–84.

KORPIMÄKI, E. 1984. Population dynamics of birds of prey in relation to fluctuations in small mammal populations in western Finland. *Ann. Zool. Fennici* 21: 287–293.

KORPIMÄKI, E. 1986. Gradients in population fluctuations of Tengmalm's owl *Aegolius funereus* in Europe. *Oecologia* 69: 195–201.

KORPIMÄKI, E. 1988. Effects of territory quality on occupancy, breeding performance and breeding dispersal in Tengmalm's owl. *J. Anim. Ecol.* 57: 97–108.

KORPIMÄKI, E. 1992. Diet composition, prey choice, and breeding success of Long-eared Owls: effects of multi-annual fluctuations in food abundance. *Can. J. Ecol.* 70: 2373–2381.

KORPIMÄKI, E. and K. NORRDAHL. 1991. Numerical and functional responses of kestrels, short-eared owls, and long-eared owls to vole densities. *Ecology* 72: 814–826.

KORPIMÄKI, E., M. LAGERSTRÖM and P. SAUROLA. 1987. Field evidence for nomadism in Tengmalm's owl *Aegolius funereus*. *Ornis Scand.* 18: 1–4.

KORTE, J. de. 1986. Ecology of the Long-tailed Skua, *Stercorarius longicaudus* Vieillot, 1819, at Scoresby Sund, East Greenland. Part four: breeding success and growth of young. *Bijdr. Dierk.* 56: 1–23.

KORZYUKOV, A. and O. POTAPOV. 1992. Distribution, numbers and biological aspects of Kentish Plovers in the South Ukraine. *Wader Study Group Bull.* 65: 22.

KOSHELEV, A.I. 1994. Baillon's Crake *Porzana pusilla*. In: Tucker, G.M. and M.F. Heath (Eds) *Birds in Europe – their conservation status*. BirdLife International, Cambridge: 226–227.

KOSHELEV, A.I., A.I. KORZIUKOV, V.A. LOBKOV and L.V. PERESADKO. 1991. [Analysis of number of several rare birds of the district of Odessa.] In: A.I. Korziukov, A.I. Koshelev and I.I. Tchernitko (Eds) *Redkie ptitsy Pritchernomoria*. Lybid Kiev-Odessa: 9–36 (in Russian).

KOSHELEV, A.I., V. SIOKHIN and I. BERLASHKOV. 1992. Population dynamics and ecological characteristics of Cormorant (*Phalacrocorax carbo*) in the Azov–Black Sea region. *Wader Study Group Bull.* 66: 38.

KOSKIMIES, J. 1957. Verhalten und Ökologie der Jungen und der jungenführenden Weibchen der Samtente. *Ann. Zool. Soc. 'Vanamo'* 18 (9).

KOSKIMIES, P. 1980. Breeding biology of Blyth's Reed Warbler *Acrocephalus dumetorum* in SE Finland. *Ornis Fennica* 57: 26–32.

KOSKIMIES, P. 1982. [The night-singers in Finland – newcomers in changing environments.] *Ornis Karelica* 8: 100–109 (in Finnish, with English summary).

KOSKIMIES, P. 1984. Polygyny in Blyth's Reed Warbler *Acrocephalus dumetorum*. *Ann. Zool. Fennici* 21: 239–242.

KOSKIMIES, P. 1989a. *Distribution and Numbers of Finnish Breeding Birds*. Appendix to Suomen lintuatlas. SLY:n Lintutieto Oy, Helsinki.

KOSKIMIES, P. 1989b. [*Breeding bird fauna of Lake Siikalahti, Parikkala (SE Finland).*] Publication No. 139, National Board of Waters and the Environment: 1–132 (in Finnish).

KOSKIMIES, P. 1989c. Faunistical report 1987. *Lintumies* 24: 12–20 (in Finnish, with English summary).

KOSKIMIES, P. 1990. [Faunistical report 1988.] *Lintumies* 25: 189–198 (in Finnish, with English summary).

KOSKIMIES, P. 1992a. Population sizes and recent trends of breeding birds in the Nordic countries. *Bird Census News* 5(3): 41–79.

KOSKIMIES, P. 1992b. Faunistic report 1990. *Lintumies* 27: 48–59 (in Finnish, with English summary).

KOSKIMIES, P. 1993a. Population sizes and recent trends of breeding and wintering birds in Finland. *Linnut* 28(2): 6–15.

KOSKIMIES, P. 1993b. *Population Sizes and Recent Trends of Breeding Birds in the Nordic Countries*. Publication No. 177, National Board of Waters and Environment: 1–73.

KOSKIMIES, P. 1994. Broad-billed Sandpiper. In: Tucker, G.M. and M.F. Heath (Eds) *Birds in Europe: their conservation status*. Conservation Series No. 3, BirdLife International, Cambridge: 264–265.

KOSKIMIES, P. 1995. [Gyrfalcons in Finland.] *Linnut* 30(3): 4 (in Finnish, with English summary).

KOSTIN, Yu.V. 1983. *The Birds of Crimea*. Nauka, Moscow (in Russian).

KOSTRZEWA, A. 1991. Die Ökologie des Wespenbussards *Pernis apivorus* L. in der niederrheinischen Bucht 1979–89: Dichte, Bruterfolg, Habitatpräferenzen und limitierende Faktoren. *Populationsökologie Greifvogel- und Eulenarten* 2: 230–254.

KOSTRZEWA, A. and G. SPEER (Eds). 1995. *Greifvögel in Deutschland: Bestand, Situation und Schutz*. AULA-Verlag, Wiesbaden.

KOTLYAKOV, V.M. and G.A. AGRANAT. 1994. The Russian North: problems and propects. *Polar Geography and Geology* 18: 285–295.

KOVÁCS, G. 1993. [Population changes of the Collared Pratincole (*Glareola pratincola*) at Hortobágy.] *Partimadár* 1993/1: 16–18 (in Hungarian, with English summary).

KOVÁCS, G. 1994a. Population increase and expansion of the Aquatic Warbler *Acrocephalus paludicola* on the Hortobágy between 1977 and 1994. *Aquila* 101: 133–143.

KOVÁCS, G. 1994b. The Nesting of Rose-coloured Starlings (*Pastor roseus*) on the Hortobágy in 1994. *Aquila* 101: 159–171.

KOVSHAR' (=KOWSCHAR), A.F. (Ed). 1974. *Ptitsy Kazakhstana*, Vol. 5. Alma-Ata. (*The Birds of Kazakhstan*) (in Russian).

KOVSHAR', A.F. 1979. [*Song-birds in the subalpine Tien-Shan*]. Alma-Ata (in Russian).

KOWSCHAR, A.F. and B.P. SCHUJKO. 1984. Biologische Daten zur Verstädterung der Amsel (*Turdus merula*) in Alma-Ata, Kasachstan, UdSSR. *Ann. Ornithol.* 8: 97–105 (abstract in *Ornithologische Schriftenschau* 63: 19–20).

KOZLOVA, E.V. 1961. *Fauna SSSR Ptitsy*, Vol. 2, No. 1, Part 2. USSR Academy of Sciences, Moscow–Leningrad (in Russian).

KOZLOVA, E.V. 1962. [Charadriiformes. Suborder *Limicolae*]. In: *Fauna of the USSR*, Vol. 2, No. 1, Part 3, *Birds*. USSR Academy of Sciences, Moscow–Leningrad (in Russian).

KOZLOVA, E.V. 1975. [*The Birds of the Steppe and Desert Zones in Central Asia*.] Nauka, Leningrad (in Russian).

KOZULIN, A. and M. FLADE. 1997. Habitatansprüche und aktuelle Gefährdungssituation des Seggenrohrsängers *Acrocephalus paludicola* unter besonderer Berücksichtigung der Polessje (Belarus, Ukraine). *Vogelwelt* 118.

KRASNOV, Y.V. and R.T. BARRETT. 1995. Large-scale interactions among seabirds, their prey and humans in the southern Barents Sea. In: Skjoldahl, H.R., C. Hopkins, K.E. Erikstad and H.P. Leinaas (Eds) *Ecology of Fjords and Coastal Waters*. Elsevier Science. B.V.

KREBS, J.R. and N.B. DAVIES. 1993. *An Introduction to Behavioural Ecology*, 3rd edn. Blackwell Scientific Publications, Oxford.

KRECHMAR, E.V. 1986. Nesting ecology of the White-fronted Goose *Anser albifrons* in different parts of its range. *Zool. Zh.* 65: 889–900.

KRESSE, A. and O. KEPKA. 1988. Haubenmaina, *Acridotheres cristatellus* (L.) ansässig in Graz (Aves, Sturnidae). *Mitt. Abt. Zool. Landesmus. Joanneum* 41: 49–50.

KRIŠTÍN, A. 1991a. Brutbestand und Brutbiologie des Schwarzstirnwürgers (*Lanius minor*) in der Mittelslowakei/CSFR. *Orn. Mitt.* 43: 131–133.

KRIŠTÍN, A. 1991b. On the present status and ecology of Rock Bunting, *Emberiza cia*, in Czechoslovakia. *Sylvia* 28: 115–120.

KRIŠTÍN, A. 1992. Zur Oekologie des Bienenfressers, *Merops apiaster* Linné, in der Tschechoslowakei. *Falke 39*: 222–225.

KRIVENKO, V.G., V.G. VINOGRADOV, A. GREEN and C. PERENNOU. 1994. Ferruginous Duck *Aythya nyroca*. In: Tucker, G.M. and M.F. Heath (Eds) *Birds in Europe – their conservation status*. BirdLife International, Cambridge: 130–131.

KROGULEC, J. and A.B.A. LEROUX. 1994. Breeding ecology of Montagu's Harrier *Circus pygargus* on natural and reclaimed marshes in Poland and France. In: Meyburg, B-U. and R.D. Chancellor (Eds) *Raptor Conservation Today*. WWGBPO/Pica Press, Sussex: 151–152.

KRÓL, W. 1985. Breeding density of diurnal raptors in the neighbourhood of Susz/Ilawa lakeland, Poland, in the years 1977–1979. *Acta Ornithol.* 21: 95–114.

KRÜGER, S. 1979. *Der Kernbeisser*. Neue Brehm-Bücherei 525, Ziemsen, Wittenberg.

KRÜGER, S. 1989. *Der Brachpieper*. Neue Brehm-Bücherei 598, Ziemsen, Wittenberg.

KUHNEN, K. 1975. Bestandsentwicklung, Verbreitung, Biotop und Siedlungsdichte der Uferschwalbe (*Riparia riparia*) 1966–1973 am Niederrhein. *Charadrius* 11: 1–24.

KUITUNEN, M. and P. HELLE. 1988. Relationship of the Common Treecreeper *Certhia familiaris* to edge effect and forest fragmentation. *Ornis Fennica* 65: 150–155.

KUITUNEN, M. and M. MÄKINEN. 1993. An experiment on nest site choice of the Common Treecreeper in fragmented boreal forest. *Ornis Fennica* 70: 163–167.

KUKISH, A.I. 1990. [Influence of irrigation on the colonial birds of Sarpinski Lakes.] In: *Fauna and Ecology of Animals in Irrigation Conditions*. Elista: 12–21 (in Russian).

KUMERLOEVE, H. 1967. Doğu ve kuzeydoğu Kuçilk Asya'nin Kusiari. Neue Beiträge zur Kenntnis der Avifauna Nordost- und Ost-Kleinasiens. *Istan. Univ. Fen. Fak.* Mecmuasi B. 32: 79–213 (in Turkish, with German summary).

KUNYSZ, P. 1994. [Occurrence of Lesser Spotted Eagle *Aquila pomarina* in the Pogorze Przemyskie mountains 1980–1984.] *Badania nad ornitofauna Ziemi Przemyskiej* 2: 91–94 (in Polish).

KURLAVIČIUS, P. 1987. [*Distribution of Birds amongst Habitats in Woodland of Agricultural Landscape*.] Moklas, Vilnius (in Lithuanian).

KUROČHKIN, E.N. and A.I. KOŠELEV. 1989. Gattung *Fulica* Linnaeus, 1758. In: Potapov, R.L. and V.E. Flint (Eds) *Handbuch der Vögel der Sowjetunion*, Vol. 4. AULA-Verlag, Wiesbaden: 339–362.

KUSCHERT, H. and F. ZIESEMER. 1991. Knäckente *Anas querquedula*. In: Berndt, R.K. and G. Busche (Eds) *Vogelwelt Schleswig-Holsteins*, Vol. 3.1. Wachholtz, Neumünster: 168–172.

KUYKEN, E. and P. MEIRE. 1990. Questions of the actual and future status of White-fronted Geese *Anser a. albifrons* in Europe. Publication No.3, International Waterfowl and Wetlands Research Bureau, Slimbridge: 15–18.

KUZMINA, M.A. 1977. *Tetraonidae and Phasianidae of the U.S.S.R.* Nauka, Alma-Ata.

KUŽNIAK, S. 1991. Breeding ecology of the Red-backed Shrike *Lanius collurio* in the Wielkopolska region (Western Poland). *Acta Ornithol.* 26: 67–84.

KUŽNIAK, S. and E. PUGACHEVICH. 1992. Wystepowanie brodzca pławnego (*Tringa stagnatilis*) w Polsce. *Notatki Ornitologiczne* 33: 227–240 (in Polish).

LACK, P. 1989. Overall and regional trends in warbler populations of British farmland over 25 years. *Ann. Zool. Fennici* 26: 219–225.

LACK, P. and D. FERGUSON. 1993. *The Birds of Buckinghamshire*. The Buckinghamshire Bird Club, UK.

LAGERSTRÖM, M. 1993: Piekana *Buteo lagopus*. In: Forsman, D. (Ed) *Suomen haukat ja kotkat* [*Finnish Hawks and Eagles*]. Kirjayhtymä, Helsinki: 149–157 (in Finnish, with English summaries).

LAMANI, F. and V. PUZANOV. 1962. Inventari i shpendeve te Squiperise. *Bul. Univ. Trivanes, Ser. Shk. Nat.* 3: 87–103 (in Albanian).

LAMBERTINI, M. 1994. Lanner *Falco biarmicus*. In: Tucker G.M. and M.F. Heath (Eds) *Birds in Europe – their conservation status*. BirdLife International, Cambridge: 196–197.

LAMMI, E. 1983. Mustakurkku-uikku. In: Hyytiä, K., E. Kellomäki and J. Koistinen (Eds) *Suomen lintuatlas*. SLY:n Lintutieto Oy, Helsinki: 22–23.

LANG, M., H. BANDORF, W. DORNBERGER, H. KLEIN, H. and U. MATTERN. 1990. Verbreitung, Bestandsentwicklung und Ökologie des Ortolans (*Emberiza hortulana*) in Franken. *Ökol. Vögel* 12: 97–126.

LANNER, R.M. and T. NIKKANEN. 1990. Establishment of a *Nucifraga-Pinus* mutualism in Finland. *Ornis Fennica* 67: 24–27.

LANSDOWN, P., N. RIDDIFORD and A. KNOX. 1991. Identification of Arctic Redpoll *Carduelis hornemanni exilipes*. *Brit. Birds* 84: 41–56.

LARSEN, T. and I. TOMBRE. 1989. Cyclic irruptions of Two-barred Crossbills in Scandinavia. *Fauna norv. Ser. C, Cinclus* 12: 3–10.

LARSON, S. 1960. On the influence of the Arctic Fox *Alopex lagopus* on the distribution of Arctic birds. *Oikos* 11: 276–305.

LARSSON, K. and P. FORSLUND. 1994. Population dynamics of Barnacle Geese *Branta leucopsis* in the Baltic area: density dependent effects on reproduction. *J. Anim. Ecol.* 63: 945–962.

LAURSEN, K. 1989. Estimates of sea duck wintering populations of the western Palearctic. *Dan. Rev. Game Biol.* 13: 1–22.

LAURSSON, K. and P. FORSLUND. 1994. Population dynamics of Barnacle Geese *Branta leucopsis* in the Baltic area: density dependent effects on reproduction. *J. Anim. Ecol.* 63: 945–962.

LEBEDEVA, M.I. 1979. [Migrations of Bean Geese according to banding results obtained in the USSR.] In: Il'ichev, V.D. and A.A. Kistchinskiy (Eds) [*Migrations of Birds of Eastern Europe and Northern Asia.*] Nauka, Moscow: 131–142 (in Russian).

LEBRERO, F. 1991. Caracterización de las comunidades orníticas de las lagunas de Cádiz en un ciclo anual. *Plan Rector de Uso y Gestión de las Reservas Naturales de las Lagunas de Cádiz*: 73–96.

LEBRETON, J-D., 1975. Distribution française du Moineau soulcie *P. petronia* (L.). *L'Oiseau et R.F.O.* 45: 65–71.

LEBRETON, P. (Ed). 1977. *Atlas ornithologiques Rhône-Alpes*. CORA, Lyon.

LEBRUN, P. 1994. Niverolle alpine *Montifringilla nivalis*. In: Yeatman-Berthelot, D. and G. Jarry (Eds) *Nouvel Atlas des Oiseaux Nicheurs de France 1985–1989*. Société Ornithologique de France, Paris: 684–687.

LEEUW, J.J. de and M.R. van EERDEN. 1992. Size selection in diving Tufted Ducks *Aythya fuligula* explained by differential handling of small and large mussels *Dreissena polymorpha*. *Ardea* 80: 353–362.

LEFRANC, N. 1980. Biologie et fluctuations des populations de Laniidés en Europe occidentale. *L'Oiseau et R.F.O.* 50: 89–116.

LEFRANC, N. 1993. *Les Pies-grièches d'Europe, d'Afrique du Nord et du Moyen-Orient*. Delachaux et Niestlé S.A., Lausanne.

LEHTONEN, L. 1970. Zur Biologie des Prachttauchers, *Gavia a. arctica* (L.). *Ann. Zool. Fennici* 7: 25–60.

LEIBAK, E., V. LILLELEHT and H. VEROMANN (Eds). 1994. *Birds in Estonia. Status, Distribution and Numbers*. Estonian Academy Publishers, Tallinn.

LEINONEN, M. 1974. The white wagtail *Motacilla alba* as a semi-hole nester. *Ornis Fennica* 51: 110–116.

LEIPE, T. 1990. Die letzten Triele – werden sie überleben? *Falke* 37: 106–111.

LEISLER, B., P. HEIDRICH, K. SCHULZE-HAGEN and M. WINK. In prep (1997). Toxonomy and phylogeny of Reed Warblers (genus *Acrocephalus*) inferred from nucleotide sequences of mtDNA and morphology. *J. Ornithol.* 138.

LENSINK, R. 1994. Broedgeval van een Indische Gans *Anser indicus*. *Limosa* 67: 109–110. (Confirmed breeding of a Bar-headed Goose *Anser indicus*) (in Dutch, with English summary).

LENSINK, R. In press (1996). Die opkomst van exoten in de Nederlandse avifauna; verleden, heden en toekomst. *Limosa* 69: 103–130.

LEOPOLD, M.F., H.J.M. BAPTIST, P.A. WOLF and H.R. OFFRINGA. 1995. De Zwarte Zeeëend *Melanitta nigra* in Nederland. *Limosa* 68: 49–64. (Common Scoters *Melanitta nigra* in The Netherlands) (in Dutch, with English summary).

LER, P.A., V.A. KOSTENKO, V.A. NECHAEV and Yu. V. SHIBAEV (Eds). 1989. [*Rare Vertebrates of the Soviet Far East and their Protection.*] Nauka, Leningrad (in Russian).

LESHEM, Y. 1994. Global raptor migration 'bottlenecks' as a parameter of long-term variations in raptor populations. In: Meyburg, B-U. and R.D. Chancellor (Eds) *Raptor Conservation Today*. WWGBPO, Berlin: 49–53.

LESLIE, R. 1993. Nightjar. In: Gibbons, D.W., J.B. Reid, and R.A. Chapman (Eds) *The New Atlas of Breeding Birds in Britain and Ireland: 1988–1991*. Poyser, London: 256–257.

LÉVÊQUE, R. 1956. Une colonie de Sternes hansel en Camargue. *Nos Oiseaux* 23: 233–246.

LEVER, C. 1977. *The Naturalized Animals of the British Isles*. Hutchinson, London.

LEVER, C. 1987. *Naturalized birds of the world*. Longman, London.

LEVER, C. 1993a. Wood Duck *Aix sponsa*. In: Gibbons, D.W., J.B. Reid and R.A. Chapman (Eds) *The New Atlas of Breeding Birds in Britain and Ireland: 1988–1991*. Poyser, London: 62–63.

LEVER, C. 1993b. Mandarin *Aix galericulata*. In: Gibbons, D.W., J.B. Reid and R.A. Chapman (Eds) *The New Atlas of Breeding Birds in Britain and Ireland: 1988–1991*. Poyser, London: 64–65.

LEVER, C. 1993c. Ring-necked Parakeet *Psittacula krameri*. In: Gibbons, D.W., J.B. Reid and R.A. Chapman (Eds) *The New Atlas of Breeding Birds in Britain and Ireland: 1988–1991*. Poyser, London: 62–63.

LEWARTOWSKI, Z. 1986. [The decline in numbers of the Roller, *Coracias garrulus*, in eastern Wielkopolska (Major Poland).] *Chrońmy Przyr.* 3: 27–34 (in Polish, with English summary).

LEWINGTON, I., P. ALSTRÖM and P. COLSTON. 1991. *A Field Guide to the Rare Birds of Britain and Europe*. HarperCollins, London.

LEWIS, J. and S.J. ROBERTS, 1993. Woodcock *Scolopax rusticola*. In: Gibbons, D.W., J.B. Reid, and R.A. Chapman (Eds) *The New Atlas of Breeding Birds in Britain and Ireland: 1988–1991*. Poyser, London: 178–179.

LEYS, H.N. 1988. Ringonderzoek in een vijftal gierzwaluwpopulaties (1954–1969). *Vogeljaar* 36: 185–196 (in Dutch).

LEYS, H.N. 1993. De Oeverzwaluw in 1991 in Nederland. *Vogeljaar* 41: 123–129. (The Sand Martin in The Netherlands in 1991) (in Dutch).

LIAKHOV, A.G. 1989. [The notes on avifauna of Karpinsk district (Sverdlovsk region, Middle Ural).] In: Davigora, A.V. (Ed) *The Distribution of the Birds and Avifauna of the Urals*. Sverdlovsk: 62–63 (in Russian).

LIBOIS, R.M. 1994. Démographie du martin-pêcheur (*Alcedo atthis*): incidences climatiques sur le succès reproducteur. *Gerfaut* 84: 19–38.

LIBOIS, R.M. and C. HALLET-LIBOIS. 1989. Expansion et régression: deux mots-clés de la dynamique des populations du martin-pêcheur (*Alcedo atthis*). *Aves* 26 spécial: 93–101.

LIBOIS, R.M. and C. HALLET-LIBOIS. 1994. Martin-pêcheur d'Europe *Alcedo atthis*. In: Yeatman-Berthelot, D. and G. Jarry (Eds) *Atlas des Oiseaux Nicheurs de France 1985–1989*. Société Ornithologique de France, Paris: 418–421.

LIEDEKERKE, R. de. 1980. Recensements des Cincles plongeurs (*Cinclus cinclus*), Bergeronnette des ruisseaux (*Motacilla cinerea*) et Martin-pêcheur (*Alcedo atthis*) sur les rivières wallonnes en 1978 et 1979. *Aves* 18: 57–71.

LIEDER, K. 1987. Zur Entwicklung der Brutbestände des Zwergtauchers *Tachybaptus ruficollis* (Pall.), im Bezirk Gera im Zeitraum von 1960–1984. *Thür. ornithol. Mitt.* 37: 51–55.

LINARD, J-C. 1994. Goéland marin *Larus marinus*. In: Yeatman-Berthelot, D. and G. Jarry (Eds) *Nouvel Atlas des Oiseaux Nicheurs de France 1985–1989*. Société Ornithologique de France, Paris: 330–333.

LINDBERG, P., P.J. SCHEI and M. WIKMAN. 1988. The Peregrine Falcon in Fennoscandia. In: Cade, T.J., J.H. Enderson, C.G. Thelander and C.M. White (Eds) *Peregrine Falcon Populations. Their management and recovery*. The Peregrine Fund, Inc., Boise, Idaho: 159–172.

LINDSTRÖM, Å. 1987. Breeding nomadism and site tenacity in the Brambling *Fringilla montifringilla*. *Ornis Fennica* 64: 50–56.

LINDSTRÖM, Å., D.J. PEARSON, D. HASSELQUIST, A. HEDENSTRÖM, S. BENSCH and S. ÅKESSON. 1993. The moult of Barred Warblers *Sylvia nisoria* in Kenya – evidence for a split wing-moult pattern initiated during the birds' first winter. *Ibis* 135: 403–409.

LINKOV, A.B. 1994. *Pelecanus onocrotalus* and *P. crispus* in Kalmykia. In: Crivelli, A.J., V.G. Krivenko, and V.G. Vinogradov (Eds) *Pelicans in the Former USSR*. Special Publication No. 27, International Waterfowl & Wetlands Research Bureau, Slimbridge: 20–24.

LINTON, E. and A.D. FOX. 1991. Inland breeding of Shelduck *Tadorna tadorna* in Britain. *Bird Study* 38: 123–127.

LIPU. 1995. *Popolazioni di rapaci minacciati in Italia centro-meridionale*. Internal report for the European Commission and Italian Ministry of Environment under the LIFE regulation, Parma.

LISETSKI, A.S. 1978. [New data about bird distribution in NE Ukraine. Abstract from: *Bird Ecology and Conservation*]. Kisheneu: 139 (in Russian).

LITTLE, B. and R.W. FURNESS. 1985. Long-distance moult migration by British Goosanders *Mergus merganser*. *Ringing and Migration* 6: 77–82.

LITVINOV, V.P. 1977. [Density dynamics of the Black Francolin in Kizil-Agach Reserve. *Abstracts of the Ornithological Conference of USSR*], Vol. 2. Kiev (in Russian).

LITZBARSKI, H. 1993. Das Schutzprojekt Grosstrappe in Brandenburg. *Berichte zum Vogelschutz* 31: 61–66.

LLANDRES, C. and C. URDIALES. 1991. *Las Aves de Doñana*. Lynx Ediciones, Barcelona.

LLOYD, C., M.L. TASKER and K. PARTRIDGE. 1991. *The Status of Seabirds in Britain and Ireland*. Poyser, London.

LOCKLEY, A.K. 1992. The position of the hybrid zone between the House Sparrow *Passer domesticus* and the Italian Sparrow *P.d. italiae* in the Alps Maritimes. *J. Ornithol.* 133: 77–82.

LØFALDLI, L., J.A. KÅLÅS and P. FISKE. 1992. Habitat selection and diet of Great Snipe *Gallinago media* during breeding. *Ibis* 134: 35–43.

LÖHRL, H. 1960. Vergleichende Studien über Brutbiologie und Verhalten der Kleiber *Sitta whiteheadi* Sharpe und *Sitta canadensis* L. *J. Ornithol.* 101: 245–264.

LÖHRL, H. 1966. Zur Biologie der Trauermeise (*Parus lugubris*) (Mit Bemerkungen über die Untergattung *Poecile*). *J. Ornithol.* 107: 167–186.

LÖHRL, H. 1974. *Die Tannenmeise*. Neue Brehm-Bücherei 472, Ziemsen, Wittenberg.

LÖHRL, H. 1988. Der Kleiber. *Bonn. Zool. Monogr.* 26.

LÖHRL, H. 1991. *Die Haubenmeise*. Neue Brehm-Bücherei 609, Ziemsen, Wittenberg.

LONG, J.L. 1981. *Introduced Birds of the World: The worldwide history, distribution and influence of birds introduced to new environments*. David and Charles, London.

LOONEN, M.J.J.E., M. ZIJLSTRA and M.R. van EERDEN. 1991. Timing of wing moult in Greylag Geese *Anser anser* in relation to the availability of their food plants. *Ardea* 79: 253–260.

LÓPEZ, G. and J.A. GIL-DELGADO. 1988. Aspects of the breeding ecology of Rufous Bush Robins *Cercotrichas galactotes* in southeast Spain. *Bird Study* 35: 85–89.

LOSKE, K-H. 1987. Habitatwahl des Baumpiepers (*Anthus trivialis*). *J. Ornithol.* 128: 33–47.

LOSKE, K-H. 1993. *Untersuchungen zu Überlebensstrategien der Rauchschwalbe (*Hirundo rustica*) im Brutgebiet*. Cuvillier Verlag, Göttingen.

LOSKE, K-H. and W. LEDERER. 1987. Bestandsentwicklung und Fluktuationsrate von Weitstreckenziehern in Westfalen: Uferschwalbe (*Riparia riparia*), Rauchschwalbe (*Hirundo rustica*), Baumpieper (*Anthus trivialis*) und Grauschnäpper (*Muscicapa striata*). *Charadrius* 23: 101–127.

LOSKOT, V.M. 1986. Geographic variations of Pallas's Reed Bunting *Emberiza pallasi* (Cabanis) and its taxonomic value. In: *The Distribution and Biology of Birds of the Altai and Far East. Proceedings of the Zoological Institute USSR Academy of Sciences, Leningrad*. 150: 147–170.

LOSKOT, V. 1994a. Radde's Accentor *Prunella ocularis*. In: Tucker, G.M. and M.F. Heath (Eds) *Birds in Europe – their conservation status*. Conservation Series No. 3, BirdLife International, Cambridge: 374–375..

LOSKOT, V. 1994b. Güldenstädt's Redstart *Phoenicurus erythrogaster*. In: Tucker, G.M. and M.F. Heath (Eds) *Birds in Europe – their conservation status*. Conservation Series No. 3, BirdLife International, Cambridge: 389.

LOSKOT, V. 1994c. Great Rosefinch *Carpodacus rubicilla*. In: Tucker, G.M. and M.F. Heath (Eds) *Birds in Europe – their conservation status*. Conservation Series No. 3, BirdLife International, Cambridge: 438.

LOSKOT, V.M. and E. von VIETINGHOFF-SCHEEL. 1978. *Oenanthe xanthoprymna*. In: Dathe, A. and I.A. Neufeldt (Eds) *Atlas der Verbreitung paläarktischer Vögel*, Vol. 7. Academia Verlag, Berlin.

LOVATY, F. 1990a. Sur la présence de la Fauvette à lunettes (*Sylvia conspicillata*) en Lozère (France). *Nos Oiseaux* 40: 285–288.

LOVATY, F. 1990b. Distribution et densités des oiseaux nicheurs sur les pelouses des causses de la région de Mende (Lozére). *L'Oiseau et R.F.O.* 60: 10–15.

LOVATY, F. 1993. Notes sur l'abondance de la Fauvette sarde (*Sylvia sarda*) près d'Ajaccio (Corse du Sud). *L'Oiseau et R.F.O.* 63: 194–201.

LOVATY, F. 1995. Aspects de la biologie de reproduction de la Fauvette sarde (*Sylvia sarda*) en Corse. *Nos Oiseaux* 43: 61–83.

LOVE, J.A. 1983. *The Return of the Sea Eagle*. Cambridge University Press, Cambridge.

LOVEGROVE, R., G. WILLIAMS and I. WILLIAMS. 1994. *Birds in Wales*. Poyser, London.

LØVENSKIOLD, H.L. 1964. Avifauna Svalbardensis: with a discussion on the geographical distribution of the birds in Spitsbergen and adjacent islands. *Norsk Polarinst. Skrifter* No. 129: 1–460.

LÜBCKE, W. and R. FURRER. 1985. *Die Wacholderdrossel*. Neue Brehm-Bücherei 569, Ziemsen, Wittenberg.

LUCIO, A.J. and F.J. PURROY. 1992a. Red-legged Partridge (*Alectoris rufa*) habitat selection in northwest Spain. *Gibier Faune Sauvage* 9: 417–429.

LUCIO, A.J. and F.J. PURROY. 1992b. Caza y conservación de aves en España. *Ardeola* 39: 85–98.

LUND-HANSEN, L.C. and P. LANGE. 1991. The numbers and distribution of the Great Skua, *Stercorarius skua*, breeding in Iceland 1984–1985. *Acta Nat. Isl.* 34: 1–16.

LUNDBERG, A. 1979. Residency, migration and a compromise: adaptations to nest-site scarcity and food specialisation in three Fennoscandian owl species. *Oecologia (Berl.)* 41: 273–281.

LUNDBERG, A. 1980. Why are the Ural Owl *Strix uralensis* and the Tawny Owl *Strix aluco* parapatric in Scandinavia? *Ornis Scand.* 11: 116–120.

LUNDBERG, A. and R.V. ALATALO. 1992. *The Pied Flycatcher*. Poyser, London.

LUNDIN, G., P.O. SWANBERG and S. TRAVENING (Eds). 1993. Tranan: studier i den euroasiatiska tranans biologi. *Vår Fågelvärld*, Suppl. 17. Sveriges Ornitologiska Förening, Stockholm (in Swedish).

LYAISTER, A.F. and G.V. SOSNIN. 1944. [*Materials on Ornithofauna of Armenian SSR*.] Armfan, Erevan (in Russian).

LYNES, H. 1934. Contribution to the ornithology of southern Tanganyika Territory. *J. Ornithol.* 82: 1–147.

LYNGS, P. 1992. Ynglefuglene på Graesholmen 1925–90. *Dansk Orn. Foren. Tidsskr.* 86: 1–93 (in Danish).

LYSENKO, V.I. 1994. The Dalmatian Pelican (*Pelecanus crispus*, Bruch) in the Ukraine. In: Crivelli, A.J., V.G. Krivenko and V.G. Vinogradov (Eds) *Pelicans in the former USSR*. Special Publication No. 27, International Waterfowl & Wetlands Research Bureau, Slimbridge: 5.

MACKAY, V.M. and W.M. HUGHES. 1963. Crested Mynah in British Columbia. *Can. Field-Nat.* 77: 154–162.

MACKOWICZ, R. 1989. Breeding biology of the River Warbler *Locustella fluviatilis* (WOLF, 1810) in north-eastern Poland. *Acta Zool. Cracov* 32: 331–437.

MADSEN, J. 1991. Status and trends of goose populations in the Western Paleartic in the 1980s. *Ardea* 79: 113–122.

MADSEN, J. and A. ANDERSSON. 1990. Status and management of *Branta canadensis* in Europe. In: Matthews, G.V.T. (Ed) *Managing Waterfowl Populations*. Special Publication No. 12, International Waterfowl and Wetlands Research Bureau, Slimbridge.

MADSEN, J. and C. MITCHELL. 1994. Status of the Pink-footed Goose, 1990–1993. *IWRB Goose Res. Group Bull.* 5: 8–11.

MADSEN, J., T. BREGNBALLE and F. MEHLUM. 1989. Study of the breeding ecology and behaviour of the Svalbard population of Light-bellied Brent Goose *Branta bernicla hrota*. *Polar Res.* 7: 1–21.

MADSEN, J., T. BREGNBALLE and A. HASTRUP. 1992. Impact of the Arctic Fox *Alopex lagopus* on nesting success of geese in southeast Svalbard, 1989. *Polar Res.* 11: 35–39.

MAESTRI, R. and L. VOLTOLINI. 1985. Nidificazione di Fringuello alpino, *Montifringilla nivalis*, a 1680 m sulle Prealpi Bresciane. *Riv. ital. Orn.* 54: 99–100.

MÄGI, E., T. PAAKSPU and T. KASTEPÕLD. 1992. [On the nesting of the Mute Swan (*Cygnus olor*) on Moonsund Islands at Matsalu Nature reserve in 1977–1992.] *Loodusevaatlusi* 1: 23–40 (in Estonian).

MAGIORIS, S.N. 1992. Nidification des Fauvettes sarde *Sylvia sarda* et de Rüppel *Sylvia rueppelli* dans les îles Cyclades en Mer Egée (Grèce). *Alauda* 60: 123.

MAGYAR, G. and G. HADARICS. 1996. Magyarország madarainak jegyzéke. *Túzok* 1: 42–48.

MAHER, W.J. 1974. Ecology of Pomarine, Parasitic and Long-tailed Jaegers in northern Alaska. *Pacific Coast Avifauna* 37: 1–148.

MAL'CHEVSKI, A. S. and PUKINSKI, Y.B. 1983. [*Birds of the Leningrad Region and Neighbouring Areas.*] Leningrad University Press, Leningrad (in Russian).

MALANDZIYA, V.I. 1990. [Notes on some rare and little-studied birds of Abkhazia.] In: *Redkie, malochislennye i maloizuchennye ptitsy Severnogo Kavkaza [Rare, Scarce and Little-studied Birds of the Northern Caucasus]*. Stavropol': 35–40 (in Russian).

MALVAUD, F. 1995. L'Oedicnème criard *Burhinus oedicnemus* en France: répartition et effectifs. *Ornithos* 2: 77–81.

MÁÑEZ, M. 1991. Estado actual en el Parque Nacional de Doñana de las especies de aves incluídas en la 'Lista Roja de los Vertebrados de España' dentro de las categorías de 'En peligro' y 'Vulnerable'. *Jornadas de Zonas Humedas Andaluzas. Fuente de Piedra 20–22 Abril 1990*: 41–49.

MANN, P., H. HERLYN and H. UNTHEIM. 1990. Bestandssituation und Habitat der Zippammer *Emberiza cia* im Südschwarzwald. *Vogelwelt* 111: 142–155.

MAÑOSA, S. 1994. Goshawk diet in a Mediterranean area of Northeastern Spain. *J. Raptor Res.* 28: 84–92.

MANRIQUE, J. and J.M. MIRALLES. 1988. El camachuelo trompetero. *Quercus* 32: 34–36.

MARCHANT, J.H. 1992. Recent trends in breeding populations of some common trans-Saharan migrant birds in northern Europe. *Ibis* 134, Suppl. 1: 113–119.

MARCHANT, J.H. 1993. Firecrest *Regulus ignicapillus*. In: Gibbons, D.W., J.B. Reid and R.A. Chapman (Eds) *The New Atlas of Breeding Birds in Britain and Ireland: 1988–1991*. Poyser, London: 354–355.

MARCHANT, J. and D. BALMER. 1994. Common Bird Census: 1992–93 index report. *BTO News* 193: 11–14.

MARCHANT, J.H. and R.D. GREGORY. 1994. Recent population changes among seed-eating passerines in the United Kingdom. In: Hagemeijer, E.J.M. and T.J. Verstrael (Eds) *Bird Numbers 1992. Distribution, monitoring and ecological aspects. Proceedings of the 12th International Conference of IBCC and EOAC, Noordwijkerhout, The Netherlands.* Statistics Netherlands, Voorburg/Heerlen and SOVON, Beek-Ubbergen: 87–95.

MARCHANT, J.H., R. HUDSON, S.P. CARTER and P. WHITTINGTON. 1990. *Population Trends in British Breeding Birds*. NCC/BTO, Tring.

MARCHANT, S. 1963. Notes on five species of Iraqi birds. *Bull. Brit. Orn. Club* 83: 52–56.

MARCSTRÖM, V. and R. KENWARD. 1981. Movements of wintering goshawks in Sweden. *Viltrevy* 12(1): 1–35.

MARÉCHAL, P. and J. TAAPKEN (Eds). 1989. Themanummer over de Nachtzwaluw. *Vogeljaar* 37: 241–376 (Special issue on the Nightjar in The Netherlands: many contributions in Dutch, some with English summary).

MARION, L. 1994a. Evolution numérique et préférences écologiques des Grands Cormorans *Phalacrocorax carbo* hivernant en France. *Alauda* 62: 13–26.

MARION, L. 1994b. Little Bittern *Ixobrychus minutus*. In: Tucker, G.M. and M.F. Heath (Eds) *Birds in Europe – their conservation status*. Conservation Series No. 3, BirdLife International, Cambridge: 90–91.

MARION, L., J. VAN VESSEM and P. ULENAERS. In press. Status of Herons in Europe. In: Kushlan, J. and H. Hafner (Eds) *Status and Conservation of Herons of the World*. Academic Press, London.

MARISOVA, I.V. and D.V. VLADYSHEVSKY. 1961. On the biology of *Turdus torquatus* L. in the Ukraine. *Zool. Zhurnal.* 40: 1240–1245.

MARJAKANGAS, A. 1982. Poor breeding success in the Spotted Flycatcher *Muscicapa striata* in 1981 due to bad weather. *Ornis Fennica* 59: 36–37.

MÄRKI, H. 1976. Brutverbreitung und Winterquartier des Zitronenzeisigs *Serinus citrinella* nördlich der Pyrenäen. *Orn. Beob.* 73: 67–88.

MAROVA, I.M. 1993. [Interrelationships of taxonomically closely related forms and the initial stages of speciation in Palearctic leaf-warblers.]. Resumé of dissertation presented for the Scientific Degree of Candidate of Biological Sciences, Moscow (in Russian).

MARQUISS, M. and R. RAE. 1994. Seasonal trends in abundance, diet and breeding of Common Crossbills (*Loxia curvirostra*) in an area of mixed species conifer plantation following the 1990 Crossbill 'Irruption'. *Forestry* 67: 31–47.

MARTÍ, R., A. GÓMEZ-MANZANEQUE and J.A. PERALES. 1989. Diferencias según edad y sexo en los movimientos dispersivos de una población de Accentor Alpina *Prunella collaris* en España Central. *Ardeola* 36: 224–226.

MARTÍN, A. 1987. *Atlas de las aves nidificantes en la Isla de Tenerife*. Instituto de Estudios Canarios, Tenerife.

MARTÍN, A., E. FERNANDEZ, G. DELGADO and V. QUILIS. 1984. (Nesting of the Madeiran Storm-petrel *Oceanodroma castro* (Harcourt 1851) in the Canary Islands.) *Donana Acta Vertebrata* 11: 337–341 (in Spanish).

MARTÍN, A., G. DELGADO, M. NOGALES, V. QUILIS, O. TRUJILLO, E. HERNANDES and F. SANTANA. 1989. Premières données sur la nidification du Puffin des Anglais (*Puffinus puffinus*), du Pétrel-fregate (*Pelagodroma marina*) et de la Sterne de Dougall (*Sterna dougallii*) aux Iles Canaries. *Oiseau et R.F.O.* 59: 73–83.

MARTIN, J-L. 1991. The *Parus caeruleus* complex revisited. *Ardea* 79: 429–438.

MARTIN, J-L. and M-D. BELLOT. 1990. Variation in morphology, laying date and clutch size between non-Mediterranean and Mediterranean Blue Tits. In: Blondel, J., A. Gosler, J-D. Lebreton and R. McCleery (Eds) *Population Biology of Passerine Birds*. Springer-Verlag, Berlin: 157–164.

MASON, C. F. and A. HUSSEY. 1984. Bird population trends as shown by chick ringing data. *Ringing and Migration* 5: 113–120.

MASSA, B. 1987. Variations in Mediterranean Crossbills *Loxia curvirostra*. *Bull. Brit. Orn. Club* 107: 118–129.

MASSA, B. 1989. Comments on *Passer italiae* (Vieillot, 1817). *Bull. Brit. Orn. Club* 109: 196–198.

MASSA, B. and J. SULTANA. 1991. Status and conservation of the Storm Petrel *Hydrobates pelagicus* in the Mediterranean. *Il Merill* 27: 1–5.

MASSA, B. and M. Lo VALVO. 1986. Biometrical and biological considerations on the Cory's Shearwater *Calonectris diomedea*. In: MEDMARAVIS and X. MONBAILLIU (Eds) *Mediterranean Marine Avifauna. Population studies and conservation*. NATO ASI series, Springer Verlag, Berlin: 293–313.

MASSA, B., F. Lo VALVO, M. SIRACUSA and A. CIACCIO. 1991. Il Lanario (*Falco biarmicus feldeggii*, Schlegel) in Italia: status, biologia e tassonomia. *Naturalista siciliano* 15: 27–63.

MASSA, Q., L. BOTTONI, and C. VIOLANI. 1993. *Lista in lingua italiana degli uccelli di tutto il mondo*. Università degli studi di Milano, Milano.

MASSOLI-NOVELLI, R. 1987. Contribution to the knowledge of the migration of Great Snipe *Gallinago media*. *Riv. ital. Orn.* 57: 14–20 (in Italian).

MATTES, H. 1978. Der Tannenhäher im Engadin. Studien zu seiner Ökologie und Funktion im Arvenwald. *Münstersche Geogr. Arb.* 2, Münster.

MATTHYSEN, E. 1990. Non-breeding social organization in *Parus*. In: Power, D. (Ed) *Current Ornithology* 7: 209–249.

MATVEJEV, S.D. 1976. *Survey of the Balkan Peninsula Bird Fauna*, Vol. 1. Serbian Academy of Sciences and Arts, Beograd (in Serbo-Croatian, with English summary).

MAUERSBERGER, G. and R. MÖCKEL. 1987. Über Arealerweiterungen bei vier Vogelarten im kaukasischen Raum. *Mitt. Zool. Mus. Berlin* 63, Suppl: *Ann. Orn.* 11: 97–111.

MAUMARY, L. and J-M. DUFLON. 1989. Le Pluvier guignard (*Eudromias morinellus*): Migration en Europe et synthèse des observations en Suisse de 1927 à 1988. *Nos Oiseaux* 40: 207–216.

MAUMARY, L., H. DUPERREX and R. DELARZE. 1990. Nidification de la Fauvette à lunettes en Valais (Alpes suisses). *Nos Oiseaux* 40: 355–372.

MAUMARY, L., T. GUILLAUME, F. RAPIN and L. VALLOTTON. 1993. Le Roselin cramoisi (*Carpodacus erythrinus*) nicheur à la Vallée de Joux (Jura vaudois) et rétrospective de la progression de l'espèce en Suisse. *Nos Oiseaux* 42: 143–157.

MAYR, E. 1951. Speciation in birds. *Proc. Xth Ornithol. Congr., Uppsala*: 29–47.

MAYR, E. 1972. Geography and ecology as faunal determinants. In: Voous, K.H. (Ed) *Proceedings of the XVth International Ornithological Congress, The Hague, 1970*. E.J. Brill, Leiden: 551–561.

McCAFFERY, B.J. and J.L. MARON. 1993. Speciation in golden-plovers, *Pluvialis dominica* and *P. fulva*: evidence from the breeding grounds. *Auk* 110: 9–20.

McCANN, K.I. 1994. *Habitat utilization and time-energy budgets of the Lesser Kestrel* Falco naumanni *in its southern African non-breeding range*. MSc Thesis, Department of Zoology, University of Witwatersrand, South Africa.

McCULLOCH, M.N., G.M. TUCKER and S.R. BAILLIE. 1992. The hunting of migratory birds in Europe: a ringing recovery analysis. *Ibis* 134, Suppl. 1: 55–65.

McGOWAN, R.Y. and B. MASSA. 1990. Evidence for breeding of the Lanner Falcon *Falco biarmicus erlangeri* in Spain in the 19th century. *Bull. Brit. Orn. Club* 110: 64–65.

MEAD, C.J. 1974. Results of ringing auks in Britain and Ireland. *Bird Study* 21: 45–86.

MEAD, C.J. 1984. *Robins*. Whittet, London.

MEAD, C.J. 1993a. Lesser Whitethroat *Sylvia curruca*. In: Gibbons, D.W., J.B. Reid and R.A. Chapman (Eds) *The New Atlas of Breeding Birds in Britain and Ireland, 1988–1991*. Poyser, London: 338–339.

MEAD, C.J. 1993b. Marsh Tit *Parus palustris*. In: Gibbons, D.W., J.B. Reid and R.A. Chapman (Eds) *The New Atlas of Breeding Birds in Britain and Ireland: 1988–1991*. Poyser, London: 364–365.

MEAD, C.J. and R. HUDSON. 1985. Report on bird-ringing for 1984. *Ringing and Migration* 6: 125–172.

MEAD, C.J., P.M. NORTH and B.R. WATMOUGH. 1979. The mortality of British Grey Herons. *Bird Study* 26: 12–22.

MEDVEDEV, N.V. 1992. [Nesting of Canada Goose (*Branta canadensis* L.) on the Valaam archipelago of Lake Ladoga.] *Russ. J. Ornithol.* 1(1): 113–114 (in Russian).

MEES, G.F. 1979. Verspreiding en getalssterkte van de Witwangstern, *Chlidonias hybridus* (Pallas), in Europa en Noord Afrika. *Zool. Bijdragen* 26: 3–63 (in Dutch).

MEHLUM, F. 1994. Steinskvett *Oenanthe oenanthe*. In: Gjershaug, J.O., P.G. Thingstad, S. Eldøy and S. Byrkjeland (Eds) *Norsk Fugleatlas*. Norsk Ornitologisk Forening, Klæbu: 362–363 (in Norwegian).

MEHLUM, F. and V. BAKKEN. 1994. Seabirds in Svalbard (Norway): status, recent changes and management. In: Nettleship, D.N., J. Burger and M. Gochfeld (Eds) *Seabirds on Islands: threats, case studies and action plans*. Conservation Series No. 1, BirdLife International, Cambridge: 155–171.

MEIJER, R. and J. VAN DER NAT. 1989. De Witgesterde Blawborst *Luscinia svecica cyanecula* gered door de Biesbosch? *Limosa* 62: 67–74. (Bluethroat *Luscinia svecica cyanecula* saved by the Biesbosch?) (in Dutch, with English summary).

MEIKLEJOHN, R.F. 1934. Notes on Rüppell's Warbler (*Sylvia rueppelli* Temm.). *Ibis* 13th series IV: 301–305.

MEIKLEJOHN, R.F. 1935. Nesting of Rüppell's Warbler (*Sylvia rueppelli* Temm.). *Ibis* 13th series V: 432–435.

MEIKLEJOHN, R.F. 1936. Nesting notes on Rüppell's Warbler and Black-headed Bunting. *Ibis* 13th series VI: 377–378.

MEINERTZHAGEN, R. 1920. Note on the birds of Southern Palestine IV. *Ibis* 11: 195–259.

MEININGER, P.L. 1993. Breeding Black-winged Stilts in the Netherlands in 1989–93, including one paired with Black-necked Stilt. *Dutch Birding* 15: 193–197.

MEININGER, P.L. 1995. Little Gulls breeding in south-western Netherlands. *Dutch Birding* 17: 152–154.

MEININGER, P.L. and G.A.M. ATTA (Eds). 1994.

Ornithological Studies in Egyptian Wetlands 1989/90. FORE-report 94–01, WIWO-report 40, Vlissingen/ Zeist.

MEININGER, P.L. and J.F. BEKHUIS. 1990. De Zwartkopmeeuw *Larus melanocephalus* als broedvogel in Nederland en Europa. *Limosa* 63: 121–134. (The Mediterranean Gull (*Larus melanocephalus*) as a breeding bird in The Netherlands and Europe) (in Dutch, with English summary).

MEININGER, P.L. and K. de KRAKER. 1992. De Middelste Zaagbek *Mergus serrator* als broedvogel in het Deltagebied, ZW-Nederland, 1977–91. *Limosa* 65: 49–51. (Red-breasted Merganser as a breeding bird in the SW-Netherlands, 1977–91) (in Dutch, with English summary).

MEININGER, P.L. and U.G. SØRENSEN. 1992. Armenian Gulls *Larus armenicus* in Egypt, 1989/90, with notes on the winter distribution of the large gulls. *Avocetta* 16: 89–92.

MEININGER, P.L. and U.G. SØRENSEN. 1993. Egypt as a major wintering area of Little Gulls. *Brit. Birds* 86: 407–410.

MEININGER, P.L. and N.D. van SWELM. 1994. Brandganzen *Branta leucopsis* als broedvogel in het Deltagebied. *Limosa* 67: 1–5. (Barnacle Geese as breeding birds in the Delta area, SW-Netherlands) (in Dutch, with English summary).

MEININGER, P.L. and P.A. WOLF. 1995. Voorjaarstrek van Rouwkwikstaarten bij Breskens. *Dutch Birding* 17: 157–159. (Spring migration of Pied Wagtails at Breskens) (in Dutch, with English summary).

MEININGER, P.L., N.D. van SWELM and C. SWENNEN. 1987. Biometrie, rui en herkomst van Dwergsterns *Sterna albifrons* in het deltagebied. *Limosa* 60: 75–83. (Biometrics, moult and origin of Little Terns *Sterna albifrons* in SW Netherlands) (in Dutch, with English summary).

MEININGER, P.L., A-M. BLOMERT and E.C.L. MARTEIJN. 1991. Watervogelsterfte in het Deltagebied, ZW-Nederland, gedurende de drie koude winters van 1985, 1986 en 1987. *Limosa* 64: 89–102. (Mortality of waterbirds in the Delta area, SW Netherlands during the three cold winters of 1985, 1986 and 1987) (in Dutch, with English summary).

MEININGER, P.L., P.A. WOLF, D.A. HADOUD and M.F.A. ESSGHAIER. 1994. Rediscovery of Lesser Crested Terns breeding in Libya. *Brit. Birds* 87: 160–170.

MEININGER, P.L., C.M. BERREVOETS and R.C.W. STRUCKER. 1995. *Kustbroedvogels in het Deltagebied in 1994 met een samenvatting van zestien jaar monitoring 1979–1994.* Werkdocument RIKZ OS-95.807X. RIKZ, Middelburg/NIOO, Yerseke. (*Coastal breeding birds in the Delta area in 1994, with a summary of 16 years of monitoring 1979–1994*) (in Dutch).

MELCHIOR, E., E. MENTGEN, R. PELTZER, R. SCHMITT and J. WEISS (Eds). 1987. *Atlas of breeding birds in Luxembourg.* Lëtzebuerger Natur-a Vulleschutzliga, Luxembourg: 305–306.

MELDE, F. and M. MELDE. 1991. *Die Singdrossel* Turdus philomelos. Neue Brehm-Bücherei 611, Ziemsen, Wittenberg.

MELLQUIST, H. and R. von BOTHMER. 1984. Effects of haymaking on Bean Goose, *Anser fabalis*, breeding habitats in Sweden. *Swedish Wildlife Res.* 13: 49–58.

MELTOFTE, H. 1985. Populations and breeding schedules of waders, *Charadrii*, in high arctic Greenland. *Meddr. Gronland, Biosci.* 16: 1–43.

MELTOFTE, H. 1993. Vadefugletraekket gennem Danmark. *Dansk. Orn. Foren. Tidsskr.* 87: 1–180 (in Danish).

MENDELSSOHN, H. 1980. Populations of *Alectoris chukar* in Israel and problems of management. In: Coles, C.L., M. Reydellet, G. van Tuyll, L. van Maltzahn and J. Bugalho (Eds) *Partridges of the Genus* Alectoris. International Council for Game and Wildlife Conservation, Paris: 82–86.

MERIGGI, A., A. GARIBOLDI and B. MAGNANI. 1992. Habitat requirements of bobwhite quail in northern Italy. *Boll. Zool.* 59: 73–78.

MERIKALLIO, E. 1958. Finnish birds. Their distribution and numbers. *Fauna Fennica* 5: 1–181.

MESCHINI, E. and S. FRUGIS (Eds). 1993. Atlante degli uccelli nidificanti in Italia. *Suppl. Ric. Biol. Selv.* 20.

MESSENGER, D. 1993. Spring passage of Little Gulls across northern England. *Brit. Birds* 86: 397–406.

MESTRE, P., S. PERIS, T. SANTOS, F. SUAREZ and B. SOLER. 1987. The decrease of the Black-eared Wheatear *Oenanthe hispanica* on the Iberian Peninsula. *Bird Study* 34: 239–243.

MEURY, R. 1989. Siedlungsdichte und Raumnutzung des Baumpiepers *Anthus trivialis* im inselartig verteilten Habitat des aargauischen Reusstals. *Orn. Beob.* 86: 105–135.

MEWES, W. 1995. *Bestandsentwicklung des Kranichs* Grus grus *in Deutschland und deren Ursachen.* Thesis, Martin-Luther-Universität, Halle-Wittenberg.

MEYBURG, B-U., T. MIZERA and T. NEUMANN. 1992. See- und Schreiadlertagung in Polen. *Orn. Mitt.* 44(6): 148–149.

MEYBURG, B-U., X. EICHAKER, C. MEYBURG and P. PAILLAT 1995. Migrations of an adult Spotted Eagle tracked by satellite. *Brit. Birds* 88: 357–361.

MEZHNEV, A. 1994. Common quail in European Russia. *J. Ornithol.* 135, Suppl.: 222.

MICHEV, T., I. VATEV, P. SIMEONOV and P. PROFIROV. 1984. Distribution and Nesting of Long-legged Buzzard (*Buteo rufinus*) in Bulgaria. *Ekologia* 13: 74–82.

MIKHALEVICH, I., V. SEREBRYAKOV and V. GRISHCHENKO. 1994. Atlas of breeding herons in Ukraine. *Bird Census News* 7: 32–37.

MIKKOLA, H. 1983. *Owls of Europe.* Poyser, Calton.

MIKKONEN, A.V. 1983. Breeding site tenacity of the Chaffinch *Fringilla coelebs* and the Brambling *F. montifringilla* in northern Finland. *Ornis Scand.* 14: 36–47.

MIKOLA, J., M. MIETTINEN, E. LEHIKOINEN and K. LEHTILÄ. 1994. The effects of disturbance caused by boating on survival and behaviour of Velvet Scoter *Melanitta fusca* ducklings. *Biol. Conservation* 67: 119–124.

MILCHEV, B. 1992. Häherkuckuck (*Clamator glandarius*) – Brutvogel in Bulgarien. *J. Ornithol.* 133: 86–88.

MILD, K. 1993. Die Bestimmung der europäischen

schwarzweissen Fliegenschnäpper *Ficedula*. *Limicola* 7: 221–226.

MILDENBERGER, H. 1984. *Die Vögel des Rheinlandes*. Vol. 2, *Papageien–Rabenvögel (Psittaculidae–Corvidae)*. Kilda-Verlag, Greven.

MILES, P. 1986. Die Vögel des Krkonoše Gebirges. *Acta Universitatis Carolinae -Biol.* 1985: 1–101.

MILES, P. and J. FORMÁNEK. 1989. Slavík modráek (*Luscinia svecica svecica* L.) hnízdí v Krkonošském národním parku. *Opera corcontica* 26: 117–130 (in Czech).

MILWRIGHT, R.D.P. 1994. Fieldfare *Turdus pilaris* ringing recoveries during autumn, winter and spring, analysed in relation to river basins and watersheds in Europe and the Near east. *Ringing and Migration* 15: 129–189.

MINEYEV, Yu.N. 1982a. Seasonal distributions and numbers of waterfowl on the Malozemel'skaya tundra. *Polar Geography and Geology* 6: 41–46.

MINEYEV, Yu.N. 1982b. [Waterfowl birds of the tundras of the European North–East of the USSR.] In: [*Fauna and Ecology of Birds and Mammals of the European North–East of the USSR.*] Syktyvkar, Trudy Koim Filiala AN USSR, No. 51: 29–39 (in Russian).

MINEYEV, Yu.N. 1987. [*Wildfowl of the Bol'shezemel'skaya Tundra. Fauna and ecology.*] Nauka, Leningrad (in Russian).

MINEYEV, Yu.N. 1990. Seasonal concentrations of *Anser fabalis* in the European Northeast of the USSR. In: Matthews, G.V.T. (Ed) *Managing Waterfowl Populations.* Special Publication No. 12, International Waterfowl & Wetlands Research Bureau, Slimbridge: 50–51.

MINEYEV, Yu.N. 1991. Distribution and numbers of Bewick's Swans *Cygnus bewickii* in the European Northeast of the USSR. In: Sears, J. and P.J. Bacon (Eds.) *Proceedings of the Third IWRB International Swan Symposium, Oxford 1989. Wildfowl.* Special Supplement No. 1: 62–67.

MINEYEV, Yu.N. 1994. [*Waterfowl of the Yugorski Peninsula.*] Syktyvkar, Komi Scientific Centre, Ural Branch, Russian Academy of Sciences (in Russian).

MINGOZZI, T., G. BOANO and C. PULCHER (Eds). 1988. *Atlante degli uccelli nidificanti in Piemonte e Val d'Aosta*. Monografia VIII del Museo Regionale di Scienze Naturali, Torino.

MINGOZZI, T., L. BIDDAU, F. RINALDI and D. ROSSELLI. In press (1994). The Rock Sparrow *Petronia petronia* (L.) in the Western Alps: a multidisciplinary programme. In: Baldaccini, N.E., T. Mingozzi and C. Violani (Eds) *Atti del VI Convegno Italiano di Ornitologia*. Museo Regionale di Scienze Naturali, Torino: 363–374.

MITCHELL, C. 1994. Shoveler *Anas clypeata*. In: Gibbons, D.W., J.B. Reid and R.A. Chapman (Eds) *The New Atlas of Breeding Birds in Britain and Ireland: 1988–1991*. Poyser, London: 78–79.

MIZERA, T. 1995. Why is the Osprey *Pandion haliaetus* a rare breeding species in Poland? *Vogelwelt* 116: 197–198.

MIZERA, T. and M. SZYMKIEWICZ. 1990. Trends, status and management of the White-tailed Sea Eagle *Haliaeetus albicilla* in Poland. *Birds of Prey Bull.* 4: 1–10.

MIZERA, T., R. UHLIG, M. KALISINSKI, J. MUNDT and R. CZERASZKIEWICZ. 1994. Brutverbreitung, Mauser, Nichtbrüter- und Winterbestand des Gänsesägers *Mergus merganser* im Einzugsgebiet der Oder. *Vogelwelt* 115: 155–162.

MJELSTAD, H. and M. SÆTERSDAL. 1986. Density, population size and breeding distribution of Spotted Redshank *Tringa erythropus*, Bar-tailed Godwit *Limosa lapponica* and Jack Snipe *Lymnocryptes minimus* in Norway. *Fauna norv. Ser. C, Cinclus* 9: 13–16.

MOCCI DEMARTIS, A. 1992. Pernice sarda *Alectoris barbara* (Bonnaterre, 1790). In: Brichetti, P., P. de Franceschi and N. Baccetti (Eds) *Fauna d'Italia, Aves I: Gaviidae – Phasianidae*. Calderini, Bologna: 787–791.

MOCCI DEMARTIS, A. and R. MASSOLI-NOVELLI. 1978. Distribuzione, caratteristiche e possibilità di ripopolamento della pernice sarda: *Alectoris barbara* (Bonnaterre). *Boll. Soc. Sarda Sci. Nat.* 17: 71–107.

MÖCKEL, R. 1988. *Die Hohltaube*. Neue Brehm-Bücherei 590, Ziemsen, Wittenberg.

MÖCKEL, R. 1992. Auswirkungen des "Waldsterbens" auf die Populationsdynamik von Tannen- und Haubenmeise (*Parus ater, P. cristatus*) im Westerzgebirge. *Ökol. Vögel* 14: 1–100.

MOKSNES, A. 1973. Quantitative surveys of the breeding bird populations in some subalpine and alpine habitats in the Nedal area in Central Norway (1967–71). *Norwegian J. Zool.* 21: 113–138.

MOLAMUSOV, Kh.T. 1967. [*Birds of the central part of the northern Caucasus.*] Kabardino-Balkar, Nal'chik (in Russian).

MØLLER, A.P. 1978. [Distribution, population sizes and changes in gulls *Larinae* breeding in Denmark, with a review of the situation in other parts of Europe.] *Dansk Orn. Foren. Tidsskr.* 72: 15–39 (in Danish).

MØLLER, A.P. 1980. Effekten på ynglefaunaen af ændringer i landbrugsdriften. Et eksempel fra Vendsyssel. *Dansk Orn. Foren. Tidsskr.* 74: 27–34 (in Danish, with English summary).

MØLLER, A.P. 1983. Changes in Danish farmland habitats and their populations of breeding birds. *Holarctic Ecol.* 6: 95–100.

MØLLER, A.P. 1989. Population dynamics of a declining swallow *Hirundo rustica* population. *J. Anim. Ecol.* 58: 1051–1063.

MOLODAN, G.N. 1988. [Collared Pratincole.] In: Voinstvensky, M.A. (Ed) [*Colonial Waterbirds of the Southern Ukraine.*] Naukova Dumka, Kiev: 111–117 (in Russian).

MOLTONI, E. 1938. Escursione ornitologica all'Isola degli Uccelli (Golfo della Gran Sirte, Cirenaica). *Riv. ital. Orn.* 8: 1–16.

MOLTONI, E. 1964. L'ornitofauna della Sila (Calabria). *Riv. ital. Orn.* 34: 1–183.

MONAGHAN, P., E. BIGNAL, S. BIGNAL, N. EASTERBEE and C.R. McKAY. 1989. The distribution and status of the chough in Scotland, 1986. *Scottish Birds* 15: 114–118.

MONTEIRO, L.R. and R.W. FURNESS. 1995. Fea's Petrel *Pterodroma feae* from the Azores. *Bull. Brit. Orn. Club* 115: 9–14.

MONTELL, J. 1917. Fågelfaunan i Muonio socken och angränsande delar av Enontekis och Kittilä socknar. *Acta Soc. Fauna Flora Fennica* 44(7): 1–260 (in Swedish).

MONTEMAGGIORI, A., A. MASSI and F. SPINA. 1993. Progetto Piccole Isole. Risultati generali e resoconto del

VI anno di attività. *Bollettino attività di inanellamento* 4 (Suppl): 1–132.
MONVAL, J-Y. and J-Y. PIROT. 1989. *Results of the IWRB International Waterfowl Census 1967–1986*. Special Publication No. 8, International Waterfowl & Wetlands Research Bureau, Slimbridge: 1–145.
MOREAU, R.E. 1954. The main vicissitudes of the European avifauna since the Pliocene. *Ibis* 96: 411–431.
MOREAU, R.E. 1966. *The Bird Faunas of Africa and its Islands*. Academic Press, New York.
MORGAN, R.A. and D.E. GLUE. 1977. Breeding, mortality and movements of kingfishers. *Bird Study* 24: 15–24.
MORGAN, R.A. and D.E. GLUE. 1981. Breeding survey of Black Redstarts in Britain, 1977. *Bird Study* 28: 163–168.
MORITZ, D. 1990. Der Feldschwirl *Locustella naevia* auf Helgoland: Bestandsdynamik und Herkunft der Durchzügler. *Vogelwarte* 35: 202–207.
MOROZOV, V.V. 1987. [New Data on fauna and distribution of birds for the eastern part of the Bol'shezemel'skaya Tundra.] *Ornitologiya* 22: 134–147 (in Russian).
MOROZOV, V.V. 1989. [The birds of the Western Macroslope of the Polar Urals.] In: Davygora A.V. (Ed) [*The Distribution of the Birds and Avifauna of the Urals*.] Sverdlovsk: 69–72 (in Russian).
MOROZOV, V.V. 1990. [Rare breeding waders of flood-plain meadows of Moscow and Klyaz'ma rivers.] In: Butjev, V.T. (Ed.) [*Rare Bird Species in the Central Non-Chernozem Zone*.] USSR Orn. Soc., Moscow: 144–149 (in Russian).
MOROZOV, V.V. 1992. The distribution of breeding waders in the extreme North-East of European Tundra. *Abstr. Odessa Conference of Wader Study Group. Wader Study Group Bull.* 65: 22–23.
MOROZOV, V.V. 1993. [Territoriality and mating behaviour of Pintail Snipe *Gallinago stenura* males in the European tundra.] *Russian J. Ornithol.* 2(2): 181–189 (in Russian).
MOROZOV, V.V. In press (1996). [Peculiarities of biology of Pintail Snipe at the western limit of the species breeding area.] *Ornitologiya* 27: 241–253 (in Russian).
MORRIS, A., D. BURGES, R.J. FULLER, A.D. EVANS and K.W. SMITH. 1994. The status and distribution of Nightjars *Caprimulgus europaeus* in Britain in 1992. A report to the British Trust for Ornithology. *Bird Study* 41: 181–191.
MORTENSEN, A., S. UNANDER, M. KOLSTAD and A.S. BLIX. 1983. Seasonal changes in body composition and crop contents of Spitsbergen Ptarmigan *Lagopus mutus hyperboreus*. *Ornis Scand.* 14: 144–148.
MOSEYKIN, V.N. 1992. Ecology and protection of the Little Bustard in the Saratov Region. *Bustard Studies* 5: 78–91.
MOSKÁT, C. 1987. Estimating bird densities during the breeding season in Hungarian deciduous forest. *Acta Regiae Soc. Sci. Litt. Gothob. Zool.* 14: 153–161.
MOSS, R. 1986. Rain, breeding success and distribution of Capercaillie *Tetrao urogallus* and Black Grouse *Tetrao tetrix* in Scotland. *Ibis* 128: 65–72.
MOSS, R. and N. PICOZZI. 1994. *Management of Forests for Capercaillie in Scotland*. Bulletin 113, HMSO, London.
MOSS, R. and A. WATSON. 1985. Adaptive value of spacing behaviour in population cycles of Red Grouse and other animals. In: Sibley, R.M. and R.H. Smith (Eds) *Behavioural Ecology. Consequences of adaptive behaviour*. Blackwell Scientific Publications, Oxford: 275–294.
MOTIS, A. 1992. Mixed breeding pairs of European Starling *Sturnus vulgaris* and Spotless Starling *Sturnus unicolor* in the north-east of Spain. *Bull. GCA* 9: 19–23.
MOTYLEV, K.V. 1989. [The most interesting ornithological findings in the Middle Urals for last 60 years.] In: Davygora, A.V. (Ed) [*The Distribution of the Birds and Avifauna of the Urals*]. Sverdlovsk: 72–73 (in Russian).
MOUGIN, J-L. 1988. Sur la nidification et l'élèvage du poussin chez le Pétrel fregate *Pelagodroma marina hypoleuca* de l'île Selvagem Grande. *Cyanopica* 4: 167–184.
MOUGIN, J-L., C. JOUANIN and F. ROUX. 1987. Structure et dynamique de la population de Puffins cendrés *Calonectris diomedea borealis* de l'Ile Selvagem Grande (30°09'N, 15°52'W). *L'Oiseau et R.F.O.* 57: 201–225.
MOUGIN, J-L., J.P. GRANADEIRO and F. ROUX. In press a. L'évolution des effectifs de Puffin cendrés *Calonectris diomedea borealis* de Selvagem Grande (30°09'N, 15°52'W) de 1989 a 1992. *Bull. Mus. Mun. Funchal*
MOUGIN, J-L., J.P. GRANADEIRO and P. OLIVEIRA. In press b. L'évolution des effectifs des reproducteurs chez le Puffin cendrés *Calonectris diomedea borealis* de Selvagem Grande (30°09'N, 15°52'W) de 1992 a 1995. *Bull. Mus. Mun. Funchal*
MOUNTFORT, G. 1957. *The Hawfinch*. Collins, London.
MOURER-CHAUVIRÉ, C. 1975. *Les Oiseaux du Pléistocène Moyen et Supérieur de France*. PhD Thesis, Université Claude Bernard, Lyon.
MOURER-CHAUVIRÉ, C. 1982. Les oiseaux fossiles des Phosphorites du Quercy (France) (Eocene Supérieur à Oligocene Supérieur): implications paléographiques. *Geobios Mem. Spec.* 6: 413–426.
MUDGE, G.P. 1978. *Ecological studies of Herring Gulls (*Larus argentatus *Pont.) and other Larini, in an urban environment*. PhD Thesis, University of Wales, Cardiff.
MÜLLER, C.Y. 1984. Bestandsentwicklung und Zugverhalten der Löffler (*Platalea leucorodia* L.) im österreichisch-ungarischen Raum. *Egretta* 27: 45–67.
MÜLLER, H.E.J. and H. WEBER. 1980. Über Lebenserwartung, Höchstalter und Ortstreue bei der Tannenmeise. *Falke* 27: 52–55.
MÜLLER, Th. and C. ROHDE. 1991. Bestandssituation des Baumfalken (*Falco subbuteo*) im Donaudelta. *Birds of Prey Bull.* 4: 87–95 (in Romanian).
MÜLLER, W. 1982. Die Besiedlung der Eichenwälder im Kanton Zürich durch den Mittelspecht *Dendrocopos medius*. *Orn. Beob.* 79: 105–119.
MULLER, Y. 1987. L'avifaune nicheuse des deux successions écologiques du pin sylvestre et du hêtre dans les Vosges du Nord. *Acta Œcoligica* 8: 185–189.
MULLIÉ, W.C. and J.O. KEITH. 1993. The effects of aerially applied fenitrothion and chlorpyrifos on birds in the savannah of northern Senegal. *J. appl. Ecol.* 30: 536–550.

MUÑOZ-COBOS, J. 1990. Evolución de la avifauna nidificante en olivares viejos de Jaén. *Testudo* 1: 99–117.

MUNTANER, J. 1980. Sur la colonisation récente de l'île de Minorque (Baléares) par la Fauvette pitchou *Sylvia undata*. *Alauda* 48: 185–192.

MUNTANER, J., X. FERRER and A. MARTINEZ-VILALTA. 1984a. *Atlas dels Ocells nidificants de Catalunya i Andorra.* Ketres, Barcelona.

MUNTANER, J., A. ESCANDEL, E. RAMOS and G. ORFILA. 1984b. Adición y revisión faunística de la publicación 'Avifauna de Menorca'. In: Muntaner, J. and J. Congost (Eds) *Avifauna de Menorca*. Treb. Mus. Zool., Barcelona 1: 175–205.

MUNTEANU, D. 1968. Syrian Woodpecker (*Dendrocopos syriacus*) in Romania. *Lucrarile* 1: 351–358.

MURTON, R.K. 1965. *The Woodpigeon*. Collins, London.

MURTON, R.K. and J. KEAR. 1978. Photoperiodism in waterfowl: phasing of breeding cycles and zoogeography. *J. Zool., London* 186: 243–283.

MUSELET, D. 1985. Les quartiers d'hivernage des Sternes naines européennes (*Sterna albifrons albifrons*). *L'Oiseau et R.F.O.* 55: 183–193.

MUSELET, D. 1987. Statut de la Sterne naine (*Sterna albifrons*) en France. In: Sternes continentales. *Ann. Biol. Centre* 2: 13–37.

MYRBERGET, S. 1988. Demography of an island population of Willow Ptarmigan in Northern Norway. In: Bergerud, A.T. and M.W. Gratson (Eds) *Adaptive Strategies and Population Ecology of Northern Grouse*. University of Minnesota Press, Minneapolis: 379–419.

MYSTERUD, I. and H. DUNKER. 1982. Food and nesting ecology of the Eagle Owl, *Bubo bubo* (L.), in four neighbouring territories in southern Norway. *Swedish Wildlife Res.* 12: 71–113.

NADLER, K. 1994. Spätwinterliche Eulenbeobachtungen im Böhmerwald, besonders zum Sperlingskauz (*Glaucidium passerinum*). *Vogelkdl. Nachr. OÖ* 2, 1: 30–34.

NADLER, T. and U. IHLE. 1988. Beobachtungen am Feldrohrsänger *Acrocephalus agricola* in Bulgarien. *Limicola* 2: 205–217.

NANKINOV, D. 1989. Früherer und jetziger Stand der Bestandsentwicklung der Zwergscharbe (*Phalacrocorax pygmeus*) in Bulgarien. *Faunistische Abhandlungen Staatl. Mus. für Tierkunde Dresden* 17(8): 79–84.

NANKINOV, D.N. 1993. Distribution of the Olive-tree Warbler, *Hippolais olivetorum*, in Bulgaria. *Riv. ital. Orn.* 63: 181–186.

NANKINOV, D. 1994. The breeding biology of the Turtle Dove (*Streptopelia turtur*) in Bulgaria. *Gibier Faune Sauvage* 11: 155–165.

NANKINOV, D., T. MICHEV, W. KOSTOVA, B. IVANOV and W. PENKOV. 1977. Pervie resultati ornitologicheskich isledovanii na stanzii 'Rupite' (jugozapadnaja Bulgaria). *Vestnik zool.* 3: 45–52 (in Bulgarian).

NANKINOV, D., G. STOYANOV, G. KOUZMANOV, and R. TODOROV. 1991. Informations sur la situation des rapaces diurnes en Bulgarie. *Birds of Prey Bull.* 4: 293–302.

NANKINOV, D., S. SIMEONOV, T. MICHEV and B. IVANOV. 1995. [*The Fauna of Bulgaria*], Vol. 20, *Aves*, Part 2. BAS, Sofia (in Bulgarian).

NAUROIS, R. de. 1969. Notes brèves sur l'avifaune de l'archipel du Cap-vert. Faunistique, endémisme, écologie. *Bull. Inst. Fond. Afrique Noire* 31: 143–218.

NAVARRO, J.D. and F. ROBLEDANO. 1992. Marbled Teal in Southern Alicante (Comunidad Valenciana, Eastern Spain). *IWRB Threatened Waterfowl Research Group Newsletter* 2.

NECHAYEV, V.A. 1993. [*Birds of Russia*, Vol. 4, *Cuculiformes*.] Nauka, Moscow: 225–236 (in Russian).

NEHLS, G., N. KEMPF and M. THIEL. 1992. Bestand und Verteilung mausernder Brandenten (*Tadorna tadorna*) im deutschen Wattenmeer. *Vogelwarte* 36: 221–232.

NELSON, J.B. 1978. *The Gannet*. Poyser, Berkhamsted.

NETHERSOLE-THOMPSON, D. 1975. *Pine Crossbills*. Poyser, Berkhamsted.

NETHERSOLE-THOMPSON, D. 1993. *The Snow Bunting*, 2nd edn. Peregrine Books, Leeds.

NETHERSOLE-THOMPSON, D. and M. NETHERSOLE-THOMPSON. 1979. *Greenshanks*. Poyser, Berkhamsted.

NETHERSOLE-THOMPSON, D. and M. NETHERSOLE-THOMPSON. 1986. *Waders, their Breeding, Haunts and Watchers*. Poyser, Calton.

NETTLESHIP, D.N. 1974. The breeding of the Knot *Calidris canutus* at Hazen Camp, Ellesmere Island N.W.T. *Polarforschung* 44: 8–26.

NETTLESHIP, D.N. and T.R. BIRKHEAD (Eds). 1985. *The Atlantic Alcidae*. Academic Press, London.

NETTLESHIP, D.N. and P.G.H. EVANS. 1985. Distribution and status of the Atlantic Alcidae. In: Nettleship, D.N. and T.R. Birkhead (Eds) *The Atlantic Alcidae*. Academic Press, London: 53–154.

NEUFELDT, I.A. and A.F. KOVSHAR. 1991. *The Demoiselle Crane in the USSR*. Alma-Ata.

NEUSCHULZ, F. 1988. Lebensraum, Bestandsdichte und Synökologie von Sperbergrasmücke (*Sylvia nisoria*) und Neuntöter (*Lanius collurio*) im Landkreis Lüchow Dannenberg. *Jb. Naturw. Verein. Fstm. Lüneburg* 38: 121–130.

NEVES, R. and R. RUFINO. 1995. The Salinas in Portugal: their ornithological importance. *Estudos de Biologia e Conservação*. CEMPA/ICN, Lisboa (in Portuguese).

NEWTON, I. 1964. Bud-eating by Bullfinches in relation to the natural food-supply. *J. appl. Ecol.* 1: 265–279.

NEWTON, I. 1967. The adaptive radiation and feeding ecology of some European finches. *Ibis* 109: 33–98.

NEWTON, I. 1972. *Finches*. Collins, London.

NEWTON, I. 1985. *Finches*, 2nd edn. Collins, London.

NEWTON, I. 1986. *The Sparrowhawk*. Poyser, Calton.

NEWTON, I. 1993a. Sparrowhawk *Accipiter nisus*. In: Gibbons, D.W., J.B. Reid and R.A. Chapman (Eds) *The New Atlas of Breeding Birds in Britain and Ireland: 1988–1991*. Poyser, London: 110–111.

NEWTON, I. 1993b. Studies of West Palaearctic birds, 192. Bullfinch. *Brit. Birds* 86: 638–648.

NEWTON, I. and M.B. HAAS. 1988. Pollutants in Merlin eggs and their effects on breeding. *Brit. Birds* 81: 258–269.

NEWTON, I. and I. WYLLIE. 1992. Recovery of a sparrowhawk population in relation to declining pesticide contamination. *J. Appl. Ecol.* 29: 476–484.

NEWTON, I., E.R. MEEK and B. LITTLE. 1978.

Breeding ecology of the Merlin in Northumberland. *Brit. Birds* 71: 376–398.

NEWTON, I., I. WYLLIE and A. ASHER. 1991. Mortality causes in British Barn Owls *Tyto alba*, with a discussion of aldrin-dieldrin poisoning. *Ibis* 133: 162–169.

NICKLAUS, G., F. LOTZ and J. WEISS. 1994. Die Wiesenweihe (*Circus pygargus*) im Saar-Lor-Lux-Raum. *Regulus, Wiss. Ber.* 13: 1–13.

NICOLAI, B. 1990. Spätbruten des Hausrotschwanzes (*Phoenicurus ochruros*) und ihre Einordnung in die Brutphänologie. *Ornithol. Rundbr. Mecklemb.-Vorpomm.* 33: 38–43.

NICOLAI, B. 1993a. Siedlungsdichte der Greifvögel (Accipitridae) im nördlichen Harzvorland unter besonderer Berücksichtigung des Rotmilans (*Milvus milvus*). *Orn. Jahresberichte Museum Heineanum* 11: 11–25.

NICOLAI, B. 1993b. *Atlas der Brutvögel Ostdeutschlands.* Fischer, Stuttgart.

NICOLAI, B. In press. Bestand und Bestandsentwicklung des Rotmilans (*Milvus milvus*) in Ostdeutschland. *Vogel und Umwelt.*

NICOLAU-GUILLAUMET, P. 1994. Bouscarle de Cetti *Cettia cetti*. In: Yeatman-Berthelot, D. and G. Jarry (Eds) *Nouvel Atlas des Oiseaux Nicheurs de France 1985–1989.* Société Ornithologique de France, Paris: 536–537.

NICOLAU-GUILLAUMET, P. and R. PRODON. 1994. Hirondelle rousseline *Hirundo daurica*. In: Yeatman-Berthelot, D. and G. Jarry (Eds) *Nouvel Atlas des Oiseaux Nicheurs de France 1985–1989.* Société Ornithologique de France, Paris: 464–465.

NIEHUIS, M. 1968. Die Bestandsentwicklung des Schwarzstirnwürgers (*Lanius minor*) in Deutschland unter besonderer Berücksichtigung des Nahetals und Rheinhessen. *Mainzer Naturw. Arch.* 7: 185–224.

NIELSEN, Ó. 1995. Hróliönd sest að á Íslandi. *Bliki* 15: 1–15 (in Icelandic).

NIETHAMMER, G. 1963. *Die Einbürgerung von Säugetieren und Vögeln in Europa.* Parey, Hamburg.

NIEUWENHUYSE, D. van and K. VANDEKERKHOVE. 1989. Populatiestijging van de Grauwe Klauwier *Lanius collurio* in het zuiden van de Gaume (België) in de periode 1979–1988. *Oriolus* 55: 60–65. (Increasing population of the Red-backed Shrike *Lanius collurio* in the South of the Gaume (Belgium) during the period 1979–1988) (in Dutch, with English summary).

NIITTYLÄ, J. 1980. On the development of some Goosander (*Mergus merganser* L.) populations in Finland. *Danske Fugle* 32: 158–165.

NIKIFOROV, M.E. 1992. Size and mobility of grey partridge winter coveys in Belorussia. *Gibier Faune Sauvage* 9: 447–453.

NIKIFOROV, M.E., B.V. YAMINSKI and L.P. SKLYAROV. 1989. [*Birds of Byelorussia.*] Visheishaya Shkola Minsk (in Russian).

NIKOLAEVA, N.G., Y.V. KRASNOV and R.T. BARRETT. In press (1996). Movements of Common *Uria aalge* and Brünnich's Guillemots *U. lomvia* breeding in the southern Barents Sea. *Fauna norv. Ser. C. Cinclus* 19: 9–20.

NILSSON, I.N. 1984. Prey weight, food overlap and reproductive output of potentially competing long-eared and tawny owls. *Ornis Scand.* 15: 176–182.

NILSSON, J-Å. 1984. The evolution of nest-site selection among hole-nesting birds: the impact of nest predation and competition. *Ornis Scand.* 15: 167–175.

NILSSON, J-Å. 1989. Causes and consequences of natal dispersal in the marsh tit, *Parus palustris*. *J. Anim. Ecol.* 58: 619–636.

NILSSON, L. 1994. Trettio års midvinterinventeringar av sjöfåglar utmed Skånes kuster, 1964–1993. *Anser* 33: 245–256. (Thirty years of midwinter counts along the coasts of Scania 1964–1993) (in Swedish).

NILSSON, L. and H. PERSSON. 1984. Non-breeding distribution, numbers and ecology of Bean Goose, *Anser fabalis*, in Sweden. *Swedish Wildlife Res.* 13: 107–170.

NILSSON, L. and M.K. PIRKOLA. 1991. Migration pattern of Finnish Bean Geese *Anser fabalis*. *Ornis Svecica* 1: 69–80.

NILSSON, S.G. 1977. Estimates of population density and changes for titmice, nuthatch and treecreeper in southern Sweden – an evaluation of the territory-mapping method. *Ornis Scand.* 8(1): 9–16.

NILSSON, S.G. 1986a. Different patterns of population fluctuation in the Wood Warbler *Phylloscopus sibilatrix* and the Willow Warbler *Phylloscopus trochilus*. *Vår Fågelvärld*, Suppl. 11: 161–164.

NILSSON, S.G. 1986b. Density-independence and density-dependence in the population dynamics of the Wren *Troglodytes troglodytes* and the Goldcrest *Regulus regulus*. *Vår Fågelvärld*, Suppl. 11: 155–160.

NILSSON, S.G. and S. ÅS. 1985. Species richness and composition of bird assemblages in south Swedish lakes. In: Ås, S. (Ed) *Biological Community Patterns in an Insular Environment. Acta Univ. Upsaliensis* 792: 1–27.

NILSSON, S.G., O. OLSSON, S. SVENSSON and U. WIKTANDER. 1992. Population trends and fluctuations in Swedish woodpeckers. *Ornis Svecica* 2: 13–21.

NIPKOW, M. 1988. Auswirkungen des landwirtschaftlichen Strukturwandels auf die Bestandsentwicklung der elsässischen Trielpopulation *(Burhinus oedicnemus)*. *Mitteilungen des Badischen Landesvereins für Naturkunde und Naturschutz* 14: 779–787.

NIPKOW, M. 1990. Habitatwahl des Triels *(Burhinus oedicnemus)* im Elsaß. *J. Ornithol.* 131: 371–380.

NIPKOW, M. 1994. Potentielle Brutbiotope des Triels *Burhinus oedicnemus* im Land Brandenburg und ihre gegenwärtige Bedeutung. *Naturschutz und Landschaftspflege in Brandenburg* 3: 27–32.

NOBEL, P. de, F.E. de RODER, E.C.L. MARTEIJN, P.L. MEININGER, J.J. STUART, F. SCHEPERS and R. van WESTRIENEN. 1990. Birds in NE-Greece, spring 1987. In: Meininger, P.L. (Ed) *Birds of the Wetlands in North-east Greece, Spring 1987.* WIWO Report 20, WIWO, Zeist: 109–263.

NOER, H. and H. SECHER. 1990. Effects of legislative protection on survival rates and status improvements of birds of prey in Denmark. *Danish Rev. Game Biol.* 14(2): 1–63.

NOORDHUIS, R. and A.L. SPAANS. 1992. Interspecific competition for food between Herring *Larus argentatus* and Lesser Black-backed Gulls *L. fuscus* in the Dutch Wadden Sea area. *Ardea* 80: 115–132.

NORDAHL, K. 1990. (The rise and fall of Finnish

skylarks.) *Lintumies* 25: 278–283 (in Finnish, with English summary).

NORDERHAUG, A. and M. NORDERHAUG. 1984. Status of the Lesser White-fronted Goose in Fennoscandia. *Swedish Wildlife Res.* 13(1): 171–185.

NORE, T. 1994. Aigle botté *Hieraaetus pennatus*. In: Yeatman-Berthelot, D. and G. Jarry (Eds) *Nouvel Atlas des Oiseaux Nicheurs de France 1985–1989*. Société Ornithologique de France, Paris: 198–199.

NÖSEL, H. 1992. Grey partridge population dynamics in East Germany. *Gibier Faune Sauvage* 9: 351–357.

NOSKOV, G. (Ed) 1981. *Polevoi Vorobei*. Izdatelstvo Leningradskogo Universiteta, Leningrad (in Russian).

NOWAK, E. 1989. Ausbreitung der Türkentaube *(Streptopelia decaocto)* in der USSR: Umfrage 1988. *J. Ornithol.* 130: 513–527.

NUMMI, P. and H. PÖYSÄ. 1993. Habitat associations of ducks during different phases of the breeding season. *Ecography* 16: 319–328.

NYGÅRD, T., B. FRANTZEN and S. ŠVAŽAS. 1995. Steller's eiders *Polysticta stelleri* wintering in Europe: numbers, distribution and origin. *Wildfowl* 46: 140–155.

NYSTRÖM, B. and H. NYSTRÖM. 1987. [Habitat preferences and breeding biology of Common Redpoll and Arctic Redpoll in southern Lapland, a comparative study.] *Vår Fågelvärld* 46: 119–128 (in Swedish, with English summary).

OAG MÜNSTER. 1989. Zugphänologie und Rastbestandsentwicklung des Kampfläufers *(Philomachus pugnax)* in den Rieselfeldern Münster anhand von Fangergebnissen und Sichtbeobachtungen. *Vogelwarte* 35: 132–155.

O'CONNOR, R.J. and C.J. MEAD. 1984. The Stock Dove in Britain, 1930–80. *Brit. Birds* 77: 181–201.

O'CONNOR, R.J. and M. SHRUBB. 1986. *Farming and Birds*. Cambridge University Press, Cambridge.

OELKE, H. 1975. Wasseramsel (*Cinclus cinclus*) und Gebirgsstelze (*Motacilla cinerea*) im Westharz (Bestandsaufnahme 1973). *Vogelkundliche Berichte Niedersachsen* 7: 19–31.

OGILVIE, M.A. 1978. *Wild Geese*. Poyser, Berkhamsted.

OJANEN, M. 1983. [*Apus caffer* found in Finland.] *Lintumies* 18(1): 48–49 (in Finnish, with English summary).

OJANEN, M and M. ORELL. 1985. Changes in the breeding parameters of the Crested Tit *Parus cristatus*. *Ornis Fennica* 62: 161–167.

OKULEWICZ, J. 1989. Biologia i ekologia rozrodu potrzosa *Emberiza schoeniclus* w rejonie stawów Milickich. Ptaki Śląska 7: 1–39 (in Polish, with English summary).

OLIOSO, G. 1994. Alouette calandrelle *Calandrella brachydactyla*. In: Yeatman-Berthelot, D. and G. Jarry (Eds) *Nouvel Atlas des Oiseaux Nicheurs de France 1985–1989*. Société Ornithologique de France, Paris: 448–449.

OLIVEIRA, P. 1992. *Alguns aspectos da ecologia, biologia e comportamento do pombo trocaz*. Relatório de licenciatura na Unversidade de Lisboa.

OLIVEIRA, P. and M. JONES. In press. Population numbers, habitat preferences, and the impact of the Madeira Laurel Pigeon, *Columba trocaz*, in agricultural fields. *Bol. Mus. Mun. Funchal.*

OLIVEIRA, P. and P. MONIZ. 1995. Population size, breeding chronology, annual cycle and effects of interspecific competition on the reproduction success of Little Shearwater, *Puffinus assimilis*, in Selvagem Grande. In: Tasker, M.L. (Ed) *The Threats to Seabirds. Proceedings of the 5th International Seabird Group Conference*. Seabird Group, Sandy: 35–36.

OLNEY, P.J.S. 1963. The food and feeding habits of Tufted Duck *Aythya fuligula*. *Ibis* 105: 55–62.

ÖLSCHLEGEL, H. 1985. *Die Bachstelze*. Neue Brehm-Bücherei 571, Ziemsen, Wittenberg.

OLSON, S.L. 1985. The fossil record of birds. In: Farner, D.S., J.R. King and D.C. Parkes (Eds) *Avian Biology*, Vol. VIII. Academic Press, New York: 80–238.

OLSSON, O., I.N. NILSSON, S.G. NILSSON, B. PETTERSSON, S. STAGEN and U. WIKTANDER. 1992. Habitat preferences of the Lesser Spotted Woodpecker *Dendrocopos minor*. *Ornis Fennica* 69: 119–125.

OLSSON, V. 1980. Förändringar i varfågelns, *Lanius excubitor*, utbredning i Sverige under de senaste årtiondena. *Fauna och flora* 75: 247–255. (Recent changes in the distribution of the Great Grey Shrike in Sweden).

OPDAM, P. and A. SCHOTMAN. 1987. Small woods in rural landscape as habitat islands for woodland birds. *Acta Œcologica* 8: 269–274.

OPITZ, H. 1982. Bestand und Bestandsentwicklung des Grossen Brachvogels (*Numenius arquata*) in Baden-Württemberg. *Beih. Veröff. Naturschutz Landschaftspflege Bad.-Württ.* 25: 15–31.

ORBÅN, G., TÖRÖK, J. and M. KUITUNEN. 1988. Nest-box project in the Pilis Biosphere Reserve. II. Breeding of *Certhia* species in artificial nest-boxes. *Ornithological Researches in Pilis Biosphere Reserve*: 26–29.

ORMEROD, S.J. and S.J. TYLER. 1987. *Dippers* Cinclus cinclus *and Grey Wagtails* Motacilla cinerea *as Indicators of Stream Acidity in Upland Wales*. Technical Publication No. 6, International Council for Bird Preservation, Cambridge: 191–208.

ORMEROD, S.J. and S.J. TYLER. 1991. The influence of stream acidification and riparian land use on the feeding ecology of Grey Wagtails *Motacilla cinerea* in Wales. *Ibis* 133: 53–61.

ORMEROD, S.J. and S.J. TYLER. 1993. Grey Wagtail. In: Gibbons, D.W., J.B. Reid and R.A. Chapman (Eds) *The New Atlas of Breeding Birds in Britain and Ireland: 1988–1991*. Poyser, London: 288–289.

ORÓ, D. and A. MARTÍNEZ VILALTA. 1992. The colony of the Audouin's Gull at the Ebro Delta. *Avocetta* 16: 98–101.

ORR, C.D., R.M.P. WARD, N.A. WILLIAMS and R.G. BROWN. 1982. Migration patterns of Red and Northern Phalaropes in southwest Davis Strait and in the northern Labrador Sea. *Wilson Bull.* 94: 303–312.

ORSINI, P. 1994. Grimpereau des jardins *Certhia brachydactyla*. In: Yeatman-Berthelot, D. and G. Jarry (Eds) *Nouvel Atlas des Oiseaux Nicheurs de France 1985–1989*. Société Ornithologique de France, Paris: 626–627.

ORTLIEB, R. 1989. *Der Rotmilan* Milvus milvus. Neue Brehm-Bücherei 532, Ziemsen, Wittenberg.

OSIECK, E.R. and F. HUSTINGS. 1994. *Rode lijst van*

bedreigde en kwetsbare vogelsoorten in Nederland. Technisch Rapport 12, Vogelbescherming Nederland, Zeist. (*Red List of Threatened and Vulnerable Bird Species in The Netherlands*) (in Dutch, with English summary).

OSTENDORP, W. 1993. Schilf als Lebensraum. *Beih. Veröff. Naturschutz Landschaftspflege Bad.-Württ.* 68: 173–280.

OTTERLIND, G. and I. LENNERSTEDT. 1964. Den svenska fagelfaunan och biocidskadorna. *Vår Fågelvärld* 23: 363–415 (in Swedish).

OWEN, M. and J.M. BLACK. 1989. Factors affecting the survival of Barnacle Geese on migration from breeding grounds. *J. Anim. Ecol.* 58: 603–617.

OWEN, M. and M. NORDERHAUG. 1977. Population dynamics of Barnacle Geese *Branta leucopsis* breeding in Svalbard, 1948–1976. *Ornis Scand.* 8: 161–174.

PAIN, D., C. AMIARD-TRIQUET, Ch. BAVOUX, G. BURNELEAU, L. EON, and P. NICOLAU-GUILLAUMET. 1993. Lead poisoning in wild populations of Marsh Harrier *Circus aeruginosus* in the Camargue and Charente-Maritime, France. *Ibis* 135: 379–386.

PAKARINEN, R. 1989. A survey of the Black-throated Diver population in 1985–86 in Finland. *Lintumies* 24: 2–11 (in Finnish, with an English summary).

PAKARINEN, R. and O. JÄRVINEN. 1984. The Red-throated Diver *Gavia stellata* in Finland: a population ecological analysis of its status and population trends. *Lintumies* 19: 46–53 (in Finnish, with an English summary).

PAKARINEN, R. and H. SIIKAVIRTA. 1993. Lintuja Karjalan merellä. *Linnut* 5: 36–39. (Breeding birds on northwestern Lake Ladoga) (in Finnish, with English summary).

PALMA, L. 1985. The present situation of birds of prey in Portugal. In: I. Newton and R.D. Chancellor (Eds) *Conservation Studies on Raptors*. Technical Publication No. 5, International Council for Bird Preservation, Cambridge: 3–14.

PALMA, L. 1994. Nidificación de águilas perdiceras sobre árboles en Portugal. *Quercus* 98: 11–12.

PALUDAN, K. 1959. On the Birds of Afghanistan. *Vidensk. Medd. Dansk nat. For.* 122: 1–332.

PANOV, E.N. 1973. *Ptitsy juznogo Primor'ja*. Minsk (in Russian).

PANOV, E.N. 1974. *Die Steinschmätzer der nördlichen Paläarktis*. Neue Brehm-Bücherei 482, Ziemsen, Wittenberg.

PANOV, E.N. and N. Sh. BULATOVA. 1972. [On the coexistence and inter-relationships of Trumpeter Finches (*Bucanetes githagineus* Licht. and *Bucanetes mongolicus* Swinh.) in Transcaucasia.] *Bull. Moscow Soc. Naturalists, Biol.* 4: 86–94 (in Russian).

PANTELIS, V.S. 1980. The Cyprian Chukars (*Alectoris chukar cypriotes*). In: Coles, C.L., M. Reydellet, G. van Tuyll, L. van Maltzahn and J. Bugalho (Eds) *Partridges of the Genus* Alectoris. International Council for Game and Wildlife Conservation, Paris: 18–24.

PAPAEVANGELOU, E. 1980. General situation of the partridge species in Greece. In: Coles, C.L., M. Reydellet, G. van Tuyll, L. van Maltzahn and J. Bugalho (Eds) *Partridges of the Genus* Alectoris. International Council for Game and Wildlife Conservation, Paris: 71–79.

PAPAEVANGELOU, E., C. THOMAIDES, G. HANDRINOS and A. HARALAMBIDES. In press. Status of partridge species in Greece. *Gibier Faune Sauvage*.

PARR, R. 1979. Sequential breeding by Golden Plovers. *Brit. Birds* 72: 499–503.

PARR, S.J. 1994. Changes in the population size and nest sites of Merlins *Falco columbarius* in Wales between 1970 and 1991. *Bird Study* 41: 42–47.

PARRINDER, E.D. 1989. Little Ringed Plover *Charadrius dubius* in Britain in 1984. *Bird Study* 36: 147–153.

PASCUAL, P. and R.J. APARICIO. 1990. Noticiario ornitológico. *Ardeola* 37: 342.

PASPALEVA-ANTONOVA, M. 1965. Data on some new and rare Bulgarian birds. *Bull. Inst. zool. and Museum Sofia* 19: 33–38 (in Bulgarian, with German summary).

PATERSON, A.M. 1994. Distribuzione degli uccelli marini nidificanti nel Mediterraneo, Mar nero e Mar di azov. MEDMARAVIS. Edizioni del Sole. *Collana Mediterranea*: 23–42.

PATTERSON, I.J. 1982. *The Shelduck*. Cambridge University Press, Cambridge.

PATTERSON, I.J. 1993. Shelduck. In: Gibbons, D.W., J.B. Reid and R.A. Chapman (Eds) *The New Atlas of Breeding Birds in Britain and Ireland: 1988–1991*. Poyser, London: 60–61.

PAYEVSKI, V.A. 1994. Age and sex structure, mortality and spatial winter distribution of Siskins (*Carduelis spinus*) migrating through eastern Baltic area. *Vogelwarte* 37: 190–198.

PAZ, U. 1987. *The Birds of Israel*. Christopher Helm, Bromley.

PEACH, W.J., S.R. BAILLIE and L. UNDERHILL. 1991. Survival of British Sedge Warblers *Acrocephalus schoenobaenus* in relation to west African rainfall. *Ibis* 133: 300–305.

PEACH, W.J., P.S. THOMPSON and J.C. COULSON. 1994. Annual and long-term variation in the survival rates of British lapwings *Vanellus vanellus*. *J. Anim. Ecol.* 63: 60–70.

PEACH, W.J., H.Q.P. CRICK and J.H. MARCHANT. 1995. The demography of the decline in the British Willow Warbler population. *J. appl. Stat.* 22: 905–922.

PEARSON, D.J. and G.C. BACKHURST. 1988. Characters and taxonomic position of the Basra Reed Warbler. *Brit. Birds* 81: 171–178.

PEARSON, D.J., G. NIKOLAUS and J.S. ASH. 1988. The southward migration of Palearctic passerines through northeast and east tropical Africa: a review. *Proc. Pan-Afric. Orn. Congr.* 6: 243–261.

PEDERSEN, M.B. 1990. Projekt Dvärgbeckasin. *Vår Fågelvärld* 49: 485–487.

PEDERSEN, M.B. 1994. Jack Snipe. In: Tucker, G.M. and M.F. Heath (Eds) *Birds in Europe – their conservation status*. Conservation Series No. 3, BirdLife International, Cambridge: 266–267.

PEITZMEIER, J. 1952. Oekologische Umstellung und starke Vermehrung des Grossen Brachvogels (*Numenius arquata* L.) im oberen Emsgebiet. *Natur u. Heimat (Münster)* 12: 65–68.

PEKLO, A.M. 1987. [*Flycatchers of the USSR Fauna.*] Kiev (in Russian).

PERDECK, A.C. and B.J. SPEEK. 1964. Bird ringing in the Netherlands, 1962. *Limosa* 37: 96–186.

PEREA, J.L., M. MORALES and J.L. VELASCO. 1991. *El alimoche (*Neophron percnopterus*) en España.* Colección Técnica, ICONA, Madrid.

PERENNOU, C., P. ROSE and C. POOLE. 1990. *Asian Waterfowl Census.* IWRB and AWB. International Wetlands Research Bureau, Slimbridge.

PERIS, S.J. and J.I. CARNERO. 1988. *Atlas Ornitológico de la provincia de Salamanca.* Diputación de Salamanca, Salamanca.

PERIS, S.J, F. SUÁREZ and J.L.TELLERÍA. 1975. Estudio ornitológico del sabinar (*Juniperus thurifera*, L.) de Maranchón (Guadalajara). Descrición de la vegetación y aplicación del método de la parcela. *Ardeola* 22: 3–27.

PERIS, S.J., A. MOTIS and A. MARTINEZ. 1987. La distribución del Estornino Negro (*Sturnus unicolor* Temm.) y del Estornino Pinto (*S. vulgaris* L.) en la Peninsula Ibérica: aumento del àrea de nidificación de ambas especies. *Act. VIII B.R.S.E. Hist. Nat., Pamplona*: 151–156.

PERRINS, C.M. 1979. *British Tits.* Collins, London.

PERRINS, C. 1993. Swift. In: Gibbons, D.W., J.B. Reid and R.A. Chapman (Eds) *The New Atlas of Breeding Birds in Britain and Ireland: 1988–1991.* Poyser, London: 258–259.

PERSSON, B. 1971. Habitat selection and nesting of a south Swedish Whitethroat *Sylvia communis* Lath. population. *Ornis Scand.* 2: 119–126.

PERSSON, C. 1987. Population processes in south-west Scanian Sand Martins (*Riparia riparia*). *J. Zool. London (B)* 1: 671–691.

PERSSON, H. and C. URDIALES. 1995. The disappearance of the Tundra Bean Goose *Anser fabalis rossicus* from the Iberian Peninsula. *IWRB Goose Research Group Bull.* 6: 17–19.

PEŠKE, L. 1990a. [The population of Sparrowhawks living in Prague.] In: [*Birds in the Human Landscape.*] KSSPPOP, Praha: 293–300 (in Czech, with English summary).

PEŠKE, L. 1990b. Study of the Sparrowhawk (*Accipiter nisus*) population in Prague: The possibility to compare the results of bird breeding distribution mapping and the actual situation. In: Šťastny, K. and V. Bejček. (Eds) *Bird Census and Atlas Studies.* Institute of Applied and Ecotechnology, Agricultural University, Praha: 99–101.

PETERSEN, B.S. 1995. Interactions between birds and agriculture in Denmark: from simple counts to detailed studies of breeding success and foraging behaviour. In: Hagemeijer, E.J.M. and T.J. Verstrael (Eds) *Bird Numbers 1992: Distribution, monitoring and ecological aspects.* Statistics Netherlands, Voorburg/SOVON, Beek-Ubbergen: 49–56.

PETIT, P. 1976. Présence et nidification d'une Sterne voyageuse (*Sterna bengalensis*) dans une colonie de Sterne caugek (*Sterna sandvicensis*) sur le Banc d'Arguin (France). *Ardea* 64: 81–82.

PETRETTI, F. 1988. Notes on the behaviour and ecology of the Short-toed Eagle in Italy. *Gerfaut* 78: 261–286.

PETRETTI, F. 1991. Status of lowland dry grassland and birds in Italy. In: Goriup, P.D., I.A. Batten and J.A. Norton (Eds) *The Conservation of Lowland Dry Grassland Birds in Europe.* Joint Nature Conservation Committee, Peterborough: 69–76.

PETROV, P., P. DRAGOEV and Z.H. GEORGIEV. 1969. On the subspecies appartenance of the Rock partridge (*Alectoris graeca* Meisner) in the Eastern Rhodope. *Gorkostopanska Nauka (Forest Science)* 6(5): 91–106.

PETROV, T. 1973. [Concerning the biology and ecology of the Bee-eater (*Merops apiaster* L.) in the district of Plovdiv.] *Collection of the Natural History Museum, Plovdiv* 2: 65–88 (in Bulgarian).

PETROV, T. 1982. [Ornithological studies on Sredna Gora Mountain.] *Bull. Mus. South. Bulg.* 8: 21–41 (in Bulgarian).

PETROV, T., P. IANKOV, B. MICHEV and L. PROFIROV. In press a. Distribution, numbers and measures for the protection of the Black Stork in Bulgaria. In: Brouwer, K., C. King and M. Strazds (Eds) *The Black Stork in the Changing World. Proceedings of the 1st International Black Stork Conservation and Ecology Symposium, Jurmala, Latvia. Latvian Ornithological Society, Riga.*

PETROV, T., P. IANKOV, A. DARAKCHIEV, K. NIKOLOV, T. MICHEV, L. PROFIROV and B. MICHEV. 1996b. State of the Imperial Eagle (*Aquila heliaca*) in Bulgaria in the period between 1890 and 1993. In: Meyburg, B-U. and R.D. Chancellor (Eds) *Eagle Studies.* WWGBPO. *Birds of Prey Bull.* 5: 429–434.

PETTERSSON, B. 1984. *Ecology of an Isolated Population of the Middle Spotted Woodpecker* Dendrocopos medius *(L.), in the Extinction Phase.* Report No. 23, Swedish University of Agricultural Sciences, Department of Wildlife Ecology, Uppsala.

PETTY, S.J. 1992. *Ecology of the Tawny Owl* Strix aluco *in the Spruce Forests of Northumberland and Argyll.* PhD Thesis, The Open University, Milton Keynes.

PICOZZI, N., D.C. CATT and R. MOSS. 1993. Evaluation of Capercaillie habitat. *J. appl. Ecol.* 29: 751–762.

PIECHOCKI, R. 1968. Beiträge zur Avifauna der Mongolei. Part I. Non-Passeriformes. *Mitteilungen aus dem Zoologischen Museum in Berlin* 44(2): 1–175.

PIENKOWSKI, M.W. 1984. Breeding biology and population dynamics of ringed plovers *Charadrius hiaticula* in Britain and Greenland: nest-predation as a possible factor limiting distribution and timing of breeding. *J. Zool., London* 202: 83–114.

PIENKOWSKI, M.W. 1993. The impact of tourism on coastal breeding waders in western and southern Europe: an overview. *Wader Study Group Bull.* 68: 92–96.

PIERSMA, T. 1994. *Close to the Edge: Energetic bottlenecks and the evolution of migratory pathways in knots.* Het Open Boek, Den Burg.

PIERSMA, T. and N. DAVIDSON. 1992. The migrations and annual cycles of five subspecies of Knots in perspective. In: Piersma, T. and N. Davidson (Eds) *The Migration of the Knot. Wader Study Group Bull.* 64, Suppl: 187–197.

PIETIÄINEN, H. 1983. In: Hyytiä, K., E. Kellomäki and J. Koistinen (Eds) *Suomen Lintuatlas.* SLY:n Lintutieto Oy, Helsinki: 328–329.

PIETIÄINEN, H. 1989. Seasonal and individual variation in the production of offspring in the Ural Owl *Strix uralensis*. *J. Anim. Ecol.* 58: 905–920.

PIETRI, C. 1993. *Le Colin de Californie,* Callipepla californica *(Shaw) 1798 – Historique, distribution et habitat en Corse.* Mémoire de Diplôme EPHE, École Pratique des Hautes Études, Montpellier.

PIIROINEN, J., J. TIAINEN, T. PAKKALA and J. YLIMAUNU. 1985. [Birds of Finnish farmland in 1984.] *Lintumies* 20: 126–138 (in Finnish, with English summary).

PIOTROWSKA, M. and T. WESOŁOWSKI. 1989. The breeding ecology and behaviour of the chiffchaff *Phylloscopus collybita* in primaeval and managed stands of Białowieża Forest (Poland). *Acta Ornithol.* 25: 25–76.

PIRKOLA, M.K. and P. KALINAINEN. 1984a. The status, distribution and habitats of Bean Goose *Anser f. fabalis* in Finland. *Suomen Riista* 31: 83–91.

PIRKOLA, M.K. and P. KALINAINEN. 1984b. The status, habitats and productivity of breeding populations of Bean Goose, *Anser fabalis fabalis*, in Finland. *Swedish Wildlife Res.* 13: 9–48.

PLAISIER, F. 1992. Zur Bionomie der Hohltaube (*Columba oenas*) auf der Nordseeinsel Langeoog. *Beitr. Vogelk.* 38: 167–174.

PLAN COORDINADO DE ACTUACIONES DE LA GAVIOTA DE AUDOUIN 1994. Ecología y situación de la Gaviota de Audouin en España. *Quercus* 100: 4–11.

PLEGUEZUELOS, J.M. 1992. *Avifauna nidificante de las Sierras Béticas Orientales y Depresiones de Guadix, Baza y Granada.* Colección Monográfica Tierras del Sur. Universidad de Granada, Granada.

POJER, F. In press. Black Stork (*Ciconia nigra* L.) in the Czech Republic – present status and conservation. In: Brewer, K., C. King and M. Strazds (Eds) *The Black Stork in the Changing World. Proceedings of the 1st International Black Stork Conservation and Ecology Symposium, Jurmala, Latvia. Latvian Ornithological Society, Riga.*

POLIVANOV, V.M. and N.N. POLIVANOVA. 1990. [Population status of Krüper's Nuthatch in Stavropol' territory.] In: *Redkie, malochislennye i maloizuchennye ptitsy Severnogo Kavkaza* [*Rare, Scarce and Little-studied Birds of the Northern Caucasus*]. Stavropol': 77–80 (in Russian).

POLJAK, A., D. HUBER and J. GREGURIC. 1990. (Estimation of the Street Pigeon population size in Zagreb.) *Larus* 41/42: 141–150.

PONS, A. 1981. The history of the Mediterranean shrublands. In: di Castri, F., D.W. Goodall and R.L. Specht (Eds) *Maquis and Chaparrals. Ecosystems of the World.* Elsevier, Amsterdam: 131–138.

POOLE, A.F. 1989. *Ospreys: A natural and unnatural history.* Cambridge University Press, Cambridge.

POORTER, E.P.R. 1982. Migration et dispersion des Spatules néerlandaises. *L'Oiseau et R.F.O.* 52: 305–334.

POORTER, E.P.R. 1991. *Bewick's Swans* Cygnus columbianus bewickii, *an analysis of breeding success and changing resources.* Ministerie van Verkeer en Waterstaat, Rijkswaterstaat, Directie Flevoland.

PORTENKO, L.A. 1937. [*Avifauna of the Polar Urals.*] Academy of Sciences of the USSR, Moscow–Leningrad (in Russian).

PORTENKO, L.A., J. STÜBS and K. WUNDERLICH. 1982. *Parus caeruleus* (L.) und *Parus cyaneus* (Pallas) ein geschlossen die *flavipectus*-Gruppe. In: Dathe, H. and I.A. Neufeldt (Eds) *Atlas der Verbreitung paläarktischer Vögel*, Vol. 9. Berlin.

POTAPOV, R.L. 1978. [Caucasian Black Grouse – an endemic of the Caucasus Mountains.] *Priroda* 3: 118–123 (in Russian).

POTAPOV, R.L. 1982. New data on the Caucasian Black Grouse, *Lyrurus mlokosiewiczi* (Taczanowski). *Ornithological Studies in the USSR* 1: 101–120.

POTAPOV, R.L. 1984. [Caucasian Black Grouse.] In: Borodin, A.M. (Ed) *Red Data Book of the USSR*, Vol. 1. Department of Nature Conservation, Moscow (in Russian).

POTAPOV, R.L. 1985. *Fauna of the USSR: Tetraonidae.* Nauka, Leningrad (in Russian).

POTAPOV, R.L. 1987. [Order Galliformes]. In: Iluichev, V.L., V.E. Flint, R.L. Beme, V.M. Galushin, J.A. Isakov, E.V. Kumari, E.N. Kurochkin, R.L. Potapov, S.G. Priklonsky, A.K. Rustamov, L.S. Stepanyan and V.E. Fomin (Eds) [*Birds of the USSR: Galliformes and Gruiformes.*] Nauka, Leningrad: 248–260 (in Russian).

POTAPOV, R.L. 1988. *Handbuch der Vögel der Sowjetunion. Galliformes.* AULA Verlag, Wiesbaden.

POTAPOV, R.L. 1989a. *Bonasa bonasia* (Linnaeus, 1758) Haselhuhn. In: Potapov, R.L. and V.E. Flint (Eds) *Handbuch der Vögel der Sowjetunion*, Vol. 4. AULA Verlag, Wiesbaden: 103–117.

POTAPOV, R.L. 1989b. Gattung *Tetraogallus* Gray, 1832. In: Potapov, R.L. and V.E. Flint (Eds) *Handbuch der Vögel der Sowjetunion*, Vol. 4. AULA Verlag, Wiesbaden: 67–91.

POTTS, G.R. 1980. The effects of modern agriculture, nest predation and game management on the population ecology of partridges *Perdix perdix* and *Alectoris rufa.* *Adv. Ecol. Res.* 11: 2–79.

POTTS, G.R. 1986. *The Partridge: Pesticides, predation and conservation.* Collins, London.

POTTS, G.R. 1991. The environmental and ecological importance of cereal fields. In: Firbank, L.G., N. Carter, J.F. Derbyshire and G.R. Potts (Eds) *The Ecology of Temperate Cereal Fields.* Blackwell, Oxford: 3–21.

POXTON, I.R. 1986. Breeding Ring Ouzels in the Pentland Hills. *Scottish Birds* 14: 44–48.

POXTON, I.R. 1987. Breeding status of the Ring Ouzel in Southeast Scotland 1985–86. *Scottish Birds* 14: 205–208.

PÖYSÄ, H., E. LAMMI, R.A. VÄISÄNEN and M. WIKMAN. 1993. Monitoring of waterbirds in the breeding season: the programme used in Finland 1986–92. In: Moser, M., R.C. Prentice and J. van Vessem (Eds) *Waterfowl and Wetland Conservation in the 1990s – a global perspective. Proceedings of an IWRB Symposium, St Petersburg Beach, Florida, USA, 12–19 November 1992.* Special Publication No. 26, International Wetlands Research Bureau, Slimbridge: 7–12.

PRANAITIS, A. 1990. [Citrine Wagtails (*Motacilla citreola*) breed in Lithuania.] *Acta. orn. Lituanica* 2: 140–142 (in Lithuanian).

PRANGE, H. (Ed). 1989. *Der Graue Kranich.* Neue Brehm-Bücherei, Wittenberg, Lutherstadt.

PRANGE, H. 1994. Zur Situation des Kranichs in Europa – Entwicklungen, Schutzmaßnahmen und künftige Aufgaben. *Bucephala, Berlin* 1: 83–96.

PRANGE, H. (Ed). 1995. *Crane Research and Protection in Europe.* Martin-Luther-Universität, Halle-Wittenberg.

PRATER, A.J. 1989. Ringed Plover *Charadrius hiaticula* breeding population in the United Kingdom in 1984. *Bird Study* 36: 154–159.

PRATER, A.J. 1993. Greylag Goose. In: Gibbons, D.W., J.B. Reid and R.A. Chapman (Eds) *The New Atlas of Breeding Birds in Britain and Ireland: 1988–1991*. Poyser, London: 54–55.

PRESTRUD, P., J.M. BLACK and M. OWEN. 1989. The relationship between the increasing Barnacle Goose population and the number and size of colonies in Svalbard. *Wildfowl* 40: 32–37.

PRIEDNIEKS, J., M. STRAZDS, A. STRAZDS and A. PETRINŠ. 1989. *Latvijas Ligzdojošo Putnu Atlants 1980–1984*. Zinātne, Riga (in Latvian, with English summary).

PRIESZHEV, G.P. 1978. [*Emberizidae. Birds of the Volga–Kama Region*, Vol. II, *Passerines*. Nauka, Moscow: 203–221 (in Russian).

PRINCE, P. and R. CLARKE. 1993. The Hobby's breeding range in Britain: What factors have allowed it to expand? *British Wildlife* 4: 341–346.

PRINS, H.H.T. 1986. Spring migration of Cuckoo through the Rift Valley in northern Tanzania. *Ardea* 74: 215–217.

PRINZINGER, R. 1979. *Der Schwarzhalstaucher*. Neue Brehm-Bücherei, Ziemsen, Wittenberg.

PRIOLO, A. and M. BOCCA. 1992. Coturnice *Alectoris graeca*. In: Brichetti, P., P. de Franceschi and N. Baccetti (Eds) *Fauna d'Italia XXIX*, Aves I. Calderini, Bologna: 766–777.

PRODON, R. 1985. Introduction à la biologie du Traquet rieur (*Oenanthe leucura*) en France. *Alauda* 53: 295–305.

PRODON, R. 1991. Traquet rieur *Oenanthe leucura*. In: Yeatman-Berthelot, D. (Ed) *Atlas des Oiseaux de France en Hiver*. Société Ornithologique de France, Paris: 392–393.

PRODON, R. 1994. Cochevis de Thékla. In: Yeatman-Berthelot, D. and G. Jarry (Eds) *Nouvel Atlas des Oiseaux Nicheurs de France 1985–1989*. Société Ornithologique de France, Paris: 452–453.

PRODON, R. and P. ISENMANN. 1994. Traquet oreillard *Oenanthe hispanica*. In: Yeatman-Berthelot, D. and G. Jarry (Eds) *Nouvel Atlas des Oiseaux Nicheurs de France 1985–1989*. Société Ornithologique de France, Paris: 518–519.

PROKOSCH, P. 1984. Breeding sites and distribution of geese in the northwest Isfjord area, Svalbard, 1982. *Nor. Polarinst. Skr.* 181: 135–139.

PROSTOV, A. and D. SMILOVA. 1983. [Ornithological collection of Department 'Priroda' Burgas.] *Sofia, Ornithol. inf. Bull.* 13–14: 14–30 (in Bulgarian).

PRŶS-JONES, R.P. 1984. Migration patterns of the Reed Bunting *Emberiza schoeniclus schoeniclus* and the dependence of wintering distribution on environmental conditions. *Gerfaut* 74: 15–37.

PRŶS-JONES, R.P., L.G. UNDERHILL and R.J. WATERS. 1994. Index numbers for waterbird populations. II. Coastal wintering waders in the United Kingdom 1970/71–1990/91. *J. appl. Ecol.* 31: 481–492.

PTUSHENKO, E.S. 1952. Order Geese Anseres, Anseriformes. In: Dementiev, G.P. and N.A. Gladkov (Eds) [*Birds of the Soviet Union*, Vol. 4]. Nauka, Moscow: 247–344.

PTUSHENKO, E.S. and A.A. INOZEMTSEV. 1968. [*Biology and Economic Importance of Birds of the Moscow Region and Neighbouring Areas*.] University of Moscow, Moscow (in Russian).

PUGACEWICZ, E. 1995. [Population of the Spotted Eagle (*Aquila clanga*) at Biebrza Marshes in 1989–1993.] *Notatki Ornitologiczne* 36: 3–4 (in Polish, with English summary).

PUIGCERVER, M. 1990. *Contribución al conocimiento de la biología y ecoetología de la codorniz (*Coturnix coturnix*)*. PhD Thesis, Universitat de Barcelona, Barcelona.

PUIGCERVER, M., J.D. RODRIGUEZ-TEIJEIRO and S. GALLEGO. 1989. Migración y/o nomadismo en la codorniz *Coturnix c. coturnix*? *Etología* 1: 39–45.

PULLIAINEN, E. 1974. Winter nutrition of the common crossbill (*Loxia curvirostra*) and the pine grosbeak (*Pinicola enucleator*) in northeastern Lapland in 1973. *Ann. Zool. Fennici* 11: 204–206.

PULLIAINEN, E. 1979. On the breeding of the Pine Grosbeak *Pinicola enucleator* in NE Finland. *Ornis Fennica* 56: 156–162.

PULLIAINEN, E. 1983. Kirjosiipikäpylintu *Loxia leucoptera*. In: Hyytiä, K., E. Kellomäki and J. Koistinen (Eds) *Suomen Lintuatlas*. SLY:n Lintutieto Oy, Helsinki: 452–453. (*The Finnish Bird Atlas*) (in Finnish).

PULLIAINEN, E. and L. SAARI. 1989. Breeding biology of Rustic Buntings *Emberiza rustica* in eastern Finnish Lapland. *Ornis Fennica* 66: 161–165.

PULLIAINEN, E. and L. SAARI. 1991. Breeding biology of the Wood Sandpiper *Tringa glareola* in eastern Finnish Lapland. *Ornis Fennica* 68: 127–128.

PULLIAINEN, E. and L. SAARI. 1993. Breeding biology of the Whimbrel *Numenius phaeopus* in eastern Finnish Lapland. *Ornis Fennica* 70: 110–116.

PULLIAINEN, E., J. MÄKELÄ and L. SAARI. 1990. [On the breeding biology and behaviour of Arctic Warblers *Phylloscopus borealis* in Finnish Forest Lapland.] *Lintumies* 25: 217–222 (in Finnish, with English summary).

PULYAKH, V. 1977. In: Voinstvenski, M.A. (Ed) *Tez. dokl. VII Vsesoyuz. orn. Konf.* 1: 306–307.

PURROY, F.J., Á. ÁLVAREZ and B. PETTERSSON. 1984. La población de Pico Mediano, *Dendrocopos medius* (L.), de la Cordillera Cantábrica. *Ardeola* 31: 81–90.

PURROY, F.J., M. RODERO and L. TOMIAŁOJĆ. 1987. The ecology of Woodpigeons *Columba palumbus* wintering on the Iberian Peninsula. *Acta Ornithol.* 20: 111–176.

RABOSEE, D., H. de WAVRIN, J. TRICOT and D. van der ELST (Eds). 1995. *Atlas des Oiseaux Nicheurs de Bruxelles*. Centrale Ornithologique Aves. Liège.

RABOUD, C. 1988. Das räumliche und zeitliche Verteilungsmuster einer Population der Alpendohle während der Brutzeit. *Orn. Beob.* 85: 385–392.

RAINES, R.J. 1962. The distribution of birds in northeast Greece in summer. *Ibis* 104: 490–502.

RAJALA, P. and T. ORMIO. 1970. On the nesting of the Goldeneye, *Bucephala clangula* (L.), in the Meltaus game research area in northern Finland, 1959–1966. *Finnish Game Res.* 31: 3–9.

RAMOS, J.A. 1989. *Ecologia e Conservacão do Caimão Comum,* Porphyrio porphyrio, *com especial referência ao Ludo, Parque Natural da Ria Formosa*. Relatório de

Estágio do Curso de Licenciatura, Universidade do Algarve.

RAMOS, J.A. 1993. *The Status and Ecology of the Priolo or Azores Bullfinch* Pyrrhula murina. DPhil Thesis, University of Oxford, Oxford.

RAMOS, J.A. 1994. The annual cycle of the Azores bullfinch, *Pyrrhula murina* Godman 1866 (Aves: Passeriformes). *Arquipélago Life and Marine Sciences* 12A: 101–109.

RAMOS, J.A. 1995. The diet of the Azores bullfinch and floristic variation within its range. *Biol. Conservation* 71: 237–249.

RAMOS, J.A. In press. Introduction of exotic trees as a threat to the Azores bullfinch population. *J. appl. Ecol.*

RANDI, E., F. SPINA and B. MASSA. 1989. Genetic variability in Cory's Shearwater (*Calonectris diomedea*). *Auk* 106: 411–417.

RANDS, M.R.W. 1986. Effect of hedgerow characteristics on partridge breeding densities. *J. appl. Ecol.* 23: 479–487.

RANFTL, H. 1982. Zur Situation des Grossen Brachvogels (*Numenius arquata*) in Bayern. *Beih. Veröff. Naturschutz Landschaftspflege Bad.-Württ.* 25: 45–60.

RATCLIFFE, D.A. 1976. Observations on the breeding of the Golden Plover in Great Britain. *Bird Study* 23: 63–116.

RATCLIFFE, D.A., 1993. *The Peregrine Falcon*, 2nd edn. Poyser, London.

RAVKIN, Yu.S. 1993. *Aquatic Warbler in Russia*. Unpublished Technical Report to Birdlife International, Cambridge.

RAVKIN, Yu.S., I.I. GLEICH and O.A. CHERNIKOV. 1988. [Numbers and distribution of birds in subtaiga forests of Central Siberia (the Kolyma River basin).] In: *Contributions to the Fauna of Central Siberia and the Adjacent Regions of Mongolia*.] Inst. Animal Morph. and Ecol., USSR Academy of Sciences, Moscow: 81–96 (in Russian).

RAYA, C. In prep (1993). Seguimiento de la población de la focha cornuda (*Fulica cristata*), tarro canelo (*Tadorna ferruginea*), cercerta pardilla (*Marmaronetta angustirostris*) y porrón pardo (*Aythya nyroca*), así como ejemplares marcados, procedentes de cría en cautividad, de malvasía (*Oxyura leucocephala*) y focha cornuda, en el territorio de Andalucía occidental y la provincia de Almería. Unpublished report.

REAL, J. 1991. *L'àliga perdiguera Hieraaetus fasciatus a Catalunya: status, ecologia tròfica, biologia reproductora i demografia*. PhD Thesis, University of Barcelona, Barcelona.

REAL, J., S. MAÑOSA, R. del AMO, J.A. SANCHEZ, M.A. SANCHEZ, D. CARMONA and J.E. MARTINEZ. 1992. La regresión del águila perdicera una cuestión de demografía. *Quercus* 70: 6–12.

REAL, J., S. MAÑOSA, G. CHEYLAN, P. BAYLE, J.M. CUGNASSE, J.A. SANCHEZ-ZAPATA, M.A. SANCHEZ, D. CARMONA, J.E. MARTINEZ, L. RICO, J. CODINA, R. del AMO and S. EGUIA. 1995. A preliminary demographic approach to the Bonelli's eagle population decrease in Spain and France. In: Meyburg, B.-U. (Ed) *Proceedings of the IV World Conference on Birds of Prey and Owls, Berlin 1992*. WWGBPO, Berlin.

REAL, J., S. MAÑOSA and J. CODINA. In press. Estatus, demografía y conservación del águila perdicera en el Mediterráneo. *Proceedings of the VI Conference on Mediterranean Birds of Prey, Palma de Mallorca 1994*.

REDDIG, E. 1981. *Die Bekassine*. Neue Brehm-Bücherei 533, Ziemsen, Wittenberg.

REDONDO, T. and F. CASTRO. 1992. The increase in risk of predation with begging activity in broods of Magpies. *Ibis* 134: 180–287.

REE, V. 1994. Bydue *Columba livia* var. *domestica*. In: Gjershaug J.O., P.G. Thingstad, S. Eldøy and S. Byrkjeland (Eds) *Norsk fugleatlas*. Norsk Ornitologisk Forening, Klæbu: 260–261.

REED, A. and A. BOURGET. 1977. Distribution and abundance of waterfowl wintering in southern Quebec. *Canadian Field-Naturalist* 91: 1–7.

REGAL, P.J. 1977. Ecology and evolution of flowering plant dominance. *Science* 196: 622–662.

REID, J.B. 1993. Rook *Corvus frugilegus*. In: Gibbons, D.W., J.B. Reid and R.A. Chapman (Eds) *The New Atlas of Breeding Birds in Britain and Ireland 1988–1991*. Poyser, London: 392–393.

REINERTSEN, R.E. and S. HAFTORN. 1983. Nocturnal hypothermia and metabolism in the Willow Tit *Parus montanus* at 63°N. *J. Comp. Physiol. B* 151: 109–118.

REINERTSEN, R.E., S. HAFTORN and E. THALER. 1988. Is hypothermia necessary for the winter survival of the Goldcrest *Regulus regulus*? *J. Ornithol.* 129: 433–437.

REINSCH, A. 1995. Der Raubwürger (*Lanius excubitor*) bei Hilpoltstein/Mittelfranken. *Avifaunistischer Informationsdienst Bayern* 2: 19–26.

REITZ, F. 1992. La Perdix grise en 1991 dans le Nord, le Bassin parisien et le Centre. *Bulletin mensuel de l'O.N.C.* 165: 7–15.

RENARD, A. 1994. Étourneau unicolore *Sturnus unicolor*. In: Yeatman-Berthelot, D. and G. Jarry (Eds) *Nouvel Atlas des Oiseaux Nicheurs de France 1985–1989*. Société Ornithologique de France, Paris: 674–675.

RENDON, M., J.M. VARGAS and J.M. RAMIREZ. 1991. Dinamica temporal y reproduccion del Flamenco comun (*Phoenicopterus ruber roseus*) en la Laguna de Fuente de Piedra (sur de España). In: Junta de Andalucia (Ed) *Reunion Tecnica sobre la Situacion y Problematica del Flamenco rosa (*Phoenicopterus ruber roseus*) en el Mediterraneo occidental y Africa Noroccidental*. Imprenta Galan, Sevilla: 135–153.

RENSSEN, T.A. and R.L. VOGEL. 1993. Recente ontwikkelingen van de Raaf *Corvus corax* in Nederland. *Limosa* 66: 107–116. (Recent developments of the Raven *Corvus corax* population in The Netherlands) (in Dutch, with English summary).

REPA, P. 1984. The qualitative and quantitative composition of bird communities of the forest upland moor in the State Reserve Farske Baziny near Tachov (southwestern Bohemia). *Folia Mus. Rerum nat. Bohemiae occident. (Zool.)* 19: 1–24.

RHEINWALD, G. 1994. A method to calculate totals of bird populations. *Bird Census News* 7: 7–15.

RHIJN, J.G. van. 1991. *The Ruff*. Poyser, London.

RICHARDSON, M.G. 1990. The distribution and status of Whimbrel *Numenius p. phaeopus* in Shetland and Britain. *Bird Study* 37: 61–68.

RICHARDSON, M.G. 1993. Whimbrel *Numenius phaeopus*. In: Gibbons, D.W., J.B. Reid and R.A.

Chapman (Eds) *The New Atlas of Breeding Birds in Britain and Ireland: 1988–1991*. Poyser, London: 182–183.

RIDGILL, S.C. and A.D. FOX. 1990. *Cold Weather Movements of Waterfowl in Western Europe*. Special Publication No. 13, International Waterfowl & Wetlands Research Bureau, Slimbridge.

RISBERG, L. 1979. Härfågelns *Upupa epops* förekomst i Sverige 1958–77. *Vår Fågelvärld* 38: 221–230 (in Swedish).

RISBERG, L. 1990. Sveriges fåglar. *Vår Fågelvärld* Suppl. 14 (in Swedish).

RISBERG, L. and B. RISBERG. 1975. Rosenfinken *Carpodacus erythrinus* i Sverige 1969 och 1974. *Vår Fågelvärld* 34: 139–151. (The Scarlet Rosefinch *Carpodacus erythrinus* in Sweden in 1969 and 1974) (in Swedish, with English summary).

RISBERG, L., G. AULÉN, K. BYLIN and T. TYRBERG. 1990. *Sveriges fåglar*. SOF, Stockholm (in Swedish).

RISTOW, D. and M. WINK. 1985. Breeding success and conservation management of Eleonora's Falcon. In: Newton, I. and R.D. Chancellor (Eds) *Conservation Studies on Raptors*. Technical Publication No. 5, International Council for Bird Preservation, Cambridge: 147–152.

RITTER, M. and J. HÖLZINGER. 1987. Zaunammer *Emberiza cirlus*. In: Hölzinger, J. (Ed) *Die Vögel Baden-Württembergs*, Vol. 1.2. Eugen Ulmer, Stuttgart: 1270–1275.

ROBEL, D. 1991. Die bisher letzte Brut der Blauracke *Coracias garrulus* in Deutschland – gescheitert. *Vogelwelt* 112: 148–149.

ROBERTS, T.J. 1992. *The Birds of Pakistan*, Vol. 2. Oxford University Press, Karachi.

ROBERTSON, H.A. 1990. Breeding of Collared Dove *Streptopelia decaocto* in rural Oxfordshire, England. *Bird Study* 37: 73–83.

ROBERTSON, J. and Å. BERG. 1992. Status and population changes of farmland birds in southern Sweden. *Ornis Svecica* 2: 119–130.

ROBERTSON, P.A., M.I.A. WOODBURN and D.A. HILL. 1993. Factors affecting winter pheasant density in British woodlands. *J. appl. Ecol.* 30: 459–464.

ROBERTSON, W.B. 1969. Transatlantic migration of juvenile Sooty Terns. *Nature* 223: 623–634.

ROBLEDANO, F. and J.F. CALVO. 1989. La expansion del Tarro Blanco, *Tadorna tadorna* (L.) como reproductor en España. *Ardeola* 36: 91–95. (The expansion of the breeding range of the Shelduck *Tadorna tadorna* (L.) in Spain) (in Spanish, with English summary).

ROCAMORA, G. In prep (1998). Sittelle corse *Sitta whiteheadi* In: Rocamora, G., D. Berthelot and G. Jarry. *Oiseaux menacés de France : statut et conservation des espèces vulnérables et à surveiller. Listes rouges et priorités nationales.* Ministère de l'Environnement, M.N.H.N. and LPO, Paris.

ROCKENBAUCH, D. 1978. Brutbiologie und den Bestand steuernde Faktoren bei Waldkauz (*Strix aluco*) und Waldohreule (*Asio otus*) in der Schwäbischen Alb. *J. Ornithol.* 119: 429–440.

RODRIGUEZ de los SANTOS, M. and J.C. RUBIO GARCIA. 1986. Biology and biometry of the Pallid Swift (*Apus pallidus*) in southern Spain. *Gerfaut* 76: 19–30.

RODRIGUEZ MARISCAL, A. 1990. Noticiario ornitológico. *Ardeola* 37: 342.

RODRIGUEZ-TEIJEIRO, J.D., M. PUIGCERVER and S. GALLEGO. 1992. Mating strategy in the European Quail (*Coturnix c. coturnix*) revealed by male population density and sex ratio in Catalonia (Spain). *Gibier Faune Sauvage* 9: 377–386.

ROGACHEVA, E.V. 1992. *The Birds of Central Siberia*. Husum Druck- und Verlagsgesellschaft, Husum: 110–124, 149–150, 458.

ROGACHEVA, E.V., E.E. SYROECHKOVSKI, O.V. BURSKY, N.V. ANZIGITOVA and A.B. GOTTFRIED. 1978. [Birds of the Yenisey mid-taiga.] In: [*Protection of the Fauna of the Far North, and its Rational Use*.] Union Inst. for Nature Conservation, Moscow: 42–96 (in Russian).

ROLANDO, A. and I.J. PATTERSON. 1993. Range and movements of the Alpine Chough *Pyrrhocorax graculus* in relation to human developments in the Italian Alps in summer. *J. Ornithol.* 134: 338–344.

ROOBROUCK, A. 1994. Faisan vénéré *Syrmaticus reevesii*. In: Yeatman-Berthelot, D. and G. Jarry (Eds) *Nouvel Atlas des Oiseaux Nicheurs de France 1985–1989*. Société Ornithologique de France, Paris: 234–235.

ROOS, G. 1984. Flyttning, övervintring och livslängd hos fåglar ringmärkta vid Falsterbo (1947–1980). *Anser* Suppl 13. (Migration, wintering and longevity of birds ringed at Falsterbo (1947–1980)) (in Swedish, with English summary).

ROOTH, J. 1989. De Nederlandse broedpopulatie van de Grote Stern *Sterna sandvicensis* in 1961–88. *Limosa* 62: 121–124. (Numbers of Sandwich Tern *Sterna sandvicensis* breeding in the Netherlands in 1961–88) (in Dutch, with English summary).

ROSE, P. 1994. Ruddy Shelduck. In: Tucker, G.M. and M.F. Heath (Eds) *Birds in Europe – their conservation status*. Conservation Series No. 3, BirdLife International, Cambridge, UK: 118–119.

ROSE, P.M. and D.A. SCOTT (Eds). 1994. *Waterfowl Population Estimates*. Special Publication No. 29, International Waterfowl & Wetlands Research Bureau, Slimbridge.

ROSELAAR, C.S. 1995. *Taxonomy, Morphology, and Distribution of the Songbirds of Turkey: an atlas of biodiversity of Turkish passerine birds*. GMB uitgeverij, Haarlem.

RØSKAFT, E., T. JÄRVI, N.E.I. NYHOLM, M. VIROLAINEN, M. WINKEL and H. ZANG. 1986. Geographic variation in secondary sexual plumage colour characteristics of the male Pied Flycatcher. *Ornis Scand.* 17: 293–298.

ROTHAUPT, G. 1992. Zur Situation des Raubwürgers *Lanius excubitor* in Bayern unter Berücksichtigung überregionaler Daten. *Orn. Verh.* 25: 151–167.

ROUX, F. and G. JARRY. 1984. Numbers, composition and distribution of populations of *Anatidae* wintering in West Africa. *Wildfowl* 35: 48–60.

RØV, N. 1990. Population studies of shags *Phalacrocorax aristotelis* in Norway. *NINA Forskningsrapport* 7: 1–28.

RUDENKO, A.G. 1992. [The first record of breeding

Great Black-headed Gull in the Black Sea Reserve.] *Studies of Colonial Seabirds in the USSR*. Information, Magadan: 35–36 (in Russian).

RUFINO, R. (Ed). 1989. *Atlas das Aves que nidificam em Portugal Continental*. CEMPA, Lisboa. (*Atlas of the Breeding Birds of Mainland Portugal*) (in Portuguese, with English summary).

RUFINO, R. and R. NEVES. 1991. [Census of Black-winged Stilt *Himantopus himantopus* breeding in Portugal]. *AIRO* 2: 10–11 (in Portuguese).

RUFINO, R. and R. NEVES. 1992. The effects on wader populations of the conversion of salinas into fish farms. In: Finlayson, C.M., G.E. Hollis and T.J. Davis (Eds) *Managing Mediterranean Wetlands and their Birds. Proceedings of a Symposium, Grado, Italy, 1991*. Special Publication No. 20, International Wetlands Research Bureau, Slimbridge: 177–182.

RUGE, K. 1982. *Picus canus* – Grauspecht. In: Schifferli, A., P. Géroudet and R. Winkler (Eds) *Verbreitungsatlas der Brutvögel der Schweiz*. Schweizerische Vogelwarte, Sempach: 202–203.

RUGE, K. and F. BRETZENDORFER. 1981. Biotopstrukturen und Siedlungsdichte beim Schwarzspecht (*Dryocopus martius*). *Beih. Veröff. Naturschutz Landschaftspflege Bad.-Württ.* 20: 37–48.

RUGE, K. and W. WEBER. 1974. Brutgebiet des Dreizehenspechts (*Picoides tridactylus*) im Eisenerzer Raum, Steiermark. *Anz. orn. Ges. Bayern* 13: 300–304.

RÜGER, A., C. PRENTICE and M. OWEN. 1986. *Population Estimates and Trends in Selected Species of Ducks, Swans and Coot from January Counts in the Western Palearctic*. Special Publication No. 6, International Waterfowl & Wetlands Research Bureau, Slimbridge.

RUITERS P.S., R. NOORDHUIS and M.S. VAN DEN BERG. 1994. Kranswieren verklaren aantalsfluctuaties van Krooneenden *Netta rufina* in Nederland. *Limosa* 67: 147–158. (Stoneworts account for fluctuations in Red-crested Pochard *Netta rufina* numbers in The Netherlands) (in Dutch, with English summary).

RUSANEN, P. 1993. [Waterfowl migration in western Estonia.] *Linnut* 28: 7–10 (in Finnish, with English summary).

RUTSCHKE, E. 1989. *Ducks of Europe*. VEB Deutscher Landwirtschaftsverlag, Berlin.

RUTTLEDGE, R.F. 1966. *Ireland's Birds*. Witherby, London.

RUWET, J.C., S. FONTAINE, S. HANON and S. HOUBART. 1986. Ecologie, éthologie, conservation du tétras lyre (*Tetrao tetrix*) sur le plateau des Hautes-Fagnes. Le point de la situation. *Hautes Fagnes* 181: 11–20.

RYABITSEV, V.K. and N.S. ALEKSEEVA. 1992. Nesting density dynamics and site tenacity in waders of the middle and northern Yamal. *Abstr. Odessa Conference of Wader Study Group. Wader Study Group Bull.* 65: 17.

RYKOVA, S.Y. 1986. [*Abundance and Territorial Distribution of Birds in the Pinega Reserve. Distribution and abundance of animals in North-East European USSR*]. Syktyvkar: 46–55 (in Russian).

RYMKEVIC, T.A. 1979. Materialy po ekologii ovsjanki-remeza (*Emberiza rustica* Pall.) v Leningradskoi oblasti. *Vestnik Leningrad gos. Univ. 3 Biol.* 1: 37–47 (in Russian).

RYTTMAN, H. 1994. Överlevnadsberäckningar och försök att skatta populationsutvecklingen hos fiskgjuse *Pandion haliaetus*, ormvråk *Buteo buteo* och sparvhök *Accipiter nisus* i Sverige. *Ornis Svecica* 4: 159–172. (Estimates of survival and population development of the Osprey *Pandion haliaetus*, Common Buzzard *Buteo buteo*, and Sparrowhawk *Accipiter nisus* in Sweden) (in Swedish, with English summary).

SAARI, L. 1984. The ecology of Woodpigeon (*Columba palumbus* L.) and Stock Dove (*C. oenas* L.) populations on an island in the SW Finnish archipelago. *Finnish Game Res.* 43: 13–67.

SAARI, L. 1995. Population trends of the Dotterel *Charadrius morinellus* in Finland during the past 150 years. *Ornis Fennica* 72: 29–36.

SACARRÃO, G.F. 1974. [On some problematic aspects of the geographical ecology of *Cyanopica cyana* (Pall.) [Aves-Corvidae]]. *Est. Fauna Port.* 1: 1–88 (in Portuguese).

SACHSLEHNER, L.M. 1992. Zur Siedlungsdichte der Fliegenschnäpper (*Muscicapinae s. str.*) auf stadtnahen Wienerwaldflächen Wiens mit Aspekten des Waldsterbens und der Durchforstung. *Egretta* 35: 121–153.

SACKL, P. 1993. A review of the current situation of Dotterel *Eudromias morinellus* in the central Alps of Austria. *Wader Study Group Bull.* 71: 39–40.

SÆTER, S.A. 1994. Dvergsnipe, *Calidris minuta*. In: Gjershaug, J.O., P.G. Thingstad, S. Eldøy and S. Byrkjeland (Eds) *Norsk Fugleatlas*. Norsk Ornitologisk Forening, Klæbu: 180–181 (in Norwegian).

SAGE, B.L. 1971. A study of White-billed Divers in arctic Alaska. *Brit. Birds* 64: 519–527.

SAGE, B.L. and P.A. WHITTINGTON. 1985. The 1980 sample survey of rookeries. *Bird Study* 32: 77–81.

SAGERS, M.J. 1994. First year of oil production from 'Polar Lights'. *Polar Geogr. Geol.* 18: 279–284.

SAGITOV, A.K and S.B. BAKAEV. 1980. *Ekologiya gnezdovaniya massovykh vidov ptits yugo-zapadnogo Uzbekistana*. Tashkent. (*Ecology of the Breeding Birds of the Uzbekistan Region*) (in Russian).

SAINT-JALME, M. and J.C. GUYOMARC'H. 1990. Recent changes in population dynamics of European quail in the western parts of its breeding range. *Transactions of the 19th International Union of Game Biologists Congress, Trondheim, 1989*.

SALOMONSEN, F. 1948. The distribution of birds and the recent climatic change in the North Atlantic area. *Dansk Orn. Foren. Tidsskr.* 42: 85–99.

SALOMONSEN, F. 1950. *The Birds of Greenland*. Munksgaard, Copenhagen.

SALOMONSEN, F. 1972. Zoogeographical and ecological problems in arctic birds. In: Voous, K.H. (Ed) *Proceedings of the XVth International Ornithological Congress, The Hague 1970*. Leiden, the Netherlands: 25–77.

SAMWALD, O. and F. SAMWALD. 1989. Die Blauracke (*Coracias g. garrulus*) in der Steiermark – Bestandsentwicklung, Phänologie, Brutbiologie, Gefährdung. *Egretta* 32: 37–57.

SAN SEGUNDO ONTIN, C. In press. The Black Stork in Spain: a review. In: Brouwer, K., C. King and M. Strazds (Eds) *The Black Stork in the Changing World.*

Proceedings of the 1st International Black Stork Conservation and Ecology Symposium, Jurmala, Latvia. Latvian Ornithological Society, Riga.

SÁNCHEZ, J.A. 1991. Terrera marismeña. In: Urios, V., J.V. Escobar, R. Pardo and J.A. Gómez (Eds) *Atlas de las aves nidificantes de la Comunidad Valenciana.* Conselleria d'Agricultura i Pesca, Generalitat Valenciana, Valencia: 244–245.

SÁNCHEZ, J.J. In press. The recovery of the Black Vulture in Spain. *Proceedings of the International Black Vulture Workshop, Dadia, Greece, 1993.*

SÁNCHEZ-LAFUENTE, A.M., J. MUÑOZ-COBO, F. VALERA and P. REY. 1987. Sobre los nuevos núcleos de Calamón (*Porphyrio porphyrio* L.) en la provincia de Jaén. *IX J. Orn. Españolas, Madrid SEO, Madrid.*

SANDBERG, R. 1992. European Bird Names – in fifteen languages. *Anser* (Lund) suppl. 28: 1–212.

SANTOS Jr., J.R. 1960. Ocorrência da *Hirundo daurica* do norte de Portugal. *Publ. Inst. Zool. Dr. Augusto Nobre* No. 72. (The occurrence of *Hirundo daurica* in the north of Portugal) (in Portuguese).

SANTOS Jr., J.R. 1968. The Ecology of Azure-winged Magpie in the Barca D'Alva region. *Cyanopica* 1: 9–28.

SARASA, C.G., J. BARTOLOME, M. FERNANDEZ-CRUZ and J.C. FARINHA. 1993. Segundo Censos de Ardeidas invernantes en la Peninsula Ibérica y Baleares (1992–1993). *Airo* 4(2): 41–50.

SATUNIN, K.A. 1907. [Contributions to the knowledge of the birds of the Caucasian area.] [*Notes of the Caucasus Department of the Russian Geographical Society*] 26: 1–144 (in Russian).

SAUROLA, P. 1983. Raptors and owls in Finland; status and research. *Proceedings of the Third Nordic Congress of Ornithology, 1981*: 45–52.

SAUROLA, P. 1985. Finnish birds of prey: status and population changes. *Ornis Fennica* 62: 64–72.

SAUROLA, P. 1987. Mate and nest-site fidelity in Ural and Tawny Owls. In: Nero, R. W., R.J. Clark, R.J. Knapton and R.H. Hamre (Eds) *Biology & Conservation of Northern Forest Owls.* General Technical Report RM-142, USDA Forest Service: 81–86.

SAUROLA, P. 1989. Ural Owl. In: Newton, I. (Ed) *Lifetime Reproduction in Birds.* Academic Press, London: 327–345.

SAUROLA, P. 1994. African non-breeding areas of Fennoscandian Ospreys *Pandion haliaetus*: a ring recovery analysis. *Ostrich* 65: 127–136.

SAUROLA, P. 1995. Finnish Ospreys *Pandion haliaetus* 1971–1994. *Vogelwelt* 116: 119–204.

SAVAGE, C. 1952. *The Mandarin Duck.* A&C Black, London.

SAVOLAINEN, J. 1987. [Movements of the Bullfinch (*Pyrrhula pyrrhula*)]. *Lintumies* 22: 190–192 (in Finnish, with English summary).

SCHADILOV, Ju.M. and G.V. KHAKHIN. 1991. Number of the Little Bustard during autumn migration in the Kura-Araks lowland. In: *Materials of the 10th Ornithology Conference of Soviet Union*, Part 2/2. Minsk: 307–308.

SCHÄFFER, N. 1994. Methoden zum Nachweis von Bruten des Wachtelkönigs *Crex crex. Vogelwelt* 115: 69–73.

SCHEPERS, F.J. 1994. Taigaboomkruipers in Zuid-Limburg. *Dutch Birding* 16: 221–225. (Eurasian Treecreepers in S Limburg) (in Dutch, with English summary).

SCHEPERS, F., J. RUTTEN and F. HUSTINGS. 1992. De Grauwe Gors, een verdwijnende broedvogel in Belgisch en Nederlands Limburg? *Limburgse Vogels* 3: 8–16. (Is the Corn Bunting a vanishing breeding bird in the Belgian and Dutch provinces of Limburg?) (in Dutch)

SCHERZINGER, W. 1970. Zum Aktionssystem des Sperlingskauzes (*Glaucidium passerinum* L.). *Zoologica* 41: 1–130.

SCHERZINGER, W. 1974. Zur Ökologie des Sperlingskauzes *Glaucidium passerinum* im National Park Bayerischer Wald. *Anz. orn. Ges. Bayern* 13: 121–156.

SCHERZINGER, W. 1982. Die Spechte im Nationalpark Bayerischer Wald. *Schriftenreihe des Bayerischen Staatsministeriums für Ernährung, Landwirtschaft und Forsten* 9. Passau: 1–119.

SCHERZINGER, W. 1985. Die Vogelwelt der Urwaldgebiete im Inneren Bayerischen Wald. *Schriftenreihe des Bayerischen Staatsministeriums für Ernährung, Landwirtschaft und Forsten* 12: 1–188.

SCHIFFERLI, A., P. GÉROUDET and R. WINKLER (Eds). 1980. *Verbreitungsatlas der Brutvögel der Schweiz.* Schweizerische Vogelwarte, Sempach.

SCHIFFERLI, L. 1989. Die naturnahen Walliser Kulturlandschaften: Biotope von nationaler Bedeutung für Vogelarten. *Bull. Murithienne* 107: 9–19.

SCHLÄPFER, A. 1988. Populationsökologie der Feldlerche *Alauda arvensis* in der intensiv genutzten Agrarlandschaft. *Orn. Beob.* 85: 309–371.

SCHLEMMER, R. 1988. Untersuchungen zur Habitatstruktur des Weißsternigen Blaukehlchens *Luscinia svecica cyanecula*, Wolf 1810, im unteren Isartal. *Verh. orn. Ges. Bayern* 24: 607–650.

SCHMID, H. 1990. Die Bestandsentwicklung des Turmfalken *Falco tinnunculus* in der Schweiz. *Orn. Beob.* 87: 327–349.

SCHMIDT, A. 1983. Ohrenlerche – *Eremophila alpestris.* In: Rutschke, E. (Ed) *Die Vogelwelt Brandenburgs.* Fischer Verlag, Jena: 278–279.

SCHMIDT, D. (Ed). 1994. *Fischadler in Mitteleuropa. Tagungsband. Internationale Fachtagung 25–27 Februar 1994, Singen.* Institut für Landschaftsökologie und Naturschutz, Singen.

SCHMIDT, E. 1977. Auffallende Zunahme des Silberreihers (*Casmerodius albus*) in Ungarn im Jahre 1976. *Egretta* 20: 68–70.

SCHMIDT, G.A.J. 1988. Zum Vorkommen von *Calidris minuta* auf der Varanger-Halbinsel, Nord-Norwegen. Ein Beitrag der Vogelkundlichen Arbeitsgruppe Schleswig-Holstein zur Biologie des Zwergstrandläufers. *Vogelkundliches Tagebuch Schleswig-Holstein* 16: 267–280.

SCHMITZ, L. 1987. Les Sizerins flammés (*Carduelis flammea cabaret*) nicheurs de la région des Hautes-Fagnes, résultats des recensements de 1985 et 1986. *Aves* 24: 1–18.

SCHMITZ, L. 1993. Distribution et habitat du Pic mar (*Dendrocopos medius*) en Belgique. *Aves* 30: 145–166.

SCHNEBEL, G. 1972. Die Ökologie der Baumläufer (*Certhia brachydactyla*) und (*Certhia familiaris*) in Ostniedersachsen. *Vogelwelt* 93(6): 201–205.

SCHNEIDER-JACOBY, M. and V.F. VASIC. 1989. The Red-crested Pochard breeding and wintering in Yugoslavia. *Wildfowl* 40: 39–44.

SCHÖNFELD, M. 1978. *Der Weidenlaubsänger*. Neue Brehm-Bücherei 511, Ziemsen, Wittenberg.

SCHÖNFELD, M. 1983. Beiträge zur Ökologie und zum intraspezifischen Verhalten der Baumläufer *Certhia familiaris* und *C. brachydactyla* in Eichen-Hainbuchen-Lindenwäldern unter dem Aspekt der erholten Siedlungsdichte durch eingebrachte Nisthöhlen. *Hercynia N.F.* 20(3): 290–311.

SCHÖNFELD, M. 1994. *Die Beutelmeise*. Neue Brehm-Bücherei 559, Westarp Wissenschaften, Magdeburg.

SCHÖNN, M. 1994a. Zur Brutbiologie des Raubwürgers (*Lanius e. excubitor*): Gelege-, Brut-Grösse und Bruterfolg im Gebiet der südwestlichen Schwäbischen Alb im Vergleich mit anderen Populationen. *Ökol. Vögel* 16: 173–218.

SCHÖNN, M. 1994b. Bestandsdichte und -entwicklung, Geschlechts-, Altersverteilung und Gruppen-Bildung in einer Raubwürger-Population (*Lanius e. excubitor*) im Gebiet der südwestlichen Schwäbischen Alb. *Ökol. Vögel* 16: 219–252.

SCHÖNN, S. 1980. *Der Sperlingskauz*. Neue Brehm-Bücherei 513, Ziemsen, Wittenberg.

SCHÖNN, S., W. SCHERZINGER, K-M. EXO and I. ROTRAUT. 1991. *Der Steinkauz*. Neue Brehm-Bücherei 606, Ziemsen, Wittenberg.

SCHOUTEN, C. 1985. Vijf jaar tellingen van Zwarte Sterns *Chlidonias niger* in het IJsselmeergebied. *Limosa* 58: 124. (Five years of counting Black Terns *Chlidonias niger* in the IJsselmeer area) (in Dutch, with English summary).

SCHUBERT, W. 1979. Dornbuschspötter *Hippolais languida* als Brutvogel in Mittelanatolien (Türkei). *Bonn. Zool. Beitr.* 30: 158–159.

SCHULZ, H. 1985. *Grundlagenforschung zur Biologie der Zwergtrappe Tetrax tetrax*. Staatliches Naturhistorisches Museum, Braunschweig.

SCHULZE-HAGEN, K., H. FLINKS and A. DYRCZ. 1989. Brutzeitliche Beutewahl beim Seggenrohrsänger *Acrocephalus paludicola*. *J. Ornithol.* 130: 251–255.

SCHULZE-HAGEN, K., B. LEISLER, T.R. BIRKHEAD and A. DYRCZ. 1995. Prolonged copulation, sperm reserves and sperm competition in the Aquatic Warbler *Acrocephalus paludicola*. *Ibis* 137: 85–91.

SCHUYTER, T.de and G. de SCHUTTER. 1989. Le retour de la Sterne naine (*Sterna albifrons*) comme nicheuse en Belgique. *Aves* 26, No. spécial: 113–115.

SCHÜZ, E. 1959. *Die Vogelwelt des südkaspischen Tieflandes*. E. Scheizer-bart'sche Verlagsbuchhandlung, Stuttgart.

SCHWABL, H. 1983. Ausprägung und Bedeutung des Teilzugverhaltens einer südwestdeutschen Population der Amsel *Turdus merula*. *J. Ornithol.* 124: 101–116.

SCHWERDTFEGER, O. 1984. Verhalten und Populationsdynamik des Rauhfusskauzes (*Aegolius funereus*). *Vogelwarte* 32: 183–200.

SCOTT, S.L. (Ed). 1986. *The Birds of North America*, 2nd edn. National Geographic, Washington D.C.

SEEBOHM, H. and J.A. HARVIE-BROWN. 1876. Notes on the birds of the lower Petschora. *Ibis* 6: 222–230.

SELL, H. and P. OODERSKÆR. 1990. Tornsgarens *Sylvia communis* ynglebiologi i danske læhegn. *Dansk Orn. Foren. Tidsskr.* 84: 21–29. (The breeding biology of the Whitethroat *Sylvia communis* in Danish hedges) (in Danish, with English summary).

SEMYONOV-TYAN-SHANSKY, O.I. and A.S. GUYLYAZOV. 1991. [*Birds of Lapland*.] Nauka, Moscow (in Russian).

SENAR, J.C. and D. SOL. 1991. (Census of Feral pigeons *Columba livia var.* from the city of Barcelona: use of stratified sampling with a correction factor.) *Butll. Grup Català d'Anellam.* 8: 19–24 (in Catalonian, with English summary).

SENAR, J.C., A. BORRAS, T. CABRERA and J. CABRERA. 1993. Testing for the relationship between coniferous crop stability and common crossbill residence. *J. Field Ornithol.* 64: 464–469.

ŠERE, D. 1989. Skalna lastovka *Ptyonoprogne rupestris* gnezdi v Sloveniji. *Acrocephalus* 10: 6–13 (in Slovenian).

SEREBRYAKOV, V.V. and V.N. GRISHCHENKO. 1990. The number of Rooks *Corvus frugilegus* in the Ukraine in 1984. *Bird Census News* 3(1): 15–19.

SERMET, E. 1980a. Schwarzmilan *Milvus migrans*. In: Schifferli, A., P. Géroudet and R. Winkler (Eds) *Verbreitungsatlas der Brutvögel der Schweiz*. Schweizerische Vogelwarte, Sempach: 88–89.

SERMET, E. 1980b. Gelbspötter *Hippolais icterina*. In: Schifferli, A., P. Géroudet and R. Winkler (Eds) Verbreitungsatlas der Brutvögel der Schweiz. Schweizerische Vogelwarte, Sempach: 296–297.

SHARLEMAN, M.V. 1938. [*The Birds of Ukraine*.] Kiev (in Russian).

SHARROCK, J.T.R. 1976. *The Atlas of Breeding Birds in Britain and Ireland*. Poyser, Berkhamsted.

SHAW, G. 1990. Timing and fidelity of breeding for Siskins *Carduelis spinus* in Scottish conifer plantations. *Bird Study* 37: 30–35.

SHAWYER, C.R. 1987. *The Barn Owl in the British Isles: its past, present and future*. The Hawk Trust, London.

SHAWYER, C.R. 1994. *The Barn Owl*. Hamlyn, London.

SHIRIHAI, H. 1996. *The Birds of Israel*. Academic Press, London: 503–505, 526–527.

SHIRIHAI, H. and D.A. CHRISTIE. 1992. Raptor migration at Eilat. *Brit. Birds* 85: 141–186.

SHISHKIN, V.S. 1976. [Annual and seasonal fluctuations of the population density of larks in NW Kazakhstan.] *Zool. J. (USSR)* 55: 402–407 (in Russian).

SHRUBB, M. 1990. Effects of agricultural change on nesting Lapwings *Vanellus vanellus* in England and Wales. *Bird Study* 37: 115–127.

SHRUBB, M. and P.C. LACK. 1991. The numbers and distribution of Lapwings *V. vanellus* nesting in England and Wales in 1987. *Bird Study* 38: 20–37.

SHRUBB, M. and P.C. LACK. 1993. The Lapwing. In: Gibbons, D.W., J.B. Reid and R.A. Chapman (Eds) *The New Atlas of Breeding Birds in Britain and Ireland: 1988–1991*. Poyser, London.

SHUBIN, A.O. [Number and distribution of the Merlin (*Falco columbarius*) in some regions of the North-European part of the USSR.] *Ornitologiya* 19: 75–80 (in Russian, with English summary).

SHURAKOV, A.I., Ju.N. KAMENSKY and M. Ph. PANTALEEV. 1989. [Some tendencies in the changing of avifauna in Kama Ural (Middle Ural).] In: Davygora,

A.V. (Ed) *The Distribution of the Birds and Avifauna of the Urals*. Sverdlovsk: 102–104 (in Russian).

SHUTOV, S.V. 1989. [Avifauna of the western foothills of the Subpolar Urals and the spring weather influences on its year-to-year composition.] In: Davygora, A.V. (Ed) *The Distribution of the Birds and Avifauna of the Urals*. Sverdlovsk: 102–104 (in Russian).

SIBLET, J-P. 1994. Nidification de la Sterne naine (*Sterna albifrons*) en Bassée: conséquence de l'aménagement réussi d'un site artificiel. *Assoc. Natur. Vallée du Loing* 70: 15–19.

SIEFKE, A. 1982. Größe und Struktur eines Brutbestandes des Sandregenpfeifers, *Charadrius hiaticula*, in ihrer Beziehung zu Dismigration und lokalen Umwelteinflüssen. *Beitr. Vogelk.* 28: 89–106.

SIEFKE, A. 1994. Wanderungen ostdeutscher Raben- und Nebelkrähen *Corvus corone* nach Beringungsergebnissen. *Vogelwelt* 115: 83–89.

SIERRO A. 1991. Écologie de l'Engoulevent, *Caprimulgus europaeus*, en Valais (Alpes suisses): biotopes, répartition spatiale et protection. *Nos Oiseaux* 41: 209–235.

SIGWALT, P. 1994. Courlis cendré *Numenius arquata*. In: Yeatman-Berthelot, D. and G. Jarry (Eds) *Nouvel Atlas des Oiseaux Nicheurs de France 1985–1989*. Société Ornithologique de France, Paris: 302–305.

SIIVONEN, L. 1939. Zur Ökologie und Verbreitung der Singdrossel (*Turdus ericetorum philomelos* Brehm). *Ann. Zool. Soc. Zool.-Bot. Fennicae Vanamo* 7: 1–289.

SIKHARULIDZE, Z.D. 1974. [On the biology of the Caucasian Black Grouse.] *Ornitologiya* 11: 410–415 (in Russian).

SIKHARULIDZE, Z.D. 1977. [Ecology and results of a census of gallinaceous birds in the Saguramskiy Nature Reserve and Pshav-Khevsureti.] *Tez. Dokl. VII Vsesoyuz. orn. Kouf.* Kiev. 1: 103 (in Russian).

SIMEONOV, S.D. 1965. Über die Verbreitung der Rötelschwalbe *Hirundo daurica rufula* (Temminck) in Bulgarien. *Fragmenta Balcanica* V(16): 115–120.

SIMEONOV, S.D. 1970. Über die Verbreitung mediterraner Vogelarten in Bulgarien. *Vogelwelt* 91: 59–67.

SIMEONOV, S.D. 1984 [On the diets and numbers of Hawks (Genus *Accipiter*) in Bulgaria.] *Ekologiya, Sofiya* 13: 83–95 (in Bulgarian, with English summary).

SIMEONOV, S.D. and V. DELOV. 1989. [The birds of Konjavska planina.] *Acta Zool. Bulg.* 38: 65–80 (in Bulgarian).

SIMEONOV, S.D. and T. MICHEV. 1980. [Studies on the Distribution and Numbers of Red-rumped Swallow *Hirundo daurica rufula* (Temminck) in Bulgaria.] *Ecology, Sofia* 7: 84–92 (in Bulgarian, with English summary).

SIMEONOV, S.D. and T. MICHEV. 1991. *The Birds of the Balkan Peninsula*. P. Beron, Sofia: 1–250.

SIMEONOV, S.D., M.T. MITCHEV and D.N. NANKINOV. 1990. *Fauna Bulgarica. 20, Aves*. Sofia: 129–131 (in Bulgarian).

SIMMS, E. 1979. *The Public Life of the Street Pigeon*. Hutchinson, London.

SIMMS, E. 1985. *British Warblers*. Collins, London: 125–126.

SIMMS, E. 1992. *British Larks, Pipits and Wagtails*. The New Naturalist, HarperCollins, London.

SIOKHIN, V.D., I.I. CHERNICHKO, T.B. ARDAMATSKAYA, V.I. LYSENKO, S.Yu. KOSTIN, A.B. GRINCHENKO, L.I. KORZYYUKOV, M.E. ZHMUD, V.P. STOYLOVSKIY, G.N. MOLODAN, I.V. SHCHLEGOLEV, V.S. GREKOV, L.D. STEPANKOVSKAYA, M.V. MALIKOVA, R.M. SOLOMKO, Z.N. NEKHOROSHIKH, L.A. SMOGORZHEVSKAYA, V.V. KORNYUSHIN and N.I. ISKOVA. 1988. [*Colonial Waterbirds of Southern Ukraine – Charadriiformes*.] Naukova Dumka, Kiev.

SIORAT, F. 1992. *Évolution comparée des effectifs de Fou de Bassan, Macareux moine et Puffin des Anglais sur l'archipel des Sept-Iles (Bretagne)*. Rapport: Ligue pour la Protection des Oiseaux à Ministère de l'Environnement, Sretie.

SITTERS, H.P. 1986. Woodlarks in Britain, 1968–83. *Brit. Birds* 79: 105–116.

SITTERS, H.P. 1988. *Tetrad Atlas of the Breeding Birds of Devon*. Devon Bird Watching and Preservation Society, Yelverton.

SITTERS, H. and A. EVANS. 1993. Cirl Bunting *Emberiza cirlus*. In: Gibbons, D.W., J.B. Reid and R.A. Chapman (Eds) *The New Atlas of Breeding Birds in Britain and Ireland: 1988–1991*. Poyser, London: 434–435.

SKINNER, J. 1987. Complément d'information sur les Tourterelles des bois dans la zone d'inondation du Niger au Mali. *Malimbus* 9: 133–134.

SKORNIK, I. 1992. Prispevek k poznavanju ekologije rumenonogega galeba (*Larus cachinnans* Pall.) (AVES, Laridae). *Annales* 2: 53–66 (in Slovenian).

SKOV, H., J. DURINCK, M.F. LEOPOLD and M.L. TASKER. 1995. *Important Bird Areas in the North Sea, including the Channel and the Kattegat*. BirdLife International, Cambridge.

SLUYS, R. 1982. Bearded Tits *Panurus biarmicus* in The Netherlands and England: comments on the hybridization theory. *J. Ornithol.* 123: 175–182.

SMIT, C.J. and T. PIERSMA. 1989. Numbers, midwinter distribution and migration of wader populations using the East Atlantic flyway. In: Boyd, H. and J-Y. Pirot (Eds) *Flyways and Reserve Networks for Waterbirds*. Special Publication No. 9, International Waterfowl and Wetlands Research Bureau, Slimbridge: 24–63.

SMITH, K. 1993. Great Spotted Woodpecker. In: Gibbons, D.W., J.B. Reid and R.A. Chapman (Eds) *The New Atlas of Breeding Birds in Britain and Ireland: 1988–1991*. Poyser, London: 266–267.

SMITH, K.W. and G.A. TYLER. 1993. Trends in the numbers of breeding Bitterns in the U.K. In: Andrews, J. and S.P. Carter (Eds) *Britain's Birds in 1990–91*. BTO/JNCC, Thetford/Peterborough: 139–140.

SMITH, R.D. and M. MARQUISS. 1995. Production and costs of nesting attempts in Snow Buntings *Plectrophenax nivalis*: why do they attempt second broods? *Ibis* 137: 469–476.

SMOGORGEVSKIY, L.O. 1979. *Tachybaptus ruficollis. Fauna of Ukraine. Birds*, Vol. 5. Naukova Dumka, Kiev: 47–50.

SNOW, B.K. and D.W. SNOW. 1984. Long-term defence of fruit by Mistle Thrushes *Turdus viscivorus*. *Ibis* 126: 39–49.

SNOW, D.W. 1978. Relationships between the European and African avifaunas. *Bird Study* 25: 134–148.

SNOW, D.W. and B. SNOW. 1988. *Birds and Berries*. T & AD Poyser, Calton.

SOLER, M. 1990. Relationships between the Great Spotted Cuckoo *Clamator glandarius* and its corvid hosts in a recently colonized area. *Ornis Scand.* 21: 212–223.

SOLER, M., J. ZUÑIGA and I. CAMACHO. 1983. Alimentación y reproducción de algunas aves de la Hoya de Guadix (Sur de España). *Trab. Monogr. Dep. Zool. Univ. Granada (N.S.)* 6: 27–100.

SOLER, M., J.J. SOLER, A.P. MØLLER, J. MORENO and M. LINDÉN. 1996. The functional significance of sexual display: stone carrying in the black wheatear. *Animal Behav.* 51: 247–254.

SOLONEN, T. 1979. Population dynamics of the Garden Warbler *Sylvia borin* in southern Finland. *Ornis Fennica* 56: 3–12.

SOLONEN, T. 1986. [Breeding of the Great Grey Owl *Strix nebulosa* in Finland.] *Lintumies* 21: 11–18 (in Finnish, with English summary).

SOLONEN, T., J. TIAINEN, E. KORPIMÄKI and P. SAUROLA. 1991. Dynamics of Finnish Starling *Sturnus vulgaris* populations in recent decades. *Ornis Fennica* 68: 158–169.

SONNABEND, H. and W. POLTZ. 1978. 30-jährige Bestandsaufnahme von Raubwürger *Lanius excubitor* und Rotkopfwürger *Lanius senator* am nordwestlichen Bodensee. *Anz. orn. Ges. Bayern* 17: 133–139.

SØRENSEN, U.G. 1995. Truede og sjældne danske ynglefugle 1976–1991. Status i relation til den generelle landskabsudvikling. *Dansk Orn. Foren. Tidsskr.* 89: 1–48. (Rare and endangered breeding birds in Denmark, 1976–1991) (in Danish, with English summary).

SOUSA, D. de, P. PILARD, Y. ROY and F. PORTIER. 1994. Le Faucon kobez *Falco vespertinus* nicheur en France en 1993. *Ornithos* 1: 46–48.

SOUTHERN, H.N. 1970. The natural control of a population of Tawny Owls (*Strix aluco*). *J. Zool., London* 162: 197–285.

SOVON. 1987. *Atlas van de Nederlandse Vogels*. SOVON, Arnhem. (*Atlas of Dutch Birds*) (in Dutch, with English summary).

SPAANS, B., M. STOCK, A. St.JOSEPH, H-H. BERGMANN and B.S. EBBINGE. 1993. Breeding biology of Dark-bellied Brent Geese *Branta b. bernicla* in Taimyr in 1990 in the absence of arctic foxes and under favourable weather conditions. *Polar Res.* 12: 117–130.

SPANGENBERG, E.P. and V.V. LEONOVICH. 1958. [New data on the geographical distribution and biology of birds on the eastern coast of the White Sea.] In: Shcherbakov, D.I. (Ed) *The Problems of the North*, Vol. 2. USSR Academy of Sciences, Moscow (in Russian).

SPANGENBERG, E.P. and V.V. LEONOVICH. 1960. [Birds of north-eastern coast of the White Sea.] In: Novikov, G.A. (Ed) [*Annals of Kandalaksha State Reserve*.] Issue 2. Murmansk Book Publ.: 213–336 (in Russian).

SPANGENBERG, E.P. and A.M. SUDILOVSKAYA. 1954. [Pine Bunting.] In: [*Birds of the Soviet Union*, Vol. 5, *Passerines*.] Soviet Science, Moscow: 390–395 (in Russian).

SPANÓ, S. 1975. Considerazioni biogeografiche sul genere *Alectoris* Kaup, 1829 (Galliformes, Phasianidae). *Ann. Mus. Civ. Storia Nat. Genova* 80: 286–293.

SPANÓ, S., G. TRAVERSO and M. SARA. 1986. Distribuzione attuale di *Alectoris graeca* e *A. barbara* in Italia. In: Fasola, M. (Ed) *Atti III Conv. Ital. Orn. 1985*: 58–61.

SPENCER, R. and RBBP. 1993. Rare breeding birds in the United Kingdom in 1990. *Brit. Birds* 86: 62–90.

SPIRIDINOV, G. 1985. [The southern White-backed Woodpecker *Dendrocopos leucotos lilfordi*.] In: *Red Data Book of the People's Republic of Bulgaria*. Bulgarian Academy of Sciences, Sofia: 126–127 (in Bulgarian).

SPITZ, F. 1994. Bruant zizi *Emberiza cirlus*. In: Yeatman-Berthelot, D. and G. Jarry (Eds) *Nouvel Atlas des Oiseaux Nicheurs de France 1985–1989*. Société Ornithologique de France, Paris: 712–713.

SPITZNAGEL, A. 1990. The influence of forest management on woodpecker density and habitat use in floodplain forests of the Upper Rhine Valley. In: Carlson, A. and G. Aulén (Eds) *Conservation and Management of Woodpecker Populations*. Report No. 17, Swedish University of Agricultural Sciences, Department of Wildlife Ecology, Uppsala: 117–145.

SPITZNAGEL, A. 1993. Warum sind Spechte schwierig zu erfassende Arten? *Beih. Veröff. Naturschutz Landschaftspfl. Bad.-Württ.* 67: 59–70.

STAGG, A. 1985. *The Birds of South-West Saudi Arabia*. Privately published, Riyadh.

STANEVIČIUS, V. 1992. [*Abundance, Structure and Spatial Distribution of Bird Communities in the Lakes of South Lithuania*]. Doctoral Thesis, Moscow University (in Russian).

STARK, H. and F. LIECHTI. 1993. Do Levant Sparrowhawks *Accipiter brevipes* also migrate at night? *Ibis* 135: 233–236.

ŠŤASTNÝ, K., A. RANDÍK and K. HUDEC. 1987. *Atlas Hnízdního Rozšíření Ptáků V ČSSR 1973–77*. Academia Praha: 50–51. (*The Atlas of Breeding Birds in Czechoslovakia 1973–1977*) (in Czech).

ŠŤASTNÝ, K., V. BEJČEK, and K. HUDEC. 1995. *Atlas hnízdního roz šíoení ptákù v Èeské republice 1985–1989*. Praha. (*Atlas of the Breeding Birds in the Czech Republic 1985–89*) (in Czech).

STEFANSSON, O. 1986. Projekt Lappuggla [Great Grey Owl Project]. *Vår Fågelvärld* 45: 301–302 (in Swedish).

STEGMANN, B. 1938. Das Problem der atlantischen Landverbindung in ornithogeographischer Beleuchtung. In: *Proceedings of the Eighth International Ornithological Congress (1934), Oxford*: 476–500.

STEGMANN, B. 1958. Herkunft der eurasiatischen Steppenvögel. *Bonn. Zool. Beitr.* 9: 208–230.

STEINFATT, O. 1939. Weitere Beobachtungen über die Vögel der Rominter Heirle und Ihrer Randgebiete. *Schr. Physikal-Oekon. Gos Königsberg (Pr)* 71: 335–375.

STENBERG, I. 1990. Preliminary results of a study on woodpeckers in Møre and Romsdal county, Western Norway. In: Carlson, A. and G. Aulén (Eds) *Conservation and Management of Woodpecker Populations*. Report No. 17, Department of Wildlife Ecology, Swedish University of Agricultural Sciences, Uppsala: 67–79.

STENBERG, I. and O. HOGSTAD. 1992. Habitat use and density of breeding woodpeckers in the 1990s in Møre og Romsdal county, western Norway. *Fauna norv. Ser. C, Cinclus* 15: 49–61.

STEPANYAN, L.S. 1978. [*Composition and Distribution of the Bird Fauna of the USSR – Passeriformes.*] Nauka, Moscow (in Russian).

STEPANYAN, L.S. 1990. [*Catalogue of Ornithological Fauna of the USSR.*] Nauka, Moscow (in Russian).

STEPHAN, B. 1986. Die Evolutionstheorie und der taxonomische Status des Italiensperlings. *Mitt. Zool. Mus. Berl.* 62 (Suppl.): *Ann.Ornithol.* 10: 25–68.

STERBETZ, I. 1982. Migration of *Anser erythropus* and *Branta ruficollis* in Hungary 1971–1980. *Aquila* 89: 107–114.

STJERNBERG, T. 1979. Breeding biology and population dynamics of the Scarlet Rosefinch *Carpodacus erythrinus. Acta Zool. Fennica* 157: 1–88.

STJERNBERG, T. 1985. Recent expansion of the Scarlet Rosefinch (*Carpodacus erythrinus*) in Europe. In: *Proceedings of the XVIII International Ornithological Congress, Moscow, 16–25 August 1982*, Vol. II: 743–753.

STOEPEL, B. 1984. Folgen der Witterungskatastrophe 1983 in Oberschwaben auf Bestand und Alterszusammensetzung bei der Mehlschwalbe (*Delichon urbica*). *Ökol. Vögel* 6: 159–167.

STOLT, B-O. 1993. Notes on reproduction in a declining population of the Ortolan Bunting *Emberiza hortulana. J. Ornithol.* 134: 59–68.

STORCH, I. 1993. Habitat selection of Capercaillie in summer and autumn: Is bilberry important? *Oecologia* 95: 257–265.

STØRKERSEN, Ø.R. 1994. Svartstrupe *Saxicola torquata.* In: Gjershaug, J.O., P.G. Thingstad, S. Eldøy and S. Byrkjeland (Eds) *Norsk Fugleatlas.* Norsk Ornitologisk Forening, Klæbu: 360–361.

STOWE, T.J. 1993. Corncrake *Crex crex.* In: Gibbons, D.W., J.B. Reid and R.A. Chapman (Eds) *The New Atlas of Breeding Birds in Britain and Ireland: 1988–1991.* Poyser, London: 150–151.

STOWE, T.J. and D. BECKER. 1992. Status and conservation of Corncrakes *Crex crex* outside the breeding grounds. *Tauraco* 2: 1–23.

STRANN, K-B. and W. VADER. 1992. The nominate Lesser Black-backed Gull *Larus fuscus fuscus*, a gull with a tern-like feeding biology, and its recent decline in northern Norway. *Ardea* 80 : 133–142.

STRAUTMAN, F.I. 1957. *Ptitsy Sovietski Karpat. Izd. Acad.* Nauk USSR, Kiev (in Russian).

STRAUTMAN, F.I. 1963. [*Birds of the Western Regions of Ukraine.*] Lviv University, Lviv (in Russian).

STRESEMANN, E. 1920. Die Herkunft der Hochgebirgsvögel Europas. *Jaarbericht Club Ned. Vogelkundigen* 10: 71–91.

STRØM, H., I.J. ØIEN, J. OPHEIM, E.A. KUZNETSOV and G.V. KHAIKHIN. 1994. *Seabird Censuses on Novaya Zemlya 1994.* Working Report No. 2/1994, Norsk Ornitologisk Forening Rapportserie.

STROUD, D.A., T.M. REED, M.W. PIENKOWSKI and R.A. LINDSAY. 1987. *Birds, Bogs and Forestry.* Nature Conservancy Council, Peterborough.

STUBBE, M. 1982. Brutdichte und Altersstruktur einer Rotmilan-Population – *Milvus milvus* (L., 1758) – im nördlichen Harzvorland der DDR im Vergleich zum Mäusebussard – *Buteo buteo* (L., 1758). *Arch. Naturschutz Landschaftsforschung* 22: 205–214.

STUBBE, M., H. ZÖRNER, H. MATTHES and W. BÖHM. 1991. Reproduktionsrate und gegenwärtiges Nahrungsspektrum einiger Greifvogelarten im nördlichen Harzvorland. *Populationsökologie Greifvogel- und Eulenarten* 2: 39–60.

STUEFLOTTEN, S. 1994. Fjellerke *Eremophila alpestris.* In: Gjershaug, J.O., P.G. Thingstad, S. Eldøy and S. Byrkjeland (Eds) *Norsk Fugleatlas.* Norsk Ornitologisk Forening, Klæbu: 318–319 (in Norwegian).

SUÁREZ, F. 1987. *Historia natural de la Collalba Rubia (Oenanthe hispanica, L.) durante la época de reproducción.* PhD Thesis, Universidad Complutense de Madrid.

SUÁREZ, F., M. YANES, J. HERRANZ and J. MANRIQUE. 1993. Nature reserves and the conservation of iberian shrubsteppe passerines: The paradox of nest predation. *Biol. Conservation* 63: 77–81.

SUC, J.P. 1978. Analyse pollinique de dépôts plio-pléistocènes du sud du massif basaltique de l'Escandorgue. *Pollen et Spores* 20: 497–512.

SÜDBECK, P. 1981. Zunahme des Bestandes der Heidelerche (*Lullula arborea*) bei Cloppenburg. *J. Orn. Arb.-Gem. Oldenburg* 4: 53–55.

SULLIVAN, M.A. 1978. Common Gulls successfully nesting on a roof in Aberdeen. *Brit. Birds* 81: 324–325.

SULTANA, J. and C. GAUCI. 1981–83. Some notes on breeding species for 1982. *Il Merill* 22: 21.

SULTANA, J. and C. GAUCI. 1990–91. The year of the first confirmed breeding record of the Sardinian warbler *Sylvia melanocephala* in the Maltese Islands. *Il Merill* 27: 26.

SUMMERS, R.W. and M. ROGERS. 1991. Seasonal and long-term changes in the numbers of Purple Sandpipers *Calidris maritima* at Portland Bill, Dorset. *Ringing and Migration* 12: 72–74.

SUMMERS, R.W., L.G. UNDERHILL, M. WALTNER and D.A. WHITELAW. 1987a. Population, biometrics and movements of the Sanderling *Calidris alba* in southern Africa. *Ostrich* 58: 24–39.

SUMMERS, R.W., C.J. CORSE and D.P. WHITFIELD. 1987b. *Purple Sandpiper Studies in North Iceland 1986.* Tay, Orkney and Grampian Ringing Groups, Kirkwall, Orkney.

SUMMERS, R.W., K-B. STRANN, R. RAE and J. HEGGÅS. 1990. Wintering Purple Sandpipers *Calidris maritima* in Troms county, northern Norway. *Ornis Scand.* 21: 248–254.

SUMMERS, R.W., L.G. UNDERHILL, E.E. SYROECHKOVSKI Jr., H.G. LAPPO, R.P. PRŶS-JONES and V. KARPOV. 1994. The breeding biology of Dark-bellied Brent *Branta b. bernicla* and King Eiders *Somateria spectabilis* on the northeastern Taimyr Peninsula, especially in relation to Snowy Owl *Nyctea scandiaca* nests. *Wildfowl* 45: 110–118.

SUMMERS-SMITH, J.D. 1988. *The Sparrows.* Poyser, Calton.

SUMMERS-SMITH, J.D. 1989. A history of the status of the Tree Sparrow *Passer montanus* in the British Isles. *Bird Study* 38: 23–31.

SUMYA, D. and N.G. SKRYABIN. 1989. [*The birds of Hubsugul Lake and adjacent territories, the Mongolian People's Republic.*] Irkutsk (in Russian).

SUSIC, G. 1994. Wing-marking of Eurasian Griffons *Gyps fulvus* in Croatia – Evaluation and initial results. In:

Meyburg, B-U. and R.D. Chancellor (Eds) *Raptor Conservation Today*. WWGBPO, Berlin: 373–380.

SUTER, W. 1995. Are Cormorants *Phalacrocorax carbo* wintering in Switzerland approaching carrying capacity? An analysis of increase patterns and habitat choice. *Ardea* 83: 255–266.

SUTER, W. and M.R. van EERDEN. 1992. Simultaneous mass starvation of wintering diving ducks in Switzerland and The Netherlands: a wrong decision in the right strategy? *Ardea* 80: 229–242.

SUTER, W. and L. SCHIFFERLI. 1988. Überwinternde Wasservögel in der Schweiz und ihren Grenzgebieten: Bestandsentwicklungen 1967–1987 im internationalen Vergleich. *Orn. Beob.* 85: 261–298.

SUTHERLAND, W.J. and G. ALLPORT. 1991. The distribution and ecology of naturalized Egyptian Geese *Alopochen aegyptiacus* in Britain. *Bird Study* 38: 128–134.

SUTTON, G.M. 1962. Life History. In: Bannerman, D.A. *The Birds of the British Isles*. Vol. 11. Oliver and Boyd, Edinburgh and London: 202–219.

SVAZAS, S., W. MEISSNER and H.W. NEHLS 1994. Wintering populations of Goosander (*Mergus merganser*) and Smew (*Mergellus albellus*) at the south eastern Baltic coast. *Acta Ornithol. Lituanica* 9–10: 56–69.

SVENSSON, S. 1981. Populationsfluktuationer hos mesar *Parus*, nötväcka *Sitta europaea* och trädkrypare *Certhia familiaris* i södra Sverige. *Proc. 2nd Nordic Congr. Ornithol. 1979*: 9–18. (Population fluctuations in tits *Parus*, Nuthatch *Sitta europaea*, and Treecreeper *Certhia familiaris* in South Sweden) (in Swedish, with English summary).

SVENSSON, S. 1990a. An alarming decline of the Shore Lark *Eremophila alpestris* in Sweden. *Proc. 6th Nordic Congr. Ornithol., 1987*: 5–11.

SVENSSON, S. 1990b. Recent population trends of common birds and modern forestry in Sweden. *Proc. 7th Nordic Congr. Ornithol.*: 43–52.

SVENSSON, S.E. and O. BERGLUND. 1995. Monitoring of small and endangered populations, with special regard to the Shore Lark *Eremophila alpestris*. In: Hagemeijer E.J.M. and T.J. Verstrael (Eds) *Bird Numbers 1992. Distribution, monitoring and ecological aspects.* Statistics Netherlands, Voorburg/Heerlen and SOVON, Beek-Ubbergen: 153–162.

SVENSSON, S., O. OLSSON and M. SVENSSON. 1992. *Förändringar i fågelfaunan. Beståndsprognoser och forskningsbehov för vissa arter – en litteraturstudie.* Naturvårdsverket, Solna (in Swedish).

SVERIGES ORNITOLOGISKA FÖRENING. 1990. *Sveriges Fåglar. Vår Fågelvärld* Suppl. 14 SOF, Stockholm (in Swedish).

SWANBERG, P.O. 1956. Territory in the Thick-billed Nutcracker. *Ibis* 98: 412–419.

SWANBERG, P.O. 1976. Ortolansparven *Emberiza hortulana* i Valle, Västergötland, 1940, 1961 och 1975. *Vår Fågelvärld* 35: 235–236 (in Swedish).

SWENNEN, C. 1983. Reproductive output of Eiders *Somateria m. mollissima* on the southern border of its breeding range. *Ardea* 71: 245–254.

SWENNEN, C. 1989. Gull predation upon Eider *Somateria mollissima* ducklings: destruction or elimination of the unfit? *Ardea* 77: 21–45.

SWENNEN, C. 1990. Dispersal and migratory movements of Eiders *Somateria mollissima* breeding in The Netherlands. *Ornis Scand.* 21: 17–27.

SWENNEN, C. and Th. MULDER. 1995. Ruiende Bergeenden *Tadorna tadorna* in de Nederlandse Waddenzee. *Limosa* 68: 15–20. (Moulting Shelducks *Tadorna tadorna* in the Dutch Wadden Sea) (in Dutch, with English summary).

SWENSON, J.E. 1993. The importance of alder to Hazel Grouse in Fennoscandian boreal forest: Evidence from four levels of scale. *Ecography* 16: 37–46.

SYKES, J.M., V.P.W. LOWE and D.R. BRIGGS. 1989. Some effects of afforestation on the flora and fauna of an upland sheepwalk during 12 years after planting. *J. appl. Ecol.* 26: 299–320.

SYROECHKOVSKIY, Y.V., K.Ye. LITVIN and B.S. EBBINGE. 1991. Breeding success of geese and swans on Vaygach Island (USSR) during 1986–1988; interplay of weather and Arctic Fox predation. *Ardea* 79: 373–382.

SZABÓ, L.V. 1976. [Das Nisten des Zwergsumpfhuhnes (*Porzana pusilla*) in der Puszta von Hortobágy.] *Aquila* 82: 165–175 (in Hungarian, with German summary).

SZÉKELY, T. 1992. Reproduction of Kentish Plover *Charadrius alexandrinus* in grasslands and fish-ponds: the habitat mal-assessment hypothesis. *Aquila* 99: 59–68.

SZÉLL, A. 1993. [Breeding habitat selection of the Collared Pratincole (*Glareola pratincola*) at agricultural sites.] *Partimadár* 1993/1 (in Hungarian, with English summary).

SZÉP, T. 1995. Relationship between West African rainfall and the survival of the Central European adult Sand Martin (*Riparia riparia*) population. *Ibis* 137: 162–168.

SZIJJ, J. 1975. Probleme des Anatidenzuges, dargestellt an der Verlagerung des europäischen Kolbenentenbestandes. *Ardeola* 21: 153–171.

TAILLANDIER, J. 1993. Reproduction de la Cisticole des joncs *Cisticola juncidis* dans les prairies d'un marais salant (Guérande, Loire-Atlantique). *Alauda* 61: 39–51.

TALPOSH, V.S. 1977. O biologii razmozheniya evropeiskoi alpiiskoi zavirushki v SSSR. *Nauchnye doklady vysshei shkoly, biologicheskie nauky – zoologiya* 9: 54–59 (in Russian).

TANGER, D. and P. ZOMERDIJK. 1985. De slobeend in Noord-Holland. *Graspieper* 5: 10–23 (The Shoveler in Noord-Holland) (in Dutch).

TASKER, M.L., A. WEBB, A.J. HALL, M.W. PIENKOWSKI and D.R. LANGSLOW. 1987. *Seabirds in the North Sea.* Nature Conservancy Council, Peterborough.

TASKER, M.L., P.R. MOORE and R.A. SCHOFIELD. 1988. The seabirds of St Kilda, 1987. *Scottish Birds* 15: 21–29.

TASKER, M.L., A. WEBB and J.M. MATTHEWS. 1991. A census of the large inland Common Gull colonies of Grampian. *Scottish Birds* 16: 106–112.

TAYLOR, I. 1994. *Barn Owls: Predator–prey relationships and conservation.* Cambridge University Press, Cambridge.

TAYLOR, K., R. HUDSON and G. HORNE. 1988. Buzzard breeding distribution and abundance in Britain and Northern Ireland in 1983. *Bird Study* 35: 109–118.

TAYLOR, S. 1993. Wryneck *Jynx torquilla*. In: Gibbons, D.W., J.B. Reid and R.A. Chapman (Eds) *The New Atlas of Breeding Birds in Britain and Ireland: 1988–1991.* Poyser, London: 262–263.

TCHERNITCHKO, I.I. 1980. [The structure of an avocet colony on the north-west shore of the Black Sea.] *Ornitologiya* 15: 80–83 (in Russian).

TCHERNITCHKO, I.I., A.N. TCHERNAYA and S.A. TCHERNYI. 1991. [Biology of the Glossy Ibis in the Tiligulsk valley.] In: Korziukov, A.I, A.I. Koshelev and I.I. Tchernitko (Eds) *Redkie ptitsy Pritchernomoria.* Kiev–Odessa: 113–128 (in Russian).

TEGELSTRÖM, H. and G. SJÖBERG. 1995. Introduced Swedish Canada Geese (*Branta canadensis*) have low levels of genetic variation as revealed by DNA fingerprinting. *J. Evol. Biol.* 8: 195–207.

TEIXEIRA, A.M. 1983. Seabirds breeding at the Berlengas, forty-two years after Lockley's visit. *Ibis* 125: 417–420.

TEIXEIRA, A.M. and C. MOORE. 1983. The breeding of Madeira Storm-petrel *Oceanodroma castro* on Farilhão Grande, Portugal. *Ibis* 125: 382–384.

TEIXEIRA, R.M. 1979. *Atlas van de Nederlandse Broedvogels.* Natuurmonumenten, 's-Graveland: 42–43.

TELLERIA, J.L. 1981. *La migración de las aves en el Estrecho de Gibraltar,* Vol. 2, *Aves no planeadoras.* Universidad Complutense, Madrid.

TELLERIA, J.L., T. SANTOS, G. ALVAREZ and C. SAEZ-ROYUELA. 1988a. Avifauna de los campos de cereales del interior de España. In: Bernis, F. (Ed) *Aves de los medios urbanos y agrícola.* Monografías No. 3, Sociedad Espanola de Ornitologia, Madrid.

TELLERIA, J.L., F. SUAREZ and T. SANTOS. 1988b. Bird communities of the Iberian shrubsteppes. *Holarctic Ecol.* 11: 171–177.

TELLERIA, J.L., T. SANTOS and M. DIAZ. 1995. Effects of agricultural practices on bird populations in the Mediterranean region: the case of Spain. In: Hagemeijer, E.J.M. and T.J. Verstrael (Eds) *Bird Numbers 1992. Distribution, monitoring and ecological aspects.* Statistics Netherlands, Voorburg/Heerlen and SOVON, Beek-Ubbergen: 57–74.

TERRASSE, J.F. 1991. Le Gypaète barbu dans les Pyrenées françaises. In: Heredia, R. and B. Heredia (Eds) *El Quebrantahuesos en los Pirineos. Caracteristicas ecológicas y biología de la conservación.* Serie Técnica, ICONA, Madrid.

TEWES, E. In press. Situation of the European Black Vulture and the Eurasian Griffon Vulture in the Mediterranean. *Proceedings of the Conference on Mediterranean Raptors, Mallorca, 1994.*

THALER-KOTTEK, E. 1990. *Die Goldhähnchen: Winter- und Sommergoldhähnchen, Regulus regulus, Regulus ignicapillus.* Neue Brehm-Bücherei 597, Ziemsen, Wittenberg.

THIBAULT, J-C. 1983. *Les oiseaux de la Corse.* Parc Naturel régional de la Corse, Ajaccio.

THIBAULT, J-C. 1993. Breeding distribution and numbers of Cory's Shearwater (*Calonectris diomedea*) in the Mediterranean. In: *Proceedings of the 2nd Mediterranean Seabird Symposium.* SEO/BirdLife International, Cambridge: 25–35.

THIBAULT, J-C. and O. PATRIMONIO. 1991. Hibou petit-duc *Otus scops.* In: Yeatman-Berthelot, D. (Ed) *Atlas des oiseaux de France en hiver.* Société Ornithologique de France, Paris: 312–313.

THIBAULT, J-C., D. BRUNSTEIN, E. PASQUET and I. GUYOT. 1987. La reproduction du Martinet pâle (*Apus pallidus*, Shelley) sur les ilots satellites de la Corse: ses relations avec les facteurs climatiques. *Rev. Ecol. (Terre et Vie)* 42: 277–296.

THINGSTAD, P.G. 1994a. Ærfugl *Somateria mollissima.* In: Gjershaug, J.O., P.G. Thingstad, S. Eldøy, S. and S. Byrkjeland (Eds) *Norsk Fugleatlas.* Norsk Ornitologisk Forening, Klæbu: 94 (in Norwegian).

THINGSTAD, P.G. 1994b. Blåstrupe *Luscinia svecica.* In: Gjershaug, J.O., P.G. Thingstad, S. Eldøy and S. Byrkjeland (Eds) *Norsk Fugleatlas.* Norsk Ornitologisk Forening, Klæbu: 352–353 (in Norwegian).

THIOLLAY, J-M. 1989. Distribution and ecology of Palearctic birds of prey wintering in West and Central Africa. In: Meyburg, B-U. and R.D. Chancellor (Eds) *Raptors in the Modern World.* WWGBPO, Berlin: 95–107.

THOMAS, A. 1994. Sterne de Dougall *Sterna dougallii.* In: Yeatman-Berthelot, D. and G. Jarry (Eds) *Nouvel Atlas des Oiseaux Nicheurs de France 1985–1989.* Société Ornithologique de France, Paris: 342–343.

THOMAS, G.J. 1980. *Breeding Terns in Britain and Ireland 1975–79. Seabird Report* 6: 59–69.

THOMPSON, D.B.A. and G. BOOBYER. 1993. Golden Plover *Pluvialis apricaria.* In: Gibbons, D.W., J.B. Reid and R.A. Chapman (Eds) *The New Atlas of Breeding Birds in Britain and Ireland: 1988–1991.* Poyser, London: 168–169.

THOMPSON, P.S. and W.G. HALE. 1993. Adult survival and numbers in a coastal breeding population of Redshank *Tringa totanus* in northwest England. *Ibis* 135: 61–69.

THOMPSON, P.S. and D.B.A. THOMPSON. 1991. Greenshanks *Tringa nebularia* and long-term studies of breeding waders. *Ibis* 133 (Suppl. 1): 99–112.

TIAINEN, J. 1983. Dynamics of a local population of the Willow Warbler *Phylloscopus trochilus* in southern Finland. *Ornis Scand.* 14: 1–15.

TIAINEN, J., M. VICKHOLM, T. PAKKALA, J. PIIROINEN and E. VIROLAINEN. 1983a. The habitat and spatial relations of breeding *Phylloscopus* warblers and the goldcrest *Regulus regulus* in southern Finland. *Ann. Zool. Fennici* 20: 1–12.

TIAINEN, J., I.K. HANSKI and J. MEHTÄLÄ. 1983b. Insulation of nests and the northern limits of three *Phylloscopus* warblers in Finland. *Ornis Scand.* 14: 149–153.

TIAINEN, J., T. PAKKALA, J. PIIROINEN, M. VICKHOLM and E. VIROLAINEN. 1985. [Changes in the avifauna of farmland at Lammi, southern Finland during the past 50 years.] *Lintumies* 20: 30–42 (in Finnish, with English summary).

TIAINEN, J., I.K. HANSKI, T. PAKKALA, J. PIIROINEN and R. YRJÖLÄ. 1989. Clutch size, nestling growth and nestling mortality of the Starling *Sturnus vulgaris* in south Finnish agroenvironments. *Ornis Fennica* 66: 41–48.

TIL'BA, P.A. 1994. [Population status of the Caucasian Black Grouse in the central part of the Western Caucasus.] *Kavkaz. orn. Vestnik (Stavropol')* 6: 42–58 (in Russian).

TIL'BA, P.A. and B.A. KAZAKOV. 1985. [Structure of the summer bird population in the central part of the

Western Caucasus.] In: Amirkhanov, A.M. (Ed) *Ptitsy Severo-Zapadnago Kavkaza [Birds of the Western Caucasus]*. Moscow: 34–53 (in Russian).

TIL'BA, P.A., R.A. MNACEKANOV, M.X. EMTIL, G.K. PLOTNIKOV, S.A. SOLOVIYOV and A.M. IVANENKO. 1990. [Concerning rare birds of the Eastern part of the Sea of Azov.] *Rare, Dispersed and Less-studied Birds of the North Caucasus*. Stavropol': 91–96.

TINARELLI, R. 1990. [Results of a national inventory of Black-winged Stilt *Himantopus himantopus* (Linnaeus, 1758).] *Ric. Biol. Selvagginna* 87: 1–102 (in Italian).

TINARELLI, R. and N. BACCETTI. 1989. Breeding waders in Italy. *Wader Study Group Bull.* 56: 7–15.

TJERNBERG, M. 1983. *Breeding Ecology of the Golden Eagle in Sweden*. Report No. 10, Department of Wildlife Ecology, Swedish University of Agricultural Sciences, Uppsala.

TJERNBERG, M. and H. RYTTMAN. 1994. Bivråkens *Pernis apivorus* överlevnad och beståndsutveckling i Sverige. *Ornis Svecica* 4: 133–139. (Survival and population development of the Honey Buzzard *Pernis apivorus* in Sweden) (in Swedish with English summary).

TJERNBERG, M., K. JOHNSON and S.G. NILSSON. 1993. Density variation and breeding success of the Black Woodpecker *Dryocopus martius* in relation to forest fragmentation. *Ornis Fennica* 70: 155–162.

TKACHENKO, V.I. 1966a. [The birds of the Teberda Nature Reserve.] *Trudy Teberdinsk. Zapoved. (Stavropol')* 6: 5–144, 147–230 (in Russian).

TOMIAŁOJĆ, L. 1976. The urban population of the Woodpigeon *Columba palumbus* Linnaeus, 1758, in Europe – its origin, increase and distribution. *Acta Zool. Cracov* 21: 585–631.

TOMIAŁOJĆ, L. 1990. *Ptaki Polski: rozmieszczenie i liczebność*. Państwowe Wydawnictwo Naukowe, Warszawa. (*The Birds of Poland. Their distribution and abundance*) (in Polish, with English summary).

TOMIAŁOJĆ, L. 1992. Colonization of dry habitats by the Song Thrush *Turdus philomelos*: is the type of nest material an important constraint? *Bull. Brit. Orn. Club* 112: 27–34.

TOMIAŁOJĆ, L. 1994. Lesser Grey Shrike *Lanius minor*. In: Tucker, G.M. and M.F. Heath (Eds) *Birds in Europe – their conservation status*. Conservation Series No. 3, BirdLife International, Cambridge.

TOMIAŁOJĆ, L. 1995. Accuracy of the mapping technique estimates for the Hawfinch – preliminary results. In: Hagemeijer, E.J.M. and T.J. Verstrael (Eds) *Bird Numbers 1992: Distribution, monitoring and ecological aspects. Poster appendix*. Statistics Netherlands, Voorburg/SOVON, Beek-Ubbergen: 145–147.

TOMIAŁOJĆ, L. and J. LONTKOWSKI. 1989. A technique for censusing territorial song thrushes *Turdus philomelos*. *Ann. Zool. Fennici* 26: 235–243.

TOMIAŁOJĆ, L. and T. WESOŁOWSKI. 1990. Bird communities of the primaeval temperate forest of Białowieża, Poland. In: Keast, A. (Ed) *Biogeography and Ecology of Forest Bird Communities*. Academic Publishing, The Hague: 141–165.

TOMIAŁOJĆ, L., T. WESOŁOWSKI and W. WALANKIEWICZ. 1984. Breeding bird community of a primaeval temperate forest (Białowieża National Park, Poland). *Acta Ornithol.* 20: 241–310.

TOMKOVICH, P.S. 1992. Breeding-range and population changes of waders in the former Soviet Union. *Brit. Birds* 85: 344–365.

TØMMERAAS, P.J. 1993. The status of Gyrfalcon *Falco rusticolus* research in northern Fennoscandia 1992. *Fauna Norv. Ser. C. Cinclus* 16: 75–83.

TØMMERAAS, P.J. 1994. Jaktfalk *Falco rusticolus*. In: Gjershaug, J.O., P.J. Thingstad, S. Eldøy and S. Byrkjeland (Eds) *Norsk fugleatlas*. Norwegian Ornithological Society, Klæbu: 134–135 (in Norwegian).

TOMPA, F.S. 1967. Reproductive success in relation to breeding density in pied flycatchers, *Ficedula hypoleuca* (Pallas). *Acta Zool. Fennica* 118: 1–28.

TORRES, J.A., R. ARENAS, and J.M. AYALA. 1986. Evolución histórica de la población Española de Malvasía (*Oxyura leucocephala*). *Oxyura* 3: 5–19.

TORRES ESQUIVIAS, J.A. 1995. Spanish national report. In: Rose, P. (Ed) *Ruddy Duck (*Oxyura jamaicensis*) European status report – 1994*. International Waterfowl and Wetlands Research Bureau, Slimbridge: 2–10.

TORTOSA, F.S., M. MAÑEZ and M. BARCELL. 1995. Wintering White Storks (*Ciconia ciconia*) in South West Spain in the years 1991 and 1992. *Vogelwarte* 38: 41–45.

TRODD, P. and D. KRAMER. 1991. *Birds of Bedfordshire*. Castlemead Publications, Welwyn Garden City.

TRONTELJ, P. 1992. Breeding of the Little Ringed Plover *Charadrius dubius* at anthropogenic habitats of Ljubljana. *Acrocephalus* 51: 38–43.

TROTIGNON, J., T. WILLIAMS and G. HÉMERY. 1994. Reproduction et dynamique des colonies de la population de Guifettes (*Chlidonias hybrida*) de la Brenne. *Alauda* 62: 89–104.

TROUVILLIEZ, J. 1988. *Contribution à l'étude des relations interspécifiques chez les oiseaux aquatiques. L'association entre le Grèbe à cou noir* Podiceps nigricollis, *et la Mouette rieuse* Larus ridibundus, *en période de nidification*. Thèse doctorat, Université Lyon I.

TUCK, L.M. 1972. *The Snipes: a study of the genus* Capella. Canadian Wildlife Service, Ottawa.

TUCKER, G.M. and M.F. HEATH (Eds). 1994. *Birds in Europe – their conservation status*. Conservation Series No. 3, BirdLife International, Cambridge.

TYLER, S.J. 1993. Yellow Wagtail *Motacilla flava*. In: Gibbons, D.W., J.B. Reid and R.A Chapman (Eds) *The New Atlas of Breeding Birds in Britain and Ireland: 1988–1991*. Poyser, London: 286–287.

TYLER, S.J. and S.J. ORMEROD. 1992. A review of the likely causal pathways relating the reduced density of breeding Dipper *Cinclus cinclus* to the acidification of upland streams. *Environ. Pollution* 78: 49–56.

TYLER, S.J. and S.J. ORMEROD. 1994. *The Dippers*. Poyser, London.

TYRVÄINEN, H. 1969. The breeding biology of the Redwing (*Turdus iliacus L.*). *Ann. Zool. Fennici* 6: 1–46.

TYRVÄINEN, H. 1975. The winter irruption of the Fieldfare *Turdus pilaris* and the supply of rowan-berries. *Ornis Fennica* 52: 23–31.

TYSSANDIER, P. 1991. La Fauvette orphée *Sylvia hortensis* en France. *Alauda* 59: 148–154.

UHLIG, R. and W. BAUMGART. 1995. Verbreitung und

Bestand des Triels *Burhinus oedicnemus* in Bulgarien. *Vogelwelt* 116 : 11–17.

UKKONEN, M. 1983. *Pohjansirkun (*Emberiza rustica*) pesimäbiologiasta (Breeding biology of the Rustic Bunting)*. Unpublished MSc Thesis, University of Helsinki, Department of Zoology (in Finnish).

ULFVENS, J. 1988. Comparative breeding ecology of the Horned Grebe *Podiceps auritus* and the Great Crested Grebe *Podiceps cristatus*: archipelago versus lake habitats. *Acta Zool. Fennica* 183: 1–75.

ULFVENS, J. 1989. Clutch size, productivity and population changes in a population of the Horned Grebe *Podiceps auritus* in an exposed habitat. *Ornis Fennica* 66: 75–77.

UNDERHILL, L.G., R.P. PRŶS-JONES, E.E. SYROECHKOVSKI Jr., N.M. GROEN, V. KARPOV, H.G. LAPPO, M.W.J. van ROOMEN, A. RYBKIN, H. SCHEKKERMAN, H. SPIEKMAN and R.W. SUMMERS. 1993. Breeding of waders (Charadrii) and Brent Geese *Branta bernicla bernicla* at Pronchishcheva Lake, northeastern Taimyr, Russia, in a peak and a decreasing lemming year. *Ibis* 135: 277–292.

UNDERHILL-DAY, J. 1993. Marsh Harrier. In: Gibbons, D.W., J.B. Reid and R.A. Chapman (Eds) *The New Atlas of Breeding Birds in Britain and Ireland: 1988–91*. Poyser, London: 102–103.

URDIALES, C. 1993. *Estudio de prospección en relación con la puesta en marcha de un Plan de Manejo del Torillo en el Parque Nacional de Doñana*. ICONA, P.N. Doñana. Unpublished report.

URDIALES, C. 1994. Andalusian Hemipode *Turnix sylvatica*. In: Tucker, G. M. and M.F. Heath (Eds) *Birds in Europe – their conservation status*. Conservation Series No. 3, BirdLife International, Cambridge: 224–225.

USHAKOV, V.E. 1916. Nest and eggs of *Numenius tenuirostris*, Veill. *Orn. Vestnik* 3: 185–187 (in Russian).

USHAKOV, V.E. 1925. [Colonial nesting of the Slender-billed Curlew in Tara district of Omsk government.] *Ural'sky okhotnik* 2(3): 32–35 (in Russian).

USPENSKI, S.M. 1958. *The Bird Bazaars of Novaya Zemlya*. Trans. of Russian Game Reports, Vol. 4. Canadian Department of Northern Affairs and National Resources.

USPENSKI, S.M. 1965. [Birds of the Eastern Bol'shezemel'skaya Tundra, the Yugorski peninsula and Vaigach Island.] In: *Proceedings of the Biological Institute, Urals Branch*, Vol. 38. USSR Academy of Sciences, Sverdlovsk: 65–102 (in Russian).

USPENSKI, S.M. 1970. [*Proceedings of the International Regional Meeting on the Conservation of Wildfowl Resources, Leningrad 1968*] (in Russian).

VAGLIANO, C. 1981. Contribution au statut des rapaces diurnes et nocturnes nicheurs en Crète. In: Cheylan, G. and J-C. Thibault (Eds) *Rapaces méditerranéens. Annales du CROP* 1: 14–16.

VÄISÄNEN, R.A. 1983. Long-term population changes of the most abundant north Finnish land birds during the past 40 years. *Aureola* 8: 58–65 (in Finnish, with English summary).

VÄISÄNEN, R.A. 1989. Renewal of methodology in the second bird atlas of Finland, 1986–89. *Ann. Zool. Fennici* 26: 167–172.

VÄISÄNEN, R.A. 1994. *Suomen pesivän maalinnuston vuosivaihtelu 15 vuoden jaksolla 1979–93*. Mimeograph, Finnish Museum of Natural History. (*Annual Variation of Breeding Land Bird Populations in Finland in 1979–93*) (in Finnish, with English captions).

VÄISÄNEN, R.A. and P. KOSKIMIES. 1989. [Winter birds in Finland in 1988/89, their long-term trends and densities in different habitats.] *Lintumies* 24: 190–203 (in Finnish, with English summary).

VÄISÄNEN, R.A. and P. RAUHALA. 1983. Succession of land bird communities on large areas of peatland drained for forestry. *Ann. Zool. Fennici* 20: 115–127.

VÄISÄNEN, R.A., O. JÄRVINEN and P. RAUHALA. 1986. How are extensive, human-caused habitat alterations expressed on the scale of local bird populations in boreal forests? *Ornis Scand.* 17: 282–292.

VÄISÄNEN, R.A., O. HILDÉN and E. PULLIAINEN. 1989. Monitoring of Finnish land bird populations in 1979–88. *Lintumies* 24: 60–67 (in Finnish, with English summary).

VALERA, F., P. REY, A.M. SANCHEZ-LAFUENTE and J. MUNOZ-COBO. 1990. The situation of Penduline Tit (*Remiz pendulinus*) in southern Europe: A new stage of its expansion. *J. Ornithol.* 131: 413–420.

VALVERDE, J.A. 1960. Vertebrados de las Marismas del Guadalguivir. *Archivos del Instituto de Aclimatación*, Vol. IX. Almería.

VALVERDE, J.A. 1964. Datos sobre Cerceta Pardilla en las Marismas. *Ardeola* 9: 121–132.

VALVO, F. Lo and G. Lo VERDE. 1987. Studio della variabilità fenotipica delle popolazioni italiane di Passere e loro posizione tassonomica. *Riv. ital. Orn.* 57: 97–110.

VALVO, M. Lo 1993. Aquila del Bonelli *Hieraaetus fasciatus*. In: Meschini, E. and S. Frugis (Eds) *Atlante degli uccelli nidificanti in Italia. Centro Italiano Studi Ornitogici, I.N.S.S., Supp. Ric. Biol. Selvagginna* 20.

VALVO, M. Lo and B. MASSA. 1992. Aquila del Bonelli *Hieraaetus fasciatus* (Viellot, 1822). In: Brichetti, P., P. de Franceschi and N. Baccetti (Eds) *Fauna d'Italia. Aves I.* Edizione Calderini, Bologna: 616–621.

VALVO, M. Lo, B. MASSA and M. SARA'. 1993. Uccelli e paesaggio in Sicilia alle soeglie del terzo millennio. *Il Naturalista siciliano* XVII (Suppl.): 1–373.

VARADINOV, E. and D. NANKINOV. 1978. Subspecies-affiliation and biology of the Crested Lark in the area around Sofia. *Orn. Inform. Bjull.* 3: 18–25 (in Bulgarian).

VARSHAVSKI, S.N. 1965. *Landshafty i faunisticheskie komplesky nazemnikh pozvonochnikh Severnogo Priaralia*. Saratov (in Russian).

VASIC, V.F. 1985. [Geographic distribution of Crag Martin *Hirundo rupestris rupestris*, Scopoli 1769, in Yugoslavia.] *Proc. Fauna SR Serbia* 3: 193–208 (in Russian).

VASIC, V.F., B. GRUBAC, G. SUSIC, and S. MARINKOVIC. 1985. *The Status of Birds of Prey in Yugoslavia, with Particular Reference to Macedonia*. Technical Publication No. 5, International Council for Bird Preservation, Cambridge: 45–53.

VASILIU, G.D. 1968. *Systema Avium Romaniae*. *Alauda* (Suppl.): 1–120.

VATEV, I. 1987. Notes on the Breeding Biology of the Long-legged Buzzard (*Buteo rufinus*) in Bulgaria. *J. Raptor Res.* 21: 8–13.

VATEV, I. and P. SIMEONOV. 1972. [Notes on some birds

observed in the southern part of Kresna gorge.] *Orn. Bull. Zool. Inst. Bulg. Acad. Sci.* 4: 15–20.

VEEN, J. 1977. *The Sandwich Tern: functional and causal aspects of nest distribution*. Brill, Leiden.

VEEN, J. 1980. Breeding behaviour and breeding success of a colony of Little Gulls *Larus minutus* in the Netherlands. *Limosa* 53: 73–83.

VERBEEK, N.A.M. 1988. Development of a stable body temperature and growth rates in nestlings of three ground nesting passerines in alpine tundra. *J. Ornithol.* 129: 449–456.

VERCRUIJSSE, H.J.P. and A.L. SPAANS. 1994. Eerste broedgeval van de Grote Mantelmeeuw *Larus marinus* in Nederland. *Limosa* 67: 111–113. (First breeding record of the Great Black-backed Gull *Larus marinus* in The Netherlands) (in Dutch, with English summary).

VEROMANN, H. 1976. Distribution dynamics of the White Stork (*Ciconia ciconia*) in the Baltic area. *Ornis Fennica* 53: 150–152.

VEROMANN, H. 1994a. White Stork. In: Leibak, E., V. Lilleleht and H. Veromann (Eds) *Birds of Estonia: Status, distribution and numbers*. Estonian Academy Publishers, Tallinn: 39.

VEROMANN, H. 1994b. Greenish Warbler. In: Leibak, E., V. Lilleleht, and H. Veromann (Eds) *Bird of Estonia: Status, distribution and numbers*. Estonian Academy Publishers, Tallinn: 198.

VICENS, P. 1993. Registres Ornitològics: *Porphyrio porphyrio*. *Anuari Ornitològic de Les Balears 1992*: 86.

VICKHOLM, M. 1983. *Avointen reunojen vaikutus metsälinnustoon*. Unpublished MSc Thesis, Department of Zoology, University of Helsinki (in Finnish).

VIDAL, P. 1986. Le Hibou petit-duc *Otus scops* dans les files d'Hyères (Var), répartition et densité. *Faune de Provence (Bull. C.E.E.P.)* 7: 74–79.

VIETINGHOFF-RIESCH, A. von. 1955. *Die Rauchschwalbe*. Duncker und Humblot, Berlin.

VIKER, M. 1994. Ringdue *Columba palumbus*. In: Gjershaug, J.D., P.G. Thingstad, S. Eldøy and S. Byrkjeland (Eds) *Norsk fugleatlas*. Norsk Ornitologisk Forening, Klæbu: 264–265 (in Norwegian).

VIKSNE, J. and M. JANAUS. 1989. [Colonies of gulls, terns and the Grey Heron in Latvia in 1986.] *Putni Daba* 2: 55–71 (in Latvian with English summary).

VIKSNE, J., M. JANAUS and A. STIPNIECE. 1996. Recent trends of the Black-headed Gull *Larus ridibundus* population in Latvia. *Ornis Svecica* 6: 39–44.

VILLAGE, A. 1987. Numbers, territory-size and turnover of Short-eared Owls *Asio flammeus* in relation to vole abundance. *Ornis Scand.* 18: 198–204.

VILLAGE, A. 1990. *The Kestrel*. Poyser, London.

VINOGRADOV, V.G. 1990. *Anser erythropus* in the USSR. In: Matthews, G.V.T. (Ed) *Proceedings of the IWRB Symposium. Astrakhan 1989*. IWRB Spec. Pub. 12, Slimbridge.

VINOGRADOV, V.G. 1994. Population trends of Smew *Mergus albellus* on East European Plain in the 19th and 20th centuries. *J. Ornithol.* 135, Sonderheft: 212–213.

VIOLANI, C.G. and B. MASSA. 1993. Extinction of the Andalusian Hemipode *Turnix s. sylvatica* (Desf.) in the Mediterranean region. *Bull. Brit. Orn. Club* 113: 225–229.

VIRKKALA, R. 1987a. Geographical variation in bird communities of old, intact forests in northern Finland. *Ornis Fennica* 64: 107–118.

VIRKKALA, R. 1987b. Effects of forest management on birds breeding in northern Finland. *Ann. Zool. Fennici* 24: 281–294.

VIRKKALA, R. 1989. Short-term fluctuations of bird communities and populations in virgin and managed forests in northern Finland. *Ann. Zool. Fennici* 26: 277–285.

VIRKKALA, R. 1990. Ecology of the Siberian Tit *Parus cinctus* in relation to habitat quality: effects of forest management. *Ornis Scand.* 21: 139–146.

VIRKKALA, R. 1991a. Population trends of forest birds in a Finnish Lapland landscape of large habitat blocks: consequences of stochastic environmental variation or regional habitat alternation? *Biol. Conservation* 56: 223–240.

VIRKKALA, R. 1991b. Spatial and temporal variation in bird communities and populations in north-boreal coniferous forests: a multiscale approach. *Oikos* 62: 59–66.

VIRKKALA, R. and H. LIEHU. 1990. Habitat selection of the Siberian Tit *Parus cinctus* in virgin and managed forests in northern Finland. *Ornis Fennica* 67: 1–12.

VIRKKALA, R., T. ALANKO, T. LAINE and J. TIAINEN. 1993. Population contraction of the White-backed Woodpecker *Dendrocopos leucotos* in Finland as a consequence of habitat alteration. *Biol. Conservation* 66: 47–53.

VIRTANEN, H. 1991. [The appearance and the nesting biology of the Woodlark in south-western Finland in 1989–91.] *Lintumies* 26: 269–276 (in Finnish).

VITOVICH, O.A. 1977. Re-establishment of Caucasian Black Grouse density after the cessation of grazing. In: *Proceedings of the VIIIth Ornithological Conference of the USSR, Kiev* (in Russian).

VLACHOS, C.G. and N.K. PAPAGEORGIOU. 1994. Diet, breeding success, and nest-site selection of the Short-toed Eagle (*Circaetus gallicus*) in northeastern Greece. *J. Raptor Res.* 28: 39–42.

VLUG, J.J. 1983. De Fuut (*Podiceps cristatus*). *Wetenschappelijke mededelingen K.N.N.V.* 160: 1–87.

VLUG, J.J. 1993. Habitatwahl des Rothalstauchers *Podiceps grisegena* in Schleswig-Holstein, in Zusammenhang mit seiner Nahrungsökologie. *Corax* 15: 91–117.

VOET, H., H. MEEUS and P. MAES. 1982. Broedvogelinventarisatie van de steltlopers in Vlaanderen – 1981. *Wielewaal* 48: 201–218 (in Dutch).

VOGEL, R.L. and R. van de WAL. 1988. Het Porseleinhoen *Porzana porzana* langs de IJssel in 1987. *Limosa* 61: 45–46. (Occurrence of the Spotted Crake *Porzana porzana* along the river IJssel in 1987) (in Dutch, with English summary).

VOISIN, J-F. 1994. Colin de Virginie *Colinus virginianus*. In: Yeatman-Berthelot, D. and G. Jarry (Eds) *Nouvel Atlas des Oiseaux Nicheurs de France 1985–1989*. Société Ornithologique de France, Paris: 240–241.

VOLKOV, A.E. and J. de KORTE. 1995. Ivory Gulls *Pagophila eburnea* on Severnaya Zemlya, Siberia. *Sula* 9: 41–54.

VOOUS, K.H. 1960. *Atlas of European Birds*. Nelson, Edinburgh.

VOOUS, K.H. 1963. The concept of Faunal elements of Faunal types. *Proc. XIII Int. Ornithol. Congr.*: 1104–1108.

VOOUS, K.H. 1977. *List of Recent Holarctic Species.* British Ornithologists' Union, London.

VOROBYEV, K.A. 1931. [New data about the distribution and biology of the birds of S. Turkmeniya.] *Reports of the USSR Academy of Sciences*, Vol. 33. No. 5. Moscow: 381–384 (in Russian).

VOROBYOBA, T. D. 1992. Wintering of the Little Bustard on the south-western coast of the Caspian Sea. *Bustard Studies* 5: 92–94.

VORONTSOV, E.M. 1949. [*Birds of the Kama Pre-Urals.*] Gorky (in Russian).

VOSLAMBER, B. 1989. De Kwartelkoning *Crex crex* in het Oldambt: aantallen en biotoopkeuze. *Limosa* 62: 15–21. (The Corncrake *Crex crex* in the Oldambt (Groningen): numbers and habitat selection) (in Dutch, with English summary).

VOSLAMBER, B. 1994. De ontwikkeling van de broedvogelaantallen van de Lepelaar (*Platalea leucorodia*) in Nederland in de periode 1961–93. *Limosa* 67: 89–94. (History of the Dutch Spoonbill *Platalea leucorodia* breeding population, 1961–1993) (in Dutch, with English summary).

VUOLANTO, S. 1968. On the breeding biology of the Turnstone at Norrskär, Gulf of Bothnia. *Ornis Fennica* 45: 19–24 (in Finnish, with English summary).

VUORISALO, T. and J. TIAINEN. 1993. *Kaupungin linnut – Turun kaupunkilinnustotutkimus. Stadens fåglar – Stadsfågelundersökning I Åbo.* Turun Biologinen Museo, Turku (in Finnish and Swedish).

WALASZ, K. and P. MIELCZAREK (Eds). 1992. *The Atlas of Breeding Birds in Małopolska 1985–1991 (south-eastern Poland).* Biologica Silesiae, Wrocław (in Polish and English).

WALKER, F.J. 1981. Notes on the birds of Dhofar, Oman. *Sandgrouse* 2: 56–85.

WALLGREN, H. 1954. Energy metabolism of two species of the genus *Emberiza* as correlated with distribution and migration. *Acta Zool. Fennica* 84: 1–110.

WALTER, H. 1979. *Eleonora's Falcon: Adaptations to prey and habitat in a social raptor.* University of Chicago Press, Chicago.

WALTER, H. 1988. Temporal and spatial dynamics of *Sylvia* warblers in the Tyrrhenis. *Bull. Ecol.* 19: 375–401.

WALTER, H. and A.M. DEMARTIS. 1972. Brutdichte and ökologische Nische sardischer Stadtvögel. *J. Ornithol.* 113: 391–406.

WANLESS, S. 1987. *A Survey of the Numbers and Breeding Distribution of the North Atlantic Gannet.* Research and Survey in Nature Conservation No. 4, Nature Conservancy Council, Peterborough.

WARTMANN, B. 1977. Die Vögel des Prättigaus und ihre Höhenverbreitung. *J. Natf. Ges. Graubünden* 97: 21–95.

WATERS, R.J. and P.A. CRANSWICK. 1993. *The Wetland Bird Survey 1992–1993: Wildfowl and Wader Counts.* BTO, WWT, RSPB and JNCC, Slimbridge.

WATKINS, D. 1993. *A National Plan for Shorebird Conservation in Australia.* RAOU Report No. 90, Australian Wader Study Group, Royal Australasian Ornithologists' Union and World Wide Fund for Nature.

WATSON, A. 1965. A population study of Ptarmigan (*Lagopus mutus*) in Scotland. *J. Anim. Ecol.* 34: 135–172.

WATSON, A. and R. MOSS. 1979. Population cycles in the Tetraonidae. *Ornis Fennica* 56: 87–109.

WATSON, G.E. 1962. Three sibling species of *Alectoris. Ibis* 104: 353–367.

WEBB, A., N.M. HARRISON, G.M. LEAPER, R.D. STEELE, M.L. TASKER and M.W. PIENKOWSKI. 1990. *Seabird Distribution West of Britain.* Nature Conservancy Council, Peterborough.

WEBER, P., D. MUNTEANU and A. PAPADOPOL (Eds). 1994. *Atlasul provisoriu al pasarilor clocitoare din România.* Societatea Ornitologica, Medias. (*Atlas of the Breeding Birds of Romania*) (in German and Romanian).

WEGNER, P. 1994. Die Wiederkehr des Wanderfalken (*Falco peregrinus*) in Nordrhein–Westfalen. *Charadrius* 30: 2–14.

WEIR, D.N., R.Y. McGOWAN, A.C. KITCHENER, S. McORIST, B. ZONFRILLO and M. HEUBECK. 1995. Iceland Gulls from the 'Braer' disaster, Shetland 1993. *Brit. Birds* 88: 15–25.

WEISHU, H. 1989. The status of Reeves's Pheasant in China, 1988: a preliminary report. *W.P.A. News* 26: 5–7.

WEITNAUER, E. 1975. Lebensdauer, Partnertreue, Ortstreue sowie Fernfunde beringter Mauersegler. *Orn. Beob.* 74: 89–94.

WESŁAWSKI, J.M. and M. MALINGA. 1993. *The Wildlife of Franz Josef Land.* Arctic Ecology Group, Institute of Oceanology, Polish Academy of Sciences, Gdansk.

WESOŁOWSKI, T. 1983. The breeding ecology and behaviour of Wrens *Troglodytes troglodytes* under primaeval and secondary conditions. *Ibis* 125: 499–515.

WESOŁOWSKI, T. 1985. The breeding ecology of the Wood Warbler *Phylloscopus sibilatrix* in primaeval forest. *Ornis Scand.* 16: 49–60.

WESOŁOWSKI, T. 1986. Riverine populations of gulls and terns in Poland and problems of their protection. *Vår Fågelvärld* Suppl. 11: 233–237.

WESOŁOWSKI, T. 1987. Polygyny in three temperate forest Passerines (with a critical reevaluation of hypotheses for the evolution of polygyny). *Acta Ornithol.* 23: 273–302.

WESOŁOWSKI, T. 1991. Bedeutung des Bruterfolgs für die Abnahme des Feldsperlings *Passer montanus* in der Schweiz. *Orn. Beob.* 88: 253–263.

WESOŁOWSKI, T. 1995a. Ecology and behaviour of White-backed Woodpecker (*Dendrocopos leucotos*) in a primaeval temperate forest (Białowieża National Park, Poland). *Vogelwarte* 38: 61–75.

WESOŁOWSKI, T. 1995b. Value of Białowieża forest for the conservation of the white-backed woodpecker *Dendrocopos leucotos* in Poland. *Biol. Conservation* 71: 69–75.

WESOŁOWSKI, T. and L. TOMIAŁOJĆ. 1986. The breeding ecology of woodpeckers in a temperate primaeval forest – preliminary data. *Acta Ornithol.* 22: 1–21.

WHILDE, A. 1985. The All-Ireland Tern Survey. *Irish Birds* 3: 1–32.

WHILDE, A., D.C.F. COTTON and J.R. SHEPPARD. 1993. A repeat survey of gulls breeding inland in Counties Donegal, Sligo, Mayo and Galway with recent counts from Leitrim and Fermanagh. *Irish Birds* 5(1): 67–72.

WHITFIELD, D.P. 1996. Waders (*Charadrii*) on Scotland's blanket bogs: recent changes in numbers of breeding birds. In: Stoneman, R. (Ed) *Peatlands: Proceedings of the 1995 Peatlands Convention:* 103–111. Scottish Wildlife Trust, Edinburgh.

WIDMER, M. 1993. Brutbiologie einer Gebirgspopulation der Gartengrasmücke *Sylvia borin. Orn. Beob.* 90: 58–113.

WIELOCH, M. 1984. Numbers and distribution of the Mute Swan *Cygnus olor* in Poland against the situation of this species in Europe. *Acta Ornithol.* 20: 187–240.

WIELOCH, M. 1991. Population trends of the Mute Swan *Cygnus olor* in the Palearctic. In: Sears, J. and P.J. Bacon (Eds) *Third IWRB International Swan Symposium,* Oxford 1989. *Wildfowl* Suppl. 1: 22–32.

WIJNANDTS, H. 1984. Ecological energetics of the Long-eared Owl (*Asio otus*). *Ardea* 72: 1–92.

WIKLUND, C.G. and J. STIGH. 1983. Nest defence and evolution of reversed sexual size dimorphism in Snowy Owls *Nyctea scandiaca. Ornis Scand.* 14: 58–62.

WIKLUND, C.G. and J. STIGH. 1986. Breeding density of Snowy Owls *Nyctea scandiaca* in relation to food, nest sites and weather. *Ornis Scand.* 17: 268–274.

WIKTANDER, U., I.N. NILSSON, S.G. NILSSON, O. OLSSON, B. PETTERSSON and A. STAGEN. 1992. Occurrence of the Lesser Spotted Woodpecker *Dendrocopos minor* in relation to area of deciduous forest. *Ornis Fennica* 69: 113–118.

WIKTANDER, U., S.G. NILSSON, O. OLSSON and A. STAGEN. 1994. Breeding success of a Lesser Spotted Woodpecker *Dendrocopos minor* population. *Ibis* 136: 318–322.

WILLGOHS, J.F. 1961. The White-tailed Eagle *Haliaeetus albicilla* (Linné) in Norway. *Univ. Bergen Aarb., Math.-Naturv. Ser.* 12: 1–212.

WILLIAMSON, K. 1975. Birds and climatic change. *Bird Study* 22: 143–164.

WILSON, J. 1993. Raven *Corvus corax*. In: Gibbons, D.W., J.B. Reid and R.A. Chapman (Eds) *The New Atlas of Breeding Birds in Britain and Ireland: 1988–1991.* Poyser, London: 400–401.

WINDEN, J. van der. 1995. The breeding population of the Red-footed Falcon (*Falco vespertinus*) in the Sivash, Ukraine. *J. Ornithol.* 136: 285–288.

WINDEN, J. van der, I.I. CHERNICHKO, T.M. van der HAVE, V.D. SIOKHIN and Y. VERKUIL. 1993. The migration of Broad-billed Sandpiper *Limicola falcinellus* during May 1992 in the Sivash, Ukraine. *Wader Study Group Bull.* 71: 41–43.

WINDEN, J. van der, W. HAGEMEIJER, F. HUSTINGS and R. NOORDHUIS. 1994. Hoe vergaat het de Krooneend *Netta rufina* in Nederland? *Limosa* 67: 137–145. (Vicissitudes of the Dutch Red-crested Pochard *Netta rufina* population) (in Dutch, with English summary).

WINDING, N. 1985. Gemeinschaftsstruktur, Territorialität und anthropogene Beeinflussungen der Kleinvögel im Glocknergebiet (Hohe Tauern, Österreichische Zentralalpen). *Veröff. österr. MaB Progr.* 9: 133–173.

WINK, M., H. BIEBACH, F. FELDMANN, W. SCHARLAU, I. SWATSCHECK, C. WINK and D. RISTOW. 1993. Contribution to the breeding biology of Eleonora's Falcon *Falco eleonorae*. In: Nicholls, M.K. and R. Clarke (Eds) *Biology and Conservation of Small Falcons.* Hawk and Owl Trust, London: 59–72.

WINKEL, W. 1992. Der Wendehals (*Jynx torquilla*) als Brutvogel in Nisthöhlen-Untersuchungsgebieten bei Braunschweig. *Beih. Veröff. Naturschutz Landschaftspflege Bad.-Württ.* 66: 31–41.

WINKEL, W. 1994. Zur langfristigen Bestandsentwicklung des Feldsperlings (*Passer montanus*) im Braunschweiger Raum. *Vogelwarte* 37: 307–309.

WINKEL, W. and M. FRANTZEN. 1991. Zur Populationsdynamik der Blaumeise (*Parus caeruleus*): Langfristige Studien bei Braunschweig. *J. Ornithol.* 132: 81–96.

WINKEL, W. and D. WINKEL. 1988. Zur Abwanderung von Kohl- und Tannenmeisen (*Parus major, P. ater*) eines Lärchen-Versuchsgebietes. *Vogelwarte* 34: 225–232.

WINKLER, R. 1984. Avifauna der Schweiz, eine kommentierte Artenliste. I. Passeriformes. *Orn. Beob.* Suppl. 5.

WINSTANLEY, D., R. SPENCER and K. WILLIAMSON. 1974. Where have all the Whitethroats gone? *Bird Study* 21: 1–14.

WITKOWSKI, J. 1989. Breeding biology and ecology of the marsh harrier *Circus aeruginosus* in the Barycz valley, Poland. *Acta Ornithol.* 25: 223–320.

WITT, H-H. 1982. Ernährung und Brutverbreitung der Korallenmöwe *Larus audouinii* im Vergleich zur Mittelmeersilbermöwe *Larus argentatus michahellis. Seevögel* 3: 87–91.

WITT, K. 1982. Der Bergpieper (*Anthus sp. spinoletta*) als Gast im nördlichen Mitteleuropa. *Vogelwelt* 103: 90–111.

WITT, K. 1985. Bestandszählung der Mehlschwalbe (Delichon urbica) in Berlin (West) 1983/84. *Ornithol. Ber. f. Berlin (West)* 10: 131–153.

WITT, K. 1996. The decline of the House Sparrow. *Brit. Birds* 89: 146.

WIWO. 1990. *The Eastern Mediterranean Wader Project 1990. Preliminary report.* WIWO, Zeist.

WOOD, B. 1992. Yellow Wagtail *Motacilla flava* migration from West Africa to Europe: pointers towards a conservation strategy for migrants on passage. *Ibis* 134 (Suppl. 1): 66–76.

WOROBIEW, K.A. 1929. Neue Angaben über die Verbreitung der Vögel im Wolgadelta und den anliegenden Steppen. *J. Ornithol.* 77: 315–322.

WOUTERSEN, K. 1992. De Stormmeeuw *Larus canus* als broedvogel in de Schoorlse Duinen. *Sula* 6: 81–92. (The Common Gull *Larus canus* as breeding bird in the dunes of Schoorl) (in Dutch, with English summary).

WÜRFELS, M. 1994. Entwicklung einer städtischen Population des Habichts *(Accipiter gentilis)* und die Rolle der Elster *(Pica pica)* im Nahrungsspektrum des Habichts. *Charadrius* 30: 82–93.

WYLLIE, I. 1981. *The Cuckoo.* Batsford, London.

WYLLIE, I. 1994. Cuckoo, *Cuculus canorus.* In: Gibbons, D.W., J.B. Reid and R.A. Chapman (Eds) *The New Atlas of Breeding Birds in Britain and Ireland: 1988–1991.* Poyser, London: 244–245.

WYNDE, R. (Ed) 1993. *Roseate Tern News* 7.

XAVIER, A. 1968. [Common Waxbill at the Lagoa de Óbidos.] *Cyanopica* 1(1): 77–81 (in Portuguese).

YALDEN, D.W. 1993. Common Sandpiper *Actitis*

hypoleucos. In: Gibbons, D.W., J.B. Reid and R.A. Chapman (Eds) *The New Atlas of Breeding Birds in Britain and Ireland: 1988–1991*. Poyser, London: 192–193.

YAMINNSKI, B.V. and M.Y. NIKIFOROV. 1986. [The Citrine Wagtail (*Motacilla citreola* Pall.) – A new species of Belarussian fauna.] *Vestsi AN BSSR*. Ser. biyalagichnykh Navuk (in Belarussian).

YANES, M. 1993. La estepa gienense: crónica de una agonia. *Quercus* 94: 12–15 (in Spanish).

YANES, M. 1994. The importance of land management in the conservation of birds associated with the Spanish steppes. In: Bignal, E.M., D.I. McCracken and D.J. Curtis (Eds) *Nature Conservation and Pastoralism in Europe*. Joint Nature Conservation Committee, Peterborough: 34–40.

YANES, M., F. MARTÍN, J. MANRIQUE and F. SUÁREZ. In press. Aspectos ecológicos del zorro *Vulpes vulpes* en la R.O. de Las Amoladeras, Almería: su implicación en la gestión de un enclave estepario protegido. *Investigación y gestión*.

YEATMAN, L. 1976. *Atlas des oiseaux nicheurs de France de 1970 à 1975* . Ministère de la Qualité de la Vie Environnement, Paris.

YEATMAN-BERTHELOT, D. and G. JARRY (Eds). 1994. *Nouvel Atlas des Oiseaux Nicheurs de France 1985–1988*. Société Ornithologique de France, Paris.

YÉSOU, P. 1991a. Reproduction de la Mouette de Sabine *Larus sabini* dans l'estuaire de la Taimyra, Sibérie. *L'Oiseau et R.F.O.* 61: 142–147.

YÉSOU, P. 1991b. The sympatric breeding of *Larus fuscus*, *L. cachinnans* and *L. argentatus* in western France. *Ibis* 133: 256–263.

YÉSOU, P. 1994. Puffin des Anglais *Puffinus puffinus*. In: Yeatman-Berthelot, D. and G. Jarry (Eds) *Nouvel Atlas des Oiseaux Nicheurs de France 1985–1988*. Société Ornithologique de France, Paris: 72–73.

YÉSOU, P. and H.G. LAPPO. 1992. Nidification de l'Eider de Steller *Polysticta stelleri* du Taïmyr à la péninsule de Yamal, Sibérie. *Alauda* 60: 193–198.

ZAHAVI, A. 1971. The function of pre-roost gatherings and communal roosts. *Ibis* 113: 203–211.

ZANG, H. 1990. Abnahme der Tannenmeise *Parus ater*-Population im Harz als Folge der Waldschäden (Waldsterben). *Vogelwelt* 111: 18–28.

ZARUDNI, N.A. 1911. [Some remarks about the ornithological fauna of Kharkov and Poltava gubernia (districts).] *Ornithological Records* 3–4: 272–277 (in Russian).

ZATSEPINA, R. A. 1978. Sylvidae. In: [*Birds of the Volga-Kama Region. Passeriformes*]. Nauka, Moscow: 94–133 (in Russian).

ZBINDEN, N. 1979. Zur Ökologie des Haselhuhns *Bonasa bonasia* in den Buchenwäldern des Chasseral, Faltenjura. *Orn. Beob.* 76: 169–214.

ZBINDEN, N. and O. BIBER. 1989. *L'évolution de l'avifaune en Suisse*. Stat. Orn. Suisse, Sempach.

ZEUNER, F.E. 1952. *Dating the Past*, 3rd edn. Methuen, London.

ZHMUD, M.Y. 1992. Territorial relations and population structure of the Redshank *Tringa totanus* during the nesting period in the south of Ukraine. *Wader Study Group Bull.* 64: 45–46.

ZIJLSTRA, M. 1994. Grote Zilverreigers *Egretta alba* in Nederland en de Oostvaardersplassen. *Vogels in Flevoland* 2: 20–26. (Great White Egrets *Egretta alba* in The Netherlands and the Oostvaardersplassen) (in Dutch).

ZIJLSTRA, M. and F. HUSTINGS. 1992. Teloorgang van de Grauwe Kiekendief *Circus pygargus* als broedvogel in Nederland. *Limosa* 65: 7–18. (Near-disappearance of Montagu's Harrier *Circus pygargus* as a breeding bird in The Netherlands) (in Dutch, with English summary).

ZIMIN, V.B., S.V. SAZONOV, N.V. LAPSHIN, T.Yu. KHOKHLOVA, A.V. ARTEMIEV, V.G. ANNENKOV and M.V. YAKOVLEVA. 1993. [*The Avifauna of Karelia*]. Karelian Science Centre of the Russian Academy of Sciences, Petrosavodsk (in Russian).

ZINK, G. 1981. *Der Zug Europäischer Singvögel*, Vol. 3. Vogelzug-Verlag, Möggingen.

ZINK, G. 1987. *Der Zug Europäischer Singvögel*, Vol. 2. AULA-Verlag, Wiesbaden.

ZINO, F.J.A. 1992. Cat amongst the Freiras. *Oryx* 26: 174.

ZINO, F.J.A. and M.J. BISCOITO. 1994. Breeding seabirds in the Madeira archipelago. In: Nettleship, D.N., J. Burger and M. Gochfeld (Eds) *Seabirds on Islands. Threats, case studies and action plans*. Conservation Series No. 1, BirdLife International, Cambridge: 172–185.

ZINO, F.J.A. and P.A. ZINO. 1986. An account of the habitat, feeding habits, density, breeding and need of protection of the Long-toed Pigeon *Columba trocaz*. *Bocagiana* 97: 1–16.

ZINO, F.J.A., M.J. BISCOITO and P.A. ZINO. 1994a. Fea's Petrel *Pterodroma feae*. In: Tucker, G.M. and M.F. Heath (Eds) *Birds in Europe – their conservation status*. Conservation Series No. 3, BirdLife International, Cambridge: 60–61.

ZINO, F.J.A., M.J. BISCOITO and P.A. ZINO. 1994b. Zino's Petrel, *Pterodroma madeira*. In: Tucker, G.M. and M.F. Heath (Eds) *Birds in Europe – their conservation status*. Conservation Series No. 3, BirdLife International, Cambridge: 62–63.

ZINO, P.A. and F.J.A. ZINO. 1986. Contributions to the study of the petrels of the genus *Pterodroma* in the archipelago of Madeira. *Bol. Mus. Mun. Funchal* 38: 141–165.

ZOHA, L. 1993. Hnízdění mníška šedého ve volné přírodě v okolí Sázavy. *Mor. ornitolog* 1/93: 8–11 (in Czech).

ZOLLINGER, R. and E.J.M. HAGEMEIJER. 1994. The Lesser Kestrel *Falco naumanni*: review of the status of a globally threatened species. In: Meyburg, B-U. and R.D. Chancellor (Eds) *Raptor Conservation Today*. WWGBPO, Berlin: 219–228.

ZOMERDIJK, P.J. 1986. De Zomertaling in Noord Holland-Noord – analyse naar aanleiding van drie totaaltellingen. *Graspieper* 6: 67–75. (The Garganey in the northern Noord-Holland – an analysis based on three complete counts) (in Dutch).

ZOMERDIJK, P.J. 1990a. Slobeend *Anas clypeata*. In: Ruitenbeek, W., C.J.G. Scharringa and P.J. Zomerdijk (Eds) *Broedvogels van Noord-Holland*. Stichting Samenwerkende Vogelwerkgroepen Noord-Holland, Assendelft: 247–248 (in Dutch).

ZOMERDIJK, P.J. 1990b. Kuifeend *Aythya fuligula*. In: Ruitenbeek, W., C.J.G. Scharringa and P.J. Zomerdijk

(Eds) *Broedvogels van Noord-Holland.* Stichting Samenwerkende Vogelwerkgroepen Noord-Holland, Assendelft: 250–251 (in Dutch).

ZOTIER, R., J.C. THIBAULT and I. GUYOT. 1992. Known population and distribution of cormorants, shearwaters and Storm Petrel in the Mediterranean. *Avocetta* 16: 118–126.

ZUBAROVSKY, V.M. 1977. *Fauna Ukrainy 5: Ptitsy, vypusk 2; Khishchenye ptitsy.* [*Fauna of Ukraine*, Vol. 5, *Birds*, Part 2, *Birds of Prey*]. Naukova Dumka, Kiev (in Ukrainian).

ZUPPKE, U. 1984. Der Einfluß der Intensivierung der Graslandwirtschaft auf die wiesenbewohnenden Vogelarten des Landschaftsschutzgebietes 'Mittelelbe'. *Hercynia N.F., Leipzig* 21: 354–387.

Index of Scientific Names

Index – English

Indeks – Český

Index – Deutsche

Indice – Castellano

Index – Français

Hakemisto – suomenkielinen

Ευρετήριο - Ελληνικά

Tárgymutató – Magyar

Indice – Italiano

Index – Nederlands

Índice – Português

Indeks – Polski

Указатель - русский

Index – Svenska